D1450666

ISIS Cumulative Bibliography

ISIS Cumulative Bibliography

A Bibliography of the History of Science
formed from ISIS Critical Bibliographies 1—90
1913—65

Edited by MAGDA WHITROW

Volume 3

SUBJECTS

MANSELL
in conjunction with the History of Science Society
1976

Mansell Information/Publishing Ltd.,
3 Bloomsbury Place, London WC1A 2QA, England

International Standard Book Numbers: 0 7201 0296 0 Volume 3
0 7201 0629 X The series

British Library Cataloguing in Publication Data
Isis cumulative bibliography: a bibliography of the history of science formed from Isis critical bibliographies 1–90, 1913–65.
Vol. 3. Subjects.
Index.
ISBN 0-7201-0296-0
1. Whitrow, Magda 2. History of Science Society
016.509 Z7405.H6
Science–History–Bibliography

*Text reproduced from typed cards,
printed by photolithography and bound in Great Britain at
The Scolar Press Limited, Ilkley, Yorkshire*

Contents

Volume 3

*These disciplines when applied to the preceding subject are included under them.

Introduction

The third volume of the *Isis Cumulative Bibliography* like its two predecessors, comprises references that were published in the Critical Bibliographies no. 1–90 printed in *Isis* during the period 1913–65. The first two volumes are in two parts, Part I: Personalities and Part II: Institutions. The present volume contains Part III: Subjects. It includes all those entries that deal with the history of science or of individual sciences without reference to a particular period or civilization, those that refer to more than two centuries during the modern period, and those that deal with two or more civilizations but are not restricted to a particular period in history. Moreover, it contains twentieth century material and material covering the nineteenth and twentieth centuries together, a departure from the current *Isis* scheme.

The reason for this change was that, when all the material for the subject volume had been cumulated, I found that all those sections covering subjects that originated in the nineteenth or twentieth century were empty: there was nothing on the history of relativity or quantum physics, vitamins, antibiotics, telegraph or telephone, nothing on aviation, and so on. I, therefore, decided to adopt the rule that historical writings which follow the subject into the modern period or to the present day be included in the subject volume. Entries that deal with the ancient world, the Middle Ages and Eastern civilizations, as well as those that cover fewer than three numbered centuries during the modern period will appear in Part IV: Periods.

As explained in the Introduction to Volumes 1 and 2, the *Isis Cumulative Bibliography* is basically a cumulation of the *Isis* Critical Bibliographies published from 1913 to 1965 rather than a fully comprehensive guide to the literature of the history of science; nevertheless, it should provide more extensive and detailed coverage of the subject than is elsewhere available. Indeed, the reviewers of Volumes 1 and 2 have referred to those volumes as indispensable tools of reference. No attempt has been made to add significantly to the number of entries, but as far as possible insufficient references have been amplified and verified and missing volumes of multi-volume works added.

On the other hand, not all titles originally listed in the Critical Bibliographies have been included in the Cumulative Bibliography. The range of subjects covered since Sarton began to publish the Critical Bibliographies has changed greatly over the years, particularly since 1952 when he ceased to be the Editor. The Committee, under Professor Henry Guerlac, which was appointed to explore 'the feasibility of continuing the *Isis* Critical Bibliography' recommended that items on philosophy, literature, art, religion and education be severely restricted and only included if they were directly relevant to the history of science. When I came to collect and organize the entries of CB 1–90, I realized that in some subjects there were no recent titles, and with the revised policy in mind entries on these subjects have been omitted from the present volume. Another practice that seems to have been largely abandoned was the inclusion of non-technical studies and textbooks relative to each discipline; however, it has not been easy to decide which non-technical studies and textbooks to retain and which to omit. Many of these contain important historical material. In some cases this was mentioned in the annotation, but not in all. It has been quite impossible to look at every such book to see whether it was included for its historical value or merely to give information on the science in question, and no doubt some titles have been retained that might have been omitted.

Entries dealing with specific topics that were included in Parts I and II have been repeated in this volume, but it has not been possible to refer to biographical studies or obituary notices of twentieth century personalities.

Corrigenda and addenda to Volumes 1, 2 and 3 will be included in Volume 4.

Classified arrangement

The arrangement of subjects follows very closely that used in the current *Isis* Critical Bibliographies. There are some minor changes in the order of subjects within the larger subject fields and the scheme is far more detailed. I need hardly emphasize that the problems of organizing a cumulative bibliography in which entries stemming from ninety bibliographies are collected are very different from those that arise in arranging the material in each one of these. Although with the ever increasing rate of publication even the scanning of one annual bibliography takes more time than many scholars have to spare, this becomes clearly impossible with the vast number of entries in the volumes of the Cumulative Bibliography. Nor does the Cumulative Bibliography serve quite the same purpose. It is after all a tool for information retrieval. Consequently, the classification scheme must be more detailed and more rigorous in its application than that currently used in *Isis*. Moreover, to make the *Isis Cumulative Bibliography* an efficient tool for information retrieval it must have an alphabetical subject index and a notation or code that will guide the user to the particular information he is seeking.

The need to break down each subject into comparatively narrow fields and to divide each field into special aspects has led to considerable fragmentation of the material. Most historians do not like bibliographies to be divided into too many sections; they like to look at a long list of entries without too many sub-headings. On the other hand, some break-down is needed to locate specific information through the subject index. To accommodate these two requirements it was decided to omit sub-headings of aspects and form unless the number of entries makes a clear subdivision necessary, but to retain the classmarks that enable the user to go from the alphabetical subject index direct to the information he is seeking.

There is no need for the user to try to understand the classification scheme unless he wishes to do so. An explanatory note on the scheme precedes the schedules printed on page 633, but the reader who wants merely to browse in the Bibliography, should find the table of contents a sufficient guide. He need only consult the alphabetical subject index when he requires information on a specific topic. An explanation of the symbols used and their arrangement is given in the Guide to users on page xcii.

Acknowledgments

I should like to take this opportunity of expressing my deep gratitude to all who have made this project possible: the History of Science Society, who sponsored and financially supported it, and the following foundations, societies and individuals who have so generously given the financial support needed to carry it on: the National Science Foundation and the United States Steel Foundation (they provided most of the funds until 1973), the British Academy, the British Library, the Royal Society, the Wellcome Trust, the American Council of Learned Societies, Imperial Chemical Industries, IBM, Bell Laboratories, the International Union of the History and Philosophy of Science, and Mr. Bern Dibner; and to those who generously provided accommodation for the project, first the Imperial College (through the kind offices of Professor A. Rupert Hall), and until recently the Science Museum (by the kindness of its directors, Sir David Follett and his successor, Dr. Margaret Weston). We are now once again indebted to the Imperial College (through the kindness of its librarian Mr. Adrian Whitworth) for its hospitality.

I should also like to express my appreciation of the kindness and forbearance shown to me by successive Presidents and Treasurers of the History of Science Society, particularly Professor E. N. Hiebert and Professor John C. Greene, during whose terms of office this volume reached completion, and to thank the members of the Editorial Committee, especially its present Chairman, Mr. John Neu, for their support. I am most grateful to them and particularly to Professor I. B. Cohen, until recently Chairman and now Co-Chairman of the Editorial Committee, who over the years has done so much in every way for the success of the project.

My thanks are due to all members of my staff, in particular to Miss Margaret Skerl who has given unsparingly of her time and energy and has shown complete devotion to her work; to Mrs. Patricia Bradshaw; to Mrs. Joyce Lancaster Jones, who volunteered help in many ways; to members of the Classification Research Group, especially its Chairman, Mr. Jack Mills, and Mr. Eric Coates, Professor Jason Farradane, Mrs. Vanda Broughton and Mrs. I. McIlwaine, for their helpful suggestions and comments; to Dr. Herbert Spencer of the School of Graphic Design (Readability of Print Research), Royal College of Art, for advice on the layout; to the directors and staff of Mansell, especially Miss Veronica Higgs and Mrs. Brunetta Jayakody for their helpful and friendly co-operation; and to Mrs. Jane Galletti for her speedy and accurate typing of the entries.

Finally, I want to say how grateful I am to the many libraries which allowed my staff and me to use their resources, in particular the Science Museum Library and its Keeper, Dr. John Chaldecott, the Lyon Playfair Library, Imperial College, and its Librarian, Mr. Adrian Whitworth, and to the Wellcome Historical Medical Library. I am also greatly indebted to all the scholars who have given valuable specialist advice, in particular Professor Edwin Clarke, Dr. Melvin Earles, Dr. Frank Greenaway, Professor A. Rupert Hall and Dr. Marie Boas Hall, Dr. Robert Heller, Dr. Norman Smith, Dr. Thaddeus Trenn, and last but not least my husband Professor G. J. Whitrow, particularly for his help with the sections on the history of mathematics, physics and astronomy, and the philosophy of science. Without his constant help and support this volume would not have been completed.

MAGDA WHITROW

Lyon Playfair Library,
Imperial College,
London, SW7 2AZ.

March 1976

Critical Bibliographies in ISIS Volumes

Critical Bibliographies	ISIS Volume	Critical Bibliographies	ISIS Volume	Critical Bibliographies	ISIS Volume
CB 1–4	1	CB 35–7	19	CB 70	37
CB 5–6	2	CB 38	20	CB 71–2	39
CB 7–9	3	CB 39	21	CB 73–4	40
CB 10–12	4	CB 40–1	22	CB 75–6	41
CB 13–14	5	CB 42	23	CB 77	42
CB 15	6	CB 43–4	24	CB 78	43
CB 16–17	7	CB 45–6	25	CB 79	44
CB 18–19	8	CB 47–8	26	CB 80	46
CB 20–1	9	CB 49–50	27	CB 81	47
CB 22	10	CB 51–2	28	CB 82	48
CB 23–4	11	CB 53–4	29	CB 83	49
CB 25	12	CB 55–6	30	CB 84	50
CB 26–7	13	CB 57–8	31	CB 85	51
CB 28	14	CB 59	32	CB 86	52
CB 29–30	15	CB 60–1	33	CB 87	53
CB 31	16	CB 62–4	34	CB 88	54
CB 32	17	CB 65–7	35	CB 89	55
CB 33–4	18	CB 68–9	36	CB 90	56

Abbreviations of Periodicals and Serials Cited

A

A.I.R. Archives of Interamerican Rheumatology

A.M.A. Arch.Neurol.Psychiat. A.M.A. Archives of Neurology and Psychiatry

Aar Der Aar: illustrierte Monatsschrift für das gesamte katholische Geistesleben der Gegenwart

Aberdeen Univ.Rev. Aberdeen University Review

Abhandl.Akad.Wiss.Lit.Geistes.Sozialwiss.Kl. Akademie der Wissenschaften und der Literatur: Abhandlungen der geistes- und sozialwissenschaftlichen Klasse

Abhandl.Akad.Wiss.Lit.Mainz Math.Naturwiss.Kl. Abhandlungen der Akademie der Wissenschaften und der Literatur zu Mainz: Mathematisch-naturwissenschaftliche Klasse

Abhandl.Bayer.Akad.Wiss.Math.Naturwiss.Abt. Abhandlungen der Bayerischen Akademie der Wissenschaften: Mathematisch-naturwissenschaftliche Abteilung

Abhandl.Bayer.Akad.Wiss.Math.Phys.Kl. Abhandlungen der Bayerischen Akademie der Wissenschaften: Mathematisch-physikalische Klasse

Abhandl.Bayer.Akad.Wiss.Phil.Hist.Abt. Abhandlungen der Bayerischen Akademie der Wissenschaften: Philosophisch-historische Abteilung

Abhandl.Bayer.Akad.Wiss.Phil.Philol.Hist.Kl. Abhandlungen der Bayerischen Akademie der Wissenschaften: Philosophisch-philologische und historische Klasse

Abhandl.Ber.Deut.Mus. Abhandlungen und Berichte des Deutschen Museums

Abhandl.Ber.Ver.Naturk. Abhandlungen und Berichte des Vereins für Naturkunde zu Cassel

Abhandl.Braunschweig.Wiss.Ges. Abhandlungen der Braunschweigischen Wissenschaftlichen Gesellschaft

Abhandl.Deut.Akad.Wiss.Kl.Math.Phys.Tech. Abhandlungen der Deutschen Akademie der Wissenschaften zu Berlin: Klasse für Mathematik, Physik und Technik

Abhandl.Deut.Akad.Wiss.Math.Naturwiss.Kl. Abhandlungen der Deutschen Akademie der Wissenschaften: Mathematisch-naturwissenschaftliche Klasse

Abhandl.Deut.Akad.Wiss.Phil.Hist.Kl. Abhandlungen der Deutschen Akademie der Wissenschaften: Philosophisch-historische Klasse

Abhandl.Fritz Haber Inst.Max Planck Ges. Abhandlungen aus dem Fritz-Haber Institut der Max-Planck-Gesellschaft

Abhandl.Geb.Auslandsk. Abhandlungen aus dem Gebiet der Auslandskunde

Abhandl.Geb.Naturwiss. Abhandlungen aus dem Gebiete der Naturwissenschaften

Abhandl.Ges.Wiss.Göttingen Math.Phys.Kl. Abhandlungen (der Königlichen) Gesellschaft der Wissenschaften zu Göttingen: Mathematisch-physikalische Klasse

Abhandl.Ges.Wiss.Göttingen Philol.Hist.Kl. Abhandlungen der (Königlichen) Gesellschaft der Wissenschaften zu Göttingen: Philologisch-historische Klasse

Abhandl.Gesamtgeb.Med. Abhandlungen aus dem Gesamtgebiet der Medizin

Abhandl.Gesch.Math.Wiss. Abhandlungen zur Geschichte der mathematischen Wissenschaften mit Einschluss ihrer Anwendungen

Abhandl.Gesch.Med.Naturwiss. Abhandlungen zur Geschichte der Medizin und der Naturwissenschaften

Abhandl.Gesch.Naturwiss.Med. Abhandlungen zur Geschichte der Naturwissenschaften und der Medizin

Abhandl.Gesch.Veterinärmed. Abhandlungen aus der Geschichte der Veterinärmedizin

Abhandl.Herder-Ges.Herder Inst. Abhandlungen der Herder-Gesellschaft und des Herder Instituts (zu Riga)

Abhandl.Kunde Morgenlandes Abhandlungen für die Kunde des Morgenlandes [Herausgegeben von der Deutschen Morgenländischen Gesellschaft]

Abhandl.Math.Seminar Hamburg.Univ. Abhandlungen aus dem Mathematischen Seminar der Hamburgischen Universität

Abhandl.Med.Fak.Sun Yatsen-Univ.Canton Abhandlungen der Medizinischen Fakultät der Sun Yatsen-Universität Canton

Abhandl.Naturforsch.Ges.Görlitz Abhandlungen der Naturforschenden Gesellschaft zu Görlitz

Abhandl.Naturhist.Ges.Nürnberg Abhandlungen der Naturhistorischen Gesellschaft zu Nürnberg

Abhandl.Naturwiss.Ver.Bremen Abhandlungen herausgegeben vom Naturwissenschaftlichen Verein zu Bremen

Abhandl.Neurol.Psychiat.Psychol. Abhandlungen aus der Neurologie, Psychiatrie, Psychologie und ihren Grenzgebieten

Abhandl.Preuss.Akad.Wiss.Math.Naturwiss.Kl. Abhandlungen der Preussischen Akademie der Wissenschaften: Mathematisch-naturwissenschaftliche Klasse

Abhandl.Preuss.Akad.Wiss.Phil.Hist.Kl. Abhandlungen der Preussischen Akademie der Wissenschaften: Philosophisch-historische Klasse

Abhandl.Preuss.Akad.Wiss.Phys.Math.Kl. Abhandlungen der Preussischen Akademie der Wissenschaften: Physikalisch-mathematische Klasse

Abhandl.Sächs.Akad.Wiss.Philol.Hist.Kl. Abhandlungen der Sächsischen Akademie der Wissenschaften: Philologisch-historische Klasse

Abhandl.Sächs.Ges.Wiss.Math.Phys.Kl. Abhandlungen der Sächsischen Gesellschaft der Wissenschaften: Mathematisch-physikalische Klasse

Abhandl.Sächs.Ges.Wiss.Philol.Hist.Kl. Abhandlungen der Sächsischen Gesellschaft der Wissenschaften: Philologisch-historische Klasse

Abhandl.Schlesischen Ges.Vaterländ.Cult.Geisteswiss.Reihe Abhandlungen der Schlesischen Gesellschaft für vaterländische Cultur: Geisteswissenschaftliche Reihe

Abhandl.Theor.Biol. Abhandlungen zur theoretischen Biologie

Abhandl.Verkehrs- Seegesch. Abhandlungen zur Verkehrs- und Seegeschichte

Acad.Bookman Academy Bookman [Friends of the Rare Bookroom, Library, New York Academy of Medicine]

Acad.Rev.Calif.Acad.Periodontol. Academy Review of the California Academy of Periodontology

Accad.Bibl.Ital. Accademie e Biblioteche d'Italia

Accounting Rev. Accounting Review

Acropole L'Acropole: Revue du monde hellénique

Act.Acad.Sci.Belles Lettres Arts Bordeaux Actes de l'Academie des Sciences, Belles Lettres et Arts de Bordeaux

Act.Colloq.Int.Inst.Étud.Renaissance Hum. Actes du Colloque International de l'Institut pour l'Étude de la Renaissance et de l'Humanisme, Université libre de Bruxelles

Act.Congr.Ass.Guillaume Budé Actes du Congrès de l'Association Guillaume Budé

Act.Congr.Bénélux Hist.Sci. Actes du Congrès Bénélux d'Histoire des Sciences

Act.Congr.Int.Étud.Byzantines Actes du Congrès International des Études Byzantines

Actas Congr.Int.Hist.Med. Actas del Congreso Internacional de Historia de la Medicina

Act.Congr.Int.Hist.Sci. Actes du Congrès International d'Histoire des Sciences

Act.Congr.Int.Phil.Sci. Actes du Congrès International de l'Union Internationale de Philosophie des Sciences

Act.Mus.Hist.Natur.Rouen Actes du Muséum d'Histoire Naturelle de Rouen

Act.Soc.Linn.Bordeaux Actes. Société Linnéenne de Bordeaux

Act.Symp.Int.Sci.Phys.Math.XVIIe Siècle Actes du Symposium International des Sciences Physiques et Mathématiques dans la Première Moitié du 17e Siècle

Acta Antiq.Magyar Tud.Akad. Acta Antiqua: Magyar Tudományos Akadémia [Budapest]

Acta Archaeol.Acad.Sci.Hung. Acta Archaeologica Academiae Scientiarum Hungaricae

Acta Astron.Sinica Acta Astronomica Sinica

Acta Bibl.Gotoburgensis Acta Bibliothecae Gotoburgensis

Acta Cardiol. Acta Cardiologia

Acta Chem.Fenn. Acta Chemica Fennica (Suomen Kemistilehti)

Acta Chir.Acad.Sci.Hung. Acta Chirurgica Academiae Scientiarum Hungaricae

Acta Embryol.Morphol.Exp. Acta Embryologiae et Morphologiae Experimentalis

Acta Genet.Med.Gemellol. Acta Geneticae Medicae et Gemellologiae

Acta Lapponica Acta Lapponica

Acta Math. Acta Mathematica

Acta Med.Hist.Patavina Acta Medicae Historiae Patavina

Acta Med.Ital. Acta Medica Italica

Acta Med.Orient. Acta Medica Orientalia: the Palestine and Near East medical journal

Acta Med.Scand.Suppl. Acta Medica Scandinavica. Supplementum

Acta Neurol.Psychiat.Belg. Acta Neurologica et Psychiatrica Belgica

Acta Orient. Acta Orientalia: Societates Orientales Batava, Danica, Norvegica [Oosters Genootschap in Nederland]

Acta Orient.Acad.Sci.Hungar. Acta Orientalia: Academia Scientiarum Hungarica

Acta Paediat. Acta Paediatrica

Acta Paediat.Suppl. Acta Paediatrica Supplement

Acta Paracelsica Acta Paracelsica [Paracelsus-Gesellschaft]

Acta Phaenol. Acta Phaenologica. International Phenological Journal. Internationale Phaenologische Zeitschrift

Acta Pharm.Jugoslav. Acta Pharmaceutica Jugoslavica

Acta Phil.Fenn. Acta Philosophica Fennica

Acta Phys.Austriaca Acta Physica Austriaca

Acta Physiol.Scand. Acta Physiologica Scandinavica

Acta Phytotaxonom.Geobot. Acta Phytotaxonomica et Geobotanica

Acta Pontif.Acad.Sci. Acta Pontificia Academia Scientiarum

Acta Psychotherap.Psychosom.Orthopaedagog. Acta Psychotherapeutica, Psychosomatica et Orthopaedagogica

Acta Soc.Hum.Litt.Lundensis Acta R. Societatis Humaniarum Litterarum Lundensis

Acta Soc.Sci.Natur.Moravicae Acta Societatis Scientiarum Naturalium Moravicae

Acta Tuberc.Belg. Acta Tuberculosea Belgica

Acta Univ.Gothoburgensis Acta Universitatis Gothoburgensis

Acta Univ.Latviensis Acta Universitatis Latviensis

Actas Acad.Nac.Cienc.Exact.Fís.Natur.Lima Actas de la Academia Nacional de Ciencias Exactas, Físicas y Naturales de Lima

Actas Congr.Int.Hist.Descobrimentos Actas del Congresso Internacional de História dos Descobrimentos

Action Univ. L'Action Universitaire [Montreal. Université. Association des Diplomés.]

Actualidad Méd.Mundial Actualidad Médica Mundial

Additional Ser.Roy.Bot.Gard.Kew Additional Series: Royal Botanic Gardens, Kew

Advance.Sci. Advancement of Science

Advances Carbohyd.Chem. Advances in Carbohydrate Chemistry

Advances Phys.Sci. Advances in Physical Sciences [English translation of *Usp.Fiz.Nauk.*]

Ägyptologische Forsch. Ägyptologische Forschungen

Aegyptus Aegyptus. Rivista Italiana di Egittologia e di Papirologia

Aeron.J. The Aeronautical Journal. [Aeronautical Society of Great Britain]

Aerotecnica L'Aerotecnica: Giornale ed Atti dell'Associazione Italiana di Aerotecnica

Ärztl.Mitt.Baden Ärztliche Mitteilungen aus und für Baden

Ärztl.Rundsch. Ärztliche Rundschau

Aesculape Aesculape

Aesthet.Med. Aesthetische Medizin

Aevum Aevum: Rivista di scienze storiche, linguistiche e filologiche

Afinidad Afinidad

Afr.Franç. L'Afrique Française

Afr.Franç.Renseign.Colon.Doc. L'Afrique Française. Renseignements Coloniaux et Documents

Afr.Ital. Africa Italiana. Rivista di Storia e d'Arte

Afr.Tervuren Africa-Tervuren [Amis du Musée Royal de l'Afrique Centrale]

Âge Or L'Âge d'Or

Agr.Hist. Agricultural History (Agricultural History Society)

Agr.Hist.Rev. Agricultural History Review

Akad.Rundsch. Akademische Rundschau: Zeitschrift für das gesamte Hochschulwesen und die akademischen Berufsstände

Al-Amâlî Al-Amâlî

Al-Andalus Al-Andalus: Revista de las Escuelas de Estudios Árabes de Madrid y Granada

Al-'Irfān Al-'Irfān

Al-Kulliyah Al-Kulliyah [American University of Beirut. Alumni Association]

Al-Machriq Al-Machriq: Revue catholique orientale bimensuelle [Sous la direction des pères de l'Université de St. Joseph]

Al-Muqtataf Al-Muqtataf: an Arabic scientific review

Al-Mustami' al-'Arabī Al-Mustami' al-'Arabī: The Arabic Listener [British Broadcasting Corporation]

Al-Ulum Al-Ulum

Ala.Rev. Alabama Review: A journal of Alabama history [Alabama historical association: University of Alabama]

Albrecht v.Graefes Arch.Ophthalmol. Albrecht von Graefes Archiv für Ophthalmologie

Alexander Turnbull Libr.Bull. Alexander Turnbull Library Bulletin

Allg.Bot.Z. Allgemeine botanische Zeitschrift

Allg.Missions Stud. Allgemeine Missions-Studien

Allg.Rundsch. Allgemeine Rundschau

Allg.Vermessungsnachr. Allgemeine Vermessungsnachrichten

Allg.Z.Psychiat. Allgemeine Zeitschrift für Psychiatrie

Alma Mater (Geneva) Alma Mater: Revue Universitaire de la Suisse Romande

Almanach Matot Braine (Reims) Almanach Matot Braine (Reims)

Alpen Die Alpen

Alpha Omegan Alpha Omegan [Alpha Omega Fraternity]

Alt Hildesheim Alt Hildesheim: eine Zeitschrift für Stadt und Stift Hildesheim

Alte Orient Der alte Orient

Alte Orient Beih. Alte Orient Beihefte

Altertum Das Altertum

Alumni Alumni [Cercle des Alumni, Fondation Universitaire de Belgique, Bruxelles]

Alumni Bull.Univ.Virginia Alumni Bulletin, University of Virginia

Alumni Gaz.Coll.William Mary Alumni Gazette of the College of William and Mary in Virginia

Amâlî, see *Al-Amâlî*

Ambix Ambix: being the journal of the Society for the Study of Alchemy and Early Chemistry

Amer.Anthropol. American Anthropologist

Amer.Antiquity American Antiquity

Amer.Benedictine Rev. American Benedictine Review

Amer.Biol.Teacher American Biology Teacher

Amer.Bookman The American Bookman

Amer.Doc. American Documentation

Amer.Drug. The American Druggist

Amer.Dyestuff Reporter The American Dyestuff Reporter

Amer.Fern J. The American Fern Journal

Amer.Forests American Forests (and Forest Life)

Amer.Ger.Rev. American-German Review

Amer.Heart J. The American Heart Journal

Amer.Hist.Rev. American Historical Review

Amer.Imago American Imago

Amer.Indig. America Indigena

Amer.J.Archaeol. American Journal of Archaeology

Amer.J.Bot. American Journal of Botany

Amer.J.Cardiol. American Journal of Cardiology

Amer.J.Clin.Pathol. American Journal for Clinical Pathology

Amer.J.Dig.Dis. American Journal of Digestive Diseases

Amer.J.Gastroenterol. American Journal of Gastroenterology

Amer.J.Hosp.Pharm. American Journal of Hospital Pharmacy [American Society of Hospital Pharmacists]

Amer.J.Hum.Genet. American Journal of Human Genetics

Amer.J.Hyg. American Journal of Hygiene

Amer.J.Med.Sci. American Journal of Medical Sciences

Amer.J.Ment.Defic. American Journal of Mental Deficiency

Amer.J.Mining American Journal of Mining

Amer.J.Nursing The American Journal of Nursing [American Nurses' Association]

Amer.J.Obstet. American Journal of Obstetrics

Amer.J.Obstet.Gynaecol. American Journal of Obstetrics and Gynaecology

Amer.J.Ophthalmol. American Journal of Ophthalmology

Amer.J.Orthopsychiat. American Journal of Orthopsychiatry

Amer.J.Pharm. American Journal of Pharmacy

Amer.J.Pharm.Educ. American Journal of Pharmaceutical Education

Amer.J.Philol. American Journal of Philology

Amer.J.Phys. American Journal of Physics

Amer.J.Phys.Anthropol. The American Journal of Physical Anthropology

Amer.J.Psychiat. American Journal of Psychiatry

Amer.J.Psychol. American Journal of Psychology

Amer.J.Psychotherap. American Journal of Psychotherapy

Amer.J.Public Health American Journal of Public Health

Amer.J.Roentgenol. American Journal of Roentgenology

Amer.J.Sci. The American Journal of Science

Amer.J.Semitic Lang. American Journal of Semitic Languages: Journal of the Department of Oriental Languages and Literature of the University of Chicag

Amer.J.Sociol. American Journal of Sociology

Amer.J.Surg. American Journal of Surgery and Gynecology

Amer.J.Syph. American Journal of Syphilis

Amer.J.Trop.Med. American Journal of Tropical Medicine

Amer.Jew.Yearb. The American Jewish Yearbook

Amer.Lit. American Literature

Amer.Mag.Art American Magazine of Art

Amer.Math.Mon. American Mathematical Monthly

Amer.Midland Natur. The American Midland Naturalist

Amer.Mineral. The American Mineralogist

Amer.Mus.J. American Museum Journal

Amer.Mus.Novitates American Museum Novitates

Amer.Natur. The American Naturalis'

Amer.Neptune The American Neptune

Amer.Notes Quer. American Notes and Queries

Amer.Numismatic Soc.Mus.Notes American Numismatic Society Museum Notes

Amer.Orient.Ser. American Oriental Series [American Oriental Society]

Amer.Phys.Teacher The American Physics Teacher

Amer.Prof.Pharm. American Professional Pharmacist

Amer.Psychol. The American Psychologist

Amer.Quart. American Quarterly

Amer.Rev.Resp.Dis. American Review of Respiratory Diseases

Amer.Rev.Soviet Med. American Review of Soviet Medicine

Amer.Rev.Tuberc. The American Review of Tuberculosis

Amer.Sch. The American Scholar [*Phi* Society]

Amer.Scient. The American Scientist

Amer.Slavic East Europe.Rev. American Slavic and East European Review

Amer.Sociol.Rev. American Sociological Review

America America: a Catholic review of the week

Amherst Grad.Quart. Amherst Graduates' Quarterly

Amsterdam Natur. Amsterdam Naturalist: Bulletin of the Zoological Museum Amsterdam

An.Acad.Brasil.Ciênc. Anais da Academia Brasileira de Ciências

An.Acad.Farm.Madrid Anales: [Real] Academia de Farmacia, Madrid

An.Ateneo Clín.Quir. Anales del Ateneo de Clínica Quirúrgica

An.Chilenos Hist.Med. Anales Chilenos de Historia de la Medicina

An.Cienc.Natur. Anales de Ciencias Naturales

An.Enseñanza Secundaria Anales de la Enseñanza Secundaria

An.Escuela Nac.Cienc.Biol. Anales de la Escuela Nacional de Ciencias Biológica-

An.Fac.Cienc.Méd. Anales de la Facultad de Ciencias Médicas

An.Fac.Ciênc.Porto Anais de Faculdade de Ciências do Porto

An.Hist.Inst.Dubrovniku Anali: Historijski Institut u Dubrovniku

An.Inst.Biol.Univ.Méx. Anales del Instituto de Biología, Universidad de México

An.Inst.Psicol. Anales del Instituto de Psicología [Buenos Aires]

An.Jard.Bot.Madrid Anales del Jardin Botánico de Madrid

An.Soc.Cient.Argent. Anales de la Sociedad Científica Argentina

An.Soc.Españ.Fís.Quím. Anales de la Sociedad Española de Física y Química

An.Soc.Peruana Hist.Med. Anales de la Sociedad Peruana de Historia de la Medicina

An.Univ.Barcelona Anales de la Universidad de Barcelona

An.Univ.Chile Anales de la Universidad de Chile

An.Univ.Madrid Anales de la Universidad de Madrid

An.Univ.Téc.Lisboa Inst.Super.Agron. Anais do Instituto Superior de Agronomia da Universidade Técnica de Lisboa

Anal.Acad.Rom.Mem.Secţ.Ştiinţ. Analele Academiei Romane Memoriile Secţiunii Ştiinţifice

Anal.Aegyptiaca Analecta Aegyptiaca

Anal.Bollandiana Analecta Bollandiana [Société des Bollandistes]

Anal.Praemonstratensia Analecta Praemonstratensia

Anal.Sacra Tarraconensia Analecta Sacra Tarraconensia: Annuari de la Biblioteca Balmes

Analysis Analysis

Anat.Anz. Anatomischer Anzeiger [Anatomische Gesellschaft]

Anat.Rec. The Anatomical Record

Anatolian Stud. Anatolian Studies. Journal of the British Institute of Archaeology at Ankara

Ancient Egypt Ancient Egypt (and the East)

Andalus, see *Al-Andalus*

Anesthesia Analg. Anesthesia and Analgesia

Angelsport Der Angelsport. Illustrierte Monatsschrift für Angel- und Fischereisport

Angew.Chem. Angewandte Chemie

Angiology Angiology

Anglia Anglia: Zeitschrift für englische Philologie

Anim.Kingdom Animal Kingdom

Ann.ACFAS Annales de l'Association Canadienne-Française pour l'Avancement des Sciences

Ann.Acad.Roy.Archéol.Belg. Annales de l'Academie Royale d'Archéologie de Belgique

Ann.Acad.Sci.Fennicae Annales Academiae Scientiarum Fennicae

Ann.Amer.Acad.Polit.Soc.Sci. Annals of the American Academy of Political and Social Science

Ann.Appl.Biol. The Annals of Applied Biology [Association of Economic (Applied) Biologists]

Ann.Ass.Amer.Geogr. Annals of the Association of American Geographers

Ann.Astron.Observ.Harvard Coll. Annals of the Astronomical Observatory of Harvard College

Ann.Bhandarkar Inst. Annals of the Bhandarkar (Oriental Research) Institute

Ann.Bourgogne Annales de Bourgogne: Revue historique trimestrielle publiée sous le patronage de l'Université de Dijon et de l'Académie des Sciences, Arts et Belles Lettres de Dijon

Ann.Bull.Soc.Méd.Gand Annales et Bulletin de la Société de Médecine de Gand

Ann.Cattedra Petrarchesca Annali della Cattedra Petrarchesca: R. Accademia Petrarca di Lettere, Arti e Scienze, Arezzo

Ann.Chim.Anal. Annales de Chimie Analytique

Ann.Congr.Féderation Archéol.Hist.Belg. Annales du Congrès de la Féderation Archéologique et Historique de Belgique

Ann.Dermatol.Syphiligr. Annales de Dermatologie et Syphiligraphie

Ann.École Nat.Eaux Forêts Annales de l'École Nationale des Eaux et Forêts

Ann.Écon.Soc.Civilizations Annales Économies, Sociétés, Civilizations

Ann.Entomol.Soc.Amer. Annals of the Entomological Society of America

Ann.Fac.Lett.Fil.Univ.Cagliari Annali della Facoltà di Lettere e Filosofia, Università di Cagliari

Ann.Franç.Chronom. Annales Françaises de Chronométrie

Ann.Gen.Pract. Annals of General Practice

Ann.Géogr. Annales de Géographie

Ann.Guébhard-Séverine Annales Guébhard-Séverine

Ann.Hist.Écon.Soc. Annales d'Histoire Économique et Sociale

Ann.Hist.Natur.Mus.Nat.Hung. Annales Historico-Naturales Musei Nationalis Hungarici

Ann.Hist.Natur.Mus.Nat.Hung.Pars Zool. Annales Historico-Naturales Musei Nationalis Hungarici: Pars Zoologica

Ann.Hydrogr. Annales Hydrographiques

Ann.Hydrogr.Marit.Meteorol. Annalen der Hydrographie und maritimen Meteorologie

Ann.Hyg.Méd.Colon. Annales d'Hygiène et de Médecine Coloniales

Ann.Hyg.Publique Ind.Soc. Annales d'Hygiène Publique, Industrielle et Sociale

Ann.Inst.Archéol.Luxemb. Annales de l'Institut Archéologique du Luxembourg

Ann.Inst.Étud.Orient.Univ.Alger Annales de l'Institut d'Études Orientales, Université d'Alger

Ann.Inst.Nat.Agron. Annales de l'Institut National Agronomique

Ann.Inst.Phys.Globe Univ.Paris Annales de l'Institut de Physique du Globe de l'Université de Paris

Ann.Inst.Supér.Phil.Univ.Cath.Louvain Annales de l'Institut Supérieur de Philosophie de l'Université Catholique de Louvain

Ann.Intern.Med. Annals of Internal Medicine [American College of Physicians]

Ann.Intern.Med.Suppl. Annals of Internal Medicine: Supplement

Ann.Lateranensi Annali Lateranensi

Ann.Litt.Franche-Comté Annales Littéraires de Franche-Comté

Ann.Mag.Natur.Hist. Annals and Magazine of Natural History; including Zoology, Botany and Geology

Ann.Mal.Vénér. Annales des Maladies Vénériennes

Ann.Mat.Pura Appl. Annali di Matematica Pura ed Applicata

Ann.Math.Statist. Annals of Mathematical Statistics [Institute of Mathematical Statistics]

Ann.Med.Hist. Annals of Medical History

Ann.Med.Nav. Annali di Medicina Navale

Ann.Med.Nav.Colon. Annale di Medicina Navale e Coloniale

Ann.Med.Nav.Trop. Annali di Medicina Navale e Tropicale

Ann.Méd.Psychol. Annales Médico-Psychologiques [Société Médico-Psychologique]

Ann.Meteorol. Annalen der Meteorologie

Ann.Midi Annales du Midi

Ann.Mines Annales des Mines

Ann.Mines Belg. Annales des Mines de Belgique: Annalen der Mijnen van Belgie

Ann.Missouri Bot.Gard. Annals of Missouri Botanical Garden

Ann.Mus.Guimet Annales Musée Guimet [Paris]

Ann.Mus.Guimet Bibl.Art Annales du Musée Guimet. Bibliothèque d'Art

Ann.Mus.Guimet Bibl.Étud. Annales du Musée Guimet, Bibliothèque d'Études

Ann.Mus.Guimet Bibl.Vulg. Annales du Musée Guimet. Bibliothèque de Vulgarisation

Ann.N.Y.Acad.Sci. Annals of the New York Academy of Sciences

Ann.Natur.Kulturphil. Annalen der Natur- und Kulturphilosophie

Ann.Naturhist.Hofmus. Annalen des (K.K.) Naturhistorischen Hofmuseums. Wien

Ann.Naturphil. Annalen der Naturphilosophie

Ann.Nestlé Annales Nestlé

Ann.Oculist. Annales d'Oculistique

Ann.Osserv.Astron.Torino Annali: Osservatorio Astronomico, Università di Torino

Ann.Oto-laryngol. Annales d'Oto-laryngologie

Ann.Ottalmol.Clin.Oculist. Annali di Ottalmologia e Clinica Oculistica

Ann.Oudheidk.Kring Land Waas Annalen van de Oudheidkundige Kring van het Land van Waas

Ann.Paléontol. Annales de Paléontologie

Ann.Parasitol. Annales de Parasitologie humaine et comparée

Ann.Phil. Annalen der Philosophie (und philosophischen Kritik)

Ann.Phys. Annales de Physique

Ann.Phys.(Leipzig) Annalen der Physik, etc.

Ann.Radiol.Diagn. Annali di Radiologia Diagnostica

Ann.Roy.Coll.Surg. Annals of the Royal College of Surgeons of England

Ann.Sanit.Pubblica Annali della Sanità Pubblica

Ann.Sci. Annals of Science

Ann.Sci.Acad.Polytech.Porto Annaes Scientificos da Academia Polytechnica do Porto

Ann.Serv.Antiquités Égypte Annales du Service des Antiquités de l'Égypte

Ann.Soc.Belg.Méd.Trop. Annales de la Société Belge de Médecine Tropicale

Ann.Soc.Émulation Bruges Annales de la Société d'Émulation de Bruges (Handelingen van het Genootschap voor Geschiedenis te Brugge)

Ann.Soc.Entomol.France Annales de la Société Entomologique de France

Ann.Soc.Géol.Belg. Annales de la Société Géologique de Belgique

Ann.Soc.Hist.Archéol.Arrondissement Saint-Malo Annales de la Société Historique et Archéologique de l'Arrondissement de Saint-Malo

Ann.Soc.Roy.Archéol.Bruxelles Annales de la Société Royale d'Archéologie de Bruxelles

Ann.Soc.Sci.Bruxelles Annales de la Société Scientifique de Bruxelles

Ann.Soc.Sci.Bruxelles, sér.A Annales de la Société Scientifique de Bruxelles, série A: Sciences Mathématiques

Ann.Soc.Sci.Bruxelles, sér.B Annales de la Société Scientifique de Bruxelles, série B: Sciences Physiques et Naturelles

Ann.Soc.Sci.Bruxelles, sér.C Annales de la Société Scientifique de Bruxelles, série C: Sciences Médicales

Ann.Soc.Sci.Bruxelles, sér.D Annales de la Société Scientifique de Bruxelles, série D: Sciences Économiques et Techniques

Ann.Soc.Sci.Bruxelles, sér.1 Annales de la Société Scientifique de Bruxelles, série 1: Sciences Mathématiques, Physiques et Astronomiques

Ann.Soc.Sci.Bruxelles, sér.2 Annales de la Société Scientifique de Bruxelles, série 2: Sciences Naturelles et Médicales

Ann.Soc.Sci.Litt.Cannes Annales: Société Scientifique et Littéraire de Cannes et de l'Arrondissement de Grasse

Ann.Soc.Sci.Natur.Charente-Marit. Annales de la Société des Sciences Naturelles de la Charente-Maritime

Ann.Soc.Zool.Belg. Annales de la Société [Royale] Zoologique de Belgique

Ann.Soc.Zool.Malacol.Belg. Annales de la Société [Royale] Zoologique et Malacologique de Belgique

Ann.Sta.Sperim.Agrumicoltura Annali della [Reale] Stazione Sperimentale di Agrumicoltura e Frutticoltura in Acireale

Ann.Städt.Allg.Krankenhäuser München Annalen: Städtische Allgemeine Krankenhäuser zu München

Ann.Surg. Annals of Surgery

Ann.Trop.Med.Parasitol. Annals of Tropical Medicine and Parasitology

Ann.Univ.Ankara Annales de l'Université d'Ankara

Ann.Univ.Ferrara, sez.1 Annali dell'Università di Ferrara, sezione I: Anatomia umana

Ann.Univ.Genova Annali della Reale Università di Genova

Ann.Univ.Lyon, nouv.sér.2 Annales de l'Université de Lyon, nouvelle série 2: Droit, lettres

Ann.Univ.Lyon, 3e sér.Lett. Annales de l'Université de Lyon, 3e série, Lettres

Ann.Univ.Paris Annales de l'Université de Paris [Société des Amis de l'Université de Paris]

Ann.Univ.Saraviensis Math.Naturwiss.Fak. Annales Universitatis Saraviensis: Mathematisch-naturwissenschaftliche Fakultät

Ann.Univ.Saraviensis Med. Annales Universitatis Saraviensis: Medizin

Ann.Univ.Saraviensis Naturwiss. Annales Universitatis Saraviensis: Naturwissenschaften [formerly *Ann.Univ.Saraviensis Wiss.*]

Ann.Univ.Saraviensis Phil. Annales Universitatis Saraviensis: Philosophie

Ann.Univ.Saraviensis Sci. Annales Universitatis Saraviensis: Scientia [formerly *Ann.Univ.Saraviensis Naturwiss.*]

Ann.Univ.Saraviensis Wiss. Annales Universitatis Saraviensis: Wissenschaften

Ann.Univ.Toscane Annali delle Università Toscane [Pisa]

Ann.Valaisannes Annales Valaisannes

Ann.Western Med.Surg. Annals of Western Medicine and Surgery [Los Angeles County Medical Association]

Année Biol. L'Année Biologique: Comptes Rendus Annuels des Travaux de Biologie Générale [Fédération des Sociétés de Sciences Naturelles]

Année Méd. L'Année Médicale [Société de Médecine de Caen et du Calvados]

Année Pédagog. L'Année Pédagogique [Ministère de l'Instruction Publique]

Année Phil. L'Année Philosophique

Annu.Acad.Int.Hist.Sci. Annuaire de l'Académie Internationale d'Histoire des Sciences

Annu.Acad.Roy.Belg. Annuaire de l'Académie Royale de Belgique

Annu.Acad.Sci. (Paris) Annuaire de l'Académie des Sciences, Institut de France

Annu.Accad.Ital. Annuario della [Reale] Accademia d'Italia

Annu.Accad.Univ.Stud.Siena Annuario Accademico: [Regia] Università degli Studi de Siena

Annu.Amer.Sch.Orient.Res.Jerusalem Annual of the American School of Oriental Research in Jerusalem

Annu.Ass.Ott.Ital. Annuario: Associazione Ottica Italiana

Annu.Astron.Osserv.Astron.Torino Annuario Astronomico: Osservatorio Astronomico, Università di Torino

Annu.Bibl.Fil. Annuario della Bibliotheca Filosofica [Società per gli Studi Filosofici]

Annu.Bibliogr.Indian Archaeol. Annual Bibliography of Indian Archaeology

Annu.Bur.Longitudes (Paris) Annuaire publié par le Bureau de Longitudes [Paris]

Annu.Hebrew Union Coll. Annual: Hebrew Union College [Cincinnati, Ohio]

Annu.Inst.Philol.Hist.Orient. Annuaire de l'Institut de Philologie et d'Historie Orientales et Slaves, Université Libre de Bruxelles

Annu.Observ.Belg.Annu.Météorol. Annuaire de l'Observatoire Royale de Belgique, 2ieme série: Annuaire Météorologique

Annu.Rep.Amer.Hist.Ass. Annual Report of the American Historical Association

Annu.Rep.Archaeol.Surv.India Annual Report of the Archaeological Survey of India

Annu.Rep.Can.Hist.Ass. Annual Report. Canadian Historical Association

Annu.Rep.Dante Soc. Annual Report of the Dante Society

Annu.Rep.Peterborough Natur.Hist.Sci.Archaeol.Soc. Annual Report of the Peterborough Natural History, Scientific, and Archaeological Society

Annu.Rep.Progr.Chem. Annual Reports on the Progress of Chemistry

Annu.Rep.Smithsonian Inst. Annual Report of the [Board of Regents of the] Smithsonian Institution

Annu.Rev.Entomol. Annual Review of Entomology

Annu.Rev.Phys.Chem. Annual Review of Physical Chemistry

Annu.Rev.Physiol. Annual Review of Physiology

Annu.Sta.Bacol.Sperim.Padova Annuario della R. Stazione Bacologica Sperimentale di Padova

Annu.Univ.Modena Annuario della Reale Università di Modena

Annu.Vie Int. Annuaire de la Vie Internationale

Anthropol.Pap.Amer.Mus.Natur.Hist. Anthropological Papers of the American Museum of Natural History

Anthropologie (Paris) L'Anthropologie

Anthropologie (Prague) L'Anthropologie [Publiée par l'Institut d'Anthropologie de l'Université Charles à Prague]

Anthropos Anthropos: ephemeris internationalis ethnologica et linguistica, etc.

Antike Die Antike: Zeitschrift für Kunst und Kultur des klassischen Altertums

Antiq.Horology Antiquarian Horology and the Proceedings of the Antiquarian Horological Society

Antiquité Cl. L'Antiquité Classique

Antiquity Antiquity

Antonie van Leeuwenhoek Antonie van Leeuwenhoek: Journal of Microbiology and Serology

Antwerpen Tijdschr. Antwerpen Tijdschrift der Stad Antwerpen

Antwerpsch Archievenbl. Antwerpsch Archievenblad

Anu.Arh.Folklor. Anuarul Arhivei de Folklor

Anu.Inst.Ist.Nat.Univ.Cluj Anuarul Institutului de Istorie Nationala, Universitate din Cluj

Anu.Inst.Stud.Cl.Univ.Cluj Anuarul [pe anii 1928-1932]: Institut de Studii Clasice, Universitate din Cluj

Appl.Anthropol. Applied Anthropology

Appl.Mech.Rev. Applied Mechanics Reviews

Appl.Opt. Applied Optics

Aquarist The Aquarist and Pondkeeper

Arastirma Arastirma [Institute for Research in Philosophy, the History of Science, Psychology and Sociology, Ankara]

Arb.Anat.Inst. Arbeiten aus anatomischen Instituten

Arb.Deut.Nord.Ges.Gesch.Med. Arbeiten der Deutsch-Nordischen Gesellschaft für Geschichte der Medezin der Jahrheilkunde und der Naturwissenschaften

Arb.Inst.Gesch.Med.Univ.Leipzig Arbeiten des Instituts für Geschichte der Medizin an der Universität Leipzig

Arb.Kunsthist.Inst.Univ.Wien Arbeiten des Kunsthistorisches Instituts, Universität Wien

Arbor Arbor [Consejo Superior de Investigaciones Cientificas]

Arch.Anat.Physiol.Anat.Abt. Archiv für Anatomie und Physiologie: Anatomische Abteilung

Arch.Anat.Physiol.Physiol.Abt. Archiv für Anatomie und Physiologie: Physiologische Abteilung

Arch.Anthropol. Archiv für Anthropologie (Völkerforschung und kolonialen Kulturwandel) [Deutsche Gesellschaft für Anthropologie, Ethnologie und Urgeschichte]

Arch.Anthropol.Criminelle Archives d'Anthropologie Criminelle de Médecine Légale et de Psychologie Normale et Pathologique

Arch.Augenheilk. Archiv für Augenheilkunde

Arch.Bádáni Životě Spisech J.A. Komenského Archiv pro bádáni o životě a spisech J.A. Komenského. Acta comeniana

Arch.Balkaniques Méd.Chir.Spéc. Archives Balkaniques de Médicine, Chirurgie et leurs Spécialités

Arch.Begriffsgesch. Archiv für Begriffsgeschichte. Bausteine zu einem historischen Wörterbuch der Philosophie

Arch.Belg.Dermatol.Syhpiligr. Archives Belges de Dermatologie et de Syphiligraphie

Arch.Bibl.Mus.Belg. Archives, Bibliothèques, et Musées de Belgique

Arch.Biol. Archives de Biologie

Arch.Bot. Archivio Botanico e Biogeografico Italiano

Arch.Buchgewerbe Archiv für Buchgewerbe

Arch.Deputazione Romana Stor.Patria Archivio della [Reale] Deputazione Romana di Storia Patria

Arch.Dermatol.Syph. Archiv für Dermatologie und Syphilis

Arch.Eisenhüttenwesen Archiv für das Eisenhüttenwesen

Arch.Farmacogn. Archivio di Farmacognosia e Scienze Affini

Arch.Fil. Archivio di Filosofia

Arch.Fischereigesch. Archiv für Fischereigeschichte

Arch.Fisiol. Archivio di Fisiologia

Arch.Franciscanum Hist. Archivum Franciscanum Historicum [Collegium S. Bonaventura, Quaracchi]

Arch.Franco-Belg.Chir. Archives Franco-Belges de Chirurgie

Arch.Fratrum Praedicatorum Archivum Fratrum Praedicatorum [Institutum Historicum ff. Praedicatorum Romae

Arch.Gesamte Psychol. Archiv für die gesamte Psychologie

Arch.Gesch.Math.Naturwiss.Tech. Archiv für Geschichte der Mathematik, der Naturwissenschaften und der Technik

Arch.Gesch.Med. Archiv für Geschichte der Medizin (Universität Leipzig) [subsequently Sudhoffs Archiv für Geschichte der Medizin und der Naturwissenschaften]

Arch.Gesch.Naturwiss.Tech. Archiv für die Geschichte der Naturwissenschaften und der Technik [Berliner Gesellschaft für Geschichte der Naturwissenschaften und Medizin]

Arch.Gesch.Phil. Archiv für Geschichte der Philosophie

Arch.Gynäkol. Archiv für Gynäkologie

Arch.Hist.Doctrinale Litt.Moyen Âge Archives d'Histoire Doctrinale et Littéraire du Moyen Âge

Arch.Hist.Exact Sci. Archive for History of Exact Sciences

Arch.Hist.Fil.Med. Archiwum historji i filozofji medycyny

Arch.Hist.Med.(Warszawa) Archiwum Historji Medycyny: Organ Polskiego Towarzystwa Historii Medycyny

Arch.Hist.Méd.Venezuela Archivos de Histŏria Médica de Venezuela

Arch.Hist.Soc.Iesu Archivum Historicum Societatis Iesu

Arch.Hist.Ver.Unterfranken Archiv des historischen Vereins von Unterfranken und Aschaffenburg

Arch.Histol.Norm.Patol. Archivos de Histologia Normal y Patológica

Arch.Hydrobiol. Archiv für Hydrobiologie (und Plankton Kunde)

Arch.Hydrobiol.Suppl. Archiv für Hydrobiologie. Supplement

Arch.Iberoamer.Hist.Med. Archivos Iberoamericanos de Historia de la Medicina y Antropologia Médica

Arch.Inst.Grand-Ducal Luxemb.Sect.Sci. Archives de l'Institut Grand-Ducal de Luxembourg, Section des Sciences Naturelles, Physiques et Mathématiques

Arch.Inst.Int.Sci.Théor.Sér.A.Bull.Acad.Int.Phil.Sci. Archives de l'Institut International des Sciences Théoriques, série A. Bulletin de l'Académie Internationale de Philosophie des Sciences

Arch.Inst.Pasteur Algerie Archives de l'Institut Pasteur d'Algerie

Arch.Inst.Pasteur Tunis Archives de l'Institut Pasteur de Tunis

Arch.Int.Hist.Sci. Archives Internationales d'Histoire des Sciences

Arch.Int.Neurol. Archives Internationales de Neurologie

Arch.Int.Pharmacodyn.Thérap. Archives Internationales de Pharmacodynamie et de Thérapie

Arch.Int.Physiol. Archives Internationales de Physiologie

Arch.Intern.Med. Archives of Internal Medicine

Arch.Ital.Anat.Embriol. Archivio Italiano di Anatomia e di Embriologia

Arch.Ital.Biol. Archives Italiennes de Biologie

Arch.Ital.Chir. Archivio Italiano di Chirurgia

Arch.Klärung Wünschelrutenfrage Archiv zur Klärung der Wünschelrutenfrage

Arch.Klin.Chirurg. Archiv für Klinische Chirurgie

Arch.Komisji Badania Hist.Fil.Polsce Archiwum Komisji do badania historji filozofii w Polsce [Akademja Umiejętności]

Arch.Kriminalanthropol.Kriminalistik Archiv für Kriminal-Anthropologie und Kriminalistik

Arch.Kriminol. Archiv für Kriminologie

Arch.Kulturgesch. Archiv für Kulturgeschichte

Arch.Laryngol.Rhinol. Archiv für Laryngologie und Rhinologie

Arch.Math.(Karlsruhe) Archiv der Mathematik (Karlsruhe)

Arch.Math.Naturvidensk. Archiv for Mathematik og Naturvidenskab

Arch.Math.Phys. Archiv der Mathematik und Physik

Arch.Méd.Angers Archives Médicales d'Angers

Arch.Méd.Enfants Archives de Médecine des Enfants

Arch.Med.Hydrol. Archives of Medical Hydrology

Arch.Med.Leg. Archivos de Medicina Legal

Arch.Medico-chir.Provence Archives Médico-chirurgicales de Provence

Arch.Morphol.Gén.Exp. Archives de Morphologie Générale et Expérimentale

Arch.Mus.Hist.Natur. Archives du Muséum d'Histoire Naturelle

Arch.Mus.Teyler Archives Musée Teyler [Haarlem

Arch.Musikwiss. Archiv für Musikwissenschaft

Arch.Néer.Zool. Archives Néerlandaises de Zoologie [Nederlandsche Dierkundige Vereeniging]

Arch.Neurol.Psychiat. Archives of Neurology and Psychiatry

Arch.Österr.Gesch. Archiv für Österreische Geschichte

Arch.Ohren.Nasen.Kehlkopfheilk. Archiv für Ohren-, Nasen-, und Kehlkopfheilkunde

Arch.Ophthalmol. Archives of Ophthalmology

Arch.Orient. Archiv Orientální: Journal of the Czechoslovak Oriental Institute: Zeitschrift des Orientalischen Instituts in Prag

Arch.Orient.Pragense Archivum Orientale Pragense (Československý Orientálni Ústav v Praze) [formerly and subsequently *Arch.Orient.*]

Arch.Orientforsch. Archiv für Orientforschung

Arch.Orientforsch Beih. Archiv für Orientforschung: Beiheft

Arch.Otolaryngol. Archives of Otolaryngology

Arch.Papyrusforsch. Archiv für Papyrusforschung und verwandte Gebiete

Arch.Parasitol. Archives de Parasitologie

Arch.Pathol. Archives of Pathology

Arch.Pathol.Lab.Med. Archives of Pathology and Laboratory Medicine

Arch.Patol.Clin.Med. Archivio di Patologia e Clinica Medica

Arch.Pharm.Ber.Deut.Pharm.Ges. Archiv der Pharmazie und Berichte der Deutschen Pharmazeutischen Gesellschaft

Arch.Pharm.Chem. Archiv for Pharmaci og Chemi

Arch.Phil.(N.Y.) Archives of Philosophy, Psychology and Scientific Method

Arch.Phil.(Paris) Archives de Philosophie [Maison d'Études Philosophiques]

Arch.Phys.Terap. Archiv für physikalische Therapie, Balneologie und Klimatologie

Arch.Prov.Chir. Archives Provinciales de Chirurgie

Arch.Psychiat. Archiv für Psychiatrie und Nervenkrankheiten

Arch.Psychoanal. Archives of Psychoanalysis

Arch.Reformationsgesch. Archiv für Reformationsgeschichte

Arch.Religionspsychol. Archiv für Religionspsychologie (und Seelenführung)

Arch.Religionswiss. Archiv für Religionswissenschaft [Heidelberger Akademie der Wissenschaften *and* Religionswissenschaftliche Gesellschaft in Stockholm]

Arch.Romanicum Archivum Romanicum: nuova rivista di filologia romanza

Arch.Schiffs- Trop.Hyg. Archiv für Schiffs- und Tropen-Hygiene, unter besonderer Berücksichtigung der Pathologie und Therapie

Arch.Schriftk. Archiv für Schriftkunde: Offizielles Organ des Deutschen Schriftmuseums zu Leipzig

Arch.Sci.Phys.Natur. Archives des Sciences physiques et naturelles

Arch.Soc.Belg.Phil. Archives de la Société Belge de Philosophie

Arch.Soc.Franç.Collect.Ex Libris Archives de la Société Française des Collectionneurs d'*ex libris*

Arch.Stor.Calabria Lucania Archivio Storico per la Calabria e la Lucania: supplemento trimestriale to *Atti Mem.Soc.Magna Grecia*

Arch.Stor.Ital. Archivio Storico Italiano [R. Deputazione Toscana di Storia Patria]

Arch.Stor.Prov.Parmensi Archivio Storico per le Provincie Parmensi

Arch.Stor.Sci. Archivio di Storia della Scienza

Arch.Surg. Archives of Surgery

Arch.Syst.Phil.Soziol. Archiv für Systematische Philosophie und Soziologie

Arch.Tisiol. Archivos de Tisiología

Arch.Tisiol. (Naples) Archivio di Tisiologia e delle Malattie dell'Apparato Respiratorio

Arch.Tow.Nauk.Lwow. Archiwum Towarzystwa Naukowego we Lwowie

Arch.Wirtschaftsforsch.Orient Archiv für Wirtschaftsforschung im (naheren) Orient

Arch.Wiss.Prakt.Tierheilk. Archiv für wissenschaftliche und praktische Tierheilkunde

Arch.Zool.Ital. Archivio Zoologico (Italiano)

Archaeol.Cambrensis Archaeologia Cambrensis

Archaeol.Cantiana Archaeologia Cantiana [Kent Archaeological Society, Maidstone]

Archaeol.J. Archaeological Journal

Archaeol.Orient. Archaeologia Orientalis [Toa-kokogaku-kwai. Far Eastern Archaeological Society]

Archaeologia Archaeologia, or miscellaneous tracts relating to antiquity

Archaeology Archaeology

Archeion Archeion: Archivio di storia della scienza

Archeografo Triestino L'Archeografo Triestino

Archiginnasio L'Archiginnasio: Bullettino della Biblioteca Comunale dell' Archiginnasio [Bologna]

Archimede Archimede: Rivista per gli insegnanti e i cultori di matematiche pure e applicate

Archimede (Palermo) Archimede: Rassegna Bimestrale di Matematica, Fisica e Ingegneria

Architects' J. The Architects' Journal

Archivalische Z. Archivalische Zeitschrift

Archivalische Z.Beih. Archivalische Zeitschrift Beiheft

Archivar Der Archivar [Verein Deutscher Archivare]

Archives Archives [British Records Association]

Arcisped.S.Anna Ferrara Arcispedale S. Anna di Ferrara: Revista Bimstrale di Scienze Mediche

Ardenne Famenne Ardenne et Famenne: art-archéologie-histoire-folklore

Arduo L'Arduo: Rivista mensile de scienza, filosofia e storia

Argosy (Sackville, N.B.) Argosy [published by the students of Mount Allison University and Mount Allison Ladies' College, Sackville, New Brunswick]

Ark.Astron. Arkiv för Astronomi [Svenska Vetenskaps Akademien]

Ark.Mat.Astron.Fys. Arkiv för Matematik, Astronomi och Fysik

Arkansas Hist.Quart. Arkansas Historical Quarterly [Arkansas Historical Association]

Arkh.Anat.Gistol.Émbriol. Arkhiv Anatomii Gistologii i Émbriologii

Arkh.Ist.Nauk.Tekh. Arkhiv Istorii Nauki i Tekhniki [Trudy Instituta Istorii Nauki i Tekhniki, Leningrad]

Arktis Arktis. Vierteljahrschrift der internationalen Studiengesellschaft zur Erforschung der Arktis mit dem Luftschiff

Armed Forces Chem.J. Armed Forces Chemical Journal

Armenian Aff. Armenian Affairs

Armenian Quart. Armenian Quarterly

Army Ordnance Army Ordnance [Army Ordnance Association, Washington, D.C.]

Arq.Anat.Antropol. Arquivo de Anatomia e Antropologia [Instituto de Anatomia da Faculdade de Medecina da Universidade de Lisboa]

Arq.Hist.Port. Arquivo Histórico de Portugal

Ars Islamica Ars Islamica

Arsberät.K.Hum.Vetenskapssamfundet Arsberättelse. Kungliga Humanistika Vetenskapssamfundet. Bulletin de la Société Royale des Lettres de Lund

Årsberet.Kjøbenhavns Univ.Med.Hist.Mus. Årsberetning: Medicinsk-historisk Museum, Kjøbenhavns Universitet

Årsbok Sydsvenska Geogr.Sällsk.Lund Årsbok: Sydsvenska Geografiska Sällskapet i Lund

Art Archaeol. Art and Archaeology

Art Bull. Art Bulletin

Art Lett. Art and Letters: India and Pakistan [Royal India and Pakistan Society, London]

Art Quart. Art Quarterly

Arte L'Arte

Arthritis Rheum. Arthritis and Rheumatism

Artibus Asiae Artibus Asiae [Ascona]

Artilleriiskii Zh. Artilleriiskii Zhurnal

Arts France Arts de France

Aryan Path The Aryan Path

Asa Gray Bull. Asa Gray Bulletin

Asia Major Asia Major

Asiatic Rev. Asiatic Review

Asiatica Asiatica: bollettino dell'Istituto Italiano per il Medio ed Estremo Oriente

Asiatische Stud. Asiatische Studien: Études Asiatiques [Schweizerische Gesellschaft für Asienkunde]

Astron.Abhandl.Ergänzungshefte Astron.Nachr. Astronomische Abhandlungen als Ergänzungshefte zu den Astronomischen Nachrichten

Astron.J. Astronomical Journal

Astron.Jahresber. Astronomischer Jahresbericht

Astron.Nachr. Astronomische Nachrichten

Astron.Sällsk. Astronomiska Sällskapet

Astronautics Aerospace Eng. Astronautics and Aerospace Engineering

Astronomie L'Astronomie: Bulletin de la Société Astronomique de France

Astrophys.J. Astrophysical Journal

Ateneo Parmense Ateneo Parmense [Società Medica di Parma]

Athena (Athens) Athena

Athena (Rome) Athena: Rassegna mensile di biologia, clinica e terapia

Atlantic Med.J. Atlantic Medical Journal

Atlantic Mon. The Atlantic Monthly

Atlantis Atlantis. Länder, Volker, Reisen

Atomes Atomes: tous les Aspects Scientifiques d'un Nouvel Âge

Atti Accad.Crusca Atti della Reale Accademia della Crusca [Florence]

Atti Accad.Fisiocrit.Siena Atti della [R.] Accademia dei Fisiocritici di Siena

Atti Accad.Georgofili Atti della Real Accademia dei Georgofili di Firenze

Atti Accad.Ital.Mem.Cl.Sci.Fis.Mat.Natur. Atti della [Reale] Accademia d'Italia: Memorie delle Classe di Scienze Fisiche, Matematiche e Naturali

Atti Accad.Ital.Mem.Cl.Sci.Morali Stor.Filol. Atti della [Reale] Accademia Italia: Memorie della Classe di Scienze Morali, Storiche e Filologich

Atti Accad.Ital.Rendic.Cl.Sci.Fis.Mat.Natur. Atti della [Reale] Accademia d'Italia: Rendiconti della Classe di Scienze Fisiche, Matematiche e Naturali

Atti Accad.Ital.Rendic.Cl.Sci.Morali Stor.Filol. Atti della [Reale] Accademia d'Italia: Rendiconti della Classe di Scienze Morali, Storiche e Filologiche

Atti Accad.Lincei Mem.Cl.Sci.Fis.Mat.Natur. Atti della [Reale] Accademia dei Lincei: Memorie della Classe di Scienze Fisiche, Matematiche e Naturali

Atti Accad.Lincei Mem.Cl.Sci.Morali Stor.Filol. Atti della [Reale] Accademia dei Lincei: Memorie della Classe di Scienze Morali, Storiche e Filologiche

Atti Accad.Lincei Rendic.Cl.Sci.Fis.Mat.Natur. Atti della [Reale] Accademia dei Lincei: Rendiconti della Classe di Scienze Fisiche, Matematiche e Naturali

Atti Accad.Lincei Rendic.Cl.Sci.Morali Stor.Filol. Atti della [Reale] Accademia dei Lincei: Rendiconti della Classe di Scienze Morali, Storiche e Filologiche

Atti Accad.Lincei Rendic.Sedute Solenni Atti della [Reale] Accademia dei Lincei: Rendiconti delle Sedute Solenni

Atti Accad.Med.Chir.Napoli Atti della Reale Accademia Medico-Chirurgica, Napoli

Atti Accad.Naz.Lincei Mem.Cl.Sci.Fis.Mat.Natur. Atti della [Reale] Accademia Nazionale dei Lincei: Memorie della Classe di Scienze Fisiche, Matematiche e Naturali

Atti Accad.Naz.Lincei Mem.Cl.Sci.Morali Stor.Filol. Atti della [Reale] Accademia Nazionale dei Lincei: Memorie della Classe di Scienze Morali, Storiche e Filologiche

Atti Accad.Naz.Lincei Rendic.Cl.Sci.Fis.Mat.Natur. Atti della [Reale] Accademia Nazionale dei Lincei: Rendiconti della Classe di Scienze Fisiche, Matematiche e Naturali

Atti Accad.Naz.Lincei Rendic.Cl.Sci.Morali Stor.Filol. Atti della [Reale] Accademia Nazionale dei Lincei: Rendiconti della Classe di Scienze Morali, Storiche e Filologiche

Atti Accad.Naz.Lincei Rendic.Sedute Solenni Atti della [Reale] Accademia Nazionale dei Lincei: Rendiconti delle Sedute Solenni

Atti Accad.Peloritana Atti della [Reale] Accademia Peloritana

Atti Accad.Peloritana Cl.Sci.Fis.Mat.Biol. Atti della [Reale] Accademia Peloritana: Classe di Scienze Fisiche, Matematiche e Biologiche

Atti Accad.Pontaniana Atti della Accademia Pontaniana

Atti Accad.Sci.Fis.Mat.Napoli Atti della Reale Accademia delle Scienze Fisiche e Matematiche, Società Reale di Napoli

Atti Accad.Sci.Ist.Bologna Cl.Sci.Fis.Rendic. Atti della Accademia delle Scienze dell'Istituto di Bologna, Classe di Scienze Fisiche: Rendiconti

Atti Accad.Sci.Med.Chir.Napoli Atti: [Reale] Accademia delle Scienze Medico-Chirurgiche, Napoli

Atti Accad.Sci.Torino Atti della [Reale] Accademia delle Scienze di Torino

Atti Accad.Sci.Torino Cl.Sci.Fis.Mat.Natur. Atti della [Reale] Accademia delle Scienze di Torino: Classe di Scienze Fisiche, Matematiche e Naturali

Atti Accad.Sci.Torino Cl.Sci.Morali Stor.Filol. Atti della [Reale] Accademia delle Scienze di Torino: Classe di Scienze Morali, Storiche e Filologiche

Atti Ass.Ital.Aerotec. Atti dell'Associazione Italiana di Aerotecnica

Atti Clin.Oto-rino-laringoiatrica Univ.Roma Atti della Clinica Oto-rino-laringoiatrica della R. Università di Roma

Atti Congr.Geogr.Ital. Atti del Congresso Geografico Italiano

Atti Congr.Int.Amer. Atti del Congresso Internazionale degli Americanisti

Atti Congr.Int.Fil. Atti del Congresso Internazionale di Filosofia

Atti Congr.Int.Mat. Atti del Congresso Internazionale dei Matematici

Atti Congr.Int.Stor.Med. Atti del Congresso Internazionale di Storia della Medicina

Atti Congr.Int.Stud.Bizantini Atti del Congresso Internazionale dei Studi Bizantini

Atti Congr.Mathesis Atti del Congresso della Mathesis, Societa' Italiana di Matematica

Atti Congr.Naz.Soc.Ital.Stor.Sci.Med.Natur. Atti del Congresso Nazionale della Società Italiana di Storia delle Scienze Mediche e Naturali

Atti Congr.Unione Mat.Ital. Atti del Congresso dell'Unione Matematica Italiana

Atti Conv.Internaz.Anniv.Nascita R.G. Boscovich Anniv.Fond. Osserv.Brera Atti del Convegno Internazionale Celebrativo del Anniversario della Nascita di R.G. Boscovich e del Anniversario della Fondazione dell' Osservatorio di Brera

Atti Conv.Naz.Logica Atti del Convegno Nazionale di Logica

Atti Deputazione Stor.Prov.Modenesi Atti della Deputazione di Storia Patria per le Provincie Modenesi

Atti Fond.Ronchi Atti della Fondazione "Giorgio Ronchi"

Atti Ist.Veneto Sci. Atti del Reale Istituto Veneto di Scienze, Lettere ed Arti

Atti Mem.Accad.Agr.Sci.Lett.Verona Atti e Memorie dell'Accademia di Agricoltura, Scienze e Lettere di Verona

Atti Mem.Accad.Patavina Sci.Lett.Arti Atti e Memorie dell'Accademia Patavina di Scienze, Lettere ed Arti

Atti Mem.Accad.Petrarca Lett.Arti Sci. Atti e Memorie della Reale Accademia Petrarca di Lettere, Arti e Scienze

Atti Mem.Accad.Sci.Lett.Arti Modena Atti e Memorie: Reale Accademia di Scienze, Lettere ed Arti di Modena

Atti Mem.Accad.Sci.Lett.Arti Padova Atti e Memorie della Reale Accademia di Scienze, Lettere ed Arti di Padova

Atti Mem.Accad.Stor.Arte Sanit. Atti e Memorie dell'Accademia di Storia dell'Arte Sanitaria

Atti Mem.Deputazione Stor.Antiche Prov.Modenesi, 8th ser. Atti e Memorie della Deputazione di Storia [Patria] per le Antiche Provincie Modenesi

Atti Mem.Deputazione Stor.Emilia Romagna Atti e Memorie della [R.] Deputazione di Storia [Patria] per l'Emilia e la Romagna

Atti Mem.Deputazione Stor.Modenesi Atti e Memorie della [R.] Deputazione di Storia [Patria] per le [Provincie] Modenesi

Atti Mem.Deputazione Stor.Modenesi Parmensi Atti e Memorie della [Reale] Deputazione di Storia [Patria] per le [Provincie] Modenesi e Parmensi

Atti Mem.Deputazione Stor.Romagna Atti e Memorie della [Reale] Deputazione di Storia [Patria] per le [Provincie] di Romagna

Atti Mem.Deputazioni Stor.Emilia, new ser. Atti e Memorie delle [R.R.] Deputazioni di Storia [Patria] per le [Provincie] dell'Emilia

Atti Mem.Soc.Magna Grecia Atti e Memorie della Società Magna Grecia

Atti Pontif.Accad.Romana Nuovi Lincei Atti della Pontificia Accademia Romana dei Nuovi Lincei

Atti Pontif.Accad.Sci. Atti della Pontificia Accademia delle Scienze

Atti Pontif.Accad.Sci.Nuovi Lincei Atti della Pontificia Accademia delle Scienze Nuovi Lincei

Atti Sind.Ing.Lombardia Atti dei Sindacati Ingegneri di Lombardia

Atti Soc.Ital.Anat. Atti della Società Italiana di Anatomia

Atti Soc.Ital.Progr.Sci.Riunione Atti della Società Italiana per il Progresso delle Scienze ... Riunione

Atti Soc.Ital.Stor.Crit.Sci.Med.Natur. Atti della Società Italiana di Storia Critica delle Scienze Mediche e Naturali

Atti Soc.Ligure Stor.Patria Atti delle Società Ligure di Storia Patria

Atti Soc.Ligustica Sci.Lett. Atti della Società Ligustica di Scienze e Lettere

Atti Soc.Ligustica Sci.Natur.Geogr. Atti della Società Ligustica di Scienze Naturali e Geografiche

Atti Soc.Natur.Mat.Modena Atti della Società dei Naturalisti e Matematici di Modena

Atti Soc.Toscana Ig. Atti della Società Toscana d'Igiene

Atti Soc.Toscana Sci.Natur. Atti della Società Toscana di Scienze Naturali [Pisa]

Attualità Sci. Attualità Scientifiche

Auk The Auk

Aus Heimat Aus der Heimat: eine naturwissenschaftliche Zeitschrift [Deutscher Verein für Naturkunde]

Aus Natur Aus der Natur: Zeitschrift für alle Naturfreunde

Aus Unterricht Forsch. Aus Unterricht und Forschung: Korrespondenzblatt der höheren Schulen Würtembergs, neue Folge

Aus Welt Tech. Aus der Welt der Technik

Australasian J.Pharm. Australasian Journal of Pharmacy

Australasian J.Phil. Australasian Journal of Philosophy

Australian Geogr. Australian Geographer

Australian J.Sci. Australian Journal of Science [Australian National Research Council]

Australian Math.Teacher Australian Mathematics Teacher

Australian Mus.Mag. The Australian Museum Magazine

Australian New Zeal.J.Obstet.Gynaecol. Australian and New Zealand Journal of Obstetrics and Gynaecology

Australian New Zeal.J.Surg. Australian and New Zealand Journal of Surgery

Autograph Collect.J. Autograph Collectors Journal

Avhandl.Norske Videnskapsakad.Oslo Hist.Fil.Kl. Avhandlinger utgitt av Det Norske Videnskapsakademi i Oslo: Historisk-filosofisk Klasse

Avhandl.Norske Videnskapsakad.Oslo Matematisk-naturvidensk.Kl. Avhandlinger utgitt av det Norske Videnskapsakademi i Oslo, Matematisk-naturvidenskapelig Klasse

Aviazione Aviazione

B

BASF BASF: Badische Anilin- und Soda-Fabrik

Babyloniaca Babyloniaca. Études de Philologie Assyro-babylonienne (et l'Histoire de l'Orient)

Bacteriol.News Bacteriological News

Bacteriol.Rev. Bacteriological Reviews

Badger Pharm. The Badger Pharmacist [Wisconsin Pharmaceutical Association]

Baessler Arch. Baessler Archiv. Beitrage zur Völkerkunde

Baltic Scand.Countries Baltic and Scandinavian Countries: a survey of the peoples and states of the Baltic

Banta's Greek Exch. Banta's Greek Exchange

Bartonia Bartonia: Proceedings of the Philadelphia Botanical Society

Basic Coll.Quart. Basic College Quarterly

Basler Veröffentl.Gesch.Med.Biol. Basler Veröffentlichungen zur Geschichte der Medizin und der Biologie

Basler Z.Gesch.Altertumsk. Basler Zeitschrift für Geschichte und Altertumskunde

Basteria Basteria: Tijdschrift van de Nederlandsche Malacologische Vereeniging [Rijks-Museum van Natuurlijke Historie]

Bayer.Bildungswesen Bayerisches Bildungswesen

Bayer.Z.Vermessungswesen Bayerische Zeitschrift für Vermessungswesen

Bayerland Bayerland: Illustrierte Wochenschrift für bayerische Geschichte und Landeskunde

Beaufortia Beaufortia

Beaux-Arts Les Beaux-Arts. Hebdomadaire d'Information Artistique

Bee-Hive Bee-Hive [Pratt and Whitney Company, United Aircraft Corporation]

Behav.Sci. Behavioral Science

Beibl.Veröffentl.Geobot.Inst.Rübel Beiblatt zu den Veröffentlichungen des Geobotanischen Instituts Rübel

Beih.Repert.Novarum Specierum Regni Veg. Beihefte zum Repertorium Novarum Specierum Regni Vegetabilis

Beitr.Geburtsh.Gynaekol. Beiträge zur Geburtshilfe und Gynaekologie

Beitr.Geol.Thüringen Beiträge zur Geologie von Thüringen [Geologische Landesuntersuchung und Thüringischer geologischer Verein]

Beitr.Gesch.Landwirtschaftswiss. Beiträge zur Geschichte der Landwirtschaftswissenschaften

Beitr.Gesch.Meteorol. Beiträge zur Geschichte der Meteorologie

Beitr.Gesch.Mönchtums Benediktinerordens Beiträge zur Geschichte des alten Mönchtums und des Benediktinerordens

Beitr.Gesch.Phil.Mittelalters Beiträge zur Geschichte der Philosophie [und Theologie] des Mittelalters

Beitr.Gesch.Tech.Ind. Beiträge zur Geschichte der Technik und Industrie: Jahrbuch des Vereines Deutscher Ingenieure

Beitr.Gesch.Univ.Halle-Wittenberg Beiträge zur Geschichte der Universität Halle-Wittenberg

Beitr.Gesch.Veterinär-med. Beitrage zur Geschichte de Veterinär-Medizin

Beitr.Hist.Theol. Beitrage zur Historischen Theologie

Beitr.Indischen Sprachwiss.Religionsgesch. Beiträge zur Indischen Sprachwissenschaft und Religionsgeschichte

Beitr.Inkunabelk. Beiträge zur Inkunabelkunde [Gesellschaft für Typenkunde des 15. Jahrhunderts - Wiegendruck-Gesellschaft]

Beitr.Klin.Tuberk. Beiträge zur Klinik der Tuberkulose und spezifischen Tuberkuloseforschung

Belgium Belgium [Belgian Press Association, New York]

Bell Syst.Tech.J. The Bell System Technical Journal

Bell Telephone Quart. Bell Telephone Quarterly

Belleten Belleten [Türk Tarih Kurumu. Société d'Histoire Turque]

Belvedere Belvedere: Monatsschrift für Sammler und Kunstfreunde

Benediktinische Monatsschr. Benediktinische Monatsschrift zur Pflege religiösen und geistigen Lebens

Ber.Bayer.Bot.Ges. Bericht der Bayerischen Botanischen Gesellschaft zur Erforschung der heimischen Flora

Ber.Deut.Bot.Ges. Berichte der Deutschen Botanischen Gesellschaft

Ber.Deut.Chem.Ges. Bericht der Deutschen Chemischen Gesellschaft

Ber.Deut.Pharm.Ges. Bericht der Deutschen pharmazeutischen Gesellschaft

Ber.Geobot.Forschungsinst.Rübel Zürich Bericht über das Geobotanische Forschungsinstitut Rübel in Zürich

Ber.Gesamte Gynäkol.Geburtsh. Berichte über die gesamte Gynäkologie und Geburtshilfe

Ber.Hist.Ver.Bamberg Bericht [und Jahrbuch] des Historischen Vereins für die Pflege der Geschichte des ehemaligen Fürstbistums zu Bamberg

Ber.Naturforsch.Ges.Bamberg Berichte der Naturforschenden Gesellschaft zu Bamberg

Ber.Naturforsch.Ges.Freiburg Berichte der Naturforschenden Gesellschaft zu Freiburg i Br.

Ber.Naturwiss.Ver.Regensburg Berichte des Naturwissenschaftlichen Vereins zu Regensburg

Ber.Oberhess.Ges.Natur-Heilk.Naturwiss.Abt. Bericht der Oberhessischen Gesellschaft für Natur- und Heilkunde. Naturwissenschaftliche Abteilung

Ber.Phys.Med.Ges.Würzb. Bericht der Physikalisch-medizinischen Gesellschaft zu Würzburg

Ber.Röm.-Ger.Komm.Deut.Archaeol.Inst. Bericht der Römisch-germanischen Kommission des Deutschen Archaeologischen Instituts

Ber.Schweiz.Bot.Ges. Berichte der Schweizerischen Botanischen Gesellschaft: Bulletin: Société Botanique Suisse

Ber.Senckenberg.Naturforsch.Ges. Bericht der Senckenbergischen Naturforschenden Gesellschaft

Ber.Tätigkeit Naturwiss.Ges.Isis Bautzen Bericht über die Tätigkeit der Naturwissenschaftlichen Gesellschaft Isis, Bautzen

Ber.Verhandl.Sächs.Akad.Wiss.Leipzig Math.Naturwiss.Kl. Berichte über die Verhandlungen der Sächsischen Akademie der Wissenschaften zu Leipzig: Mathematisch-naturwissenschaftliche Klasse.

Ber.Verhandl.Sächs.Akad.Wiss.Leipzig Math.Phys.Kl. Berichte über die Verhandlungen der Sächsischen Akademie der Wissenschaften zu Leipzig: Mathematisch-physische Klasse

Ber.Verhandl.Sächs.Akad.Wiss.Leipzig Philol.Hist.Kl. Berichte über die Verhandlungen der Sächsischen Akademie der Wissenschaften zu Leipzig: Philologisch-historische Klasse

Ber.Verhandl.Sächs.Ges.Wiss.Leipzig Philol.Hist.Kl. Berichte über die Verhandlungen der Sächsischen Gesellschaft der Wissenschaften zu Leipzig: Philologisch-historische Klasse

Bergstadt Die Bergstadt

Berks.Bucks.Oxon.Archaeol.J. Berks, Bucks, and Oxon Archaeological Journal [Berks Archaeological and Architectural Society]

Berliner Gesundheitsbl. Berliner Gesundheitsblatt

Berliner Klin.Wochenschr. Berliner klinische Wochenschrift

Berliner Med.Z. Berliner medizinische Zeitschrift

Berliner Münch.Tierärztl.Wochenschr. Berliner und Münchener tierärztliche Wochenschrift

Berliner Philol.Wochenschr. Berliner philologische Wochenschrift

Berliner Tierärztl.Wochenschr. Berliner tierärztliche Wochenschrift

Berlingske Tid. Den Berlingske Tidende

Berner Beitr.Gesch.Med.Naturwiss. Berner Beiträge zur Geschichte der Medizin und der Naturwissenschaften

Bernstein Forsch. Bernstein Forschungen. Amber Studies

Berytus Berytus. Archaeological studies published by the Museum of Archaeology of the American University of Beirut

Bibl.École Chartes Bibliothèque de l'École des Chartes: Revue d'érudition, consacrée spécialement à l'étude du moyen âge

Bibl.Etud.Reg. Bibliothèque d'Etudes Régionales

Bibl.Hist.Sueo-Gothica Bibliotheca Historica Sueo-Gothica

Bibl.Hum.Renaiss. Bibliothèque d'Humanisme et Renaissance

Bibl.Laeger Bibliotek for Laeger

Bibl.Math. Bibliotheca Mathematica: Zeitschrift für Geschichte der mathematischen Wissenschaften

Bibl.Méridionale Bibliothèque Méridionale

Bibl.Orient. Bibliotheca Orientalis

Bibl.Quadrivium Ser.Filol. Biblioteca di Quadrivium. Serie Filologica

Bibl.Sacra The Bibliotheca Sacra. A Religious and Sociological Quarterly

Bibl.Universelle Arch.Sci.Phys.Math. Bibliothèque Universelle: Archives des Sciences Physiques et Naturelles

Bibl.Universelle Rev.Suisse Bibliothèque Universelle et Revue Suisse

Biblica Biblica. Commentarii editi a Pontificio Instituto Biblico

Biblical Archaeol. The Biblical Archaeologist

Biblical Rev. The Biblical Review

Bibliofilia La Bibliofilia

Bibliogr.Bouddhique Bibliographie Bouddhique

Bibliogr.Géogr. Bibliographie Géographique (Internationale)

Bibliogr.Med.Biol. Bibliografia Medico-Biologica

Bibliogr.Meteorol.Lit. Bibliography of Meteorological Literature [Royal Meteorological Society]

Bibliogr.Rev.Chem. Bibliography of Reviews in Chemistry

Bibliogr.Seismol. Bibliography of Seismology

Bibliogr.Stud. Bibliographien und Studien

Bibliogr.Vostoka Bibliografiia Vostoka [Akademiia Nauk. Institut Vostokovedeniia]

Biekorf Biekorf: Leer- en leesblad voor alle verstandige Vlamingen

Bijdr.Dierk. Bijdragen tot de Dierkunde [K Zoologisch Genootschap Natura Artis Magistra, Amsterdam]

Bijdr.Gesch.Geneesk. Bijdragen tot de Geschiedenis der Geneeskunde [Nederlandsche Maatschappij tot Bevordering der Geneeskunst]

Bilten Drushtvo Mat.Fiz.Nar.Repub.Makedonija Bilten: Drushtvo na Matematicharite i Fizicharite od Narodna Republika Makedonija

Biochem.Bull. Biochemical Bulletin

Bio-Chem.J. Bio-Chemical Journal

Biogr.Mem.Fellows Roy.Soc. Biographical Memoirs of Fellows of the Royal Society

Biogr.Mem.Nat.Acad.Sci. Biographical Memoirs of the National Academy of Sciences

Biogr.Nat.Acad.Roy.Belg. Biographie Nationale: Publiée par l'Académie Royale des Sciences, des Lettres et des Beaux-arts de Belgique

Biol.Abstr. Biological Abstracts

Biol.Bull. Biological Bulletin

Biol.Heilkunst. Biologische Heilkunst

Biol.Jaarb. Biologisch Jaarboek

Biol.Listy Biologické Listy [supplement to *Čas.Lék.Českých*]

Biol.Méd. Biologie Médicale

Biol.Medd.Danske Vidensk.Selsk. Biologiske Meddelelser: [Kongelige] Danske Videnskabernes Selskab [Académie Royale des Sciences et des Lettres de Danemark]

Biol.Rev. Biological Reviews

Biol.Zentralbl. Biologisches Zentralblatt [or Centralblatt]

Biologica Biologica: Revue scientifique du médecin

Biologist The Biologist

Biometrics Biometrics [Biometrics Section, American Statistical Association]

Biometrika Biometrika: a journal for the statistical study of biological problems

Bios Bios [Beta Beta Beta Biological Fraternity, Mount Vernon, Ia.]

Bios (Genoa) Bios. Rivista di Biologia Sperimentale e Generale

Bios (Leipzig) Bios: Abhandlungen zur theoretischen Biologie und ihrer Geschichte

Biotypologie Biotypologie: Bulletin de la Société de Biotypologie

Bitumen Bitumen

Biul.Gl.Bot.Sada (Leningrad) Biulleten' Glavnogo Botanicheskogo Sada [Leningrad]

Biul.Moskov.Obshchest.Ispytatelei Prirody Otd.Biol. Biulleten' Moskovskogo Obshchestva Ispytatelei Prirody: Otdel biologicheskii

Biul.Sredne-aziat.Gos.Univ. Biulleten Sredne-aziatskogo Gosudarstvennogo Universiteta. Bulletin de l'Université de l'Asie Centrale

Bl.Angew.Ophthalmol.Physiol.Iriskopie Blätter für angewandte ophthalmologische Physiologie und Iriskopie

Bl.Deut.Phil. Blätter für deutsche Philosophie

Bl.Gesch.Tech. Blätter für Geschichte der Technik [Österreichisches Forschungsinstitut für Geschichte der Technik]

Bl.Gymnasialschulwesen Blätter für das [bayerische] Gymnasialschulwesen

Bl.Münzfreunde Blätter für Münzfreunde

Bl.Technikgesch. Blätter für Technikgeschichte [Forschungsinstitut für Technikgeschichte in Wien]

Boabe Grău Boabe de Grău

Bodleian Libr.Rec. Bodleian Library Record

Bodleian Quart.Rec. Bodleian Quarterly Record

Börsenbl.Deut.Buchhandel Börsenblatt für den deutschen Buchhandel

Boghazköi Stud. Boghazköi-Studien [Vorderasiatische Ägyptische Gesellschaft]

Bol.Acad.Buenas Letras Barcelona Boletín de la Real Academia de Buenas Letras de Barcelona

Bol.Acad.Hist. Boletín de la Real Academia de la Historia, Madrid

Bol.Acad.Nac.Cienc.Cordoba Boletín de la Academia Nacional de Ciencias en Cordoba

Bol.Acad.Nac.Hist. Boletin de la Academia Nacional de Historia, Quito

Bol.Agencia Géral Colón. Boletin da Agencia Géral das Colónias

Bol.Bibl.Menendez y Pelayo Boletín de la Biblioteca Menendez y Pelayo

Bol.Bibl.Univ.Coimbra Boletim da Biblioteca (Geral) da Universidade de Coimbra

Bol.Bibliogr.Antropol.Amer. Boletin Bibliográfico de Antropologia Americana. [Instituto Panamericano de Geografia e Historia]

Bol.Inst.Geol.Miner.Españ. Boletín del Instituto Geológico y Minero de España

Bol.Mat. Boletín Matemático

Bol.Mus.Nac.Rio de Janeiro Boletim do Museu Nacional de Rio de Janeiro

Bol.Real Acad.Gallega Boletin de la Real Academia Gallega

Bol.Seminar.Estud.Pedagóg. Boletin del Seminario de Estudios Pedagógicos

Bol.Soc.Cient.Hispano-Marroqui Alcazarquivir Boletín de la Sociedad Científica Hispano-Marroqui de Alcazarquivir

Bol.Soc.Geogr.Lisboa Boletim da Sociedade de Geographia de Lisboa

Bol.Soc.Geogr.Madrid Boletín de la Real Sociedad Geográfia de Madrid

Bol.Soc.Quím.Perú Boletín de la Sociedad Química del Perú

Bol.Univ.Granada Boletin de la Universidad de Granada

Boll.Ass.Int.Stud.Mediterranei Bollettino della Associazione Internazionale degli Studi Mediterranei

Boll.Ass.Ott.Ital. Bollettino dell' Associazione Ottica Italiana

Boll.Bibliogr.Stor.Sci.Mat. Bollettino di Bibliografia e Storia delle Scienze Matematiche

Boll.Com.Prep.Ed.Naz.Class.Greci Lat. Bollettino del Comitato per la Preparazione dell' Edizione Nazionale dei Classici Greci e Latini

Boll.Ist.Ital.Medio Estremo Orient. Bollettino dell Istituto Italiano per il Medio ed Estremo Oriente

Boll.Ist.Stor.Cult.Arma Genio Bollettino dell'Istituto Storico e di Cultura dell'Arma del Genio, Roma

Boll.Ist.Stor.Ital.Arte Sanit. Bollettino dell'Istituto Storico Italiano dell'Arte Sanitaria

Boll.Mat. Il Bollettino di Matematica

Boll.Mathesis Bollettino dell'Associazione Mathesis [Società Italiana di Matematica]

Boll.Mens.Inform.Notiz.Sta.Patol.Vegetale Roma Bollettino Mensile di Informazioni e Notizie della [Reale] Stazione di Patologia Vegetale di Roma *and* [Reale] Osservatorio Fitopatologico per la Provincia di Roma e gli Abruzzi

Boll.Mus.Civico Padova Bollettino del Museo Civico di Padova

Boll.Sci.Med. Bollettino delle Scienze Mediche [Società di Bologna]

Boll.Soc.Adriat.Sci.Natur.Trieste Bollettino della Società Adriatica di Scienze Naturali in Trieste

Boll.Soc.Geogr.Ital. Bollettino della (Real) Società Geografica Italiana

Boll.Soc.Geol.Ital. Bollettino della Società Geologica Italiana

Boll.Soc.Natur.Napoli Bollettino della Società di Naturalisti i Napoli

Boll.Sta.Patol.Vegetale Bollettino della [Reale] Stazione di Patologia Vegetale di Roma

Boll.Stor.Pisano Bolletino Storico Pisano

Boll.Unione Mat.Ital. Bollettino della Unione Matematica Italiana

Bologna Med. Bologna Medica

Bonner Jahrb. Bonner Jahrbücher

Book Collect. The Book Collector

Book Week Book Week [World Journal Tribune]

Boston Med.Surg.J. Boston Medical and Surgical Journal

Bostonia Bostonia [Boston University Alumni Magazine]

Bot.Arch. Botanisches Archiv

Bot.Centralbl.Beih.2.Abt. Botanisches Centralblatt, Beihefte: Zweite Abteilung - Systematik, Pflanzengeographie, angewandte botanik

Bot.Mag. (Tokyo) The Botanical Magazine (Tokyo Botanical Society)

Bot.Mus.Leafl.Harvard Univ. Botanical Museum Leaflets. Harvard University

Bot.Rev. The Botanical Review

Bot.Zh. Botanicheskiĭ Zhurnal [Botanical Society of the USSR]

Botanica Botanica

Bowdoin Alumnus The Bowdoin Alumnus [Bowdoin College, Brunswick, Me.]

Brabant Brabant: Bulletin d'information de la Féderation Touristique de la Province de Brabant

Brain Brain: a journal of neurology

Brandenburgia Brandenburgia. Monatsblatt der Gesellschaft für Heimatkunde der Provinz Brandenburg zu Berlin

Brasil Médico-cirûrg. Brasil Médico-cirûrgico

Braunschweiger G.N.C. Monatsschr. Die Braunschweiger G.N.C. Monatsschrift

Bremer Beitr.Naturwiss. Bremer Beiträge zur Naturwissenschaft

Breslauer Stud.Hist.Theologie Breslauer Studien zur historischen Theologie

Bristol Medico-chir.J. The Bristol Medico-Chirurgical Journal

Brit.Dent.J. The British Dental Journal

Brit.Heart J. British Heart Journal

Brit.J.Appl.Phys. British Journal of Applied Physics

Brit.J.Dermatol. British Journal of Dermatology

Brit.J.Dis.Chest British Journal for the Diseases of the Chest

Brit.J.Hist.Sci. British Journal for the History of Science

Brit.J.Med.Psychol. British Journal of Medical Psychology

Brit.J.Ophthalmol. British Journal of Ophthalmology

Brit.J.Phil.Sci. British Journal for the Philosophy of Science

Brit.J.Physiol.Opt. British Journal of Physiological Optics

Brit.J.Plast.Surg. British Journal for Plastic Surgery

Brit.J.Psychol. British Journal of Psychology

Brit.J.Sociol. British Journal of Sociology

Brit.J.Surg. British Journal of Surgery

Brit.J.Tuberc. British Journal of Tuberculosis

Brit.J.Vener.Dis. British Journal of Venereal Diseases

Brit.Med.Bull. British Medical Bulletin

Brit.Med.J. British Medical Journal

Brit.Mus.Quart. British Museum Quarterly

Brit.Veterinary J. British Veterinary Journal

Brooklyn Bot.Gard.Leafl. Brooklyn Botanic Garden Leaflets

Brooklyn Bot.Gard.Rec. Brooklyn Botanic Garden Record

Brooklyn Eng.Club.Proc. Brooklyn Engineers' Club Proceedings

Brooklyn Mus.Quart. Brooklyn Museum Quarterly

Brotéria Sér.Mens. Brotéria: Série Mensal

Brotéria Sér.Vulg.Sci. Brotéria: Série de Vulgarização Scientifica

Brug De Brug [Rijksuniversiteit, Ghent]

Bruxelles Méd. Bruxelles-médical

Bryologist Bryologist

Bucknell Rev. Bucknell Review

Bul.Inst.Politechnic Iaşi Buletinul Institutul Politechnic din Iaşi

Bul.Soc.Rom.Geogr. Buletinul Societăţii [Regale] Române de Geografie

Bul.Soc.Ştiinţ.Cluj Buletinul Societătii de Ştiinţe din Cluj

Bul.Univ.V. Babes Ser.Ştiinţ.Natur. Buletinul Universitătilor "V. Babes" si "Bolyai" Ser. Ştiinţele Naturii

Bull.Acad.Méd. Bulletin de l'Académie de Médecine

Bull.Acad.Méd.Belg. Bulletin de l'Académie [Royale] de Médecine de Belgique: Mededeelingen van de Koninklijke Belgische Academie voor Geneeskunde

Bull.Acad.Nat.Méd. Bulletin de l'Académie Nationale de Médecine

Bull.Acad.Pol.Sci. Bulletin de l'Académie Polonaise des Sciences

Bull.Acad.Pol.Sci.Sér.Sci.Chim.Géol.Géogr. Bulletin de l'Académie Polonaise des Sciences: Série des Sciences Chimiques, Géologiques et Géographiques

Bull.Acad.Pol.Sci.Sér.Sci.Géol.Géogr. Bulletin de l'Académie Polonaise des Sciences: Série des Sciences Géologiques et Géographiques

Bull.Acad.Roy.Belg.Cl.Beaux Arts Bulletin de l'Académie Royale de Belgique, Classe des Beaux-Arts

Bull.Acad.Roy.Belg.Cl.Lett. Bulletin de l'Académie Royale de Belgique, Classe des Lettres et des Sciences Morales et Politiques

Bull.Acad.Roy.Belg.Cl.Sci. Bulletin de l'Académie Royale de Belgique, Classe des Sciences

Bull.Acad.Sci.Lett.Montpellier Bulletin de l'Académie des Sciences et Lettres de Montpellier

Bull.Acad.Sci.Math.Natur.(Belgrade), *A* Bulletin de l'Académie des Sciences Mathématiques et Naturelles, A: Sciences mathématiques et physiques [Académie Royale Serbe]

Bull.Acad.Sci.St.Louis Bulletin of the Academy of Sciences of St. Louis

Bull.Acad.Var Bulletin de l'Académie du Var

Bull.Albertus Magnus Guild Bulletin. Albertus Magnus Guild. [Spring Hill College, Mobile, Ala.]

Bull.Alexandria Univ.Fac.Arts Bulletin of the Faculty of Arts, Alexandria University: Majallat Kullīyat al-ādāb, Jāmi'at al-Iskandarūyah

Bull.Amer.Acad.Arts Sci. Bulletin of the American Academy of Arts and Sciences

Bull.Amer.Ass.Univ.Professors Bulletin of the American Association of University Professors

Bull.Amer.Coll.Surg. Bulletin of the American College of Surgeons

Bull.Amer.Counc.Learned Soc. Bulletin of the American Council of Learned Societies

Bull.Amer.Libr.Ass. Bulletin of the American Library Association

Bull.Amer.Math.Soc. Bulletin of the American Mathematical Society

Bull.Amer.Meteorol.Soc. Bulletin of the American Meteorological Society

Bull.Amer.Mus.Natur.Hist. Bulletin of the American Museum of Natural History [New York]

Bull.Amer.Sch.Orient.Res. Bulletin of the American Schools of Oriental Research

Bull.Amer.Soc.Hosp.Pharm. Bulletin of the American Society of Hospital Pharmacists

Bull.Anal. Bulletin Analytique

Bull.Annu.Soc.Suisse Chronom. Bulletin Annuel de la Société Suisse de Chronométrie et du Laboratoire Suisse de Recherches Horlogères

Bull.Arménologique Bulletin Arménologique

Bull.Ass.Franç.Avance.Sci. Bulletin de l'Association Française pour l'Avancement des Sciences

Bull.Ass.Franç.Tech.Pétrol. Bulletin. Association Française des Techniciens du Pétrole

Bull.Ass.Guillaume Budé Bulletin de l'Association Guillaume Budé

Bull.Ass.Int.Hydrol.Sci. Bulletin. Association Internationale de Hydrologie Scientifique

Bull.Ass.Philomath.Alsace Lorraine Bulletin de l'Association Philomathique d'Alsace et de Lorraine

Bull.Ass.Rég.Étud.Rech.Sci. Bulletin. Association Régionale pour l'Étude et la Recherche Scientifique

Bull.Astron.Observ.Belg. Bulletin Astronomique de l'Observatoire Royal de Belgique

Bull.Astron.Observ.Harvard Univ. Bulletin of the Astronomical Observatory Harvard University

Bull.Atom.Sci. Bulletin of Atomic Scientists

Bull.Belg.Metrol. Bulletin Belge de Metrologie [Service de la Metrologie, Brussels]

Bull.Bibl.France Bulletin des Bibliothèques de France

Bull.Bibliogr. Bulletin of Bibliography

Bull.Biol.France Belg. Bulletin Biologique de la France et de la Belgique

Bull.Bot.Surv.India Bulletin of the Botanical Survey of India

Bull.Brit.Mus.(Natur.Hist.)Hist.Ser. Bulletin of the British Museum (Natural History): Historical Series

Bull.Brit.Psychol.Soc. Bulletin of the British Psychological Society

Bull.Brit.Soc.Hist.Sci. Bulletin of the British Society for the History of Science

Bull.Buffalo Soc.Natur.Sci. Bulletin of the Buffalo Society of Natural Sciences

Bull.Bur.Amer.Ethnol. Bulletin of the Bureau of American Ethnology

Bull.Bus.Hist.Soc. Bulletin of the Business Historical Society

Bull.Calcutta Math.Soc. Bulletin of the Calcutta Mathematical Society

Bull.Centre Pol.Rech.Sci.Paris Bulletin du Centre Polonais de Recherches Scientifiques de Paris

Bull.Cercle Benelux Hist.Pharm. Bulletin du Cercle Benelux d'Histoire de la Pharmacie

Bull.Cercle Géogr.Liégeois Bulletin du Cercle des Géographes Liégeois

Bull.Cercle Pédagog.Univ.Louvain Bulletin du Cercle Pédagogique. Université de Louvain

Bull.Cercle Zool.Congolais Bulletin du Cercle Zoologique Congolais

Bull.Cleveland Med.Libr. Bulletin of the Cleveland Medical Library [Cleveland Medical Library Association]

Bull.Coll.Art.Ass. Bulletin of the College Art Association (of America)

Bull.Comité Étud.Hist.Sci.Afr.Occident.Franç. Bulletin du Comité d'Études Historiques et Scientifiques de l'Afrique Occidentale Française

Bull.Comm.Hist.Archéol.Mayenne Bulletin de la Commission Historique et Archéologique de la Mayenne

Bull.Comm.Roy.Hist.Acad.Roy.Belg. Bulletin de la Commission Royale d'Histoire, Académie Royale de Belgique

Bull.Corresp.Hellén. Bulletin de Correspondance Hellénique

Bull.Czech.Med.Ass.Great Brit. Bulletin of the Czechoslovak Medical Association in Great Britain

Bull.Dent.Soc.State N.Y. Bulletin of the Dental Society of the State of New York

Bull.Dep.Hist.Med.Osmania Med.Coll. Bulletin of the Department of History of Medicine of Osmania Medical College

Bull.Du Cange Bulletin Du Cange: archivvm latinitatis medii aevi

Bull.École Franç.Extrême-Orient Bulletin de l'École Française d'Extrême-Orient, Hanoi

Bull.Egypt.Univ.Fac.Arts Bulletin of the Faculty of Arts, Egyptian University

Bull.Enseign.Public Gouvernement Chérifien Bulletin de l'Enseignement Public du Gouvernement Chérifien

Bull.Enseign.Public Maroc Bulletin de l'Enseignement Public du Maroc

Bull.Étud.Arabes Bulletin des Études Arabes

Bull.Étud.Orient. Bulletin d'Études Orientales

Bull.Far East.Bibliogr. Bulletin of Far Eastern Bibliography. [American Council of Learned Societies]

Bull.Farouk I Univ.Fac.Arts Bulletin: Farouk I University, Faculty of Arts [Cairo]

Bull.Féd.Belg.Soc.Sci. Bulletin de la Fédération Belge des Sociétés de Sciences mathématiques, physiques, chimiques, naturelles, médicalés, et appliquées

Bull.Fogg Art Mus. Bulletin of the Fogg Art Museum

Bull.Fouad I Univ.Fac.Arts Bulletin: Fouad I University, Faculty of Arts [Giza]

Bull.Franç.Piscicult. Bulletin Français de Pisciculture

Bull.Friends Hist.Ass. Bulletin of the Friends Historical Association

Bull.Gard.Club Amer. Bulletin of the Garden Club of America

Bull.Gén.Thérap. Bulletin Générale de Thérapeutique Médicale, Chirurgicale, Obstétricale et Pharmaceutique

Bull.Géogr.Hist. Bulletin de Géographie Historique et Descriptive

Bull.Geogr.Soc.Phila. Bulletin of the Geographical Society of Philadelphia

Bull.Geol.Soc.Amer. Bulletin of the Geological Society of America

Bull.Harvard Med.Alumni Ass. Bulletin of the Harvard Medical Alumni Association

Bull.Health Organ.League Nat. Bulletin of the Health Organisation. League of Nations

Bull.Hispanique Bulletin Hispanique

Bull.Hist.Dent. Bulletin of the History of Dentistry

Bull.Hist.Med. Bulletin of the History of Medicine

Bull.Inst.Agron.Gembloux Bulletin de l'Institut Agronomique de l'État et des Stations de Recherches de Gembloux, Belgium

Bull.Inst.Archéol.Liégeois Bulletin de l'Institut Archéologique Liégeois

Bull.Inst.Égypte Bulletin de l'Institut d'Égypte

Bull.Inst.Franç.Archéol.Orient. Bulletin de l'Institut Français d'Archéologie Orientale, Le Caire

Bull.Inst.Gén.Psychol. Bulletin de l'Institut Général Psychologique

Bull.Inst.Hist.Belg.Rome Bulletin de l'Institut Historique Belge de Rome

Bull.Inst.Hist.Med. Bulletin of the Institute of the History of Medicine [Johns Hopkins University]

Bull.Inst.Hist.Res. Bulletin of the Institute of Historical Research [London University]

Bull.Inst.Hyg.Maroc Bulletin de l'Institut d'Hygiène du Maroc

Bull.Inst.Int.Bibliogr. Bulletin de l'Institut International de Bibliographie

Bull.Inst.Nat.Genevois Bulletin de l'Institut National Genevois

Bull.Inst.Océanogr.Monaco Bulletin de l'Institut Océanographique de Monaco

Bull.Inst.Pasteur Bulletin de l'Institut Pasteur

Bull.Inst.Phys.Lond. Bulletin of the Institute of Physics [and the Physical Society, London]

Bull.Inst.Psychol.Int. Bulletin de l'Institut Psychologique International

Bull.Inst.Sci.Natur.Belg. Bulletin de l'Institut Royal des Sciences Naturelles de Belgique

Bull.Inst.Sociol.Solvay Bulletin de l'Institut de Sociologie Solvay

Bull.Int.Acad.Sci.Cracovie Cl.Sci.Math.Natur. Bulletin International de l'Académie des Sciences du Cracovie: Classe de Sciences Mathématiques et Naturelles

Bull.Int.Acad.Sci.Cracovie Cl.Sci.Math.Natur., sér.A Bulletin International de l'Académie des Sciences du Cracovie: Classe des Sciences Mathématiques et Naturelles, série A - Sciences Mathématiques

Bull.Int.Acad.Sci.Lett.Cracovie Bulletin International de l'Académie des Sciences et des Lettres du Cracovie

Bull.Int.Acad.Yougoslave Cl.Sci.Math.Natur. Bulletin International de l'Académie Yougoslave [des Sciences et des Beaux-Arts]: Classe des Sciences Mathématiques et Naturelles

Bull.Int.Ass.Med.Mus. Bulletin of the International Association of Medical Museums

Bull.Int.Comm.Hist.Sci. Bulletin of the International Committee of Historical Sciences [Comité International des Sciences Historiques; Comitato Internazionale di Scienze Storiche]

Bull.Isaac Ray Med.Libr. Bulletin of the Isaac Ray Medical Library

Bull.Jard.Bot.État Bulletin du Jardin Botanique de l'État, Bruxelles

Bull.John Rylands Libr. Bulletin of the John Rylands Library [Manchester]

Bull.Johns Hopkins Hosp. Bulletin of the Johns Hopkins Hospital

Bull.Karachi Geogr.Soc. Bulletin of the Karachi Geographical Society

Bull.Kwasan Observ. Bulletin published by the Kwasan Observatory [Kyoto Imperial University, Kyoto

Bull.Lloyd Libr.Bot.Pharm.Mater.Med. Bulletin of the Lloyd Library of Botany, Pharmacy and Materia Medica

Bull.Los Angeles County Med.Ass. Bulletin of the Los Angeles County Medical Association

Bull.Maison Franç.Col.Univ. Bulletin de la Maison Française de Columbia University

Bull.Math.Ass.Univ.Allahabad Bulletin of the Mathematical Association, University of Allahabad

Bull.Méd.(Paris) Bulletin Médical[Paris]

Bull.Med.Chir.Fac.Maryland Bulletin of the Medical and Chirurgical Faculty of Maryland

Bull.Med.Libr.Ass. Bulletin of the Medical Library Association

Bull.Mém.Soc.Anthropol.Paris Bulletins et Mémoires de la Société d'Anthropologie de Paris

Bull.Mém.Soc.Archéol.Hist.Charente Bulletin et Mémoires de la Société Archéologique et Historique de la Charente

Bull.Mém.Soc.Chir.Paris Bulletins et Mémoires de la Société de Chirurgie de Paris

Bull.Menninger Clin. Bulletin of the Menninger Clinic

Bull.Mens.Comité Afr.Franç. Bulletin Mensuel du Comité Afrique Français.

Bull.Mens.Soc.Natur.Luxembourgeois Bulletin Mensuel de la Société des Naturalistes Luxembourgeois

Bull.Metrop.Mus.Art The Metropolitan Museum of Art Bulletin [New York]

Bull.Millard Fillmore Hosp.Buffalo Bulletin of the Millard Fillmore Hospital, Buffalo

Bull.Misc.Inform.Roy.Bot.Gard.Kew Bulletin of Miscellaneous Information: Royal Botanic Gardens, Kew

Bull.Missouri Hist.Soc. Bulletin of the Missouri Historical Society

Bull.Monumental Bulletin Monumental

Bull.Mus.Art Hist.Genève Bulletin du Musée d'Art et d'Histoire de Genève

Bull.Mus.Far East.Antiquities Bulletin of the Museum of Far Eastern Antiquities [Östasiatiska Samlingarna, Stockholm]

Bull.Mus.Fine Arts (Boston) Bulletin of the Museum of Fine Arts, Boston

Bull.Mus.Hist.Natur.Belg. Bulletin du Musée Royale d'Histoire Naturelle de Belgique: Mededeelingen van het Koninklijk Natuurhistorisch Museum van België

Bull.Mus.Nat.Hist.Natur. Bulletin du Muséum National d'Histoire Naturelle [Paris]

Bull.Mus.Roy.Art Hist. Bulletin des Musées Royaux d'Art et d'Histoire

Bull.N.J.Acad.Sci. Bulletin. New Jersey Academy of Sciences

Bull.N.Y.Acad.Med. Bulletin of the New York Academy of Medicine

Bull.N.Y.Public Libr. Bulletin of the New York [City] Public Library

Bull.N.Y.State Mus. Bulletin of the New York State Museum (Natural History) [Albany, N.Y.]

Bull.N.Y.Zool.Soc. Bulletin of the New York Zoological Society

Bull.Nat.Arch. Bulletins of the National Archives [U.S.A.]

Bull.Nat.Ass.Watch Clock Collect. Bulletin of the National Association of Watch and Clock Collectors

Bull.Nat.Formulary Comm. Bulletin of the National Formulary Committee

Bull.Nat.Geogr.Soc.India Bulletin of the National Geographic Society of India

Bull.Nat.Inst.Hist.Philol.Acad.Sinica Bulletin of the National Institute of History and Philology, Academia Sinica.

Bull.Nat.Inst.Sci.India Bulletin of the National Institute of Sciences of India

Bull.Nat.Res.Counc. Bulletin of the National Research Council

Bull.Nat.Res.Counc.Philippines Bulletin of the National Research Council of the Philippine Islands

Bull.Neth.Neth.Indies Counc.Inst.Pacific Relat. Bulletin of the Netherlands and Netherlands Indies Council of the Institute of Pacific Relations

Bull.Ophthalmol.Soc.Egypt Bulletin of the Ophthalmological Society of Egypt

Bull.Phil.Soc.Wash. Bulletin of the Philosophical Society of Washington [Washington, D.C.]

Bull.Philol.Hist. Bulletin Philologique et Historique [Comité des Travaux Historiques et Scientifiques, France]

Bull.Pol.Inst.Arts Sci.Amer. Bulletin of the Polish Institute of Arts and Sciences in America

Bull.Public Mus.Milwaukee Bulletin of the Public Museum of the City of Milwaukee

Bull.Railway Locomotive Hist.Soc. Bulletin of the Railway and Locomotive Historical Society

Bull.Relat.Sci. Bulletin des Relations Scientifiques

Bull.Res.Counc.Israel Bulletin of the Research Council of Israel

Bull.Sch.Med.Univ.Maryland Bulletin of the School of Medicine, University of Maryland

Bull.Sch.Orient.Afr.Stud. Bulletin of the School of Oriental and African Studies [University of London]

Bull.Sch.Orient.Stud. Bulletin of the School of Oriental Studies [University of London]

Bull.Sci.Acad.Imp.Sci.Saint Petersbourg Bulletin Scientifique de l'Académie Impériale des Sciences de Saint Petersbourg

Bull.Sci.École Polytech.Timişoara Bulletin Scientifique de l'École Polytechnique de Timişoara: Comptes Rendus des Séances de la Société Scientifique de Timişoara

Bull.Sci.Math. Bulletin des Sciences Mathématiques

Bull.Sci.Pharmacol. Bulletin des Sciences Pharmacologiques

Bull.Sci.Relat. Bulletin for Scientific Relations. Bulletin des Relations Scientifiques. [International Institute of Intellectual Co-operation]

Bull.Sci.Roumain Bulletin Scientifique Roumain [Institut Universitaire Roumain Charles Ier, Paris]

Bull.Séances Acad.Roy.Sci.Colon. Bulletin des Séances. Académie des Sciences Coloniales

Bull.Séances Acad.Roy.Sci.Outremer Bulletin des Séances. Académie Royale des Sciences d'Outremer

Bull.Séances Inst.Roy.Colon.Belg. Bulletin des Séances. Institut Royal Colonial Belge

Bull.Sect.Géogr.Comité Trav.Hist.Sci. Bulletin de la Section de Géographie du Comité des Travaux Historiques et Scientifiques [Ministère de l'Instruction Publique et des Beaux Arts: Ministère de l'Éducation Nationale]

Bull.Sect.Hist.Acad.Roumaine Bulletin de la Section Historique de l'Academie Roumaine

Bull.Seismol.Soc.America Bulletin of the Seismological Society of America

Bull.Senese Stor.Patria Bullettino Senese di Storia Patria [Istituto Comunale d'Arte e di Storia, Sienna]

Bull.Serv.Géol.Indochine Bulletin du Service Géologique de l'Indo-Chine

Bull.Sign. Bulletin Signalétique: Centre National de la Recherche Scientifique

Bull.Soc.Agr.Sci.Arts Sarthe Bulletin de la Société d'Agriculture, Sciences et Arts de la Sarthe

Bull.Soc.Amis André-Marie Ampère Bulletin de la Société des Amis d'André-Marie Ampère

Bull.Soc.Amis Sci.Natur.Rouen Bulletin de la Société des Amis des Sciences Naturelles de Rouen

Bull.Soc.Anthropol. Bulletins et Mémoires de la Société d'Anthropologie de Paris

Bull.Soc.Anthropol.Bruxelles Bulletin de la Société (Royale) d'Anthropologie (et de Préhistoire) de Bruxelles

Bull.Soc.Antiquaires Ouest Bulletin de la Société des Antiquaires de l'Ouest

Bull.Soc.Archéol.Alexandrie Bulletin. Société Archéologique d'Alexandrie

Bull.Soc.Archéol.Bruxelles Bulletin de la Société Royale d'Archéologie de Bruxelles

Bull.Soc.Archéol.Copte Bulletin de la Société d'Archéologie Copte

Bull.Soc.Archéol.Hist.Limousin Bulletin de la Société d'Archéologie et d'Histoire Limousin

Bull.Soc.Archéol.Hist.Orléannais Bulletin de la Société Archéologique et Historique de l'Orléannais

Bull.Soc.Archéol.Sci.Litt.Vendômois Bulletin de la Société Archéologique, Scientifique et Littéraire du Vendômois

Bull.Soc.Astron.Pop.Toulouse Bulletin de la Société d'Astronomie Populaire de Toulouse

Bull.Soc.Belg.Anthrop.Préhist. Bulletins et mémoires de la Société [Royale] Belge d'Anthropologie et de Préhistoire de Bruxelles

Bull.Soc.Belg.Astron. Bulletin de la Société Belge d'Astronomie, de Météorologie et de Physique du Globe

Bull.Soc.Belg.Élec. Bulletin de la Société Belge d'Électriciens

Bull.Soc.Belg.Géogr. Bulletin de la Société Royale Belge de Géographie

Bull.Soc.Belg.Géol.Paléontol.Hydrol. Bulletin de la Société Belge de Géologie, de Paléontologie et d'Hydrologie

Bull.Soc.Belg.Photogram. Bulletin (trimestriel) de la Société Belge de Photogrammetrie

Bull.Soc.Borda Bulletin de la Société de Borda à Dax

Bull.Soc.Bot.Belg. Bulletin de la Société Royale de Botanique de Belgique

Bull.Soc.Bot.France Bulletin de la Société Botanique de France

Bull.Soc.Chim.Belg. Bulletin de la Société Chimique de Belgique

Bull.Soc.Chim.France Bulletin de la Société Chimique de France

Bull.Soc.Chim.France Mém. Bulletin de la Société Chimique de France: Mémoires

Bull.Soc.Chir.Lyon Bulletin de la Société de Chirurgie de Lyon

Bull.Soc.Étud.Indo-Chinoises Saïgon Bulletin de la Société des Études Indo-Chinoises de Saïgon

Bull.Soc.Étud.Océaniennes Bulletin de la Société d'Études Océaniennes [Papeeté, Tahiti]

Bull.Soc.Étud.Phil.Sud-Est Bulletin de la Société d'Études Philosophiques du Sud-Est

Bull.Soc.Étud.Psychiques Lyon Bulletin de la Société d'Études Psychiques de Lyon

Bull.Soc.Étud.Sci.Natur.Vaucluse Bulletin de la Société d'Étude des Sciences Naturelles de Vaucluse

Bull.Soc.Franç.Élec. Bulletin de la Société Française des Électriciens

Bull.Soc.Franç.Hist.Méd. Bulletin de la Société Française d'Histoire de la Médecine

Bull.Soc.Franç.Minéral. Bulletin de la Société Française de Minéralogie

Bull.Soc.Franç.Minéral.Cristallogr. Bulletin de la Société Française de Minéralogie et de Cristallographie

Bull.Soc.Franç.Pédagog. Bulletin de la Société Française de Pédagogie

Bull.Soc.Franç.Phil. Bulletin de la Société Française de Philosophie

Bull.Soc.Franç.Photogr. Bulletin de la Société Française de Photographie

Bull.Soc.Freedom Sci. Bulletin of the Society for Freedom in Science [Great Britain]

Bull.Soc.Fribourgeoise Sci.Natur. Bulletin de la Société Fribourgeoise des Sciences Naturelles

Bull.Soc.Géogr.(Paris) Bulletin de la Société de Géographie [Paris]

Bull.Soc.Géogr.Alger Bulletin de la Société de Géographie d'Alger (de l'Afrique du Nord)

Bull.Soc.Géogr.Anvers Bulletin de la Société [Royale] de Géographie d'Anvers

Bull.Soc.Géogr.Égypte Bulletin de la Société [Royale] de Géographie d'Égypte

Bull.Soc.Géogr.Lille Bulletin de la Société de Géographie de Lille

Bull.Soc.Géogr.Québec Bulletin de la Société de Géographie de Québec

Bull.Soc.Géol.France Bulletin de la Société Géologique de France

Bull.Soc.Hist.Archéol.Gand Bulletin de la Société d'Histoire et d'Archéologie de Gand

Bull.Soc.Hist.Natur.Afr.Nord Bulletin de la Société d'Histoire Naturelle de l'Afrique du Nor

Bull.Soc.Hist.Natur.Anthropol.Loir-et-Cher Bulletin de la Société d'Histoire Naturelle et d'Anthropologie de Loir-et-Cher

Bull.Soc.Hist.Pharm. Bulletin de la Société d'Histoire de la Pharmacie

Bull.Soc.Hist.Protestantisme Franç. Bulletin de la Société de l'Histoire du Protestantisme Français: études, documents, chronique littéraire

Bull.Soc.Ing.Civils France Bulletin de la Société des Ingénieurs Civils de France

Bull.Soc.Linn.Nord France Bulletin de la Société Linnéenne du Nord de la France

Bull.Soc.Math.Belg. Bulletin de la Société Mathématique de Belgique

Bull.Soc.Math.France Bulletin de la Société Mathématique de France

Bull.Soc.Med.Hist.Chicago Bulletin of the Society of Medical History of Chicago

Bull.Soc.Natur.Luxembourgeois Bulletin de la Société des Naturalistes Luxembourgeois

Bull.Soc.Natur.Mons Borinage Bulletin Mensuel de la Société Royale "Les Naturalistes" de Mons et du Borinage

Bull.Soc.Natur.Moscou Bulletin de la Société Impériale des Naturalistes de Moscou

Bull.Soc.Neuchâteloise Géogr. Bulletin de la Société Neuchâteloise de Géographie

Bull.Soc.Neuchâteloise Sci.Natur. Bulletin de la Société Neuchâteloise des Sciences Naturelles

Bull.Soc.Philomath.Vosgienne Bulletin de la Société Philomathique Vosgienne

Bull.Soc.Préhist.Franç. Bulletin de la Société Préhistorique Française

Bull.Soc.Sci.Agr.Arts Lille Bulletin (des Séances) de la Société des Sciences, de l'Agriculture et des Arts de Lille

Bull.Soc.Sci.Anciennes Bulletin de la Société des Sciences Anciennes

Bull.Soc.Sci.Bas-Rhin Bulletin de la Société des Sciences du Bas-Rhin

Bull.Soc.Sci.Hyg.Aliment. Bulletin de la Société Scientifique d'Hygiène Alimentaire

Bull.Soc.Sci.Liège Bulletin de la Société Royale des Sciences de Liège

Bull.Soc.Sci.Natur.Maroc Bulletin de la Société des Sciences Naturelles du Maroc

Bull.Soc.Suisse Amis Extrême-Orient Bulletin de la Société Suisse des Amis de l'Extrême-Orient: Mitteilungen der Schweizerischen Gesellschaft der Freunde Ostasiatischer Kultur

Bull.Soc.Topogr.France Bulletin (bimestriel) de la Société de Topographie de France

Bull.Soc.Vieux-Liège Bulletin de la Société Royale le Vieux-Liège

Bull.Soc.Zool.France Bulletin de la Société Zoologique de France

Bull.State Univ.Iowa Stud.Eng. Bulletin. State University of Iowa Studies in Engineering

Bull.Storrs Agr.Exp.Sta. Bulletin of Storrs Agricultural Experiment Station

Bull.Synd.Maîtres Imprimeurs France Bulletin officiel du Syndicat des Maîtres Imprimeurs de France

Bull.Tech.Ass.Ing.Bruxelles Bulletin Technique de l'Association des Ingénieurs sortis de l'École Polytechnique de l'Université Libre de Bruxelles

Bull.Torrey Bot.Club Bulletin of the Torrey Botanical Club [New York]

Bull.Trim.Inst.Archéol.Luxembourg Bulletin trimestriel de l' Institut Archéologique du Luxembourg

Bull.U.S.Geol.Surv. Bulletin of the United States Geological Survey

Bull.U.S.Nat.Mus. Bulletin of the United States National Museum: monograph series

Bull.Union Cath.Sci.Franç. Bulletin de l'Union Catholique des Scientifiques Français

Bull.Union Nat.Assoc.Étudiants France Bulletin de l'Union Nationale des Étudiants de France

Bull.Union Vérité Bulletin de l'Union pour la Vérité [Paris]

Bull.Univ.Aurore Bulletin de l'Université de l'Aurore

Bull.Univ.Ill. Bulletin of the University of Illinois [Urbana, Ill.]

Bull.Univ.Rochester Libr. Bulletin of the University of Rochester Library

Bull.Univ.Wis. Bulletin of the University of Wisconsin

Bull.Yacht Club France Bulletin du Yacht Club de France

Bull.Zool.Nomencl. Bulletin of Zoological Nomenclature

Bülteni Istanbul Tek.Üniv. Istanbul Teknik Üniversitesi Bülteni; Bulletin of the Technical University of Istanbul

Burlington Mag. Burlington Magazine for Connoisseurs

Bus.Equip.Top. Business Equipment Topics

Bus.Hist.Rev. Business History Review

Butlletí Assoc.Catalana Antropol.Etnol.Prehist. Butlletí de l'Associació Catalana d'Antropología, Etnología i Prehistória

Byzantina Metabyzantina Byzantina Metabyzantina: a journal of Byzantine and modern Greek studies

Byzantinisch-Neugriechische Jahrb. Byzantinisch-neugriechische Jahrbücher

Byzantinische Z. Byzantinische Zeitschrift

Byzantion Byzantion: Revue internationale des études Byzantines

C

Cah.Archéol.Hist.Alsace Cahiers d'Archéologie et d'Histoire d'Alsace

Cah.Biloque Cahiers de la Biloque [Ghent. Biloke]

Cah.Bruxellois Cahiers Bruxellois: Revue Historique Trimestrielle

Cah.Cercle Thomiste Cairo Cahiers: Cercle Thomiste, Cairo

Cah.Civilisation Médiévale Cahiers de Civilisation Médiévale: Xe-XIIe siècles

Cah.Droits Homme Les Cahiers des Droits de l'Homme

Cah.Hist.Bibliogr. Cahiers d'Histoire et de Bibliographie

Cah.Hist.Mond. Cahiers d'Histoire Mondiale; Journal of World History; Cuadernos de Historia Mundial

Cah.Inst.Sci.Écon.Appl.Sér.AD Cahiers de l'Institut de Science Économique Appliquée. Série AD. Évolution de Techniques et Progrès de l'Économie

Cah.Int.Sociol. Cahiers Internationaux de Sociologie

Cah.Léopoldiens Cahiers Léopoldiens: deux mille ans d'histoire des Belges

Cah.Nord Cahiers du Nord

Cah.Orient Contemp. Cahiers de l'Orient Contemporain

Cah.Phil.Natur. Cahiers de Philosophie de la Nature [Société de Philosophie de la Nature]

Cah.Quinzaine Cahiers de la Quinzaine

Cah.Radio-Paris Cahiers de Radio-Paris

Cah.Rationalistes Cahiers Rationalistes [Union Rationaliste, Paris]

Cah.Sud Cahiers du Sud

Cah.Tunisie Cahiers de Tunisie [Institut des Hautes Études, Tunis]

Calcutta Rev. The Calcutta Review

Calif.Fish Game California Fish and Game

Calif.Folklore Quart. California Folklore Quarterly

Calif.Western Med. California and Western Medicine

Cambridge Hist.J. Cambridge Historical Journal

Can.Geogr.J. Canadian Geographical Journal

Can.Hist.Rev. Canadian Historical Review

Can.J.Public Health Canadian Journal of Public Health

Can.J.Res. Canadian Journal of Research

Can.Med.Ass.J. Canadian Medical Association Journal

Can.Psychiat.Ass.J. Canadian Psychiatric Association Journal

Can.Surveyor The Canadian Surveyor

Cancer Cancer: diagnosis, treatment, research [American Cancer Society]

Cancer Res. Cancer Research

Cap.Chemist The Capital Chemist

Carbone Acciaio Il Carbone e l'Acciaio

Cardiologia Cardiologia. Internationales Archiv für Kreislaufforschung

Caribbean Stud. Caribbean Studies [University of Puerto Rico. Institute of Caribbean Studies]

Carnegie Sch.Mem. Carnegie Scholarship Memoirs

Čas.Lék.Českých Časopis Lékařů Českých: orgán Českého Lékařstva

Čas.Pěstování Mat.Fys. Časopis pro Pěstování Matematiky a Fysiky

Cassier's Eng.Mon. Cassier's Engineering Monthly

Castalia (Milano) Castalia: la medicina nella storia e nell' arte

Cath.Hist.Rev. The Catholic Historical Review

Ce Fastu? Ce Fastu? [Società Filologica Friulana G.I. Ascoli]

Cellule Cellule: recueil de cytologie et d'histologie générale

Cent.Asiatic J. Central Asiatic Journal: international periodical for the languages, literature, history and archaeology of Central Asia

Centaur Alpha Kappa Kappa The Centaur of Alpha Kappa Kappa

Centaurus Centaurus: international magazine of the history of science and medicine

Centennial Rev. Centennial Review of Arts and Science

Century Illus.Mon.Mag. The Century Illustrated Monthly Magazine

Century Mon.Mag. The Century Monthly Magazine

Céram.Verrerie Céramique et Verrerie

Cesalpino Cesalpino: giornale medico della Provincia di Arezzo

Česk.Čas.Hist. Československý Časopis Historický [Historický Ústav. Československá Akademie Věd.]

Česká Myšl Česká Myšl

Česká Rev. Česká Revue: měsíčník narodní strony svobodomyslné venovaný verejným otázkám

Chem.App. Chemische Apparatur

Chem.Ber. Chemische Berichte

Chem.Chem.Eng.News Chemistry and Chemical Engineering News [American Chemical Society]

Chem.Courant De Chemische Courant voor Nederland en Koloniën

Chem.Drug. Chemist and Druggist

Chem.Drug.Pharm. Chemist and Druggist and Pharmacist of Australasia

Chem.Eng.News Chemical and Engineering News [American Chemical Society]

Chem.Ind. Chemistry and Industry

Chem.Ind.Rev. Chemistry and Industry Review

Chem.Novitäten Chemische Novitäten: Bibliographie für die neuerscheinende Literatur auf dem Gesamtgebiet der reinen und angewandten Chemie und der chemischen Technologie

Chem.Tech.Rundsch. Chemisch-Technische Rundschau: Mitteilungsblatt der Chemischen Innung Österreichs und der ihr angeschlossenen Zünfte

Chem.Warf. Chemical Warfare [Department of the Army, United States]

Chem.Weekbl. Chemisch Weekbladj: orgaan der Nederlandsche Chemische Vereeniging en der Vereeniging van de Nederlandsche Chemische Industrie

Chem.Zeitung Chemiker-Zeitung

Chemie Die Chemie

Chemist Chemist. Bulletin of the American Institute of Chemists

Chim.Ind. Chimie et Industrie

Chim.Ind.(Milan) Chimica e l'Industria, Milano

Chimica Chimica [Istituto Italiano di Storia della Chimica]

Chin.J.Pediat. Chinese Journal of Pediatrics

Chin.Med.J. Chinese Medical Journal

Chin.Rev. The Chinese Review

Chin.Soc.Polit.Sci.Rev. Chinese Social and Political Science Review

Chin.Stud.Mon. The Chinese Students' Monthly (Bulletin)

China China [China Society of America]

China J. The China Journal

China Med.J. China Medical Journal

Chir.Organi Movimento Chirurgia degli Organi di Movimento

Chirurg Chirurg: Zeitschrift für alle Gebiete der operativen Medizin

Christ.Register The Christian Register

Christiaan Huygens Christiaan Huygens: internationaal mathematisch tijdschrift

Chron.Archéol.Pays Liége Chronique Archéologique du Pays de Liége

Chron.Bot. Chronica Botanica: international plant science news

Chron.Égypte Chronique d'Égypte: Bulletin périodique de la Fondation Égyptologique Reine Élisabeth

Chron.Méd. Chronique Médicale

Chron.Spinozanum Chronicon Spinozanum [Societas Spinozana, The Hague]

Chung Chi J. Chung Chi Journal

Chuo K'oron Chuo K'oron; Central Review

Church Hist. Church History [American Society of Church History]

Chymia Chymia: Annual studies in the history of chemistry [University of Pennsylvania]

Ciba Rev. Ciba Review

Ciba Rundsch. Ciba Rundschau [Gesellschaft für chemische Industrie in Basel]

Ciba Symp. Ciba-Symposium [Society of Chemical Industry in Basle]

Ciba Symp.(Summit, N.J.) Ciba-Symposia [Ciba Pharmaceutical Products, Inc.]

Ciba Z. Ciba Zeitschrift [Gesellschaft für chemische Industrie in Basel]

Ciba Z. Ciba Zeitschrift [German edition: Wehr, Baden]

Ciel Terre Ciel et Terre: Revue populaire d'astronomie

Cienc.Tecnol. Ciencia y Tecnologia

Ciencia Ciencia: Revista hispano-americana de ciencias puras y aplicadas

Ciencias Las Ciencias: Anales de la Asociación Española para el Progreso de las Ciencias

Cincinnati J.Med. The Cincinnati Journal of Medicine

Circ.N.Y.State Mus. Circular: New York State Museum

Ciudad Dios La Ciudad de Dios

Civiltà Macchine Civiltà delle Macchine [Gruppo Industriale della Società Finanziaria Meccanica "Finmeccanica"]

Cl.J. The Classical Journal [Classical Association of the Middle West and South, Chicago]

Cl.Mediaevalia Classica et Mediaevalia: Revue danoise de philologie et d'histoire [Societas Danica Indagationis Antiquitatis et Mediiaevi]

Cl.Philol. Classical Philology [Chicago University]

Cl.Quart. The Classical Quarterly [Classical Association, London]

Cl.Rev. Classical Review [Classical Association, London]

Cl.Weekly The Classical Weekly [The Classical Association of the Middle States and Maryland (of the Atlantic States)]

Cl.World Classical World

Clessidra Clessidra [Associazione Orologiai d'Italia]

Cleveland Clin.Quart. Cleveland Clinic Quarterly

Clin.Anesth. Clinical Anesthesia

Clin.Lab. Clinica y Laboratorio: Revista mensual española de ciencias médicas

Clin.Neurosurg. Clinical Neurosurgery

Clin.Oculist. Clinica Oculistica

Clin.Pediat. (Philadelphia) Clinical Pediatrics

Clujul Med. Clujul Medical

Coelum Coelum [Osservatorio Astronomico, Università, Bologna]

Coimbra Méd. Coimbra Médica

Coll.Art.J. College Art Journal

Collect.Theologica Collectanea Theologica [Societas Theologorum Poloniae]

Colloq.Math. Colloquium Mathematicum

Colo.Coll.Publ.Sci.Ser. Colorado College Publications. Science Series

Colo.Coll.Stud. Colorado College Studies: studies series

Colombo Colombo

Colophon The Colophon: a book collectors' quarterly

Columbia Law Rev. Columbia Law Review

Columbia Univ.Quart. Columbia University Quarterly

Comment.Ateneo Brescia Commentari dell'Ateneo di Brescia

Comment.Math.Helvet. Commentarii Mathematici Helvetici

Comment.Vindobonenses Commentationes Vindobonenses

Commentationes Commentationes. Pontifica Academia Scientiarum

Commonhealth The Commonhealth

Commun.Acad.Mar.Belg. Communications de l'Académie de Marine de Belgique (Mededeelingen: Akademie van Marine de België)

Commun.Appl.Math. Communications on Applied Mathematics

Commun.Mém.Acad.Mar. Communications et Mémoires de l'Académie de Marine, Paris

Communist De Communist

Comp.Ethnogr.Stud. Comparative Ethnographical Studies

Comp.Lit. Comparative Literature

Compr.Psychiat. Comprehensive Psychiatry

Compress.Air.Hydraul.Eng. Compressed Air and Hydraulic Engineering

Compress.Air Mag. Compressed Air Magazine

Compt.Rend.Acad.Inscriptions Belles Lett. Comptes Rendus [des Séances de l'Année...] de l'Académie des Inscriptions et Belles-Lettres [Institut de France]

Compt.Rend.Acad.Sci. Compte Rendu Hebdomadaire des Séances de l'Académie des Sciences [France]

Compt.Rend.Acad.Sci.Morales Polit. Compte Rendu des Séances et Travaux de l'Académie des Sciences Morales et Politiques [Paris]

Compt.Rend.Ass.Franç.Avance.Sci. Compte-Rendu de l'Association Française pour l'Avancement des Sciences

Compt.Rend.Conf.Gén.Poids Mesures Compte Rendu de la Conférence Générale des Poids et Mesures

Compt.Rend.Conf.Int.Africanistes Ouest Compte-rendu de la Conférence Internationale des Africanistes de l'Ouest

Compt.Rend.Congr.Chim.Ind. Compte Rendu du Congrès de Chimie Industrielle

Compt.Rend.Congr.Géol.Int. Comptes Rendus du Congrès Géologique International

Compt.Rend.Congr.Int.Amér. Comptes Rendus du Congrès International des Américanistes

Compt.Rend.Congr.Int.Anthropol.Archéol.Préhist. Compte Rendu du Congrès International d'Anthropologie et d'Archéologie Préhistorique

Compt.Rend.Congr.Int.Géogr. Comptes Rendus du Congrès International de Géographie

Compt.Rend.Congr.Int.Géol. Comptes Rendus du Congrès International de Géologie

Compt.Rend.Congr.Int.Hist.Méd. Comptes Rendus du Congrès International d'Histoire de la Médecine

Compt.Rend.Congr.Int.Hist.Sci. Comptes Rendus du Congrès International d'Histoire des Sciences

Compt.Rend.Congr.Int.Math. Comptes Rendus du Congrès International des Mathématiciens

Compt.Rend.Congr.Int.Méd.Trop.Hyg. Comptes Rendus du Congrès International de Médecine Tropicale et d'Hygièn

Compt.Rend.Congr.Int.Navigation Aérienne Comptes Rendus du Congrès International de la Navigation Aérienne

Compt.Rend.Congr.Int.Path.Comp. Comptes Rendus du Congrès International de Pathologie Comparée

Compt.Rend.Congr.Int.Sci.Hist. Compte rendu du Congrès International des Sciences Historiques

Compt.Rend.Congr.Math.Pays Slaves Compte-rendu du Congrès des Mathématiciens des Pays Slaves

Compt.Rend.Congr.Nat.Natur.Roum. Compte rendu des Séances. Congrès National des Naturalistes de Roumanie. (Congrès al Naturaliştor din România. Dare de Seamă)

Compt.Rend.Congr.Nat.Sci. Comptes Rendus du Congrès National des Sciences

Compt.Rend.Congr.Préhist.France Compte-rendu du Congrès Préhistorique de France

Compt.Rend.Séances Acad.Agr.France Comptes Rendus des Séances de l'Académie d'Agriculture de France

Compt.Rend.Sem.Méd.Balkanique Compte-rendu de la Semaine Médicale Balkanique

Compt.Rend.Soc.Biol. Compte Rendu des Séances et Mémoires de la Société de Biologie

Compt.Rend.Trav.Congr.Eau Compte Rendu des Travaux du Congrès de l'Eau

Concours Méd. Le Concours Médical

Condor Condor: Bulletin of the Cooper Ornithological Club

Conf.Empire Meteorol.Agr.Sect. Conference of Empire Meteorologists, Agricultural Section

Conf.Int.Counc.Mus. Conference of International Council of Museums (ICOM)

Conf.Proluzioni Conferenze e Proluzioni

Confinia Psychiat. Confinia Psychiatrica

Confluence Confluence: an International Forum

Congo Tervuren Congo-Tervuren [Amis du Musée Royal de l'Afrique Centrale]

Congr.Bénélux Hist.Sci. Congrès Bénélux d'Histoire des Sciences

Congr.Chim.Ind. Congrès de Chimie Industrielle

Congr.Fédération Archéol.Hist.Belg. Congrès de la Fédération Archéologique et Historique de Belgique

Congr.Fédération Soc.Savantes Afr.Nord Congrès de la Fédération des Sociétés Savantes de l'Afrique du Nord

Congr.Geogr.Ital. Congresso Geografico Italiano

Congr.Hist.Art Guérir Congrès d'Histoire de l'Art de Guérir [1st International Congress of the History of Medicine]

Congr.Int.Amér. Congrès International des Américanistes

Congr.Int.Anthropol. Congrès International d'Anthropologie

Congr.Int.Étud.Byzantines Congrès International des Études Byzantines

Congr.Int.Fil. Congresso Internazionale di Filosofia

Congr.Int.Géogr. Congrès International de Géographie

Congr.Int.Hist.Descobrimentos Congresso Internacional de História dos Descobrimentos

Congr.Int.Hist.Méd. Congrès International d'Histoire de la Medecine

Congr.Int.Hist.Sci. Congrès International d'Histoire des Sciences

Congr.Int.Math. Congrès International des Mathématiciens

Congr.Int.Méd.Trop.Hyg. Congrès International de Médecine Tropicale et d'Hygiène

Congr.Int.Mines Mét.Géol.Appl. Congrès International des Mines, de la Métallurgie et de la Géologie Appliquée.

Congr.Int.Navigazione Aerea Congresso Internazionale di Navigazione Aerea

Congr.Int.Path.Comp. Congrès International de Pathologie Comparée

Congr.Int.Phil. Congrès International de Philosophie

Congr.Int.Phil.Médiévale Congrès International de Philosophie Médiévale

Congr.Int.Phil.Sci. Congrès International de Philosophie des Sciences

Congr.Int.Quím.Pura Apl. Congreso Internacional de Química Pura y Aplicada

Congr.Méd.Fédération Soc.Sci.Méd.Afrique Nord Congrès de Médecine de la Fédération des Sociétes des Sciences Médicales de l'Afrique du Nord

Congr.Nat.Méd.Prof. Congrès National de Médecine Professionnelle [Belgium]

Congr.Nat.Sci. Congrès National des Sciences [Bruxelles]

Congr.Naz.Soc.Ital.Stor.Sci.Med.Natur. Congresso Nazionale della Società Italiana di Storia delle Scienze Mediche e Naturali

Congr.Rech.Sci.Ter.Outre-Mer Congrès de la Recherche Scientifique dans les Territoires d'Outre-Mer

Congr.Soc.Int.Chir. Congrès de la Société Internationale de Chirurgie

Congr.Unione Mat.Ital. Congresso dell'Unione Matematica Italiana

Conn.Hist.Soc.Bull. Bulletin of the Connecticut Historical Society

Connaiss.Arts Connaissance des Arts

Connoisseur The Connoisseur: an illustrated magazine for collectors

Contemp.Phys. Comtemporary Physics

Contemp.Psychol. Contemporary Psychology [American Psychological Association]

Contemp.Rev. Contemporary Review

Contrib.Astron.Osserv.Astron.Brera Contributi Astronomici: Osservatorio Astronomico di Brera

Contrib.Astron.Specola Merate Contributi Astronomici della [R.] Specola di Merate

Contrib.Gray Herb.Harvard Univ. Contributions from the Gray Herbarium of Harvard University

Contrib.Orient.Hist.Philol. Contributions to Oriental History and Philology [Columbia University, New York]

Contrib.Osserv.Astron.Milano Merate Contributi del Osservatorio Astronomico di Milano-Merate

Convivium Convivium [Società Editrice Internazionale]

Coop.Elec.Res. Co-operative Electrical Research

Copeia Copeia [American Society of Ichthyologists and Herpetologists]

Cornhill Mag. The Cornhill Magazine

Courr.Méd. Le Courrier Médical

Critique Critique: Revue générale des publications françaises et étrangères

Crón.Méd.Quir. Crónica Médico Quirúrgica

Crozer Quart. The Crozer Quarterly

Cryobiology Cryobiology

Cryogenics Cryogenics: Bibliography of low temperature engineering and research

Cuad.Amer. Cuadernos Americanos

Cuad.Hist.Jeronimo Zurita Cuadernos de Historia "Jeronimo Zurita"

Cuad.Hist.Med.Españ. Cuadernos de Historia de Medicina de España

Cuadernos (Paris) Cuadernos: Revista del Congresso por la Libertad de la Cultura

Cult.Franco-Japonaise, Tokyo. La Culture Franco-Japonaise, Tokyo

Cult.Life Culture and Life [English edition of Russian periodical, *Voks*]

Cult.Med.Mod. Cultura Medica Moderna

Cultura (Cluj) Cultura: sciences, lettres, arts

Cultura, La See *La Cultura*

Curator The Curator [American Museum of Natural History]

Curr.Sci. Current Science [Indian Institute of Science, Bangalore]

Current Current

Czech.J.Phys. Czechoslovak Journal of Physics

D

Dacoromania Dacoromania [Cluj Universitatea]

Daedalus Daedalus: Tekniska Museets årsbok [Ingeniörsvetenskapsakademien]

Daedalus Amer.Acad.Arts Sci. Daedalus: American Academy of Arts and Sciences

Danish Med.Bull. Danish Medical Bulletin [Almindelige Danske Laegeforening]

Danmarks Geol.Undersøgelse Danmarks Geologiske Undersøgelse

Dansk Ornithol.Foren.Tidsskr. Dansk Ornithologisk Forenings Tidsskrift

Dansk Veterinaerhist.Aarb. Dansk Veterinaerhistorisk Aarbog

Danske Stud. Danske Studier

Dapim Refuiim Dapim Refuiim: Medical Quarterly: Revue Médicale ["Kupat-Holim" (Workers' Sick-Fund of Israel)]

Dauphiné Le Dauphiné

Dearborn Independ. The Dearborn Independent: the Ford International Weekly

Debreceni Szemle Debreceni Szemle

Deccan Coll.Res.Inst.Bull. Deccan College Research Institute Bulletin

Del-Chem Bull. Del-Chem Bulletin [American Chemical Society: Delaware Section]

Del.Hist. Delaware History

Del.State Med.J. Delaware State Medical Journal

Deliberationes Congr.Dermatol.Int. Deliberationes Congressus Dermatologorum Internationalis

Delta Delta: Cuadernos Universitarios del Litoral [Rosario de Santa Fé]

Deltion Hestais Phus Hepist Deltion Hestais Phus Hepist

Denkmäler Tonkunst Oesterr. Denkmäler der Tonkunst in Oesterreich

Denkschr.Akad.Wiss.Wien Math.Naturwiss.Kl. Denkschriften der Akademie der Wissenschaften in Wien: Mathematisch-naturwissenschaftliche Klasse

Denkschr.Akad.Wiss.Wien Phil.Hist.Kl. Denkschriften der [Kaiserliche] Akademie der Wissenschaften in Wien: Philosophisch-historische Klasse

Denkschr.Österr.Akad.Wiss.Phil.Hist.Kl. Denkschriften der Österreichischen Akademie der Wissenschaften: Philosophisch-historische Klasse

Dent.Cosmos Dental Cosmos

Dent.Dig. Dental Digest

Dent.Items Dental Items of Interest

Dent.Mag. Dental Magazine (and Oral Topics)

Dent.Pract. Dental Practitioner (and Dental Record)

Dent.Surv. Dental Survey

Dep.State Bull. The Department of State Bulletin

Dergisi Ankara Üniv.Dil Tarih-Coğrafya Fak. Dergisi: Dil ve Tarih-coğrafy Fakültesi, Ankara Üniversitesi [Revue: Faculté de Langues, d'Histoire et de Géographie de l'Université d'Ankara]

Deri Hastaliklari Frengi Klin.Arşivi Deri Hastaliklari ve Frengi Klinigī Arşivi. Archives de Dermatologie et Siphiligraphie

Dermatol.Wochenschr. Dermatologische Wochenschrift

Dermatol Z. Dermatologische Zeitschrift

Dermatologia (Mexico) Dermatologia

Detroit Med.News Detroit Medical News [Wayne County Medical Society]

Deut.Ärztebl. Deutsches Ärzteblatt [Deutscher Ärztevereinsbund *and* Verband der Ärzte Deutschlands]

Deut.Allg.Zeitung Deutsche Allgemeine Zeitung

Deut.Apoth.Zeitung Deutsche Apotheker-Zeitung

Deut.Apoth.Zeitung Gesch.Beil. Deutsche Apotheker-Zeitung: Geschichtliche Beilage: "Zur Geschichte der deutschen Apotheke"

Deut.Bergwerkszeitung Tech.Bl. Deutsche Bergwerkszeitung. Technische Blätter

Deut.Biogr.Jahrb. Deutsches Biographisches Jahrbuch

Deut.Chem.Z. Deutsche Chemiker Zeitschrift

Deut.Chem.Zeitung Deutsche Chemiker-Zeitung [Centralblatt für die chemische Praxis und öffentliche Gesundheitspflege]

Deut.Dante Jahrb. Deutsche Dante-Gesellschaft: Jahrbuch

Deut.Erde (Gotha) Deutsche Erde

Deut.Erde (Munich) Deutsche Erde

Deut.Geogr.Bl. Deutsche Geographische Blätter

Deut.Geschichtsbl. Deutsche Geschichtsblätter

Deut.Geschlechterbuch Deutsches Geschlechterbuch

Deut.Gesundheitswesen Das Deutsche Gesundheitswesen [Deutsche Zentralverwaltung für das Gesundheitswesen]

Deut.Lit.Zeitung Deutsche Literaturzeitung für Kritik der internationalen Wissenschaften

Deut.Luftfahrerz. Deutsche Luftfahrerzeitschrift

Deut.Math. Deutsche Mathematik

Deut.Med.J. Deutsches medizinisches Journal

Deut.Med.Wochenschr. Deutsche medizinische Wochenschrift

Deut.Militärärztl.Z. Deutsche militärärztliche Zeitschrift

Deut.Opt.Wochenschr. Deutsche optische Wochenschrift

Deut.Rev. Deutsche Revue

Deut.Tech. Der deutsche Techniker

Deut.Texte Mittelalters Deutsche Texte des Mittelalters [Akademie der Wissenschaften, Berlin]

Deut.Tierärztl.Wochenschr. Deutsche tierärztliche Wochenschrift

Deut.Vierteljahrsschr.Literaturwiss.Geistesgesch. Deutsche Vierteljahrsschrift für Literaturwissenschaft und Geistesgeschichte

Deut.Z.Chir. Deutsche Zeitschrift für Chirurgie

Deut.Z.Gesamte Gerichtl.Med. Deutsche Zeitung für die gesamte gerichtliche Medizin

Deut.Z.Phil. Deutsche Zeitschrift für Philosophie

Deut.Zahnärztl.Z. Deutsche zahnärztliche Zeitschrift [Bayerische Landeskammer für Zahnärzte]

Deut.Zahnheilk. Deutsche Zahnheilkunde

Deut.Zahn- Mund- Kieferheilk. Deutsche Zahn- Mund- und Kieferheilkunde

Deut.Zeitung Spanien Deutsche Zeitung für Spanien. Revista Alemana de España

Deut.Zuckerind. Deutsche Zuckerindustrie

Deut.Zündwaren-Zeitung Deutsche Zündwaren-Zeitung

Develop.Biol. Developmental Biology

Devir Devir

Día Méd.Urug. El Día Médico Uruguayo

Dialectica Dialectica: International review of philosophy of knowledge

Dialogue Dialogue: Canadian philosophical review

Diogène Diogène: Revue internationale des sciences humaines

Diogenes Diogenes [International Council for Philosophy and Humanistic Studies]

Dioptric Rev. Dioptric Review

Dirim Dirim. Aylik Tip Gazetesi

Dis.Nerv.Syst. Diseases of the Nervous System

Discovery Discovery

Diss.Abstr. Dissertation Abstracts

XVIIe Siècle XVIIe Siècle. Bulletin de la Société d'Étude du XVIIe Siècle

Doc.Commerciale Comptable La Documentation Commerciale et Comptable [Association des Élèves et Anciens Élèves de l'Institut Professionnel Supérieur de Belgique]

Doc.France La Documentation en France

Doc.Hist.Tech. Documents pour l'Histoire des Techniques [Centre de Documentation d'Histoire des Techniques, Paris]

Dokl.Akad.Nauk SSSR B Doklady̆ Akademii Nauk Soyuza Sovetskikh Sotsialisticheskikh Respublik [Seriya] B: Comptes Rendus de l'Académie des Sciences de l'Union des Républiques Soviétiques Socialistes

Draeger-Hefte Mitteilungen des Drägerwerkes, Lübeck

Dresdner Neueste Nachr. Dresdner Neueste Nachrichten

Duisburger Forsch. Duisburger Forschungen: Schriftenreihe für Geschichte und Heimatkunde Duisburgs [Hrsg. vom Stadtarchiv Duisburg in Verbindung mit der Mercator-Gesellschaft]

Durham Univ.J. Durham University Journal

E

EB.Essent.Books E B. Essential Books

E.L.H. E.L.H: a journal of English literary history [Tudor and Stuart Club, Johns Hopkins University]

ETC ETC. A Review of General Semantics

East.Art Eastern Art

East.Churches Quart. Eastern Churches Quarterly [St. Augustine's Abbey, Ramsgate]

Eclectic Rev. Eclectic Review: a monthly journal devoted to eclectic medicine and surgery [Eclectic Medical College]

Eclogae Graecolatinae Eclogae Graecolatinae

Ecology Ecology [Ecological Society of America]

Écon.Appl. Économie Appliquée [Institut de Science Économique Appliquée, Paris]

Econ.Bot. Economic Botany: devoted to applied botany and plant utilization

Econ.Geogr. Economic Geography

Econ.Geol. Economic Geology (and the Bulletin of the Society of Economic Geologists)

Econ.Hist. Economic History: supplement to *Economic Journal* [Royal Economic Society]

Econ.Hist.Rev. Economic History Review

Econ.J. Economic Journal

Econometrica Econometrica [Econometric Society]

Edgar Allen News Edgar Allen News

Edinb.Acad. Edinburgh Academy: the Edinburgh Academy chronicle

Edinb.Med.J. Edinburgh Medical Journal

Edinb.Rev. The Edinburgh Review

Edoth Edoth [Palestine Institute of Folklore and Ethnology]

Educ.Admin.Superv. Educational Administration and Supervision

Educ.Forum Educational Forum

Éducation (Saigon) Éducation [Le Haut Commissariat de France pour l'Indochine]

Eesti Arst Eesti Arst: Médecin Estonien [Organe de la Ligue des Médecins d'Estonie]

Efficiency Mag. Efficiency Magazine

Egypt.Relig. Egyptian Religion [Alma Egan Hyatt Foundation]

Eiszeit Die Eiszeit. Zeitschrift für allgemeine Eiszeitforschung

Ekkehard, Mitteilungsbl.Deut.Geneal.Abende Ekkehard, Mitteilungsblatt deutscher Genealogischer Abende

Elec.Commun. Electrical Communication

Elec.Eng. Electrical Engineering

Elektrotech.Z. Elektrotechnische Zeitschrift

Elektrotechnika Elektrotechnika

Elem.Math. Elemente der Mathematik: Revue de Mathématiques Élémentaires: Rivista di Matematica Elementare [Organ für den Verein Schweizerischer Mathematiklehrer]

Elem.Math.Beih. Beihefte zur Elemente der Mathematik

Emporium Emporium [Istituto Italiano d'Arte Grafiche]

En Terre Islam En Terre d'Islam

Encéphale Encéphale: Journal de psychiatrie

Endeavour Endeavour

Eng.Bull. (Denver) Engineers' Bulletin [Colorado Society of Engineers]

Eng.Mining J. Engineering and Mining Journal

Eng.Mining J.Press The Engineering and Mining Journal-Press

Engineer Engineer

Engineering Engineering: an Illustrated Weekly Journal

Engl.Hist.Rev. English Historical Review

Engl.Stud. Englische Studien

Enseign.Math. L'Enseignement Mathématique [Commission International de l'Enseignement Mathématique]

Enseign.Sci. L'Enseignement Scientifique

Entomol.News Entomological News [Academy of Natural Sciences, Philadelphia]

Enzymologia Enzymologia

Ephemerides Orient. Ephemerides Orientalistes

Epistēmonikē Epetēris Physikomath.Scholē Ethnikon Kapodistriakon Panepistēmion Epistēmonikē Epēteris: Physikomathematikē Scholē, Ethnikon kai Kapodistriakon Panepistēmion

Epistolae Logistorici Epistolae et Logistorici

Épitöipari Közlekedési Müszaki Egyetem Tud.Közl. Az Épitöipari és Közlekedési Müszaki Egyetem Tudományos Közleményei

Épreuves Syn. Épreuves et Synthèses

Eranos Eranos: Acta philologica suecana

Eranos-Jahrb. Eranos-Jahrbuch

Erasmus Erasmus: Speculum Scientiarum

Erdball Erdball

Erde Die Erde: Zeitschrift der Gesellschaft für Erdkunde

Erdkunde Erdkunde: Archiv für wissenschaftliche Geographie

Ergeb.Anat. Ergebnisse der Anatomie und Entwicklungsgeschichte

Ergeb.Inn.Med.Kinderheilk. Ergebnisse der inneren Medizin und Kinderheilkunde

Ergeb.Physiol. Ergebnisse der Physiologie

Erkenntnis Erkenntnis

Ernähr.Pflanze Die Ernährung der Pflanze

Ernährungsforschung Ernährungsforschung: Berichte und Mitteilungen aus dem Institut für Ernährung

Erudicíon Ibero-Ultramar. Erudicíon Ibero-Ultramarina

Esercitazioni Mat. Esercitazioni Matematiche [Circolo Matematico, Catania]

Essays Stud.Tokyo Wom.Christ.Coll. Essays and Studies by Members of Tokyo Woman's Christian College: Tokyo Joshi Daigaku Ronshu

Estud.Eclesiásticos Estudios Eclesiásticos

Estud.Franciscanos Estudios Franciscanos [Publicación dirigida par los padres de Cataluña]

Estud.Franciscans Estudis Franciscans [Convent de Fra-Menors Caputxins Barcelona-Sarria]

Estud.Lulianos Estudios Lulianos

Estud.Univ.Catalans Estudis Universitaris Catalans

Ethics Ethics

Ethnographie L'Ethnographie

Ethnohistory Ethnohistory [American Indian Ethnohistorical Conference]

Ethnos Ethnos [Instituto Português de Arqueologia, História e Etnografia]

Étud.Art Éthnol.Asiatiques Études d'Art et d'Éthnologie Asiatiques

Étud.Cl. Les Études Classiques

Étud.Doc.Inst.Franco-Chinois Lyon Études et Documents publiés par l'Institut Franco-Chinois de l'Université de Lyon

Étud.Franciscaines Études Franciscaines

Étud.Grecques Études Grecques

Étud.Hist.Phil.Relig. Études d'Histoire et de Philosophie Religieuses [Faculté de Théologie Protestante de l'Université de Strasbourg]

Étud.Métaphys.Morale Études de Métaphysique et de Morale

Étud.Papyrologie Études de Papyrologie

Étud.Phil. Études Philosophiques: organe officiel de la Société d'Études Philosophiques

Étud.Phil.Médiévale Études de Philosophie Médiévale

Étud.Rabelaisiennes Études Rabelaisiennes

Euclides Euclides: Tijdschrift voor de didactiek der exacte vakken

Eudemus Eudemus. An International Journal devoted to the History of Mathematics and Astronomy

Eugen.Rev. The Eugenics Review

Euphorion Euphorion: Zeitschrift fur Literaturgeschichte

Eurasia Septentrionalis Antiqua Eurasia Septentrionalis Antiqua

Europa Seculo XIX L'Europa nel seculo XIX

Évolut.Hum. L'Évolution de l'Humanité

Évolut.Psychiat. Évolution Psychiatrique

Evolution Evolution. International Journal of Organic Evolution [Society for the Study of Evolution]

Ex Orient. Ex Oriente [Eastern Culture Association: Daito Bunka Kyokai]

Ex Orient.Lux Ex Oriente Lux

Exp.Parasitol. Experimental Parasitology

Experientia Experientia: Monatsschrift für das gesamte Gebiet der Naturwissenschaft

Explor.Pyrénéennes Explorations Pyrénéennes: Bulletin de la Société Ramond, Bagnères-de-Bigorre

Explorations Explorations: Studies in Culture and Communications

Explosives Eng. Explosives Engineer

Extrême-Orient Méd. L'Extrême-Orient Médicale

Eye Ear Nose Throat Mon. The Eye, Ear, Nose and Throat Monthly

F

Fac.Pap.Union Coll. Faculty Papers: Union College [Schenectady, N.Y.]

Far East.Ceram.Bull. Far Eastern Ceramic Bulletin

Far East.Quart. The Far Eastern Quarterly [Far Eastern Association]

Faraday Faraday [Vereniging van Leraren in Natuuren Scheikunde, Groningen]

Farlowia Farlowia: a journal of cryptogamic botany [Farlow Library and Herbarium, Harvard University]

Farm Res. Farm Research

Farm.Revy Farmacevtisk Revy [Organ för Sveriges Farmacevtförbund]

Farm.Tid. Farmaceutisk Tidende [Dansk Farmaceutforening]

Farmacêutico El Farmacêutico

Fenix Fenix: Revista de la Sociedad Cientifica Alemana de Buenos Aires

Fennia Fennia. Bulletins de la Société de Géographie Finlandaise

Fette Seifen Fette und Seifen

Fibonacci Quart. Fibonacci Quarterly

Field The Field

Field Artillery J. Field Artillery Journal [U.S. Field Artillery Association]

Field Lab. Field and Laboratory [Science Departments, Southern Methodist University, Dallas, Texas]

Fieldiana Anthropol. Fieldiana: Anthropology

Fight Dis. Fight Against Disease [Research Defence Society, London]

Fil.Čas. Filosofický Časopis

Fil.Nauk. Filosofskie Nauki

Filosofia Filosofia

Fiz.Tverd.Tela Fizika Tverdogo Tela [English translation in *Soviet Phys.: Solid State*]

Flambeau Flambeau: Revue belge des questions politiques et littéraires

Florence Florence: a periodical of the Italian Tourist Board

Földrajzi Közlemények Földrajzi Közlemények: Bulletin de la Société Hongroise de Géographie; Mitteilungen der Ungarischen Geographischen Gesellschaft

Folia Biol. Folia Biologica [Czechoslovakia]

Folia Clin.Int. Folia Clinica Internacional

Folia Morphol. Folia Morphologica

Folia Neuro-Biol. Folia Neuro-Biologica

Folia Oto-Laryngol.Orient. Folia Oto-Laryngologica Orientalia: [Folia Medica Orientalia, Sectio II]

Folium Folium: librorum vitae deditum

Folklore Brabançon Le Folklore Brabançon: Bulletin du Service de Recherches Historiques et Folkloriques de Brabant

Fonderia Ital. Fonderia Italiana

Food Drug Cosmet.Law J. Food, Drug and Cosmetic Law Journal

Fornvännen Fornvännen: Meddelanden från K. Vitterhets-Historie-och Antikvitetsakademien [Stockholm]

Försäkringsfören.Tidskr. Försäkringsföreningens Tidskrift

Forsch.Fortschr. Forschungen und Fortschritte: Korrespondenzblatt (Nachrichtenblatt) der deutschen Wissenschaft und Technik

Forsch.Funde Forschungen und Funde

Forsch.Gesch.Opt. Forschungen zur Geschichte der Optik [Supplement to *Z.Instrumentenk.*]

Forsch.Gesch.Phil.Pädagogik Forschungen zur Geschichte der Philosophie und der Pädagogik

Fortn.Rev. Fortnightly Review

Fortschr.Chem.Organischer Naturst. Fortschritte der Chemie organischer Naturstoffe

Fortschr.Geol.Paläontol. Fortschritte der Geologie und Paläontologie

Fortschr.Med. Fortschritte der Medizin

Fortschr.Mineral. Fortschritte der Mineralogie

Fortschr.Mineral.Kristallogr.Petrogr. Fortschritte der Mineralogie, Kristallographie und Petrographie

Fortschr.Naturwiss.Forsch. Fortschritte der naturwissenschaftlichen Forschung

Fortschr.Therap. Fortschritte der Therapie

Fortschr.Zahnheilk. Fortschritte der Zahnheilkunde

Forum The Forum

Fra Ark.Mus. Fra Arkiv og Museum [Östifternes Historisk-Topografisk Selskab]

Franç.Mod. Le Français Moderne

France-Asie France-Asie. Revue de Culture et de Synthèse Franco-Asiatique

France Illus. France Illustration

France Méd. La France Médicale: Revue d'études d'histoire de la médecine [from 1861-1914]

France Méd. La France Médicale: Revue générale de médecine et chirurgie [from 1938]

France Monde France et Monde

Frankf.Bücher-Freund Der Frankfurter Bücher-Freund

Frankf.Geogr.Hefte Frankfurter geographische Hefte [Verein für Geographie und Statistik]

Franziskanische Stud. Franziskanische Studien

Franziskanische Stud.Beih. Franziskanische Studien Beiheft

Fraser's Mag. Fraser's Magazine

Frau Die Frau

Freemason Freemason

French Rev. French Review [American Association of Teachers of French]

Frontiers Frontiers: a magazine of natural history [Academy of Natural Sciences of Philadelphia]

Fys.Tidsskr. Fysisk Tidsskrift [Selskab for Naturlaerens Udbredelse]

G

G.Batteriol.Virol.Immunol. Giornale di Batteriologia, Virologia ed Immunologia ed Annali Ospedale Maria Vittoria di Torino

G.Crit.Fil.Ital. Giornale Critico della Filosofia Italiana

G.Dantesco Giornale Dantesco

G.Econ.Riv.Statist. Giornale degli Economisti e Rivista di Statistica

G.Ital. Il Giornale d'Italia

G.Ital.Filol. Giornale Italiano di Filologia

G.Mat.Battaglini Giornale di Matematiche di Battaglini per il Progresso degli Studi nelle Università Italiane

G.Med.Mil. Giornale di Medicina Militare [Ministero della Guerra: Direzione ed Amministrazione]

G.Univ. Il Giornale dell'Università. Organo degli Atenei d'Italia

Gac.Méd.Mex. Gaceta Médica de Mexico [Academia Nacional de Medicina de Mexico]

Gaea Gaea: Anales de la Sociedad Argentina de Estudios Geográficos

Gallia Gallia [Department of French Literature in the University of Osaka]

Gândirea Gândirea

Gants Ciel Gants du Ciel

Gard.Bull. The Gardens' Bulletin [Botanic Gardens, Straits Settlements, *afterwards* Singapore]

Gard.Chron. Gardener's Chronicle

Gard.J. The Garden Journal of the New York Botanical Garden

Gastroenterology Gastroenterology [American Gastroenterological Association]

Gaz.Beaux-Arts Gazette des Beaux-Arts: Courrier européen de l'art et de la curiosité

Gaz.Hôp. Gazette des Hôpitaux

Gaz.Mat. Gazeta Matematică

Gaz.Méd. Gazette Médicale de Paris

Gaz.Méd.Centre Gazette Médicale du Centre

Gazz.Chim.Ital. Gazzetta Chimica Italiana [Società Chimica Italiana]

Gazz.Int.Med.Chir. Gazzetta Internazionale di Medicina e Chirurgia

Gazz.Med.Marche Gazzetta Medica delle Marche

Geist Ostens Geist des Ostens. Monatsschrift für volkstümliche Asiatenkunde

Geisteskultur Geisteskultur (und Volksbildung) [Comenius Gesellschaft]

Geisteswissenschaften Die Geisteswissenschaften

Geistige Arb. Geistige Arbeit: Zeitung aus der wissenschaftlichen Welt

Geloof Wetensch. Geloof en Wetenschap

Gen.Elec.Rev. General Electric Review

Gen.Mag.Hist.Chron. General Magazine and Historical Chronicle [Pennsylvania University, General Alumni Society]

Gen.Mot.Eng.J. General Motors Engineering Journal

Gen.Sci.Quart. General Science Quarterly [National Association for Research in Science Teaching, New York]

Genava Genava [Musée d'Art et d'Histoire, Genève]

Genealogical Quart. Genealogical Quarterly: notes and queries dealing with British and American family and clan history and biography

Geneesk.Gids Geneeskundige Gids: Tijdschrift voor Geneeskunst en Volksgezondheit

Geneesk.Tijdschr.Ned.Indie Geneeskundige Tijdschrift voor Nederlandsch-Indie

Genesis Genesis

Genetics Genetics [Brooklyn Botanic Garden]

Génie Civil Le Génie Civil

Gentleman's Mag. Gentleman's Magazine

Geo Times Geo Times [American Geological Institute]

Geofys.Sb. (Praha) Geofysikálni Sbornik

Geogr.Ann. Geografiska Annaler [Svenska Sällskapet för Antropologi och Geografi]

Geogr.Anz. Geographischer Anzeiger: Blätter für den geographischen Unterricht

Geogr.Geol.Mededeel.Anthropogeogr.Reeks Geographische en Geologische Mededeelingen: Anthropogeographische Reeks [Publicaties uit het Geografisch en uit het Mineralogisch-Geologisch Instituut der Rijksuniversiteit te Utrecht]

Geogr.Geol.Mededeel.Physiogr.Geol.Reeks Geographische en Geologische Mededeelingen: Physiographisch-geologische Reeks [Geographisch Instituut, Rijksuniversiteit, Utrecht]

Geogr.Helv. Geographica Helvetica

Geogr.J. Geographical Journal: including the proceedings, etc. [Royal Geographical Society of London]

Geogr.Jahrb. Geographisches Jahrbuch

Geogr.Mag. Geographical Magazine

Geogr.Rev. Geographical Review [American Geographical Society of New York]

Geogr.Tidsskr. Geografisk Tidsskrift [K. Dansk Geografisk Selskab]

Geogr.Z. Geographische Zeitschrift

Geografia La Geografia: communicazioni dell'Instituto Geografico de Agostini, Novara

Géographie La Géographie

Geography Geography [Geographical Association, London]

Geokhimiya Geokhimiya [Akademiya Nauk SSSR]

Geol.Hung.Ser.Geol. Geologica Hungarica: Series Geologica

Geol.Hung.Ser.Palaentol. Geologica Hungarica: Series Palaeontologica

Geol.Mag. Geological Magazine

Geol.Mijnbouw Geologie en Mijnbouw

Geol.Rundsch. Geologische Rundschau [Geologische Vereinigung]

Geologe Der Geologe: Auskunftsblatt für Geologen und Mineralogen, zugleich Nachtrag und Ergänzung zum Geologen-Kalender

Geophysics Geophysics [Society of Exploration Geophysicists]

Georgia Hist.Quart. Georgia Historical Quarterly

Georgofili I Georgofili: Atti della R. Accademia dei Georgofili di Firenze

Ger.Life Lett. German Life and Letters

Ger.Rev. Germanic Review [Department of Germanic Languages, Columbia University]

Geriatrics Geriatrics [American Geriatrics Society, Minneapolis]

Gerlands Beitr.Geophys. Gerlands Beiträge zur Geophysik

Gesch.Einzeldarstell.Electrotech. Geschichtliche Einzeldarstellungen aus der Elektrotechnik

Gesch.Islandischen Geogr. Geschichte der Islandischen Geographie

Gesch.Pharm. Zur Geschichte der Pharmazie

Geschichtsbl.Tech.Ind. Geschichtsblätter für Technik und Industrie [und Gewerbe]: illustrierte Monatsschrift

Geschlecht Ges. Geschlecht und Gesellschaft

Gesnerus Gesnerus: Vierteljahrsschrift hrsg. von der Schweizerischen Gesellschaft für Geschichte der Medizin und der Naturwissenschaften

Gesundheitslehrer Gesundheitslehrer

Gewina Gewina

Gids De Gids: nieuwe vaderlandsche letteroefeningen

Giesserei Die Giesserei

Ginecol.Prat. La Ginecologia Pratica

Glas Srpske Akad. Glas Srpske [Kral'evske] Akademije [Beograd]

Glas.Srpsko Geogr.Društvo Glasnik Srpsko Geografsko Društvo: Bulletin de la Société Serbo de Géographie

Glasgow Med.J. Glasgow Medical Journal

Glasgow Univ.Mag. Glasgow University Magazine

Glashütte Die Glashütte (und Keramik)

Globe Globe [Société de Géographie de Genève]

Globusfreund Der Globusfreund [Coronelli-Weltbund der Globusfreunde: Societas Coronelliana Amicorum Globorum]

Glückauf Glückauf: Berg- und hüttenmannische Zeitschrift

Glückauf (Freiberg) Glückauf; Industrie- und Familienblatt (Sächsische Gewerbe-Vereins-Zeitung)

Gnomon Gnomon: Kritische Zeitschrift für die gesamte klassische Altertumswissenschaft

Göteborgs Högsk.Årsskr. Göteborgs Högskolas Årsskrift

Göteborgs Univ.Årsskr. Göteborgs Universitets Årsskrift: Acta Universitatis Gothoburgensis

Goethe Goethe: Vierteljahrsschrift der Goethe-Gesellschaft

Göttingische Gelehrte Anz. Göttingische Gelehrte Anzeigen

Göttingische Nebenstunden Göttingische Nebenstunden

Goldene Tor Das Goldene Tor

Grad.J. Graduate Journal

Greek Roman Byzantine Stud. Greek, Roman and Byzantine Studies

Gregorianum Gregorianum: Rivista Trimestrale di Studi Teologici e Filosofici

Greifsw.Beitr.Lit.Stilforsch. Greifswalder Beiträge zur Literatur- und Stilforschung

Grenz.Med. Grenzgebiete der Medizin

Grünenthal-Waage Die Grünenthal-Waage [Medizinisch-wissenschaftliche Abteilung der Chemie Grünenthal GmbH]

Gruźlica Gruźlica

Gulden Passer De Gulden Passer: Le Compas d'Or [Vereeniging der Antwerpsche Bibliophilen]

Gut Gut: Journal of the British Society of Gastroenterology

Gutenberg-Jahrb. Gutenberg-Jahrbuch

Gutenbergmuseum Gutenbergmuseum [Organ der Schweizer Bibliophilen-Gesellschaft]

Gutenbergstube Gutenbergstube: Mitteilungen des Vereins zur Förderung des Schweizer Gutenbergmuseums in Bern

Guy's Hosp.Gaz. Guy's Hospital Gazette

Guy's Hosp.Rep. Guy's Hospital Reports

Gymnasium Das Gymnasium: Zeitschrift des Deutschen Gymnasialvereins

Gypsy Folklore Gaz. Gypsy and Folk Lore Gazette

H

HMW Jahrb. HMW-Jahrbuch

Ha'aretz Ha'aretz [Israel]

Hamburger Akad.Rundsch. Hamburger Akademische Rundschau

Hamdard Med.Digest Hamdard Medical Digest

Handel.Hydrobiol.Club Handelingen van de Hydrobiologische Club [Amsterdam]

Handel.Levensber.Maatschappij Ned.Lett.Leiden Handelingen en Levensberichten van de Maatschappij der Nederlandsche Letterkunde te Leiden

Handel.Vlaam.Natuur- Geneesk.Congr. Handelingen van het Vlaamsch Natuur- en Geneeskundig Congres

Handel.Zuidned.Maatschappij Taal.Lett.Gesch. Handelingen: Zuidnederlandse Maatschappij voor Taal- en Letterkunde en Geschiedenis

Handl.Svenska Vetenskapsakad. Handlingar: Svenska Vetenskapsakademien

Handl.Vitterhets.Hist.Antiquitets Acad. Handlingar: Vitterhets-, Historie- och Antiquitets Academien

Hansa Hansa. Deutsche nautische Zeitschrift

Hansische Geschichtsbl. Hansische Geschichtsblätter

Harper's Mag. Harper's Magazine

Harvard Afr.Stud. Harvard African Studies

Harvard Alumni Bull. Harvard Alumni Bulletin

Harvard Educ.Rev. Harvard Educational Review

Harvard Grad.Mag. Harvard Graduates' Magazine

Harvard J. Asiatic Stud. Harvard Journal of Asiatic Studies [Harvard-Yenching Institute]

Harvard Libr.Bull. Harvard Library Bulletin

Harvard Libr.Notes Harvard Library Notes [Harvard University Library]

Harvard Med.Alumni Bull. Harvard Medical Alumni Bulletin

Harvard Stud.Cl.Philol. Harvard Studies in Classical Philology

Harvard Stud.Comp.Lit. Harvard Studies in Comparative Literature

Harvard Stud.Philol.Lit. Harvard Studies and Notes in Philology and Literature

Harvard Theol.Rev. Harvard Theological Review

Harvard Univ.Gaz. Harvard University Gazette

Harvey Lect. The Harvey Lectures

Hastings East Sussex Natur. The Hastings and East Sussex Naturalist

Hautarzt Der Hautarzt

Health Educ.J. The Health Education Journal

Heavens The Heavens [Kwasan Observatory, Imperial University, Kyoto; Oriental Astronomical Association]

Hebrew Med.J. The Hebrew Medical Journal: Harofé Haivri

Hebrew Physician Hebrew Physician

Hebrew Union Coll.Annu. Hebrew Union College Annual

Heidelb.Abhandl.Phil. Heidelberger Abhandlungen zur Philosophie und ihrer Geschichte

Heil- Gewürzpflanzen Heil- und Gewürzpflanzen

Heimatbilder Oberfranken Heimatbilden aus Oberfranken

Heimatkal.Kreises Züllichau-Schwiebus Heimatkalender des Kreises Züllichau-Schwiebus

Hellēn.Contemp. Hellénisme Contemporain

Hēllen.Dēmiourgia Hēllenikē Dēmiourgia

Hēllen.Iatrike Hēllenikē Iatrike

Hellēnika Hellēnika: philologikon, historikon kai laographilcon periodikon syngramma

Hellēnika Parartēma Hellēnika Parartēma

Helv.Phys.Acta Helvetica Physica Acta [Schweizerische Physikalische Gesellschaft]

Hémecht T'Hémecht. Zeitschrift für Luxemburger Geschichte

Hemel Dampkring Hemel en Dampkring [Nederlandsche Vereeniging voor Weer- en Sterrenkunde]

Henschel's Janus Henschel's Janus: Zeitschrift für Geschichte und Literatur der Medicin

Herbarium Herbarium: Organ zur Förderung des Austausches wissenschaftlicher Exsiccatensammlungen

Herbertia Herbertia [American Plant Life Society]

Heredity Heredity: an international journal of genetics

Hermathena Hermathena: a series of papers on literature, science, and philosophy by members of Trinity College, Dublin

Hermeneus Hermeneus: Maandblad voor de antieke cultuur

Hermes Z.Kl.Philol. Hermes: Zeitschrift für klassische Philologie

Herpetologica Herpetologica [Herpetologists League, Chicago]

Hesperia Hesperia: Journal of the American School of Classical Studies at Athens

Hesperia (Zurich) Hesperia [Swiss Institute of International Studies]

Hesperia Suppl. Hesperia Supplements

Hespéris Hespéris: Archives berbères et Bulletin de l'Institut des Hautes-Études Marocaines

Hess.Bl.Volksk. Hessische Blätter für Volkskunde [Hessische Vereinigung für Volkskunde]

Hess.Kron. Hessische Kronik. Monatsschrift für Familien und Ortgeschichte in Hessen und Hessen-Nassau.

Hibbert J. Hibbert Journal: a quarterly review of religion, theology and philosophy

Higher Educ. Higher Education [Higher Education Division U.S. Office of Education]

Hilgardia Hilgardia. A Journal of Agricultural Science

Himmelswelt Himmelswelt

Hinrichsen's Musical Year Book Hinrichsen's Musical Year Book

Hippocrate (Paris) Hippocrate: Revue d'humanisme médical

Hippocrates (London) Hippocrates: towards synthesis in medicine

Hippokrates (Stuttgart) Hippokrates: Zeitschrift für praktische Heilkunde

Hispanic-Amer.Hist.Rev. Hispanic-American Historical Review

Hispanic Rev. Hispanic Review

Hist.Collect.Essex Inst. Historical Collections: Essex Institute [Salem, Mass.]

Hist.Fil.Medd.Danske Vidensk.Selsk. Historisk-filosofiske Meddelelser: [Kongelige] Danske Videnskabernes Selskab [Académie Royale des Sciences et des Lettres de Danemark]

Hist.Fil.Skr.Danske Vidensk.Selsk. Historisk-filosofiske Skrifter: [Kongelige] Danske Videnskabernes Selskab [Académie Royale des Sciences et des Lettres de Danemark]

Hist.Filol.Medd.Danske Vidensk.Selsk. Historisk-filologiske Meddelelser: [Kongelige] Danske Videnskabernes Selskab [Académie Royale des Sciences et des Lettres de Danemark]

Hist.J. The Historical Journal

Hist.Jahrb.Görres-Ges. Historisches Jahrbuch. Herausgegeben von der Historischen Section der Görres-Gesellschaft

Hist.Méd. Histoire de la Médecine [Société Française d'Histoire de la Médecine]

Hist.Natur. Historia Naturalis [Unione Italiana Naturalisti]

Hist.Notes Pap.Observ.Lund Historical Notes and Papers, Observatory of Lund

Hist.Polit.Bl.Katholische Deut. Historisch-politische Blätter für das katholische Deutschland

Hist.Reference Bull. The History Reference Bulletin

Hist.Rev.Berks County Historical Review of Berks County [Historical Society of Berks County, Pennsylvania]

Hist.Sci. History of Science: an annual review of literature, research and teaching

Hist.Soc.Southern Calif.Quart.Publ. Historical Society of Southern California Quarterly Publications

Hist.Today History Today

Hist.Z. Historische Zeitschrift

Hist.Z.Beih. Historische Zeitschrift Beiheft

Historia Historia: Revista trimestral de Historia Argentina, Americana y Española

Historia (Baden) Historia. Zeitschrift für alte Geschichte

Historian The Historian

History History: the quarterly journal of the Historical Association

History (New York) History [from 1959-61]

Home Gard. (New Orleans) Home Gardening [New Orleans Gardening Society]

Homme Préhist. L'Homme Préhistorique

Hôpital Hôpital

Horological J. The Horological Journal [British Horological Institute]

Hosp.Tidings (Philadelphia) Hospital Tidings (Philadelphia)

Hospitals Hospitals

Hospitalstidende Hospitalstidende [Dansk Medicinsk Selskab]

Houille Blanche La Houille Blanche

Hum.Biol. Human Biology: a record of research

Hum.Gymnasium Das humanistische Gymnasium

Hum.Renaiss. Humanisme et Renaissance

Hum.Stud. Humana Studia. ser. 2

Hum.Tech. Humanismus und Technik. Zeitschrift zur Erforschung und Pflege der Menschlichkeit

Humanidades (Buenos Aires) Humanidades [Facultad de Humanidades, *etc.*, Universidad de La Plata]

Humanitas (Brescia) Humanitas: Rivista Mensile di Cultura

Huntington Libr.Bull. Huntington Library Bulletin [Henry E. Huntington Library and Art Gallery, San Marino, California]

Huntington Libr.Quart. Huntington Library Quarterly [Henry E. Huntington Library and Art Gallery, San Marino, California]

Hydrogr.Rev. Hydrographic Review [International Hydrographic Bureau]

Hydrologica Hydrologica

Hyg.Ment. Hygiène Mentale [Supplement to *Encéphale*]

Hyg.Wegweiser Hygienischer Wegweiser. Zentralblatt für Technik und Methodik der hygienischen Volksbelehrung

Hygiea Hygieà: Medicinisk och pharmaceutisk månadskrift [Svenska Läkare-Sällskapet]

I

IEEE Trans.Educ. Institute of Electrical and Electronics Engineers, Transactions on Education

Ibérica Ibérica: el progreso de las ciencias

Iberica (Hamburg) Iberica [Hamburg. Ibero-amerikanisches Institut]

Ibero-Amer.Arch. Ibero-Amerikanisches Archiv: Zeitschrift des Ibero-Amerikanischen Forschungs-Instituts der Universität Bonn

Ibis Ibis [British Ornithologists Union]

Idrol.Climatol. Idrologia e la Climatologia

Ig.Sanit.Pubblica Igiene e Sanità Pubblica

Ill.Tech.Eng.Alumnus Illinois Technical Engineer and Alumnus

Illus.Franç. Illustration Française

Illus.Ital. Illustrazione Italiana

Illus.London News Illustrated London News

Illustration L'Illustration

Imago Imago: Zeitschrift für Anwendung der Psychoanalyse

Imago Mundi Imago Mundi: a review of early cartography

Imago Mundi (Buenos Aires) Imago Mundi. Revista de Historia de la Cultura

Impact Impact of Science on Society [UNESCO]

Impr.Coll.Univ.Teaching Improving College and University Teaching

Ind.Chim.Belg. Industrie Chimique Belge [Fédération des Industries Chimiques de Belgique]

Ind.Chim.Mineraria Met. L'Industria Chimica, Mineraria e Metallurgica

Ind.Educ.Mag. Industrial Education Magazine

Ind.Eng.Chem. Industrial and Engineering Chemistry [American Chemical Society]

Ind.Mineraria Industria Mineraria

Ind.Mus.N.Y. Industrial Museum of New York [New York Museum of Science and Industry]

Ind.Quim. Industria y Quimica: Revista de la Asociacion Quimica Argentina

Ind.Tech. Industrie und Technik

Indian Antiq. Indian Antiquary

Indian Art Lett. Indian Art and Letters [India Society, London]

Indian Cult. Indian Culture: Journal of the Indian Research Institute

Indian Hist.Quart. Indian Historical Quarterly

Indian J.Entomol. Indian Journal of Entomology

Indian J.Hist.Med. Indian Journal of the History of Medicine [Indian Association of the History of Medicine]

Indian J.Psychol. Indian Journal of Psychology

Indian J.Vener.Dis. Indian Journal of Venereal Diseases (and Dermatology)

Indiana Mag.Hist. Indiana Magazine of History [Indiana Historical Society]

Indische Gids De Indische Gids

Indo-Iranica Indo-Iranica: quarterly organ of the Iran Society [Calcutta]

Industrie Industrie (Fédération des Industries Belges)

Inform.Aliénistes Neurol. Informateur des Aliénistes et des Neurologistes

Inform.Circ.Dep.Mines Tech.Surv.Can.Mines Br. Information Circular: Department of Mines and Technical Surveys, Canada: Mines Branch

Inform.Cult. Informazioni Culturali

Infrared Phys. Infrared Physics

Ingegneria Ingegneria

Ingenieur Ingenieur [K. Instituut van Ingenieurs, The Hague]

Ingeniorvidenskab.Skr. Ingeniorvidenskabelige Skriften

Initiation Islam Initiation à l'Islam

Int.Arch.Ethnogr. Internationales Archiv für Ethnographie

Int.Bibliogr.Hist.Sci. International Bibliography of Historical Sciences

Int.Conciliation International Conciliation [Division of Intercourse and Education, Carnegie Endowment for International Peace]

Int.Congr.Amer. International Congress of Americanists

Int.Congr.Byzantine Stud. International Congress of Byzantine Studies

Int.Congr.Hist.Med. International Congress of the History of Medicine

Int.Congr.Hist.Sci. International Congress of the History of Science

Int.Congr.Math. International Congress of Mathematicians

Int.Congr.Med. International Congress of Medicine

Int.Congr.Orient. International Congress of Orientalists

Int.Congr.Phil. International Congress of Philosophy

Int.Congr.Zool. International Congress of Zoology

Int.Geogr.Congr. International Geographical Congress

Int.J.Ethics International Journal of Ethics

Int.J.Leprosy The International Journal of Leprosy

Int.J.Orthodont. International Journal of Orthodontia

Int.J.Psychoanal. International Journal of Psychoanalysis

Int.J.Soc.Psychiat. The International Journal of Social Psychiatry

Int.Math.Nachr. Internationale mathematische Nachrichten: International Mathematical News: Nouvelles Mathématiques Internationales

Int.Math.News International Mathematical News: Internationale mathematische Nachrichten: Nouvelles Mathématiques Internationales

Int.Med.Monatsh. Internationale medizinische Monatshefte

Int.Monatsschr.Erforsch.Alkoholismus Internationale Monatsschrift zur Erforschung des Alkoholismus

Int.Monatsschr.Wiss.Kunst Tech. Internationale Monatsschrift für Wissenschaft, Kunst und Technik

Int.Office Equip.Mag. International Office Equipment Magazine

Int.Rec.Med. International Record of Medicine

Int.Rev.Missions The International Review of Missions

Int.Sci. International Science [New World Club, New York]

Int.Sugar J. International Sugar Journal

Int.Z.Phys.-Chem.Biol. Internationale Zeitschrift für physikalisch-chemische Biologie

Int.Z.Psychoanal.Imago Internationale Zeitschrift für Psychoanalyse und Imago

Interchem.Rev. Interchemical Review [Interchemical Corporation]

Intermédiaire Chercheurs Curieux L'Intermédiaire des Chercheurs et Curieux

Interne Interne

Interstate Med.J. Interstate Medical Journal

Iraq Iraq [British School of Archaeology in Iraq]

'Irfān, see *Al-'Irfān*

Irish Astron.J. Irish Astronomical Journal

Irish J.Med.Sci. Irish Journal of Medical Science

Iron Worker The Iron Worker

Isis Isis: an International Review devoted to the History of Science and its Cultural Influences [History of Science Society]

Islam Der Islam: Zeitschrift für Geschichte und Kultur des Islamischen Orients

Islamic Cult. Islamic Culture: the Hyderabad quarterly review

Islamic Rev. Islamic Review

Islamica Islamica: Zeitschrift für die Erforschung der Sprachen, der Geschichte und der Kulturen der islamischen Völker [Supplement to *Asia Major*]

Israel Ann.Psychiat. Israel Annals of Psychiatry and Related Disciplines

Israel Explor.J. Israel Exploration Journal

Ist.Arkh. Istoricheski Arkhiv [Akademiya Nauk SSSR]

Ist.Astron.Issled. Istoriko-Astronomicheskie Issledovaniia: Studies in the history of astronomy

Ist.Mat.Issled. Istoriko-Matematicheskie Issledovaniia: Works of the seminar for the history of mathematics of Moscow State University

Ist.Naz.Ott. Istituto Nazionale di Ottica

Istanbuler Mitt. Istanbuler Mitteilungen [Hrsg. von der Abteilung Istanbul des Archäologischen Institutes des Deutschen Reiches]

Ital.Medioevale Umanistica Italia Medioevale e Umanistica

Ital.Sacra Italia Sacra: le chiese d'Italia nell'arte e nella storia

Italica Italica [American Association of Teachers of Italian]

Items Items

Iz Ist.Nauk.Tekh.Stranakh Vostoka Iz Istorii Nauki i Tekhniki v Stranakh Vostoka

Izv.Akad.Nauk Azerbaidzh.SSSR Ser.Fiziko-Tekh.Mat.Nauk Izvestiya Akademii Nauk Azerbaidzhanskoi SSSR. Seriya Fiziko-tekhnicheskikh i Matematicheskikh Nauk

Izv.Akad.Nauk SSSR Otd.Fiz.Mat.Nauk Izvestiya Akademii Nauk SSSR: Otdelenie Fiziko-Matematicheskikh Nauk

Izv.Akad.Nauk SSSR Otd.Ist.Filol.Nauk Izvestiya Akademii Nauk SSSR: Otdelenie Istoriko-Filologicheskikh Nauk

Izv.Akad.Nauk SSSR Otd.Mat.Estestv.Nauk Izvestiya Akademii Nauk SSSR: Otdelenie Matematicheskikh i Estestvennyi Nauk

Izv.Akad.Nauk SSSR Otd.Mat.Estestv.Nauk Ser.Biol. Izvestiya Akademii Nauk SSSR: Otdelenie Matematicheskikh i Estestvennyi Nauk - Seriya Biologicheskaya [formerly *Izv.Akad.Nauk SSSR Otd.Mat.Estestv.Nauk Ser.Biol.*]

Izv.Akad.Nauk SSSR Otd.Obshchest.Nauk Izvestiya Akademii Nauk SSSR: Otdelenie Obshchestvennuikh Nauk

Izv.Akad.Nauk SSSR Otd.Tekh.Nauk Mekh.Mashinostr. Izvestiya Akademii Nauk SSSR: Otdelenie Tekhnicheskikh Nauk: Mekhanika i Mashinostroenie

Izv.Akad.Nauk SSSR Ser.Biol. Izvestiya Akademii Nauk SSSR: Seriya Biologicheskaya

Izv.Akad.Nauk SSSR Ser.Geogr. Izvestiya Akademii Nauk SSSR: Seriya Geograficheskaia

Izv.Gos.Geogr.Obshchest. Izvestiya Gosudarstvennogo Geograficheskogo Obshchestva [formerly *Izv.Gos.Russ.Geogr.Obshchest.*]

Izv.Gos.Russ.Geogr.Obshchest. Izvestiya Gosudarstvennogo Russkogo Geograficheskogo Obshchestva [formerly *Izv.Russ.Geogr. Obshchest.*]

Izv.Imperatorskoi Akad.Nauk Izvestiya Imperatorskoi Akademii Nauk

Izv.Leningr.Nauch.Inst.Im.P.F.Lesgafta Izvestiya Leningradskogo Nauchnogo Instituta Imeni P.F. Lesgafta [formerly *Izv. Petrogradskogo Nauch.Inst.Im.P.F.Lesgafta*]

Izv.Nauch.Inst.Im.P.F.Lesgafta Izvestiya Nauchnogo Instituta Imeni P.F. Lesgafta [formerly *Izv.Leningr.Nauch.Inst.Im.P.F. Lesgafta*]

Izv.Petrogradskogo Nauch.Inst.Im.P.F.Lesgafta Izvestiya Petrogradskogo Nauchnogo Instituta Imeni P.F. Lesgafta

Izv.Ross.Akad.Nauk Izvestiya Rossiiskoi Akademii Nauk

Izv.Russ.Geogr.Obshchest. Izvestiya Russkogo Geograficheskogo Obshchestva

Izv.Vses.Geogr.Obshchest. Izvestiya Vsesoyuznogo Geograficheskogo Obshchestva

J

J.Abnorm.Soc.Psychol. Journal of Abnormal and Social Psychology

J.Acoust.Soc.Amer. Journal of the Acoustical Society of America

J.Adult Educ. (New York) Journal of Adult Education [American Association for Adult Education]

J.Afr.Soc. Journal of the Royal African Society

J.Agr.Res. Journal of Agricultural Research

J.Ala.Acad.Sci. Journal of the Alabama Academy of Sciences

J.Allergy Journal of Allergy

J.Amer.Chem.Soc. Journal of the American Chemical Society

J.Amer.Coll.Dent. Journal of the American College of Dentists

J.Amer.Dent.Ass. Journal of the American Dental Association

J.Amer.Diet.Ass. Journal of the American Dietetic Association

J.Amer.Folklore Journal of American Folklore

J.Amer.Hist. Journal of American History

J.Amer.Inst.Elec.Eng. Journal of the American Institute of Electrical Engineers

J.Amer.Med.Ass. Journal of the American Medical Association

J.Amer.Orient.Soc. Journal of the American Oriental Society

J.Amer.Orient.Soc.Suppl. Supplement to the Journal of the American Oriental Society

J.Amer.Osteopath.Ass. Journal of the American Osteopathic Association

J.Amer.Pharm.Ass. Journal of the American Pharmaceutical Association

J.Amer.Psychoanal.Ass. Journal of the American Psychoanalytic Association

J.Amer.Soc.Nav.Eng. Journal of the American Society of Naval Engineers

J.Amer.Statist.Ass. Journal of the American Statistical Association

J.Amer.Veterinary Med.Ass. Journal of the American Veterinary Medical Association

J.Anat. Journal of Anatomy

J.Arnold Arboretum Journal of the Arnold Arboretum [Harvard University]

J.Asian Stud. Journal of Asian Studies

J.Asiatic Soc. Journal of the Asiatic Society

J.Asiatique Journal Asiatique

J.Ass.Comput.Mach. Journal of the Association for Computing Machinery

J.Aviat.Med. Journal of Aviation Medicine

J.Ayurveda (Calcutta) Journal of Ayurveda, or, The Hindu System of Medicine

J.Bacteriol. Journal of Bacteriology

J.Biblical Lit. Journal of Biblical Literature

J.Bihar Orissa Res.Soc. Journal of the Bihar and Orissa Research Society

J.Bombay Br.Roy.Asiatic Soc. Journal of the Bombay Branch of the Royal Asiatic Society

J.Bombay Natur.Hist.Soc. Journal of the Bombay Natural History Society

J.Bot. Journal of Botany

J.Bot.Brit.Foreign Journal of Botany, British and Foreign

J.Brit.Archaeol.Ass. Journal of the British Archaeological Association

J.Brit.Astron.Ass. Journal of the British Astronomical Association

J.Brit.Interplanet.Soc. Journal of the British Interplanetary Society

J.Cal.Reform Journal of Calendar Reform

J.Calcutta Univ.Dept.Lett. Journal of the Calcutta University, Department of Letters

J.Cama Orient.Inst. Journal [K.R.] Cama Oriental Institute

J.Ceylon Br.Roy.Asiatic Soc. Journal of the Ceylon Branch of the Royal Asiatic Society

J.Chem.Educ. Journal of Chemical Education

J.Chem.Phys. Journal of Chemical Physics [American Institute of Physics, New York]

J.Chem.Soc. Journal of the Chemical Society

J.Chim.Phys. Journal de Chimie Physique [Société de Chimie Physique, Paris]

J.Chir.Ann.Soc.Belg.Chir. Journal de Chirurgie et Annales de la Société Belge de Chirurgie

J.Cincinnati Soc.Natur.Hist. Journal of the Cincinnati Society of Natural History

J.Clin.Exp.Psychopathol. Journal of Clinical and Experimental Psychopathology and Quarterly Review of Psychiatry and Neurology

J.Comp.Neurol. Journal of Comparative Neurology

J.Comp.Pathol.Therap. Journal of Comparative Pathology and Therapeutics

J.Crim.Psychopathol. Journal of Criminal Psychopathology

J.Cuneiform Stud. Journal of Cuneiform Studies [American School of Oriental Research]

J.Cycle Res. Journal of Cycle Research

J.Dent.Res. Journal of Dental Research

J.Dep.Lett.Univ.Calcutta Journal of Department of Letters. University of Calcutta

J.Doc. The Journal of Documentation

J.Ecol. The Journal of Ecology [British Ecological Society]

J.École Polytech. Journal de l'École Polytechnique [Paris]

J.Econ.Bus.Hist. Journal of Economic and Business History [Graduate School of Business Administration, Harvard University]

J.Econ.Hist. The Journal of Economic History [Economic History Association]

J.Econ.Soc.Hist.Orient. Journal of the Economic and Social History of the Orient

J.Educ.Method Journal of Educational Method

J.Egypt.Archaeol. Journal of Egyptian Archaeology

J.Egypt.Med.Ass. Journal of the Egyptian Medical Association

J.Electrochem.Soc. Journal of the (American) Electrochemical Society

J.Elisha Mitchell Sci.Soc. Journal of the Elisha Mitchell Scientific Society [University of North Carolina]

J.Eng.Educ. The Journal of Engineering Education

J.Engl.Ger.Philol. Journal of English and Germanic Philology [University of Illinois]

J.Forest. Journal of Forestry

J.Franklin Inst. Journal of the Franklin Institute

J.Gasbeleucht. Journal für Gasbeleuchtung

J.Gen.Chem.USSR Journal of General Chemistry of the USSR: English translation of *Zhurnal Obshcheĭ Khimii*

J.Gen.Educ. Journal of General Education

J.Gen.Physiol. Journal of General Physiology [Rockefeller Institute for Medical Research, New York]

J.Gen.Psychol. The Journal of General Psychology

J.Genet.Psychol. Journal of Genetic Psychology

J.Geogr. Journal of Geography

J.Geogr. (Tokyo) Journal of Geography

J.Geol. Journal of Geology [Department of Geology, Chicago University]

J.Geol.Educ. Journal of Geological Education

J.Geophys.Res. Journal of Geophysical Research

J.Gerontol. Journal of Gerontology [Gerontological Society, Springfield, Ill.]

J.Glaciol. Journal of Glaciology

J.Grad.Res.Cent. Journal of the Graduate Research Center [Southern Methodist University]

J.Greater India Soc. Journal of the Greater India Society

J.Hellen.Stud. Journal of Hellenic Studies [Society for the Promotion of Hellenic Studies, London]

J.Hered. Journal of Heredity

J.Higher Educ. Journal of Higher Education [Ohio State University. Bureau of Educational Research]

J.Hist.Ideas Journal of the History of Ideas [College of the City of New York]

J.Hist.Med. Journal of the History of Medicine and Allied Sciences

J.Hist.Phil. Journal for History of Philosophy

J.Hist.Sci.Japan Journal of History of Science: Kagaku-shi Kenkyū [History of Science Society of Japan: Nippon Kagaku-shi Gakkai]

J.Hum.Relat. The Journal of Human Relations

J.Hydraul.Div.Amer.Soc.Civil Eng. Journal of the Hydraulics Division, American Society of Civil Engineers [forms part of *Proc.Amer.Soc.Civil Eng.*]

J.Ill.State Hist.Soc. Journal of the Illinois State Historical Society

J.Immunol. Journal of Immunology

J.Ind.Eng.Chem. Journal of Industrial and Engineering Chemistry

J.Indian Art The Journal of Indian Art (and Industry)

J.Indian Hist. Journal of Indian History

J.Indian Math.Soc. Journal of the Indian Mathematical Society

J.Indian Soc.Orient.Art Journal of the Indian Society of Oriental Art

J.Inst.Brewing Journal of the Institute of Brewing

J.Inst.Elec.Eng. Journal of the Institute of Electrical Engineers

J.Inst.Metals Journal of the Institute of Metals

J.Inst.Navigation Journal of the Institute of Navigation

J.Inst.Petrol.Technol. Journal of the Institution of Petroleum Technologists

J.Iran Soc. Journal of the Iran Society

J.Iron Steel Inst. Journal of the Iron and Steel Institute

J.Int.Coll.Surg. Journal of the International College of Surgeons

J.Jap.Veterinary Med.Ass. Journal of the Japanese Veterinary Medical Association

J.Japan Med.Ass. Journal of the Japan Medical Association

J.Kans.Med.Soc. Journal of the Kansas Medical Society

J.Kentucky State Med.Ass. Journal of the Kentucky State Medical Association

J.Korean Acad.Hist.Dent. The Journal of the Korean Academy of the History of Dentistry

J.Lab.Clin.Med. Journal of Laboratory and Clinical Medicine

J.Lancet Journal Lancet

J.Laryngol. Journal of Laryngology and Rhinology

J.Liberal Religion Journal of Liberal Religion

J.Linnean Soc.Bot. Journal of the Linnean Society. Botany

J.Linnean Soc.Zool. Journal of the Linnean Society. Zoology

J.Madras Geogr.Ass. Journal of the Madras Geographical Association

J.Madras Univ.Sect.B Journal of the Madras University. Section B. Contributions in Mathematics, Physical & Biological Sciences

J.Malayan Br.Roy.Asiatic Soc. Journal of the Malayan Branch of the Royal Asiatic Society

J.Mammalogy Journal of Mammalogy

J.Manchester Geogr.Soc. Journal of the Manchester Geographical Society

J.Maryland Acad.Sci. Journal of the Maryland Academy of Sciences

J.Math.Anal.Appl. Journal of Mathematical Analysis and Application

J.Math.Ass.Japan Secondary Educ. Journal of the Mathematical Association of Japan for Secondary Education

J.Math.Mech. Journal of Mathematics and Mechanics

J.Math.Phys. Journal of Mathematics and Physics [Massachusetts Institute of Technology]

J.Math.Pures Appl. Journal de Mathématiques Pures et Appliqueés

J.Math.Soc.Japan Journal of the Mathematical Society of Japan

J.Med.Ass.Georgia Journal of the Medical Association of Georgia

J.Med.Ass.Israel Journal of the Medical Association of Israel

J.Méd.Bordeaux Journal de Médecine de Bordeaux

J.Méd.Bruxelles Journal Médical de Bruxelles

J.Med.Educ. Journal of Medical Education

J.Med.Soc.N.J. Journal of the Medical Society of New Jersey

J.Ment.Sci. Journal of Mental Science

J.Mich.State Med.Soc. Journal of the Michigan State Medical Society

J.Middle East Soc. Journal of the Middle East Society

J.Missouri State Med.Ass. Journal of the Missouri State Medical Association

J.Mod.Hist. Journal of Modern History [University of Chicago]

J.Mond.Pharm. Journal Mondial de Pharmacie

J.Morphol. Journal of Morphology

J.Mt.Sinai Hosp. Journal of the Mount Sinai Hospital [New York]

J.N.China Br.Roy.Asiatic Soc. Journal of the North-China Branch of the Royal Asiatic Society of Great Britain and Ireland

J.N.J.State Dent.Soc. Journal of the New Jersey State Dental Society

J.N.Y.Bot.Gard. Journal of the New York Botanical Garden

J.N.Y.Entomol.Soc. Journal of the New York Entomological Society

J.Nat.Med.Ass. Journal of the National Medical Association

J.Near East.Stud. Journal of Near Eastern Studies

J.Negro Hist. The Journal of Negro History

J.Nerv.Ment.Dis. Journal of Nervous and Mental Diseases

J.Neurophysiol. Journal of Neurophysiology

J.Neurosurg. Journal of Neurosurgery

J.Nutr. Journal of Nutrition

J.Offic.Répub.Franç. Journal Officiel de la République Française

J.Opt. Journal d'Optique et l'Optique Française Réunis [Union Nationale des Syndicats d'Opticiens de France]

J.Opt.Soc.Amer. Journal of the Optical Society of America

J.Orient.Res. Journal of Oriental Research

J.Ornithol. Journal für Ornithologie: ein Centralorgan für die gesammte Ornithologie

J.Osmania Univ. Journal of the Osmania University

J.Palestine Orient.Soc. Journal of the Palestine Oriental Society

J.Parasitol. Journal of Parasitology

J.Paris Journal de Paris

J.Pastoral Care Journal of Pastoral Care [Council for the Clinical Training of Theological Students]

J.Pat.Office Soc. Journal of the Patent Office Society

J.Pathol.Bacteriol. The Journal of Pathology and Bacteriology [Pathological Society of Great Britain and Ireland]

J.Pharm.Alsace-Lorraine Journal de Pharmacie d'Alsace-Lorraine

J.Pharm.Belg. Journal de Pharmacie de Belgique [Féderation des Unions et des Oeuvres Pharmaceutiques Belges]

J.Pharm.Chim. Journal de Pharmacie et de Chimie

J.Pharm.Soc.Japan Journal of the Pharmaceutical Society of Japan

J.Pharmacol.Exp.Therap. Journal of Pharmacology and Experimental Therapeutics

J.Phil. Journal of Philosophy [psychology and scientific methods]

J.Phil.Stud. Journal of Philosophical Studies

J.Philol. Journal of Philology

J.Phys.Soc.Japan Journal of the Physical Society of Japan

J.Physiol. Journal of Physiology

J.Pract.Pharm. The Journal of Practical Pharmacy

J.Prakt.Chem. Journal für Praktische Chemie

J.Proc.Asiatic Soc.Bengal Journal and Proceedings of the Asiatic Society of Bengal

J.Proc.Roy.Australian Hist.Soc. Journal and Proceedings of the Royal Australian Historical Society

J.Proc.Roy.Soc.New S.Wales Journal and Proceedings of the Royal Society of New South Wales

J.Psychol.Norm.Pathol. Journal de Psychologie Normale et Pathologique

J.Quekett Microscop.Club Journal of the Quekett Microscopical Club

J.Ration.Mech. Journal of Rational Mechanics and Analysis

J.Reine Angew.Math. Journal für die Reine und Angewandte Mathematik

J.Relig. Journal of Religion [Chicago University]

J.Relig.Psychol. The Journal of Religious Psychology

J.Renaiss.Baroque Music Journal of Renaissance and Baroque Music

J.Res.Nat.Bur.Stand. Journal of Research of the National Bureau of Standards

J.Roman Stud. Journal of Roman Studies

J.Roy.Aeron.Soc. Journal of the Royal Aeronautical Society

J.Roy.Anthropol.Inst. Journal of the Royal Anthropological Institute of Great Britain and Ireland

J.Roy.Army Med.Corps Journal of the Royal Army Medical Corps

J.Roy.Asiatic Soc. Journal of the Royal Asiatic Society of Great Britain and Ireland

J.Roy.Asiatic Soc.Bengal, Lett. Journal of the Royal Asiatic Society of Bengal, Letters edition

J.Roy.Asiatic Soc.Bengal, Sci. Journal of the Royal Asiatic Society of Bengal, Science edition

J.Roy.Asiatic Soc.Bengal, Yearbook Journal of the Royal Asiatic Society of Bengal, Yearbook edition

J.Roy.Astron.Soc.Can. Journal of the Royal Astronomical Society of Canada

J.Roy.Cent.Asian Soc. Journal of the Royal Central Asian Society

J.Roy.Coll.Surg.Edinb. Journal of the Royal College of Surgeons of Edinburgh

J.Roy.Hort.Soc. Journal of the Royal Horticultural Society

J.Roy.Inst.Chem. Journal of the Royal Institute of Chemistry

J.Roy.Inst.Public Health Hyg. Journal of the Royal Institute of Public Health and Hygiene

J.Roy.Microscop.Soc. Journal of the Royal Microscopical Society

J.Roy.Nav.Med.Serv. Journal of the Royal Naval Medical Service

J.Roy.Soc.Arts Journal of the Royal Society of Arts

J.Rubber Res. Journal of Rubber Research

J.Rutgers Univ.Libr. Journal of the Rutgers University Library [New Brunswick, N.J.]

J.S.C.Med.Ass. Journal of the South Carolina Medical Association

J.S.West Essex Tech.Coll. Journal of the South-West Essex Technical College and School of Art

J.Savants Journal des Savants [Académie des Inscriptions et Belles-Lettres]

J.Sci.Instrum. Journal of Scientific Instruments [Institute of Physics, London]

J.Shanghai Sci.Inst. Journal of the Shanghai Science Institute

J.Soc.Amer.Paris Journal de la Société des Americanistes de Paris

J.Soc.Arch. Journal of the Society of Archivists [London]

J.Soc.Bibliogr.Natur.Hist. Journal of the Society for the Bibliography of Natural History

J.Soc.Chem.Ind. Journal of the Society of Chemical Industry

J.Soc.Chem.Ind.J.Rev.Sect. Journal of the Society of Chemical Industry: Journal and Review Section

J.Soc.Forces Journal of Social Forces

J.Soc.Hyg. Journal of Social Hygiene

J.Soc.Orient.Res. Journal of the Society of Oriental Research

J.Soc.Phil. Journal of Social Philosophy (& Jurisprudence)

J.Soc.Psychical Res. Journal of the Society for Psychical Research

J.Soc.Psychol. Journal of Social Psychology

J.Soc.Sci.Med.Lisboa Jornal da Sociedade das Sciencias Medicas de Lisboa

J.Soc.Statist.Paris Journal de la Société de Statistique de Paris

J.Southern Calif.State Dent.Ass. Journal of the Southern California State Dental Association

J.Southern Hist. Journal of Southern History

J.Suisse Horlogerie Journal Suisse d'Horlogerie et de Bijouterie

J.Symbolic Logic Journal of Symbolic Logic

J.Telev.Soc. Journal of the Television Society

J.Theol.Stud. Journal of Theological Studies

J.Torquay Natur.Hist.Soc. Journal of the Torquay Natural History Society

J.Trop.Med.Hyg. The Journal of Tropical Medicine and Hygiene

J.Unified Sci. The Journal of Unified Science (Erkenntnis)

J.Univ.Bombay Journal of the University of Bombay

J.Univ.Malaya Singapore Chin.Soc. Journal of the University of Malaya in Singapore, Chinese Society

J.Urol. Journal d'Urologie Médicale et Chirurgicale

J.Urusvati Journal of Urusvati [Himalayan Research Institute Roerich Museum, New York]

J.Walters Art Gallery Journal of the Walters Art Gallery

J.Warburg Courtauld Inst. Journal of the Warburg and Courtauld Institutes

J.Warburg Inst. Journal of the Warburg Institute

J.Wash.Acad.Sci. Journal of the Washington Academy of Sciences

J.West China Border Res.Soc. Journal of the West China Border Research Society

Jaarb.Genoot.Amstelodamum Jaarboek: Genootschap Amstelodamum für Geschichte und Gegenwart Amsterdams

Jaarb.Maatschappij Ned.Lett.Leiden Jaarboek: Maatschappij der Nederlandsche Letterkunde te Leiden

Jaarb.Munt- Penningk. Jaarboek voor Munt- en Penningkunde

Jaarb.Ned.Dendrol.Ver. Jaarboek: Nederlandsche Dendrologische Vereeniging

Jaarb.Vlaam.Acad.Wetensch.Lett.Schoone Kunst.Belg. Jaarboek van de Koninklijke Vlaamsche Academie voor Wetenschappen, Letteren en Schoone Kunsten van België

Jaarber.Vooraziatisch Egyptisch Gezelschap Ex Orient Lux Jaarbericht: Vooraziatisch Egyptisch Gezelschap "Ex Orient Lux" [Leiden]

Jahr Das Jahr

Jahrb.Akad.Gemeinnütziger Wiss.Erfurt Jahrbücher der [K.] Akademie gemeinnütziger Wissenschaften zu Erfurt

Jahrb.Altertumsk. Jahrbuch für Altertumskünde

Jahrb.Archäol.Inst.Deut.Reiches Jahrbuch des Archäologischen Instituts des Deutschen Reiches

Jahrb.Bayer.Akad.Wiss. Jahrbuch der Bayerischen Akademie der Wissenschaften

Jahrb.Bernischen Hist.Mus. Jahrbuch des Bernischen historischen Museums

Jahrb.Charakterologie Jahrbuch der Charakterologie

Jahrb.Chem. Jahrbuch der Chemie

Jahrb.Deut.Archäol.Inst. Jahrbuch des Deutschen Archäologischen Instituts

Jahrb.Deut.Ges.Chronometrie Jahrbuch der Deutschen Gesellschaft für Chronometrie

Jahrb.Freien Deut.Hochstifts Jahrbuch des Freien Deutschen Hochstifts für Wissenschaften, Künste und allgemeine Bildung zu Frankfurt am Main

Jahrb.Geogr.Ges.Hannover Jahrbuch der Geographischen Gesellschaft zu Hannover

Jahrb.Geol.Reichsanst. Jahrbuch der [kaiserlich-königlichen] geologischen Reichsanstalt

Jahrb.Ges.Gesch.Bibliogr.Brauw. Jahrbuch der Gesellschaft für die Geschichte und Bibliographie des Brauwesens

Jahrb.Ges.Gesch.Lit.Landwirt. Jahrbuch der Gesellschaft für Geschichte und Literatur der Landwirtschaft

Jahrb.Goethe-Ges. Jahrbuch der Goethe-Gesellschaft

Jahrb.Jüdisch-Lit.Ges. Jahrbuch der Jüdisch-literarischen Gesellschaft

Jahrb.Kaiserl.Deut.Archaeol.Inst. Jahrbuch des Kaiserlich Deutschen Archaeologischen Instituts

Jahrb.Kunsthist.Samml.Wien Jahrbuch der kunsthistorischen Sammlungen in Wien

Jahrb.Landeskunde Niederösterreich Jahrbuch für Landeskunde von Niederösterreich

Jahrb.Phil. Jahrbücher der Philosophie

Jahrb.Phil.Phänomenolog.Forsch. Jahrbuch für Philosophie und phänomenologische Forschung

Jahrb.Phil.Spekulative Theol. Jahrbuch für Philosophie und spekulative Theologie

Jahrb.Photogr.Reproduktionstech. Jahrbuch für Photographie und Reproduktionstechnik

Jahrb.Preuss.Kunstamml. Jahrbuch der [K] Preussischen Kunstsammlungen

Jahrb.Psychiat.Neurol. Jahrbücher für Psychiatrie und Neurologie

Jahrb.Ungar.Karpathenver. Jahrbuch des Ungarischen Karpathenvereins

Jahrb.Ver.Schutze Alpenpflanzen Jahrbuch des Vereins zum Schutze der Alpenpflanzen

Jahrb.Ver.Schweiz.Gymnasiallehrer Jahrbuch des Vereins schweizerischer Gymnasiallehrer

Jahresber.Deut.Math.Ver. Jahresberichte der Deutschen Mathematiker-Vereinigung

Jahresber.Forschungsinst.Gesch.Naturwiss.Berlin Jahresberichte des Forschungsinstituts für Geschichte der Naturwissenschaften in Berlin

Jahresber.Fortschr.Kl.Altertumswiss. Jahresberichte über die Fortschritte der klassischen Altertumswissenschaft

Jahresber.Geogr.Ges.Greifswald Jahresbericht der Geographischen Gesellschaft zu Greifswald

Jahresber.Geogr.Ges.Hannover Jahresbericht der Geographischen Gesellschaft zu Hannover

Jahresber.Gymnasiums Realsch.Töchtersch.Basel Jahresberichte des Gymnasiums, der Realschule und der Töchterschule in Basel

Jahresber.Leist.Fortschr.Gesamten Med. Jahresbericht über die Leistungen und Fortschritte in der gesamten Medizin

Jahresber.Naturwiss.Ver.Osnabrück Jahresbericht des Naturwissenschaftlichen Vereins zu Osnabrück

Jahresber.Phys.Vereins Frankfurt a.M. Jahresbericht des Physikalischen Vereins zu Frankfurt a.M.

Jahresber.Schlesische Ges.Vaterländ.Cult. Jahresbericht der Schlesischen Gesellschaft für vaterländische Cultur

Jahresber.Sonnblick Ver. Jahresbericht des Sonnblick- Vereins

Jahresber.Ver.Naturwiss.Braunschweig Jahresbericht des Vereins für Naturwissenschaft zu Braunschweig

Jahresh.Ver.Math.Naturwiss.Ulm Jahreshefte des Vereins für Mathematik und Naturwissenschaften in Ulm a.D.

Jahreskurse Ärztl.Fortbild. Jahreskurse für ärztliche Fortbildung

Jain Antiq. The Jain Antiquary

Janus Janus: Archives internationales pour l'histoire de la médecine

Janus Suppl. Janus Supplement

Jap.Stud.Hist.Sci. Japanese Studies in the History of Science [History of Science Society of Japan]

Japanisch-Deut.Z.Wiss.Tech. Japanisch-deutsche Zeitschrift für Wissenschaft und Technik

Jena Rev. Jena Review

Jenaer Med.Hist.Beitr. Jenaer medizin-historische Beiträge

Jenaer Rundsch. Jenaer Rundschau

Jenaische Z.Naturwiss. Jenaische Zeitschrift für Naturwissenschaft

Jeschurun (Berlin) Jeschurun

Jesuit Sci.Bull. Jesuit Science Bulletin: Bulletin of the Eastern States Division of the American Association of Jesuit Scientists

Jew.Forum Jewish Forum

Jew.Quart.Rev. Jewish Quarterly Review: edited for the Dropsie College for Hebrew and Cognate Learning

Jew.Soc.Stud. Jewish Social Studies

Johns Hopkins Alumni Mag. Johns Hopkins Alumni Magazine

Johns Hopkins Hosp.Bull. Johns Hopkins Hospital Bulletin

Johns Hopkins Mag. The Johns Hopkins Magazine

Jökull Jökull

Jorden Runt Jorden Runt. Magasin för Geografi och Resor

Jungarzt Der Jungarzt

Jungdeutsche Der Jungdeutsche

Justs Bot.Jahresber. Justs botanischer Jahresbericht

K

Kagaku Kisoron Kenkyu Kagaku Kisoron Kenkyu: Journal of the Japan Association for Philosophy of Science [Kagaku Kisoron Gakkai]

Kagaku Kôgyô Kagaku to Kôgyô: Chemistry and Chemical Industry [Chemical Society of Japan]

Kaizo Kaizo - la rekonstruo

Kans.State Coll.Bull. Kansas State College Bulletin

Kans.Univ.Sci.Bull. Kansas University Science Bulletin

Kant Stud. Kantstudien [Kantgesellschaft]

Karlsbader Ärztl.Vortr. Karlsbader ärztliche Vorträge

Kartographische Schulgeogr.Z. Kartographische und Schulgeographische Zeitschrift

Keizyô J.Med. The Keizyô Journal of Medicine

Kenya East Afr.Med.J. Kenya and East African Medical Journal

Kêmi Kêmi. Revue de Philologie et d'Archéologie Égyptiennes et Coptes

Kenyon Rev. The Kenyon Review

Keram.Rundsch. Keramische Rundschau

Keramos Keramos

Kieler Bl. Kieler Blätter [Gemeinschaft Kieler Professoren, Universität, Kiel]

Kinderärztl.Prax. Kinderärztliche Praxis

Kirchenmusikalisches Jahrb. Kirchenmusikalisches Jahrbuch [Allgemeiner Cäcilien-Verein für Deutschland, Österreich und die Schweiz]

Kirjath Sefer Kirjath Sefer: the organ of the Hebrew University [Jewish National and University] Library in Jerusalem

Klin.Med. Klinische Medizin

Klin.Monatsbl.Augenheilk. Klinische Monatsblätter für Augenheilkunde

Klin.Therap.Wochenschr. Klinisch-therapeutische Wochenschrift

Klin.Wochenschr. Klinische Wochenschrift

Klio Klio: Beiträge zur alten Geschichte

Klio Beih. Klio: Beihefte

Knoll's Mitt.Ärzte Knoll's Mitteilungen für Ärzte

K'o Hsueh K'o Hsüeh; Science [Science Society of China]

K'o Hsueh Shi Chi K'an K'o Hsüeh Shi Chi K'an: Chinese Journal of History of Science [K'o Hsueh Ch'u Pan Shê, Peking]

Köl.Z.Soziologie Kölner Zeitschrift für Soziologie und Sozialpsychologie

Kolon.Rundsch. Koloniale Rundschau

Komunhwa Komunhwa; Korean Antiquity [Korean Association of University Museum]

Koroth Koroth: a quarterly journal devoted to the history of medicine and science [Israel Society of the History of Medicine and Science, Jerusalem]

Korrespondenzbl.Gesamtver.Deut.Geschichts-Altertumsver. Korrespondenzblatt des Gesamtvereins der Deutschen Geschichts- und Altertumsvereins

Korrespondenzbl.Höheren Sch.Württemb. Korrespondenzblatt für die Höheren Schulen Württembergs

Korrespondenzbl.Schweiz.Ärzte Korrespondenzblatt für Schweizer Ärzte

Korrespondenzbl.Zahnärzte Korrespondenzblatt für Zahnärzte

Kosmos (Kaunas) Kosmos

Kosmos (Stuttgart) Kosmos [Kosmos, Gesellschaft für Naturfreunde]

Kosmos, ser.A Kosmos, seria A: Biologia [Polskie Towarzystwo Prsyrodników im. Kopernika]

Krefelder Zeitung Krefelder Zeitung

Kristall Der Kristall: das Wissen der Zeit

Kühn-Arch. Kühn-Archiv: Arbeiten aus dem landwirtschaftlichen Institut der Universität Halle-Wittenberg

Kulliyah, see *Al-Kulliyah*

Kunstchronik Kunstchronik: Nachrichten aus Kunstwissenschaft

Kwart.Hist. Kwartalnik Historyczny

Kwart.Hist.Kult.Mater. Kwartalnik Historii Kultury Materialnej [Polska Akademia Nauk, Instytut Historii Kultury Materialnej]

Kwart.Hist.Nauk.Tech. Kwartalnik Historii Nauki i Techniki: Istoriya Nauki i Tekhniki: History of Science and Technology [Komitet Historii Nauk, Polska Akademia Nauk]

Kyklos Kyklos: Jahrbuch des Instituts für Geschichte der Medizin an der Universität Leipzig

Kyklos (Bern) Kyklos: internationale Zeitschrift für Sozialwissenschaften (Bern)

L

La Cultura La Cultura: Rivista mensile di filosofia, lettere, arte

La Nature La Nature: Revue des sciences et de leurs applications aux arts et à l'industrie

La Revue See *Revue*

Laboratory Laboratory [Fisher Scientific Company, Technical Department, Pittsburg, Pa.]

Lancet Lancet

Landarzt (Stuttgart) Der Landarzt

Landmarks Med. Landmarks in Medicine [New York Academy of Medicine]

Language Language [Linguistic Society of America]

Lapidarium Vondel.Koninklijke Vlaam.Acad.Taal- Lett.Verslagen Mededeel. Lapidarium van Vondel. Koninklijke Vlaamsche Academie voor Taal- en Letterkunde, Verslagen en Mededeelingen

Larousse Mens. Larousse Mensuel Illustré

Laryngoscope The Laryngoscope

Latomus Latomus

Law Quart.Rev. Law Quarterly Review

Leafl.Astron.Soc.Pacific Leaflets of the Astronomical Society of the Pacific

Leban.Pharm.J. Lebanese Pharmaceutical Journal

Lebendige Med. Lebendige Medizin. Ein Querschnitt durch die Medizinische Klinik

Leipziger Illus.Zeitung Leipziger illustrierte Zeitung

Lék.Listy Lékařské Listy: Časopis Lékařských spolků a žup Moravskoslezských

Leodium Leodium

Leopoldina Leopoldina: Berichte der K. Leopoldinischen deutschen Akademie der Naturforscher zu Halle

Leopoldina, new ser. Leopoldina: Berichte der Kaiserlich Deutschen Akademie der Naturforscher zu Halle, new series

Lepidopterists' News The Lepidopterists' News [Lepidopterists' Society, Cambridge, Mass.]

Lepra Lepra. Bibliotheca Internationalis

Leprosy Rev. Leprosy Review

Leshonenu Leshonenu. A quarterly for the study of Hebrew

Lett.Franç. Les Lettres Françaises

Lett.Mod. Letterature Moderne

Levnadsteckningar Svenska Vetenskapsakad.Ledamöter Levnadsteckningar över [K.] Svenska Vetenskapsakademiens Ledamöter Stockholm

Lexington Herald Lexington Herald [newspaper]

Liberal Relig. Liberal Religion

Libr.Ass.Rec. The Library Association Record [Library Association, London]

Libr.Chron. The Library Chronicle

Libr.Congr.Quart.J.Curr.Acquis. Library of Congress Quarterly Journal of Current Acquisitions

Libr.J. Library Journal

Libr.Quart. Library Quarterly: a journal of investigation and discussion in the field of library science [Chicago University, Graduate Library School]

Libr.Resources Tech.Serv. Library Resources and Technical Services

Librarium Librarium [Schweizerische Bibliophilen Gesellschaft]

Library The Library: a magazine of bibliography and literature

Libre Pharm. La Libre Pharmacie

Libri Libri: international library review [International Federation of Library Associations, Copenhagen]

Liburni Civitas Liburni Civitas

Licht Lampe Licht und Lampe

Life Life

Liječnički Vjesnik Liječnički Vjesnik

Limosa Limosa [Club van Nederlandsche Vogelkundigen]

Lincolnshire Mag. Lincolnshire Magazine

Linschoten Ver.Jaarverslag Linschoten Vereeniging Jaarverslag

Linschoten Ver.Werken Werken uitgegeven door de Linschoten-vereeniging

List Doctoral Diss.Hist.U.S.Canada List of Doctoral Dissertations in History now in progress at universities in the United States and Canada

List Res.Proj.Hist.U.S.Canada List of Research Projects in History now in progress in the United States and Canada

Listener The Listener

Lit.Guide Literary Guide and Rationalist Review

Litterae Orient. Litterae Orientales: orientalistischer Literaturbericht

Litteris Litteris: an international critical review of the humanities [New Society of Letters, Lund]

Livre Le Livre: Philosophie-Histoire-Sciences Économiques et Sociales

Lloydia Lloydia: a quarterly journal of biological science [Lloyd Library, Cincinnati, Ohio]

Los Angeles Daily J. Los Angeles Daily Journal

Lotos Lotos: Naturwissenschaftliche Zeitschrift [Prague]

Luce Immag. Luce e Immagini

Lunds Univ.Årsskr. Lunds Universitets Årsskrift: Acta Universitatis Lundensis

Lunds Univ.Årsskr.Avd.1, new ser. Lunds Universitets Årsskrift, ny följd, Avdelning 1: Teologi, juridik och humanistiska ämnen

Lunds Univ.Årsskr.Avd.2, new ser. Lunds Universitets Årsskrift, ny följd, Avdelning 2: Medicin samt matematiska och naturvetenskapliga ämnen

Lychnos Lychnos: Lärdomshistoriska Samfundets Årsbok: Annual of the Swedish History of Science Society

Lyon Méd. Lyon Médical [Société de Médecine de Lyon]

M

M.D.(Med.J.Residents Interns Med.Stud.) M.D. (Medical Journal for Residents, Interns and Medical Students)

MSN MSN: Monthly Science News [Science Department, British Council]

Maandbl.Natuurhist.Genoot.Limburg. Maandblad. Natuurhistorisch Genootschap in Limburg

McGill Med.J. McGill Medical Journal [McGill Medical Society, Montreal]

Machriq, see *Al-Machriq*

Maclean's Mag. (Toronto) Maclean's Magazine

Madroño Madroño: a West American journal of botany [California Botanical Society]

Mag.Inst.Istanbul Magazine of the Institute of Istanbul

Magdeburger Zeitung Magdeburger Zeitung

Magyar Nöorv.Lapja Magyar Nöorvosok Lapja

Maia Maia: Rivista di letterature classiche

Malpighia Malpighia. Rassegna Mensuale di Botanica

Man Man: a monthly record of anthropological science [Royal Anthropological Institute of Great Britain and Ireland]

Manchester Guardian Manchester Guardian [Newspaper]

Manchester Guardian Weekly Manchester Guardian Weekly

Mannheimer Geschichtsbl. Mannheimer Geschichtsblätter

Mannus Mannus: Zeitschrift für Vorgeschichte

Manuscripta Manuscripta [St. Louis University Library]

Mar.Geol. Marine Geology. International Journal of Marine Geology, Geochemistry & Geophysics

Mar.Observ. The Marine Observer [Meteorological Office]

Mar.Rundsch. Marine Rundschau. Zeitschrift für Seewesen

Margarita Philosophica Margarita Philosophica

Marginales Marginales: Revue bimestrielle des idées et des lettres

Mariner's Mirror Mariner's Mirror

Marseille Méd. Marseille-Médical [Société Nationale de Médecine de Marseille]

Mary Mellish Archibald Mem.Libr.Bull Mary Mellish Archibald Memorial Library Bulletin [Mount Allison University, Sackville, New Brunswick]

Masch.Buchhaltung Maschinen-Buchhaltung

Masch.Buchhaltung Euklid Feldhaus Beil. Maschinen-Buchhaltung: Euklid-Feldhaus-Beilage

Mass Wert Mass und Wert: Zweimonatsschrift für freie deutsche Kultur

Mat.Elem. Matematica Elemental

Mat.Fiz.Lapok Matematikai és Fizikai Lapok

Mat.Fiz.Sredneĭ Shkole Matematika i Fizika v Sredneĭ Shkole

Mat.Lapok Matematikai Lapok [formerly *Mat.Fiz.Lapok*]

Mat.Természettud.Értesito Matematikai és természettudományi értesito a Magyar Tudományos Akadémia: Mathematischer und naturwissenschaftlicher Anzeiger der Ungarischen Akademie der Wissenschaften

Mat.Tidsskr. Matematisk Tidsskrift [Dansk Matematisk Forening i København]

Matér.Étud.Calamités Matériaux pour l'Étude des Calamités [Société de Géographie de Genève]

Mater.Med.Nordmark Materia Medica Nordmark

Math.Ann. Mathematische Annalen

Math.Fys.Medd.Danske Vidensk.Selsk. Mathematisk-fysiske Meddelelser: [Kongelige] Danske Videnskabernes Selskab

Math.Gaz. Mathematical Gazette

Math.Nachr. Mathematische Nachrichten [Forschungsinstitut für Mathematik, Deutsche Akademie der Wissenschaften]

Math.Naturwiss.Bl. Mathematisch-naturwissenschaftliche Blätter

Math.Naturwiss.Unterricht Der mathematische und naturwissenschaftliche Unterricht

Math.Phys.Semesterber. Mathematisch-physikalische Semesterberichte zur Pflege des Zusammenhangs von Schule und Universität

Math.Rev. Mathematical Reviews

Math.Tables Aids Comput. Mathematical Tables and [other] Aids to Computation [National Research Council, Menasha, Wis.]

Math.Teacher Mathematics Teacher [National Council of Teachers of Mathematics]

Mathematica Mathematica [Seminarul de Matematici, Cluj Universitatea]

Mathésis (Gand) Mathésis: recueil mathématique

Mathesis ('s Gravenhage) Mathesis: tijdschrift voor wiskunde

Mayo Clin.Proc. Mayo Clinic Proceedings

Mech.Eng. Mechanical Engineering

Mecmuasi Istanbul Üniv.Tip.Fak. Istanbul Üniversitesi Tip Fakültesi Mecmuasi: Bulletin de la Faculté de Médecine de l'Université d'Istanbul

Med.Arts Sci. Medical Arts and Sciences

Med.Biol.Ill. Medical and Biological Illustration

Med.Bookman Hist. The Medical Bookman and Historian

Med.Chir.Rev. Medico-Chirurgical Review

Med.Cir.Farm. Medicinia, Cirurgia, Farmácia

Med.Cl. Medical Classics

Med.Contemp. Medicina Contemporanea: jornal Portugues de ciencias medicas

Med.Españ. Medicina Española

Med.Forum Medicinisk Forum

Méd.France Médecine de France [Société Parisienne d'Expansion Chimique]

Med.Germano-Hispano-Amer. Medicina Germano-Hispano-Americano. Revista mensual de Medicina, Cirugia y Especialidades

Med Hammare Fackla Med Hammare och Fackla. Årsbok utgiven av Sancte Örjens Gille

Med.Hist. Medical History

Med.Illus. Medicine Illustrated

Méd.Int. La Médecine Internationale

Med.Ital. (Milan) Medicina Italiana

Med.J.Australia The Medical Journal of Australia [BMA Australian Branch]

Med.J.Rec. The Medical Journal and Record

Med.Klin. Medizinische Klinik [Berliner medizinische Gesellschaft]

Med.Leaves Medical Leaves: a Review of the Jewish Medical World and Medical History

Med.Life Medical Life [American Society of Medical History]

Med.Logik Medizinische Logik

Med.Mitt.Schering-Kahlbaum Medizinische Mitteilungen. Schering-Kahlbaum A.G.

Med.Monatsschr. Medizinische Monatsschrift: Zeitschrift für allgemeine Medizin und Therapie

Med.Morale Medicina e Morale

Med.Press The Medical Press [and Circular]

Med.Rec. The Medical Record

Med.Rundsch. Medizinische Rundschau

Med.Sci.Law Medicine, Science and the Law

Med.Searchlight Medical Searchlight

Med.Times (London) Medical Times [General Practitioners Alliance, London]

Med.Times (N.Y.) Medical Times [New York]

Med.Way Medical Way

Med.Welt Medizinische Welt

Med.Wochenschr. Medizinische Wochenschrift

Med.Z. Medizinische Zeitschrift

Medd.Kunglica Armésmus. Meddelander fran Kunglica Armésmuseum

Medd.Lunds Astron.Observ. Meddelanden från Lunds Astronomiska Observatorium

Meddelelser Grønland Meddelelser om Grønland

Mededel.Bestendige Commissie Gesch.Wet. Mededeling aan de Bestendige Commissie voor de Geschiedenis der Wetenschappen

Mededel.Bibl.Wasiana Mededelingen Bibliotheca Wasiana

Mededel.Ned.Akad.Wetensch.Afd.Lett. Mededelingen der [Koninklijke] Nederlandse Akademie van Wetenschappen: Afdeeling Letterkunde

Mededel.Ned.Hist.Inst.Rome Mededeling van het Nederlandsch Historisch Institut te Rome

Mededel.Ned.Mycol.Ver. Mededelingen. Nederlandsche Mycologische Vereeniging

Mededel.Vlaam.Acad.Wetensch.Lett.Schoone Kunsten Belg.Kl.Lett. Mededelingen van de [Koninklijke] Vlaamsche Academie voor Wetenschappen, Letteren en Schoone Kunsten van België: Klasse der Letteren

Mededel.Vlaam.Acad.Wetensch.Lett.Schoone Kunsten Belg.Kl. Wetensch. Mededelingen van de [Koninklijke] Vlaamse Academie voor Wetenschappen, Letteren en Schoone Kunsten van België: Klasse der Wetenschappen

Mededel.Vlaam.Chem.Ver. Mededelingen van de Vlaamse Chemische Vereeniging

Mediaeval Renaiss.Stud. Mediaeval and Renaissance Studies

Mediaeval Stud. Mediaeval Studies [Toronto University: St. Michael's College, Institute of Mediaeval Studies]

Medicina Medicina

Medicina (Madrid) Medicina: Revista mensual de ciencias médicas

Medicinhist.Årsbok Medicinhistorisk Årsbok. Yearbook of the Medical-Historical Museum, Stockholm

Medico-Leg.J. The Medico-Legal Journal

Medievalia Hum. Medievalia et Humanistica: an American journal for the middle ages and renaissance

Medium Aevum Medium Aevum

Medycyna Medycyna doświadczalna i społeczna [Warsaw]

Meereskunde Meereskunde: Sammlung volkstümlicher Vorträge zum Verständnis der nationalen Bedeutung von Meer und Seewesen [Institut für Meereskunde, Friedrich Wilhelms Universität]

Mélanges Chinois Bouddhiques Mélanges Chinois Bouddhiques

Mélanges Univ.Saint Joseph Mélanges [de la Faculté Orientale], Université St. Joseph [Beirut]

Mém.Acad.Chir. Mémoires de l'Académie de Chirurgie

Mem.Acad.Cienc.Arts Barcelona Memorias de l'Academia de Ciencias y Arts de Barcelona

Mém.Acad.Lang.Litt.Franc.Belg. Mémoires de l'Académie [Royale] de Langue et de Littérature Françaises de Belgique

Mém.Acad.Malgache Mémoires de l'Académie Malgache

Mém.Acad.Med.Belg. Mémoires de l'Académie [Royale] de Médecine de Belgique

Mem.Acad.Mex.Hist. Memorias de la Academia Mexicana de la Historia

Mem.Acad.Nac.Cienc. (Mexico) Memorias Academia Nacional de Ciencias "Antonio Alzate", Mexico

Mém.Acad.Roy.Belg.Cl.Lett. Mémoires de l'Académie Royale de Belgique, Classe des Lettres et des Sciences Morales et Politiques

Mém.Acad.Roy.Belg.Cl.Sci. Mémoires de l'Académie Royale de Belgique, Classe des Sciences

Mém.Acad.Sci. Mémoires de l'Académie des Sciences de l'Institut de France

Mém.Acad.Sci.Arts Belles Lett.Caen Mémoires de l'Académie des Sciences, Arts et Belles-Lettres de Caen

Mém.Acad.Sci.Arts Belles Lett.Dijon Mémoires de l'Académie des Sciences, Arts et Belles-Lettres de Dijon

Mém.Acad.Sci.Belles Lett.Arts Angers Mémoires de l'Académie des Sciences, Belles-Lettres et des Arts d'Angers

Mém.Acad.Sci.Belles Lett.Arts Lyon Mémoires de l'Académie des Sciences, Belles-Lettres et Arts de Lyon

Mém.Acad.Sci.Belles Lett.Arts Lyon Cl.Sci.Lett. Mémoires de l'Académie des Sciences, Belles-Lettres et Arts de Lyon, Classe des Sciences et Lettres

Mém.Acad.Sci.Inscriptions Belles Lett.Toulouse Mémoires de l'Academie des Sciences, Inscriptions et Belles Lettres de Toulouse

Mem.Accad.Ital.Cl.Sci.Fis.Mat.Natur. Memorie della [Reale] Accademia d'Italia: Classe di Scienze Fisiche, Matematiche e Naturali

Mem.Accad.Petrarca Memorie della Reale Accademia Petrarca di Lettere, Arti e Scienze

Mem.Accad.Sci.Ist.Bologna Cl.Sci.Fis.Sez.Med.Chir. Memorie della [Reale] Accademia delle Scienze dell'Istituto di Bologna: Classe di Scienze Fisiche: Sezione di Medicina e Chirurgia

Mem.Accad.Sci.Ist.Bologna Cl.Sci.Fis.Sez.Sci.Fis.Mat. Memorie della [Reale] Accademia delle Scienze dell' Istituto di Bologna: Classe di Scienze Fisiche: Sezione delle Scienze Fisiche e Matematiche

Mem.Accad.Sci.Ist.Bologna Cl.Sci.Fis.Sez.Sci.Natur. Memorie della [Reale] Accademia delle Scienze dell'Istituto di Bologna: Classe di Scienze Fisiche: Sezione delle Scienze Naturali

Mem.Accad.Sci.Ist.Bologna Suppl. Memorie della [Reale] Accademia delle Scienze dell'Istituto di Bologna: Supplemento

Mem.Accad.Sci.Lett.Arti Modena Memorie della Reale Accademia di Scienze, Lettere ed Arti di Modena

Mem.Accad.Sci.Torino Memorie della [Reale] Accademia delle Scienze di Torino

Mem.Amer.Acad.Arts Sci. Memoirs of the American Academy of Arts and Sciences

Mem.Amer.Phil.Soc. Memoirs of the American Philosophical Society

Mem.Archaeol.Surv.India Memoirs of the Archaeological Survey of India

Mem.Asiatic Soc.Bengal Memoirs of the Asiatic Society of Bengal

Mém.Asie Orient. Mémoires concernant l'Asie Orientale [Académie des Inscriptions et Belles-lettres]

Mem.Brit.Astron.Ass. Memoirs of the British Astronomical Association

Mém.Compt.Rend.Soc.Ing.Civils France Mémoires et Comptes Rendus [des travaux] de la Société des Ingénieurs Civils de France

Mem.Comun.Congr.Mundo Port. Memorias e Comunicaçoes. Congresso do Mundo Português

Mém.Couronnés Mém.Savants Étrang.Acad.Roy.Belg. Mémoires Couronnés et Mémoires des Savants Étrangers de l'Académie Royale des Sciences de Belgique

Mém.Divers Savants Acad.Inscriptions Belles Lett. Mémoires présentées par divers savants de l'Académie des Inscriptions et Belles-lettres

Mém.Doc.Soc.Hist.Archéol.Genève Mémoires et Documents de la Société d'Histoire et d'Archéologie de Genève

Mem.Doc.Stor.Univ.Padova Memorie e Documenti per la Storia della Università di Padova

Mém.Inst.Colon.Belg.Sect.Sci.Natur.Méd. Mémoires de l'Institut Royal Colonial Belge, Section des Sciences Naturelles et Médicales

Mém.Inst.Égypte Mémoires de l'Institut d'Égypte

Mém.Inst.Égyptien Mémoires de l'Institut Égyptien

Mém.Inst.Franç.Archéol.Orient.Caire Mémoires publiés par les membres de l'Institut Français d'Archéologie Orientale du Caire

Mem.Inst.Oswaldo Cruz Memorias do Instituto Oswaldo Cruz [Rio de Janeiro]

Mem.Lect.Chem.Soc. Memorial Lectures delivered before the Chemical Society, London

Mem.Litt.Port.Acad.Ciênc.Lisboa Memorias da Litteratura Portugueza. Academia das Ciências de Lisboa

Mem.Manchester Lit.Phil.Soc. Memoirs and Proceedings of the Manchester Literary and Philosophical Society: Manchester Memoirs

Mem.Mat.Sci.Fis.Natur.Soc.Ital.Sci.(XL) Memorie di Matematica e di Scienze Fisiche e Naturali della Società Italiana delle Scienze (detta dei XL)

Mém.Mission Archéol.Franç.Caire Mémoires publiés par les membres de la Mission Archéologique Française au Caire

Mém.Mission Archéol.Perse Mémoires de la Mission Archéologique de Perse

Mém.Mus.Hist.Natur.Belg. Mémoires du Musée [Royale] d'Histoire Naturelle de Belgique

Mém.Mus.Nat.Hist.Natur.,sér.A Mémoires du Muséum National d'Histoire Naturelle [Paris], série A, Zoologie

Mém.Mus.Nat.Hist.Natur.,sér.C Mémoires du Muséum National d'Histoire Naturelle [Paris], série C, Sciences de la Terre

Mem.Nat.Acad.Sci. Memoirs of the National Academy of Sciences [Washington, D.C.]

Mem.Phila.Soc.Promoting Agr. Memoirs of the Philadelphia Society for Promoting Agriculture

Mem.Pontif.Accad.Sci.Nuovi Lincei Memorie della Pontificia Accademia delle Scienze Nuovi Lincei

Mem.Res.Dep.Toyo Bunko Memoirs of the Research Department of the Toyo Bunko

Mém.Soc.Agr.Sci.Arts Angers Mémoires de la Société d'Agriculture, Sciences et Arts d'Angers

Mem.Soc.Amer.Archaeol. Memoirs of the Society for American Archaeology

Mem.Soc.Astron.Ital. Memorie della Società Astronomica Italiana

Mém.Soc.Finno-Ougrienne Mémoires de la Société Finno-Ougrienne

Mém.Soc.Franç.Hist.Méd. Mémoires de la Société Française d'Histoire de la Médecine

Mém.Soc.Géogr.Égypte Mémoires de la Société de Géographie d'Égypte

Mem.Soc.Geogr.Ital. Memorie della [Reale] Società Geografica Italiana

Mém.Soc.Hist.Paris Île France Mémoire de la Société de l'Histoire de Paris et de l'Île de France

Mem.Soc.Ital.Sci.XL Memorie della Società Italiana delle Scienze detta dei XL

Mém.Soc.Sci.Liége Mémoires de la Société [Royale] des Sciences de Liége

Mém.Soc.Sci.Natur.Cherbourg Mémoires de la Société des Sciences Naturelles de Cherbourg

Mém.Soc.Sci.Natur.Maroc Mémoires de la Société des Sciences Naturelles (et Physiques) du Maroc

Mém.Soc.Vaudoise Sci.Natur. Mémoires de la Société Vaudoise des Sciences Naturelles [Lausanne]

Mém.Univ.Neuchâtel Mémoires de l'Université de Neuchâtel

Memorille Acad.Română Secţiunea Istorică Memorille: Academia Română, Secţiunea Istorică

Menorah J. Menorah Journal

Merc.France Le Mercure de France

Merchistonian Merchistonian

Merck Rep. Merck Report

Message Message: Belgian Review

Met.Ital. Metallurgia Italiana

Metalen Metalen

Metallurgia Metallurgia

Metanoia Metanoia. Revue Internationale Scientifique, Spiritualiste, Adogmatique et Éclectique

Métaux Civilisations Métaux et Civilisations

Meteorol.Mag. Meteorological Magazine

Meteorol.Prat. Meteorologia Pratica [Osservatorio Meteorico-aerologico-geodinamico de Montecassino]

Meteorol.Z. Meteorologische Zeitschrift

Météorologie La Météorologie

Methodist Rev. The Methodist Review

Metron Metron. Rivista Internazionale di Statistica

Metrop.Detroit Sci.Rev. Metropolitan Detroit Science Review

Metrop.Mus.Stud. Metropolitan Museum Studies

Mich.Alumnus Michigan Alumnus

Mich.Alumnus Quart.Rev. Michigan Alumnus Quarterly Review

Mich.Hist.Mag. Michigan History Magazine

Microscope The Microscope

Middle East.Aff. Middle Eastern Affairs [St. Anthony's Papers, Oxford]

Middle East Forum Middle East Forum

Middle East J. The Middle East Journal

Middlesex Hosp.J. Middlesex Hospital Journal

Midwest J. Polit.Sci. Midwest Journal of Political Science

Mikrochim.Acta Mikrochimica Acta

Mikroskopie Mikroskopie: Zentralblatt für mikroskopische Forschung und Methodik

Mil.Eng. The Military Engineer. Journal of the Society of American Military Engineers

Mil.Med. Military Medicine

Mil.Surg. Military Surgeon

Mind Mind: a quarterly review of psychology and philosophy

Mineral Ind. Mineral Industries [Pennsylvania State University]

Mineral.Mag. Mineralogical Magazine and Journal of the Mineralogical Society of Great Britain and Ireland

Mineralogist The Mineralogist

Minerva Minerva: a Review of Science, Learning and Policy

Minerva(Buenos Aires) Minerva: Revista Continental de Filosofia [Buenos Aires]

Minerva Farm. Minerva Farmaceutica

Minerva Med. Minerva Medica

Minerva Pediat. Minerva Pediatrica

Mining Eng. Mining Engineering

Mining Met. Mining and Metallurgy

Minn.Hist. Minnesota History

Minn.Hist.Bull. Minnesota History Bulletin

Minn.Med. Minnesota Medicine

Misc.Amer. Miscelánea Americanista [Consejo Superior de Investigaciones Científicas, Instituto Gonzalo Fernandez de Oviedo]

Misc.Comillas Miscelánea Comillas [Universidad Pontificia, Comillas, Spain]

Misc.Hist.Pontif. Miscellanea Historiae Pontificiae [Pontificia Università Gregoriana, Facoltà di Storia Ecclesiastica: Collegium Romanum Societatis Jesu, Facultas Historiae Ecclesiasticae]

Misc.Inst.Météorol.Belg. Miscellaneés de l'Institut [Royal] Météorologique de Belgique

Miss.Val.Hist.Rev. Mississippi Valley Historical Review

Missouri Bot.Gard.Bull. Missouri Botanical Garden Bulletin

Missouri Hist.Rev. Missouri Historical Review [State Historical Society of Missouri]

Mitra Mitra. Monatsschrift für vergleichende Mythenforschung

Mitt.Aegyptischen Samml. Mitteilungen aus der Aegyptischen Sammlung [Stadtliche Museen zu Berlin. Aegyptische Abteilung]

Mitt.Anthropol.Ges.Wien Mitteilungen der Anthropologischen Gesellschaft in Wien

Mitt.Antiq.Ges.Zürich Mitteilungen der Antiquarischen Gesellschaft in Zürich

Mitt.Astron.Rechen-Inst.Berlin-Dahlem Mitteilungen des Astronomischen Rechen-Instituts zu Berlin-Dahlem

Mitt.Bayer.Bot.Ges. Mitteilungen der Bayerischen Botanischen Gesellschaft zur Erforschung der Heimischen Flora

Mitt.Bayer.Numismat.Ges. Mitteilungen der Bayerischen numismatischen Gesellschaft

Mitt.Bundes Asienkämpfer Mitteilungen des Bundes der Asienkämpfer

Mitt.Deut.Archaeol.Inst.Roemische Abt. Mitteilungen des [Kaiserlich] Deutschen Archaeologischen Instituts, Roemische Abteilung: Bullettino dell' [Imperiale] Istituto Archeologico Germanico, Sezione Romana

Mitt.Deut.Dendrol.Ges. Mitteilungen der Deutschen dendrologischen Gesellschaft

Mitt.Deut.Ges.Erforsch.Sprache Altertümer Leipzig Mitteilungen der Deutschen Gesellschaft zur Erforschung [vaterländischer] Sprache und Altertümer zu Leipzig

Mitt.Deut.Ges.Natur.Völkerk.Ostasiens Mitteilungen der Deutschen Gesellschaft für Natur- und Völkerkunde Ostasiens

Mitt.Deut.Ges.Natur.Völkerk.Ostasiens Suppl. Mitteilungen der Deutschen Gesellschaft für Natur- und Völkerkunde Ostasiens: Supplement

Mitt.Deut.Inst.Ägyptische Altertumskunde Mitteilungen des Deutschen Instituts für Ägyptische Altertumskunde in Kairo

Mitt.Deut.Orient Ges. Mitteilungen der Deutschen Orient-Gesellschaft

Mitt.Geogr.Ethnogr.Ges.Zürich Mitteilungen der Geographisch-ethnographischen Gesellschaft im Zürich

Mitt.Geogr.Ges.Hamburg Mitteilungen der Geographischen Gesellschaft in Hamburg

Mitt.Geogr.Ges.München Mitteilungen Geographische Gesellschaft in München

Mitt.Geogr.Ges.Wien Mitteilungen der Geographischen Gesellschaft in Wien

Mitt.Gesch.Altertums Ver.Liegnitz Mitteilungen des Geschichts- und Altertums-Vereins zu Liegnitz

Mitt.Gesch.Med. Mitteilungen zur Geschichte der Medizin, der Naturwissenschaften und der Technik [Deutsche Gesellschaft für Geschichte der Medizin, Naturwissenschaft und Technik]

Mitt.Inst.Österr.Geschichtsforsch. Mitteilungen des Instituts für Österreichische Geschichtsforschung

Mitt.Jahresber.Geogr.Ges.Nürnberg Mitteilungen und Jahresberichte der Geographischen Gesellschaft in Nürnberg

Mitt.Naturforsch.Ges.Bern Mitteilungen der Naturforschenden Gesellschaft in Bern

Mitt.Naturforsch.Ges.Schaffhausen Mitteilungen der Naturforschenden Gesellschaft, Schaffhausen

Mitt.Nordböhmischen Exkursionsklubs Mitteilungen des Nordböhmischen Excursions-Clubs [Leipa]

Mitt.Oekon.Ges.Sachsen Mitteilungen der Oekonomischen Gesellschaft in Sachsen

Mitt.Papyrussamml.Nationalbibl.Wien Mitteilungen aus der Papyrussammlung der Nationalbibliothek in Wien

Mitt.Pfälz.Ver.Naturk.Pollichia Mitteilungen des Pfälzischen Vereins für Naturkunde 'Pollichia'

Mitt.Provinzialstelle Naturdenkmalpflege Hannover Mitteilungen der Provinzialstelle für Naturdenkmalpflege Hannover

Mitt.Reichsamts Landesaufn. Mitteilungen des Reichsamts für Landesaufnahme

Mitt.Seminar.Orient.Sprachen Friedrich-Wilhelms-Univ.Berlin Mitteilungen des Seminars für Orientalische Sprachen an der Königlichen Friedrich-Wilhelms-Universität zu Berlin

Mitt.Septuaginta-Unternehmens Ges.Wiss.Göttingen Mitteilungen des Septuaginta-Unternehmens der [K.] Gesellschaft der Wissenschaften zu Göttingen

Mitt.Thüringischen Bot.Ver. Mitteilungen des Thüringischen Botanischen Vereins

Mitt.Thurgauischen Naturforsch.Ges. Mitteilungen der Thurgauischen Naturforschenden Gesellschaft

Mitt.Tierärztl.Ges.Bekämpfung Kurpfuschertums Mitteilungen der tierärztlichen Gesellschaft zur Bekämpfung des Kurpfuschertums

Mitt.Universitätsbund Göttingen Mitteilungen des Universitätsbunds Göttingen

Mitt.Ver.Erdk.Dresden Mitteilungen des Vereins für Erdkunde, Dresden

Mitt.Ver.Freunden Astron.Kosm.Phys. Mitteilungen der Vereinigung von Freunden der Astronomie und Kosmischen Physik

Mitt.Ver.Gesch.Stadt Nürnberg Mitteilungen des Vereins für Geschichte der Stadt Nürnberg

Mitt.Ver.Gothaische Gesch.Altertumsforsch Mitteilungen der Vereinigung für Gothaische Geschichte und Altertumsforschung

Mitt.Ver.Math.Naturwiss.Ulm Mitteilungen des Vereins für Mathematik und Naturwissenschaften in Ulm a.D.

Mitt.Ver.Sächsischer Ornithol. Mitteilungen des Vereins Sächsischer Ornithologen [Dresden]

Mitt.Vorderasiatischen Ges. Mitteilungen der Vorderasiatischen Gesellschaft

Mitteilungsbl.Deut.Genealogischer Abende Mitteilungsblatt Deutscher Genealogischer Abende

Mitteilungsbl.Ver.Jüdischer Ärzte Mitteilungsblatt der Vereinigung jüdischer Ärzte

Mitteldeut.Bl.Volksk. Mitteldeutsche Blätter für Volkskunde

Mizraim Mizraim. Journal of Papyrology, Egyptology, History of Ancient Laws, and their relations to the Civilizations of Bible Lands

Mnemosyne Mnemosyne: Bibliotheca philologica classica batava: Tijdschrift voor classiek litteratuur

Mnemosyne Suppl. Mnemosyne: Bibliotheca philologica classica batava: Supplementum

Mod.Hum. Modern Humanist

Mod.Lang.J. The Modern Language Journal. [National Federation of Modern Language Teachers]

Mod.Lang.Notes Modern Language Notes

Mod.Lang.Quart. Modern Language Quarterly

Mod.Lang.Rev. Modern Language Review

Mod.Med. Modern Medicine [American Association of Industrial Physicians and Surgeons]

Mod.Med. (Minneapolis) Modern Medicine: the newsmagazine of medicine [Minneapolis]

Mod.Philol. Modern Philology [University of Chicago]

Mod.Quart. The Modern Quarterly

Mod.Schoolman The Modern Schoolman: a quarterly journal of philosophy [St. Louis University]

Mois Le Mois: Synthèse de l'Activité Mondiale

Mon.Bull.Econ.China Monthly Bulletin on Economic China

Mon.Cyclopaedia Med.Bull. The Monthly Cyclopaedia and Medical Bulletin

Mon.Not.Roy.Astron.Soc. Monthly Notices of the Royal Astronomical Society

Mon.Not.Roy.Astron.Soc.Geophys.Suppl. Monthly Notices of the Royal Astronomical Society. Geophysical Supplement

Mon.Weather Rev. (United States) Monthly Weather Review [U.S. Weather Bureau]

Monatsber.Deut.Akad.Wiss.Berlin Monatsberichte der Deutschen Akademie der Wissenschaften zu Berlin

Monatsbl.Ges.Pommersche Gesch.Altertumsk. Monatsblätter der Gesellschaft für Pommersche Geschichte und Altertumskunde

Monatsh.Deut.Unterricht Monatshefte für deutschen Unterricht, deutsche Sprache und Literatur [Nationaler deutsch-amerikanischer Lehrerbund]

Monatsh.Math.Phys. Monatshefte für Mathematik und Physik

Monatsh.Naturwiss.Unterricht Monatshefte für den naturwissenschaftlichen Unterricht

Monatsschr.Gesch.Wiss.Judentums Monatsschrift für die Geschichte und Wissenschaft des Judentums

Monatsschr.Kinderheilk. Monatsschrift für Kinderheilkunde

Monatsschr.Krebsbekämpf. Monatsschrift für Krebsbekämpfung

Monatsschr.Psychiat.Neurol. Monatsschrift für Psychiatrie und Neurologie

Monde Orient. Monde Oriental

Monde Plantes Le Monde des Plantes

Mondo Odontostomatol. Mondo Odontostomatologico

Monist The Monist: a quarterly magazine devoted to the philosophy of science

Monist.Jahrhundert Das monistische Jahrhundert

Monit.Sci. Moniteur Scientifique

Montagne La Montagne

Month The Month. A Magazine of Literature, Science and Art

Montpellier Méd. Montpellier Médical

Monumenta Germ.Hist. Monumenta Germaniae Historica

Monumenta Nippon. Monumenta Nipponica: Studies on Japanese Culture, Past and Present

Monumenta Serica Monumenta Serica: Journal of Oriental Studies

Monumenta Sinica Monumenta Sinica [Published by the National Commission for the Preservation of Antiques, Nanking]

Monuments Mém.Acad.Inscriptions Monuments et Mémoires [Fondation Eugène Piot] publiés par l'Académie des Inscriptions

More Books More Books [Boston Public Library]

Morgen Morgen (Goldstein)

Morgenland Morgenland: Darstellungen aus Geschichte und Kultur des alten Orients

Moslem World Moslem World

Mouvement Sci.Belg. Mouvement Scientifique en Belgique: Wetenschapelijke Beweging in Belgie [Belgisch Verbond der Wetenschappelijke Verenigingen]

Moyen Âge Le Moyen Âge

Mühlhäuser Geschichtsblatt Mühlhäuser Geschichtsblatt

Münch.Beitr.Gesch.Lit.Naturwiss.Med. Münchener Beiträge zur Geschichte und Literatur der Naturwissenschaften und Medizin

Münch.Geogr.Stud. Münchener Geographische Studien

Münch.Jahrbuch Bildenden Kunst Münchner Jahrbuch der Bildenden Kunst

Münch.Med.Wochenschr. Münchener Medizinische Wochenschrift

Münch.Tierärztl.Wochenschr. Münchener Tierärztliche Wochenschrift

Mugtaṭaf, see *Al-Mugtaṭaf*

Multa Paucis Méd. Multa Paucis Médica

Mus.Genève Les Musées de Genève: Bulletin des musées et collections de la ville de Genève [Service des Musées et Collections]

Mus.Helv. Museum Helveticum: schweizerische Zeitschrift für klassische Altertumswissenschaft

Mus.J. Museums Journal [The Museums Association]

Mus.Livre Publ.Fasc. Le Musée du Livre. Publications: Fascicules

Muséon Le Muséon: Revue d'études orientales

Museumskunde Museumskunde

Muslim World Muslim World [formerly *Moslem World*]

Mustanie al-'Arabī, see *Al-Mustanie al-'Arabī*

Mycologia Mycologia [New York Botanical Gardens]

Mycopathol.Mycol.Appl. Mycopathologia et Mycologia Applicata

N

N.C.Med.J. North Carolina Medical Journal

N.Mex.Hist.Rev. New Mexico Historical Review [New Mexico Historical Society, Santa Fé]

NTM Z.Gesch.Naturwiss.Tech.Med. NTM, Zeitschrift für Geschichte der Naturwissenschaften, Technik und Medizin

N.Y.Hist. New York History

N.Y.Med.J. New York Medical Journal

N.Y.Rev.Books New York Review of Books

N.Y.State J.Med. New York State Journal of Medicine

N.Y.Times New York Times [Newspaper]

N.Y.Times Book Rev. New York Times Book Review

Nachr.Akad.Wiss.Göttingen Math.Phys.Kl. Nachrichten von der Akademie der Wissenschaften in Göttingen: Mathematisch-physikalische Klasse [formerly *Nachr.Ges.Wiss.Göttingen*]

Nachr.Ges.Wiss.Göttingen Nachrichten von der Gesellschaft der Wissenschaften zu Göttingen

Nachr.Ges.Wiss.Göttingen Geschäftliche Mitt. Nachrichten von der Gesellschaft der Wissenschaften zu Göttingen: Geschäftliche Mitteilungen

Nachr.Ges.Wiss.Göttingen Jahresber. Nachrichten von der Gesellschaft der Wissenschaften zu Göttingen: Jahresbericht über das Geschäftsjahr

Nachr.Ges.Wiss.Göttingen Math.Phys.Kl. Nachrichten von der Gesellschaft der Wissenschaften zu Göttingen: Mathematisch-physikalische Klasse

Nachr.Ges.Wiss.Göttingen Philol.Hist.Kl. Nachrichten von der Gesellschaft der Wissenschaften zu Göttingen: Philologisch-historische Klasse

Nachr.Giessener Hochschulges. Nachrichten der Giessener Hochschulgesellschaft

Nachr.Graetzel Ges.Göttingen Nachrichten von der Graetzel-Gesellschaft zu Göttingen

Nachr.Niedersachsens Urgeschichte Nachrichten aus Niedersachsens Urgeschichte

Nachrichtenbl.Deut.Vereinig.Gesch.Med.Naturwiss.Tech. Nachrichtenblatt der Deutschen Vereinigung für Geschichte der Medizin, Naturwissenschaft und Technik

Nankai Soc.Econ.Quart. Nankai Social and Economic Quarterly

Nár.Listy Národni Listy [Praha]

Nat.Geogr.Mag. National Geographic Magazine

Nat.Libr.Wales J. National Library of Wales Journal

Nat.Math.Mag. National Mathematics Magazine

Nat.Med.J.China National Medical Journal of China

Nat.Rev. National Review

Nation Nation: a weekly journal devoted to politics, literature, science and art

Nationalsozialistische Monatsh. Nationalsozialistische Monatshefte

Natur.Belg. Les Naturalistes Belges

Natur.Can. Le Naturaliste Canadien [Université Laval]

Natur.Hist. Natural History: devoted to natural history, exploration and the development of public education through the museums [American Museum of Natural History, New York]

Natur.Hist.Mag. Natural History Magazine

Natur Kult. Natur und Kultur: Monatschrift für Naturwissenschaft und ihre Grenzgebiete

Natur Mus. Natur und Museum: Bericht der Senckenbergischen Naturforschenden Gesellschaft

Natur.Phil. Natural Philosopher

Natur.Verden Naturens Verden

Natur Volk Natur und Volk: Bericht der Senckenbergischen Naturforschenden Gesellschaft

Natura Natura: Maandorgaan der Nederlandsche Natuurhistoriche Vereeniging

Natura(Bucharest) Natura: Revista Stiintifica de Popularizare [Bucharest]

Naturaleza La Naturaleza [Museo Nacional de Historia Natural, Mexico; Sociedad Mexicana de Historia Natural, Mexico]

Nature Nature [London]

Nature, La See *La Nature*

Nature Mag. Nature Magazine [American Nature Association]

Naturforscher Der Naturforscher: vereint mit *Natur und Technik*

Naturwiss.Rundsch. Naturwissenschaftliche Rundschau

Naturwiss.Rundsch (Braunschweig) Naturwissenschaftliche Rundschau [Braunschweig]

Naturwiss.Wochenschr. Naturwissenschaftliche Wochenschrift

Naturwissenschaften Die Naturwissenschaften: Organ der Gesellschaft Deutscher Naturforscher und Ärzte und Organ der Kaiser Wilhelm-Gesellschaft zur Förderung der Wissenschaften

Natuur De Natuur

Natuur Mensch Natuur en Mensch

Natuur Tech. Natuur en Techniek: Tijdschrift voor natuur, natuurwetenschappen en techniek

Natuurhist.Maandbl. Natuurhistorisch Maandblad [Natuurhistorisch Genootschap in Limburg]

Natuurk.Tijdschr.Ned.Indië Natuurkundig Tijdschrift voor Nederlandsch-Indië

Natuurwetensch.Tijdschr. Natuurwetenschappelijk Tijdschrift

Natuurwetensch.Tijdschr.Ned.Indië Natuurwetenschappelijk Tijdschrift voor Nederlandsch-Indië

Nauk.Polska Nauka Polska jej Potrzeby, Organizacja i Rozwój: Science and Letters in Poland,their Needs, Organization and Progress [Mianowski Institute for the Promotion of Science and Letters in Poland]

Navigation (Los Angeles) Navigation: Journal of the Institute of Navigation

Navigation (Paris) Navigation: Revue technique de navigation maritime et aérienne

Ned.Kruidkundig Arch. Nederlandsch Kruidkundig Archief: Verslagen en mededeelingen der Nederlandsche Botanische Vereeniging [Leyden]

Ned.Kunsthist.Jaarb. Nederlands Kunsthistorisch Jaarboek

Ned.Leeuw Nederlandsche Leeuw

Ned.Tijdschr.Geneesk. Nederlands Tijdschrift voor Geneeskunde

Ned.Tijdschr.Hyg.Microbiol.Serol. Nederlands Tijdschrift voor Hygiëne, Microbiologie en Serologie

Ned.Tijdschr.Natuurk. Nederlandsch Tijdschrift voor Natuurkunde

Ned.Tijdschr.Volksk. Nederlandsch Tijdschrift voor Volkskunde

Nef La Nef

Neue Bl.Sozialismus Neue Blätter für den Sozialismus: Zeitschrift für geistige und politische Gestaltung

Neue Deut.Chir. Neue deutsche Chirurgie

Neue Jahrb.Kl.Altertum Gesch.Deut.Lit. Neue Jahrbücher für das Klassische Altertum, Geschichte und deutsche Literatur

Neue Jahrb.Pädagogik Neue Jahrbücher für Pädagogik

Neue Jahrb.Wiss.Jugendbild. Neue Jahrbücher für Wissenschaft und Jugendbildung

Neue Med.Welt Neue Medizinische Welt

Neue Phys. Neue Physik: Zeitschrift für die Gebiete der Atom- und Strahlungsphysik

Neue Psychol.Stud. Neue Psychologische Studien

Neue Schweiz.Rundsch. Neue Schweizer Rundschau

Neue Uhrmacher-Zeitung Neue Uhrmacher-Zeitung: Fachzeitschrift für das Uhrmachergewerbe

Neue Weg Der neue Weg: Blätter ehemaliger oesterreichischer Pfadfinder in Ausland

Neue Weltansch. Neue Weltanschauung

Neue Züricher Zeitung Neue Züricher Zeitung

Neues Arch.Sächsische Gesch.Altertumsk. Neues Archiv für Sächsische Geschichte und Altertumskunde

Neues Lausitzisches Mag. Neues Lausitzisches Magazin [Oberlausitzische Gesellschaft der Wissenschaften]

Neujahrsbl.Naturforsch.Ges.Schaffhausen Neujahrsblatt der Naturforschenden Gesellschaft, Schaffhausen

Neujahrsbl.Naturforsch.Ges.Zürich Neujahrsblatt, herausgegeben von der Naturforschenden Gesellschaft in Zürich

Neumologia Cir.Tōrax Neumologia y Cirugia de Tōrax [Mexico]

Neuphilol.Mitt. Neuphilologische Mitteilungen [Neuphilologischer Verein in Helsingfors]

Neurol.Zentralbl. Neurologisches Zentralblatt

Neurology Neurology

Neutestamentliche Abhandl. Neutestamentliche Abhandlungen

New China Rev. New China Review

New Engl.J.Med. New England Journal of Medicine

New Engl.Quart. New England Quarterly

New Indian Antiq. The New Indian Antiquary

New Ireland Rev. New Ireland Review

New Mexico New Mexico: the State Magazine of National Interest

New Zeal.Libr. New Zealand Libraries

New Palestine The New Palestine [Zionist Organization of America]

New Repub. New Republic

New Sch. The New Scholasticism [Journal of the American Catholic Philosophical Association]

New Sci. The New Scientist

New Yorker The New Yorker

New Zeal.J.Geol. New Zealand Journal of Geology and Geophysics

New Zeal.Med.J. New Zealand Medical Journal [New Zealand Medical Association]

News Edition Amer.Chem.Soc. American Chemical Society's News Edition

News Serv.Bull.Carnegie Inst.Wash. News Service Bulletin. Carnegie Institution of Washington

Newsletter Soc.Amer.Bacteriol. Newsletter. Society of American Bacteriologists

Nieuw Arch.Wisk. Nieuw Archief voor Wiskunde

Nieuw Tijdschr.Wisk. Nieuw Tijdschrift voor Wiskunde

Nieuwe Rotterdamsche Courant Nieuwe Rotterdamsche Courant

Nihon Sūgaku Butsuri Gakkaishi Nihon Sūgaku Butsuri Gakkaishi [Journal of the Japanese Mathematical and Physical Society]

Nineteenth Century The Nineteenth Century

Nord.Astron.Tidsskr. Nordisk Astronomisk Tidsskrift [Astronomisk Selskab]

Nord.Försäkringstidskr. Nordisk Försäkringstidskrift

Nord.Mat.Tidsskr. Nordisk Matematisk Tidsskrift

Nord.Med. Nordisk Medicin

Nord.Psykiat.Tidsskr. Nordisk Psykiatrisk Tidsskrift

Nord Süd Nord und Süd: Monatsschrift für internationale Zusammenarbeit

Nord.Tidskr.Bok.Biblioteksväs. Nordisk Tidskrift för Bok- och Biblioteksväsen

Nord.Tidskr.Vetenskap Nordisk Tidskrift för Vetenskap, Konst och Industri

Normandie Pharm. Normandie Pharmaceutique

Northwest Med. Northwest Medicine

Nosokomeion Nosokomeion. Quarterly Hospital Review

Notes Conf.Univ.Libre Bruxelles Notes et Conférences. Université Libre de Bruxelles

Notes Queries Notes and Queries for readers and writers, collectors and librarians

Notes Roy.Soc.Lond. Notes and Records of the Royal Society of London

Notic.Discours Acad.Sci. Notices et Discours: Académie des Sciences

Notiz.Scavi Antichità Notizie degli Scavi di Antichità. [R. Accademia Nazionale dei Lincei]

Notizbl.Bot.Garten.Mus. Notizblatt des Botanischen Gartens und Museums zu Berlin-Dahlem

Notre Dame J.Formal Logic Notre Dame Journal of Formal Logic

Nouv.Arch.Missions Sci.Litt. Nouvelles Archives des Missions Scientifiques et Littéraires [Ministère de l'Instruction Publique et des Beaux-Arts, France]

Nouv.Clio Nouvelle Clio

Nouv.Iconographie Salpêtrière Nouvelle Iconographie de la Salpêtrière

Nouv.Litt. Nouvelles Littéraires

Nouv.Math.Int. Nouvelles Mathématiques Internationales [International Mathematical News]

Nouv.Rev. Nouvelle Revue

Nouv.Rev.Hist.Droit Franç.Étrang. Nouvelle Revue Historique de Droit Français et Étranger

Nouv.Rev.Ital. Nouvelle Revue d'Italie

Nouv.Rev.Théol. Nouvelle Revue Théologique [Collège Philosophique et Théologique S.J. Saint-Albert à Louvain]

Nova Acta Acad.Caesareae Leopoldino-Carolina Nova Acta Academiae Caesareae Leopoldino-Carolinae Germanicae Naturae Curiosorum: Verhandlungen [Abhandlungen] der Kaiserlichen Leopoldinisch-Carolinischen Deutschen Akademie der Naturforscher

Nova Acta Leopoldina Nova Acta Leopoldina: Abhandlungen der Kaiserlich Leopoldinisch-Carolinisch Deutschen Akademie der Naturforscher, neue Folge

Nova Acta Regiae Soc.Sci.Upsaliensis Nova Acta Regiae Societatis Scientiarum Upsaliensis

Nova Vetera Nova et Vetera [Fédération Nationale de l'Enseignement Moyen Catholique de Belgique]

Nowe Drogi Nowe Drogi [Polska Zjednoczona Partia Robotnicza]

Nucl.Phys. Nuclear Physics: journal devoted to the experimental and theoretical study of the fundamental constituents of matter and their interactions

Nucleus Nucleus [American Chemical Society, North Eastern Section]

Nuova Antologia Nuova Antologia: rivista di lettere, scienze ed arti

Nuova Riv.Stor. Nuova Rivista Storica

Nuovo Arch.Veneto Nuovo Archivio Veneto

Nuovo Cim. Il Nuovo Cimento [Società Italiana di Fisica, Pisa]

Nuovo Cim.Suppl. Nuovo Cimento Supplemento

Nuovo G.Bot.Ital. Nuovo Giornale Botanico Italiano [e Bollettino della Società Botanica Italiana]

Nutrition Rev. Nutrition Reviews

Oberbayer Arch.Vaterländische Gesch. Oberbayerisches Archiv für Vaterländische Geschichte

O

Oberdeut.Z.Volksk. Oberdeutsche Zeitschrift für Volkskunde

Obit.Not.Fellows Roy.Soc. Obituary Notices of Fellows of the Royal Society

Observatory The Observatory: a monthly review of astronomy

Occas.Notes Roy.Astron.Soc. Occasional Notes of the Royal Astronomical Society

Occas.Pap.Bernice P.Bishop Mus. Occasional Papers of the Bernice P. Bishop Museum [Hawaii]

Occult Rev. The Occult Review

Occup.Med. Occupational Medicine [American Medical Association]

Ocherki Ist.Geol.Znaniĭ Ocherki po Istorii Geologicheskikh Znaniĭ [Institut Geologicheskikh Nauk, Akademiia Nauk SSSR]

Ocherki Ist.Znaniĭ Ocherki po Istoriĭ Znanii [Akademiia Nauk, Leningrad]

Oeffentl.Gesundheitsdienst Der oeffentliche Gesundheitsdienst

Oesterr.Bot.Z. Oesterreichische Botanische Zeitschrift

Oesterr.Chem.Zeitung Oesterreichische Chemiker-Zeitung

Oesterr.Fisch.Zeitung Oesterreichische Fischerei Zeitung

Oesterr.Rettungswesen Oesterreichisches Rettungswesen

Oesterreichisch-ungar.Z.Zuckerind.Landwirt. Oesterreichisch-ungarische Zeitschrift für Zuckerindustrie und Landwirtschaft

Offic.Quart.J.Cleveland Med.Libr.Ass. Official Quarterly Journal of the Cleveland Medical Library Association

Ohio Hist.Quart. Ohio Historical Quarterly [Ohio State Archaeological and Historical Society]

Ohio J.Sci. Ohio Journal of Science [Scientific Society, Ohio State University]

Ohio State Archaeol.Hist.Quart. Ohio State Archaeological and Historical Quarterly [Ohio State Archaeological and Historical Society]

Ohio State Med.J. Ohio State Medical Journal [Ohio State Medical Association]

Old Time New Engl. Old Time New England: the Bulletin of the Society for the Preservation of New England Antiquities

Olie Olie

Ons Heem Ons Heem: Mededelingen van het Verbond voor Heemkunde

Oost Vlaanderen Oost-Vlaanderen

Oostvlaam.Zanten Oostvlaamsche Zanten

Open Court Open Court: a fortnightly journal devoted to the work of establishing ethics and religion upon a scientific basis

Opportunity Opportunity: A Journal of Negro Life

Opt.J.Rev.Optom. Optical Journal and Review of Optometry

Opt.Rundsch. Optische Rundschau und Photo-optiker

Optician Optician: the British optical and instrument journal

Optik Optik

Oregon Hist.Quart. Oregon Historical Quarterly

Orgaan Ver.Tech.Ambtenaren Kadaster Orgaan der Vereniging van Technische Ambtenaren van het Kadaster

Organon Organon: international review [Instytut Popierania Nauki Polskiej "Kasa im. Mianowskiegs". 1936-38]

Organon Organon [Instytut Historii Nauki i Techniki. Polska Akademia Nauk. From 1964]

Oriens Oriens: Journal of the International Society for Oriental Research

Oriens Extremus Oriens Extremus. Zeitschrift für Sprache, Kunst und Kultur der Länder des Ostens

Orient.Arch. Orientalisches Archiv

Orient.Christ.Period. Orientalia Christiana Periodica

Orient.Inst.Commun.Univ.Chicago Oriental Institute Communications ... of the University of Chicago

Orient.Lit.Zeitung Orientalistische Literatur-Zeitung [*OLZ*]

Orient.Mod. L'Oriente Moderno [Istituto per l'Oriente]

Orient.Neer. Orientalia Neerlandica

Orientalia Orientalia [Pontificio Istituto per gli Studi Orientalia, Roma]

Oriento Oriento. Bulletin of the Society of Near Eastern Studies in Japan. [Nihon Orient Gakkai]

Orion Orion: naturwissenschaftlich-technische Zeitschrift für Jedermann

Országos Orv.Könyvtar Közleményei Országos Orvostörteneti Könyvtar Közleményei: Communicationes ex Bibliotheca Historiae Medicae Hungarica

Orv.Hétil. Orvosi Hétilap

Orvosképzés Orvosképzés

Osiris Osiris: studies on the history and philosophy of science, and on the history of learning and culture

Osped.Magg. Ospedale Maggiore

Ostasiatische Z. Ostasiatische Zeitschrift: The Far East: L'Extrême Orient: Beiträge zur Kenntnis der Kultur und Kunst des fernen Ostens

Ostbairische Grenzmarken Ostbairische Grenzmarken: Passauer Jahrbuch für Geschichte, Kunst und Volkskunde

Otechestvenÿya Zapiski Otechestvenÿya Zapiski

Otsar ha-Ḥayyim Otsar ha-Ḥayyim

Oud Holland Oud-Holland: Tweemaandelijksch Tijdschrift voor Nederlandsche Kunstgeschiedenis

Oudheidkundig Jaarb. Oudheidkundig Jaarboek

Ouest Méd. Ouest-Médical

Outlook Bull.Southern Dent.Soc.N.J. Outlook and Bulletin. Southern Dental Society of New Jersey

Oversigt Danske Vidensk.Selsk.Forhandl. Oversigt over det [Kgl.] Danske Videnskabernes Selskabs Forhandlinger: Bulletin de l'Académie Royale des Sciences et des Lettres de Danemark

Oversigt Videnskabs-Selsk.Møder Oversigt over Videnskabs-Selskapets Møder

Oxford Mail Oxford Mail [Newspaper]

P

Pacific Aff. Pacific Affairs [Institute of Pacific Relations]

Pacific Discovery Pacific Discovery

Pacific Hist.Rev. Pacific Historical Review

Pacific Spectator The Pacific Spectator

Pädagog.Arch. Pädagogisches Archiv

Paginae Bibliogr. Paginae Bibliographicae

Pagine Stor.Med. Pagine di Storia della Medicina [Istituto di Storia della Medicina dell'Università di Roma]

Paideuma Paideuma: Mitteilungen zur Kulturkunde

Paix Droit Le Paix par le Droit

Pakistan Geogr.Rev. Pakistan Geographical Review

Pakistan Phil.J. Pakistan Philosophical Journal

Paläontol.Z. Paläontologische Zeitschrift

Palästinajahrbuch Palästinajahrbuch des Deutschen evangelischen Instituts für Altertumswissenschaft des Heiligen Landes

Palestine Explor.Fund Quart.Statement Palestine Exploration Fund Quarterly Statement

Palimpsest The Palimpsest

Pan-Amer.Geol. Pan-American Geologist

Pantheon München Pantheon München: Monatsschrift für Freunde und Sammler der Kunst

Pap.Bibliogr.Soc.Amer. Papers of the Bibliographical Society of America

Pap.Gesch. Papiergeschichte: Zeitschrift der Forschungsstelle Papiergeschichte

Pap.Maker Paper Maker and British Paper Trade Journal

Pap.Maker (Wilmington) Paper Maker, Wilmington

Pap.Mich.Acad.Sci.Arts Lett. Papers of the Michigan Academy of Science, Arts and Letters

Pap.Roy.Soc.Tasmania Papers and Proceedings of the Royal Society of Tasmania

Pap.Tortugas Lab.Carnegie Inst. Papers from the Tortugas Laboratory, Carnegie Institution

Papyri Osloenses Papyri Osloenses

Papyrus Papyrus. Annuaire de Toutes les Industries du Papier

Parasitology Parasitology: a supplement to the *Journal of Hygiene*

Parfum.Mod. Parfumerie Moderne

Paris Méd. Paris Médical: la semaine du clinicien

Parnassus Parnassus [College Art Association, New York]

Parola Passato Parola del Passato: Rivista di Studi Antichi

Past Present Past and Present: a journal of scientific history

Pathol.Biol. Pathologie et Biologie

Pathol.Gén. Pathologie Générale

Pays Gaumais Les Pays Gaumais

Pedagog.Seminar. Pedagogical Seminary

Peking Natur.Hist.Bull. Peking Natural History Bulletin

Penn.Genealogical Mag. Pennsylvania Genealogical Magazine [Genealogical Society of Pennsylvania]

Penn.Hist. Pennsylvania History [Pennsylvania Historical Association, Philadelphia]

Penn.Lit.Rev. Pennsylvania Literary Review

Penn.Mag.Hist.Biogr. Pennsylvania Magazine of History and Biography

Penn.Med.J. The Pennsylvania Medical Journal

Pensée(Bruxelles) La Pensée [Bruxelles]

Pensée(Paris) La Pensée: Revue du rationalisme moderne, arts, sciences, philosophie [Paris]

Pensiero Med. Pensiero Medico

Pensiero Missionario Il Pensiero Missionario

Percept.Mot.Skills Perceptual and Motor Skills

Period.Mat. Periodico di Matematica per l'Insegnamento Secondario [Società Italiana "Mathesis"]

Period.Mineral. Periodico di Mineralogia

Periodiek Periodiek: Maanblad van het Vlaams Geneesheren Verbond

Personalist The Personalist: an international review of philosophy, religion and literature [University of Southern California]

Personhist.Tidskr. Personhistorisk Tidskrift

Perspect.Biol.Med. Perspectives in Biology and Medicine

Perspectiva Communis Perspectiva Communis

Petermanns Geogr.Mitt. Petermanns Geographische Mitteilungen [formerly *Petermanns Mitt.*]

Petermanns Geogr.Mitt.Ergänzungsheft Petermanns Geographische Mitteilungen Ergänzungsheft [formerly *Petermanns Mitt. Ergänzungsheft*]

Petermanns Mitt. Dr. A. Petermann's Mitteilungen aus Justus Perthes Geographischer Anstalt: Illustrierte Zeitschrift für Länder- und Völkerkunde

Petermanns Mitt.Ergänzungsheft Petermanns Mitteilungen Ergänzungsheft

Petrus Nonius Petrus Nonius [Grupo Português da História das Ciências]

Peuples Civilisations Peuples et Civilisations

Pfälz.Mus. Pfälzisches Museum

Pflanzenbau Pflanzenbau

Pflanzenschutz Nachr.Bayer Pflanzenschutz. Nachrichten Bayer

Pharm.Arch. Pharmaceutical Archives

Pharm.Franç. La Pharmacie Française

Pharm.Hist. Pharmacy in History

Pharm.Ind. Die pharmazeutische Industrie

Pharm.J. Pharmaceutical Journal and Pharmacist

Pharm.Monatsh. Pharmazeutische Monatshefte: supplement to *Pharmazeutische Post*

Pharm.Tijdschr.Belg. Pharmaceutisch Tijdschrift voor België

Pharm.Weekbl. Pharmaceutisch Weekblad voor Nederland

Pharm.Zeitung Pharmazeutische Zeitung

Pharm.Zentralhalle Pharmazeutische Zentralhalle für Deutschland

Pharma-Med. Pharma-Medico

Pharmacia Pharmacia

Phi Beta Kappa Key Rep. The Phi Beta Kappa Key Reporter

Phi Beta Pi Quart. Phi Beta Pi Quarterly

Phi Chi Quart. Phi Chi Quarterly [Phi Chi Medical Fraternity]

Phil.East West Philosophy East and West

Phil.Forum Philosophical Forum [Boston University Philosophical Club]

Phil.Gesch. Philosophie und Geschichte

Phil.Jahrb.Görres-Ges. Philosophisches Jahrbuch der Görres Gesellschaft

Phil.Mag. [London, Edinburgh and Dublin] Philosophical Magazine [and journal of science]

Phil.Natur. Philosophia Naturalis: Archiv für Naturphilosophie

Phil.Phenomenol.Res. Philosophy and Phenomenological Research [International Phenomenological Society, New York]

Phil.Rev. The Philosophical Review

Phil.Sci. Philosophy of Science

Phil.Trans. Philosophical Transactions of the Royal Society

Philips Tech.Rev. Philips Technical Review [Research Laboratory, Philips' Gloeilampenfabrieken, Eindhoven]

Philobiblon Philobiblon: eine Zeitschrift für Bücherliebhaber

Philol.Jahrb. Philologisches Jahrbuch

Philol.Quart. Philological Quarterly [Iowa University]

Philol.Stud. Philologische Studien: Tijdschrift voor classiek philologie [Universite Catholique, Louvain]

Philol.Wochenschr. Philologische Wochenschrift

Philologus Philologus: Zeitschrift für das klassische Altertum

Philologus Suppl.Band Philologus: Zeitschrift für das klassische Altertum: Supplement-Band

Philosophy Philosophy: Journal of the British Institute of Philosophical Studies

Phoenix The Phoenix: Journal of the Classical Association of Canada

Phoenix Suppl.Vol. The Phoenix: supplementary volume

Photogr.J. Photographic Journal

Photogr.Korresp. Photographische Korrespondenz

Phronesis Phronesis: a journal for ancient philosophy

Phylon Phylon. The Atlanta University Review of Race and Culture

Phys.Bl. Physikalische Blätter

Phys.Can. Physics in Canada [Canadian Association of Physicists]

Phys.Teacher Physics Teacher

Phys.Today Physics Today [American Institute of Physics]

Phys.Verhandl. Physikalische Verhandlungen [Supplement to *Phys.Bl.*]

Phys.Z. Physikalische Zeitschrift

Physica Physica: Nederlandsch tijdschrift voor natuurkunde

Physics Physics

Physis Physis: Rivista di storia della scienza

Physis (Stuttgart) Physis: Beiträge zur naturwissenschaftlichen Synthese

Phytomorphology Phytomorphology

Phytopathology Phytopathology [American Phytopathological Society]

Pi Mu Epsilon J. Pi Mu Epsilon Journal: the official publication of the Honorary Mathematical Fraternity

Planetary Space Sci. Planetary and Space Science

Plant Physiol. Plant Physiology

Plant Sci.Bull. Plant Science Bulletin

Platinum Metals Rev. Platinum Metals Review

Platon Platon. Deltion tes Hetaireias Hellenon Philologon

Pochvovedenie Pochvovedenie

Pol.Gaz.Lek. Polska Gazeta Lekarska

Pol.Przegl.Chir. Polski Przegląd Chirurgiczny

Pol.Przegl.Kartogr. Polski Przegląd Kartograficzny

Pol.Rev. Polish Review [Polish Institute of Arts and Sciences in America]

Policlinico Sez.Chir. Policlinico: Sezione Chirurgica

Policlinico Sez.Med. Policlinico: Sezione Medica

Policlinico Sez.Prat. Policlinico: Sezione Pratica

Polit.Quart. Political Quarterly [from 1914-16]

Polit.Quart. Political Quarterly [from 1930]

Polit.Sci.Quart. Political Science Quarterly

Politiken Politiken [Newspaper: Copenhagen]

Pollen Anal.Circ. Pollen Analysis Circular [Oberlin College. Department of Botany]

Pop.Astron. Popular Astronomy: a review of astronomy and allied sciences [Goodsell Observatory, Carleton College, Minn.]

Pop.Sci.Mon. Popular Science Monthly

Port.Acta Biol.Ser.A Portugaliae Acta Biologica Series A

Port.Acta Biol.Ser.B Portugaliae Acta Biologica Series B

Posebna Izdanja Geogr.Društvo Posebna Izdanja Geografsko Društvo: Société Serbe de Géographie; Société de Géographie de Béograd

Post Iucundam Iuventutem Post Iucundam Iuventutem. Orgaan van het Utrechts Universiteitsfond

Post Office Elec.Eng.J. The Post Office Electrical Engineers' Journal

Prace Geogr. Prace Geograficzne

Prace Mat.Fiz. Prace Matematyczno-fizyczne

Prace Wrocławskiego Tow.Nauk. Prace Wrocławskiego Towarzystwa Naukowego: Travaux de la Société des Sciences et des Lettres de Wroclaw

Pract.Pharm. Practical Pharmacy. Tokio

Practitioner The Practitioner

Praehist.Z. Prähistorische Zeitschrift

Prager Arch.Tiermed. Prager Archiv für Tiermedizin und vergleichende Pathologie

Prager Med.Wochenschr. Prager Medizinische Wochenschrift

Prairie Schooner Prairie Schooner

Prakt.Akad.Athēnōn Praktika tēs Akadēmias 'Athēnōn

Prat.Doktor Pratik Doktor

Prax.Kinderpsychol.Kinderpsychiat. Praxis der Kinderpsychologie und Kinderpsychiatrie

Prax.Math. Praxis der Mathematik

Préhistoire Préhistoire

Prensa Méd.Argent. Prensa Médica Argentina

Présence Ardennaise Présence Ardennaise

Presse Méd. Presse Médicale

Preuss.Jahrbücher Preussische Jahrbücher

Preussag Werks Zeitung Preussag-Werks-Zeitung

Princeton Alumni Weekly Princeton Alumni Weekly

Princeton Univ.Libr.Chron. Princeton University Library Chronicle

Printing Art The Printing Art

Priroda Priroda [Akademiia Nauk SSSR]

Příroda (Brno) Příroda [Brno]

Probl.Aliment. Problema Alimentare

Probl.Attuali Sci.Cult.Quad. Problemi Attuali di Scienza e di Cultura: Quaderni [Accademia Nazionale dei Lincei, Rome]

Proc.Alumni Ass.King Edward VII Coll.Med.Singapore Proceedings of the Alumni Association of the King Edward VII College of Medicine, Singapore

Proc.Amer.Acad.Arts Sci. Proceedings of the American Academy of Arts and Sciences

Proc.Amer.Acad.Jew.Res. Proceedings of the American Academy for Jewish Research

Proc.Amer.Antiq.Soc. Proceedings of the American Antiquarian Society

Proc.Amer.Cath.Phil.Ass. Proceedings of the American Catholic Philosophical Association

Proc.Amer.Inst.Elec.Eng. Proceedings of the American Institute of Electrical Engineering

Proc.Amer.Phil.Soc. Proceedings of the American Philosophical Society

Proc.Annu.Congr.Med.Educ.Licensure Proceedings of the Annual Congress on Medical Education and Licensure [American Medical Association]

Proc.Aristotelian Soc. Proceedings of the Aristotelian Society for the Systematic Study of Philosophy

Proc.Belfast Natur.Hist.Phil.Soc. Proceedings [and Report] of the Belfast Natural History and Philosophy Society

Proc.Benares Math.Soc. Proceedings of the Benares Mathematical Society

Proc.Biol.Soc.Wash. Proceedings of the Biological Society of Washington

Proc.Brit.Acad. Proceedings of the British Academy

Proc.Cambridge Phil.Soc. Proceedings of the Cambridge Philosophical Society

Proc.Charaka Club Proceedings of the Charaka Club [New York]

Proc.Chem.Soc. Proceedings of the Chemical Society [London]

Proc.Colo.Mus.Natur.Hist. Proceedings of the Colorado Museum of Natural History

Proc.Congr.Int.Fed.Mod.Lang.Lit. Proceedings of the Congress of the International Federation for Modern Languages and Literatures

Proc.Congr.Prehist.Far East Proceedings of the Congress of Prehistorians of the Far East

Proc.Del.County Inst.Sci. Proceedings of the Delaware County Institute of Science

Proc.Edinb.Math.Soc. Proceedings of the Edinburgh Mathematical Society

Proc.Geol.Ass.Can. Proceedings of the Geological Association of Canada

Proc.Geol.Soc.Amer. Proceedings of the Geological Society of America

Proc.Imp.Acad.Japan Proceedings of the Imperial Academy of Japan

Proc.Indian Sci.Congr. Proceedings of the Indian Science Congress

Proc.Indiana Acad.Sci. Proceedings of the Indiana Academy of Science

Proc.Inst.Mech.Eng. Proceedings of the Institution of Mechanical Engineers

Proc.Inst.Radio Eng. Proceedings of the Institute of Radio Engineers [New York]

Proc.Int.Assembly Inter-State Post Grad.Med.Ass.N.Amer. Proceedings of the International Assembly of the Inter-State Post Graduate Medical Association of North America

Proc.Int.Bot.Congr. Proceedings of the International Botanical Congress

Proc.Int.Congr.Amer. Proceedings of the International Congress of Americanists

Proc.Int.Congr.Hist.Med. Proceedings of the International Congress of the History of Medicine

Proc.Int.Congr.Hist.Sci. Proceedings of the International Congress of the History of Science

Proc.Int.Congr.Math. Proceedings of the International Congress of Mathematicians

Proc.Int.Congr.Med. Proceedings of the International Congress of Medicine

Proc.Int.Congr.Phil. Proceedings of the International Congress of Philosophy

Proc.Int.Congr.Zool. Proceedings of the International Congress of Zoology

Proc.Leeds Phil.Lit.Soc. Proceedings of the Leeds Philosophical and Literary Society

Proc.Linnean Soc.Lond. Proceedings of the Linnean Society of London

Proc.Malacol.Soc. Proceedings of the Malacological Society [London]

Proc.Mass.Hist.Soc. Proceedings of the Massachusetts Historical Society

Proc.Math.Phys.Soc.Egypt Proceedings of the Mathematical and Physical Society of Egypt

Proc.Math.Phys.Soc.U.A.R. Proceedings of the Mathematical and Physical Society of the United Arab Republic

Proc.Math.Phys.Soc.U.A.R.(Egypt) Proceedings of the Mathematical and Physical Society of the United Arab Republic (Egypt)

Proc.Myrin Inst. Proceedings. Myrin Institute for Adult Education

Proc.N.Dak.Acad.Sci. Proceedings of the North Dakota Academy of Science

Proc.Nat.Acad.Sci. Proceedings of the National Academy of Sciences of the United States of America

Proc.Nat.Cancer Conf. Proceedings of the National Cancer Conference

Proc.Nat.Lab.Psychical Res. Proceedings of the National Laboratory of Psychical Research

Proc.Ned.Akad.Wetensch.Sect.Sci. Proceedings: Koninklijke Nederlandsche Akademie van Wetenschappen: Section of Sciences

Proc.Ned.Akad.Wetensch.Ser.A Proceedings: Koninklijke Nederlandse Akademie van Wetenschappen, Series A: Mathematical Sciences [formerly *Proc.Ned.Akad.Wetensch.Sect.Sci.Ser.A*]

Proc.Ned.Akad.Wetensch.Ser.B Proceedings: Koninklijke Nederlandse Akademie van Wetenschappen, Series B: Physical Sciences [formerly *Proc.Ned.Akad.Wetensch.Sect.Sci.Ser.B*]

Proc.Ned.Akad.Wetensch.Ser.C Proceedings: Koninklijke Nederlandse Akademie van Wetenschappen, Series C: Biological and Medical Sciences [formerly *Proc.Ned.Akad.Wetensch.Sect.Sci.Ser.C*]

Proc.Okla.Acad.Sci. Proceedings of the Oklahoma Academy of Science

Proc.Oxford Bibliogr.Soc. Proceedings and Papers of the Oxford Bibliographical Society

Proc.Pan-Pacific Sci.Conf. Proceedings of the Pan-Pacific Scientific Conference

Proc.Penn.Acad.Sci. Proceedings of the Pennsylvania Acadamy of Science

Proc.Phil.Soc.Tex. Proceedings of the Philosophical Society of Texas

Proc.Phys.Math.Soc.Japan Proceedings of the Physico-Mathematical Society of Japan [Nippon Sugaku-buturigakkwai]

Proc.Phys.Soc. Proceedings of the [Institute of Physics and the] Physical Society of London

Proc.Prehist.Soc. Proceedings of the Prehistoric Society

Proc.Rochester Acad.Sci. Proceedings of the Rochester Academy of Science [Rochester, N.Y.]

Proc.Roy.Entomol.Soc.London Proceedings of the Royal Entomological Society of London

Proc.Roy.Geogr.Soc.Australasia S.Australia Br. Proceedings of the Royal Geographical Society of Australasia: South Australian Branch

Proc.Roy.Inst. Proceedings of the Royal Institution of Great Britain

Proc.Roy.Irish Acad. Proceedings of the Royal Irish Academy

Proc.Roy.Phil.Soc.Glasgow Proceedings of the Royal Philosophical Society of Glasgow

Proc.Roy.Soc.Can. Proceedings and Transactions of the Royal Society of Canada

Proc.Roy.Soc.Edinb. Proceedings of the Royal Society of Edinburgh

Proc.Roy.Soc.Edinb.Sect.A Proceedings of the Royal Society of Edinburgh, Section A: Mathematical and Physical Sciences

Proc.Roy.Soc.Edinb.Sect.B Proceedings of the Royal Society of Edinburgh, Section B: Biology

Proc.Roy.Soc.Med. Proceedings of the Royal Society of Medicine

Proc.Roy.Soc.Ser.A Proceedings of the Royal Society [London]: Series A: Physical Sciences

Proc.Roy.Soc.Ser.B Proceedings of the Royal Society [London]: Series B: Biological Sciences

Proc.S.Wales Inst.Eng. Proceedings of the South Wales Institute of Engineers

Proc.Scot.Anthropol.Soc. Proceedings of the Scottish Anthropological (and Folklore) Society

Proc.Soc.Antiq.Scot. Proceedings of the Society of Antiquaries of Scotland

Proc.Soc.Biblical Archaeol. Proceedings of the Society of Biblical Archaeology

Proc.Somersetshire Archaeol.Natur.Hist.Soc. Proceedings of the Somersetshire Archaeological and Natural History Society

Proc.Staff Meetings Mayo Clin. Proceedings of the Staff Meetings of the Mayo Clinic

Proc.U.S.Nat.Congr.Appl.Mech. Proceedings of the United States National Congress of Applied Mechanics

Proc.U.S.Nat.Mus. Proceedings of the United States National Museum [Washington, D.C.]

Proc.U.S.Nav.Inst. Proceedings of the United States Naval Institute

Proc.Univ.Durham Phil.Soc. Proceedings of the University of Durham Philosophical Society

Proc.Virchow Med.Soc.N.Y. Proceedings of the Rudolf Virchow Medical Society in the City of New York

Proc.West Virginia Acad.Sci. Proceedings of West Virginia Academy of Science

Proc.Wireless Inst. Proceedings of the Wireless Institute

Proc.Wis.Pharm.Ass. Proceedings of the Wisconsin Pharmaceutical Association

Proc.World Poultry Congr. Proceedings of the World Poultry Congress and Exposition

Proc.Yorkshire Geol.Polytech.Soc. Proceedings of the Yorkshire Geological and Polytechnic Society

Proc.Zool.Soc.London Proceedings of the Zoological Society of London

Procès-Verbaux Congr.Soc.Int.Chir. Procès-verbaux du Congrès de la Société Internationale de Chirurgie

Procès-Verbaux Mém.Congr.Int.Bibl.Bibliophiles Procès-Verbaux et Mémoires du Congrès International des Bibliothécaires (et des Bibliophiles)

Procès-Verbaux Séances Soc.Sci.Phys.Natur.Bordeaux Procès-verbaux des Séances de la Société des Sciences Physiques et Naturelles de Bordeaux

Procès-Verbaux Soc.Méd.Athènes Procès-verbaux de la Société Médicale d'Athènes

Produits Pharm. Produits Pharmaceutiques

Prof.Geogr. The Professional Geographer: Journal of the Association of American Geographers

Progr.Méd. Le Progrès Médical

Progr.Medieval Renaiss.Stud.Bull. Progress of Medieval and Renaissance Studies in the United States of America (and Canada). Bulletin

Progr.Phys.Sci. Progress of Physical Sciences [English abstract of *Usp.Fiz.Nauk*]

Progr.Terap. Progressi di Terapia

Prometheus (Leipzig) Prometheus. Illustrierte Wochenschrift über die Fortschritte der angewandten Naturwissenschriften

Prophylaxie Antivénér. La Prophylaxie Antivénérienne: organe officiel de la Société Française de Prophylaxie Sanitaire et Morale et de la Ligue Nationale Française contre le Péril Vénérien

Prophylaxie Sanit.Morale Prophylaxie Sanitaire et Morale

Proteus (Bonn) Proteus: Verhandlungsberichte der Rheinischen Gesellschaft für Geschichte der Naturwissenschaft, Medizin und Technik

Proteus (London) Proteus: a journal of the science, philosophy and therapy of nature

Protoplasma Protoplasma

Przegl.Dermatol. Przeglad Dermatologiczny

Przegl.Epidemiol. Przeglad Epidemiologiczny

Przegl.Geogr. Przegląd Geograficzny

Przegl.Wspólczesny Przeglad Wspólczesny

Psyche (Cambridge, Mass.) Psyche: a Journal of Entomology (Cambridge Entomological Club)

Psychiat.Quart. Psychiatric Quarterly [Department of Mental Hygiene, New York State]

Psychiatrisch-Neurol.Wochenschr. Psychiatrisch-neurologische Wochenschrift

Psychiatry Psychiatry. Journal of the Biology and Pathology of Interpersonal Relations

Psychic Res.Quart. The Psychic Research Quarterly

Psychoanal.Quart. Psychoanalytic Quarterly

Psychoanal.Rev. Psychoanalytic Review

Psychol.Abstr. Psychological Abstracts

Psychol.Bull. The Psychological Bulletin

Psychol.Forsch. Psychologische Forschung

Psychol.Rec. The Psychological Record

Psychol.Rev. Psychological Review

Pubbl.Ist.Naz.Ott. Pubblicazioni dell'Istituto Nazionale di Ottica [Florence]

Pubbl.Osserv.Astron.Univ.Bologna Pubblicazioni dell'Osservatorio Astronomico della R. Università di Bologna

Pubbl.Sci.Accad.Navale Pubblicazioni Scientifiche a cura dell' Accademia Navale [Leghorn]

Publ.Astron.Soc.Pacific Publications of the Astronomical Society of the Pacific

Publ.Brit.Sch.Archaeol.Egypt Publications of the British School of Archaeology in Egypt

Publ.Bur.Cent.Séismol.Int.Sér.A Trav.Sci. Publications de Bureau Central Séismologique International. Série A. Travaux Scientifiques

Publ.Carnegie Inst.Wash. Publications of the Carnegie Institution of Washington

Publ.Cátedra Hist.Med.Univ.Buenos Aires Publicaciones de la Cátedra de Historia de la Medicina, Universidad de Buenos Aires

Publ.Colon.Soc.Mass. Publications of the Colonial Society of Massachusetts

Publ.Comm.Roy.Hist.Acad.Roy.Belg. Publications de la Commission Royale d'Histoire de l'Académie des Sciences, des Lettres et des Beaux-Arts de Belgique

Publ.Ecole Franç.Extrême-Orient Publications de l'École Française d'Extrême-Orient [Hanoi]

Publ.Field Mus.Natur.Hist.Anthropol.Ser. Publications of the Field Museum of Natural History, Anthropological Series

Publ.Florida State Hist.Soc. Publications of the Florida State Historical Society

Publ.Ill.State Hist.Libr. Publications of the Illinois State Historical Library

Publ.Indiana Hist.Soc. Publications of the Indiana Historical Society

Publ.Inst.Comp.Stud.Cult.Tokyo Publications of the Institute for Comparative Studies of Culture affiliated to Tokyo Woman's Christian College: Tokyo Jyoshi Daigaku Fuzoku Hikaku Bunka Kenkyusho Kiyo

Publ.Inst.Hist.Filosof.Cienc.Univ.Nac.Litoral Publicación del Instituto de Historia y Filosofia de la Ciencia, Universidad Nacional del Litoral [Rosario de Santa Fé, Argentina]

Publ.Inst.Hist.Med.Univ.Buenos Aires Publicaciones del Instituto de Historia de la Medicina, Facultad de Ciencias Médicas, Universidad de Buenos Aires

Publ.Int.Electrotech.Comm. Publications of the International Electrotechnical Commission

Publ.Kwasan Observ. Publications of the Kwasan Observatory

Publ.Metrop.Mus.Art Egypt.Exped. Publications of the Metropolitan Museum of Art Egyptian Expedition

Publ.Mod.Lang.Ass.Amer. Publications of the Modern Language Association of America [PMLA]

Publ.Observ.Univ.Mich. Publications of the Observatory of the University of Michigan

Publ.Public Arch.Can. Publications of the Public Archives of Canada

Publ.Seminar.Hist.Med.Univ.Salamanca Publicaciones del seminario de Historia de la Medicina de la Universidad de Salamanca

Publ.Soc.Étud.Iraniennes Publications de la Société des Études Iraniennes [Paris]

Publ.Soc.Géogr.Hanoi Publications de la Société de Géographie de Hanoi

Publ.Vassar Coll.Observ. Publications of the Vassar College Observatory [Poughkeepsie, N.Y.]

Publ.Week. Publisher's Weekly

Public Health Rep. Public Health Reports

Publikationen Stift.Vulkaninst.Immanuel Friedländer Publikationen der Stiftung Vulkaninstitut Immanuel Friedländer

Pyramide Wochenschr.Karlsruher Tagbl. Die Pyramide: Wochenschrift zum Karlsruher Tagblatt

Q

Quad.Merceol. Quaderni di Merceologia

Quad.Nutr. Quaderni della Nutrizione

Quad.Stor.Crit.Sci. Quaderni di Storia e Critica della Scienza

Quad.Stor.Sci.Med. Quaderni di Storia della Scienza e della Medicina [Università degli Studi di Ferrara]

Quadrige Quadrige. Pensée, Art, Vie, Élégance

Quarry Managers' J. Quarry Managers' Journal

Quart.Bull.Chin.Bibliogr. Quarterly Bulletin of Chinese Bibliography

Quart.Bull.N.Y.Hist.Soc. Quarterly Bulletin of the New York Historical Society

Quart.Bull.Northwestern Univ.Med.Sch. Quarterly Bulletin of the Northwestern University Medical School

Quart.Calif.Hist.Soc. Quarterly of the California Historical Society

Quart.J.Agr. Quarterly Journal of Agriculture

Quart.J.Econ. The Quarterly Journal of Economics

Quart.J.Geol.Soc.Lond. Quarterly Journal of the Geological Society of London

Quart.J.Microscop.Sci. Quarterly Journal of Microscopical Science

Quart.J.N.Y.State Hist.Ass. Quarterly Journal of the New York State Historical Association

Quart.J.Roy.Astron.Soc. Quarterly Journal of the Royal Astronomical Society

Quart.J.Roy.Meteorol.Soc. Quarterly Journal of the Royal Meteorological Society

Quart.Phi Beta Pi Med.Fraternity Quarterly of the Phi Beta Pi Medical Fraternity

Quart.Publ.Amer.Statist.Ass. Quarterly Publications of the American Statistical Association

Quart.Rev. The Quarterly Review

Quart.Rev.Biol. Quarterly Review of Biology

Queen's Quart. Queen's Quarterly

Queensland Geogr.J. Queensland Geographical Journal

Quellen Aufsätze Russ.Gesch. Quellen und Aufsätze zur Russischen Geschichte

Quellen Stud.Gesch.Kult.Altertums Mittelalters, ser. D Quellen und Studien zur Geschichte und Kultur des Altertums und des Mittelalters, Reihe D: Untersuchungen und Mitteilungen

Quellen Stud.Gesch.Math.Abt.A Quellen und Studien zur Geschichte der Mathematik, Abteilung A: Quellen

Quellen Stud.Gesch.Math.Abt.B Quellen und Studien zur Geschichte der Mathematik, Abteilung B: Studien

Quellen Stud.Gesch.Naturwiss.Med. Quellen und Studien zur Geschichte der Naturwissenschaften und der Medizin [Institut für Geschichte der Medizin und der Naturwissenschaften in Berlin]

Quinzaine Thérap. Quinzaine Thérapeutique

R

Raccolta Vinciana Raccolta Vinciana

Radio Actual. Radio Actualités

Radio Eng. Radio Engineering

Radiology Radiology [Radiological Society of North America]

Rapp.Annu.Inst.Rech.Sci.Afr.Cent. Rapport Annuel. Institut pour la Recherche Scientifique en Afrique Centrale (IRSAC)

Rapp.Congr.Int.Sci.Hist. Rapports du Congrès International des Sciences Historiques

Rapp.Procès-Verbaux Cons.Perma.Int.Explor.Mer Rapport et Procès-Verbaux des Réunions. Conseil Permanent International pour l'Exploration de la Mer

Rapp.Univ.Libre Bruxelles Rapport de l'Université Libre de Bruxelles sur l'Année Académique

Rare Books Rare Books: notes on the history of old books and manuscripts

Rasprave Grada Povijest Nauk. Rasprave i Grada za Povijest Nauka

Rass.Clin.Sci.Ist.Biochim.Ital. Rassegna Clinico Scientifica dell'Istituto Biochimico Italiano

Rass.Clin.Terap. Rassegna di Clinica, Terapia e Scienze Affini

Rass.Ital. Rassegna Italiana

Rass.Mat.Fis. Rassegna di Matematica e Fisica

Rass.Med. Rassegna Medica

Rass.Med.Sarda La Rassegna Medica Sarda

Rass.Naz. Rassegna Nazionale

Rass.Stor.Univ.Modena Cult.Sup.Modenese Rassegna per la Storia della Università di Modena e della Cultura Superiore Modenese

Rass.Stud.Sessuali Rassegna di Studi Sessuali

Rass.Terap. Rassegna di Terapia

Rauch Staub Rauch und Staub. Zeitschrift für ihre Bekämpfung

Realidad Realidad. Revista de ideas

Realist The Realist: a Journal of Scientific Humanism

Realités Realités. Monthly magazine. International edition

Rec.Amer.Cath.Hist.Soc.Phila. Records of the American Catholic Historical Society of Philadelphia

Rec.Bot.Surv.India Records of the Botanical Survey of India

Rec.Glasgow Bibliogr.Soc. Records of the Glasgow Bibliographical Society

Rec.Indian Mus. Records of the Indian Museum: a Journal of Indian Zoology

Rec.Méd.Vétérinaire Recueil de Médecine Vétérinaire

Rec.Publ.Soc.Havraise Étud.Diverses Recueil des Publications de la Société [Nationale] Havraise d'Études Diverses

Rec.Trav.Conf.Hist.Philol.Univ.Louvain Recueil de Travaux de la Conférence d'Histoire et de Philologie, Université [Catholique] de Louvain

Rec.Trav.Fac.Phil.Lett.Gand Recueil des Travaux de la Faculté de Philosophie et Lettres de Gand

Rec.Trav.Hist.Philol.Univ.Louvain Recueil de travaux d'histoire et de philologie [Université Catholique de Louvain] [formerly *Rec.Trav.Conf.Hist.Philol.Univ.Louvain*]

Rec.Voyages Doc.Hist.Geogr. Recueil de Voyages et de Documents pour servir à l'Histoire de la Géographie

Rech.Phil. Recherches Philosophiques

Rech.Sci.Relig. Recherches de Science Religieuse

Rech.Théol.Ancienne Medièvale Recherches de Théologie Ancienne et Médiévale

Reclams Universum Reclams Universum

Reddingwezen Reddingwezen

Reflets Monde Reflets du Monde

Reforma Méd. La Reforma Médica

Refractionist The Refractionist [Institute of Ophthalmic Opticians]

Refuah Veterinarith Refuah Veterinarith [Quarterly of the Israel Veterinary Medical Association]

Regensburger Jahrb.Ärztl.Fortbild. Regensburger Jahrbuch für ärztliche Fortbildung

Register Phi Lamda Upsilon Register of Phi Lamda Upsilon

Reichsmed.Anz. Reichsmedizinal Anzeiger

Reichspost (Vienna) Reichspost [Newspaper]

Rekishi Chiri Rekishi chiri [Nippon Rekishi Chiri Gakkai: Japanese Historical and Geographical Society]

Relig.Educ. Religious Education

Religionsgeschichtl.Versuche Vorarb. Religionsgeschichtliche Versuche und Vorarbeiten

Religionswiss.Bibl. Religionswissenschaftliche Bibliothek

Renaiss.Mod.Stud. Renaissance and Modern Studies

Renaiss.News Renaissance News

Renaiss.Phil. Renaissance und Philosophie: Beiträge zur Geschichte der Philosophie

Renaissance Renaissance [New School for Social Research, New York]

Rendic.Accad.Sci.Fis.Mat.Napoli Rendiconti della Accademia delle Science Fisiche e Matematiche di Napoli

Rendic.Accad.Sci.Med.Chir.Napoli Rendiconti della Accademia di Scienze Mediche e Chirurgiche della Società Nazionale di Scienze, Lettere ed Arti in Napoli

Rendic.Ist.Lombardo Sci.Lett. Rendiconti dell' Istituto Lombardo di Scienze e Lettere

Rendic.Ist.Lombardo Sci.Lett.Cl.Lett. Rendiconti dell' Istituto Lombardo di Scienze e Lettere: Classe di Lettere

Rendic.Ist.Lombardo Sci.Lett.Cl.Sci.Mat. Rendiconti dell' Istituto Lombardo di Scienze e Lettere: Classe di Scienze Matematiche e Naturali

Rendic.Ist.Lombardo Sci.Lett.Parte Gen.Atti Uffic. Rendiconti. (Reale) Istituto Lombardo di Scienze e Lettere. Parte Generale e Atti Ufficiali

Rendic.Ist.Super.Sanit. Rendiconti. Istituto Superiore di Sanità

Rendic.Seminar.Fac.Sci.Univ.Cagliari Rendiconti del Seminario della Facolta di Scienze, Università di Cagliari

Rendic.Seminar.Mat.Fis.Milano Rendiconti del Seminario Matematico e Fisico di Milano

Rendic.Seminar.Mat.Univ.Roma Rendiconti del Seminario Matematico, Università di Roma

Rendic.Sess.Accad.Sci.Ist.Bologna Cl.Sci.Fis. Rendiconti delle Sessioni dell'[Reale] Accademia delle Scienze dell' Istituto di Bologna: Classe di Scienze Fisiche

Rendic.Soc.Chim.Ital. Rendiconti della Società Chimica Italiana

Rendic.Soc.Ital.Sci.Accad.XL Rendiconti della Società Italiana delle Scienze dell' Accademia dei XL

Rep.Annu.Conf.Nat.Ass.Matern.Child Welfare Report of Annual Conference of the National Association for Maternity and Child Welfare

Rep.Australasian Ass.Advance.Sci. Report of the Australasian Association for the Advancement of Science

Rep.Australian New Zeal.Ass.Advance.Sci. Report of the Australian and New Zealand Association for the Advancement of Science

Rep.Brit.Ass.Advance.Sci. Report of the British Association for the Advancement of Science

Rep.Libr.Congr. Report of the Librarian of Congress

Rep.New Engl.Ass.Chem.Teachers Report of the New England Association of Chemistry Teachers

Rep.Proc.Int.Geogr.Congr. Report and Proceedings of the International Geographical Congress

Rep.State Geol.Mineral Ind.Vermont Report of the State Geologist on the Mineral Industries and Geology of certain areas of Vermont

Repert.Kunstwiss. Repertorium für Kunstwissenschaft

Répert.Méd.Int. Répertoire de Médicine Internationale

Reporter The Reporter

Reproduktion Reproduktion

Répub.Franç. La République Française. Revue Mensuelle de l'Idéologie Républicaine et Démocratique

Res.Progr. Research and Progress: quarterly review of German science [English edition of *Forsch.Fortschr.*]

Res.Publ.Ass.Res.Nerv.Ment.Dis. Research Publications. Association for Research in Nervous and Mental Diseases

Res.Publ.Ill.Inst.Tech. Research Publications. Illinois Institute of Technology

Res.Rev. Research Review [Institute of Education: Durham University]

Research Research: a Journal of Science and its Applications

Residencia Residencia

Rev.Acad.Arabe Revue de l'Académie Arabe: Maǧallat al-Maǧna' al-'ilmī al-'arabī

Rev.Acad.Cienc.Exact.Fis.Natur.Madrid Revista de la [Real] Academia de Ciencias Exactas, Fisicas y Naturales de Madrid

Rev.Acad.Cienc.Exact.Fisico-Quim.Nat.Zaragoza Revista de l'Academia de Ciencias Exactas Fisico-quimicas y Naturales de Zaragoza

Rev.Acad.Colomb.Cienc.Exact.Fis.Natur. Revista de la Academia Colombiana di Ciencias Exactas, Fisicas y Naturales

Rev.Afr. Revue Africaine: Journal des travaux de la Société Historique Algérienne

Rev.Anthropol. Revue Anthropologique

Rev.Arch.Bibl.Mus. Revista de Archivos, Bibliotecas y Museos [Madrid]

Rev.Archéol. Revue Archéologique

Rev.Argent.Hist.Med. Revista Argentina de Historia de la Medicina [Ateneo de Historia de la Medicina, Buenos Aires]

Rev.Arq. (São Paulo) Revista do Arquivo [São Paulo]

Rev.Art Ancien Mod. Revue de l'Art Ancien et Moderne

Rev.Arts Asiatiques Revue des Arts Asiatiques

Rev.Asoc.Odontol.Argent. Revista. Asociación Odontológica Argentina

Rev.Ass.Méd.Univ.Libre Bruxelles Revue de l'Association des Médecins Sortis de l'Université Libre de Bruxelles

Rev.Assyriologie Revue d'Assyriologie et d'Archéologie Orientale

Rev.Belg. Revue Belge

Rev.Belg.Doc.Méd. Revue Belge de Documentation Médicale

Rev.Belg.Numismatique Revue Belge de Numismatique et de Sigillographie

Rev.Belg.Philol.Hist. Revue Belge de Philologie et d'Histoire: Belgisch Tijdschrift voor Philologie en Geschiedenis

Rev.Bénédictine Revue Bénédictine

Rev.Bibl. Revue des Bibliothèques

Rev.Bibl.Arch.Mus.Ayuntamiento Revista de la Biblioteca, Archivo y Museo del Ayuntamiento

Rev.Bibliogr.Nac. Revista de Bibliografía Nacional

Rev.Biblique Revue Biblique

Rev.Bleue Revue Bleue, Politique et Littéraire

Rev.Bourgogne Revue de Bourgogne

Rev.Brasil.Geogr. Revista Brasileira da Geografia

Rev.Brasil.Hist.Med. Revista Brasileira de Historia da Medicina

Rev.Bretonne Bot. Revue Bretonne de Botanique Pure et Appliquée

Rev.Can.Biol. Revue Canadienne de Biologie

Rev.Cath.Idées Faits La Revue Catholique des Idées et des Faits Bruxelles

Rev.Celtique Revue Celtique

Rev.Centro Estud.Hist.Granada Reino Revista del Centro de Estudios Historicos de Granada y su Reino

Rev.Cercle Alumni Fondation Univ.Belg. Revue du Cercle des Alumni de la Fondation Universitaire de Belgique

Rev.Chilena Hist.Geogr. Revista Chilena de Historia y Geografía [Sociedad Chilena de Historia y Geografía]

Rev.Chir. Revue de Chirurgie

Rev.Ciba Revue Ciba

Rev.Cienc. (Lima) Revista de Ciencias. Órgano de la Facultad de Ciencias Biológicas, Fisicas y Matemáticas de la Universidad Mayor de San Marcos

Rev.Clin.São Paulo Revista Clinica de São Paulo

Rev.Clube Eng. Revista do Clube de Engenharia

Rev.Colomb.Antropol. Revista Colombiana de Antropología: organo del Instituto Colombiano de Antropología

Rev.Colon.Belg. La Revue Coloniale Belge

Rev.Cons.Écon.Wallon Revue du Conseil Économique Wallon [Belgium]

Rev.Cours Conf. Revue des Cours et Conférences

Rev.Deux Mondes Revue des Deux Mondes [formerly *La Revue*]

Rev.Dix-Huitième Siècle Revue du Dix-Huitième Siècle [Société du Dix-Huitième Siècle, France]

Rev.Écon.Int. Revue Économique Internationale

Rev.Econ.Stat. Review of Economic Statistics, *afterwards* Review of Economics and Statistics

Rev.Égypte Ancienne Revue de l'Égypte Ancienne

Rev.Égyptologie Revue d'Égyptologie

Rev.Engl.Stud. Review of English Studies

Rev.Espan.Estomatologia Revista Española de Estomatologia

Rev.Ethnogr.Sociol. Revue d'Ethnographie et de Sociologie

Rev.Étud.Anciennes Revue des Études Anciennes

Rev.Étud.Arméniennes Revue des Études Arméniennes

Rev.Étud.Grec. Revue des Études Grecques

Rev.Étud.Islamiques Revue des Études Islamiques

Rev.Étud.Juives Revue des Études Juives: publication de la Société des Études Juives

Rev.Étud.Lat. Revue des Études Latines: publiée par la Société des Études Latines

Rev.Étud.Roumaines Revue des Études Roumaines [Institut Universitaire Roumain Charles 1er]

Rev.Fac.Cienc.Quím.Univ.Nac.La Plata Revista de la Facultad de Ciencias Químicas, Universidad Nacional de La Plata

Rev.Fac.Ciênc.Univ.Coimbra Revista da Faculdade de Ciências, Universidade de Coimbra

Rev.Fac.Hum.Cienc.Univ.Montevideo Revista de la Facultad de Humanidades y Ciencias, Universidad de [la República] Montevideo

Rev.Fac.Ing.Quím.Univ.Nac.Litoral Rosario de Santa Fé Revista de la Facultad de Ingenieria Química, Universidad Nacional del Litoral, Rosario de Santa Fé

Rev.Fac.Let.Univ.Lisboa Revista da Faculdade de Letras, Universidade de Lisboa

Rev.Fac.Quím.Ind.Agr.Univ.Nac.Litoral Rosario de Santa Fé Revista de la Facultad de Química Industrial y Agrícola, Universidad Nacional del Litoral, Rosario de Santa Fé

Rev.Fil. (Bucharest) Revista de Filosofie [Societatea Romana de Filosofie]

Rev.Filol.Españ. Revista de Filología Española [Centro de Estudios Históricos; Junta para Ampliacion de Estudios e Investigaciones Cientificas]

Rev.Franç.Bijout.Horlogers Revue Française des Bijoutiers-Horlogers

Rev.Franç.Élite Europé. Revue Française de l'Élite Européene

Rev.France La Revue de France

Rev.Franco-Belge Revue Franco-Belge

Rev.Fundatiilor Regale Revista Fundatiilor Regale

Rev.Gastroenterol. Review of Gastroenterology

Rev.Gén.Appl.Ind. Revue Générale des Applications Industrielles

Rev.Gén.Belge Revue Générale Belge

Rev.Gén.Bot. Revue Générale de Botanique

Rev.Gén.Élec. Revue Générale de l'Électricité

Rev.Gén.Sci. Revue Générale des Sciences Pures et Appliquées

Rev.Geogr.Colon.Merc. Revista de Geografia Colonial y Mercantil [Real Sociedad Geográfica de Madrid]

Rev.Géogr.Com. Revue de Géographie Commerciale

Rev.Géogr.Hum.Ethnol. Revue de Géographie Humaine et d'Ethnologie

Rev.Ger. Revue Germanique

Rev.Hébd. Revue Hébdomadaire

Rev.Hébd.Laryngol. Revue Hébdomadaire de Laryngologie, d'Otologie et de Rhinologie

Rev.Hispanique Revue Hispanique [Hispanic Society of America]

Rev.Hist. Revue Historique

Rev.Hist. (São Paulo) Revista de Historia [São Paulo]

Rev.Hist.Amér. Revista de Historia de América [Instituto Panamericano de Geografía e Historia, Mexico]

Rev.Hist.Amér.Franç. Revue d'Histoire de l'Amérique Française

Rev.Hist.Colon.Franç. Revue de l'Histoire des Colonies Françaises

Rev.Hist.Doctrinale Litt.Moyen Âge Revue d'Histoire Doctrinale et Littéraire du Moyen Âge

Rev.Hist.Ecclésiastique Revue d'Histoire Ecclésiastique

Rev.Hist.Écon.Soc. Revue d'Histoire Économique et Sociale

Rev.Hist.Église France Revue d'Histoire de l'Église de France [Société d'Histoire Ecclésiastique de la France]

Rev.Hist.Litt.Relig. Revue d'Histoire et de Littérature Religieuses

Rev.Hist.Lyon Revue d'Histoire de Lyon: études, documents, bibliographie

Rev.Hist.Méd.Hébraique Revue d'Histoire de la Médecine Hébraique

Rev.Hist.Mod. Revue d'Histoire Moderne

Rev.Hist.Pharm. Revue d'Histoire de la Pharmacie

Rev.Hist.Phil. Revue d'Histoire de la Philosophie (et d'Histoire Générale de la Civilization) [Faculté des Lettres de l'Université de Lille]

Rev.Hist.Relig. Revue de l'Histoire des Religions [Museé Guimet, Paris]

Rev.Hist.Sci. Revue d'Histoire des Sciences et de leurs Applications: organe de la Section d'Histoire des Sciences, Centre International de Synthèse

Rev.Hist.Sidérurg. Revue d'Histoire de la Sidérurgie

Rev.Hist.Sud-Est Europé. Revue Historique du Sud-Est Européen

Rev.Hist.Vaudoise Revue Historique Vaudoise [Société Vaudoise d'Histoire et d'Archéologie]

Rev.Hittite Asianique Revue Hittite et Asianique

Rev.Hommes Mondes Revue des Hommes et des Mondes

Rev.Hort. Revue Horticole

Rev.Hort.Belg. Revue de l'Horticulture Belge et Étrangère

Rev.Idées Revue des Idées

Rev.Inform.Terap. Revista de Información Terapéutica

Rev.Inst.Antropol.Univ.Nac.Tucumán Revista del Instituto de Antropologia, Universidad de Tucumán

Rev.Inst.Archeol.Hist.Geogr.Pernambucano Revista do Instituto Archeologico, Historico e Geografico Pernambucano

Rev.Inst.Egipcio Estud.Islamicos Revista. Instituto Egipcio de Estudios Islamicos

Rev.Inst.Etnol.Nac. Revista de Instituto Etnologico Nacional

Rev.Inst.Int.Statist. Revue de l'Institut International de Statistique

Rev.Inst.Sociol. Revue de l'Institut de Sociologie [Université Libre, Brussels]

Rev.Instr.Publique Belg. Revue de l'Instruction Publique en Belgique

Rev.Int.Croix Rouge Revue Internationale de la Croix Rouge

Rev.Int.Enseign. Revue Internationale de l'Enseignement

Rev.Int.Phil. Revue International de Philosophie [Société Belge de Philosophie]

Rev.Int.Sociol. Revue Internationale de Sociologie

Rev.Lang.Vivantes Revue des Langues Vivantes

Rev.Litt.Comp. Revue de Littérature Comparée

Rev.Livre Revue du Livre (et des Bibliothèques)

Rev.Livres Anciens Revue des Livres Anciens: Documents d'Histoire Littéraire, de Bibliographie et de Bibliophilie

Rev.Maritime Revue Maritime

Rev.Mat.Hispano-Amer. Revista Matemática Hispano-Americana [Sociedad Matemática Española]

Rev.Méd. Revue de Médecine

Rev.Méd.Chile Revista Médica de Chile

Rev.Med.Cir.Pract. Revista de Medicina y Cirugia Practicas [Academia Médicó Quereirgica Jerezana, Madrid]

Rev.Méd.Cubana Revista Médica Cubana

Rev.Méd.Franç.Extrême Orient Revue Médicale Française d'Extrême Orient

Rev.Méd.Liège Revue Médicale de Liège

Rev.Méd.Louvain Revue Médicale de Louvain [Faculte de Médecine, Université Catholique, Louvain]

Rev.Méd.Pharm. Revue de Médecine et de Pharmacie. [Bulletin Officiel du Cercle de Médecine et de Pharmacie de l'Université Libre de Bruxelles]

Rev.Méd.Roum. Revue Médicale Roumaine

Rev.Méd.Suisse Romande Revue Médicale de la Suisse Romande

Rev.Méditer. Revue de la Méditerranée

Rev.Mens.Oeuvre Nat.Enfance Revue Mensuelle. Oeuvre National de l'Enfance

Rev.Mét. Revue de Métallurgie

Rev.Metaphys. Review of Metaphysics

Rev.Métaphys.Morale Revue de Métaphysique et de Morale

Rev.Métrol. Revue de Métrologie Pratique (et Légale)

Rev.Mod.Phys. Reviews of Modern Physics

Rev.Mois Revue du Mois

Rev.Monde Musulman Revue du Monde Musulman [Mission Scientifique du Maroc]

Rev.Moyen Âge Lat. Revue du Moyen Âge Latin: études, textes, chronique, bibliographie

Rev.Mus.La Platâ Revista del Museo de La Platâ

Rev.Musicale La Revue Musicale

Rev.Néo-Scolastique Revue Néo-Scolastique de Philosophie

Rev.Neuro-Psiquiat. Revista de Neuro-Psiquiatría

Rev.Nord Revue du Nord [Revue Trimestrielle de l'Université de Lille]

Rev.Nouv. La Revue Nouvelle

Rev.Occidente Revista de Occidente

Rev.Odontol. Revue Odontologique

Rev.Orient Algérie Revue de l'Orient de l'Algérie

Rev.Orient Chrétien Revue de l'Orient Chrétien

Rev.Paludisme Med.Trop. Revue du Paludisme et de Médecine Tropicale

Rev.Paris Revue de Paris

Rev.Pathol.Comp. Revue de Pathologie Comparée

Rev.Pathol.Gén.Comp. Revue de Pathologie Générale et Comparée

Rev.Pathol.Gén.Physiol.Clin. Revue de Pathologie Générale et de Physiologie Clinique [Société de Pathologie Comparée]

Rev.Pensée Juive Revue de la Pensée Juive

Rev.Phil. Revue Philosophique de la France et de l'Étranger

Rev.Phil.Louvain Revue de Philosophie de Louvain

Rev.Philol. Revue de Philologie, de Littérature et d'Histoire Anciennes

Rev.Philomath.Bordeaux Revue philomathique de Bordeaux et du Sud-Ouest

Rev.Pol.Acad.Sci. Review of the Polish Academy of Sciences

Rev.Polit.Parlementaire Revue Politique et Parlementaire

Rev.Polytech. Revue Polytechnique

Rev.Port.Fil. Revista Portuguesa de Filosofia [Faculdade Pontificia de Filosofia, Braga, Portugal]

Rev.Positiviste Int. Revue Positiviste Internationale

Rev.Prat. Revue du Praticien

Rev.Prat.Biol.Appl.Clin.Thérap. Revue Pratique de Biologie Appliquée à la Clinique et à la Thérapeutique

Rev.Produits Chim. Revue des Produits Chimiques

Rev.Psicoanál. Revista de Psicoanálisis

Rev.Psychiat. Revue de Psychiatrie, de Neurologie et d'Hypnologie

Rev.Quest.Hist. Revue des Questions Historiques

Rev.Quest.Sci. Revue des Questions Scientifiques [Société Scientifique de Bruxelles]

Rev.Religion Review of Religion

Rev.Savoisienne Revue Savoisienne [Société Florimontaine d'Annecy]

Rev.Sci. Revue Scientifique: revue rose illustrée

Rev.Sci.Phil.Théol. Revue des Sciences Philosophiques et Théologiques

Rev.Sci.Psychol. Revue des Sciences Psychologiques

Rev.Seizième Siècle Revue du Seizième Siècle [Société des Études Rabelaisiennes]

Rev.Siemens Revue Siemens

Rev.Soc.Mex.Hist.Natur. Revista de la Sociedad Mexicana de Historia Natural

Rev.Soc.Venezolana Hist.Med. Revista de la Sociedad Venezolana de Historia de la Medicina

Rev.Ştiinţ.Adamachi Revista Ştiinţifica 'V. Adamachi'

Rev.Ştiinţ.Med. Revista Ştiinţelor Medicale

Rev.Stomatol. Revue de Stomatologie

Rev.Suisse Méd. Revue Suisse de Médecine

Rev.Suisse Numismatique Revue Suisse de Numismatique

Rev.Syn. Revue de Synthèse: organe du Centre International de Synthèse

Rev.Syn.Hist. Revue de Synthèse Historique

Rev.Tech.Méd. Revue de Technique Médicale

Rev.Théol.Phil. (Lausanne) Revue de Théologie et de Philosophie

Rev.Thom. Revue Thomiste

Rev.Transylvanie Revue de Transylvanie [Astra, Association Littéraire et Scientifique]

Rev.Trav.Acad.Sci.Morales Polit. Revue des Travaux de l'Académie des Sciences Morales et Politiques

Rev.Trim.Can. Revue Trimestrielle Canadienne

Rev.Trim.Cult.Mod.Univ.Nat.Colombia Revista Trimestral de Cultura Moderna, Universidad National Colombia

Rev.Tunisienne Revue Tunisienne

Rev.Union Mat.Argent. Revista de la Unión Matemática Argentina y de la Asociación Física Argentina

Rev.Univ.Bruxelles Revue de l'Université de Bruxelles

Rev.Univ.Católica Perú Revista de la [Pontificia] Universidad Católica del Perú

Rev.Univ.Coímbra Revista da Universidade de Coímbra

Rev.Univ.Lyon Revue de l'Université de Lyon

Rev.Univ.San Carlos Revista de la Universidad de San Carlos [Guatemala]

Rev.Universelle Mines Revue Universelle des Mines

Rev.Zool.Bot.Africaines Revue de Zoologie et de Botanique Africaines

Revue La Revue: littérature, histoire, arts et sciences des deux mondes

Rheinisches Mus.Philol. Rheinisches Museum für Philologie

Rheumatism Rheumatism

Rhode Island Hist. Rhode Island History

Rhodora Rhodora: Journal of the New England Botanical Club

Ric.Sci. Ricerca Scientifica

Riedel Arch. Riedel-Archiv

Riforma Med. Riforma Medica

Rigascher Almanach Rigascher Almanach

Rinascenza Salentina Rinascenza Salentina: revista bimestrale di arti, lettere, scienze

Rinascimento Rinascimento [Centro Nazionale di Studi sul Rinascimento]

Rinascita Rinascita [Centro Nazionale di Studi sul Rinascimento]

Říše Hvězd Říše Hvězd [Česká Společnost Astronomická v Praze]

Riv.Aeron. Rivista Aeronautica

Riv.Antropol. Rivista di Antropologia

Riv.Ateneo Veneto Rivista dell' Ateneo Veneto

Riv.Bibl.Arch. Rivista delle Biblioteche e degli Archivi [Società Bibliografica Italiana]

Riv.Crit.Stor.Fil. Rivista Critica di Storia della Filosofia

Riv.Cult.Mar. Rivista di Cultura Marinara

Riv.Fil. Rivista di Filosofia

Riv.Fis.Mat.Sci.Natur. Rivista di Fisica, Matematica e Scienze Naturali

Riv.Geogr.Ital. Rivista Geografica Italiana... e Bollettino della Società di Studi Geografice e Coloniali in Firenze

Riv.Geogr.Ital.Mem.Geogr. Rivista Geografica Italiana: Memorie Geografiche [Supplemento]

Riv.Indo-Greco-Ital.Filol.Lingua Antichità Rivista Indo-Greco-Italica di filologia, linqua, antichità

Riv.Ing. Rivista di Ingegneria

Riv.Ital. Rivista d'Italia: lettere, scienza, ed arte

Riv.Ital.Sociol. Rivista Italiana di Sociologia

Riv.Ital.Stomatol. Rivista Italiana di Stomatologia

Riv.Livorno Rivista di Livorno: rassegna di attivita municipale a cura del Comune

Riv.Marit. Rivista Marittima [Italy. Ministero della Marina]

Riv.Mat.Univ.Parma Rivista di Matematica della Università di Parma

Riv.Med. Rivista Medica [Rome]

Riv.Med.Bologna Rivista Medica di Bologna

Riv.Med.Clero Rivista Medica per il Clero

Riv.Mil. Rivista Militare

Riv.Osped. Rivista Ospedaliera

Riv.Parassit. Rivista di Parassitologia

Riv.Sanit. Rivista Sanitaria

Riv.Soc.Filol.Frinlana Rivista della Societa Filologica Frinlana

Riv.Stor.Crit.Sci. Rivista di Storia Critica delle Scienze Mediche e Naturali

Riv.Stor.Fil. Rivista di Storia della Filosofia

Riv.Stor.Med. Rivista di Storia della Medicina

Riv.Stor.Sci. Rivista di Storia della Scienze Mediche e Naturali: organo ufficiale della Società Italiana di Storia della Scienze Mediche e Naturali

Riv.Stud.Orient. Rivista degli Studi Orientali

Roads Road Constr. Roads and Road Construction

Rochester Hist. Rochester History [Rochester Public Library, Rochester, N.Y.]

Rochester Hist.Soc.Publ. Rochester Historical Society Publications Fund Series [Rochester, N.Y.]

Rockefeller Inst.Rev. Rockefeller Institute Review

Rodo Kagaku Rodo Kagaku: Journal of Science of Labour [Japan Institute for Science of Labour]

Röm.Quartalschr.Christl.Altertumsk. Römische Quartalschrift für christliche Altertumskunde (und für Kirchengeschichte)

Roentgenpraxis Roentgenpraxis: Diagnostik, Rontgen-, Radium, Lichttherapie

Rohstoffe Tierreichs Die Rohstoffe des Tierreichs

Romagna Romagna: rivista di storia e di lettere

Romana Romana

Romance Philol. Romance Philology [University of California]

Romania Romania: recueil trimestriel consacré à l'étude des langues et des littératures romanes

Romanic Rev. The Romanic Review

Romanische Forsch. Romanische Forschungen

Rotterdamsch Jaarb. Rotterdamsch Jaarboekje

Rozhl.Chir. Rozhledy v Chirurigii

Rozpr.Česk.Akad.Věd Řada Mat.Přírodn.Věd Rozpravy: Československá Akademie Věd: Řada Matematických a Přírodních Věd

Rozpr.Hist.Tow.Nauk Warszawskiego Rozprawy Historyczne Towarzystwa Naukowego Warszawskiego

Rozpr.Polska Akad.Umiejętności Wydz.Filol. Rozprawy: Polska Akademia Umiejętności: Wydział Filologiczny

Rozpr.Polskie Tow.Mat. Rozprawy: Polskie Towarzystwo Matematyczne

Rubber J. Rubber Journal and International Plastics

Ruch Filozof. Ruch Filozoficzny [Polskie Towarzystwo Filozoficzney]

Rūpam Rūpam: an Illustrated Quarterly Journal of Oriental Art

Russ.J.Inorg.Chem. Russian Journal of Inorganic Chemistry [English translation of *Zh.Neorg.Khim*; Chemical Society, London]

Russ.Rev. Russian Review: an American journal devoted to Russia past and present

S

S.Afr.J.Sci. South African Journal of Science

S.Afr.Med.J. South African Medical Journal: Suid-Afrikaanse Tydskrif vir Geneeskunde

S.Afr.Surv.J. South African Survey Journal

S.Atlantic Quart. South Atlantic Quarterly

S.E.T.Struct.Évolut.Tech. S.E.T. Structure et Évolution des Techniques

Saarpfälzische Abhandl.Landes-Volksforsch. Saarpfälzische Abhandlungen zur Landes- und Volksforschung

Sächs.Gärtnerbl. Sächsisches Gärtnerblatt

Saeculum Saeculum. Jahrbuch für Universalgeschichte

St. Bartholomew's Hosp.J. St. Bartholomew's Hospital Journal

Salmon Trout Mag. Salmon and Trout Magazine

Salut Public (Lyon) Le Salut Public [Lyon]

Salzburger Beitr.Paracelsusforsch. Salzburger Beiträge zur Paracelsusforschung

Samlaren Samlaren [Svenska Literatursällskapet]

Sammler Der Sammler

Saturday Rev. (London) Saturday Review

Saturday Rev. (New York) Saturday Review

Sb.Bŭlgarska Akad.Nauk.: Klon Istoriko-Filol.Fil.Obshtestven Sbornik: Bŭlgarska Akademiya na Naukitĕ: Klon Istoriko-filologichen i Filosofsko-obshtestven

Sb.Česk.Společnosti Zeměpisné Sbornik Československé Společnosti Zeměpisné [Bulletin of the Czechoslovak Geographical Society]

Sb.Dějiny Přírodn.Věd Tech. Sborník pro Dějiny Přírodnich Věd a Techniky [Československá Akademie Věd]

Sb.Inst.Inzh.Putei Soobshch. Sbornik Instituta Inzhenerov Putei Soobshcheniia

Sb.Přírodovědecký Sbornik Přírodovědecký

Scalpel Scalpel [Fédération Médicale Belge] [formerly *Scalpel Liége Méd*]

Scalpel (Alpha Epsilon Delta) Scalpel of Alpha Epsilon Delta

Scalpel Liége Méd. Scalpel et Liége Médical [Fédération Médicale Belge]

Sch.Sci. School Science [Central Association of Science and Mathematics Teachers]

Sch.Sci.Math. School Science and Mathematics [Central Association of Science and Mathematics Teachers] [formerly *Sch.Sci.*]

Sch.Sci.Rev. School Science Review: a quarterly magazine for science teachers

Sch.Soc. School and Society

Schering-Kahlbaum Med.Mitt. Schering-Kahlbaum Aktiengesellschaft: Medizinische Mitteilungen

Schlesische Monatsh. Schlesische Monatshefte

Schmerz Narkose Anaesth. Schmerz, Narkose, Anaesthesie

Schola Vita Schola et Vita: Organo de Academia pro Interlingua

Scholastik Scholastik: Vierteljahresschrift für Theologie und Philosophie

Schr.Elsass-Lothringischen Wiss.Ges.Strasbourg. Reihe C Schriften der Elsass-Lothringischen wissenschaftliche Gesellschaft zu Strasburg. Reihe C. Geschichte und Literatur

Schr.Ges.Förder.Wiss.Judentums Schriften der Gesellschaft zur Förderung der Wissenschaft des Judentums

Schr.Goethe Ges. Schriften der Goethe-Gesellschaft

Schr.Königsberger Gelehrten Ges.Geisteswiss Kl. Schriften der Königsberger Gelehrten Gesellschaft:Geisteswissenschaftliche Klasse

Schr.Naturforsch.Ges.Danzig Schriften der Naturforschenden Gesellschaft in Danzig

Schr.Prakt Erzieh. Schriften zur praktischen Erziehungskunde

Schr.Schweiz.Ges.Volksk. Schriften der Schweizerischen Gesellschaft für Volkskunde

Schr.Sekt.Altertumswiss.Deut.Akad.Wiss.Berlin Schriften der Sektion für Altertumswissenschaft der Deutschen Akademie der Wissenschaften zu Berlin

Schr.Strassburger Wiss.Ges.Heidelberg Schriften der Strassburger Wissenschaftlichen Gesellschaft in Heidelberg

Schr.Strassburger Wiss.Ges.Univ.Frankfurt Schriften der Strassburger Wissenschaftlichen Gesellschaft an der Universität Frankfurt

Schr.Ver.Verbr.Naturwiss.Kennt. Schriften des Vereins zur Verbreitung Naturwissenschaftlicher Kenntnisse im Wien

Schr.Verbands Klärung Wünschelrütenfrage Schriften des Verbands zur Klärung der Wünschelrütenfrage

Schr.Wiss.Ges.Strassburg Schriften der Wissenschaftlichen Gesellschaft in Strassburg

Schweiz.Apoth.Zeitung Schweizerische Apotheker Zeitung

Schweiz.Arch.Angew.Wiss.Tech. Schweizer Archiv für angewandte Wissenschaft und Technik

Schweiz.Arch.Volksk. Schweizerisches Archiv für Volkskunde

Schweiz Deut.Geistesleben Die Schweiz im deutschen Geistesleben

Schweiz.Gutenbergmus. Schweizerisches Gutenbergmuseum: Zeitschrift für Buchdruck- und Pressegeschichte, Bibliophilie und Bibliothekwesen [Verein zur Förderung des schweizerischen Gutenbergmuseums]

Schweiz.Hochschulzeitung Schweizerische Hochschulzeitung: Revue Universitaire Suisse: Rivista Universitaria Suizzera

Schweiz.Med.Jahrb. Schweizerisches Medizinisches Jahrbuch

Schweiz.Med.Wochenschr. Schweizerische Medizinische Wochenschrift

Schweiz.Mineral.Petrogr.Mitt. Schweizerische Mineralogische und Petrographische Mitteilungen

Schweiz.Monatsh. Schweizer Monatshefte

Schweiz.Sammler Schweizer Sammler: le collectionneur suisse [Schweizer Bibliophilen-Gesellschaft: Vereinigung Schweizerischer Bibliothekare]

Schweiz.Stud.Geschichtswiss. Schweizer Studien zur Geschichtswissenschaft

Schweiz.Z.Gesch. Schweizerische Zeitschrift für Geschichte

Schweiz.Z.Gesundheitspfl. Schweizerische Zeitschrift für Gesundheitspflege

Schweiz.Z.Hydrol. Schweizerische Zeitschrift für Hydrologie

Schweiz.Z.Pathol.Bacteriol. Schweizerische Zeitschrift für Pathologie und Bacteriologie

Schwenckfeldiana Schwenckfeldiana

Sci.Amer. Scientific American

Sci.Cult. Science and Culture: a monthly journal of natural and cultural sciences published by the Indian Science News Association

Sci.Educ. Science Education [National Association for Research in Science Teaching]

Sci.Fortn. Science Fortnightly

Sci.Hist. Scientiarum Historia

Sci.Med.Ital. Scientia Medica Italica

Sci.Méd.Prat. Science Médicale Pratique et Bulletin de l'Association Professionnelle des Externes et Anciens Externes des Hôpitaux de Paris

Sci.Mod. Science Moderne

Sci.Mon. The Scientific Monthly

Sci.Natur.Bibliogr. Scientiae Naturalis Bibliographia

Sci.News Lett. Science News Letter

Sci.Pap.Coll.Gen.Educ.Tokyo Scientific Papers of the College of General Education. University of Tokyo

Sci.Proc.Roy.Dublin Soc. Scientific Proceedings of the Royal Dublin Society

Sci.Progr. Science Progress

Sci.Religion Science and Religion: a Review of Current Literature and Thought

Sci.Soc. Science and Society

Sci.Teacher Science Teacher [Illinois Association of Chemistry Teachers]

Sci.Tec. Scienza e Tecnica

Sci.Veterum Scientia Veterum. Collana di Studii di Storia della Medicina

Sci.Vita Scienze e la Vita

Science Science: offical organ of the American Association for the Advancement of Science

Sciences Sciences [Association Française pour l'Avancement des Sciences]

Scientia Scientia: rivista di scienza

Scot.Geogr.Mag. Scottish Geographical Magazine [Royal Scottish Geographical Society]

Scot.Hist.Rev. Scottish Historical Review

Scot.Med.J. Scottish Medical Journal

Scotsman The Scotsman

Scr.Biol. Scritti Biologici (Istituto Anatomico di Cagliari)

Scr.Math. Scripta Mathematica: quarterly journal devoted to the philosophy. history and expository treatment of mathematics

Scr.Med. Scripta Medica [Facultatum Medicinae Universitatum Brunensis et Olomucensis, Brno]

Scri.Pontif.Inst.Biblici Scripta Pontificii Instituti Biblici

Scribner's Mag. Scribner's Magazine

Scriptorium Scriptorium: Revue internationale des études relatives aux manuscrits: International review of manuscript studies

Seara Nova Seara Nova

Sechenov Physiol.J.USSR Sechenov Physiological Journal of the U.S.S.R. [English translation of *Fiziologicheskii Zhurnal SSSR*]

Sefarad Sefarad: Revista de la Escuela de Estudios Hebraicos [Instituto Arias Montana, Madrid]

Selec.Chim. Selecta chímica. Boletim da Associação dos ex-alunos de química da Faculdade de Filosofia, Ciências e Letras da Universidade de São Paulo

Sem.Dent. Semaine Dentaire

Sem.Hôp.Inform. Semaine des Hôpitaux Informations [Association d'Enseignemenet Médical des Hôpitaux de Paris]

Sem.Hôp.Paris Semaine des Hôpitaux de Paris

Sem.Méd. La Semaine Médicale

Semana Méd. Semana Médica

Senckenbergiana Senckenbergiana [Senckenbergische Naturforschende Gesellschaft, Frankfurt a.M]

Shell Mag. Shell Magazine: the house organ of the Shell Group of Oil Companies

Shigaku Zasshi Shigaku Zasshi (Zeitschrift für Geschichtswissenschaft)

Shinjlekh Ukhaan Tekhnik Shinjlekh Ukhaan Tekhnik

Shisô Shisô

Sibrium Sibrium. Collana di Studi e Documentazioni [Centro di Studi Preistorici e Archeologici. Civici Musei di Varese]

Sicilia Med. Sicilia Medica

Sierra Club Bull. Sierra Club Bulletin

Sigma Xi Quart. Sigma Xi Quarterly (Society of the Sigma Xi)

Simon Stevin Simon Stevin: Wis- en Natuurkundig Tijdschrift

Sinica Sinica: Zeitschrift für Chinakunde und Chinaforschung

Sinica Franciscana Sinica Franciscana

Sinologica Sinologica

Sirius Sirius

Sitzungsber.Abhandl.Flora Sächs.Ges.Bot. Sitzungsberichte und Abhandlungen "Flora", Sächsische Gesellschaft für Botanik und Gartenbau [Dresden]

Sitzungsber.Abhandl.Naturforsch.Ges.Rostock Sitzungsberichte und Abhandlungen der Naturforschenden Gesellschaft zu Rostock

Sitzungsber.Abhandl.Naturwiss.Ges.Isis Bautzen Sitzungsberichte und Abhandlungen der Naturwissenschaftlichen Gesellschaft Isis zu Bautzen

Sitzungsber.Abhandl.Naturwiss.Ges.Isis Dresden Sitzungsberichte und Abhandlungen der Naturwissenschaftlichen Gesellschaft 'Isis' in Dresden

Sitzungsber.Akad.Wiss.Wien Math.Naturwiss.Kl. Sitzungsberichte der Akademie der Wissenschaften in Wien: Mathematisch-naturwissenschaftliche Klasse

Sitzungsber.Akad.Wiss.Wien Phil.Hist.Kl. Sitzungsberichte der Akademie der Wissenschaften in Wien: Philosophisch-historische Klasse

Sitzungsber.Bayer.Akad.Wiss.Math.Naturwiss.Abt. Sitzungsberichte der mathematisch-naturwissenschaftlichen Abteilung der Bayerischen Akademie der Wissenschaften [zu München]

Sitzungsber.Bayer.Akad.Wiss.Math.Naturwiss.Kl. Sitzungsberichte der Bayerischen Akademie der Wissenschaften: Mathematisch-naturwissenschaftliche Klasse

Sitzungsber.Bayer.Akad.Wiss.Math.Phys.Kl. Sitzungsberichte der mathematisch-physikalischen Klasse der [Königlich] Bayerischen Akademie der Wissenschaften [zu München]

Sitzungsber.Bayer.Akad.Wiss.Phil.Hist.Abt. Sitzungsberichte der Bayerischen Akademie der Wissenschaften zu München: Philosophisch-historische Abteilung

Sitzungsber.Bayer.Akad.Wiss.Phil.Philol.Hist.Kl. Sitzungsberichte der Bayerischen Akademie der Wissenschaften: Philosophisch-philologische und historische Klasse

Sitzungsber.Berliner Math.Ges. Sitzungsberichte der Berliner Mathematischen Gesellschaft

Sitzungsber.Deut.Akad.Wiss.Kl.Phil.Gesch. Sitzungsberichte der Deutschen Akademie der Wissenschaften zu Berlin: Klasse für Philosophie, Geschichte, Staats-,Rechts- und Wirtschaftswissenschaften

Sitzungsber.Deut.Akad.Wiss.Kl.Sprachen Lit.Kunst Sitzungsberichte der Deutschen Akademie der Wissenschaften zu Berlin: Klasse für Sprachen, Literatur, und Kunst

Sitzungsber.Deut.Akad.Wiss.Math.Naturwiss.Kl. Sitzungsberichte der Deutschen Akademie der Wissenschaften: Mathematisch-naturwissenschaftliche Klasse

Sitzungsber.Deut.Akad.Wiss.Phil.Hist.Kl. Sitzungsberichte der Deutschen Akademie der Wissenschaften: Philosophisch-historische Klasse

Sitzungsber.Ges.Beförd.Naturwiss.Marburg Sitzungsberichte der Gesellschaft zur Beförderung der gesamten Naturwissenschaften zu Marburg

Sitzungsber.Ges.Naturforsch.Freunde Berlin Sitzungsberichte der Gesellschaft Naturforschender Freunde zu Berlin

Sitzungsber.Heidelb.Akad.Wiss.Math.Naturwiss.Kl. Sitzungsberichte der Heidelberger Akademie der Wissenschaften: Mathematisch-naturwissenschaftliche Klasse

Sitzungsber.Heidelb.Akad.Wiss.Math.Naturwiss.Kl.Abt.A Math. Phys.Wiss. Sitzungsberichte der Heidelberger Akademie der Wissenschaften: Mathematisch-naturwissenschaftliche Klasse; Abt. A - Mathematisch-physikalische Wissenschaften

Sitzungsber.Heidelb.Akad.Wiss.Math.Naturwiss.Kl.Abt.B Biol. Wiss. Sitzungsberichte der Heidelberger Akademie der Wissenschaften: Mathematisch-naturwissenschaftliche Klasse; Abt. B - Biologische Wissenschaften

Sitzungsber.Heidelb.Akad.Wiss.Phil.Hist.Kl. Sitzungsberichte der Heidelberger Akademie der Wissenschaften: Philosophisch-historische Klasse

Sitzungsber.Oesterr.Akad.Wiss.Phil.Hist.Kl. Sitzungsberichte der Österreichischen Akademie der Wissenschaften: Philosophisch-historische Klasse

Sitzungsber.Phys.Med.Ges.Würzburg Sitzungsberichte der Physikalisch-medizinischen Gesellschaft zu Würzburg

Sitzungsber.Phys.Med.Soz.Erlangen Sitzungsberichte der Physikalisch-medizinischen Sozietät in Erlangen

Sitzungsber.Preuss.Akad.Wiss. Sitzungsberichte der [Königlich] Preussischen Akademie der Wissenschaften

Sitzungsber.Preuss.Akad.Wiss.Phil.Hist.Kl. Sitzungsberichte der Preussischen Akademie der Wissenschaften: Philosophisch-historische Klasse

Sitzungsber.Preuss.Akad.Wiss.Phys.Math.Kl. Sitzungsberichte der Preussischen Akademie der Wissenschaften: Physikalisch-mathematische Klasse

Skr.Danske Vidensk.Selsk.Hist.Phil.Afd. [Kongelige] Danske Videnskabernes Selskabs Skrifter: Historisk og philosophisk Afdeling

Skr.Norsk Polarinst. Skrifter om Norsk Polarinstitutt

Skr.Norske Vidensk.Akad.Hist.Fil.Kl. Skrifter utgitt av det Norske Videnskaps-Akademie i Oslo, Historisk-Filosofisk Klasse

Skr.Norske Vidensk.Akad.Mat.Natur.Kl. Skrifter utgitt av det Norske Videnskaps-Akademie i Oslo, Matematisk Naturvidenskabelig Klasse

Skr.Svenska Linné-Sällsk. Skrifter utgivna av Svenska Linné-Sällskapet [Uppsala]

Sky Telesc. Sky and Telescope

Slavonic East Europe.Rev. The Slavonic and East European Review

Slovanska Knihověda Slovanska Knihověda [Československá Společnost Knihovědná]

Smithsonian Contrib.Astrophys. Smithsonian Contributions to Astrophysics

Smithsonian Misc.Collect. Smithsonian Miscellaneous Collections [Smithsonian Institution, Washington, D.C.]

Smithsonian Rep. Smithsonian Report on the Progress and Condition of the United States National Museum [Smithsonian Institution, Washington, D.C.]

Soc.Forces Social Forces [University of North Carolina]

Soc.Ital.Progr.Sci. Società Italiano per il Progresso delle Scienze

Soc.Ital.Stor.Sci.Med.Natur.Congr.Naz. Società Italiana di Storia delle Scienze Mediche e Naturali: Congresso Nazionale

Soc.Res. Social Research [Graduate Faculty of Political and Social Science, New School for Social Research, New York]

Soc.Sci.Abstr. Social Science Abstracts

Soc.Sci.Fenn.Årsbok Societas Scientiarum Fennica Årsbok

Società Società

Sociol.Rev. Sociological Review: Journal of the Sociological Society

Sociometry Sociometry: a Journal of Inter-personal Relations

Soil Conserv. Soil Conservation [U.S. Department of Agriculture, Soil Conservation Service]

Sophia Sophia: Rivista internazionale di fonti e studi di storia della filosofia

Sotsialist.Rekonstruktsiia Nauk. Sotsialisticheskaia Rekonstruktsiia i Nauka

Sound Sound: its Uses and Control

Southern Med.J. Southern Medical Journal

Southwest.Hist.Quart. Southwestern Historical Quarterly [Texas State Historical Association]

Southwest.J.Anthropol. Southwestern Journal of Anthropology

Southwest.Lore Southwestern Lore

Southwest Rev. Southwest Review

Southwest.Soc.Sci.Quart. Southwestern Social Science Quarterly

Sovet.Arkheol. Sovetskaya Arkheologiya

Sovet.Geol. Sovetskaia Geologiia

Sovet.Vostokovedenie Sovetskoe Vostokovedenie [Institut Vostokovedenia, Akademiia Nauk SSSR]

Sovet.Zdravookhr. Sovetskoe Zdravookhranenie

Soviet Phys.Solid State Soviet Physics: Solid State [English translation of *Fiz.Tverd.Tela*]

Soviet Phys.Usp. Soviet Physics: Uspekhi [English translation of *Usp.Fiz.Nauk*]

Soviet Stud.Phil. Soviet Studies in Philosophy

Soz.Med. Soziale Medizin

Spanische Forsch.Ser.1 Spanische Forschungen der Görres gesellschaft. Series 1

Spec.Libr. Special Libraries

Spec.Libr.Ass.Geogr.Map Div.Bull. Special Libraries Association Geography and Map Division Bulletin

Speculum Speculum: a journal of mediaeval studies

Sperimentale Sperimentale [Archivio di Biologia Normale e Patologica, Firenze]

Sperry Eng.Rev. Sperry Engineering Review

Sphinx (Brussels) Sphinx. Revue Mensuelle des Questions Récréatives

Sphinx Oedipe Sphinx Oedipe

Spisy Vydávané Přirodovědeckou Fak.Karlovy Univ. Spisy Vydávané Přirodovědeckou Fakultôu Karlovy University [Praha]

Ssu Hsiang Yü Shih Tai Ssu Hsiang Yü Shih Tai: Thought and Time [Ssu Hsiang Yü Shih Tai Yueh K'an She, Tai-pei]

Stader Jahrb. Stader Jahrbuch [Stader Geschichts- und Heimatverein]

Stadt Hafen Duisburg Stadt und Hafen Duisburg

Stahl Eisen Stahl und Eisen. Zeitschrift für das deutsche Eisenhüttenwesen

Stanford Illus.Rev. Stanford Illustrated Review [Stanford University, Calif.]

Stanford Med.Bull. Stanford Medical Bulletin [Stanford Medical Alumni Association]

State Hosp.Quart. State Hospitals Quarterly [New York State Hospital Commission]

Stechert-Hafner Book News Stechert-Hafner Book News

Stemmen Tijds. Stemmen des Tijds

Sterne Die Sterne

Stevens Indic. Stevens Indicator [Stevens Institute of Technology, Hoboken, N.J.]

Stimmen Maria Laach Stimmen aus Maria-Laach. Katholische Monatsschrift

Stirpe La Stirpe [Confederazione delle Corporazioni Sindacali Fasciste]

Stomatologija Stomatologija

Stor.Religioni Storia delle Religioni

Strahlentherapie Strahlentherapie

Strasbourg Méd. Strasbourg Médical

Strědni Škol. Strědni Škola

Struct.Évolut.Tech. Structure et Évolution des Techniques (S.E.T.)

Stud.Bauforsch. Studien zur Bauforschung [Koldewey Gesellschaft]

Stud.Cl. Studii Clasice

Stud.Colombiani Studi Colombiani

Stud.Darstell.Geb.Gesch. Studien und Darstellung aus dem Gebiete der Geschichte

Stud.Gen. Studium Generale

Stud.Graeca Lat.Gothoburgensia Studia Graeca et Latina Gothoburgensia [Klassiska Institutionen K. Universitet i Göteborg]

Stud.Hist.Ideas Studies in the History of Ideas [Department of Philosophy, Columbia University]

Stud.Hyderabad Acad. Hyderabad Academy Studies

Stud.Islamica Studia Islamica

Stud.Ital.Filol.Cl. Studi Italiani di Filologia Classica

Stud.Mater.Dziej.Nauk.Pol. Studia i Materiały z Dziejów Nauki Polskiej [Polska Akademia Nauk: Komitet Historii Nauki]

Stud.Mater.Dziej.Nauk.Pol., ser.A Studia i Materiały z Dziejów Nauki Polskiej, seria A: Historia Nauk Społecznych [Polska Akademia Nauk: Komitet Historii Nauki]

Stud.Mater.Dziej.Nauk.Pol., ser.B Studia i Materiały z Dziejów Nauki Polskiej, seria B: Historia Nauk Biologicznych i Medycznych [Polska Akademia Nauk: Komitet Historii Nauki]

Stud.Mater.Dziej.Nauk.Pol., ser.C Studia i Materiały z Dziejów Nauki Polskiej, seria C: Historia Nauk Matematycznych, Fizyko-chemicznych i Geologo-geograficznych [Polska Akademia Nauk: Komitet Historii Nauki]

Stud.Mater.Dziej.Nauk.Pol., ser.D Studia i Materiały z Dziejów Nauki Polskiej, seria D: Historia Techniki i Nauk Technicznych [Polska Akademia Nauk: Komitet Historii Nauki]

Stud.Mater.Dziej.Nauk.Pol., ser.E Studia i Materiały z Dziejów Nauki Polskiej, seria E: Zagadnienia Ogólne [Zakład Historii Nauki i Techniki Polskiej Akademii Nauk]

Stud.Medievali Studi Medievali

Stud.Mem.Stor.Univ.Bologna. Studi e Memorie per la Storia dell' Università di Bologna

Stud.Mitt.Gesch.Benediktinerordens Studien und Mitteilungen zur Geschichte des Benediktinerordens und seiner Zweige

Stud.Neophilol. Studia Neophilologica

Stud.Orient. Studia Orientalia [Societas Orientalis Fennica]

Stud.Philol. Studies in Philology

Stud.Renaiss. Studies in the Renaissance [Renaissance Society of America]

Stud.Romantic. Studies in Romanticism

Stud.Semitica Orient. Studia Semitica et Orientalia [Glasgow University Oriental Society]

Stud.Spätantik.Kunstgesch. Studien zur spätantiken Kunstgeschichte [Archäologisches Institut des Deutschen Reiches]

Stud.Sprog- Oldtidsforsk. Studier fra Sprog- og Oldtidsforskning utgivne af det Philologisk-historiske Samfund

Stud.Stor. Studi Storici.

Stud.Testi Studi e Testi [Biblioteca Vaticana]

Stud.Trentini Sci.Natur. Studi Trentini di Scienze Naturali

Stud.Univ.Babeş-Bolyai Ser.Math.Phys. Studia Universitatis Babeş-Bolyai, I: Series Mathematica-Physica [Universitate din Cluj]

Stud.Voltaire Studies on Voltaire and the 18th Century [Institut et Musée Voltaire, Genève]

Studio The Studio: an illustrated magazine of fine and applied art

Stultifera Navis Stultifera Navis: Mitteilungsblatt der Schweizerischen Bibliophilen-Gesellschaft: Bulletin de la Société Suisse des Bibliophiles

Sudan Notes Rec. Sudan Notes and Records

Sudetendeut.Z.Volksk. Sudetendeutsche Zeitschrift für Volkskunde

Sudhoffs Arch. Sudhoffs Archiv für Geschichte der Medizin [und der Naturwissenschaften]

Süddeut.Monatsh. Süddeutsche Monatshefte

Südostdeut.Forsch. Südostdeutsche Forschungen

Suisse Horlogère La Suisse Horlogère [Federation Horlogère Suisse]

Sum.Theses Degree Doctor Phil.Harvard Coll. Summaries of Theses for the Degree of Doctor of Philosophy, Harvard College

Sumer Sumer: a Journal of Archaeology in Iraq

Suppl.Annu.Encicl.Chim.Sci.Ind. Supplemento Annuale alla Enciclopedia di Chimica Scientifica e Industriale

Surg.Gynecol.Obstet. Surgery, Gynecology and Obstetrics

Svensk Bot.Tidskr. Svensk Botanisk Tidskrift

Svensk Farm.Tidskr. Svensk Farmaceutisk Tidskrift

Svensk Geogr.Årsbok Svensk Geografisk Årsbok: Swedish Geographical Yearbook [Sydsvenska Geografiska Sällskapet i Lund]

Svenska Boktryckarefören.Medd. Svenska Boktryckareföreningens Meddelanden

Svenska Läkartidn. Svenska Läkartidningen

Svenska Linné-Sällsk.Årsskr. Svenska Linné-Sällskapets Årsskrift

Svenska Vetenskapsakad.Årsbok [Kungliga] Svenska Vetenskapsakademiens Årsbok

Symbolae Osloenses Symbolae Osloenses [Societas Graeco-Latina: Klassisk Forening]

Symbolae Osloenses Fasc.Suppl. Symbolae Osloenses Fascicule Supplement [Societas Graeco-Latina: Klassisk Forening]

Symbolae Philol.Gotoburgenses Symbolae Philologicae Gotoburgenses

Symp.Int.Sci.Phys.Math.XVIIe Siècle Symposium International des Sciences Physiques et Mathématiques dans la Première Moitié du 17e Siècle

Symposion Symposion: Jahrbuch für Philosophie

Symposion (Erlangen) Symposion: philosophische Zeitschrift für Forschung und Aussprache

Symposium Symposium: a journal devoted to modern foreign languages and literatures [Syracuse University, N.Y.]

Synthèse Synthèse [Paris]

Synthese Synthese: an international quarterly for the logical and the psychological study of the foundations of science

Synthèses Synthèses

Syria Syria

Syst.Zool. Systematic Zoology

T

TAPPI Publ.Tech.Assoc.Pulp Pap.Ind. TAPPI: Publications of the Technical Association of the Pulp and Paper Industry

TIC TIC [Ticonium Company, CMP Industries, Albany, N.Y.]

Table Ronde La Table Ronde

Tablettes Connaissance Tablettes de la Connaissance

Tabulae Anat. Tabulae Anatomicae

Tabulae Biol. Tabulae Biologicae

Tätigkeitsber.Museumsges.Teplitz-Schönau Tätigkeitsberichte der Museumsgesellschaft in Teplitz-Schönau

Tageszeitung Brau. Tageszeitung für Brauerei, Mälzerei, Hopfenhandel, Brauerei- und Kellereimaschinenindustrie [Verein Versuchs- und Lehranstalt für Brauerei]

Talpioth Talpioth [New York]

Tamuda Tamuda: Revista de investigaciones marroquíes [Delegación de Educación y Cultura, Alta Comisaría de España en Marruecos]

Tarbiz Tarbiz: a quarterly review of the humanities [Jewish National and University Library, Jerusalem]

Tarih Dergisi Tarih Dergisi [Edebiyat Fakültesi, Beyazit, Istanbul University]

Teacher Educ.Quart. Teacher Education Quarterly

Teachers' Coll.Rec. Teachers' College Record

Tech The Tech: Engineering News. The Professional Journal of the Alumni and Undergraduates of the Massachusetts Institute of Technology

Tech.Civilisations Techniques et Civilisations

Tech.Kult. Technik und Kultur

Tech.Monatsh. Technische Monatshefte

Tech.Rundsch. Technische Rundschau

Tech.Stud.Fine Arts Technical Studies in the Field of the Fine Arts [William Hays Fogg Art Museum, Harvard University]

Tech.Wetensch.Tijdschr. Technisch Wetenschappelijk Tijdschrift en Ingenieurs Tijdingen

Tech.Yearbook Technion Yearbook [American Technion Society]

Technikgeschichte Technikgeschichte

Technisch-Wetensch.Tijdschr. Technisch-wetenschappelijk Tijdschrift en Ingenieurs Tijdingen

Technol.Cult. Technology and Culture

Technol.Rev. Technology Review

Technos Technos

Tedavi Klin.Laboratuvari Tedavi Kliniği ve Laboratuvari

Tekh.Ėkon.Vestnik Tekhniko-Ėkonomicheskiĭ Vestnik [Biuro Inostrannoĭ Nauki i Tekhniki]

Tekh.Prom.Khoz. Tekhnika i Promyshlennoe Khoziaistvo [Biuro Inostrannoĭ Nauki i Tekhniki v Berline]

Telescope The Telescope: a quarterly review of the progress of astronomy

Temmon Geppô Temmon Geppô; Astronomical Herald [Astronomical Society of Japan]

Temps Le Temps [Newspaper]

Tenger Tenger: Népszerű folyóirat a tengerre vonatkozó ismeretek terjesztésére [Magyar Adria Egyesület]

Terre, Air, Mer Terre, Air, Mer: La Géographie

Terre Hommes Terre des Hommes

Terrest.Magnet.Atmos.Elec. Terrestrial Magnetism and Atmospheric Electricity

Tetrahedron Tetrahedron: International Journal of Organic Chemistry

Tetrahedron Suppl. Tetrahedron Supplement

Tex.Geogr.Mag. Texas Geographic Magazine [Texas Geographic Society]

Tex.J.Sci. Texas Journal of Science

Tex.Quart. Texas Quarterly

Tex.Rep.Biol.Med. Texas Reports on Biology and Medicine

Tex.Water Comm.Circ. Texas Water Commission. Circular

Texte Commun.Congr.Mond.Doc.Universelle Texte des Communications, Congrès Mondial de la Documentation Universelle

Texte Untersuch.Gesch.Altchristl.Lit. Texte und Untersuchungen zur Geschichte der Altchristlichen Literatur

Texts Stud.Jew.Theological Seminar.Amer. Texts and Studies of the Jewish Theological Seminary of America

Thalès Thalès: Recueil annuel des travaux de l'Institut d'Histoire des Sciences et des Techniques de l'Université de Paris

Theol.Lit.Zeitung Theologische Literaturzeitung

Theol.Today Theology Today

Theol.Z. Theologische Zeitschrift [Universität Basel: Theologische Fakultät]

Theoria Theoria: Tidskrift för filosofi och psykologi

Therap.Ber. Therapeutische Berichte

Think Think: a spotlight on new things and thoughts

Thomist The Thomist: a speculative quarterly review

Thomist Reader The Thomist Reader [Dominican Fathers of the Province of St. Joseph]

Thüringisch-Sächsische Z.Gesch.Kunst Thüringisch-Sächsische Zeitschrift für Geschichte und Kunst

Tib Dünyasi Tib Dünyasi

Tidskr.Elem.Mat.Fys.Kem. Tidskrift för Elementär Matematik, Fysik och Kemi

Tidsskr.Ind. Tidsskrift for Industri

Tidsskr.Sygeplejersker Tidsskrift for Sygeplejersker

Tierärztl.Zentralbl. Tierärztliches Zentralblatt

Tierseele Tierseele. Zeitschrift für vergleichende Seelenkunde

Tijdschr.Belg.Ver.Aardrijksk.Stud. Tijdschrift van de Belgische Vereenigung voor Aardrijkskundige Studies

Tijdschr.Econ.Geogr. Tijdschrift voor Economische Geographie

Tijdschr.Entomol. Tijdschrift voor Entomologie

Tijdschr.Gesch. Tijdschrift voor Geschiednis

Tijdschr.Indische Taal Land Volkenk. Tijdschrift voor Indische Taal-Land- en Volkenkunde

Tijdschr.Ned.Aardrijksk.Genoot. Tijdschrift van het (Koninklijk) Nederlandsch Aardrijkskundig Genootschap

Tijdschr.Ned.Taal- Letterk. Tijdschrift voor Nederlandsche Taal- en Letterkunde

Tijdschr.Phil. Tijdschrift voor Philosophie

Tijdschr.Stad Antwerpen Tijdschrift der Stad Antwerpen

Tijdschr.Vergelijkende Geneesk. Tijdschrift voor vergelijkende geneeskunde

Times(London) The Times [London]

Times Educ.Suppl. Times Educational Supplement

Times Lit.Suppl. Times Literary Supplement

Times Sci.Rev. The Times Science Review

Timotheus Timotheus

Toerist De Toerist: halfmaandelijks orgaan van de Vlaamse Toeristen-Bond

Tôho Gakuhô(Kyoto) Tôhô Gakuhô: Journal of Oriental Studies

Tôhoku Math.J. The Tôhoku Mathematical Journal [Tôhoku Imperial University]

Tōkyō Sūgaku-butsurigakukwaiv kizi Tōkyō Sūgaku-butsurigakukwaiv Kizi: Transactions of the Physico-mathematical Society of Japan

Torreya Torreya [Torrey Botanical Club, Lancaster, Pa.]

T'oung Pao T'oung Pao: Archives concernant l'histoire, les langues, la géographie et l'ethnographie de l'Asie orientale

Tow.Nauk.Scislych Paryzu Tam. Towarzystwo Nauk Scislych w Paryzu: Tamietnik

Town Planning Rev. Town Planning Review

Tôyô-Gakuhô (Tokyo) Tôyô-Gakuhô

Tr.Ark.Akad.Nauk SSSR Trudy Arkhiva Akademiia Nauk SSSR

Tr.Inst.Ist.Est. Trudy Institut Istorii Estestvoznaniia [Akademiia Nauk SSSR]

Tr.Inst.Ist.Est.Tekh. Trudy Institut Istorii Estestvoznaniia i Tekhniki [Akademiia Nauk SSSR]

Tr.Inst.Ist.Nauk.Tekh. Trudy Instituta Istorii Nauki i Tekhniki [Leningrad]

Tr.Inst.Kn. Trudy Instituta Knigi, Dokumenta, Pisma [Akademiia Nauk SSSR]

Tr.Inst.Russ.Lit.Otd.Drevne-Russ.Lit. Trudy Otdela Drevne-russkoi Literatury Instituta Russkoi Literatury [Akademiia Nauk SSSR]

Tr.Inst.Vostokovedeniya Trudy Instituta Vostokovdeniya

Tr.Kom.Ist.Znaniǐ Trudy Komissii po Istorii Znaniǐ [Instītut Īstorīī Naukī Tekhnīkī]

Tr.Prikl.Bot.Genet.Selek. Trudy po Prikladnoǐ Botanikē Genetike i Selektsii

Trab.Cátedra Hist.Crit.Med.Univ.Madrid Trabajos de la Cátedra de Historia Critica de la Medicina, Universidad de Madrid

Traditio Traditio: Studies in ancient and mediaeval history and religion

Tradition Tradition: Zeitschrift für Firmengeschichte und Unternehmerbiographie

Trained Nurse Trained Nurse

Trans.Amer.Acad.Ophthalmol.Oto-laryngol. Transactions of the American Academy of Ophthalmology and Oto-laryngology

Trans.Amer.Climatol.Clin.Ass. Transactions of the American Climatological and Clinical Association

Trans.Amer.Electrochem.Soc. Transactions of the American Electrochemical Society

Trans.Amer.Gynecol.Soc. Transactions of the American Gynecological Society

Trans.Amer.Inst.Elec.Eng. Transactions of the American Institute of Electrical Engineers

Trans.Amer.Neurol.Ass. Transactions of the American Neurological Association

Trans.Amer.Phil.Soc. Transactions of the American Philosophical Society

Trans.Amer.Philol.Ass. Transactions (and Proceedings) of the American Philological Association

Trans.Amer.Soc.Civil Eng. Transactions of the American Society of Civil Engineers

Trans.Ass.Amer.Physicians Transactions of the Association of American Physicians

Trans.Bibliogr.Soc. Transactions of the Bibliographical Society

Trans.Bristol Gloucestershire Archaeol.Soc. Transactions of the Bristol and Gloucestershire Archaeological Society

Trans.Brit.Mycol.Soc. Transactions of the British Mycological Society

Trans.Coll.Physicians Phila. Transactions [and studies] of the College of Physicians of Philadelphia

Trans.Coll.Physicians Surg.Gynaecol.S.Afr. Transactions of the Colleges of Physicians, Surgeons and Gynaecologists of South Africa

Trans.Colon.Soc.Mass. Transactions of the Colonial Society of Massachusetts

Trans.Conf.Cent.Nerv.Syst. Transactions of the Conference on the Central Nervous System and Behavior

Trans.Conn.Acad.Arts Sci. Transactions of the Connecticut Academy of Arts and Sciences

Trans.Edin.Geol.Soc. Transactions of the Edinburgh Geological Society

Trans.Edinb.Obstet.Soc. Transactions of the Edinburgh Obstetrical Society

Trans.Faraday Soc. Transactions of the Faraday Society [London]

Trans.Glasgow Univ.Orient.Soc. Transactions of the Glasgow University Oriental Society

Trans.Highland Agr.Soc.Scot. Transactions of the Highland and Agricultural Society of Scotland

Trans.Ill.Acad.Sci. Transactions of the Illinois State Academy of Science

Trans.Ill.State Hist.Soc. Transactions. Illinois State Historical Society

Trans.Int.Congr.Entomol. Transactions of the International Congress of Entomology

Trans.Int.Numismatic Congr. Transactions of the International Numismatic Congress

Trans.Jew.Hist.Soc.Engl. Transactions of the Jewish Historical Society of England

Trans.Kans.Acad.Sci. Transactions of the Kansas Academy of Science

Trans.Korea Br.Roy.Asiatic Soc. Transactions of the Korea Branch of the Royal Asiatic Society

Trans.Med.Soc.London Transactions of the Medical Society of London

Trans.Med.Soc.State N.Y. Transactions of the Medical Society of the State of New York

Trans.N.Y.Acad.Sci. Transactions of the New York Academy of Sciences

Trans.Newcomen Soc. Transactions of the Newcomen Society

Trans.Opt.Soc. Transactions of the Optical Society

Trans.Proc.Japan Soc. Transactions and Proceedings of the Japan Society

Trans.Roy.Entomol.Soc.London Transactions of the Royal Entomological Society of London

Trans.Roy.Soc.S.Afr. Transactions of the Royal Society of South Africa

Trans.Swedenborg Soc. Transactions of the Swedenborg Society [London]

Trans.Ulster Med.Soc. Transactions of the Ulster Medical Society

Trans.Wis.Acad.Sci.Arts Lett. Transactions of the Wisconsin Academy of Sciences, Arts and Letters

Transilvania Transilvania [Asociatiunea Pentru Literatura Română]

Transylvania Coll.Bull. Transylvania College Bulletin

Trav.Inst.Anat.École Supér.Méd.Indochine Travaux de l'Institut Anatomique, École Supérieure de Médecine de l'Indochine

Trav.Inst.Anat.Fac.Méd.Indochine Travaux de l'Institut Anatomique, Faculté de Médecine de l'Indochine

Trav.Méth. Travail et Méthodes

Travalhos Ass.Arqueólogos Port. Travalhos: Associacão dos Arqueólogos Portugueses

Trinity Coll.Bull. (Hartford) Trinity College Bulletin [Trinity College, Hartford, Conn.]

Trop.Agr. Tropical Agriculture [Imperial College of Tropical Agriculture, Trinidad]

Tsitologiia Tsitologiia

Tübinger Naturwiss.Abhandl. Tübinger Naturwissenschaftliche Abhandlungen: Württembergische Gesellschaft [zur Förderung] der Wissenschaften; Abteilung Tübingen; Naturwissenschaftlich-medizinische Klasse

Türmer Der Türmer [Monatschrift für Gemüt und Geist]

Tufts Med.Alumni Bull. Tufts Medical Alumni Bulletin

Tulane Stud.Phil. Tulane Studies in Philosophy

Tunisie Médicale Tunisie Médicale

Türk Tib Cem.Mecmuasi Türk Tib Cemiyeti Mecmuasi. Bulletin de la Société Turque de Médecine

Türk Tib Tarihi Arkivi Türk Tib Tarihi Arkivi: Archives d'Histoire de la Médecine Turque

Turtox News Turtox News

Typewriter Top. Typewriter Topics

Typographica Typographica

U

U.S.Nav.Med.Bull. United States Naval Medical Bulletin

Uch.Zap.Moskovskogo Gos.Univ. Uchenye Zapiski Moskovskogo Gosudarstevennogo Universiteta

Über Land Meer Über Land und Meer: deutsche illustrierte Zeitschrift

Ugeskr.Laeger Ugeskrift for Laeger [Almindelige Danske Laegeforening]

Uhr Die Uhr: Fachzeitschrift der Deutschen Uhrmacher

Uhrmacherkunst Uhrmacherkunst

Ukrain.Bot.Zh. Ukrayins'kyi Botanichnȳi Zhurnal

Ukrain.Fiz.Zh. Ukrains'kyi Fizychnyi Zhurnal

Ulisse Ulisse

Ulster Med.J. Ulster Medical Journal [Ulster Medical Society, Belfast]

Ulum, see *Al-Ulum*

Umschau Die Umschau

Ungar.Jahrb. Ungarische Jahrbücher

Union Coll.Bull. (Albany N.Y.) Union College Bulletin [Albany N.Y.]

Union Méd.Can. Union Médicale du Canada

Union Méd.Nord-Est Union Médicale (et scientifique) du Nord-Est

Union Méd.Provence Union Médicale de la Provence: organ officiel des sociétés locales des médecins de France

Unitas (Manila) Unitas: Revista de cultura y vida universitaria [Universidad de Manila]

United Asia United Asia

United Synagogue Rec. United Synagogue Recorder

Univ.Calif.Agr.Bull. University of California Agricultural Experiment Station Bulletin

Univ.Calif.Chron. University of California Chronicle

Univ.Calif.Publ.Amer.Archaeol. University of California Publications in American Archaeology and Ethnology

Univ.Calif.Publ.Bot. University of California Publications in Botany

Univ.Calif.Publ.Bull.Dep.Geol. University of California Publications. Bulletin of the Department of Geology

Univ.Calif.Publ.Cl.Philol. University of California Publications in Classical Philology

Univ.Calif.Publ.Egypt.Archaeol. University of California Publications in Egyptian Archaeology

Univ.Calif.Publ.Eng. University of California Publications in English

Univ.Calif.Publ.Math. University of California Publications in Mathematics

Univ.Calif.Publ.Mod.Philol. University of California Publications in Modern Philology

Univ.Calif.Publ.Phil. University of California Publications in Philosophy [Monograph series]

Univ.Calif.Publ.Zool. University of California Publications in Zoology

Univ.Colo.Stud.Ser.A University of Colorado Studies, Series A: General series

Univ.Colo.Stud.Ser.B Universitv of Colorado Studies, Series B: Studies in the humanities

Univ.Edinb.J. University of Edinburgh Journal [University of Edinburgh Alumni Association]

Univ.Ill.Stud.Lang.Lit. University of Illinois Studies in Language and Literature

Univ.Leeds Med.J. University of Leeds Medical Journal

Univ.Manitoba Med.J. University of Manitoba Medical Journal

Univ.Mich.Med.Bull. University of Michigan Medical Bulletin

Univ.Mich.Stud.Hum.Ser. University of Michigan Studies, Humanistic Series

Univ.Missouri Stud. University of Missouri Studies

Univ.Penn.Libr.Chron. University of Pennsylvania Library Chronicle [Friends of the University of Pennsylvania Library]

Univ.Quart. Universities Quarterly

Univ.Rochester Libr.Bull. University of Rochester Library Bulletin

Univ.Toronto Quart. University of Toronto Quarterly

Univ.Virginia Alumni News University of Virginia Alumni News

Univ.Wichita Bull. Municipal University Wichita [Kansas]: University Studies Bulletin

Universitas (Stuttgart) Universitas: Zeitschrift für Wissenschaften, Kunst und Literatur

Universo Universo: pubblicazione dell' Istituto Geografico Militare [Firenze]

Unsere Welt Unsere Welt

Unterrichtsbl.Math.Naturwiss. Unterrichtsblätter für Mathematik und Naturwissenschaften [Verein zur Förderung des mathematischen und naturwissenschaftlichen Unterrichts]

Untersuch.Gesch.Buddhismus Untersuchungen zur Geschichte des Buddhismus

Urania(Jena) Urania: Monatsschrift über Natur und Gesellschaft [Jena]

Urania Soc.Astrôn.Españ. Urania: Revista cientifica [Sociedad Astrônomica de España (y Amêrica)]

Usp.Fiz.Nauk Uspekhi Fizicheskikh Nauk

Usp.Khim. Uspekhi Khimii: Progress in Chemistry [Akademiia Nauk SSSR]

Usp.Mat.Nauk Uspekhi Matematicheskikh Nauk [Akademiia Nauk SSSR, Moskovskoye Matematicheskoye Obshchestvo]

Usp.Prom.Tekh. Uspekhi Promyshlennoĭ Tekhniki

V

Vacuum Vacuum

Vakbl.Biol. Vakblad voor Biologen

Valsalva Valsalva: Rivista mensile di oto-rino-laringo-iatria

Valvoja-Aika Valvoja-Aika

Vassar J.Undergrad.Stud. Vassar Journal of Undergraduate Studies [Vassar College, Poughkeepsie, N.Y.]

Věda Život Věda a Život

Verfkroniek Verfkroniek

Vergangenheit Gegenwart Vergangenheit und Gegenwart

Verhandel.Akad.Wetensch.Afd.Lett. Verhandelingen der Koninklijke Akademie van Wetenschappen [Amsterdam]: Afdeeling Letterkunde

Verhandel.Akad.Wetensch.Afd.Natuur. Verhandelingen der Koninklijke Akademie van Wetenschappen [Amsterdam]: Afdeeling Natuurkunde

Verhandel.Ned.Akad.Wetensch.Afd.Lett. Verhandelingen der [Koninklijke] Nederlandsche Akademie van Wetenschappen: Afdeeling Letterkunde [formerly *Verhandel.Akad.Wetensch.Afd. Natuur.*]

Verhandel.Ned.Akad.Wetensch.Afd.Natuur. Verhandelingen der [Koninklijke] Nederlandsche Akademie van Wetenschappen: Afdeeling Natuurkunde [formerly *Verhandel.Akad.Wetensch.Afd. Natuur.*]

Verhandel.Vlaam.Acad.Geneesk.Belg. Verhandelingen Vlaamse Academie voor Geneeskunde van Belgie

Verhandel.Vlaam.Acad.Wetensch.Lett.Schone Kunsten Belg.Kl. Wetensch. Verhandelingen van de [Koninklijke] Vlaamse Academie voor Wetenschappen, Letteren en Schone Kunsten van België: Klasse der Wetenschappen

Verhandl.Anat.Ges.Jena Verhandlungen der Anatomischen Gesellschaft, Jena

Verhandl.Deut.Pathol.Ges. Verhandlungen der Deutschen Pathologischen Gesellschaft [Jena]

Verhandl.Deut.Phys.Ges.Berlin Verhandlungen der Deutschen Physikalischen Gesellschaft, Berlin

Verhandl.Deut.Wiss.Ver.Santiago Chile Verhandlungen des Deutschen Wissenschaftlichen Vereins zu Santiago de Chile

Verhandl.Ges.Deut.Naturforsch.Aerzte Verhandlungen der Gesellschaft Deutscher Naturforscher und Ärzte

Verhandl.Int.Amerikanisten-Kongr. Verhandlungen des Internationalen Amerikanisten-Kongresses

Verhandl.Int.Math.Kongr. Verhandlungen des Internationalen Mathematiker-Kongresses

Verhandl.Naturforsch.Ges.Basel. Verhandlungen der Naturforschenden Gesellschaft in Basel

Verhandl.Naturforsch.Ver.Brünn Verhandlungen des Naturforschenden Vereins in Brünn

Verhandl.Phys.Med.Ges.Würzb. Verhandlungen der Physikalisch-medizinischen Gesellschaft, Würzburg

Verhandl.Schweiz.Naturforsch.Ges. Verhandlungen der Schweizerischen Naturforschenden Gesellschaft: Actes de la Sociêtê Helvêtique des Sciences Naturelles

Veröffentl.Akad.Wiss.Judentums Veröffentlichungen der Akademie für die Wissenschaft des Judentums

Veröffentl.Ges.Erforsch.Musik Orients Veröffentlichungen der Gesellschaft zur Erforschung der Musik des Orients

Veröffentl.Ges.Typenk.15 Jahrhunderts, Reihe B Veröffentlichungen der Gesellschaft für Typenkunde des 15. Jahrhunderts: Reihe B: Seltene Frühdrucke in Nachbildungen

Veröffentl.Hist.Seminar Univ.Graz Veröffentlichungen des Historischen Seminars der Universität Graz

Veröffentl.Indogermanischen Seminars Univ.Erlangen Veröffentlichungen des Indogermanischen Seminars der Universität Erlangen

Veröffentl.Int.Ges.Gesch.Pharm. Veröffentlichungen der Internationalen Gesellschaft für Geschichte der Pharmazie

Veröffentl.Missionswiss.Inst.Westfälischen Landesuniv.Münster Veröffentlichungen des Missionswissenschaftlichen Instituts der Westfälischen Landesuniversität zu Münster in Westfalen

Veröffentl.Mus.Ferdinandeum Innsbruck Veröffentlichungen des Museums Ferdinandeum in Innsbruck

Veröffentl.Naturwiss.Ver.Osnabrück Veröffentlichungen des Naturwissenschaftlichen Vereins zu Osnabrück

Veröffentl.Remeis-Sternwarte Bamberg Veröffentlichungen der Remeis-Sternwarte zu Bamberg

Veröffentl.Remeis-Sternwarte Bamberg, 2nd ser. Veröffentlichungen der Remeis-Sternwarte zu Bamberg, 2nd series: Astrophysikalische Abteilung

Veröffentl.Schweiz.Ges.Gesch.Med.Naturwiss. Veröffentlichungen der Schweizerischen Gesellschaft für Geschichte der Medizin und der Naturwissenschaften

Veröffentl.Schweiz.Math.Ges. Veröffentlichungen der Schweizerischen Mathematischen Gesellschaft

Veröffentl.Zool.Staatsamml.München Veröffentlichungen der Zoologischen Staatsammlung, München

Verslagen Mededeel.Vlaam.Acad.Taal- Letterk. Verslagen en Mededeelingen Koninklijke Vlaamsche Academie voor Taal- en Letterkunde

Verslagen Ned.Akad.Wetensch.Afd.Natuurk. Verslagen van de gewone vergadering der Afdeling Natuurkunde, Koninklijke Nederlandse Akademie van Wetenschappen

Vesmír Vesmír [Ústav pro Obecnou Přírodovědu, Česka Universita, Praha]

Vestnik Akad.Med.Nauk SSSR Vestnik Akademii Meditsinskikh Nauk SSSR

Vestnik Akad.Nauk SSSR Vestnik Akademii Nauk SSSR

Věstník České Společnosti Nauk Třida Mat.Přirodovědecká Věstník [Královské] České Společnosti Nauk Třida Matematicko-Přírodovedecká

Vestnik Drevnei Ist. Vestnik Drevnei Istorii

Vestnik Društvo Mat.Fiz.Nar.Repub.Srbije Vestnik Društvo Matematicara i Fizičara Narodne Republike Srbije

Vestnik Ist.Mirovoi Kult. Vestnik Istorii Mirovoi Kulturny: Revue de la Civilisation Mondiale

Vestnik Leningr.Univ. Vestnik Leningradskogo Gosudarstvennogo Universiteta

Vestnik Leningr.Univ.Ser.Mat.Mekh.Astron. Vestnik Leningradskogo Universiteta: Seriya Matematiki, Mekhaniki i Astronomii

Vestnik Moskovskogo Gos.Univ.Fiz.Astron. Vestnik Moskovskogo Gosudarstvennogo Universiteta, Sér. 3. Fizika, astronomia

Vestnik Moskovskogo Gos.Univ.Mat.Mekh. Vestnik Moskovskogo G - sudarstvennogo Universiteta, Ser. 1: Matematika Mekhanika

Věstník Nár.Tech.Mus. Věstník Národního Technického Musea

Vetenskaps-Soc.Årsbok [Kungl.] Vetenskaps-Societetens Årsbok

Veterinärhist.Jahrb. Veterinär-historisches Jahrbuch [Gesellschaft für Geschichte und Literatur der Veterinärmedizin]

Veterinärhist.Mitt. Veterinärhistorische Mitteilungen [Gesellschaft für Geschichte und Literatur der Veterinärmedizin]

Viata Med. Viata Medicalà

Victorian Stud. Victorian Studies [Indiana University]

Vie Int. La Vie Internationale: Revue mensuelle des ideés des faits et des organismes internationaux [Union des Associations Internationales]

Vie Ital. Vie d'Italia (e dell' America Latina) [Touring Club Italiano]

Vie Méd. La Vie Médicale [Association Générale des Médecins de France]

Vie Peuples Vie des Peuples

Vierteljahrsschr.Astron.Ges. Vierteljahrsschrift der astronomischen Gesellschaft [Leipzig]

Vierteljahrsschr.Gerichtl.Med. Vierteljahrsschrift für gerichtliche Medizin und öffentliches Sanitätswesen

Vierteljahrsschr.Naturforsch.Ges.Zürich Vierteljahrsschrift der naturforschenden Gesellschaft in Zürich

Vierteljahrsschr.Naturforsch.Ges.Zürich Beibl. Vierteljahrsschrift der naturforschenden Gesellschaft in Zürich: Beiblätter

Vierteljahrsschr.Soz.Wirtschaftsgesch. Vierteljahrsschrift für Sozial- und Wirtschaftsgeschichte

Vierteljahrsschr.Wiss.Phil. Vierteljahrsschrift für wissenschaftliche Philosophie

Vieux Pap. Vieux Papier: Bulletin de la Société Archéologique, Historique et Artistique

Virchows Arch.Pathol.Anat.Physiol. Virchows Archiv für pathologische Anatomie und Physiologie und für klinische Medizin

Virginia Mag.Hist.Biogr. Virginia Magazine of History and Biography

Virginia Med.Mon. Virginia Medical Monthly

Virginia Quart.Rev. Virginia Quarterly Review

Vistas Astron. Vistas in Astronomy

Visva-Bharati Ann. Visva-Bharati Annals

Visva-Bharati Quart. The Visva-Bharati Quarterly

Vlaam.Geneesk.Tijdschr. Vlaamsch Geneeskundig Tijdschrift

Vlaam.Gids De Vlaamsche Gids

Voeding Voeding

Volksgesundheit Volksgesundheit: Zeitschrift für soziale Hygiene

Volkshochschule Volklshochschule

Vop.Fil. Voprosi Filosofii [Akademiia Nauk SSSR, Institut Filosofii]

Vop.Fil.Psikhol. Voprosy Filosofii i Psikhologii

Vop.Ist.Est.Tekh. Voprosy Istorii Estestvoznaniia i Tekhniki

Vortr.Ber.Deut.Mus. Vorträge und Berichte des Deutscher Museums [München]

Vortr.Bibl.Warburg Vorträge der Bibliothek Warburg

Vortr.Ges.Gesch.Pharm. Vorträge der Gesellschaft für Geschichte der Pharmazie

Vouno To Vouno. Revue du Club Alpin Hellenique

Vox Vox: Internationales Zentralblatt für experimentelle Phonetik

Vragen Dag Vragen van den Dag

Vrije Fries De Vrije Fries

W

Wash.Evening Star Washington Evening Star [Newspaper]

Wash.Hist.Quart. Washington Historical Quarterly

Wasserwirtsch.Tech. Wasserwirtschaft und Technik

Water Supply Irrig.Pap.U.S.Geol.Surv. Water-Supply and Irrigation Papers. U.S. Geological Survey

Wear Wear - Usure - Verschleiss

Weather Weather: a monthly magazine for all interested in meteorology

Weatherwise Weatherwise

Weekly Bull.St.Louis Med.Soc. Weekly Bulletin of the St. Louis Medical Society

Welt Islams Die Welt des Islams. Zeitschrift der Deutschen Gesellschaft für Islamkunde

Weltall Weltall: Illustrierte Zeitschrift für Astronomie

Weltkreis Der Weltkreis

Werken Rijksuniv.Gent Fac.Wijsbegeerte Lett. Werken uitgegeven door de Faculteit van de Wijsbegeerte en Letteren, Rijksuniversiteit te Gent

Wessex Geogr. Wessex Geographer

West-Indische Gids De West-Indische Gids

West.J.Surg.Obstet.Gynecol. Western Journal of Surgery, Obstetrics and Gynecology

West Lond.Med.J. West London Medical Journal

West.Penn.Hist.Mag. Western Pennsylvania Historical Magazine [Historical Society of Western Pennsylvania]

West Virginia Hist. West Virginia History

Westdeut.Ärztezeitung Westdeutsche Ärztezeitung für Standesfragen und soziale Medizin

Wetensch.Tijdingen Wetenschappelijke Tijdingen

Wetensch.Vlaanderen Wetenschap in Vlaanderen [Vereeniging voor Wetenschap, Ghent]

What's New What's New [Abbott Laboratories, North Chicago]

Wiad.Mat. Wiadomości Matematyczne

Wiener Klin.Wochenschr. Wiener Klinische Wochenschrift

Wiener Med.Wochenschr. Wiener Medizinische Wochenschrift

Wiener Prähist.Z. Wiener Prähistorische Zeitschrift

Wiener Stud. Wiener Studien: Zeitschrift für klassische Philologie

Wiener Z. Kunde Morgenlandes Wiener Zeitschrift für die Kunde des Morgenlandes

William Mary Coll.Quart.Hist.Pap. William and Mary College Quarterly Historical Paper

William Mary Quart. William and Mary Quarterly

Wis.Drug. Wisconsin Druggist

Wis.Med.J. Wisconsin Medical Journal

Wis.Mortar Quill Wisconsin Mortar and Quill

Wis- Natuurk.Tijdschr. Wis- en Natuurkundig Tijdschrift [Vlaamsch Natuur-, Wis- en Geneeskundig Congres]

Wis.Pharm. Wisconsin Pharmacist

Wisk.Post Wiskunde Post

Wiss.Ann.Verbr.Forsch. Wissenschaftliche Annalen zur Verbreitung neuer Forschungsergebnisse

Wiss.Hypothese Wissenschaft und Hypothese: Sammlung von Einzeldarstellungen aus dem Gesamtgebiet der Wissenschaften

Wiss.Ind. Wissenschaft und Industrie

Wiss.Rundsch. Wissenschaftliche Rundschau: Zeitschrift für die allgemeinwissenschaftliche Fortbildung des Lehrers

Wiss.Veröffentl.Ver.Erdk.Leipzig Wissenschaftliche Veröffentlichungen des Vereins für Erdkunde zu Leipzig

Wiss.Z.Friedrich-Schiller-Univ.Jena Wissenschaftliche Zeitschrift der Friedrich-Schiller-Universität, Jena

Wiss.Z.Humboldt Univ.Berlin Math.Naturwiss.Reihe Wissenschaftliche Zeitschrift der Humboldt-Universität zu Berlin: Mathematisch-naturwissenschaftliche Reihe

Wiss.Z.Karl-Marx Univ.Leipzig Mathematisch-naturwiss.Reihe Wissenschaftliche Zeitschrift der Karl-Marx Universität, Leipzig. Mathematisch-naturwissenschaftliche Reihe

Wochenschr.Tierheilk.Viehzucht Wochenschrift für Tierheilkunde und Viehzucht

Wörter Sachen Wörter und Sachen

Württemb.Vierteljahrsh.Landesgesch. Württembergische Vierteljahrshefte für Landesgeschichte

Würzburger Abhandl.Gesamtgeb.Prakt.Med. Würzburger Abhandlungen auf dem Gesamgebiet der praktischen Medizin

X

Xaveriana Xaveriana

Xi Trans. Xi Transactions

Y

Yale J.Biol.Med. Yale Journal of Biology and Medicine

Yale Law J. Yale Law Journal [Yale University, Institute of Advanced Legal Studies]

Yale Rev. The Yale Review

Yale Sci.Mag. Yale Scientific Magazine

Yale Univ.Libr.Gaz. Yale University Library Gazette

Yale Univ.Publ.Anthropol. Yale University Publications in Anthropology

Yayinlarindan Tege Laboratuvar Yayinlarindan Tege Laboratuvar

Yearbook Amer.Phil.Soc. Yearbook of the American Philosophical Society

Year Book Carnegie Inst.Wash. Year Book of the Carnegie Institution of Washington

Yearbook Phys.Soc.Lond. Yearbook of the Physical Society of London

Year Book Roy.Soc.Edinb. Year Book of the Royal Society of Edinburgh

Yenching J.Chin.Stud. Yenching Journal of Chinese Studies

Ymer Ymer: tidskrift utg. af Svenska Sällskapet för Antropologi och Geografi

Yoga Yoga. Internationale Zeitschrift für wissenschaftliche Yoga-Forschung

Yokohama Shiritsu Daigaku Kiyo, ser.A Yokohama Shiritsu Daigaku Kiyo [Journal of Yokohama Municipal University] Series A

Yperman Yperman: Bulletin de la Société Belge d'Histoire de la Médecine: Bulletijn der Belgische Vereeniging voor Geschiedenis der Geneeskunde

Yu-Shih Hsueh-Chih Yu-Shih Hsueh-Chih: Youth Quarterly [Chung-kuo Ch'ing-nien Fan-king Chiu-kuo Tuan, T'ai-pei]

Z

Z.Ägypt.Sprache Altertumsk. Zeitschrift für Ägyptische Sprache und Altertumskunde [Deutsche morgenländische Gesellschaft]

Z.Ärztl.Fortbild. Zeitschrift für Ärztliche Fortbildung

Z.Ästhetik Zeitschrift für Ästhetik und Allgemeine Kunstwissenschaft

Z.Alttestamentliche Wiss. Zeitschrift für die alttestamentliche Wissenschaft (und die Kunde des nachbiblischen Judentums)

Z.Alttestamentliche Wiss.Beih. Zeitschrift für die alttestamentliche Wissenschaft: Beihefte

Z.Anat.Entwicklungsgesch. Zeitschrift für Anatomie und Entwicklungsgeschichte

Z.Angew.Anat.Konstitutionslehre Zeitschrift für angewandte Anatomie und Konstitutionslehre

Z.Angew.Chem. Zeitschrift für angewandte Chemie

Z.Angew.Math.Mech. Zeitschrift für angewandte Mathematik und Mechanik [Ingenieurwissenschaftliche Forschungsarbeiten]

Z.Angew.Math.Phys. Zeitschrift für angewandte Mathematik und Physik

Z.Angew.Phys. Zeitschrift für angewandte Physik

Z.Assyrologie Zeitschrift für Assyrologie und verwandte Gebiete

Z.Balneol.Klim. Zeitschrift für Balneologie, Klimatologie und Kurorthygienc

Z.Bekämpfung Geschlechtskrankheiten Zeitschrift für Bekämpfung der Geschlechtskrankheiten

Z.Bot. Zeitschrift für Botanik

Z.Buddhismus Zeitschrift für Buddhismus

Z.Bücherfreunde Zeitschrift für Bücherfreunde

Z.Deut.Alpenver. Zeitschrift des Deutschen Alpenvereins

Z.Deut.Geol.Ges. Zeitschrift der Deutschen Geologischen Gesellschaft

Z.Deut.Ges.Edelsteink. Zeitschrift der Deutschen Gesellschaft für Edelsteinkunde

Z.Deut.Morgenländ.Ges. Zeitschrift der Deutschen Morgenländischen Gesellschaft

Z.Deut.Palästina-Ver. Zeitschrift des Deutschen Palästina-Vereins

Z.Deut.Philol. Zeitschrift für deutsche Philologie

Z.Deut.Wortforsch. Zeitschrift für deutsche Wortforschung

Z.Deut.Zuckerind. Zeitschrift für die deutsche Zuckerindustrie

Z.Eingeborenen Sprachen Festschrift für Eingeborenen Sprachen

Z.Erzbergbau Metallhüttenwesen Zeitschrift für Erzbergbau und Metallhüttenwesen

Z.Ethnol. Zeitschrift für Ethnologie

Z.Fleisch- Milchhyg. Zeitschrift für Fleisch- und Milchhygiene

Z.Flugwiss. Zeitschrift für Flugwissenschaften

Z.Geburtsh.Gynäkol. Zeitschrift für Geburtshilfe und Gynäkologie

Z.Ges.Erdk.Berlin Zeitschrift der Gesellschaft für Erdkunde zu Berlin

Z.Gesamte Kohlensäureind. Zeitschrift für die gesamte Kohlensäureindustrie

Z.Gesamte Naturwiss. Zeitschrift für die gesamte Naturwissenschaft, einschliesslich Naturphilosophie und Geschichte der Naturwissenschaft und Medizin

Z.Gesamte Neurol.Psychiat. Zeitschrift für die gesamte Neurologie und Psychiatrie

Z.Gesch.Oberrheins Zeitschrift für die Geschichte des Oberrheins

Z.Geschiebeforsch. Zeitschrift für Geschiebeforschung [Gesellschaft für Geschiebeforschung, Berlin]

Z.Harz-Ver.Gesch.Altertumsk. Zeitschrift der Harz-Vereinigung für Geschichte und Altertumskunde

Z.Heimatk.Regierungsbezirke Coblenz Zeitschrift für Heimatkunde der Regierungsbezirke Coblenz und Trier und der angrenzenden Gebiete

Z.Indologie Iran. Zeitschrift für Indologie und Iranistik

Z.Instrumentenk. Zeitschrift für Instrumentenkunde [Physikalischtechnische Reichsanstalt]

Z.Kath.Theol. Zeitschrift für Katholische Theologie

Z.Kelt.Philol. Zeitschrift für keltische (celtische) Philologie

Z.Kinderheilk. Zeitschrift für Kinderheilkunde

Z.Konstitutionslehre Zeitschrift für Konstitutionslehre

Z.Kristallogr.Kristallgeom. Zeitschrift für Kristallographie, Kristallgeometrie, Kristallphysik, Kristallchemie

Z.Kristallogr.Mineral. Zeitschrift für Kristallographie und Mineralogie

Z.Krit.Okkultismus Zeitschrift für kritischen Okkultismus und Grenzfrage des Seelenlebens

Z.Krüppelfürsorge Zeitschrift für Krüppelfürsorge

Z.Kunstgesch. Zeitschrift für Kunstgeschichte

Z.Laryngol.Rhinol.Otol. Zeitschrift für Laryngologie, Rhinologie, Otologie und ihre Grenzgebiete

Z.Math.Naturwiss.Unterricht Zeitschrift für mathematischen und naturwissenschaftlichen Unterricht [Verein zur Förderung des Unterrichts in der Mathematik und den Naturwissenschaften]

Z.Metallk. Zeitschrift für Metallkunde [Deutsche Gesellschaft für Metallkunde, Berlin]

Z.Österr.Ing.- Architekt.Ver. Zeitschrift des Österreichischen Ingenieur- und Architektenvereins

Z.Ophthalmol.Opt. Zeitschrift für ophthalmologische Optik

Z.Phil.Forsch. Zeitschrift für philosophische Forschung

Z.Phys. Zeitschrift für Physik [Deutsche physikalische Gesellschaft]

Z.Phys.Chem. Zeitschrift für physikalische Chemie, Stöchiometrie und Verwandtschaftslehre

Z.Phys.Chem.Unterricht Zeitschrift für den physikalischen und chemischen Unterricht

Z.Phys.Diät.Therap. Zeitschrift für physikalische und diätetische Therapie

Z.Pilzk. Zeitschrift für Pilzkunde [Deutsche Gesellschaft für Pilzkunde]

Z.Positivistische Phil. Zeitschrift für die positivistische Philosophie [Gesellschaft für positivistische Philosophie]

Z.Psychol. Zeitschrift für Psychologie

Z.Rassenk. Zeitschrift für Rassenkunde und ihre Nachbargebiete (und die gesamte Forschung am Menschen)

Z.Rassenphysiol. Zeitschrift für Rassenphysiologie [Deutsche Gesellschaft für Blutgruppenforschung]

Z.Relig.Geistesgesch. Zeitschrift für Religions- und Geistesgeschichte

Z.Relig.Geistesgesch.Beih. Zeitschrift für Religions- und Geistesgeschichte: Beiheft

Z.Säugetierkunde Zeitschrift für Säugetierkunde

Z.Semitistik Zeitschrift für Semitistik und verwandte Gebiete

Z.Spiritusind. Zeitschrift für Spiritusindustrie

Z.Stomatol. Zeitschrift für Stomatologie

Z.Tech.Phys. Zeitschrift für technische Physik

Z.Tierzücht.Züchtungsbiol. Zeitschrift für Tierzüchtung und Züchtungsbiologie

Z.Urol. Zeitschrift für Urologie

Z.Ver.Deut.Ing. Zeitschrift des Vereins Deutscher Ingenieure

Z.Ver.Deut.Zuckerind. Zeitschrift des Vereins der deutschen Zuckerindustrie

Z.Ver.Deut.Zuckerind.Tech.Teil Zeitschrift des Vereins der deutschen Zuckerindustrie. Technischer Teil

Z.Ver.Gas- Wasserfachmännern Zeitschrift des Vereins von Gas- und Wasserfachmannern in Österreich-Ungarn

Z.Ver.Hess.Gesch.Landeskunde Zeitschrift des Vereins für Hessische Geschichte und Landeskunde

Z.Ver.Höheren Bayer.Vermessungsbeamten Zeitschrift des Vereins der Höheren Bayerischen Vermessungsbeamten

Z.Ver.Thüringische Gesch.Altertumskunde Zeitschrift des Vereins für thüringische Geschichte und Altertumskunde

Z.Ver.Thüringische Gesch.Altertumskunde Beih. Zeitschrift des Vereins für thüringische Geschichte und Altertumskunde: Beiheft

Z.Ver.Volksk. Zeitschrift des Vereins für Volkskunde

Z.Vergleichende Seelenk. Zeitschrift für vergleichende Seelenkunde

Z.Vermessungswesen Zeitschrift für Vermessungswesen [Deutscher Verein für Vermessungswesen]

Z.Völkerpsychol.Soziol.Beil. Zeitschrift für Völkerpsychologie und Soziologie. Beilage

Z.Volksk. Zeitschrift für Volkskunde

Z.Vorgeschichte Zeitschrift für Vorgeschichte

Z.Vulkanol. Zeitschrift für Vulkanologie: Revista Vulcanologica: Volcanological Review: Revue Vulcanologique

Z.Wahrscheinlichkeitstheorie Zeitschrift für Wahrscheinlichkeitstheorie

Z.Wirtsch.Zuckerind.Allg.Teil Zeitschrift der Wirtschaftsgruppe Zuckerindustrie. Allgemeiner Teil

Z.Wirtsch.Zuckerind.Tech.Teil Zeitschrift der Wirtschaftsgruppe Zuckerindustrie: Technischer Teil

Zahnärztl.Mitt. Zahnärztliche Mitteilungen

Zalmoxis Zalmoxis: Revue des études religieuses

Zap.Russ.Nauch.Inst.Belg. Zapiski Russkogo Nauchnogo Instituta v Belgrade

Zee De Zee: Zeevaartkundig Tijdschrift

Zeiss Werkz. Zeiss-Werkzeitschrift. Bulletin Technique Zeiss

Zeitwende Zeitwende: Die Neue Furche

Zeměměřický Věstník Zeměměřický Věstník

Zemlevedenie Zemlevedenie: Sbornik [Moskovskogo Obshchestva Ispytateleĭ Prirody. I. Moskovsky Universitet]

Zentralbl.Allg.Path. Zentralblatt für allgemeine Pathologie und pathologische Anatomie

Zentralbl.Arbeitsmed. Zentralblatt für Arbeitsmedizin und Arbeitsschutz

Zentralbl.Bakteriol. Zentralblatt für Bakteriologie, Parasitenkunde, Infektionskrankheiten (und Hygiene)

Zentralbl.Bibl. Zentralblatt für Bibliothekswesen

Zentralbl.Chir. Zentralblatt für Chirurgie

Zentralbl.Gynäkol. Zentralblatt für Gynäkologie

Zentralbl.Prakt.Augenheilk. Zentralblatt für praktische Augenheilkunde

Zentralbl.Psychoanal.Psychotherap. Zentralblatt für Psychoanalyse und Psychotherapie

Zentralbl.Zuckerind. Zentralblatt für die Zuckerindustrie [Verein deutscher Zuckertechniker]

Zentralzeitung Opt.Mech. Zentralzeitung für Optik und Mechanik, Elektrotechnik, etc.

Zh.Min.Nar.Prosveshcheniia Zhurnal Ministerstva Narodnago Prosveshcheniia

Zh.Neorg.Khim. Zhurnal Neorganicheskoĭ khimii

Zh.Neuropatol.Psikhiat. Zhurnal Neuropatologii i Psikhiatrii

Zh.Obshch.Khim. Zhurnal Obshcheĭ Khimii

Zh.Russ.Fiz.Khim.Obshchest. Zhurnal Russkogo Fiziko-Khimicheskogo Obshchestva

Zinbun Zinbun [or Zimbun]: [Research Institute for Humanistic Studies, Kyoto University]

Zool.Ann. Zoologische Annalen: Zeitschrift für Geschichte der Zoologie

Zool.Anz. Zoologischer Anzeiger [Deutsche zoologische Gesellschaft]

Zool.Garten Der Zoologische Garten

Zool.Mededeel. Zoologische Mededeelingen [Rijksmuseum van Natuurlijke Historie te Leiden]

Zool.Soc.Bull.N.Y. Zoological Society Bulletin. New York Zoological Society

Züchter Der Züchter: Zeitschrift für theoretische und angewandte Genetik, Organ des Forschungsdienstes

Zürcher Medizingesch.Abhandl. Zürcher medizingeschichtliche Abhandlungen

Życie Nauk. Życie Nauki: miesięcznik naukoznawczy

XVIIe Siècle XVIIe Siècle. Bulletin de la Société d'Étude du XVIIe Siècle

Guide to Users

The Bibliography has been arranged in a systematic sequence, but it is not necessary for the user to understand the way in which the classification scheme has been constructed. To avoid fragmentation, subheadings have been omitted unless the number of entries makes a clear subdivision necessary. Classmarks have, however, been retained to enable the user to go from the alphabetical subject index direct to the information he is seeking. For the reader who wishes merely to browse, the table of contents is a sufficient guide, but he will also be helped by the running heads on the inside corners of the pages which indicate the main subject and the subdivision. The full schedules* may be found on pages 633-41 and an explanatory note on the scheme is on pages 621-31.

Search procedure

The user who requires information on a particular topic should turn to the alphabetical index to subjects which appears, with classmarks, at the end of the volume, pages 643-78. If the topic is very specific, there may be no entry under it in the index because there is no special section on the topic in the Bibliography. In that case, reference should be made to a more general heading. For example, although the word 'copper' does not appear in the index, under 'metals' there are classmarks of the sections which may contain references to copper. Having found the code or classmark (a sequence of letters) in the index, the user should turn to the body of the Bibliography. The code in the left hand top corner of a page is the classmark of the first item on the page, whereas that in the right hand top corner refers to the last item.

Codes

The codes in this volume are composed of capital and lower case letters. The capital letters represent the main subject divisions; the lower case letters symbolize form and aspect subdivisions. It must be emphasized that the notation does *not* set out to reflect the hierarchy of the classification; it is *ordinal*. Although frequently one letter represents a main subject, this is not always so. Thus, FZ, indicating earth sciences has a two letter code, but meteorology, which is one of the earth sciences, is represented by one letter, G. Similarly, RB, standing for surgery, contains as many letters as RC, meaning regional surgery, although the latter is a subdivision of the former.

The codes are arranged in alphabetical order. It is essential to remember that in the filing sequence a stop must be imagined between the capital letters and the lower case letters, with the result that Bce (B.ce) files before BAce (BA.ce). Apart from capital and lower case letters, the only other symbols used are the hyphen and

---

* These differ in some respects from the brief outline of the scheme which appeared on pages xvii-xviii of Volume 1.

the oblique stroke, both with their conventional filing values. The hyphen separates two sets of codes and in filing is considered like a stop; for example, Lc-be (L.c.be) files before Lcb (L.cb). The oblique stroke is an inclusion sign, meaning for example that p/s includes sections, p, q, r, s, and consequently precedes them, e.g. LUp/s comes before LUp, LUq, LUr, LUs. It is mainly used to indicate the range of sections in the body of the Bibliography.

Apart from representing form and aspect subdivisions, the lower case letters are also used as connecting symbols: (1) to denote a conceptual relationship between subject fields, the code used being mz (for example, TmzA, relation of technology and science); (2) to form compound subjects (the letter used is y, for example, LUyLO = insect behaviour, LU being the code for entomology and LO for animal behaviour); and (3) to extend the subject field in a non-systematic way (the letter used is z, for example, QPzpl = plague, QP representing named infectious and communicable diseases, and pl short for plague).

Aspect subdivisions

Each subject field, however narrow, is subdivided in exactly the same way. The main aspect subdivisions are:

c	general history of the subject
c-bu/cv	bibliography; literature; sources
d	biography
f	history of the subject as a study
g	teaching the history of the subject
h	historiography and particular aspects of the history of the subject
j	psychological aspects
k	philosophy and methodology
m	fundamental concepts
mz	relation with other scientific subject fields
n	communication
o	study and teaching
p/s	social relations of the subject
p	organization
q	institutions
r	the profession
s	society
t	humanistic relations of the subject
u	popular aspects
v	ethnic and linguistic groups
w	national histories (the subject in different countries)
x	techniques and instruments; equipment
xx	museology
y	connecting symbol to form compound subjects
z	connecting symbol for extension of subject

a and b, which represent geographical subdivisions and bibliographical form (for example, encyclopaedias, large scale works, essays, etc.) respectively, are only used in conjunction with one of the above sections.

If the subject is considered from more than one aspect, they are combined by a hyphen and are alphabetized in the usual way. Thus, SAwb-qd signifies North American agricultural learned societies (SA = agriculture; wb = North America; qd = learned societies).

Abbreviations

1: and 2:	For references to Volumes 1 and 2 of the *ISIS CUMULATIVE BIBLIOGRAPHY* the form 1: or 2: followed by the page number is used.
:	The colon, :, after a number indicates the volume in references to articles in periodicals.
[CB 81/256]	This signifies that the original entry in *Isis* was followed by an annotation or a review which can be found in *Isis* Critical Bibliography no. 81, p. 256.* A table correlating the numbers of the Critical Bibliographies with the volume numbers of *Isis* is on page xiii.

Abbreviations used for periodicals will be found on pages xv-xci. Standard bibliographical abbreviations are used in the entries. The form of entry is explained in detail below.

Form of Entry
The form of entry adopted is the same as in Volumes 1 and 2. It follows that used in the *Isis* Critical Bibliographies during the last few years. It is:

(a) in the case of books

Author. Title. Edition where applicable. Collation (number of pages, etc) (Series) Imprint (Place of publication: publisher, year). [CB /] if entry is annotated. Reviews.

Example:

DUNN, Leslie Clarence, ed. Genetics in the 20th century: essays in the progress of genetics during its first 50 years. xi, 634 p., portr. New York: Macmillan, 1951. [CB 79/178]
Reviewed by Conway Zirkle, *Arch.Int.Hist.Sci.*, 1952, 31: 150-1; by Bentley Glass, *Bull.Hist.Med.*, 1953. 27: 294-6.

(b) in the case of periodical articles

Author. Title. Title of periodical (usually abbreviated), year, volume: (part), pages. [CB /] if entry is annotated.

Example:

LEVY-VALENSI, J. Chaire d'histoire de la medicine. Leçon inaugurale. *Semp.Hôp.Paris*, 1946, 22: 1709-19. [CB 71/310]

---

* Readers are advised that the entry in the *Cumulative Bibliography* may be in a different form from that in the *Isis* Critical Bibliography. It was, of course, essential to make the cataloguing consistent and we have followed the Anglo-American Cataloguing Rules (North American Text).

A SCIENCE

Ac general history

Ac-be *encyclopaedias; systematic compendia*

THE BRITANNICA Year-Book: a survey of the world's progress since the completion in 1910 of the Encyclopedia Britannica. 11th ed. xliv, 1226 p. London/New York: Encyclopedia Britannica Company, 1913.
Reviewed by George Sarton, *Isis*, 1913, 1: 290-2.

DARMSTÄDTER, Ludwig. Handbuch zur Geschichte der Naturwissenschaften und der Technik in chronologischer Darstellung. 2nd ed. x, 1262 p. Berlin: Springer, 1908.
Reprinted by Kraus, 1960.

THE HARPER Encyclopedia of Science. Ed. by James R. Newman. 4 vol. 1379 p., ill. New York: Harper and Row, 1963.
Reviewed by John Walsh, *Science*, 1964, 145: 806-7.

McGRAW-HILL Encyclopedia of Science and Technology. Ed. by William H. Crouse. 15 vol. 9100 p. New York: McGraw-Hill Book Co., 1960.
For reviews *see* CB 87/555.

MAYERHÖFER, Josef, ed. Lexikon der Geschichte der Naturwissenschaften. Biographien, Sachwörter und Bibliographien. Vol. 1- Vienna: Verlag Brüder Hollinek, 1959-
Vol. 1, pt. 1-2 reviewed by Sten Lindroth, *Lychnos*, 1962, 390-1; by W. Baron, *Sudhoffs Arch.*, 1962, 46: 186-8. Pt. 2 separately reviewed by P. Boeynaems, *Sci.Hist.*, 1961, 3: 207.

POPULAR science. Encyclopedia of the sciences. Ed. by W.B. Sill and N. Hoss. 762 p., ill. New York: Popular Science Publishing Co., 1963.

SCHUDER, Werner, ed. Universitas litterarum. Handbuch der Wissenschaftskunde. Unter Mitarbeit zahlreicher Fachgelehrter in Verbindung mit Willy Hoppe, Günther Ludwig, Wieland Schmidt. xx, 819 p., bibliogr. Berlin: W. de Gruyter, 1953-55. [CB 81/258]
Issued in parts.

UCCELLI, Arturo, ed. Enciclopedia storica delle scienze e delle loro applicazioni. Opera compilata con la collaborazione di eminenti specialisti. 2 vol. in 3. 1. Le scienze fisiche e matematiche; 2. i and ii. Le scienze applicate e la tecnica. Milano: Ulrico Hoepli, 1941-43. [CB 68/51]

UCCELLI, Arturo, ed. Scienza e tecnica del tempo nostro nei principii e nelle applicazioni. Opera compilata con la collaborazione di eminenti specialisti. 2 vol. in 3. Milan: Hoepli, 1946-58. [CB 75/85]
Originally planned as the last part of the Editor's Enciclopedia storica delle scienze.

VAN NOSTRAND'S Scientific Encyclopedia. 3rd ed. vii, 1839 p. Princeton, N.J./London: D. Van Nostrand Company, 1958.
Reviewed by L.S. Goddard, *Nature*, 1958, 182: 1587.

Ac-bm *large scale works*

ABBAGNANO, Nicola, ed. Storia delle scienze, coordinata da Nicola Abbagnano. 3 vol. in 4. 1. A cura di N. Abbagnano [*et al.*]. xii, 662 p., ill.; 2. A cura di M. Gliozzi e M. Gina. xvii, 802 p., ill.; 3.i. A cura di G. Montalenti. vii, 620 p., ill.; 3.ii. A cura di A. Massucco Costa e F. Ferrarotti. 621-1071 p., ill. Torino: Unione Tipografico-Editrice Torinese, 1962.

ABBOT, Charles Greeley. Adventures in the world of science. x, 150 p., ill., bibliogr. Washington: Public Affairs Press, 1958.
At the Smithsonian Institution from 1895.
Reviewed by Richard E. Hewlett, *Isis*, 1959, 50: 516-17; for other reviews *see* CB 85/465 and CB 86/512.

ACADEMIA REPUBLICII POPULARE ROMÎNE. Études d'histoire et de philosophie des sciences. 311 p. Bucharest: L'Académie de la République Populaire Roumaine, 1962.
Reviewed by R. Bruce Lindsay, *Phys.Today*, 1964, 17: no. 1, 80-2.

ALBÈRGAMO, Francesco. Il pensiero scientifico contemporaneo. Antologia storica. 2 vol. 1. Le scienze esatte e le scienze fisiche. 170 p.; 2. Le scienze naturali. 172 p. Firenze: La Nuova Italia, 1952.
These two anthologies contain accounts of twentieth-century science by men of many nationalities. These are not classic papers.
Reviewed by A. Natucci, *Arch.Int.Hist.Sci.*, 1953, 6: 323-5.

ANTHONY, H.D. Science and its background. 4th ed. 368 p. London: Macmillan, 1963.
First publ. 1948.
Reviewed by W.L. Sumner, *Nature*, 1948, 161: 354; in *Sch. Sci.Rev.*, 1956, 37: 288.

AUGER, Pierre. Current trends in scientific research. Survey of the main trends of inquiry in the field of natural sciences, the dissemination of scientific knowledge, and the application of such knowledge for peaceful ends. 245 p. New York: Columbia University Press (for UNESCO), 1961.
Reviewed by James W. Moyer, *Phys.Today*, 1963, 16: 82-4.

BABINI, José. Historia sucinta de la ciencia. 226 p. (Coleccion Austral) Buenos Aires: Espasa-Calpe, 1951. [CB 78/175]

BARBAGALLO, Corrado. Storia delle scienze. vi, 179 p. Milano: Albrighi Segati, 1925.

BARKER, Ernest; CLARK, George; VAUCHER, P. The European inheritance. 3 vol. 1. Prehistory; Greece and Rome; The Jews and the beginnings of the Christian Church; The Middle Ages. xxviii, 543 p., 24 pl., 12 maps; 2. The early modern period; Political, economic and social development in the 18th century; the development of literature and culture in the 18th century. xxviii, 391 p., 15 pl., 5 maps; 3. The nineteenth century (1815-1914), 1914-50; Review and epilogue. xxviii, 406 p., 12 pl., 7 maps. Oxford: Clarendon Press, 1954. [CB 81/256]

BARNES, Harry Elmer. The history of western civilization. With the collaboration of Henry David. 2 vol. xxv, 911 p.; xxv, 1,170 p. New York: Harcourt, Brace, 1935. [CB 46/598]

BARYCZ, Henryk. [Développement de l'histoire de la culture intellectuelle. (In Polish with summary in French)]. 79 p. (Polska Akademia Umiejetności, Historia Nauki Polskiej w Monografiach, 31) Krakow: 1949.

BECCARI, Arturo. Storia della filosofia e della scienza. viii, 408 p. Torino: Soc. Editr. Internazionale, 1928. [CB 27/533]

BEITRÄGE zur Geschichte der Medizin und der Naturwissenschaften. Festschrift für Professor Dr. Rudolph Zaunick zum 70. Geburtstag am 26.VIII.1963. 411 p., ill. (Acta Leopoldina no. 167, new ser., vol. 27) Leipzig: Johann Ambrosius Barth, 1963. [CB 89/483]

BENEDETTI, Rinaldo de. Aneddotica delle scienze [di] Sagredo [pseud.]. Con disegni di Leo Spaventa-Filippi. 354 p. Milan: Hoepli, 1948.
Reviewed by Gino Loria, *Arch.Int.Hist.Sci.*, 1948, 2: 220-1.

BOULIGAND, Georges, *et al.* L'évolution des sciences physiques et mathématiques. 267 p. (Bibliothèque de Philosophie Scientifique) Paris: Flammarion, 1935.

BOURGOUIN, Louis. Histoire des sciences et de leurs applications. 325 p., 21 ill. Montréal: Editions de l'Arbre, 1945. [CB 77/361]

BRINTON, Crane. Ideas and men. The story of Western thought. x, 587 p. New York: Prentice-Hall, 1950.
Reviewed by I. Bernard Cohen, *Isis*, 1951, 42: 88-9.

BRINTON, Crane; CHRISTOPHER, John B.; WOLFF, Robert Lee. A history of civilization. 2 vol. 1. Prehistory to 1715. xviii, 686 p.; 2. 1715 to the present. xiv, 722 p. New York: Prentice-Hall, 1955. [CB 81/256]

BRONOWSKI, J.; MAZLISH, Bruce. The Western intellectual tradition. From Leonardo to Hegel. xviii, 522 p. London: Hutchinson & Co.; New York: Harper & Brothers, 1960.
Reviewed by A. Rupert Hall, *Isis*, 1962, 53: 231-2; for other reviews *see* CB 86/460, CB 87/560 and CB 88/537.

BUTTERFIELD, Herbert. The origins of modern science, 1300-1800. Rev. ed. x, 242 p. New York: Macmillan Company, 1957.
First publ. 1949.
Reviewed by I. Bernard Cohen, *Isis*, 1950. 41: 231-3; for other reviews *see* CB 84/295.

CAHEN, Gustave. Les conquêtes de la pensée scientifique. vi, 390 p. (Heures Scientifiques) Paris: Dunod, 1953.
Reviewed by Suzanne Colnort, *Rev.Hist.Sci.*, 1954, 7: 378-9.

CALIFORNIA ACADEMY OF SCIENCES. A century of progress in the natural sciences, 1853-1953. (Published in celebration of the centennial of the Academy.) x, 807 p., ill. San Francisco: California Academy of Sciences, 1955. [CB 82/208]

CANDOLLE, Alphonse de. Zur Geschichte der Wissenschaften und der Gelehrten seit zwei Jahrhunderten. Deutsch hrsg. von Wilhelm Ostwald. xx, 466 p. (Grosse Männer, 2) Leipzig: Akademische Verlagsgesellschaft, 1911.
Reviewed by G. Sarton, *Isis*, 1913, 1: 132-3.

CARDIFF, Ira D. A million years of human progress. With an introduction by Melvin A. Brannon. Rev. ed. xii, 146 p. New York: Pageant Press, 1955. [CB 81/252]
First publ. 1942.

COLLINGWOOD, Robin George. The idea of nature. viii, 183 p. Oxford: Clarendon Press, 1945; New York: Oxford University Press, 1960. [CB 74/395]

CONANT, James Bryant. On understanding science. An historical approach. xv, 145 p., 10 fig. (Terry Lectures) New Haven: Yale University Press, 1947.
Reviewed by John F. Fulton, *Isis*, 1947, 38: 125-7.

CONANT, James Bryant; NASH, Leonard K.; ed. Harvard case histories in experimental science. 2 vol. xvi, 322 p.; v, 323-639 p. London: Oxford University Press; Cambridge, Mass.: Harvard University Press, 1957.
First publ. in separate parts, 1950-55.
Reviewed by V.F. Lenzen, *Isis*, 1951, 42: 65; by J.A. Ratcliffe, *Nature*, 1958, 182: 348; by E.J. Holmyard, *Endeavour*, 1959, 8: 51.

COURNOT, Antoine Augustin. Considérations sur la marche des idées et des événements dans les temps modernes. 2 vol. 351 p.; 376 p. Paris: Boivin, 1934.
First edition, Paris, 1872.
Reviewed by Pierre Brunet, *Archeion*, 1934, 16: 255.

CRESSY, Edward. Discoveries and inventions of the twentieth century. 3rd rev. ed. xxi, 476 p., ill. London: Routledge, 1930.

CROMBIE, Alistair C. Augustine to Galileo. The history of science A.D. 400-1650. 436 p. London: Falcon Educational Books, 1952. Reissued Cambridge, Mass.: Harvard University Press, 1953; London: Heinemann, 1957.
2nd ed. 2 vol. xxiv, 296 p.; xx, 380 p. London: Heinemann, 1961. Also republished under the title "Medieval and modern science", Cambridge, Mass.: Harvard University Press, 1961 and New York: Doubleday, 1959.
Reviewed by Marshall Clagett, *Isis*, 1953, 44: 398-403; by Edward Grant, *ibid.*, 1960, 51: 591-3; for further reviews *see* CB 81/252 and CB 89/483.

CROMBIE, Alistair C. Robert Grosseteste and the origins of experimental science, 1100-1700. xii, 369 p., 16 ill. Oxford: Clarendon Press, 1953.
Reviewed by Marshall Clagett, *Isis*, 1955, 46: 66-9; for other reviews *see* CB 80/155, CB 81/296 and CB 82/225.

CURT, Ralph H. The story of discovery and invention. How the wonders of the modern world came into being. viii, 568 p., 16 pl., 125 fig. New York: Hilman-Curl, 1937. [CB 55/172]

D'ABRO, A. The evolution of scientific thought. From Newton to Einstein. 2nd ed. 482 p., 15 portr. New York: Dover Publications, 1950.
First publ. 1927.
Reviewed by V.F. Lenzen, *Isis*, 1951, 42: 70; by D.J. Struik, *Scr.Math.*, 1952, 18: 137-9.

DAMPIER, William Cecil. A history of science and its relations with philosophy and religion. 4th rev. ed. xxvii, 527 p. Cambridge University Press; New York: Macmillan Co., 1949. [CB 64/448 and CB 75/84]
First publ. 1929.
Reviewed by George Sarton, *Isis*, 1930, 14: 263-5; for other reviews *see* CB 63/269 and CB 83/184.
French translation (Paris: Payot, 1951) reviewed by Jean Itard, *Rev.Hist.Sci.*, 1953, 6: 70-1.

DAMPIER, William Cecil. A shorter history of science. x, 190 p., 9 pl. Cambridge University Press; New York: Macmillan Co., 1944. [CB 68/50]
Reviewed by A.D. Ritchie, *Nature*, 1944, 154: 3.

DAMPIER, William Cecil; DAMPIER-WHETHAM, Catherine Durning. Science and the human mind. A critical and historical account of the development of natural knowledge. 304 p. London: Longmans, Green & Co., 1912.
Reviewed in *Isis*, 1913, 1: 125-32.

DANNEMANN, Friedrich. Die Naturwissenschaften in ihrer Entwicklung und in ihrem Zusammenhange. 2nd ed. 4 vol. fig. Leipzig: Engelmann, 1920-23.
First publ. 1911-13.
Reviewed by George Sarton, *Isis*, 1914, 2: 218-22; 1921, 4: 110-11, 563-4; 1924, 6: 115-16.

DANNEMANN, Friedrich. Vom Werden der naturwissenschaftlichen Probleme: Grundriss einer Geschichte der Naturwissenschaften. xii, 376 p. Leipzig: Engelmann, 1928. [CB 38/589]
This is a summary of the author's larger work "Die Naturwissenschaften in ihrer Entwicklung und in ihrem Zusammenhange", *see* above.

DAUMAS, Maurice, ed. Histoire de la science. xlviii, 1908 p. (Encyclopédie de la Pléiade, 5) Paris: Librairie Gallimard, 1957.
Reviewed by I. Bernard Cohen, *Isis*, 1961, 52: 106-7; for other reviews *see* CB 84/295, CB 85/377 and CB 87/551.

DAVIES, Mansel. An outline of the development of science. vii, 214 p., pl. (The Thinker's Library, 120) London: Watts, 1947.

DAVIS, Watson. The century of science. vi, 313 p., ill. New York: Duell, Sloan, and Pearce, 1963.
Reviewed by P.C. Fraley, *Science*, 1963, 142: 1050.

DE LUIGI, Emilio. Brevi considerazioni sulla scienza. 131 p. Asmara, Ethiopia: Stabilimento Tipografico Zuco, 1958.

DIJKSTERHUIS, E.J. De mechanisiering van het wereldbeeld. [The mechanization of the world picture. (In Dutch)] ix, 590 p. Amsterdam: Meulenhoff, 1950.
Reviewed by D.J. Struik, *Isis*, 1951, 42: 66-7.
German translation (Berlin: Springer-Verlag, 1956) reviewed by Serge Moscovici, *Rev.Hist.Sci.*, 1960, 13: 149-51; by M. de Tollenaire, *Rev.Quest.Sci.*, 1956, 17: 635-6.
For English translation *see* below.

DIJKSTERHUIS, E.J. The mechanization of the world picture. Transl. by C. Dikshoorn. 539 p., fig., bibliogr. Oxford: Clarendon Press, 1961.
For reviews *see* CB 87/551 and CB 88/542; for reviews of Dutch and German editions *see* above.

DIJKSTERHUIS, E.J.; FORBES, R.J. Overwinning door gehoorzaamheid. Geschiedenis van natuurwetenschap en techniek. [Victory through obedience. The history of science and technology. (In Dutch)] 2 vol. Zeist: Standard-Boekhandel, 1961.

DINGLE, Herbert. The scientific adventure. Essays in the history and philosophy of science. ix, 372 p. London: Isaac Pitman and Sons Ltd., 1952; New York: Philosophical Library, 1953.
For reviews *see* CB 80/113 and CB 81/252.

DINGLE, Herbert, ed. A century of science, 1851-1951. 338 p. London and New York: Hutchinson's Scientific and Technical Publications, 1951.
Reviewed by I. Bernard Cohen, *Isis*, 1952, 43: 377-8.

DINGLER, Hugo. Geschichte der Naturphilosophie. 174 p. Berlin: Junker u. Dünnhaupt, 1932.
Reviewed by V.F. Lenzen, *Isis*, 1934, 22: 284-5.

EASTON, Stewart C. The heritage of the past from the earliest times to 1715. xx, 845 p., ill. New York: Rinehart & Co., 1957. [CB 83/185]

ENRIQUES, F.; DE SANTILLANA, G. Compendio di storia del pensiero scientifico. vi, 481 p. Bologna: Zanichelli, 1937. [CB 52/577]

FORBES, R.J. Cultuurgeschiedenis van wetenschap en techniek. [Cultural history of science and technology. (In Dutch)]. 502 p., 105 ill., 37 fig. (Universiteit voor Zelfstudie) The Hague: N.V. Maandblad Succes, 1948.

FORBES, R.J.; DIJKSTERHUIS, E.J. A history of science and technology. 2 vol. 1. Ancient times to the seventeenth century. 294 p.; 2. The eighteenth and nineteenth centuries. p. 300-535, pl., bibliogr. Baltimore: Penguin Books, 1963.
Reviewed by J. Morton Briggs, Jr., *Isis*, 1964, 55: 101-2; by A.G. Drachman, *Centaurus*, 1963, 9: 131-2.

FORTUNE. The mighty force of research. ix, 308 p. New York: McGraw-Hill, 1956. [CB 83/193]
A series of essays describing current advances in various aspects of scientific effort.

FRIEDELL, Egon. Kulturgeschichte der Neuzeit. Die Krisis der europäischen Seele von der schwarzen Pest bis zum Weltkrieg. 3 vol. 1. Einleitung. Renaissance und Reformation. xii, 414 p. 1927; 2. Barock und Rokoko. Aufklärung und Revolution. xi, 536 p. 1930; 3. Romantik und Liberalismus. Imperialismus und Impressionismus. xi, 594 p. 1931. München: C.H. Beck, 1927-31.
Reviewed by W. Haberling, *Mitt.Gesch.Med.*, 1928, 27: 146-7.

FUENTES GUERRA, Rafael. La evolución de las ciencias exactas y aplicades en el intercambio cultural de Oriente y Occidente. 155 p., ill. Madrid: Artística, 1962.
Brief sketches, based on a series of articles published in *Boletín del Colegio Oficial de Ingenieros Industriales* of Madrid.

GARBEDIAN, H. Gordon. Major mysteries of science. 355 p., 64 pl. New York: Corvici, Friede, 1933.
Popular account of the current status of scientific discovery and hypothesis in the major fields of chemistry, physics, biology, geology, cosmology, and astronomy, with brief historical data.

GILLISPIE, Charles Coulston. The edge of objectivity. An essay in the history of scientific ideas. x, 562 p. Princeton, N.J.: Princeton University Press, 1960.
Reviewed by A. Rupert Hall, *Isis*, 1960, 51: 344-7; for other reviews *see* CB 86/451 and CB 88/521.

GINZBURG, Benjamin. The adventure of science. xvi, 487 p., 8 portr. New York: Simon and Schuster, 1930
Reviewed by Charles A. Kofoid, *Isis*, 1931, 16: 157-8.

GRAY, George W. The advancing front of science. xiii, 364 p. New York: Whittlesey House, 1937.
Popular account of recent advances in physics, astronomy, chemistry, and biology.

GUERLAC, Henry. Science in western civilization: a syllabus. 198 p. New York: The Ronald Press, 1952.
Reviewed by I. Bernard Cohen, *Isis*, 1953, 44: 293-5.

GUZZO, Augusto. La scienza. cxlii, 528 p. (Biblioteca di Filosofia, 10) Torino: Edizioni di "Filosofia," 1955.
Most of the essays deal with problems of the philosophy of science, but Part Two is historical.
Reviewed by Francesco Albèrgamo, *Arch.Int.Hist.Sci.*, 1956, 35: 51-3.

HALDANE, J.B.S. Science advances. 253 p. New York: Macmillan Co., 1947.
Reviewed by I.B. Cohen, *Isis*, 1948, 38: 255-6.

HALL, A. Rupert. The scientific revolution, 1500-1800. The formation of the modern scientific attitude. xvii, 390 p., ill. London/New York/Toronto; Longmans, Green, 1954; Boston: Beacon Press, 1956.
Reviewed by Marie Boas, *Isis*, 1955, 46: 304-5; for other reviews *see* CB 81/253, CB 82/192, CB 83/185 and CB 84/296.
2nd edition. London: 1962.

HALL, A. Rupert; BOAS HALL, Marie. A brief history of science. vi, 352 p., 14 fig. New York: New American Library, 1964.

HAMMOND, D.B. Stories of scientific discovery. vii, 199 p. Cambridge University Press, 1923.

HARIG, Gerhard, ed. Sowjetische Beiträge zur Geschichte der Naturwissenschaft. Übersetzung aus dem Russischen. viii, 243 p. Berlin: VEB Deutscher Verlag der Wissenschaften, 1960.
Reviewed by Friedrich Klemm, *Isis*, 1963, 54: 141-3; by J. O. Fleckenstein, *Arch.Int.Hist.Sci.*, 1962, 15: 158-66; by Anna Beckman, *Lychnos*, 1962, 394-6.

HARVEY-GIBSON, Robert John. Two thousand years of science: the wonders of nature and their discoverers. viii, 362 p. Rev. ed. London: Black, 1929.
Reviewed by E.J.H., *Nature*, 1930, 125: 404-5.

HEATH, A.E., ed. Scientific thought in the twentieth century. An authoritative account of fifty years progress in science. xv, 387 p. London: Watts, 1951; New York: Frederick Ungar Publishing Co., 1954. [CB 80/202]

HOLLANDER, Bernard. In search of the soul and the mechanism of thought, emotion and conduct. 2 vol. 1. The history of philosophy and science from ancient times to the present day. 526 p.; 2. The origin and the mental capacities and dispositions of man and their normal, abnormal and supernatural manifestations. vii, 361 p. London: Kegan Paul, 1920.

HOLMYARD, E.J. General science ... mainly chemistry and biology. xiii, 236 p., 8 portr. London: Dent, [1928]. [CB 24/521]

HOLMYARD, E.J. Science. An introductory text book. vi, 230 p., 98 fig. London: J.M. Dent and Sons, 1926. [CB 21/563]
Contains many historical notices.

HOMMAGE à Gaston Bachelard. Études de philosophie et d'histoire des sciences. 216 p. Paris: Presses Universitaires de France, 1957. [CB 83/280]
Reviewed by B. Rochot, *Arch.Int.Hist.Sci.*, 1958, 11: 50-2.

HULL, L.W.H. History and philosophy of science: an introduction. xi, 340 p. New York: Longmans, Green and Company, 1959.
Reviewed by Carl B. Boyer, *Isis*, 1960, 51: 347-8; for other reviews *see* CB 85/377 and CB 86/452.

HUMBERT, Pierre. Histoire des sciences. 81 p. (Initiations, 5) Pau: Editions de la Revue des Jeunes, 1943.
Reviewed by Pierre Brunet, *Rev.Hist.Sci.*, 1947, 1: 93.

HUNGER, Edgar. Von Demokrit bis Heisenberg. Quellen und Betrachtungen zur naturwissenschaftlichen Erkenntnis. 328 p., 11 portr. Braunschweig: Friedr. Vieweg & Sohn, 1958.
Reprinted 1963.
Reviewed by W. Berger, *Naturwiss.Rundsch.*, 1959, 12: 397.

HURD, David Leonard; KIPLING, J.J.; ed. The origins and growth of physical science. 2 vol., ill. Baltimore: Penguin Books, 1964.
Based on "Moments of discovery", *see* Schwartz, George; Bishop, Philip W.; ed. below.

HUTCHINSON, G.E. The itinerant ivory tower. Scientific and literary essays. xi, 261 p., ill. New Haven: Yale University Press; London: Oxford University Press, 1953. [CB 80/117]

HUTTEN, Ernest H. The origins of science. An inquiry into the foundations of Western thought. 241 p. London: George Allen and Unwin; New York: Humanities Press, 1962.
Reviewed by Paul K. Feyerabend, *Isis*, 1963, 54: 487-8.

JAMMER, Max. [The history of science. An introduction to the study of the historical development of scientific thought. (In Hebrew)]. 190 p. [Jerusalem: Kiryat Sepher, 1951]. [CB 79/164]

JASTROW, Joseph, ed. The story of human error. xviii, 445 p., 18 pl. New York: Appleton-Century, 1936.
Reviewed by Charles A. Kofoid, *Isis*, 1939, 30: 545-47.

JEANS, James Hopwood; *et al.* Scientific progress. 210 p., 31 fig. New York: Macmillan, 1936. [CB 53/256]
In the main historical in content.

KAEMPFFERT, Waldemar. Science, today and tomorrow. 279 p. New York: Viking Press, 1945.
Account of science in the making by the science editor of *The New York Times*.

LAIN ENTRALGO, Pedro; LÓPEZ PIÑERO, José Maria. Panorama histórico de la ciencia moderna. 865 p., ill. Madrid: Ediciones Guadarrama, 1963.

LARK-HOROVITZ, K.; CARMICHAEL, Eleanor. A chronology of scientific development, 1848-1948. 99 p. Washington, D.C.: American Association for the Advancement of Science, 1948. [CB 78/177]

LEE, Richard E. Man the universe builder. The backgrounds and foundations of the scientific technique. Rev. ed. xix 443 p., 16 fig., 4 pl., 10 tables. Baltimore: Williams and Wilkins, 1935. [CB 48/564]

LEPRINCE-RINGUET, Louis; FIGAL, Jean-Louis, ed. La science contemporaine. 1. Les sciences physiques et leurs applications. 360 p., ill. Paris: Librairie Larousse, 1964. [CB 90/505]
This is an addition to the familiar Larousse series of illustrated popular expositions of various subjects.

LEVY, Hyman. Modern science. A study of physical science in the world to-day. x, 736 p. London: Hamilton, 1939.
Reviewed by J.D. Bernal, *Nature*, 1939, 144: 3-4.

LIBBY, Walter. Introduction to contemporary civilization. An orientation course for college students. xiii, 272, xix p. New York: Knopf, 1929. [CB 28/560]

LIBBY, Walter. An introduction to the history of science. xi, 288 p., 8 pl. Boston: Houghton Mifflin Co., 1917.
Reviewed by George Sarton, *Isis*, 1923, 5: 478-9.

LIPPMANN, Edmund O. von. Abhandlungen und Vorträge zur Geschichte der Naturwissenschaften. 2 vol. Leipzig: Veit, 1909, 1913.

LIPPMANN, Edmund O. von. Beiträge zur Geschichte der Naturwissenschaften und Technik. 2 vol. viii, 314 p.; xii, 357 p., 1 ill. Berlin: Springer, 1923; Weinheim: Verlag Chemie, 1953.
Reviewed by George Sarton, *Isis*, 1924, 6: 116-19; by Eduard Farber, *ibid.*, 1953, 44: 404; for other reviews *see* CB 80/114.

LORENZEN, Paul. Die Entstehung der exakten Wissenschaften. v, 163 p., 70 fig. (Verständliche Wissenschaft, 72) Berlin: Springer-Verlag, 1960.
Reviewed by P. Collinder, *Lychnos*, 1960-61, 309-10.

LORIA, Gino. Pagine di storia della scienza. 151 p. Turin: G.B. Paravia, 1925. [CB 17/601]

McKENZIE, A.E.E. The major achievements of science. 2 vol. 1. xvi, 368 p., fig., pl., bibliogr.; 2. Selections from the literature. xii, 196 p., fig., bibliogr. Cambridge/New York: Cambridge University Press, 1960.
Reviewed by Robert E. Schofield, *Isis*, 1962, 53: 394-5; for other reviews *see* CB 87/552 and CB 88/522.

McLEAN, George F., ed. History and philosophy of science. 282 p. (Proceedings of the American Catholic Philosophical Association, 38) Washington: Catholic University of America, 1964.

THE MARCH of science: a first quinquennial review, 1931-1935. By various authors. Issued under the authority of the Council of the British Association for the Advancement of Science. viii, 215 p. London: Pitman, 1937. [CB 53/240]
Reviewed by A.S.R., *Nature*, 1937, 139: 216.

MARVIN, Francis S. The living past. A sketch of western progress. 288 p. Oxford: Clarendon Press, 1913.

MARVIN, Francis S., ed. The new world-order. Essays arranged and edited by F.S. Marvin. vi, 188 p. (Unity Series, 9) Oxford University Press, 1932.
Reviewed by E.J.H., *Nature*, 1932, 130: 76-7.

MASON, Stephen Finney. Main currents of scientific thought. A history of the sciences. viii, 520 p. New York: Henry Schuman; London: Routledge & Kegan Paul, 1953.
Reviewed by Robert C. Stauffer, *Isis*, 1954, 45: 201-2; for other reviews *see* CB 81/253. For reviews of French edition (Paris: Colin, 1956) *see* CB 82/193 and CB 83/186; of German edition (Stuttgart: Alfred Kröner, 1961) *see* CB 88/522.

MAYER, Joseph. The seven seals of science. An account of the unfoldment of orderly knowledge and its influence on human affairs. ix, 444 p., 43 ill., pl. New York: Century Co., 1927. [CB 22/253]
A popular account of the history of science.

MELSEN, Andrew G. van. Science and technology. x, 374 p. (Duquesne Studies, Philosophical Series, 13) Pittsburgh, Pa.: Duquesne University Press; Louvain: Nauwelaerts, 1961.
Reviewed by M. de Tollenaere, *Rev.Quest.Sci.*, 1962, 23: 455-6; by W.E.K. Middleton, *Technol.Cult.*, 1963, 4: 120-2.

MÉTRAUX, Guy S.; CROUZET, François; ed. The evolution of science. Readings from the history of mankind. 432 p., ill. New York: New American Library, 1963. [CB 89/484]
Reviewed by David L. Anderson, *Technol.Cult.*, 1964, 5: 598-600.

MIELI, Aldo. El desarrollo de la historia de la ciencia a traves de ciento veinte acontecimientos fundamentales. *Universidad*, 1942, 13: 55-199.
History of science summarized in 120 chapters. First part, no. 1-60, to Boerhaave.

MIELI, Aldo. Panorama general de historia de la ciencia. 1. El mundo antiquo: griegos y romanos. xxiv, 295 p. 1945. 2. La época medieval: mundo islamico y occidente cristiano. xviii, 354 p. 1946. 3. La eclosion del Renacimento. xxii, 400 p. 1951. 4. Lionardo da Vinci, sabio. xv, 223 p. 1950. 5. La ciencia del Renacimiento: matemàtica y ciencias naturales. Buenos Aires: Espasa-Calpe, 1945-51. [CB 78/143 and CB 78/177]
Work continued by D. Papp, *see* below.
Vol. 1 and 2 reviewed by Pierre Brunet, *Arch.Int.Hist.Sci.*, 1947, 1: 172-6; vol. 2 by J. Vernet, *Al-Andalus*, 1948, 13: 232-4; vol. 3 and 4 by P. Sergescu, *Rev.Hist.Sci.*, 1952, 5: 372-3; vol. 5 by R. Taton, *ibid.*, 1956, 9: 93-4.

MIELI, Aldo. Sumario de un curso de historia de la ciencia en ciento veinte numeros. I. No. 1-74. vii, 251 p. Santa Fe, Argentina: 1943. [CB 65/78]
Reviewed by Pierre Brunet, *Arch.Int.Hist.Sci.*, 1947, 1: 172-6.

MÖRL, Anton von. Die grosse Weltordnung. 3 vol. 1. Die Geburt der Wissenschaft. 525 p.; 2. Verfall der antiken Wissenschaft. 291 p. Vienna: Zsolnay, 1947-48; 3. Die Wiedergeburt der Wissenschaft. 471 p. Innsbruck: Wagner, 1952.
Volumes 1 and 2 reviewed by Robert Eisler, *Arch.Int.Hist.Sci.*, 1949, 2: 1162-3.

MOULTON, Forest Ray; SCHIFFERES, Justus J.; ed. The autobiography of science. 2nd ed. xxxiii, 748 p. Garden City, N.Y.: Doubleday & Company, 1960. [CB 86/452]
Spanish translation of first edition (Mexico: Fondo de Cultura Económica, 1947) reviewed by Aldo Mieli, *Arch.Int. Hist.Sci.*, 1948, 1: 724-6.

NEEDHAM, Joseph; PAGEL, Walter; ed. Background to modern science. xii, 243 p. New York: Macmillan, 1938.
Reviewed by M.F. Ashley Montagu, *Isis*, 1940, 31: 465-6.

NEW frontiers of knowledge. A symposium by distinguished writers, notable scholars and public figures. By Arnold Toynbee [*et al.*] x, 125 p. Washington: Public Affairs Press, 1957. [CB 83/277]
Based upon a series of talks broadcast by the United States Information Agency. The contributors are scientists, educators, artists, and statesmen, many but not all Americans.

NEWMAN, James R. Science and sensibility. 2 vol. xii, 372 p., ill.; xii, 309 p., ill. New York: Simon and Schuster, 1961.
A collection of essays by the editor of the *Scientific American*.
Reviewed by J.E. McGuire, *Arch.Int.Hist.Sci.*, 1964, 16: 70-1.

OSBORN, Henry Fairfield. From the Greeks to Darwin. 2nd ed. xvi, 398 p. New York: Scribner's, 1929.
Reviewed by George Sarton, *Isis*, 1930, 13: 386-8.

PANORAMA of science: annual supplement to the Smithsonian Scientific Series, 1951-52. 2 vol. ill. New York: Series Publishers, 1951-52. [CB 79/149]
Volume for 1951 edited by T.P. True.
Reviewed by A.J. Hatch, *Amer.J.Phys.*, 1952, 20: 316-17.

PAPP, Desiderio; BABINI, José. Panorama general de historia de la ciencia. 7 vol. 6. La ciencia del Renacimiento: astronomía, física, biologia. 193 p. 1952; 7. La ciencia del Renacimiento: las ciencias exactas en el siglo XVII. xii, 234 p. 1954; 8. El siglo del iluminismo. xii, 256 p. 1955; 9. Biologia y medicina en los siglos XVII y XVIII. xii, 258 p. 1959; 10. Las ciencias exactas en el siglo XIX. xv, 310 p. 1958; 11. Biologia y medicina del siglo XIX. xii, 276 p. 1961; 12. Ciencia de la tierra y técnica del siglo XIX. xii, 257 p. 1961. Buenos Aires: Espasa Calpe Argentina, 1952-61.
Continuation of work begun by A. Mieli, *see* above.
Reviewed by R. Taton, *Rev.Hist.Sci.*, 1956, 9: 93-4 (vol. 6-7); 1964, 17: 166-7 (vol. 8-12); *Arch.Int.Hist.Sci.*, 1964, 16: 66-7 (vol. 10).

PARMELEE, Maurice. The history of modern culture. 1295 p. New York: Philosophical Library, 1960.

PÉRÈS, J. Les sciences exactes. 198 p. (Histoire du Monde, 3) Paris: De Boccard, 1930.
Reviewed by L. Guinet, *Isis*, 1931, 15: 188-90.

PERRIN, Jean; *et al.* L'orientation actuelle des sciences. Introduction de Léon Brunschvicg. 158 p. (Bibliothèque de Philosophie Contemporaine) Paris: Alcan, 1930. [CB 33/392]

PICARD, Emile. Un coup d'oeil sur l'histoire des sciences et des théories physiques. 101 p. Paris: Gauthier-Villars, 1930. [CB 30/464]
Also printed in part in *Rev.Sci.*, 1930.

PICARD, Emile. Discours et mélanges. 294 p. Paris Gauthier-Villars, 1922. [CB 14/519]
A collection of essays of a biographical and historical nature.

PICARD, Emile. Discours et notices. viii, 363 p. Paris: Gauthier-Villars, 1936.
Reviewed by George Sarton, *Isis*, 1937, 27: 342-4.

PICARD, Emile. Eloges et discours académiques. viii, 400 p. Paris: Gauthier-Villars, 1931.
Reviewed by George Sarton, *Isis*, 1932, 17: 443.

PICARD, Emile. Mélanges de mathématiques et de physique. 366 p. Paris: Gauthier-Villars, 1924. [CB 18/562]
A collection of essays of a biographical and historical nature.

PICARD, Emile. Das Wissen der Gegenwart in Mathematik und Naturwissenschaft. Transl. by F. and L. Lindemann. iv, 292 p. (Wissenschaft und Hypothese, 16) Leipzig: Teubner, 1913.
Translation of: La science moderne et son état actuel. Paris: 1905.

A PICTORIAL history of science and engineering. The story of man's technological and scientific progress from the dawn of history to the present, told in 1,000 pictures and 75,000 words. By the editors of *Year*. 263 p., ill. New York: *Year*, 1958.
Reviewed by Robert P. Multhauf, *Science*, 1958, 128: 1170.

PLEDGE, H.T. Science since 1500. A short history of mathematics, physics, chemistry, and biology. 357 p., ill., bibliogr. New York: Harper & Brothers, 1959.
First publ. London: H.M.S.O., 1939.
Reviewed by I. Bernard Cohen, *Isis*, 1941, 33: 74-9; by P. Bockstaele, *Sci.Hist.*, 1960, 2: 24-6; in *Sci.Amer.*, 1960, 202: no. 1, 181-2.

PRICE, Derek J. de Solla. Science since Babylon. x, 149 p., graphs. New Haven: Yale University Press, 1961.
Reviewed by Herbert Butterfield, *Isis*, 1962, 53: 395-6; for other reviews *see* CB 87/552, CB 88/522 and CB 89/495.

PRICE, George McCready. A history of some scientific blunders. 138 p. London: Oliphant, 1930.

PRINGLE, Patrick. Great discoveries in modern science. 206 p. London: George G. Harrap and Co., 1955.
Reviewed in *Sch.Sci.Rev.*, 1956, 37: 469.

REASON, H.A. The road to modern science. 3rd ed. v, 344 p., fig., pl. London: G. Bell & Sons Ltd., 1959. [CB 87/552]
First publ. New York: Appleton-Century, 1940. [CB 60/141]
This is a volume intended specifically for English students in the sixth form.

REICHENBACH, Hans. From Copernicus to Einstein. Translated by Ralph B. Winn. 123 p. New York: Philosophical Library, 1942.
Reviewed by Gordon Ferrie Hull, *Science*, 1943, 98: 85-6.

REY PASTOR, Julio, ed. Colección de historia y filosofía de la ciencia. Buenos Aires: Espasa-Calpe, 1945-
Reviewed by Aldo Mieli, *Arch.Int.Hist.Sci.*, 1947, 1: 165-72.

REYMOND, Arnold. Philosophie spiritualiste. Études et méditations, recherches critiques. 2 vol. xxiii, 429 p.; viii, 448 p., bibliogr. (Recueil publié par la Faculté des Lettres de l'Université de Lausanne) Lausanne: Rouge, 1942. [CB 70/270]
Includes many articles on the philosophy and history of science.

RICCI, Mario, ed. Momenti del pensiero scientifico e della tecnica. 313 p., ill. Bologna: Casa Editrice Ponti Nuovo, 1962.

RITCHIE, Arthur David. Studies in the history and methods of the sciences. vi, 230 p. (Edinburgh University Publications: History, Philosophy and Economics, 2) Edinburgh: University Press, 1958.
Reviewed by A.V. Hill, *Nature*, 1959, 184: 4-5; by Stephen Toulmin, *Bull.Brit.Soc.Hist.Sci.*, 1960, 10: 346-9; by P. Collinder, *Lychnos*, 1960-61, 306-8.

ROSSITER, A.P. The growth of science. An outline history. 372 p. London: Pitman (for the Orthological Institute), 1939.
Reviewed by I. Bernard Cohen, *Isis*, 1941, 33: 74-9.

ROUSSEAU, Pierre. Histoire de la science. 825 p. Paris: Fayard, 1945.

RUSSO, François. Histoire de la pensée scientifique. 125 p. (Collection "La Colombe") Paris: Édit. du Vieux Colombier, 1951.
Reviewed by H. Dopp, *Rev.Quest.Sci.*, 1951, 12: 319; by Pierre Costabel, *Rev.Hist.Sci.*, 1953, 6: 69-70; by P. Sergescu, *Arch.Int.Hist.Sci.*, 1953, 6: 93-4.

SARTON, George. The life of science: essays in the history of civilization. viii, 197 p. New York: Schuman, 1948; Bloomington, Ind.: Indiana University Press (paper back ed.), 1960.
Reviewed by Chauncey D. Leake, *Isis*, 1949, 40: 282-3; for other reviews *see* CB 73/164, CB 74/384, CB 75/85, CB 76/390, CB 77/363, CB 78/178 and CB 79/166.
Japanese translation Tokyo: Chukyo Shuppan Sha, 1951; Persian translation Teheran: Ebnesina, 1955.

SARTON, George. Sarton on the history of science. Essays. Selected and ed. by Dorothy Stimson. xvi, 383 p. Cambridge, Mass.: Harvard University Press; London: Oxford University Press, 1962.
Reviewed by A. Armitage, *Ann.Sci.*, 1962, 18: 129-30; by Marshall Clagett, *J.Hist.Med.*, 1964, 19: 84-5.

SCHNEER, Cecil J. The search for order: the development of the major ideas in the physical sciences from the earliest times to the present. Foreword by Henry Margenau. xvii, 397 p., ill. New York: Harper & Brothers, 1960.
Reviewed by Robert P. Multhauf, *Isis*, 1961, 52: 589-90; for other reviews *see* CB 86/453 and CB 87/552.

SCHWARTZ, George; BISHOP, Philip W.; ed. Moments of discovery. 2 vol. 1. The origins of science. xviii, 500 p., ill.; 2. The development of modern science. xii, 510 p. New York: Basic Books, Inc., 1958.
Reviewed by Robert E. Schofield, *Isis*, 1959, 50: 484-6; for other reviews *see* CB 84/297 and CB 85/378.

SCIENCE, medicine and history. *See* Nc-bm

SEDGWICK, W.T.; TYLER, H.W.; BIGELOW, R.P. A short history of science. xxi, 512 p., 61 fig., maps. New York: Macmillan, 1939. [CB 59/464]
First publ. 1917. Spanish translation by José Babini, Buenos Aires: Argos, 1950.
Reviewed by I. Bernard Cohen, *Isis*, 1941, 33: 74-9.

SEN, Samarendranath. Bijnaner itihas. [A history of science. (In Bengali)] Vol. 1, 2. xv, 348 p., 13 pl., 1955; xvi, 430 p., 18 pl., 1958. Calcutta: Indian Association for the Cultivation of Science, 1955- [CB 82/235]
Volume 3 not yet published. 2nd ed. of vol. 1, 1961.
Reviewed by F.A. Allchin, *Nature*, 1956, 178: 1367; 1959, 183: 1353-4.

SERGESCU, Pierre. Coups d'oeil sur les origines de la science exacte moderne. 203 p. (Collection "Esprit et Méthode", 2) Paris: Société d'Edition d'Enseignement Supérieur, 1951. [CB 79/166]
Reviewed by Andrea Corsini, *Riv.Stor.Sci.*, 1952, 43: 280-1.

SHAPLEY, Harlow; RAPPORT, Samuel; WRIGHT, Helen; ed. A treasury of science. 5th rev. ed. xii, 788 p., ill. New York: Harper and Row, [1963].
First published 1943.

SINGER, Charles. From magic to science. Essays on the scientific twilight. 254 p. New York: Dover Publications, 1958.
First published London and New York, 1928. [CB 26/225]
Reviewed by Jean Beaujeu, *Arch.Int.Hist.Sci.*, 1962, 15: 179; by Albert Lejeune, *Rev.Quest.Sci.*, 1960, 21: 590.

SINGER, Charles. New worlds and old. Essays. vii, 178 p. London: Heinemann, 1951. [CB 79/166]

SINGER, Charles. A short history of science to the nineteenth century. xiv, 399 p., 94 ill. Oxford: Clarendon Press, 1941.
Reviewed by I. Bernard Cohen and Charles A. Kofoid, *Isis*, 1942, 34: 177-80; by Sten Lindroth, *Lychnos*, 1943, 360-4.

SINGER, Charles. A short history of scientific ideas to 1900. xviii, 525 p., fig., front. Oxford: Clarendon Press, 1959.
Publ. in paperback 1962.
For reviews *see* CB 85/378, CB 86/453 and CB 87/552.

SLICHTER, C.S. Science in a tavern. xi, 186 p. Madison, Wisc.: University of Wisconsin Press, 1939. [CB 57/232]

SLOSSON, Edwin E. Chats on science. xi, 273 p., ill. New York: Century Co., 1924. [CB 16/338]

SLOSSON, Edwin E., ed. Keeping up with science: notes on recent progress in the various sciences for unscientific readers. xv, 355 p., 30 pl. London: Cape, 1924.

SMITHSONIAN scientific series. Editor-in-chief: Charles Greeley Abbot. 12 vol., ill. New York: Smithsonian Institution Series, Inc., 1943.

STÖRIG, Hans Joachim. Kleine Weltgeschichte der Wissenschaft. xix, 778 p. Stuttgart: W. Kohlhammer Verlag, 1954.
Reviewed by Erwin N. Hiebert, *Isis*, 1956, 47: 424-6; by Sten Lindroth, *Lychnos*, 1956, 244-5.

STUDIES and essays offered to George Sarton. Ed. by M.F. Ashley Montagu. xiv, 595 p., fig., pl. New York: Schuman, 1947.
Reviewed by George Sarton, *Isis*, 1947, 38: 127-8; for other reviews *see* CB 72/268, CB 74/384 and CB 76/390.

STUDIES in the history and method of science. Ed. by Charles Singer. 2 vol. xiv, 304 p., 41 pl., ill.; xxii, 559 p., 55 pl., ill. Oxford: Clarendon Press, 1917, 1921.
Reviewed by George Sarton, *Isis*, 1922, 4: 380-2 and *Science*, 1918, 47: 316-19.

SULLIVAN, John William Navin. The bases of modern science. x, 246 p. London: Benn, 1928.
Reviewed by J.A.C., *Nature*, 1929, 123: 273.

TANNERY, Paul. Mémoires scientifiques. 17 vol. Toulouse: Privat; Paris: Gauthier Villars, 1912-50. [CB 70/249, CB 78/178 and CB 81/346]
Vol. 6 (Sciences modernes (1883-1904)) and vol. 10 (Suppl. to vol. 6) reviewed by George Sarton, *Isis*, 1927, 9: 472-6; *Ibid.*, 1931, 16: 155-7.

TATON, René, ed. Histoire générale des sciences. 4 vol. 1. La science antique et médiévale (des origines à 1450). viii, 627 p.; 2. La science moderne (de 1450 à 1800). viii, 800 p., ill.; 3. La science contemporaine. (i) Le XIXe siècle. 755 p., ill. (ii) Le XXe siècle. viii, 1080 p. Paris: Presses Universitaires de France, 1957-64.
Reviewed in *Isis*, 1958, 49: 445-6 (Aydin Sayili); 1960, 51: 574-6 (Marie Boas Hall); 1963, 54: 305-6 (L. Pearce Williams); and CB 90/623. For other reviews *see*: for vol. 1, CB 83/187, CB 84/296, CB 85/378; for vol. 2, CB 85/378, CB 86/453, CB 87/552, CB 89/485; for vol. 3, CB 88/618 and CB 89/560.

TATON, René, ed. History of science. Transl. by A.J. Pomerans. 4 vol. 1. Ancient and medieval sciences from prehistory to A.D.1450. 552 p., ill.; 2. The beginnings of modern science, from 1450 to 1800. xx, 667 p.; 3. Science in the nineteenth century. xix, 623 p.; 4. Science in the twentieth century. xxiv, 638 p. New York: Basic Books; London: Thames & Hudson, 1963-66. [CB 89/485]
For reviews in *Isis* and other reviews *see* French original above.

TAYLOR, F. Sherwood. An illustrated history of science. 178 p., 118 fig. New York: F.A. Praeger; London: William Heinemann, 1955. [CB 81/254]
Reviewed by R.J. Forbes, *Arch.Int.Hist.Sci.*, 1956, 9: 53.

TAYLOR, F. Sherwood. The march of mind. A short history of science. xiv, 320 p., 36 fig., 14 pl. London: Heinemann; New York: Macmillan, 1939. [CB 59/465]
Reviewed by I. Bernard Cohen, *Isis*, 1941, 33: 74-9.

TAYLOR, F. Sherwood. Science, past and present. viii, 275 p., 22 pl. London: Heinemann, 1945.
New ed. (x, 368 p., 28 pl., 53 ill.) 1949; reprinted 1958. Paperback reprint, 1962.
Reviewed by H.D. Anthony, *Nature*, 1946, 127: 144.
For American edition *see* below.

TAYLOR, F. Sherwood. A short history of science and scientific thought: with readings from the great scientists from the Babylonians to Einstein. 368 p. New York: W.W. Norton & Co., 1949. [CB 76/391]
American edition of "Science, past and present". 2nd ed., 1949. Reprinted 1963.
Reviewed by Richard Harrison Shryock, *Scr.Math.*, 1953, 19: 251-2.

TAYLOR, F. Sherwood. The world of science. 2nd ed. 1114 p., ill. London: Heinemann; New York: Norton, 1950. [CB 78/179]
First published 1936; 3rd edition 1952.

THORNDIKE, Lynn. A history of magic and experimental science. 8 vol. New York: Columbia University Press, 1923-58.
Vol. 1-2, 3-4 reviewed by G. Sarton, *Isis*, 1924, 6: 74-89 and 1935, 23: 471-5; vol. 5-6 by D.B. Durand, *ibid.* 1942, 33: 691-712; vol.7-8 by I.B. Cohen, *ibid.* 1958, 49: 453-5.

THORNDIKE, Lynn. A short history of civilization. xiv, 619 p., ill., maps. New York: F.S. Crofts, 1926. [CB 21/591]

TIMPANARO, Sebastiano. Scritti di storia e critica della scienza. 334 p. Florence: Sansoni, [1952]. [CB 79/166]
Reviewed in *Sci.Veterum*, 1953, 2: no. 2, 7.

TRUE, Webster P., ed. Smithsonian treasury of science. 3 vol. xvi, 1208 p. New York: Simon and Schuster, 1960.
A selection of articles from the *Annual Reports of the Smithsonian Institution*.
Reviewed by I. Bernard Cohen, *Isis*, 1962, 53: 513-14; W.J. Cunningham, *Amer.Scient.*, 1961, 49: 172A-173A.

TURNER, D.M. The book of scientific discovery. How science has aided human welfare. 259 p., 39 fig., 31 pl. London: Harrap, 1933. [CB 42/577]

URBAIN, Georges; BOLL, Marcel. La science, ses progrès, ses applications. 2 vol. 1. La science jusqu'à la fin du XIXe siècle. 384 p., 1160 fig., 6 pl.; 2. Les applications et les théories actuelles. 424 p., 1200 fig., 6 pl. Paris; Larousse, 1933-34. [CB 40/397 and CB 41/578]

VALJAVEC, Fritz, ed. Das 19. und 20. Jahrhundert. Foreword by the editor. 818 p. (Historia Mundi, 10) Bern/Munich: Francke Verlag, 1961. [CB 89/560]

VASSILIEV, S.F. [Some features of the evolution of scientific theories (in memory of the 40th anniversary of Engels's death). (In Russian, with English summary)] *Arkh.Ist.Nauk. Tekh.*, 1936, 8: 1-27.

VERA, Francisco. Historia de la ciencia. xvi, 684 p. Barcelona, Iberia: Joaquín Gil, 1937. [CB 63/269]
This work covers the entire field of the sciences and also includes some material on inventions and industry.

VOICE of America. History of science. 102 p., portr. Washington, 1964.
For contents *see* CB 90/502.

WALTER, Emil J. Erforschte Welt. Die wichtigsten Ergebnisse der naturwissenschaftlichen Forschung. 2nd ed. 363 p., 65 fig., 15 pl. (Sammlung Dalp, 5) Bern: Francke Verlag, 1953.

WALTER, Emil J. Unser naturwissenschaftliches Weltbild. Sein Werden vom Altertum bis zur Gegenwart. 247 p., 84 fig. Zürich: Niehans Verlag, 1938. [CB 57/233]

WATANABE, Masao. [Science in the history of modern culture. (In Japanese with English summary)] iv, 353 p. Tokyo: Mirai-Sha, 1962.
Reviewed by Edward E. Daub, *Isis*, 1964, 55: 374-5.

WESTAWAY, F.W. The endless quest. 3000 years of science. xix, 1080 p., 193 fig., 51 pl. London: Blackie, 1934. [CB 42/577]

WHETHAM, William Cecil Dampier-, *see* DAMPIER, William Cecil

WIENER, Philip P.; NOLAND, Aaron; ed. Roots of scientific thought. A cultural perspective. x, 677 p. New York: Basic Books, 1957. [CB 83/187]
Reviewed by L. Marton, *Phys.Today*, 1958, 11: 32-4; by Arthur C. Danto, *Science*, 1958, 127: 973-4; by E.H. Hutten, *Brit.J.Phil.Sci.*, 1960, 11: 261-2.

WIGHTMAN, William P.D. The growth of scientific ideas. xii, 495 p., 34 fig., 8 pl. Edinburgh: Oliver and Boyd, 1950; New Haven: Yale University Press, 1964.

WOODRUFF, L.L., ed. The development of the sciences. xiv, 327 p., 28 pl. New Haven: Yale University Press, 1923. [CB 15/243]
Six public lectures organized in 1920 before the Yale Chapter of the Gamma Alpha Graduate Scientific Fraternity.

WOODRUFF, L.L., ed. The development of the sciences. 2nd series. iv, 336 p., front. New Haven: Yale University Press, 1941. [CB 62/71]
Eight lectures given in 1939-40, under the auspices of the Yale Chapter of the Gamma Alpha Scientific Fraternity.

YERKES, Robert M., ed. The new world of science. Its development during the war. xx, 443 p., ill. New York: Century, 1920. [CB 11/422]

Ac-bn *essays; articles*

ALLEN, Frank. Physical science, ancient and modern. *Univ. Toronto Quart.*, 1934, 3: 146-66.

BOCCARDI, Jean. Les sciences d'observation à travers les âges. *Rev.Sci.*, 1933, 71: 225-30.

BUTTERFIELD, Herbert. The scientific revolution. *Sci.Amer.*, 1960, 203: no. 3, 173-92.

CARDWELL, D.S.L. Reflections on some problems in the history of science. *Mem.Manchester Lit.Phil.Soc.*, 1963-64, 106: 108-23.

COHEN, I. Bernard. The wonderful century. *Atlantic Mon.*, Oct. 1957, 200: 80-4.
"The *Atlantic's* hundred years have seen science and technology transform our world not once but repeatedly."

COLOMBO, Giuseppe. Le scienze fisiche e le loro applicazioni nel cinquantennio, 1865-1915. *Scientia*, 1916, 19: 333-47.

DANNEMANN, Friedrich, ed. Der Werdegang der Entdeckungen und Erfindungen. Unter Berücksichtigung der Sammlungen des Deutschen Museums und ähnlicher wissenschaftlich-technischer Anstalten. München: R. Oldenbourg, 1922-27. [CB 14/564]
Series of popular pamphlets on the history of science and technology.

DELTHEIL, A. Quelques caractères essentiels de l'évolution des sciences depuis un siècle. *Rev.Sci.*, 1933, 71: 129-34.

DIJKSTERHUIS, E.J. Die Mechanisierung des Weltbildes. *Abhandlungen zur Wissenschaftsgeschichte und Wissenschaftslehre*, p. 33-63. (Veröffentlichungen der Gesellschaft für Internationale Wissenschaftsgeschichte. 1952, no. 1) Bremen: 1952.

DIJKSTERHUIS, E.J. Die Mechanisierung des Weltbildes. *Phys. Bl.*, 1956, 12: 481-93.

DINGLE, Herbert. The scientific outlook in 1851 and in 1951. *Proc.Roy.Inst.*, 1951-54, 35: 68-89.

DONATH, Eduard. Die wichtigsten Momente für die Entwicklung der Naturwissenschaft in den letzten fünfzig Jahren. *Verhandl.Naturforsch.Ver.Brünn*, 1912, vol. 50.

DuBRIDGE, Lee A. Science, the endless adventure. *Sci.Teacher*, 1956, 23: 273-6, 307.

DUFOURCQ, A. Les origines de la science moderne d'après les découvertes récentes. *Rev.Deux Mondes*, 1913, 83: 349-78.

FLOREY, Howard. Development of modern science. *Nature*, 1963, 200: 397-402.

FUETER, Eduard. Über Bedingungen wissenschaftlicher Leistung in der europäischen Kultur der Neuzeit. *Gesnerus*, 1951, 8: 66-84.
Largely apropos of A. de Candolle's book, *see* Ac-bm.

GREGORY, Richard. Science in a changing world: recollections and reflections. *Nature*, 1936, 137: 981-8, 3 fig.

HALL, A. Rupert, ed. The making of modern science. Six essays. 55 p. Leicester: Leicester University Press, 1960. Reviewed by Fredrik Neumeyer, *Lychnos*, 1962, 407; by W.H. Brock, *Hist.Sci.*, 1962, 1: 117-18.

HEYL, Paul R. The genealogical tree of modern science. *Amer. Scient.*, 1944, 32: 135-44.
A sketch of the origins of science.

HOPKINS, Frederick Gowland. A survey of progressive science. *Nature*, 1933, 132: 878-80.
From the presidential address to the Royal Society, delivered on 30 November.

KOL'MAN, E. Nekotorye teoreticheskie problemy istorii estestvoznaniia i tekhniki i trud Dzh. Bernala *Nauka v istorii obshchestva*. [Some theoretical problems in the history of natural science and technology and the work of John Bernal *Science in history*. (In Russian)]. *Vop.Ist.Est.Tekh.*, 1958, 6: 84-94.

LACOIN, Maurice. De la scolastique à la science moderne. Pierre Duhem et Anneliese Maier. *Rev.Quest.Sci.*, 1956, 17: 325-43.

LACOIN, Maurice. Naissance de la science moderne. *Act.VIIIe Congr.Int.Hist.Sci.* (Florence, 1956), p. 1171-5. Paris: Hermann, 1958.

LECLAINCHE, X. Aperçu sur le développement des sciences et de la médecine à travers les âges. *Rev.Gén.Sci.*, 1961, 14: 197-206.

NAGEL, Ernest. Science as history. *N.Y.Rev.Books*, 1964, 1: no. 12, 14-16.
Essay review of A.C. Crombie's "Scientific change", *see* Ac-bq

OPPENHEIMER, J.R. The age of science: 1900-1950. *Sci.Amer.*, 1950, 183: no. 3, 20-3.

PATRI, Aimé. Achievements, 1900-1950. *Univ.Penn.Libr.Chron.*, 1950, 17: 43-60. [CB 77/345]

RAINOV, T.I. [Fundamental scientific discoveries. (In Russian)]. *Sotsialist.Rekonstruktsiia Nauk.*, 1935, no. 9, 84-95; no. 10, 82-96. [CB 47/281]

REYMOND, Arnold. Les étapes de la pensée scientifique. *Archeion*, 1935, 17: 133-48.

SAGERET, J. La genèse des sciences. *Rev.Mois*, 1912, 13: 513-40.

SCHURMANN, Paul F. En feuilletant l'histoire des sciences. L'évolution de l'esprit scientifique. 40 p. Montevideo: Urta y Curbelo, 1942.

SCIENTIFIC centenaries. (Calendar of centenaries) [Annual article appearing in a January issue of each year of *Nature*, 1930, vol. 125 to 1962, vol. 193]
Edited from 1933-53 by Edgar C. Smith; from 1954-62 by Joan M. Eyles.

SETH, George. From Galton to Crowther. *Advance.Sci.*, 1961, 18: 273-83.

SHAPLEY, Harlow; *et al.* The age of science, 1900-1950, with introduction by J.R. Oppenheimer. *Sci.Amer.*, 1950, 183: no. 3, 118 p., ill. [CB 77/345]

SINGER, Charles. The beginnings of science. *Nature*, 1931, 128: 7-10.
Inaugural address delivered to the 2nd International Congress of the History of Science and Technology.

SINGER, Charles. Les progrès de l'esprit scientifique au cours de l'histoire. *Act.Ve Congr.Int.Hist.Sci.* (Lausanne, 1947), p. 36-44. Paris: Hermann, 1948. Also in *Arch.Int.Hist.Sci.*, 1948, 1: 222-30.

SMUTS, J.C. The scientific world-picture of today. *Nature*, 1931, 128: 521-9.
Presidential address delivered in London on Sept. 23, 1931, at the centenary meeting of the British Association.

TESTI, Gino. Alcuni notevoli anniversari scientifici per il 1932. *Riv.Stor.Sci.*, 1932, 23: 34-5.

THOMPSON, D'Arcy Wentworth. The Golden Ages. *Science, Medicine and History. Essays in honour of Charles Singer*, p. 409-18, 6 fig. London: Oxford University Press, 1953.

THORNDIKE, Lynn. The historical background of modern science. *Sci.Mon.*, 1923, 16: 488-97.

TRIBUTE of science to the Royal Jubilee. *Nature*, 1935, 135: 669-755.
Reviewed by G. Sarton, *Isis*, 1936, 24: 433.

VETTER, Quido. [Dawn of new science from Copernicus to Laplace. (In Czech)] In: *Dějiny lidstva od pravěkv k dnešku*, vol. 6, pt. 1, 14 p. Prague: Melantrich, [193-].

WATERMAN, Alan T. Science in the sixties. *Amer.Scient.*, 1961, 49: 1-8.

WINTER, H.J.J. The history of scientific thought with special reference to Asia. 15 p. (Transaction, 5) Basavangudi, Bangalore: Indian Institute of Culture, 1951.

Ac-bq *Symposia; Conference Proceedings*

for accounts and impressions of history of science conferences *see* Afqv and Afqx

BRITISH ASSOCIATION FOR THE ADVANCEMENT OF SCIENCE. The advancement of science, 1931. Addresses delivered at the Centenary Meeting of the Association, London, Sept. 23-30, 1931. 275 p., ill. London: British Association, 1932.

CRITICAL problems in the history of science. Proceedings of the Institute for the History of Science at the University of Wisconsin, September 1-11, 1957. Ed. by Marshall Clagett. xiv, 555 p., ill. Madison, Wisc.: University of Wisconsin Press, 1959.
Reviewed by M.A. Hoskin, *Isis*, 1962, 53: 230-1; for other reviews *see* CB 85/377, CB 86/451 and CB 87/551.
A brief account of the Wisconsin meeting was given in *Isis*, 1957, 48: 461-2.

CROMBIE, Alistair C., ed. Scientific change. Historical studies in the intellectual, social, and technical conditions for scientific discovery and technical invention, from antiquity to the present. (Symposium on the History of Science, University of Oxford, 9-15 July 1961.) xii, 896 p. New York: Basic Books, 1963.
For reviews *see* CB 90/600.

THE HISTORY of science; origins and results of the scientific revolution: a symposium [by Herbert Butterfield and others]. 184 p. London: Cohen and West; Glencoe, Ill.: Free Press, 1951. [CB 78/177]
A series of broadcast talks delivered on the Third Programme of the B.B.C. during 1949-50.
Reviewed by Bern Dibner, *Scr.Math.*, 1953, 19: 45-8. For later edition, *see* below A SHORT history of science ...

HOLTON, Gerald, ed. Science and the modern mind. A symposium. 110 p. Boston: The Beacon Press, 1958.
Reviewed by Herbert Dingle, *Isis*, 1960, 51: 90-1; by Norwood Russell Hanson, *Phys.Today*, 1960, 13: 68-72.

A SHORT history of science; origins and results of the scientific revolution: a symposium [by Herbert Butterfield and others]. xiv, 138 p., fig., tables, bibliogr. Garden City, N.Y.: Doubleday, 1959. [CB 85/378]
See also above THE HISTORY of science ...

SOVESHCHANIE po istorii estestvoznaniia, Moscow, 1946. Trudy. [All-Union conference on the history of natural sciences, Moscow, 1946. Ed. by Kh.S. Koshtoyants. (In Russian)]. 376 p. Moscow: Akademiia Nauk SSSR, 1948. [CB 75/85]

STUDIES in the history of science. 123 p. (University of Pennsylvania Bicentennial Conference). Philadelphia: University of Pennsylvania Press, 1941.
Reviewed by Solomon Gandz, *Isis*, 1943, 34: 226. A short note on the Conference appeared in *Isis*, 1941, 33: 64.

WISCONSIN UNIVERSITY. Science and civilization, edited by Robert C. Stauffer. xiii, 212 p. Madison: University of Wisconsin Press, 1949. [CB 76/391]
Symposium of the Wisconsin History of Science Group.

Ac-br *periodicals*

Abhandlungen zur Wissenschaftsgeschichte und Wissenschaftslehre. Ed. by Hans Schimank. No. 1, 1951- Bremen: 1951-

Annals of Science. A quarterly review of the history of science since the Renaissance. Vol. 1, no. 1, January 15, 1936- London: Taylor and Francis, 1936-
Vol. 1, no. 1 reviewed by George Sarton, *Isis*, 1936, 25: 488; by A. Pogo, *Astrophys.J.*, 1936, 83: 256.

Archeion. Archivio di Storia della Scienza. Ed. by Aldo Mieli. Vol. 1-25, no. 1. Roma: 1919-43.
Entitled *Archivio di Storia della Scienza* from 1919-26, vol. 1-7, fasc. 2. Vol. 22-25 published in Santa Fé (Argentina).
For accounts of the history of *Archeion*, *see* prefaces by Aldo Mieli, *Archeion*, 1938, 21: 1-9; *Arch.Int.Hist.Sci.*, 1947, 1: 5-8.

Archiv für Geschichte der Mathematik, der Naturwissenschaften und der Technik. *Isis*, 1928, 10: 57.
See also Schuster, Julius, Af

Archives Internationales d'Histoire des Sciences. Publication trimestrielle de l'Union Internationale d'Histoire des Sciences. New ser. of *Archeion*. Vol. 1- Paris: Académie Internationale d'Histoire des Sciences, 1947-

Archivio di Storia della Scienza. [Ed. by Aldo Mieli] Roma: Attilip Nardecchia, 1919-26.
Vol. 1 reviewed by George Sarton, *Isis*, 1920, 3: 59.

Arkhiv Istorii Nauki i Tekhniki. [In Russian with index in German and Russian] Trudy Instituta Istorii Nauki i Tekhniki, Leningrad. no. 1-9. Leningrad: Akademiia Nauk, 1933-36.
Brief note on no. 1 in *Isis,* 1934, 21: 440.

British Journal for the History of Science. Vol. 1- London: 1962-
Under the auspices of the British Society for the History of Science.

Bulletin of the British Society for the History of Science. Vol. 1-2. London: 1949-61. [CB 74/383]

Centaurus. International magazine of the history of science and medicine. Vol. I, no. 1- Copenhagen: Munksgaard, 1950-
Brief note on no. 1 in *Isis,* 1951, 42: 361.

Discovery. A monthly popular journal of knowledge. Jan. 1920- Vol. 1- London: Murray, 1920-
Vol. 1, no. 1 reviewed by George Sarton, *Isis,* 1920, 3: 309-10.

Experientia. Monthly journal of pure and applied science. Vol. 1- 1945- [CB 69/224]

Gesnerus. Revue trimestrielle, publiée par la Société Suisse d'Histoire de la Médecine et des Sciences Naturelles. Volume 1- 1943-44- Aarau: Verlag Sauerländer, 1944- [CB 70/248]

History of Science. An annual review of literature, research and teaching. Ed. by A.C. Crombie and M.A. Hoskin. Vol. 1- Cambridge: Heffer, 1962-
Vol. 1 reviewed by A. Armitage, *Brit.J.Hist.Sci.,* 1962, 1: 187-8; by I. Bernard Cohen, *Science,* 1962, 138: 803-4; by A. Yushkevich, *Rev.Hist.Sci.,* 1963, 16: 287-8.

Isis. For notes and articles on *Isis, see* Ac-br *(Isis)* below

Japanese Studies in the History of Science. No. 1- Tokyo: History of Science Society of Japan, 1962-
Reviewed by Robert P. Multhauf, *Bull.Hist.Med.,* 1963, 37: 585.

Journal of the History of Science, Japan. Kagakushi Kenkyu. Dec. 1941-; no. 1- Tokyo: Iwanami Co., 1941-
For note on Parts 1-8 *see* CB 73/160, Parts 18-20, CB 78/177.

Kwartalnik Historii Nauki i Techniki. Vol. 1- Warszawa: Polska Akademia Nauk, Komitet Historii Nauk, 1956-
Vol. 6 (1961) reviewed bv Paul Bockstaele, *Sci.Hist.,* 1962, 4: 40-1.

Lychnos. Lärdomshistoriska Samfundets Årsbok. [Annual of the Swedish History of Science Society, ed. by Johan Nordström.] Vol. 1- Uppsala: Almqvist & Wiksells, 1936-
Vol. 1 reviewed by George Sarton, *Isis,* 1936, 26: 177-80; 1960 volume reviewed by P. Boeynaems, *Sci.Hist.,* 1960, 2: 199.

Notes and Records of the Royal Society. [First volume, 1938, noted by George Sarton] *Isis,* 1940, 32: 123.

Osiris. Studies on the history and philosophy of science, and on the history of learning and culture. Vol. 1- Bruges: 1936-
For reviews of vol. 1 and 2 *see* CB 49/162, CB 51/244 and CB 54/526; vol. 7 CB 60/84; vol. 8 CB 76/390; vol. 9 and 10 reviewed by I. Bernard Cohen, *Isis,* 1952, 43: 289-90; for other reviews of vol. 9 *see* CB 78/177 and CB 79/165; for note on vol. 12 *see* CB 82/193.

Petrus Nonius. Publicação de Grupo português da história das ciências patrocinada pelos Presidentes das secçoes do Porto, Coimbra e Lisboa e pelos membros do Comité central. Vol. 1, fasc. 1 e 2- Lisboa: 1937-

Rasprave i Građa za Povijest Nauka. [Ed. by Hrvoje Iveković and Mirko Dražen Grmek. [Discussions and observations on the history of science.] Vol. 1- Zagreb: Jugoslavenska Akademija Znanosti i Umjetnosti. Institut za Povijest Prirodnih, Matematičkih i Medicinskih Nauka, 1963-
A new periodical devoted to the history of science, including medicine. English, French, and German summaries.

Science. L'encyclopédie annuelle. Journal hebdomadaire. No. 1, Octobre 1936. Paris: Centre International de Synthèse, 1936. [CB 49/165]

Science in Progress. (Sigma Xi Society National Lectureships) 1st series, 1937-38- Edited by George Baitsell. New Haven: Yale University Press, 1939- [CB 61/380, CB 63/269, CB 69/207 and 398, CB 72/259, CB 78/159, CB 80/202 and CB 81/258]
1st series, 1937-38 reviewed by M.F. Ashley Montagu, *Isis,* 1947, 32: 166-7; 4th series, 1943-44 reviewed by Karl K. Darrow, *Science,* 1945, 101: 679-80.

Sudhoffs Archiv für Geschichte der Medizin und der Naturwissenschaften. Vol. 1- Leipzig, Wiesbaden: 1907- [CB 79/193]
Volumes 1-20, 1907-28, entitled: Archiv für Geschichte der Medizin.
Not published 1944-52.

Thalès. Recueil des travaux de l'Institut d'Histoire des Sciences et des Techniques de l'Université de Paris. Vol. 1 -, 1934 - Paris: 1935- [CB 45/272]

Trudy Instituta Istorii Estestvoznanija i Tekhniki (Akademiia Nauk SSSR) Tom 1 -. [Transactions of the Institute of the History of Science and Technology. (In Russian)] Moscow: Academy of Sciences of the U.S.S.R., 1954 -
Vol. 1 and 5 reviewed by Q. Vetter, *Arch.Int.Hist.Sci.,* 1956, 35: 246-7.

Voprosy Istorii Estestvoznaniia i Tekhniki. [Problems in the history of science and of technology]. Vypusk 1- Moscow: Academy of Sciences of the U.S.S.R., 1956-
Part 1 reviewed by Claude Backvis, *Arch.Int.Hist.Sci.,* 1956, 35: 240-1; announced in *Isis,* 1957, 48: 70.

Vorträge der Bibliothek Warburg. Hrsg. von Fritz Saxl. 1921/1922-1930/1931. Leipzig: Teubner, 1923-32.
For 1921/22 vol. *see* CB 15/236; for 1923/24 vol. CB 22/301.

Zprávy Komise pro Dějiny Přírodních, Lékařských a Technických Věd CSAV. [Report of the Commission for the History of Science, Medicine and Technology of the Czechoslovak Academy of Sciences. (In Czech)]. No. 1- Prague: 1959-

Ac-br *(Isis)*

for articles on the *ISIS* Critical Bibliographies *see* Ac-bu under Guerlac, Henry and Sarton, George.

Isis: an international review devoted to the history of science and its cultural influences. [From vol. 6, 1924] official quarterly journal of the History of Science Society. Vol. 1- Wordelgem lez Gand, Belgique; Washington, D.C., *etc.:* 1913-

Isis. Microcarded volumes of early issues. *Isis,* 1954, 45: 197.

NOTES sur la revue Isis. *Isis,* 1914, 1: 704-5.

SARTON, George. Avant-propos. *Isis,* 1919, 2: 313-14.
Preface explaining why the publication of *Isis* was interrupted during five years and stating new policy.

SARTON, George. Le but d'*Isis*. *Isis,* 1913, 1: 193-6.
Reprinted *ibid.* 1963, 54: 7-10.

SARTON, George. Early volumes of *Isis*. *Isis,* 1927, 9: 117-18.

SARTON, George. The end of the Belgian *Isis*. List of articles and reviews which will eventually appear in no. 84 and in vol. 32 of *Isis,* and in vol. 8 and 9 of *Osiris*. *Isis,* 1941, 33: 41-54.

SARTON, George. Notes sur la revue *Isis*. *Isis,* 1914, 2: 162-3.

SARTON, George. Preface to the nineteenth volume of *Isis*. *Isis,* 1933, 19: 6-10.
Brief statement of the work done thus far by *Isis* and its many short-comings.

SARTON, George. Preface to Volume 8. *Isis,* 1926, 8: 7-11.
Regarding *Isis*.

SARTON, George. The publication of *Isis*. *Science,* 19 July 1940, 92: 59-60.

SARTON, George. Le sentiment du passé. *Isis,* 1926, 8: 391-402. [CB 21/564]
On the aims of *Isis*.

SARTON, George. Second preface to volume 32. Reconstruction. *Isis*, 1949, 32: 245-7.
Giving reasons for reduced size of *Isis* volume as a result of the war.

SARTON, George. To the Republic of Letters. Preface to volume 33. *Isis*, 1941, 33: 1-3, 1 facs.

SARTON, George. Why *Isis*? *Isis*, 1953, 44: 232-42.
Explanations of his choice of name.

SARTON, George; ZIRKLE, Conway. O columns! *Isis*, 1942, 34: 3-4.
Explaining the need of printing *Isis* in two-columned pages. With technical note by Conway Zirkle.

STIMSON, Dorothy. The editing of *Isis*. *Isis*, 1953, 44: 3-4.
End of Sarton's editorship.

WOOLF, Harry. *Isis*: 1913-1963. *Isis*, 1963, 54: 5

Ac-bt *charts*

BABINI, Rosa D. de. Los siglos de la historia. Tablas cronológicas. 352 p. Mexico/Buenos Aires: Fondo de Cultura Económica, 1960.
Reviewed by Juan A. Paniagua, *Arch.Int.Hist.Sci.*, 1962, 15: 177-8.

BERTHIER, J.; LAUVERNIER, C. Tableaux d'histoire générale. Présentation synchronique des principaux événements contemporains à travers les siècles. Politiques, religions, philosophies, lettres, arts, sciences, découvertes, inventions, institutions. Introduction de Emile Picard. x, 7 p., 43 tables. Paris: Société Mercasia, 1930. [CB 34/400]

MIELI, Aldo. Tables chronologiques d'histoire des sciences. *Arch.Int.Hist.Sci.*, 1949, 28: 728-9.

PETERS, Arno; PETERS, Anneliese. Synchronoptische Weltgeschichte. 4 p., 32 fold. l. Frankfurt a. M.: Universum Verlag, 1952.
Reviewed by F.S. Bodenheimer, *Arch.Int.Hist.Sci.*, 1953, 6: 91-2.

WYER, Samuel S. Shift of civilization. Chart 42" x 28". Columbus, Ohio: 1949. [CB 75/96]

Ac-bu/cv bibliography; literature; sources

Ac-bu history of science: documentation

COLLINDER, M. Une cartothèque générale concernant l'histoire des sciences en voie d'élaboration sous les auspices de l'Académie pour l'histoire de l'astronomie de Lund. *Congr.Mond.Doc.Universelle* (Paris, 1937) *Texte Commun.*, p. 70-2. Paris: Secrétariat, 1937.

GUERLAC, Henry. A proposed revision of the ISIS critical bibliography. *Isis*, 1953, 44: 226-31.
Explains the classification of the current Critical Bibliography.

MIELI, Aldo. La documentation en "histoire des sciences". *Texte Commun.Congr.Mond.Doc.Universelle* (Paris, 1937), p. 238-40. Paris: Secretariat, 1937.

RUSSO, F. Conception et méthode moderne de la documentation. *Rev.Quest.Sci.*, 1958, 19: 263-89.

RUSSO, F. La documentation en histoire des sciences et des techniques. *Arch.Int.Hist.Sci.*, 1959, 12: 253-66. [CB 85/380]
A report on the present status of bibliographical services in the history of science.

RUSSO, F. L'histoire des sciences. *Bull.Bibl.France*, 1960, 5: 209-31.

RUSSO, F. Rapport sur une experience d'indexation et de selection documentaires en histoire des sciences et des techniques. *Doc.France*, 1960, 22-4.

SALIÉ, Hans. Ein Standardwerk zur Geschichte der Naturwissenschaften. Hundert Jahre "Poggendorff". *Forsch.Fortschr.*, 1963, 37: 202-5.
For Poggendorff *see* Ada

SARTON, George. La bibliographie de l'histoire de la science. *Rev.Gén.Sci.*, 1912, 23: 131-2.

SARTON, George. Bibliographie synthétique des revues et des collections de livres. Introduction générale. *Isis*, 1914-19, 2: 125-31.

SARTON, George. La bibliographie de l'histoire des sciences. *Arch.Int.Hist.Sci.*, 1953, 6: 395-419.

SARTON, George. The critical bibliographies of "Isis". *Isis*, 1950, 41: 291-8.

SARTON, George. Introduction à la bibliographie analytique des publications relatives à l'histoire de la science. *Isis*, 1913, 1: 136-43.

SARTON, George. Synthetic bibliography with special reference to the history of science. *Isis*, 1920-21, 3: 159-70. [CB 9/483]
On the organization of the *Isis* Critical Bibliography.

WHITROW, Magda. Classification schemes for the history of science. A comparison. *J.Doc.*, 1964, 20: 120-36.

Ac-bv bibliographies; literature surveys

see also Acd-bv and Ace-bv

Annual Reports of the Smithsonian Institution. Author-subject index to articles in Smithsonian annual reports, 1849-1961, compiled by Ruth M. Stemple. v, 200 p. (Smithsonian Publication 4503.) Washington: Smithsonian Institution, 1963.

BIBLIOGRAFIE dějin přírodních věd a techniky. [Bibliography of the history of science and technology. (In Czech)]. *Cesk.Cas.Hist.*, 1963, 11: Supplement to no. 6.

BOCKSTAELE, P. Bibliografie van de geschiedenis der wetenschappen in de Nederlanden. *Sci.Hist.*, 1959, 1: 31-52, 107-16, 162-75, 219-28; 1960, 2: 30-45, 86-100, 143-55, 203-21; 1961, 3: 50-6, 102-13, 209-26; 1962, 4: 91-112, 212-25; 1963, 5: 82-96, 178-94; 1964, 6: 97-107, 222-35.

BOCKSTAELE, P. [Writings on the history of science in the Netherlands. (In Dutch)]. *Wetensch.Tijdingen*, 1951, 11: 218-29.

BRUNET, Lucien, *et al.* Bibliographie des années 1937 à 1939. Histoire des sciences. Histoire de la philosophie dans ses rapports avec les sciences. Philosophie et théorie des sciences. *Thalès*, 1940, 4: 287-315.

Bulletin Signalétique. 22. Histoire des sciences et des techniques, 1961, 15: no. 1- Paris: Centre du Documentation du C.N.R.S., 1961-
Quarterly.

Bullettino di Bibliografia e di Storia delle Scienze Matematiche e Fisiche. Publicato da B. Boncompagni. Indici dei venti tomi componenti il presente Bullettino (anni 1868-1887). 52 p. (Serie di indici generali di opere periodiche italiane estinte, 1) Roma: Nardecchia, 1915.

DIJKSTERHUIS, E.J. Historische revue. [Historical review. (In Dutch)] *Euclides*, 1930-31, 7: 185-95.
Reviews of forty recent works on the history of mathematics and science.

DIJKSTERHUIS, E.J. Works on history of science published in the Netherlands in the years 1930-1947. *Scr.Math.*, 1950, 16: 43-59.

Endeavour. A quarterly review designed to record the progress of the sciences in the service of mankind. Index to vol. I-X, 1942-51. xvi p. London: 1951.

FUETER, Eduard. Geschichte der exakten Wissenschaften. *Schweiz.Hochschulzeitung*, 1947, 20: 275-81.
General review of a number of recent publications on the history of science, mostly Swiss.

GEISER, Samuel W.; GEISER, Bessie T. A brief short-title list of published works on the history of science. 35 p. (Southern Methodist University Studies, 1) Dallas, Texas: University Press Southern Methodist University, 1947. [CB 71/114]
List of about 700 titles of books.

HISTORY OF SCIENCE SOCIETY. List of publications. *Isis*, 1943, 34: 411.

Index to theses accepted for higher degrees in the Universities of Great Britain and Ireland. Vol. 1 (1950/51) - London: Aslib, 1953- [CB 83/187]
Includes a section on the history and philosophy of science.

INDEX zur Geschichte der Medizin, Naturwissenschaft und Technik. Unter Mitwirkung von J. Steudel, W. Hartner, O. Mahr, hrsg. von W. Artelt. 398 p. München-Berlin: Urban & Schwarzenberg, 1953.
Reviewed by Walter Pagel, *Isis*, 1954, 45: 109; for other reviews *see* CB 81/255.

ISIS Critical Bibliographies, no. 1-90. *Isis*, 1913- vol. 1-
For page and volume number of the Critical Bibliographies *see* at the beginning of this volume.
See also Ac-bu under Guerlac, Henry and Sarton, George.

JOSEPHSON, Aksel G. A list of books on the history of science. x, 297 p.; Supplement, vi, 139 p. Chicago: John Crerar Library, 1911, 1917.

KLOPFER, Leopold E. A history of science bibliography for high school students and teachers. 10 p. Hebron, Conn.: The Author, 1957. [CB 83/188]

KLOPFER, Leopold E. Paperbound books in the history and philosophy of science. 16 p. Cambridge, Mass.: The Author, 1959.

LEBEDOVÁ, Anna. Česká bibliografie dějin přírodních věd, lékařství a techniky 1954-60. [Czech bibliography of history of science, medicine and technology. (In Czech)]. *Sb. Dějiny Přírodn. Věd Tech.*, 1957, 3: 272-81; 1958, 4: 271-85; 1960, 5: 235-79; 1961, 6: 277-307; 1962, 7: 309-32; 1963, 8: 247-68; 1964, 9: 295-316.

LINDROTH, Sten. History of science in Sweden. *Isis*, 1945, 36: 16-19.
A review of recent literature published in Sweden.

LINDSAY, Jean Olivia. The early history of science, a short handlist. 64 p. (Helps for Students of History, 52) London: The Historical Association, 1950.
Reviewed by R.J. Forbes, *Arch.Int.Hist.Sci.*, 1951, 4: 743.

MAY, Eduard. Ueber einige neuere Werke zur Geschichte der Naturwissenschaft und Naturphilosophie. *Phil.Natur.*, 1955, 3: 274-8.

MIELI, Aldo. Bibliografia metodica dei lavori di storia della scienza in Italia. *Arch.Stor.Sci.*, 1919-20, 1: 84-6, 195-217, 332-56, 397-420; 1924, 5: 163-75, 284-98; 1925, 6: 159-68, 347-59; 1926, 7: 152-76, 411-13; 1927, 8: 274-87; *Archeion*, 1929, 10: 36-9. [CB 8/367 and CB 6/336]

MIELI, Aldo. Storia delle scienze. 12 p. (Catalogo ragionato per una biblioteca di cultura generale). Milano: Fed. Ital. delle Biblioteche Popolare, [191?]

MIELI, Aldo. Storia delle scienze; rassegna e note sulle pubblicazioni ad esse relative. 1. Prologo. 2. Cina, India, Arabia. 3. Alcune osservazioni sull'indole di questa rassegna e sulla nuova rivista "Isis". 4. Pubblicazioni periodiche italiane dedicate alla storia delle scienze. 5. Testi di storia di varie discipline scientifiche. *Riv.Fil.*, 1912, 4: 509-21; 1913, 5: 289-300.

POGGENDORFF, J.C. *See* Ada

RAINOV, T.I. [Important foreign periodicals devoted to the history of science. (In Russian)]. *Sotsialist.Rekonstruktsiia Nauk.*, 1933, 3: no. 2, 129-43. [CB 39/440]

REY, Abel. Revue d'histoire des sciences et d'histoire de la philosophie dans ses rapports avec les sciences (année 1920). *Rev.Syn.Hist.*, 1920, 31: 121-35. [CB 11/451]

RUSSO, F. Bibliographie d'histoire des sciences. *Bull.Union Cath.Sci.Fran.*, 1948, no. 7, 24 p.
Reviewed by R. Taton, *Rev.Hist.Sci.*, 1950, 3: 92.

RUSSO, F. Histoire des sciences et des techniques. Bibliographie. 2 vol. 186 p. (Actualités scientifiques et industrielles, 1204) Supplément. [Unpaged]. Paris: Hermann, 1954-55.
Mimeographed supplement distributed by author.
Reviewed by George Sarton, *Isis*, 1954, 45: 204-5; by Marie Boas, *Scr.Math.*, 1955, 21: 176-7; by J.P., *Arch. Int.Hist.Sci.*, 1955, 8: 273-4.

SARTON, George. Horus. A guide to the history of science: a first guide for the study of the history of science, with introductory essays on science and tradition. xviii, 316 p. Waltham, Mass.: Chronica Botanica Company; New York: Stechert-Hafner; London: William Dawson and Sons Ltd., 1952.
Reviewed by Marshall Clagett, *Isis*, 1953, 44: 91-3; for other reviews *see* CB 80/115, CB 81/254 and CB 82/195.

SARTON, George. Soixante-deux revues et collections relatives à l'histoire des sciences. (Bibliographie Synthétique, 1) *Isis*, 1914, 2: 132-61.

Ac-bx exhibitions

ISTITUTO E MUSEO DI STORIA DELLA SCIENZA. Esposizione nazionale di storia delle scienze (Firenze, maggio-ottobre, 1929). Catalogo con aggiornamenti. 127 p., ill. Firenze: Olschki, 1952. [CB 83/191]
Reviewed by P. Sergescu, *Arch.Int.Hist.Sci.*, 1952, 5: 376.

ROYAL SOCIETY OF LONDON. Phases of modern science. Published in connection with the Science Exhibit arranged by a Committee of the Royal Society in the Pavilion of His Majesty's Government at the British Empire Exhibition, 1925. vii, 232 p. London: Denny, 1925.
Enlarged and revised edition of the Society's Handbook to the Exhibition of Pure Science, 1924. [CB 16/338]

Acb science libraries

BIENKOWSKA, B.; SIDOROWIEZ, Z. [The library of the former Warsaw Scientific Society (1907-1915). (In Polish with summaries in English and Russian)] *Stud.Mater.Dziej.Nauk. Pol., ser. A.*, 1962, vol. 6.

GRAY, Austin Kayingham. Benjamin Franklin's library (printed, 1936, as "The first American library"), a short account of the Library Company of Philadelphia, 1731-1931. xi, 80 p., front., pl., portr., facs. New York: Macmillan, 1937. [CB 57/179]

GUNTHER, Robert T. Plea for the preservation of a scientific library. *Nature*, 1935, 135: 432. [CB 44/491]
Apropos of the library of Stephen Peter Rigaud.

VERNON, Kenneth D.C. The library of the Royal Institution, 1799-1954. *Nature*, 1954, 174: 242-4.

Acb-bd

ASLIB directory; a guide to sources of information in Great Britain and Ireland. Ed. by Miriam Alman. 2 vol. London: Aslib, 1957.
Replaces: The Aslib directory (London: 1928). [CB 25/440]

Acc historical sources

BRUNET, Pierre. Souvenirs des savants. *Rev.Hist.Sci.*, 1947-48, 1: 351-4.
"Souvenirs" means here *reliquiae* (objects, instruments, MSS) which men of science have left behind.

Acd archives and manuscripts

ALPERT, Harry. Science records. Viewpoints of the sociology of science. *Isis*, 1962, 53: 67-71.

BENISON, Saul. Oral history and manuscript collecting. *Isis*, 1962, 53: 113-17.

BIRR, Kendall. "What shall we save?" An historian's view. *Isis*, 1962, 53: 72-9.

CORSI, Domenico. Fonti dell'Archivio di Stato in Lucca per la storia delle scienze. *Act.VIIIe Congr.Int.Hist.Sci.* (Florence 1956), p. 1113-26. Paris: Hermann, [n.d.]

DUPREE, A. Hunter. What manuscripts the historian wants saved. *Isis*, 1962, 53: 63-6.

EVANS, Luther H. Some proposals for action. *Isis*, 1962, 53: 101-5.

FREDERKING, H. Conservation des archives. *Chim.Ind.*, 1931, 26: 148. [CB 56/408]

GLASS, H. Bentley. The scientist and the preservation of science manuscripts. *Isis*, 1962, 53: 136-42.

GROVER, Wayne C. The role of the archivist in the preservation of scientific records. *Isis,* 1962, 53: 55-62.

GRUMAN, Gerald J. Preserving the stuff of history. *Science,* 1958, 127: 1471.

GRUMAN, Gerald J. Saving our primary source materials. *Isis,* 1957, 48: 183-5.

GUERLAC, Henry. Case studies of research experience. *Isis,* 1962, 53: 7-8.
Opening remarks at a Conference on Scientific Manuscripts.

JEFFREYS, Alan. Locating the manuscript sources of science. *Brit.J.Hist.Sci.,* 1964, 2: 157-61.

JOHNSON, E.H. History of science source material in college libraries. *Science,* 1930, 72: 340-1.

LEAKE, Chauncey D. Responsibility for science archives. *Isis,* 1962, 53: 143-6.
The paper deals with problems of preservation.

MERCATI, Angelo. Lettere di scienziati dall' archivio segreto vaticano. *Pont.Acad.Sci.Comm.,* 1941, 5: no. 2. [CB 71/114]
Reviewed by L. Castaldi, *Riv.Stor.Sci.,* 1943, 34: 59.

PELSENEER, Jean. Documents manuscrits intéressant l'histoire des sciences au Musée de Mariemont (Belgique). *Bull.Acad. Roy.Belg.Cl.Sci.,* 1951, 406-8.

PROOSDIJ, B.A. van. Matériaux pour l'histoire des sciences du temps moderne. *Janus,* 1957, 46: 3.

SIMONS, Lao G. Among the autograph letters in the David Eugene Smith collection. *Scr.Math.,* 1945, 11: 247-62.

WALDE, O. Bokanteckningar och lärdomshistoria. [Bucheintragungen als wissenschaftsgeschichtliches Material. (In Swedish, with summary in German)] *Lychnos,* 1941, 28-48.

WOOLF, Harry. Manuscripts and the history of science. *Isis,* 1962, 53: 3-4.

Acd-br

Manuscripta, a new journal. *Isis,* 1957, 48: 187-8.

Acd-bu

ALBAREDA, Anselm M. The preservation and reproduction of the manuscripts of the Vatican Library through the centuries. *Proc.Amer.Phil.Soc.,* 1960, 104: 413-18.

COUSTET, Ernest. La reconstitution des documents brulés. *La Nature,* 1917, no. 2,294, 170. [CB 51/298]

REINGOLD, Nathan. Subject analysis and description of manuscript collections. *Isis,* 1962, 53: 106-12.

SHRYOCK, Richard H. The viewpoint of an historian and a manuscript librarian. *Isis,* 1962, 53: 9-13.

SOCIETY OF AMERICAN ARCHIVISTS. The care of records in a national emergency. [Joint report of committees.] *Bull. Nat.Arch.,* 1941, no. 3, 25-36, bibliogr.

WILSON, William Jerome. Manuscript cataloguing. *Traditio,* 1956, 12: 457-555. [CB 84/298]

WILSON, William Jerome. Manuscripts in microfilm. Problems of librarian and custodian. (Problems of cataloger and bibliographer). *Libr.Quart.,* 1943, 13: 212-26, 293-309.

Acd-bv

ACADEMY OF NATURAL SCIENCES OF PHILADELPHIA. Guide to the manuscript collections in the Academy. Compiled by Venia T. Phillips and Maurice E. Phillips. xxvi, 553 p. (Special Publication, no. 5) Philadelphia, Pa.: The Academy, 1963.
Reviewed by Brooke Hindle, *J.Hist.Med.,* 1964, 19: 177-8.

BALLIOL COLLEGE, Oxford. Catalogue of the manuscripts of [the] College. Compiled by R.A.B. Mynors. lvii, 401 p. Oxford University Press, 1963.
Reviewed in *Times Lit.Suppl.,* June 14, 1963, 451.

BEIRUT. UNIVERSITÉ DE SAINT JOSEPH. Bibliothèque. Catalogue raisonné des manuscrits historiques de la Bibliothèque Orientale de l'Université St. Joseph. Par P.L. Cheiko. 6 vol. (*Mélanges Univ.Saint Joseph*) Beyrouth: 1913-29.

FISCHER, Hans, ed. Katalog der Handschriften der Universitätsbibliothek Erlangen. Erlangen: Universitätsbibliothek, 1928-
Vol. 1 reviewed by E.K. Rand, *Speculum,* 1929, 231-3.

GREAT BRITAIN. Public Record Office. Catalogue of manuscripts and other objects in the Museum of the Public Record Office. With brief descriptive and historical notes. 16th ed. compiled by J.H. Collingridge. xi, 91 p. London: His Majesty's Stationery Office, 1948.

HAMER, Philip M., ed. A guide to archives and manuscripts in the United States. Compiled for the National Historical Publications Commission. xxiii, 775 p. New Haven: Yale University Press, 1961.

HOYOUX, Jean. Catalogue des manuscrits scientifiques de la Bibliothèque de l'Université de Liège. Acquisitions faites de 1886 à 1950. iv, 267 p. Liège: Centre National d'Histoire des Sciences, 1959.

THE NATIONAL Union Catalog of manuscript collections. Based on reports from American repositories of manuscripts. (U.S. Library of Congress). 1959, 1961- Ann Arbor: J.W. Edwards, 1962- [CB 88/524]

RAU, Arthur. Bibliotheca Bodmeriana. 1. Manuscripts. *Book Collect.,* 1958, 7: 386. [CB 85/379]
Short descriptions of scientific manuscripts in the famous private collection of Dr. Martin Bodmer, Switzerland.

RUSKA, Julius; HARTNER, Willy. Katalog der orientalischen und lateinischen Originalhandschriften, Abschriften und Photokopien des Instituts für Geschichte der Medizin und der Naturwissenschaften in Berlin. *Quellen Stud.Gesch.Naturwiss. Med.,* 1939, 7: 155-303.

TURSKA, J. Indeks do inventarza rekopisow Biblioteki Zaktadu Narodowego im. Ossolinskich we wroctawiu. [An index to the inventory of manuscripts in the Ossolineum Library, Wroclaw. (In Polish)] 2 vol. 576 p. Wroclaw/Warsaw/Cracow: Polish Academy of Sciences, 1962.

Ace literature

ABGARYAN, G.V. The Matenadaran. 67 p., 19 col. pl., ill. Yerevan SSR: Armenian State Publishing House, 1962. [CB 90/503]
MSS in the great Library at Yerevan.

DOWNS, Robert B. Rare books in American state university libraries. *Book Collect.,* 1957, 6: 232-43. [CB 85/379]

GOSSEN, Hans. Medizin- und naturwissenschaftshistorische Lesefrüchte. *Med.Welt,* 1937, 11: 333-5.

OTLET, Paul. Le livre dans les sciences. *Mus.Livre Publ. Fasc.,* 1913, 25-26: 379-89.

RAY, J. Christian. Some vital books in science, 1848-1947. *Science,* 1948, 107: 485-91.

SARTON, George. Second preface to Volume 38. The study of early scientific textbooks. *Isis,* 1948, 38: 137-48, 6 fig.
With comments by I. Bernard Cohen, *ibid.,* p. 149-50.

SCIENTIFIC Books at California Institute of Technology. *Isis,* 1956, 47: 187.

SORKIN, A.M. Iz istorii bibliografii fiziko-matematicheskikh i estestvennykh nauk v nachale XX v. [On the history of bibliography of the physical-mathematical and natural sciences in the beginning of the 20th century. (In Russian)] *Vop.Ist.Est.Tekh.,* 1961, 11: 79-82.

TAYLOR, Archer; MOSHER, Frederic J. The bibliographical history of anonyma and pseudonyma. 297 p. (Newberry Library Publication). Chicago: University of Chicago Press, 1951. [CB 78/197]

THORNTON, John L.; TULLY, R.I.J. Scientific books, libraries and collectors. A study of bibliography and the book trade in relation to science. 2nd rev. ed. xiii, 406 p., pl., bibliogr. London: Library Association, 1962. [CB 81/256]
First publ. 1954.
For reviews *see* CB 81/256, CB 88/525 and CB 89/486.

WOOD, A.M. Historic scientific books at Oxford. *Discovery,* 1959, 20: 204-5.

Ace-br

Essential Books, a new periodical. *Isis,* 1956, 47: 56-7.
Five issues published 1955-56.

Revue des Livres Anciens. Documents d'histoire littéraire, de bibliographie et de bibliophilie. Direction: Pierre Louys. Vol. 1-2. Paris: Fontemoing, 1913-17. [CB 5/305]

Ace-bu literature: documentation

BIRKENMAJER, Alexandre. Esquisse du plan d'un manuel de bibliothéconomie scientifique. *Congr.Int.Bibl.Bibliophiles* (Paris, 1923) *Procès-Verb.Mém.*, p. 91-5. Paris: Jouve, 1925. Also publ. separately, 1924.

HAMOR, William A.; BASS, Lawrence W. Bibliochresis: the pilot of research. *Science*, 1930, 71: 375-8. Bibliochresis - the scientific use of literature.

LA FONTAINE, H.; OTLET, P. La vie internationale et l'effort pour son organisation. *Vie Int.*, 1912, 1: 5-8, 9-34.

OTLET, Paul. L'avenir du catalogue international de la littérature scientifique. *Rev.Gén.Sci.*, 1918, 29: 71-5.

OTLET, Paul. L'organisation des travaux scientifiques. *Compt. Rend.Acad.Sci.*, 1919-20, 15-50. [CB 10/211]

OTLET, Paul. Le traitement de la littérature scientifique. *Rev.Gén.Sci.*, 1918, 29: 494-502.

REICHARDT, Günther. Die Bedeutung der Annotation für Bibliographie und Katalog. *Bibliothek-Bibliothekar-Bibliothekswissenschaft, Festschrift Joris Vorstius zum 60. Geburtstag dargebracht*, p. 86-109. Leipzig: Harrassowitz, 1954.

RIDER, Fremont. The scholar and the future of the research library: a problem and its solution. xiii, 236 p. New York: Hadham Press, 1944. Reviewed by William Jerome Wilson, *Isis*, 1945, 36: 83-6.

SORKIN, A.M. Zur Entstehungsgeschichte des "International catalogue of scientific literature". *NTM Z.Gesch.Naturwiss. Tech.Med.*, [1963], 1: no. 4, 67-84.

Ace-bv literature: bibliographies

BIBLIOTHECA chemico-mathematica. Catalogue of works in many tongues on exact and applied science; compiled and annotated by H. Zeitlinger and H.C. Sotheran. 2 vol. xii, 964 p., pl., 1921. 1st-3rd supplements. 3 vol. in 4, 1932, 1937, 1957. London: Sotheran, 1921-57. [CB 80/115] Original work reviewed by G. Sarton, *Isis*, 1921-22, 4: 111-12.

BUFFALO Museum of science. Milestones of science. A reference list of epochal books now being assembled by the Museum. 28 p., ill. Buffalo, N.Y.: 1938.

BURNDY LIBRARY. Heralds of science as represented by two hundred epochal books and pamphlets selected from the Library. With notes by Bern Dibner. 96 p., pl. (Burndy Library Publication, 12) Norwalk, Conn.: The Library, 1955. [CB 81/255] Reviewed by Marshall Clagett, *J.Hist.Med.*, 1956, 11: 115.

CHAO CHI-SHENG, ed. K'o-hsueh chi-shu ts'ank'ao-shu t'i yao. [An annotated bibliography of reference books on science and technology. (In Chinese)] 539 p. Peking: Commercial Press, 1958. [CB 88/585]

CHOULANT, Ludovicus. Bibliotheca Medico-Historica sive Catalogus librorum historicum de re medica et scientia naturali systematicus. x, 270 p. Leipzig: 1842. Reprinted Hildesheim: Olms, 1960.

DEASON, Hilary J.; BLACKLOW, William; ed. A guide to science reading. xiv, 220 p. (Signet Science Library Book) New York: The New American Library, 1963.

EVANS, Herbert McLean. Exhibition of first editions of epochal achievements in the history of science. 48 p. Berkeley: University of California Press, 1934. Catalogue raisonné of 114 items with introduction.

INTERNATIONAL catalogue of scientific literature ... 1901-1914. Published for the International Council by the Royal Society of London. 254 vol. London: 1902-21. An annual classified index to scientific literature for the years 1901-1914.

MASSART, Jean. Liste des recueils bibliographiques des sciences mathématiques, physiques, chimiques et naturelles. *Bull.Acad.Roy.Belg.Cl.Sci.*, 1919, 237-48. [CB 12/640]

MEDICINE and science. A bibliographical catalogue of historical and rare books from the 15th to the 20th century. 610 p., 70 pl. London: Wm. Dawson & Sons, 1956. [CB 82/195]

OKLAHOMA. UNIVERSITY. Library. An exhibition list of works selected from the De Golyer Collection in the history of science and technology, shown at the Library of the University of Oklahoma, 2-14 February 1953. 15 p. Norman: University of Oklahoma Press, 1953.

OKLAHOMA. UNIVERSITY. Library. A check list of the E. De Golyer Collection in the History of Science and Technology as of August 1, 1954. Compiled by Arthur McAnally and Duane H.D. Roller. vi, 127 p., facs. Norman: University of Oklahoma Press, 1954. [CB 81/255] Reviewed by George W. White, *J.Geol.*, 1956, 64: 98-9.

OSLER, William. Bibliotheca Osleriana: a catalogue of books illustrating the history of medicine and science, collected, arranged and annotated by Sir William Osler and bequeathed to McGill University. xxxvi, 786 p. Oxford: Clarendon Press 1929.

SALLANDER, Hans. Bibliotheca Walleriana. The books illustrating the history of medicine and science collected by Dr. Erik Waller and bequeathed to the library of the Royal University of Uppsala. 2 vol. xii, 471 p., 48 pl.; 494 p., 7 pl. (Acta Bibliothecae R. Universitatis Upsaliensis, 8-9) Stockholm: Almqvist & Wiksells, 1955. [CB 82/268] Reviewed by I. Bernard Cohen, *Isis*, 1957, 48: 353-5; for other reviews see CB 82/195, 85/401, and 87/554.

SAUVENIER-GOFFIN, Elisabeth. Les sciences mathématiques et physiques à travers le fonds ancien de la Bibliothèque de l'Université de Liége. 2 pt. (Mémoires de la Société Royale des Sciences de Liége, *sér. 4*, 19: fasc. 2; *sér. 5*, 5) Liége: 1957, 1961.

SHIPMAN, Joseph T. Some milestones in the history of science, to 1800. 56 p., 8 pl., front. Kansas City, Mo.: Linda Hall Library, 1956. [CB 82/194]

TOWNSEND, A.C. Guides to scientific literature. *J.Doc.*, 1955, 11: 73-8.

VELDE, Albert J.J. van de. Zuid- en Noord- Nederlandsche bibliographie over natuur- en geneeskunde tot 1800. 12 parts. *Verslagen Mededeel.Vlaam.Acad.Taal Lett.*, 1937, 255-301, 425-87, 659-700; 1938, 199-265, 439-505; 1939, 47-111, 173-261, 525-603, 827-87; 1940, 53-133, 365-443; 1941, 195-301. [CB 73/165] Supplement *ibid.*, 1947, 47-64.

WILSON, Wiliam Jerome. The Union Catalog of the Library of Congress. *Isis*, 1942, 33: 625-9.

Ace-by book collecting

DE RICCI, Seymour. English collectors of books and manuscripts (1530-1930) and their marks of ownership. ix, 203 p., pl., facs. (Sandars Lectures 1929-1930). Cambridge University Press, 1930. Reviewed by Ernst Crous, *Deut.Lit.Zeitung*, 1933, (ser. 3), 4: 1-4.

JACKSON, Holbrook. The anatomy of bibliomania. 2 vol. New York: Scribners, 1931.

Acf encyclopaedic literature

COLLISON, Robert. Encyclopaedias. Their history throughout the ages. 319 p. New York: Hafner, 1964.

LEHMANN, Ernst Herbert. Geschichte des Konversationslexikons. 63 p., 36 fig. Leipzig: Brockhaus, 1934.

WELLS, H.G. The idea of a world encyclopaedia. *Nature*, 1936, 138: 917-24. Friday evening discourse delivered at the Royal Institution on November 20. Also printed *Proc.Roy.Inst.*, 1937, 29: 371-96.

Aci Festschriften

ROUNDS, Dorothy; DOW, Sterling. Festschriften. *Harvard Libr. Bull.*, 1954, 8: 283-98. [CB 81/255]

Acj periodical literature

RANC, Albert. L'évolution de la presse de diffusion des sciences depuis le début du XIXe siècle. *Sciences*, 1949, 76: 87-107.

SHERRINGTON, C.S. Language distribution of scientific periodicals. *Nature*, 1934, 134: 625. [CB 42/578]

Acj-bv periodical literature: bibliographies

BHATTACHARYYA, K. Catalogue of scientific periodicals in Calcutta libraries. Calcutta: Asiatic Society, 1962.
As of 1962 available only in a limited number of cyclostyled copies.
Reviewed in *Sci.Cult.*, 1962, 28: 69-70.

BRITISH union-catalogue of periodicals: a record of the periodicals of the world from the seventeenth century to the present day in British libraries. Edited ... by James D. Stewart [*et al.*]. 4 vol. London: Butterworth Scientific Publications; New York: Academic Press, 1955
Supplements published.

COBB, Ruth. Periodical bibliographies and abstracts for the scientific and technological journals of the world. *Bull. Nat.Res.Counc.*, 1919-21, 1: 131-54.

JOHN CRERAR LIBRARY. A list of current periodicals. 2nd ed. 237 p. Chicago, Ill.: The Library, 1924. [CB 16/288]

SCIENCE MUSEUM. Hand-list of short titles of current periodicals in the Science library. Part 1. Alphabetical. Ed. by S.C. Bradford. 5th ed. 262 p. London: H.M. Stationery Off., 1938. [CB 57/229]

WORLD list of scientific periodicals published in the years 1900-1960. 4th ed. Ed. by Peter Brown and G.B. Stratton. 3 vol. London: Butterworth, 1963-65.
1st edition 1925-27; 2nd edition (London: 1934).
Reviewed by C.S.S., *Nature*, 1934, 134: 435-7.

Acm illustrations

IVINS, William M., Jr. Prints and visual communication. xxv, 190 p., 84 ill. Cambridge, Mass.: Harvard University Press, 1953. [CB 80/116]

NISSEN, Claus. Die naturwissenschaftliche Illustration. Ein geschichtlicher Überblick. 63 p., bibliogr. Bad Münster, am Stein: Lothar Hempe Verlag, 1950.

RIDGWAY, John L. Scientific illustration. xiv, 173 p. Stanford University Press, 1938. [CB 56/383]

STOCK, Chester. A tribute to John L. Ridgway. *Science*, 1938, 88: 145-6.

SUDHOFF, Karl. Drei Jahrtausende Graphik im Dienste der Wissenschaft (1914). *Sudhoffs Arch.*, 1929, 21: 283-95.
Originally published in Internationale Ausstellung für Buchgewerbe und Graphik, Leipzig, 1914. Amtlicher Führer, p. 251-62. Leipzig: R. Schick, 1914.

Acp non-bibliographical material

DAVIS, Tenney L. Decorative bronzes in the George Eastman Research Laboratory of the Massachusetts Institute of Technology. *J.Chem.Educ.*, 1939, 16: 3-6, 3 fig.

Act

BISHOP, W.J.; MATHESON, N.M. Medicine and science in postage stamps. 82 p., 33 pl. London: Harvey and Blythe, 1948.
Reviewed in *Nature*, 1949, 163: 270.

Acv

PELSENEER, Jean. Pour des archives cinématographiques des sciences. *Arch.Int.Hist.Sci.*, 1951, 4: 600-1; also *Act.VIe Congr.Int.Hist.Sci.* (Amsterdam, 1950), (1), p. 403-4. Paris: Hermann, 1951.

SERGESCU, P. Pour les archives photographiques de l'histoire des sciences. *Act.VIIe Congr.Int.Hist.Sci.* (Jérusalem, 1953), p. 568-70. Paris: Hermann, [n.d.]

Ad biography

Ad-bv

SIMPSON, Donald H. Biography catalogue of the library of the Royal Commonwealth Society. xxiv, 512 p. London: Royal Commonwealth Society, 1961.
Reviewed by Rolf Du Rietz, *Lychnos*, 1962, 417-20.

Ad-cc

BARR, E. Scott. Biographical material in the *Philosophical Magazine* to 1900. *Isis*, 1964, 55: 88-90.

MATERIALS for the biography of contemporary scientists (chiefly obituary notices). *Isis*, 1913, 1: 172-3, 311-12, 560; 1920, 3: 120-3; 1921, 4: 161-71; 1923, 5: 244-62; 1924, 6: 460-74.
The early lists entitled: Scientists and scholars who died between 1909 and 1918.

Ada collective biography

ASIMOV, Isaac. Biographical encyclopedia of science and technology. The living stories of more than 1000 great scientists from the age of Greece to the space age, chronologically arranged. x, 662 p., portr. Garden City, N.Y.: Doubleday, 1964.

ASTER, E. von. Grosse Denker. 2 vol. 384 p.; 380 p. Leipzig: Quelle & Meyer, 1912.

BALMER, Heinz. Antlitze grosser Schöpfer. Geplant und eingeleitet von Bettina Holzapfel. Mit Beiträgen von Adolf Portmann und Ernst Bohnenblust. 524 p. (Wissenschaft und Kultur, 13). Basel: Birkhäuser, 1961. [CB 87/551]
Reviewed by H. Degen, *Sudhoffs Arch.*, 1962, 46: 283; by M.D. Grmek, *Arch.Int.Hist.Sci.*, 1962, 15: 414-15.

BIXBY, William. Great experimenters. x, 182 p., portr. New York: McKay, 1964.

BRASCH, Frederick E. Medical men in mathematics, astronomy, and physics. *Med.Life*, 1929, 36: 219-36, portr.

BRIDGES, Thomas Charles; TILTMAN, H. Hessell. Master minds of modern science. 278 p., 32 pl. London: Harrap, 1930.

BROGLIE, Louis de. Savants et découvertes. 396 p. (Savants et le Monde) Paris: Michel, 1951.

CROWTHER, J.G. Men of science. xiii, 332 p. New York: Norton, 1936.
Reviewed by M.F. Ashley-Montagu, *Isis*, 1938, 28: 507-8.

DARMSTAEDTER, Ludwig. Naturforscher und Erfinder: Biographische Miniaturen. vii, 182 p., 16 pl. Bielefeld: Velhagen und Klasing, 1926.

DARROW, Floyd L. Masters of science and invention. v, 350 p., 24 pl. London: Chapman and Hall, 1924.

DE FORD, Miriam Allen. Who was when? A dictionary of contemporaries. 2nd ed. 1 vol. (unpaged). New York: Wilson, 1950.
First published 1940.

DEVAUX, Pierre. Les aventuriers de la science. 233 p. Paris: N.R.F. Gallimard, 1943.
Watt, Ampère, Galois, Edison.

DIAMOND, D.M.; INNES, R. Three hundred scientists. 1. Biologists. 74 p.; 2. Chemists. 59 p.; 3. Physicists. 101 p. London: Science Club Publications, 1961.
Reviewed by J.H. White, *J.Roy.Inst.Chem.*, 1962, 86: 144.

DIEPGEN, Paul. Unvollendete. Vom Leben und Wirken frühverstorbener Forscher und Ärzte aus anderthalb Jahrhunderten. 223 p., ill. Stuttgart: Georg Thieme Verlag, 1960.
For reviews *see* CB 87/572 and CB 88/557.

EVANS, Herbert M., ed. Men and moments in the history of science. viii, 226 p., ill. Seattle: University of Washington Press, 1959.
Reviewed by I. Bernard Cohen, *Isis*, 1960, 51: 571-2; for other reviews *see* CB 86/451 and CB 88/521.

FALKENHAGEN, Hans. Die Naturwissenschaft in Lebensbildern grosser Forscher. 224 p. Stuttgart: Hirzel, 1948.
Reviewed by W. Hartner, *Angew.Chem.*, 1950, 62: 440-1.

GREENE, Jay E., ed. 100 great scientists. xiv, 498 p. New York: Washington Square Press, 1964. [CB 90/505]

GUMPERT, Martin. Trail-blazers of science. Life stories of some half-forgotten pioneers of modern research. Transl. from the German by Edwin L. Shuman. x, 306 p. New York: Funk & Wagnalls, 1936.
Reviewed by Charles A. Kofoid, *Isis*, 1938, 29: 460-1.

GUMPRECHT, F. Leben und Gedankenwelt grosser Naturforscher. v, 166 p. (Wissenschaft und Bildung, 232) Leipzig: Quelle und Meyer, 1927.
Deals with Alexander von Humboldt, Helmholtz, R. Mayer, Darwin, Haeckel.

HART, Ivor B. Makers of science. Mathematics, physics, astronomy. 320 p., 120 ill. New York: Oxford University Press, American Branch, 1923. [CB 15/241]

HOWARD, A.V. Chamber's dictionary of scientists. 505 p. New York: Dutton, 1951. [CB 79/164]

HUMBERT, Pierre. Philosophes et savants. 224 p. (Bibliothèque de Philosophie Scientifique) Paris: Flammarion, 1953.
Reviewed by Bernard Rochot, *Rev.Hist.Sci.*, 1953, 6: 278-9.

HYAMSON, Albert Montefiore. A dictionary of universal biography of all ages and of all peoples. 744 p. London: Routledge, 1916.

IRELAND, Norma Olin. Index to scientists of the world from ancient to modern times. Biographies and portraits. xliii, 662 p. Boston: F.W. Faxon Company, Inc., 1962.

JAFFE, Bernard. Outposts of science: a journey to the workshops of our leading men of science. xxvi, 547 p., 32 pl. New York: Simon and Schuster, 1935.
Reviewed in *Nature*, 1936, 138: 740-1.

LACROIX, Alfred. Figures de savants. 4 vol. 1. x, 325 p., 32 pl.; 2. 357 p., 26 pl.; 3 & 4. L'Académie des Sciences et l'étude de la France d'outre-mer de la fin du XVIIe siècle au début du XIXe. xiii, 220 p., 38 pl.; 259 p., 59 pl. Paris: Gauthier-Villars, 1932, 1938. [CB 35/309]
Reviewed by George Sarton, *Isis*, 1938, 29: 436-40; vol. 1 and 2 by Hélène Metzger, *Archeion*, 1933, 15: 281-2.

LARSEN, Egon. Men who changed the world. 2nd rev. ed. 227 p. London: English Language Book Society, Phoenix House Ltd., 1962.
Reviewed by D.M.B., *Sci.Cult.*, 1963, 29: 554-5.

LAURENT, Gaston. Les grands écrivains scientifiques de Copernic à Berthelot. Extraits, introduction, biographies et notes. 5th ed. xi, 384 p. Paris: Colin, 1913.
Reviewed by E. Turrière, *Isis*, 1919, 2: 424-5.

LENARD, Philipp. Great men of science: a history of scientific progress. Transl. from the 2nd German ed. by H. Stafford Hatfield. xix, 389 p., 48 pl. London: Bell; New York: Macmillan, 1933. [CB 41/596]
Reviewed by Rutherford, *Nature*, 1933, 132: 367-9.

LENARD, Philipp. Grosse Naturforscher. Eine Geschichte der Naturforschung in Lebensbeschreibungen. 2nd rev. ed. 332 p., 70 portr. München: Lehmann, 1930. [CB 34/493]
First publ. 1929.
Reviewed by H. Wieleitner, *Mitt.Gesch.Med.*, 1931, 30: 7.

LEPRINCE-RINGUET, Louis, ed. Les inventeurs célèbres. Sciences physiques et applications. 403 p. (La Galerie des Hommes Célèbres) Paris: Mazenod, 1950. [CB 77/370]
German translation (Cologne: 1963) reviewed by Heinz Degen, *Naturwiss.Rundsch.*, 1964, 17: 284.

LIVES in science. xiv, 214 p. New York: Simon and Schuster, 1957. [CB 83/189]
Reviewed by M. Daumas, *Rev.Hist.Sci.*, 1958, 11: 280.

LODGE, Oliver. Pioneers of science and the development of their scientific theories. 2nd ed. xiv, 406 p., fig. New York: Dover Publications, 1960.
Reviewed by Nénad Yankovitch, *Arch.Int.Hist.Sci.*, 1962, 15: 175-7; by Albert Lejeune, *Rev.Quest.Sci.*, 1962, 5th ser., 23: 274.

MAKERS of modern science. 44 p., 10 portr. London: Times Publishing Company, Ltd., 1956. [CB 83/187]

POGGENDORFF, J.C. Biographisch-literarisches Handwörterbuch zur Geschichte der exacten Wissenschaften. Vol. 1 - Leipzig: J.A. Barth, 1863-1904; Leipzig/Berlin: Verlag Chemie, 1925-40; Berlin: Akademie Verlag, 1955-.
Vol. 1-2 covers scientists to 1857; vol. 3, 1858-83; vol. 4, 1883-1903; vol. 5, 1904-22; vol. 6, 1923-31; vol. 7, 1932-53.

POOLE, Lynn; POOLE, Gray. Scientists who changed the world. xvi, 164 p., pl. New York: Dodd, Mead and Company, Inc., 1960.

SARTON, George. Third preface to volume 34: the years "forty-three". *Isis*, 1943, 34: 193-5, 4 fig. [CB 64/449]
Apropos of some centenaries occurring in 1943: the fourth centenaries of Copernicus and Vesalius, the third centenary of Torricelli, the second centenary of d'Alembert and the first centenaries of Joseph Plateau and Stuart Mill.

SCHURMAN, Paul F. Grandes efemérides de la ciencia: monografías y ensayos sobre magnas figuras y etapas de la ciencia. 119 p. Montevideo: Oficina de Representación de Editoriales, 1953. [CB 82/196]
Reviewed by P. Sergescu, *Arch.Int.Hist.Sci.*, 1953, 6: 319.

SCHUSTER, Arthur. Biographical fragments. xiii, 268 p. London: Macmillan, 1932.
Originally published under the title, Biographical byways, in *Nature*, 1925, 115: 55-7 *et seq.*

SCIENCE milestones. The story of the epic scientific achievements and the men who made them possible. 1. 460 B.C.-1640 A.D., In which some principles are established; 2. 1641-1821, In which some applications are made; 3. 1822-1954, The march toward new horizons. Edited by George B. Clementson. 312 p., ill. Chicago/New York: Windsor Press, 1954.
This volume contains stories of great scientists, which have been published in *Science Digest*.

SUTER, Rufus. A gallery of scientists. 132 p., 5 pl. New York: Vantage Press, 1955. [CB 82/194]

TRATTNER, Ernest R. Architects of ideas. 426 p. New York: Carrick & Evans, 1938.
Reviewed by M.F. Ashley-Montagu, *Isis*, 1939, 30: 295-7.

VELDE, A.J.J. van de. Vijf Groten in 1852 geboren (Becquerel, Fischer, Moissan, Ramsay, Van't Hoff). [Five great men born in 1852 ... (In Dutch)] *Mededel.Vlaam.Acad.Wetensch.Lett. Schone Kunsten Belg.Kl.Wetensch.*, 1952, 14: no. 6, 17 p.

WILSON, Grove. Great men of science. Their lives and discoveries. xi, 397 p., 11 portr. New York: Garden City, 1932. [CB 37/587]

ZISCHKA, Gert A. Allgemeines Gelehrten-Lexikon. Biographisches Handwörterbuch zur Geschichte der Wissenschaften. 701 p. (Kröners Taschenausgabe, 306) Stuttgart: Alfred Kröners Verlag, 1961.
Reviewed by M. Michler, *Sudhoffs Arch.*, 1962, 46: 372-3; by M. Habacher, *Bl.Technikgesch.*, 1964, 26: 174.

Ada-bv

RICHES, Phyllis M. An analytical bibliography of universal collected biography comprising books published in the English tongue in Great Britain and Ireland, America and the British Dominions. ix, 709 p. London: Library Association, 1934.
Reviewed by R.C. Archibald, *Scr.Math.*, 1935, 3: 178-9.

Ada-py Nobel prize winners

JUNK, Victor. Die Nobelpreisträger. Dreissig Jahre Nobelstiftung. 303 p., portr. Wien: Winkler, 1930.

NOBELSTIFTELSEN, Stockholm. Nobelprisen 50 år. Forskare, diktare, fredskämpar. [The Nobel prizes during 50 years. Scientists, writers, workers for peace. (In Swedish)]. 512 p., ill. Stockholm: Sohlmans Förlag, 1950.
Reviewed by Sten Lindroth, *Lychnos*, 1952, 373-4.

NOBELSTIFTELSEN, Stockholm. Les Prix Nobel en 1950. Avec une table des auteurs des années 1901 à 1950. 281, 9 p. Stockholm: Imprimerie royale, 1951.
Reviewed by J.P., *Arch.Int.Hist.Sci.*, 1952, 5: 388.

Ada-rw women

SABIN, Florence R. Women in science. *Science*, 1936, 83: 24-6.
Apropos of Mme Curie, Agnes Pockels and Emmy Noether.

Adae portraits

BLUM, André. Les sources iconographiques et leur enseignement; leur valeur artistique et historique. *Bull.Int.Comm. Hist.Sci.*, 1926-28, 1: 736-46.

DEPRÉAUX, Albert. L'iconographie, science auxiliaire de l'histoire. *Bull.Int.Comm.Hist.Sci.*, 1926-28, 1: 725-35.

ENQUÊTE sur l'organisation de la documentation iconographique. *Bull.Int.Comm.Hist.Sci.*, 1928, 1: 525-31.
Valuable information on iconographical materials relative to Denmark by Otto Andrup, and to France, by André Blum and Albert Depréaux.

SARTON, George. Iconography of science. *Isis*, 1921-22, 4: 45.
A few lines to suggest the publication of iconographical notes in *Isis*.

SARTON, George. Query no. 92. Falsely identified portraits of scientists and scholars. *Isis*, 1947, 32: 121.

SARTON, George. Second preface to Vol. XXX. Iconographic honesty. (Followed by a Bibliography of iconographic studies and a note on altered portraits). *Isis*, 1939, 30: 222-35.

Adae-bv

SCHRECKER, Paul. Bibliography of iconographic studies (additions to the list published in *Isis*, 1939, 30: 230-2). *Isis*, 1947, 32: 126.

Adae-bw

SACHSE, J.D.W. Verzeichnis von Bildnissen von Aerzten und Naturforschern seit den ältesten bis auf unsre Zeiten, mit Biographien. Erstes Heft: Abano-Azzoguijoi. vi, 93 p. Schwerin: Marcus, 1847.
No more published.
Reviewed by L. Spengler, *Henschel's Janus*, 1848, 3: 813-4; reprinted, Alfred Lorentz, Leipzig, 1931.

Adae-cs

SARTON, George, ed. Medallic illustrations of the history of science. First series: XIXth and XXth centuries. 9 articles. *Isis*, 1926, 8: 333-5; 1927, 9: 359-62, 420-3; 1928, 10: 485-8; 1929, 12: 146-8, 320-2; 1930, 13: 333-5; 1930, 14: 215-18, 417-19; plates passim.
See also note by G. Sarton, *Isis*, 1947, 38: 101.

Adaj collections of texts

BAUMER, Franklin Levan, ed. Main currents of western thought. Readings in Western European intellectual history from the Middle Ages to the present. xvi, 700 p. New York: Alfred A. Knopf, 1952. [CB 79/188]
Reviewed by Thomas S. Kuhn, *Isis*, 1954, 45: 100.

BOYNTON, Holmes, ed. The beginnings of modern science. Scientific writings of the 16th, 17th and 18th centuries. xxi, 634 p. New York: Walter J. Black, 1948. [CB 73/163]

CLASSICS in science. *See* INTERNATIONAL University Society, below.

DAMPIER, William Cecil; WHETHAM, Margaret Dampier. Cambridge readings in the literature of science: being extracts from the writings of men of science to illustrate the development of scientific thought. xii, 276 p., 8 pl. Cambridge University Press, 1924.
Reprinted as Readings in the literature of science (New York: Harper, 1959).

DANNEMANN, Friedrich. Aus der Werkstatt grosser Forscher. Allgemeinverständliche, erläuterte Abschnitte aus den Werken hervorragender Naturforscher aller Völker und Zeiten. 4th ed. xii, 442 p. Leipzig: Engelmann, 1922.
Reviewed by G. Sarton, *Isis*, 1923, 5: 198-200.

DAVIS, Mrs. Watson. Classics of science. [Extracts from writings of men of science of all ages]. *Sci.News Lett.*
Feature began September 1927 issue.
Reviewed by G. Sarton, *Isis*, 1930, 13: 362.

GUERLAC, Henry. Selected readings in the history of science. 1. From antiquity to the time of Galileo. 464 p.; 2. From the time of Galileo to the present. 3 pts. Ithaca, N.Y.: Henry Guerlac, 1950-53.
Reviewed by J. Pelseneer, *Arch.Int.Hist.Sci.*, 1951, 4: 742-3.

GUINET, L. Classiques de la Science. *Isis*, 1922, 4: 324.
Apropos of the new collection of scientific classics published in France by Gauthier-Villars.

INTERNATIONAL University Society. Science: a course of selected readings by authorities. 2nd rev. ed. Introduction by E.N. da C. Andrade. xxiii, 322 p. Nottingham: Cultural Publications, 1958.
First publ. 1957.
Reviewed by John K. Wood, *Amer.J.Phys.*, 1959, 27: 373-4; by James Maclachlan, *Phys.Today*, 1959, 12: no. 5, 52-4; American edition: CLASSICS in science, 1960 (New York: Philosophical Library), reviewed by Bentley Glass, *Isis*, 1964, 55: 213-4.

KNICKERBOCKER, William S. Classics of modern science (Copernicus to Pasteur). xvi, 384 p. New York: Alfred A. Knopf, 1927. [CB 23/232]

LALOUP, Jean. Anthologie de littérature scientifique. 222 p., ill. Tournai: Casterman, 1960.
Reviewed by Vilma Fritsch, *Arch.Int.Hist.Sci.*, 1960, 13: 305-6.

MIELI, Aldo; TROILO, Ermiulo. Classici delle scienze e della filosofia. Serie Scientifica. 3 vol. Bari: Società Tipografica Editrice Barese, 1914.
Reviewed by George Sarton, *Isis*, 1913, 1: 99-100, 246.

MOULTON, Forest Ray; SCHIFFERES, Justus J.; ed. The autobiography of science. xxxi, 666 p. New York: Doubleday, Doran, 1945. [CB 69/223]

RUNES, Dagobert D., ed. A treasury of world science. 978 p., fig., pl. New York: Philosophical Library, 1962.
Short readings from 99 famous men of science from Archimedes to Einstein.
Reviewed in *Sky Telesc.*, 1962, 23: 344; by Joseph K. Kowalewski, *Amer.J.Pharm.Educ.*, 1962, 26: 569-70.

RYAN, Lawrence V., ed. A science reader. xii, 308 p., fig., bibliogr. New York: Rinehart, 1959.
An anthology of readings in and about science essentially designed to demonstrate good scientific prose.

SAMPSON, George, ed. Pages of science. viii, 147 p. London: Methuen, 1922.

SARTON, George. Les classiques de la science. *Rev.Gén.Sci.*, 1912, 23: 217.
Includes account of Ostwalds Klassiker der exakten Wissenschaften (Leipzig: Engelmann, 1889-).

SARTON, George. [Les collections des classiques de la science]. *Isis*, 1913, 1: 99-100, 246-7, 476, 706-7; 1914, 2: 125-61, 168-70.
Reports on various series.

SOKOL, Anthony Eugene; NYE, Helena May. Berühmte Forscher und ihre Beiträge; ein wissenschaftliches Lesebuch. 595 p. New York: American Book Co., 1938. [CB 56/380]

WARD, Harold, ed. New worlds in science. An anthology. With commentary and introduction. 670 p., 17 fig. New York: McBride, 1941. [CB 62/72]
Selections from 33 prominent writers.

Af history of science as a study

BABINI, José. Algunos aspectos de la historia de la ciencia *Scientia*, 1957, 92: 201-6.

BABINI, José. La historia de la ciencia como disciplina científica. *Archeion*, 1943, 25: 101-7.

BACHELARD, G. L'actualité de l'histoire des sciences. 16 p. (Les Conférences du Palais de la Découverte, 20 Oct. 1951). Paris: Université de Paris, 1951.

BARNES, Harry Elmer. The historian and the history of science. *Sci.Mon.*, 1920, 11: 112-16. [CB 12/640]

BARRY, Frederick. A short critique of the history of science. *Columbia Univ.Quart.*, 1934, 26: 95-111, 259-78. [CB 43/265]

BODENHEIMER, F. Simon. History of science on the cross-read [*sic*], with especial consideration of the history of biology. *Act.VIIIe Congr.Int.Hist.Sci.* (Florence, 1956), p. 819-23. Paris: Hermann, 1958.

BORING, Edwin. Science and the meaning of its history. *Phi Beta Kappa Key Report*, 1959, 24: no. 4, 2-3.

BROWN, Harcourt. An odd lot. Presidential address delivered at the close of the meeting of the History of Science Society at Brown University, 5 April 1952. *Isis*, 1952, 43: 307-11.

BUTTERFIELD, Herbert. The historian and the history of science. *Bull.Brit.Soc.Hist.Sci.*, 1950, 1: 49-58.

BUTTERFIELD, Herbert. The history of science and the study of history. *Harvard Lib.Bull.*, 1959, 13: 329-47.

CHERNIAVSKII, A. L'humanisation de l'histoire de la science. *Act.VIIe Congr.Int.Hist.Sci.* (Jerusalem, 1953), p. 594-600. Paris: Hermann, [n.d.]

COHEN, I. Bernard. Creative science: an art for moderns. *Sperry Eng.Rev.*, 1958, 11: no. 1, [41].
Reprinted from the *New York Herald Tribune*, February 20, 1958.
Plea for the humanistic study of science.

COHEN, I. Bernard. History of science: the imagination of nature. In: White, Lynn, ed. Frontiers of knowledge in the study of man, p. 150-65. New York: Harper, 1956.

COHEN, I. Bernard. Present status and needs of the history of science. *Proc.Amer.Phil.Soc.*, 1955, 99: 343-47.

COHEN, I. Bernard. A sense of history in science. *Amer.J. Phys.*, 1950, 18: 343-59, 1 fig.

CROMMELIN, C.A. Ansprache bei der Eröffnung des Niederländischen Museums zur Geschichte der Naturwissenschaften zu Leiden. (Gehalten am 5. Juni 1931). *Naturwissenschaften*, 1931, 19: 673-5.

CYSARZ, Herbert. Geschichtswissenschaft, Kunstwissenschaft, Lebenswissenschaft. 51 p. Wien: Braumüller, 1928.
Reviewed by Julius Schuster, *Arch.Gesch.Math.Naturwiss. Tech.*, 1929, 11: 341.

DANNEMANN, Friedrich. Die Geschichte der Naturwissenschaften in ihrer Bedeutung für die Gegenwart. (Programm) Barmen: 1912.

DANNEMANN, Friedrich. Wissenschaft als Einheit. *Isis*, 1924, 6: 395-9.
Summary of the inaugural lecture of a course on the history of science at the University of Bonn.

DEL GUERRA, G. La storia come scienza; la storia della scienza e la storia della medicina. *Sci.Veterum*, 1954, 2: no. 4, 1-5.

DIJKSTERHUIS, E.J. Ad quanta intelligenda condita. 27 p. Amsterdam: J.M. Meulenhoff, [1955]. [CB 81/252]
Inaugural address of the professor of the history of mathematics and exact sciences at the State University at Leiden.

DIJKSTERHUIS, E.J. Clio's Stiefkind. 24 p. Groningen, Djarkarta: J.B. Wolters, 1953.
Closing address on the occasion of the 22nd Netherlands Congress of Philologists at the State University of Utrecht. "Clio's Stiefkind" is the history of science.

DIJKSTERHUIS, E.J. Doel en Methode van de Geschiedenis der Exacte Wetenschappen. [Aim and method of the history of the exact sciences. (In Dutch)]. 27 p. Amsterdam: J.M. Meulenhoff, 1953.

DINGLE, Herbert. The dependence of science on its history. Presidential address delivered to the British Society for the History of Science on 6 May 1957. *Bull.Brit.Soc.Hist. Sci.*, 1957, 2: 65-73.

DINGLE, Herbert. The missing factor in science. Inaugural lecture. 18 p. London: Lewis, 1947. [CB 71/114]
Summary in *Nature*, 1947, 160: 108-10. Discussion by J.D. Bernal and the author in *Nature*, 1947, 160: 612-13.

DINGLE, Herbert. The place of the history of science within the world of learning. *Act.VIIIe Congr.Int.Hist.Sci.* (Florence, 1956), p. 1107-10. Paris: Hermann, 1958.

FORBES, R.J. The history of science and technology. *Rapp. XIe Congr.Int.Sci.Hist.* (Stockholm, 1960), (1), p. 59-72. Göteborg: Almqvist & Wiksell, 1960.

FULTON, John F. A prolegomenon to the sciences. *Isis*, 1949, 40: 99-106.
Address at a joint session of the History of Science Society and the Modern Language Association.

GINSBURG, Benjamin. The value of the history of science. *Archeion*, 1933, 15: 27-33.

GRAINGER, Thomas H. Why study the history of science? *Impr. Coll.Univ.Teach.*, Autumn 1956, 79-82.

GULLI, Luciano. A proposito della storia della scienza come storia dello spirito umano. *Act.VIIIe Congr.Int.Hist.Sci.* (Florence, 1956), p. 1176-81. Paris: Hermann, 1958.

GULLI, Luciano. Historia nauki jako historia ducha ludzkiego. [History of science as the history of man's intellectual development. (In Polish)]. *Kwart.Hist.Nauk.Tech.*, 1958, 3: 355-75.
Translation of "A proposito della storia della scienza come storia dello spirito umano", *see* above.

INTERNATIONAL CONGRESS OF THE HISTORY OF SCIENCE, 2nd, London. The sciences as an integral part of general historical study. *Archeion*, 1932, 14: 271-88. [CB 38/590]

JOHNSON, E.H. Some observations concerning the history of science. *Sch.Sci.Math.*, 1921, 21: 450-3.

JONES, B. Mouat. The scientist and the historian: a plea for cooperation. *Mem.Manchester Lit.Phil.Soc.*, 1931-32, 76: 19-30.

KRANZBERG, Melvin. The newest history: science and technology. *Science*, 1962, 136: 463-8.

KUZNETSOV, Boris. L'histoire des sciences sous le jour de la science actuelle. *Proc.10th Int.Congr.Hist.Sci.* (Ithaca, 1962), (1), p. 315-16. Paris: Hermann, 1964.

LAIGNEL-LAVASTINE, Maxime. Histoire de la médecine et histoire des sciences. *Act.Ve Congr.Int.Hist.Sci.* (Lausanne, 1947), p. 185-8. Paris: Hermann, 1948. Also in *Arch.Int.Hist.Sci.*, 1948, 1: 490-3.

LORIA, Gino. La storia della scienza è una scienza? *Atti Soc.Ital.Progr.Sci.VI Rivnione* (Genoa, 1912), 19 p. Rome: Bertero, 1913.

MEYER, Adolf. Was heisst und zu welchem Ende studieren wir die Geschichte der Naturwissenschaften? *Arch.Gesch.Math. Naturwiss.Tech.*, 1927, 10: 37-53.

MEYERSON, Emile. De l'étude de l'histoire des sciences. *Archeion*, 1931, 13: 297-9. [CB 35/293]
Message to the 2nd International Congress of the History of Science, London, 1931.

MIELI, Aldo. Le réveil récent des études d'histoire des sciences et sa signification. *Scientia*, 1915, 17: 86-91.

MIELI, Aldo. La storia della scienza come disciplina scientifica. *Proteus*, 1931, 1: 13-16.

MIELI, Aldo. Sul concetto di storia della scienza. Appunti introduttivi. *Riv.Stor.Crit.Sci.*, 1916, 7: 42-46, 88-89.
The history of science as understood and defined by Gino Loria, George Sarton, Aldo Mieli.

MILLER, Genevieve. Backgrounds of current activities in the history of science and medicine. *J.Hist.Med.*, 1958, 13: 160-78, 10 fig.

MIZUKAMI, D.; HIROSHIGE, T. [On the article "Essentials of the history of science", by K. Oka. (In Japanese)]. *J.Hist. Sci.Japan*, 1952, no. 23, 24-5.

NATUCCI, A. Storia generale della scienza o storie particolari? *Scientia*, 1951, 86: 110-14.

OKA, Kunio. [Essentials of the history of science. (In Japanese)]. *J.Hist.Sci.Japan*, Oct. 1951, no. 20, 1-7.

OSTOL'SKII, VS. I. K voprosu o meste istorii estestvoznaniia i tekhniki v sisteme istoricheskikh nauk. [On the question of the place of the history of science and technology in the system of historical sciences. (In Russian)]. *Vop.Ist. Est.Tekh.*, 1963, 15: 75-81.
A comment on R.J. Forbes's paper "The history of science and technology", *see* above.

PELSENEER, Jean. L'histoire de la science. *Rev.Univ. Bruxelles*, 1932, 124-49.
Lecture inaugurating the course of the history of physical and mathematical sciences at the Université Libre of Brussels.

PELSENEER, Jean. L'histoire des sciences physiques. *Notes Conf.Univ.Libre Bruxelles*, 1946, 3: 62-89.
Leçon inaugurale faite à l'Université Libre de Bruxelles le 12 avril 1945.

PELSENEER, Jean; PUTMAN, Jacques. L'histoire des sciences. *Congr.Int.Phil.Sci.* (Paris, 1949), (8), p. 23-35. (Actualités Scientifiques et Industrielles, 1166) Paris: Hermann, 1952.

PLESSNER, Martin. The place of the history of science within the world of learning. *Act.VIIIe Congr.Int.Hist.Sci.* (Florence, 1956), p. 1146-50. Paris: Hermann, 1958.

PLOTKIN, S.IA. Vazhnye zadachi istorikov estestvoznaniia i tekhniki. [Important tasks of historians of science and technology. (In Russian)]. *Vop.Ist.Est.Tekh.*, 1962, 13: 3-6. [CB 88/535]

PRICE, Derek J. de Solla. Little science, big science. 144 p. New York: Columbia University Press, 1963.
Reviewed by Stanley Goldberg, *Science*, 1963, 140: 639-41; by L. Pearce Williams, *Arch.Int.Hist.Sci.*, 1964, 17: 168-70.

PRICE, Derek J. de Solla. The science of science. *Discovery*, 1956, 17: 179-80.
Stresses the importance of the study of the history and philosophy of science for a better understanding of scientific needs.

PRICE, Derek J. de Solla. Scholarship about science. *Yale Sci.Mag.*, 1962, 37: no. 2.

PRICE, Derek J. de Solla. Two cultures - and one historian of science. *Teach.Coll.Rec.*, 1963, 64: 527-35.

REINKE, Johannes. Geschichte und Naturwissenschaft. *Arch. Gesch.Math.Naturwiss.Tech.*, 1927, 10: 12-15.

RUDY, Z. [On the study of the history of science. (In Hebrew)]. *Koroth*, 1962, 2: 514-15.

RUSKA, Julius. Die Naturwissenschaften und ihre Geschichte. *Kristall*, 1928-29, 1: 88-93.
General views on the history of science.

RUSSO, F. Les dimensions de l'histoire des sciences. *Kwart. Hist.Nauk.Tech.*, 1962, 6: (Special issue), 43-53.

SARTON, George. Acta atque agenda. *Arch.Int.Hist.Sci.*, 1951, 4: 323-56.
Speech for the opening session of the 6th International Congress of the History of Science, 1950.

SARTON, George. Henri Berr (1863-1954): la synthèse de l'histoire et l'histoire de la science. *Centaurus*, 1956, 4 185-97, 1 pl.

SARTON, George. L'histoire de la science. *Isis*, 1913, 1: 3-46.

SARTON, George. L'histoire de la science. *Rev.Gén.Sci.*, 1912, 23: 93-4.

SARTON, George. The history of science. *Monist*, 1916, 26: 321-65.
Reviewed by P.E.B. Jourdain, *Isis*, 1920, 3: 310-11.

SARTON, George. The history of science. *Science*, 1919, 49: 497.
To support the proposition made by Felix Neumann (*Science*, April 4, 1919) to create a new section of the American Association for the Advancement of Science, to be devoted to the history of science.

SARTON, George. The history of science and the new humanism. xx, 196 p. (Colver lectures in Brown University, Elihu Root lecture at the Carnegie Institution of Washington). Cambridge, Mass.: Harvard University Press, 1937.
First publ. New York: Holt, 1931 and reviewed by H.T. Davis, *Isis*, 1931, 16: 451-5. Reissued New York: George Braziller, Inc., 1956. For other reviews *see* CB 32/573, CB 34/494, CB 35/293, CB 36/432, CB 49/163, CB 53/255 and CB 58/565.
Spanish translation (Rosario, Argentina: Editorial Rosario, 1948) of 2nd edition reviewed by Arlindo Camilo Monteiro, *Petrus Nonius*, 1951, 7: 206-14. Japanese translation of 2nd edition Tokyo: Iwanami Shoten, 1950.

SARTON, George. The history of science and the problems of to-day. iii, 30 p. (Carnegie Institution of Washington, Elihu Root Lecture, Suppl. Publ. 20). Washington: Roberts, 1936.
Reviewed in Swedish by Johan Nordström, *Lychnos*, 1936, 1: 331-4; by A.B., *Organon*, 1938, 2: 277.

SARTON, George. The history of science versus the history of learning. *Structure, Method and Meaning, Essays in Honor of Henry M. Sheffer*, p. 145-51. New York: 1951.

SARTON, George. Knowledge and charity. *Isis*, 1923, 5: 5-19. [CB 15/242]

SARTON, George. The new humanism. *Isis*, 1924, 6: 9-42.
German translation publ. in *Arch.Gesch.Math.Naturwiss. Tech.*, 1927, 10: 16-36.

SARTON, George. Le nouvel humanisme. *Scientia*, 1918, 23: 161-75.

SARTON, George. Oriente y occidente en la historia de la ciencia. *Al-Andalus* 1934, 2: 261-97.
Spanish translation by Alfonso Gámir Sandoval of chapter 2 of "The history of science and the new humanism" (New York: 1931).

SARTON, George. Science et tradition. *Arch.Int.Hist.Sci.*, 1948, 2: 10-31.
Lecture delivered at the Universities of London and Paris, Spring 1948.

SARTON, George. Les sciences et les humanités: l'histoire des sciences. *Act.VIIe Congr.Int.Hist.Sci.* (Jerusalem, 1953), p. 97-114. Paris: Hermann, [n.d.] [CB 80/114]

SARTON, George. Sixth preface to vol. XXXIV. Defence of the history of science (Philadelphia 1940). *Isis*, 1943, 34: 465-6. [CB 66/261]

SCHUSTER, Julius. Die Geschichte der Naturwissenschaften und wir. Dem *Archiv für Geschichte der Mathematik, der Naturwissenschaften und der Technik* zum Geleit. *Arch.Gesch. Math.Naturwiss.Tech.*, 1927, 10: 1-6.

SHRYOCK, Richard H. The history and sociology of science. *Items*, 1956, 10: 13-16.

SINGER, Charles. One increasing purpose. The spirit of science in history. *Times Lit.Suppl.*, July 18, 1936.
Leading article apropos of the works of Lynn Thorndike, George Sarton and J.R. Partington.

SINGER, Charles. Presidential address delivered on 3rd May, 1949. *Bull.Brit.Soc.Hist.Sci.*, 1950, 1: 59-63. [CB 77/363]
Reminiscences concerning the study of the history of science during the last fifty years.

STICKER, Bernhard. Wege und Ziele. Sechzig Jahre Wissenschaftgeschichte, Bestand, und Wandel, 1901-1961. Wiesbaden: Franz Steiner Verlag, 1961.
Reviewed by E. Wickersheimer, *Sudhoffs Arch.*, 1962, 46: 185-6.

SUCHODOLSKI, Bogdan. History of science in continuity and change. *Kwart.Hist.Nauk.Tech.*, 1962, 6: (Special issue), 5-17.

TATON, R. Sur les buts et les méthodes de l'histoire de la science. *Kwart.Hist.Nauk.Tech.*, 1962, 6: (Special issue), 19-27.

TIMPANARO, Sebastiano. La storia della scienza. *Arduo*, 1921, 1: 10-17.

VELDE, A.J.J. van de. L'histoire des sciences et la division de l'histoire de l'humanité. *Rev.Hist.Sci.*, 1955, 8: 97-102.

VELDE, A.J.J. van de. Voor een ruimere belangstelling van de intellectuëelen in de geschiedenis der wetenschappen. Beroep op hun medewerking. [A plea for scholars to take more interest in the history of science. (In Dutch)]. *Jaarb. Vlaam.Acad.Wetensch.Lett.Schoone Kunst.Belg.*, 1945, 141-7.

VERNADSKII, V.I. [Ideas on the present importance of the history of science. (In Russian)]. *Tr.Kom.Ist.Znanii*, 1927, 1: 1-17.

VOISÉ, W. Les germes des sciences modernes et l'objet de l'histoire des sciences. *Kwart.Hist.Nauk.Tech.*, 1962, 6: (Special issue), 73-7.

VRAGALI, J. L'histoire de la science - facteur du développement scientifique et de la paix des nations. *Act.VIIe Congr.Int.Hist.Sci.* (Jerusalem, 1953), (2), p. 625-8. Paris: Hermann, [n.d.].

WALTER, Emil J. Aufgaben, Ziele und Methoden der Wissenschaftgeschichte. *Abhandlungen zur Wissenschaftsgeschichte und Wissenschaftslehre*, p. 13-31. (Veröffentlichungen der Gesellschaft für Internationale Wissenschaftsgeschichte, 1951, no. 4) Bremen: Carl Schünemann, [n.d.]

WILLIAMS, W. Roger. Science and its history. 19 p. London: Burrow, 1933.

Af-a the study of the history of science in different countries

for history of science research institutes *see* Afqg
history of science societies *see* Afqd

Af-ab

DIJKSTERHUIS, E.J. Amerikaanse indrukken. [American impressions. (In Dutch)]. *Gids*, 1957, no. 11, 311-17.
Reflections on the study of the history of science in America occasioned by the meeting at the University of Wisconsin in Sept. 1957 (*see Isis*, 1957, 48: 461-2).

LEIKIND, Morris C. The history of science movement in Washington D.C. *Isis*, 1934, 22: 230-32.

SARTON, George. Report [on his work in the history of science] to the Trustees of the Carnegie Institution of Washington. *Year Book Carnegie Inst.Wash.*, 1919, vol. 18 - 1949, vol. 48.
During the thirty-one years of his association with the Carnegie Institution Sarton contributed annual reports. [CB 8/363, CB 10/210, CB 12/641, CB 14/564, CB 17/602, CB 24/520 and CB 26/224]
The twelfth, thirteenth and fourteenth reports were fully given in *Isis*, 1931, 15: 170-1; 1932, 17: 209-17; 1933, 19: 15-18.

Af-ac

IZQUIERDO, J. Joaquin. Importancia de los estudios históricos de las ciencias en México. *Mem.Acad.Mex.Hist.*, 1961, 20: 325-47.

Af-ag

MIELI, Aldo. Un viaggio in Germania. Impressioni ed appunti di uno storico della scienza. *Arch.Stor.Sci.*, 1926, 7: 342-81. [CB 23/211]

Af-ah

SARTON, George. The history of science in Poland. *Isis*, 1955, 46: 279.

VETTER, Quido. L'histoire des sciences en Tchécoslovaquie. *Bull.Int.Comm.Hist.Sci.*, 1933, 19: 333-52.

VETTER, Quido. L'histoire des sciences en Tchécoslovaquie. *Lychnos*, 1937, 2: 243-7.

Af-ai

CORSINI, Andrea. Origine e sviluppo degli studi di storia della scienza. *Ulisse*, 1957, 5: 1305-10.

METZGER, Hélène. La settimana della Scuola di storia delle scienze a Roma. *Archeion*, 1935, 17: 203-12.

MIELI, Aldo. La storia della scienza in Italia. viii, 130 p. Firenze: La Voce, 1916. [CB 7/151]

MIELI, Aldo. La storia della scienza in Italia. *Arch.Stor.Sci.*, 1926, 7: 36-48.
Introduction to a History of Science course held at the University of Perugia, 9 March 1926.

RONCHI, Vasco. La storia della scienza in Italia. *G.Univ.*, 1957, 7: 1-8.

Af-ak

DIJKSTERHUIS, E.J. L'histoire des sciences en Hollande de 1940 à 1950. *Rev.Hist.Sci.*, 1950, 3: 273-6.

GENOOTSCHAP VOORGESCHIEDENIS DER GENEESKUNDE, WISKUNDE EN NATUURWETENSCHAPPEN. Vijftig jaren. Beoefening van de geschiedenis der geneeskunde, wiskunde en natuurwetenschappen in Nederland 1913-1963. [Fifty years: the study of the history of medicine, mathematics and the natural sciences. Published under the supervision of B.P.M. Schulte. (In Dutch)]. 118 p., bibliogr., 1963.

Af-an

FIGUROVSKII, N.A. [Some results and problems of the development of the history of science and technology in the USSR in the light of decisions of the 21st Congress of the Soviet Communist Party] *Vop.Ist.Est.Tekh.*, 1960, 9: 7-17.

FIGUROVSKII, N.A.; ZUBOV, V.P. Discours prononcé à la session de l'Union Internationale d'Histoire de la Science à Florence, Septembre, 1956. *Isis*, 1958, 49: 78-9.

GRIGORIAN, A.T.; ZUBOV, V.P. L'état actuel de l'histoire des sciences en URSS. *Lychnos*, 1962, 128-37.

JORAVSKY, David. Soviet views on the history of science. *Isis*, 1955, 46: 3-15.

Af-ao

BOLOGA, Valeriu L. Universitas litterarum und Wissenschaftsgeschichte. (Mit besonderer Berücksichtigung der Verhältnisse in Rumänien). 26 p. (*Abhandl.Gesch.Med.Naturwiss.*, 7) Berlin: Ebering, 1935.

SARTON, George. The study and teaching of the history of science and of medicine in Rumania. *Isis*, 1935, 23: 445.

Af-mzAke history of science as scientific method

KANTOR, J.R. History of science as scientific method. (Perspectives in Psychology, 15) *Psychol.Rec.*, 1960, 10: 187-9.

Af-mzNf relation with history of medicine as a study

for the study of the history of science in relation to the study of the history of medicine *see* Nf-mzAf

Afb history and philosophy of science as a study

for philosophical aspects of the history of science *see* Ahf
philosophy and methodology of science *see* Ak

DINGLE, Herbert. History and philosophy of science. *Univ.Quart.*, 1952, 6: 337-45.

MIELI, Aldo. La historia y la filosofía de la ciencia. *Essays in the History of Medicine presented to Prof. Arturo Castiglioni*, p. 205-16. Baltimore: Johns Hopkins Press, 1944.

MILLER, Hugh. Philosophy of science and history of science. *Isis*, 1939, 30: 52-64.

SEEGER, Raymond J. On the history and philosophy of science. After-dinner address given at the annual meeting of the History of Science Society in New York City on 30 December 1954. *Amer.Scient.*, 1956, 44: 151-7. [CB 82/193]

Afd biography of historians of science

MIELI, Aldo. Per una biografia degli storici della scienza italiani. *Riv.Stor.Crit.Sci.*, 1916-17, 7: 59-60, 86, 125-7, 165-7; 8: 225-7, 250-1, 320-3. [CB 8/367]

SARTON, George. Acta atque agenda. *Act.VIe Congr.Int.Hist.Sci.* (Amsterdam, 1950), p. 45-78. Paris: Hermann, 1951-53.
Includes short biographies of Moritz Cantor, Paul Tannery, Karl Sudhoff, J.L. Heiberg, Pierre Duhem, Sir Thomas Heath, Aldo Mieli.

SARTON, George. "Historians and philosophers" of science. Biographies available in *Isis* and *Osiris*. *Isis*, 1955, 46: 360-6.

SARTON, George. Materials for the history of the history of science. *Isis*, 1937, 27: 6-8. [CB 51/246]
A list of articles devoted to historians and philosophers of science.

WOHLWILL, Emil. Naturforscher als Historiker der Naturwissenschaften. *Mitt.Gesch.Med.*, 1912, 11: 1-5.

FOR biographies and bibliographies of individual historians of science (20th century) *see* volumes 1 and 2 under:-

Barry, Frederick; Cannizzaro, Stanislao; Dampier-Whetham, William Cecil; De Milt, Clara; Diergart, Paul; Duhem, Pierre; Favaro, Antonio; Irsay, Stephen d'; Koyré, Alexandre; Langevin, Paul; Menéndez y Pelayo, Marcelino; Metzger, Hélène; Mieli, Aldo; Milhaud, Gaston; Ostwald, Wilhelm; Pagel, Julius Leopold; Procházka, Jan Svatopluk; Sarton, George Alfred Léon; Sergescu, Petre; Singer, Charles Joseph; Tannery, Jules; Tannery, Marie Alexandrine Prisset; Tannery, Paul; Thorndike, Lynn; Tyler, Harry Walter; Vavilov, Sergei Ivanovich; Velde, Albert Jacques Joseph van de; Windle, Bertram Coghill Alan; Wyrouboff, Grégoire Nicolaevich.

FOR biographies and bibliographies of contemporary historians specialising in the different subject fields *see* INDEX.

Afp historical studies: organization

Afph

ALPERT, Harry. National Science Foundation program for basic research in the history, philosophy and sociology of science. *Isis*, 1956, 47: 56.

Afpx

DELORME, Suzanne. Médaille George Sarton. *Rev.Hist.Sci.*, 1959, 12: 367-8.

THE GEORGE SARTON medal. *Isis*, 1956, 47: 31-2, 3 pl.

PRIX Binoux (1889) [Académie des Sciences] *Isis*, 1926, 8: 161-3, 725; 1927, 9: 370-2; 1928, 10: 58, 502-5; 1929, 11: 232; 1932, 17: 429; 1934, 21: 210; 1935, 22: 531; 1936, 25: 136-7; 1947, 37: 79; 1950, 41: 303; 1954, 45: 293; 1956, 47: 55; 1960, 51: 86.
The Prix Binoux is an academic award open to historians of science.

SCHUMAN PRIZE in the history of science. [An annual award established by Henry and Ida Schuman of New York City for an original prize essay in the history of science and its cultural influences in 1955 and continued by Mrs. Schuman in memory of her husband who died in 1962. Particulars of the prize were given on the fly leaves of] *Isis*, 1955, 46: part 4 and 1964, 55: part 1.
For awards of the prize *see Isis*, 1956, 47: 418; 1961, 52: 104.

SUDHOFF medals. *Isis*, 1927, 9: 428.
Awarded by the Deutsche Gesellschaft für Geschichte der Medizin und der Naturwissenschaften.

Afq historical studies: institutions

MIELI, Aldo. Organizzazzioni italiane per promuovere lo studio della storia della scienza. *Arch.Stor.Sci.*, 1919, 1: 94-6.

Afqd history of science societies

see also British Society for the History of Science, 2: 674
History of Science Society, 2: 701-2

ARTELT, Walter. Wege und Ziele. Rückblicke auf ein Vierteljahrhundert der deutschen Gesellschaft für Geschichte der Medizin, Naturwissenschaft, und Technik, 1930-1955. 55 p., ill. (Beiträge zur Geschichte der Wissenschaft und der Technik, 3) Wiesbaden: Franz Steiner Verlag, 1961.
Reviewed by E. Wickersheimer, *Sudhoffs Arch.*, 1962, 46: 185-6.

BLOKH, M.A. Kommission für Geschichte des Wissens an der Akademie der Wissenschaften d. U.S.S.R. *Mitt.Gesch.Med.*, 1927, 26: 281-2.

BRASCH, Frederick E. The history of science section [of the American Association for the Advancement of Science] and the progress of science. *Science*, 1920, 52: 559-62.

BUESS, Heinrich. Tagung der schweizerischen Gesellschaft für Geschichte der Medizin und der Naturwissenschaften in Basel. *Gesnerus*, 1956, 13: 219-21.

BURGER, D. Overzicht van de eerste 25 jaren (1913-1938) van de Vereeniging voor Geschiedenis der Genees-, Natuur- en Wiskunde, sinds 1928: Genootschap voor Geschiedenis der Genees-, Natuur- en Wiskunde gevestigd te Leiden. [Chronicle of the first twenty-five years of the Dutch Society for the History of Medicine, Mathematics and Natural Science. (In Dutch)] 46 p. Amsterdam: 1938.

DEUTSCHE GESELLSCHAFT FÜR GESCHICHTE DER MEDIZIN, DER NATURWISSENSCHAFTEN UND DER TECHNIK. Verhandlungsbericht der Sektion für Geschichte der Medizin und der Naturwissenschaften auf der Versammlung Deutscher Naturforscher und Aerzte zu Nauheim, Sept. 1920. Zugleich wissenschaftliche Tagung der deutschen Gesellschaft für Geschichte der Medizin. *Janus*, 1921, 25: 101-22.
From 1921 to 1934 reports of the annual meetings of the Society were published in *Janus*.

GESELLSCHAFT FÜR GESCHICHTE DER NATURWISSENSCHAFTEN, DER MEDIZIN UND DER TECHNIK AM NIEDERRHEIN. *Isis*, 1913, 1: 251.

INDIAN SOCIETY FOR THE HISTORY OF SCIENCE. [Announcement of its formation] *Isis*, 1958, 49: 76.

PELSENEER, Jean. Comité Belge d'Histoire des Sciences [1946-47]. *Isis*, 1948, 38: 245.
First 5 annual reports for 1933-38 appeared in *Archeion*, vol. 16-21; 6th (1938-39) in *Isis*, 1940, 32: 129-30.

RHEINISCHE GESELLSCHAFT FÜR GESCHICHTE DER NATURWISSENSCHAFT, MEDIZIN UND TECHNIK. Verhandlungsberichte. *Proteus*, 1931, 1: 47-281. [CB 31/544]
Concerning the activities of the Rheinische Gesellschaft.

SAUVENIER-GOFFIN, E. L'activité du centre national (Belge) d'histoire des sciences au cours de l'exercice 1958. *Arch.Int.Hist.Sci.*, 1959, 12: 56-65.

SOCIETÀ DI STORIA CRITICA DELLE SCIENZE MEDICHE E NATURALI. [Notice of first national congress, 1912] *Isis*, 1913, 1: 110-11.

WASHINGTON ACADEMY OF SCIENCES. [Announcement of the appointment of a Special Committee on the History of Science.] *Isis*, 1958, 49: 80.

Afqg history of science research institutes

see also Istituto e Museo di Storia della Scienza, Florence, 2: 708

ARTELT, Walter. Das Institut für Geschichte der Medizin und der Naturwissenschaften in Berlin. *Mitt.Gesch.Med.*, 1937, 36: 281-4, fig.

BURGER, Dionys. L'Institut d'Histoire de la Médecine, des Mathématiques et des Sciences en 1948. *Arch.Int.Hist.Sci.*, 1949, 2: 936-8.
Genootschap voor Geschiedenis der Genees-, Natuur- en Wiskunde, Leyden.

DIEPGEN, Paul. Die Aufgaben und Ziele des Institutes für Geschichte der Medizin und der Naturwissenschaften in Berlin. *Klin.Wochenschr.*, 1931, 10: 269-71.

DIEPGEN, Paul. Das Berliner Institut für Geschichte der Medizin und der Naturwissenschaften. *Lychnos*, 1936, 1: 230-4.

HISTORY of science in the Soviet Union. *Isis*, 1946, 36: 131.
The new Institute of the History of Natural Sciences of the USSR.

L'INSTITUT POUR L'HISTOIRE DES SCIENCES de l'Université de Hambourg. *Doc.Hist.Tech.*, 1962, 2: 68.

MATOUŠEK, Otakar. Czechoslovak Academy of Sciences. [Notice of the establishment of a new department for the history of science & technology] *Isis*, 1958, 49: 80.

MIELI, Aldo. El desarrollo histórico de la historia de la ciencia y la función actual de los Institutos de historia de la ciencia. *Publ.Inst.Hist.Filosof.Cienc., Univ.Nac. Litoral,* 1939, no. 1, 5-45. Also in *Archeion,* 1940, 22: 1-41. [CB 49/483]
Inaugural lecture opening the new Institute of the History and Philosophy of Science established in the University of Santa Fé, Argentina.

RUDNYKH, Semyon P. The history of science in Russia. Creation of an institute for its study. *Isis,* 1947, 37: 77.

SARTON, George. An institute for the history of science. *Isis,* 1924, 6: 408-10.

SARTON, George. An institute for the history of science and civilization. [First and second articles] *Science,* 1917, 45: 284-6; 46: 399-402; [third article] *Isis,* 1938, 28: 7-17.
His plan for an institute in the United States.

SIGERIST, Henry E. Forschungsinstitute für Geschichte der Medizin und der Naturwissenschaften. 15 p. In: Brauer, Ludolph, ed. Forschungsinstitute; ihre Geschichte, Organisation und Ziele. Hamburg: P. Hartung, 1930.

SIGERIST, Henry E. An institute for the history of science in Leningrad. *Bull.Inst.Hist.Med.,* 1935, 3: 92-3.

SKUBALA, Z. Ten years of history of science at the Polish Academy of Sciences (1952-1962). *Kwart.Hist.Nauk.Tech.,* 1962, 6: Special issue, 141-64.

ZEISS, Heinz. Das neugegründete Forschungsinstitut für Geschichte der Naturwissenschaften in Moskau. *Arch.Gesch. Math.Naturwiss.Tech.,* 1929, 11: 308-16.

Afqv history of science national congresses

see also American Association for the Advancement of Science, 2: 662
American Historical Association, 2: 663

BASHMAKOVA, I.G.; SOROKINA, L.A. [Interuniversity conference on the history of exact sciences held in the Soviet Union in May 1960] (In Russian) *Usp.Mat.Nauk,* 1960, no. 6, 205-14.
Includes list of papers presented.

BUESS, Heinrich. Tagung der Schweizerischen Gesellschaft für Geschichte der Medizin und der Naturwissenschaften in Basel. *Gesnerus,* 1956, 13: 219-21.

CONFERENCE on the history, philosophy, and sociology of science. Sponsored by the American Philosophical Society and the National Science Foundation in the Hall of the Society, 10-11 February 1955. *Proc.Amer.Phil.Soc.,* 1955, 99: 327-54. [CB 81/253 and CB 82/192]

PRIMO convegno nazionale di storia della scienza in Palermo. *Universo,* 1926, 7: 595-6. [CB 22/252]

RUBINSTEIN, Bertha W. Conference on the history, philosophy and sociology of science. (Philadelphia, 1955) *Isis,* 1955, 46: 282-3.

SHRYOCK, Richard H. The nature of the Conference [on the history, philosophy and sociology of science]. *Proc.Amer. Phil.Soc.,* 1955, 99: 327-31.

THORNDIKE, Lynn. The conference at Cleveland on the history of science. *Science,* 1920, 51: 193-4.
Took place during the Annual Meeting of the American Historical Association, December 1919.

THORNDIKE, Lynn. The Washington conference on the history of science. *Science,* 1921, 53: 122.
Report of conference held in Washington, December 1920.

WOODS HOLE Seminar in the History and Philosophy of Science. [1st-3rd, 1961-63] *Isis,* 1962, 53: 227; 1963, 54: 136-7; 1964, 55: 94-5.

WOOLF, Harry. Annual meeting of the Pacific Coast branch of the American Historical Association. *Isis,* 1957, 48: 187.
For the first time in the history of the branch, a section was devoted to the history of science.

Afqx international congresses for the history of science

see also International Congress of the History of Science, 2: 707

BENELUX Congress (First) on the History of Science. *Isis,* 1954, 45: 197-8.
Conference held in Leiden, April 1954. Papers listed.

INTERNATIONAL CONGRESS OF HISTORICAL SCIENCES, Warsaw 1933. [The setting up of a preliminary committee for a Section of the History of Science, including medicine] *Isis,* 1931, 16: 129-30.

INTERNATIONAL CONGRESS OF THE HISTORY OF SCIENCE. [Publication dates of Proceedings and accounts of congresses.]

1st (Paris, 1929)
Archeion, 1929, vol. 11; suppl.
2nd (London, 1931) Resumés in *Archeion,* 1931, vol. 13; 1932, vol. 14.
Isis, 1931, 16: 126-9.
3rd (Portugal, 1934) Lisboa: 1936
Isis, 1938, 28: 135-8; *Archeion,* 1934, 16: 100-2, 337-72.
4th (Prague, 1937) [Not printed]
Isis, 1937, 26: 452-3; *Archeion,* 1937, 19: 374-6.
5th (Lausanne, 1947) Paris: 1948.
Isis, 1948, 39: 65-6; *Arch.Int.Hist.Sci.,* 1948, 1: 323-5.
6th (Amsterdam, 1950) Paris: 1951-53.
Isis, 1951, 42: 45 and CB 79/163; *Arch.Int.Hist.Sci.,* 1951, 4: 135-7.
7th (Jerusalem, 1953) Paris: [1954?]
Isis, 1954, 45: 63-77; *Arch.Int.Hist.Sci.,* 1953, 6: 453-79.
8th (Florence, 1956) Paris: 1958.
Isis, 1957, 48: 176-81; *Arch.Int.Hist.Sci.,* 1958, 11: 43-4.
9th (Barcelona, Madrid, 1959) Paris: 1960.
Arch.Int.Hist.Sci., 1959, 12: 225-52.
10th (Ithaca, 1962) Paris: 1964.
Arch.Int.Hist.Sci., 1962, 15: 399-40; *Sterne,* 1963, 39: no. 9-10, 200-4.

SERGESCU, Pierre. Rapport général sur les travaux du colloque d'histoire des sciences. *Congr.Int.Phil.Sci.* (Paris, 1949), (8), p. 3-12. (Actualités Scientifiques et Industrielles, 1166) Paris: Hermann, 1952.

ZUBOV, V.P. Problemy istorii estestvoznaniya na VII Mezhdunarodnom kongresse po istorii nauki. [Problems of the history of natural science at the Seventh International Congress for the History of Science. (In Russian)] *Vop.Ist.Est.Tekh.,* 1956, part 2, 294-7.
Apropos of the *Act.VIIe Congr.Int.Hist.Sci.* (Jerusalem, 1953).

Afqy international institutions for the history of science

see also Académie Internationale d'Histoire des Sciences, 2: 657

CORTESAO, Armando. L'UNESCO. Sa tâche et son but concernant les sciences et leur développement historique. *Act.Ve Congr. Int.Hist.Sci.* (Lausanne, 1947), p. 25-35. Paris: Hermann, 1948.

INTERNATIONAL COMMITTEE OF THE HISTORY OF SCIENCE. *Isis,* 1929, 12: 323.

SARTON, George. L'histoire de la science et l'organisation internationale. *Doc.Prélim.IIe Congr.Mond.Ass.Int.* (Ghent, Brussels, 1913), (37), 14 p. Bruxelles: 1913. Also published, *Vie Int.,* 1913, 4: 27-40. [CB 5/283]
Reprinted, with new preface, *Isis,* 1938, 29: 311-25.

UNESCO and the history of science. *Arch.Int.Hist.Sci.,* 1947, 1: 3-4.

UNION INTERNATIONALE D'HISTOIRE DES SCIENCES. Compte rendu de la IVe Assemblée Générale, Florence-Milan, 3-9 septembre 1956. *Arch.Int.Hist.Sci.,* 1956, 35: 390-405. [CB 83/187]

Afqy-br

Annuaire de l'Académie Internationale d'Histoire des Sciences. 1-, 1934- Paris: 1934-

Ag teaching history of science

ALBRECHT-CARRIÉ, René. Of science, its history, and the teaching thereof. *Sci.Mon.*, 1951, 73: 16-24.

BARNES, Harry Elmer, ed. The teaching of the history of science and personalia. *Isis*, 1924, 6: 534-8; 1925, 7: 105-10; 1926, 8: 158-61; 1927, 9: 112-17; 1928, 10: 47-52; 1929, 12: 149-50; 1930, 13: 356-8.

DELEVSKY, J. L'histoire des sciences dans l'enseignement. *Enseign.Sci.*, 1937, 10: 241-7.

DINGLE, Herbert; *et al.* History of science in education. *Bull.Brit.Soc.Hist.Sci.*, 1950, 1: 89-93.

HAMSHAW THOMAS, H. The history of science in modern education. (Presidential address, 1954). *Bull.Brit.Soc.Hist.Sci.*, 1955, 2: 1-8; also in *Nature*, 1954, 174: 481-3.

LHÉRITIER, Michel. L'enseignement de l'histoire des sciences. Projet d'enquête. *Archeion*, 1931, 13: 159-67. [CB 33/391]

MIELI, Aldo, ed. L'enseignement de l'histoire des sciences. *Archeion*, 1931, 13: 467-90; 1932, 14: 88-110, 161-2, 261-6. [CB 35/292-3]
Collection of short notes, of which some were read at the 2nd International History of Science Congress (London, 1931), and a bibliography of material which appeared in *Archeion*, 1929-31.

PINA, Luiz de. O ensino da história das ciências, em especial da medicina. *An.Fac.Ciênc.Porto*, 1934, 18: 42 p.

PRICE, Derek J. de Solla. The scientific humanities - an urgent program. Presented at the Second American Humanities Seminar, General Session V, Skinner Hall Auditorium, 29 June 1957. Washington, D.C.: The author, [1957?]; also in *Basic Coll.Quart.*, 1959, 4: 6-14.

QUINTANA Y MARI, Antonio. Valor de la historia de la ciencia como medio de educación integral y específica del individuo. *Archeion*, 1935, 17: 218-23.

REYMOND, Arnold. Réflexions sur l'enseignement de l'histoire des sciences. *Act.IIIe Congr.Int.Hist.Sci.* (Portugal, 1934), p. 120-6. Lisbon: 1936; also in *Archeion*, 1934, 16: 265-72.

RONCHI, V. A propos de l'enseignement de l'histoire de la science. *Kwart.Hist.Nauk.Tech.*, 1962, 6: (Special issue), 109-27.

SARTON, George. Est-il possible d'enseigner l'histoire de la science? *Arch.Int.Hist.Sci.*, 1950, 29: 3-38.

SARTON, George. Primum herbam deinde spicam deinde plenum frumentum in spica. Preface to Volume XXIX. *Isis*, 1938, 29: 9-14.

SARTON, George. The teaching of the history of science. [First article] *Sci.Mon.*, 1918, 7: 193-211; [second article] *Isis*, 1922, 4: 225-49; *Med.Life*, 1923, 30: 515-38; [third article] *Isis*, 1930, 13: 272-97.

SIGERIST, Henry E. The history of science in post-war education. *Science*, 1944, 100: 415-20.

TATON, René. Teaching the history of science. *Impact*, 1959, 9: 137-49.

WINTER, Henry James Jacques. The history of science and the history of civilization; its reflection in the process of education. *Archeion*, 1943, 25: 13-30.

WINTER, Henry James Jacques. Remarks on the teaching of the history and philosophy of science. *Arch.Int.Hist.Sci.*, 1947-48, 1: 574-8.

Agg curriculum

COHEN, I. Bernard. Principles of physical science. An outline of the topics covered in Natural Sciences 3, together with a selected group of readings illustrative of the development of science. Mimeographed notes for students, fig., ill. Cambridge, Mass.: The Author, 1949. [CB 76/389]

STIMSON, Dorothy. The development of the scientific point of view, a syllabus. 2nd rev. ed. 17 p. Baltimore, Maryland, 1932. [CB 36/433]

TANNERY, Paul. Programme pour un cours d'histoire des sciences. *Enseign.Sci.*, 1932, 5: 135-40. [CB 36/433]
Program first proposed in 1892 and published in 1907.

Agm at primary and secondary level

See also Agt

BENTWICH, J. The teaching of scientific method in secondary schools. *Act.VIIe Congr.Int.Hist.Sci.* (Jerusalem, 1953), p. 206-9. Paris: Hermann, 1954.
A discussion of the teaching of the history of science and scientific method in the Reali School at Haifa.

EWEN, A.H. A sixth form course in the history and philosophy of science. *Hist.Sci.*, 1963, 2: 84-90.

FETTWEIS, Ewald. Bericht über die Stellung der Wissenschaftsgeschichte im Unterricht der höheren Schulen Deutschlands. *Archeion*, 1935, 17: 213-17.

FOWLES, G. The place of the history of science in education. *Sch.Sci.Rev.*, Oct. 1949, 31: 2-6.

HIRATA, Yutaka. [Critics of the treatment of history of science in the secondary school textbooks, 1. (In Japanese)]. *J.Hist.Sci.Japan*, 1952, no. 22, 20-2.

KIMURA, Kimio. [On education in the history of science in the secondary school. (In Japanese)]. *J.Hist.Sci.Japan*, 1953, no. 27, 29-31.

KLOPFER, L.E. A secondary school course in the history of science. *Isis*, 1956, 47: 63.
At the Bronx High School of Science in New York City.

MUTÔ, Tôru. [Present state of the history of science in high school education. (In Japanese)]. *J.Hist.Sci.Japan*, 1953, no. 25, 29-31.

ÔYA, Shin-Ichi. [Criticism of the treatment of the history of science in secondary school text-books. (In Japanese)]. *J.Hist.Sci.Japan*, 1952, no. 24, 18-21; *ibid.*, no. 26, 27-9.

OYE, Paul V. van. De geschiedenis der wetenschappen doet haar intrede in het middelbaar onderwijs. [The history of science makes its entry into secondary education. (In Dutch)]. *Vlaam.Gids*, 1959, 43: 638-40.

REYMOND, Arnold. L'histoire des sciences et sa valeur dans l'enseignement secondaire. *Jahrb.Ver.Schweiz.Gymnasiallehrer*, 1928, 12 p. [CB 26/534]

TEACHING the history of science. [Paul D. Schreiber High School, Port Washington, New York.] *Isis*, 1964, 55: 444.

Agp at university level

CREW, Henry. The problem of the history of science in the college curriculum. *Sci.Mon.*, 1920, 10: 475-81. [CB 9/494]

DIJKSTERHUIS, E.J. La place de l'histoire des sciences dans l'instruction supérieure. (Rapport presenté à la Commission pour l'Enseignement et la Diffusion de l'Histoire des Sciences instituée par l'Académie Internationale des Sciences.) *Arch.Int.Hist.Sci.*, 1950, 3: 39-76. [CB 76/389]

ENGLEY, Donald B. A report of a study of the provision of history of science materials and their use in the undergraduate college. 11 p. Hartford 6, Conn.: The author, 1957.
Mimeographed.

SIMMONS, R.H. The history and philosophy of science: a challenge to higher education. *Sci.Educ.*, 1957, 41: 57-61.

SIMMONS, R.H. The history of science: a neglected area in college teaching. *Turtox News*, 1954, no. 7, 3 p.

WOODBURY, Robert S. The teaching of the history of science in an engineering school. *Ann.Sci.*, 1936, 1: 226-32.

Agp-a

MAYS, W. History and philosophy of science in British Commonwealth universities. *Brit.J.Phil.Sci.*, 1960, 11: 192-211.

MAYS, W. History and philosophy of science in the Commonwealth. *Nature*, 1961, 189: 971-2.

Agp-ab

BRASCH, Fred. E. The teaching of the history of science [in the U.S.]. Its present status in our universities, colleges and technical schools. *Science*, 1915, 42: 746-60.

COHEN, I. Bernard. The history of science. *Science*, 1951, 114, AAAS Supplement to 21 December, p. 3.
Discussing opportunities for the study of the history of science in the United States.

HISTORY of science teaching. [In American universities]
Brooklyn Polytechnic Institute. *Isis*, 1959, 50: 158; 1964, 55: 210.
Brown University. *Isis*, 1947, 37: 78; 1948, 39: 67; 1951, 42: 41.
Bryn Mawr College. *Isis*, 1951, 42: 308.
Butler University. *Isis*, 1958, 49: 77.
California, University of. *Isis*, 1933, 20: 6-14; 1958, 49: 172-3; 1960, 51: 86; 1963, 54: 137.
Carnegie-Mellon University. *Isis*, 1959, 50: 483.
Chicago, University of. *Isis*, 1959, 50: 158; 1960, 51: 343.
Clarkson College of Technology. *Isis*, 1955, 46: 284.
Columbia University. *Isis*, 1964, 55: 210.
Cornell University. *Isis*, 1947, 38: 99.
Delaware, University of. *Isis*, 1949, 40: 123.
Harvard University. *Isis*, 1936, 26: 154; 1938, 28: 95-6; 1940, 32: 125; 1941, 33: 65-6, 340-1.
Indiana University. *Isis*, 1960, 51: 209-10.
Iowa State College. *Isis*, 1958, 49: 77.
Johns Hopkins University. *Isis*, 1964, 55: 96.
Kansas, University of. *Isis*, 1958, 49: 77; 1964, 55: 210.
Kent State University. *Isis*, 1962, 53: 511.
Lawrence College. *Isis*, 1955, 46: 284.
Lehigh University. *Isis*, 1959, 50: 158.
Massachusetts Institute of Technology. *Isis*, 1936, 24: 432; 1940, 32: 123-4.
Minnesota, University of. *Isis*, 1949, 40: 123.
Northwestern University. *Isis*, 1955, 46: 283-5.
Oklahoma, University of. *Isis*, 1956, 47: 61-2.
Princeton University. *Isis*, 1956, 47: 62; 1960, 51: 86-7.
Washington, D.C. National University. *Isis*, 1931, 16: 131.
Washington, University of. *Isis*, 1956, 47: 61; 1958, 49: 78; 1964, 55: 445.
Washington and Lee University. *Isis*, 1960, 51: 569; 1962, 53: 227-8.
Williams College, Williamstown. *Isis*, 1947, 38: 98.
Wisconsin, University of. *Isis*, 1952, 43: 51-3, 368; 1956, 47: 62-3.
Yale University. *Isis*, 1960, 51: 209, 569.

JOHNSON, E.H. The present status of the history of science in American colleges and universities. *Science*, 1921, 54: 585-95.

RUBINSTEIN, Joseph. The history of science: library resources and academic programs of teaching and research in the Middle West. *Libr.Resources Tech.Serv.*, 1958, 2: 3-15.

SHRYOCK, Richard H. Training historians of science in the United States. *Act.VIe Congr.Int.Hist.Sci.* (Amsterdam, 1950), (1), p. 393-7. Paris: Hermann, 1951; also *Arch.Int. Hist.Sci.*, 1951, 30: 595-9.

STIMSON, Dorothy. A case report on a history of scientific ideas. *Sci.Mon.*, 1947, 64: 148-54.
A summary of twenty-five years of experience in teaching the history of science in a liberal arts college (Goucher College in Baltimore).

STIMSON, Dorothy. The teaching of the history of science in a liberal arts college for women. *Ann.Sci.*, 1937, 2: 460-4.

Agp-ae

ARMITAGE, A. The teaching of the history of science in the University of London. *Lychnos*, 1936, 1: 302-7.

BUCHDAHL, Gerd. History and philosophy of science at Cambridge. *Hist.Sci.*, 1962, 1: 62-6.

CAMBRIDGE UNIVERSITY. Lectures on the history of science. *Isis*, 1937, 27: 329-30; 1938, 29: 411-12; 1940, 32: 126; 1944, 35: 179-80, 335.

COURSES on the history of science at University College, London. *Isis*, 1920, 3: 419-20.
Short note on the courses provided for summer term 1920.

CROMBIE, A.C. History and philosophy of science at Oxford. *Hist.Sci.*, 1962, 1: 57-61.

HALL, A. Rupert. Teaching of the history of science. Cambridge University, England. *Isis*, 1955, 46: 285-6.

HANSON, N.R. History and philosophy of science in an undergraduate physics course. *Phys.Today*, 1955, 8: no. 8, 4-9.
Polish translation: *Kwart.Hist.Nauk.Tech.*, 1957, 2: 663-79.

HISTORY of science in the University of London. [Appointment of Professor H. Dingle to the chair at University College, London] *Isis*, 1947, 37: 77.

IMPERIAL College, London. [A new Department of History of Science and Technology.] *Isis*, 1963, 54: 278.

SARTON, George. The teaching of the history of science at the University of London. *Isis*, 1924, 6: 406-7.

Agp-af

BORDEAUX. [Establishment of chair for the history of philosophy and science] *Isis*, 1932, 17: 427.

BRUNET, Pierre. L'école lyonnaise d'histoire des sciences (A. Hannequin, E. Goblot, A. Georges-Berthier). *Archeion*, 1936, 18: 146-59.

MAY, Raoul Michel. Faculté des Sciences, Paris. Histoire des sciences, Enseignement (3ème Cycle). *Isis*, 1956, 47: 186-7.

PARIS. UNIVERSITÉ. Institut d'Histoire des Sciences. *Isis*, 1933, 19: 501; 20: 265-6; 1934, 21: 210.

PARIS. UNIVERSITÉ. Institut d'Histoire des Sciences et des Techniques. Rapport sur l'activité de l'Institut pendant l'année scolaire, 1937-1938. *Ann.Univ.Paris*, 1938, 325-32.

Agp-ag

MEYER-ABICH, Adolf. Teaching the history of science. Hamburg. *Isis*, 1950, 41: 45.

STICKER, Bernhard. Die Stellung der Geschichte der Naturwissenschaften im Rahmen unserer heutigen Universitäten. *Phil.Natur.*, 1964, 8: 109-16.

SWISS Federal Institute of Technology (E.T.H., Zürich). *Isis*, 1963, 54: 485.

WALTER, Emil J. The history of science in Switzerland, 1946-47. *Isis*, 1948, 38: 244.

Agp-ah

TESKE, A. The history of science and its place in our educational system. *Kwart.Hist.Nauk.Tech.*, 1962, 6: (Special issue), 129-40.

VETTER, Quido. L'enseignement de l'histoire des sciences en Tchécoslovaquie. *Archeion*, 1931, 13: 477-82.

Agp-ai

CARDINI, Maria Timpanaro. Per una Cattedra di Storia delle Scienze in Pisa. *Sci.Veterum*, 1953, 2: 1-3.

MIELI, Aldo. Per una cattedra di storia della scienza. *Atti Soc.Ital.Progr.Sci.VIII Riunione* (Rome, 1916) 32 p. Florence: 1916.

PERNA, Alfredo. Corsi di storia delle scienze in Italia. *Archeion*, 1934, 16: 329-36.

PERNA, Alfredo. Les cours d'histoire des sciences en Italie. *Act.IIIe Congr.Int.Hist.Sci.* (Portugal, 1934), p. 113-20. Lisbon: 1936.

Agp-ak

FORBES, R.J. The teaching of the history of science. In post-war Holland. *Isis*, 1947, 38: 98-9.

GARDEDIEU, Alex. L'enseignement de l'histoire des sciences en Belgique. *Compt.Rend.IIe Congr.Nat.Sci.* (Bruxelles, 1935), (1), p. 131-7. Brussels: 1935.

PELSENEER, Jean. L'histoire de la science en Belgique. *Isis*, 1947, 37: 76.

SARTON, George. History of science in Holland. *Isis*, 1948, 39: 67.

Agp-am

UPPSALA. Une chaire d'histoire des sciences et des idées. *Isis*, 1934, 22: 232.

Agp-ao

BOLOGA, Valeriu L. L'enseignement de l'histoire de la science aux universités. *Compt.Rend.I Congr.Nat.Natur.Roum.* (Cluj, 1928), p. 61-73. Cluj: Societatea de Stünțe, 1930

BOLOGA, Valeriu L. [History of the natural sciences and medicine in Roumanian education. (In Rumanian)]. *Liječnički Vjesnik*, 1933, no. 4.

Agp-at

TEACHING the history of science. [University of Tokyo.] *Isis*, 1961, 52: 102-3.

Agp-aw

ROSENTHAL-SCHNEIDER, Ilse. History of science in Australia. *Isis*, 1946, 36: 130.

THE TEACHING of the history of science in Australia. *Isis*, 1947, 37: 76-7.

TEACHING the history of science. [University of Melbourne.] *Isis*, 1959, 50: 158.

Agr

SARTON, George. Qualifications of teachers of the history of science. Preface to volume 37 and third preface to volume 40. *Isis*, 1947, 37: 5-7; 1949, 40: 311-13.

Agt in teaching science

BRUNET, Pierre. Enquête sur l'histoire des sciences dans l'enseignement. *Enseign.Sci.*, 1932, 5: 182-4.

BRUNOLD, Charles. Enseignement scientifique et histoire des sciences. *Rev.Hist.Sci.*, 1957, 10: 193-204.

BRUNOLD, Charles. Esquisse d'une pédagogie de la redécouverte dans l'enseignement scientifique. 48 p. Paris: Masson, 1948.
Reviewed by Jean Itard, *Rev.Hist.Sci.*, 1949, 2: 194.

BRUNOLD, Charles. Rôle de l'histoire dans l'enseignement des sciences physiques. *Rev.Hist.Sci.*, 1958, 11: 97-107.

CONANT, James Bryant. The growth of the experimental sciences. An experiment in general education. Progress report on the use of the case method in teaching the principles of the tactics and strategy of science. iv, 67 p. Cambridge, Mass.: Harvard University Press, 1949. [CB 75/86]

CONANT, James Bryant. History in the education of scientists. *Harvard Libr.Bull.*, 1960, 14: 315-33.
Reprinted in *Amer.Scient.*, 1960, 48: 528-43.

COURTIN, Madeleine. La méthode historique dans l'enseignement des sciences physiques. *Act.VIIe Congr.Int.Hist.Sci.* (Jerusalem, 1953), p. 246-51. Paris: Hermann, [n.d.].

DONY-HÉNAULT, Oct. L'ornement des sciences expérimentales. *Bull.Acad.Roy.Belg.Cl.Sci.*, 1936, 22: 1415-35. [CB 54/524]

ENQUÊTE sur l'histoire des sciences dans l'enseignement. *Enseign.Sci.*, 1932, 5: 209-15.

HISTORY of science in general education. *Isis*, 1948, 38: 245.
Note on Joint Committee set up by American Association of the History of Medicine and the History of Science Society.

IHDE, Aaron J. Learning the scientific method through the historical approach. *Sch.Sci.Math.*, 1953, 637-43.

KLOPFER, Leo E.; FLETCHER, G. Watson. Historical materials and high school science teaching. *Sci.Teacher*, 1957, 24: 264-5, 292-3.

LALANDE, A.; REY, Abel. L'histoire des sciences dans l'enseignement. *Enseign.Sci.*, 1932, 5: 129-32.

LANGEVIN, P. La valeur éducative de l'histoire des sciences. *Bull.Soc.Franç.Pédagog.*, 1926, 692-700.

LOEFFLER, Eugen. Die Geschichte der Mathematik und der Naturwissenschaften im Unterricht. *Korrespondenzbl.Höheren Sch. Würitemb.*, 1915, 22: 174-200. [CB 16/335]

LORIA, Gino. La storia della scienza e la storia di una scienza nel pubblico insegnamento. *Archeion*, 1943, 25: 1-12.

McGRATH, Earl J., ed. Science in general education. viii, 400 p. Dubuque: Brown, 1948. [CB 75/85]
Emphasis on the historical approach in science teaching.

MILHAUD, Gérard. Conclusions à l'enquête sur l'histoire des sciences dans l'enseignement. *Enseign.Sci.*, 1933, 6: 148-53.

MILLER, George Abram. The historical point of view in the teaching of science. *Science*, 1919, 50: 489-93.

SCHURMANN, Pablo F. La historia de la ciencia y su introducción en la enseñanza secundaria. *An.Enseñanza Secundaria*, 1937, 2: 347-51; also in *Archeion*, 1937, 19: 368-71.

TELLER, James D. Humanizing science and mathematics by commemorating November anniversaries. *Sch.Sci.Math.*, 1942, 42: 737-52.

WEBER, Maurice. Sur l'introduction de l'histoire des sciences dans les humanités scientifiques. *Enseign.Sci.*, 1932, 6: 8-15.

WIELEITNER, Heinrich. Geschichte der Wissenschaften und Unterricht. *Unterrichtsbl.Math.Naturwiss.*, 1923, 29: 50-4. [CB 16/337]

WINTER, Henry James Jacques. Humanism in science teaching. *Sch.Sci.Rev.*, 1940, 86: 177-9.

Agv history of science: popularization

STASIEWICZ, Irena; BURDOWICZNOWICKA, Maria; ORLOWSKI, Boleslaw. [Social significance of popular scientific works from the domain of the history of science and technology. (In Polish)]. *Kwart.Hist.Nauk.Tech.*, 1962, 7: 285-305.

Ah historiography and particular aspects of the history of science

BOYER, Carl B. Current thoughts in the history of science. *Science*, 1955, 121: 541-3.
A running account of the meeting of the History of Science Society in New York during 29-30 December 1954.

CUNEO, Ernest. Science and history. 237 p. New York: Duell, Sloan and Pearce; London: Cassell, 1963.

MARVIN, Francis Sydney. Old and new thoughts on the modern study of history. 224 p. London: Nicholson and Watson, 1935. [CB 45/297]
Deals with certain selected aspects of history, including scientific topics.

ROSENTHAL-SCHNEIDER, Ilse. Various approaches to the history of science. *Australian J.Sci.*, 1951, 13: 125-30.
Discussion of various forms of historical work apropos of George Sarton, Max von Laue, Harvey Cushing's biography and Darwin's autobiography.

THORNDIKE, Lynn. Whatever was, was right. Presidential address read at the annual dinner of the American Historical Association, Washington, 29 December 1955. *Amer. Hist.Rev.*, 1956, 61: 265-83.

Ahc historical techniques

BROWNE, Charles Albert. The comparative value of methods for estimating fame. *Science*, 1911, 33: 770-3.
Reply to F.A. Woods' article, *see* below.

DARMSTAEDTER, Ernst. Einige Bemerkungen zu der Nachprüfung älterer Angaben. *Sudhoffs Arch.*, 1933, 26: 277-80.

GARFIELD, E.; SHER, I.H.; TORPIE, R.J. The use of citation data in writing the history of science. v, 75 p. Philadelphia: Institute for Scientific Information, 1964.
Report of research for the U.S. Air Force Office of Scientific Research.

KLINCKOWSTROEM, Carl von. Quellenangaben zur Geschichte der Naturwissenschaften. *Mitt.Gesch.Med.*, 1912, 11: 106-8.

STEPHANIDES, Michael. [Explanation and criticism of scientific texts. (In Greek)]. *Athena*, 1928, 40: 184-93.
The author explains how to handle the primary sources, giving rules for the critical interpretation of ancient texts.

WOODS, Frederick Adams. Historiometry as an exact science. *Science*, 1911, 33: 568-74.

Ahd historiography; historical method and research

BRUINS, E.M. Sur la méthode de recherche en histoire des sciences. *Congr.Int.Phil.Sci.* (Paris, 1949), (8), p. 69-78. (Actualités Scientifiques et Industrielles, 1166) Paris: Hermann, 1952.

CHALUS, Paul. Importance de l'histoire des sciences. A propos d'une collection en cours de publication. *Rev. Syn.*, 1957, 78: 496-500.
Apropos of Taton, René, ed. Histoire générale des sciences, *see* Ac-bm.

GREENE, John C. Objectives and methods in intellectual history. *Miss.Val.Hist.Rev.*, 1957, 44: 58-74.

HEWLETT, R.G. A pilot study in contemporary scientific history. *Isis*, 1962, 53: 31-8.
Regarding the feasibility of a general history of the Atomic Energy Commission and raising some general points on methods of historical research.

MILLER, George Abram. The history of science as an error breeder. *Sci.Mon.*, 1921, 12: 439-43.

OSTWALD, Wilhelm. Geschichtswissenschaft und Wissenschaftsgeschichte. *Arch.Gesch.Math.Naturwiss.Tech.*, 1927, 10: 1-11.

REY, Abel. Indications concernant une direction d'étude relative à l'histoire des sciences, du point de vue de leurs méthodes (d'après une conférence de Abel Rey). *Thalès*, 1935, 2: 34-48.

ROSENFELD, L. On the method of history of science. *Arch. Int.Hist.Sci.*, 1947, 1: 126-9.

SARTON, George. Remarks concerning the history of twentieth century science. *Isis*, 1936, 26: 53-62.
Explaining methods for the historical study of contemporary science.

SARTON, George. The scientific basis of the history of science. *Cooperation in research: [a testimonial volume for John Campbell Merriam]*, p. 465-81. Washington: Carnegie Institution of Washington, 1938.

SUGITA, Motonobu. [Methodology and history of science. (In Japanese)]. *J.Hist.Sci.Japan*, 1953, no. 26, 1-7.

SZYFMAN, L. [La méthode irrationaliste dans l'histoire des sciences italienne. (In Polish, with summaries in Russian and French)]. *Kwart.Hist.Nauk.Tech.*, 1959, 4: 713-25. [CB 85/378]

TAYLOR, F. Sherwood. Reflections on the writing of the history of science. (Presidential address, 1953). *Bull.Brit. Soc.Hist.Sci.*, 1954, 1: 239-45.

WOHLWILL, Emil. Naturforscher als Historiker der Naturwissenschaften. *Mitt.Gesch.Med.*, 1912, 11: 1-5.
The author maintains that eminent scientists are not always accurate historians. He quotes as an example William Ramsay's essay on Boyle's "Sceptical Chemist".

Ahd-d biography in historiography

METZGER, Hélène. L'historien des sciences doit-il se faire le contemporain des savants dont il parle? *Archeion*, 1933, 15: 34-44.

SHARLIN, Harold I. The scientist in biography. *Bull.Atom. Sci.*, 1963, 19: no. 9, 27-8.

YASUGI, Ryūichi. [On the necessity of hypothesis in the biography of a scientist. (In Japanese)]. *J.Hist.Sci.Japan*, 1952, no. 23, 24-5.

ZUBOV, V.P. L'histoire de la science et la biographie des savants. *Kwart.Hist.Nauk.Tech.*, 1962, 6: (Special issue), 29-42.

Ahf philosophical aspects

AGASSI, Joseph. Towards an historiography of science. vii, 117 p. (History and Theory. Studies in the Philosophy of History, 2). The Hague: Mouton and Co., 1963.
Reviewed by W.A. Smeaton, *Ann.Sci.*, 1962, 18: 125-7; by Safford Finlay, *Ann.Sci.*, 1962, 18: 127-9.

ARBER, Agnes. Analogy in the history of science. *Studies and Essays offered to George Sarton*, p. 219-33. New York: Schuman, 1947. [CB 71/114]

BENDA, Julien. Une conception moderne de l'histoire de la science. *Congr.Int.Phil.Sci.* (Paris, 1949), (8), p. 45-50. (Actualités Scientifiques et Industrielles, 1166) Paris: Hermann, 1952.
A discussion of the Hegelian-Marxist conception.

BOULIGAND, Georges. L'histoire des sciences devant le présent afflux théorique. *Arch.Int.Hist.Sci.*, 1964, 17: 113-20.

CANGUILHEM, Georges. L'histoire des sciences dans l'oeuvre épistémologique de Gaston Bachelard. *Ann.Univ.Paris*, 1963, 33: 24-39.

COHEN, Robert S. Alternative interpretations in the history of science. *Sci.Mon.*, 1955, 80: 111-16.

COHEN, Robert S. [Is the philosophy of science germane to the history of science? (In Polish)]. *Kwart.Hist.Nauk.Tech.*, 1963, 8: 163-78.

COHEN, Robert S. Is philosophy of science germane to the history of science? The work of Meyerson and Needham. *Proc.10th Int.Congr.Hist.Sci.* (Ithaca, 1962), (1), p. 213-23. Paris: Hermann, 1964.

COWAN, Thomas A. The historian and the philosophy of science. *Isis*, 1947, 38: 11-18.

DELEVSKY, J. L'évolution des sciences et la thèse historico-matérialiste. *Mois*, 1938, 8: 251-9.

DELEVSKY, J. L'histoire des sciences et la philosophie de l'histoire. *Trav.IXe Congr.Int.Phil.Congr.Descartes* (Paris, 1937), (5), p. 33-48. (Actualités Scientifiques et Industrielles, 534) Paris: Hermann, 1937.

DELEVSKY, J. La prévision historique dans la nature. 54 p. (Exposés de Philosophie des Sciences, 7) Paris: Hermann, 1935.

DELEVSKY, J. Les tendances dialectiques dans l'évolution de la science. *Rev.Phil.*, 1938, 63: 278-306.

DE RUGGIERO, Guido. Science, history and philosophy. *Philosophy*, 1931, 6: 166-79.

DINGLER, Hugo. La notion de système dans l'histoire et la philosophie des sciences. *Archeion*, 1931, 13: 210-25.

EDELSTEIN, Ludwig. Platonism or Aristotelianism? A contribution to the history of medicine and science. *Bull. Hist.Med.*, 1940, 8: 757-69.

FARBER, Eduard. Theories of types in the history of sciences. *J.Wash.Acad.Sci.*, 1964, 54: no. 9, 349-56.

GIUA, Michele. Storia delle scienze ed epistemologia: Galileo, Boyle, Planck. viii, 298 p. Torino: Chiantore, 1945.
Reviewed by Aldo Mieli, *Arch.Int.Hist.Sci.*, 1948, 1: 726-28.

GRÜNBAUM, A. The bearing of philosophy on the history of science. *Science*, 1964, 143: 1406-12.

HANSON, Norwood Russell. The irrelevance of history of science to philosophy of science. *J.Phil.*, 1962, 59: 574-86.

HATCH, Melville H. The limitations of science. An historical survey. *Biologist*, 1938, 19: 189-203.

HOSIASSON-LINDENBAUM, Janina. Theoretical aspects of the advancement of knowledge. *Synthese*, 1948-49, 7: 253-301.

KOYRÉ, Alexander. Influence of philosophic trends on the formulation of scientific theories. *Sci.Mon.*, 1955, 80: 107-10.

MARCUCCI, Silvestro. Filosofia, scienza e storia della scienza in Emilio Meyerson. *Physis*, 1961, 3: 5-19.

MASSON-OURSEL, P. Synthèse historique et philosophie de l'histoire. *Rev.Syn.Hist.*, 1913, 26: 282-92.

METZGER, Hélène. L'a priori dans la doctrine scientifique et l'histoire des sciences. *Archeion*, 1936, 18: 29-42.

METZGER, Hélène. La méthode philosophique dans l'histoire des sciences. *Archeion*, 1937, 19: 204-16.

METZGER, Hélène. La philosophie de Lucien Lévy-Bruhl et l'histoire des sciences. *Archeion*, 1930, 12: 15-24.

METZGER, Hélène. La philosophie d'Émile Meyerson et l'histoire des sciences. (*Compt.Rend.1er Congr.Int.Hist.Sci.*, Paris, 1929) *Archeion*, 1929, 11: xxxii-xliii.

METZGER, Hélène. Tribunal de l'histoire et théorie de la connaissance scientifique. *Archeion*, 1935, 17: 1-14. [CB 45/272]

MILNE, E.A. On the origin of laws of nature. *Nature*, 1937, 139: 997-9. [CB 51/248]

NEEDHAM, Joseph. The pattern of nature-mysticism and empiricism in the philosophy of science: third century B.C. China, tenth century A.D. Arabia, and seventeenth century A.D. Europe. *Science, medicine and history. Essays in honour of Charles Singer*, (2), p. 361-87. London: Oxford University Press, 1953. [CB 80/114]

PUTMAN, Jacques. Pour une histoire irrationaliste des sciences. *Arch.Int.Hist.Sci.*, 1955, 8: 56-8.

RÁDL, Emil. Zur Philosophie der Wissenschaftsgeschichte. *Scientia*, 1933, 54: 309-15. Trad. française, ibid., 133-8. [CB 40/398]

REYMOND, Arnold. L'histoire des sciences et la philosophie des sciences. *Congr.Int.Phil.Sci.* (Paris, 1949), (8), p. 13-23. (Actualités Scientifiques et Industrielles, 1166) Paris: Hermann, 1952.

REYMOND, Arnold. La philosophie des sciences et son influence sur l'histoire des sciences. *Act.VIIe Congr.Int. Hist.Sci.* (Jerusalem, 1953), p. 498-509. Paris: Hermann, [n.d.]

RUSKA, Julius. Weltbild und Naturforschung im Wandel der Zeiten. *Fortschr.Med.*, 1932, 50: 88-91. [CB 36/432]

SARTON, George. The historical basis of philosophical unification. *J.Unified Sci.*, 1939, 9: 90-3.
Summary of a lecture delivered at the beginning of the Vth International Congress for the Unity of Science, Harvard University, Labor Day, 1939.

SUCHODOLSKI, Bogdan. A new approach to the history of science. *Rev.Pol.Acad.Sci.*, 1963, 8: no. 1, 17-25.
Marxist methodology in history of science.

TOULMIN, Stephen. Philosophy and the history of science. *Proc.10th Int.Congr.Hist.Sci.* (Ithaca, 1962), 1: 225-30. Paris: Hermann, 1964.

WHITEHEAD, Alfred North. Science and the modern world. xi, 296 p. (Lowell Lectures, 1925) Cambridge University Press, 1926.
Reviewed by S. Alexander, *Nature*, 1926, 117: 847-50.
French translation: La science et le monde moderne (Paris: 1930) reviewed by R. de Montessus de Ballore, *Rev.Gén. Sci.*, 1931, 42: 191.

Ahg evolution; progress

BORING, Edwin G. Great men and scientific progress. *Proc. Amer.Phil.Soc.*, 1950, 94: 339-51.

BUSH, Vannevar. Science and progress? *Amer.Scient.*, 1955, 43: 241-58.

COHEN, I. Bernard. An open mind. *Tech.Yearbook*, 1949, 8: 64-7, ill.
Collection of anecdotes which illustrate the misconceptions of great scientists concerning the progress of science.

COHEN, I. Bernard. Orthodoxy and scientific progress. *Proc. Amer.Phil.Soc.*, 1952, 96: 505-12.

CROMBIE, A.C. Historians and the scientific revolution. *Endeavour*, 1960, 19: 9-13.

DODD, Stuart Carter. A mass-time triangle. *Phil.Sci.*, 1944, 11: 233-44, ill.
Diagramatic representation of the development of the universe and the sciences.

FELLOWS, Erwin W. Cyclical variation in scientific activity. *J.Cycle Res.*, 1959, 8: 108-20.
An attempt to determine whether there is a cyclic variation in scientific activity. Data on Greek, Arabic and Chinese scientists and the dates of their work are used.

FELLOWS, Erwin W. On the order of development of sciences. *Centennial Rev.*, 1962, 6: 84-97.

FLECK, Ludwik. Entstehung und Entwicklung einer wissenschaftlichen Tatsache. Einführung in die Lehre vom Denkstil und Denkkollektiv. 150 p., ill. Basel: Schwabe, 1935.
Reviewed in *Klin.Wochenschr.*, 1936, 15: 239-42.

GILFILLAN, S.C. The coldward course of progress. *Pol.Sci. Quart.*, 1920, 35: 393-410. [CB 10/196]

HADAMARD, Jacques. Les diverses formes et les diverses étapes de l'esprit scientifique. *Thalès*, 1937-39, 4: 23-7.

HOLTON, Gerald. A heuristic model for the growth process of modern physical science. (Based on the paper given before the Seventh International Significs Conference, Amersfoort.) *Synthèse*, 1957, 10: 190-202.

HORTON, Paul B. Does history show long-time trends? *Sci. Mon.*, 1942, 55: 461-70.
The author holds that knowledge continually increases and that this in itself is sufficient to give history a trend in a definite direction.

HUBERT, René. Essai sur l'histoire de l'idée de progrès. *Rev.Hist.Phil.*, 1934, *new ser.* 2: 289-305; 1935, *new ser.* 3: 1-32.

HUBERT, René, *et al.* La notion de progrès devant la science actuelle: exposés par René Hubert, Guglielmo Ferrero, Pierre Janet, Edouard Le Roy, René Legendre, Jean Rostand, Ed. Bauer, Abel Rey. 189 p. (Discussions. VIe Semaine Internationale de Synthèse, 1934). Paris: Alcan, 1938.
Reviewed by Hélène Metzger Bruhl, *Archeion*, 1940, 22: 132.

JOHNSON, Francis R. Preparation and innovation in the progress of science. *J.Hist.Ideas*, 1943, 4: 56-9.

KUHN, Thomas S. Historical structure of scientific discovery. *Science*, 1962, 136: 760-4.

KUHN, Thomas S. The structure of scientific revolutions. xv, 172 p. (Foundations in the Unity of Science, 2: no. 2). Chicago: University of Chicago Press, 1962.
Paperback edition publ. 1964.
Reviewed by Mary Hesse, *Isis*, 1963, 54: 286-7; for other reviews *see* CB 88/529, CB 89/489 and CB 90/501.

LILLEY, S. Cause and effect in the history of science. *Centaurus*, 1953, 3: 58-72.

MASON, S.F. The idea of progress and theories of evolution in science. *Centaurus*, 1953, 3: 90-106.

MAYER, Charles. Matérialisme progressiste. Préface de André Maurois. 181 p. Paris: Société française de Presse, 1947.
Defense of science and of the belief in progress.

MORGAN, Jacques de. La notion innée du progrès dans l'esprit humain. *Rev.Syn.Hist.*, 1923, 35: 15-36. [CB 16/308]

NAYRAC, Jean Paul. Science, morale et progrès. 68 p. Paris: J. Vrin, 1928. [CB 27/573]

NICEFORO, Alfredo. Les indices numériques de la civilisation et du progrès. 211 p. Paris: Flammarion, 1921.

PELSENEER, Jean. Pour une histoire négative des sciences. *Scientia*, 1952, 46: 105-7. [CB 80/114]

POPPER, Karl R. Conjectures and refutations. The growth of scientific knowledge. 412 p. New York/London: Basic Books, 1962.
Reviewed by George E. Hudson, *Phys.Today*, 1963, 16: no. 11, 80-2.

PRICE, Derek J. The exponential curve of science. *Discovery*, 1956, 17: 240-3, 4 fig.

PRICE, Derek J. Quantitative measures of the development of science. *Arch.Int.Hist.Sci.*, 1951, 4: 85-93, 2 fig.; also *Act.VIe Congr.Int.Hist.Sci.* (Amsterdam, 1950), (1), p. 413-21, 2 fig. Paris: Hermann, 1951.

REYMOND, Arnold. L'évolution de la pensée scientifique et l'histoire des sciences. *Rev.Hist.Sci.*, 1947, 1: 97-113.

SPOEHR, H.A. The nature of progress in science. With: Angell, James R. Popular and unpopular science, p. 25-54. (Elihu Root Lectures on the Influence of Science and Research on Current Thought) Washington: Carnegie Institution of Washington, 1935.

WEBER, Louis. Le rythme du progrès. 311 p. Paris: Alcan, 1913.

ZILSEL, Edgar. The genesis of the concept of scientific progress. *J.Hist.Ideas*, 1945, 6: 325-49.

ZINNER, E. Die Kulturkurven der Naturerkenntnis. *Arch. Kulturgesch.*, 1934, 25: 98-100, 1 fig.

Ahg-mzNhg relation with MEDICINE: evolution

DANNEMANN, Friedrich. Über den Parallelismus in der Entwicklung der Naturwissenschaften und der Heilkunde nebst einigen Vorbemerkungen über die Einführung der Geschichte der Naturwissenschaften und ihrer Anwendungen in den Hochschulunterricht. *Essays on the History of Medicine presented to Karl Sudhoff*, p. 349-68. London: Oxford University Press; Zurich: 1924.

Ahh historical chronology; periodization

HEATH, A.E. Time perspectives in science. *Nature*, 1943, 152: 434-7, 3 fig.

OLSZEWSKI, Eugeniusz. Les problèmes de périodisation dans l'histoire de la science et de la technique. *Arch.Int.Hist. Sci.*, 1960, 13: 110-14.

SARTON, George. La chronologie de l'histoire de la science. *Rev.Gén.Sci.*, 1912, 23: 341-2.

YUASA, Mitsuo. [Chronological division of the history of modern science. (In Japanese)]. *J.Hist.Sci.Japan*, 1953, no. 25, 1-5.

Ahj precursors and influences

DINGLE, Herbert. Modern Aristotelianism. *Nature*, 1937, 139: 784-6.

DOWNEY, Glanville. Aristotle and modern science. *Cl.World*, 1963, 57: 41-5.

JEANS, James. Newton and the science of to-day. *Nature*, 1942, 150: 710-15.
Address delivered at the Royal Society's commemorative meeting, 30 November 1942.

KLIBANSKY, Raymond. "Standing on the shoulders of giants". Answer to *query* no. 53 (*Isis*, 1935, 24: 107-9.) *Isis*, 1936, 26: 147-9.
See Sarton, George, below.

LEVY, H. Modern Aristotelianism. *Nature*, 1937, 139: 1025-6.

LÖWENHEIM, L. Die Wissenschaft Demokrits und ihr Einfluss auf die moderne Naturwissenschaft. xi, 244 p. Berlin: L. Simion, 1914.

MERTON, Robert K. Priorities in scientific discovery: a chapter in the sociology of science. *Amer.Sociol.Rev.*, 1957, 22: 635-59.
Presidential address read at the annual meeting of the American Sociological Society, August 1957.

METZGER, Hélène. La role des précurseurs dans l'évolution de la science. *Thalès*, 1937-39, 4: 199-209.

MIELI, Aldo. Le questioni di priorità e dei precursori. *Arch.Int.Hist.Sci.*, 1947, 1: 9-17.

NADOV, Gyorgy. L'importance de la doctrine heuristique de Descartes dans l'histoire de la science. *Dialectica*, 1962, 16: 25-38.

OCKENDEN, R.E. "Standing on the shoulders of giants". Answer to *query* no. 53 (*Isis*, 1935, 24: 107-9.) *Isis*, 1936, 25: 451.
See Sarton, George, below.

PELSENEER, Jean. Les influences dans l'histoire aes sciences. *Arch.Int.Hist.Sci.*, 1948, 1: 347-53.

PELSENEER, Jean; PUTMAN, Jacques. L'histoire des sciences, l'université et les influences. *Arch.Int.Hist.Sci.*, 1951, 4: 879-83; also *Act.VIe Congr.Int.Hist.Sci.* (Amsterdam, 1950), (1), p. 398-401. Paris: Hermann, 1951.

REYMOND, Arnold. Brèves remarques sur "influences et précurseurs". *Arch.Int.Hist.Sci.*, 1951, 4: 357-64; also *Act. VIe Congr.Int.Hist.Sci.* (Amsterdam, 1950), (1), p. 357-64. Paris: Hermann, 1951.

ROSENFELD, Léon. Remarques sur la question des précurseurs. *Archeion*, 1938, 21: 74-83.

SARTON, George. "Standing on the shoulders of giants". *Query* no. 53. *Isis*, 1935, 24: 107-9.
Apropos of the history of the idea of scientific progress. For answers *see* Klibansky, Raymond, and Ockenden, R.E., above.

WEIZSÄCKER, Carl F.F. von. Descartes und die neuzeitliche Naturwissenschaft. 30 p. (Hamburger Universitätsreden, 23) Hamburg: Im Selbstverlag der Universität Hamburg, 1962.

Ahm ideas in science

ARONS, Arnold Boris; BORK, A.M.; ed. Science and ideas; selective readings. 278 p. Englewood Cliffs, N.J.: Prentice-Hall, 1964.

AUGER, P. Structures et complexités dans l'univers de l'antiquité à nos jours. *Cah.Hist.Mond.*, 1960, 6: 457-75.
A historical account of the ideas of continuity and discontinuity, law and structure, size and complexity, quantity and quality.

BIRCH, L.C. The concept of nature. *Amer.Scient.*, 1951, 39: 294-302.
Traces the historical development of various ideas as to the basic organization of nature.

DESSAUER, Friedrich. Die Teleologie in der Natur. 72 p. (Glauben und Wissen, 3) München: Reinhardt, 1949.

DRIESCH, Hans. Über die grundsätzliche Unmöglichkeit einer "Vereinigung" von universeller Teleologie und Mechanismus. 20 p. (*Sitzungsber.Heidelb.Akad.Wiss.Phil.Hist.Kl.*, 1914, 5) Heidelberg: 1914.

EVOLUTION in the light of modern knowledge. A collective work. xvi, 528 p. London: Blackie, 1925. [CB 18/603]
The idea of evolution in the different sciences.

GILLISPIE, Charles Coulston. *See* Ac-bm

GOOD, Irving J., ed. The scientist speculates. An anthology of partly-baked ideas. xvii, 413 p., fig. London: Heinemann, 1962.
Reviewed by Jean Walch, *Arch.Int.Hist.Sci.*, 1964, 16: 68-9.

LENOBLE, Robert. L'évolution de l'idée de "nature" du 16e au 18e siècle. *Rev.Métaphys.Morale*, 1953, no. 1-2, 108-29.

MASON, Frances. The great design: order and progress in nature. Introduction by J. Arthur Thomson. 324 p. London: Duckworth, 1934.

PAINTER, George Stephen. Science and evolutionary theory. 323 p. Washington D.C.: Washington College Press, 1940. [CB 62/71]

PETRONIJEVIĆ, Branislav. L'Evolution universelle. Exposé des preuves et des lois de l'évolution mondiale et des évolutions particulières (inorganique, intellectuelle et sociale). 1. L'Evolution mondiale, inorganique et organique, 214 p., 3 fig. et 1 tableau dans le texte. Paris: Félix Alcan, 1921.
Reviewed by L. Guinet, *Isis*, 1922, 4: 564-5.

SEARES, Frederick H. The concept of uniformity: growth and reactions. 50 p. (Elihu Root Lectures on the Influence of Science and Research on Current Thought) Washington: Carnegie Institution of Washington, 1938.

ZILSEL, Edgar. History and biological evolution. *Phil.Sci.*, 1940, 7: 121-8.

Aht transmission of ideas

BENNETT, Jesse Lee. The diffusion of science. ix, 141 p. Baltimore: Johns Hopkins Press, 1942.
Reviewed by M.F.A. Montagu, *Isis*, 1943, 34: 374-5.

BREASTED, James Henry; ROBINSON, James Harvey. The human adventure. 2 vol. 1. The conquest of civilization, by J.H. Breasted. xxv, 717 p., 50 pl., 17 maps; 2. The ordeal of civilization: a sketch of the development and world-wide diffusion of our present-day institutions and ideas, by J.H. Robinson. xii, 769 p., 59 pl., 12 maps. New York: Harper and Bros., 1926.
Reviewed by F.S. Marvin, *Nature*, 1927, 119: 591-3.

CHAYAPPA, M. Modern science and ancient thought. *Aryan Path*, 1949, 490-4.

DUSTIN, Albert P. Succès et diffusion des idées scientifiques. *Rev.Univ.Bruxelles*, 1938-39, 44: 235-65.

HARVARD TERCENTENARY CONFERENCE ON ARTS AND SCIENCES, 1936. Independence, convergence and borrowing, in institutions, thought, and art. x, 272 p. Cambridge, Mass.: Harvard University Press, 1937. [CB 51/289]

KLEBS, A.C. Moyens matériels de diffusion de la pensée scientifique. Démonstration d'une carte géographique (monde occidental connu au XVe siècle). *Verhandl.Allg. Schweiz.Ges.Gesammten Naturwiss.*, 1931, 112: 376-7.

MOESE, Henryk. [Some notes on the history of the dissemination of knowledge. (In Polish)]. *Kwart.Hist.Nauk.Tech.*, 1963, 8: 179-213.

ROGERS, Everett M. Diffusion of innovations. xiii, 367 p., ill. New York: Free Press of Glencoe, 1962.
Reviewed by Bernard Barber, *Isis*, 1963, 54: 296-7.

SARTON, George. La transmission au monde moderne de la science ancienne et médiévale. *Rev.Hist.Sci.*, 1949, 2: 101-38, 2 fig.
Summary of lectures delivered in the spring of 1948 in London, Liége and Paris.

SCHIMANK, Hans. Mittel und Wege wissenschaftlicher, insbesondere naturwissenschaftlicher Überlieferung bis zum Aufkommen der ersten wissenschaftlichen Zeitschriften. *Sudhoffs Arch.*, 1952, 36: 159-82.

SCHOVE, D.J. East and west in science. *Nature*, 1952, 169: 774-6.
Apropos of "a symposium of the British Society for the History of Science on 'Historical scientific contacts between East and West'".

SMITH, Grafton Elliot. The diffusion of culture. x, 244 p. London: Watts, 1933.
Reviewed by H.S. Harrison, *Nature*, 1933, 132: 763-5.

SMITH, Grafton Elliot, *et al.* Culture: the diffusion controversy. 98 p. (Psyche Miniatures, General Series, 18) London: Kegan Paul, 1928.

VETTER, Quido. Co spojuje nasi kulturu s kulturou antickou v matematice a vědách exaktních. (Rapport entre les civilisations antique et moderne concernant les mathématiques et les sciences). *Česká Rev.*, 1923-24, 17: no. 4.

Aj psychological aspects

ARMSTRONG, D.M. Perception and the physical world. xiii, 196 p. London: Routledge and Kegan Paul, 1961.
Reviewed by Walter B. Carter, *Dialogue*, 1962, 1: 338-40.

BORING, Edwin G. Cognitive dissonance: its use in science. *Science*, 1964, 145: 680-5.

DE SARLO, Francesco. La storia della scienza e la psicologia. *Arch.Stor.Sci.*, 1920, 1: 253-61.
Insists on the psychologic aspect of the history of science.

LOUCH, A.R. Science and psychology. *Brit.J.Phil.Sci.*, 1962, 12: 314-27.

MYERS, Charles Samuel. Psychological conceptions in other sciences. 24 p. (Herbert Spencer Lecture delivered at Oxford, 14 May 1929) Oxford: Clarendon Press, 1929.

SAUSSURE, Raymond de. Psychologie de la pensée scientifique. *Ann.Guébhard-Séverine*, 1931, 7: 151-5.

STEVENS, S.S. Psychology and the science of science. *Psychol. Bull.*, 1939, 36: 221-63.

Ajd personality of the scientist

BARBER, Bernard. Resistance by scientists to scientific discovery. *Science*, 1961, 134: 596-602.
This source of resistance has yet to be given the scrutiny accorded religious and ideological sources.

FEUER, Lewis S. The scientific intellectual. The psychological and sociological origins of modern science. xii, 441 p. New York: Basic Books, Inc., 1963.
Reviewed by Melvin Kranzberg, *Amer.Hist.Rev.*, 1963, 69: 409-10; by A.R. Hall, *Sci.Amer.*, 1963, 209: no. 2, 129.

HATCH, Melville H. The rôle of the individual in the history of science. *Biologist*, 1933, 15: 9-26.

KRETSCHMER, Ernst. The psychology of men of genius. Transl. by R.B. Cattell. xx, 256 p. (International Library of Psychology, Philosophy and Scientific Method.) London: Kegan Paul, 1931.
Translation of "Geniale Menschen" (Berlin: Springer, 1929).

PELSENEER, Jean. L'abandon de la science par le savant de génie. *Act.IIIe Congr.Bénélux Hist.Sci.* (Luxembourg, 1960). *Janus*, 1960, 49: 142-4.
How and why scientists of genius abandoned science.

PELSENEER, Jean. La psychologie du savant de génie. *Janus*, 1964, 51: 62-4.

PUTMAN, Jacques. Les idéaux extra-scientifiques et leur contrôle par le savant, à la lumière de l'histoire des sciences. *Compt.Rend.IIIe Congr.Nat.Sci.* (Bruxelles, 1950), (1), p. 6-9. Liége: 1951.

RADNER, David B. The intolerance of great men. *Ann.Med. Hist.*, 1933, 5: 561-5.

RAINOV, T.I. [The many-sided scientist as a type. (In Russian)]. *Sotsialist.Rekonstruktsiia Nauk.*, 1934, 4: 101-27. [CB 45/273]

ROE, Anne. The making of a scientist. ix, 244 p., 4 fig., 1 ill. New York: Dodd, Mead & Co., 1952.
A general account of Anne Roe's research project of psychological interviews with leading American scientists.

SCHWINGE, Erich. Welt und Werkstatt des Forschers. vi, 305 p. Wiesbaden: Franz Steiner Verlag, G.m.b.H., 1957.
Reviewed by Matthias Schramm, *Isis*, 1961, 52: 107-8.

WALDEN, P. Zur Biologie und Tragik grosser Naturforscher. *Scientia*, 1951, 86: 200-7.

WATSON, David Lindsay. Scientists are human. With a foreword by John Dewey. xx, 249 p. London: Watts, 1938.
Microfilm copies of complete original manuscript, Document 1015, American Documentation Institute, Washington, D.C.
Reviewed by R.K. Merton, *Isis*, 1940, 31: 466-7.

Ajg psychology of discovery; creativity

BENJAMIN, A. Cornelius. The mystery of scientific discovery. *Phil.Sci.*, 1934, 1: 224-36.

BLOKH, M.A. [On scientific creativity. (In Russian)] *Zh. Russ.Fiz.Khim.Obshchest.*, *B.Fiz.Otd.*, 1925, 57: 179-208. [CB 28/539]

BLOKH, M.A. Tvorchestvo v nauke i tekhnike. [Creativity in science and technology. (In Russian)] 64 p., bibliogr. Petrograd: Nauk Khimiko-Tekh. Izd-vo, 1920.

BOREL, Emile. Documents sur la psychologie de l'invention dans le domaine de la science: exposé par Emile Borel. *Organon*, 1936, 1: 33-42.

BORING, Edwin G. Dual role of the Zeitgeist in scientific creativity. *Sci.Mon.*, 1955, 80: 101-6.

BORING, Edwin G. The problem of originality in science. *Amer.J.Psychol.*, 1927, 39: 70-90. [CB 24/545]

BOSSIÈRE, Claude-Georges. Les chemins de la découverte. *Temps*, 1938, 78: 19 juillet, 8; 26 juillet, 6; 28 juillet, 8; 2 août, 6; 3 août, 8; 5 août, 6; 6 août, 6; 7 août, 6; 9 août, 6; 14 août, 6; 22 août, 6; 29 août, 6. [CB 56/381]

BROGLIE, Louis de. Rôle de la curiosité, du jeu, de l'imagination et de l'intuition dans la recherche scientifique. In: La méthode dans les sciences modernes, présenté par François Le Lionnais, p. 249-53. (Travail et Méthodes) Paris: Editions Science et Industrie, 1958.

BROWN, Harcourt, ed. Science and the creative spirit. xxvii, 165 p. Toronto: University of Toronto Press, 1958.
Reviewed by Jan Belehradek, *Brit.J.Phil.Sci.*, 1961, 11: 347-8.

BUSH, Vannevar. Scientific motivation. (R.A.F. Penrose, Jr., Memorial Lecture). *Proc.Amer.Phil.Soc.*, 1954, 98: 225-32.

COLER, Myron A., ed. Essays on creativity in the sciences. Foreword by Paul A. McGhee. xix, 235 p. New York: New York University Press, 1963. [CB 89/488]

CYSARZ, Herbert. Das Gesetz des Schaffens; Fragen eines Geschichtforschers an die Naturforschung. *Nova Acta Leopoldina*, 1941, 10: 123-46. [CB 79/168]

DOBROWOLSKI, Antoni Boleslaw. On the psychology of creative thought. *Organon*, 1936, 1: 290-4.

DUPRÉEL, E. Sur les conditions de l'invention scientifique. *Bull.Inst.Sociol.Solvay*, 1913, no. 26, 652-6. [CB 2/323]

GALDSTON, Iago. The ideological basis of discovery. *Bull. Hist.Med.*, 1939, 7: 729-35.

GARRETT, Alfred Benjamin, ed. The flash of genius. 249 p., ill. Princeton, N.J.: D. Van Nostrand, 1963. [CB 88/641 and CB 90/625]
First publ. *J.Chem.Educ.*, 1962, vol. 39; 1963, vol. 40.

GHISELIN, Brewster. The creative process. A symposium. 259 p. Berkeley and Los Angeles: University of California Press, 1952. [CB 79/184]

HADAMARD, J. Histoire des sciences et psychologie de l'invention. *Act.VIIe Congr.Int.Hist.Sci.* (Jerusalem, 1953), p. 350-7. Paris: Hermann, [n.d.]

HANSON, Norwood Russell. The logic of discovery. *J.Phil.*, 1958, 55: 1073-89.
Comment by Donald Schon, *J.Phil.*, 1959, 56: 500-3.

HANSON, Norwood Russell. Patterns of discovery. An inquiry into the conceptual foundations of science. x, 241 p., ill. New York/London: Cambridge University Press, 1958.
Reviewed by Max Black, *Isis*, 1959, 50: 267-8; for other reviews *see* CB 85/381 and CB 87/555, and Pyke, Magnus, below.

HARDING, Rosamond E.M. An anatomy of inspiration and an essay on the creative mood. xvi, 190 p. Cambridge: W. Heffer & Sons Ltd., 1948.

HUMBERSTONE, T. Ll. Scientific discoveries by accident. *Nature*, 1943, 151: 215-16.

IHDE, Aaron J. The inevitability of scientific discovery. *Sci.Mon.*, 1948, 67: 427-9. [CB 74/383]

INNOVATION in science. *Sci.Amer.*, 1958, 199: 1-240. [CB 84/297]

KNOWLSON, Thomas Sharper. Originality. A popular study of the creative mind. xvi, 304 p. London: Werner Laurie, 1917.

KOESTLER, Arthur. The act of creation. 751 p., ill. New York: Macmillan, 1964. [CB 90/507]

LIBBY, Walter. Conceptual thinking. *Sci.Mon.*, 1923, 15: 435-42.
Lecture of a series entitled "The psychology and logic of research", Mellon Institute, 1922.

LIBBY, Walter. The scientific imagination. *Sci.Mon.*, 1923, 15: 263-70.
Lecture of a series entitled "The psychology and logic of research" given before the Industrial Fellows of the Mellon Institute, 1922.

LOCKEMANN, Georg. The varieties of scientific discovery. (Translated by Ralph E. Oesper). *J.Chem.Educ.*, 1959, 36: 220-4.
Appeared originally in German in *Naturwiss.Rundsch.*, 1957, 10: 219-24.

LORIA, Gino. Osservazioni e documenti relativi al fenomeno della scoperta scientifica. *Boll.Unione Mat.Ital.*, 1947, 1: 35-45. [CB 71/114]

LOT, Fernand. Les jeux du hasard et du génie. Le rôle de la chance dans la découverte. vii, 280 p., 30 ill. Paris: Librairie Plon, 1956. [CB 83/186]

MACH, Ernst. Erkenntnis und Irrtum. Skizzen zur Psychologie der Forschung. 5th ed. xi, 476 p., 35 ill. Leipzig: Barth, 1926.
First ed., 1905.
Reviewed by E. Zilsel, *Deut.Lit.Zeitung*, 1928, 5: 2285-8.

MACH, Ernst. [Translation into English of "Gedächtnis, Reproduktion und Association".] *Open Court*, 1913, 27: 1-16.
From "Erkenntnis und Irrtum", 2nd ed. (Leipzig: 1906).

MOLES, Abraham A. La création scientifique. vi, 237 p., fig. Genève: Éditions René Kister, 1957.
Reviewed by R. Martin, *Arch.Int.Hist.Sci.*, 1958, 11: 402; by R. Bruce Lindsay, *Phys.Today*, 1958, 11: no. 4, 40-2.

MONTMASSON, Joseph-Marie. Invention and the unconscious. Translated, with a preface, by H. Stafford Hatfield. xxiv, 338 p. (International Library of Psychology, Philosophy and Scientific Method) London: Kegan Paul, 1931.

NICOLLE, Charles. Biologie de l'invention. xvi, 162 p. Paris: Alcan, 1932. [CB 35/301]

OSTWALD, Wilhelm. Genie und Vererbung. *Isis*, 1913, 1: 208-14.

OSTWALD, Wilhelm. Grosse Männer. xii, 424 p. Leipzig: Akademische Verlagsgesellschaft, 1909.
This volume consists of studies of some 19th century scientists and a general study of the nature of scientific genius. It was later considered as volume 1 of the series "Grosse Männer: Studien zur Biologie des Genies", edited by W. Ostwald.
French translation Paris: Flammarion, 1912.
Note by George Sarton, *Isis*, 1913, 1: 124.

PELSENEER, Jean. Science pure et science appliquée, à la lumière de l'histoire des sciences. (Society for Freedom in Science, occasional pamphlet 7) Oxford: 1948.
Indicates the fallacy of planning original discoveries.

PICARD, Jacques. Essai sur les conditions positives de l'invention dans les sciences. 324 p. (Bibliothèque de Philosophie Contemporaine) Paris: Alcan, 1928. [CB 44/540]

PYKE, Magnus. Thinking and discovery. *Discovery*, 1959, 21: 74-6.
Review article treating N.R. Hanson's "Patterns of discovery", *see* above, and R. Taton's "Reason and chance in scientific discovery", *see* below.

RUGG, Harold. Imagination. An inquiry into the source and conditions that stimulate creativity. Foreword and editorial comments by Kenneth D. Benne. 361 p. New York: Harper & Row, 1963.

SARTON, George. Comment augmenter le rendement intellectuel de l'humanité? Introduction. 1. Le génie scientifique; 2. Le génie et la race; 3. L'hérédité; 4. L'hérédité des aptitudes intellectuelles; 5. Le milieu et l'hérédité. *Isis*, 1913, 1: 219-42, 416-73.

TATON, René. Causalités et accidents de la découverte scientifique. Illustration de quelques étapes caractéristiques de l'évolution des sciences. 171 p., 7 fig., 32 pl. Paris: Masson et Cie., 1955.
Reviewed by Roger Hahn, *Isis*, 1957, 48: 352-3; for other reviews *see* CB 83/186 and CB 84/297.

TATON, René. Reason and chance in scientific discovery. Transl. by A.J. Pomerans. 171 p., 32 pl. London: Hutchinson & Co. Ltd.; New York: Philosophical Library, 1957. [CB 83/189]
Reviewed by Edward V. Appleton, *Nature*, 1958, 181: 983; by James R. Newman, *Sci.Amer.*, 1958, 200: 141-8; by Magnus Pyke, *Discovery*, 1959, 21: 74-6.
For French original *see* above.

TRAMER, M. Philosophie des Schöpferischen (naturwissenschaftlich fundiert). 87 p. Bern: Francke, 1957.

TRAMER, M. Le problème des traces en science et en philosophie. *Rev.Syn.*, 1956, 77: 343-9.

Ajj age and creativity

ADAMS, C.W. The age at which scientists do their best work. *Isis*, 1946, 36: 166-9.

DENNIS, Wayne. Age and productivity among scientists. *Science*, 1956, 123: 724-5.

HILL, A.V. Age of election to the Royal Society. *Notes Roy. Soc.Lond.*, 1954, 2: 14-16, 1 fig.

LEHMAN, Harvey C. Men's creative production rate at different ages and in different countries. *Sci.Mon.*, 1954, 78: 321-6, 7 fig.

LEHMAN, Harvey C. Man's most creative years: then and now. *Science*, 1943, 98: 393-9, 13 fig. [CB 65/78]

LEHMAN, Harvey C. Young thinkers and memorable creative achievements. *J.Genet.Psychol.*, 1964, 105: 237-55.

MEADE, George P. Youthful achievements of great scientists. *Sci.Mon.*, 1925, 21: 522-32. [CB 21/563]

Ak philosophy and methodology of science

for philosophical aspects of the history of science *see* Ahf
for philosophy of the separate sciences *see* INDEX

Ak-bm *large scale works*

ACADEMIA REPUBLICII POPULARE ROMÎNE. Études d'histoire et de philosophie des sciences. 311 p. Bucharest: L'Académie de la République Populaire Roumaine, 1962.
Reviewed by R. Bruce Lindsay, *Phys.Today*, 1964, 17: no. 1, 80-2.

BACHELARD, Gaston. La formation de l'esprit scientifique. 257 p. Paris: Vrin, 1947.
Reviewed by Harcourt Brown, *Isis*, 1949, 40: 283-5.

BACHELARD, Gaston. Le nouvel esprit scientifique. 179 p. Paris: Alcan, 1934.
Reviewed by Pierre Brunet, *Archeion*, 1934, 16: 256.

BAVINK, Bernhard. Ergebnisse und Probleme der Naturwissenschaften. Eine Einführung in die heutige Naturphilosophie. 9th ed. viii, 814 p., 91 fig. Zürich: Hirzel, 1948.
First publ. 1914.
Reviewed by P. Kirchberger, *Deut.Lit.Zeitung*, 1931, 2: 1046-50; by Zaunick, *Mitt.Gesch.Med.*, 1940, 39: 308-10; by H. Dopp, *Rev.Quest.Sci.*, 1949, 10: 316-17.

BAVINK, Bernhard. The natural sciences. An introduction to the scientific philosophy of today. Transl. from the 4th German edition by H. Stafford Hatfield. xiii, 683 p., 87 ill., bibliogr. New York: Century; London: Bell, 1932. [CB 48/565]
For original *see* above. The London edition has the title "The anatomy of modern science".
Reviewed by R.B., *Nature*, 1933, 131: 707-8.

BENJAMIN, A. Cornelius. An introduction to the philosophy of science. xvi, 469 p. New York: Macmillan, 1937.
Reviewed by H.T. Davis, *Isis*, 1938, 29: 464-9.

BUNGE, Mario. Intuition and science. x, 142 p. Englewood Cliffs, N.J.: Prentice-Hall, 1962.
Reviewed by Michael Scriven, *Amer.Math.Mon.*, 1963, 70: 232; by Jerzy A. Wojciechowski, *Dialogue*, 1963, 2: 238-9.

BUNGE, Mario. The myth of simplicity; problems of scientific philosophy. 239 p. Englewood Cliffs, N.J.: Prentice-Hall, 1963.
Reviewed by Hugues Leblanc, *Dialogue*, 1964, 3: 201-3.

BUNGE, Mario, ed. The critical approach to science and philosophy. 496 p., ill. New York: Macmillan, 1964.

CAVAILLES, Jean. Sur la logique et la théorie de la science. viii, 78 p. (Bibliothèque de philosophie contemporaine) Paris: Presses Universitaires de France, 1947.
Reviewed by G. Bouligand, *Rev.Gén.Sci.*, 1947, 54: no. 2, 26.

COHEN, Morris R. Studies in philosophy and science. 278 p. New York: Holt, 1949.
Reviewed by Mark Graubard, *Isis*, 1950, 41: 319.

COLODNY, Robert Garland, ed. Frontiers of science and philosophy. 288 p., ill. (University of Pittsburgh Series in the Philosophy of Science, 1). Pittsburgh: University of Pittsburgh Press, 1962.
Reviewed by Wesley C. Salmon, *Isis*, 1964, 55: 215-16; by Jerzy N. Wojciechowski, *Dialogue*, 1963, 2: 239-40; by J.W. Herivel, *Arch.Int.Hist.Sci.*, 1964, 17: 167-8.

CONGER, George Perrigo. Epitomizations. A study in the philosophy of the sciences. vi, 878 p. [Mimeoprinted]. Minneapolis: Burgess Co., 1949. [CB 78/180]

CONGER, George Perrigo. A world of epitomizations: a study in the philosophy of the sciences. xiv, 605 p. Princeton, N.J.: Princeton University Press, 1931

CORDEBAS, René. Les lois de l'esprit ou la science des principes. 171 p. (Philosophie Scientifique) Paris: Lesot, 1946. [CB 70/252]

DANTO, Arthur; MORGENBESSER, Sidney; ed. Philosophy of science. Preface by Ernest Nagel. 477 p., tables, bibliogr. New York: Meridian Books, Inc., 1960.
Reviewed by Stephen Toulmin, *Isis*, 1962, 53: 232-4; by Patrick Suppes, *J.Phil.*, 1961, 58: 387-91

DELAWARE SEMINAR IN THE PHILOSOPHY OF SCIENCE. Philosophy of science. 2 vol. 1. 1961-62. xvi, 370 p.; 2. 1962-63. xviii, 551 p. New York/London: Interscience Publishers, 1963. [CB 89/487]

DIDE, Maurice; JUPPONT, P. La métaphysique scientifique. 184 p. Paris: Félix Alcan, 1924. [CB 17/596]

DINGLE, Herbert. The scientific adventure. Essays in the history and philosophy of science. ix, 372 p. London: Isaac Pitman and Sons, Ltd., 1952; New York: Philosophical Library, 1953.
For reviews *see* CB 80/113 and CB 81/252.

DINGLE, Herbert. Through science to philosophy. vi, 363 p. Oxford: Clarendon Press; New York: Oxford University Press, 1937.
Lowell Institute Lectures, 1936.
Reviewed by Benjamin Ginzburg, *Isis*, 1938, 29: 160-3.

DOTTERER, Ray Harbaugh. Philosophy by way of the sciences: an introductory textbook. xv, 469 p. New York: Macmillan, 1929.
Reviewed in *Nature*, 1930, 125: 521-2.

DRIESCH, Hans. Man and the universe. Transl. by W.H. Johnston. 172 p. London: Allen and Unwin, 1929.
German original: Der Mensch und die Welt. Leipzig: Reinicke, 1928.

DRIESCH, Hans. Metaphysik der Natur. 95 p. (Handbuch der Philosophie). München: R. Oldenbourg, 1927.
Reviewed by E.O. von Lippmann, *Chem.Zeitung*, 1927, no. 58.

ENRIQUES, Federigo. Problems of science. Authorized translation by Katharine Royce. With an introductory note by Josiah Royce. xvi, 392 p. Chicago/London: Open Court Publishing Co., 1914. [CB 8/368]
This is a translation of Enriques's "Problemi della Scienza", of which the first Italian edition appeared in 1906.

FEIGL, Herbert; MAXWELL, Grover; ed. Current issues in the philosophy of science. Symposia of scientists and philosophers. ix, 484 p., tables. (Proceedings of Section L of the American Association for the Advancement of Science. 1959) New York: Holt, Rinehart and Winston, 1961.

FRANK, Philipp. Philosophy of science. The link between science and philosophy. 394 p. Englewood Cliffs, N.J.: Prentice-Hall, 1957.
Reviewed by Hilary Putnam, *Science*, 1958, 127: 750-1.

GRASSET, Joseph. Science et philosophie. 179 p. Paris: Renaissance du livre, 1918.
Reviewed by L. Guinet, *Isis*, 1920, 3: 88.

GREGG, John R.; HARRIS, F.T.C.; ed. Form and strategy in science: studies dedicated to Joseph Henry Woodger on the occasion of his seventieth birthday. vii, 475 p., bibliogr. Dordrecht: Reidel, 1964.

GRÉGOIRE, Auguste, S.J. Leçons de philosophie des sciences expérimentales. 230 p. (Bibliothèque de la Faculté de Philosophie et Lettres de Namur, 8) Paris: Vrin, 1950. [CB 77/366]

GUZZO, Augusto. La scienza. cxlii, 528 p. (Biblioteca di Filosofia, 10) Torino: Edizioni di "Filosofia", 1955.
Most of the essays deal with problems of the philosophy of science, but Part Two is historical.
Reviewed by Francesco Albèrgamo, *Arch.Int.Hist.Sci.*, 1956, 9: 51-3.

HANAPPE, Ed. L'activité. Synthèse de philosophie scientifique. 110 p., 7 fig. Bruxelles: Edition Universelle, [1934?] [CB 42/580]

HARRÉ, R. An introduction to the logic of the sciences. viii, 180 p. London: Macmillan & Co., Ltd., 1960.
Reviewed by Wesley C. Salmon, *Isis*, 1962, 53: 234-5; by F.I.G. Rawlins, *Nature*, 1960, 188: 87-8.

HARRÉ, R. Theories and things. 114 p. (Newman History and Philosophy of Science Series) London: Sheed & Ward, 1961
Reviewed by Mary B. Hesse, *Hist.Sci.*, 1962, 1: 115-17.

HARTMANN, Max. Die philosophischen Grundlagen der Naturwissenschaften. 2nd ed. 183 p. Stuttgart: Fischer, 1959.
First edition, 1948 (Jena: Fischer).
Reviewed by Curt Stern, *Science*, 1961, 133: 697.

HAWKINS, David. The language of nature. An essay in the philosophy of science. Drawings by Evan L. Gillespie. xii, 372 p., fig. San Francisco/London: W.H. Freeman, 1964.

HEISENBERG, Werner. Philosophic problems of nuclear science. Eight lectures, transl. by F.C. Hayes. 126 p. London: Faber and Faber; New York: Pantheon, 1952. [CB 80/122]
Reviewed by G.P. Thomson, *Endeavour*, 1953, 12: 105-6.
This is a translation of "Wandlungen in den Grundlagen der Naturwissenschaft" (8th enl.ed. Zürich: Hirzel, 1949). It is more general than the English title would suggest.

HEYL, Paul R. The philosophy of a scientific man. 182 p. New York: Vanguard Press, 1933.

HOMMAGE à Gaston Bachelard. Études de philosophie et d'histoire des sciences. 216 p. Paris: Presses Universitaires de France, 1957. [CB 83/280]
Reviewed by B. Rochot, *Arch.Int.Hist.Sci.*, 1958, 11: 50-2.

HULL, L.W.H. History and philosophy of science: an introduction. xi, 340 p. New York: Longmans, Green and Company, 1959.
Reviewed by Carl B. Boyer, *Isis*, 1960, 51: 347-8; for other reviews *see* CB 85/377 and CB 86/452.

INSTITUTE FOR THE UNITY OF SCIENCE. Contributions to the analysis and synthesis of knowledge. *Proc.Amer.Acad.Arts Sci.*, 1951, 80: 1-112.
Proceedings of National Conference of the Institute, Boston, Mass., April 1950; papers in 3 sections; 1. Science and man. 2. The "meaning" of scientific statements. 3. The role of "abstract objects" in science.

INTERNATIONAL ENCYCLOPEDIA OF UNIFIED SCIENCE. Editor-in-chief, Otto Neurath. Associate editors, Rudolf Carnap, Charles W. Morris. Vol. 1, no. 1-2- Chicago: University of Chicago Press, 1938- [CB 55/173 and CB 82/197]
Volume 1, no. 1-10 reprinted 1955.
Reviewed by I. Bernard Cohen, *Isis*, 1942, 33: 721-3.

INTERNATIONAL INSTITUTE OF THEORETICAL SCIENCES. Problèmes de philosophie des sciences. Premier symposium, Bruxelles, 1947. 7 vol. (Archives de l'Institut International des Sciences Théoriques, ser. A: Actualités Scientifiques et Industrielles, 1059, 1061. 1065-8, 1109) Paris: Langemark, 1948-50. [CB 73/166]

JOAD, Cyril E.M. Philosophical aspects of modern science. 344 p. London: Allen & Unwin; New York: Macmillan, 1932; reprinted 1943.
Reviewed by P. Le Corbeiller, *Isis*, 1949, 40: 77; in *Nature*, 1932, 130: 487-9.
Republished. 272 p. London: Allen & Unwin, 1963; New York: Barnes and Noble, 1964.

KEMENY, John G. A philosopher looks at science. xii, 273 p. Princeton, N.J.: D. Van Nostrand Co., 1959.
For reviews *see* CB 85/381, CB 86/456 and CB 88/529.

LAER, Pierre Henry van. Philosophico-scientific problems. Transl. by Henry J. Koren. xi, 168 p. (DuQuesne Studies, Philosophical Studies, 3) Pittsburgh: DuQuesne University Press, 1953. [CB 81/259]

LAER, Pierre Henry van. The philosophy of science. 2 vol. 1. Science in general. 181 p.; 2. A study of the division and nature of various groups of sciences. xiii, 342 p. Pittsburgh: DuQuesne University Press, 1956, 1962.
2nd edition of vol. 1 publ. 1963.

McLEAN, George F., ed. History and philosophy of science. 282 p. (Proceedings of the American Catholic Philosophical Association, 38) Washington: Catholic University of America, 1964.

MADDEN, Edward H., ed. The structure of scientific thought: an introduction to philosophy of science. ix, 381 p., bibliogr. Boston: Houghton Mifflin Company, 1960.
Reviewed by Nicholas Rescher, *Isis*, 1961, 52: 590-1; by F.I.G. Rawlins, *Nature*, 1960, 188: 831; by Patrick Suppes, *J.Phil.*, 1961, 58: 387-91.

MANDELBAUM, Maurice. Philosophy, science, and sense perception. Historical and critical studies. ix, 262 p., bibliogr. Baltimore: Johns Hopkins Press, 1964. [CB 90/507]

MARGENAU, Henry. Open vistas. Philosophical perspectives of modern science. x, 256 p., fig., bibliogr., table. (Trends in Science, 3) New Haven, Conn.: Yale University Press, 1961.
Paperback edition 1964.

MAUGE, Francis. La synthèse totale des sciences, ses conditions et son principe. 192 p. (Actualités Scientifiques et Industrielles, 1223) Paris: Hermann, 1955. [CB 81/259]

MEYERSON, Émile. Identité et réalité. 3rd ed. xix, 571 p. (Bibliothèque de Philosophie Contemporaine) Paris: Alcan, 1926.
Reviewed by Hélène Metzger, *Isis*, 1927, 9: 470-2.
First publ. 1908. For English translation *see* below; German translation, Leipzig: Akademische Verlagsgesellschaft, 1930.

MEYERSON, Émile. Identity and reality. Authorized translation by Kate Loenwenberg. 495 p. (Library of Philosophy) London: Allen and Unwin, 1930. [CB 30/393]
Reviewed by J.E. Turner, *Nature*, 1930, 126: 305-6.
For French original *see* above.

NAGEL, Ernest. Logic without metaphysics, and other studies in the philosophy of science. xviii, 433 p. Glencoe, Ill.: Free Press, 1956. [CB 83/190]

NAGEL, Ernest; SUPPES, Patrick; TARSKI, Alfred; ed. Logic, methodology, and philosophy of science. vi, 661 p. (Proceedings of the 1960 International Congress). Stanford, Cal.: Stanford University Press, 1962.
Reviewed by J. Agassi, *Isis*, 1963, 54: 405-7; by Roger Martin, *Arch.Int.Hist.Sci.*, 1963, 16: 77; in *Sci.Amer.*, 1962, 207: no. 5, 196.

NEEDHAM, Joseph. Time: the refreshing river. 280 p. New York: The Macmillan Co., 1943. [CB 65/79]
A collection of essays, mostly on philosophical aspects of science.

NEEF, F. Der Geist der Wissenschaft. 140 p. Karlsruhe in B.: G. Braun, 1925. [CB 19/798]

NORTHROP, F.S.C. Science and first principles. xiv, 299 p. Cambridge University Press; New York: Macmillan, 1931.
Reviewed by H.T. Davis, *Isis*, 1932, 17: 273-7; by C.G. Hempel, *Deut.Lit.Zeitung*, 1932, 3: 1716-21; by Thomas Greenwood, *Nature*, 1932, 130: 453-5.

PAP, Arthur. An introduction to the philosophy of science. Epilogue by Brand Blanshard. xiii, 444 p. New York: Free Press of Glencoe, 1961.
Reviewed by Henry E. Kyburg, Jr., *J.Phil.*, 1963, 15: 358-62; by William Kneale, *Brit.J.Phil.Sci.*, 1962, 13: 334-7.

PEIRCE, Charles S. Essays in the philosophy of science. Edited, with an introduction by Vincent Tomas. xxii, 271 p., fig., bibliogr., tables. (The American Heritage Series) Indianapolis/New York: Bobbs-Merrill Company, 1957.

POIRIER, R. La philosophie de la science. xxiv, 234 p. (Philosophes et Savants Français du XXe Siècle. Extraits et Notices, 2) Paris: Alcan, 1926. [CB 20/178]

POPPER, Karl R. Conjectures and refutations. The growth of scientific knowledge. 412 p. New York/London: Basic Books, 1962.
Reviewed by George E. Hudson, *Phys.Today*, 1963, 16: no. 11, 80-2.

RAMSPERGER, Albert G. Philosophies of science. xi, 304 p. New York: Crofts, 1942. [CB 63/270]

REYMOND, Arnold. Philosophie spiritualiste. Études et méditations, recherches critiques. 2 vol. xxiii, 429 p.; viii, 448 p., bibliogr. (Recueil publié par la Faculté des Lettres de l'Université de Lausanne) Lausanne: Rouge, 1942. [CB 70/270]
Includes many articles on the philosophy and history of science.

RIGNANO, Eugenio. Essays in scientific synthesis. 254 p. Chicago: Open Court, 1918.
French edition Paris: Alcan, 1912.

RUYER, R. Esquisse d'une philosophie de la structure. 370 p. Paris: Alcan, 1931. [CB 35/310]

SAGGI di critica delle scienze, di Abbagnano [et al]. 8, 176 p. (Maestri e Compagni; Biblioteca di Studi Critici e Morali, 17) Torino: De Silva, 1950.
Reviewed by A. Natucci, *Arch.Int.Hist.Sci.*, 1951, 4: 1009-12.

ST. JOHN'S UNIVERSITY, New York. Philosophy of science: the Philosophy of Science Institute Lectures. 164 p. Jamaica, N.Y.: St. John's University Press, 1960.
Reviewed by Edward C. Moore, *Phil.Sci.*, 1962, 29: 92-3.

SAMUEL, Herbert Louis Samuel, *Viscount;* DINGLE, Herbert. A threefold cord: philosophy, science, religion. 280 p. London: Geo. Allen and Unwin, 1961.
Reviewed by G.W. Scott Blair, *Brit.J.Phil.Sci.*, 1962, 13: 339-40.

SCHLICK, Moritz. Philosophy of nature. xi, 136 p. New York: Philosophical Library, 1949.
Reviewed by Wolfgang Yourgrau, *Arch.Int.Hist.Sci.*, 1951 4: 374-82; by A.P. Ushenko, *Scr.Math.*, 1951, 17: 108-10.
Translation of: Grundzuege der Naturphilosophie. Wien: Gerold, 1948.

SCHRÖDINGER, Erwin. Mind and matter. vii, 104 p. (The Tarner Lectures, 1956) Cambridge/New York: Cambridge University Press, 1958.
Reviewed by W.H. McCrea, *Nature*, 1959, 183: 1218-19; by Ian G. Barbour, *Amer.J.Phys.*, 1959, 27: 529.

SCHRÖDINGER, Erwin. Science theory and man. Transl. by James Murphy and W.H. Johnston. 233 p. London: Allen and Unwin; New York: Dover Publications, 1957.
Formerly published under the title, Science and the human temperament. 154 p. London: Allen and Unwin, 1935.
Reviewed by W.H. McCrea, *Nature*, 1959, 183: 1218-19; by H.R. Post, *Brit.J.Phil.Sci.*, 1962, 13: 80-2.

SEELY, Charles S. The philosophy of science; essays in contemporary realism. xii, 140 p. New York: Philosophical Library, 1964.

SHEEN, Fulton J. Philosophy of science. xxv, 197 p. Milwaukee: Bruce, 1934.
Reviewed by W.M. Malisoff, *Phil.Sci.*, 1935, 2: 381-3.

SMITH, Vincent Edward. The general science of nature. xii, 400 p. Milwaukee: Bruce Publishing Co., 1958.
Reviewed by Wesley C. Salmon, *Isis*, 1962, 53: 234-5.

STRONG, William Walker. The new philosophy of modern science. viii, 194 p. York, Pa.: Kyle Printing Co., 1920.

STUDY, Eduard. Denken und Darstellung in Mathematik und Naturwissenschaften. Hrsg. von Karl Scheel. 2nd ed. v, 63 p., 10 fig. (Sammlung Vieweg, 59) Braunschweig: Vieweg, 1921.

TENNANT, Frederick Robert. Philosophy of the sciences: or, The relations between the departments of knowledge. ix, 191 p. Cambridge University Press, 1932.

TONQUEDEC, J. de. La philosophie de la nature. 182 p. Paris: Lethielleux, 1959.
Reviewed by Michel Ambacher, *Dialogue*, 1962, 1: 95-6.

TOULMIN, Stephen. Contemporary scientific mythology. In: Metaphysical beliefs, three essays, by S. Toulmin, Ronald W. Hepburn, and Alasdair MacIntyre, p. 1-83. London: SCM Press, 1957. [CB 83/190]

TOULMIN, Stephen. Foresight and understanding. An inquiry into the aims of science. 115 p. Bloomington: Indiana University Press, 1961; London: Hutchinson, 1961; New York: Harper and Row, 1963.
Reviewed by Peter Achinstein, *Isis*, 1963, 54: 408-10; by P. Collinder, *Lychnos*, 1962, 393-4.

TOULMIN, Stephen. The philosophy of science. An introduction. viii, 176 p. (Hutchinson's University Library, 1055). London/New York: Hutchinson & Co., 1953. [CB 81/259]
Reprinted New York: Harper Torchbooks, 1960.

ULLMO, Jean. La pensée scientifique moderne. 284 p. (Bibliothèque de Philosophie Scientifique) Paris: Flammarion, 1958.
Reviewed by H. Dopp, *Rev.Quest.Sci.*, 1958, 19: 479-80; by V. Mathieu, *Filosofia*, 1958, 9: 736-7.

VARIA. 497 p. (Studia Philosophica Academiae Scientiarum Hungaricae, 3) Budapest: Akadémiai Kiadó, 1963.
The papers in this volume are published in English, German, and French and include subjects as varied as problems of cognition, Hegelian logic and chemistry, and dialectical materialism.

VOICE OF AMERICA. Philosophy of science. 152 p., portr. Washington: 1964. [CB 90/508] 408
Annotation contains contents list.

WARTOFSKY, Marx W., ed. Boston studies in the philosophy of science. viii, 212 p. (Proceedings of the Boston Colloquium for the Philosophy of Science, 1961/1962; Synthese Library). Dordrecht, Holland: D. Reidel Publishing Co., 1963. [CB 89/491]

WEIZSÄCKER, Carl Friedrich von. The history of nature. 191 p. Chicago: University of Chicago Press, 1949. Paperback reprint, 1959. [CB 76/393]
Reviewed by S. Moser, *Phil.Natur.*, 1951, 1: 435-8; by H. Wein, *ibid.*, 438-46.

WENZL, Aloys. Wissenschaft und Weltanschauung. Natur und Geist als Probleme der Metaphysik. xi, 374 p. Leipzig: Meiner, 1936.

WERKMEISTER, W.H. A philosophy of science. xii, 551 p. New York: Harper, 1940. [CB 60/144]

WEYL, Hermann. Mind and nature. viii, 100 p. Philadelphia: University of Pennsylvania Press, 1934.
Reviewed by H.T. Davis, *Isis*, 1935, 23: 281-4; by W.H. McCrea, *Math.Gaz.*, 1935, 19: 58-9.

WEYL, Hermann. The open world (Three lectures on the metaphysical implications of science). v, 84 p. New Haven: Yale University Press, 1932.
Reviewed by H.T. Davis, *Isis*, 1935, 23: 281-4.

WEYL, Hermann. Philosophy of mathematics and natural science. Rev. and augmented English edition based on a translation by Olaf Helmer. vii, 311 p. Princeton, N.J.: Princeton University Press, 1949.
Reprinted New York: Atheneum, 1963.
Reviewed by V.F. Lenzen, *Isis*, 1950, 41: 236-7.
German original first published Munich: 1926. [CB 21/566 and CB 27/536]. 2nd edition 1948.

WHITEHEAD, Alfred North. Essays in science and philosophy. vii, 348 p. New York: Philosophical Library, 1947.
Reviewed by Edmund Whittaker, *Nature*, 1947, 160: 415-16.

WHITEHEAD, Alfred North. The interpretation of science. Selected essays. Ed., with an introd. by A.H. Johnson. xlv, 274 p., bibliogr. (Library of Liberal Arts, 117) Indianapolis, Ind./New York: Bobbs-Merrill, 1961.

WHITEHEAD, Alfred North. Nature and life. (Two lectures). 95 p. Cambridge University Press; Chicago: University of Chicago Press, 1934.
Spanish translation Naturaleza y vida, ed. by Risieri Frondizi. 93 p. Buenos Aires: Universidad de Buenos Aires, Instituto de Filosofia, 1941.
Reviewed by Ricardo Resta, *Archeion*, 1942, 24: 468-9.

WHYTE, Lancelot Law. The unitary principle in physics and biology. x, 182 p. London: Cresset Press, 1949.

YOUNG, John Zachary. Doubt and certainty in science. 168 p., ill. Oxford: Clarendon Press, 1951

Ak-bn *essays; articles*

BENJAMIN, A. Cornelius. Science and its presuppositions. *Sci.Mon.*, 1951, 73: 150-53.

BENJAMIN, A. Cornelius. Science and the philosophy of science. *Phil.Sci.*, 1938, 5: 421-33.

BETH, E.W. La cosmologie, dite naturelle, et les sciences mathématiques de la nature. *Arch.Inst.Int.Sci.Théor.Sér.A Bull.Acad.Int.Phil.Sci.*, 1. Problèmes de philosophie des sciences, 1, Les méthodes de la connaissance, p. 17-24. Discussion p. 25-41. (Actualités Scientifiques et Industrielles, 1059) Paris: Hermann, 1948.

BETH, E.W. Fundamental features of contemporary theory of science. *Brit.J.Phil.Sci.*, 1951, 1: 291-302.

BIALOBRZESKI, G. Memorandum concernant la méthodologie et la synthèse philosophique des sciences. *Arch.Int.Hist.Sci.*, 1947, 1: 157-64.

BLUMBERG, Albert E. The nature of philosophic analysis. *Phil. Sci.*, 1935, 2: 1-8.

BOHR, Niels. Analysis and synthesis in science. *International Encyclopedia of Unified Science*, (1), p. 28. Chicago: University of Chicago Press; Cambridge University Press, 1938.

BOODIN, John Elof. A revolution in metaphysics and in science. *Phil.Sci.*, 1938, 5: 267-75.

BRODBECK, May. Structure of science. Philosophy of science, a separate discipline, meets philosophy proper on the question, "What exists?". *Science*, 1961, 134: 997-9.

CAWS, Peter. Science, computers and the complexity of nature. *Phil.Sci.*, 1963, 30: 158-64.

DAUJAT, J. La représentation intelligible et le réel. *Arch. Inst.Int.Sci.Théor.Sér.A Bull.Acad.Int.Phil.Sci.*, 2. Problèmes de philosophie des sciences, 2, Les sciences et le réel, p. 7-19. Discussion p. 20-9. (Actualités Scientifiques et Industrielles, 1061) Paris: Hermann, 1948

DE SANTILLANA, Giorgio. Lights and shadows in the philosophy of science. *Confluence*, 1954, 3: 187-95.
Reprinted Cambridge, Mass.: M.I.T. Press, 1954 (Publications in the Humanities, 9).

DINGLE, Herbert. Knowledge without understanding. *Atlantic Mon.*, July 1937, 116-24.

DINGLE, Herbert. The nature of scientific philosophy. *Proc. Roy.Soc.Edinb.Sect.A*, 1949, 62: 400-11.

DINGLER, Hugo. La notion de système dans l'histoire et la philosophie des sciences. *Archeion*, 1931, 13: 210-25.

ELSBACH, A.C. Der Lebensgehalt der Wissenschaften. Wissenschaftstheoretische Grundfragen. 39 p. Berlin: Walter de Gruyter, 1926. [CB 21/565]

FRANK, Lawrence K. Structure, function and growth. *Phil.Sci.*, 1935, 2: 210-35.

FRANK, Philipp. The mechanical versus the mathematical conception of nature. *Phil.Sci.*, 1937, 4: 41-74.

FRANK, Philipp. The origin of the separation between science and philosophy. *Proc.Amer.Acad.Arts Sci.*, 1952, 80: 115-39.

FRANK, Philipp. Three aspects of science (logical-empirical, metaphysical and sociological). Abstract of paper read on 16th October, 1950. *Bull.Brit.Soc.Hist.Sci.*, 1951, 1: 163-4.

GONSETH, F. Les conceptions mathématiques et le réel. *Arch. Inst.Int.Sci.Théor.Sér.A Bull.Acad.Int.Phil.Sci.*, 2. Problèmes de philosophie des sciences, 2. Les sciences et le réel, p. 31-49, Discussion, p. 50-60. (Actualités Scientifiques et Industrielles, 1061) Paris: Hermann, 1948.

HARTMANN, Max. Prozess und Gesetz in Physik und Biologie. *Phil.Natur.*, 1953, 2: 277-92.

HINSHELWOOD, C.N. The vision of nature. 33 p. (The fifteenth Arthur Stanley Eddington Memorial Lecture, 10 November 1961) New York: Cambridge University Press, 1961.

HÖNIGSWALD, Richard. Naturphilosophie. *Jahrb.Phil.*, 1913, 1: 60-98, 366-9.

HOFERT, Hans Joachim. Nicolai Hartmanns Ontologie und die Naturphilosophie. *Phil.Natur.*, 1950, 1: 36-55.

JEFFREYS, Harold. Science, logic and philosophy. *Nature*, 1938, 141: 672-6, 716-19.

JENKINSON, J.W. Science and metaphysics. In: Singer, Charles, ed. Studies in the history of science, vol. 2, p. 447-71. Oxford: Clarendon Press, 1921.

JOURDAIN, Philip E.B. The economy of thought. *Monist*, 1914, 24: 134-5.
Account of a discussion between N.R. Campbell and Philip E.B. Jourdain on Mach's principle of economy.

KAPP, Reginald O.; GRANT, C.K. The metaphysics of science. *Nature*, 1956, 177: 997-8.

KURSANOV, G.A. Philipp Frank and his philosophy of science. *Daedalus Amer.Acad.Arts Sci.*, 1962, 91: 617-41.
A translation by A.G. Korol of the introductory essay for the Russian translation of Philipp Frank's "Philosophy of science: the link between science and philosophy" (1957).

LAPAN, Arthur. Preface to a theory of nature. *Phil.Sci.*, 1938, 5: 393-409.

LODGE, Oliver. The philosophy of science or the principles of scientific procedure. *Scientia*, 1922, 32: 361-77; French transl., suppl., 51-66. [CB 14/566]

LOSACCO. È possibile una filosofia della natura? *Atti IVo Congr.Int.Fil.* (Bologna, 1911), (2), p. 150-6. Genova: 1913.

LUCHINS, Abraham S.; LUCHINS, Edith H. Two philosophies of science: a study in contrasts. *Synthese*, 1963, 15: 292-316.
A discussion of R.B. Braithwaite's "Scientific explanation" (*see* Akd) and S. Toulmin's "The philosophy of science".

MARITAIN, Jacques. Philosophy of nature. To which is added Maritain's Philosophy of the sciences, by Yves R. Simon. x, 198 p. New York: Philosophical Library, 1951.
Reviewed by F.I.G. Rawlins, *Nature*, 1952, 169: 254-5.

MILLER, David L. Things and potentiality. *Phil.Sci.*, 1936, 3: 19-25.

MOORE, Merritt Hadden. A metaphysics of design without purpose. *Phil.Sci.*, 1936, 3: 1-8.

OSSOWSKA, Marja; OSSOWSKI, Stanislaw. The science of science. *Organon*, 1936, 1: 1-12.

OSTWALD, Wilhelm. Théorie des unités. *Vie Int.*, 1913, 4: 113-63.

REICHENBACH, Hans. La philosophie scientifique, vues nouvelles sur les buts et les méthodes. Traduction de Ernest Vouillemin, revue et mise à jour par l'auteur. Introduction de Marcel Boll. 44 p. Paris: Hermann, 1932.
Translation of "Ziele und Wege der heutigen Naturphilosophie" (Leipzig: F. Meiner, 1931).

REYMOND, Arnold. Réflexions sur la philosophie des sciences, la philosophe et la métaphysique. *Arch.Int.Hist.Sci.*, 1948, 2: 32-49.

SCHLICK, Moritz. Les énoncés scientifiques et la réalité du monde extérieur. Traduction de l'allemand par Ernest Vouillemin, revue et mise à jour par l'auteur. 54 p. (Actualités Scientifiques et Industrielles, 152) Paris: Hermann, 1934.
Translation based on articles in German which appeared in *Erkenntnis*.

STERN, Alfred. Science and philosopher. *Amer.Scient.*, 1956, 44: 281-95.

STIERNOTTE, A.P. Scientists as philosophers. *Amer.Scient.*, 1954, 42: 650-7.

Ak-br *periodicals*

British Journal for the Philosophy of Science. Vol. 1- Edinburgh/London: Nelson, 1950- [CB 77/365]
Quarterly.

Philosophy of Science. Quarterly. Vol. 1 - Baltimore, Md.: Williams & Wilkins (for the Philosophy of Science Association), 1934 - [CB 40/398]

Philosophy of Science Group Supplement, 1-8, to the *Bulletin of the British Society for the History of Science*, 1949-54, 1: 39-48, 67-72, 97-104, 127-8, 161-7, 191-4, 237-8, 253-8.

Physis. Beiträge zur naturwissenschaftlichen Synthese. Vol. 1, 2/3. Stuttgart: Hippokrates Verlag, 1942-49.
Vol. 2/3 edited by Adolph Meyer-Abich. [CB 76/393]
No more published.

Ak-bv bibliographies

BRUNET, Lucien, *et al.* Bibliographie des années 1937 à 1939. Histoire des sciences. Histoire de la philosophie dans ses rapports avec les sciences. Philosophie et théorie des sciences. *Thalès*, 1940, 4: 287-315.

MAY, Eduard. "Monographien zur Naturphilosophie, Erkenntnistheorie und Geschichte der Naturwissenschaft" und "Beihefte zur Philosophia Naturalis." *Phil.Natur.*, 1952, 2: 131.

SELVAGGI, F. Rassegna di filosofia delle scienze. *Gregorianum*, 1958, 39: 611-27.
A review of some twenty books on the philosophy of science.

Ak-c history

ALBÈRGAMO, Francesco. Storia della logica delle scienze esatte. xv, 366 p. Bari: Laterza & Figli, 1947. [CB 75/86]

BLAKE, Ralph M.; DUCASSE, Curt J.; MADDEN, Edward H. *See* Ake-c.

BUCHDAHL, Gerd. The relevance of Descartes's philosophy for modern philosophy of science. *Brit.J.Hist.Sci.*, 1963, 1: 227-49.

CURTH, Hermann. Das instrumentale Weltmodell Diderots, zugleich ein Beitrag zur Problematik des modernen Wissenschaftsbegriffs. *Phil.Natur.*, 1956, 3: 495-526.

ENRIQUES, Federigo. Signification de l'histoire de la pensée scientifique. 68 p. (Actualités Scientifiques et Industrielles, 161; Philosophie et Histoire de la Pensée Scientifique, 1) Paris: Hermann, 1934. [CB 42/576]

FILIPOVIĆ, Vladimir. Rudjer Bošković und seine Bedeutung für die gegenwärtige Naturphilosophie. *Actes du Symposium International R.J. Bošković* (1961), p. 227-34. Beograd: 1962.

FLECKENSTEIN, Joachim Otto. Scholastik, Barock, exakte Wissenschaften. 71 p. (*Christ Heute*, 1: no. 7) Einsiedeln: Johannes-Verlag, 1949. [CB 76/392]

HENDERSON, Lawrence Joseph. The order of nature: an essay. v, 234 p. Cambridge: Harvard University Press, 1917. [CB 7/152]
French translation. L'ordre de la nature. viii, 188 p. Paris: Alcan, 1924.

LOVEJOY, Arthur O. The revolt against dualism. xii, 325 p. Chicago: Open Court, 1930.
Reviewed by H.T. Davis, *Isis*, 1931, 15: 190-3.

McRAE, Robert. The problem of the unity of the sciences: Bacon to Kant. xii, 148 p. Toronto: University of Toronto Press, 1961.
Reviewed by Rolf Lindborg, *Lychnos*, 1962, 402-5; by Peter Remnant, *Dialogue*, 1962, 1: 97-8.

McRAE, Robert. The unity of the sciences: Bacon, Descartes, and Leibniz. *J.Hist.Ideas*, 1957, 18: 27-48.

MEYERSON, Émile. Du cheminement de la pensée. 3 vol. xxvii, 294, 422, 320 p. (Bibliothèque de Philosophie Contemporaine) Paris: Alcan, 1931.
Reviewed by Hélène Metzger, *Isis*, 1932, 17: 444-5; by Federigo Enriques, *Scientia*, 1932, 51: 366-8.

MOSER, Simon. Der Begriff der Natur in aristotelischer und moderner Sicht. *Phil.Natur.*, 1961, 6: 261-87.

REICHENBACH, Hans. The rise of scientific philosophy. xi, 333 p. Berkeley: University of California Press; London: Cambridge University Press, 1951.
Reviewed by W.H. Werkmeister, *Isis*, 1951, 42: 277-8; by I. Bernard Cohen, *Sci.Mon.*, 1951, 73: 328-9; by Adolf Grünbaum, *Scr.Math.*, 1953, 19: 48-54.

SAGERET, Jules. La révolution philosophique et la science: Bergson, Einstein, Le Dantec, J.H. Rosny ainé. 252 p. Paris: Félix Alcan, 1924. [CB 16/340]

SEGOND, J. La sagesse cartésienne et la doctrine de la science. 321 p. Paris: Vrin, 1932.

WALLACE, William A. St. Thomas Aquinas, Galileo, and Einstein. *Thomist*, 1961, 24: 1-22.

Ak-o teaching philosophy of science

BERTALANFFY, Ludwig von. Philosophy of science in scientific education. *Sci.Mon.*, 1953, 77: 233-39.

FRANK, Philipp. The place of the philosophy of science in the curriculum of the physics student. *Amer.J.Phys.*, 1947, 15: 202-18.

HANSON, N.R. History and philosophy of science in an undergraduate physics course. *Phys.Today*, 1955, 8: no. 8, 4-9.
Polish translation: *Kwart.Hist.Nauk.Tech.*, 1957, 2: 663-79.

SIMMONS, R.H. The history and philosophy of science: a challenge to higher education. *Sci.Educ.*, 1957, 41: 57-61.

WINTER, Henry James Jacques. Remarks on the teaching of the history and philosophy of science. *Arch.Int.Hist.Sci.*, 1947-48, 1: 574-8.

Ak-ob philosophy of science as a study

GONSETH, F. Gibt es eine neue wissenschaftliche Philosophie? *Schweiz.Hochschulzeitung*, 1940, no. 6, 344-60.

GONSETH, F. Sur le statut de la philosophie des sciences. *Act.IIe Congr.Int.Phil.Sci.* (Zurich, 1954), p. 10-23. Zurich: Editions du Griffon, 1955.

KLUBERTANZ, George P. A program for progress in the philosophy of science. *Act.IIe Congr.Int.Phil.Sci.* (Zurich, 1954), p. 78-84. Zurich: Editions du Griffon, 1955.

MARGENAU, Henry. Present status and needs of the philosophy of science. *Proc.Amer.Phil.Soc.*, 1955, 99: 334-7.

MARGENAU, Henry. The task of the coming philosophy; perspectives of science. *Phi Beta Kappa Key Reporter*, 1959, 25: 2-3, 8.

MEYER, Adolf. Die gegenwärtige Krise der Wissenschaften und die Aufgabe der Philosophie bei ihrer Beseitigung. *Hippokrates* (Stuttgart), 1931, 3: 393-416.

TUMMERS, J.H. La tâche de la philosophie des sciences. *Act. IIe Congr.Int.Phil.Sci.* (Zurich, 1954), p. 91-4. Zurich: Editions du Griffon, 1955.

WHITROW, G.J. The study of the philosophy of science. *Brit. J.Phil.Sci.*, 1956, 7: 189-205.

WHYTE, Lancelot Law. The philosophy of science, today and tomorrow. Abstract of paper read on 11th June, 1951. *Bull. Brit.Soc.Hist.Sci.*, 1951, 1: 167.

Ak-qx international congresses

CONGRÈS INTERNATIONAL DE PHILOSOPHIE SCIENTIFIQUE, Paris, 1935. Actes. 8 vol. (Actualités Scientifiques et Industrielles, 388-95) Paris: Hermann, 1936. [CB 51/247]

CONGRÈS INTERNATIONAL DE PHILOSOPHIE SCIENTIFIQUE. Einheit der Wissenschaft. [Proceedings of preliminary congress, Prague, 1934] 204 p. Leipzig: Meiner, 1934.

FIFTH International Congress for the Unity of Science, Harvard University, September 5-10, 1939. *Isis*, 1939, 30: 279-80; 1940, 32: 340-4.

Ak-qy

DOCKX, S.I. De la nature et du but de l'Institut International des Sciences Théoriques. *Arch.Inst.Int.Sci.Théor.Sér.A Bull. Acad.Int.Phil.Sci.*, 1. Problèmes de philosophie des sciences, 1, Les méthodes de la connaissance, p. 7-10. (Actualités Scientifiques et Industrielles, 1059) Paris: Hermann, 1948.

Akb the nature of science

Akb-bm *large scale works*

AMERICAN ACADEMY OF ARTS AND SCIENCES. Science and the modern mind: a symposium edited by Gerald Holton. ix, 110 p. Boston: Beacon Press, 1958.

AUERBACH, Felix. Das naturwissenschaftliche Weltbild. 135 p. Berlin-Lichterfeld: Bermüller, 1933.

BRIDGMAN, P.W. The way things are. x, 333 p. Cambridge, Mass.: Harvard University Press, 1959.
Reviewed by A. Cornelius Benjamin, *Science*, 1959, 130: 31-2; by R. Bruce Lindsay, *Phys.Today*, 1959, 12: 48; by C.K. Grant, *Nature*, 1959, 184: 1975.

BROAD, Charles Dunbar. Scientific thought. 555 p. London: Kegan Paul, 1923.

BRONOWSKI, Jacob. The common sense of science. 154 p. London: Heinemann, 1951.
Reviewed by John R. Baker, *Endeavour*, 1952, 11: 108.

BRONOWSKI, Jacob. Insight. Ideas of modern science. 108 p., ill. New York: Harper and Row, 1964. [CB 90/620]

CALDER, Ritchie. Profile of science. 326 p. London: Allen & Unwin, 1951.

CALDIN, E.F. The power and limits of science. A philosophical study. ix, 196 p. London: Chapman & Hall, 1949. [CB 77/365]

CAMPBELL, Norman. What is science? ix, 186 p. New York: Dover Publications, 1952.
First publ. 1921.

CHWISTEK, Leon. The limits of science. With an introduction and appendix by Helen Charlotte Brodie. lvii, 347 p. New York: Harcourt, Brace, 1948.
Reviewed by Ernest Nagel, *Phys.Today*, 1948, 1: no. 6, 25, 35.

COHEN, I. Bernard. Science, servant of man: a layman's primer for the age of science. Foreword by Harlow Shapley. xiv, 362 p., 7 pl. Boston: Little, Brown, 1948; London: Sigma Books, 1949.
Reviewed by Conway Zirkle, *Isis*, 1949, 40: 73-5; for other reviews *see* CB 74/383, CB 75/84, CB 76/389 and CB 77/362.

DELBET, P. La science et la réalité. 349 p. Paris: Flammarion, 1913.

FRIEND, Julius W.; FEIBLEMAN, James. Science and the spirit of man: a new ordering of experience. 336 p. London: Allen and Unwin, 1933.
Reviewed by W.G.L.C., *Nature*, 1934, 134: 233-4.

FRIEND, Julius W.; FEIBLEMAN, James. What science really means. An explanation of the history and empirical method of general science. 222 p. London: Allen & Unwin, 1937.
Reviewed by M.F. Ashley-Montagu, *Isis*, 1939, 31: 105-8.

GRASSI, E., *et al.* Die Einheit unseres Wirklichkeitsbildes und die Grenzen der Einzelwissenschaften. 196 p. Bern: Francke, 1951.
Reviewed by Heinrich Meyer, *Isis*, 1952, 43: 381-2.

GREENWOOD, David. The nature of science and other essays. xiii, 95 p. New York: Philosophical Library, 1960.
Reviewed by Wesley C. Salmon, *Isis*, 1962, 53: 234-5.

GREGORY, R.A. Discovery, or the spirit and service of science. xii, 340 p., 8 pl. London: Macmillan, 1916.

HEITLER, Walter H. Der Mensch und die naturwissenschaftliche Erkenntnis. 82 p., ill. (Die Wissenschaft, 2, vol. 116). Braunschweig: F. Vieweg & Sohn, 1962.
Engl. translation by Robert Schlapp, Man and science, vii, 100 p., ill. New York: Basic Books, 1963.
Reviewed by K.H. Simon, *Naturwiss.Rundsch.*, 1963, 16: 459.

HOBSON, Ernest William. The domain of natural science. The Gifford Lectures delivered in the University of Aberdeen in 1921 and 1922. xvi, 510 p. Aberdeen: The University; Cambridge University Press, 1923.

HOGBEN, Lancelot. Science in authority. 157 p. New York: Norton, 1963.
Reviewed by Michael Scriven, *Phil.Sci.*, 1964, 31: 184-6.

HUBBLE, Edwin. The nature of science, and other lectures. viii, 83 p., front. San Marino, Cal.: Huntington Library, 1954. [CB 80/120]

HUTCHINGS, Edward, ed. Frontiers in science. 362 p. New York: Basic Books, 1958; Pasadena: California Institute of Technology, 1960.
Reviewed by Leon E. Gold, *Sky Telesc.*, 1958, 18: 40-3; by Aleksander Gella, *Kwart.Hist.Nauk.Tech.*, 1961, 6: 308-9.

JEFFARES, A. Norman; DAVIES, M. Bryn. The scientific background. xii, 306 p. London: Pitman & Sons, Ltd., 1958.
Reviewed by W.L. Sumner, *Nature*, 1959, 184: 6; by H. Dobb, *Rev.Quest.Sci.*, 1959, 20: 618.

LANGDON-DAVIES, John. Science and common sense. 284 p. London: Hamilton, 1931.

LECLERC DU SABLON, M. L'unité de la science. 284 p. (Nouvelle Collection Scientifique) Paris: Félix Alcan, 1919.
Reviewed by L. Guinet, *Isis*, 1921, 4: 115.

LEVY, Hyman. The universe of science. xiii, 224 p. London: Century, 1932. 2nd ed. London: Watts, 1947.
Reviewed by H.T. Davis, *Isis*, 1934, 21: 328-30; by T.G., *Nature*, 1939, 143: 224.

LEWIS, Gilbert Newton. The anatomy of science. x, 221 p. (Yale University, Mrs. Hepsa Ely Silliman Memorial Lectures) New Haven: Yale University Press, 1926.
Reviewed by Alex. Findlay, *Nature*, 1927, 119: 228-9.

LYNCH, Arthur. Science: leading and misleading. 376 p. London: John Murray, 1927.
Reviewed in *Nature*, 1927, 120: 469-70.

MEHLBERG, Henryk. The reach of science. xii, 356 p. Toronto: University of Toronto Press; Oxford University Press, 1958.
Reviewed by Stephen Toulmin, *Bull.Brit.Soc.Hist.Sci.*, 1960, 10: 346-9.

MORE, Louis Trenchard. The limitations of science. 268 p. New York: Holt, 1915.

NASH, Leonard K. The nature of the natural sciences. xix, 406 p., ill. Boston/Toronto: Little, Brown, 1963.
Reviewed by Arnold B. Levison, *Science*, 1964, 144: 167.

NEWMAN, James R. What is science? Twelve eminent scientists and philosophers explain their various fields to the layman. 493 p. New York: Simon and Schuster, 1955. [CB 81/258]

OBLER, Paul C.; ESTRIN, Herman A.; ed. The new scientist. Essays on the methods and values of modern science. 316 p. (Anchor Books) Garden City, N.Y.: Doubleday & Co., 1962. [CB 87/556]

RUSSELL, Bertrand. The scientific outlook. 285 p. London: Allen & Unwin, 1931.
Reviewed by E.S.R., *Nature*, 1932, 129: 295-6.

RUYTINX, Jacques. La problématique philosophique de l'unité de la science. viii, 368 p. Paris: Belles Lettres, 1962.

SULLIVAN, John William Navin. Aspects of science. 190 p. London: Cobden-Sanderson, 1923.

SULLIVAN, John William Navin. Limitations of science. v, 303 p. London: Chatto and Windus, 1933.
Reprinted New York: Mentor Books, Viking Press, 1949 (192 p.).
Reviewed by F.S. Marvin, *Nature,* 1933, 132: 872-3.

SYNGE, J.L. Science: sense and nonsense. 156 p. London: Cape, 1951.

THOMSON, George. The inspiration of science. x, 150 p., ill. New York: Oxford University Press, 1961.
Reviewed by Jean M. Calloway, *Amer.Math.Mon.,* 1963, 70: 343.

WALKER, Marshall. The nature of scientific thought. viii, 184 p. Englewood Cliffs, N.J.: Prentice-Hall, 1963.

Akb-bn *essays; articles*

BENJAMIN, A. Cornelius On defining "science". *Sci.Mon.,* 1949, 68: 192-8.

CHECCHIA, Nicolas. Scienza e scientismo. 47 p. Castellamare Adriatico: Camillo di Sciullo, 1914.

CHIANG KAI-SHEK. The way and spirit of science. *Nature,* 1943, 152: 180-2.

COMPTON, John J. Understanding science. *Dialectica,* 1962, 16: 155-76.

DANNEMANN, Friedrich. Wissenschaft als Einheit. *Arch.Gesch. Math.Naturwiss.Tech.,* 1929, 11: 321-9.
This paper was partly published in *Isis,* 1924, 6: 395-9.

DEGOLYER, E. Science. A method, not a field. 15 p. Norman: University of Oklahoma Press, 1948.
Commencement address delivered at the University of Oklahoma, the evening of 31 May 1948.

DELAHAY, Paul. Reflections of the cultivation of science. *Amer.Scient.,* 1960, 48: 20-9.

DIJKSTERHUIS, E.J. Grensverschuivingen in den Orbis Scientiarum. [Changing frontiers in the world of sciences. (In Dutch)] *Verslag van het 9e Nederlands Congres van Leraren in de Wiskunde en de Natuurwetenschappen,* April 1952, 19 p. Groningen: J.B. Wolters, 1952.

DINGLE, Herbert. Science and the unobservable. *Proc.Roy. Inst.,* 1937-38, 30: 68-98. [CB 53/256]
Reprinted in *Nature,* 1938, 141: 21-8 and in *Annu.Rep. Smithsonian Inst.* for 1938, p. 209-26. Washington: 1939.

DUCASSE, C.J. Science: its nature, method, and scope. 20 p. (3rd David Wight Prall Memorial Lecture) [Piedmont, Calif.: 1947].

GRÜNBAUM, Adolf. The structure of science. *Phil.Sci.,* 1962, 29: 294-305.

GRUENBERG, Benjamin C. The chains of Prometheus. *Sci.Mon.,* 1927, 25: 504-10. [CB 41/597]

JORDAN, David Starr. Science and sciosophy. Address of the President, Pacific Division of the American Association for the Advancement of Science at Stanford University, June 26, 1924. *Science,* 1924, 59: 563-9.
"Sciosophy is systematized ignorance".

KALLEN, Horace M. The meanings of "unity" among the sciences. *Educ.Admin.Superv.,* 1940, 81-97.

KALLEN, Horace M. The meanings of unity among the sciences. *Structure, Method and Meaning, Essays in Honor of Henry M. Sheffer,* p. 225-41. New York: Liberal Arts Press, 1951.

KAUFMAN, Felix. The structure of science. *J.Phil.,* 1941, 38: 281-93.

LALANDE, André. La pensée scientifique et sa tendance fondamentale. *Rev.Gén.Sci.,* 1932, 43: 309-13.

LE CHÂTELIER, H. De la science. Sa nature, son utilité et son enseignement. *Rev.Sci.,* 1913, 2e sem., 449-58.

MAST, S.O. Science. *Bios,* 1943, 14: 7-24.

MERRIAM, John C. Ultimate values of science. 8 p. (Carnegie Institution of Washington, Supplementary Publications, 15) Washington: 1935.

MOULTON, F.R. Science. *Science,* 1937, 85: 571-5

NESMEIANOV, A.N. Les voies de la science. *Pensée,* 1961, no. 99, 27-35.

NEURATH, Otto. The departmentalization of unified science. *Erkenntnis,* 1938, 7: 240-6.

NEURATH, Otto. Encyclopaedism as a pedagogical aim: a Danish approach. *Phil.Sci.,* 1938, 5: 484-92.

NEURATH, Otto. Unified science and its encyclopedia. *Phil. Sci.,* 1937, 4: 265-77.

NEURATH, Otto. Unified science as encyclopedic integration. 27 p. (International Encyclopedia of Unified Science, I: no. 1) Chicago: University of Chicago Press, 1938.

PICARD, Émile. Quelques vues générales sur la science. *Bull. Sci.Math.,* 1938, 62: 163-6.

PICARD, Émile. Quelques vues sur la science. *Rev.Sci.,* 1938, 76: 269-70.
Part of speech delivered to the Société de Secours des Amis des Sciences.

SCHATZMAN, E. Qu'est-ce que la science? *Cah.Rationalistes,* 1958, no. 175, 282-93.

SOMERVILLE, John. The forgotten problem: aims in science. *Phil.Sci.,* 1935, 2: 246-54.

STERN, Curt. The journey, not the goal. *Sci.Mon.,* 1944, 58: 96-100.

THOMSON, George. The two aspects of science. Control over nature and understanding of nature must both be held in equal honor. *Science,* 1960, 132: 996-1000; *Advanc.Sci.,* 1960, 17: 191-6.

TOULMIN, Stephen. Science and our intellectual tradition. *Advanc.Sci.,* 1963, 20: 28-34.

VIVAS, Eliseo. Nature, common sense and science. *Phil.Sci.,* 1938, 5: 300-9.

WALLACE, R.C. The changing values of science. *Science,* 1938, 88: 265-71.
The Maiben lecture delivered at the meeting of the American Association for the Advancement of Science, Ottawa, June 30, 1938.

WEAVER, Warren. The imperfections of science. *Amer.Scient.,* 1961, 49: 99-113.

WEAVER, Warren. Science and complexity. *Amer.Scient.,* 1948, 36: 536-44.

WHITE, Leslie A. Science is sciencing. *Phil.Sci.,* 1938, 5: 369-89.

WOJCIECHOWSKI, Jerzy A. L'Unité de la science. *Dialogue,* 1963, 2: 346-58.
An analysis of Jacques Ruytinx' "La Problématique philosophique de l'unité de la science".

Akd hypotheses and theories; explanation

ALEXANDER, Peter. Sensationalism and scientific explanation. v, 149 p., ill. New York: Humanities Press, 1963.
Reviewed by Peter Achinstein, *Isis,* 1964, 55: 448-9.

ALEXANDER, Peter. Speculations and theories. *Synthese,* 1963, 15: 187-203.

BANCROFT, Wilder D. Une loi universelle. *Rev.Sci.,* 1912, 50: 2e sem., 385-94.

BARTLEY, W.W., III. Achilles, the tortoise, and explanation in science and history. *Brit.J.Phil.Sci.,* 1962, 13: 15-33.

BAUCH, Bruno. Das Naturgesetz: ein Beitrag zur Philosophie der exakten Wissenschaften. viii, 76 p. (Wissenschaftliche Grundfragen. Philosophische Abhandlungen, 1) Leipzig: Teubner, 1924.

BRAITHWAITE, Richard Bevan. Scientific explanation. A study of the function of theory, probability and law in science. Based upon the Tarner Lectures, 1946. xii, 376 p. Cambridge/New York: Cambridge University Press, 1953. [CB 80/117]
Reprinted in the Harper Torchbook Series 1960.
Reviewed by E.T. Bell, *Scr.Math.,* 1955, 21: 282-3.

CRAIK, K.J.W. The nature of explanation. viii, 123 p. Cambridge University Press; New York: Macmillan Co., 1943. [CB 66/261]

DELEVSKY, J. La simplicité des lois. *Rev.Phil.*, 1934, 49: 232-73.

DINGLER, H. Ueber den Zusammenhang der a priorischen Gesetze mit der Erfahrung in den exakten Wissenschaften. *Atti IVº Congr.Int.Fil.* (Bologna, 1911), (2), p. 325-30. Genoa: 1913.

ESSERTIER, Daniel. Les formes inférieures de l'explication. iv, 358 p. Paris: Félix Alcan, 1927. [CB 24/523]

FRANK, Philipp. The variety of reasons for the acceptance of scientific theories. *Sci.Mon.*, 1954, 79: 139-45.

GEIRINGER, Hilda. Über die Wahrscheinlichkeit von Hypothesen. *J.Unified Sci.*, 1939, 8: 151-76.

GOODMAN, Nelson. Fact, fiction and forecast. 126 p. Cambridge, Mass.: Harvard University Press, 1955.
This discussion of "the nature of scientific laws and lawlike (or projectible) hypotheses" will be of interest to the philosopher of science.

GRÜNBAUM, Adolf. Temporally asymmetric principles, parity between explanation and prediction, and mechanism versus teleology. *Phil.Sci.*, 1962, 29: 146-74.

HANSON, Norwood Russell. On the symmetry between explanation and prediction. *Phil.Rev.*, 1959, 68: 349-58.

HENSON, Richard G. Discussion: Mr. [N.R.] Hanson on the symmetry of explanation and prediction. *Phil.Sci.*, 1963, 30: 60-1.
For Hanson's article *see* above.

HEYDE, Johannes Erich. Annahme und Möglichkeit. Vorgedanken zur Wissenschaftstheorie der Hypothese. *Phil.Natur.*, 1957, 4: 223-44.

KAHL, Russell. Studies in explanation: a reader in the philosophy of science. xi, 363 p. Englewood Cliffs, N.J.: Prentice-Hall, 1963.

LENOBLE, Robert. Types d'explication et types logiques au cours de l'histoire des sciences. *Act.XIe Congr.Int.Phil.* (Brussels, 1953), (6), p. 10-15. Amsterdam: North Holland Publishing Co., 1953.

MADDEN, Edward H. Discussion: Ernest Nagel's "Structure of science". *Phil.Sci.*, 1963, 30: 64-71.
For Nagel's work *see* below.

MEYERSON, Émile. De l'explication dans les sciences. 2 vol. xiv, 338 p.; 470 p. Paris: Payot, 1921.
Reviewed by H. Metzger, *Isis*, 1921-22, 4: 382-5.

MEYERSON, Emile. La tendance apriorique et l'expérience. *Rev. Phil.*, 1924, 97: 161-80.
These pages form the 22nd chapter of the author's "La déduction relativiste", *see* CBk.

NAGEL, Ernest. The structure of science. Problems in the logic of scientific explanation. xiii, 618 p. New York/Burlingame: Harcourt Brace and World, 1961.
Reviewed by J.J.C. Smart, *J.Phil.*, 1962, 59: 216-23; by Jon Wheatley, *Dialogue*, 1962, 1: 233-4; by R.B. Lindsay, *Phys.Today*, 1962, 15: no. 5, 71-2; for essay review by Madden, Edward H., *see* above.

NELSON, Everett J. A note on parsimony. *Phil.Sci.*, 1936, 3: 62-6.

NICKEL, Erwin. Was heisst für einen Naturforscher "verstehen"? *Phil.Natur.*, 1964, 8: 242-9.

OWEN, E.C. The nature of scientific and other hypotheses. *Bull.Brit.Soc.Hist.Sci.*, 1950, 1: 98-9.

RAHMAN, Fazlur. The concept of objectivity. *Pakistan Phil. J.*, October 1957, 1: 25-36.

RESCHER, Nicholas. On prediction and explanation. *Brit.J. Phil.Sci.*, 1958, 8: 281-90.

RESCHER, Nicholas. Scientific explanation. *Synthese*, 1962, 14: 200-15.

SCHILLER, F.C.S. Hypothesis. In: Singer, Charles, ed. Studies in the history and method of science, vol. 2, p. 46. Oxford: Clarendon Press, 1921.

SCHILPP, Paul Arthur. The nature of the "given". *Phil.Sci.*, 1935, 2: 128-38.

TREISMAN, Michel. Psychological explanation: the "private data" hypothesis. *Brit.J.Phil.Sci.*, 1962, 13: 130-43.

WEINBERG, Julius R. Are there ultimate simples? *Phil.Sci.*, 1935, 2: 387-99.

WOODGER, J.H. The technique of theory construction. vii, 81 p. (International Encyclopedia of Unified Science, 2: no. 5) Chicago: University of Chicago Press, 1939.

Ake scientific method

for logic and scientific method *see* Akk

ACHINSTEIN, Peter. Theoretical terms and partial interpretation. *Brit.J.Phil.Sci.*, 1963, 14: 89-105.

AMBACHER, Michel. Méthode de la philosophie de la nature. 233 p. (Bibliothèque de Philosophie Contemporaine) Paris: Presses Universitaires de France, 1961.
Reviewed by Vincent E. Smith, *Dialogue*, 1962, 1: 202-3.

BAUER, Edmond. Présentation du problème scientifique (l'expérience dans les sciences). *Rev.Syn.*, 1963, 84: 13-27.

BEVERIDGE, W.I.B. The art of scientific investigation. xii, 172 p., 4 pl. New York: Norton, 1950. [CB 77/363]

BIRKHOFF, George D. Intuition, reason and faith in science. *Science*, 1938, 88: 601-9; also in *Nature*, 1939, 143: 60-7.

BOULIGAND, Georges. L'expérience dans les sciences théoriques. *Rev.Syn.*, 1963, 34: 59-102.

BOUTROUX, P. En quel sens la recherche scientifique est elle une analyse? *Atti IVº Congr.Int.Fil.* (Bologna, 1911), (2), p. 419-23. Genoa: 1913.

BRIDGMAN, P.W. Operational analysis. *Phil.Sci.*, 1938, 5: 114-31.

BRIDGMAN, P.W. Science and common sense. *Sci.Mon.*, 1954, 79: 32-9.

BROWN, G. Burniston. Science, its method and its philosophy. 190 p., 8 pl. London: Allen and Unwin, 1950.

BUCHDAHL, Gerd. Induction and scientific method. *Mind*, 1951, 60: 16-34.

CALDER, Ritchie. Speculative research. *Discovery*, 1960, 21: 420-5.
Speculative research is defined and examined in the light of the history of the development of polythene.

COHEN, Morris Raphael. Reason and nature. An essay on the meaning of scientific method. xxv, 470 p. London: Kegan Paul, 1931

CONANT, James B. Science and common sense. xii, 372 p. New Haven: Yale University Press, 1951.
Reviewed by Conway Zirkle, *Isis*, 1951, 42: 269-71; by Eleanor R. Webster, *Arch.Int.Hist.Sci.*, 1953, 6: 93.

THE CONCEPT and the role of the model in mathematics and natural and social sciences. Proceedings of the Colloquium sponsored by the Division of Philosophy of Sciences of the International Union of History and Philosophy of Sciences organized at Utrecht, January, 1960, by Hans Freudenthal. 194 p. (Synthese Library) Dordrecht: D. Reidel Publishing Company; New York: Gordon and Breach, 1961. [CB 88/528]
Reviewed by R. Harré, *Hist.Sci.*, 1963, 2: 172-3.

DINGLER, Hugo. Das Experiment. Sein Wesen und seine Geschichte. viii, 263 p. München: E. Reinhardt, 1928.

DUBARLE, H.D. La synthèse inductive. *Arch.Inst.Int.Sci.Théor. Sér.A Bull.Acad.Int.Phil.Sci.*, 1. Problèmes de philosophie des sciences, 1, Les méthodes de la connaissance, p. 43-60. Discussion p. 61-9. (Actualités Scientifiques et Industrielles, 1059) Paris: Hermann, 1948.

EASTRUCCI, Carlo L. The scientific approach: basic principles of the scientific method. xi, 257 p. Cambridge, Mass.: Schenkman, 1963.

ELLSON, D.G. The scientists' criterion of true observation. *Phil.Sci.*, 1963, 30: 41-52.

EMERY, A. Dialectics versus mechanics. A Communist debate on scientific method. *Phil.Sci.*, 1935, 2: 9-38.

FIESER, Louis Frederick. The scientific method; a personal account of unusual projects in war and in peace. 242 p., pl. New York: Reinhold, 1964.

GEORGE, William Henry. The scientist in action. ix, 355 p. London: Williams & Norgate, 1936.
Reviewed by Robert K. Merton, *Isis*, 1938, 29: 159; by Norman R. Campbell, *Nature*, 1936, 138: 381-2.

GLANSDORFF, Maxime. Essai sur l'avènement de la raison expérimentale. Suivi de réflexions sur la philosophie naturelle de la liberté. 141 p. (Grande Collection de la Société Humaine) Bruxelles: Editions du Temple, 1948. [CB 76/390]

HAMBLIN, C.L. Discussion: questions aren't statements. *Phil.Sci.*, 1963, 30: 62.

HILDEBRAND, Joel H. Science in the making. 116 p. New York: Columbia University Press, 1957. [CB 83/278]
Paperback edition 1962.

JEVONS, W. Stanley. *See* Akk

KRAFT, Viktor. Die Grundformen der wissenschaftlichen Methoden. 304 p. (*Sitzungsber.Akad.Wiss.Wien Phil.Hist.Kl.*, 203: no. 3) Wien: Hölder-Pichler-Tempsky, 1926.
Reviewed by Wilhelm Burkamp, *Deut.Lit.Zeitung*, 1929, 6: 608-10.

LAMOUCHE, André. La méthode générale des sciences pures et appliquées. 298 p. Paris: Gauthier-Villars, 1924.

LAMOUCHE, André. Essai sur la méthode des sciences. *Rev. Phil.*, 1929, 54: 48-104.

LA VAISSIÈRE, Jules de. Méthodologie scientifique; méthodologie, dynamique, interne. 2, 109 p. (*Arch.Phil.* (Paris), 10) Paris: Beauchesne, 1933.
Reviewed by R.P., *Rev.Gén.Sci.*, 1935, 46: 96.

LE CHATELIER, Henry. De la méthode dans les sciences expérimentales. 319 p. Paris: Dunod, 1936.
Reviewed by Tenney L. Davis, *Isis*, 1937, 27: 519-22.

LE LIONNAIS, François. La méthode dans les sciences modernes. 343 p. (Numéro Hors Série de "Travail et Méthodes") Paris: Éditions Science et Industrie, 1958.
Reviewed by René Taton, *Rev.Hist.Sci.*, 1959, 12: 175-6.

LENZEN, Victor F. Procedures of empirical science. vii, 59 p. (International Encyclopedia of Unified Science, 1: no. 5) Chicago: University of Chicago Press, 1938.

LERNER, Daniel, ed. Parts and wholes. ix, 180 p. (The Hayden Colloquium on Scientific Method and Concept) New York: The Free Press of Glencoe, 1963.

LEWONTEN, R.C. Models, mathematics and metapnors. *Synthese*, 1963, 15: 222-4.

PÉRIÉTEANU, Alexandre. La méthode scientifique. 204 p. (Bibliothèque de Philosophie Contemporaine) Paris: Alcan, 1932. [CB 39/444]

PRESCOTT, C.H. The scientific method and its extension to systems of many degrees of freedom. *Phil.Sci.*, 1938, 5: 237-66.

RAMÓN Y CAJAL, Santiago. Regeln und Ratschläge zur wissenschaftlichen Forschung. Ins Deutsche übersetzt von D. Miskolzcy. 134 p. München: Reinhardt, 1933.

RAPPORT, Samuel; WRIGHT, Helen; ed. Science: method and meaning. xii, 258 p. New York: New York University Press, 1963. [CB 89/490]
Reviewed by J.R. Ravetz, *Arch.Int.Hist.Sci.*, 1964, 17: 173.

RITCHIE, Arthur David. Scientific method. An inquiry into the character and validity of natural laws. xiii, 204 p. London: Kegan Paul, 1923.

ROWLAND, John. Mysteries of science: a study of the limitations of the scientific method. ix, 214 p. New York: Philosophical Library, 1957. [CB 83/195]
Reviewed by J.C. Polkinghorne, *Phys.Today*, 1958, 11: no. 1, 35-6.

ROYCE, Joseph. The mechanical, the historical, and the statistical. *Science*, April 1914, 39: 551-66. [CB 6/451]

SACKSTEDER, William. Structural variation in science. *Synthese*, 1963, 15: 412-23.

SCHEFFLER, Israel. The anatomy of inquiry. Philosophical studies in the theory of science. xii, 332, v p., bibliogr. (Borzoi Books in the Philosophy of Science) New York: Alfred A. Knopf, 1963.

SCHILLER, F.C.S. Scientific discovery and logical proof. In: Singer, Charles, ed. Studies in the history and method of science, vol. 1, p. 235-89. Oxford: Clarendon Press, 1917.

SCHLESINGER, G. Method in the physical sciences. vii, 140 p. (International Library of Philosophy and Scientific Method) New York: Humanities Press, 1963.
Reviewed by M.F. Partridge, *Isis*, 1964, 55: 104-6.

SCHMIDT, Paul F. Some merits and misinterpretations of scientific method. *Sci.Mon.*, 1956, 82: 20-4.

SIMARD, Emile. La nature et la portée de la méthode scientifique. Exposé et textes choisis de philosophie des sciences. Préface de Mgr. Alphonse-Marie Parent, P.A. Dessin de René Thibault. 408 p. Quebec: Presses Universitaires Laval; Paris: J. Vrin, 1956. [CB 82/198]

SPILLER, G. A new system of scientific procedure. Being an attempt to ascertain, develop and systematize the general methods employed in modern enquiries at their best. ix, 441 p. London: Watts, 1921.

SUPPES, Patrick. A comparison of the meaning and uses of models in mathematics and the empirical sciences. *Synthese*, 1960, 12: 287-301.

VERNOTTE, Pierre. Les principes de la méthode scientifique. *Act.IIe Congr.Int.Phil.Sci.* (Zurich, 1954), p. 7-8. La Neuveville: Editions du Griffon, 1955.

WEINBERG, Alvin M. Criteria for scientific choice. *Minerva*, 1963, 1: 159-71.

WESTAWAY, F.W. Scientific method. Its philosophy and its practice. 5th ed. xxi, 588 p. London: Blackie; New York: Curl, 1937.
First published 1912; 2nd edition, 1919, reviewed by G. Sarton, *Isis*, 1921, 4: 119-22.

WOLF, Abraham. Essentials of scientific method. 2nd rev. ed. 174 p. London: George Allen and Unwin, 1928. [CB 18/604]
First publ. 1925.

ZICH, Otakar; MÁLEK, Ivan; TONDL, Ladislav. K metodologii experimentálních věd. [Concerning the methodology of experimental science. (In Czech)] 342 p. Praha: Nakladatelství Československé Akademie Věd, 1959.

Ake-c

BELL, A.E. Hypotheses non fingo. *Nature*, 1942, 149: 238-40.

BLAKE, Ralph M.; DUCASSE, Curt J.; MADDEN, Edward H. Theories of scientific method. The Renaissance through the nineteenth century. iv, 346 p. Seattle: University of Washington Press, 1960.
Reviewed by M.D. Grmek, *Arch.Int.Hist.Sci.*, 1963, 16: 78; in *Times Lit.Suppl.*, August 1960, 26: 551.

DINGLER, Hugo. *See* Ake

DUCASSÉ, Pierre. *See* Akw

FOWLER, W.S. The development of scientific method. xiii, 116 p. (Commonwealth and International Library of Science, Technology and Engineering, History of Science and Technology Division, 1) Oxford: Pergamon Press, 1962.
Reviewed by Olaf Pedersen, *Centaurus*, 1963, 9: 62.

LECLERCQ, René. Histoire et avenir de la méthode expérimentale. 138 p., ill. (Evolution des Sciences, 17) Paris: Masson, 1960.
Reviewed by Heinz Degen, *Naturwiss.Rundsch.*, 1961, 14: 449.

PELSENEER, Jean. Y-a-t-il une méthode scientifique? Ce que nous dit l'histoire des sciences. *Act.VIIe Congr.Int.Hist.Sci.* (Jerusalem, 1953), p. 465-8. Paris: Hermann, [n.d.]

SAIDLA, Leo E.; GIBBS, Warren E.; ed. Science and the scientific mind. xiv, 506 p. New York: McGraw-Hill, 1931.
Twenty-four essays by leading scientists, each dealing with the scientific method in its relation to the various phases of culture.

Ake-mzAf

KANTOR, J.R. History of science as scientific method. (Perspectives in Psychology, 15) *Psychol.Rec.*, 1960, 10: 187-9.

Ake-mzTke

HOSTELET, Georges. Confrontation entre la méthodologie scientifique des faits de nature et celle des faits d'activité humaine. *Compt.Rend.IIe Congr.Nat.Sci.* (Bruxelles, 1935), p. 60-7. Brussels: 1935.

HOSTELET, Georges. La méthodologie scientifique de l'investigation des faits de la nature et des faits de l'activité humaine. *Bull.Soc.Franç.Phil.*, 1935, 35: 1-3.

HOSTELET, Georges. La méthodologie comparée des sciences et des techniques. [1]. 2. La méthodologie de l'investigation scientifique des faits d'activité humaine. *Rev.Syn.*, 1956, 77: 279-310; 1958, 79: 67-102.

Akg inference; deduction and induction; probability

BELOT, Emile. Le danger de l'application du calcul des probabilités aux sciences de la nature et en particulier à l'astronomie. *Scientia*, 1919, 26: 242-6. [CB 9/496]

BROWN, G. Spencer. Probability and scientific inference. 154 p., ill. New York/London: Longmans, Green and Company, 1957.
Reviewed by Ernest Nagel, *Sci.Amer.*, 1957, 197: 155-62.

BUCHDAHL, Gerd. Induction and scientific method. *Mind*, 1951, 60: 16-34.

BUCHDAHL, Gerd. Inductive process and inductive inference. *Australasian J.Phil.*, 1956, 34: 164-81.

BURES, Charles E. The concept of probability. A critical survey of recent contributions. *Phil.Sci.*, 1938, 5: 1-20.

CHURCHMAN, C. West. Theory of experimental inference. ix, 292 p. New York: The Macmillan Co., 1948.
Reviewed by V.F. Lenzen, *Isis*, 1949, 40: 78; by Francis A.C. Sévier, *Scr.Math.*, 1952, 18: 273-5.

DOROLLE, Maurice. Les problèmes de l'induction. Préface de André Lalande. xii, 148 p. (Bibliothèque de Philosophie Contemporaine) Paris: Félix Alcan, 1926. [CB 22/255]

FEIGL, Herbert. The logical character of the principle of induction. *Phil.Sci.*, 1934, 1: 20-9.

GOBLOT, E. Théorie nouvelle du raisonnement déductif. *Atti IV° Congr.Int.Fil.* (Bologna, 1911), (2), p. 337-42. Genoa: 1913.

HARRÉ, R. Counter-induction. *Theoria*, 1963, 29: 244-6

HEPP, Maylon H. Thinking things through. An introduction to logic. xviii, 455 p. New York: Charles Scribner's Sons, 1956.
Part 3, which occupies about half the volume, deals with the methods of science and problems of induction.

HUNTINGTON, Edward V. The method of postulates. *Phil.Sci.*, 1937, 4: 482-95.

JEFFREYS, Harold. Scientific inference. 2nd ed. viii, 236 p. Cambridge University Press, 1957. (First published 1931; reissued with addenda, 1937.) [CB 83/190]

JUHOS, Bela. Die "Warscheinlichkeit" als physikalische Beschreibungsform. *Phil.Natur.*, 1957, 4: 297-336.

KATTSOFF, Louis Osgood. Postulational methods. *Phil.Sci.*, 1935, 2: 139-63; 1936, 3: 67-89.

KING-FARLOW, John. Toulmin's analysis of probability. *Theoria*, 1963, 29: 12-26.

KNEALE, William. Probability and induction. viii, 264 p. Oxford: Clarendon Press, 1949. [CB 75/97]

KYBURG, Henry E. Probability and randomness. *Theoria*, 1963, 29: 27-55.

KYBURG, Henry E. Probability and the logic of rational belief. 346 p., bibliogr. Middletown, Conn.: Wesleyan University Press, 1961.

KYBURG, Henry E.; NAGEL, Ernest; ed. Induction: some current issues. 220 p. (Proceedings of Symposium at Wesleyan University, June 1961). Middletown, Conn.: Wesleyan University Press, 1963.

LALANDE, André. Las teorías de la inducción y de la experimentación. Trad. José Ferrater Mora. 296 p. Buenos Aires: Losada, 1945.
Reviewed by M.B., *Minerva*, (Buenos Aires), 1945, 2: 209.
For original French edition *see* below.

LALANDE, André. Les théories de l'induction et de l'expérimentation. vi, 288 p. Paris: Boivin, 1929. [CB 26/227]

LAMOUCHE, A. Le principe d'harmonie. Essai de synthèse physico-mécanique. *Rev.Gén.Sci.*, 1923, 34: 172-81. [CB 15/244]
The author calls the inductive principle the principle of harmony.

LEBLANC, Hughes. The algebra of logic and the theory of deduction. *J.Phil.*, 1961, 58: 553-8.

MADDEN, Edward H.; KITELEY, Murray J. Postulates and meaning. *Phil.Sci.*, 1962, 29: 66-78.

NAGEL, Ernest. *See* Aks

POIRIER, René. Remarques sur la probabilité des inductions. 226 p. Paris: Vrin, 1931.

POPPER, Karl R. Creative and non-creative definitions in the calculus of probability. *Synthese*, 1963, 15: 167-86.

REICHENBACH, Hans. On probability and induction. *Phil.Sci.*, 1938, 5: 21-45.

REICHENBACH, Hans. Über die semantische und die Objekt-Auffassung von Wahrscheinlichkeitsausdrücken. *J.Unified Sci.*, 1939, 8: 50-68.

ROUGIER, Louis. Enoncés indéterminés, indécidables, contradictoires, vides de sens. *Proc.10th Int.Congr.Phil.* (Amsterdam, 1948), p. 610-17. Amsterdam: North Holland Publishing Co., 1949.

ROUGIER, Louis. La structure des théories déductives. xv, 136 p. Paris: Alcan, 1922.
Reviewed by Marcel Dufour, *Rev.Gén.Sci.*, 1922, 33: 628.

ROUSTAN, Désiré. Déduction et induction. *Atti IV° Congr.Int.Fil.* (Bologna, 1911), (2), p. 404-18. Genoa: 1913.

RUSSELL, Bertrand. Postulates of scientific inference. *Proc. 10th Int.Congr.Phil.* (Amsterdam, 1948), p. 33-41. Amsterdam: North Holland Publishing Co., 1949.

VON WRIGHT, Georg Henrik. The logical problem of induction. 2nd rev. ed. xii, 249 p. Oxford: Basil Blackwell; New York: MacMillan, 1957. [CB 83/195]
Reviewed by F.I.G. Rawlins, *Nature*, 1958, 181: 981.

WILLIAMS, Donald. The ground of induction. viii, 213 p. Cambridge, Mass.: Harvard University Press, 1947.
Reviewed by V.F. Lenzen, *Isis*, 1947, 38: 128-9.

Akh quantification and statistical aspects

HILLMAN, Donald J. The measurement of simplicity. *Phil.Sci.*, 1962, 29: 225-52.

KUHN, Thomas S. The function of measurement in modern physical science. *Isis*, 1961, 52: 161-93.

MARCH, Lucien. Les principes de la méthode statistique. Avec quelques applications aux sciences naturelles et à la science des affaires. 808, xii p., 50 fig. Paris: Alcan, 1930.

SIMIAND, François. La statistique comme moyen d'expérimentation et de preuve. *J.Soc.Statis.Paris*, February 1921, 37-49.

WILKS, Samuel S. Some aspects of quantification in science. *Isis*, 1961, 52: 135-42.

WILKS, Samuel S. Statistical aspects of the design of experiments. *Proc.Amer.Phil.Soc.*, 1955, 99: 169-73.

WOOLF, Harry. The conference on the history of quantification in the sciences. *Isis*, 1961, 52: 133-4.

WOOLF, Harry, ed. Quantification. A history of the meaning of measurement in the natural and social sciences. 224 p. Indianapolis/New York: Bobbs-Merrill, 1961.
Reviewed by Mary Hesse, *Hist.Sci.*, 1963, 2: 152-5.

Yearbook of Research and Statistical Methodology. Books and Reviews. (2nd ed. by Oscar Krisen Buros). 383, xx p. Highland Park, N.J.: Gryphon Press, 1941.
Reviewed by Helen M. Walker, *Isis*, 1943, 34: 375-7.
Volume 1 entitled *Research and Statistical Methodology*; continued as *Statistical Methodology Reviews*.

Akk logic and foundations of science

ACHINSTEIN, Peter. The identity hypothesis. *Brit.J.Phil. Sci.*, 1962, 13: 167-71.

BENJAMIN, A. Cornelius. The logical structure of science. 344 p. (Psyche Monographs. 9) London: Kegan Paul, 1936. [CB 51/249]
Reviewed by H.T. Davis, *Isis*, 1938, 29: 461-4.

BOLL, Marcel. La logique et sa caricature. 49 p. Paris: Rieder, 1935.
Reviewed by Harry Malisoff, *Phil.Sci.*, 1936, 3: 130.

BRONOWSKI, J. The logic of experiment. *Nature*, 1953, 171: 194-5.

BUSHNELL, J.C. The logic of the sciences. *Monist*, 1919, 29: 481-508.

CARMICHAEL, R.D. The logic of discovery. ix, 280 p. Chicago: Open Court, 1930.
Reviewed by H.T. Davis, *Isis*, 1931, 15: 373-6.

CARMICHAEL, R.D. The structure of exact thought. *Monist*, 1924, 34: 63-95.

CARNAP, Rudolf. Abriss der Logistik. Mit besonderer Berücksichtigung der Relationstheorie und ihrer Anwendungen. vi, 114 p. (Schriften zur wissenschaftlichen Weltauffassung, 2) Wien: Springer, 1929.
Reviewed by Adolf Fraenkel, *Deut.Lit.Zeitung*, 1930, 1: 89-90.

CARNAP, Rudolf. Die Aufgabe der Wissenschaftslogik. 30 p. (Einheitswissenschaft, 3) Wien: Gerold, 1934.

CARNAP, Rudolf. Logical foundations of the unity of science. In: International Encyclopedia of Unified Science 1: no. 1, p. 42-62. Chicago: University of Chicago Press, 1938.

CARNAP, Rudolf. Le problème de la logique de la science: science formelle et science du réel. Traduction du général Ernest Vouillemin. 39 p. Paris: Hermann, 1935.
Reviewed by Hélène Metzger, *Archeion*, 1936, 18: 104-8.

COHEN, Morris R.; NAGEL, Ernest. An introduction to logic and scientific method. xii, 467 p. London: Routledge; New York: Harcourt, Brace, 1934.
Reviewed by Charles Mâlik, *Isis*, 1935, 23: 284-7; and in *Nature*, 1935, 135: 51.

DUBOS, René. Logic and choices in science. *Proc.Amer.Phil. Soc.*, 1963, 107: 365-74.

ENRIQUES, Federigo. Per la storia della logica: i principii e l'ordine della scienza nel concetto dei pensatori matematici. 302 p. Bologna: Nicola Zanichelli, 1922.
Reviewed by H.M. Sheffer, *Isis*, 1923, 5: 469-70.
French translation Paris: Etienne Chiron, 1926; German translation Leipzig: Teubner, 1927.

HANSON, Norwood Russell. Scientists and logicians: a confrontation. *Science*, 1962, 138: 1311-14.

HILBERT, D. La connaissance de la nature et la logique. *Enseign.Math.*, 1931, 30: 22-33

JEVONS, W. Stanley. The principles of science. A treatise on logic and scientific method. (2nd ed., 1877) with a new introd. by Ernest Nagel. liii, 786 p. New York: Dover, 1958. [CB 84/373]
Reviewed by Herbert Dingle, *Arch.Int.Hist.Sci.*, 1958, 11: 405-6; by M. de Tollenaere, *Rev.Quest.Sci.*, 1959, 20: 319-20; by William Kneale, *Brit.J.Phil.Sci.*, 1960, 11: 260-1.

JOHNSON, William Ernest. Logic. Part 3. The logical foundation of science. xxxvi, 192 p. Cambridge University Press, 1924.
Reviewed by H. Wildon Carr, *Nature*, 1924, 113: 522.

JOJA, Athanase. Le principe d'identité concrète comme fondement logique de la science. *Proc.10th Int.Congr.Hist.Sci.* (Ithaca, 1962), (1), p. 253-5. Paris: Hermann, 1964.

KAUFMANN, Felix. The logical rules of scientific procedure. *Phil.Phenomenol.Res.*, 1942, 3: 457-71.

KÖRNER, Stephan. Conceptual thinking. A logical enquiry viii, 301 p. New York: Dover Publications, 1959.
Reviewed by Herbert Dingle, *Arch.Int.Hist.Sci.*, 1960, 13: 140.

LALANDE, André. Du parallélisme formel des sciences normatives. *Atti IV° Congr.Int.Fil.* (Bologna, 1911), (2), p. 477-82. Genoa: 1913.

NAGEL, Ernest. Some theses in the philosophy of logic. *Phil. Sci.*, 1938, 5: 46-51.

NORRIS, O.O. The logic of science and technology. *Phil.Sci.*, 1936, 3: 286-306.

NORTHROP, F.S.C. The logic of the sciences and the humanities. xi, 402 p. New York: Macmillan, 1947; reprinted New York: Meridian Books, 1959.
Reviewed by P.W. Bridgman, *Isis*, 1948, 39: 192-4.

POPPER, Karl R. The logic of scientific discovery. 480 p. London: Hutchinson and Co., Ltd.; New York: Basic Books, Inc., 1959.
Reviewed by Y. Bar-Hillel and S. Sambursky, *Isis*, 1960, 51: 91-4; for other reviews *see* CB 85/382.

SAMBURSKY, S. Some comments on 'Imaginary experiments'. *Brit. J.Phil.Sci.*, 1960, 11: 62-4.
Comment on Appendix xi of Karl Popper's "The logic of scientific discovery", *see* above.

SAUER, Wilhelm. Grundlagen der Wissenschaft und der Wissenschaften. Eine logische und sozialphilosophische Untersuchung. xvi, 439 p. Berlin-Grunewald: Dr. Walther Rothschild, 1926.
Reviewed by H. Wieleitner, *Mitt.Gesch.Med.*, 1926, 25: 281.

SMART, Harold R. The logic of science. viii, 237 p. New York: 1931.

SMITH, Vincent Edward, ed. The logic of science. 90 p. New York: St. John's University Press, 1964.

TARSKI, Alfred. Introduction to logic and to the methodology of deductive sciences. xvii, 239 p. New York: Oxford University Press, 1941.
Reviewed by Keith R. Symon, *Isis*, 1941, 33: 546-8.

WHEELER, Raymond Holder. Organismic logic in the history of science. *Phil.Sci.*, 1936, 3: 26-61.

YOURGRAU, Wolfgang. On the logical status of so-called thought-experiments. *Proc.10th Int.Congr.Hist.Sci.* (Ithaca, 1962), (1), p. 359-62. Paris: Hermann, 1958.

Akm verification and falsification

ACHINSTEIN, Peter. Confirmation theory, order, and periodicity. *Phil.Sci.*, 1963, 30: 17-35.

BAVINK, Bernhard. Was ist Wahrheit in den Naturwissenschaften? 88 p. Wiesbaden: Brockhaus, 1947. [CB 71/116]

BENJAMIN, A. Cornelius. Philosophy of science: the problem of factual truth. In: Winn, Ralph B., ed. American philosophy. New York: Philosophical Library, 1955.

DINGLER, Hugo. Das Geltungsproblem als Fundament aller strengen Naturwissenschaften und das Irrationale. *Naturwissenschaft, Religion, Weltanschauung, Arbeitstag.Gmelin Inst.Anorg.Chem.Grenz.* (Clausthal, 1948), p. 273-97. Clausthal: Gmelin Verlag, 1949

FRANK, Philipp, ed. The validation of scientific theories. xi, 242 p. Boston: Beacon Press, 1957. [CB 83/189]

FRANKARD, P. Analyse critique de la notion de validité. Préface by R. Buyse. 160 p. Louvain: Nauwelaerts, 1958.
Reviewed by J.-M. de Buck, *Rev.Quest.Sci.*, 1959, 20: 319.

GIEDYMIN, Jerzy. Reliability of informants. *Brit.J.Phil.Sci.*, 1962-63, 13: 287-302.

GOBLOT, Edmond. Le système des sciences (le vrai, l'intelligible, le réel). 259 p. Paris: Armand Colin, 1922.
Reviewed by L. Guinet, *Isis*, 1922, 4: 565.

GREENWOOD, David. Truth and meaning. xii, 114 p. New York: Philosophical Library, 1957.

GRÜNBAUM, Adolf. The falsifiability of theories: Total or partial? A contemporary evaluation of the Duhem-Quine thesis. *Synthese*, 1962, 14: 17-34.

KAUFMANN, Felix. Verification, meaning and truth. *Phil. Phenomenol.Res.*, 1943, 4: 267-83.

KING-FARLOW, John. Truth preference and neuter propositions. *Phil.Sci.*, 1963, 30: 53-9.

LEPLEY, Ray. The verifiability of facts and values. *Phil. Sci.*, 1938, 5: 310-20.

LEPLEY, Ray. Verifiability of value. ix, 267 p. New York: Columbia University Press, 1944. [CB 68/60]

LE ROY, Edouard. La pensée intuitive. 2 vol. 1. Au delà du discours. vii, 204 p.; 2. Invention et vérification. 296 p. (Bibliothèque de la Revue des Cours et Conférences) Paris: Boivin, 1929-30. [CB 33/393]

LEVI, I. Corroboration and rules of acceptance. *Brit.J. Phil.Sci.*, 1962, 13: 307-13.

LEVI, I. On the seriousness of mistakes. *Phil.Sci.*, 1962, 29: 47-65.

MACKIE, J.L. The paradox of confirmation. *Brit.J.Phil.Sci.*, 1962-63, 13: 265-77.

MACLEOD, Andries H.D. What is a true assertion? *Theoria*, 1947, 13: 183-214.

RESCHER, Nicholas. A theory of evidence. *Phil.Sci.*, 1958, 25: 83-94.

ROSENTHAL-SCHNEIDER, Ilse. The interpretation of scientific evidence. *Australian J.Sci.*, 1947, 9: 161-6.

SAPPER, Karl. Das Element der Wirklichkeit und die Welt der Erfahrung. Grundlinien einer anthropozentrischen Naturphilosophie. xv, 250 p. München: Beck, 1924.
Reviewed by M. Kronenberg, *Naturwissenschaften*, 1926, 735-8.

UEXKÜLL, Thure von; GRASSI, Ernesto. Wirklichkeit als Geheimnis und Auftrag. Die Exaktheit der Naturwissenschaften und die philosophische Erfahrung. 130 p. Bern: Francke, 1945.
Reviewed by H. Kunz, *Experientia*, 1946, 2: 72.

WISDOM, J.O. The refutability of "irrefutable" laws. *Brit. J.Phil.Sci.*, 1962, 13: 303-6.

Akn linguistic and semantic problems

ADAMS, George P.; DENNES, William R.; MacKAY, Donald S.; ed. Meaning and interpretation. Lectures delivered before the Philosophical Union of the University of California, 1948-1949. vi, 352 p. Berkeley: University of California Press, 1950. [CB 79/169]

ALLENDE LEZAMA, Luciano. Lenguaje cientifico. Introducción a la epistemologia y metodologia de las ciencias. 107 p., 10 fig. Buenos Aires: El Ateneo, 1942. [CB 75/86]

BENTLEY, Arthur F. Behavior, knowledge, fact. xii, 391 p. Bloomington, Ind.: Principia Press, 1935. [CB 46/598]
Explores the linguistic conditioning of science and knowledge.

BLOOMFIELD, Leonard. Linguistic aspects of science. viii, 59 p. (International Encyclopaedia of Unified Science, 1: no. 4) Chicago: University of Chicago Press, 1939.

BLOOMFIELD, Leonard. Linguistic aspects of science. *Phil. Sci.*, 1935, 2: 499-517.

CARNAP, Rudolf. Introduction to semantics. x, 256 p. (Studies in Semantics, 1) Cambridge, Mass.: Harvard University Press, 1942.
Reviewed by Keith R. Symon, *Isis*, 1943, 34: 229.

CARNAP, Rudolf. The logical syntax of language. Translated from the German by Amethe Smeaton (Countess von Zeppelin). xvi, 352 p. New York: Harcourt, Brace, 1937.
Reviewed by Henry S. Leonard, *Isis*, 1938, 29: 163-7.
German original Wien: Springer, 1934.

CARNAP, Rudolf. La science et la métaphysique devant l'analyse logique du langage. Traduction du général Ernest Vouillemin. Introduction de Marcel Boll. 45 p. (Actualités Scientifiques et Industrielles, 172) Paris: Hermann, 1934.
Reviewed by L.P., *Rev.Gén.Sci.*, 1935, 46: 95.

FENSTAD, Jens Erik. Notes on synonymy. *Synthese*, 1962, 14: 35-77.

GRANGER, Gilles-G. Logique, langage, communication. In: *Hommage à Gaston Bachelard*, p. 31-57. Paris: Presses Universitaires de France, 1957.

HARDING, T. Swann. Science at the tower of Babel. *Phil.Sci.*, 1938, 5: 338-53.

JANET, Pierre. L'intelligence avant le langage. 292 p. (Bibliothèque de Philosophie Scientifique) Paris: Flammarion, 1936.

KORZYBSKI, Alfred. Science and sanity. An introduction to non-Aristotelian systems and general semantics. xx, 798 p. Lancaster: Science Printing Co., 1933.
Reviewed by T.E. Bell, *Amer.Math.Mon.*, 1934, 41: 570-3.

LENNEBERG, Eric H. The relationship of language to the formation of concepts. *Synthese*, 1962, 14: 103-9.

RAPOPORT, Anatol. Science and the goals of man: a semantic orientation. 290 p. New York: Harper, 1950. [CB 77/364]

ROUGIER, Louis. La métaphysique et le language. 252 p. Paris: Flammarion, 1960.

SELLARS, Wilfrid. Naming and saying. *Phil.Sci.*, 1962, 29: 7-26.

TURBAYNE, Colin Murray. The myth of metaphor. ix, 224 p. New Haven/London: Yale University Press, 1962.
Reviewed by Silvestro Marcucci, *Physis*, 1962, 4: 396-9.

Akq classification in science

BETH, E.W. Science and classification. *Synthese*, 1959, 11: 231-44.

BLISS, Henry Evelyn. The organization of knowledge and the system of the sciences. With an introduction by John Dewey. xx, 433 p. New York: Holt, 1929.
Reviewed by George Sarton, *Isis*, 1930, 13: 378-9.

BLISS, Henry Evelyn. The system of the sciences and the organization of knowledge. *Phil.Sci.*, 1935, 2: 86-103.

COUNILLON, Jean-François. Réflexions sur la classification des sciences. *Rev.Syn.*, 1958, 79: 53-66.

GUICHOT Y SIERRA, Alejandro. Noticia historica de las classificaciones de las ciencias y de las artes. 200 p. Sevilla: Artes graficas, 1912.

HARA, Mitsuo. [Classification of natural sciences. (In Japanese)] *J.Hist.Sci.Japan*, 1953, no. 26, July, 39-46; no. 27, November, 6-14.

KEDROW, B. [On the problem of the classification of sciences. (In Polish. Summary in English)]. *Stud.Mater.Dziej.Nauk. Pol.*, 1956, no. 4, 5-31.

LE CORBEILLER, Philippe. Stars, proteins and nations. *Atlantic Mon.*, December 1946, 6 p.
Restatement of the Comtian classification or hierarchy of sciences.

MALISOFF, William Marias. Arranging the sciences. 1. An experiment; 2. Another experiment. *Phil.Sci.*, 1937, 4: 261-4, 1 fig.; 1938, 5: 390-2.

NATUCCI, A. Specimine de classificatione de scientias. *Schola Vita*, 1931, 6: 241-3. [CB 35/294]

NAVILLE, Adrien. Classification des sciences. Les idées maîtresses des sciences et leurs rapports. 3rd rev. ed. iv, 322 p. Paris: Alcan, 1920.
Reviewed by George Sarton, *Isis*, 1921, 4: 118.

OPPENHEIM, Paul. Die natürliche Ordnung der Wissenschaften. Grundgesetze der vergleichenden Wissenschaftslehre. viii, 288 p., ill. Jena: Gustav Fischer, 1926. [CB 21/565]

PACOTTE, Julien. Le réseau arborescent, schème primordial de la pensée. 54 p. (Actualités Scientifiques et Industrielles, 429) Paris: Hermann, 1936.

RUSSO, François. Introduction à l'étude de la structure des sciences et techniques du monde physique. *Thalès*, 1948, 5: 26-39.

RUSSO, François. Le système des sciences et des techniques et l'évolution de la classification des sciences. *Trav. Méth.*, 1958, no. 1 (hors série), 17-23.

TATARKIEWICZ, L. Sciences nomologiques et typologiques: essais d'une classification des sciences. *Proc.10th Int. Congr.Phil.* (Amsterdam, 1948), p. 621-3. Amsterdam: North Holland Publishing Co., 1949.

Aks epistemology

AYER, A.J. The foundations of empirical knowledge. x, 275 p. New York: Macmillan, 1940. [CB 61/396]

BACHELARD, Gaston. Essai sur la connaissance approchée. 312 p. Paris: J. Vrin, 1927. [CB 24/522]

BARRY, Frederick. The scientific habit of thought. An informal discussion of the source and character of dependable knowledge. xiii, 358 p. New York: Columbia University Press, 1927.
Reviewed by George Sarton, *Isis*, 1930, 14: 265-8.

BARTHEL, Ernst. Die Welt als Spannung und Rhythmus. Erkenntnistheorie, Ästhetik, Naturphilosophie, Ethik. xviii, 411 p. Leipzig: Noske, 1932.

BEGGEROW, Hans. Die Erkenntnis der Wirklichkeiten. xxvi, 558 p., 3 pl. Halle: Max Niemeyer, 1927.
Reviewed by Julius Schuster, *Arch.Gesch.Math.Naturwiss. Tech.*, 1929, 11: 332-5.

BLANSHARD, Brand. Reason and analysis. 505 p. (The Paul Carus Lectures, Series 12) La Salle, Ill.: Open Court Publishing Company, 1962.

CASSIRER, Ernst. Erkenntnistheorie nebst den Grenzfragen der Logik. *Jahrb.Phil.*, 1913, 1: 1-59, 365-6.

CASSIRER, Ernst. The philosophy of symbolic forms. Transl. by Ralph Manheim. 3 vol. Newhaven: Yale University Press, 1953-57.
Translation of: Philosophie der symbolischen Formen. 4 pt. Berlin: 1923-31.
For volume 3. The phenomenology of knowledge *see* CB 83/195.

CENTRE INTERNATIONAL DE SYNTHÈSE. XXe semaine de synthèse: notion de structure et structure de la connaissance, 18-27 avril 1956. xxiv, 436 p. Paris: Albin Michel (avec le concours du Centre National de la Recherche Scientifique), 1957. [CB 83/189]
Reviewed by J. Dopp, *Rev.Quest.Sci.*, 1958, 129: 157-8.

COLLINGWOOD, Robin George. Speculum mentis, or the map of knowledge. 327 p. Oxford: Clarendon Press, 1924.
Reviewed by F.S. Marvin, *Nature*, 1925, 115: 79.

DESSAUER, Friedrich. Naturwissenschaftliches Erkennen. 445 p. Frankfurt/Main: Josef Knecht, 1958.
Reviewed by Joseph Meurers, *Phil.Natur.*, 1959, 5: 369-73.

DOCKX, S.I. Vers une synthèse moderne du savoir. *Arch.Inst. Int.Sci.Théor.Sér.A Bull.Acad.Int.Phil.Sci.*, 7. Problèmes de philosophie des sciences, p. 7-46. (Actualités Scientifiques et Industrielles, 1109) Paris: Hermann, 1950.

DRIESCH, Hans. Wissen und Denken, ein Prolegomenon zu aller Philosophie. 2nd ed. vi, 152 p. Leipzig: E. Reinicke, 1922.

FRANK, Philipp, *et al.* Contributions to the analysis and synthesis of knowledge. (Published in cooperation with the Institute for the Unity of Science). *Proc.Amer.Acad.Arts Sci.*, 1951, 80: 1-112.
Reviewed by V.F. Lenzen, *Isis*, 1952, 43: 87.

GOMPERZ, Heinrich. Limits of cognition and exigencies of action. *Univ.Calif.Publ.Phil.*, 1938, 16: 53-70.

GOODMAN, Nelson. The structure of appearance. xv, 315 p., fig. Cambridge, Mass.: Harvard University Press, 1951.
Reviewed by Morton White, *Isis*, 1952, 43: 85-7.

HELMER, Olaf; RESCHER, Nicholas. On the epistemology of the inexact sciences. (U.S. Air Force Project). v, 40 p. Santa Monica, Calif.: Rand Corporation, 1960.

HUBERT, René. Essai sur la systématisation du savoir scientifique. *Rev.Métaphys Morale*, 1922, 29: 311-58. [CB 14/565]

KRAFT, Viktor. Erkenntnislehre. v, 375 p. Vienna: Springer-Verlag, 1960.
Reviewed by P.K. Feyerabend, *Brit.J.Phil.Sci.*, 1962, 13: 319-23.

LE CORBEILLER, Philippe. A new pattern in science. *J.Chem. Educ.*, 1951, 28: 553-5. [CB 78/184]
The author believes that knowledge of certain subjects can be complete on a certain level.

LEWIS, Clarence I. Mind and the world order. Outline of a theory of knowledge. xiv, 446 p. New York: Dover Publications, 1956.
First publ. 1929.
Reviewed by Leo Apostel, *Arch.Int.Hist.Sci.*, 1957, 10: 123-7.

MANLEY, R.M. Synthetische Naturerkenntnis. 66 p., 3 fig. Cleveland: 1931.
Reviewed by E.O. von Lippmann, *Chem.Zeitung*, 1931, 55: 821.

MARTIN, Roger. Epistémologie et philosophie. *Hommage à Gaston Bachelard*, p. 59-69. Paris: Presses Universitaires de France, 1957.

MEYERSON, Emile. Le sens commun vise-t-il à la connaissance? *Rev.Métaphys.Morale*, 1923, 30: 12-28. [CB 14/559]

MILLER, Hugh. History and science. A study of the relation of historical and theoretical knowledge. xi, 201 p. Berkeley: University of California Press, 1939.
Reviewed by F.S. Marvin, *Nature*, 1940, 146: 316.

MOCHI, Alberto. La connaissance scientifique. 272 p. Paris: Alcan, 1927. [CB 24/522]

NAGEL, Ernest. Probability and the theory of knowledge. *Phil.Sci.*, 1939, 6: 212-53.

NORRIS, O.O. A preamble to an organismic theory of knowledge. *Phil.Sci.*, 1934, 1: 460-78.

PARDO, Raymundo. El carácter evolutivo de la razón en la epistemologia de L. Rougier y en la epistemologia del empirismo filosófico. Estudio comparativo. 12 p. Buenos Aires: Sociedad Argentina de Filosofía, 1954.

PARDO, Raymundo. Del origén a la esencia del conocimiento. Los datos de la ciencia y el problema del mundo exterior. 117 p. Buenos Aires: Sociedad Argentina de Filosofía, 1954.

PARDO, Raymundo. Ensayo sobre los integrantes racionales (esquema). Con estudios críticos de los profesores Amadeo A. Mininni, Alberto J. Sanz, Anselmo Leoz, y de los ingenieros Carlos Ferri, Edelmiro Valdés y Juan Carlos Grimberg. Prólogo del Dr. Carlos E. Prélat. 190 p. Buenos Aires: Sociedad Argentina de Filosofía, 1949.
A publication of the Sección, Epistemologia y historia de la ciencia, of the Sociedad Argentina de Filosofía.

POLANYI, Michael. Personal knowledge: towards a post-critical philosophy. xiv, 428 p. London: Routledge and Kegan Paul; Chicago: University of Chicago Press, 1958.
Reviewed by J.H. Woodger, *Brit.J.Hist.Sci.*, 1960, 11: 65-71; for other reviews *see* CB 84/301, CB 85/382 and 465.

POPPER, Karl R. Three views concerning human knowledge. In: Contemporary British Philosophy, 3rd ser., p. 355-88. London: Allen and Unwin, 1956.

POS, H.J. Le symbolisme de la connaissance et l'idée de l'unité du savoir. *Arch.Inst.Int.Sci.Théor.Sér.A Bull.Acad. Int.Phil.Sci.*, 1. Problèmes de philosophie des sciences, 1, Les méthodes de la connaissance, p. 11-16. Discussion p. 25-41. (Actualités Scientifiques et Industrielles, 1059) Paris: Hermann, 1948.

REID, Louis Arnaud. Knowledge and truth: an epistemological essay. xiii, 243 p. London: Macmillan, 1923.

RENAUD, Paul. Structure de la pensée et définitions expérimentales. 24 p. (Exposés de Philosophie des Sciences, 2) Paris: Hermann, 1934.
Reviewed by G.P., *Rev.Gén.Sci.*, 1935, 46: 216.

ROUGIER, Louis. Les paralogismes du rationalisme. Essai sur la théorie de la connaissance. xiv, 540 p. Paris: Alcan, 1920.

ROUGIER, Louis. Traité de la connaissance. 450 p. Paris: Gauthiers-Villars, 1955.
Reviewed by J. Porte, *Arch.Int.Hist.Sci.*, 1958, 11: 52-5.

RUSSELL, Bertrand. Human knowledge. Its scope and limits. 538 p. London: Allen and Unwin, 1948.
Reviewed by A.D. Ritchie, *Nature*, 1949, 163: 267-8; by Robert Eisler, *Arch.Int.Hist.Sci.*, 1949, 2: 754-8.

RUSSELL, Bertrand. An inquiry into meaning and truth. 445 p. New York: Norton, 1940. [CB 61/396]

SCHLEGEL, Richard. On the possibility of universal knowledge. *J.Gen.Educ.*, 1952, 6: 129-35.

SCHLICK, Moritz. Sur le fondement de la connaissance. Trad. du Général Vouillemin. 56 p. Paris: Hermann, 1935.

SCHNEIDER, Friedrich. Die Problemsituation der Erkenntnistheorie und das naturwissenschaftliche Erkennen. *Phil. Natur.*, 1957, 4: 245-65.

STACE, Walter Terence. The theory of knowledge and existence. xii, 455 p. Oxford: Clarendon Press, 1932.
Reviewed by H.T. Davis, *Isis*, 1934, 20: 485-8.

STRONG, Charles Augustus. A theory of knowledge. xii, 102 p. New York: Macmillan, 1923.

TURRÓ, R. Les origines de la connaissance. 274 p. Paris: Alcan, 1914.

WERKMEISTER, W.H. The basis and structure of knowledge. xi, 451 p. New York: Harper, 1948.
Reviewed by Philipp Frank, *Isis*, 1951, 42: 68.

WHITEHEAD, Alfred North. Modes of thought. ix, 241 p. New York: The Macmillan Co., 1938.
Reprinted New York: Capricorn Books, 1958.
Reviewed by M.F. Ashley Montagu, *Isis*, 1947, 32: 239.

WOOD, Ledger. The analysis of knowledge. 263 p. Princeton, N.J.: Princeton University Press, 1941. [CB 62/73]

ZIEHEN, Theodor. Erkenntnistheorie auf psychophysiologischer und physikalischer Grundlage. xi, 571 p. Jena: 1913.

ZINKERNAGEL, Peter. Conditions for description. Transl. by Olaf Lindum from the Danish. 264 p. (International Library of Philosophy and Scientific Method) New York: Humanities Press, 1962.
Translation of Omverdensproblemat (Copenhagen: G.E.C. Gad, 1957).

Aks-c

BLOCH, Ernst. Ueber Wirklichkeit und Wahrheit. Ein Beitrag zur entwicklungsgeschichtlichen Begründung der Erkenntnistheorie. *Ann.Naturphil.*, 1919, 14: 54-82.

BOLL, Marcel; PAGES, Jean Claude. Les étapes de la connaissance. 91 p. (Actualités scientifiques et industrielles, 1193) Paris: 1953.

BUZELLO, H. Kritische Untersuchungen von Ernst Mach's Erkenntnistheorie. 94 p. (*Kant Stud.*, 23. Ergänzungsheft) Berlin: 1911.

CASSIRER, Ernst. The problem of knowledge: philosophy, science, and history since Hegel. Transl. by William H. Woglom and Charles W. Hendel. With a preface by Charles W. Hendel. 334 p. New Haven: Yale University Press, 1950.
Reviewed by Philip P. Wiener, *J.Hist.Ideas*, 1951, 12: 305-9.
Spanish translation Mexico: Fondo de Cultura Económica, 1948.

DÜRR, Karl. Wesen und Geschichte der Erkenntnistheorie. 176 p. Zurich: Seldwyla, 1924. [CB 16/309]

ENRIQUES, Federigo. La théorie de la connaissance scientifique de Kant à nos jours. 46 p. (Actualités Scientifiques et Industrielles, 638) Paris: Hermann, 1938.

HÖNIGSWALD, Richard. Geschichte der Erkenntnistheorie. vi, 192 p. (Geschichte der Philosophie in Längsschnitten, 9) Berlin: Junker und Dünnhaupt, 1933.

LOWY, H. Die Erkenntnistheorie von Popper-Lynkeus und ihre Beziehung zur Machschen Philosophie. *Naturwissenschaften*, 1932, 20: 767-70.

MILMED, Bella K. Kant and current philosophical issues: some modern developments of his theory of knowledge. 262 p., bibliogr. New York: New York University Press, 1961.
Reviewed by Stephen Korner, *J.Phil.*, 1962, 59: 802-5.

Aks-mzOP

KESTNER, Otto. Die Abhängigkeit der wissenschaftlichen Erkenntnis von der Eigenart unserer Sinnesorgane. *Sudhoffs Arch.*, 1934, 27: 267-76.

Akt philosophical systems

BACHELARD, Gaston. Le rationalisme appliqué. 215 p. Paris: Presses Universitaires de France, 1949.
Reviewed by Bernard Rochot, *Rev.Hist.Sci.*, 1951, 4: 91-2.

BECK, M. L'irrationalisme actuel. Sa nature, ses origines et le moyen de le surmonter. *Rev.Métaphys.Morale*, 1934, 41: 459-70.

BLANCHÉ, Robert. La science physique et la réalité. Réalisme, positivisme, mathématisme. 213 p. Paris: Presses Universitaires de France, 1948.
Reviewed by D. Dubarle, *Rev.Quest.Sci.*, 1949, 10: 158-60.

BRUNSCHVICG, Léon. L'orientation du rationalisme. Représentation, concept, jugement. *Rev.Métaphys.Morale*, 1920, 27: 261-343. [CB 13/298]

CARUS, Paul. The mechanistic principle and the non-mechanical. An inquiry into fundamentals with extracts from representatives of either sides. 128 p. Chicago: Open Court, 1913.

CARUS, Paul. The monism of *The Monist* compared with Professor Haeckel's monism. *Monist*, 1913, 23: 435-9.

ELLIOT, Hugh Samuel Roger. Modern science and materialism. 211 p. London/New York: Longmans, 1919.

ENRIQUES, Federigo. Scienza e razionalismo. 302 p. Bologna: Nicola Zanichelli, 1912.
Reviewed by Aldo Mieli, *Isis*, 1913, 1: 541-2.

FEIBLEMAN, James K. Philosophical empiricism from the scientific standpoint. *Dialectica*, 1962, 16: 5-14.

JOERGENSEN, Joergen. The development of logical empiricism. iii, 100 p. (International Encyclopedia of Unified Science, 2: no. 9) Chicago: University of Chicago Press, 1951.

KEETON, Morris T. Edmund Montgomery - pioneer of organicism. *J.Hist.Ideas*, 1947, 8: 309-41.

KLASSICHESKOE proizvedenie marksistskoi filosofii. [A classic of Marxist philosophy. (In Russian)] *Usp.Fiz.Nauk,* 1959, 68: (3), 369-76.
Apropos of the 40th anniversary of the publication of Lenin's "Materializm i emporiokrititsizm".

KOCIAN, Vojtech. [Dialectical materialism in the natural sciences. (In Czech)]. *Vesmír,* 1948, 49: 26-32, ill.

MORRIS, Charles W. Scientific empiricism. In: International encyclopedia of unified science,1: no. 1, p. 63-75. Chicago: University of Chicago Press, 1938.

PACOTTE, Julien. La logique et l'empirisme intégral. 56 p. (Exposés de Philosophie des Sciences, 5) Paris: Hermann, 1935.

PLAUT, H.C. Empiricism, solipsism, and realism. *Brit.J.Phil. Sci.,* 1962, 13: 216-28.

REY, Abel. Pour le réalisme de la science et de la raison. *Atti IV.Congr.Int.Fil* (Bologna, 1911), (2), p. 16-24. Genoa: Formiggini, 1913.

ROSNY, J.H., pseud. of Joseph Henri Honoré Boex-Borel. Les sciences et le pluralisme. 2nd ed. xvi, 220 p. (Nouvelle Collection Scientifique) Paris: Alcan, 1930. [CB 32/606]
First published 1922.

SAGERET, Jules. Le pluralisme et le monisme scientifiques. Leur conciliation. *Rev.Phil.,* 1923, 95: 206-24. [CB 15/235]

SIU, R.G.H. The Tao of science. An essay on Western knowledge and Eastern wisdom. Decorations by Veronica Ruzicka. xvi, 180 p. New York: John Wiley & Sons, Inc. (with the Technology Press of the Massachusetts Institute of Technology); London: Chapman & Hall, Ltd., 1957. [CB 83/190]

SMART, J.J.C. Philosophy and scientific realism. 160 p. New York: Humanities Press, 1963; London: Routledge and Kegan Paul, 1964.
Reviewed by W.V. Quine, *N.Y.Rev.Books,* 1964, 2: no. 11, 3.

SPAULDING, Edward Gleason. The new rationalism. The development of a constructive realism upon the basis of modern logic and science and through the criticism of opposed philosophical systems. xviii, 532 p. New York: H. Holt, 1918.

TAUBE, Mortimer. A re-examination of some arguments for realism. *Phil.Sci.,* 1938, 5: 410-20.

WETTER, Gustav A. Dialectical materialism of modern science. In: Wetter, Gustav A. Dialectical materialism. *See* AFwn

WIGHTMAN, William Persehouse Delisle. Science and monism. 416 p. (History of Science Library) London: Allen and Unwin, 1934.
Reviewed in *Nature,* 1935, 135: 388.

WITTENBERG, A. May philosophy of science preach empiricism and practice apriorism? *Dialectica,* 1962, 16: 15-24.

WORRALL, Ralph Lyndal. The outlook of science: modern materialism. v, 203 p. London: Bale and Danielsson, 1933.

Akv causality; determinism and indeterminism

for causality in different subjects
see INDEX

BENNETT, Jonathan. The status of determinism. *Brit.J.Phil. Sci.,* 1963, 14: 106-19.

BIRKHOFF, G.D.; LEWIS, D.C. Stability in causal systems. *Phil.Sci.,* 1935, 2: 304-33.

BUNGE, Mario. Causality, chance, and law. *Amer.Scient.,* 1961, 49: 432-48.

BUNGE, Mario. Causality. The place of the causal principle in modern science. xx, 380 p., fig., bibliogr. Cambridge, Mass.: Harvard University Press, 1959.
Reprinted New York: World Publishing Co., 1963.
Reviewed by C.J. Ducasse, *Isis,* 1960, 51: 88-90; for other reviews *see* CB 85/381, CB 86/456 and CB 87/555.

BUNGE, Mario. Causality. A rejoinder. *Phil.Sci.,* 1962, 29: 306-17.

CONGRÈS INTERNATIONAL DE PHILOSOPHIE SCIENTIFIQUE, Copenhagen, 1936. Das Kausalproblem. 180 p. Leipzig: 1937.
Proceedings reprinted from *Erkenntnis,* volume 6.

DAVIDSON, M. The free will controversy. ix, 118 p. London: Watts, 1942.
Reviewed by H. Dingle, *Nature,* 1943, 152: 229-30.

EDDINGTON, Arthur Stanley. The decline of determinism. *Nature,* 1932, 129: 233-40.
Presidential address to the Mathematical Association delivered on 4 Jan., 1932.

FRANK, Philipp. Das Kausalgesetz und seine Grenzen. xv, 308 p., 4 fig. (Schriften zur wissenschaftlichen Weltauffassung, 6) Wien: Springer, 1932.

FRANKLIN, Wm. S. Indeterminism in the physical world. *Proc. Amer.Acad.Arts Sci.,* 1925, 60: 485-502. [CB 28/541]

FREY, Gerhard. Inhaltliche Aussagefunktionen. Logische Analyse des Ursache-und Zweckbegriffes. *Phil.Natur.,* 1964, 8: 134-52.

HOOK, Sidney, ed. Determinism and freedom in the age of modern science. A philosophical symposium. xv, 237 p. New York: New York University Press, 1958; Collier Books, 1962.

HOUSSAY, Fr. Force et cause. 210 p. (Bibliothèque de Philosophie Scientifique) Paris: Flammarion, 1920.
Reviewed by L. Guinet, *Isis,* 1921, 4: 115-17.

HUTTEN, E.H. Indeterminism. *Brit.J.Phil.Sci.,* 1954-55, 5: 159-64.

KAPP, Reginald O. Problems and theories of causation. *Bull. Brit.Soc.Hist.Sci.,* 1952, 1: 192-4.

KELSEN, Hans. Causality and retribution. *Phil.Sci.,* 1941, 8: 533-56.

KOCH, Richard. Ueber Kausalität. *Arch.Gesch.Math.Naturwiss. Tech.,* 1928, 10: 369-96.

LENZEN, Victor F. Causality in natural science. 121 p. (American Lecture Series, Publ. 213) Springfield, Ill.: Charles C. Thomas; Oxford: Blackwell Scientific Publications; Toronto: Ryerson Press, 1954. [CB 81/259]

LILLIE, Ralph S. Physical indeterminism and vital action. *Science,* 1927, 66: 139-44.

LIPPMANN, Edmund O. von. Zur Geschichte der "Kausalitäts-Schmerzen". *Chem. Zeitung,* 1929, 53: 257.

MARGENAU, Henry. Meaning and scientific status of causality. *Phil.Sci.,* 1934, 1: 133-48

MARKOVIĆ, Mihailo. The continuum of deterministic methods. *Proc.10th Int.Congr.Hist.Sci.* (Ithaca, 1962), (1), p. 347-50. Paris: Hermann, 1964.

MATISSE, Georges. Interprétation philosophique des relations d'incertitude et déterminisme. 30 p. (Actualités Scientifiques et Industrielles, 361) Paris: Hermann, 1936.

MITTASCH, Alwin. Akausalität? *Phil.Natur.,* 1950, 1: 577-88.

POIRIER, René. Déterminisme physique et liberté humaine. *Hommage à Gaston Bachelard,* p. 119-158. Paris: Presses Universitaires de France, 1957.

ROSENFELD, L. L'évolution de l'idée de causalité. *Mém.Soc. Sci.Liége,* 1942, ser. 4, 6: 57-88.

ROSENTHAL-SCHNEIDER, Ilse. The scientist's interference with the things he studies. *Australian J.Sci.,* 1945, 7: 166-9.

SCHLICK, Moritz. Gesetze, Kausalitaet und Wahrscheinlichkeit. 116 p. Vienna: Gerold, 1948.

SILBERSTEIN, Ludwik. Causality: a law of nature or a maxim of the naturalist? Lecture delivered at the Royal York Hotel, Toronto, on May 14th, 1932, much enlarged. viii, 159 p. London: Macmillan, 1933.
Reviewed in *Nature,* 1934, 133: 235.

UEDA, Daisuke. Zen and science. A treatise on causality and freedom. 95 p. Tokyo: Risosha Co., 1963.

WENTSCHER, Else. Geschichte des Kausalproblems in der neueren Philosophie. Von der preussischen Akademie der Wissenschaften gekrönte Preisschrift. viii, 389 p. Leipzig: Felix Meiner, 1921.

WILKIE, J.S. The problem of the temporal relation of cause and effect. *Brit.J.Phil.Sci.*, 1950, 1: 211-29.

Akw positivism

see also Vienna Circle, 2: 770

BERGMANN, Gustav. The metaphysics of logical positivism. x, 341 p. London: Longmans, Green, 1954.
Reviewed by F.I.G. Rawlins, *Nature*, 1955, 175: 1097-8.

BLACK, M. Relations between logical positivism and the Cambridge School of Analysis. *J.Unified Sci.*, 1939, 8: 24-35.

BOLL, Marcel. La science et l'esprit positif chez les penseurs contemporains. 262 p. Paris: Félix Alcan, 1921.
Reviewed by L. Guinet, *Isis*, 1923, 5: 200-1.

DUCASSÉ, Pierre. Méthode positive et méthode cartésienne. *Rev.Syn.*, 1937, 14: 51-66. [CB 51/209]

DUCASSÉ, Pierre. Méthode positive et méthode cartésienne. *Scientia*, juillet 1937, 62: no. 303, 1-6. [CB 52/562]

DUCASSÉ, Pierre. Méthode positive et méthode cartésienne. *Trav.IXe Congr.Int.Phil.*, *Congr.Descartes* (Paris, 1937), vol. 3, pt. 3, p. 81-7. (Actualités Scientifiques et Industrielles, 532) Paris: Hermann, 1937.

DUCASSÉ, Pierre. Le positivisme comme philosophie intuitive. *Thalès*, 1939, 4: 79-90.

FEIGL, Herbert. Logical analysis of the psycho-physical problem. A contribution of the new positivism. *Phil.Sci.*, 1934, 1: 420-45.

FRANK, Philipp. Concerning an interpretation of positivism. *Isis*, 1942, 33: 683-7.

GRASSET, Joseph. L'idéalisme positif. *Rev.Phil.*, February and March, 1917.
Reviewed by L. Guinet, *Isis*, 1920, 3: 88.

LADRIÈRE, Jean. Athéisme et néo-positivisme. *Rev.Quest.Sci.*, 1964, 135: 479-500.

MISES, Richard von. Positivism, a study in human understanding. 404 p. Cambridge, Mass.: Harvard University Press, 1951. [CB 78/180]

MOURÉLOS, Georges. L'épistémologie positive et la critique meyersonienne. 230 p. Paris: P.U.F., 1962.
Reviewed by Silvestro Marcucci, *Physis*, 1963, 5: 199-205.

PETZOLDT, Joseph. Positivistische Philosophie. *Z.Positivistische Phil.*, 1913, 1: 1-16.

PETZOLDT, Joseph. Das Weltproblem vom Standpunkte des relativischen Positivismus aus, historisch-kritisch dargestellt. 3rd ed. x, 223 p. (Wissenschaft und Hypothese, 14) Leipzig: Teubner, 1921.
2nd ed. 1912.

PLANCK, Max. Positivismus und reale Aussenwelt. Vortrag gehalten am 12. November 1930 im Harnack-Haus der Kaiser Wilhelm-Gesellschaft für Förderung der Wissenschaften. iii, 35 p. Leipzig: Akademische Verlagsgesellschaft, 1931.

QADIR, Abdul. Logical positivism. *Pakistan Phil.J.*, 1957, 1: 75-81.

Akw-bv

DUCASSÉ, Pierre. La méthode positive et l'intuition comtienne: bibliographie. 172 p. Paris: Alcan, 1939.

Akw-cd

MILNE, H.J.M. A positivist archive. *Brit.Mus.Quart.*, 1939, 13: 54

Akw-qy

UNE NOUVELLE société positiviste internationale, fondée à Berlin en 1912. *Isis*, 1913, 1: 107-10.

Akz the future of science

BRIDGMAN, Percy Williams. Quo vadis? *Daedalus Amer.Acad. Arts Sci.*, 1958, 87: no. 1, 85-93.

DECOMTE DU NOÜY, Pierre. L'avenir de l'esprit. 308 p. Paris: Gallimard, 1941; New York: Brentano's, 1943.

DINGLER, Hugo. Der Zusammenbruch der Wissenschaft und der Primat der Philosophie. 400 p. München: Ernst Reinhardt, 1926. [CB 21/593]
Reviewed by Dietrich Mahnke, *Arch.Gesch.Math.Naturwiss. Tech.*, 1927, 10: 216-32; by Heinrich Wieleitner, *Süddeut. Monatsh.*, October 1926, 24: 61-6.

FURNAS, C.C. The next hundred years. The unfinished business of science. xiv, 434 p. Baltimore: Williams & Wilkins, 1936. [CB 47/266]

HARTMANN, Hans. Die Gedanken Plancks und Einsteins als Pole künftiger Naturphilosophie. *Act.IIe Congr.Int.Phil.Sci.* (Zurich, 1954), (4), p. 114-16. Zurich: Éditions du Griffon, 1955.

HUBBARD, N.S. The future of science and technology. 15 p. (Society for Freedom in Science, Occasional Pamphlet, 5) Oxford: 1946.

MAHNKE, Dietrich. Untergang der abendländischen Wissenschaft? *Arch.Gesch.Math.Naturwiss.Tech.*, 1927, 10: 216-32.
Review of Hugo Dingler's Der Zusammenbruch der Wissenschaft und der Primat der Philosophie, *see* above.

MOSER, Simon. Wissenschaft und Zukunft. *Phil.Natur.*, 1964, 8: 117-33.

PLANCK, Max. Where is science going? Prologue by Albert Einstein. Translation and biographical note by James Murphy. 222 p. New York: Norton, 1932; London: Allen & Unwin, 1933.
Reviewed by Cassius Jackson Keyser, *Scr.Math.*, 1933, 1: 327-41; by Thomas Greenwood, *Nature*, 1933, 132: 947-8.

RUSSELL, Bertrand. Icarus, or the future of science. 64 p. London: Kegan Paul, 1924.

SARTON, George. L'avenir de la science. *Renaissance*, 1943, 1: 218-37.

Am fundamental concepts in science

ENRIQUES, Fed. Les concepts fondamentaux de la science. 312 p. (Bibliothèque de Philosophie Scientifique) Paris: Flammarion, 1913.

METZGER, Hélène. Les concepts scientifiques. Préface de M. André Lalande. 195 p. Paris: Alcan, 1926.
Reviewed by George Sarton, *Isis*, 1927, 9: 467-70.

Amd time

for the role of time in different subjects *see* INDEX

ASIMOV, I. The clock we live on. 160 p. New York: Abelard-Schuman, 1959.
A history of time, for the lay reader.
Reviewed by Morris Silverman, *Scr.Math.*, 1961, 26: 74-5.

BACHELARD, Gaston. La dialectique de la durée. 172 p. Paris: Boivin, 1936.

BONACINA, L.C.W. The real meaning of the new conception of time. *Nature*, 1926, 117: 556.

CLEUGH, Mary Frances. Time and its importance in modern thought. Foreword by L. Susan Stebbing. viii, 308 p. London: Methuen, 1937.

FRISCHEISEN-KÖHLER, Max. Das Zeitproblem. *Jahrb.Phil.*, 1913, 1: 129-66, 370.

GUNN, John Alexander. The problem of time: an historical and critical study. 460 p. London: Allen and Unwin, 1929.
Reviewed by Thomas Greenwood, *Nature*, 1930, 126: 677-9.

HABER, Francis C. Revolution in the concept of historical time: a study in the relationship between Biblical chronology and the rise of modern science. *Isis*, 1955, 46: 56.

HELLMANN, Winfried. Der Begriff der Zeit bei Henri Bergson. *Phil.Natur.*, 1957, 4: 126-39.

IRSAY, Stephen d'. Time-implied function: an historical aperçu. *Kyklos*, 1928, 1: 52-9.

KURTH, Rudolf. Ueber Zeit und Zeitmessung. *Phil.Natur.*, 1964, 8: 65-90.

LECHALAS, Georges. Le nouveau temps. *Année Phil.*, 1913, 23: 19-44.

LOVEJOY, Arthur O. The reason, the understanding, and time. xiii, 210 p. Baltimore: Johns Hopkins Press, 1961.

MAN and time. By H. Corbin [et al.]. xx, 414 p. (*Eranos Jahrbuch*. Papers, 3) New York: Pantheon Books, 1957; London: Routledge & Kegan Paul, 1958.
These papers originally published in French or German in *Eranos Jahrbuch*, 1949, vol. 17 and 1951, vol. 20.

MENSCH und Zeit. 459 p., ill. (*Eranos-Jahrbuch*, 1951, vol. 20) Zürich: Rhein-Verlag, 1952. [CB 79/190]
This volume is devoted to man's conception of time in various epochs or climates.
For English translation of some of this volume *see* above.

MILLIKAN, Robert Andrews. Time, matter and values. x, 99 p., 10 pl. (John Calvin McNair Lectures) Chapel Hill, N.C.: University of North Carolina Press, 1932.

MINEUR, Henri. Qu'est-ce que le temps? *La Nature*, 1934, 53-60, 106-11, 157-66, 245-50

NORDMANN, Charles. The tyranny of time: Einstein or Bergson? Translated from the French by E.E. Fournier d'Albe. 217 p. London: T. Fisher Unwin, 1925.

PÉRÈS, Jean. Vers une nouvelle conception du temps. *Rev. Phil.*, 1912, 2e sem., 602-16.

REICHENBACH, Hans. The direction of time. Ed. by Maria Reichenbach. xi, 280 p. Berkeley/Los Angeles: University of California Press, 1956.
Reviewed by Hilary Putnam, *J.Phil.*, 1962, 59: 213-16.

RUSSELL, Bertrand. On the experience of time. *Monist*, 1915, 25: 212-33. [CB 8/361]

SIVADJIAN, Joseph. Le temps. Étude philosophique, physiologique et psychologique. 425 p. Paris: Hermann, 1938.
Reviewed by Hélène Metzger Bruhl, *Archeion*, 1940, 22: 121-2.

SKULSKY, Samuel. A theory of time. *Phil.Sci.*, 1938, 5: 52-9.

TIME and its mysteries. Lectures given on the James Arthur Foundation, New York University. 3 vol. 1. By R.A. Millikan [et al.]. viii, 102 p.; 2. By D.W. Hering [et al.]. 146 p.; 3. By Henry Norris Russell [et al.]. x, 126 p. New York: New York University Press, 1936-49. [CB 76/393]
Volumes 1 and 2 reprinted New York: Collier Books, 1962.

TOULMIN, Stephen. The discovery of time. *Mem.Manchester Lit. Phil.Soc.*, 1963, 105: 100-12. [CB 89/560]

WHITROW, G.J. The natural philosophy of time. xi, 324 p. London/Edinburgh: Nelson, 1961.
Reviewed by Richard Schlegel, *Isis*, 1963, 54: 410-11; for further reviews *see* CB 88/531 and CB 89/491.

WHITROW, G.J. On the nature of time. *Rev.Int.Phil.*, 1962, no. 61-2, 1-14.

Amd-fpx

PRIX Eugenio Rignano. [On the evolution of the concept of time.] *Isis*, 1932, 17: 263-4; 1934, 21: 304.

Amd-kv

BRUNSCHVICG, Léon. Le temps et la causalité. *Rev.Métaphys. Morale*, 1922, 29: 1-33. [CB 13/298]

ZILSEL, Edgar. Über die Asymmetrie der Kausalität und die Einsinnigkeit der Zeit. *Naturwissenschaften*, 1927, 15: 280-6.

Amf symmetry

FIALA, F. Structure formelle et signification extérieure de la notion de symétrie. *Arch.Inst.Int.Sci.Théor.Sér.A Bull.Acad. Int.Phil.Sci.*, 4. Problèmes de philosophie des sciences, 4. Problèmes de connaissance en physique moderne, p. 81-98, Discussion, p. 99-102. (Actualités Scientifiques et Industrielles, 1066) Paris: Hermann, 1949.

JAEGER, F.M. Lectures on the principle of symmetry and its applications in all natural sciences. 2nd ed. xii, 348 p. Amsterdam: Elsevier; Cambridge University Press, 1920.
First publ. 1917. French translation Paris: Gauthier-Villars, 1925.
Reviewed by G. Sarton, *Isis*, 1921, 4: 32-8.

RENAUD, Paul. Sur le principe de symétrie. *Thalès*, 1936, 3: 44-54.

SARTON, George. The principle of symmetry and its application to science and to art. *Isis*, 1921, 4: 32-8.
Essay suggested by F.M. Jaeger's lectures, *see* above.

SCHOPPER, H. Symmetrieprinzipien und Naturgesetze. *Naturwissenschaften*, 1963, 50: 205-11. [CB 89/582]
General review of discussions connected with symmetry principles and the related question of the structure of physical space.

Amz relation of science with other subject fields

AmzAC

GRUENDER, David. On distinguishing science from magic. *Proc.10th Int.Congr.Hist.Sci.* (Ithaca, 1962), (1), p. 257-60. Paris: Hermann, 1964.

AmzAF

BOUTROUX, Emile. Du rapport de la philosophie aux sciences. *Atti IVo Congr.Int.Fil.* (Bologna, 1911), (1), p. 23-40. Genova: Formiggini, 1912.

BOUTROUX, Emile. La nature de l'esprit. 274 p. (Bibliothèque d'Histoire de la Philosophie) Paris: Vrin, 1926. [CB 22/299]
Includes a lecture on the relation between philosophy and the sciences.

DAVIS, Harold T. Philosophy and modern science. xiv, 335 p., 9 fig. Bloomington, Indiana: Principia Press, 1931.
Reviewed by Carol Jane Anger, *Isis*, 1932, 18: 204-6.

DE SARLO, Francesco. Scienza e filosofia. *Scientia*, 1930, 47: 81-90, 149-64, 225-44; French transl., suppl., 37-46, 63-75, 95-112.

DEVAUX, Ph. Savants et philosophes. *Rev.Univ.Bruxelles*, 1931, 67-75. [CB 35/294]

GEMELLI, Agostino. Sui rapporti tra scienza e filosofia. *Atti IVo Congr.Int.Fil.* (Bologna, 1911), (2), p. 25-77. Genova: 1913.

HALDANE, John Scott. The sciences and philosophy. ix, 344 p. (Gifford Lectures, University of Glasgow, 1927 and 1928). London: Hodder and Stoughton, 1928.
Reviewed by F.S. Marvin, *Nature*, 1929, 124: 259-60.

MEURERS, Joseph. Philosophie und Naturwissenschaft. *Phil. Natur.*, 1950, 1: 337-47.

MORRIS, Charles W. Philosophy of science and science of philosophy. *Phil.Sci.*, 1935, 2: 271-86.

REISER, Oliver Leslie. Philosophy and the concepts of modern science. xviii, 315 p. New York: Macmillan, 1935.
Reviewed by David Lindsay Watson, *Phil.Sci.*, 1936, 3: 364-5.

TANNERY, Jules. Science et philosophie, avec une notice par Émile Borel. xvi, 336 p. (Nouvelle Collection Scientifique) Paris: F. Alcan, 1912.

UNITY SCHOOLS. (14th) Farnham meeting, 1937. (F.S. Marvin, chairman) *Isis*, 1938, 28: 465.
Theme of meeting, Relation of philosophy and science.

WEIN, Hermann. Heutiges Verhältnis und Missverhältnis von Philosophie und Naturwissenschaft. *Phil.Natur.*, 1950, 1: 56-75, 189-222.

WHITTAKER, Edmund T. The modern approach to Descartes' problem: the relation of the mathematical and physical sciences to philosophy. (Herbert Spencer Lecture) 30 p. London: Nelson, 1948.

ZAWIRSKI, Zygmunt. Science et philosophie. *Organon*, 1938, 2: 1-16.

AmzAH

BUCHDAHL, Gerd. Science and metaphysics. In: The nature of metaphysics, p. 61-82. London: Macmillan, 1957.

MERLAN, Philip. Metaphysics and science - some remarks. *J.Phil.*, 1959, 56: 612-18.

RUSSELL, John. Science and metaphysics. 40 p. London: Sheed & Ward, 1958; New York: Sheed & Ward, 1960.
Reviewed by H. Dopp, *Rev.Quest.Sci.*, 1959, 20: 320.

AmzB

BOYER, Carl B. Mathematical inutility and the advance of science. *Science*, 1959, 130: 22-5.

DANTZIG, Tobias. Aspects of science. xi, 285 p. New York: Macmillan, 1937.
The part played by mathematics in the conceptual structure of exact science.
Reviewed by Richard Hocking, *Isis*, 1938, 29: 155-7.

HÖLDER, Otto. Die mathematische Methode. Logisch erkenntnistheoretische Untersuchungen im Gebiete der Mathematik, Mechanik und Physik. x, 563 p., 235 ill. Berlin: Julius Springer, 1924.
Reviewed by H. Wieleitner, *Isis*, 1925, 7: 155-6.

KARPINSKI, Louis C. Mathematics and the progress of science. *Sch.Sci.Math.*, 1929, 29: 126-32.

KEYSER, Cassius Jackson. Panthetics. *Scr.Math.*, 1936, 4: 126-38.
Panthetics is the author's term for relating scientific, mathematical and other types of propositions.

KEYSER, Cassius Jackson. The pastures of wonder: the realm of mathematics and realm of science. xii, 208 p. New York: Columbia University Press, 1929.

LÖFFLER, E. Forschung und Schule. Denkmittel der Mathematik im Dienste anderer Wissenschaften. *Unterrichtsbl.Math. Naturwiss.*, 1928, 34: 225-34.

AmzMP

TOPITSCH, Ernst. Das Verhältnis zwischen Sozial- und Naturwissenschaften. Eine methodologisch-ideologiekritische Untersuchung. *Dialectica*, 1962, 16: 211-31.

AmzT for relations between science and technology *see* TmzA

An communication in science

Anb symbolism

ARRÉAT, L. Signes et symboles. *Rev.Phil.*, January, 1913, 51-70.

FOSSEY, Charles. Notices sur les caractères étrangers anciens et modernes, rédigées par un groupe de savants. x, 326 p. Paris: Imprimerie nationale, 1927.
Reviewed by E. Dhorme, *Rev.Hist.Relig.*, 1933, 107: 224.

MAY, Rollo, ed. Symbolism in religion and literature. 253 p. New York: George Braziller, 1960.
Reviewed by Richard F. Grabau, *Phil.Sci.*, 1962, 29: 98-9.
Includes symbolism in science.

PLEDGE, H.T. Symbolism as a limiting factor in the history of science. *Science, medicine and history. Essays in honour of Charles Singer*, (2), p. 450-9. London: Oxford University Press, 1953.

REISER, Oliver L. Unified symbolism for world understanding in science, including Bliss symbols (semantography) and logic, cybernetics and semantics. 52 p. Sydney, Australia: Semantography Publishing Company, 1953.

SCHLESINGER, Max. Geschichte des Symbols. viii, 474 p. Berlin: L. Simion, 1912.

SHEPPARD, H.J. Egg symbolism in the history of sciences. *Scientia*, 1960, 95: 356-60.

STREETER, George L. Archetypes and symbolism. *Science*, 1927, 65: 405-12.

URBAN, Wilbur Marshall. Symbolism in science and philosophy. *Phil.Sci.*, 1938, 5: 276-99.

WHITEHEAD, Alfred North. Symbolism, its meaning and effect. x, 88 p. (Barbour-Page Lectures, 1927, University of Virginia). New York: Macmillan Company, 1927.
Reprinted 1959 (New York: Capricorn Books).

Anb-kk

MORRIS, Charles W. Foundations of the theory of signs. In: International Encyclopedia of Unified Science, 1: no. 2, p. 1-59. Chicago: University of Chicago Press, 1938.

And transliteration

MIELI, Aldo. Per raggiungere l'uniformità di scrittura dei nomi propri di persona. *Isis*, 1914, 1: 707-8.

Anh terminology

ASIMOV, Isaac. Words of science and the history behind them. 266 p. Boston: Houghton Mifflin Company, 1959.

BROWN, Roland Wilbur. Composition of scientific words. A manual of methods and a lexicon of materials for the practice of logotechnics. 885 p. Washington, D.C.: The author, 1954. [CB 81/285]
Another printing [c. 1956] [CB 85/380]. Rev. and enl. edition of "Materials for word study" (New Haven, Conn.: Van Dyck, 1927).

COCULESCO, Pius Servien. Principes d'esthétique: problèmes d'art et langage des sciences. viii, 228 p. Paris: Boivin, 1935.
Reviewed by Hélène Metzger, *Archeion*, 1935, 17: 342-3.

GILBERT, E.J. Langage de la science. 320 p. Paris: Biologica, 1945. [CB 75/86]

NEUGEBAUER, O. Sense or nonsense in scientific jargon. *J. Warburg Inst.*, 1960, 23: 175-6. [CB 86/459]

ROSS, Sydney. Scientist: the story of a word. *Ann.Sci.*, 1962, 18: 65-85.

SAVORY, Theodore H. The language of science. Its growth and usage. 184 p. London: Andre Deutsch, 1953. 1,036
Reviewed by Gösta Langenfelt, *Lychnos*, 1954-55, 371-2.

STEIN, Robert. Naturwissenschaftliche Philosophien. Eine terminologische Studie. *Mitt.Gesch.Med.*, 1917, 16: 11-18.
Bibliographical study on the use of the word philosophy, philosophia, etc. in connection with the name of some branch of science. Additional information, *ibid.*, 259-60, 427-531.

TOLMER, L. A travers les vocabulaires scientifiques (1573-1834). Datations nouvelles. *Franç.Mod.*, 1946, 14: 281-300.

WHITMORE, Charles E. The language of science. *Sci.Mon.*, 1955, 80: 185-91.

Anh-bd

HOLMSTROM, J.E. Report on interlingual scientific and technical dictionaries. 2nd ed. 36 p. Paris: UNESCO, 1951.
Reviewed in *Nature*, 1952, 169: 25-6.

HOLMSTROM, J.E. Bibliography of interlingual scientific and technical dictionaries. 2nd ed. with corrections and supplement. 232 p. Paris: UNESCO, 1951.
Reviewed in *Nature*, 1952, 169: 25-6.

STEFFANIDES, George F. The scientist's thesaurus; a treasury of the stock words of science. 3rd ed. 142 p. Fitchburg, Mass.: Steffanides, 1963.

UNESCO Bibliography of interlingual scientific and technical dictionaries. xxxvi, 236 p. Paris: 1961

Anp writing; reviewing

ALLBUTT, T. Clifford. Notes on the composition of scientific papers. 3rd ed. xii, 192 p. London: Macmillan, 1923.

BAKER, J.R. English style in scientific papers. *Nature*, 1955, 176: 851-2.
Reprinted in *Science*, 1956, 123: 713-14.

EMBERGER, Meta R.; HALL, Marian R. Scientific writing. xii, 468 p., ill. New York: Harcourt, Brace, 1955.
Reviewed by Raymund L. Zwemer, *Sci.Mon.*, 1956, 82: 269.

ERNST, Juliette. Book-reviews: the bibliographer's point of view. *Eranos*, 1951, 49: 1-4

GREGORY, Richard. Science in the public press. *Science*, 1934, 80: 323-30.

KNOX, Crawford. The idiom of contemporary thought. A re-interpretation of some of the problems to which it gives rise. x, 206 p. London: Chapman & Hall, 1956. [CB 82/201]

MENZEL, Donald Howard. Writing a technical paper [by] D.H. Menzel, H.M. Jones & L.G. Boyd. 132 p., ill. (McGraw-Hill paperback series, 41493) New York: McGraw-Hill, 1961.

SARTON, George. Notes on the reviewing of learned books. (Second preface to vol. 41). *Isis*, 1950, 41: 149-88.

SARTON, George. Notes on the reviewing of learned books. *Science*, 1960, 131: 1182-7.

TRELEASE, Sam Farlow. The scientific paper. xii, 152 p. Baltimore: Williams & Wilkins, 1947. [CB 72/269]

TRELEASE, Sam Farlow; YULE, Emma Sarepta. Preparation of scientific and technical papers. 113 p. Baltimore: Williams & Wilkins, 1925

TROAN, John. Science reporting - today and tomorrow. *Science*, 1960, 131: 1193-6.

UDDEN, J.A. Science in newspapers. *Pop.Sci.Mon.*, 1914, 84: 483-9. [CB 6/451]

USE and abuse of English in science. *Nature*, 1955, 176: 845-6.
Leading article; part reprinted in *Science*, 1956, 123: 720-1.

Anq linguistic problems of communication

ADAMS, C.W. Linguistic distribution of (1) scientific incunabula, (2) scientific papers during the period 1795-1863. *Isis*, 1947, 37: 75.

DIJKSTERHUIS, E.J. Taalstrijd in de geschiedenis der wetenschap. [The linguistic conflict in the history of science. (In Dutch)]. *Gids*, 1959, 122(1): 305-24.

FAVARO, Giuseppe. Corso di conversazione latina scientifica alla R. Università di Modena. *Isis*, 1936, 24: 433.

MACKAY, A.L. Scientific and technical translation. *Nature*, 1958, 181: 1044-5.
Apropos of Aslib conference.

SHERRINGTON, C.S. Language distribution of scientific periodicals. *Nature*, 1934, 134: 625. [CB 42/578]

WASHINGTON (STATE) UNIVERSITY. DEPARTMENT OF FAR EASTERN AND SLAVIC LANGUAGES AND LITERATURE and DEPARTMENT OF ELECTRICAL ENGINEERING. Linguistic and engineering studies in the automatic language translation of scientific Russian into English: technical report. (Prepared for the Intelligence Laboratory, Rome Air Development Center, Griffiss Air Force Base, New York). 2 vol. 1. [Phase 1]. 658 p. (Report no. RADC-TN-58-321). 2. Phase 2. 492 p. (Report no. RADC-TR-60-11). Seattle: 1958-60. [CB 85/406]
Vol. 2 published by the University of Washington Press.

Ans publishing

MUMBY, Frank Arthur. Publishing and bookselling. A history from the earliest times to the present day. With a bibliography by W.H. Peet. xii, 480 p. London: Cape, 1930.

ROSSI, Carlo. The new centre of consultation for the technical and scientific press at the National Museum of Science and Technics, Milan. *Riv.Ing.*, 1953, 2: 1-3, 4 fig.

SARTON, George. On a petty form of dishonesty in the publishing trade. *Isis*, 1923, 5: 145.

SCHRAMM, J.R. Cost analysis of scholarly periodical printing. Preliminary report of the Committee on abstracting and documentation of scientific literature of the National Research Council. *Proc.Amer.Phil.Soc.*, 1939, 80: 1-24.

THOMPSON, G.P.; BAKER, John R. Proposed central publications of scientific papers. *Nature*, 1948, 161: 771. [CB 73/166]

Ans-jd

DENNIS, Wayne. Bibliographies of eminent scientists. *Sci. Mon.*, 1954, 79: 180-2.
A study of the rate at which eminent scientists publish.

PELSENEER, Jean. La répugnance à publier, chez le savant de génie. *Act.VIIIe Congr.Int.Hist.Sci.* (Florence, 1956), p. 1155-7. Paris: Hermann, 1958.

Ao study and teaching of science

BARKER, Edwin. Scientific and technological education. An essay. 37 p. (Technics & Purpose, 2) London: Student Christian Movement Press, Ltd., 1957.

BODE, Hendrik, *et al.* The education of a scientific generalist. *Science*, 1949, 109: 553-8.

BREED, Frederick S. Education and the new realism. xx, 237 p. New York: Macmillan, 1939. [CB 59/493]
Includes a discussion on the place of science in modern education.

BURNS, R.M. The crisis in science teaching. *J.Electrochem. Soc.*, 1954, 101: 261C-2C.

COHEN, I. Bernard; WATSON, Fletcher G.; ed. General education in science. vi, 217 p. Cambridge, Mass.: Harvard University Press, 1952.
Reviewed by Aaron J. Ihde, *Isis*, 1952, 43: 300.

CRISIS in science education. *Sci.Mon.*, 1956, 82: 277-94. [CB 82/199]

CURTIS, Francis D. A digest of investigations in the teaching of science. 3 vol. [First digest], 1926; Second digest. xx, 424 p., 1931; Third digest. 419 p., 1938. Philadelphia: Blakiston, 1926-38. [CB 32/529]

DUNGEN, Frans van den. Les vertus éducatives des sciences. *Rev.Univ.Bruxelles*, 1938-39, 44: 22-44.

GRUENBERG, Benjamin C. Light and smoke from the torch of science. *Sci.Educ.*, 1936, 20: 60-5.

HILDEBRAND, Joel H. Role of sciences in education. *Science*, 1955, 121: 840-3.

KENYON, Frederic G., ed. Education, scientific and humane: a report of the proceedings of the Council for Humanistic Studies. 32 p. London: Murray, 1917.

KERSCHENSTEINER, G. Wesen und Wert des naturwissenschaftlichen Unterrichtes. Neue Untersuchungen einer alten Frage. xii, 141 p. (Die Schule der Naturwissenschaft in der Erziehung). Leipzig: Teubner, 1914.

MERRIAM, John C. The inquiring mind in a changing world. An address delivered at the nineteenth commencement convocation of the Rice Institute. *Rice Institute Pamphlet*, 21, no. 3, p. 194-206. Houston: 1934.

MERRIAM, John C. The research spirit in every day life of the average man. *Science*, 1920, 52: 473-8.

NORTHROP, E.P. Efforts to strengthen education in the sciences. *Science*, 1955, 122: 505-7.

PAUCOT, R. Le rôle des sciences dans l'éducation. 255 p. Paris: A. Colin, 1920.
Reviewed by L. Guinet, *Isis*, 1921, 4: 114-15.

ROUCEK, Joseph S., ed. The challenge of science education. 491 p., tables. New York: Philosophical Library, 1959.

SALISBURY, Edward. Science and education. (Presidential address to the Science Masters' Association given on Wednesday, December 28, 1955). *Sch.Sci.Rev.*, 1956, 37: 170-8.

STILL, Joseph W. Science and education at the crossroads. A view from the laboratory. xii, 140 p. Washington: Public Affairs Press, 1958.
Reviewed by George A. Gullette, *Technol.Cult.*, 1961, 2: 300-1.

SUITS, Guy. Education and science. *Amer.Scient.*, 1959, 47: 60-7.

Ao-c

DAINVILLE, F. de. Sciences et enseignement. D'hier à aujourd'hui. 124 p. Paris: Centre d'Etudes Pédagogiques, 1957.
Reviewed by R. Taton, *Rev.Hist.Sci.*, 1958, 11: 279-80.

PAHL, Franz. Geschichte des naturwissenschaftlichen und mathematischen Unterrichts. ix, 368 p. (Handbuch des naturwissenschaftlichen und mathematischen Unterrichts, 1) Leipzig: Quelle und Meyer, 1913.

WESTAWAY, Frederick William. Science teaching: what it was, what it is, what it might be. xxii, 442 p. London: Blackie, 1929.
Reviewed by E.J. Holmyard, *Nature,* 1929, 124: 436-7.

Aoc

CONANT, James Bryant. Two modes of thought. My encounters with science and education. 128 p. New York: Trident, 1964.

TURNER, Dorothy M. The philosophical aspect of education in science. *Isis,* 1927, 9: 402-19.
Section 2 deals with Herbert Spencer and education for complete living.

Aod

ABEL, John J. The education of the superior student. *J.Chem. Educ.,* 1930, 7: 283-93.

AMERICAN COUNCIL ON EDUCATION. COOPERATIVE STUDY OF EVALUATION IN GENERAL EDUCATION. Science reasoning and understanding. A handbook for college teachers. vii, 233 p., ill. Dubuque, Iowa: Brown, 1954.
Reviewed by I. Bernard Cohen, *Sci.Mon.,* 1955, 81: 202-3.

GRUENBERG, Benjamin C. Hypothesis and doctrine in science teaching. *Sch.Soc.,* 1933, 37: 8 p. [CB 41/598]

HEISS, Elwood D.; OBOURN, Ellsworth S.; HOFFMAN, C. Wesley. Modern methods and materials for teaching science. x, 351 p. New York: Macmillan, 1940. [CB 59/465]

LAMPKIN, Richard H. Variability in recognizing scientific inquiry. An analysis of high school science textbooks. ix, 79 p. New York: Bureau of Publications, Teachers College, Columbia University, 1949.

ROLLER, Duane H.D. How can we use the knowledge of current science? *Sci.Teacher,* 1958, 25: 244-50, 280-1

Aop

BLÜH, Otto. Men of science and higher education in a democracy. *Sci.Educ.,* 1941, 25: 1-9.

TAYLOR, Lloyd W. Science in general education at the college level. *Science,* 1940, 91: 560-5.

U.S. PRESIDENT'S SCIENCE ADVISORY COMMITTEE. Meeting manpower needs in science and technology: a report. 1. Graduate training in engineering, mathematics and physical sciences. vi, 45 p. Washington, D.C.: U.S. Govt. Print. Off., 1962.
Resumé with extracts in *Minerva,* 1963, 1: 381-91.

WEISS, Paul. Science in the university. *Daedalus, Amer. Acad.Arts Sci.,* 1964, 93: 1184-218.

Aop-bv

MILES, Vaden W. Bibliography with annotations of college science in general education, 1951-1953. *Sci.Educ.,* 1954, 38: 366-90.

Aorf

HERZOG, M.A. Sind den Fachlehrern für Naturwissenschaften altsprachliche Kenntnisse vonnöten? Mit einem sozialistischen Nachwort und einem Anhang: 1. Der Philosoph Aristoteles in den Quellenschriften zur Geschichte der Erziehungslehre: 2. Aufbau und Ausbau des grossstädtischen Schulwesens [Basels]. Als Manuskript gedruckt. 120 p., 1 pl. Basel: [Druckerei Leykam, Graz], 1921.

Aos

BROWN, W. Sterry. Science - education - good citizenship. 8 p. Bloomington, Ill.: The author, 1935.

Aov popularization of science

ASHBY, Eric. Dons or crooners? *Science,* 1960, 131: 1165-70. [CB 86/458]
Apropos of the popularization of science.

BASSO, L. Le problème de la vulgarisation scientifique. *Rev. Phil.,* 1924, 97: 104-39, 268-305. [CB 17/602]

COHEN, I. Bernard. The education of the public in science. *Impact,* 1952, 3: 67-100.

COHEN, I. Bernard. For the education of the layman. *N.Y. Times Book Rev.,* Sept. 7, 1947.
Criticizing a number of recent scientific books written for the general reader and explaining the standards which such books should meet.

CONANT, James Bryant. The scientific education of the layman. *Yale Rev.*, 1946-47, 36: 15-36.

DUPREE, A. Hunter. Public education for science and technology. *Science,* 1961, 134: 716-18.
The role that the universities should play in dispelling popular myths about science.

GRUENBERG, Benjamin C. Science and the public mind. xiii, 196 p. New York: McGraw-Hill, 1935. [CB 45/273]

GRUENBERG, Benjamin C. Scientific education as a defense against propaganda and dogma. *J.Educ.Method,* 1925, 5: 8 p.

PIEL, G. Need for public understanding of science. *Science,* 1955, 121: 317-22.

SLOSSON, Edwin E. A plea for popular science. 15 p. Washington, D.C.: The Author; New York: Eilert Printing Company, 1920.

Ap organization of science

ALBAREDA HERRERA, Jose Maria. Consideraciones sobre la investigacion cientifica. 466 p. Madrid: 1951. [CB 78/179]

BOYD, Thomas Alvin. Research. The pathfinder of science and industry. xvi, 319 p. New York: Appleton-Century, 1935. [CB 45/283]

BUJAK, Franciszek. The man of action and the student. *Organon,* 1936, 1: 20-32.
A comparison of the characteristics, methods and standards of work.

BUSH, George P.; HATTERY, Lowell H.; ed. Scientific research: its administration and organization. viii, 190 p. Washington, D.C.: American University Press, 1950. [CB 77/364]

CIM, Albert. Le travail intellectuel. 188 p. Paris: Felix Alcan, 1924. [CB 16/337]

CLAUDE, Georges. La recherche scientifique, ses applications à l'industrie et à la synthèse industrielle de l'ammoniaque. *Rev.Gén.Sci.,* 1921, 32: 534-43, 570-81.

COHEN, I. Bernard. Fundamental scientific research and its applications. *Proc.1st Nat.Cancer Conf.* (Memphis, 1949), p. 109-19. [New York?]: American Cancer Society, 1949.

CONNELL, Vera, ed. The application of results of research. vii, 212 p. (British Commonwealth Scientific Conference) New York: Academic Press, Inc.; London: Butterworth Scientific Publications, 1954. [CB 80/120]

FREEDMAN, Paul. The principles of scientific research. 222 p. London: Macdonald, 1949; Washington: Public Affairs Press, 1950. [CB 77/364]
2nd edition New York/Oxford: Pergamon Press, 1960.

HATCH, Melville H. Obstacles to research. *Biologist,* 1938, 20: 66-78.

HILL, Karl, ed. The management of scientists. xvi, 143 p., ill. Boston: Beacon Press, 1964.
Includes essays by Everett Mendelsohn, Anne Roe, Royden C. Saunders, Jr., Albert F. Siepert, Norman Kaplan, and Herbert A. Shepard.
Reviewed by Albert V. Crewe, *Science,* 1964, 146: 1289-90.

HOLTON, Gerald. Scientific research and scholarship; notes toward the design of proper scales. *Daedalus Amer.Acad. Arts Sci.,* 1962, 91: 362-99.

LOEB, Leonard B. The maintenance of scientific proficiency in nonacademic research laboratories. *Science,* 1948, 108: 267-73. [CB 73/165]

LUMIÈRE, Auguste. A propos de la recherche scientifique libre ou dirigée. *Rev.Gén.Sci.,* 1947, 54: no. 2, 3-6.

McKENZIE, Lawson M. Echoes of science administration. *Bull. Phil.Soc.Wash.*, 1962, 16: 25-46.

MEES, C.E. Kenneth. The path of science. xii, 250 p. New York: John Wiley & Sons, 1946. [CB 70/251]

MEYER, Adolf. Organisationsformen der Forschung seit der Renaissance und ihre gegenwärtigen Hauptprobleme. 16 p. In: Brauer, Ludolph, ed. Forschungsinstitute, ihre Geschichte, Organisation und Ziele. Hamburg: Paul Hartung, 1929.

NATIONAL PHYSICAL LABORATORY. Direction of research establishments. Proceedings of a symposium held at the National Physical Laboratory on 26th, 27th & 28th September 1956. 1 vol. (unpaged), ill. London: H.M. Stationery Off., 1957. [CB 83/192]

NATIONAL SCIENCE FOUNDATION. Basic research. A national resource. viii, 64 p. Washington: 1957.

PELSENEER, Jean. Science pure et science appliquée à la lumière de l'histoire des sciences. *Rev.Cercle Alumni Fondation Univ.Belg., new ser.*, 1947, no. 16, 194-201.

POLANYI, Michael. The planning of science. 14 p. (Society for Freedom in Science, Occasional Pamphlet, 4) Oxford: The Society, 1946.
Reprinted from *The Political Quarterly*.

POLYANI, Michael. Pure and applied science and their appropriate forms of organization. 13 p. (Society for Freedom in Science, Occasional Pamphlet, 14) Oxford: The Society, 1953.

ROBERTSON, Thorburn Brailsford. The spirit of research. Edited by Jane W. Robertson. xiv, 210 p., 2 pl. Adelaide: Preece, 1931.
Reviewed by E.F.S., *Nature*, 1933, 131: 111-12.

WEAVER, Warren, ed. The scientists speak. xiii, 369 p. New York: Boni & Gaer, 1947.
Reviewed by George Sarton, *Isis*, 1948, 39: 191-2.
Includes lectures on the present and future of scientific research.

WHEELER, William Morton. The organization of research. *Science*, 1920, 53: 53-67.

WOODWARD, Robert S. The needs of research. *Science*, 1914, 40: 217-29. [CB 8/368]
Address read at the Dedication of the Marine Biological Laboratory, Woods Hole, Mass., July 10, 1914.

Ap-kq

MAHALANOBIS, P.C. The need of a standard terminology for classification of different types of research. *Sci.Cult.*, 1963, 29: 224-5.

Ap-xm

YAGI, Eri. On the measurements of science. *Sci.Pap.Coll.Gen. Educ.Tokyo*, 1964, 14: 129-38.
Proposes possible types of measurement of research results, numbers of scientists, investment, time and money, and notes their use in government documents.

Apd

BEER, John J.; LEWIS, W. David. Aspects of the professionalization of science. *Daedalus Amer.Acad.Arts Sci.*, 1963, 92: 754-84.

THOMAS, W. Stephen. The amateur scientist. Science as a hobby. 291 p., 16 ill. New York: Norton, 1942. [CB 63/269]

Apf

MERTON, Robert K. Singletons and multiples in scientific discovery: a chapter in the sociology of science. *Proc. Amer.Phil.Soc.*, 1961, 105: 470-86.

Aph governmental

BAKER, John R. Science and the planned state. 120 p. London: Allen & Unwin; New York: The Macmillan Co., 1945. [CB 69/224 & 70/250]

COHEN, Felix. The role of science in government. *Sci.Mon.*, 1947, 65: 155-64.
A paper at the Boston Meeting (1946) of the AAAS "How far can scientific method determine the ends for which scientific discoveries are used?".

COLE, W. Sterling. Science and statecraft. *Science*, 1955, 121: 885-7.

DEDIJER, Stefan. Research policy - its makings and measurement. *Sci.Cult.*, 1963, 29: 3-12.

DEDIJER, Stefan. Scientists and the national research policy. *Sci.Cult.*, 1963, 29: 61-73.

DUPRE, J. Stefan; LAKOFF, Sanford A. Science and the nation. Policy and politics. 181 p. Englewood Cliffs, N.J.: Prentice-Hall, 1962.
Reviewed by R.B. Lindsay, *Phys.Today*, 1963, 16: no. 2, 70.

GILPIN, Robert George; WRIGHT, C.; ed. Scientists and national policy-making. 307 p. New York: Columbia University Press, 1964.
Reviewed by Alan T. Waterman, *Science*, 1964, 144: 1438-9.

HILL, A.V. The use and misuse of science in government. *Engineer*, 1941, 172: 222-4. [CB 62/72]
Published in part in *Advance.Sci.*, 1942-43, 2: 6-9; also in *Science*, 1941, 94: 475-7.

KAEMPFFERT, Waldemar. Should the government support science? 32 p. (Public Affairs Pamphlet, 119) New York: Public Affairs Committee, 1946.

MERRIAM, John C. Some responsibilities of science with relation to government. *Science*, 1934, 80: 597-601.

THE SCIENTIFIC community and research policy. *Sci.Cult.*, 1963, 29: 53-8.

SNOW, C.P. Science and government. 88 p. Cambridge, Mass.: Harvard University Press, 1961.
Reviewed in *Amer.Scient.*, 1961, 49: 219A-20A; by P.M.S. Blackett, *Sci.Amer.*, 1961, 204: no. 4; in *Discovery*, 1961, 22: 264-7.

SNOW, C.P. Science and government. viii, 128 p., (Mentor Books). (The Godkin Lectures at Harvard University, 1960, with a new appendix) New York: New American Library of World Literature, Inc., 1962.

Apq academic

CONANT, James B. Academic patronage and superintendence. *Harvard Educ.Rev.*, 1938, 8: 312-34.

LIPSCHUTZ, Alejandro. La organización de la universidad y la investigación científica. 216 p. Santiago, Chile: Editorial Nascimento, 1943. [CB 65/78]

LUCKHARDT, Arno B. Academic or unsuccessful research. *Amer. J.Pharm.Educ.*, 1939, 3: 165-77.
Defense of pure research. Examples drawn from author's own research in physiology.

Apw international relations

CANNON, Walter B.; FIELD, Richard M. International relations in science. A review of their aims and methods in the past and in the future. *Chron.Bot.*, 1945, 9: 253-98.

DALE, Henry. International activities in science. *Nature*, 1944, 154: 724-6.

DENNY, Margaret. The Royal Society and American scholars. *Sci. Mon.*, 1947, 65: 415-27. [CB 73/163]

DUNN, L.G., *et al.* The American-Soviet Science Society. *Science*, 1948, 108: 279. [CB 73/151]

FERREIRA, H. Amorim. Relações científicas entre Portugal e a Grã-Bretanha. viii, 76 p. Lisbon: Academia das Ciências de Lisboa, 1943.
Reviewed by Sir George Thomson, *Nature*, 1943, 152: 618-19.

HALE, George Ellery. Cooperation in research. *Science*, 1920, 51: 149-55.

HEINDEL, Richard H. The American impact on Great Britain, 1898-1914. ix, 439 p. Philadelphia: University of Pennsylvania Press; London: Oxford University Press, 1940.
For Anglo-American relations in science, *see* p. 181, 215, 219, 224, 275, 276, 280, 282, 285 ff., 303, 380-96.

HEINDEL, Richard H. Americans and the Royal Society, 1783-1937. *Science*, 1938, 87: 267-72.

HILL, A.V. Science, national and international, and the basis of cooperation. *Science*, 1941, 93: 579-84.
Read at the Annual General Meeting of the Parliamentary and Scientific Committee held in the House of Commons.

JORGE, Ricardo. Relations médicales et scientifiques entre l'Angleterre et le Portugal. *Proc.3rd Int.Congr.Hist.Med.* (London, 1922), p. 82-4. Antwerp: de Vlijt, 1923.

KELLNER, L. Alexander von Humboldt and the history of international scientific collaboration. *Scientia*, 1960, 95: 252-6.

MERRIAM, John C. Cultural objectives as a basis for international understanding. *Los Angeles Daily J.*, August 21, 1941.

PACE, Antonio. The American Philosophical Society and Italy. *Proc.Amer.Phil.Soc.*, 1946, 90: 387-421. [CB 70/275]

RADOVSKII, M.I. Iz istorii anglo-russkikh nauchnykh sviazei. [From the history of Anglo-Russian scientific relations. (In Russian)]. 216 p. Moscow: Akademiia Nauk SSSR, 1961.
An extensively documented survey, ranging from Chancellor's expedition in the mid-16th century through Mendeleev's trips at the turn of the 19th century.

RADOVSKII, M.I. Nauchnye sviazi Lanzhevena s sovetskimi Uchenymi. [Scientific relations of Langevin with Soviet scientists. (In Russian)] *Priroda*, 1962, no. 10, 96-8.
Letters from Langevin to S.F. Oldenburg and P.P. Lazarev, 1924-1928.

RIABUSHINSKII, Dimitrii. Les rapports scientifiques entre la France et la Russie. *Rev.Gén.Sci.*, 1934, 45: 46-50.

SARTON, George. Collaboration with Germany and with other countries whose currency is debased. *Isis*, 1924, 6: 44-5.

SARTON, George. The international organization of science. *Isis*, 1921, 3: 420-1. [CB 9/496]

SCHUSTER, A. International cooperation in research. *Science*, 1913, 37: 691-701.

VERDOORN, Frans. The development of scientific publications and their importance in the promotion of international scientific relations. *Science*, 1948, 107: 492-7.

WATANABE, Masao. [Kenjiro Yamagawa and the Sheffield Scientific School of Yale University. An early contact in the field of science between Japan and the United States of America. (In Japanese, with English summary)] *Publ.Inst.Comp.Stud. Cult.Tokyo*, 1959, 8: 127-68.

ZIMMERN, Alfred. Learning and leadership; a study of the needs and possibilities of international cooperation. 112 p. London: Oxford University Press, 1928.

Apw-br

Bulletin for Scientific Relations. Bulletin des Relations Scientifiques. (League of nations. International Institute of Intellectual Co-operation) Vol. 1-3. Paris: Presses Universitaires de France, 1926-28. [CB 21/564]

Apw-bx

THE HERITAGE from Newton and Linnaeus. Scientific links between England and Sweden in bygone times. 116, 21 p., 14 ill. (Bidrag till Kungl. Svenska Vetenskaps-Akademiens Historia, 2) Stockholm: Almquist & Wiksells, 1962.
A catalogue of an exhibition held under the sponsorship of Swedish scholarly institutions commemorating the interrelation of Swedish and English savants since the 17th century.

Aq societies and institutions

for national societies *see* under the countries concerned.

SCOPE of the associations for the advancement of science. [Extract, with brief comment, from editorial in the London *Times*, 15 September, 1919, on the recent meeting of the British Association] *Isis*, 1920, 3: 62.

Aq-bd

Index Generalis, 1919-1939; 1952/53-1954/55; general yearbook of universities and of higher educational institutions, academies, archives, libraries, scientific institutes, botanical and zoological gardens, museums, observatories, learned societies ... Paris: Dunod, 1920-39; 1953-55. [CB 14/564 and CB 29/318]
Title varies: 1920-39 in French. Publisher varies.

WORLD of learning. 1963-64. xvi, 1424 p. London: Europa Publications, 1964.
The 14th edition of an international guide to scientific educational and cultural institutions; first edition, 1947.

Aqd

HALE, George Ellery. National academies and the progress of research. 167 p., ill. Lancaster, Pa.: New Era Printing Company, 1915.
Reprinted from *Science*, 1913, 38: 681-98; 1914, 39: 189-200; 1914, 40: 907-19; 1915, 41: 12-22.

McKIE, Douglas. Scientific societies to the end of the eighteenth century. *Phil.Mag.*, 1948, Commemoration number, 133-43.

SCHOFIELD, Robert E. Histories of scientific societies. Needs and opportunities for research. *Hist.Sci.*, 1963, 2: 70-83.

SCHUSTER, Julius. Die wissenschaftliche Akademie als Geschichte und Problem. In: Brauer, Ludolph; Bartholdy, Mendelssohn; Meyer, Adolf. Forschungsinstitute, ihre Geschichte, Organisation und Ziele, 13 p. Hamburg: Paul Hartung Verlag, 1930.

SPARN, Enrique. Las sociedades científicas literarias y tecnicas del mundo con mas de 1000 miembros. 76 p. (Republica Argentina. Academia Nacional de Ciencias. Miscelanea, 18) Cordoba: 1931.
Reviewed by H.D., *J.Savants*, 1932, 140-1.

Aqd-nj

PELSENEER, Jean. Query 78 apropos of scientific societies named after illustrious scientists. *Isis*, 1938, 29: 407-8.

SARTON, George. Réponse à la question 78. Sociétés dont le nom commémore des savants illustres (*Isis*, 1938, 29: 407-8). *Isis*, 1939, 30: 508.

Aqg

BRAUER, Ludolph. Ueber die Bedeutung freier Forschungsinstitute. *Beitr.Klin.Tuberk.*, 1928, 68: 671-9.

BRAUER, Ludolph, ed. Forschungsinstitute; ihre Geschichte, Organisation und Ziele. 2 vol. Hamburg: P. Hartung, 1930.

Aqu

ORGANISATION des congrès scientifiques. *Organon*, 1938, 2: 133-236.

Aqu-bv

NATIONAL LIBRARY OF MEDICINE. Congresses. Tentative chronological and bibliographical reference list of national and international meetings of physicians, scientists, and experts. Second supplement, fourth series, Index-catalogue, United States Army (Army Medical Library). 288 p. Washington, D.C.: 1938.

Aqx

MARGERIE, Emmanuel de. Discours prononcé à la séance de clôture du Congrès des Sociétés Savantes à Paris, le samedi, 22 mai 1937. 23 p. Paris: Imprimerie Nationale, 1937.
This presidential lecture contains a history of scientific congresses. The author deals chiefly with the international congresses of geology, of geography, of history, and with the meetings of the Association française pour l'avancement des sciences.

RITTER, Wm. E. The Australian meeting of the Pan-Pacific Science Congress. *Science*, 1924, 59: 285-8. [CB 16/338]

Aqy international organizations

BESTERMAN, Theodore. UNESCO. Peace in the minds of men. xi, 133 p., front. London: Methuen: 1951. [CB 79/186]

BIDEZ, J. L'Union Académique Internationale. *Flambeau*, 1937, 8 p.

BORCHGRAVE, Emile Jacques Yvon Marie de, *baron*. L'Association des Académies. Son organisation et ses travaux. *Vie Int.*, 1913, 4: 41-4.

DARBOUX, Jean Gaston. Éloges académiques et discours. 525 p., portr. Paris: Hermann, 1912. [CB 9/468]
Contains a series of documents relating to the history of the Association Internationale des Académies.

HALE, George Ellery. The international organization of scientific research. *Int.Conciliation*, 1920, no. 154, 431-41. [CB 10/210]
Explains the aims and organisation of the International Research Council.

HUXLEY, Julian. UNESCO. Its purpose and its philosophy. 62 p. Washington, D.C.: Public Affairs Press, American Council on Public Affairs, 1947. [CB 71/116]

INTERNATIONAL COUNCIL OF SCIENTIFIC UNIONS. A description of the council, of its commissions, and of its affiliated scientific unions and commissions with some account of their history and scientific activities. v, 137 p. Cambridge: 1950.

INTERNATIONAL COUNCIL OF SCIENTIFIC UNIONS. Reports of proceedings of the General Assembly. London: 1920-
From 1919-28 called International Research Council.

LELAND, Waldo G. The International Union of Academies and the American Council of Learned Societies. *Int.Conciliation*, 1920, no. 154, 423-30. [CB 10/211]

NEEDHAM, Joseph. An international science cooperation service. *Nature*, 1944, 154: 657-60.

NEEDHAM, Joseph. The place of science and international scientific cooperation in post-war world organization. Memorandum III, 42 typewritten pages. Dated Chungking, 28th April, 1945. [CB 70/251]
Concerning UNESCO.

RICHARDSON, Hugh. Science and international cooperation. [Letter, dated] Wheelbirks, Stocksfield, Northumberland, October, 6, 1929. *Isis*, 1930, 14: 222-5.
Development of international scientific societies.

SARTON, George. Conférence pour le développement des institutions du Palais Mondial (Bruxelles, 1922). *Isis*, 1923, 5: 419-20.

SCIENCE and UNESCO. International scientific cooperation. Tasks and functions of the Secretariat's Division of Natural Sciences. 64 p. London: Pilot Press, [1947?]

UNESCO. The field scientific liaison work of UNESCO. 67 p. Paris: 1949. [CB 76/392]

UNION OF INTERNATIONAL ASSOCIATIONS. Conceptions et programme de l'internationalisme. Organismes internationaux et Union des Associations Internationales. Etablissements scientifiques installés au Palais Mondial. 130 p., 15 pl. Bruxelles: 1921. [CB 12/642]

UNION OF INTERNATIONAL ASSOCIATIONS. Union des Associations Internationales. Mundaneum. Le Nouveau Palais Mondial organisé en Centre Intellectuel International. 32 p. (Publication, 116) Bruxelles: 1925. [CB 18/654]

WILSON, Howard E. The development of UNESCO. *Int.Conciliation*, 1947, no. 431, 293-343.

Aqy-bd

Annual of International Associations and Organisations - Annuaire de la Vie Internationale. 1-3; *ser. 2*, 1-2, 1905-1910/11. Brussels: 1906-12.
Reviewed by G. Sarton, *Isis*, 1913, 1: 289-90.

Ar the profession

ALMAN, David. Conquest. A book about scientists, their inquiries and achievements. 179 p. Garden City, N.Y.: Doubleday & Co., 1963.

BAKER, John R. The scientific life. 154 p. New York: Macmillan & Co., 1943. [CB 69/224]

BAKER, Robert A. The stress analysis of a strapless evening gown and other essays for a scientific age. 192 p. Englewood Cliffs, N.J.: Prentice Hall, 1963.
A collection of essays about scientists.
Reviewed by J. Gillis, *Phys.Today*, 1964, 17: no. 2, 62.

CONANT, James B. Scientists, inventors and executives. *Sci. Cult.*, 1951, 17: 118-22.

FORTUNE MAGAZINE. The scientists. *Amer.Scient.*, 1949, 37: 107-18.
Discussion of the problems of science, of scientific research and of the scientists themselves as of the middle of the twentieth century. Reprinted from *Fortune Magazine*, October 1948.

GLASS, Bentley. The academic scientist, 1940-1960. *Science*, 1960, 132: 598-603.

HILDEBRAND, E.M. Scientists and society. *Amer.Scient.*, 1954, 42: 495-7.

KUBIE, Lawrence S. Problems of the scientific career. *Amer. Scient.*, 1953, 41: 596-613.

MERTON, Robert E. Rôle of the intellectual in public bureaucracy. *Studies and Essays offered to George Sarton*, p. 521-43. New York: Schuman, 1947.

MORISON, Robert Swain. Scientist. xiv, 207 p. New York: Macmillan, 1964.

ROBINSON, James Harvey. An outline of the history of the intellectual class in Western Europe. 3rd rev. ed. vii, 56 p. New York: The Marion Press, 1915.

SCOTT, Christopher. The science of science. What scientists read and why. *Discovery*, 1959, 20: 110-14, 4 fig.

SHAPIRO, Theresa R. What scientists look for in their jobs. *Sci.Mon.*, 1953, 76: 335-40.

Arc

LONG, Esmond R. Democrats and aristocrats in scientific research. *Sci.Mon.*, 1921, 12: 414-23. [CB 12/640]

Ard social responsibility; attitudes

AHLBERG, Clark D.; HONEY, John C.; ed. Attitudes of scientists and engineers about their government employment. I. ii, 223 p. Syracuse, N.Y.: Syracuse University, Maxwell Graduate School of Citizenship and Public Affairs, 1950.
Mimeographed.

ASTIN, Allen V. Scientists and public responsibility. *Phys. Today*, 1957, 10: no. 11, 23-7.

BARBER, Bernard; HIRSCH, Walter. The sociology of science. The role and responsibilities of the scientist - discussed as social phenomena. viii, 662 p. New York: Free Press of Glencoe, 1962.

BRIDGMAN, P.W. Scientists and social responsibility. *Sci. Mon.*, 1947, 65: 148-53.
A paper presented in the AAAS symposium in Boston (1946) on "How far can scientific method determine the ends for which scientific discoveries are used?".

COHEN, I. Bernard. Savants & social conscience. *Saturday Rev.* (New York), June 16, 1951, 35-6.

COMPTON, Arthur H. The religion of a scientist. 28 p. New York: Jewish Theological Seminary of America, 1938.
An address delivered at the Jewish Theological Seminary of America on Monday, November 21, 1938.

DRAWBRIDGE, Cyprian Leycester, ed. The religion of scientists: being recent opinions expressed by two hundred Fellows of the Royal Society on the subject of religion and theology. Edited ... on behalf of the Christian Evidence Society. 160 p. London: Benn, 1932.

HALL, Daniel, *et al.* The frustration of science. Foreword by Frederick Soddy. 144 p. London: Allen and Unwin, 1935.
Reviewed by R.B., *Nature*, 1935, 135: 414-15.

HILDEBRAND, Joel H. The social responsibility of scientists. *Amer.Scient.*, 1955, 43: 450-6. [CB 81/262]

HOLTON, Gerald. Notes on the religious orientation of scientists. In: Shapley, Harlow, ed. Science ponders religion, p. 52-64. New York: Appleton-Century-Crofts, 1960.

IHDE, Aaron J. Responsibility of the scientist to society. *Sci.Mon.*, 1953, 77: 244-9.

NIELSEN, J. Rud. Our responsibilities as scientists. *Sci. Mon.*, 1955, 81: 65-70.

PELSENEER, Jean. Un faux problème: la responsabilité sociale du savant. *Rev.Inst.Sociol.*, 1961, 449-51.

ZHMUDSKY, A.Z. The scientist's responsibility toward society. *Impact*, 1963, 13: 301-10.

ZNANIECKI, Florian. The social role of the man of knowledge. v, 212 p. New York: Columbia University Press, 1940.
Reviewed by R.K. Merton, *Amer.Sociol.Rev.*, 1941, 6: 111-15.

Ard-q

SOCIETY FOR SOCIAL RESPONSIBILITY IN SCIENCE. *Science*, 1950, 112: 760-1.

Arf status; remuneration

ZIRKLE, Conway. Our splintered learning and the status of scientists. *Science*, 1955, 121: 513-19.

Arj professional ethics

HALL, Maurice C. Scientists sometimes tell the truth. *Sci. Mon.*, 1938, 47: 152-60. [CB 60/143]

PELSENEER, Jean. Morale de savants d'Hippocrate à Einstein. Pages choisies. 130 p. (Collection Lebègue, 77) Bruxelles: Office de Publicité, 1946.
Reviewed by P. Sergescu, *Arch.Int.Hist.Sci.*, 1947, 1: 185.
Texts to illustrate the ethics of scientists.

Arw women in science

CASTLE, Cora Sutton. A statistical study of eminent women. vii, 90 p. (Archives of Psychology, 27) New York: Science Press, 1913. [CB 5/301]

DUSTIN, Albert. La science et la femme. Discours rectoral prononcé à la séance solennelle de rentrée, le 15 octobre 1937. *Rev.Univ.Bruxelles*, 1937-38, 43: 21-44.

MOZANS, H.J. [pseud. of John Augustine Zahm]. Woman in science. With an introductory chapter on woman's long struggle for things of the mind. xi, 452 p., ill. London: D. Appleton, 1913.

As relations with society

As-bm *large scale works*

ADAMS, Mary, ed. Science in the changing world, by Thomas Holland, H. Levy, Julian Huxley, John R. Baker, Bertrand Russell, Aldous Huxley, Hugh I'A. Fausset, Hilaire Belloc, J.B.S. Haldane, Oliver Lodge. 286 p. London: Allen & Unwin; New York: Century, 1933. [CB 39/442]
Series of radio talks of the British Broadcasting Corporation.
Reviewed by F.S. Marvin, *Nature*, 1933, 131: 674-5.

ANSHEN, Ruth Nanda, ed. Beyond victory. 291 p. New York: Harcourt, Brace, 1943. [CB 69/234]

ANSHEN, Ruth Nanda, ed. Science and man. viii, 494 p. New York: Harcourt Brace, 1942. [CB 63/270]

BARBER, Bernard. Science and the social order. With a foreword by Robert K. Merton. xxiii, 288 p. Glencoe, Ill.: Free Press, 1952; London: Allen & Unwin, 1953. [CB 79/167]
Reviewed by Conway Zirkle, *Isis*, 1953, 44: 296-8; in *Nature*, 1953, 172: 1014-15.

BARZUN, Jacques Martin. Science: the glorious entertainment. 322 p. New York: Harper and Row, 1964.
For reviews *see* CB 90/511.

BAWDEN, Arthur Talbot. Man's physical universe. xvii, 812 p., ill. New York: Macmillan, 1937. [CB 52/579]

BERKNER, L.V. The scientific age; the impact of science on society. xvi, 137 p. New Haven, Conn./London: Yale University Press, 1964.

BERNAL, John Desmond. The social function of science. xvi, 482 p. London: Routledge, 1939.
Reviewed by Herbert Dingle, *Sci.Progr.*, 1949, no. 146, 232-43.

BROOKS, John. The one and the many, the individual in the modern world. With essays by Charles Habib Malik [and others]. xvi, 331 p. (The Second Corning Conference) New York: Harper & Row, 1962.

BURCHARD, J.E., ed. Mid-century. The social implications of scientific progress. xx, 549 p. Cambridge, Mass.: Technology Press of M.I.T., 1949.

BUTLER, J.A.V. Science and human life. Successes and limitations. viii, 163 p. London/New York: Pergamon Press; New York: Basic Books, 1957. [CB 83/189]
Reviewed by F.I.G. Rawlins, *Nature*, 1958, 181: 299; by R. Bruce Lindsay, *Phys.Today*, 1958, 11: 32-3.

CATTELL, R.B.; COHEN, J.; TRAVERS, R.M.W.; ed. Human affairs. ix, 360 p. New York: Macmillan, 1937.
Reviewed by M.F. Ashley-Montagu, *Isis*, 1938, 28: 508-10.

COLLIN, Rémy. Message social du savant. 350 p. Paris: Michel, 1941.

CONANT, James B. Modern science and modern man. 111 p. (Bampton Lectures, 5, for 1952) New York: Columbia University Press, 1952. [CB 80/113]
Reviewed by Eleanor R. Webster, *Arch.Int.Hist.Sci.*, 1954, 7: 76-7; by Francis A.Sevier, *Scr.Math.*, 1954, 20: 81.

CROWTHER, J.G. The social relations of science. xxxii, 665 p. New York: Macmillan, 1941.
Reviewed by M.F. Ashley Montagu, *Isis*, 1941, 33: 345-7.

DANIELS, Farrington; SMITH, Thomas M.; ed. The challenge of our times. Contemporary trends in science and human affairs as seen by twenty professors at the University of Wisconsin. viii, 364 p. Minneapolis: Burgess Publishing Co., 1953. [CB 82/263]

DIBNER, Bern, ed. Science and Technion. A selection of major essays on science and society contributed to the "Technion Yearbook" by some of the foremost among those who helped to shape the mid-twentieth century. 178 p., ill. New York: American Technion Society, [1959].

DINGLE, Herbert. Science and human experience. 141 p. London: Williams and Norgate, 1931.
Reviewed by Oliver Lodge, *Nature*, 1932, 129: 147-50.

ELBERS, Gerald W.; DUNCAN, Paul; ed. The scientific revolution. Challenge and promise. A symposium. viii, 280 p. Washington, D.C.: Public Affairs Press, 1959.
Reviewed by George A. Cullette, *Technol.Cult.*, 1961, 2: 88-9.

HALDANE, J.B.S. Science and everyday life. 284 p. New York: Macmillan, 1940. [CB 60/142]
Seventy short essays.

HARRIS, Franklin Stewart; BUTT, Newbern I. Scientific research and human welfare. ix, 406 p. New York: Macmillan, 1924.

HILL, D.W. The impact and value of science. 88 p. London: Hutchinson, 1944.
Reviewed by E.T. Whittaker, *Endeavour*, 1944, 3: 163.

HUIZINGA, Jan. In the shadow of to-morrow. A diagnosis of the spiritual distemper of our time. Translated from the Dutch by J.H. Huizinga. ix, 228 p. London: Heinemann, 1936.
Includes chapters on science.
Reviewed by George Sarton, *Isis*, 1937, 26: 487-9.

HUXLEY, Julian. Scientific research and social needs. With an introductory chapter by Sir William Bragg, and discussions with H. Levy, Sir Thomas D. Barlow, and P.M.S. Blackett. xvi, 287 p., 41 pl. London: Watts, 1934; New York: Harper, 1935.
Title of American ed., Science and social needs.
Reviewed by Robert K. Merton, *Isis*, 1935, 24: 188; by J.W.W., *Nature*, 1934, 134: 83-4.

LEVY, Hyman. Science in an irrational society. viii, 82 p. (Conway Memorial Lecture) London: Watts, 1934.
Reviewed by R. Brightman, *Nature*, 1934, 134: 889.

LODGE, Oliver J. Modern problems. 320 p. London: Methuen, 1912.
On a variety of topics relating to social aspects of science.

MAN and learning in modern society. Papers and addresses delivered at the inauguration of Charles E. Odegaard as President of the University of Washington November 6 and 7, 1958. vii, 186 p., fig., pl. Seattle: University of Washington, 1959.

MATSON, Floyd W. The broken image; man, science and society. 355 p. New York: Braziller, 1964.
Reviewed by Peter F. Drucker, *Science*, 1964, 144: 829-30; by Bert James Loewenberg, *Amer.Quart.*, 1964, 16: 492-500.

MEAD, George H. Mind, self and society. Edited, with introduction, by Charles W. Morris. 401 p., xxxviii. Chicago: University of Chicago Press, 1934.
Reviewed by Robert K. Merton, *Isis*, 1935, 24: 189-91.

MERTON, Robert K. Social theory and social structure. Rev. ed. xviii, 645 p. Glencoe, Ill.: Free Press, 1957. [CB 83/193]
1st ed. 1949.

PEARSON, Karl. The function of science in the modern state. 2nd ed. vii, 97 p. Cambridge University Press, 1919.
First published as introduction to vol. 32 of the 10th ed. of the Encyclopaedia Britannica, 1902.

PLA, Cortés. Ciencia y sociedad. 232 p. (Coleccion Oro de Cultura General, 130-131) Buenos Aires: Atlantida, 1950. [CB 77/364]

PLATT, John Rader. The excitement of science. 176 p. Boston: Houghton Mifflin, 1962. [CB 90/512]
Reviewed by Duane Roller, *Technol.Cult.*, 1964, 5: 117-18.

RABINOWITCH, Eugene. The dawn of a new age. Reflections on science and human affairs. viii, 332 p. Chicago: University of Chicago Press, 1963.

RUSSELL, E. John. Science and modern life. 101 p. London: Epworth Press; New York: Philosophical Library, 1955. [CB 82/263]

SPROTT, W.J.H. Science and social action. 164 p. (The Josiah Mason Lectures, delivered at the University of Birmingham) London: Watts, 1954; Glencoe, Ill.: Free Press, 1955.
Reviewed by Bernard Barber, *Isis*, 1956, 47: 191-2.

WESTINGHOUSE EDUCATIONAL FOUNDATION. Science and life in the world. The George Westinghouse centennial forum, May 16-18, 1946. 3 vol. 1. Science and civilization. The future of atomic energy. ix, 125 p., 11 pl.; 2. Transportation - a measure of civilization. Light, life and man. ix, 236 p., 12 pl.; 3. A challenge to the world. ix, 198 p., 28 pl. New York: McGraw Hill, 1946. [CB 40/166]

WOOLF, Harry, ed. Science as a cultural force. vii, 110 p. (Shell Companies Foundation Lectures) Baltimore: Johns Hopkins Press, 1964. [CB 90/512]

As-bn *essays; articles*

ALPERT, Harry. The knowledge we need most. *Saturday Rev.* (New York), 1 February 1958, 36-8, 2 fig.

BLAKESLEE, Albert Francis. Individuality and science. *Science*, 1942, 95: 1-10.
Presidential address to the AAAS on the value of science to the community.

BOGGS, S.W. Mapping some of the effects of science and technology on human relations. *Dep.State Bull.*, 1945, 12: 183-8, 3 fig.

BOLT, Richard H. Statesmanship in science. *Phys.Today*, 1961, 14: no. 3, 30-2.

BOUTRY, G.A. Contacts of science with social problems. *Nature*, 1938, 142: 422-3.

BRIDGMAN, P.W. Some of the broader implications of science. *Phys.Today*, 1957, 10: no. 10, 17-24.

BRIDGMAN, P.W. The task before us. *Proc.Amer.Acad.Arts Sci.*, 1953, 83: 97-112.

COHEN, I. Bernard. The impact of science on society. *Sci. Teacher*, 1957, 24: 213-15, 240-1, 1 portr.

COMPTON, Karl T. The social implications of scientific discovery. 33 p. (Jayne Memorial Lecture, American Philosophical Society, 1938) Lancaster, Pa.: Lancaster Press, 1938.

DALE, Henry. The mission of science. *Nature*, 1945, 156: 677-80.

DARLINGTON, C.D. The conflict of science and society. x, 51 p. (Conway Memorial Lecture) London: Watts, 1948.
Reviewed by Conway Zirkle, *Isis*, 1950, 41: 319.

DE GRÉ, Gerard. Science as a social institution: an introduction to the sociology of science. 49 p. (Doubleday Short Studies in Sociology) Garden City, N.Y.: Doubleday & Co., 1955.

DEWEY, John. Unity of science as a social problem. In: International Encyclopedia of Unified Science, 1: no. 1, p. 29-38. Chicago: University of Chicago Press, 1938.

DINGLE, Herbert. Science and Professor Bernal. *Sci.Progr.*, 1949, 146: 232-43.
Apropos of J.D. Bernal "The social function of science", *see* As-bm.

FEIBLEMAN, James K. The impact of science on society. In: Studies in social philosophy, p. 39-75. (Tulane Studies in Philosophy, 11) New Orleans: Tulane University, 1962.

GEORGE, André. L'homme devant la science moderne. *Rev.Quest. Sci.*, 1949, 10: 481-97.

GRAUBARD, Mark. Human goals in the light of science. *Crozer Quart.*, 1949, 26: 289-98.

GRUENBERG, Benjamin C. The scientific temper and social values. *Sci.Educ.*, 1938, 22: 128-33.

HADAMARD, Jacques. La science et le monde moderne. *Renaissance*, 1943, 1: 523-58.

HAFSTAD, Lawrence R. Science, technology and society. *Amer.Scient.*, 1957, 45: 157-68, 6 fig.

HOPKINS, Frederick Gowland. Science in modern life. *Nature*, 1935, 136: 893-5.
From the anniversary address to the Royal Society, delivered on November 30, 1935.

HORDER, Thomas Jeeves Horder, *baron*. The strain of modern civilization. *Nature*, 1936, 138: 529-31.
From the introduction to a discussion in section I (physiology) of the British Association at Blackpool on September 15, 1936.

HUSKINS, C. Leonard. Science, cytology and society. *Amer. Scient.*, 1951, 39: 688-99. [CB 78/180 and 191]

LOEWENBERG, Bert James. Toward a new birth of freedom. *Amer.Quart.*, 1964, 16: 492-500.

MERRIAM, John C. Science and the constructive life. *Univ. Virginia Alumni News*, 1933, 21: no. 7, 153-8.
Lecture delivered as the Founder's day address at the University of Virginia, April 13, 1933.

MERTON, Robert K. Science and the social order. *Phil.Sci.*, 1938, 5: 321-37. [CB 56/382]

MERTON, Robert K. Science, population and society. *Sci. Mon.*, 1937, 44: 165-71. [CB 51/288]

MERTON, Robert K.; BARBER, Bernard. Sorokin's formulations in the sociology of science. In: Allen, Philip James, ed. Pitirim A. Sorokin in review, p. 332-68. Durham, N.C.: Duke University Press; Cambridge University Press, 1963.

MOULTON, F.R. Science and society. *Science*, 1937, 86: 387-91.

PELSENEER, Jean. Science et technique; aspects sociologiques. *Rev.Inst.Sociol.*, 1959, 32: 145-56.

PIERCE, J.R. The social uses of science. *Amer.Scient.*, 1954, 42: 646-9.

POTTER, Van Rensselaer. Society and science. *Science*, 1964, 146: 1018-22.

SARTON, George. Preface to volume XXXI. Quousque tandem? *Isis*, 1939, 31: 6-7.

SCIENCE and society. *Nature*, 1958, 181: 1183-4.

SEEGER, Raymond J. Man and science. *J.Wash.Acad.Sci.*, 1956, 46: 169-76.
Discusses the question whether science is inherently individualistic or essentially social.

SOCIAL aspects of science. Preliminary report of AAAS interim committee. *Science*, 1957, 125: 143-7.

STAKMAN, Elvin Charles. Science and human affairs. *Science*, 1951, 113: 137-42.

STAMP, Josiah. The impact of science upon society. *Science*, 1936, 84: 236-9; also *Nature*, 1936, 138: 435-48. [CB 49/165]

TOPCHIEV, A.V. Interdependence of science and society. *Bull.Atom.Sci.*, 1963, 19: no. 3, 7-12.

VON LAUE, Theodore H. Modern science and the old Adam. *Bull.Atom.Sci.*, 1963, 19: no. 1, 2-5.

WATERMAN, Alan T. Science in the service of man. *Bull. Atom.Sci.*, 1963, 19: no. 5, 3-6.

WEAVER, Warren. Science and people. *Science*, 1955, 122: 1255-9.
Presidential address to the meeting of the AAAS in December 1955.

WELLS, Herbert George. What are we to do with our lives? vi, 148 p. New York: Doubleday, Doran, 1931.
Reviewed by L.A.F., *Nature*, 1932, 129: 415-17.

As-br periodicals

Impact of Science on Society. Vol. 1 - New York: Columbia University Press for UNESCO, 1950 - [CB 79/168]

Organon. International review. Published by the Mianowski Institute for the Promotion of Science and Letters. Warsaw, Poland. Editor: Stanisław Michalski. Vol. 1-2. Warszawa: 1936-38. [CB 48/562]
Reviewed by Charles W. Morris, *Isis*, 1939, 30: 297-8.
On the organization and sociology of science.

Science and Society. A Marxian quarterly. Vol. 1 - Cambridge, Mass.: 1936 - [CB 49/165]

As-bv bibliographies

ADAMS, Charles C. Selected references on the relation of science to modern life. *N.Y.State Mus.Bull.*, 1940, 322: 79-96.

BARBER, Bernard; MERTON, Robert K. Brief bibliography for the sociology of science. *Proc.Amer.Acad.Arts Sci.*, 1952, 80: 140-54.

LIBRARY OF CONGRESS. GENERAL BIBLIOGRAPHICAL AND REFERENCE SECTION. The social impact of science: a select bibliography with a section on atomic power. vii, 51 p. (Subcommittee on War Mobilization of the Committee on Military Affairs, United States Senate) Washington: U.S. Gov. Print. Off., 1945.
This includes 505 items divided as follows: 1. Government publications, 50 items; 2. Books and pamphlets, 172; 3. Periodical articles, 260; 4. Atomic power, 23.

As-ob the sociology of science as a study

BARBER, Bernard. Present status and needs of the sociology of science. *Proc.Amer.Phil.Soc.*, 1955, 99: 338-42.

BARBER, Bernard. The sociology of science. In: Sociology today: problems and prospects, p. 215-28. New York: Basic Books, 1959.

DINGLE, Herbert. History of science and the sociology of science. *Sci.Mon.*, 1956, 82: 107-11. [CB 82/192]

SHRYOCK, Richard H. The history and sociology of science. *Items*, 1956, 10: 13-16.

Asb social background of science

BOSE, D.M. Impact of society on science. *Sci.Cult.*, 1960, 25: 447-50.

CHILD, Arthur. The problem of imputation in the sociology of knowledge. *Ethics*, 1941, 51: 200-19.

CHILD, Arthur. The theoretical possibility of the sociology of knowledge. *Ethics*, 1941, 51: 392-418.

CHILDE, V. Gordon. Social worlds of knowledge. 26 p. London: Oxford University Press, 1949.

CROMBIE, Alistair C., ed. Scientific change. Historical studies in the intellectual, social, and technical conditions for scientific discovery and technical invention, from antiquity to the present. (Symposium on the History of Science, University of Oxford, 9-15 July 1961.) xii, 896 p. New York: Basic Books, 1963.
For reviews *see* CB 90/600.

DE GRÉ, Gerard. The sociology of knowledge and the problem of truth. *J.Hist.Ideas*, 1941, 2: 110-15.

DELEVSKY, J. L'évolution des sciences et les intérêts matériels. C'est la soif de savoir qui a été le principal stimulant du progrès des sciences exactes. *Mois*, 1938, no. 86, 251-9.

DELEVSKY, J. L'évolution des sciences et les techniques industrielles. *Rev.Hist.Écon.Soc.*, 1939, 311-33.

DELEVSKY, J. Influences diverses du milieu humain sur l'évolution des sciences. *Mois*, 1938, no. 90, 251-7.

DELEVSKY, J. L'intérêt économique matériel de l'homme, joue-t-il un rôle dans l'évolution des sciences? Il est difficile de le soutenir. *Mois*, 1937, 251-60.

GRÜNWALD, Ernst. Das Problem der Soziologie des Wissens. viii, 279 p. Wien/Leipzig: Wilhelm Braumüller, 1934.

HOFSTRA, Sjoerd. De sociale aspecten van kennis en wetenschap. [The social aspects of learning and science. (In Dutch)]. 76 p. Amsterdam: Scheltema & Holkema, 1937. [CB 58/566]

HOGBEN, Lancelot. Science for the citizen: a self educator based on the social background of scientific discovery. 3rd rev. ed. 1146 p. (Primers for the Age of Plenty, 2) London: Allen & Unwin; New York: W.W. Norton, 1951.
First published 1938 (London: Allen & Unwin; New York: Knopf).
Reviewed by M.F. Ashley Montagu, *Isis*, 1940, 31: 467-9.

MANNHEIM, Karl. Ideology and utopia: an introduction to the sociology of knowledge. With a preface by L. Wirth. Translation of Ideologie und Utopie [Bonn: 1929] and two essays. xxxi, 318 p. London: Kegan Paul; New York: Harcourt, Brace, 1936.
Reviewed by R.K. Merton, *Isis*, 1937, 27: 493-503.
Spanish edition, Mexico: Fondo de Cultura Económica, 1941, reviewed by Angela Romera, *Archeion*, 1942, 24: 276-8.

MERTON, Robert K. Karl Mannheim and the sociology of knowledge. *J.Liberal Relig.*, 1941, 2: 23 p.

MERTON, Robert K. Priorities in scientific discovery: a chapter in the sociology of science. *Amer.Sociol.Rev.*, 1957, 22: 635-59.
Presidential address read at the annual meeting of the American Sociological Society, August 1957.

MERTON, Robert K. The sociology of knowledge. *Isis*, 1937, 27: 493-503.

ROSENTHAL-SCHNEIDER, Ilse. Science and utilitarianism. Some aspects of the history of science. [With discussion] *Australian J.Sci.*, 1944-45, 7: 9-13, 60, 97, 127.

SCHELER, Max, ed. Versuche zu einer Soziologie des Wissens. vii, 450 p. München/Leipzig: Duncker und Humbolt, 1924.

WAXWEILER, E. Sur les conditions sociales de la formation et de la diffusion d'une doctrine scientifique dans ses rapports avec la religion et la magie. *Bull.Inst.Sociol. Solvay*, 1912, 21: 916-36.

WEINBERG, Boris. Les lois d'évolution des découvertes de l'humanité. *Rev.Gén.Sci.*, 1926, 37: 43-7. [CB 20/191]

WOLFF, Kurt H. The sociology of knowledge: emphasis on an empirical attitude. *Phil.Sci.*, 1943, 10: 104-23.

ZILSEL, Edgar. The social roots of science. *J.Unified Sci.*, 1939, 9: 216-20.

ZILSEL, Edgar. The sociological roots of science. *Amer.J. Sociol.*, 1942, 47: 544-62.

Asc relation with the history of civilization

ANSHEN, Ruth Nanda, ed. Our emergent civilisation. x, 330 p. (Science of Culture Series, 4) New York: Harper, 1947.
Reviewed by Mark Graubard, *Isis*, 1949, 40: 76.

ARCHER, Simon. Science as human evolution. 103 p. Paterson, N.J.: Pageant Press, 1963.

BERNAL, J.D. Science in history. xxiv, 967 p., ill. London: Watts & Co., 1954.
Reviewed by L. Pearce Williams, *Isis*, 1957, 48: 471-3; by L. Rosenfeld, *Centaurus*, 1956, 4: 285-92; by Bogdan Suchodolski, *Stud.Mater.Dziej.Nauk.Pol.*, 1955, no. 3, 443-51.

BRINTON, Crane. From many one. 126 p. Cambridge: Harvard University Press, 1948.
On world government in the light of the history of civilization.
Reviewed by Sidney Jackman, *Isis*, 1949, 40: 85.

CALDER, Ritchie. After the seventh day, the world man created. 348 p., ill. New York: The New American Library (Mentor Book), 1962.

COHEN, John. The scientific revolution and leisure. *Nature*, 1963, 198: 1028-33.

CORTESÃO, Armando. Science and the development of culture. *Act.VI° Congr.Int.Hist.Sci.* (Amsterdam, 1950), p. 96-108. Paris: Hermann, 1951.
Also published in *Arch.Int.Hist.Sci.*, 1951, 4: 3-15.

COUNSON, Albert. La civilisation; action de la science sur la foi. 192 p. Paris: Alcan, 1929. [CB 35/308]

CUSHING, Harvey. The humanizing of science. *Science*, 1935, 81: 137-43.
Presidential address before the History of Science Society, Washington, December 28, 1934.

DUBOS, René Jules. The cultural roots and the social fruits of science. 33 p., ill., portr., bibliogr. (Condon Lectures, 1963) Eugene: Oregon State System of Higher Education, 1963.

FIGUROVSKI, N.A. Istoriia estestvoznaniia i tekhniki i ee mesto v istorii olshchestva. [The history of natural science and technology and its place in the history of society. (In Russian)]. *Vop.Ist.Est.Tekh.*, 1958, 6: 75-83.

FORBES, R.J. Cultuurgeschiedenis van wetenschap en techniek. [Cultural history of science and technology. (In Dutch)]. 502 p., 105 ill., 37 fig. (Universiteit voor Zelfstudie) The Hague: N.V. Maandblad Succes, 1948.

FORBES, R.J. Science, technology and social evolution. *Congr.Int.Phil.Sci.* (Paris, 1949), (8), p. 51-8. (Actualités Scientifiques et Industrielles, 1166) Paris: Hermann, 1952.

FORD, Guy Stanton. Science and civilization. 29 p. (The Day and Hour Series of the University of Minnesota) Minneapolis: University of Minnesota Press, 1933.

GREGORY, Richard. Civilization and the pursuit of knowledge. *Nature*, 1946, 158: 114-18, 148-51.
Presidential address to the British Association for the Advancement of Science, delivered on July 20, 1946.

JONES, R.V. Science, technology and civilization. *Nature*, 1962, 194: 1211-14.

JORDAN, Pascual. Science and the course of history: the influence of scientific research on human events. Translated by Ralph Manheim. x, 139 p. New Haven: Yale University Press, 1955.
Reviewed by Charles C. Gillispie, *Amer.Hist.Rev.*, 1956, 61: 998; by I. Bernard Cohen, *Sci.Mon.*, 1956, 83: 109-10; by Per Collinder, *Lychnos*, 1957-58, 393.

KENNEDY, Foster. Science, civilization and faith. *Trans. Amer.Neurol.Ass.*, 1940, 66: 1-9.

KOL'MAN, E. Nekotorye teoreticheskie problemy istorii estestvoznaniia i tekhniki i trud Dzh. Bernala *Nauka v istorii obshchestva.* [Some theoretical problems in the history of natural science and technology and the work of John Bernal *Science in history.* (In Russian)]. *Vop.Ist.Est.Tekh.*, 1958, 6: 84-94.

KROEBER, A.L. Configuration of culture growth. x, 882 p. Berkeley; University of California Press, 1944.
Reviewed by Mark Graubard, *Isis*, 1947, 37: 118-19; by G. Levi Della Vida, *J.Amer.Orient.Soc.*, 1945, 65: 207-10. *See also* Scherman's article, *ibidem*, 133-44.

LILLEY, S., ed. Essays on the social history of science. 182 p. (*Centaurus*, 1953, 3: no. 1-2) Copenhagen: Ejnar Munksgaard, 1953.
Reviewed by Donald Fleming, *Isis*, 1956, 47: 65-6; for other reviews *see* CB 81/262, CB 82/200 and CB 84/305.

LILLEY, S. Social aspects of the history of science. *Arch. Int.Hist.Sci.*, 1949, 2: 376-443.

LINDSAY, Robert Bruce. The impact of science on contemporary civilization. *Sigma Xi Quart.*, 1942, 30: 51-65.

LINDSAY, Robert Bruce. The role of science in civilization. 318 p., ill. New York: Harper and Row, 1963. [CB 89/495]
Reviewed by H.L. Nieburg, *Science*, 1963, 142: 220; by Phyllis A. Richmond, *Phys.Today*, 1964, 17: no. 6, 63-4.

LODGE, Oliver. Science and human progress. 187 p. (Halley Stewart Lectures, 1926) London: Allen and Unwin, 1927.
Reviewed by E.S.R., *Nature*, 1927, 120: 435-6.

MARVIN, Francis Sydney, ed. Science and civilization. 350 p. (The Unity Series, 6) New York: Oxford University Press, 1923.
Reviewed by George Sarton, *Isis*, 1924, 6: 119-21.

MARVIN, Francis Sydney. Science and the unity of mankind. In: Singer, Charles, ed. Studies in the history and method of science, vol. 2, p. 344-58. Oxford: Clarendon Press, 1921. [CB 11/452]

MARVIN, Francis Sydney. The social influence of science. *Nature*, 1923, 111: 209-11. [CB 15/244]

NEEDHAM, Joseph. Science and society in East and West. *Centaurus*, 1964, 10: 174-97.

NEEDHAM, Joseph. Science and society in China and the West. *Sci.Progr.*, 1964, 52: 50-65.
An abridgment of Needham's contribution to "Scientific change", ed. by A.C. Crombie, p. 117-53, *see* Ac-bq.

NORDEN, Eduard, ed. Vom Altertum zur Gegenwart. Die Kulturzusammenhänge in den Hauptepochen und auf den Hauptgebieten. Skizzen von F. Boll, A. Curtius, u. s. w. viii, 308 p. Leipzig: Teubner, 1919.
Reviewed by George Sarton, *Isis*, 1921, 4: 89.

PELSENEER, Jean. Science, technique et société, à la lumière de l'histoire des sciences. *Rev.Inst.Sociol.*, 1953, no. 4, 461-74.

ROBINSON, James Harvey. Civilization. 62 p. London/New York: Encyclopaedia Britannica, 1929.
Reviewed by George Sarton, *Isis*, 1929, 13: 136-7.

ROUTH, H.V. Towards the twentieth century. x, 392 p. New York: Macmillan, 1937.
Reviewed by M.F. Ashley-Montagu, *Isis*, 1939, 30: 554-5.

RUSSELL, Bertrand. The impact of science on society. ix, 64 p. (Matchette Foundation Lectures, 3) New York: Columbia University Press, 1951; London: Allen and Unwin, 1952 (140 p.). [CB 78/179]

SARTON, George. Secret history. *Scribner's Mag.*, 1920, 67: 187-92. [CB 8/368]
Showing the relation of the development of science to the development of civilization.

SAYILI, Aydin. [The truest guide in life is science. (In Turkish)] 201 p. (Publications of the Institute of Education, no. 5) Ankara: 1948.
Reviewed by Richard N. Frye, *Isis*, 1949, 40: 286.
On the role of science in history.

SUCHODOLSKI, Bogdan. O społeczna role historii nauki. [The social role of the history of science. (In Polish, with summaries in English and Russian)]. *Kwart.Hist.Nauk.Tech.*, 1959, 4: 3-14.

THORNTON, Jesse E., ed. Science and social change. xi, 577 p. Washington, D.C.: Brookings Institution, 1939. [CB 59/465]

TIZARD, Henry. The passing world. *Nature*, 1948, 162: 392-9.
From the Presidential address, British Association, delivered at Brighton, on September 8, 1948. A review of the social effects of science since 1885.

VEBLEN, Thornstein B. The place of science in modern civilization. 509 p. New York: Huebsch, 1919.

WISCONSIN UNIVERSITY. *See* Ac-bq

Asc-br

GUINET, L. "Collection science et civilisation". *Isis*, 1922, 4: 493.
Apropos of an encyclopedic series edited by Maurice Solovine and published by Gauthier-Villars in Paris.

Ase public opinion

DARLINGTON, C.D. The dead hand on discovery. *Discovery*, 1948, *new ser.* 9: 358-62; 1949, *new ser.* 10: 7-11.
Discusses the social opposition to scientific discoveries.

DUBARLE, D. The proper public of science: reflections on a Cartesian theme concerning humanity and the state as audiences of the scientific community. *Minerva*, 1963, 1: 405-27.

DUBOS, René. Scientist and public. *Science*, 1961, 133: 1207-11.

GRUENBERG, Benjamin C. Science and the layman. *Sci.Mon.*, 1935, 40: 450-7.

PELSENEER, Jean. Les dangers de la prolétarisation de la science. *Rev.Univ.Bruxelles*, Jan.-Feb. 1956, 167-72.

WATERMAN, Alan T. Acceptance of science. *Sci.Mon.*, 1955, 80: 10-14.
Illustrates the lack of understanding by the public of new scientific ideas by examples from the history of science.

Asg relation with economics

BERNAL, J.D. Vliianie ekonomicheskikh i tekhnicheskikh faktorov na sovremennuiu nauku. [Influence of economic and technological factors on contemporary science. (In Russian)]. *Vop.Ist.Est.Tekh.*, 1958, 6: 95-110.

BERNAL, J.D., ed. Science for a developing world; an account of a symposium organized by the World Federation of Scientific Workers on science and the development of economy and welfare of mankind, Warsaw, September 1959. 131 p. London: World Federation of Scientific Workers, [1962].

BOWMAN, Isaiah. Commanding our wealth. *Science*, 1944, 100: 229-41.
Address of the retiring president, American Association for the Advancement of Science, Cleveland, Ohio, September 11, 1944.

CARTER, C.F. The distribution of scientific effort. *Minerva*, 1963, 1: 172-81.

CONANT, James Bryant. The impact of science on industry and medicine. *Amer.Scient.*, 1951, 39: 33-49.
Based upon chapter IX of President Conant's book "Science and Common Sense", see Ake.

DEDIJER, Stefan. Underdeveloped science in underdeveloped countries. *Minerva*, 1963, 2: 61-81.

DERAEVE, Ed. A. L'économie et la science. *Rev.Écon.Int.*, 1938, 30: (3), 347-68.

FLECK, Alexander. Science and business: a balanced partnership. (British Association Meeting in Glasgow). *Nature*, 1958, 182: 573-8.

LE CHATELIER, Henri. Science et industrie. 284 p. Paris: Ernest Flammarion, 1925.

MEIER, Richard L. Science and economic consequences of scientific discovery. *Amer.J.Phys.*, 1957, 25: 602-13.

MEIER, Richard L. Science and economic development: new patterns of living. xviii, 266 p. Cambridge, Mass.: Technology Press of Massachusetts Institute of Technology, Inc.; London: Chapman and Hall, 1956.
Reviewed by Suzanne Colnort, *Rev.Hist.Sci.*, 1958, 11: 96.

REDMAN, L.V.; MORY, A.V.H. The romance of research. viii, 149 p., 6 fig. New York: Appleton-Century, 1933. [CB 41/596]
This is a survey of the applications of science to industry.

SODDY, Frederick, ed. The frustration of science. With a foreword by Frederick Soddy. 144 p. New York: Norton, 1935. [CB 45/274]

SOMBART, Werner. Weltanschauung, science and economy. ix, 60 p. New York: Piest, 1939. [CB 61/411]

TAYLOR, F. Sherwood. Is the progress of science controlled by the material wants of man? 15 p. (Society for Freedom in Science, Occasional Pamphlet, 1) Oxford: The Society, 1945. [CB 69/224]

ZVORIKINE, A.A. Science as a direct productive force. *Cah.Hist.Mond.*, 1963, 7: 959-71.

Asg-bv

KATZ, Saul M.; McGOWAN, Frank. A selected list of U.S. readings on development. Prepared for the United Nations Conference on the Application of Science and Technology for the Benefit of the Less Developed Areas. 363 p. Washington, D.C.: Agency for International Development, 1963.
Reviewed by Eugene Staley, *Science*, 1963, 142: 216-17.

NATIONAL SCIENCE FOUNDATION. Selected bibliography of research and development and its impact on the economy. Foreword by Jacob Perlman. v, 21 p. (NSF-58-18) Washington, D.C.: Office of Special Studies, National Science Foundation, 1958.

Ask relation with politics

BERNAL, J.D. Science and Marxist philosophy. *Nature*, 1941, 148: 280-1.

BOREL, E. La science dans une société socialiste. *Scientia*, 1922, 31: 223-9. [CB 11/641]

CONFERENCE ON THE SCIENTIFIC SPIRIT AND DEMOCRATIC FAITH, New York, 1943. The scientific spirit and democratic faith. Papers from the conference. xii, 92 p. New York: King's Crown Press, 1944. [CB 66/261]

DE SANTILLANA, Giorgio. Galileo and J. Robert Oppenheimer. *Reporter*, 1957, 17: (12), 10-18, 3 fig.

DEUTSCH, Karl W. The impact of science and technology on international politics. *Daedalus Amer.Acad.Arts Sci.*, 1959, 88: 669-85.

ESSLINGER, William. Politics and sciences. With a foreword by Albert Einstein. xi, 167 p. New York: Philosophical Library, 1955.

FRIEDRICH, Carl J., ed. Totalitarianism. Proceedings of a conference held at the American Academy of Arts and Sciences, March 1953. x, 386 p. Cambridge, Mass.: Harvard University Press, 1954. [CB 80/120]

GREGORY, Richard. Science and world order. *Nature*, 1941, 148: 331.

GRODZINS, Morton; RABINOWITCH, Eugene; ed. The atomic age. Scientists in national and world affairs. xiii, 616 p. (Articles from the *Bull.Atom.Sci.*, 1945-62) New York: Basic Books, 1963.

HALDANE, J.B.S. The Marxist philosophy and the sciences. 183 p. London: Allen & Unwin, 1938.
Reviewed by P.J., *Sci.Progr.*, 1939, 34: 432.

HASKINS, Caryl P. The scientific revolution and world politics. 125 p. New York: Harper and Row, 1964.

HODGSON, P.E. The role of scientists in world affairs. *Nature*, 1956, 178: 460.

HUTCHINS, Robert M., *et al.* Science, scientists, and politics; an occasional paper on the role of science and technology in the free society. 15 p. Santa Barbara, Calif.: Center for the Study of Democratic Institutions, 1963.

JOUVENEL, Bertrand de. The political consequences of the rise of science. *Bull.Atom.Sci.*, 1963, 19: no. 10, 2-8.

KROPOTKIN, Peter Alekseevich. La science moderne et l'anarchie. xi, 391 p. (Bibliothèque Sociologique, 49) Paris: Stock, 1913.

LINDSAY, Jack. Marxism and contemporary science. 261 p. London: Dobson, 1949.
Reviewed by Sydney W. Jackman, *Isis*, 1950, 41: 320.

McDOUGALL, William. World chaos: the responsibility of science. vi, 119 p. London: Kegan Paul, 1931.
Reviewed by E.S.R., *Nature*, 1932, 129: 295-6.

MORGENTHAU, Hans J. Scientific man vs. power politics. 245 p. Chicago: University of Chicago Press, 1947.
Reviewed by Mark Graubard, *Isis*, 1948, 38: 267-8.

NATHANSON, Jerome, ed. Science for democracy. x, 170 p. New York: King's Crown Press, 1946. [CB 74/385]

RABINOWITCH, Eugene. Scientific revolution. 1. Man's new outlook; 2. The new content of politics; 3. The end of history; 4. The beginning of world community. *Bull.Atom. Sci.*, 1963, 19: no. 7, 15-18; no. 8, 11-16; no. 9, 9-12; no. 10, 14-17.

RABINOWITCH, Eugene. The scientist and the cold war. *Current*, 1961, no. 11, 39.

SAYRE, Wallace S. The scientist as politician. *Current*, 1961, no. 11, 37-8.

SCHRADER, Rudolf. Science and policy; on the interaction of scientific and political affairs. 81 p. New York: Pergamon, 1963.

TIZARD, Henry. Science and democracy. 34 p. (Arthur Dehon Little Memorial Lecture at the Massachusetts Institute of Technology) Cambridge, Mass.: 1951.

VON ECKARDT, Ursula M. The pursuit of happiness in the democratic creed; an analysis of political ethics. xvi, 414 p., bibliogr. New York: Frederick A. Praeger, 1959. [CB 85/383]
A section deals with the effect of science on political creeds.

Ask-qx

ROTBLAT, J. Science and world affairs. History of the Pugwash conferences. 92 p., ill. London: Dawsons of Pall Mall, 1962.

Asp peace and war

for military technology *see* XR

BRY, Ilse; DOE, Janet. War and men of science. *Science*, 1955, 122: 911-13. [CB 82/200]

CONFERENCE ON SCIENCE, PHILOSOPHY AND RELIGION IN THEIR RELATION TO THE DEMOCRATIC WAY OF LIFE. Learning and world peace. 8th symposium. Ed. by L. Bryson. xix, 694 p. New York: 1948. [CB 73/179]
Includes an appendix on UNESCO.

CROWTHER, J.G.; WHIDDINGTON, R. Science at war. vi, 185 p., 51 pl. London: H.M. Stationery Office, 1947; New York: Philosophical Library, 1948. [CB 73/148]
Reviewed by S. Weintroub, *Nature*, 1948, 161: 907.

HUXLEY, Julian. Science, war and reconstruction. *Science*, 1940, 91: 151-8.

KAEMPFFERT, Waldemar. Science and war. *Science*, 1943. 97: 532-3. [CB 65/78]

KANSAS ACADEMY OF SCIENCE. Science and the war. A symposium presented at the seventy-fifth anniversary meeting of the Kansas Academy of Science, Lawrence, Kansas, April 10, 1943. 47 p. (*Trans.Kansas Acad.Sci.*, 46) Lawrence: 1943.
Preprint.

LANGEVIN, Paul. La science et la paix. *Quadrige*, 1946, no. 5, 15-19.

NEF, John U. War and human progress. An essay on the rise of industrial civilization. ix, 464 p. Cambridge, Mass.: Harvard University Press, 1950. [CB 79/177]

RAY, J.N. Scientists and defense preparedness. *Sci.Cult.*, 1963, 29: 114-18.

RAYLEIGH, Robert John Strutt, *4th baron.* Vision in nature and vision aided by science; science and warfare. *Science*, 1938, 88: 175-81, 204-8.

SARTON, George. Preface to Volume 42. Science and peace. The development of international law. *Isis*, 1951, 42: 3-9.

SEEGER, Raymond J. Imperatives for peace. Keynote address, 12th National Conference on Citizenship, Hotel Statler, Washington, D.C., 16 September 1957. 26 p. [Washington: National Science Foundation, 1957]
Mimeographed.

SIGERIST, Henry E. War and culture. *Bull.Hist.Med.*, 1942, 11: 1-11.

STERN, Curt. Peacetime research in wartime - a report. *Science*, 1944, 99: 278-80.

Asr freedom and secrecy

ADRIAN, Edgar Douglas. Freedom and responsibility of science. *News Report, National Academy of Sciences, National Research Council*, 1952, 2: 49-52.

BAKER, John R. Freedom and authority in scientific publications. 13 p. (Society for Freedom in Science, Occasional Pamphlet, 15) Oxford: The Society, 1953.

BAKER, John R. The scientific life. 154 p. New York: Macmillan, 1943.
On scientific freedom. *See also* Aph, Baker, John R.
Reviewed by M.F. Ashley Montagu, *Isis*, 1944, 35: 191-2.

BAKER, John R.; TANSLEY, A.G. The course of the controversy on freedom in science. *Nature*, 1946, 158: 574-6.

BECKNER, Lloyd V. Secrecy and scientific progress. *Science*, 1956, 123: 783-7.
The testimony of the President of Associated Universities, Inc., before the Government Information Subcommittee of the House of Representatives.

BOAS, Franz, *et al.* Manifesto on freedom of science. 31 p. New York: 1938. [CB 57/234]

BRIDGMAN, Percy W. Science and freedom. Reflections of a physicist. *Isis*, 1947, 37: 128-31, portr.

BRYSON, Lyman. Science and freedom. xi, 191 p. New York: Columbia University Press, 1947. [CB 74/384]

CHENEY, Edward P., ed. Freedom of inquiry and expression. A collection of facts and judgments concerning freedom and suppression of freedom of all forms of intellectual life. xii, 365 p. (*Ann.Amer.Acad.Polit.Soc.Sci.*, 200) Philadelphia: 1938.
Reviewed by Hans H. Gerth, *Isis*, 1947, 32: 200-3.

EDSALL, J.T. Government and the freedom of science. *Science*, 1955, 121: 615-18.

A FREE voice at the Moscow University Bicentennial, 1755-1955. 29 p. New York: American Committee for Liberation from Bolshevism, 1955.
Excerpts from radio broadcasts to Moscow from American educators and scientists, émigré scholars and scientists, and from student newspapers.

FREEDOM and restriction in science and its aspects in society. Congress promoted by the Netherlands University, at The Hague, 17-18 September 1954. ix, 196 p. The Hague: Martinus Nijhoff, 1955.

GELLHORN, Walter. Security, loyalty and science. viii, 300 p. Ithaca: Cornell University Press, 1950.
Reviewed by I.I. Rabbi, *Sci.Amer.*, Jan. 1951, 184: no. 1, 56-7.

GOUDSMIT, S.A. Freedom of science. *Research*, 1949, 2: 49-51. [CB 74/384]

GREGORY, Richard. The commonwealth of science. *Isis,* 1942, 34: 27-8.
On the need for freedom in science. Reprinted from *Nature,* 1941, 148: 393.

GREGORY, Richard. Science in chains. 32 p. (Macmillan War Pamphlets, 12) London: Macmillan, 1941.

HAYEK, F.A. Planning, science and freedom. *Nature,* 1941, 148: 580.

HUXLEY, Aldous. Science, liberty and peace. 64 p. London: Chatto and Windus, 1947.
Reviewed by R. Brightman, *Nature,* 1947, 160: 733-4.

LEAKE, Chauncey D. Science implies freedom. *Studies in the History of Culture,* p. 310-20. Menasha, Wisc.: American Council of Learned Societies, 1942.

LEAKE, Chauncey D. Science implies freedom. A timely topic for the New Year's amusement of the friends of Chauncey and Elizabeth Leake. 11 p., ill. San Francisco: 1940.

McCORMICK, John; MacINNES, Mairi; ed. Versions of censorship: an anthology. xviii, 374 p. Chicago: Aldine Publishing Co., 1962. [CB 87/559]

PHYSICS and engineering in a free society. A panel discussion. *Phys.Today,* 1961, 14: no. 3, 19-28. [CB 87/559]

POLANYI, Michael. The autonomy of science. *Mem.Manchester Lit.Phil.Soc.,* 1941-43, 85: 19-38. Also published *Sci.Mon.,* 1945, 60: 141-50. [CB 69/224]

POLANYI, Michael. The contempt of freedom. The Russian experiment and after. ix, 116 p. London: Watts, 1940. [CB 61/413]

POLANYI, Michael. The foundations of academic freedom. 18 p. (Occasional Pamphlet of the Society for Freedom in Science, 6) Oxford: The Society, 1947.

POLANYI, Michael. The logic of liberty. Reflections and rejoinders. viii, 206 p. London: Routledge and Kegan Paul, 1951.
Reviewed by J.P., *Arch.Int.Hist.Sci.,* 1952, 5: 388.

RAEYMAEKER, Louis de, *et al.* Truth and freedom. vii, 133 p. (Duquesne Studies, Philosophical Series, 5) Pittsburgh: Duquesne University; Louvain: Editions E. Nauwelaerts, 1954. [CB 81/263]

ROBERTSON, John Mackinnon. A history of free thought. Ancient and modern, to the period of the French Revolution. 4th ed. rev. 2 vol. London: Watts, 1936.

SARTON, George. Preface to Volume 27. Unification of good will. *Isis,* 1937, 27: 211-15.
On freedom in science.

SCHRECKER, Paul. The freedom of civilization. *Conference on Science, Philosophy and Religion, 12th Symposium, Freedom and Authority in our time,* p. 647-57. New York: Harper, 1953.

SMYTH, Henry DeWolf. The place of science in a free society. *Amer.Scient.,* 1950, 38: 426-36.

UNESCO. Freedom and culture. 270 p. New York: Columbia University Press, 1951. [CB 78/195]

UNESCO. Human rights. Comments and interpretations. 288 p. New York: Columbia University Press, 1949.
Reviewed by M.F. Ashley Montagu, *Isis,* 1951, 42: 92.

WATERMAN, Alan T.; WARD, J. Carlton; KELLY, Mervin J. Scientific research and national security. *Sci.Mon.,* 1954, 78: 214-21.

WEAVER, Warren. Free science. 4 p. (Occasional Pamphlet of the Society for Freedom in Science, 3) Oxford: The Society, 1945.

WEAVER, Warren. Free science sought. Letter. *N.Y.Times,* Sept. 2, 1945.

ZUCKERMAN, Solly. Liberty in an age of science. *Nature,* 1959, 184: 135-8.
Substance of the address delivered at the Sixty-fifth Commencement Exercises of the California Institute of Technology on 12 June 1959.

Asr-br

Science and Freedom: a bulletin of the Committee on Science and Freedom. No. 1- Manchester: 1954-
For contents of no. 2 *see* CB 81/263.

Asr-qb

THE OBJECTS of the Society for Freedom in Science. 8 p. Oxford: Committee of the Society for Freedom in Science, 1944. [CB 70/251]

TANSLEY, Arthur George. The psychological connexion of two basic principles of the Society for Freedom in Science. 4 p. (Occasional Pamphlet of the Society for Freedom in Science, 12) Oxford: The Society, 1952.

THOMSON, George; DALE, Henry. Speeches made at the dinner held to celebrate the tenth anniversary of the Foundation of the Society. 11 p. (Occasional Pamphlet of the Society for Freedom in Science, 11) Oxford: The Society, 1951.

Asy science and the future; scientific utopias

for the future of science *see* Akz

ADAMS, Robert P. The social responsibilities of science in Utopia, New Atlantis and after. *J.Hist.Ideas,* 1949, 10: 374-98.

BERNERI, Marie Louise. Journey through Utopia. xii, 339 p. London: Routledge and Kegan Paul, 1950.

DUBOS, René. The dreams of reason. Science and utopias. xxi, 167 p. New York/London: Columbia University Press, 1961.
For reviews *see* CB 88/536.

HALDANE, J.B.S. Daedalus; or, Science and the future. A paper read to the Heretics, Cambridge, on February 4, 1923. vii, 93 p. London: Kegan Paul, 1923.

HERTZLER, Joyce Oramel. The history of Utopian thought. viii, 321 p. New York: Macmillan, 1923. [CB 15/246]

HINSHELWOOD, Cyril. The scientist and the future. *New Scient.,* 1960, 8: 228-31. [CB 86/456]

LE CORBEILLER, Philippe. Man in transit. *Atlantic Mon.,* May 1947, 6. [CB 71/116]

MUMFORD, Lewis. The story of Utopias. With an introduction by Hendrik Willem Van Loon. 315 p. New York: Boni and Liveright, 1923.

PERRIN, Jean. La science et l'espérance. xxxv, 216 p. Paris: Presses Universitaires de France, 1948.
Reviewed by Jacques Putnam, *Arch.Int.Hist.Sci.,* 1949, 2: 771-7.

STEIN, Robert. Naturwissenschaft in Utopia. *Deut.Geschichtsbl.,* 1916, 17: 48-59.

WHYTE, L.L. The next development in man. 275 p. London: Cresset Press, 1944. [CB 77/366]
Publ. New York: H. Holt, 1948, and New American Library, 1950 (Mentor Book).

At relations with the humanities

for relations of science with philosophy *see* AmzAF

ANGELL, James R. Popular and unpopular science. 22 p. (Elihu Root Lecture on the Influence of Science and Research on Current Thought) Washington, D.C.: Carnegie Institution of Washington, 1935.

ASHMORE, Jerome. Some reflections on science and the humanities. *Phys.Today,* 1963, 16: no. 11, 46-54.

BECHER, Erich. Geisteswissenschaften und Naturwissenschaften. Untersuchungen zur Theorie und Einteilung der Realwissenschaften. 385 p. München: Duncker, 1921.

BERNARD, Jessie. Can science transcend culture? *Sci.Mon.,* 1950, 71: 268-73.

BHATIA, S.L. Science and the humanities. 124 p. Calcutta: Orient Longmans, 1962.
Reviewed by D.M. B[ose], *Sci.Cult.,* 1963, 29: 136.

BIAŁOBRZESKI, Czesław. La science et la culture. *Organon,* 1938, 2: 17-42.

BIBBY, Cyril. Science as an instrument of culture. *Nature,* 1964, 202: 331-3.

BROGLIE, Louis de. Science et humanisme. *Nef,* 1946, 3: 57-63.

BRONK, Detlev W. The unity of the sciences and the humanities. 23 p. Cambridge: Massachusetts Institute of Technology, 1949.
Fourth annual Arthur Dehon Little Memorial Lecture at the Massachusetts Institute of Technology, November 22, 1949.

BRONOWSKI, J. The common sense of science. 154 p. Cambridge, Mass.: Harvard University Press, 1953.
About modern science, historically and philosophically oriented, stressing the belief "that the layman's key to science is its unity with the arts".

BRONOWSKI, J. Science and human values. 94 p., ill. New York: Harper & Brothers, 1959.
First publ. New York: Julian Messner, 1956.
Reviewed in *Amer.Scient,*, 1959, 47: 356A-8A; in *Sci.Amer.,* 1960, 202: no. 1, 181-2; by P. Bockstaele, *Sci.Hist.,* 1960, 2: 24-6.

BROWN, Harcourt. Science, humanities, and artifacts. *Sci.Mon.,* 1956, 83: 169-75.

BROWN, Harcourt, ed. Science and the creative spirit: essays on humanistic aspects of science by Karl W. Deutsch, F.E.L. Priestley, Harcourt Brown, and David Hawkins. 165 p. Toronto: University of Toronto Press, 1958.
Reviewed by Lawrence H. Bennett, *Phys.Today,* 1958, 11: 38.

CHAYAPPA, M. The cultural value of modern science. *Aryan Path,* 1949, 365-70.

COUTANT, Victor. Science and the humanities. *J.Higher Educ.,* 1957, 28: 315-18.

DUCASSÉ, Pierre. La science et l'humanisme gréco-latin. *Thalès,* 1937-39, 4: 66-75.

FARRINGTON, B. Science and the classics. *Nature,* 1961, 191: 1337-42.
The place of science in civilization and education.

FASSETT, Frederick, C. Science and culture. Does the dignity of life become greater as we learn more of its complexity? *Technol.Rev.,* May 1938, 312-14.

FLEXNER, Abraham. The burden of humanism. 25 p. (The Taylorian Lecture, 1928) Oxford: Clarendon Press, 1928. [CB 39/443]

FRANK, Philipp. Contemporary science and the contemporary world view. *Daedalus Amer.Acad.Arts Sci.,* 1958, 87: 57-66.

GREENE, T.M., ed. The meaning of the humanities. xi, 178 p. Princeton, N.J.: Princeton University Press, 1938.
Reviewed by M.F. Ashley Montagu, *Isis,* 1947, 32: 225-6.

GREGORY, Richard. Cultural contacts of science. 56 p. (Elihu Root Lectures on the Influence of Science and Research on Current Thought, 5) Washington: Carnegie Institution of Washington, 1938.
Parts of this lecture were printed in *Science,* 1939, 89: 163-6; *Sci.Mon.,* 1939, 48: 99-108; *Nature,* 1939, 143: 68-70. A portion was delivered at the meeting of the AAAS in Richmond, Va. on Dec. 27, 1938.

GUERLAC, Henry. Humanism in science. In: Harris, Julian, ed. The humanities: an appraisal, p. 87-115. Madison: University of Wisconsin Press, 1950.

HARDMAN, David, ed. Reflections on our age. 347 p. New York: Columbia University Press, 1949. [CB 77/345]
Includes several essays on science.

HARRISON, George Russell. What man may be. The human side of science. iv, 262 p. London: Cassell, 1957.
Reviewed by C.A. Coulson, *Nature,* 1958, 181: 7.

HOGBEN, Lancelot. Science and humanism. *Realist,* 1929, 2: 370-83.

HOLTON, Gerald. Modern science and the intellectual tradition. The dissociation of science from the rest of our culture has deep seated causes and disturbing implications. *Science,* 1960, 131: 1187-93.
Reprinted with some amplification from "The Intellectuals". Ed. by B. de Huszar. Chicago: Free Press, 1960, *see* MV.

HOLTON, Gerald. Perspectives on the issue "Science and the modern world view". *Daedalus Amer.Acad.Arts Sci.,* 1958, 87: 3-7.

HUTCHINSON, G. Evelyn. The enchanted voyage and other studies. xi, 163 p., ill. New Haven/London: Yale University Press, 1962.
Insights into the unsuspected liaisons between science and the humanities.

HUTCHISSON, Elmer. Can we merge our "two cultures"? *Bull. Phil.Soc.Wash.,* 1962, 16: 47-57.

JONES, Howard Mumford. A humanist looks at science. *Daedalus Amer.Acad.Arts Sci.,* 1958, 87: 102-10.

KEYSER, Cassius Jackson. Humanism and science. vii, 243 p. New York: Columbia University Press, 1931.
Reviewed by H.T. Davis, *Isis,* 1931, 16: 451-5.

KLIBANSKY, Raymond; PANOFSKY, Erwin; SAXL, Fritz. Saturn and melancholy. Studies in the history of natural philosophy, religion, and art. xviii, 429 p., 5 fig., 146 pl. New York: Basic Books, 1964.

KOENIG, Frederick O. Science and the humanities. In: The humanities look ahead. Report of the first annual conference held by the Stanford School of Humanities, p. 15-24. Stanford: Stanford University Press, 1943.

LEAVIS, F.R. Two cultures? The significance of C.P. Snow. 64 p. New York: Pantheon, 1963.
With an essay by Michael Yudkin.
Reviewed by Jean Le Corbeiller, *Technol.Cult.,* 1964, 5: 119-20.

LORIA, Gino. Cultura classica e scienza moderna. Discorso. 33 p. Genova, 1912.

MATHER, Kirtley F. The problem of anti-scientific trends today. *Science,* 1952, 115: 533-7.

MILLIKAN, Robert A. Science and the new civilization. 194 p. New York: Scribner's, 1930.
Reviewed by George Sarton, *Isis,* 1930, 14: 446-9.

MORRIS, Charles. Prospects for a new synthesis: science and the humanities as complementary activities. *Daedalus Amer. Acad.Arts Sci.,* 1958, 87: 94-101.

OPPENHEIMER, Robert. The growth of science and the structure of culture. *Daedalus Amer.Acad.Arts Sci.,* 1958, 87: 67-76.
Comment on Philipp Frank's paper, *see* above.

PAYNE-GAPOSCHKIN, Cecilia. The scholar and the world. *Amer. Scient.,* 1943, 31: 329-37.

PRIOR, Moody E. Science and the humanities. xii, 124 p. Evanston, Ill.: North-western University Press, 1962.
Reviewed by Robert M. Gray, *Amer.J.Pharm.Educ.,* 1963, 27: 188.

RABI, I.I. Science and the humanities. *Science,* 1955, 122: 961.
Excerpts from an address given at Harvard on 21 October 1955.

ROBINSON, James Harvey. The humanizing of knowledge. *Science,* 1922, 56: 89-100.
Address before the A.A.A.S., Salt Lake City, June 1922.

RYBICKI, P. On the relation between the natural sciences and humanistic knowledge. *Kwart.Hist.Nauk.Tech.,* 1962, 6: (Special issue), 55-72.

SARTON, George. Casting bread upon the face of the waters. (Jamaica). Preface to volume 21. *Isis,* 1934, 21: 488-501.
On science and human values.

SARTON, George. Humanism versus grammar. Preface to volume 25. *Isis,* 1936, 25: 6-8.
Remarks made at the annual dinner of the American Council of Learned Societies, Hotel Mayflower, Washington, D.C., on January 31, 1936.

SARTON, George. Preface to volume 9. *Isis*, 1927, 9: 226-33.
On the unity of thought.

SARTON, George. Two fundamental problems. Second preface to volume 24. *Isis*, 1936, 24: 308-9. [CB 47/282]
The two fundamental problems are the humanization of industry and labor and the humanization of science.

SCIENCE and the humanities. *Nature*, 1961, 189: 695-7.

SEABORG, Glenn T. Science and the humanities: a new level of symbiosis. *Science*, 1964, 144: 1199-203.

SNOW, C.P. The two cultures and the scientific revolution. 58 p. (Rede Lecture, 1959) Cambridge/New York: Cambridge University Press, 1959.
Reviewed by Asa Briggs, *Sci.Amer.*, 1959, 201: no. 4, 201-6.

STANDEN, Anthony. Science is a sacred cow. 221 p. New York: Dutton, 1950.
Reviewed by Bernard Barber, *Isis*, 1951, 42: 91.

STONEQUIST, Everett V. The marginal man: a study in personality and culture conflict. xviii, 228 p. New York: Scribner's, 1937. [CB 56/401]

STUDIES in the history of culture. The disciplines of the humanities. (A tribute presented to Waldo Gifford Leland). xxiii, 343 p., ill. Menasha, Wis.: Banta Publishing Company for the American Council of Learned Societies, 1942.

TESKE, Armin. O elementy humanistyczne w stuciach nauk przyrodniczych. [For some humanist elements in science studies. (In Polish with English summary)]. *Kwart.Hist. Nauk.Tech.*, 1957, 2: 681-93.
French version, *ibid.*, 1957-58, Special issue, 109-21.

VAN VLECK, J.H. "The so-called age of science". Science and the humanities. In: Casimir, H.B.G.; Van Vleck, J.H. The Cherwell-Simon memorial lectures 1961 and 1962, p. 25-50. Edinburgh/London: Oliver and Boyd, 1962.
Reviewed by R. Bruce Lindsay, *Phys.Today*, 1964, 17: no. 4, 70.

VIRIEUX-RAYMOND, A. Histoire des sciences et vie culturelle. *Rev.Théol.Phil.* (Lausanne), 1957, no. 3, 13.
Inaugural lecture of a course on the History of Science at the University of Lausanne, November 1956.

WHITEHEAD, T. North. Humanism in a scientific age. *Amer. Scient.*, 1958, 46: 309-22.

At-o

DAVIS, Tenney L. Toward a liberal education. Relations of science to the humanities. *Technol.Rev.*, 1936, 39: 4.

Atc relation with ethics

for professional ethics *see* Arj

BAYET, Albert. La morale de la science. 139 p. Paris: Presses Universitaires de France, 1931.
Reviewed by J. Pelseneer, *Isis*, 1933, 19: 241-5.

BROWN, Harcourt. A duty to the devil: some suggestions for a humanistic theory. *French Rev.*, 1952, 25: 437-43.

COCKERELL, T.D.A. Science and social ethics. *Science*, 1925, 62: 236-7.

CONKLIN, Edwin Grant. Science and ethics. *Science*, 1937, 86: 595-603; *Nature*, 1938, 141: 101-5.
Address of the retiring president of the A.A.A.S., delivered at Indianapolis on December 27, 1937.

DEWEY, John. Theory of valuation. 67 p. (International Encyclopedia of Unified Science, 2: no. 4) Chicago: University of Chicago Press, 1939.

DINGLE, Herbert. Science and ethics. *Nature*, 1946, 158: 184-7.
Substance of paper for the Conference on 'The problems of communal life: the ethical and scientific approach' organized by the British Social Hygiene Council, 1946.

EDEL, Abraham. Ethical judgment. The use of science in ethics. 348 p. Glencoe, Ill.: Free Press, 1955. [CB 81/263]

EDEL, Abraham. Science and the structure of ethics. iv, 101 p. (International Encyclopedia of Unified Science, 2: no. 3) Chicago: University of Chicago Press, 1961.
Reviewed by Kenneth Stern, *J.Phil.*, 1962, 59: 554-6.

FELLOWS, Erwin. Science and values. *Sci.Mon.*, 1951, 73: 111-13.

GRAUBARD, Mark. Science and brotherly love. *Conference on Science, Philosophy and Religion, 8th Symposium, Learning and World peace*, p. 138-53. New York: Harper, 1948.

GREGORY, Richard. Education in world ethics and science. viii, 40 p. (Conway Memorial Lecture, 1943) London: Watts, 1943.
Reviewed by T. Raymont, *Nature*, 1943, 152: 284-5.

HALDANE, John Burdon Sanderson. Science and ethics. 46 p. (Conway Memorial Lecture, 1928) London: Watts, 1928.

HELLPACH, Willy. Gesinnung, Gewissen und Gesittung der Wissenschaftlichkeit als positive Werte im öffentlichen Leben. 29 p. (Forum Academicum) Frankfurt/Main: Schulte-Bulmke, 1947.

HILL, A.V. The ethical dilemma of science. *Nature*, 1952, 170: 388-93.

HUXLEY, Julian. Essays of a humanist. 288 p. New York: Harper and Row, 1964.
Reviewed by Edward S. Deevey, *Science*, 1964, 145: 147.

HUXLEY, Julian. Knowledge, morality and destiny. xi, 287 p., fig., pl. New York: New American Library of World Literature, 1960.
Original title: New bottles for new wine (London: Chatto and Windus; New York: Harper, 1957).

INGE, William Ralph. Scientific ethics. 20 p. (3rd Norman Lockyer Lecture, 1927) London: British Science Guild, 1927.

JOHNSON, Martin Christopher. Science and the meaning of truth. 179 p. London: Faber and Faber, 1946.
Reviewed by V.F. Lenzen, *Isis*, 1947, 38: 129.

KÖHLER, Wolfgang. The place of value in a world of facts. ix, 418 p., fig. New York: Meridian Books, 1959.
A reprint of the 1938 edition.

KRUSE, Frederik Vinding. The foundation of human thought. The problem of science and ethics. 404 p. London: Oxford University Press, 1949.
Translation of: Erkendelse og Vurdering (Copenhagen: 1942).

LANGMUIR, Irving. Science, common sense and decency. *Science*, 1943, 97: 1-7. [CB 64/449]

LEAKE, Chauncey D. Ethicogenesis. *Studies and Essays offered to George Sarton*, p. 261-75. New York: Schuman, 1947. [CB 71/128]

LEAKE, Chauncey D.; ROMANELL, Patrick. Can we agree? A scientist and a philosopher argue about ethics. xiii, 110 p. Austin: University of Texas Press, 1950. [CB 77/382]

LONSDALE, Kathleen. Science and ethics. *Nature*, 1962, 193: 209-14.

MALISOFF, William Marias. Virtue and the scientist. *Phil. Sci.*, 1939, 6: 127-36.

MARGENAU, Henry. Ethics and science. 314 p., ill. Princeton, N.J.: Van Nostrand, 1964.

MARGENAU, Henry. Western culture, scientific method and the problem of ethics. *Amer.J.Phys.*, 1947, 15: 218-28.

OTTO, Max. Science and the moral life. Selected writings. Preface by Eduard C. Lindeman. 192 p. (A Mentor Book) New York: New American Library, 1949. [CB 76/409]

RAVEN, Charles E. Science, medicine, and morals. A survey and a suggestion. 189 p. New York: Harper, 1959.

RIGNANO, Eugenio. Science et morale. *Rev.Métaphys.Morale*, 1927, 34: 325-35.

ROSHWALD, M. The development of sciences and moral progress. *Act.VIIe Congr.Int.Hist.Sci.* (Jerusalem, 1953), p. 531-6. Paris: Hermann, [n.d.]

RYLE, John A. Science and ethics. *Nature*, 1945, 156: 619-21.

SARTON, George. Sur la tolérance intellectuelle. *Isis,* 1926, 8: 241-53. [CB 21/593]

SHERRINGTON, Charles. Man on his nature. ix, 413 p., 7 pl. (Gifford Lectures, Edinburgh, 1937-38) Cambridge University Press, 1940.
2nd edition 1951.
Reviewed by M.F. Ashley Montagu, *Isis,* 1941, 33: 544-5; by A.D. Ritchie, *Nature,* 1941, 147: 127-9.

SNOW, C.P. The moral un-neutrality of science. Remarks by W. Weaver, T.M. Hesburgh and W.O. Baker. *Science,* 1961, 133: 255-62.

WADDINGTON, C.H. The ethical animal. 230 p. London: George Allen and Unwin, 1960.
Reviewed by Marjorie Grene, *Brit.J.Phil.Sci.,* 1962, 13: 172-6.

WADDINGTON, C.H. The relations between science and ethics. [With commentaries from scientists, etc.]. *Nature,* 1941, 148: 270-80, 342-5, 533-5, 783-4.

WADDINGTON, C.H. Science and ethics. 144 p. London: Allen and Unwin, 1942. [CB 65/79]
Reprints with additions from a series of articles appearing in volume 148 of *Nature,* in 1941, *see* above.

Atd science and religion

for the religious beliefs of scientists *see* Ard

BAILLIE, John. Natural science and the spiritual life. Being the philosophical discourse delivered before the British Association for the Advancement of Science at Edinburgh on 12 August 1951. 44 p. London: Oxford University Press, 1951.
Reviewed by W.R. Matthews, *Nature,* 1951, 168: 968.

BAILLIE, John, *et al.* Science and faith today. 60 p. London: Lutterworth Press, 1953.
Reviewed by R. Brightman, *Nature,* 1953, 172: 557-8.

BARNES, Ernest William. The influence of science on Christianity. From a sermon preached in Liverpool Cathedral on September 16, in connexion with the visit of the British Association to the city. *Nature,* 1923, 112: 477-8.

BARNES, Ernest William. Science, religion and moral judgments. *Nature,* 1950, 166: 455-7.
Substance of the Evening discourse delivered on September 3 at the meeting of the British Association in Birmingham.

BARNES, Ernest William. Scientific theory and religion: the world described by science and its spiritual interpretation. xxiv, 685 p. (The Gifford Lectures at Aberdeen 1927-29) Cambridge University Press, 1933.

BAVINK, Bernhard. Science and God. Transl. by H. Stafford Hatfield. ix, 174 p. London: Bell, 1933.

BEST, John H. From the seen to the unseen. xii, 552 p. London: Longmans, 1929.

BOOTH, Edwin P., ed. Religion ponders science. 314 p. New York: Appleton-Century, 1964.

BRAGG, William Henry. Science and faith. 24 p. (University of Durham, Riddell Memorial Lectures, 13th series, 1941) London: Oxford University Press, 1941.

BRAIN, Russell. Science, philosophy and religion. 31 p. (The Twelfth Arthur Stanley Eddington Memorial Lecture, 1959) Cambridge University Press, 1959.

BREWSTER, Edwin Tenney. The understanding of religion. xiv, 133 p., 9 ill. Boston: Houghton Mifflin, 1923.
Attempt to interpret religion in the light of scientific knowledge.
Reviewed by George Sarton, *Isis,* 1925, 7: 162-5.

BURDELL, Edwin Sharp. Scientific humanism. *Sch.Soc.,* 1938, 48: 611-19.
Address on the occasion of the installation of Dr. Burdell as the director of Cooper Union, New York City, November 3, 1938.

CHWOLSON, O.D. Das Problem Wissenschaft und Religion: Versuch einer Lösung in neuer Richtung. iv, 37 p. Braunschweig: Vieweg, 1925.

CLARK, Robert Edward David. The universe and God. v, 252 p. London: Hodder and Stoughton, 1939.
Reviewed by Richard Hocking, *Isis,* 1949, 32: 403-5.

COMPTON, Arthur H. The human meaning of science. xiv, 88 p. (John Calvin McNair Lectures) Chapel Hill, N.C.: University of North Carolina Press, 1940.
Reviewed by W.R. Matthews, *Nature,* 1942, 150: 130-1.

CONFERENCE ON SCIENCE, PHILOSOPHY AND RELIGION IN THEIR RELATIONS TO THE DEMOCRATIC WAY OF LIFE. [Papers of the meeting] 1st-16th symposium. New York: Harpers for the Conference, 1941-62. [CB 64/449, CB 68/58-9, CB 69/235 and CB 71/128]

COULSON, C.A. Science and Christian belief. vii, 127 p. (The John Calvin McNair Lectures) Chapel Hill, N.C.: University of North Carolina Press, 1955.
Reviewed by George A. Foote, *Isis,* 1956, 47: 427-8.

COULSON, C.A. Science and the idea of God. 51 p. (Arthur Stanley Eddington Memorial Lecture, 11) Cambridge/New York: Cambridge University Press, 1958.

COULSON, C.A. Science, technology and the Christian. 111 p. (The Beckly Social Service Lecture, 1960) London: Epworth Press, 1960.
Reviewed by R. Brightman, *Nature,* 1961, 189: 173-4.

CROSS, Frank Leslie. Religion and the reign of science. xi, 111 p. (Anglican Library of Faith and Thought) London: Longmans, Green, 1930.

D'ARCY, Charles F. Science and creation: the Christian interpretation. vi, 126 p. London: Longmans, 1925.

DINGLE, Reginald James. The faith and modern science. xvii, 195 p. London: Burns, Oates and Washbourne, 1935.
Reviewed by T.G., *Nature,* 1936, 137: 92.

DONAT, Josef. Die Freiheit der Wissenschaft. Ein Gang durch das moderne Geistesleben. 3rd ed. (reprint). xii, 520 p. Innsbruck: F. Rauch, 1925.
First published 1910; 2nd edition 1912.
Reviewed by H. Wieleitner, *Mitt.Gesch.Med.,* 1926, 25: 215-16.

DUNHAM, Chester Forrester. Christianity in a world of science. 185 p. New York: Macmillan, 1930.

EDDINGTON, Arthur Stanley. Science and the unseen world. 56 p. (Swarthmore Lecture, 1929) London: Allen and Unwin, 1929.

GAGER, Charles Stuart. The relation between science and theology: how to think about it. vi, 87 p. Chicago: Open Court Publishing Company, 1925.

GEMELLI, Agostino. Religione e scienza. xii, 347 p. (Saggi Apologetici, 2) Milano: Vita e Pensiero, 1920. [CB 10/208]

GREGORY, Richard. Gods and men. ix, 214 p. London: Stuart and Richards; New York: Macmillan, 1949. [CB 76/410]
Reviewed by Arthur Keith, *Nature,* 1949, 163: 856.

GREGORY, Richard. Religion in science and civilization. xiii, 306 p. London: Macmillan, 1940. [CB 76/410]

GREGORY, Richard. Religion in science. *Sci.Mon.,* 1939, 48: 99-108. [CB 57/269]
Points out the significance of faith in carrying forward work and discusses the relation of science to social ethics.

HEIM, Karl. Christian faith and natural science. 256 p. New York: Harper, 1953.

HEIM, Karl. The transformation of the scientific world view. 262 p. New York: Harper, 1953. [CB 80/202]
The problems of Protestant theology and modern science.

HOCKING, William Ernest. Science and the idea of God. xi, 124 p. (John Calvin McNair Lectures) Chapel Hill, N.C.: University of North Carolina Press, 1944.
Reviewed in *Nature,* 1945, 156: 281.

HUXLEY, Julian. Science and religion. *Listener,* 1930, 4: 503-4, 535-7.

HUXLEY, Julian. What dare I think? The challenge of modern science to human action and belief. Including the Henry La Barre Jayne Foundation Lectures (Philadelphia) for 1931. ix, 278 p. London: Chatto and Windus, 1931.

INGE, William Ralph. Science and ultimate truth. 32 p. (Fison Memorial Lecture, 1926) London: Longmans, Green, 1926.

LEAKE, Chauncey D. Religio scientiae. *Sci.Mon.*, 1941, 52: 166-73.

LINDSAY, Alexander D. Religion, science and society in the modern world. 64 p. (Terry Lectures delivered at Yale University, 1943) London: Oxford University Press, 1943.
Reviewed by F. Ian G. Rawlins, *Nature*, 1944, 153: 150-1.

LUNN, Arnold; HALDANE, J.B.S. Science and the supernatural. A correspondence between Arnold Lunn and J.B.S. Haldane. vii, 412 p. London: Eyre and Spottiswoode, 1935.
Reviewed by J.C. Hardwick, *Nature*, 1935, 136: 288.

MACPHERSON, Hector Copland. The church and science: a study of the inter-relation of theological and scientific thought. 254 p. (The Living Church Series) London: James Clarke, 1927.

MATHEWS, Shailer, ed. Contributions of science to religion. With the cooperation of William E. Ritter, Robert A. Millikan, Edwin B. Frost, and others. vii, 427 p., 5 pl. New York: Appleton, 1924.

MATTHEWS, W.R. Relation of religion and science. *Nature*, 1953, 172: 376-7.

METZGER, Helene. La science, l'appel de la religion et la volonté humaine. 61 p. Paris: E. de Boccard, 1954. [CB 81/263]
Reviewed by S. Delorme, *Rev.Hist.Sci.*, 1954, 7: 378.

MILLIKAN, Robert A. Science and religion. *Isis*, 1924, 6: 43-4.

MOREUX, Théophile. Les confins de la science et de la foi. 2 vol., ill. Paris: G. Doin, 1924-25.

MULLER, Camille. L'encyclique *Humani generis* et les problèmes scientifiques. 36 p. Louvain: Nauwelaerts, 1951.

NEEDHAM, Joseph, ed. Science, religion and reality. Introductory essay by George Sarton. 355 p. New York: George Braziller, 1955. [CB 81/264]
First published 1925 (London: Sheldon Press; New York: Macmillan): corrected reprint 1926. [CB 68/50]

PELSENEER, Jean. Science, religion et technique. *IIIe Congr. Nat.Sci.* (Bruxelles, 1950), (1), p. 10-12. [Liège: 1951].

POLANYI, M. Science, faith and society. 80 p. (University of Durham, Riddell Memorial Lectures, 18th series) London: Oxford University Press, 1946.
Reviewed by F. Ian G. Rawlins, *Nature*, 1947, 159: 793.

POLLARD, William G. Chance and providence. God's action in a world governed by scientific thought. 190 p. New York: Scribner's, 1958.

PUPIN, Michael Idvorsky. The new reformation: from physical to spiritual realities. xvii, 273 p., 8 pl. New York: Scribner's, 1927.

RAHN, Carl. Science and the religious life. A psycho-physiological approach. ix, 221 p. New Haven: Yale University Press, 1928.

RAVEN, Charles E. Experience and interpretation. vii, 227 p. (Gifford Lectures on Natural Religion and Christian Theology, 1951-52, 2nd series) Cambridge University Press, 1953.

RAVEN, Charles E. Science and religion. vii, 224 p. (Gifford Lecture on Natural Religion and Christian Theology, 1951-52, 1st series) Cambridge University Press, 1953.
Reviewed by Marie Boas, *Isis*, 1954, 45: 205-6.

RAVEN, Charles E. Science and the Christian man. 60 p. London: SCM Press, 1952. [CB 79/169]

RAVEN, Charles E. Science, religion, and the future. A course of eight lectures. x, 125 p. Cambridge University Press, 1943. [CB 53/87]
Reviewed by T. Raymont, *Nature*, 1943, 152: 284-5.

REISER, Oliver L. A philosophy for world unification. Scientific humanism as an ideology for cultural integration. 20 p. Girard, Kan.: Haldeman-Julius, 1946.

REISER, Oliver L. The promise of scientific humanism. xviii, 364 p. New York: Piest, 1940.
Reviewed by M.F. Ashley Montagu, *Isis*, 1943, 34: 226-9.

REISER, Oliver L. Scientific humanism as creative morality. 23 p. Girard, Kan.: Haldeman-Julius, 1949.

RICHARDSON, Alan. Science and existence; two ways of knowing. 30 p. (Technics and Purpose, 1) London: Student Christian Movement Press, Ltd., 1957.

ROZWADOWSKI, Jan. La science, la religion et l'art. *Organon*, 1936, 1: 13-19.

RUSSELL, Bertrand. Religion and science. 256 p. (Home University Library of Modern Knowledge, 178) London: Butterworth, 1935.
Reprinted 1956 (London/New York: Oxford University Press) and 1961 (New York: Galaxy Books).

SAMUEL, Herbert Louis Samuel, *Viscount;* DINGLE, Herbert. A threefold cord: philosophy, science, religion. 280 p. London: Geo. Allen and Unwin, 1961.
Reviewed by G.W. Scott Blair, *Brit.J.Phil.Sci.*, 1962, 13: 339-40.

SCIENCE and religion: a symposium. vii, 175 p. London: Howe, 1931. [CB 36/454]
Twelve talks by Julian Huxley, J. Arthur Thomson, J.S. Haldane and others, broadcast September-December 1930 by the British Broadcasting Corporation. American edition (New York: Scribner's, 1931) has foreword by Michael Pupin.

SHAPLEY, Harlow, ed. Science ponders religion. 308 p., bibliogr. New York: Appleton-Century-Crofts, 1960.

SIMPSON, James Young. The garment of the Living God. Studies in the relations of science and religion. With a memoir by G.F. Barbour. 281 p. London: Hodder and Stoughton, 1934.

SINGER, Charles. Scientific humanism. *Realist*, 1929, 1: 12-18.

SMITH, Homer W. Man and his gods. 500 p. Boston: Little, Brown and Co., 1952.
Reviewed by Mark Graubard, *Isis*, 1953, 44: 88-9.

SMYTH, Nathan A. Through science to God. vii, 213 p. New York: Macmillan, 1936.
Reviewed by M.F. Ashley-Montagu, *Isis*, 1937, 27: 114-16.

STREETER, Burnett Hillman. Reality: a new correlation of science and religion. xiii, 350 p. London: Macmillan, 1926.
Reviewed in *Nature*, 1927, 119: 273-4.

STREETER, Burnett Hillman, *et al.* Adventure: the faith of science and the science of faith. ix, 247 p. London: Macmillan, 1927.
Reviewed by E.S.R., *Nature*, 1928, 121: 448.

TAYLOR, F. Sherwood. Man and matter. Essays scientific and Christian. 238 p. London: Chapman & Hall, 1951. [CB 80/121]

THOMSON, John Arthur. Science and religion. ix, 238 p. (Morse Lectures, Union Theological Seminary, New York, 1924) New York: Methuen, 1925.

TITIUS, Arthur. Natur und Gott. Ein Versuch zur Verständigung zwischen Naturwissenschaft und Theologie. x, 851 p. Göttingen: Vandenhoeck und Ruprecht, 1926.
Reviewed by H. Wieleitner, *Mitt.Gesch.Med.*, 1926, 214-15.

URBAN, Wilbur Marshall. Humanity and deity. 479 p. London: Allen & Unwin, 1951; New York: Macmillan. [CB 79/191]

WALKER, Leslie Joseph. Science and revelation. vii, 87 p. London: Oates, 1932.

WEIZSÄCKER, Carl Friedrich von. The history of nature. 191 p. Chicago: University of Chicago Press, 1949. Paperback reprint, 1959. [CB 76/393]
Reviewed by S. Moser, *Phil.Natur.*, 1951, 1: 435-8; by H. Wein, *ibid.*, 438-46.

WESTAWAY, F.W. Science and theology. Their common aims and methods. iv, 346 p. London: Blackie, 1920.
Reviewed by George Sarton, *Isis*, 1921, 4: 119-22.

WHITE, Lynn. Christian myth and Christian history. *J.Hist. Ideas*, 1942, 3: 145-58.

WHITEHEAD, Alfred North. Religion in the making. 160 p. (Lowell Lectures, 1926) Cambridge University Press, 1926.

WIEMAN, Henry Nelson. Religious experience and scientific method. v, 387 p. New York: Macmillan, 1926.

WOOD, Alexander. In pursuit of truth: a comparative study ir science and religion. 122 p. London: S.C.M., 1927.

WOOD, H.G. Belief and unbelief since 1850. viii, 143 p. New York: Cambridge University Press, 1955.
Reviewed by George A. Foote, *Isis*, 1956, 47: 427-8.

WOODBURNE, Angus Stewart. The relation between religion and science. A biological approach. vii, 103 p. Chicago, Ill.: Chicago University Press, 1920.

Atd-br

Science and Religion: a review of current literature and thought. Edited by Robert E.D. Clark. 1- London: Paternoster Press, 1948-. [CB 73/181]
Journal devoted to the study of interrelationships of science with religion and philosophy.

Atf religion and science in history

ADNAN-ADIVAR, Abdulhak. [Science and religion in the course of history. 2 vol. 1. From the beginnings to the 19th century. xxii, 360 p. 2. 19th and 20th centuries. xi, 286 p. (In Turkish)]. Istanbul: Kitabevi, 1944.
Reviewed by Lewis V. Thomas, *Isis*, 1949, 40: 285-6.

AGAR, William M. Catholicism and the progress of science. ix, 109 p. New York: Macmillan, 1940. [CB 62/84]

BAUMER, Franklin L. Religion and the rise of scepticism. 308 p. New York: Harcourt, Brace, 1960.

COULTON, G.G. Inquisition and liberty. xiii, 354 p. London: Heinemann; New York: Macmillan, 1938. [CB 53/568]
Reviewed by M.F. Ashley-Montagu, *Isis*, 1939, 30: 558-60.

DELEVSKY, J. L'évolution des sciences et les croyances. *Rev. Syn.*, 1938, 16: 97-106.

DILLENBERGER, John. Protestant thought and natural science. A historical interpretation. 320 p. London: Collins, 1961.
Reviewed by Sten Lindroth, *Lychnos*, 1962, 320-1.

DRAPER, John William. History of the conflict between religion and science. New edition. xxii, 373 p. London: Pioneer Press (for the Secular Society), 1923.
First edition New York: 1874.

HARDWICK, John Charlton. Religion and science. From Galileo to Bergson. ix, 148 p. London: Society for Promoting Christian Knowledge, 1920.

HOOYKAAS, R. Natural law and divine miracle. xiv, 237 p. Leiden: Brill, 1959.
Reviewed by M.J.S. Rudwick, *Hist.Sci.*, 1962, 1: 82-6.

HOOYKAAS, R. Natuurwetenschap en religie in het licht der historie. [Science and religion in the light of history. (In Dutch)]. Referaat voor de negentiende Wetenschappelijke samenkomst der Vrije Universiteit. 31 p. Assen: G.F. Hummelen, 1934.

HOOYKAAS, R. Philosophia libera. Christian faith and the freedom of science. 24 p. London: Tyndale Press, 1957.
Reviewed by J.A. Vollgraff, *Janus*, 1957, 46: 232.

PELSENEER, Jean. La réforme et l'origine de la science moderne. *Rev.Univ.Bruxelles*, 1953-4, 6: 406-18.

RITTER, Eugène. Trois chapitres de l'histoire des sciences. *Compt.Rend.Acad.Sci.Morales Polit.*, Oct.-Dec. 1926, 346-54. [CB 23/233]
On the struggle between the ecclesiastical authority and the Copernicans, between dogma and the idea of the evolution of the earth and between biblical tradition and the evolution of the human species.

SHIPLEY, Maynard. The war on modern science: a short history of the fundamentalist attack on evolution and modernism. xiv, 415 p. London/New York: Knopf, 1927.

SIMPSON, James Young. Landmarks in the struggle between science and religion. xiv, 288 p. London: Hodder and Stoughton, 1925.

SINGER, Charles. Religion and science. Considered in their historical relations. 79 p. (Benn's Sixpenny Library, 144) London: Benn, 1928.

UĬBO, Arkadiĭ Aleksandrovich. Iz istorii bor'by nauk protiv religii. [From the history of the struggle of science against religion. (In Russian)]. 30 p., ill. Moscow: Znanie, 1956.

VERNES, Maurice. Histoire social des religions. 1. Les religions occidentales dans leur rapport avec le progrès politique et social. 539 p. Paris: V. Giard et E. Brière, 1911.
Refers to the encouragement of arts and sciences by religious establishments of education.
Reviewed by George Sarton, *Isis*, 1913, 1: 538-9.

WALSH, James J. Rôle of Catholic physicians and scientists in the advancement of civilization. *Med.Life*, 1929, 36: 169-88, pl.

WHITE, Andrew Dickson. A history of the warfare of science with theology in Christendom. 2 vol. New York: Dover Publications, Inc., 1960.
"Unabridged and unaltered republication of the 1st ed., 1896." Also reprinted 1955 (2 vol. in 1, New York: George Braziller).
Reviewed by Francis C. Haber, *Hispanic Amer.Hist.Rev.*, 1961, 41: 307.

Ath relation with literature

DINGLE, Herbert. Science and literary criticism. 184 p. London: Nelson, 1949.

EASTMAN, Max. Literature in an age of science. (Address at the awarding of the Avery Hopwood prizes at the University of Michigan, June 1934) *Mich.Alumnus*, 1934, 40: 108-16.

EVANS, B. Ifor. Literature and science. 114 p. London: George Allen & Unwin, 1954. [CB 81/263]

FULTON, John Farquhar. Humanism in an age of science. 26 p. New York: Schuman, 1950. [CB 77/362]
The author illustrates the interrelations between science and literature.

GLASS, Bentley. The scientist in contemporary fiction. *Sci. Mon.*, 1957, 85: 288-93.

GLICKSBERG, Charles I. Literature and science: a study in conflict. *Sci.Mon.*, 1944, 59: 467-72.

GLICKSBERG, Charles I. Science and the literary mind. *Sci. Mon.*, 1950, 70: 352-7.
An account of some literary opposition to what the litterateurs thought was the belittling of man by science.

HUXLEY, Aldous. Literature and science. 118 p. New York: Harper & Row, 1963.

HYMAN, Stanley Edgar. The tangled bank: Darwin, Marx, Frazer and Freud as imaginative writers. 492 p. New York: Atheneum, 1962.
Reviewed by Morse Peckham, *Victorian Stud.*, 1962, 6: 180-2.

JEFFARES, A. Norman. Language, literature and science. An inaugural lecture. 24 p. Leeds: Leeds University Press, 1959.

Literature and Science. Proceedings of the Sixth Triennial Congress, International Federation for Modern Languages and Literature, (Oxford, 1954). xiii, 330 p. Oxford: Basil Blackwell, 1955. [CB 83/194]

McCOLLEY, Grant. Literature and science. xii, 528 p. Chicago: Packard, 1940.
Reviewed by M.F. Ashley Montagu, *Isis*, 1941, 33: 285-7.

MESSAC, Regis. Micromégas. 93 p. Nimes: La Laborieuse, [1936?].
Essay on the literary repercussions of the scientific knowledge of the microscopic world.

MONTAGU, M.F. Ashley. Suggestions for the better correlation of literature & science. *Studies and Essays offered to George Sarton*, p. 235-46. New York: Schuman, 1947. [CB 71/115]

MULLER, Herbert J. Science and criticism. xiv, 303 p. New Haven: Yale University Press, 1943. [CB 65/79]
The value of contemporary scientific thought for the literary critic.

NICOLSON, Marjorie Hope. Mountain gloom and mountain glory: the development of the aesthetics of the infinite. xv, 403 p. Ithaca, N.Y.: Cornell University Press, 1959.
Reviewed by D.C. Allen, *Isis*, 1960, 51: 222-3.

NICOLSON, Marjorie Hope. Science and imagination. ix, 238 p. (Great Seal Books) Ithaca, N.Y.: Cornell University Press, 1957. [CB 83/194]

READ, John. Science, literature, and human thought. *J.Chem. Educ.*, 1960, 37: 110-17.
A rapid view of scientific references and influences in literature from the Ebers Papyrus to Ezra Pound.

ROSENBERG, Charles E. Martin Arrowsmith: the scientist as hero. *Amer.Quart.*, 1963, 15: 447-58.
A revelation of the role played by Paul de Kruif in providing Sinclair Lewis with motivation and information in this novel.

THOMPSON, D'Arcy Wentworth. Science and the classics. *Nature*, 1929, 123: 800-3.
Presidential address to the Classical Association, Cardiff, April 9, 1929.

Ath-bv

DUDLEY, Fred A., ed. The relations of literature and science: a selected bibliography 1930-1967. Combining annual bibliographies assembled by various hands for "General Topic 7", a discussion group of the Modern Language Association of America and published in *Symposium*. viii, 137 p. Ann Arbor, Mich.: University Microfilms, 1968.
Earlier edition covered 1930-49. [CB 76/408]

Ath-md

BURGER, D. [The concept of time in literature. (In Dutch)]. *Faraday*, June 1949, 89-99.

Atk relation with poetry

BAILEY, C.E.G. Poetry and science. *Nature*, 1954, 173: 113.

BUSH, Douglas. Science and English poetry. A historical sketch, 1590-1950. viii, 166 p. (The Patten Lectures, 1949, Indiana University) New York: Oxford University Press, 1950. [CB 79/189]

COCULESCO, Pius Servien. Science et poésie. 249 p. (Bibliothèque de Philosophie Scientifique) Paris: Flammarion, 1947. [CB 78/181]

CRUM, Ralph B. Scientific thought in poetry. vi, 246 p. (Columbia University Studies in English and Comparative Literature) New York: Columbia University Press, 1931.

EASTWOOD, W., ed. A book of science verse. 279 p. London: Macmillan, 1960.
Reviewed by Donald Davie, *Hist.Sci.*, 1962, 1: 100-2.

HENN, T.R. Science and poetry. *Nature*, 1961, 191: 534-9.

OEHSER, Paul H. The lion and the lamb. Essay on science and poetry. *Amer.Scient.*, 1955, 43: 89-96.

PEACOCK, Roland. Abstraction and reality in modern science, art and poetry. In: *Literature and science, Proc.Congr.Int. Fed.Mod.Lang.Lit.* (Oxford, 1954), p. 324-30. Oxford: Blackwell, 1955.

SEEGER, Raymond J. Scientist and poet. *Amer.Scient.*, 1959, 47: 350-60.

WOOD, H.G. Thought, life and time as reflected in science and poetry. 58 p. (The Tenth Arthur Stanley Eddington Memorial Lecture, 1957) Cambridge University Press, 1957.

Atk-nq

ARTHOS, Joh. Poetic diction and scientific language. *Isis*, 1949, 32: 324-38.

Atn science fiction

MOSKOWITZ, Sam. Explorers of the infinite: shapers of science fiction. 353 p. Cleveland/New York: World Publishing Co., 1963.

Atp aesthetic aspects

READ, Herbert. The forms of things unknown. Essays towards an aesthetic philosophy. 248 p., ill. Cleveland/New York: World Publishing Co., 1963.

SEEGER, Raymond J. Phenomena and imagination. *Sci.Mon.*, 1951, 72: 148-52.
The author emphasizes that science can be a source of aesthetic enjoyment.

WEISS, Paul. Beauty and the beast: life and the rule of order. *Sci.Mon.*, 1955, 81: 286-99, ill.
Describes aesthetic patterns found in nature.

WHYTE, L.L., ed. Aspects of form, a symposium on form in nature and art. ix, 249 p., 32 pl. New York: Pellegrini & Cudahy; London: Lund Humphries, 1951. [CB 79/169]
Reviewed by F.I.G. Rawlins, *Nature*, 1951, 168: 574.

Atp-nq

COCULESCO, Pius Servien. Principes d'esthétique: problèmes d'art et langage des sciences. viii, 228 p. Paris: Boivin, 1935.
Reviewed by Hélène Metzger, *Archeion*, 1935, 17: 342-3.

Atq relation with art

for illustrations in scientific literature *see* Acm

BRÉHIER, Louis. L'art chrétien. Son développement iconographique des origines à nos jours. 456 p., 233 pl. Paris: H. Laurens, 1918.
Reviewed by G. Sarton, *Isis*, 1921-22, 4: 540-4.

DE MOTT, Benjamin. Science and the rejection of realism in art. *Synthese*, 1963, 15: 389-400.

FLORISOONE, Michel. Aperçus sur certains rapports de la science et de l'art. 23 p. (Conférences du Palais de la Découverte, 5 juin 1948) Paris: Université de Paris, [1949?]

GIBSON, R.E. Science, art, and education. *Annu.Rep.Smithsonian Inst.* for year ended June 1953, p. 169-203. Washington, D.C.: 1954.

JOHNSON, Martin. Art and scientific thought. viii, 192 p. London: Faber and Faber, 1944. [CB 75/85]
Reviewed by M.F.A. Montagu, *Isis*, 1947, 37: 122.
American edition, 1949 (New York: Columbia University Press).

HOURTICQ, Louis. L'art et la science. 243 p. (Bibliothèque de Philosophie Scientifique) Paris: Flammarion, 1943.

HOURTICQ, Louis. La vie des images. 246 p., 16 pl., 397 ill. Paris: Hachette, 1927.
Reviewed by George Sarton, *Isis*, 1931, 16: 181-4.

LANGER, Susanne K. Abstraction in science and abstraction in art. *Structure, Method and Meaning, Essays in Honor of Henry M. Sheffer*, p. 171-82. New York: Liberal Arts Press, 1951.

LAPAGE, Geoffrey. Art and the scientist. xii, 115 p., pl., fig., bibliogr. Bristol: John Wright; Baltimore: Williams and Wilkins, 1961.
Reviewed by Jacob Kainen, *Isis*, 1963, 54: 411-12; by Claus Nissen, *Sudhoffs Arch.*, 1963, 47: 192.

PIRENNE, M.H. Art, science and the million. *Message*, 1942, no. 9, 39-43, ill.

RAWLINS, F. Ian G. Natural science and the fine arts. *Proc. Roy.Inst.*, 1947-50, 34: 40-6, 2 pl.
A Friday evening discourse delivered at the Royal Institution on February 14, 1947. Also in *Nature*, 1947, 159: 628-30.

SAXL, F.; WITTKOWER, R. British art and the Mediterranean. 86 pl. and pages of explanatory text. (Warburg Institute, University of London) London: Oxford University Press, 1948.
This extends to science, medicine and philosophy.
Reviewed by W. Pagel, *Isis*, 1950, 41: 143.

SCIENTIFIC AMERICAN. Art in science. A portfolio of 32 paintings, drawings and photographs from *Scientific American*. With a preface by György Kepes. New York: Simon and Schuster, [1955]. [CB 81/263]

SIEGEL, Armand. Operational aspects of hidden-variable quantum theories with a postscript on the impact of scientific rends on art. *Synthese*, 1962, 14: 171-88.

Att relation with music

JEANS, James Hopwood. Science and music. x, 258 p. New York: Macmillan, 1937.
Reviewed by V.F. Lenzen, *Isis*, 1938, 29: 172.

NOVAK, Benjamin J.; BARNETT, Gladys R. Scientists and musicians. *Sci.Teacher*, 1956, 23: 229-32, 1 portr.

Au popular aspects of science

MARINUS, Albert. Folklore et science. *Folklore Brabançon*, 1933, 13: 5-52.

MARINUS, Albert. La pensée scientifique et le sens commun. *Compt.Rend.IIe Congr.Nat.Sci.* (Bruxelles, 1935), (1), p. 45-50. Bruxelles: 1935.

PELSENEER, Jean. Le folklore et l'histoire de la pensée scientifique. *Archeion*, 1934, 16: 186-204. [CB 43/286]

PELSENEER, Jean. Questionnaire de folklore pour servir à l'histoire de la pensée scientifique. *Compt.Rend.XVIe Congr.Int.Anthropol.Archéol.Prehist.* (Brussels, 1935), p. 993-7. Bruxelles: Imprimerie Médicale et Scientifique, 1936.
Also published in *Folklore Brabançon*, 1936, 16: 269-72.

Av ethnic and linguistic groups

Avf Latin races and languages

Avf-ce

SARTON, George. Scientific literature in Romansh. *Osiris*, 1950, 9: 602-23, 9 fig.

Avh Slavs

Avh-be

ROUCEK, Joseph S., ed. Slavonic encyclopaedia. xi, 1445 p. New York: Philosophical Library, 1949. [CB 75/96]

Avh-da

PETRONIEVICS, Branislav. Slav achievement in advanced science. 32 p. London: American Book Supply Co., 1917. [CB 8/367]
Biographies of Copernicus, Mendeleev, Lobachevskiĭ and Boscovich.

Avm Jews

GERSHENFELD, Louis. The Jew in science. viii, 224 p. Philadelphia: Jewish Publication Society, 1934. [CB 41/572]

JACOBS, Joseph. Jewish contributions to civilization. An estimate. 334 p. Philadelphia: The Jewish Publication Society of America, 1919.

MAGNUS, Laurie. The Jews in the Christian era. From the first to the eighteenth century and their contributions to its civilization. 432 p. London: Benn, 1929.

NEWMAN, H., ed. The real Jew: some aspects of the Jewish contribution to civilization. With an introduction by Israel Zangwill. xxiv, 291 p. London: Black, 1925.

ROBACK, A.A. The Jew in modern science. In: Runes, Dagobert D., ed. The Hebrew impact on Western civilization, p. 187-318. New York: Philosophical Library, 1951.

ROBACK, A.A. Jewish influence in modern thought. 506 p., 16 ill. Cambridge, Mass.: Sci-Art, 1929. [CB 27/522]

ROTH, Cecil. The Jewish contribution to civilization. New ed. xiii, 369 p. Oxford: East and West Library, 1943.
Spanish edition (Buenos Aires: Editorial Israel, 1945) reviewed by F.P.C., *Sefarad*, 1946, 6: 206-8.

RUNES, Dagobert D., ed. The Hebrew impact on Western civilization. xiv, 922 p. New York: Philosophical Library, 1951. [CB 78/171]

Avm-bv

STONEHILL, C.A., ed. The Jewish contribution to civilization. A collection of books formed and offered by C.A. Stonehill, Ltd. With a preface by Stephen Zweig. 198 p. [Birmingham: Printed at the press of F. Juckes Ltd., 1940]. 2585 items.

Avm-da

RAISIN, Max. Great Jews I have known. A gallery of portraits. xv, 249 p. New York: Philosophical Library, 1952.

Avs Turkish and Finno-Ugrian

Avs-ce

WITTEK, Paul. Neuere wissenschaftliche Literatur in osmanisch-türkischer Sprache. *Orient.Lit.Zeitung*, 1931, 34: 411-20.

Aw in different countries

BRILLOUIN, Léon. Science française et science américaine. *Répub.Franç.*, 1945, 2: 27-30.

FELLOWS, Erwin W. Intercultural comparison in the history of science. *J.Hum.Relat.*, 1959, 7: 15, bibliogr.
An attempt to explain the failure of systematic scientific inquiry to develop to any great extent in literate societies other than the Western European. Chinese, Arabic, Indian and Greek science are examined.

FLEMING, Donald. Science in Australia, Canada, and the United States. Some comparative remarks. *Proc.10th Int. Congr.Hist.Sci.* (Ithaca, 1962),(1),p. 179-96. Paris: Hermann, 1964.

LACROIX, Alfred. La recherche scientifique dans les territoires d'outre-mer. *Thalès*, 1940, 4: 13-22.

Iz Istorii Nauki i Tekhniki v Stranakh Vostoka. [On the history of science and technology in the countries of the East. (In Russian)] Vol. 1- Moskva: Izdatel'stvo Vostochnoi Literatury, 1960-
Volume 2, 1961, reviewed by M. Wong, *Arch.Int.Hist.Sci.*, 1962, 15: 419-20.

MIELI, A. Il contributo dato dai diversi paesi allo svilluppo della storia della scienza. *Scientia*, 1921, 29: 89-100; French transl. supplement, 21-32. [CB 10/209]

YUASA, Mitutomo. Center of scientific activity; its shift from the 16th to the 20th century. *Jap.Stud.Hist.Sci.*, 1962, 1: 57-75.

Awb North America

AMERICA'S role in the growth of science. Present trends and international implications of science. Problems of international cooperation in science and the Pilgrim Trust Lecture. Papers read before the American Philosophical Society and the National Academy of Sciences, October 17-23, 1946. *Proc.Amer.Phil.Soc.*, 1947, 91: 1-136. [CB 71/115]

AMERICAN PHILOSOPHICAL SOCIETY. The early history of science and learning in America with especial reference to the work of the American Philosophical Society during the eighteenth and nineteenth centuries. [Papers by E.G. Conklin, *et al.*] *Proc.Amer.Phil.Soc.*, 1942, 86: 1-204; 1943, 87: 1-119, ill. [CB 63/268 and CB 65/78]

BELL, Whitfield J. Early American science: needs and opportunities for study. ix, 85 p. Williamsburg, Va.: Institute of Early American History and Culture, 1955.
Reviewed by Theodore Hornberger, *Amer.Hist.Rev.*, 1956, 61: 473.

BRADFORD, Richard. The sciences, pure and applied, in the first century of the landgrant institutions. *Sci.Educ.*, 1962, 46: 240-7.

BRILLOUIN, Léon. *See* Aw

CARGILL, Oscar. Intellectual America. xxi, 777 p. New York: Macmillan, 1941. [CB 62/82]

CARMICHAEL, Emmett B. The South's contribution to science. *Science*, 1931, 74: 421-7.

CHRISTIAN, Schuyler Medlock. The history of science in the South. (Southern Scientists' Meeting, Mobile, Alabama, March 20, 1941). 19 p.
Mimeographed.

COHEN, Morris R. American thought. A critical sketch. 360 p. Glencoe, Ill.: Free Press, 1954.
Reviewed by Philip B. Perlman, *Sci.Mon.*, 1955, 80: 378-9.

CONANT, James B. The advancement of learning in the United States in the post-war world. *Proc.Amer.Phil.Soc.*, 1944, 87: 291-8; also in *Science*, 1944, 99: 87-94.

CURTI, Merle, *et al.* An American history. 2 vol. xiv, 657 p.; xiv, 683 p., maps, charts. New York: Harper, 1950. [CB 78/196]
Large amount of space given to science, invention and technology.

DANA, Edward Salisbury, *et al.* A century of science in America. With special reference to the *American Journal of Science*, 1818-1918. 458 p., 22 portr. New Haven, Conn.: Yale University Press, 1918. [CB 7/116]

DUPREE, A. Hunter, ed. Science and the emergence of modern America, 1865-1916. 59 p. (Berkeley Series in American History) Chicago: Rand McNally & Co., 1963.

EATON, Clement. A history of the Old South. ix, 636 p. New York: Macmillan, 1949.
Some pages devoted to science.

EISENHART, Luther P., ed. Historic Philadelphia, from the founding until the early nineteenth century. Papers dealing with its people and buildings with an illustrative map. 331 p., front., pl. and fig. in text, map. (*Trans.Amer. Phil.Soc.*, 1953, vol. 43) Philadelphia: American Philosophical Society, 1953. [CB 80/113]

FLEMING, Donald. *See* Aw

HOCKETT, Homer Carey. Political and social growth of the American people, 1492-1865. 3rd ed. xxi, 861 p. New York: Macmillan, 1940. [CB 61/413]
See also Schlesinger, Arthur Meier, below.

KILGOUR, Frederick G. How good are our science and engineering? *Yale Rev.*, Summer, 1955, 555-63.

KULL, Irving S.; KULL, Nell M. A short chronology of American history 1492-1950. 388 p. New Brunswick, N.J.: Rutgers University Press, 1952.

PIERCE, John Robinson; TRESSLER, Arthur G. The research state. A history of science in New Jersey. xv, 167 p., ill., maps, portr. (New Jersey Historical Series, 15) Princeton, N.J.: Van Nostrand, 1964.

SCHLESINGER, Arthur Meier. An American historian looks at science and technology. *Isis*, 1946, 36: 162-6.

SCHLESINGER, Arthur Meier. Political and social growth of the American people, 1865-1940. xxi, 783 p. New York: Macmillan, 1941. [CB 61/414]
Includes an account of the development of science.

STRUIK, Dirk J. Yankee science in the making. xiii, 430 p. Boston: Little, Brown, 1948.
Reviewed by Leo Marx, *Isis*, 1949, 40: 62-4.
Rev.ed. (544 p.) New York: Collier Books, 1962.

TORY, H.M., ed. A history of science in Canada. vi, 152 p. Toronto: Ryerson Press, 1939. [CB 60/142]

WILLIAMS, Howard R. Edward Williams Morley (1838-1923), his influence on science in America. xi, 282 p., portr., 27 pl. Easton, Pa.: Chemical Education Publishing Company, 1957.
Reviewed by Aaron Ihde, *Isis*, 1959, 50: 81-2; by R. Siegfried, ibid., 1962, 53: 426-8; for other reviews, see CB 84/377.

WILSON, Mitchell. Science and invention. A pictorial history. The fabulous story of how American dreamers, wizards, and inspired tinkerers converted a wilderness into the wonder of the world. xi, 437 p., ill. New York: Simon & Schuster, 1954.
Reviewed by Donald Fleming, *Isis*, 1956, 47: 188-90.

Awb-br

Review of Science in U.S.A. for the year ending June 1952-June 1954. (British Commonwealth Scientific Office) 3 vol. London: H.M. Stationery Off., 1953-55.

Awb-bu/cv bibliography; literature; sources

Awb-bv

KOSTER, Donald N., *et al.* Articles in American studies, 1959. *Amer.Quart.*, 1960, 12: 242-94.
Followed by a listing of dissertations in progress in the field of American studies.

Awb-bx

HORNBERGER, Theodore. Science and the New World (1526-1800). An exhibition to illustrate the scientific contributions of the New World and the spread of scientific ideas in America. 18 p., 2 fig. San Marino: Henry E. Huntington Library, 1937. [CB 51/244]

Awb-cb

CLEMENTS, William Lawrence. The William L. Clements Library of Americana at the University of Michigan. xiii, 228 p. Ann Arbor: The University, 1923. [CB 15/223]

Awb-cd

BERKELEY, Francis L. History and problems of the control of manuscripts in the United States. *Proc.Amer.Phil.Soc.*, 1954, 98: 171-8.

FLEMING, Donald. The ends in view of the preservation of the private papers of American scientists. *Isis*, 1962, 53: 118-21.

HAMER, Philip M., ed. A guide to archives and manuscripts in the United States. Compiled for the National Historical Publications Commission. xxiii, 775 p. New Haven: Yale University Press, 1961.

HEINDEL, Richard H. Historical manuscripts in the Academy of Natural Sciences, Philadelphia. *Penn.Hist.*, 1937, 5: 30-1.

MATTESON, David M. List of manuscripts concerning American history preserved in European libraries and notes in their published catalogues and similar printed lists. viii, 203 p. Washington: Carnegie Institution, 1925. [CB 18/644]

MEARNS, David C. Comments on the symposium on the manuscript sources of American history: problems of their control, use, and publication. *Proc.Amer.Phil.Soc.*, 1954, 98: 185-8.

REINGOLD, Nathan. Manuscript resources for the history of science and technology in the Library of Congress. *Libr. Congr.Quart.J.Curr.Acquis.*, 1960, 17: 161-9.

REINGOLD, Nathan. The National Archives and the history of science in America. *Isis*, 1955, 46: 22-8.

Awb-cd-bv

UNITED STATES. NATIONAL ARCHIVES. Guide to the material in the Archives. xviii, 303 p. Washington, D.C.: U.S. Govt. Print. Off., 1940. [CB 60/171]
A considerable amount of the material preserved in the National Archives in Washington is of interest to the historian of science.

Awb-ce

JACKSON, Sidney L. Old book catalogs and early American bibliography of science. 20 p. (Aspects of Librarianship, 22). Kent, Ohio: Kent State University, 1959.

STILLWELL, Margaret Bingham. Incunabula and Americana, 1450-1800. A key to bibliographical study. xviii, 483 p. New York: Columbia University Press, 1931.
Reviewed by George Sarton, *Isis*, 1931, 16: 178-81.

Awb-ce-by

CANNON, Carl L. American book collectors and collecting. xi, 399 p. New York: Wilson, 1941. [CB 61/422]

Awb-cj

DANA, Edward Salisbury, *et al.* *See* Awb

DAUGHERTY, D.H. American learned journals. *Bull.Amer.Counc. Learned Soc.*, 1940, 30: 129-86.

MOTT, Frank Luther. A history of American magazines. 3 vol. 1. 1741-1850. xix, 848 p., 1939; 2. 1850-65, xvii. 608 p., 1938; 3. 1865-85. xiv, 649 p., 1938. Cambridge, Mass.: Harvard University Press, 1939, 1938. [CB 62/84]

Awb-d biography

Awb-d-bv

KAPLAN, Louis. A bibliography of American autobiographies. xi, 372 p. Madison: University of Wisconsin Press, 1961. [CB 80/454]

Awb-da

AMERICAN men of science: a biographical directory. [1st ed.-] New York/Lancaster, Pa.: Science Press, 1906-49; Tempe, Ariz.: Jaques Cattell Press, 1960-.
For 3rd ed. (by J. McKeen Cattell and Dean R. Brimhall), 1921, *see* CB 11/451; 5th ed. (by J. McKeen Cattell and Jaques Cattell), 1933, reviewed by C.A. Kofoid, *Isis*, 1934, 22: 259-61; for 6th ed. (by J. McKeen Cattell and Jaques Cattell), 1938, *see* CB 56/382; 10th ed. (by Jaques Cattell), 1960-61): part 1 and 2 reviewed by Joseph Turner, *Science*, 1960, 132: 1657.

Biographical Memoirs. National Academy of Sciences. Vol. 1- Washington: 1877-. [CB 82/263, CB 83/276, CB 84/299, CB 85/380, CB 86/455, CB 87/554, CB 88/526 and CB 90/505]

CROWTHER, J.G. Famous American men of science. xvi, 414 p. New York: Norton, 1937.
Reviewed by M.F. Ashley-Montagu, *Isis*, 1938, 28: 507-8.

DICTIONARY of American biography. Published under the auspices of the American Council of Learned Societies. 22 vol. New York: Scribner's, 1928-58.
Second Supplement (Vol. 22) reviewed by I. Bernard Cohen, *Isis*, 1958, 49: 446-7.

DIRECTORY of American Scholars. Edited by Jacques Cattell. vii, 928 p. Lancaster, Pa.: Science Press, 1942. [CB 63/261]

HYLANDER, Clarence John. American scientists. xiii, 186 p., 16 pl. New York: Macmillan, 1935. [CB 45/272]

JAFFE, Bernard. Men of science in America. The role of science in the growth of our country. xl, 600 p., 25 fig., 28 pl. New York: Simon and Schuster, 1944.
Reviewed by Philippe Le Corbeiller, *Isis*, 1945, 36: 73-4; by I.E. Drabkin, *Bull.Hist.Med.*, 1944, 16: 327-8.
German and French translation New York: Overseas Editions; Italian translation Rome: Apollon; for French translation *see* CB 70/248.

JAFFE, Bernard. Men of science in America. The story of American science told through the lives and achievements of twenty outstanding men from earliest Colonial times to the present day. Rev. ed. xlii, 716 p., 16 pl. New York: Simon and Schuster, 1958. [CB 84/299]
Reviewed by John C. Greene, *Isis*, 1959, 50: 486-7.
For first edition *see* above.

VISHER, Stephen Sargent. Indiana scientists. 286 p. Indianapolis: Indiana Academy of Science, 1951.
A biographical dictionary and an analysis.

WRIGHT, John S. Men of science in Indiana, past and present. *Proc.Indiana Acad.Sci.*, 1945, 54: 179-83.
Lists some scientists who had contacts with the state of Indiana from George Rogers Clark (1778) to the present.

Awb-dae

AMERICAN PHILOSOPHICAL SOCIETY. A catalogue of portraits and other works of art in the possession of the Society. viii, 173 p. Philadelphia, Pa.: The Society, 1961.

AMERICAN PHILOSOPHICAL SOCIETY. Catalogue of the Portraits. Exhibition marking the 250th anniversary of the birth of the Society's founder, Benjamin Franklin, Jan. 17 - April 20, 1956. By Charles Coleman Sellers. 27 p., ill. Philadelphia, Pa.: The Society, 1956.

Awb-f historical study

SHRYOCK, Richard H. The need for studies in the history of American science. *Isis*, 1944, 35: 10-13.

Awb-fpx

BOOK Prize of the Institute of Early American History and Culture awarded to I. Bernard Cohen. *J.Hist.Med.*, 1957, 12: 521-2.

Awb-k/n philosophv: communication

Awb-kt

ROBET, H. L'école de Chicago et l'instrumentalisme. *Rev.Métaphys.Morale*, 1913, 21: 537-75.

Awb-np

KRIEGHBAUM, Hillier. American newspaper reporting of science news. *Kans.State Coll.Bull.*, 1941, 25: no. 5, 73 p., pl.

LARSEN, J.A. Wisconsin's science writing program. *Science*, 1956, 123: 720.

Awb-o science teaching in North America

Awb-og

SEEGER, R.J. On the classics and science in American education. *Cl.World*, 1958, 51: 121-2, 133-6.

Awb-om

CRAIG, Gerald S. Elementary school science in the past century. *Sci.Teacher*, 1957, 24: 11-14, 37, ill.

ROSEN, Sidney. A century of high-school science. *Sci.Teacher*, November 1956, 23: 4 p.

Awb-op

CALIFORNIA. UNIVERSITY. Science in the University. By members of the Faculties of the University of California. x, 332 p., pl., fig. Berkeley, Calif.: University of California Press, 1944. [CB 66/243]

CAULLERY, Maurice. Les universités et la vie scientifique aux États-Unis. xii, 302 p. Paris: A. Colin, 1917.
English translation, 1922 (Cambridge, Mass.: Harvard University Press).

FULTON, John F. Science in American universities 1636-1946. With particular reference to Harvard and Yale. *Bull.Hist. Med.*, 1946, 20: 97-111.

U.S. PRESIDENT'S SCIENCE ADVISORY COMMITTEE. *See* Awb-sm

Awb-oq

BAKER, Ray Palmer. Rensselaer Polytechnic Institute and the beginnings of science in the United States. *Sci.Mon.*, 1924, 19: 337-55, portr.
Founded at Troy, New York, in 1824, by Stephen var Rensselaer, and first headed by Amos Eaton.

CARMICHAEL, Leonard. Tufts College, its science and technology, a centennial view (1852-1952). 24 p. New York/San Francisco/Montreal: Newcomen Society in North America, 1952.

CHITTENDEN, Russell H. History of the Sheffield Scientific School of Yale University, 1846-1922. 2 vol. ix, 298 p., 36 pl; x, 299-610 p., 57 pl. New Haven, Conn.: Yale University Press, 1928.
Reviewed by F.S.M., *Nature*, 1929, 124: 48-9.

COHEN, I. Bernard. Centenary of the Lawrence Scientific School of Harvard University. *Isis*, 1948, 39: 59.

COHEN, I. Bernard. Harvard and the scientific spirit. *Harvard Alumni Bull.*, Feb. 1948, 50: 6 p., ill.

DEXTER, Ralph W. Science education and the Ohio Academy of Science. An historical review. *Ohio.J.Sci.*, 1961, 4: 235-41.

FLEMING, Donald. Science and technology in Providence 1760-1914: an essay on the history of Brown University in the metropolitan community. 54 p., ill. (Brown University Papers, 26) Providence, R.I.: The University, 1952. [CB 79/164]
Reviewed by John B. Blake, *J.Hist.Med.*, 1955, 10: 254-5.

FULTON, John F. The centenary of the Sheffield Scientific School. *Isis*, 1947, 38: 100.

Awb-or

SHRYOCK, Richard H. The academic profession in the United States. *Bull.Amer.Ass.Univ.Professors*, 1952, 38: 32-70.

THWING, Charles Franklin. The college president. x, 345 p. New York: Macmillan, 1926.

Awb-osp

SIGERIST, Henry E. The university at the crossroads. *Bull. Hist.Med.*, 1944, 15: 233-45.
The effect of the war on university education and research in the United States.

Awb-p organization of science in North America

AMERICAN FEDERATION OF LABOR. [Resolution on] the organisation of labor and the organization of science. *Isis*, 1923, 5: 144-5.
Adopted at its 39th Annual Convention, 1919.

McDONALD, Ellice. Research and its organization. [92] p. Newark, Del.: Biochemical Research Foundation, 1950. [CB 77/364]
Various pagings.

WEINBERG, Alvin M. Impact of large-scale science on the United States. *Science*, 1961, 134: 161-4.

Awb-ph

COX, Donald William. America's new policy makers; the scientists' rise to power. xiv, 298 p., ill., bibliogr. Philadelphia: Chilton, 1964.

DUPREE, A. Hunter. Central scientific organisation in the United States Government. *Minerva*, 1963, 1: 453-69.

DUPREE, A. Hunter. "A history of the activities of the Federal Government in science". *Isis*, 1954, 45: 198.
Project sponsored by the American Academy of Arts and Sciences.

DUPREE, A. Hunter. Science in the federal government. A history of policies and activities to 1940. x, 460 p., 4 fig. Cambridge, Mass.: Harvard University Press, 1957.
Reviewed by Brooke Hindle, *Isis*, 1957, 48: 470-1; for other reviews *see* CB 83/185 and 193, CB 84/304, CB 85/385 and CB 86/459.

DU SHANE, Graham. Evis water conditioner. *Science*, 1956, 123: 1107-8. [CB 82/200]
Concerning the criteria adopted in a test carried out by the National Bureau of Standards.

DU SHANE, Graham. Test by testimonial. *Science*, 1956, 123: 1059. [CB 82/200]

GANT, Charles G.; RUBINSTEIN, Bertha. Funds for science: the Federal Government and nonprofit institutions. *Science*, 1953, 117: 669-76, 4 fig.

PRICE, Don K. Government and science. Their dynamic relation in American democracy. ix, 203 p. New York: New York University Press, 1954. [CB 80/121]
Reprinted New York: Oxford University Press, 1962.

SAYRE, Wallace S. Scientists and American science policy. *Science*, 1961, 133: 859-64.

SMYTH, H.D. Science and the Federal Government. *Phys.Today*, 1958, 11: no. 6, 10-14.

U.S. PRESIDENT'S SCIENCE ADVISORY COMMITTEE. Science, government and information: the responsibilities of the technical community and the government in the transfer of information; a report. v, 52 p. Washington: U.S. Govt. Print. Off., 1963.
Resumé, with extracts, *Minerva*, 1963, 2: 91-117.

U.S. SENATE. COMMITTEE ON MILITARY AFFAIRS. Hearings on science legislation (S. 1297 and related bills). Hearings before a Subcommittee of the Committee on Military Affairs, United States Senate, seventy-ninth Congress, first session. Part 2 (unrevised). iv, 258 p. Washington, D.C.: U.S. Govt. Print.Off., 1945.

U.S. SENATE. COMMITTEE ON MILITARY AFFAIRS. Legislative proposals for the promotion of science. The texts of five bills and excerpts from reports. v, 89 p. (Subcommittee on War Mobilization of the Committee on Military Affairs, United States Senate) Washington: U.S. Govt. Print. Off., 1945.

Awb-ph-oq

KIDD, Charles V. American universities and federal research. 272 p. Cambridge, Mass.: Belknap Press of Harvard University Press, 1959.
Reviewed by C. Kittel, *Phys.Today*, 1960, 13: no. 6, 64.

Awb-pr

CARNEGIE INSTITUTION OF WASHINGTON. Cooperation in research; [a testimonial volume commemorating the retirement of John Campbell Merriam from the presidency of the Institution] by staff members and research associates. ix, 782 p. Washington, D.C.: The Institution, 1938.
A systematic view of the research activities of the Institution.
Reviewed by H.T. Davis, *Isis*, 1947, 32: 197-200.

CONANT, James B. Andrew Carnegie, patron of learning. *Science*, 1935, 82: 599-603.

Awb-pw for international relations involving North America and other countries *see* Apw (DENNY, Margaret; DUNN, L.G.; HEINDEL, Richard; PACE, Antonio; WATANABE, Masao)

Awb-q scientific institutions in North America

Awb-qd

BATES, Ralph S. Scientific societies in the United States. 2nd ed. xiv, 297 p. New York: Technology Press, 1958. [CB 84/302]
1st ed. published New York: Wiley, 1945; reviewed by Charles A. Kofoid, *Isis*, 1947, 38: 133.

BUFFALO SOCIETY OF NATURAL SCIENCES. Seventy-five years: a history of the Buffalo Society of Natural Sciences, 1861-1936. 204 p., 53 pl., 3 plans. (*Bull.Buffalo Soc.Natur. Sci.*, 18) Buffalo, N.Y.: [The Society], 1938. [CB 58/197]

CHAMBERLIN, Thomas Chrowder. The founding of the Wisconsin Academy of Sciences, Arts and Letters. *Science*, July 2, 1920, 52: 1-8.
It was founded on Feb. 16, 1870. The history of its first half-century is traced.

GEISER, S.W. The first Texas Academy of Science. *Field Lab.*, 1945, 13: 34-9. [CB 69/202]
The Texas Academy was organized in 1892 and existed until 1912.

JONES, Howard Mumford. The future of the Academy. Presidential address. 9 p. Boston, Mass: American Academy of Arts and Sciences, 1944.

KIGER, Joseph C. American learned societies. Foreword by Luther Evans. 217 p., bibliogr. Washington, D.C.: Public Affairs Press, 1963.

THE PHILOSOPHICAL SOCIETY OF WASHINGTON. *Bull.Phil.Soc.Wash.*, 1962, 16: 156.

RAND, Christopher. Cambridge, U.S.A. Hub of a new world. 195 p. New York: Oxford University Press, 1964.
Learned institutes and societies.

RIESS, Karlem. The New Orleans Academy of Science. Its first hundred years (1853-1953). *Sci.Mon.*, 1953, 77: 255-9.

SIGERIST, Henry E. Why academies were founded. *Trans.Coll. Physicians Phila.*, 1937, 4: 83-8.
An address at the celebration of the 150th anniversary of the founding of the College of Physicians of Philadelphia, May 15, 1937.

see also American Association for the Advancement of Science 2: 662.
American Council of Learned Societies 2: 662.
American Philosophical Society 2: 663.
National Academy of Sciences 2: 728.
New York Academy of Sciences 2: 730.

Awb-qd-bv

SKALLERUP, Harry R. Bibliography of the histories of American academies of science. *Trans.Kans.Acad.Sci.*, 1963, 66: no. 2, 274-81.

Awb-qg

FLINN, Alfred D.; PORSKIEVICS, A.J.; COBB, Ruth. Research laboratories in industrial establishments of the United States of America. *Bull.Nat.Res.Counc.*, 1920, 1: 45-130. [CB 12/641]

NORTH, S.N.D., ed. A manual of the public benefactions of Andrew Carnegie. Compiled and published by the Carnegie Endowment for International Peace. viii, 322 p., portr., ill. Washington: 1919. [CB 76/347]
Contains brief histories of the various institutions founded by Carnegie.

UNITED STATES. NATIONAL RESEARCH COUNCIL. Industrial research laboratories of the United States. 11th ed. compiled by J.H. Gribbin and S.S. Krogfus. 698 p. (Publication no. 844) Washington: The Council, 1960.
10th ed. 1956. First published 1920; *see* above: Flinn, A.D.; Porskievics, A.J.; Cobb, R.

Awb-qk

BAXTER, James Phinney. Scientists against time. With a foreword by Vannevar Bush. xv, 473 p. Boston: Little, Brown, 1946. [CB 72/269]
Reviewed by John W. Oliver, *Amer.Hist.Rev.*, 1947, 52: 491-2.
The story of the Office of Research and Development which directed American scientific research during the war.

see also National Research Council (Canada) 2: 728.
National Research Council (United States) 2: 729.
Smithsonian Institution 2: 759.

Awb-r/s professional aspects and social relations of science in North America

Awb-rc

ASHMAN, Richard. States of birth of American men of science. *J.Hered.*, 1945, 36: 99-106.

BRANSON, C.C. Another attempt at classifying American scientists. *Science*, 1954, 119: 655.

KNAPP, R.H.; GOODRICH, H.B. Origins of American scientists: a study made under the direction of a committee of the Faculty of Wesleyan University. vii, 450 p. Chicago: University of Chicago Press for Wesleyan University, 1952.
Reviewed by Edward Lurie, *Isis*, 1953, 44: 403-4.

THE SCIENTIST in American society. [A symposium]. *Sci.Mon.*, 1954, 78: 129-41. [CB 81/262]

VISHER, Stephen Sargent. Scientists starred, 1903-1943, in "American Men of Science". A study of collegiate and doctoral training, birthplace, distribution, backgrounds, and developmental influences. xxiii, 556 p., 117 fig. Baltimore: Johns Hopkins University Press, 1947. [CB 72/268]

Awb-rd

LONG, Edward Leroy. Religious beliefs of American scientists. 168 p. Philadelphia: Westminster Press, 1951. [CB 79/191]

Awb-sc

CONANT, James B. The role of science in our unique society *Science*, 1948, 107: 77-83.
Address of the retiring president of the AAAS, delivered on the evening of December 27, 1947, at the 114th meeting of the Association in Chicago, Illinois.

FOERSTER, Norman, ed. Humanism and America. Essays on the outlook of modern civilization. xvii, 294 p. New York: Farrar and Rinehart, 1930.
Reviewed by George Sarton, *Isis*, 1930, 14: 446-9.

FULTON, John F. The impact of science on American history. *Isis*, 1951, 42: 176-91, 6 fig.

Awb-sm

GREENWOOD, David C. Solving the scientist shortage. viii, 68 p. Washington, D.C.: Public Affairs Press, 1958. [CB 84/304]

NATIONAL MANPOWER COUNCIL. A policy for scientific and professional manpower. A statement by the Council with facts and issues prepared by the research staff. xix, 263 p., 5 fig., 14 tables. New York: Columbia University Press, 1953.

NATIONAL MANPOWER COUNCIL. The utilization of scientific and professional manpower. Proceedings of a conference held 7-11 October 1953 at Columbia University. xii, 197 p. New York: Columbia University Press, 1954.
The conference dealt with three professional fields: engineering, medicine, and teaching.

U.S. PRESIDENT'S SCIENCE ADVISORY COMMITTEE. Meeting manpower needs in science and technology: a report. 1. Graduate training in engineering, mathematics and physical sciences. vi, 45 p. Washington, D.C.: U.S. Govt. Print. Off., 1962.
Resumé with extracts in *Minerva*, 1963, 1: 381-91.

WOLFLE, Dael. A retreat from science? *Science*, 1955, 122: 375.
Discusses the shortage of students who specialize in science and engineering.

Awb-sp peace and war

COMPTON, Karl T. Organization of American scientists for the war. *Science*, 1943, 98: 71-6, 93-8.
Pilgrim Trust Lecture, under the auspices of the Royal Society of London, May 20, 1943.

Awb-sq

BROWNE, C.A. The role of refugees in the history of American science. *Science*, 1940, 91: 203-8.

DAVIE, Maurice R. Refugees in America. xxi, 453 p. New York: Harper, 1947. [CB 71/126]
The report of the Committee for the Study of Recent Immigration from Europe.

DUGGAN, Stephan; DRURY, Betty. The rescue of science and learning. The story of the Emergency Committee in Aid of Displaced Foreign Scholars. xii, 214 p. New York: Macmillan, 1948. [CB 73/186]

Awb-sr

COMMUNISM and academic freedom: the record of the tenure cases at the University of Washington. 125 p. Seattle; University of Washington Press, 1949. [CB 76/392]

COOK, R.C. Unamericana. *J.Hered.*, 1948, 39: 22. [CB 73/165]
The Congressional Committee on Un-American Activities and Dr. E.U. Condon.

MELLETT, Lowell. Lysenkoism in Washington. *J.Hered.*, 1953, 44: 69.
Reprinted from the *Wash.Evening Star* of 18 April 1953. A discussion of the fiasco which resulted from Secretary Weeks' attempt to fire Dr Allen V. Astin from his position as Director of the United States Bureau of Standards.

UREY, Harold C. "I greatly fear ...". *J.Hered.*, 1948, 39: 150-2. [CB 73/166]
The Condon case.

Awb-vm Jews

LEBESON, Anita Libman. Jewish pioneers in America, 1492-1848. x, 372 p. New York: Brentano, 1931.

Awc Latin America

BABINI, José. Las ciencias en la historia de la cultura argentina. De acuerdo con los nuevos programas para 6º año del ciclo superior del magisterio. 182 p., 23 fig. Buenos Aires: Estrada, 1951. [CB 78/175]

BABINI, José. La evolución del pensamiento científico en la Argentina. 249 p., 29 pl. Buenos Aires: Ediciones "La Fragua," 1954. [CB 81/252]

BABINI, José. Historia de la ciencia argentina. 218 p. México: Fondo de Cultura Económica, 1949. [CB 75/84]

GONZALEZ, Luis Felipe. Historia de la influencia extranjera en el desenvolvimiento educacional y cientifico de Costa Rica. xi, 317 p., 24 pl. San José de Costa Rica: Imprenta Nacional, 1921.
Reviewed by Philip P. Calvert, *Science*, 1923, 58: 71-3.

GORTARI, Eli de. La ciencia en la historia de México. 461 p., bibliogr. (Vida y Pensamiento de México) Mexico City: Fondo de Cultura Económica, 1963. [CB 89/483]

MEANS, Philip Ainsworth. Fall of the Inca Empire and the Spanish rule in Peru: 1530-1780. xii, 351 p., 29 ill., 1 map. New York: Scribners, 1932. [CB 36/451]

Awc-ce

PAOLI, Humberto Julio. Contributi alla scienza sud americana, ed alla sua storia, e la "Collección de libros referentes a la ciencia hispano-americana". *Arch.Stor.Sci.*, 1919-20, 1: 440-2. [CB 10/210]
Short notes to announce the publication of a collection of reprints of the early South American scientific books.

Awc-qd

BESIO MORENO, Nicolás. Sociedad Cientifica Argentina, fundada en 1872. Reseña histórica. *Archeion*, 1943, 25: 172-94.

Awd Europe

BARKER, Ernest; CLARK, George; VAUCHER, P. The European inheritance. 3 vol. Oxford: Clarendon Press, 1954. [CB 81/256] [For full entry *see* Ac-bm]

CROWTHER, J.G. Science in liberated Europe. 336 p. London: Pilot Press, 1949.

HAYES, Carlton J.H. A political and cultural history of modern Europe. 2 vol. xviii, 863 p.; xiv, 1215 p. New York: Macmillan, 1936.
Reviewed by M.F. Ashley-Montagu, *Isis*, 1937, 27: 357-8.

MARVIN, Francis Sydney, ed. Recent developments in European thought. Essays arranged and ed. by Francis Sydney Marvin. 306 p. London: Oxford University Press, 1920.
Includes several essays on science.

Awd-bv

HASKINS, Charles H. European history and American scholarship. *Amer.Hist.Rev.*, 1923, 28: 215-27.
Review of American work in the field of European history.

Awd-cc-aa

COHEN, I. Bernard. The New World as a source of science for Europe. *Act.IXe Congr.Int.Hist.Sci.* (Barcelona, Madrid, 1959), p. 96-130. Paris: Hermann, 1960.

Awd-pw

AUGER, Pierre. Scientific cooperation in Western Europe. *Minerva*, 1963, 1: 428-38.

Awd-sm

McCRENSKY, Edward. Scientific manpower in Europe. A comparative study of scientific manpower in the public service of Great Britain and selected European countries. ix, 188 p., front. New York: Pergamon Press, 1958.
Reviewed by Bernard Barber, *Isis*, 1959, 50: 487-8; and in *Nature*, 1959, 183: 489-92.

Awe British Isles

ARMYTAGE, W.H.G. Early science in Sheffield (1161-1831). In: Batey, Charles, Sheffield and its region, p. 217-27. London: Oxford University Press, 1956.

ARMYTAGE, W.H.G. Science and industry in Sheffield; some historical notes. *Proc.Chem.Soc.*, 1962, 51-5.
From about 1670 to 1900.

BRITISH ASSOCIATION FOR THE ADVANCEMENT OF SCIENCE. London and the advancement of science. Issued ... on the occasion of its centenary meeting in London, 1931. iii, 321 p. London: 1931.
Reviewed in *Nature*, 1931, 128: 687-9.

BRITISH ASSOCIATION FOR THE ADVANCEMENT OF SCIENCE. Edinburgh's place in scientific progress. Prepared for the Edinburgh meeting. xvi, 263 p., portr. Edinburgh: Chambers, 1921.

BRITISH contributions to science 1851-1951. *Endeavour*, 1951, 10: 117-18, 173-4.
A listing of the outstanding work and workers during the past hundred years.

CLEMENT, A.G.; ROBERTSON, Robert H.S. Scotland's scientific heritage. viii, 151 p. Edinburgh/London: Oliver and Boyd, 1961.
Reviewed by Fredrik Neumeyer, *Lychnos*, 1962, 405-7.

CROMBIE, A.C. Oxford's contribution to the origins of modern science. 27 p. Oxford: Basil Blackwell, 1954.
Reviewed by William B. Walker, *J.Hist.Med.*, 1955, 10: 439-40; by Friedrich Klemm, *Sudhoffs Arch.*, 1955, 39: 284.

DAVIDSON, Maurice. Memoirs of a golden age. xvi, 140 p., 30 pl. Oxford: Basil Blackwell, 1958.
Memoirs of Oxford at the turn of the century.
Reviewed by John F. Fulton, *J.Hist.Med.*, 1959, 14: 122-3.

DEMPSEY, P.J.R. Science in Ireland. *Science*, 1952, 115: 635-6.
Conditions today.

EYLES, V.A. Scientific activity in the Bristol region in the past. In: MacInnes, C.M.; Whittard, W.F., ed. Bristol and its adjoining counties, p. 123-43, 3 pl. London: 1955.

FERGUSON, Allan. Dramatic moments in the history of science in Britain. *Endeavour*, 1945, 4: 17-21, 34, 7 fig.

GOLDSMITH, Maurice. One hundred years of British science. *Sci.Mon.*, 1952, 74: 170-9.
Address delivered at the 113th annual meeting of the British Association for the Advancement of Science held in Edinburgh in August 1951.

GREGORY, Richard. Science in Britain. *Science*, 1942, 96: 213-15.

GUNTHER, Robert William Theodore. Early science in Cambridge. xii, 513 p., ill. Oxford University Press (for the author) 1937.
Reviewed by M.F. Ashley-Montagu, *Isis*, 1938, 28: 134.

GUNTHER, Robert William Theodore. Early science in Oxford. 14 vol. pl. Oxford: Printed for the subscribers, 1923-45. [CB 54/525 and CB 70/205]
Vol. 1 published in parts, 1920-3.

GUNTHER, Robert William Theodore. Oxford and the history of science. With an appendix on scientific collections in college libraries. 49 p. Oxford University Press, 1934.
Inaugural lecture delivered in the Examination Schools, 25 Oct., 1934.

McKIE, D. 1851-1951: a century of British science. *J.Roy. Soc.Arts*, 1951, 99: 316-25.

PHILIP, *Duke of Edinburgh*. The British contribution to science and technology in the past hundred years. *Nature*, 1951, 168: 219-25.

SCHUSTER, Arthur; SHIPLEY, Arthur E. Britain's heritage of science. xv, 334 p., 15 portr. London: Constable, 1917.
Reviewed by Charles Singer, *History*, 1918-19, *new ser.* 3: 205-9.

TAYLOR, F. Sherwood. A conspectus of science, 1851-1951. Festival of Britain lecture. Delivered by the President of the Society on 16th July, 1951. *Bull.Brit.Soc.Hist.Sci.*, 1951, 1: 136-43.

THOMPSON, D'Arcy Wentworth. The history of science in Scotland. 39 p. (Scotland and its people, 5) Edinburgh: St. Andrews University, 1942. [CB 63/269]

WEISINGER, Herbert. The study of the revival of learning in England from Bacon to Hallam. *Philol.Quart.*, 1946, 25: 221-47.

WINGFIELD-STRATFORD, Esmè. The history of British civilization. 2 vol. xv, 574 p.; viii, 575-1332 p. London: Routledge, 1928.
Reviewed by F.S. Marvin, *Nature*, 1929, 123: 863-4.

WITTING, Gustaf, ed. Sweden speaks. Transl. by Edith M. Nielsen. 212 p. London: Allen and Unwin, 1942. [CB 65/87]
Includes articles on science and medicine in England.

Awe-cd

BLUHM, R.K. A guide to the archives of the Royal Society and to other manuscripts in its possession. *Notes Roy.Soc.Lond.*, 1956, 12: 21-39.

BORN, Lester K., comp. British manuscripts project. A checklist of the microfilms prepared in England and Wales for the American Council of Learned Societies, 1941-1945. xvii, 179 p. Washington: Library of Congress, 1955. [CB 83/187-8]

BRAGG, William. History in the archives of the Royal Society. *Science*, 1939, 89: 445-53: *Nature*, 1939, 144: 21-8.
Pilgrim Trust Lecture, delivered before the National Academy of Sciences, April 24, 1939.

QUIRK, R.N. The problem of scientific manuscripts in Britain. *Isis*, 1962, 53: 151-4.

Awe-cj

THE JUBILEE of *Nature* (1869-1919). *Isis*, 1920, 3: 60-2. [CB 9/468]

WIGHTMAN, William P.D. *Philosophical Transactions of the Royal Society*. *Nature*, 1961, 192: 23-4.

Awe-cp

SMITH, Edgar C. Britain's scientific shrines. *Nature*, 1951, 167: 664-6, 790-2, 918-21, 1045-8; 168: 180-4, 443-6, 578-80.

Awe-da

Biographical Memoirs of Fellows of the Royal Society. Vol. 1- London: 1955-. [CB 83/277, CB 84/299, CB 86/455, CB 87/554 and CB 88/526]
Vol. 5 and 7 reviewed by R. Bruce Lindsay, *Phys.Today*, 1960, 13: no. 10, 60-2; 1962, 15: no. 6, 74.

CROWTHER, J.G. British scientists of the twentieth century. xiv, 320 p., 8 pl. London: Routledge & Kegan Paul, 1952.
Biographies of J.J. Thomson, Rutherford, Jeans, Eddington, Hopkins and Bateson.

DICTIONARY of national biography. Ed. by Leslie Stephen. 63 vol. London: Smith, Elder. 1885-1900. Supplements, 1901-

HOLMYARD, E.J. British scientists. viii, 88 p., 24 portr. New York: Philosophical Library, 1951. [CB 79/164]

Obituary Notices of Fellows of the Royal Society. New ser. Vol. 1-9, 1932-54. London: 1933-55. [CB 81/340 and CB 83/211]
Before 1901 and between 1904 and 1932, obituary notices are found in the *Proceedings of the Royal Society*. From 1955 they are published as *Biographical Memoirs of Fellows of the Royal Society* (see above).

RAYLEIGH, Robert John Strutt, 4th Baron. Some reminiscences of scientific workers of the past generation, and their surroundings. *Proc.Phys.Soc.*, 1936, 48: 217-46.
Presidential address, delivered 24 January, 1936. These reminiscences concern Lord Kelvin, the Royal Institution, Sir William Crookes, Sir Arthur Schuster.

Awe-dae

ANDRADE, E.N. da C. The Royal Society portraits. *Endeavour*, 1956, 15: 128-36, 6 pl.

JONES, S. Rees. The Royal Institution's collection of portraits. *Proc.Roy.Inst.*, 1962, 39: 240-5.

ROYAL SOCIETY OF LONDON. The Society's portraits. *Notes Roy. Soc.Lond.*, 1949, 7: 97-107, 2 pl.

Awe-dae-bw

BRITISH MUSEUM. Catalogue of engraved British portraits preserved in the Department of Prints and Drawings. (Vol. 6. Supplement and indexes). 6 vol. London: British Museum, 1908-25.

GUTHRIE, Douglas. A list of the portraits in the Royal Society of Edinburgh, with bibliographical notes. *Year Book Roy.Soc.Edinb.*, 1959/60, 5-24.

POOLE, Rachel Emily. Catalogue of portraits in the possession of the University, Colleges, City and County of Oxford. 3 vol. (Oxford Historical Society. Publications 57. 81, 82). Oxford: Clarendon Press, 1912. 1926.

Awe-nh

ATKINSON, A.D. The Royal Society and English vocabulary. *Notes Roy.Soc.Lond.*, 1956, 12: 40-3.

Awe-o science teaching in the British Isles

ARGLES, Michael. South Kensington to Robbins: an account of English technical and scientific education since 1851. xiii, 178 p., ill., bibliogr. London: Longmans, 1964.

ARMYTAGE, W.H.G. Education in Sheffield (1603-1955). In: British Association for the Advancement of Science. Sheffield and its Region, p. 201-7. Sheffield: 1956.

BLOOM, J.D. The teaching of science in Lancashire during the middle period. *Sch.Sci.Rev.*, 1958, 39: 316-18.
The author defines the middle period "from 1500 to 1850 or thereabouts" and adduces some evidence which seems to indicate that considerable science was taught in England during this time.

FOSTER, Charles. One hundred years of science teaching in Great Britain. *Ann.Sci.*, 1937, 2: 335-44.

TURNER, Dorothy M. History of science teaching in England. x, 208 p. London: Chapman and Hall, 1927.

Awe-p organization of science in the British Isles

CARDWELL, D.S.L. The organisation of science in England. A retrospect. ix, 204 p. London: William Heinemann, 1957.
Reviewed by L. Rosenfeld, *Arch.Int.Hist.Sci.*, 1957, 10: 119-20; by E. Ashby, *Endeavour*, 1957, 16: 171; by R. Taton, *Rev.Hist.Sci.*, 1959, 12: 371.

HISCOCKS, E.S. Organization of science in the United Kingdom. *Science*, 1959, 129: 689-93.

Awe-pg

HOLMYARD, E.J. Editorial: royal patronage of science. *Endeavour*, 1953, 12: 15-16.

McKIE, Douglas. The crown and science: Elizabeth I to Elizabeth II. *Discovery*, 1960, 21: 284-92.

MacNALTY, Arthur. Science and the sovereign. *Nature*, 1953, 171: 951-2.

Awe-ph

ALBU, Austen. The Member of Parliament, the executive and scientific policy. *Minerva*, 1963, 2: 1-20.

JONES, R.V. Science and the state. *Advance Sci.*, 1964, 20: 393-405; substance in *Nature*, 1963, 200: 7-14.
The relationship in Britain over the past 100 years is reviewed.

Awe-pw

ANDRADE, E.N. da C.; MARTIN, D.C. The Royal Society and its foreign relations. *Endeavour*, 1960, 19: 72-80.

FORBES, R.J. The Royal Society and the progress of science abroad. *Nature*, 1960, 187: 100-2.

for international relations involving the British Isles and other countries *see also* Apw (DENNY, Margaret; HEINDEL, Richard H.; FERREIRA, H. Amorim; RADOVSKII, M.I.) and Apw-bx

Awe-px

LANGE, Erwin F.; BUYERS, Ray F. Medals of the Royal Society of London. *Sci.Mon.*, 1955, 81: 85-90, 16 ill.

SMITH, Edgar C. The Copley medal and its founder. *Nature*, 1954, 174: 1034-7, ill.

WIGHTMAN, William P.D. The Copley medal and the work of some of the early recipients. *Physis*, 1961, 3: 344-55.

Awe-q British scientific societies

Awe-qb

GUTHRIE, Douglas. A short history of the Royal Society Club of Edinburgh, 1820 to 1962. 40 p., ill. Edinburgh: Royal Society Club, 1963.
Reviewed in *Med.Hist.*, 1963, 7: 289.

SLICHTER, C.S. Science in a tavern. xi, 186 p. Madison, Wisc.: University of Wisconsin Press, 1939. [CB 57/232]
The first essay deals with the Royal Society Club.

WARD, Thomas Humphry. History of the Athenaeum, 1824-1925. xii, 370 p., 32 pl. London: The Club, 1926.

Awe-qd

CLARK, E. Kitson. The history of 100 years of life of the Leeds Philosophical and Literary Society. viii, 249 p. Leeds: Jowett and Sowry, 1924.

COHEN, John; HANSEL, C.E.M.; MAY, Edith F. Natural history of learned and scientific societies. *Nature,* 1954, 173: 328-33, 3 fig., 3 tables.

see also British Association for the Advancement of Science, 2: 672.
Manchester Literary and Philosophical Society, 2: 721.
Royal Institution of Great Britain, 2: 748.
Royal Society of Edinburgh, 2: 749.
Royal Society of London, 2: 749.

Awe-qd-bd

SCIENTIFIC and learned societies of Great Britain. A handbook compiled from official sources. 59th ed. 215 p. London: George Allen and Unwin, 1958.
Reviewed in *Nature,* 1959, 183: 1151.

Awe-qw

HALL, A. Rupert. Cambridge and the Royal Society. 20 p., ill. Cambridge University Press, 1960.

HARTLEY, Harold; HINSHELWOOD, Cyril. Gresham College and the Royal Society. *Notes Roy.Soc.Lond.,* 1961, 16: 125-35.

SEWARD, Albert C. Christ's Hospital and the Royal Society. *Notes Roy.Soc.Lond.,* 1941, 3: 141-5.

WIGHTMAN, William P.D. Aberdeen University and the Royal Society. *Notes Roy.Soc.Lond.,* 1955, 2: 145-58, ill.

Awe-s/u social and humanistic relations; ethnic groups

Awe-sm

McCRENSKY, Edward. *See* Awd-sm

ROYAL SOCIETY. Emigration of scientists from the United Kingdom. 32 p., tables. London: Royal Society, 1963.
Also in *Minerva,* 1963, 1: 342-80.

Awe-sy

FLORKIN, Marcel. L'avenir de la science anglaise. *Alumni,* 1945, 15: 207-22.

Awe-th

GLICKSBURG, Charles I. D.H. Lawrence and science. *Sci.Mon.,* 1951, 73: 99-104.

[SCIENCE and English literature. (In Japanese)]. xi, 392 p., fig. Tokyo: Kenyusha, 1964.

Awe-vm

SALAMAN, Redcliffe N. Jews in the Royal Society. A problem in ecology. *Notes Roy.Soc.Lond.,* 1949, 7: 61-7.

Awf France

BERTHIER, A. Georges. L'histoire des sciences en France. *Rev.Syn.Hist.,* 1914, 28: 230-52.

BOUTROUX, Pierre. Science in France. *Sci.Mon.,* 1921, 13: 435-47. [CB 13/304]

BRILLOUIN, Léon. *See* Aw

BROGLIE, Louis de. La France et le progrès scientifique. *Age Or,* 1945, 1: 19-30.

CAULLERY, Maurice. French science and its principal discoveries since the seventeenth century. xi, 229 p., ill. [New York: Privately printed for the French Institute, 1934].

CAULLERY, Maurice. La science française depuis le XVIIe siècle. 215 p. (Collection Armand Colin). Paris: Colin, 1933. [CB 40/395]
For English translation *see* above.

DAINVILLE, François de. Foyers de culture scientifique dans la France méditerranéenne du XVIe au XVIIIe siècle. *Rev. Hist.Sci.,* 1948, 1: 289-300.

FRANCE. MINISTÈRE DE L'INSTRUCTION PUBLIQUE ET DES BEAUX-ARTS. La science française. 2 vol. portr. Paris: Larousse, 1915.

HADAMARD, Jacques. La pensée française dans l'évolution des sciences exactes. *France Monde,* 20 mars 1923, 321-43.

HISTOIRE de la Nation Française. Vol. XIV. Histoire des sciences en France. 1. Introduction générale, par Émile Picard. Mathématiques, mécanique, astronomie [par Henri Andoyer and Pierre Humbert], physique [par Charles Fabry] et chimie [par Albert Colson]. xx, 619 p., 12 pl., ill. Paris: Plon, 1924.
Reviewed by George Sarton, *Isis,* 1925, 7: 514-16.

IZ ISTORII frantsuzskoi nauki. Sbornik statei. [From the history of French science. A collection of articles. (In Russian)] 184 p. Moscow: Akademiia Nauk SSSR, 1960. [CB 86/452]

LEJARD, Anna; LEJARD, André; ed. 50 années de découvertes 1900-1950. Un bilan dressé par Albert Béguin, Claude-Edmonde Magny, Jean Wahl, Charles-Albert Reichen, Frank Elgar, François Le Lionnais, Jacques Bergier. 358 p. Paris: Editions du Seuil, 1950. [CB 77/345]

MADELIN, Louis, ed. La France immortelle. 2 vol. xxi, 393 p., fig., pl.; 436 p., fig., pl. Paris: Hachette, 1946. [CB 77/362]
The second volume contains three articles devoted to the history of French science.

MATISSE, G. Le mouvement scientifique contemporain en France. 3 vol. 1. Les sciences naturelles. 160 p.; 2. Les sciences physiologiques. 154 p.; 3 and 4. Les sciences physico-chimiques. Les sciences mathématiques. 320 p. Paris: Payot, 1921-5. [CB 12/626]

PICARD, Emile. L'histoire des sciences et le rôle de la France. *Rev.Deux Mondes,* 1 June 1924, 652-70.

SERGESCU, P.; ROSTAND, J.; BOUTARIC, A. Les sciences. 501 p. (Collection "Tableau du XXe siècle", 1900-1933, 2) Paris: Denoël et Steele, 1933. [CB 41/579]
Les sciences mathématiques, par P. Sergescu. Les sciences biologiques, par J. Rostand. Les sciences physico-chymiques, par Augustin Boutaric.

Awf-cd

BEAUJOUAN, Guy. L'histoire des sciences aux Archives Nationales de Paris. *Arch.Int.Hist.Sci.,* 1950, 3: 874-81; also *Act.VIe Congr.Int.Hist.Sci.* (Amsterdam, 1950), (1), p. 405-12. Paris: Hermann, 1951.

Awf-cj

BURGER, D. Het franse tijdschrift "La Nature" bestaat tachtig jaar. [The French review, *La Nature,* has existed 80 years. (In Dutch)]. *Faraday,* 1953-54, 23: 32.

SARTON, George. *La Revue Générale des Sciences. Isis,* 1920, 3: 270-1.
Short note to commemorate the 25th anniversary in 1914, of this review founded in 1890 by Louis Olivier.

STEIN, Robert. *See* Awg-ce

Awf-da

Annuaire de l'Académie des Sciences, Institut de France, pour 1917- Paris: 1917-
Contains brief biographies of members since the foundation.

BINET, Léon. Figures de savants français. 118 p., 8 portr. Paris: Vigot, 1946.
Leborgne de Savigny, Ed. Nocard, L.H. Faraboeuf, Lavoisier, Brown-Séquard, Richet, d'Arsonval, Ch. Achard.

DICTIONNAIRE de biographie française. Sous la direction de J. Balteau [et al.]. I. Aage - Alicot - Paris: Letouzey, 1933-
In continuation.

DURTAIN, Luc. Les grandes figures de la science française. 258 p. Paris: Hachette, 1952.
Reviewed by Suzanne Delorme, *Rev.Hist.Sci.,* 1952, 5: 274; by J.P., *Arch.Int.Hist.Sci.,* 1952, 5: 377.

INSTITUT DE FRANCE. Index biographique des membres et correspondants de l'Académie des Sciences, du 22 décembre 1666 au 15 novembre 1954. (2nd ed.) xi, 534 p. Paris: Gauthier-Villars, 1954.
Reviewed by J.P., *Arch.Int.Hist.Sci.,* 1955, 8: 185.
For an earlier edition covering the years 1666 to 1939 *see* CB 57/279.

LEURS DÉBUTS. *Nouv.Litt.,* 1951, 30: 5. [CB 78/159]
French scientists speak of their professional debuts.

NOTICES et discours. Académie des Sciences. 4 vol. 1. 1924-36; 2. 1937-48; 3. 1949-56; 4. 1957-62. Paris: Gauthier-Villars, 1957.
Vol. 1 and 2 reviewed by George Sarton, *Isis*, 1940, 31: 462-4 and 1950, 41: 389; for vol. 3 *see* CB 84/299.

OCAGNE, Maurice d'. Hommes et choses de science. Propos familiers. 3 vol. vii, 305 p.; 291 p.; 275 p. Paris: Vuibert, 1930, 1932, 1936. [CB 32/573]

PICARD, Emile. Mélanges de mathématiques et de physique. 366 p. Paris: Gauthier-Villars et Cie, 1924. [CB 18/562]
Contains a number of biographical sketches.

Awf-daj

DANIELS, Francis. French scientific reader, edited with introduction, notes and vocabulary. xviii, 748 p. (Oxford French Series). New York: Oxford University Press, 1917.

Awf-k

BERTHELOT, René. Sur quelques philosophies des sciences dans la France contemporaine. *Rev.Métaphys.Morale*, 1930, 37: 181-221.

POIRIER, R. Philosophes et savants français du XXe siècle. 2. La philosophie de la science. xxiv, 234 p. Paris: F. Alcan, 1926. [CB 20/178]

TATARKIEWICZ, Wladyslaw. [From the history of the theory of science. (In Polish with English summary)]. *Zycie Nauk.*, 1947, 2: 345-53. [CB 71/117]
Discussing the work of French critics of science.

Awf-nh

SMET, Roger. Le nouvel argot de l'X. Préface de Michel Corday. xiv, 306 p. Paris: Gauthier-Villars, 1936.
Study of the slang used by Polytechnicians.

Awf-p/t organization of science and other special aspects

Awf-p

APPELL, Paul. La recherche scientifique. *Rev.Sci.*, 1923, 61: 161-5.
The article lists organizations which assist scientific research in France.

LACROIX, Alfred. La recherche scientifique dans les territoires d'Outre-mer. *XIIIe Congr.Rech.Sci.Ter.Outre-Mer*, (Paris, 1937), 15 p. Paris: 1938.

PERRIN, Jean. Discours prononcé à l'Académie des Sciences, séances publique annuelle du lundi 21 décembre 1936. *Compt. Rend.Acad.Sci.*, 1936, 203: 1409-14.
Includes short account of the current organisation and support of scientific research in France.

PICARD, Emile. La science et la recherche scientifique. *Rev.Sci.*, 1912, 50: 2e sem., 577-81.
On the organization of science in France.

TASSY, Edmé; LÉRIS, Pierre. Les ressources du travail intellectuel en France. 2 vol. xvi, 711 p. Supplément (1921-23), vii, 102 p. Paris: Gauthier-Villars, 1921-24.

VILLEY, Jean. L'organisation de la recherche expérimentale en France. *Rev.Gén.Sci.*, 1923, 34: 601-7, 643-8.

Awf-pw

RADOVSKII, M.I. Nauchnye ... *See* Apw

RIABUŠHINSKII, Dimitrii. Les rapports scientifiques entre la France et la Russie. *Rev.Gén.Sci.*, 1934, 45: 46-50.

Awf-qd

MARGERIE, Emmanuel de. Discours prononcé à la séance de clôture du Congrès des Sociétés Savantes à Paris, le samedi, 22 mai 1937. 23 p. Paris: Imprimerie Nationale, 1937. [CB 57/280]
Deals with the meetings of the Association Française pour l'Avancement des Sciences.

for French learned scientific societies *see also*
Académie des Sciences, 2: 658
Collège de France, 2: 681
Institut de France, 2: 704

Awf-qg

DELAUNAY, Albert. L'Institut Pasteur des origines à aujourd'hui. 367 p. Paris: Editions France-Empire, 1962.
Reviewed by M.D. Grmek, *Arch.Int.Hist.Sci.*, 1963, 16: 105-6; by Jean Théodoridès, *Rev.Hist.Sci.*, 1963, 16: 283-4; by Albert Delorme, *Rev.Syn.*, 1963, 84: 620-1.

Awf-qk

LEGENDRE R. L'Office National des Recherches Scientifiques et Industrielles et des Inventions. *Rev.Sci.*, 1923, 61: 165-72.

Awf-sk

GUERLAC, Henry. Science and French national strength. In: Earle, E.M., ed. Modern France: problems of the Third and Fourth Republics, p. 81-105. Princeton: Princeton University Press, 1951.

Awf-th

BÉMOL, Maurice. Paul Valéry et la méthode scientifique en critique littéraire. *Literature and Science, Proc.Congr. Int.Fed.Mod.Lang.Lit.* (Oxford, 1954), p. 302-8. Oxford: Blackwell, 1955.

CATTAUI, Georges. Proust et les sciences. *Literature and Science, Proc.Congr.Int.Fed.Mod.Lang.Lit.* (Oxford, 1954), p. 287-92. Oxford: Blackwell, 1955.

RICHTHOFEN, Erich, Freiherr von. Die aus der Natur und den Wissenschaften geschöpften Gleichnisse von Paul Valéry. *Literature and Science, Proc.Congr.Int.Fed.Mod.Lang.Lit.* (Oxford, 1954), p. 308-13. Oxford: Blackwell, 1955. 128

Awg Germany; Austria; Switzerland

ABB, Gustav, ed. Aus fünfzig Jahren deutscher Wissenschaft. Die Entwicklung ihrer Fachgebiete in Einzeldarstellungen. (... Friedrich Schmidt-Ott zur Feier seines siebzigsten Geburtstages überreicht). xi, 496 p. Berlin: De Gruyter, 1930.

ARMATTOE, Raphael E.G. The Swiss contribution to Western civilisation. With a foreword by Julian S. Huxley. 91 p. Dundalk: Dundalgan Press, 1944. [CB 69/222]

DUHEM, Pierre. La science allemande. 146 p. Paris: Hermann, 1915.

ISCHER, Ad.; GAGNEBIN, S. Sciences. 113 p. Neuchâtel (Suisse): 1948.
History of science in the Pays de Neuchâtel.

MEYER, Adolf. Naturforschung und Naturlehre im alten Hamburg. viii, 99 p., 8 pl. Hamburg: Staatsbibliothek, 1928. [CB 25/407]

ROSSIER, Paul. Coup d'oeil sur l'histoire des sciences exactes à Genève. *Rev.Hist.Sci.*, 1953, 6: 231-49.

SCHMID, Bastian, ed. Deutsche Naturwissenschaft, Technik und Erfindung im Weltkriege. xvi, 1008 p., ill. München: O. Nemnich, 1919. [CB 10/160]

SIEGEL, Carl. Geschichte der deutschen Naturphilosophie. xvi, 390 p. Leipzig: Akademische Verlagsgesellschaft, 1913.
Reviewed by Ernest Bloch, *Isis*, 1913, 1: 287-9.

SRBIK, Heinrich von. Geist und Geschichte vom deutschen Humanismus bis zur Gegenwart. 2 vol. Salzburg: Müller, 1950-51.
Reviewed by E. Fueter, *Schweiz.Z.Gesch.*, 1955, 5: 376-82.

STEINHAUSEN, Georg. Geschichte der deutschen Kultur. 3rd rev. ed. x, 685 p., 151 fig., 15 pl. Leipzig: Bibliographisches Institut, 1929.
First published 1904.

STROMER VON REICHENBACH, Ernst. Die Pflege der Naturwissenschaften in Nürnberg vom Ausgange des Mittelalters an bis zur Gegenwart. Festvortrag. *Abhandl.Naturhist.Ges.Nürnberg*, 1927, 22: 233-40.

WALTER, Emil J. Die Pflege der exakten Wissenschaften (Astronomie, Mathematik, Kartenkunde, Physik und Chemie) im alten Zürich. 113 p., 39 fig. *Vierteljahrschr.Naturforsch. Ges.Zürich*, 1951, 96: no. 2.
History of mathematical and physical sciences in old Zürich, which means until about 1837. Some 40 illustrations and abundant notes.

Awg-cc

BRESSLAU, Harry. Geschichte der Monumenta Germaniae Historica, im Auftrage ihrer Zentraldirektion bearbeitet. xiii, 770 p. Hannover: Hahnsche Buchhandlung, 1921.
Reviewed by Fedor Schneider, *Deut.Lit.Zeitung*, 1923, 44: 257-71.

DAHLMANN, Friedrich C.; WAITZ, Georg. Quellenkunde der deutschen Geschichte. 9th ed. by Hermann Haering. 2 vol. xl, 1292 p. Leipzig: K.F. Koehler, 1931-32.
First published 1830.
Reviewed by G. Sarton, *Isis*, 1913, 1: 537-8.

GAMBLE, William Thomas Miller. The Monumenta Germaniae Historica: its inheritance in source-valuation and criticism. vi, 202 p. Washington, D.C.: Catholic University of America, 1927.
Reviewed by James Westfall Thompson, *Amer.Hist.Rev.*, 1928, 33: 636-8.

Awg-ce

STEIN, Robert. Alte französische Zeitschriften für deutsche medizinische und naturwissenschaftliche Literatur. *Arch. Gesch.Math.Naturwiss.Tech.*, 1928, 10: 473-5.

Awg-ce-bv

LAKOWITZ, Conrad. Hauptverzeichnis aller Veröffentlichungen der Naturforschenden Gesellschaft zu Danzig seit ihrer Begründung 1743 bis zum Abschluss des XV. Bandes der Neuen Folge ihrer Schriften 1922. 51 p. Danzig: 1924.

Awg-cj

BUCHNER, Eberhard. Das Neueste von gestern. Kulturgeschichtlich interessante Dokumente aus alten deutschen Zeitungen. 1. Vom 16. und 17. Jahrhundert. xiv, 330 p.; 2. 1700-1750. vii, 491 p.; 3. 1750-1787. v, 437 p. München: Albert Lange, 1911-12.

LAMLA, Ernst. *Die Naturwissenschaften* zum fünfzigjährigen Bestehen der Zeitschrift. *Naturwissenschaften*, 1963, 50: 8-14. [CB 89/492]

Awg-da

BAYERISCHE AKADEMIE DER WISSENSCHAFTEN. Geist und Gestalt. Biographische Beiträge zur Geschichte der Bayerischen Akademie der Wissenschaften, vornehmlich im 2. Jahrhundert ihres Bestehens. 3 vol. 1. Geisteswissenschaften. viii, 318 p.; 2. Naturwissenschaften. vii, 297 p.; 3. Bilder. xlvii p., 269 pl. Munich: Beck, 1959.

BUSCHBECK, Ernst H. Wissenschaft der letzten hundertfünfzig Jahre in Österreich. 26 p. Zürich: Europa Verlag, 1947. [CB 73/163]
Collection of very brief biographies.

Deutsches Biographisches Jahrbuch. Hrsg. vom Verbande der deutschen Akademien. 7 vol. Vol. 1, 1914/16 - vol. 11, 1929. Berlin/Leipzig: Deutsche Verlagsanstalt, 1925-32.
Vol. 6-9 not published.
Vol. 2 and 3 reviewed by H. Herzfeld, *Deut.Lit.Zeitung*, 1929, 6: 1737-8; 1928, 5: 2297-9.

DICTIONNAIRE historique et biographique de la Suisse. Publié avec la recommandation de la Société Générale Suisse d'Histoire et sous la direction de Marcel Godet, Henri Turler, et Victor Attinger. (Supplément.) 8 vol. Neuchâtel: Administration du Dictionnaire Historique et Biographique de la Suisse, 1921-34.
Volumes 1 and 2 reviewed by Albert Schinz, *Amer.Hist.Rev.*, 1926, 32: 88-9.

FINGER, Otto; HERNECK, Friedrich; ed. Von Liebig zu Laue; Ethos und Weltbild grosser deutscher Naturforscher und Ärzte. 379 p. Berlin: Deutscher Verlag der Wissenschaften, 1963.

FUETER, Eduard, ed. Grosse Schweizer Forscher. Hrsg. im Auftrage der Fachgruppe "Hochschulen und wissenschaftliche Forschung" der Schweizerischen Landesausstellung 1939 und der Schweizerischen Naturforschenden Gesellschaft unter Mitarbeit hervorragender Fachleute. 2nd ed. 340 p., ill. Zürich: Atlantis Verlag, 1941. [CB 70/247]
Text in German, French or Italian; added title pages in French: Pionniers suisses de la science, and in Italian: Pionieri svizzeri della scienza.
First edition reviewed by George Sarton, *Isis*, 1940, 32: 193-7.

HARIG, Gerhard, ed. Von Adam Ries bis Max Planck; 25 grosse deutsche Mathematiker und Naturwissenschaftler. 156 p., portr. (E Taschenbuch, 11) Leipzig: Verlag Enzyklopädie, 1961.
Second edition 1962.

HAUPT, Herman, ed. Hessische Biographien. In Verbindung mit Karl Esselborn und Georg Lehnert. 3 vol. Darmstadt: Grossherzogliche Staatsverlag, 1918-34 [1912-34].
Published in parts.

REVILLIOD, Pierre. Physiciens et naturalistes genevois. Publ. à l'occasion du 2me millénaire de Genève. 55 p., 10 pl. Geneva: Kundig, 1942.

WALTER, Emil. Schweizer Naturforscher. *Volkshochschule*, 1945, 14: 1-5, 33-7, 65-70, 97-101, 129-132, 161-6, 193-7, 225-30, 257-60, 289-94. [CB 70/249]

Awg-dae

SCHAUBUCH berühmter deutscher Zeitgenossen in Werken bildender Kunst. 142 p., 130 pl. München: Ernst Heimeran, 1925.

Awg-o/v teaching; organization; and other special aspects

Awg-o

LILGE, Fritz. Science and education in National Socialist Germany. *Harvard Educ.Rev.*, 1937, 7: 391-403.

WIELEITNER, Heinrich. Die Entwicklung des mathematischen und naturwissenschaftlichen Unterrichts in Bayern. *Festschrift des Deutschen Vereins zur Förderung des mathematischen und naturwissenschaftlichen Unterrichts*, p. 53-64. Würzburg: 1930.

Awg-op

UEBERREITER, Kurt. A statistical postwar survey on the natural sciences and German universities. 32 p., 7 charts. Washington, D.C.: Library of Congress European Affairs Division, 1950.

Awg-p

SCHREIBER, Georg. Deutsche Wissenschaftsorganisation von der Zeit Bismarcks bis zur Gegenwart. *Abhandlungen zur Wissenschaftslehre*, p. 21-23. (Veröffentlichungen des Gesellschaft für Internationale Wissenschaftsgeschichte, 1952, no. 2) Bremen: Carl Schünemann, [n.d.].

Awg-qd

HARNACK, Axel von. Erinnerungen an die Gründungszeit der "Kaiser-Wilhelm-Gesellschaft zur Förderung der Wissenschaften." *Naturwiss.Rundsch.*, 1963, 16: 435-8.

HEUSS, Theodor. Ansprache anlässlich der 200-Jahr Feier der Akademie der Wissenschaften in Göttingen. 31 p. In: Abhandlungen zur Wissenschaftsgeschichte und Wissenschaftslehre (Veröffentlichungen der Gesellschaft für Internationale Wissenschaftsgeschichte), 1951, no. 4. Bremen: Carl Schünemann, 1951.

JUBILEE of the Max-Planck-Gesellschaft. *Endeavour*, 1961, 20: 59-60.

MEISTER, Richard. Geschichte der Akademie der Wissenschaften in Wien, 1847-1947. 411 p., 58 pl. Wien: Holzhausen, 1947. [CB 75/99]

RÜBEL, Eduard. Eine allgemeine schweizerische Akademie und die bestehende Naturforscher-Akademie. *Neue Schweiz.Rundsch.*, Feb. 1934, 15 p.

SUDHOFF, Karl. Der deutschen Naturforscherversammlungen Werden und wachsende Bedeutung in ihrem ersten Jahrhundert. *Wiss.Ind.*, Sept. 1922, 1: 33-8.

SUDHOFF, Karl. Hundert Jahre Deutscher Naturforscher-Versammlungen. Gedächtnisschrift zur Jahrhundert Tagung der Gesellschaft Deutscher Naturforscher und Aerzte. 80 p., 8 pl. Leipzig: F.C.W. Vogel, 1922.

for German learned scientific societies *see also* Deutsche Akademie der Naturforscher Leopoldina, 2: 687

Awg-qk

GERMANY. REICHSMINISTERIUM FÜR WISSENSCHAFT, ERZIEHUNG UND VOLKSBILDUNG. Ein Ehrentag der deutschen Wissenschaft. Die Eröffnung des Reichsforschungsrats am 25. Mai 1937. 47 p., 19 ill. Berlin: Pressestelle des Reichserziehungsministeriums, 1937. [CB 73/151]

Awg-sb

WALTER, Emil J. Gli influssi sociologici sull'indagine scientifica naturalistica nell'antica Svizzera dal XVI al XVIII sec. *Act.VIIIe Congr.Int.Hist.Sci.* (Florence, 1956), p. 747-8. Paris: Hermann, 1958.

WALTER, Emil J. Soziale Grundlagen der Entwicklung der Naturwissenschaften in der alten Schweiz. 383 p., 8 tables. Bern: Verlag Francke, 1958.
Reviewed by Elinor G. Barber, *Isis*, 1960, 51: 576-8; by H. Fischer, *Gesnerus*, 1958, 15: 181-4.

Awg-th

CLERY, Adrien Robinet de. Rainer-Maria Rilke et la science moderne. *Literature and Science, Proc.Congr.Int.Fed.Mod. Lang.Lit.* (Oxford, 1954), p. 298-302. Oxford: Blackwell, 1955.

CLOSS, A. Scientific analysis and interpretation in modern German literary criticism. In: *Literature and science, Proc. Congr.Int.Fed.Mod.Lang.Lit.* (Oxford, 1954), p. 318-24. Oxford: Blackwell, 1955.

KOHLBRUGGE, J.H.F. Herders Verhältnis zu modernen Naturanschauungen. *Naturwissenschaften*, 1913, 1: no. 46, 1110-16.

Awg-u

LOTE, R. Les origines mystiques de la science allemande. 236 p. Paris: Alcan, 1913.

Awg-vm

MYERSON, Abraham; GOLDBERG, Isaac. The German Jew: his share in modern culture. xiii, 161, ix p. London: Hopkinson, 1933.
Reviewed in *Nature*, 1933, 132: 428.

Awh Czechoslovakia; Hungary; Poland

BIRKENMAJER, Aleksander; DICKSTEIN, Samuel. Coup d'oeil sur l'histoire des sciences exactes en Pologne. In: Histoire sommaire des sciences en Pologne, publiée à l'occasion du VIIe Congrès International des Sciences Historiques, p. 1-33. Cracow: 1933.

DRUCE, Gerald. Czechoslovakia's contributions to science: a survey and a forecast. *Nature*, 1938, 142: 942-4.

HISTOIRE sommaire des sciences en Pologne, publiée à l'occasion du VIIe Congrès International des Sciences Historiques. 155 p. Cracow: Drukarnia Narodowa, 1933.

KRASSOWSKI, Jean. L'apport de la Pologne dans les sciences exactes. *Rev.Gén.Sci.*, 1921, 32: 682-7. [CB 13/305]

LIGETI, Lajos, ed. A Magyar tudomany tiz éve, 1945-1955. [Ten years of Hungarian science. (In Hungarian)]. 432 p. Budapest: Akadémiai Kiadó, 1955.
Reviewed by C.K., *Arch.Int.Hist.Sci.*, 1957, 10: 359-60. Summary of contents of volume, *ibid.*, 360-2.

MATOUŠEK, Otakar. A methodical study of the history of science in Bohemia. *Arch.Int.Hist.Sci.*, 1955, 8: 264-9.

NOVÝ, L., ed. Dejiny exaktnich ved v ceskych zemich do konce 19. stoleti. [History of the exact sciences in Bohemian lands to the end of the 19th century. (In Czech)]. 427 p. Prague: Czechoslovak Academy of Sciences, 1961.
Reviewed by Karel Hujer, *Isis*, 1964, 55: 99-101; by Jan Koran, *Česk.Čas.Hist.*, 1963, 11: 248-50.

SARTON, George. Science in Poland. *Isis*, 1947, 37: 78-9.

STUDIA i Materialy z Dziejów Nauki Polskiej. [Studies and materials concerning the Polish history of science] Polska Akademia Nauk: Komitet Historii Nauki. Vol. 1- Warsaw: Panstwowe Wydawnictwo Naukowe, 1953-
Published in series A,B,C since 1957; series D added 1958; series E 1965.
Vol. 1 and 2 reviewed by Waldemar Voisé, *Arch.Int.Hist. Sci.*, 1956, 9: 57-60; vol. 7(3), ser. B, by Zdzislaw Kosiek, *Kwart.Hist.Nauk.Tech.*, 1961, 6: 326-8.

SUCHODOLSKI, Bogdan. Studia z dziejów polskiej myśli filozoficznej i naukowej. [Studies on the history of Polish philosophical and scientific thought. (In Polish)] 492 p., pl. Wrocław: Zakład Narodowy Imienia Ossolińskich Wydawnictwo Polskiej Akademii Nauk, 1959.

VETTER, Quido. Czech science during the war. *Scr.Math.*, 1946, 12: 141-6, 3 portr.

VETTER, Quido. L'évolution des sciences sur le territoire de la République Tchécoslovaque. (7th International Congress of Historical Sciences, Warsaw, 1933, Scientific reports). *Bull.Int.Comm.Hist.Sci.*, 1933, 5: pt. 1, 333-52.

VETTER, Quido. Přírodní vědy v Polsku. [The natural sciences in Poland. (In Czech)]. *Sb.Dějiny Přírodn.Věd Tech.*, 1957, 3: 223-35.

Z dejin vied a techniky na Slovensku. [From the history of science and technology in Slovakia. (In Czech with summaries in German and Russian)] Vol. 1- Bratislava: Vydavatel'stvo Slovenskej Akademie Vied, 1962
Collection of Slovakian works on the history of science and technology.
Vol. 1 reviewed by J. Smolka, *Cesk.Cas.Hist.*, 1963, 11: 476-9.

Awh-br

Nauka Polska: jej potrzeby, organizacja i rozwój. [Science in Poland, its needs, organization and progress. (In Polish)] Warsaw: 1918-47.

Awh-bv

BIRKENMAJER, Aleksander. [A glance at Polish historiography of the sciences in the period 1887-1937. (In Polish)]. 12 p. Lwów: Z Drukarni Zakladu Narodowego Imienia Ossolinskich, 1937.

BIRKENMAJER, Aleksander. Historia nauk matematyczno-przyrodniczych i medycyny. [History of mathematical and natural sciences and medicine in Poland in the 19th and 20th centuries. (In Polish)] *Kwart.Hist.*, 1937, 51: 425-34.

RECHCIGL, Miloslav. Czechoslovakia and its arts and sciences: A selective bibliography in the Western European languages. In: The Czechoslovak contribution to world culture, ed. Miloslav Rechcigl, p. 555-634. London/The Hague/Paris: Mouton, 1964.

Awh-ce-bv

TRYPUCKO, Jozef. Polonica vetera Upsaliensia. Catalogue des imprimés polonais ou concernant la Pologne des XVe, XVIe, XVIIe et XVIIIe siècles conservés à la Bibliothèque de l'Université Royale d'Upsala. 186 p. (Acta Bibliothecae R. Universitatis Upsaliensis, 13) Uppsala: Almqvist & Wiksells, 1958.

Awh-p

ORGANISATION de la science polonaise. *Organon*, 1936, 1: 135-289.

Awh-qd for Polish learned scientific societies *see* Polska Akademija Nauk, 2: 741

Awi Italy

BILANCIONI, Guglielmo. "Italae vires". Storia della scienza e nazionalismo. Alla ricerca di una giustizia internazionale. *Boll.Ist.Stor.Ital.Arte Sanit.*, 1924, 3: 61-9.
Criticism of Sarton's review of the author's "Veteris vestigia flammae", *see* below.

BILANCIONI, Guglielmo. Sulle rive del Lete: rievocazioni e ricorsi del pensiero scientifico italiano. 346 p. Rome: Bardi, 1930.

BILANCIONI, Guglielmo. Veteris vestigia flammae. Pagine storiche della scienza nostra. xvi, 544 p., 66 fig. Roma: Leonardo da Vinci, 1922.
Reviewed by George Sarton, *Isis*, 1923, 5: 475-7; for the author's reply *see* his "Italae vires" above.

CARUGO, Adriano; MONDELLA, Felice. Lo sviluppo delle scienze e delle tecniche in Italia dalla metà del XIX secolo alla prima guerra mondiale. In: Nuove Questioni di storia del Risorgimento e dell'Unità d'Italia, vol. 2, p. 429-509. Milano: C. Marzorrati, 1961.

IVANENKO, D.D. Fizicheskaia nauka Italii. [Physical science in Italy. (In Russian)]. *Usp.Fiz.Nauk*, 1957, 62: 523-7. English transl. in *Advances Phys.Sci.*, 1960, 62: 645-72.

MIELI, Aldo. La storia della scienza in Italia negli ultimi due secoli. *Arch.Gesch.Math.Naturwiss.Tech.*, 1929, 11: 292-308.

OLSCHKI, Leonardo. The genius of Italy. [Essays]. vii, 481 p. New York: Oxford University Press, 1949.
Italian translation (2 vol. Milan: A. Mondadori, 1953) reviewed by A. Corsini, *Riv.Stor.Sci.*, 1953, 44: 220-1.

PETRUCCI, Gino Bargagli. L'Italia e la scienza. Studi di vari autori. viii, 400 p. Firenze: Le Monnier, 1932.
Reviewed by Aldo Mieli, *Archeion*, 1933, 15: 261-6.

SILLA, Lucio, ed. Un secolo di progresso scientifico italiano, 1839-1939. Opera storica ... sotto la direzione del Comitato Scientifico della S.I.P.S. 7 vol. ill., maps, diagr. Rome: Società Italiana per il Progresso delle Scienze, [1939-40].
Vol. 1-6 reviewed by G. Sarton, *Isis*, 1944, 35: 190-1; for vol. 7 *see* CB 69/223.

Awi-bx

ENTE MANIFESTAZIONI MILANESI. Mostra storica della scienza italiana, novembre 1957-gennaio 1958, Milano, Palazzo Reale. xxxii, 109 p., 121 pl., front. Milan: Amilcare Pizzi, 1958.
Account of exhibition, *Isis*, 1958, 49: 348-9.

Awi-cj

GUINET, L. Note to celebrate the twentieth anniversary of *Scientia*. *Isis*, 1927, 9: 428-9.

Awi-da

MIELI, Aldo, ed. Gli scienziati italiani dall' inizio del medio evo ai nostri giorni. Repertorio biobibliografico dei filosofici, matematici, astronomi, fisici, chimici, naturalisti, biologi, medici, geografi italiani. 2 vol. in 3. 1, pt. 1. viii, 236 p., ill., 1921; pt. 2. 235-465 p., ill., 1923. 2, pt. 1. 104 p., ill., 1923. Rome: Nardecchia, 1921-23. [CB 16/336]
No more published.
Reviewed by G. Sarton, *Isis*, 1920-21, 3: 59-60; 1921-22, 4: 112-14.

Awi-of

NICEFORO, Alfredo. Les "classiques" et les "techniciens" dans leurs notes d'examen à la Faculté des sciences. *J. Soc.Statist.Paris*, 1913, 54: 485-507. [CB 4/785]
In Italy.

Awi-or

AGOSTINI, Amedeo. Matematici e fisici, direttori e professori della Scuola Normale Superiore di Pisa. Conferenza letta nel Salone degli Stemmi il giorno 18 maggio 1934. 18 p. Pisa: Arti Grafiche Pacini Mariotti, [n.d.].

Awi-pw

PACE, Antonio. The American Philosophical Society and Italy. *Proc.Amer.Phil.Soc.*, 1946, 90: 387-421. [CB 70/275]

Awi-qd

ATENEO DI VENEZIA. L'Ateneo Veneto nel suo primo centennio (1812-1912). Quattordici relazioni di A. Brunetti [ed altri]. viii, 336 p., ill. Venezia: A spese dell'Ateneo, 1912.

BORTOLOTTI, Ettore. Origine e progressi della R. Accademia delle Scienze dell' Istituto di Bologna. *Supplemento delle Mem.Accad.Sci.Ist.Bologna Sez.Sci.Fiz.Mat., 8th ser.*, 1923-24, 1: 20 p.

GABRIELI, G. Vita accademica in Roma nell' età moderna. 23 p. Rome: [1936?]. [CB 39/603]

SARTON, George. Società Italiana per il Progresso delle Scienze, Bari, 1914. *Isis*, 1914, 2: 172-3.

TESTI, Gino. Antiche accademie italiane di piccole città. L'Accademia degli Spensierati di Rossano in Calabria. *Archeion*, 1941, 23: 117-18.

for Italian learned scientific societies *see also* Accademia Nazionale dei Lincei, 2: 659

Awj Spain; Portugal

FERREIRA, Ernesto. O Arquipélago dos Açores na história das ciências. *Petrus Nonius*, 1937, 1: 61-79.

LAIN ENTRALGO, Pedro; LÓPEZ PIÑERO, José Maria. The Spanish contribution to world science. *Cah.Hist.Mond.*, 1961, 6: 948-68.

MILLÁS VALLICROSA, José Maria. Nuevos estudios sobre historia de la ciencia española. 364 p., pl. Barcelona: Instituto "Luis Vives" de Filosofía, 1960.
Reviewed by Carl B. Boyer, *Isis*, 1963, 54: 143-4.

MILLAS VALLICROSA, José Maria. La vindicación de la ciencia española por Menéndez y Pelayo. *Arbor*, julio-agosto, 1956, no. 127-8, 17 p.

Awj-ce

SARTON, George. Eskualherria. *Studies in the History of Culture*, p. 63-83, 6 fig. Menasha, Wisc.: American Council of Learned Societies, 1942.
With notes on Basque literature.

Awj-da

PINA, Luiz de. Os homens da Igreja na ciência nacional. *Brotéria: Sér.Mens.*, 1936, 23: 153-73.

Awj-pw

FERREIRA, H. Amorim. Relações científicas entre Portugal e a Grã-Bretanha. viii, 76 p. Lisbon: Academia das Ciências de Lisboa, 1943.
Reviewed by Sir George Thomson, *Nature*, 1943, 152: 618-19.

Awk Low Countries

BARNOUW, A.J.; LANDHEER, B.; ed. The contribution of Holland to the sciences. A symposium. xvii, 373 p., 13 ill. New York: Querido, 1943.
Reviewed by George Sarton, *Isis*, 1944, 35: 189-90.

BOCKSTAELE, Paul. Het Mercator-Muzeüm te Sint-Niklaas. Met enkels beschouwingen over de geschiedenis der wetenschappen in Vlaanderen. [The Mercator Museum at St. Niklaas. With a brief view of the history of science in Flanders. (In Dutch)] *Toerist*, 1962, 41: 548-51. [CB 88/532]

BURGER, D. Het culturele leven in Nederland. 4. De natuurwetenschappen. In: Algemene geschiedenis der Nederlanden. 12. In de schaduw van twee wereldoorlogen [Cultural life in the Netherlands. 4. The natural sciences. In: General history of the Netherlands. 12. In the shadow of two world wars. (In Dutch)], p. 346-56. Utrecht: 1958.

BURGER, D. Het geestelijk leven in Nederland. 2. De natuurwetenschappen. In: Algemene geschiedenis der Nederlanden. 11. Van liberaal naar sociaal getij, 1885-1914 [Intellectual life in the Netherlands. 2. The natural sciences. In: General history of the Netherlands. 11. From the liberal to the socialist period, 1885-1914. (In Dutch)], p. 212-21. Utrecht: 1956.

GRANDE encyclopédie de la Belgique et du Congo. 2 vol. xxxi, 677 p., ill.; 842 p., ill. Brussels: Editorial Office, H. Wauthoz-Legrand, 1938-52.
Vol. 1 reviewed by J. Pelseneer, *Arch.Int.Hist.Sci.*, 1953, 6: 319.

PELSENEER, Jean. Aspect statistique du progrès des sciences en Belgique, à travers les siècles. *Isis*, 1941, 33: 237-42. [CB 69/223]
Definitive version in *Bull.Acad.Roy.Belg.Cl.Sci.*, 1941, 27: 269-76.

PELSENEER, Jean. Bruxelles et les sciences. In: Les Belles heures de Bruxelles, p. 347-60, 18 pl. Brussels: Elsevier, 1952.

TIMMERMANS, Jean. Science in independent Belgium. In: Goris, Jan Albert, ed. Belgium, p. 239-55. Berkeley, Los Angeles: University of California Press, 1945.

VELDE, A.J.J. Van de. De natuurwetenschappen. [The sciences. (In Dutch)] In: Lamberty, Max; Lissens, R.F.; ed. Vlaanderen door de euwen heen. [Flanders through the centuries], vol. 2, p. 373-86, ill. Brussels/Amsterdam: Elsevier, 1952.

Awk-br

Le Mouvement Scientifique en Belgique. (De Wetenschappelijke Beweging in Belgie). 1- Brussels: Féderation Belge des Sociétés Scientifiques (Belgisch Verbond der Wetenschappelijke Verenigingen), 1960-.

Awk-bx

BIBLIOTHÈQUE ROYALE DE BELGIQUE. Histoire des sciences en Belgique jusqu'à la fin du XVIIIe siècle. Exposition. Bruxelles, 12 février-15 avril 1938. 160 p. [Renaix: J. Leherte-Delcour, 1938] [CB 54/526]

UNGER, W.S. Tentoonstelling betreffende de geschiedenis der genees- en natuurkunde in Zeeland. [Exhibition illustrating the history of medicine and the natural sciences in Zeeland. (In Dutch)] *Bijdr.Gesch.Geneesk.*, 1926, 6: 191-9.

Awk-ce-bv

BIERENS DE HAAN, D. Bibliographie Néerlandaise historique-scientifique des ouvrages importants dont les auteurs sont nés aux 16e, 17e, et 18e siècles, sur les sciences mathématiques et physiques, avec leurs applications. 424 p. Roma: 1883; reprinted Nieukoop: B. De Graaf, 1960.

Awk-cm

LIÉGE. UNIVERSITÉ. BIBLIOTHÈQUE. Maîtres liégois de l'illustration scientifique: catalogue (établi par E. Sauvenier-Goffin) de l'exposition organisée à la Bibliothèque ... du 13 octobre au 6 novembre 1955. 26 p., 4 pl. (Bibliotheca Universitaties Leodiensis, Publications, 7) Liége: Maison Desoer, 1955.

Awk-da

ACADÉMIE ROYALE DES SCIENCES, DES LETTRES ET DES BEAUX ARTS DE BELGIQUE. Biographie nationale. Vol. 1-28. (Première série). Vol. 29- Supplément 1- Brussels: 1866-1944, 1957- [CB 39/465; CB 55/185; CB 57/266]
Vol. 29 reviewed by J. Pelseneer, *Arch.Int.Hist.Sci.*, 1957, 10: 122.

ACADEMIE ROYALE DES SCIENCES, DES LETTRES ET DES BEAUX ARTS DE BELGIQUE. Index biographique des membres, correspondants et associés de l'Académie Royale de Belgique de 1769 à 1947. 265 p. Bruxelles: Palais des Académies, 1948. [CB 76/389]
2nd ed., 1769-1963 (Brussels: 1964).

ACADÉMIE ROYALE DES SCIENCES D'OUTRE-MER. Biographie coloniale belge. Vol. 1- Brussels: Falk, 1948- [CB 84/299]

ALDERS, J.G. Nederlandsche baanbrekers der wetenschap. [Dutch pioneers of science. (In Dutch)]. 201 p. Amsterdam: Bigot and Van Rossum, 1940.
Reviewed by Ernest Tillotson, *Nature*, 1947, 160: 449.

GERRITS, G.C. Grote Nederlanders bij de opbouw der natuurwetenschappen. [Great Dutchmen in the development of the natural sciences. (In Dutch)] 518 p. Leiden: Brill: 1948.
Reviewed by P. Sergescu, *Arch.Int.Hist.Sci.*, 1949, 2: 483.

LEBRUN, Gaston. Grandes figures de la Belgique indépendante, 1830-1930. Bruxelles: Bieleveld, 1930. [CB 39/466]
La première partie (Sciences mathématiques, physiques et naturelles) de la 5e Section comporte une introduction et 23 biographies par Lucien Hauman.

LOURIDANT, Félicien. Tables des notices biographiques publiées dans l'Annuaire de l'Académie Royale de Belgique (1835-1914). 55 p. Bruxelles: Hayez, 1919.

MOLHUYSEN, P.C.; BLOK, P.J.; ed. Nieuw Nederlandsch Biographisch Woordenboek. 10 vol. Leiden: Sijthoff, 1911-37.

Awk-da-py

SEVENSMA, T.P. Nederlandsche helden der wetenschap. Levensschetsen van negen Nobel-prijswinnaars. Hoogtepunten van wetenschappelijken arbeid in Nederland. [Dutch heroes of science. Sketches of the lives of nine Nobel prize winners. Peaks of scientific work in the Netherlands. (In Dutch)]. 351 p., fig., pl. Amsterdam: Kosmos, 1946. [CB 74/164]

Awk-hd

ARNOULD, Maurice A. Historiographie de la Belgique. Des origines à 1830. 77 p., facs. (Collection Nationale, 80) Bruxelles: Office de Publicité, 1947. [CB 71/127]

Awk-o/t teaching; organization; and other special aspects

Awk-oq

FLORKIN, Marcel. Les origines françaises de la Faculté des Sciences de Liége. *Vieux-Liége*, 1954, no. 104-105, 302-6.

ROOSEBOOM, Maria. Matériaux pour l'histoire des sciences du temps moderne. 8. Albert Einstein und die Niederländischen Universitäten. *Janus*, 1958, 47: 198-201.
Regarding Einstein's candidature for a professorship at Utrecht.

THE 350th ANNIVERSARY of the establishment of the Athenaeum of the Grand-Duchy of Luxemburg. *Scr.Math.*, 1953, 19: 217. [CB 80/119]

Awk-p

LECAT, Maurice. Notre misère scientifique. Ses causes - ses remèdes. L'appel du roi. Par Q.M. Quaeris [pseud. of Maurice Lecat] et des collaborateurs. 56 p. Bruxelles: Fr. Sacy, 1928.
Discussion of the organization of scientific research in Belgium.

Awk-pw

BRANS, P.H. Cooperation scientifique au sein du Bénélux. *Act.IIIe Congr.Bénélux Hist.Sci.* (Luxembourg, 1960), p. 137-41. (Comité Luxembourgeois d'Histoire des Sciences, Publications, 2) Leiden: E.J. Brill, 1960. Also in *Janus*, 1960, 49: 137-41.

KRAENTZEL, F. Les savants étrangers en Belgique. *Alumni*, 1932, 4: 8-19. [CB 38/615]

Awk-qd

BIERENS DE HAAN, J.A. De Hollandsche Maatschappij der Wetenschappen, 1752-1952. [The Netherlands Society of Science. (In Dutch, with a summary in English)] 422 p., 48 ill. Haarlem: Siège de la Société, 1952.
Reviewed by H. Dopp, *Rev.Quest.Sci.*, 1952, 13: 476-7.

GILLIS, J.B. Contribution des Académies Royales Flamandes de Belgique à l'histoire des sciences. *Act.VIe Congr.Int.Hist. Sci.* (Amsterdam, 1950), p. 518-25. Paris: Hermann, 1953.

ITERSON, G. van, Jr. The Netherlands East Indies and the Royal Netherlands Academy of Sciences and Literature. 32 p., ill. Amsterdam: North-Holland Publishing Company, 1946.

LOURIDANT, Félicien. Tables des notices biographiques publiées dans l'Annuaire de l'Académie Royale de Belgique (1835-1914). 55 p. Bruxelles: Hayez, 1919.
With list of documents relating to the history of the Académie published in the Annuaire.

PELSENEER, Paul, ed. L'Académie Royale de Belgique depuis sa fondation (1772-1922). 343 p. Bruxelles: Lamertin, 1922.
Reviewed by George Sarton, *Isis*, 1922, 4: 522.

RÉPERTOIRE des Sociétés Scientifiques Fédérées de Belgique. Edité par la Fédération Belge des Sociétés de Sciences Mathématiques, Physiques, Chimiques, Naturelles, Médicales et Appliquées. 56 p. Bruxelles: Éditions Techniques et Scientifiques, R. Louis, 1948.

Awk-qv

CONGRÈS NATIONAL DES SCIENCES. IIIe Congrès National des Sciences, organisé par la Fédération belge des Sociétés Scientifiques, Bruxelles, 30 mai - 3 juin 1950. Vol. 1. Historique du Congrès et Histoire des Sciences. 148 p. Liège: Desoer, 1951. [CB 77/361]
Reviewed by A.G. Drachmann, *Centaurus*, 1952, 2: 254-5.

VELDE, A.J.J. van de. Het Vlaamsch Natuur- en Geneeskundig Congres van zijn oorsprong in 1897 tot in 1944. Historische schets. [History of the Flemish Scientific Congress from its beginning in 1897 to 1944. (In Dutch)] 131 p., pl. (*Verhandel.Vlaam.Acad.Wetensch.Lett.Schoone Kunsten Belg., Kl.Wetensch.*, 6) Antwerpen: N.V. Stadaard-Boekhandel, 1944. [CB 71/116]

Awk-th

ROOS, Jacques. Maurice Maeterlinck et les sciences. *Literature and science, Proc.Congr.Int.Fed.Mod.Lang.Lit.* (Oxford, 1954), p. 276-83. Oxford: Blackwell, 1955.

Awm Scandinavia

DIE ENTWICKLUNG der Wissenschaften in Schweden. Nachtrag zu "Schweden 1941". 61 p., ill. Stockholm: 1941.
Reviewed by Sten Lindroth, *Lychnos*, 1943, 291.

WESTERGAARD, Waldemar. Danish history and Danish historians. *J.Mod.Hist.*, 1952, 24: 167-80.

Awm-da

DAHLGREN, E.W. Kungl. Svenska Vetenskapsakademien. Personförteckningar, 1739-1915. [Royal Swedish Academy of Science. List of members, 1739-1915. (In Swedish)] vii, 295 p. Stockholm: Almqvist & Wiksells, 1915. [CB 42/612]
List of members, including foreign ones.

EHRENCRON-MÜLLER, Holger. Forfatterlexikon omfattende Danmark, Norge og Island indtil 1814. [Dictionary of writers covering Denmark, Norway and Iceland up to 1814. (In Danish)] 12 vol. Copenhagen: H. Aschehoug, 1924-35.
Volumes 1-4 reviewed by Gustav Neckel, *Deut.Lit.Zeitung*, 1927, 1489-91.

LINDROTH, Sten, ed. Swedish men of science, 1650-1950. 295 p. Stockholm: Swedish Institute, Almqvist & Wiksell, 1952.
Reviewed by George Sarton, *Isis*, 1953, 44: 295-6.

MEISEN, V. Prominent Danish scientists through the ages. With facsimiles from their works. 195 p. (University Library of Copenhagen, 450th anniversary) Copenhagen: Levin & Munksgaard, 1932.
Reviewed by George Sarton, *Isis*, 1935, 23: 276-8.

Awm-n

HOLMBERG, Arne. Kungl. Vetenskapsakademiens äldre skrifter i utländska översättningar och referat. [The early publications of the Royal Academy of Sciences in foreign translations and reviews. (In Swedish with German summary)] 72 p., 7 pl. Uppsala: Almqvist & Wiksells, 1939. [CB 59/494]

Awm-p

MAJOR, Robert. Organization of scientific activities in Norway. *Science*, 1959, 129: 694-9, 6 fig.

Awm-ph

HALSEY, A.H. Science and government in Sweden. *Minerva*, 1963, 2: 54-60.

Awm-pw

THE HERITAGE from Newton and Linnaeus. Scientific links between England and Sweden in bygone times. *See* Apw-bx

Awm-qd

ALMHULT, Arthur; HOLMBERG, Arne; SCHÜCK, Adolf. Academies in Sweden. *Baltic Scand.Countries*, 1937, 3: 305-19.
The oldest Swedish academy was founded in 1739, the youngest in 1932.

LOMHOLT, Asger. Det Kongelige Danske Videnskabernes Selskab 1742-1942. Samlinger til Selskabets Historie. [History of the Royal Danish Scientific Society. (In Danish)] 2 vol. Copenhagen: Det Kongelige Danske Videnskabernes Selskab, 1960, 1961.
Reviewed by Nils Ludwig Rasmusson, *Lychnos*, 1962, 247-8; Herman Richter, *Lychnos*, 1962, 248-9.

MIDBØE, Hans. Det Kongelige Norske Videnskabers Selskabs historie 1760-1960. [The history of the Royal Norwegian Society of Sciences. (In Norwegian)] 2 vol. 407 p.; 300 p., ill. Trondheim: 1960.
Reviewed by Gunnar Eriksson, *Lychnos*, 1962, 250-1.

for Swedish learned scientific societies *see also* Svenska Vetenskapsakademien, 2: 763

Awn Russia; Baltic States; Finland

AKADEMIIA NAUK SSSR. OTDELENIE MATEMATICHESKIKH I ESTVENNYKH NAUK. Matematika i estestvoznanie v S.S.S.R. Ocherki razvitiya matematicheskikh i estestvennykh nauk za dvadtsat let. [Mathematics and natural sciences in the U.S.S.R. Outlines of their development for the past twenty years. (In Russian)] vii, 1006 p. Moscow: 1938.

BATESON, William. Science in Russia. *Nature*, 1925, 116: 681-3.
Account of visit to Russia for 200th anniversary of the Akademiia Nauk SSSR.

BILLINGTON, James H. Science in Russian culture. *Amer. Scient.*, 1964, 52: 274-80.

BORODIN, George. Soviet and tsarist Siberia. 168 p., 43 ill. London: Rich & Cowan, 1944. [CB 66/253]

CHRISTMAN, Ruth G., ed. Soviet science. A symposium presented on 27 December 1951 at the Philadelphia meeting of the American Association for the Advancement of Science. vii, 108 p. Washington: for the American Association for the Advancement of Science, 1952.
Reviewed by David Joravsky, *Isis*, 1954, 45: 408-9.

CONGRESS OF AMERICAN-SOVIET FRIENDSHIP, 2nd, New York, 1943. Science in Soviet Russia. Papers presented at Congress. Under the auspices of the National Council of American-Soviet Friendship. ix, 97 p. Lancaster, Pa.: Jaques Cattell Press, 1944. [CB 68/39]

CROWTHER, J.G. Science in Soviet Russia. 128 p., 13 pl. London: Williams and Norgate, 1930.

CROWTHER, J.G. Soviet science. x, 342 p., 16 pl. London: Kegan Paul; New York: Dutton, 1936.
Reviewed by C.A. Kofoid, *Isis*, 1937, 27: 90-2; by E.J. Russell, *Nature*, 1936, 137: 797-8; by E.H. Neville, *Math.Gaz.*, 1936, 20: 354-5.

DOBROV, Gennady M. Investigations on the history of science and technology in the Ukraine. *Proc.10th Int.Congr.Hist. Sci.* (Ithaca, 1962), (1), p. 341-2. Paris: Hermann, 1964.

FIGUROVSKII, N.A. 40 lat historii przyrodoznawstwa i techniki w ZSRR. [40 years of natural science and technology history in the USSR. (In Polish)]. *Kwart.Hist.Nauk.Tech.*, 1958, 3: 519-36.

FIGUROVSKII, N.A. Istoriia estestvoznaniia i tekhniki v SSSR za 40 let. [The history of natural science and technology in the USSR during the past 40 years. (In Russian)]. *Vop.Ist.Est.Tekh.*, 1958, 6: 3-11.

IOFFE, A.F. Development of the exact sciences in the U.S.S.R. [and] Twenty-five years of power development in the U.S.S.R. by A.V. Vinter; reports made at the jubilee session of the Academy of Sciences ... 25th anniversary of the October Revolution ... 1942. Translated by Henry F. Mins. 47 p. New York: American-Russian Institute, 1943.

ISTORIA estestvoznaniia v Rossii. [History of the natural sciences in Russia. (In Russian)]. 3 vol. in 4. 495 p., ill.; 380 p., ill.; 702 p., ill.; 603 p., ill. Moscow: Izdatel'stvo Akademii Nauk SSSR, 1957-62. [CB 83/185 and CB 86/502]
Volume 1, part 1 deals with science in Russia up to and including the 18th century; volume 1, part 2, with the first half of the 19th century. Volume 2 is devoted to mathematics, physics and chemistry in the second half of the 19th and beginning of the 20th century and volume 3 to the earth sciences and the biological sciences.
Vol. 1 reviewed by J. Théodoridès and M. Wong, *Arch.Int. Hist.Sci.*, 1957, 10: 118-19.

JOLIOT-CURIE, F. Les sciences en U.R.S.S. 16 p. Paris: Editions France-U.R.S.S., [n.d.]
Address given 30 November 1944.

KUPREVICH, V.F., *et al.* Sostoianie i razvitie nauki v soiuznykh respublikakh. [The condition and development of science in the union republics. (In Russian)]. *Vop.Ist.Est. Tekh.*, 1962, 13: 37-63.
The Soviet Republics covered are: Byelorussia, Kazakhstan, Georgia, Azerbaijan, and Latvia.

KUZNETSOV, B.G. [Essays on the history of Russian science. (In Russian)] 172 p., portr. Moscow and Leningrad: USSR Academy of Sciences, 1940.
A series of popular essays.

LAZAREV, P.P. [Outline history of Russian science. (In Russian)] 247 p., ill. Moscow: Izdatelstvo Akademii Nauk SSSR, 1950.

MAGOUN, H.W.; DARLING, Louise; BRAZIER, Mary A.B. Russian contributions to an understanding of the central nervous system and behavior - a pictorial survey. *Central nervous system and behavior, Trans.1st Conf.Cent.Nerv.Syst.Behav.*, (Madison, N.J., 1958), p. 23-136. New York: Josiah Macy, Jr. Foundation, 1959. [CB 86/452]
This pictorial survey in fact covers the development of science in Russia from Peter the Great up to the present day.

MANTON, S.M. (Mrs. J.P. Harding). Developments and science in the Soviet Union. *Nature*, 1952, 169: 729-32.

MEZHRESPUBLIKANSKAIA KONFERENTSIIA PO VOPROSAM ISTORII ESTESTVOZNANIIA I TEKHNIKI V PRIBALTIKE, 3rd, Vilna, 1959. Tezisy dokladov. [Interrepublic conference on problems of the history of natural science and technologies in the Baltic region. Précis of reports. (In Russian)] 105 p. Vilna: Gazetno-Zhurnal'noe Izdatel'stvo, 1959.

MEZHRESPUBLIKANSKAIA KONFERENTSIIA PO VOPROSAM ISTORII ESTESTVOZNANIIA I TEKHNIKI V PRIBALTIKE, 4th, Vilna, 1962. Nauka v Pribaltike v 18 - nachale 20 veka: tezisy dokladov. [Interrepublic conference on problems of the history of natural science and technologies in the Baltic region. Science in the Baltic region in the 18th - beginning of 20th century: prècis of reports. (In Russian)] 232 p. Riga: Izdatel'stvo Akademii Nauk Latviiskoĭ SSR, 1962.

SADYKOV, A.S. Puti razvitiia estestvennykh i tekhnicheskikh nauk v Uzbekistane. [The paths of development of the natural and technological sciences in Uzbekistan. (In Russian)]. *Vop.Ist.Est.Tekh.*, 1963, 14: 66-71.

VOGT, Oskar. Die Naturwissenschaft in der Sowjet-Union: Vorträge ihrer Vertreter während der "Russischen Naturforscherwoche" in Berlin 1927. Herausgegeben im Auftrage der Deutschen Gesellschaft zum Studium Osteuropas. viii, 352 p. Berlin: Ost-Europa Verlag, 1929.

VUCINICH, Alexander. Science in Russian culture: a history to 1860. Vol. 1. xv, 463 p. Stanford: Stanford University Press, 1963.
Reviewed by Loren R. Graham, *Isis*, 1964, 55: 373-4; for other reviews *see* CB 90/502.

ZIRKLE, Conway. The involuntary destruction of science in the U.S.S.R. *Sci.Mon.*, 1953, 76: 277-83.

Awn-cd

NESTERENKO, A.I. [Personal documents in the state archives of the USSR. (In Russian)]. *Sovet.Zdravookhr.*, 1964, 23: 61-3.

Awn-ce-bv

LUKOMSKAYA, A.M. Bibliografiia otechestvennoi literatury po matematike i fizike. Obzor bibliograficheskikh istochnikov. [Bibliography of Russian literature of mathematics and physics. Survey of bibliographical sources. (In Russian)] Pod redaktsiei V.I. Smirnova. 155 p. Moscow: Izdatel'stvo Akademii Nauk S.S.S.R., 1961.

Awn-da

TURKEVICH, John. Soviet men of science; academicians and corresponding members of the Academy of Sciences of the USSR. 441 p. Princeton, N.J.: Van Nostrand, 1963.

Awn-ks

BLAKELEY, Thomas J. Soviet theory of knowledge. vii, 203 p., bibliogr. (Sovietica Monographs of the Institute of East-European Studies, University of Fribourg/Switzerland) Dordrecht: Reidel, 1964.

Awn-kt

ZENKOVSKII, V.V. O mnimom materializme russkoi nauki i filosofii. [On the imaginary materialism of Russian science and philosophy. (In Russian with summary in English, French and German)]. 72 p. (Institut zur Erforschung der UdSSR. Issledovaniya i Materialy, ser. 1, no. 27) Munich: 1956. [CB 82/198]

Awn-o/t teaching; organization; social and humanistic relations

Awn-o

KOROL, Alexander G. Soviet education for science and technology. xxvi, 513 p. New York: John Wiley & Sons [and the Technology Press of Massachusetts Institute of Technology], 1957. [CB 83/192]

Awn-p

BROZEK, Josef. The current five-year plan of Soviet science in historical perspective. *Sci.Mon.*, 1950, 70: 390-4.
A clear and objective description of the stated purposes of Soviet scientific research and education.

DE WITT, Nicholas. Reorganization of science and research in the U.S.S.R. *Science*, 1961, 133: 1981-91.

SCIENCE at the cross roads. Papers presented to the [2nd] International Congress of the History of Science and Technology held in London from June 29th to July 3rd, 1931 by the delegates of the U.S.S.R. [233] p. London: Kniga, 1931. [CB 38/591]

TOPTCHIEV, Alexander. Organization of scientific research in the U.S.S.R. *Sci.Cult.*, 1956, 21: 650-5.

Awn-pw for international relations involving Russia and other countries *see* Apw (DUNN, L.G., *et al.*; RADOVSKII, M.I.; RIABUSHINSKII, Dimitrii)

Awn-qd

BRASCH, F.E. History and activities of the U.S.S.R. Academy of Sciences during the past twenty-five years. *Science*, 1944, 99: 437-41.

TIMOSHENKO, S.P.; USPENSKY, J.V. Remarks on the history of science in Russia. *Science*, 1944, 100: 193-4.
Apropos of article by F.E. Brasch, *see* above.

for Russian learned scientific societies *see also* Akademiia Nauk SSSR, 2: 660

Awn-sk

BORODIN, N.M. One man in his time. 344 p. New York: Macmillan Company, 1955.
Reviewed by Conway Zirkle, *Isis*, 1957, 48: 97-9.
Autobiographical account of a Russian who defected to the West.

BUCHHOLZ, Arnold. Ideologie und Forschung in der sowjetischen Naturwissenschaft. 127 p. Stuttgart: Deutsche Gesellschaft für Osteuropakunde, 1953.

HAINES, C. Grove, ed. The threat of Soviet imperialism. xvi, 402 p. Baltimore: Johns Hopkins Press, 1954. [CB 80/202]

JORAVSKY, David. Soviet Marxism and natural science, 1917-1932. xiv, 433 p. New York: Columbia University Press, 1961.
Reviewed by Bernard Barber, *Isis*, 1962, 53: 421-2; for other reviews *see* CB 87/630 and CB 89/576.

JORAVSKY, David. Soviet scientists and the great break. *Daedalus Amer.Acad.Arts Sci.*, 1960, 89: 562-80.

KEDROV, B.M. V.I. Lenin i estestboznanie. [Lenin and natural sciences. (In Russian)] *Priroda*, 1964, no. 4, 2-11.

MEAD, Margaret. Soviet attitudes toward authority: an interdisciplinary approach to problems of Soviet character. 148 p. New York: McGraw-Hill, 1951. [CB 78/195]

MOORE, Barrington. Influence of political creeds on the acceptance of theories. *Sci.Mon.*, 1954, 79: 146-8.
The influence of Soviet doctrine on Soviet science.

NEKRASSOFF, V.A. Human science, neither East nor West. 37 p. New York: priv. print., 1950. [CB 77/364]
Contains information on the attitudes of the Russian government towards science and philosophy during the last two hundred years.

SAX, Karl. Soviet science and political philosophy. *Sci. Mon.*, 1947, 65: 43-7. [CB 71/117]

WEISSBERG, Alexander. The accused. 518 p. New York: Simon and Schuster, 1951.
Includes a discussion of the effect of the Great Purge on Soviet scientists.
Reviewed by Mark Graubard, *Isis*, 1953, 44: 93-4.

WETTER, Gustav, Ideology and science in the Soviet Union: recent developments. *Daedalus Amer.Acad.Arts Sci.*, 1960, 89: 581-603.

Awn-sr

ACADEMIC freedom under the Soviet regime: a symposium of refugee scholars who have escaped from the U.S.S.R., on the subject "Academic Freedom in the Soviet Union as a Threat to the Theory and Practice of Bolshevik Doctrine", New York, 3-4 April, 1954. 120 p. Munich: Institute for the Study of the History and Culture of the U.S.S.R., 1954.

MULLER, Hermann Joseph. Science in bondage. *Science*, 1951, 113: 25-9.
Apropos of science in Russia and "diamat".

POLANYI, Michael. *See* Asr

SOVIET science (from "Pravda"). 4 p. (Occasional Pamphlet of the Society for Freedom in Science, 8) Oxford: The Society, 1948.

Awn-th

KOUTAISSOFF, Elisabeth. The scientific theme in post-war Soviet literature. In: *Literature and science, Proc.Congr. Int.Fed.Mod.Lang.Lit.* (Oxford, 1954), p. 313-18. Oxford: Blackwell, 1955.

Awo South Eastern Europe

BOLOGA, Valeriu L. Geschichte der Naturwissenschaften und der Medizin bei den Rumänen. (Seventh International Congress of Historical Sciences, Warsaw, 1933) *Bull.Int.Comm.Hist.Sci.*, 1933, 5: 371-88.

FLORESCU, Radu R. The origin and development of science in Rumania. *Ann.Sci.*, 1960, 16: 43-58.

GOMOIU, V. Contribution de quelques médecins roumains au progrès des sciences. *Act.Ve Congr.Int.Hist.Sci.* (Lausanne, 1947), p. 220-5. Paris: 1948. Also in *Arch.Int.Hist.Sci.*, 1948, 1: 291-6.

SERGESCU, Petre. Histoire des sciences mathématiques et physiques en Roumanie. (*7th Int.Congr.Hist.Sci.*, Warsaw, 1933) *Bull.Int.Comm.Hist.Sci.*, 1933, 5: no. 19, 319-32.

Awo-bv

SMET, A. de. Over de geschiedenis van de wetenschappen in Bulgarije (maart 1959). [On the history of the sciences in Bulgaria, March 1959. (In Dutch, with French summary)] *Sci. Hist.*, 1960, 2: 76-81.

Awo-p

SERGESCU, Petre. Obecny stan nauki w Rumunji. [Present day organisation of science in Roumania. (In Polish)]. *Nauk. Polska*, 1934, 19: 200-24.

Awo-qd

KHADZHIOLOV, A.I. K istorii Bolgarskogo literaturno-uchenogo obshchestva i Bolgarskoi Akademii nauk (1869-1944 gg). [On the history of the Bulgarian literary-scientific society and the Bulgarian Academy of Sciences (1869-1944). (In Russian)] *Vop.Ist.Est.Tekh.*, 1962, 12: 200-6.

SERGESCU, Petre. Les sociétés scientifiques roumaines. *Isis*, 1938, 29: 412-14.

Awp/wy Asia; Africa; Australia

Awp/wq Middle East; North Africa
(this section relates to modern science; a section on Islamic science will be found in Volume 4)

MASSIGNON, Louis. Mouvement intellectuel du Proche-Orient. *Hesperia* (Zurich), 1953, 4: 71-9

Awp

ZIA, Hilmi. Türk Teffekürü Tarihi. [History of Turkish thought. (In Turkish)]. 2 vol. 535 p. Istanbul: Ebuzzia, 1933.
Reviewed by A. Adnan, *Archeion*, 1935, 17: 288-91.

Aws India
(this section relates to modern science in India; a section on Indian science will be found in Volume 4)

CHATTERJEE, S.P. Fifty years of science in India. 277 p. Calcutta: Indian Science Congress Association, 1963.

LARWOOD, H.J.C. Western science in India before 1850. *Roy.Asiatic Soc.*, 1962, 62-76.

LARWOOD, H.J.C. Science and education in India before the mutiny. *Ann.Sci.*, 1961, 17: 81-96.

MUKHERJEE, J.N. Address of the General President to the Indian Science Congress, Calcutta, Jan. 1952. *Sci.Cult.*, 1952, 17: suppl. to no. 7, 17-32.
Review of science in India at present time, with particular reference to agriculture.

RUTHERFORD, Ernest, *Lord Rutherford*. Science and industry in India. *Science*, 1938, 87: 75-9.

WADIA, D.N. Thirty years of science in India. *J.Ceylon Br. Roy.Asiatic Soc.*, 1943, 35: 153-8.

Aws-ce-bx

CALCUTTA. NATIONAL LIBRARY. Indian scientific and technical publications, exhibition 1960; a bibliography. xii, 195 p. New Delhi: Council of Scientific & Industrial Research, 1960.

Aws-da

DHAR, N.R. Short life sketch of the general president and sectional presidents. *Sci.Cult.*, 1961, 27: 23-38.
Forty-eighth session of the Indian Science Congress Association, Roorkee, 1961.

INDIAN scientists: biographical sketches, with an account of their researches, discoveries and inventions. viii, 280 p., 8 pl. Madras: Natesan, 1929.

Who's who in science and research, 1961- Karachi: Bibliographical Information Bureau and Reference Centre, 1961-1961 also published New York: Heinman, 1963. (Pakistan Reference Series).

Aws-p

GHANDY, Jehangir. Some thoughts on scientific research in India. *Sci.Cult.*, 1963, 29: 73-7.

HILL, A.V. India - scientific development or disaster. *Asiatic Rev.*, 1944, 40: 351-6.

SWAMINATHAN, V.S. Scientific and industrial research in India. *Amer.Scient.*, 1954, 42: 625-38.

Aws-qd

BOSE, D.M. Asiatic Society's contribution to science studies in India. *Sci.Cult.*, 1963, 29: 219-24.

Aws-sr

SARTON, George. Science and freedom in India. *Isis*, 1948, 38: 243.
Apropos of Indian independence and the journal *Science and Culture*.

Awt Far East
(this section relates to modern science in the Far East; a section on Far Eastern science will be found in Volume 4)

HASHIMOTO, U. An historical synopsis of education and science in Japan from the Meiji restoration to the present day. *Impact*, 1963, 13: 3-23. [CB 89/494]

HUARD, Pierre. Quelques aspects de la pénétration des sciences occidentales au Japon depuis le 16e siècle. *Bull.Soc. Études Indo-Chinoises, Saïgon*, 1952, 27: 79-97.

ITO, Shuntaro. Science in Japan before the Meiji revolution. *Proc.10th Int.Congr.Hist.Sci.* (Ithaca, 1962), 1: 291-4. Paris: Hermann, 1964.

LIU CHUNGSHEE H. The advancement of science in China during the past thirty years. *Science*, 1943, 98: 47-51.

NEEDHAM, Joseph. Chinese science. 80 p., 95 ill. London: Pilot Press, 1945. [CB 70/238]

NEEDHAM, Joseph. Chinese science revisited. *Nature*, 1953, 171: 237-9, 283-5.

NEEDHAM, Joseph. Science and technology in China's Far South-East. *Nature*, 1946, 157: 175-7.

NEEDHAM, Joseph. Science and technology in the North-West of China. *Nature*, 1944, 153: 238-41.

NEEDHAM, Joseph. Science in Chungking. *Nature*, 1943, 152: 64-6.

NEEDHAM, Joseph. Science in Kweichow and Kuangsi. *Nature*, 1945, 156: 496-9.

NEEDHAM, Joseph. Science in South-West China. 1. The physico-chemical sciences. 2. The biological and social sciences. *Nature*, 1943, 152: 9-10, 36-7.

NEEDHAM, Joseph. Science in Western Szechuan. 1. Physico-chemical sciences and technology. *Nature*, 1943, 152: 343-5, 372-4.

NEEDHAM, Joseph; NEEDHAM, Dorothy; ed. Science outpost. Papers of the Sino-British Science Co-operation Office, 1942-1946. 313 p., ill. London: Pilot Press, 1948. [CB 73/159]

PEAKE, Cyrus H. Some aspects of the introduction of modern science into China. *Isis*, 1934, 22: 173-219. [CB 43/261]

SCIENTIFIC Japan, past and present. Prepared in connection with the third Pan-Pacific Science Congress, Tokyo, 1926. xii, 359 p., 47 pl., 3 maps. Tokyo: Maruzen Co., 1926.
Reviewed by George Sarton, *Isis*, 1928, 10: 83-8.

TUGE, Hideomi, ed. Historical development of science and technology in Japan. 200 p. Tokyo: Kokusai Bunka Shinkokai, 1961.

YAJIMA, S. Les sciences physiques au Japon durant l'ère de Meiji (1868-1912). *Arch.Int.Hist.Sci.*, 1956, 9: 3-12.

YAP POW-MENG. The place of science in China. 24 p. London: China Campaign Committee, [1943?]

YAP POW-MENG. Some observations on the development of science in China. *Asiatic Rev.*, 1944, 40: 226-9.

Awt-cj-bv

HOWARD, Richard C., ed. Index to learned Chinese periodicals. vi, 215 p. Boston: G.K. Hall, 1962. [CB 89/576]

Awt-ht

KOBORI, Akira. Un aspect de l'histoire de la diffusion des sciences européennes au Japon. *Jap.Stud.Hist.Sci.*, 1964, 3: 1-5.
The establishment of institutes in Japan for the study and teaching of European sciences

OTSUKI, Nyoden. Shinsen Yôgaku Nempyô. [Newly revised chronological table of Occidental learning in Japan. (In Japanese)]. xvi, 158 p. Tokyo: 1927.
Reviewed by Yoshio Mikami, *Isis*, 1928, 10: 82-3.

Awt-k

CHANG, Carsun (Chang Chün-mai). Reflections on the philosophical controversy in 1923. *Chung Chi J.*, 1963, 3: no. 1, 19-22. [CB 89/576]
Chang argues for a "balance between science on the one hand and philosophy on the other".

Awt-o

KUWAKI, Ayao. Development of the study of science in Japan. 15 p. (Western Influences in Modern Japan, 5) [Tokyo?]: Institute of Pacific Relations, Japanese Council, 1929.

Awt-p

KAMATANI, Chikayoshi. The history of research organization in Japan. *Jap.Stud.Hist.Sci.*, 1963, no. 2, 1-79.

KELLY, Harry C. A survey of Japanese science. *Sci.Mon.*, 1949, 68: 42-51.
Organization of modern Japanese science.

Awt-pw for international relations involving Japan and other countries *see* Apw (WATANABE, Masao)

Awt-qd

WANG CHI. Mainland China organizations of higher learning in science and technology and their publications: a selected guide. vi, 104 p. Washington, D.C.: Library of Congress, Science and Technology Division, Reference Department, 1961. [CB 89/493]

Awv Indonesia; Pacific Islands

HONIG, Pieter; VERDOORN, Frans; ed. Science and scientists in the Netherlands Indies. xxiii, 491 p., 134 fig. (Natuurwetenschappelijk Tijdschrift voor Nederlandsch Indie, Vol. 102, Special Supplement). New York: Board for the Netherlands Indies, Surinam and Curaçao, 1945.
Reviewed by George Sarton, *Isis*, 1946, 36: 260-1.

INTERNATIONALE CIRCUMPACIFISCHE ONDERZOEK COMMISSIE. The history and present state of scientific research in the Dutch East Indies. 8 vol. Amsterdam: Printed by De Bussy, 1923. [CB 16/33]
A series of pamphlets, listed in *Bibliogr.Géogr.*, 1924, 34: 317-18.

INTERNATIONALE CIRCUMPACIFISCHE ONDERZOEK COMMISSIE. Science in the Netherlands East Indies. [By various authors]. Ed. by L.M.R. Rutten. viii, 432 p. Amsterdam: Printed by De Bussy, 1929.
Prepared for the 4th Pacific Science Congress, Batavia and Bandong, 1929.

NATUURKUNDIGE VERENIGING IN INDONESIË. Gedenboek. Een eeuw natuurwetenschap in Indonesië 1850-1950. [A memorial volume. One century of natural science in Indonesia. (In Dutch)] 279 p., ill. Bandung, Indonesia: N.V. Mij Vorkink, 1951. [CB 79/164]

Awv-q

VERDOORN, Frans; VERDOORN, J.G. Scientific institutions, societies and research workers in the Netherlands Indies. In: Honig, Pieter; Verdoorn, Frans; ed. Science and scientists in the Netherlands Indies, p. 425-60. New York: 1945.

Awv-s

SPOEHR, Alexander. Human background of Pacific science. *Sci. Mon.*, 1955, 81: 3-9.

Aww Australia

FLEMING, Donald. *See* AW

MASSON, David Orme. Science and progress in Australia. *Nature*, 1923, 112: 507-10.

Awx Africa
for North Africa *see* Awq

GRANDE encyclopédie ... *See* Awk

HOFMEYER, Jan H. Africa and science. *Nature*, 1929, 124: 135-45; also *Science*, 1929, 70: 269-74, 294-9.
Address at the inaugural meeting of the British Association for the Advancement of Science, Cape Town, July 22, 1929, by the President of the South African Association.

Awx-qg

Rapport Annuel. Institut pour la Recherche Scientifique en Afrique Centrale (IRSAC) 1st, 1948- Brussels/Bakavu, Congo: [1950?]- [CB 77/361 and CB 79/163]

Awx-sc

WORTHINGTON, E.B. Science in the development of Africa. A review of the contribution of physical and biological knowledge south of the Sahara. xix, 462 p. London: Commission for Technical Cooperation in Africa South of the Sahara, and the Scientific Council for Africa South of the Sahara, 1958.
Reviewed by Kenneth Mellanby, *Nature*, 1958, 182: 1043.

Awy

CROCKER, H.J., ed. South Africa and science. A handbook prepared under the auspices of the South African Association for the Advancement of Science for the meeting of the British Association in Cape Town and Johannesburg, South Africa, 1929. x, 313 p. Johannesburg: Hortors, 1929.

SMUTS, Jan Christiaan. Science in South Africa. Presidential address to the South African Association for the Advancement of Science, delivered at Oudtshoorn, Cape Province, on July 6, 1925. *Nature*, 1925, 116: 245-9. [CB 18/603]

SOUTH AFRICAN COUNCIL FOR SCIENTIFIC AND INDUSTRIAL RESEARCH. Science in South Africa. 176 p. Pretoria: The Council, 1949.
Reviewed by W. Yourgrau, *Arch.Int.Hist.Sci.*, 1951, 4: 197-203.

Ax techniques and instruments

RUTHERFORD, Ernest. Science in development. *Nature*, 1936, 138: 865-9.
From the twelfth annual Norman Lockyer lecture of the British Science Guild, delivered on November 12. Deals with improvements in laboratory techniques and the development of new instruments and methods of measurement in the last 40 years.

WILSON, E. Bright. An introduction to scientific research. xiii, 375 p. London: McGraw-Hill, 1952.
Practical advice to researcher on research; methods and techniques; laboratory work; statistics, etc.
Reviewed by S. Whitehead, *Nature*, 1953, 171: 451.

Axb

IHDE, Aaron J. The development of scientific laboratories. *Sci.Teacher*, 1956, 23: 3 p.

MUNBY, A.E. Laboratories: their planning and fittings. With a historical introduction by Sir Arthur E. Shipley. xix, 220 p. London: Bell, 1921.

MURRAY, David Stark. The laboratory: its place in the modern world. 117 p. (Fen Series, 8) London: Fenland Press, 1934.
Reviewed by R. Brightman, *Nature*, 1934, 134: 889.

Axk scientific instruments

for instrument technology *see* WQ
instruments in different fields *see* INDEX

FORBES, R.J. The "precision" element in the history of science and technology. *Act.VIe Congr.Int.Hist.Sci.*, 1953, (Amsterdam, 1950), p. 489-91. Paris: Hermann, 1953; also *Arch.Int.Hist.Sci.*, 1952, 5: 227-9.
Regarding the precision of instruments and apparatus in the different historical periods.

KLOPSTEG, Paul E. The indispensable tools of science. *Science*, 1960, 132: 1913-22.
The role of instruments in scientific research from antiquity to modern times.

PRICE, Derek J. de Solla. Fake antique scientific instruments. *Act.VIIIe Congr.Int.Hist.Sci.* (Florence, 1956), p. 380-94, 4 fig. Paris: Hermann, 1958.

PRICE, Derek J. de Solla. Old scientific apparatus and instruments. *Isis*, 1958, 49: 81.

ROHDE, Alfred. Die Geschichte der wissenschaftlichen Instrumente vom Beginn der Renaissance bis zum Ausgang des 18. Jahrhunderts. viii, 119 p., ill. (Monographien des Kunstgewerbes, 16) Leipzig: Klinkhardt und Biermann, 1923.

SCHURR, Gerald. Market trends in scientific objects and "objets d'art". *Realités*, 1963, no. 154, 15-16.
A brief commentary with illustrations on the increasing rarity of antique scientific instruments with illustrations, descriptions, and prices paid at French auctions.

STREETER, Edward Clark. Intuitions versus instruments. In: *Science, medicine and history. Essays in honour of Charles Singer*, (2), p. 435-41. London: Oxford University Press, 1953.

ZINNER, E. Die Suche nach alten Sonnenuhren und wissenschaftlichen Instrumenten in Skandinavien. *Ber.Naturforsch.Ges. Bamberg*, 1954, 34: 9-12.

Axk-bw

BELGIUM. CENTRE NATIONAL D'HISTOIRE DES SCIENCES. Inventaire des instruments scientifiques historiques conservés en Belgique. 2 vol. Bruxelles: 1959-60. [CB 85/384]
Typescript facsimile.
Reviewed by M.L. Bonelli, *Physis*, 1960, 265; by Ed. Frison, *Sci.Hist.*, 1960, 2: 199-201.

CROMMELIN, C.A. Beschrijvende catalogus der historische verzameling van natuurkundige instrumenten in het Natuurkundig Laboratorium der Rijks-Universiteit te Leiden. [Descriptive catalogue of the historical collection of scientific instruments in the science laboratory of the University at Leiden. (In Dutch)] 71 p., 10 pl. Leiden: Eduard Ijdo, 1926.

GUNTHER, Robert William Theodore. Handbook of the Museum of the History of Science in the Old Ashmolean Building, Oxford. iv, 157 p. Oxford University Press, 1935.
An enlarged ed. of "Historic Instruments for the advancement of science", issued by the Lewis Evans Collection of Scientific Instruments in 1925.

GUNTHER, Robert William Theodore. Historic instruments for the advancement of science: a handbook to the Oxford Collections prepared for the opening of the Lewis Evans Collection on May 5, 1925. iv, 90 p. London: Oxford University Press, 1925.
For later editions *see* above: Handbook of the Museum of the History of Science ... and below: The Old Ashmolean.

GUNTHER, Robert William Theodore. The Lewis Evans Collection at Oxford. Recent additions. *Nature*, 1926, 118: 160-1.

GUNTHER, Robert William Theodore. The Old Ashmolean, the oldest museum for the history of the natural sciences and medicine. Prepared for the 250th anniversary of the opening of the museum. iv, 151 p. Oxford: Old Ashmolean, 1933.
An enlarged ed. of "Historic Instruments for the advancement of science".

ISTITUTO E MUSEO DI STORIA DELLA SCIENZA. Catalogo degli strumenti del Museo di Storia della Scienza. vii, 393 p., front., 16 pl., 89 ill. Firenze: Leo Olschki Editore, 1954. [CB 81/261]

LEVEILLE, A. An inventory of scientific apparatus of historical interest throughout the world. *2nd Conf.Int.Counc. Mus.* (London, 1950). 5 p. (ICOM/BI/CONF.2/19) Paris: 1950.

MENSING, Ant. W.M. Sammlung Mensing: alte wissenschaftliche Instrumente. Catalogue ed. by Max Engelmann. 2 vol. 1. Text; 2. Abbildungen. Amsterdam: Muller, 1924.
This collection now in Adler Planetarium and Astronomical Museum, Chicago.

SCIENCE MUSEUM. Handbook of the King George III collection of scientific instruments. By J.A. Chaldecott. ... Catalogue of exhibits with descriptive notes. 91 p., 8 pl. London: H.M. Stationery Office, 1951.

Axk-bx

CAMBRIDGE. UNIVERSITY. An exhibition of historic scientific instruments and books in the east room of the Old Schools, 4-11 Nov., 1944. 19 p. [Cambridge]: 1944. [CB 68/50]

CITTERT, M. van. Historische Tentoonstelling van antieke, natuurkundige Instrumenten te Utrecht. [Historical exhibition of ancient scientific instruments at Utrecht. (In Dutch)]. *Bijdr.Gesch.Geneesk.*, 1928, 8: 147-8.

EARLY scientific instruments at Harvard University. *Isis*, 1949, 40: 119.
Notes on an exhibition in the Edward Mallinckrodt Chemical Laboratory at Harvard, in 1949.

SOCIÉTÉ BELGE D'ASTRONOMIE, DE MÉTÉOROLOGIE ET DE PHYSIQUE DU GLOBE. Exposition d'instruments scientifiques et de documents anciens et modernes organisée à l'occasion du 50me anniversaire de la fondation de la Société. Catalogue. 63 p. Bruxelles: 1945. [CB 70/255]

Axk-by

HISTORIC scientific instruments in the Old Ashmolean Museum, Oxford, by H.H.T. *Nature*, 1925, 115: 783.

SCIENCE MUSEUM. The King George III collection of scientific instruments; a brief outline of the history of the collection together with notes on personalities involved and points of interest in connection with objects shown in a special exhibition held in the Science Museum during 1949. By J.A. Chaldecott. 13 p. London: H.M. Stationery Office, 1949.

Axk-wb

BEDINI, Silvio A. Early American scientific instruments and their makers. xii, 184 p., 85 fig. (*Bull.U.S.Nat.Mus.*, 231) Washington: Smithsonian Institution, 1964.

COHEN, I. Bernard. Old Harvard instruments. *Harvard Alumni Bull.*, 1949, 51: 384-8, ill.

COHEN, I. Bernard. Some early tools of American science: an account of the early scientific instruments and mineralogical and biological collections in Harvard University. xxi, 201 p., ill. Cambridge, Mass.: Harvard University Press, 1950.
Reviewed by Brooke Hindle, *Isis*, 1950, 41: 233-4. For other reviews *see* CB 77/362, CB 78/176 and CB 81/261.

FULLER, Henry M. The philosophical apparatus of Yale College. *Papers in honor of Andrew Keogh*, p. 163-80. New Haven, Conn.: 1938.

Axk-wi

ACCADEMIA DEL CIMENTO. I Saggi di naturali esperienze fatte nell'Accademia del Cimento e Strumenti e suppellettili della medesima Accademia conservati presso il Museo di Storia della Scienza di Firenze. [23], 269, [17], 61, [2] p. Pisa: Domus Galilaeana, [1957].
Facsimile reproduction of 1667 ed. of Saggi.
Reviewed by Andrea Corsini, *Arch.Int.Hist.Sci.*, 1957, 10: 246.

BONELLI, Maria Luisa. Gli strumenti superstiti dell'Accademia del Cimento. 23 p., pl. Pisa: Presso la Domus Galilaeana, 1958.

Axm measurement; metrology

for aspects of quantification in the philosophy of science *see* Akh

BERRIMAN, A.E. Historical metrology. A new analysis of the archaeological and historical evidence relating to weights and measures. xvi, 224 p., 65 ill. New York: E.P. Dutton, 1953.
Reviewed by A.W. Richeson, *Isis*, 1954, 45: 111-12.

BRANDT, Otto. Alte Normalgewichte. *Beitr.Gesch.Tech.Ind.*, 1931-32, 21: 155-7, 6 fig.

CAMPBELL, Norman Robert. An account of the principles of measurement and calculation. xii, 294 p. London: Longman, Green, 1928. [CB 27/546]

DARROW, Karl K. Who first spoke of the importance of the next place of decimals in physical measurements? Query no. 128. *Isis*, 1950, 41: 201.

DAVISON, C. St. C.B. Landmarks in the history of weighing and measuring. *Trans.Newcomen Soc.* for 1957-58 and 1958-59, 31: 131-52.

DAVISON, C. St. C.B. Origin of the footmeasure. *Engineering*, 1957, 184: 418-21.

DIEUDONNÉ, Adolphe Edmond. Manuel des poids monétaires. vii, 184 p., 16 pl. Paris: Florange, 1925

GLAZEBROOK, Richard. Standards of measurement: their history and development. *Nature*, 1931, 128: 17-28

GRUNDY, G.B. The old English mile and the Gallic league. *Geogr.J.*, 1938, 91: 251-9.

HOGBEN, Lancelot. Man must measure. 70 p. London: Rathbone Books, 1955.
Reviewed in *Sch.Sci.Rev.*, 1956, 37: 468.

IRWIN, Keith Gordon. Fathoms and feet, acres and tons. An appraisal. *Sci.Mon.*, 1951, 72: 9-17. [CB 77/370]
A very concise history of the units of measure now in use in the Anglo-Saxon world.

JONES, Stacy V. Weights and measures: an informal guide. 141 p. Washington, D.C.: Public Affairs Press, 1963.

KENNELLY, Arthur E. Vestiges of pre-metric weights and measures, persisting in metric-system Europe,1926-1927. xi, 189 p. New York: Macmillan, 1928. [CB 43/272]

LARMOR, Joseph. Physical units and their dimensions. *Nature*, 1935, 136: 548.

MACHABEY, Armand. Histoire des poids et des mesures depuis le XIIIe siècle. 512 p. Paris: Revue de Métrologie, 1962.
Reviewed by C. St. Clair B. Davison, *Arch.Int.Hist.Sci.*, 1964, 17: 185-7.

MACHABEY, Armand. Les progrès de la précision des mesures. Vue brève sur leur evolution. *J.Hist.Med.*, 1960, 15: 372-83.

MACHABEY, Armand. Les sources historiques de la métrologie. *Rev.Métrol.*, avril 1952, 4-18, 25 fig.
Reviewed by R. Taton, *Rev.Hist.Sci.*, 1953, 6: 91.

MAURER, K. Die Romantik des Messens. 79 p. (Technische Bücher für Alle.) Stuttgart: Dieck, 1932.

PÉRARD, M.A. La haute précision des mesures de longueur au laboratoire et dans l'industrie. 32 p. Paris: Hermann, 1931.
Lecture given at the Conservatoire des Arts et Métiers, 22nd April 1931.

SANDERS, L. A short history of weighing. 59 p., 52 fig. Birmingham: Avery, 1947.

SHEPPARD, T.; MUSHAM, J.F. Money-scales and weights. vi, 221 p. London: A. Brown, 1924.

WHYTE, L.L. On the history of natural lengths. *Ann.Sci.*, 1954, 10: 20-7.

WILLIAMS, W. Ewart. Light-waves as units of length. *Nature*, 1935, 135: 459-61, 496-7, 1 fig.

Axm-cb

RECORDS of a universal science. A description of the library of weights and measures of Samuel S. Dale, Brookline, Mass. *Bull.Bus.Hist.Soc.*, 1929, 8 p., pl.

Axm-k

CHURCHMAN, C. West; RATOOSH, P.; ed. Measurement: definitions and theories. 274 p. New York: Wiley, 1959.
Collection of papers read at a symposium on Measurement at the A.A.A.S. meeting December, 1956.
Reviewed by G.W. Scott Blair, *Brit.J.Phil.Sci.*, 1962, 13: 85-6.

ESNAULT-PELTERIE, Robert. L'analyse dimensionnelle. 236 p. Paris: Gauthier-Villars, 1948.

ESNAULT-PELTERIE, Robert. L'analyse dimensionnelle et métrologie. 132 p. Lausanne: Rouge, 1949.

Axm-qy

BUREAU INTERNATIONAL DES POIDS ET MESURES. Séance spéciale tenue à l'occasion du cinquantenaire de sa fondation, le mercredi 5 octobre 1927. 26 p. Paris: Palais de l'Institut, 1927. [CB 25/384]

GUILLAUME, Ch., ed. La création du Bureau International des Poids et Mesures et son oeuvre. Ouvrage publié à l'occasion du cinquantenaire de sa fondation. viii, 321 p., 129 fig., 1 pl. Paris: Gauthier-Villars, 1927. [CB 25/385]

KENNELLY, A.E. A modern Mecca. *Sci.Mon.*, 1922, 15: 570-80.
Apropos of the International Bureau of Weights and Measures at Sèvres.

Axm-sb

FETTWEIS, Ewald. Ueber die Enstehung der Messkunst. *Isis*, 1930, 13: 334-9. [CB 29/310]

FETTWEIS, Ewald. Völkerkundliche Beiträge zur Frage nach der Entstehung der Messkunde. *Technikgeschichte*, 1937, 26: 130-8.

Axm-sc

VIEWEG, Richard. Mass und Messen in kulturgeschichtlicher Sicht. 28 p., 43 ill. Wiesbaden: Franz Steiner Verlag, 1962.
Reviewed by M.O.G., *Arch.Int.Hist.Sci.*, 1963, 16: 87.

Axm-w in different countries

Axm-wb

BRIGGS, Lyman J. The [U.S.] national standards of measurement. *Annu.Rep.Smithsonian Inst.for 1940*, p. 161-76. Washington, D.C.: 1941.

BURLINGTON, R.S. The mil as an angular unit and its importance to the army. *Amer.Math.Mon.*, 1941, 48: 188-9. [CB 61/397]

FISCHER, Louis A. History of the standard weights and measures of the United States. v, 34 p. (Bureau of Standards. Miscellaneous Publications, 64) Washington: U.S. Govt. Print. Off., 1925.

FISCHER, Louis A. Recent developments in weights and measures in the United States. *Pop.Sci.Mon.*, 1914, 84: 345-69. [CB 6/456]

JUDSON, Lewis van Hagen. Weights and measures standards of the United States, a brief history. v, 30 p., ill., portr., facs., tables., bibliogr. (U.S. National Bureau of Standards, Miscellaneous Publication 247) Washington, D.C.: U.S. Government Printing Office, 1963.

MENDENHALL, T.C. The United States fundamental standards of length and mass. *Science*, 1922, 56: 377-80. [CB 14/560]

Axm-wd

SKINNER, F.G. European weights and measures derived from ancient standards of the Middle East. *Act.VIe Congr.Int.Hist.Sci.* (Amsterdam 1950), p. 230-48, 2 pl. Paris: Hermann, 1951; also, *Arch.Int.Hist.Sci.*, 1951, 4: 933-51.

Axm-we

CLOSE, Charles. The old English mile. *Geogr.J.*, 1930, 76: 338-42.
The length of the old English mile, deduced from measurements on maps dated from 1300 to 1895, varies between 0.92 and 1.35 of the present statute mile.

CONNOR, R.D. The evolution of the British yard and pound. *Sch.Sci.Rev.*, 1957, 39: 2-10.

PRELL, Heinrich. Bemerkungen zur Geschichte der Englischen Langenmass-systeme. 74 p. (*Ber.Verhandl.Sächs.Akad.Wiss. Leipzig, Math.Naturwiss.Kl.*, 104: no. 4) Berlin: Akademie der Wissenschaften zu Leipzig, 1962.
Reviewed by C. St. Clair B. Davison, *Arch.Int.Hist.Sci.*, 1963, 16: 88-9.

RUSSELL, Samuel. The unity of English weights. *Science*, 1923, 58: 442-3.

SKINNER, F.G. The English yard and pound weight. *Bull.Brit. Soc.Hist.Sci.*, 1952, 1: 179-87.

Axm-wf

MACHABEY, Armand. Poids et mesures du Languedoc et des provinces voisines. 144 p. Toulouse: Musée Paul-Dupuy, 1953.
Reviewed by Maurice Daumas, *Rev.Hist.Sci.*, 1954, 7: 98-9.

MACHABEY, Armand. Prolégomènes à l'histoire de la métrologie en France. *Act.VIII*[e] *Congr.Int.Hist.Sci.*(Florence, 1956), p. 211-14. Paris: Hermann, 1958.

Axm-wg-qk

AWECKER, Herta. Die Linzer Stadtwaage; die Geschichte des Waag- und Niederlagamtes der Stadt Linz. 187 p., ill. Linz: 1958.

Axm-wh

DAVÍDEK, Václav. Technika a staré míry délkové a plošné. [Technology and the old length and land measures. (In Czech with German summary)]. *Sb.Déjiny Přírodn.Věd Tech.*, 1964, 9: 271-94.

Axm-wk

JACOB, M. Le pied étalon de l'abbaye des Dunes est l'empreinte d'un véritable pied. *Bull.Belg.Métrol.*, fév. 1958, 209: 35-9.

WITTOP KONING, D.A. [The standard marks of Netherlandish troy weights. (In Dutch)] *Jaarb.Munt Penningk.*, 1950, 37: 123-6, 1 fig.

ZEVENBOOM, K.M.C.; KONING, D.A. Wittop. Nederlandse Gewichten. Stelsels, ijkwezen, vormen, makers en merken. [Weights in the Netherlands. Systems, inspection of weights and measures, forms, makers and marks. (In Dutch)]. 247 p., 16 pl. (Mededeling uit het Rijksmuseum voor de Geschiedenis der Natuurwetenschappen te Leiden, 86) Leiden: Rijksmuseum, 1953.
Reviewed by E.J. Dijksterhuis, *Rev.Hist.Sci.*, 1953, 6: 287-8; by R.J. Forbes, *Arch.Int.Hist.Sci.*, 1953, 6: 531-2.

Axm-wn

ORLOV, S.N. [On the subject of metrology in old Russia. (In Russian)] *Sovet.Arkheol.*, 1957, no. 4, 163-6.

Axm-ws

SILBERRAD, C.A. The weights and measures of India. *Nature*, 1922, 110: 325-9.

Axn metric system

BIREMBAUT, Arthur. Les deux determinations de l'unité de masse du système métrique. *Rev.Hist.Sci.*, 1959, 12: 25-54.

BRITISH ASSOCIATION inquiry into the metric system. *Nature*, 1958, 181: 1571.

CALVERT, H.R. Decimal division of scales before the metric system. *Isis*, 1936, 25: 433-6. [CB 49/175]

CONNOR, R.D. The evolution of the metre and kilogram. *Sch. Sci.Rev.*, 1958, 39: 193-9.

DRURY, Aubrey, ed. World metric standardization. An urgent issue. A volume of testimony urging world-wide adoption of the metric units of weights and measures. 524 p., ill. San Francisco: World Metric Standardization Council, 1922.

FAVRE, Adrien. Les origines du système métrique. 242 p. Paris: Presses Universitaires de France, 1931.
Reviewed by C. Doris Hellman, *Isis*, 1931, 16: 449-50.

FRANCE. MINISTÈRE DU COMMERCE ET DE L'INDUSTRIE. Le système métrique décimal. 256 p., 21 pl. Paris: Gauthier-Villars, 1930.

GLIOZZI, Mario. Precursori del sistema metrico decimale. *Atti Accad.Sci.Torino*, 1932, 67: 29-50. [CB 39/448]

GUILLAUME, Ch.-Ed. Les récents progrès du système métrique. *Rapport présenté à la Ve Conférence des poids et mesures*, [Paris, 1913]. iv, 118 p. Paris: Gauthier-Villars, 1913.

KARPINSKI, Louis C. A brief historical consideration of the metric system. *Science*, 1921, 53: 156-7.

LANGEVIN, Luce. The introduction of the metric system. The first example of scientific rationalization by society. *Impact*, 1961, 11: 77-95.

McKIE, Douglas. The origins of the metric system. *Endeavour*, 1963, 22: 24-6.

MÜLLER, Franz Joh. Zur Geschichte des metrischen Längenmasses. *Bayer.Z.Vermessungswesen*, 1926, 25: 153-71, 182-94, 251-4.

POZDĚNA, Rudolf. Meter und Kilogramm. Entstehung und Sicherung des internationalen metrischen Masssystems. 45 p., 15 fig. Leipzig: Teubner, 1934.

SHAW, Napier, *et al.* Quelques réflexions sur le système métrique. *Rev.Gén.Sci.*, 1918, 29: 489-91.

TANDBERG, J. Vad är 1 kilogram? En studie i metersystemet. [What is one kilogram? A study in the metric system. (In Swedish)]. *Tidskr.Elem.Mat.Fys.Kem.*, 1934, 17: 13-30, 3 fig.

TANDBERG, J. Vad väger 1 kubikdecimeter vatten? En studie i metrologi. [What does one cubic centimetre weigh? A study in metrology. (In Swedish)]. *Tidskr.Elem.Mat.Fys.Kem.*, 1933, 16: 19-31, 5 fig.

Axn-qy

GUILLAUME, Ch. Ed. Les systèmes de mesure et l'organisation internationale du système métrique. *Vie Int.*, 1913, 3: 5-44.

KENNELLY, Arthur E. Adoption of the meter-kilogram-mass-second (M.K.S.) absolute system of practical units by the International Electrotechnical Commission (I.E.C.), Bruxelles, June 1935. *Proc.Nat.Acad.Sci.*, 1935, 21: 579-83.

PICARD, Emile. Le cinquantenaire de la Convention Internationale du Mètre. *Annu.Bur.Longitudes* (Paris), 1928, Suppl. B, 11 p.
Discours prononcé dans la séance extraordinaire de l'Académie des Sciences, le 5 octobre 1927.

Axn-wb

KENNELLY, Arthur E., *et al.* The adoption of the metric system in the United States. *Sci.Mon.*, 1917, 4: 193-219.

Axn-we

SEMMEL, Bernard. Parliament and the metric system. *Isis*, 1963, 54: 125-33.

Axn-wf

LALLEMAND, Ch. Les nouvelles unités légales de mesures industrielles (système M.T.S., unités géométriques, mécaniques, électriques, calorifiques et optiques). *Annu.Bur. Longitudes* (Paris), 1920, Notice B, 1-63.
After the law passed 2 April 1919.

Axn-wk

JACOB, M. Histoire sommaire du système métrique en Belgique. *Bull.Belg.Métrol.*, 1958, 216: 232-6.

Axp measuring instruments

BENTON, W.A. The early history of the spring balance. *Trans. Newcomen Soc.*, 1941-42, 22: 65-78, 3 fig.

KRUHM, August. Die Waage im Wandel der Zeiten. 32 p., 5 fig. Frankfurt a. M.: Kramer, 1934.
Reviewed by Zaunick, *Mitt.Gesch.Med.*, 1935, 34: 190.

MACHABEY, Armand. Mémoire sur l'histoire de la balance et de la balancerie. Préface d'André Dolimier. 128 p., 18 fig. Paris: Imprimerie Nationale, 1949. [CB 77/372]

MÜNSTER, Clemens. Geschichte des Einstand-Entfernungsmessers. *Abhandl.Ber.Deut.Mus.*, 1940, 12: 107-36, ill.
Reviewed by R. Zaunick, *Mitt.Gesch.Med.*, 1940, 39: 320.

RHEINBOLDT, Heinrich. Balança e pesagens na epoca preclassica da química. 167 p., ill. (*Selec.Quím.*, 3) São Paulo: 1945. [CB 70/257]

ROLT, Frederick Henry. Gauges and fine measurements. Edited by R.T. Glazebrook. 2 vol. 1. Standards of length, measuring machines, comparators. xv, 366 p.; 2. Limit gauges, measuring instruments, general methods of measurement. viii, 357 p. London: Macmillan, 1929.
Reviewed by L.M.D., *Nature*, 1930, 125: 81-2.

SAUNDERS, L. Evolution of the pivot, with special reference to weighing instruments. *Trans.Newcomen Soc.*, 1943-45, 24: 81-7, 2 fig.

VERHAGEN, C.J.D.M. Mens en meetinstrument. [Man and measuring instrument. (In Dutch)]. 20 p. Delft: Waltmann, 1955.

Axr time measurement

see also FV ASTRONOMICAL CHRONOLOGY
HCxs MARINE CHRONOMETERS
WR CLOCKS

ABELÉ, Jean. Etat actuel du problème de la mesure du temps. *Rev.Quest.Sci.*, 1950, 121: 20-52.

BAILLAUD, R. La chronométrie, science de la mesure et de la conservation du temps, et le Congrès de Genève. *Scientia*, 1951, 86: 56-64.

BARNECK, Alfred. Die Grundlagen unserer Zeitrechnung. 2nd ed. 49 p., 9 fig. (Mathematisch-physikalische Bibliothek, 29) Leipzig: Teubner, 1932.

BOLTON, Lyndon. Time measurement: an introduction to means and ways of reckoning physical and civil time. vii, 166 p. London: Bell; New York: Van Nostrand, 1924.

BROUWER, Dirk. The accurate measure of time. *Phys.Today*, 1951, 4: no. 8, 6-15.
History of the science of measurement of time from the sundial to the atomic clock.

BROUWER, Dirk. How long is a second? Science depends upon precise standards of measurement. Involved in the establishment of these standards are problems greater than one might expect. *Yale Sci.Mag.*, 1954, 28: 18-20, *et seq.*
A list of exact time measurements and instruments.

BROWN, Ernest W. Changes in the length of the day. *Nature*, 1927, 119: 200-2. [CB 22/261]

CLEMENCE, G.M. Standards of time and frequency. *Science*, 1956, 123: 567-73.

COWAN, Harrison J. Time and its measurement: from the Stone Age to the Nuclear Age. 159 p., ill. Cleveland, Ohio: World Publishing Co., 1958.
Reviewed by F.A.B. Ward, *Isis*, 1959, 50: 496-8.

DANJON, André. Le temps et sa mesure. 16 p. (Conférences du Palais de la Découverte, 26 mars 1949) Paris: Université de Paris, 1949.

DINGLE, Herbert. The measurement of time. *Nature*, 1937, 139: 355-7.

DRECKER, Joseph. Zeitmessung und Sterndeutung in geschichtlicher Darstellung. 188 p., 67 ill. Berlin: Borntraeger, 1925.
Summary of present knowledge on chronology and horology (with historical notes) followed by an explanation of astrology.

DUCASSÉ, P. Pour l'histoire de la mesure du temps. *Thalès*, 1948, 5: 113-27.

HOOD, Peter. How time is measured. 64 p., ill. London: Oxford University Press, 1955. [CB 83/211]

JAQUEROD, Adrien. Science and chronometry. *Endeavour*, 1954, 13: 134-9.
The emphasis is upon very recent advances in the exact measurement of time.

KURTH, Rudolf. Ueber Zeit und Zeitmessung. *Phil.Natur.*, 1964, 8: 65-90.

MESURE du temps de la préhistoire à l'ère atomique. *Tech. Civilisations*, 1954, 3: 134-40.

MICHEL, Henri. La genèse des unités de temps. *J.Suisse Horlogerie*, 1948, 73: 27-34.

MICHEL, Henri. La mesure du temps. *Reflets Monde*, 1952, no. 3, 1-16, ill.

SCIENCE MUSEUM. Handbook of the collection illustrating time measurement. By F.A.B. Ward. Pt. 1. Historical review. 4th ed. 60 p., ill. London: H.M. Stationery Off., 1958. [CB 49/172 and CB 84/328]
First published 1936.

SPENCER JONES, Harold. The measurement of precise time. Summary of communication presented before the Academy, April 13, 1949. *Bull.Amer.Acad.Arts Sci.*, 1949, 2: 2-4.

SPENCER JONES, Harold. The secular increase in the length of the day. *Proc.Amer.Phil.Soc.*, 1955, 99: 195-9.

STRONG, Helen M. Universal world time. *Geogr.Rev.*, 1935, 25: 479-84.

Axr-bx

ANTIQUARIAN HOROLOGICAL SOCIETY. Tercentenary of Christiaan Huygens' pendulum clock, December, 1656-December, 1956. Exhibition arranged by the Science Museum and the Antiquarian Horological Society, December 4th, 1956, to February 24th, 1957. Catalogue. 28 p. (Publications of the ... Society, 2) London: 1956.

SCIENCE MUSEUM. Handbook of the collection illustrating time measurement. By F.A.B. Ward. Pt. 2. Descriptive catalogue. 3rd ed. 102 p., ill. London: H.M. Stationery Off., 1955. [CB 83/212]

Axt recording and recording instruments

HOFF, Hebbel E.; GEDDES, L.A. The beginnings of graphic recording. *Isis*, 1962, 53: 287-324.

Axw museology

COLEMAN, Laurence Vail. Historic house museums. xii, 187 p. Washington: American Association of Museums, 1933.
Reviewed by Leicester B. Holland, *Amer.Hist.Rev.*, 1934, 40: 133-4.

COLEMAN, Laurence Vail. Manual for small museums. xiv, 395 p., 32 pl. New York: Putnam, 1927. [CB 24/567]

COURRET, G. Le "Musée de l'avenir" de George Sarton. *Ann.Soc. Sci.Litt.Cannes, new ser.*, 1930, 2: 75-9.
Apropos of Sarton's article "The museum of to-morrow", *see* below.

GREAT BRITAIN. Department of Scientific and Industrial Research. The cleaning and restoration of museum exhibits. Third report upon investigations conducted at the British Museum. v, 70 p., 58 p. London: H.M. Stationery Office, 1926.

HUTCHINS, Robert Maynard. The value of the museum. *Science*, 1943, 98: 331-4.

KENYON, Frederic George. Museums and national life. The Romanes Lecture delivered in the Sheldonian Theatre, 17 June 1927. 32 p. Oxford: Clarendon Press, 1927.

KRAEPELIN, Karl. Naturwissenschaftlich-technische Museen. In: Hinneberg, Paul, ed. Die allgemeinen Grundlagen der Kultur der Gegenwart. 2nd ed., p. 392-409. (Kultur der Gegenwart, pt. 1, section 1) Leipzig: Teubner, 1913.

LOIR, Adrien; LEGANGNEUX, H. Précis de muséologie pratique. 107 p. Le Havre: Museum d'Histoire Naturelle, 1921.

MARINUS, Albert. L'utilité des petits musées. *Bibl.Etud. Rég.*, [1937?], no. 31, 447-56.

MULTHAUF, Robert P. The research museum of the physical sciences. *Curator*, 1960, 3: 355-60.

PLENDERLEITH, H.J. Some aspects of museum laboratory work. *Antiquity*, 1942, 16: 97-112.

PRICE, Derek J. De Solla. Comments on the role of the research museum in science. *Curator*, 1961, 4: 184-6.

RUEDEMANN, Rudolf; GOLDRING, Winifred. Some museum methods developed in the New York State Museum. *Bull.N.Y.State Mus.*, 1931, no. 288, 71-5, 1 fig., 7 pl.

SARTON, George. The museum of to-morrow. *Natur.Hist.*, 1924, 24: 710-12. [CB 16/282]

SCHUSTER, Julius. Geschichte und Idee des naturwissenschaftlichen Museums. Vortrag bei der Gründungs-Tagung des "Bundes der deutschen naturwissenschaftlichen Museen". *Arch. Gesch.Math.Naturwiss.Tech.*, 1928, 11: 178-92, ill.

SCOTT, Alexander. The cleaning and restoration of museum exhibits. 3rd report. London: H.M. Stationery Office, 1927.

Axw-bv

CLIFFORD, William. Bibliography of museums and museology. viii, 99 p. New York: Metropolitan Museum, 1923.

SMITH, Ralph Clifton. A bibliography of museums and museum work. vi, 302 p. Washington: American Association of Museums, 1928.

Axx museums

Axx-wb

ADAMS, Charles C. The proposals for a new state museum building. *Bull.N.Y.State Mus.*, 1932, no 293, 81-110.

ADAMS, Charles C. The public functions of the Division of Science and State Museum. *Bull.N.Y.State Mus.*, 1931, no. 288, 61-70.

GILMAN, Benjamin Ives. The Museum design as tested by experience. *Bull.Mus.Fine Arts*, 1924, 22: 39-45.
The design of the Boston Museum of Fine Arts.

THE HARVARD MUSEUM OF THE HISTORY OF SCIENCE. *Isis*, 1924, 6: 543.

for North American museums *see also*
New York State Museum, 2: 731
Western Museum Society of Cincinnati, 2: 773

for collections of American instruments *see also*
Axk-wb

Axx-wd

MULTHAUF, Robert P. European science museums. A tour shows how they cope with the problems of displaying famous apparatus of the past and present. *Science*, 1958, 128: 512-19, 10 fig.

WATANABE, Masao. History of science and museums in European countries. *J.Hist.Sci.Japan*, 1961, 57: 36.

Axx-we

CURTIS, William Hugh. The first hundred years of a small museum. vii, 55 p., 10 p. Alton: Curtis Museum, 1955.
Reviewed in *Nature*, 1956, 178: 6-7.

for museums in the British Isles *see also*
British Museum, 2: 673
Oxford University. Museum for the History of Science, 2: 735
Royal Scottish Museum, Edinburgh, 2: 748
Science Museum, London, 2: 757
Whipple Museum of the History of Science, 2: 773

Axx-wg for German science museums *see*
Deutsches Museum, Munich, 2: 688

Axx-wi for Italian science museums *see*
Istituto e Museo di Storia della Scienza, Florence, 2: 708
Milan. Museo Nazionale della Scienza e della Tecnica, 2: 724

Axx-wk for science museums in the Low Countries *see*
Ghent. Museum voor de Geschiedenis der Wetenschappen, 2: 697
Rijksmuseum voor de Geschiedenis der Natuurwetenschappen, Leyden, 2: 744

Axx-wr

SALMONY, Alfred. The museums of Siberia. *Parnassus*, 1930, 2: 14-16, 1 fig. [CB 28/520]

SALMONY, Alfred. Museums on the Volga and in the Ukraine. Transl. by George J. Hexter. *Parnassus*, 1932, 4: 30, 39, 2 fig.

Axx-ww

PESCOTT, R.T.M. Collections of a century. The history of the first hundred years of the National Museum of Victoria. xiv, 186 p., 25 ill. Melbourne: National Museum of Victoria, 1954. [CB 82/199]

AC NATURAL MAGIC; MYTHOLOGY; PSEUDO-SCIENCES

for popular aspects of science and the separate sciences *see* INDEX

see also MR FOLKLORE; SUPERSTITIONS

ACc general history

ACKERMANN, A.S.E. Popular fallacies. A book of common errors, explained and corrected with copious references to authorities. 4th ed. xv, 843 p. London: Old Westminster Press, 1950.
First published 1907. 3rd ed. London: Old Westminster Press, 1923; Philadelphia: Lippincott, 1924. [CB 16/344]
Reviewed in *Nature*, 1950, 166: 579.

ARAM, Kurt, *pseud.* of Hans Fischer. Magie und Mystik in Vergangenheit und Gegenwart. 626 p. Berlin: Albertus-Verlag, 1928.
Reviewed by W. Haberling, *Mitt.Gesch.Med.*, 1929, 28: 232.

BANNING, Pierson Worrall. Maker, man and matter. 248 p. (Thread of Life Series, 1) Los Angeles: International Book Concern, 1924.
Reviewed by David Starr Jordan, *Science*, 1925, 61: 68.

BOUISSON, Maurice. Magic: its history and principal rites. 319 p., ill. New York: Dutton, 1960.

BUTLER, E.M. Ritual magic. x, 329 p., 8 pl., bibliogr. Cambridge University Press, 1949.

CAMPBELL, Joseph. The historical development of mythology. *Daedalus Amer.Acad.Arts Sci.*, 1959, 88: 232-54.

CHILDE, V. Gordon. Magic, craftsmanship and science. 19 p. (The Frazer Lecture 1949) Liverpool: University Press, 1950.

CHRISTIAN, Paul, *pseud.* of Christian Pitois. The history and practice of magic. Newly transl, with additional material by modern authorities, by James Kirkup and Julian Shaw. Supplementary articles by Mir Bashir, Margery Lawrence and Julian Shaw. Edited by Ross Nichols. 2 vol. xxviii, 621 p. London: Forge Press, 1952.
Translation of: Histoire de la magie, du monde surnaturel, et de la fatalité à travers le temps et les peuples. Paris: 1870.

CLODD, Edward. Magic in names and in other things. vii, 238 p. London: Chapman and Hall, 1920.

DACQUÉ, Edgar. Natur und Seele. Ein Beitrag zur magischen Weltlehre. 200 p. München: Oldenbourg, 1926.
Reviewed by Carl von Klinckowstroem, *Isis*, 1928, 10: 95-8.

DANZEL, Theodor William. Magie und Geheimwissenschaft in ihrer Bedeutung für Kultur und Kulturgeschichte. xii, 213 p., ill. Stuttgart: Strecker & Schröder, 1924.

ELIADE, Mircea. Traité d'histoire des religions. Préface de Georges Dumézil. 405 p. (Bibliothèque Scientifique) Paris: Payot, 1949. [CB 77/383]
A history of myths, divided according to types of myths.

FRAZER, James George. Aftermath, a supplement to "The golden bough". xxi, 494 p. London: Macmillan, 1936; New York: Macmillan, 1937.
Reviewed by M.F. Ashley-Montagu, *Isis*, 1938, 29: 191-2.

FRAZER, James George. Creation and evolution in primitive cosmogonies, and other pieces. xii, 151 p. London: Macmillan, 1935. [CB 44/525]

FRAZER, James George. Garnered sheaves. Essays, addresses, and reviews. 509 p. London: Macmillan, 1931.

FRAZER, James George. The golden bough. A study in magic and religion. 3rd ed. rev. and enl. 12 vol. London: Macmillan, 1907-15.
Volume 12, 1915, is a bibliography and general index. First edition 1890; 2nd edition 1900; abridged edition. xiv, 756 p. London/New York: Macmillan, 1922; reprinted 1951.

FRAZER, James George. Man, God and immortality. Thoughts on human progress. Passages chosen from the writings of Sir James George Frazer, rev. and ed. by the author. xvi, 437 p. London: Macmillan, 1928.

FRAZER, James George. Myths of the origin of fire: an essay. vii, 238 p. London: Macmillan, 1930.
Reviewed by Henry Balfour, *Nature*, 1930, 125: 920-1.

FRAZER, James George. Le rameau d'or. Abridged edition transl. by Lady Frazer. 722 p. Paris: Paul Geuthner, 1924.
Reviewed by L. Guinet, *Isis*, 1926, 8: 234-6.
French translation of The golden bough, *see* above; for French translations of parts of complete work *see* CB 12/630, CB 19/811 and CB 21/595.

FRAZER, James George. The worship of nature. Vol. 1. The worship of the sky, the earth, and the sun. xxvi, 672 p. London: Macmillan, 1926.
Projected second volume not published.

GARDNER, Martin. Fads and fallacies in the name of science. 2nd rev. ed. 363 p. New York: Dover Publication, 1957.
First published under the title: In the name of science (New York: Putnam, 1952) and reviewed by Conway Zirkle, *Isis*, 1953, 44: 298.
2nd edition reviewed by L. Marton, *Phys.Today*, 1958, 11: 36-8.

GÖRRES, Joseph von. Mystik, Magie und Dämonie. vi, 599 p., portr. (Die Christliche Mystik in Auswahl.) München: Oldenbourg, 1927.
Reviewed by Friedrich Heiler, *Deut.Lit.Zeitung*, 1929, 6: 796-7.

GRILLOT DE GIVRY, Émile Angelo. Witchcraft, magic, and alchemy. Transl. by J. Courtenay Locke. 395 p., 10 pl. London: Harrap, 1931. Reprinted Chicago: University Books, 1958.
Translation of: Le musée des sorciers, mages et alchimistes (Paris: Librairie de France, 1929).

HERING, Daniel W. Foibles and fallacies of science. An account of celebrated scientific vagaries. xiii, 294 p., ill. New York: Van Nostrand, 1924. [CB 16/345]

HERING, Daniel W. An introduction to scientific vagaries. *Sci.Mon.*, 1921, 13: 516-22.

JORDAN, David Starr. Science and sciosophy. 54 p. (Better-healthgrams, Popular Series, 2) San Francisco: Better Health, 1926.

KLUCKHOHN, Clyde. Recurrent themes in myths and mythmaking. *Daedalus*, 1959, 88: 268-79.

KRAATZ, Walter C. Pseudoscience and antiscience in an age of science. *Ohio J.Sci.*, 1958, 58: 261-9. [CB 84/390]

KRAPPE, Alexandre Haggarty. Mythologie universelle. 453 p. Paris: Payot, 1930. [CB 33/407]

LEHMANN, Alfred G.L. Aberglaube und Zauberei, von den ältesten Zeiten bis in die Gegenwart. 3rd German ed. xvi, 752 p., ill. Stuttgart: Enke, 1925.
Reviewed by Carl von Klinckowstroem, *Isis*, 1927, 9: 142-3.
Danish original: Kjøbenhavn: 1893-96.

MAGER, Henri. Une science nouvelle: la science des vibrations atomiques. xviii, 151 p., 50 fig. Paris: Dunod, 1923.
Reviewed by L. Guinet, *Isis*, 1924, 6: 565-6.

MALINOWSKI, Bronislaw. Magic, science and religion and other essays. Introduction by Robert Redfield. xii, 327 p. Glencoe, Ill.: Free Press, 1948.

MARTINO, Ernesto de. Il mondo magico. Prolegomeni a una storia del magismo. 264 p. Torino: Einaudi, 1948.

MAXWELL, Joseph. La magie. 252 p. (Bibliothèque de Philosophie Scientifique) Paris: Flammarion, 1922.
Reviewed by L. G., *Isis*, 1924, 6: 121-2.

DER MENSCH und die mythische Welt. 515 p., 19 fig. (*Eranos-Jahrbuch*, 1949, vol. 17) Zürich: Rhein-Verlag, 1950. [CB 76/410]

MONTANDON, Raoul. Les radiations humaines. Introduction à la démonstration expérimentale de l'existence des corps subtils de l'homme. 408 p., 99 fig. Paris: Alcan, 1927. [CB 24/550]

NUMAZAWA, K. Background of myths on the separation of sky and earth from the point of view of cultural history. *Scientia*, 1953, 88: 28-35.

OTTO, Rudolf. Mysticism, east and west. Transl. by Bertha L. Bracey and Richenda C. Payne. xvii, 262 p. London/New York: Macmillan, 1932.
An enlarged form of the Haskell Lectures delivered at Oberlin College, 1923-24.

PAGE, Calvin Samuel. Rx the life atom. Key to nature. New direct explanations; radio, gravitation, magnetism, electricity, light, sound, nervous force, molecule; refuting Einstein's relativity confirmations, using new discoveries of the Earth, Mercury, Moon, volcanoes, etc. xv, 330 p. Chicago: Science Publishing Company, 1923. [CB 18/640]

PROBST, Jean Henri. Survivances magiques dans la science contemporaine. *Rev.Int.Sociol.*, 1931, 39: 391-4.

PROKOP, Otto, ed. Wünschelrute, Erdstrahlen und Wissenschaft. viii, 183 p., 39 fig. Stuttgart: Enke, 1955.
Reviewed by Johannes Steudel, *Sudhoffs Arch.*, 1956, 40: 91.

REDGROVE, H. Stanley. Bygone beliefs. Being a series of excursions in the byways of thought. xvi, 205 p., ill. London: Rider, 1920. [CB 11/453]

RIBADEAU-DUMAS, François. Histoire de la magie. 621 p., ill. Paris: Productions de Paris, [1962].

RÓHEIM, Géza. Animism, magic and the divine king. xviii, 390 p. London: Kegan Paul, 1930.

SAINTYVES, P., *pseud.* La force magique. Du mana des primitifs au dynamisme scientifique. 136 p. (Science et Magie, 2) Paris: Emile Nourry, 1914. [CB 6/478]

SELIGMANN, Kurt. The mirror of magic. 504 p., 255 ill. New York: Pantheon Books, 1948. [CB 73/170]

SINGER, Charles. From magic to science. Essays on the scientific twilight. 254 p. New York: Dover Publications, 1958.
First published London and New York, 1928. [CB 26/225]
Reviewed by Jean Beaujeu, *Arch.Int.Hist.Sci.*, 1962, 15: 179; by Albert Lejeune, *Rev.Quest.Sci.*, 1960, 21: 590.

SMITH, Catharine Cook. In defence of magic. The meaning and use of symbol and rite. 159 p. London: Rider, 1931.

SPENCE, Lewis. An introduction to mythology. 335 p. London: Harrap, 1921.
Reviewed by George Sarton, *Isis*, 1922, 4: 378-80.
A review of mythic science from its beginnings.

STRUNZ, Franz. Astrologie, Alchemie, Mystik: ein Beitrag zur Geschichte der Naturwissenschaften. 351 p. München-Planegg: Otto Wilhelm Barth, 1928.

SWANSON, Guy E. The birth of the gods. The origin of primitive beliefs. ix, 260 p., bibliogr. Ann Arbor: University of Michigan Press, 1960.

THOMPSON, Charles John Samuel. The mysteries and secrets of magic. xvii, 320 p. London: Lane, 1927; Philadelphia: Lippincott, 1928.

THORNDIKE, Lynn. A history of magic and experimental science. 8 vol. New York: Columbia University Press, 1923-58.
Vol. 1-2, 3-4 reviewed by G. Sarton, *Isis*, 1924, 6: 74-89 and 1935, 23: 471-5; vol. 5-6 by D.B. Durand, *ibid.* 1942, 33: 691-712; vol.7-8 by I.B. Cohen, *ibid.* 1958, 49: 453-5.

TROMP, Solco Walle. Psychical physics. A scientific analysis of dowsing, radiesthesia and kindred divining phenomena. xv, 534 p. Amsterdam: Elsevier, 1949.

WEISINGER, Herbert. Some meanings of myth. *Comp.Lit.*, 1959, 11: 1-10.

WESTAWAY, Frederic William. Obsessions and convictions of the human intellect. xvi, 528 p., 4 pl. London: Blackie, 1938.
Reviewed by J.C.H., *Nature*, 1938, 141: 766-7.

ACc-br

Mitra. Monatsschrift für Vergleichende Mythenforschung. Vol. 1, no. 1-12. Wien/Leipzig: Orion, 1914-20.

ACj/x special aspects

ACj

CASTIGLIONI, Arturo. Adventures of the mind. xviii, 428 p. New York: Knopf, 1946.
Deals mainly with the psychological forces behind magic, myth and fancy.
Reviewed by Mark Graubard, *Isis,* 1947, 38: 131; by Erwin H. Ackerknecht, *Bull.Hist.Med.,* 1946, 19: 570-1.
Part of this book published 1934 in Italian under the title Incantesimo e magia, *see* below.

CASTIGLIONI, Arturo. Incantesimo e magia. 468 p., bibliogr. Milano: Mondadori, 1934.
Reviewed by A. Corsini, *Riv.Stor.Sci.,* 1934, 25: 116-18.

ACk

BASTIDE, Roger. Les problèmes de la vie mystique. 216 p. Paris: Colin, 1931. [CB 33/406]

CASSIRER, Ernst. Die Begriffsform im mythischen Denken. 62 p. (*Studien der Bibliothek Warburg,* 1) Berlin: Teubner, 1922. [CB 14/558]

DORSON, Richard M. Theories of myth and the folklorist. *Daedalus Amer.Acad.Arts Sci.,* 1959, 88: 280-90.

LANGER, Fritz. Intellectualmythologie. Betrachtungen über das Wesen des Mythus und die mythologische Methode. xii, 269 p. Leipzig: Teubner, 1916.

LEVIN, Harry. Some meanings of myth. *Daedalus Amer.Acad. Arts Sci.,* 1959, 88: 223-31.

MARINUS, Albert. Quelques problèmes de méthode dans l'étude de la magie. *Bull.Soc.Anthropol.Bruxelles,* 1933, 48: 49-66.

RUYSSEN, Théodore. L'imagination mythique et sa persistance dans la pensée évoluée. *Rev.Syn.,* 1958, 79: 5-29.

SAGERET, Jules. La vague mystique. 180 p. Paris: Flammarion, 1920.
Comparison with scientific method. The author discusses points in Poincaré's philosophy.
Reviewed by Léon Guinet, *Isis,* 1920, 3: 448-9.

STAUDENMAIER, Ludwig. Die Magie als experimentelle Naturwissenschaft. 184 p. Leipzig: Akademische Verlagsgesellschaft, 1912.

ACmzA

GRUENDER, David. On distinguishing science from magic. *Proc.10th Int.Congr.Hist.Sci.* (Ithaca, 1962), (1), p. 257-60. Paris: Hermann, 1964.

ACmzDY

MAHDIHASSAN, S. Alchemy and its connection with astrology, pharmacy, magic and metallurgy. *Janus,* 1957, 46: 81-103.

ACng

SARTON, George. Notes on the history of anagrammatism. *Isis,* 1936, 26: 132-8, 1 fig.
Apropos of the anagrammatic superstition and of the use of anagrams for the purpose of publishing the truth without revealing it.

ACnh

WAGNER, Robert Léon. "Sorcier" et "magicien". Contribution à l'histoire du vocabulaire de la magie. 292 p. Paris: Droz, 1939.
Reviewed by Marcel Fosseyeux, *Bull.Soc.Franç.Hist.Méd.,* 1940, 34: 100.

ACr

FRANCESCO, Grete de. The power of the charlatan. vii, 288 p. New Haven: Yale University Press, 1939.
Reviewed by M.F. Ashley Montagu, *Isis,* 1949, 32: 406-8.

ACs

WEBSTER, Hutton. Magic, a sociological study. 524 p. Stanford: Stanford University Press, 1948.
Reviewed by Mark Graubard, *Isis,* 1950, 41: 138.

ACth

EDSMAN, Carl-Martin. Ignis divinus. Le feu comme moyen de rajeunissement et d'immortalité: contes, légendes, mythes et rites. 306 p. (Skrifter utgivna av Vetenskaps-Societeten i Lund, 34) Lund: Gleerup, 1949. [CB 75/97]

ACwe

DEXTER, T.F.G. Fire worship in Britain. 48 p. London: Watts, 1931.

ACwg

FREUDENTHAL, Herbert. Das Feuer im deutschen Glauben und Brauch. xx, 571 p., 15 fig., 11 pl. Berlin: de Gruyter, 1931.

ACxm

TRUESDELL, C. Can any reader supply examples of magic whose effect is measured? *Isis,* 1956, 47: 59.

AD HISTORY OF IDEAS

for ideas in science *see* Ahm
ideas in the separate sciences *see* INDEX

ADc

HALL, Everett W. Modern science and human values: a study in the history of ideas. x, 483 p. Princeton, N.J.: D. Van Nostrand Company, 1956. [CB 83/185]
Reviewed by George A. Foote, *Amer.Hist.Rev.,* 1957, 62: 597-9; by Paul F. Schmidt, *Scr.Math.,* 1959, 24: 91.

HUSSERL, Edmund. Erste Philosophie (1923/24). 1. Kritische Ideengeschichte. Herausgegeben von Rudolf Boehm. xxiv, 468 p. (Husserleriana, 7) The Hague: Martinus Nijhoff; London: Batsford, 1956.
Reviewed by F.I.G. Rawlins, *Nature,* 1956, 178: 714.

JOHNS HOPKINS UNIVERSITY. HISTORY OF IDEAS CLUB. Studies in intellectual history. 225 p. Baltimore: Johns Hopkins Press, 1953.
Reviewed by I. Bernard Cohen, *Isis,* 1953, 44: 404-5.

LOVEJOY, Arthur O. Essays in the history of ideas. xvii, 359 p. Baltimore: Johns Hopkins Press, 1948. [CB 73/151]
Reprinted 1960 (New York: Putnam).
Reviewed by Harry Levin, *Isis,* 1949, 40: 85-7.

MARVIN, Francis S., ed. Recent developments in European thought. Essays arranged and edited by him. 306 p. (Unity Series) Oxford University Press, 1920.

MENSCH und Wandlung. Ed. by Olga Fröbe-Kapteyn. 454 p. (Eranos-Jahrbuch, 23) Zürich: Rhein-Verlag, 1955.

STYBE, Svend Erik. Idéhistorie. Vor kulturs idéer og tanker i historisk perspektiv. [History of ideas: our cultural ideas and concepts in historical perspective. (In Danish)]. 402 p., ill. Copenhagen: Munksgaard, 1961.
Reviewed by Gunnar Eriksson, *Lychnos,* 1962, 254-5.

WHITEHEAD, Alfred North. Adventures of ideas. xii, 392 p. New York: Macmillan, 1933.
Reviewed by Sarah Youngman Keyser, *Scr.Math.,* 1933, 2: 59-63.

ADc-br

ARCHIVES INTERNATIONALES D'HISTOIRE DES IDÉES. The Hague: Martinus Nijhoff, 1963. [CB 89/497]
New monograph series dealing principally with the 16th, 17th. and 18th centuries.

Journal of the History of Ideas. Edited by Arthur O. Lovejoy Vol. 1, no. 1- New York: College of the City of New York: 1940-
Brief note on no. 1 in *Isis,* 1940, 32: 483.

Studies in the History of Ideas. Edited by the Department of Philosophy of Columbia University. Vol. 1- New York: Columbia University Press, 1918-

ADce

LINDBERG, Sten G. Från skapelsetro till naturlagar. Idéhistorisk översikt över banbrytande bokverk i Hjalmar Sjögrens bibliotek. 115 p. [From belief in creation to natural laws: analysis of the history of ideas in pioneer works in Hjalmar Sjögrens library. (In Swedish)]. Stockholm: Ingeniörs-vetenskapsakademien, 1959.
Reviewed by Gunnar Eriksson, *Lychnos*, 1960-61, 310-11.

ADhd

LOVEJOY, Arthur O. The historiography of ideas. *Proc.Amer. Phil.Soc.*, 1938, 78: 529-43.

ADhj

BRUNSCHWICG, Léon. Le rôle du pythagorisme dans l'évolution des idées. 27 p. (Actualités Scientifiques et Industrielles, 446; Conférences du Centre Universitaire Méditerranéen de Nice, 2) Paris: Hermann, 1937.

WEISSMANN, Asriel. Platonic ideas in the history of human thought. *Act.VIIIe Congr.Int.Hist.Sci.* (Florence, 1956), p. 1182-7. Paris: Hermann, 1958.

ADht

WHYTE, L.L. The growth of ideas. *Eranos-Jahrb.*, 1954, 23: 367-88.
Treats mainly of the formation and transmission of ideas.

ADk

CASSIRER, Ernst. The philosophy of symbolic forms. Transl. by Ralph Manheim. 3 vol. 1. Language. xiv, 328 p.; 2. Mythical thought. xviii, 269 p.; 3. The phenomenology of knowledge. xvii, 501 p. New Haven: Yale University Press; London: Oxford University Press, 1953, 1955, 1957. [CB 80/117 and CB 83/195]
Translation from the German (Berlin: B. Cassirer, 1923-31).
Reviewed by F.I.G. Rawlins, *Nature*, 1958, 182: 1586.
Italian translation (Florence: La Nuova, 1961). Volume 1 reviewed by Silvestro Marcucci, *Physis*, 1962, 4: 171-2.

KRISTELLER, Paul Oskar. The philosophical significance of the history of thought. *J.Hist.Ideas*, 1946, 7: 360-6.

ADke

ASPELIN, Gunnar. [The history of ideas as a science. (In Swedish with summary in English)]. *Lychnos*, 1948-49, 129-43.

ADkk

WIENER, Philip P. Logical significance of the history of thought. *J.Hist.Ideas*, 1946, 7: 366-73.

ADnh

BUCK, Carl Darling. A dictionary of selected synonyms in the principal Indo-European languages. A contribution to the history of ideas. xx, 1515 p. Chicago: University of Chicago Press, 1949.
Reviewed by E.H. Sturtevant, *J.Amer.Orient.Rev.*, 1950, 70: 329-31.

ADqg

BING, Gertrud. The Warburg Institute. *Libr.Ass.Rec.*, Aug. 1934, 36: 262-6. [CB 42/601]

ADwm-oq

UPPSALA. Une chaire d'histoire des sciences et des idées. *Isis*, 1934, 22: 232.

ADz

BERGEMA, Hendrik. De boom des levens in schrift en historie. Bijdrage tot een onderzoek naar de verhouding van schriftopenbaring en traditie betreffende den boom des levens binnen het kader der oud-testamentische wetenschap. [The tree of life in literature and history: contributions to an enquiry into the relation between literary evidence and tradition concerning the tree of life within the framework of Old Testament studies. (In Dutch)] 682 p., 127 ill. [Thesis, Amsterdam) Hilversum: Schipper, 1938.
Study of the traditions of the tree of life.

DELEVSKY, J. L'idée du cycle éternel dans l'histoire du monde. *Studies and Essays offered to George Sarton*, p. 375-401. New York: Schuman, 1947. [CB 71/116]

ELIADE, Mircea. Le mythe de l'éternel retour, archétypes et répétition. Les essais XXXIV. 254 p. Paris: Gallimard, 1949. [CB 77/383]

LOVEJOY, Arthur O. The great chain of being. ix, 382 p. Cambridge, Mass.: Harvard University Press, 1936.
2nd series of The William James Lectures on Philosophy and Psychology, Harvard University, 1933. Reprinted 1960 (New York: Harper Torchbooks).
Reviewed by H.T. Davis, *Isis*, 1937, 27: 111-14; by H.V.S. Ogden, *Isis*, 1938, 28: 537-40.

REY, Abel. Le retour éternel et la philosophie de la physique. 320 p. Paris: Flammarion, 1927.
Reviewed by George Sarton, *Isis*, 1927, 9: 477-9.

ROUSSEAU, Michel. "L'arbre de la vie", vivante image de l'évolution chez le P. Teilhard de Chardin. *Rev.Syn.*, 1958, 79: 113-21.

WIFSTRAND, Albert. Den Gyllene Kedjan. [The Golden Chain. (In Swedish)]. *Lychnos*, 1957-58, 1-13.
Concerning the allegory of the golden chain as a representation of the continuous, ordered and graded connection between all parts of the universe.

AF PHILOSOPHY

for epistemology *see* Aks
philosophy of science in general *see* Ak
philosophical aspects of the separate sciences *see* INDEX

AFc general history

ARCHIV für Begriffsgeschichte: Bausteine zu einem historischen Wörterbuch der Philosophie. (Im Auftrage der Kommission für Philosophie der Akademie der Wissenschaften und der Literatur zu Mainz) 1- Bonn: H. Bouvier, 1955-
A series of monographs.

BAKER, Herschel. The dignity of man. Studies in the persistence of an idea. xii, 365 p. Cambridge, Mass.: Harvard University Press, 1947.
A general history of philosophical, theological, ethical and political thought in Western society from the Ionians to the end of the Renaissance.
Reviewed by Crane Brinton, *Isis*, 1948, 39: 199-200.

BECCARI, Arturo. Storia della filosofia e della scienza. viii, 408 p. Torino: Soc. Editr. Internazionale, 1928. [CB 27/533]

BEER, Samuel H. The city of reason. 227 p. Cambridge, Mass.: Harvard University Press, 1949.
"The author postulates a philosophy of liberalism based upon the concepts of A.N. Whitehead."
Reviewed by Sydney Jackman, *Isis*, 1949, 40: 298.

BLACK, Max. Problems of analysis. Philosophical essays. xi, 304 p. Ithaca: Cornell University Press, 1954. [CB 80/117]

BOAS, George. Dominant themes of modern philosophy. x, 660 p. New York: Ronald Press Company, 1957.
Reviewed by John Herman Randall, *Amer.Hist.Rev.*, 1958, 63: 371-2.

BREHIER, Emile. Histoire de la philosophie. 2 vol. 1. L'antiquité et le moyen-âge. Fasc. 1. Introduction; période héllénique. 262 p. Fasc. 2. Période héllénistique et romaine. 264 p. Fasc. 3. Moyen-âge et renaissance. 274 p. 2. La philosophie moderne. Fasc. 1. Le dix-septième siècle. 314 p. Fasc. 2. Le dix-huitième siècle. 265 p. Fasc. 3. Le dix-neuvième siècle. Période des systèmes (1800-1850). 340 p. Fasc. 4. Le dix-neuvième siècle après 1850; le vingtième siècle. 278 p. Paris: F. Alcan, 1926-32. [CB 21/593, CB 24/555, CB 28/563, CB 30/425, CB 35/310 and CB 37/557]
Issued in 7 parts, each with special title page.

BROCHER, Henri. Les étapes de la pensée humaine. 149 p. Genève: Editions Labor et Fides, 1952. [CB 79/190]

BRUNSCHVICG, Léon. Les âges de l'intelligence. 152 p. (Nouvelle Encyclopédie Philosophique, 1) Paris: Alcan, 1934.

BRUNSCHVICG, Léon. Ecrits philosophiques. Textes réunis et annotés par Mme A.-R. Weill-Brunschvicg et M. Claude Lehec. 3 vol. 1. L'humanisme de l'occident; Descartes-Spinoza-Kant. 322 p.; 2. L'orientation du rationalisme. 338 p.; 3. Science-Religion. 296 p. Paris: Presses Universitaires de France, 1951, 1954, 1958. [CB 84/390]
Vol. 3 contains a bibliography of the author's writings.

BRUNSCHVICG, Léon. Le progrès de la conscience dans la philosophie occidentale. 2 vol. xxiii, 807 p. (Bibliothèque de Philosophie Contemporaine) Paris: Alcan, 1927.
Reviewed by Hélène Metzger, *Isis*, 1928, 10: 98-102.

CLARKE, F.P.; NAHM, M.C.; ed. Philosophical essays in honor of Edgar Arthur Singer, Jr. x, 377 p. Philadelphia: University of Pennsylvania Press, 1942.
Reviewed by George D.W. Berry, *Isis*, 1944, 35: 197-8.

CONGER, George Perrigo. Theories of macrocosms and microcosms in the history of philosophy. xviii, 146 p. New York: Columbia University Press, 1922. [CB 16/323]

DARLU, A. La tradition philosophique. *Rev.Métaphys.Morale*, 1920, 27: 345-53. [CB 13/299]

DE RUGGIERO, Guido. La filosofia contemporanea (Germania, Francia, Inghilterra, America, Italia). 485 p. Bari: Laterza, 1912.

DEVAUX, Philippe. De Thalès à Bergson. Introduction historique à la philosophie européenne. 607 p., 28 pl. Liège: Sciences et Lettres, 1955.
Reviewed by V.F. Lenzen, *Isis*, 1957, 48: 355-6.

FALCKENBERG, R. Geschichte der neueren Philosophie von Nikolaus von Kues bis zur Gegenwart. 7th ed. xii, 692 p. Leipzig: Veit, 1913.
First published 1886.

GIHRING, Kurt. Abendland und Kultur. Zur Kulturphilosophie der Gegenwart. 144 p. Einsiedeln-Zürich: Benziger, 1947.
Reviewed by Eduard Farber, *Isis*, 1949, 40: 88.

GILSON, Etienne. History of philosophy and philosophical education. 49 p. (Aquinas Lecture, 1947) Milwaukee: Marquette University Press, 1948.
Reviewed by Thurston N. Davis, *Speculum*, 1949, 24: 110-11.

GIRAN, Paul. Les origines de la pensée. 148 p. Paris: Félix Alcan, 1924. [CB 16/323]

HARTMANN, Nicolai. Kleinere Schriften. 1. Abhandlungen zur systematischen Philosophie. 318 p.; 2. Abhandlungen zur Philosophiegeschichte. 364 p.; 3. Vom Neukantianismus zur Ontologie. 395 p. Berlin: De Gruyter, 1955-58.
Volume 3 reviewed by Manfred Brelage, *Kant-Stud.*, 1961-62, 53: 107-11.

HÖFFDING, Harald. A history of modern philosophy: a sketch of the history of philosophy from the close of the Renaissance to our own day. Translated from the German edition by B.E. Meyer. 2 vol. 1. Renaissance to Rousseau. xvii, 532 p.; 2. Kant to German philosophers of 1850-1880. ix, 600 p. New York: Dover Publications, 1955.
An unabridged republication of the English translation, originally published in 1900 (London: Macmillan), from the German edition "Geschichte der neueren Philosophie" (Leipzig: 1895-96). Danish original: "Den nyere Filosofis Historie" (Copenhagen: 1894-95).

HOLLANDER, Bernard. In search of the soul and the mechanism of thought, emotion and conduct. 2 vol. 1. The history of philosophy and science from ancient times to the present day. 526 p.; 2. The origin and the mental capacities and dispositions of man and their normal, abnormal and supernatural manifestations. vii, 361 p. London: Kegan Paul, 1920.

JORDAN, Rudolf. The new perspective, 316 p. Chicago: University of Chicago Press, 1951.
Reviewed by V.F. Lenzen, *Isis*, 1952, 43: 88-9.

LEE, Otis. Existence and inquiry. ix, 323 p. Chicago: University of Chicago Press, 1949.
Development of modern philosophy.
Reviewed by V.F. Lenzen, *Isis*, 1949, 40: 297.

LE SENNE, R. Introduction à la philosophie. 316 p. (Bibliothèque de Philosophie Contemporaine) Paris: F. Alcan, 1925. [CB 20/208]

LEWIS, John. Introduction to philosophy. 236 p. London: Watts & Co., 1954. [CB 81/264]
This book is conceived historically.

MacDONALD, Margaret, ed. Philosophy and analysis. A selection of articles published in *Analysis* between 1933-40 and 1947-53. viii, 296 p. Oxford: Basil Blackwell; New York: Philosophical Library, 1954.

MACLEOD, Andries H.D. Geest en stof. Een inleiding tot de studie van enkele klassieke wijsgeerige problemen, inzonderheid het werkelijkheidsprobleem. [Mind and matter. An introduction to the study of a few classical philosophical problems, including the problem of reality. (In Dutch)] 96 p. Brussels: Manteau, 1939.
This book on mind and matter is partly derived from the teaching of Adolf Phalén (1884-1931) and other members of the school of Uppsala.

MASSON-OURSEL, Paul. Comparative philosophy. vi, 212 p. (International Library of Psychology, Philosophy and Scientific Method) London: Kegan Paul; New York: Harcourt Brace, 1926.
Original French text (Paris: Alcan, 1923) reviewed by George Sarton, *Isis*, 1924, 6: 99-104.

MEAD, George Herbert. The philosophy of the present. xi, 199 p. Chicago: Open Court, 1932.
Reviewed by H.T. Davis, *Isis*, 1933, 20: 307-10.

MOOG, Willy. Philosophie. x, 106 p. (Wissenschaftliche Forschungsberichte, 5) Gotha: Perthes, 1921. [CB 10/204]
Gives a general survey of the work done during the First World War.

NELSON, Leonard. Socratic method and critical philosophy: selected essays. Transl. by Thomas K. Brown III. Introd. by Julius Kraft. xxii, 211 p., front. New Haven: Yale University Press, 1949. [CB 76/409]

NICHOLSON, J.A. An introductory course in philosophy. xiii, 508 p. New York: Macmillan, 1939. [CB 57/269]
The book represents an elementary historical introduction to philosophy.

PASSMORE, John A. A hundred years of philosophy. 523 p., bibliogr. London: Gerald Duckworth, 1957.

PHILOSOPHICAL studies. Essays in memory of L. Susan Stebbing. v, 156 p. London: Allen and Unwin (for Aristotelian Society), 1948.

PHILOSOPHY and history. Essays presented to Ernst Cassirer. Edited by Raymond Klibansky and H.J. Paton. xii, 300 p. Oxford: Clarendon Press; New York: Oxford University Press, 1936.

PRATT, James Bissett. Personal realism. xi, 387 p. New York: Macmillan, 1937. [CB 53/284]

RAEYMAEKER, Louis de. Introduction to philosophy. Transl. by Harry McNeill. xi, 297 p. (Introductory Volume of the Philosophical Series of the Higher Institute of Philosophy, University of Louvain, Belgium) New York: Wagner, 1948. [CB 75/96]

RANDALL, J.H. The career of philosophy from the middle ages to the Enlightenment. xiv, 993 p. New York: Columbia University Press, 1962.
Reviewed by R.F. McRae, *Dialogue*, 1963, 2: 101-2.

REYMOND, Arnold. Brèves remarques sur l'histoire de la philosophie. *Mélanges d'Histoire et de Littérature offerts à Monsieur Charles Gilliard*, 6 p. Lausanne: Université de Lausanne, Faculté des Lettres, 1944.

RIVAUD, Albert. Histoire de la philosophie. 1. Des origines à la scolastique. xxiv, 616 p. 2. De la scolastique à l'époque classique. 456 p. 3. L'époque classique. 592 p. 4. Philosophie française et philosophie anglaise de 1700 à 1830. 594 p. Paris: Presses Universitaires de France, 1948-62.
In progress.
Second edition of volume 1, 1961; of volume 4, 1963.

ROMERO, Francisco. Historia de la filosofía moderna. 365 p., bibliogr. México: Fondo de Cultura Económica, 1959.
Reviewed by Manfredo Kempff Mercado, *Hispanic-Amer.Hist. Rev.*, 1961, 41: 456.

RUNES, Dagobert D. Pictorial history of philosophy. x, 406 p., ill. New York: Philosophical Library, 1959.
Reviewed by Gerd Buchdahl, *Nature*, 1960, 185: 67; in *Scientia*, 1961, 15: 42.

RUNES, Dagobert D., ed. Twentieth century philosophy. 571 p. New York: Philosophical Library, 1943. [CB 65/72]

RUSSELL, Bertrand. A history of Western philosophy. 895 p. New York: Simon & Shuster, 1945.
Reviewed by Lindsay of Birker, *Nature*, 1947, 159: 723-4; by George Boas, *J.Hist.Ideas*, 1947, 8: 117-23; by Leo Roberts, *Isis*, 1948, 38: 268-70.

RUSSELL, Bertrand. Outline of philosophy. vi, 317 p. London: Allen and Unwin, 1927.
German translation: Mensch und Welt. Grundriss der Philosophie. (343 p. München: Drei Masken Verlag, 1930) reviewed by Wilhelm Burkamp, *Deut.Lit.Zeitung*, 1930, 2070-2.

RUSSELL, Bertrand. The problems of philosophy. 256 p. (Home University Library of Modern Knowledge) London: T. Butterworth; New York: H. Holt, 1912.
Reprinted 1959 (New York: Oxford University Press).

RUSSELL, Bertrand. Wisdom of the West. Edited by Paul Foulkes. 320 p. London: Macdonald, 1959.
Reviewed by Gerd Buchdahl, *Nature*, 1959, 184: 1829-30.

SCHAUB, Edward Leroy, ed. Philosophy today. Essays on recent developments in the field of philosophy. x, 609 p. Chicago: Open Court, 1928. [CB 24/557]
Essays reprinted from *The Monist*.

SCHILLER, Ferdinand Canning Scott. Our human truths. Ed. by Louise S. Schiller. x, 271 p. New York: Columbia University Press, 1939. [CB 59/487]

SCHILLING, K. Geschichte der Philosophie. 2nd ed. 2 vol. 1. Die alte Welt. Das christlich germanische Mittelalter. 456 p.; 2. Die Neuzeit. 688 p., 55 pl. Munich: Ernst Reinhardt, 1951-53.
First publ. Munich: Reinhardt, 1943-44.

SOUILHÉ, Joseph; BRÉMOND, A.; MUGNIER, R. Etude historique de la philosophie. 187 p. Paris: Beauchesne, 1932.

STACE, Walter Terence. The destiny of Western man. xi, 322 p. New York: Reynal & Hitchcock, 1942.
Reviewed by Mark Graubard, *Isis*, 1943, 34: 236-7.

STUDIEN zur Geschichte der Philosophie. Festgabe zum 60. Geburtstag Clemens Baeumkers. viii, 491 p. (*Beitr.Gesch. Phil.Mittelalters Suppl.*, 1) Münster i. W.: Aschendorff, 1913.

TULANE UNIVERSITY. DEPARTMENT OF PHILOSOPHY. Centennial year number. [A collection of articles] 122 p. (Tulane Studies in Philosophy, 8) New Orleans: 1959. [CB 85/446]
The year 1959 marks the centenary of the "Origin of species" and of the births of many philosophers of the recent past.

WAHL, Jean. Vers le concret. Etudes d'histoire de la philosophie contemporaine. 272 p. Paris: Vrin, 1932. [CB 38/609]

WHITE, Morton. Toward reunion in philosophy. xii, 308 p. Cambridge, Mass.: Harvard University Press, 1956. [CB 82/201]

WIFSTRAND, Albert. Bakgrunder: uppsatser om tider och tankesätt. [Backgrounds: essays about times and ways of thought. (In Swedish)] 215 p. Lund: Gleerups Förlag, 1961.
Reviewed by E.N. Tigerstedt, *Lychnos*, 1962, 267-9.

WOLFSON, Harry Austryn. Infinite and privative judgments in Aristotle, Averroes, and Kant. *Phil.Phenomenol.Res.*, 1947, 8: 173-87.

WRIGHT, William Kelley. A history of modern philosophy. xvi, 633 p. New York: Macmillan, 1941. [CB 61/416]

ZYBURA, John S., ed. Present-day thinkers and the new scholasticism: an international symposium. xviii, 543 p. St. Louis Mo./London: Herder, 1926.
Reviewed by James H. Ryan, *Speculum*, 1926, 1: 454-6.

AFc-be

HANDBUCH der Philosophie [by various authors]; herausgegeben von A. Baeumler und M. Schröter. 4 vol. Munich: Oldenbourg, 1934, 1927, 1931, 1934.
Separate pagination for each chapter.

RUNES, Dagobert D., ed. The dictionary of philosophy. 343 p. New York: Philosophical Library, 1942. [CB 71/128]

RUSSELL, Bertrand. Dictionary of mind, matter and morals. Ed. with an introd. by Lester E. Denonn. xiv, 290 p. New York: Philosophical Library, 1952. [CB 79/148]

URMSON, J.O., ed. The concise encyclopedia of western philosophy and philosophers. 431 p. New York: Hawthorn Books, 1960.
Reviewed in *Sci.Amer.*, 1961, 204: no. 1, 202-5.

AFc-br

Annalen der Philosophie, mit besonderer Rücksicht auf die Probleme der Als-Ob-Betrachtung. Edited by H. Vaihinger and R. Schmidt. Leipzig: Meiner, 1919-30.

Jahrbücher der Philosophie. Eine kritische Übersicht der Philosophie der Gegenwart. Vol. 1-3. Berlin: Mittler, 1913-14, 1927.
Volume 1 reviewed by George Sarton, *Isis*, 1914, 2: 243-4.

Journal of the History of Philosophy. Vol. 1- Berkeley: University of California Press, 1963- [CB 89/497]

Philosophy East and West. A quarterly journal of Oriental and comparative thought. Vol. 1, no. 1- Honolulu: University of Hawaii Press, 1951- [CB 78/197]

Vorträge der Bibliothek Warburg. Hrsg. von Fritz Saxl. 1921/1922-1930/1931. Leipzig: Teubner, 1923-32.
For 1921/22 vol. *see* CB 15/236; for 1923/24 vol. CB 22/301.

AFcb/daj bibliography; literature; biography

AFcb

BING, Gertrud. The Warburg Institute. *Libr.Ass.Rec.*, Aug. 1934, 36: 262-6. [CB 42/601]

AFce-bv

BERG, Jan. Selektiv Bibliografi i Teoretisk Filosofi. [Selective bibliography in theoretical philosophy. (In Swedish)] 81 p. Stockholm: Universitet i Stockholm, 1960.

Bibliographie de la Philosophie. 1937- Paris: Vrin, 1937- Published for the International Federation of Philosophical Societies under the auspices of the International Council of Philosophy and Human Studies.

VARET, Gilbert. Manuel de bibliographie philosophique. 2 vol. in 1. 1,058 p. (Collection "Logos") Paris: Presses Universitaires de France, 1956. [CB 83/195]
Reviewed by René Taton, *Rev.Hist.Sci.*, 1959, 12: 75-6.

AFcj-bv

BAUMGARDT, David. Philosophical periodicals. An annotated world list. 89 p. Washington: Library of Congress, Reference Department, 1952. [CB 83/194]

AFda

HUMBERT, Pierre. Philosophes et savants. 224 p. (Bibliothèque de Philosophie Scientifique) Paris: Flammarion, 1953.
Reviewed by Bernard Rochot, *Rev.Hist.Sci.*, 1953, 6: 278-9.

JASPERS, Karl. The great philosophers. Edited by Hannah Arendt. Translated by Ralph Manheim. [1.] xx, 396 p. New York: Harcourt, Brace & World, 1962.
Translation of part of Die Grossen Philosophen. Vol. 1. München: R. Piper, 1957.
Reviewed in *Sci.Amer.*, 1962, 206: no. 6, 192.

McCABE, Joseph Martin. A biographical dictionary of modern Rationalists. xxxii, 934 col. London: Watts, 1920. [CB 10/204]

AFdaj

CURTIS, Charles S.; GREENSLET, Ferris; ed. The Practical Cogitator or The Thinker's Anthology. x, 577 p. Boston: Houghton Mifflin, 1945. [CB 70/269]

EDWARDS, Paul; PAP, Arthur; ed. A modern introduction to philosophy: readings from classical and contemporary sources. ix, 648 p. Glencoe, Ill.: The Free Press, 1957. [CB 83/189]

RUNES, Dagobert D., ed. Treasury of philosophy. xxiv, 1280 p. New York: Philosophical Library, 1955. [CB 81/264]

WHITE, Morton, ed. The age of analysis. 20th century philosophers, selected with introduction and interpretive commentary by the editor. 253 p. (Mentor Philosophers) New York: New American Library; Boston: Houghton Mifflin, 1955. [CB 81/340]

AFh/m historiography; methodology

AFhd

DELORME, Suzanne. La philosophie par les textes. *Rev.Syn.*, 1957, 78: 535-6.

GUINET, L., ed. Un grand traité d'histoire de la philosophie. *Isis*, 1924, 6: 407-8. [CB 16/324]

ROTHACKER, Erich. Das akademische "Wörterbuch der Philosophie". *Goldene Tor*, 1950, 5: 94-7.
Need for a dictionary of philosophy which stresses the historical point of view.

AFhj

CRUZ HERNÁNDEZ, Miguel. La distinción aviceniana de la esencia y la existencia y su interpretación en la filosofía occidental. *Homenaje a Millás-Vallicrosa*, (1), p. 351-74. Barcelona: Consejo Superior de Investigaciones Cientificas, 1954.

MOREAU, J. Platon et la crise de la civilisation contemporaine. *Proc.10th Int.Congr.Phil.* (Amsterdam, 1948), p. 1084-7. Amsterdam: North Holland Publishing Co., 1949.

ODEGARD, Douglas. Essences and discovery: Plato, Locke, and Leibnitz. *Dialogue*, 1964, 3: 219-34.

AFk

DILTHEY, Wilhelm. Gesammelte Schriften. Vol. 8. Weltanschauungslehre. xiv, 274 p. (Abhandlungen zur Philosophie der Philosophie) Leipzig: Teubner, 1931.
Reviewed by Richard Hönigswald, *Deut.Lit.Zeitung*, 1931, 2: 2068-76.

AFkb

AYER, A.J. [Philosophy and science. (In Russian)] *Vop. Fil.*, 1962, no. 1, 96-105.
English version in *Soviet Stud.Phil.*, 1962, 1: no. 1, 14-19.
A discussion of whether philosophy is a science. For reply by Kuznetsov, I.V., *see* below.

CARNAP, Rudolf. On the character of philosophic problems. *Phil.Sci.*, 1934, 1: 5-19.

KUZNETSOV, I.V. [No! Philosophy is a science. (In Russian)]. *Vop.Fil.*, 1962, 1: 106-22.
English version in *Soviet Stud.Phil.*, 1962, 1: no. 1, 20-36. A reply to Ayer, A.J., *see* above.

AFke

AGREEMENT in philosophy. [Papers on this topic by Norman K. Smith, Walter P. Pitkin and Karl Schmidt for discussion at the American Philosophical Association's 12th Annual Meeting, December 1912] *J.Phil.*, 1912, 9: 701-17.

ALQUIE, Ferdinand. Présentation du problème philosophique (l'expérience dans la philosophie). *Rev.Syn.*, 1963, 34: 29-41.

BERGSON, Henri. La pensée et le mouvant. Essais et conférences. 322 p. (Bibliothèque de Philosophie Contemporaine) Paris: Alcan, 1934. [CB 43/288 and 51/291]

CARR, H. Wildon. The scientific approach to philosophy: selected essays and reviews. viii, 278 p. London: Macmillan, 1924.

CHAUCHARD, Paul. Valeur et limites de l'apport scientifique à la philosophie. *Dialectica*, 1959, 13: 123-44.

KUNTZE, Friedrich. Von den neuen Denkmitteln der Philosophie in sechs Briefen an den Einzelnen und an die philosophischen Arbeitsgemeinschaften. vii, 262 p. Heidelberg: Winter, 1928.
Reviewed by Edmund O. von Lippmann, *Chem.Zeitung*, 1929, 53: 368.

MASSON-OURSEL, P. Objet et méthode de la philosophie comparée. *Atti IV° Congr.Int.Fil.* (Bologna, 1911), (2), p. 165-72. Genoa: Formiggini, 1913.

POLLACK, W. Perspektive und Symbol in Philosophie und Rechtswissenschaft. xvi, 533 p. Berlin: Rothschild, 1912.

RUSSELL, Bertrand. Our knowledge of the external world as a field for scientific method in philosophy. x, 245 p. Chicago: Open Court Co., 1914.
Reviewed by P. Jourdain, *Isis*, 1920, 3: 311-14.
For French translation entitled "Méthode scientifique en philosophie" (Paris: J. Vrin, 1929) *see* CB 26/227; German translation (Leipzig: Meiner, 1926) reviewed by M. Kronenberg, *Naturwissenschaften*, 1926, 945-6.

SCHMIDT, Franz. Die Theorie der Geisteswissenschaften vom Altertum bis zur Gegenwart. 150 p. München: Reinhardt, 1931.

AFkm

DUCASSE, C.J. Is scientific verification possible in philosophy? *Phil.Sci.*, 1935, 2: 121-7.

AFkz

DEWEY, John. Has philosophy a future? *Proc.10th Int.Congr. Phil.* (Amsterdam, 1948), p. 108-16. Amsterdam: North Holland Publishing Co., 1949.

AFm

COATES, Adrian. A basis of opinion. xvii, 461 p. New York: Macmillan, 1938.
Reviewed by M.F. Ashley-Montagu, *Isis*, 1939, 30: 547-9.
A critique of modern philosophical concepts.

AFmzA

for relations of science and philosophy *see* AmzAF

AFmzB

KENNEDY, E.S. Interrelations between mathematics and philosophy in the last three centuries. *Nat.Math.Mag.*, 1942, 16: 9 p.

AFmzBF

WHITTAKER, E.T. The new algebras and their significance for physics and philosophy. *Nature*, 1943, 152: 603.

AFmzMO

GATTERER, Alois. Der wissenschaftliche Okkultismus und sein Verhältnis zur Philosophie. 175 p. Innsbruck: Rauch, 1927.
Reviewed by K. Sudhoff, *Mitt.Gesch.Med.*, 1927, 26: 269.

AFn/t other special aspects

AFnh

CUVILLIER, A. Cours de philosophie à l'usage des classes de philosophie et de mathématiques et des classes préparatoires aux grandes écoles. IV. Petit vocabulaire de la langue philosophique. 109 p. Paris: Armand Colin, 1925.

LALANDE, André. Vocabulaire technique et critique de philosophie. 2 vol. 1065 p. Paris: Felix Alcan, 1926.

MEANS, Blanchard William. Selected glossary of philosophical terms. 67 p. (*Trinity Coll.Bull.*, 40) Hartford, Conn.: 1943.

AFo

GILSON, Etienne. History of philosophy and philosophical education. 49 p. (Aquinas Lecture, 1947) Milwaukee: Marquette University Press, 1948.
Reviewed by Thurston N. Davis, *Speculum*, 1949, 24: 110-11.

AFo-mzBo

GREBE, W. Mathematischer und philosophischer Unterricht in ihrer gegenseitigen Befruchtung. *Z.Math.Naturwiss.Unterricht*, 1923, 54: 193-201. [CB 17/589]

AFpw

EAST-WEST PHILOSOPHERS' CONFERENCE, 1st, Honolulu, 1939. Philosophy - East and West. Ed. by Charles A. Moore. ix, 334 p. Princeton, N.J.: Princeton University Press, 1944.

EAST-WEST PHILOSOPHERS' CONFERENCE, 2nd, Honolulu, 1949. Essays in East-West philosophy: an attempt at world philosophical synthesis. Ed. by Charles A. Moore. xii, 467 p. Honolulu: University of Hawai Press, 1951.

AFsc

DEWEY, John. Philosophy and civilization. vii, 334 p. New York: Minton, Balch, 1931.
Reviewed by F.S. Marvin, *Nature*, 1932, 129: 329-31.

GILSON, Étienne. Le rôle de la philosophie dans l'histoire de la civilisation. *Rev.Métaphys.Morale*, 1927, 34: 169-76.

JASPERS, Karl. Man in the modern age. Transl. by Eden and Cedar Paul. vii, 243 p. London: Routledge, 1933.
New edition London: Kegan Paul & Routledge, 1951
German original, Die geistige Situation der Zeit, first published Berlin: de Gruyter, 1931.

WULF, M. De. Civilisation et philosophie. *Rev.Néo-Scolastique*, 1912, 157-76.

AFtd

BEVAN, Edwyn. Symbolism and belief. 391 p. (Gifford Lectures, 1933-34) London: Allen and Unwin; New York: Macmillan, 1938.
An inquiry into the relation of religious symbols to reality.

BRADSHAW, Marion J. Philosophical foundations of faith. xl, 254 p. New York: Columbia University Press, 1941. [CB 62/85]

FRANK, Erich. Philosophical understanding and religious truth. x, 209 p. New York: Oxford University Press, 1945.
Reviewed by Leo Roberts, *Isis*, 1946, 36: 273.

RAEYMAEKER, L. de. Le climat chrétien et la philosophie. *Proc.10th Int.Congr.Phil.* (Amsterdam, 1948), p. 62-73. Amsterdam: North Holland Publishing Co., 1949.

WOLFSON, Harry Austryn. Philo. Foundations of religious philosophy in Judaism, Christianity and Islam. 2 vol. xvi, 462 p.; xiv, 531 p. Cambridge, Mass.: Harvard University Press, 1947.
Reviewed by Leo Roberts, *Isis*, 1949, 40: 199-213; for further reviews *see* CB 73/125.

AFw in different countries

PERRY, Ralph Barton. Philosophy of the recent past: an outline of European and American philosophy since 1860. viii, 230 p. New York: Charles Scribner, 1926.

AFwb

FISCH, Max H. Evolution in American philosophy. *Phil.Rev.*, 1947, 66: 357-73.

MOUVEMENT général de la pensée américaine. *Rev.Métaphys. Morale*, 1922, 29: 380-575. [CB 14/559]
Articles by American scholars.

PERRY, Ralph Barton. *See* AFw

PERSON, Stow, ed. Evolutionary thought in America. x, 462 p., 28 ill. New Haven: Yale University Press, 1950.
Reviewed by Conway Zirkle, *Isis*, 1951, 42: 275.

SCHNEIDER, Herbert W. A history of American philosophy. xiv, 646 p. New York: Columbia University Press, 1946.
Reviewed by A.D. Ritchie, *Nature*, 1947, 160: 37.

TALLMADGE, G. Kasten. The epistemology of American Humanism. The apprehension of the standard. *Petrus Nonius*, 1941, 3: 186-219.

WINN, Ralph B., ed. American philosophy. xviii, 318 p. New York: Philosophical Library, 1955. [CB 81/260]

AFwb-td

SCHNEIDER, Herbert W. The influence of Darwin and Spencer on American philosophical theology. *J.Hist.Ideas*, 1945, 6: 3-18.

AFwe

CONTEMPORARY British philosophy: personal statements. 3 vol. 1st ser. Ed. by J.H. Muirhead. 432 p. 2nd ser. Ed. by J.H. Muirhead. 365 p. 3rd ser. Ed. by H.D. Lewis. xiv, 501 p. London: Allen & Unwin; New York: Macmillan, 1924, 1925, 1956.

METZ, Rudolf. A hundred years of British philosophy. Transl. by J.W. Harvey, T.E. Jessop, Henry Sturt. Edited by J.H. Muirhead. 828 p. (Library of Philosophy) London: Allen and Unwin, 1938.
Reviewed by T. Greenwood, *Nature*, 1939, 144: 51-3.
Reprinted London: Allen & Unwin; New York: Macmillan, 1950. Translation of "Die philosophischen Strömungen der Gegenwart in Grossbritannien" (Leipzig: F. Meiner, 1935).

SETH, James. English philosophers and schools of philosophy. 372 p. London: Dent, 1912.

SORLEY, W.R. A history of English philosophy. xvi, 380 p. Cambridge University Press; New York: Macmillan, 1937. [CB 58/587]
Reprint; first published 1920.

AFwf

BARUZI, Jean. Philosophie générale et métaphysique. xxii, 220 p. (Philosophes et Savants Français du XXe Siècle. Extraits et Notices, 1) Paris: Alcan, 1926. [CB 20/178]

BENRUBI, I. Les sources et les courants de la philosophie contemporaine en France. 2 vol. viii, 1058 p. Paris: Alcan, 1933.

CRESSON, André. Les courants de la pensée philosophique française. 2 vol. 208, 212 p. Paris: Armand Colin, 1927.
Reviewed by Hélène Metzger, *Isis*, 1927, 9: 489-90.

GUNN, John Alexander. Modern French philosophy. A study of the development since Comte. With a foreword by Henri Bergson. 358 p. London: Fisher Unwin, 1922.

LOTE, René. Histoire de la philosophie. In: Histoire de la Nation Française. Vol. XV. Histoire des sciences en France, pt. 2, p. 299-605. Paris: Plon, 1925. [CB 18/602]

PARODI, Dominique. La philosophie contemporaine en France; essai de classification des doctrines. 3rd enl. ed. vi, 537 p. Paris: Félix Alcan, 1925.
First publ. 1919.
Reviewed by R. Le Senne, *Rev.Métaphys.Morale*, 1927, 34: 81-114.

LA TRADITION philosophique et la pensée française. Leçons professées à l'École des Hautes Études Sociales. Par Mme L. Prenant [*et al.*]. iv, 358 p. Paris: Alcan, 1922. [CB 14/559]

AFwg

BRÉHIER, Emile. Histoire de la philosophie allemande. 160 p. Paris: Payot, 1922.
Reviewed by L. Guinet, *Isis*, 1923, 5: 471-3.
2nd edition Paris: Vrin, 1933.

REYMOND, Arnold. Les préoccupations philosophiques actuelles en Suisse romande. *Rech.Phil.*, 1931-32, 1: 353-61.

VIRIEUX-REYMOND, Antoinette. La pensée philosophique en Suisse romande. *Rev.Syn.*, 1947, 21: 65-84.

AFwh

TATARKIEWICZ, Wladyslaw. [Esquisse de l'histoire de la philosophie en Pologne. (In Polish with summary in French)]. 37 p. (Polska Akademia Umiejetnosci, Historia Nauki Polskiej w Monografiach, 32) Cracow: 1948.

AFwi

PICCOLI, Valentino. Storia della filosofia italiana. viii, 340 p. Torino: Paravia, 1927. [CB 24/556]

AFwj

FERREIRA, Ernesto. Estudos filosóficos nos Açôres. Esbôço histórico. *Petrus Nonius*, 1940, 2: 253-66.

AFwj-vm

KARCHER, Johann. Die jüdischen Arztphilosophen Spaniens und Lusitaniens vom Mittelalter bis zur Neuzeit. *Gesnerus*, 1952, 9: 124-48.

AFwn

BOCHEŃSKI, J.M. Die dogmatischen Grundlagen der sowjetischen Philosophie (Stand 1958): Zusammenfassung der 'Osnovy marksistskoj filosofi' mit Register. xii, 84 p. (Sovietica: Veröffentlichungen des Ost-Europa Instituts, Universität Freiburg/Schweiz, 3) Dordrecht: D. Reidel Publishing Co., 1959.
Reviewed by George L. Kline, *J.Phil.*, 1962, 59: 815-20.

BOCHENSKI, J.M.; BLAKELEY, T.J.; ed. Studies in Soviet thought. ix, 141 p. Dordrecht: D. Reidel Publishing Company, 1961. [CB 88/527]

LOBKOWICZ, Nikolaus, ed. Das Widerspruchsprinzip in der neueren sowjetischen Philosophie. [Transl. by the editor.] vi, 89 p. (Sovietica: Veröffentlichungen des Ost-Europa Instituts, Universität Freiburg/Schweiz, 4) Dordrecht: Reidel, 1960.
Reviewed by George L. Kline, *J.Phil.*, 1962, 59: 815-20.

SOMERVILLE, John. Soviet philosophy. A study of theory and practice. xv, 269 p. New York: Philosophical Library, 1946.
Reviewed by Lord Lindsay of Birker, *Nature*, 1947, 160: 36.

AFwt

BRIERE, O. Fifty years of Chinese philosophy, 1898-1950. Transl. from the French by Laurence G. Thompson. 159 p. London: George Allen & Unwin, Ltd.; New York: Macmillan, 1956.
Reviewed by James R. Ware, *Isis*, 1958, 49: 94.

AG PHILOSOPHICAL SYSTEMS

for philosophical systems in the philosophy of science *see* Akt
philosophical systems in the separate sciences *see* INDEX

BERGSON, Henri, *et al.* Le matérialisme actuel par H. Bergson, H. Poincaré, Ch. Gide, Ch. Wagner, F. Roz, P. De Witt-Guizot, J. Friedel, G. Riou. 263p. Paris: E. Flammarion, 1913.

BERTHELOT, René. Le pragmatisme chez Nietzsche et chez Poincaré. 416 p. Paris: Alcan, 1911.

CRESSON, André. Les systèmes philosophiques. 220 p. Paris: Colin, 1929. [CB 29/313]

DAURIAC, Lionel. Contingence et rationalisme. xxi, 366 p. Paris: J. Vrin, 1925. [CB 18/646]

FARBER, Marvin. The foundation of phenomenology. xi, 585 p. Cambridge: Harvard University Press, 1943.
Includes English edition of the main content of Husserl's "Logische Untersuchungen".
Reviewed by Leo Roberts, *Isis*, 1948, 39: 200-1.

FARBER, Marvin, ed. Philosophical essays in memory of Edmund Husserl. viii, 332 p. Cambridge, Mass.: Harvard University Press for the University of Buffalo, 1940.
Reviewed by F.I.G. Rawlins, *Nature*, 1944, 154: 504-6.

FERM, Vergilius, ed. A history of philosophical systems. 642 p. New York: Philosophical Library, 1950. [CB 77/383]

GEX, Maurice. La philosophie d'inspiration scientifique. *Dialectica*, 1959, 13: 160-84.
Discusses the philosophies of A.N. Whitehead and Raymond Ruyer as examples of philosophical systems inspired by science.

GHOSH, Jajneswar. Samkhya and modern thought. 141 p. Calcutta: The Book Co., 1930.

GRIFFIN, James. Wittgenstein's logical atomism. viii, 166 p. Oxford: Clarendon Press, 1964.

HOERNLÉ, R.F. Alfred. Idealism as a philosophical doctrine. 189 p. (Library of Philosophy and Religion) London: Hodder and Stoughton, 1924.

HOOK, Sidney. The metaphysics of pragmatism. With an introductory word by John Dewey. 144 p. 144 p., 1 pl. Chicago: Open Court, 1927. [CB 24/556]

HUSSERL, Edmund. Die Idee der Phänomenologie. Fünf Vorlesungen. Hrsg. und eingeleitet von Walter Biemel. xi, 94 p. (Husserliana, 2) The Hague: Nijhoff, 1950.

KALLEN, H.M. La méthode de l'intuition et la méthode pragmatiste. *Rev.Métaphys.Morale*, 1922, 29: 35-62.

LANGE, Friedrich Albert. The history of materialism: and criticism of its present importance. Authorised translation by Ernest Chester Thomas. Third ed. 3 vol. in 1. xliii, 330 p.; 397 p.; 376 p. (International Library of Psychology, Philosophy and Scientific Method) London: Kegan Paul, 1925.
Translation of "Geschichte des Materialismus" first publ. 1881.

LEVINAS, Emmanuel. La théorie de l'intuition dans la phénoménologie de Husserl. 224 p. Paris: Alcan, 1930. [CB 30/488]

McKEON, Richard. Aristotelianism in western Christianity. *Environmental Factors in Christian History*, p. 206-31. Chicago, Ill.: University of Chicago Press, 1939.

MAYER, Charles. L'homme, esprit ou matière? 139 p. Paris: Marcel Rivière, 1949. [CB 76/409]

OSTWALD, Wilhelm. Le monisme comme but de la civilisation. 39 p. Hambourg: Comité International du Monisme, 1913. [CB 23/309]

PAPINI, Giovanni. Sul pragmatismo. Saggi e ricerche, 1903-1911. xii, 165 p. Milan: Libreria Editrice Milanese, 1913.
Reviewed by A. Mieli, *Isis*, 1914, 2: 245-7.

POLE, David. The later philosophy of Wittgenstein. A short introduction, with an epilogue on John Wisdom. vi, 132 p. London: Athlone Press, 1958; New York: Oxford University Press, 1963.
Reviewed by F.I.G. Rawlins, *Nature*, 1959, 183: 494.

PRATT, James Bissett. Naturalism. x, 180 p. New Haven: Yale University Press, 1939. [CB 59/486]

RAWLINS, F.I.G. Adventures in phenomenology. *Nature*, 1944, 154: 504-6.
Review of Philosophical essays in memory of Edmund Husserl, *see* Farber, Marvin, above.

RINTELEN, J. von. Beyond existentialism. 264 p. London: George Allen & Unwin, 1961; New York: Humanities Press, 1962.
Reviewed by David Baumgardt, *J.Phil.*, 1962, 59: 836-40.

SELLARS, Roy Wood; McGILL, V.J.; FARBER, Marvin. Philosophy for the future; the quest of modern materialism. xiv, 647 p. New York: Macmillan, 1949.
Reviewed by V.F. Lenzen, *Isis*, 1950, 41: 248-9.

SHOREY, Paul. Platonism ancient and modern. 259 p. (Sather Classical Lectures, 14) Berkeley: University of California Press, 1938.
Reviewed by Aubrey Diller, *Isis*, 1940, 31: 483-5.

UNOLD, J. Die drei Hauptrichtungen des modernen Monismus. *Atti IV Congr.Int.Fil.* (Bologna, 1911), (2), p. 130-43. Genoa: Formiggini, 1913.

VAIHINGER, Hans. The philosophy of "As if": a system of the theoretical, practical and religious fictions of mankind. Transl. by C.K. Ogden. xlvii, 370 p. (International Library of Psychology, Philosophy and Scientific Method) London: Kegan Paul, 1924.
Translation based on 6th edition of Die Philosophie des Als-Ob (Leipzig: F. Meiner, 1920).

WITTGENSTEIN, Ludwig. Tractatus logicophilosophicus. The German text of Ludwig Wittgenstein's Logisch-philosophische Abhandlung. Transl. by D.F. Pears and B.F. McGuinness, with an introd. by Bertrand Russell. xxii, 156 p. New York: Humanities Press, 1961. [CB 87/556]
The German text is given with the English translation on the facing pages.

AGhj

BOEHM, A. Leibniz et la scolastique contemporaine. *Proc. 10th Int.Congr.Phil.* (Amsterdam, 1948), p. 1148-52. Amsterdam: North Holland Publishing Co., 1949.

AGmc

BRETTSCHNEIDER, Bertram D. The philosophy of Samuel Alexander; idealism in "Space, time, and deity". xii, 177 p., bibliogr. New York: Humanities Press, 1964.

RUJA, Harry. Samuel Alexander's concept of space-time. *Phil. Sci.*, 1935, 2: 188-209.

STIERNOTTE, Alfred P. God and space-time. Deity in the philosophy of Samuel Alexander. xxvii, 455 p. New York: Philosophical Library, 1954.
Reviewed by V.F. Lenzen, *Isis*, 1955, 46: 287-9.

AGnh

KARUTZ, R. Der Emanismus. (Ein Vorschlag zur ethnologischen Terminologie) *Z.Ethnol.*, 1913, 45: 545-611.

AGw in different countries

LEROUX, Emmanuel. Le pragmatisme américain et anglais. Etude historique et critique suivie d'une bibliographie méthodique. 340 p. Paris: Alcan, 1923. [CB 15/235]

MUIRHEAD, John Henry. The Platonic tradition in Anglo-Saxon philosophy. Studies in the history of idealism in England and America. 446 p. London: Allen & Unwin, 1931.
Reviewed by A.E. Taylor, *Deut.Lit.Zeitung*, 1932, 3: 1118-22.

AGwb

KRIKORIAN, Yervant H. Naturalism and the human spirit. x, 397 p. New York: Columbia University Press, 1944. [CB 68/60]
This volume contains a series of essays which offer a fair summary of the position of naturalistic philosophy in America.

LEROUX, Emmanuel. *See* AGw

MOORE, Edward C. American pragmatism: Peirce, James, and Dewey. xii, 285 p. New York: Columbia University Press, 1961.
Reviewed by W.M. Sibley, *Dialogue*, 1962, 1: 223-4; by Richard J. Bernstein, *J.Phil.*, 1962, 59: 272-4.

MUIRHEAD, John Henry. *See* AGw

ROMANELL, Patrick. Toward a critical naturalism. Reflections on contemporary American philosophy. xv, 88 p. New York: Macmillan Company, 1958.
Reviewed by Virgil Hinshaw, *Isis*, 1959, 50: 82-3.

AGwe for studies relating to British philosophical systems *see* AGw

AGwg-qǿ

HERRMANN, Otto. The monism of the German Monistic League. *Monist*, 1913, 23: 543-66.

AGwn

WETTER, Gustav A. Dialectical materialism: a historical and systematic survey of philosophy in the Soviet Union. Transl. from the German [1952 ed.] by Peter Heath. xii, 609 p. London: Routledge, Kegan Paul, 1958; New York: Frederick A. Praeger, 1959. [CB 85/466]

AH METAPHYSICS

for relations of physics and metaphysics *see* Ck
relations of science and metaphysics *see* AmzAH

ALEXANDER, Hartley Burr. Nature and human nature. Essays metaphysical and historical. xi, 529 p. Chicago: Open Court, 1923. [CB 15/234]

ARBER, Agnes. The manifold and the one. xiii, 146 p. London: John Murray, 1957.
Reviewed by W.R. Matthews, *Nature*, 1958, 182: 681-2.

BERGMANN, Gustav. Meaning and existence. xi, 274 p. Madison: The University of Wisconsin Press, 1960.
Reviewed by M. Przelecki, *Brit.J.Phil.Sci.*, 1962, 13: 87.

CHEVALIER, Jacques. L'habitude. Essai de métaphysique scientifique. xviii, 256 p. Paris: Boivin, 1929. [CB 30/487]

DURAND-DOAT, Jacques. Essai sur l'étendue. 170 p. Paris: J. Vrin, 1928. [CB 27/574]

DURAND-DOAT, Jacques. Le sens de la métaphysique. 132 p. Paris: J. Vrin, 1928. [CB 27/574]

GLANSDORFF, Maxime. La vérité et le sentiment. *Synthèses*, 1949, 4: no. 2, 15 p.

HAGSTROEM, K.G. Bilderna av en okänd verklighet. [Images of an unknown reality. (In Swedish)] 159 p., front., fig. Stockholm: Fritzes K. Hovbokhandel, 1935. [CB 79/190]

HELLMUND, Heinrich. Das Wesen der Welt. 1323 p. Zürich: Amalthea-Verlag, 1927. [CB 25/410]

HÖFFDING, Harald. Les conceptions de la vie. Trad. de l'allemand par A. Koyré. 172 p. Paris: Alcan, 1928. [CB 27/574]

MACLEOD, Andries H.D. Sur diverses questions se présentant dans l'étude du concept de réalité. xi, 239 p. Paris: J. Hermann, 1927. [CB 22/255]

PETRONIEVICS, Branislav. Hauptsätze der Metaphysik. 74 p., 14 fig. (Beiträge zur Philosophie, 17) Heidelberg: Winter, 1930. [CB 30/488]

SANTAYANA, George. Realms of being. xxxii, 862 p. New York: Scribners, 1942. [CB 63/278]

TOULMIN, Stephen. Contemporary scientific mythology. In: Metaphysical beliefs, three essays, by S. Toulmin, Ronald W. Hepburn, and Alasdair MacIntyre, p. 1-83. London: SCM Press, 1957. [CB 83/190]

TSANOFF, Radoslav A. Worlds to know. A philosophy of cosmic perspectives. 230 p. New York: Humanities Press, 1962.
English edition entitled: Science and human perspectives. London: Routledge and Kegan Paul, 1963; reviewed in *Times Lit.Suppl.*, June 7, 1963, 409.

URTIN, Henri. Vers une science du réel. vii, 124 p. Paris: Alcan, 1930. [CB 32/575]

WUNDT, Max. Geschichte der Metaphysik. 123 p. (Geschichte der Philosophie in Längsschnitten, 2) Berlin: Junker u. Dünnhaupt, 1931.

AHmh

DEMPF, Alois. Das Unendliche in der mittelalterlichen Metaphysik und in der Kantischen Dialektik. viii, 91 p. (*Veröffentlichungen des katholischen Instituts für Philosophie*, 2: no. 1) Münster i. W.: Aschendorff, 1926.

AJ PHILOSOPHY OF VALUES

for the relation of science and aesthetics *see* Atp
the relation of science and ethics *see* Atc
aesthetic and ethical aspects of the separate sciences *see* INDEX
professional ethics *see* INDEX

BARUZI, Jean. Le problème moral. viii, 204 p. (Philosophes et Savants Français du XXe Siècle. Extraits et Notices, 3) Paris: Alcan, 1926. [CB 22/212]

BERGSON, Henri. Les deux sources de la morale et de la religion. 348 p. Paris: Alcan, 1932.
Reviewed by L.G., *Isis*, 1933, 19: 240.

CRESSON, André. Le problème moral et les philosophes. 204 p. Paris: Colin, 1933. [CB 39/466]

DUPRÉEL, Eugène. Esquisse d'une philosophie des valeurs. viii, 304 p. Paris: Alcan, 1939. [CB 59/486]

EBY, Louise Saxe. The quest for moral law. 284 p. New York: Columbia University Press, 1944. [CB 69/60]

HOBHOUSE, L.T. Morals in evolution. 7th ed. liv, 648 p. With an introd. by Morris Ginsberg. London: Chapman & Hall; New York: Macmillan, 1951. [CB 78/197]
First published 1906.

LANGER, Susanne K. Philosophy in a new key. A study in the symbolism of reason, rite and art. 312 p. Cambridge: Harvard University Press, 1942.
Reviewed by Milton H. Singer, *Isis*, 1943, 34: 529-30.

LEAKE, Chauncey D. Ethicogenesis. *Proc.Phil.Soc.Tex.*, 1945, 7-34. [CB 69/236]

LEDENT, Adrien. Histoire des doctrines morales. 84 p., bibliogr. (Collection Lebègue, 6me série, no. 67) Bruxelles: Office de Publicité, 1945. [CB 69/236]

MEAD, George Herbert. The philosophy of the act. Ed. with introduction by Charles W. Morris [*et al.*]. lxxix, 696 p. Chicago: University of Chicago Press, 1938.
Reviewed by R.K. Merton, *Isis*, 1940, 31: 482-3.

MITCHELL, E.T. A system of ethics. xviii, 559 p. New York: Scribner, 1950. [CB 77/382]
Meliorism. The second part of the volume considers the historical background of alternative theories of ethics.

MORRIS, Bertram. The aesthetic process. ix, 189 p. Evanston: Northwestern University, 1943. [CB 69/236]

MUNITZ, Milton Karl. The moral philosophy of Santayana. vii, 116 p. New York: Columbia University Press, 1939. [CB 59/445]

ROBERTSON, John Mackinnon. A short history of morals. vii, 460 p. London: Watts, 1920.

SIDGWICK, Henry. Outlines of the history of ethics: for English readers. With an additional chapter by Alban G. Widgery. 6th ed. xxvi, 342 p. London: Macmillan, 1931.
First published 1886.

SOURIAU, Michel. La fonction pratique de la finalité. (*Thèse*, Paris). 264 p. (Bibliothèque de Philosophie Contemporaine) Paris: Alcan, 1925. [CB 23/264]

STERN, Alfred. La philosophie des valeurs. *Thalès*, 1936, 3: 136-40.

STERN, Alfred. La philosophie des valeurs. Regard ... *See* AJwg

WENTSCHER, Max. Geschichte der Ethik. vi, 113 p. (Geschichte der Philosophie in Längsschnitten, 3) Berlin: Junker und Dünnhaupt, 1931.

AJj

FROMM, Erich. Man for himself, an inquiry into the psychology of ethics. xiv, 254 p. New York: Rinehart, 1947; London: Routledge & Kegan Paul, [1949].
Reviewed by Ruth Nanda Anshen, *Phil.Rev.*, 1948, 57: 518-23.

PARODI, Daniel. Les bases psychologiques de la vie morale. viii, 160 p. Paris: Alcan, 1928. [CB 27/573]

AJke

ROTH, Léon. The science of morals. An essay in method. 141 p. London: Benn, 1928. [CB 24/555]

AJkk

GOBLOT, Edmond. *See* AKke

TOULMIN, S.E. An examination of the place of reason in ethics. xiv, 228 p. Cambridge University Press, 1950.
Reviewed by A.D. Ritchie, *Nature*, 1951, 167: 872.

AJmzMC

NORDAU, Max Simon. Morals and the evolution of man. Transl. by Marie A. Lewenz. 278 p. London: Cassell; New York: Funk and Wagnalls, 1922.
German original, Biologie der Ethik, first published Leipzig: 1921; French translation Paris: Alcan, 1930.

AJs

HOLMES, Samuel Jackson. Life and morals. x, 232 p. New York: Macmillan, 1948. [CB 74/395]

SARTON, George. Transparency. *Scribner's Mag.*, March 1925, 308-13.

AJsc

SCHWEITZER, Albert. The philosophy of civilization. 1. The decay and the restoration of civilization. 2. Civilization and ethics. xvii, 347 p. New York: Macmillan, 1949.
Reviewed by Sydney W. Jackman, *Isis*, 1950, 41: 250.

AJwg

STERN, Alfred. La philosophie des valeurs. Regard sur ses tendances actuelles en Allemagne. 74, 62 p. (Actualités Scientifiques et Industrielles, 367-8. Exposés d'Histoire et Philosophie des Sciences, 4 et 5) Paris: Hermann, 1936.

AK LOGIC

for the logic of science *see* Akk
logical aspects of the separate sciences *see* INDEX
symbolic logic *see* Bkk

AKc general history

BACHELARD, Suzanne. La logique de Husserl. Étude sur "Logique formelle et logique transcendentale". 316 p. Collection 'Epithémée, Essais Philosophiques'. Paris: Presses Universitaires de France, 1957.
Reviewed by J. Defever, S.J., *Rev.Quest.Sci.*, 1958, 19: 480.

BETH, Evert W. Geschiedenis der logica. [History of logic. (In Dutch)] 96 p. (Encyclopaedia in Monografieën, Afdeling Logica, 37) Den Haag: N.V. Servire, 1944.

BOLL, Marcel; REINHART, Jacques. Les étapes de la logique. 127 p. (Que sais-je? 225) Paris: 1948.

CARNAP, Rudolf. L'ancienne et la nouvelle logique. Trad. de l'allemand par Ernest Vouillemin, revue et mise à jour par l'auteur. 38 p. (Actualités Scientifiques et Industrielles, 76) Paris: Hermann, 1933. [CB 51/250]
Translation of "Die alte und die neue Logik". *Erkenntnis*, 1930, 1: 12-26.

CLARK, Joseph T. Conventional logic and modern logic. A prelude to transition. With a preface by W.V. Quine. vii, i, 109 p. (Philosophical Studies of the American Philosophical Association, vol. 3) Woodstock, Md.: Woodstock College Press, 1952. [CB 79/169]
Reviewed by William W. Boone, *Isis*, 1955, 46: 57.

COHEN, Morris R. A preface to logic. ix, 212 p. New York: Holt, 1944; London: Routledge, 1946.
Reviewed in *Times Lit.Suppl.*, August 31, 1946, 409-10.

D'ERCOLE, Pasquale. La logica aristotelica, la logica kantiana ed hegeliana e la logica matematica con accenno alla logica indiana. *Mem.Accad.Sci.Torino, 2nd ser.*, 1912, 62: 101-211.

DE RUGGIERO, Guido. Il problema della deduzione delle categorie. *Atti IV° Congr.Int.Fil.* (Bologna, 1911), (2), p. 331-6. Genoa: 1913.

ENRIQUES, Federigo. Per la storia della logica: i principii e l'ordine della scienza nel concetto dei pensatori matematici. 302 p. Bologna: Nicola Zanichelli, 1922.
Reviewed by H.M. Sheffer, *Isis*, 1923, 5: 469-70.
French translation Paris: Etienne Chiron, 1926; German translation Leipzig: Teubner, 1927.

GILLOT, Frédéric. Éléments de logique appliquée d'après Wronski, Jevons, Solvay. 195 p. Paris: Albert Blanchard, 1964.

GOBLOT, Edmond. Traité de logique. Préface de M. Emile Boutroux. xxiii, 412 p. Paris: Colin, 1918.
Reviewed by G. Sarton, *Isis*, 1920, 3: 306-7.

JØRGENSEN, Jørgen. A treatise of formal logic: its evolution and main branches, with its relations to mathematics and philosophy. 3 vol. xv, 266 p.; iv, 273 p.; iv, 321 p. Copenhagen: Levin and Munksgaard, 1931.
Reviewed by Thomas Greenwood, *Nature*, 1931, 128: 1021-3.

KLEINPETER, Hans. Die alte und die neue Logik. Ein Blick auf den gegenwärtigen wissenschaftlichen Zustand der Logik. *Z. Positivistische Phil.*, 1913, 1: 157-71.

KNEALE, William; KNEALE, Martha. The development of logic. 761 p., bibliogr. London: Oxford University Press, 1962.

LASBAX, Emile. La dialectique et le rythme de l'univers. viii, 428 p. Paris: J. Vrin, 1925. [CB 19/798]

PRANTL, Carl von. Geschichte der Logik im Abendlande. Manuldruck der Orig.-Ausgabe, 1855. 4 vol. Leipzig: Gustav Fock, 1927.
First published Leipzig: 1855-1870.

QUINE, Willard van Orman. From a logical point of view. Logico-philosophical essays. vi, 184 p. Cambridge, Mass.: Harvard University Press, 1953.

QUINE, Willard van Orman. Whitehead and the rise of modern logic. In: Schilpp, P.A., ed. The philosophy of Alfred North Whitehead, p. 127-63. (The Library of Living Philosophers, 3) Chicago: Northwestern University, 1941.

SCHOLZ, Heinrich. Concise history of logic. Transl. by Kurt F. Leidecker. xiv, 140 p. New York: Philosophical Library, 1961.
Translation of "Geschichte der Logik", *see* below.
Reviewed by Nicholas Rescher, *Isis*, 1962, 53: 515-16; by Trevor Evans, *Amer.Math.Mon.*, 1963, 70: 106.

SCHOLZ, Heinrich. Geschichte der Logik. vii, 78 p. (Geschichte der Philosophie in Längsschnitten, 4) Berlin: Junker und Dünnhaupt, 1931.
2nd edition [unaltered] 1959, has title "Abriss der Geschichte der Logik".

STEBBING, L. Susan. A modern introduction to logic. xiii, 525 p. New York: Harper & Brothers, 1961.

VACCARINO, G. L'origine della logica. *Scientia*, 1961, 96: 103-9.

VIRIEUX-REYMOND, Antoinette. La logique et l'épistémologie des Stoiciens, leurs rapports avec la logique d'Aristote, la logistique et la pensée contemporaines. vi, 331 p. Chambéry: Lire, 1949.
Reviewed by Benson Mates, *Isis*, 1950, 41: 316.

VON WRIGHT, George Henrik. Logical studies. ix, 195 p. (International Library of Psychology, Philosophy, and Scientific Method) London: Routledge and Kegan Paul, Ltd., 1957.
Reviewed by F.I.G. Rawlins, *Nature*, 1958, 181: 981.

WOLF, Abraham. Textbook of logic. 2nd ed., rev. and enl. 445 p. London: Allen and Unwin, 1948; New York: Macmillan, 1949. [CB 76/393]

ZAWIRSKI, Zygmunt. Les logiques nouvelles et le champ de leur application. *Rev.Métaphys.Morale*, 1932, 39: 503-19. [CB 20/591]

AKc-be

ENCYKLOPAEDIE der philosophischen Wissenschaften. In Verbindung mit Wilhelm Windelband, hrsg. von Arnold Ruge. Vol. 1. Logik. 2 parts. viii, 275 p. Tübingen: J.C.B. Mohr, 1912.
No further volumes published.

AKce-bv

CHURCH, Alonzo. Brief bibliography of formal logic. *Proc. Amer.Acad.Arts Sci.*, 1952, 80: 155-72.

AKk methodology

AKke

CATON, Charles E. A stipulation of logical truth in a modal propositional calculus. *Synthese*, 1962, 14: 196-9.

COUTURAT, Louis. Logistique et intuition. *Rev.Métaphys. Morale*, 1913, 21: 260-8.

CRAWSHAY-WILLIAMS, Rupert. Methods and criteria of reasoning. An inquiry into the structure of controversy. viii, 296 p. (International Library of Psychology, Philosophy, and Scientific Method) London: Routledge and Kegan Paul, Ltd., 1957.
Reviewed by C.K. Grant, *Nature*, 1958, 181: 869-70.

DEWEY, John. Essays in experimental logic. 444 p. New York: Dover Publications, 1953.
Reprint of 1st edition, Chicago: University of Chicago Press, 1916.

GOBLOT, Edmond. La logique des jugements de valeur; théorie et applications. ii, 209 p. Paris: A Colin, 1927. [CB 24/523]

HUNTINGTON, Edward V. The duplicity of logic. *Scr.Math.*, 1938, 5: 149-57, 233-8.

JONES, E.E. Constance. A new "law" of thought and its logical implications. *Atti IV° Congr.Int.Fil.* (Bologna, 1911), (2), p. 440-3. Genoa: 1913.

KEMENY, John G. Analyticity versus fuzziness. *Synthese*, 1963, 15: 57-80.

MARTIN, R.M. Toward a logic of intentions. *Synthese*, 1963, 15: 81-102.

POPPER, K.R. Functional logic without axioms or primitive rules of inference. *Proc.Ned.Akad.Wetensch.Sect.Sci.*, 1947, 50: 1214-24.

QUINE, Willard van Orman. Methods of logic. xx, 264 p. New York: Henry Holt, 1950.
Reviewed by A.H. Copeland, *Scr.Math.*, 1953, 19: 62-3.

REYMOND, Arnold. Les principes de la logique et la critique contemporaine. New ed. xii, 280 p. Paris: Vrin, 1957.
First publ. Paris: Boivin, 1932. [CB 39/446]
Reviewed by S. Colnort-Bodet, *Rev.Syn.*, 1958, 79: 161-2.

SCHILLER, F.C.S. Formal logic. A scientific and social problem. xviii, 423 p. London: Macmillan, 1912.

SEALL, Robert E. Truth-valued fluents and qualitative laws. *Phil.Sci.*, 1963, 30: 36-40

SILVERMAN, Sanford L.; SILVERMAN, Martin G. Theory of relationships. xv, 111 p., fig. New York: Philosophical Library, 1963.

SMITH, Henry Bradford. Abstract logic or the science of modality. *Phil.Sci.*, 1934, 1: 369-97.

TATARKIEWICZ, Krzysztof. Modèles et systèmes deductifs. *Dialectica*, 1962, 16: 275-98.

TOULMIN, Stephen Edelston. The uses of argument. vii, 261 p. Cambridge University Press, 1958.
Reviewed by J.O. Urmson, *Nature*, 1958, 182: 212-13.

WHITEHEAD, Alfred North. The function of reason. (Louis Clark Vanuxem Foundation lectures delivered at Princeton University, March 1929) v, 72 p. Princeton, N.J.: Princeton University Press, 1929.
Reprinted, Boston: Beacon Press, 1958.

AKkk

DEWEY, John. Logic, the theory of inquiry. ix, 546 p. New York: Holt, 1938. [CB 57/236]

JEPSON, Rowland Walter. Clear thinking. New ed. ix, 250 p. New York: Longmans, Green, 1948.
First printed 1936.

MAILLY, Ernst. Gegenstandstheoretische Grundlagen der Logik und Logistik. 87 p. Leipzig: Barth, 1912.

STAMMLER, Gerhard. Begriff, Urteil, Schluss; Untersuchungen über Grundlagen und Aufbau der Logik. xii, 331 p. Halle: Berlag W. Niemeyer, 1928.
Reviewed by W. Dubislav, *Arch.Gesch.Math.Naturwiss.Tech.*, 1929, 11: 331.

AKkn

FLEW, Anthony, ed. Essays on logic and language. vii, 206 p. New York: Philosophical Library, 1951. [CB 78/181]
Reviewed by Joseph T. Clark, *Mod.Schoolman*, 1951-52, 29: 65-70.

PROT, Marcel. Langage et logique. Vers une logique nouvelle. 121 p. Paris: Hermann, 1949.

AKmz

JOURDAIN, Philip E.B. Mathematicians and philosophers. *Monist*, 1915, 25: 633-8. [CB 8/363]
A contrast between the attitudes of mathematicians and philosophers towards logic.

AKz special topics

HEMPEL, Karl. Studies in the logic of confirmation. *Mind*, 1945, *new ser.*, 54: 1-26, 97-121.

KOYRÉ, Alexandre. The liar. *Phil.Phenomenol.Res.*, 1946, 6: 344-62.
Epimenides' saying "All Cretans are liars" rediscussed in the light of Bertrand Russel, Carnap, Tarski, Husserl, etc.

NAGEL, Ernest. "Impossible numbers": a chapter in the history of modern logic. In: Studies in the history of ideas, (3), p. 429-74. New York: Columbia University Press, 1935.

MORGENBERGER, Sidney. Goodman on the ravens. *J.Phil.*, 1962, 59: 493-5.
Apropos of Nelson Goodman's discussion in Fact, fiction and forecast (*see* Akd) of Karl Hempel's paradox in Studies in the logic of confirmation (*see* above).

B MATHEMATICS

Bc general history

Bc-bm *large scale works*

AMERICAN MATHEMATICAL SOCIETY. Semicentennial addresses of the American Mathematical Society. 315 p. (Semicentennial publications, 2) New York: The Society, 1938.
Reviewed by T.A.A. Broadbent, *Math.Gaz.*, 1939, 23: 237-8; by Mina Rees, *Scr.Math.*, 1940, 7: 121-5.

ARCHIBALD, Raymond Clare. Outline of the history of mathematics. 6th ed. 114 p. (Herbert Ellsworth Slaught Memorial Papers, 2) [Menasha, Wis.: Mathematical Association of America], 1949.
First publ. 1932. [CB 36/434 and CB 62/73]. Issued as supplement to *Amer.Math.Mon.*, 1949, 56: no. 1.
Reviewed by George Sarton, *Isis*, 1949, 40: 289-90.

BALL, W. W. Rouse. A short account of the history of mathematics. xxiv, 522 p. New York: Dover, 1960.
Paperback reprint of 4th edition (1908); first publ. 1888; for annotation to 5th ed. (1912) *see* CB 3/561; for details of French and Italian translations *see* CB 3/561 and CB 24/523.
Reviewed by Albert Lejeune, *Rev.Quest.Sci.*, 1961, 22: 558-9.

BECKER, Oskar; HOFMANN, Josef E. Geschichte der Mathematik. 340 p. (Geschichte der Wissenschaften; II. Naturwissenschaften) Bonn: Athenäum-Verlag, 1951.
Reviewed by D.J. Struik, *Isis*, 1952, 43: 290-1; for other reviews *see* CB 80/122 and CB 81/265; French translation (Paris: Lamarre, 1956) reviewed by René Taton, *Rev.Hist. Sci.*, 1958, 11: 361.

BELL, Eric Temple. The development of mathematics. xiii, 583 p. New York: McGraw-Hill, 1940.
Reviewed by I. Bernard Cohen, *Isis*, 1941, 33: 291-3.

BELL, Eric Temple. The handmaiden of the sciences. viii, 216 p. New York: Reynal and Hitchcock, 1937.
Reviewed by Leo Nedelsky, *Scr.Math.*, 1938, 5: 195-8.

BELL, Eric Temple. Mathematics, queen and servant of science. xii, 437 p. New York: McGraw-Hill, 1951. [CB 78/181]
Reviewed by René Taton, *Arch.Int.Hist.Sci.*, 1951, 30: 1014-15.

BELL, Eric Temple. The queen of the sciences. iv, 138 p. (A Century of Progress Series) Baltimore: Williams and Wilkins, 1931.

BENSE, Max. Konturen einer Geistesgeschichte der Mathematik. 2 vol. 144 p.; 214 p., ill. Hamburg: Verlag Claassen & Goverts, 1946, 1949.
Reviewed by J.E. Hofmann, *Centaurus*, 1950, 1: 181-2.

BOURBAKI, Nicolas. Éléments d'histoire des mathématiques. 276 p. (Histoire de la Pensée, 4) Paris: Hermann, 1960.
For reviews *see* CB 87/561, CB 88/538 and CB 90/513.

BOYER, Jacques. Sûgaku-shi. [Japanese translation by Tsuruichi Hayashi of "Histoire des mathématiques", Paris: 1900] x, 230 p., 46 portr., facs. 6th rev. ed. Tokyo: Okura, 1930.
Reviewed by Shio Sakanishi and George Sarton, *Isis*, 1937, 27: 526.

CAJORI, Florian. A history of elementary mathematics with hints on methods of teaching. 2nd ed. viii, 324 p. New York: Macmillan, 1917.
First published 1897. Illustrated Japanese translation published 1928 (Tokyo: Sank do) [CB 25/412]

CAJORI, Florian. A history of mathematics. x, 514 p. 2nd ed. New York: Macmillan, 1919. [CB 8/362]

CALLANDREAU, Edouard. Célèbres problèmes mathématiques. 478 p. Paris: Editions Albin Michel, 1949.

CANDIDO, Giacomo. Scritti matematici (con cenno biografico di R. D'Ambrosio e ritratto), raccolti e ordinati per incarico del figlio Francesco dai Proff. Enea Bortolotti ed Enrico Nannei. (Edizione fuori commercio) xv, 802 p., front. Firenze: Marzocco, 1948. [CB 74/374]
The ninth section (p. 585-788) includes nineteen articles concerning the history of mathematics.

CARRUCCIO, Ettore. Corso di storia delle matematiche presso la Facoltà di Science dell' Università di Torino. Matematica e logica nella storia e nel pensiero contemporaneo. 578 p. Torino: Gheroni, 1951.
Reviewed by A. Natucci, *Arch.Int.Hist.Sci.*, 1952, 5: 390-1.

CASSINA, Ugo. Dalla geometria egiziana alla matematica moderna. vi, 537 p. Rome: Edizioni Cremonese, 1961.
Seventeen articles on the history of mathematics.
Reviewed by A. Gloden, *Scr.Math.*, 1961, 26: 361; by H. Freudenthal, *Math.Rev.*, 1963, 25: 2941; by René Taton, *Rev.Hist.Sci.*, 1964, 17: 64-5.

DAVIS, Harold T. A course in general mathematics. xi, 316 p., 3 fig. Bloomington, Indiana: Principia Press, 1935. [CB 46/587]
Contains many historical notes.

DEDRON, Pierre; ITARD, Jean. Mathématiques et mathématiciens. 443 p. (Collection Sciences et Savants) Paris: Magnard, 1959.
For reviews *see* CB 86/460 and CB 87/561.

DÖRRIE, Heinrich. Triumph der Mathematik. Hundert berühmte Probleme aus zwei Jahrtausenden mathematischer Kultur. 2nd rev. ed. vii, 391 p., 112 fig. Breslau: Hirt, 1940.
First publ. 1933.
Reviewed by Zaunick, *Mitt.Gesch.Med.*, 1940, 39: 314.

DZIOBEK, Otto. Mathematical theories. Transl. by Mark W. Harrington and William J. Hussey. vi, 294 p. New York: Dover Publications, 1962.
An unabridged and corrected re-issue of a work first published in 1892.

ENCYCLOPÄDIE der mathematischen Wissenschaften mit Einschluss ihrer Anwendungen. Hrsg. im Auftrage der Akademien der Wissenschaften zu Göttingen, Leipzig, München und Wien. 6 vol. in 23. Leipzig: Teubner, 1898-1935.
2nd ed. 1939- For French translation *see* below.

ENCYCLOPÉDIE des sciences mathématiques pures et appliquées publiée sous les auspices des Académies des Sciences de Göttingen, de Leipzig, de Munich, et de Vienne, avec la collaboration de nombreux savants. Edition française d'après l'édition allemande. 5 vol. in 18. Paris: Gauthier-Villars, 1904- [CB 13/292]
Not completed.
Reviewed by G. Sarton, *Isis*, 1913, 1: 256-7; 1921, 4: 39-40.

ENRIQUES, Federigo. Le matematiche nella storia e nella cultura. Lezioni pubblicate per cura di Attilo Frajese. ii, 339 p., 22 pl. Bologna: Zanichelli, 1938.
Reviewed by C. Doris Hellman, *Isis*, 1939, 31: 108-9.

EVES, Howard. An introduction to the history of mathematics. xv, 422 p. New York: Rinehart & Co., Inc., 1953. [CB 81/265]
Rev. ed. 1964.
Reviewed by Carolyn Eisele, *Scr.Math.*, 1955, 21: 59-62.

FRAJESE, Attilio. Attraverso la storia della matematica. 212 p., 24 ill. Roma: Pioda, 1949.
Reviewed by A. Natucci, *Arch.Int.Hist.Sci.*, 1951, 4: 761-2.

FREEBURY, H.A. A history of mathematics. 198 p. New York: Macmillan, 1961.
First publ. under the title "A history of mathematics for secondary schools" (London: Cassell & Co., 1958).
Reviewed by Oystein Ore, *Amer.Math.Mon.*, 1962, 69: 819-20.

GIORGI, Giovanni. Compendio di storia delle matematiche. viii, 140 p. Turin: Società Editrice Internazionale, 1948. [CB 74/385]

HOFMANN, Joseph Ehrenfried. Classical mathematics: a concise history of the classical era in mathematics. 165 p. New York: Philosophical Library, 1959.
Translation of volumes 2 and 3 of "Geschichte der Mathematik", *see* below.

HOFMANN, Joseph Ehrenfried. Geschichte der Mathematik. 3 vol. 1. Von den Anfängen bis zum Auftreten von Fermat und Descartes. 200 p.; 2. Von Fermat und Descartes bis zur Erfindung des Calculus und bis zum Ausbau der neuen Methoden. 109 p.; 3. Von den Auseinandersetzungen um den Calculus bis zur französischen Revolution. 107 p. (Sammlung Göschen, 226, 875, 882). Berlin: Walter de Gruyter, 1953, 1957.
2nd edition of volume 1, Berlin: De Gruyter, 1963.
Reviewed by Carl B. Boyer, *Isis*, 1955, 46: 57-9; 1958, 49: 350-2; for other reviews *see* CB 82/202.

HOFMANN, Joseph Ehrenfried. The history of mathematics. Translated by F. Gaynor and H.O. Midonick. 132 p. New York: Philosophical Library, 1957. [CB 83/196]
Translation of volume 1 of "Geschichte der Mathematik", *see* above.
Reviewed by Robert T. Beyer, *Phys.Today*, 1957, 10: 38.

HOGBEN, Lancelot. Mathematics for the million. xii, 647 p. New York: Norton, 1937.
Reviewed by M.F. Ashley-Montagu and by H.T. Davis, *Isis*, 1938, 28: 138-40.
Danish translation (København: Gyldendal, 1938) reviewed by O. Neugebauer, *Mat.Tidsskr.*A, 1938, no. 2-3, 50-7.

HOGBEN, Lancelot. Mathematics in the making. 320 p., ill. Garden City, N.Y.: Doubleday, 1960.
Reviewed by Carl B. Boyer, *Science*, 1962, 135: 522; by S.A. Jayawardene, *Scr.Math.*, 1964, 27: 162-3.

KLEIN, Felix. Elementarmathematik vom höheren Standpunkte aus. 3rd ed. 3 vol. 1. Arithmetik, Algebra, Analysis; 2. Geometrie; 3. Präzisions- und Approximationmathematik. Berlin: Springer, 1924-28.
Contains many historical notes.

KLINE, Morris. Mathematics in Western culture. 484 p., 27 pl., diagr. New York/London: Oxford University Press, 1953.
Publ. in paperback 1964.
Reviewed by Carl B. Boyer, *Isis*, 1954, 45: 385-7.

KOFLER, Edward. Z dziejów matematyki. [From the history of mathematics. (In Polish)]. 339 p., ill. Warsaw: Wiedza Powszechna, 1962.

KRAMER, Edna E. The main stream of mathematics. xii, 321 p. New York: Oxford University Press, 1951.
Reviewed by Ernest Nagel, *Science*, 1951, 113: 445; by Phillip S. Jones, *Scr.Math.*, 1953, 19: 151-4.

LEBESGUE, Henri. Notices d'histoire des mathématiques. 116 p. (Monographies de l'Enseignement Mathématique, 4) Genève: Institut de Mathématiques, Université de Genève, 1958. [CB 85/387]
Reviewed by A. Natucci, *Scientia*, 1959, 94: 267; by Kurt Vogel, *Sudhoffs Arch.*, 1959, 43: 376-7; by H.J. Heyman, *Lychnos*, 1959, 55; by J.E. Hofmann, *Arch.Int.Hist.Sci.*, 1959, 12: 311-12.

LECAT, Maurice. Erreurs de mathématiciens des origines à nos jours. xii, 167 p. Brussels and Louvain: 1935. [CB 44/515]

LE LIONNAIS, François, ed. Les grands courants de la pensée mathématique. 2nd ed. 559 p. (L'humanisme scientifique de demain) Paris: Albert Blanchard, 1962.
Reviewed by Carl Boyer, *Isis*, 1963, 54: 490-2.
First publ. Marseille: Cahiers du Sud, 1948 and reviewed by J. Pelseneer, *Isis*, 1949, 40: 78-9; by F. Russo, *Rev. Quest.Sci.*, 1948, 9: 434-6.

LIETZMANN, Walther. Lustiges und Merkwürdiges von Zahlen und Formen. 4th ed. vi, 307 p. Breslau: Hirt, 1930.
First publ. 1922.
Reviewed by David Eugene Smith, *Amer.Math.Mon.*, 1931, 38: 224-5.

LORIA, Gino. Scritti, conferenze, discorsi sulla storia delle matematiche, raccolti per iniziativa e pubblicati sotto gli auspici della Sezione Ligure della Società "Mathesis". xv, 589 p. Padua: Milani, 1937.
Reviewed by C. Doris Hellman, *Isis*, 1937, 27: 522-4.

LORIA, Gino. Storia delle matematiche. 3 vol. 1. Antichità, medio evo, rinascimento. 497 p.; 2. I secoli XVI e XVII. 595 p.; 3. Dall' alba del secolo XVIII al tramonto del secolo XIX. 607 p. Torino: Sten, 1929, 1931, 1933. [CB 26/228 and CB 41/598]
Vol. 2 reviewed by R.C. Archibald, *Isis*, 1933, 19: 231.

LORIA, Gino. Storia delle matematiche dall' alba della civiltà al secolo XIX. 2nd ed. xxv, 975 p., 80 fig. Milano: Hoepli, 1950.
Reviewed by George Sarton, *Isis*, 1951, 42: 63.

MALSCH, Fritz. Geschichte der Mathematik. 115 p., 40 fig. in text, 15 pl. (Wissenschaft und Bildung, 242) Leipzig: Quelle and Meyer, 1928.
Reviewed by Edmund Hoppe, *Deut.Lit.Zeitung*, 1928, 484-6.

MONTAGUE, Harriett Frances; MONTGOMERY, Mabel D. The significance of mathematics. xi, 290 p., ill. Columbus, Ohio: C.E. Merrill, 1963.
Seven out of fourteen chapters are historical.

MONTUCLA, J.F. Histoire des mathématiques. 4 vol. Nouveau tirage augmenté d'un Avant-Propos par M. Ch. Naux. xii, 739 p., pl.; 718 p., pl.; viii, 832 p., pl.; 688 p., pl. Paris: Librairie Scientifique et Technique Albert Blanchard, 1960.
Reprint of 2nd edition 1799-1803.
Reviewed by C.J. Scriba, *Math.Rev.*, 1962, 23: 269, A1485.

MORITZ, Robert Edouard. On mathematics and mathematicians. (Formerly titled: Memorabilia Mathematica or the Philomath's Quotation Book.) vii, 410 p. New York: Dover Publications, Inc., 1958.
For reviews *see* CB 85/387, CB 86/460 and CB 87/562.
Originally publ. by Macmillan, 1914.

MÜLLER, Félix. Gedenktagebuch für Mathematiker. 3rd ed. iv, 121 p. Leipzig: Teubner, 1912.

NATUCCI, Alpinolo. Sviluppo storico dell'aritmetica generale e dell'algebra. 368 p., 10 fig., bibliogr. Napoli: Edizioni Del Gaudio, 1955.
Reviewed by A. Gloden, *Arch.Int.Hist.Sci.*, 1955, 8: 388-90 and *Rev.Hist.Sci.*, 1956, 9: 271-3; in *Scientia*, 1956, 91: 107-8.

OCAGNE, Maurice d'. Histoire abrégée des sciences mathématiques. Ouvrage receuilli et achevé par René Dugas. 400 p. Paris: Edit. Vuibert, 1955.
Reviewed by Pierre Costabel, *Arch.Int.Hist.Sci.*, 1955, 8: 387-8; by K.-C. Hagstroem, *Lychnos*, 1956, 384-5.

OGURA, Kinnosuke. Sûgaku-shi kenkyû. [Studies in the history of mathematics. Series 1. (In Japanese)]. 10, 340 p., ill. Tokyo: Iwanami shoten, 1935.
Reviewed by Shio Sakanishi, *Isis*, 1937, 26: 481-2.

PELSENEER, Jean. Esquisse du progrès de la pensée mathématique. Des primitifs au IXe Congrès International des Mathématiciens. 160 p. Paris: Hermann, 1935. [CB 43/269]

QUENEAU, Raymond. Bords: mathématiciencs, précurseurs, encyclopédistes. 137 p., ill. Paris: Hermann, 1963.

RAPPORT, Samuel; WRIGHT, Helen; ed. Mathematics. xii, 319 p., fig. New York: New York University Press, 1963. [CB 89/498]
A collection of essays on the history and nature of mathematics.

REID, Constance. A long way from Euclid. ix, 292 p., diagr. New York: T.Y. Crowell, 1963.

REY PASTOR, Julio; BABINI, José. Historia de la matemática. xx, 368 p. Buenos Aires: Espasa-Calpe, 1951. [CB 79/171]

RICHARDSON, Moses. Fundamentals of mathematics. xx, 525 p., 254 fig. New York: The Macmillan Co., 1941. [CB 63/271]
This book contains pictures of great mathematicians and accounts of their lives, as well as notes on the historical evolution of some mathematical ideas.

RYBNIKOV, K.A. Istoriia matematiki. [History of mathematics. (In Russian)]. 190 p. Moscow: Izdatel'stvo Moskovskogo Universiteta, 1960.
Reviewed by E.S. Kennedy, *Scr.Math.*, 1961, 26: 363-5; by L. Lombardo-Radice, *Math.Rev.*, 1962, 23: 692, A3621.

SANFORD, Vera. A short history of mathematics. Under the editorship of John Wesley Young. With an introduction by David Eugene Smith. xii, 412 p., ill., maps, tables. Boston: Houghton Mifflin, 1930. [CB 29/293]

SCOTT, J.R. A history of mathematics. From antiquity to the beginning of the nineteenth century. xiv, 268 p., 6 pl. London: Taylor and Francis Ltd., 1958.
2nd rev. ed. 1960.
Reviewed by Phillip S. Jones, *Isis*, 1960, 51: 224-5; for other reviews *see* CB 84/308 and CB 85/388.

SCRIPTA MATHEMATICA Forum Lectures: addresses by Cassius Jackson Keyser, David Eugene Smith, Edward Kasner, and Walter Rautenstrauch. iii, 94 p. (The Scripta Mathematica Library, 3) New York: Yeshiva College, 1937.
Reviewed by J.M. Feld, *Scr.Math.*, 1939, 6: 43-6.

SMITH, David Eugene. History of mathematics. 2 vol. 1. General survey of the history of elementary mathematics. xxii, 596 p.; 2. Special topics of elementary mathematics. xii, 725 p., ill., bibliogr. New York: Dover Publications, Inc., 1958.
First publ. Boston: Ginn, 1923, 1928 and reviewed by G. Sarton, *Isis*, 1924, 6: 440-4 and 1926, 8: 221-5.
Reviewed by Carl B. Boyer, *Isis*, 1959, 50: 268-9.

SMITH, David Eugene. Mathematics. Introduction by Thomas Little Heath. 175 p. New York: Cooper, 1963.

STRUIK, Dirk. A concise history of mathematics. 2 vol. New York: Dover Publications, 1948.
Reviewed by Carl B. Boyer, *Isis*, 1949, 40: 287-9.

STRUIK, Dirk. Krótki zarys historii matematyki do końca XIX wieku. Z angielskiego tłumaczył P. Szeptycki. [A short survey of the history of mathematics up to the end of the 19th century. Transl. from the English by P. Szeptycki. (In Polish)]. 325 p. (Biblioteka "Problemów") Warszawa: Państwowe Wydawnictwo Naukowe, 1960.
Reviewed by Stanislaw Dobryzcki, *Kwart.Hist.Nauk.Tech.*, 1961, 6: 117-19.

TIETZE, Heinrich. Gelöste und ungelöste mathematische Probleme aus alter und neuer Zeit. 2 vol. xx, 256 p., 115 fig., 10 pl.; iv, 305 p., 41 fig., 8 pl. München: Biederstein-Verlag, 1949.
Reviewed by J.E. Hofmann, *Centaurus*, 1954, 3: 253-4.

TIMERDING, H.E. Die Verbreitung mathematischen Wissens und mathematischer Auffassung. v, 161 p. (Die Kultur der Gegenwart, ihre Entwicklung und ihre Ziele, III. Mathematik. Naturwissenschaften, Medizin. Part 1. Die mathematischen Wissenschaften) Leipzig: Teubner, 1914.
Reviewed by Louis C. Karpinski, *Isis*, 1936, 25: 489-91; by G. Eneström, *Bibl.Math.*, 1914, 14: 271-82.

TROPFKE, Johannes. Geschichte der Elementar-Mathematik in systematischer Darstellung mit besonderer Berücksichtigung der Fachwörter. 7 vol. 1. Rechnen; 2. Allgemeine Arithmetik; 3. Proportionen, Gleichungen; 4. Ebene Geometrie; 5. Ebene Trigonometrie; Sphärik und sphärische Trigonometrie; 6. Analysis; Analytische Geometrie; 7. Stereometrie. 2nd rev. ed. Berlin: de Gruyter, 1921-4. [CB 14/553, CB 15/229, CB 16/314 and CB 17/592]
First publ. 1902-1903; for 3rd ed. of vol. 1-4 *see* below.
Reviewed by H. Wieleitner, *Isis*, 1923, 5: 182-6 (vol. 1-3).

TROPFKE, Johannes. Geschichte der Elementar-Mathematik in systematischer Darstellung. 3rd rev. ed. 4 vol. 1. Rechnen; 2. Allgemeine Arithmetik; 3. Proportionen, Gleichungen; 4. Ebene Geometrie. Besorgt von Kurt Vogel. Berlin: de Gruyter, 1930-40. [CB 39/450]
Reviewed by T.L.H., *Nature*, 1931, 127: 921-2; by D.E. Smith, *Amer.Math.Mon.*, 1931, 42: 331-4 (vol. 1); by Solomon Gandz, *Isis*, 1938, 29: 167-9 (vol. 3).
No more published; *see* K. Vogel, *Arch.Int.Hist.Sci.*, 1953, 6: 86-8.

VERRIEST, Gustaaf. Vier voordrachten over de Wiskunde. [Four lectures on mathematics. (In Dutch)]. 168 p. (Collection Lovanium) Tournai: Casterman, 1947.
History of problems such as the squaring of the circle.

VOSS, A. Die Beziehungen der Mathematik zur Kultur der Gegenwart. Bound with Timerding, H.E., *see* above. Leipzig: Teubner, 1914.
Reviewed by L.C. Karpinski, *Isis*, 1936, 25: 489-91.

VRIES, Henrik de. Historische Studien I. iv, 192 p., ill. Groningen: P. Noordihoff, 1926. [CB 20/192]

WARGNY, C. Historia de las matematicas. 375 p. Santiago: Cervantes, [1913].

WIELEITNER, Heinrich. Der Gegenstand der Mathematik im Lichte ihrer Entwicklung. 61 p. (Mathematisch-Physikalische Bibliothek, 50) Leipzig: Teubner, 1925. [CB 18/609]

WIELEITNER, Heinrich. Geschichte der Mathematik. 2 vol. 1. Von den ältesten Zeiten bis zur Wende des 17. Jahrhunderts. 136 p.; 2. Von 1700 bis zur Mitte des 19. Jahrhunderts. 154 p. (Sammlung Göschen, 226 and 875) Berlin: de Gruyter, 1939.
Reprint of rev. ed. [CB 14/553 and CB 16/315]; Part 2 of earlier edition reviewed by D.E. Smith, *Isis*, 1921, 4: 109. Spanish translation Barcelona: Editorial Labor, 1928.

Bc-bn *essays; articles*

BORTOLOTTI, Ettore. Le matematiche disfide, e la importanza che esse ebbero nella storia delle scienze. *Atti Soc.Ital. Progr.Sci.XV Riunione* (Bologna, 1926), 20 p. Pavia: 1927. [CB 24/524]

BROWN, Ernest W. The history of mathematics. *Sci.Mon.*, 1921, 12: 385-413.
A summary of the history of mathematics.

CURTISS, D.R. Fashions in mathematics. *Amer.Math.Mon.*, 1937, 44: 559-66.

DENJOY, Arnaud. Aspects actuels de la pensée mathématique. *Ann.Univ.Paris*, 1938, 13: 151-63.

DENJOY, Arnaud. Les mathématiques et les mathématiciens. *Rev. Mois*, 1912, 13: 67-78.

DIEUDONNÉ, Jean. Recent developments in mathematics. *Amer. Math.Mon.*, 1964, 71: 239-48. [CB 90/623]

GNEDENKO, B.V. O nekotorykh zadachakh istorii matematiki. [On some problems in the history of mathematics. (In Russian)]. *Ist.Mat.Issled.*, 1958, 11: 47-62.

GNEDENKO, B.V.; RYBNIKOV, K.A.; SIMONOV, N.I. Problemy istorii matematiki novogo vremeni. [Problems in the history of modern mathematics. (In Russian)]. *Ist.Mat.Issled.*, 1963, 15: 73-96.

KREITNER, John. Man's mathematical mind: from Thales to Wiener. *Proc.Myrin Inst.*, 1956, 5: 3-26.

LORIA, Gino. Dalla tavola pitagorica alle equazioni integrali. Schizzo storico. *Europa Secolo XIX*, 1929, 3: pt. 1, 1-51.

LORIA, Gino. Le matematiche nei quaranta secoli della loro storia. *Atti Soc.Ligustica Sci.Lett.*, 1932, 11: 245-324. [CB 37/589]

MILLER, George Abram. Fundamental facts in the history of mathematics. *Sci.Mon.*, 1925, 21: 150-6.

MILLER, George Abram. Origin of our present mathematics. *Sci.Mon.*, 1928, 26: 295-8. [CB 25/413]

PRASAD, Ganesh. Mathematical research in the last 20 years. 36 p. Berlin: W. de Gruyter & Co., 1923. [CB 15/185]
Presidential address delivered on Jan. 31, 1921 before the Benares Mathematical Society.

REEVE, William David. Mathematics in the post-war period. *Scr.Math.*, 1945, 11: 275-307.

SALTYKOW, N. Histoire et évolution des mathématiques. *Enseign.Math.*, 1934, 33: 214-20.

SCHAAF, W.L. How modern is modern mathematics? *Math.Teacher*, 1964, 57: 89-97.
A comparison of twentieth-century views with those of earlier periods in the development of mathematics.

SERGESCU, Petre. Sur quelques aspects des mathématiques contemporaines. *Act.III*[e] *Congr.Int.Hist.Sci.* (Portugal, 1934), p. 167-71. Lisbon: 1936.

SERGESCU, Petre. La vie contemporaine des mathématiques. *Rev.Univ.Bruxelles*, 1937, no. 2, 110-33.

SMITH, David Eugene. On the origin of certain typical problems. *Amer.Math.Mon.*, 1917, 24: 64-71.

SMITH, David Eugene. Ten great epochs in the history of mathematics. *Scientia*, 1921, 29: 417-29. French transl. suppl. 79-89. [CB 11/445]

STONE, Marshall. The revolution in mathematics. *Amer.Math.Mon.*, 1961, 68: 715-35.
An account of some of the fundamental changes during the twentieth century.

STRUBECKER, K. Einige neuere Entwicklungslinien in der Mathematik. *Scientia*, 1960, 95: 3-10.

Bc-br *periodicals*

Bollettino di Bibliografia e Storia delle Scienze Matematiche. Vol. 1-21. Turin: 1898-1921.
Merged with: *Bollettino di Matematica.* New ser., vol. 1- Bologna: 1922-

Eudemus. An international journal devoted to the history of mathematics and astronomy. Published by Brown University, Providence, Rhode Island, U.S.A. Vol. 1. Copenhagen: Einar Munksgaard, for Brown University, 1941.
No more published.

Istoriko-matematicheskie Issledovaniia. [Historico-mathematical Investigations. (In Russian)]. Vol. 1- 1948- Moscow: Gosudarstvennoe Izdatel'stvo Fiziko-Matematicheskoi Literatury, 1948-
For vol. 1-8 *see* CB 81/266; vol. 9-11 reviewed by I.M. Gaidouk, *Vop.Ist.Est.Tekh.*, 1960, no. 9, 168-70; vol. 13 by Lubos Novy, *Arch.Int.Hist.Sci.*, 1962, 15: 425-9; for vol. 13 *see also* CB 86/460 for list of contents; vol. 14 by Kurt-R. Biermann, *Arch.Int.Hist.Sci.*, 1962, 15: 182-4.

Periodico di Matematiche: storia - didattica - filosofia. Ser. 4, vol. 1- Bologna: 1920-
First published from 1886.

Scripta Mathematica. A quarterly journal devoted to the philosophy, history, and expository treatment of mathematics. Vol. 1, no. 1- New York: Yeshiva College, September 1932-

Bc-bt *charts*

EDWARDS, E.J. An illustrated historical time chart of elementary mathematics for senior and secondary schools, training colleges and universities. 5 charts. London: University of London Press, 1936.
Reviewed by C.T. Daltry, *Math.Gaz.*, 1937, 21: 237-9.

Bc-bu/cs bibliography; literature; sources

Bc-bu

MÜLLER, Felix. Versuch einer Gruppierung der neuen mathematisch-historischen Schriften. *Z.Math.Naturwiss.Unterricht*, 1913, 44: 461-3.

Bc-bv

FOLTA, Jaroslav. K sovětským pracím "matematické historiografie". [Concerning Soviet work in mathematical historiography. (In Czech)]. *Česk Čas.Hist.*, 1964, 12: 888-92.

IUSHKEVICH, A.P. O novykh rabotakh v SSSR po istorii matematiki. [Recent research in the USSR on the history of mathematics. (In Russian)] *Ist.-Mat.Issled.*, 1958, 11: 11-46.

KROPOTOV, A.I. Istoriia matematiki na IV Vsesoiuznom Matematicheskom S'ezde. [The history of mathematics at the Fourth All-Union Mathematical Congress. (In Russian)]. *Vop. Ist.Est.Tekh.*, 1962, 13: 185-9.
The Congress met in Leningrad, 3-12 July 1961.

LORIA, Gino. Considerazioni e notizie intorno alla storia delle matematiche. *Atti Accad.Lincei, Rendic.Cl.Sci.Fis. Mat.Natur.*, 1933, 17: 768-75.
Survey of recent publications dealing with various phases of the history of mathematics from the earliest times to the present.

LUR'E, S. IA. Obzor russkoĭ literatury po istorii matematiki. [Review of Russian literature on the history of mathematics. (In Russian)]. *Arkh.Ist.Nauk.Tekh.*, 1934, 3: 273-311.

Mathematical Reviews. (Sponsored by the American Mathematical Society, the Mathematical Association of America, Academia Nacional de Ciencias Exactas, Fisicas y Naturales de Lima, het Wiskundig Genootschap te Amsterdam [and] the London Mathematical Society.) Vol. 1- Lancaster, Pa./Groningen: American Mathematical Society, 1940-

MILLER, George Abram. History of mathematics. *Amer.Math. Mon.*, 1915, 22: 299-304.
Account of some recent publications in mathematics, with a plea for the study of the history of modern mathematics as opposed to the mathematics of the past.

READ, Cecil B. Articles on the history of mathematics: a bibliography of articles in six periodicals. (*American Mathematical Monthly; Mathematical Gazette; Mathematics Teacher; National Mathematics Magazine; Scripta Mathematica; School Science and Mathematics*). *Sch.Sci.Math.*, 1959, 59: 689-717.

ROME, A. Histoire des mathématiques. (Revue des recueils périodiques) *Rev.Quest.Sci.*, 1932, 22: 261-88. [CB 37/589]
A review of recent work.

SARTON, George. The study of the history of mathematics [and] The study of the history of science. (Two vol. bound as one). 112 p.; 75 p. Unabridged and unaltered republication of the first editions. (Cambridge: Harvard University Press, 1936). New York: Dover Publications, 1957.
Reviewed by Carl B. Boyer, *Isis*, 1958, 49: 350. For reviews of the 1936 edition of "The study of the history of science" *see* CB 48/563, CB 49/163, CB 51/245, CB 53/255, CB 57/232 and CB 60/142.

VETTER, Quido. La storia della matematica presso i Cechi. *Arch.Stor.Sci.*, 1921, 2: 199-201.
A short review of Bohemian work on the history of mathematics.

Zentralblatt für Mathematik und ihre Grenzgebiete. Vol. 1 - Berlin: Springer, 1931 - [CB 34/497]
Contains sections on the history of mathematics, physics, astrophysics and geophysics.

Bcb

FRICK, Bertha Margaret. The David Eugene Smith mathematical library of Columbia University. *Osiris*, 1936, 1: 79-84.

MUNSTERBERG, Margaret. The Bowditch collection in the Boston Public Library. *Isis*, 1942, 34: 140-2.

Bcd

BJÖRNBO, Axel Anthon. Die mathematischen S. Marchandschriften in Florenz. *Bibl.Math.*, 1912, 12: 97-132, 193-224.

Bce

MILLER, George Abram. Historical introduction to mathematical literature. xiv, 302 p., bibliogr. New York: Macmillan, 1916. [CB 7/142]

PLIMPTON, George A. The history of elementary mathematics in the Plimpton Library. *Science*, 1928, 68: 390-5.

SAUVENIER-GOFFIN, Elisabeth. Les sciences mathématiques et physiques à travers le fonds ancien de la Bibliothèque de l'Université de Liège. 2 pt. (*Mémoires de la Société Royale des Sciences de Liège, sér. 4,* 19: fasc. 2; *sér. 5,* 5) Liège: 1957, 1961.

SMITH, David Eugene. In the surnamed chosen chest. 1. Association copies. 2. Orientalia. *Amer.Math.Mon.,* 1925, 32: 287-94, 393-7.
Mathematical works in the author's library.

VETTER, Quido. Nektera "rara mathematica" v prazskych knihovnach. [Some "rara mathematica" in Prague libraries. (In Czech)]. *Přirodovědecky,* 1929, 6: 35 p., 6 fig. [CB 28/543]

VETTER, Quido. Quelques remarques sur l'histoire des mathématiques dans les bibliothèques de Prague. *Compt.Rend.1er Congr.Int.Hist.Sci.* (Paris, 1929). *Archeion,* 1929, 11: liii-lviii.

Bce-bv

Acta Mathematica. Tables générales des tomes I-XXXV (1882-1912), rédigées par M. Riesz. 179 p. Stockholm: 1913.

ARCHIBALD, Raymond Clare. Bibliographia de mathematicis. *Scr.Math.,* 1932, 1: 173-81; 1933, 1: 265-74, 346-62; 1933, 2: 75-85.

Bibliografia Matematica Italiana. Ser. 1, vol. 1-9. (1950-1958); *ser. 2,* vol. 10- (1959-) Rome: Edizioni Cremonese (for Unione Matematica Italiana), 1951-59, 1961-
First series reviewed by A. Procissi, *Physis,* 1960, 2: 186-8.

KARPINSKI, Louis C. Rare mathematical books in the University of Michigan Library. *Scr.Math.,* 1932, 1: 63-5.

SÁNCHEZ PÉREZ, José A. Las matemáticas en la Biblioteca del Escorial. Obra premiada por la Real Academia de Ciencias Exactas, Fisicas y Naturales de Madrid. 365 p., 61 pl. Madrid: Imprenta de Estanislao Maestre, 1929.
Reviewed by G. Sarton, *Isis,* 1929, 13: 128-9.

STRUIK, Dirk J. A selected list of mathematical books and articles published after 1200 and translated into English. *Scr.Math.,* 1949, 15: 115-32.

Bce-bx

BOYER, Carl B. Classics in the history of mathematics. The history of mathematics, an exhibition of rare books. 32 p. Bethlehem, Pa.: Lehigh University, 1961.

Bcj

ALLEN, Edward S. Periodicals for mathematicians. *Science,* 1929, 70: 592-4.

ARCHIBALD, Raymond Clare. New mathematical periodicals. *Amer.Math.Mon.,* 1931, 38: 436-9; 1932, 39: 185-7. [CB 34/495 and CB 36/434]

KURATOWSKI, Kazimierz. Fifty volumes of *Fundamenta Mathematicae* - Recollections and notes. *Rev.Pol.Acad.Sci.,* 1963, 8: no. 2, 23-9.

Bcj-bv

LONDON UNIVERSITY. LIBRARY. Union list of periodicals on mathematics and allied subjects in London libraries. 68 p. London: 1958; 2nd ed. 147 p. 1968.

SMITH, David Eugene; SEELY, Caroline Eustis. Union list of mathematical periodicals. 60 p. Washington, D.C.: Bureau of Education, 1918.
List of 81 periodicals available in 52 American libraries.

Bcp

CARO-DELVAILLE, Henri. Mural paintings illustrating the history of mathematics, in the Lincoln school of Teachers College, Columbia University, New York. Introduction by Otis W. Caldwell. Description by David Eugene Smith, John Clark and Vera Sanford. (4 sheets, 32 by 49 cm., with colored reproductions of the paintings). New York: 1926. [CB 21/568]

Bcs

SMITH, David Eugene. In the surnamed chosen chest, 3. Numismatica mathematica. *Amer.Math.Mon.,* 1925, 32: 444-50.
Brief enumeration of some 129 mathematical medals in the author's collection.

Bd biography

Bd-bv

HIGGINS, Thomas James. Biographies and collected works of mathematicians. *Amer.Math.Mon.,* 1944, 51: 433-45. Addenda, *ibid.,* 1949, 56: 310-12.

Bda

BELL, Eric Temple. Men of mathematics. xxi, 592 p., 29 ill. New York: Simon and Schuster, 1937.
Reviewed by George Sarton, *Isis,* 1938, 28: 510-13.

COLERUS, Egmont. De Pythagore à Hilbert. Les époques de la mathématique et leurs maîtres. Trad. de l'allemand par J. du Plessis de Grenédan. 313 p. (Bibliothèque de Philosophie Scientifique) Paris: Flammarion, 1943.
For German original *see* below. Contains biographical chapters on great mathematicians.

COLERUS, Egmont. Von Pythagoras bis Hilbert. Die Epochen der Mathematik und ihre Baumeister. Geschichte der Mathematik für Jedermann. 364 p. Berlin: Zsolnay, 1937. [CB 59/466]
Reviewed by O. Neugebauer, *Naturwissenschaften,* 1937, 25: 683.

COOLIDGE, Julian Lowell. The mathematics of great amateurs. viii, 211 p., 56 fig. New York: Dover, 1963.
Reprint of the Clarendon Press edition of 1949.
Reviewed by Boris Rosenfeld, *Arch.Int.Hist.Sci.,* 1964, 17: 321-3.

EELLS, Walter Crosby. One hundred eminent mathematicians. *Math.Teacher,* 1962, 55: 582-8. [CB 88/538]

Elemente der Mathematik. (Revue de Mathématiques Elémentaires) Beihefte. No. 1 - Basel: Verlag Birkhauser, 1947 -
These supplements consist almost entirely of an un-numbered series: Kurze Mathematiker Biographien. [CB 82/202]
Reviewed by Jean Itard, *Rev.Hist.Sci.,* 1953, 6: 180-1.

HOOPER, Alfred. Makers of mathematics. ix, 402 p., 125 fig., front. New York: Random House, 1948; London: Faber and Faber, 1950. [CB 75/87]

KLEIN, Felix. Lebensbilder von eigener Hand. *Mitt.Universitätsbund Göttingen,* 1923, 5: 11-36.

KOWALEWSKI, Gerhard. Grosse Mathematiker. Eine Wanderung durch die Geschichte der Mathematik vom Altertum bis zur Neuzeit. 300 p. München: Lehmann, 1938.
Reviewed by E.J. Dijksterhuis, *Quellen Stud.Gesch.Math., Abt.B,* 1938, 4: 415-21.

MESCHKOWSKI, Herbert. Denkweisen grosser Mathematiker. Ein Weg zur Geschichte der Mathematik. viii, 94 p., ill. Braunschweig: F. Vieweg & Sohn, 1961.
Reviewed by H. Degen, *Naturwiss.Rundsch.,* 1963, 16: 75.

MESCHKOWSKI, Herbert. Ways of thought of great mathematicians. Transl. for German by John Dyer-Bennet. viii, 110 p., fig., bibliogr. (Mathesis Series) San Francisco: Holden-Day, 1964.
For German original *see* above.

MUIR, Jane. Of men and numbers: the story of the great mathematicians. 249 p. New York: Dodd, Mean & Company, 1961.

TURNBULL, Herbert Westren. The great mathematicians. 4th ed. [reprinted]. xv, 141 p., ill. London: Methuen; New York: New York University Press, 1961.
Reviewed by J.F. Scott, *Scr.Math.,* 1961, 26: 370; by Carl B. Boyer, *Science,* 1962, 135: 719; in *Sci.Amer.,* 1962, 206: no. 1, 165. 1st ed. 1929, reviewed in *Math.Gaz.,* 1930, 15: 172-3.

Bda-rw

COOLIDGE, Julian L. Six female mathematicians. *Scr.Math.,* 1951, 17: 20-31. [CB 78/181]

Bdae-ct

BOYER, Carl B. Philately and mathematics. *Scr.Math.,* 1949, 15: 104-14.
Portraits of mathematicians of all periods on postage stamps. Supplement to note by R.A. Johnson and R.C. Archibald.

JOHNSON, R.A.; ARCHIBALD, Raymond Clare. Postage-stamp or coin portraits of mathematicians. *Scr.Math.,* 1932-33, 1: 183-4.

Bdaj

LIETZMANN, Walter. Aus der neueren Mathematik. Quellen zum Zahlbegriff und zur Gleichungslehre, zum Funktionsbegriff und zur Analysis. iv, 78 p., 15 fig., 4 pl., map. (Mathematisches Unterrichtswerk, Ergänzungsheft, 5) Leipzig: Teubner, 1929.

NEWMAN, James R., ed. The world of mathematics. A small library of the literature of mathematics from A'h-mosé the Scribe to Albert Einstein, presented with commentaries and notes by the editor. 4 vol. xviii, 2,535 p. New York: Simon and Schuster, 1956.
Reviewed by Carl B. Boyer, *Isis*, 1957, 48: 476-9; by Henry W. Syer, *Sci.Mon.*, 1957, 84: 217-18.
Swedish translation: Sigma. En matematikens kulturhistoria, sammanställd och kommenterad av James R. Newman. 6 vol. Stockholm: Forum, 1959-60.
Volume 6 reviewed by F. Neumeyer, *Lychnos*, 1962, 423.

SMITH, David Eugene. A source book in mathematics. 2 vol. 1. The field of number; the field of algebra. xiii, 701 p.; 2. The field of geometry; the field of probability; the field of the calculus, functions, quaternions. xiii, 701 p.; fig., pl., front. New York: Dover Publications, Inc., 1959.
An unaltered republication of the edition first printed in 1929, save for its present format in two volumes.
Reviewed by George Sarton, *Isis*, 1930, 14: 268-70; by L. Bouckaert, *Rev.Quest.Sci.*, 1962, 23: 432.
Author's comments on the projected work, *Amer.Math.Mon.*, 1928, 35: 280-2.

SPEISER, Andreas. Klassische Stücke der Mathematik. 168 p., 16 fig. Zurich: Füssli, 1925. [CB 18/607]
An anthology.

WIELEITNER, Heinrich. Rechnen und Algebra. viii, 75 p., 5 fig. (Mathematische Quellenbücher, 1) Berlin: Otto Salle, 1927. [CB 23/240]
An anthology of mathematical texts illustrating the development of arithmetic and algebra.

WITTING, A.; GEBHARDT, M. Beispiele zur Geschichte der Mathemathik. Ein mathematisch-historisches Lesebuch. viii, 61 p. (Mathematische Bibliothek, 15) Leipzig: Teubner, 1913.

WOLFF, Peter. Breakthroughs in mathematics. 285 p., ill. New York: New American Library, 1963. [CB 89/499]
Selections from the works of nine major mathematical innovators.

Bf history of mathematics as a study

BELL, E.T. Possible projects in the history of mathematics. *Scr.Math.*, 1945, 11: 308-16.

ENESTRÖM, G. Die mathematisch-historische Forschung und der mathematisch-historische Schulunterricht. *Bibl.Math.*, 1913-14, 14: 1-8.

GNEDENKO, B.V.; POGREBYTSKII, I.B. Ob istorii matematiki i ee znachenii dlia matematiki i drugikh nauk. [On the value of the history of mathematics for mathematics and the other sciences. (In Russian)]. *Ist.-Mat.Issled.*, 1958, 11: 441-60.
Reviewed by Kenneth May, *Math.Rev.*, 1962, 23: 691, A3618.

HOFMANN, Joseph E. Geschichte der Mathematik. In: Naturforschung und Medizin in Deutschland, 1939-45, 1, Reine Mathematik, pt. 1, 9 p. Wiesbaden: Dieterich, 1948.
Report of the work on mathematical history done in Germany during the war 1939-46.

IANOVSKAIA, S.A. Vvodnaiia lekstiia k kursu "Istoriia matematiki". [Introduction to the course "History of mathematics". (In Russian)]. *Ist.-Mat.Issled.*, 1958, 11: 193-208.

LORIA, Gino. Guida allo studio della storia delle matematiche. Generalità - didattica - bibliografia. Appendice: Questioni storiche concernenti le scienze esatte. 2nd rev. ed. xix, 384 p. Milano: Hoepli, 1946. [CB 70/254]
First published 1916.

LORIA, Gino. Intorno allo stato attuale degli studi sulla storia delle matematiche. *Atti Soc.Ital.Prog.Sci.VIII Riunione*, p. 643-59. Roma: 1916.

NEUGEBAUER, Otto. The history of mathematics. *Nat.Math.Mag.*, 1936, 11: 5-11, 1 portr.
Translated by G. Waldo Dunnington, with a biography of the author and portrait.

RYBNIKOV, K.A. O predmete istorii matematiki. [The purpose of the history of mathematics. (In Russian)]. *Ist.-Mat. Issled.*, 1958, 11: 209-24.

SARTON, George. The study of the history of mathematics. *Amer.Math.Mon.*, 1934, 41: 127-9.
Summary of Sarton's informal lecture at the joint session of the Mathematical Association of America with section of A.A.A.S. on Dec. 29, 1933.

SARTON, George. The study of the history of mathematics [and] The study of the history of science. (Two volumes bound as one.) 112 p.; 75 p. Unabridged and unaltered republication of the first editions (Cambridge: Harvard University Press, 1936). New York: Dover Publications, 1957.
Reviewed by Carl B. Boyer, *Isis*, 1958, 49: 350. For reviews of the 1936 edition of "The study of the history of mathematics" *see* CB 48/567, CB 49/173, CB 50/393, CB 51/252, CB 53/259, CB 57/238 and CB 59/468.

SARTON, George. Les tendances actuelles de l'histoire des mathématiques. *Isis*, 1914, 1: 577-89.

STOTT, W. A plea for economy of thought and labour in the mathematical sciences by the study of their history. *Sci. Progr.*, 1915-16, 10: 204-17.

VETTER, Quido. Trois remarques sur l'histoire des mathématiques. *Mathematica*, 1935, 9: 304-9.

WHITROW, G.J. The importance of the history of mathematics in relation to the study of mathematical technique. *Math. Gaz.*, 1932, 16: 225-7.

WIELEITNER, Heinrich. Was lehrt die Geschichte der Mathematik über den Sinn dieser Wissenschaft? *Arch.Gesch.Med.*, 1923, 15: 27-32.

Bfd

FUETER, Eduard. Geschichte der Mathematik. *Festschrift zur 200-Jahr-Feier der Naturforschenden Gesellschaft in Zürich (1746-1946)*, p. 135-7. *(Vierteljahrsschr.Naturforsch.Ges. Zürich*, 91: no. 1-4) Zürich: 1946.
Notes on the historians of mathematics who were members of the Society.

FOR biographies and bibliographies of individual historians of mathematics (20th century) *see* volumes 1 and 2 under:-

Archibald, Raymond Clare; Bortolotti, Ettore; Bosmans, Henri; Cajori, Florian; Cantor, Moritz Benedikt; Eneström, Gustav; Favaro, Antonio; Heath, Thomas Little; Jourdain, Philip E.B.; Karpinski, Louis C.; Loria, Gino; Miller, George Abram; Peano, Giuseppe; Rouse Ball, Walter William; Sergescu, Petre; Smith, David Eugene; Vetter, Quido; Wieleitner, Heinrich; Zeuthen, Hieronymus Georg.

Bg teaching history of mathematics

GABRIEL, R.M. The history of mathematics: its relation to pupil and teacher. *Math.Gaz.*, 1937, 21: 106-16.

LORIA, Gino. Teaching the history of mathematics. *Math.Gaz.*, 1937, 21: 274-5.
A scheme of a university course.

PROGRAMMA po istorii matematiki v Moskovskom gosudarstvennom universitete. [Program for the history of mathematics course at the State University at Moscow. (In Russian)]. *Ist.-Mat. Issled.*, 1958, 11: 185-92.

RICHESON, A.W. Courses on the history of mathematics in the United States. *Scr.Math.*, 1934, 2: 161-5.

STRUIK, Dirk J. Massachusetts Institute of Technology. A course in the history of mathematics. *Isis*, 1947, 32: 123-4.

Bgt

BOCKSTAELE, Paul. Het belang van de geschiedenis der wiskunde voor het Middelbaar Onderwijs. [The importance of the history of mathematics in secondary school teaching. (In Dutch)]. *Nova Vetera*, 1949, 27: 15 p.

BUNT, L.N.H. Geschiedenis van de wiskunde als onderwerp voor het Gymnasium A. Verslag van een proefneming. [History of mathematics as a subject in the Grammar School A. An account of an experiment. (In Dutch)] 2 vol. 42 p.; vi, 171 p. (*Acta Paedagogica Ultrajectina*, 6) Groningen/ Djakarta: J.B. Wolters, 1954.

GEBHARDT, Martin. Die Geschichte der Mathematik im mathematischen Unterrichte der höheren Schulen Deutschlands, dargestellt vor allem auf Grund alter und neuer Lehrbücher und der Programmabhandlungen höherer Schulen. viii, 157 p. (Abhandlungen über den mathematischen Unterricht in Deutschland, 3: no. 6) Leipzig: Teubner, 1912.

LILLIACUS, L.A. The history of mathematics in elementary instruction. *Amer.Math.Mon.*, 1920, 27: 61-3.

MENDELSSOHN, W. Ueber die Verwendung mathematischer Originalwerke im Unterricht. *Z.Math.Naturwiss.Unterricht*, 1912, 43: 1-9.

WIELEITNER, Heinrich. Mathematische Quellenstudien im Unterricht. *Unterrichtsbl.Math.Naturwiss.*, 1927, 33: 312-15. [CB 23/240]

Bh historiography and special aspects of the history of mathematics

Bhc

ENESTRÖM, G. Ueber die Bedeutung von Quellenstudien bei mathematischer Geschichtsschreibung. *Bibl.Math.*, 1911-12, 12: 1-20.

WIELEITNER, Heinrich. Mathematische Quellenstudien. *Weltall*, 1927, 26: 186-91. [CB 23/240]

Bhd

BOULIGAND, Georges. Attitudes de la pensée mathématique et histoire des sciences. *Arch.Int.Hist.Sci.*, 1952, 5: 230-3.

BOYER, Carl B. Myth, the muse, and mathesis. *Math.Teacher*, 1964, 57: 242-53.
An account of some recent changes in view in the history of mathematics.

CAJORI, Florian. On the prevalence of inaccurate criticism. *Isis*, 1922, 4: 494-6. [CB 13/304]
A rejoinder to G.A. Miller's article Different types of mathematical history, *see* below.

ENESTRÖM, G. Wie kann die weitere Verbreitung unzuverlässiger mathematisch-historicher Angaben verhindert werden? *Bibl. Math.*, 1912-13, 13: 1-3.

KARPINSKI, Louis C. History of mathematics in the recent [11th] edition of the Encyclopaedia Britannica. *Science*, 1912, 35: 29-31.

LORIA, Gino. Projet d'une histoire universelle des mathématiques. *Act.Ve Congr.Int.Hist.Sci.* (Lausanne, 1947), p. 51-2. Paris: Hermann, 1948. Also in *Arch.Int.Hist.Sci.*, 1948, 1: 230-1.

MILLER, George Abram. Different types of mathematical history. *Isis*, 1921, 4: 5-12.
Remarks on the works of Montucla, Cantor and Cajori. *See* Cajori's rejoinder above.

MILLER, George Abram. Disagreeing with the textbook. *Sch. Soc.*, 1922, 16: 449-54. [CB 14/552]

MILLER, George Abram. A dozen mathematical errors in Webster's [New International] Dictionary, [2nd ed., 1934]. *Science*, 1936, 84: 418-19.

MILLER, George Abram. A dozen mathematical errors in the "Encyclopaedia Britannica" [14th ed.]. *Science*, 1939, 90: 512-13.

MILLER, George Abram. Histories of mathematics by Florian Cajori and D.E. Smith. *Sch.Sci.Math.*, 1924, 24: 939-47. [CB 17/591]

MILLER, George Abram. The history oı mathematics forty years ago. *Science*, 1938, 88: 375.
Pointing out historical errors in the *Encyklopädie der mathematischen Wissenschaften*, 1898-1935.

MILLER, George Abram. Inaccuracies in the mathematical literature. *Sci.Mon.*, 1923, 17: 216-28.

MILLER, George Abram. Mathematics in the New International Encyclopaedia. *Amer.Math.Mon.*, 1917, 24: 106-9.
1st ed. 1902-4; 2nd ed. 1914-17.

VETTER, Quido. Intorno al metodo nella storia della matematica. *Boll.Mat.Sez.Stor.Bibliogr.*, 1922, 18: xxxiii-xliii, lxv-lxxiv.

VETTER, Quido. O metodyce historji matematyki. [On the methodology of the history of mathematics. (In Polish)]. *Wiad.Mat.*, 1929, 30: 175-82; 31: 1-11.

VOGEL, Kurt. Legenden und Irrtümer der mathematischen Geschichtsschreibung. *Sudhoffs Arch.*, 1953, 37: 161-9.

Bhg

LORIA, Gino. Di alcuni aspetti sotti qui presentansi li ricerche storiche nel campo matematico. *Archeion*, 1932, 14: 198-206. [CB 38/593]

LORIA, Gino. La matematica, nel suo millenario sviluppo, ha seguito una direzione costante? *Science, Medicine and History, Essays in honour of Charles Singer*, (2), p. 442-9. London: Oxford University Press, 1953.

LORIA, Gino. Punti interrogativi nella storia delle matematiche. *Arch.Stor.Sci.*, 1926, 7: 4-17.

MILLER, George Abram. Harmony as a principle of mathematical development. *Proc.Nat.Acad.Sci.*, 1928, 14: 214-17.

MILLER, George Abram. Implications involved in mathematical advances. *Science*, 1943, 98: 38-9.

SMITH, David Eugene. Certain questions in the history of mathematics. *Bull.Calcutta Math.Soc.*, 1930, 20: 135-8.

Bhm

DELEVSKY, J. La philosophie des paradoxes mathématiques. *Rev.Phil.*, 1952, 142: 196-222.

KARPINSKI, Louis C. The parallel development of mathematical ideas, numerically and geometrically. *Sch.Sci.Math.*, 1920, 20: 821-8.

MILLER, George Abram. Arithmetization in the history of mathematics. *Science*, 1925, 62: 328. [CB 19/799]

SINGH, Jagjit. Great ideas of modern mathematics: their nature and use. viii, 312 p., fig. New York: Dover Publications, 1959.

Bj psychological aspects

CHASLIN, Philippe. Essai sur le mécanisme psychologique de la mathématique pure. viii, 272 p., portr. Paris: F. Alcan, 1926. [CB 22/257]

DUGAS, René. Essai sur l'incompréhension mathématique. 130 p. Paris: Vuibert, 1940.

DUGAS, René. L'incompréhension mathématique. *Thalès*, 1937-40, 4: 168-83.

FETTWEIS, Ewald. Einzelbeiträge zur Frage nach dem phylogenetischen Parallelismus auf dem Gebiet der Zahl- und Raumentwicklung bei Kindern und Primitiven. *Psychol.Forsch.*, 1951, 23: 391-8.

FETTWEIS, Ewald. Über das Verhältnis des mathematischen Denkens zum mystischen Denken auf niederen Kulturstufen. *Archeion*, 1932, 14: 207-20. [CB 38/593]

HUGH-HELLMUTH, H. v. Einige Beziehungen zwischen Erotik und Mathematik. *Imago*, 1915, 4: 52-68.
Reviewed by H. Wieleitner, *Mitt.Gesch.Med.*, 1916, 15: 17-18.

KALMUS, H. Animals as mathematicians. *Nature*, 1964, 202: 1156-60.

LUQUET, G.H. Sur l'origine des notions mathématiques. Remarques psychologiques et ethnographiques. *J.Psychol.Norm. Pathol.*, 1929, 15: 733-62, 26 fig.
Reviewed by J. Nippgen, *Ethnographie*, 1930, 123-4.

PIER, Jean-Paul. La valeur des mathématiques dans l'esprit de leurs promoteurs. *Act.IIIe Congr.Bénélux Hist.Sci.* (Luxembourg, 1960), p. 195-202. (Comité Luxembourgeois d'histoire des science, Publication no. 2) Leiden: E.J. Brill, 1960. Also in *Janus*, 1961, 49: 195-202.

SERGESCU, Petre. Gândirea matematică. [Ways of mathematical thinking. (In Rumanian)] vii, 192 p. Cluj: "Ardealul", 1928.

VERA, Francesco. Psicogénesis del razonamiento matemático. 200 p. Buenos-Aires: Editorial Poseidon, 1947.

VERLAINE, Louis. Histoire naturelle de la connaissance chez le singe inférieur. 4. La notion du nombre. *Mem.Soc.Sci. Liège, sér. 4,* 1941, 4: 145-223.

Bjg

BARLOW, Fred. Mental prodigies: an enquiry into the faculties of arithmetical, chess and musical prodigies, famous memorizers, precocious children and the like, with numerous examples of "lightning" calculations and mental magic. 256 p. New York: Philosophical Library, 1952. [CB 79/170]

BIEBERBACH, Ludwig. Stilarten mathematischen Schaffens. *Sitzungsber.Preuss.Akad.Wiss.,* 1934, 20: 351-60.
Reviewed by Klemm, *Mitt.Gesch.Med.,* 1935, 34: 160.

BOYER, Jacques. Les calculateurs prodiges. *Larousse Mens.,* septembre 1951, 709-10.

FEHR, Henri; FLOURNOY, Th.; CLAPARÈDE, Ed. Enquête de l'"Enseignement Mathématique" sur la méthode de travail des mathématiciens. 2e édition conforme à la 1re suivie d'une note sur l'invention mathématique par Henri Poincaré. viii, 137 p. Paris: Gauthier-Villars, 1912.
First published in *Enseign.Math.,* 1909.
Reviewed by George Sarton, *Isis,* 1913, 1: 719.

HADAMARD, Jacques. Essai sur la psychologie de l'invention dans le domaine mathématique. Première édition française revue et augmentée par l'auteur. 135 p. Paris: Albert Blanchard, 1959.
Reviewed by Geneviève Guitel, *Ann.Écon.Soc.Civilizations,* 1963, 18: 399-401.

HADAMARD, Jacques. The psychology of invention in the mathematical field. 2nd ed. xiii, 145 p. Princeton, N.J.: Princeton University Press, 1949.
Reprint of "An essay on the psychology of invention" with 2 page appendix, publ. 1945. [CB 69/226]

LORIA, Gino. Psicologia dei matematici. *Scientia,* 1924, 35: 10-21; French transl., suppl., 9-20.

PELSENEER, Jean. Peut-on planifier la recherche scientifique? Ce que nous dit l'histoire des mathématiques. *Isis,* 1955, 46: 95-8.
On the intellectual process of creation.

WAERDEN, B.L. van der. Einfall und Uberlegung in der Mathematik. *Elem.Math.,* 1953, 8: 121-9; 1954, 9: 1-9, 49-56, 15 fig.

WAVRE, Rolin. L'imagination du réel, l'invention et la découverte dans la science des nombres. 133 p. (Collection Etre et Penser, 23) Neuchâtel: La Baconnière, 1948.

Bk philosophy and methodology

BERNAYS, Paul. Über Nelsons Stellungsnahme in der Philosophie der Mathematik. *Naturwissenschaften,* 1928, 16: 142-4.

BOCKSTAELE, Paul. *See* Bwf-k

BOLL, Marcel. La philosophie mathématique. *Rev.Positiviste Int.,* 1913, 13: 59-80.

BOLZANO, Bernard. Philosophie der Mathematik oder Beiträge zu einer begründeteren Darstellung der Mathematik. Neu hrsg. mit Einleitung und Anmerkungen von H. Fels. 88 p. (F. Schöninghs Sammlung philosophischer Lesestoffe, 9) Paderborn: F. Schöningh, 1926. [CB 22/256]
First published 1811 (Prague: Widtmann).

BROUWER, L.E.J. Consciousness, philosophy, and mathematics. *Proc.10th Int.Congr.Phil.* (Amsterdam 1948), p. 1235-49. Amsterdam: North Holland Publishing Co., 1949.

CROISSANT-GOEDERT, Jeanne. La critique sceptique des mathématiques. *IIIe Congr.Nat.Sci.* (Bruxelles, 1950), (2), p. 16-18. [Liège: 1951].

DARBON, André. La philosophie des mathématiques. Étude sur la logistique de Russell. Publiée par Madeleine Lagarce-Darbon. Avec la collaboration de François Chatelet. xii, 203 p. (Bibliothèque de Philosophie Contemporaine) Paris: Presses Universitaires de France, 1949.

DUBISLAW, Walter. Die Philosophie der Mathematik in der Gegenwart. viii, 88 p. (Philosophische Forschungsberichte, 13) Berlin: Junker & Dünnhaupt, 1932.

DUBISLAW, Walter. Les recherches ... *See* Bwg-k

FRAENKEL, Abraham Adolf. The intuitionistic revolution in mathematics and logic. *Bull.Res.Counc.Israel,* 1954, 3: 283-9.

HAMEL, Georg. Ueber die philosophische Stellung der Mathematik. 16 p. (Akademische Schriftenreihe der technischen Hochschule Charlottenburg, 1) Charlottenburg E.V.: Verlag Studentenhaus, 1928. [CB 25/412]

KATTSOFF, Louis O. A philosophy of mathematics. ix, 266 p. Ames, Iowa: Iowa State College Press, 1948.

KENNEDY, Hubert C. The mathematical philosophy of Giuseppe Peano. *Phil.Sci.,* 1963, 30: 262-6.

KEYSER, Cassius Jackson. Mathematical philosophy, a study of fate and freedom: lectures for educated laymen. xv, 466 p. New York: E.P. Dutton, 1922.

KEYSER, Cassius Jackson. The nature of the doctrinal function and its role in rational thought. *Scr.Math.,* 1933-34, 2: 5-26, 143-54.
Originally published in the Yale Law Journal, 1932.

KEYSER, Cassius Jackson. The rational and the superrational. Studies in thinking. viii, 259 p., portr. (Collected Works, vol. 2) New York: Scripta Mathematica, Yeshiva University, 1952. [CB 79/171]
This book has special reference to mathematics.

KEYSER, Cassius Jackson. Thinking about thinking. 91 p. New York: E.P. Dutton, 1926. [CB 21/566]

KÖRNER, S. The philosophy of mathematics. 198 p. London: Hutchinson, 1960.
Reviewed by R. Harré, *Brit.J.Phil.Sci.,* 1962, 13: 337-8.

KUNTZE, Friedrich. Der Begriff der Elemente des Gedankens in der Mathematik. In his: Von den neuen Denkmitteln der Philosophie in sechs Briefen. 3, 32 p. Heidelberg: Winter, 1928.

LICHTENSTEIN, Leon. La philosophie des mathématiques selon Émile Meyerson. *Rev.Phil.,* 1932, 57: 169-206.

LÖWY, Heinrich. Die Krisis in der Mathematik und ihre philosophische Bedeutung. *Naturwissenschaften,* 1926, no. 30, 706-8.

LORENZEN, Paul. Wie ist Philosophie der Mathematik möglich? *Phil.Natur.,* 1957, 4: 192-208.

MAZIARZ, Edward A. The philosophy of mathematics. viii, 286 p. New York: Philosophical Library, 1950. [CB 77/368]

ORESTANO, Francesco. La matematica moderna e la filosofia. *Archimede* (Palermo), 1923, 1: no. 5-6, 54 p.
Lecture given at the University of Palermo.

SHAW, James Byrnie. Lectures on the philosophy of mathematics. vii, 206 p. Chicago: Open Court, 1918.

SPEISER, Andreas. Elemente der Philosophie und Mathematik. Eine Anleitung zum inhaltlichen Denken. 116 p. (Wissenschaft und Kultur, 5) Basel: Birkhäuser, 1952.

WAVRE, R. Mathématique et philosophie. *Arch.Soc.Belg.Phil.,* 1933, 5: 3-16.

WEYL, Hermann. Philosophie der Mathematik. 162 p. (Handbuch der Philosophie, IIA, parts 1 und 2) München: Oldenbourg, 1927.
Reviewed by E. Zilsel, *Naturwissenschaften,* 1927, 24-7.

Bk-c

BOUTROUX, Pierre. Les étapes de la philosophie mathématique. *Rev.Métaphys.Morale,* 1913, 21: 107-31.
Critical review of Brunschvicg's book *see* below.

BRUNSCHVICG, Léon. Les étapes de la philosophie mathématique. xi, 593 p. Paris: Alcan, 1912.
Reviewed by George Sarton, *Isis*, 1913, 1: 577-89; by E. Turrière, *ibid*, 721-34.
For essay review *see* Boutroux above.

CAVAILLÈS, Jean. Philosophie mathématique. 274 p. (Histoire de la Pensée, 6) Paris: Hermann, 1962.

Bkb the nature of mathematics

BECKER, Oskar. Grösse und Grenze der mathematischen Denkweise. iv, 174 p. Freiburg/München: Verlag Karl Alber, 1959.
Reviewed by G.L. Huxley, *Scr.Math.*, 1960, 25: 259-60; by J.E. Hofmann, *Arch.Int.Hist.Sci.*, 1960, 13: 147-8.

BOULIGAND, Georges. Le repérage de la pensée mathématique, sa part dans la recherche. 35 p. (Conférences du Palais de la Découverte, 23 juin 1956) Paris: Université de Paris, [1956].

BOULIGAND, Georges. Sur les alternances dans le dynamisme de la pensée mathématique. In: *Hommage à Gaston Bachelard*, p. 73-81. Paris: Presses Universitaires de France, 1957.

BOULIGAND, Georges. L'unité des sciences mathématiques. *Scientia*, 1929, 15: 77-84. [CB 27/538]

BOULIGAND, Georges; DESBATS, Jean. La mathématique et son unité. 312 p. Paris: Payot, 1947.
Reviewed by F. Russo, *Rev.Quest.Sci.*, 1948, 119: 109-10.

BOUTROUX, Pierre. L'idéal scientifique des mathématiciens. 274 p. Paris: Alcan, 1920.
Reviewed by George Sarton, *Isis*, 1921, 4: 93-6.
Nouvelle edition, 1955 (Paris: Presses Universitaires de France). German translation Leipzig: Teubner, 1927.

BOUTROUX, Pierre. Les mathématiques. 184 p., 51 fig. (Bibliothèque de Culture Générale) Paris: Albin Michel, 1922.

BRODETSKY, S. The meaning of mathematics. 80 p. (Benn's Sixpenny Library, 84) London: Benn, 1929.

CASSIRER, Ernst. Mathematische Mystik und mathematische Naturwissenschaft. Betrachtungen zur Entstehungsgeschichte der exakten Wissenschaft. *Lychnos*, 1940, 248-65.

CLIFFORD, William Kingdon. The common sense of the exact sciences. Edited and with a preface by Karl Pearson. Newly edited and with an introduction by James R. Newman. lxvi, 250 p. New York: Knopf, 1946.
Reviewed by Edmund Whitaker, *Nature*, 1947, 159: 248.
First publ. 1885.

COURANT, Richard; ROBBINS, Herbert. What is mathematics? An elementary approach to ideas and methods. xix, 521 p., 287 fig. New York: Oxford University Press, 1941.
Reviewed by I. Bernard Cohen, *Isis*, 1944, 35: 219.

FÉLIX, Lucienne. The modern aspect of mathematics. Transl. by Julius H. Hlavaty and Francille H. Hlavaty. xiii, 194 p. New York: Basic Books, 1960.
First publ. in French, Paris: Albert Blanchard, 1957.
Reviewed by Karl Menger, *Phil.Sci.*, 1962, 29: 95-6.

GEIRINGER, Hilda. Die Gedankenwelt der Mathematik. 200 p. Berlin: Frankfurt a M.: Verlag der Arbeitsgemeinschaft, 1922. [CB 14/551]

HARDY, Godfrey Harold. A mathematician's apology. vii, 93 p. Cambridge University Press, 1940. [CB 62/61]

JEFFREYS, Harold. The nature of mathematics. *Phil.Sci.*, 1938, 5: 434-51.

JOURDAIN, Philip E.B. The nature of mathematics. 92 p. (The People's Books) London: T.C. et E.C. Jack, 1912. [CB 3/562]
2nd edition, 126 p. London: 1919.

KASNER, Edward; NEWMAN, James. Mathematics and the imagination. With drawings and diagrams by Rufus Isaacs. xvi, 380 p. New York: Simon and Schuster, 1940.
Reviewed by I. Bernard Cohen, *Isis*, 1942, 33: 723-5.
French translation Paris: Payot, 1950; Swedish translation (Stockholm: Natur och Kultur, 1942) reviewed by Harald J. Heyman, *Lychnos*, 1942, 394-6.

KEYSER, Cassius Jackson. The bearings of mathematics. *Scr. Math.*, 1932, 1: 93-110.

KEYSER, Cassius Jackson. The human worth of rigorous thinking: essays and addresses. 2nd enl. ed. 323 p. New York: Columbia University Press, 1925.
First edition, 1916.

KEYSER, Cassius Jackson. Mathematics and the question of cosmic mind. *Scr.Math.*, 1934, 2: 125-9.

KEYSER, Cassius Jackson. Mathematics and the question of cosmic mind, with other essays. v, 121 p. (Scripta Mathematica Library, 2) New York: Scripta Mathematica, 1935. [CB 45/277]

KEYSER, Cassius Jackson. The meaning of mathematics. *Scr. Math.*, 1932, 1: 15-28.

KLINE, Morris. Mathematics and the physical world. xi, 546 p., ill. New York: Doubleday & Company (Anchor Books), 1963. [CB 89/498]
A paperback reprinting of the volume which was first publ. New York: Thomas Y. Crowell Co., 1959.

KÖNIGSBERGER, L. Die Mathematik, eine Geistes- oder Naturwissenschaft? 15 p. (*Sitzungsber.Heidelb.Akad.Wiss.Math. Naturwiss.Kl.Abt.A Math.Phys.Wiss*, 1913, 4: no. 8) Heidelberg: 1913.

LITTLEWOOD, J.E. A mathematician's miscellany. viii, 136 p. London: Methuen, 1953.
Reviewed by Geoffrey Matthews, *Scr.Math.*, 1956, 22: 70; by R.J. Gillings, *Australian Math.Teacher*, April 1954, 2 p.

PACOTTE, Julien. La pensée mathématique contemporaine. vi, 128 p. Paris: F. Alcan, 1925. [CB 20/177]

PICARD, Emile. De l'objet des sciences mathématiques. *Rev. Gén.Sci.*, 1924, 35: 325-7.

RADEMACHER, Hans; TOEPLITZ, Otto. Von Zahlen und Figuren. Proben mathematischen Denkens für Liebhaber der Mathematik. v, 164 p., 129 fig. Berlin: Springer, 1930.
Reviewed by O.D. Kellogg, *Amer.Math.Mon.*, 1931, 38: 456-7; by T.G., *Nature*, 1931, 127: 480.

SPEISER, Andreas. Die geistige Arbeit. 216 p. (Wissenschaft und Kultur, 9) Basel-Stuttgart: Birkhäuser Verlag, 1955.
On the mathematical way of thinking.
Reviewed by Carl B. Boyer, *Isis*, 1957, 48: 356-7.

SPEISER, Andreas. Die mathematische Denkweise. 3rd ed. 128 p., 9 pl., front. Basel: Verlag Birkhäuser, 1952.
First published Zürich: 1932.
Reviewed by Carl B. Boyer, *Isis*, 1956, 47: 194-5; 2nd edition reviewed by E. Schubarth, *Experientia*, 1946, 2: 262; by F. Ian G. Rawlins, *Nature*, 1946, 158: 393-5.

STEINHAUS, Hugo. Mathematical snapshots. vi, 266 p., ill., maps. New York: Oxford University Press, 1950.
First publ. New York: Stechert, 1938 and reviewed by Tomlinson Fort, *Amer.Math.Mon.*, 1939, 46: 354.

STRUBECKER, Karl. Mathematisches Denken und exakte Naturbeschreibung. *Naturwiss.Rundsch.*, 1956, 9: 261-5.

SUTTON, O.G. Mathematics in action. xvi, 236 p., ill. New York: Harper, 1960.

VIDAL ABASCAL, Enrique. La nueva matemática. xv, 189 p., ill. Madrid: Editorial Dossat, 1961.

VOSS, Aurel. Über das Wesen der Mathematik. Rede, gehalten am 11. März 1908 in der öffentlichen Sitzung der K. Bayerischen Akademie der Wissenschaften. Erweitert u. mit Anmerkungen versehen. 3rd ed. iv, 123 p. Leipzig: Teubner, 1922.
1st edition, 1908; 2nd edition, 1913.

WAISMANN, Friedrich. Introduction to mathematical thinking. The formulation of concepts in modern mathematics. Foreword by Karl Menger. x, 260 p., fig. New York: Frederick Ungar, 1951.
Reprinted 1959 (New York: Harper). Translation of Einführung in das mathematische Denken (Vienna: Gerold, 1936).

WEYL, Hermann. The mathematical way of thinking. *Science*, 1940, 92: 437-46, 4 fig.
Also published in: Pennsylvania. University. Studies in the history of science, p. 103-23, 4 fig. Philadelphia: 1941.

WIENER, Norbert. Pure and applied mathematics. In: *Structure, method and meaning, Essays in honor of Henry M. Sheffer,* p. 91-8. New York: Liberal Arts Press, 1951.

WITTENBERG, Alexander Israel. Vom Denken in Begriffen. Mathematik als Experiment des reinen Denkens. Mit einem Geleitwort von Paul Bernays. 360 p. (Wissenschaft und Kultur, 12) Basel/Stuttgart: Birkhauser Verlag, 1957. [CB 85/388]

Bke method

AGNEW, P.G. "Multiplication of pears and pence" *Monist,* 1914, 24: 155-7. [CB 5/285]

BOSMANS, Henri. Note historique sur la forme singulière de certains raisonnements par réduction à l'absurde. *Sphinx-Oedipe,* 1925, 20: 113-19.
Mémoire présenté à l'Association Française pour l'Avancement des Sciences, Congrès de Grenoble, Juillet-Août 1925.

BUSSEY, W.H. The origin of mathematical induction. *Amer. Math.Mon.,* 1917, 24: (5), 199-207.
Discussion of the use of this method, in effect, by Maurolico and by Pascal, with some of its recent applications.

DANTZIG, Tobias. The pseudomath. *Sci.Mon.,* 1954, 79: 113-17. [CB 81/265]

FREUDENTHAL, Hans. De begrippen axiom en axiomatiek in de wis- en natuurkunde. [The concepts axiom and axiomatics in mathematics and physics. (In Dutch)] *Simon Stevin,* 1955-56, 30: 156-75.

FREUDENTHAL, Hans. Zur Geschichte der vollständigen Induktion. *Arch.Int.Hist.Sci.,* 1953, 6: 17-37.

IANOVSKAIA, S.A. Iz istorii aksiomatiki. [Sur l'histoire de la méthode axiomatique. (In Russian)]. *Ist.-Mat.Issled.,* 1958, 11: 63-96.

KARPINSKI, Louis C. The methods and aims of mathematical science. *Sch.Sci.Math.,* 1922, 22: 718-22.

LAKATOS, I. Proofs and refutations. *Brit.J.Phil.Sci.,* 1963-64, 14: 1-25, 120-39, 221-45, 296-342.

LARGUIER, Everett H. Postulational methods. *Scr.Math.,* 1941, 8: 99-109.

LORIA, Gino. Metodi matematici. Essenza - tecnica - applicazioni. xv, 276 p., 51 fig. Milan: Hoepli, 1935. [CB 45/278]

MILLER, George Abram. Fundamental laws of operations in mathematics. *Science,* 1940, 91: 571-2.

MILLER, George Abram. Laws relating to mathematical operations. *Science,* 1928, 67: 104.

POLYA, G. Induction and analogy in mathematics. 2 vol. 1. Of mathematics and plausible reasoning. xvi, 280 p.; 2. Patterns of plausible inference. x, 190 p. Princeton: Princeton University Press, 1954. [CB 81/266]

STUYVAERT, Modeste. Introduction à la méthodologie mathématique. 257 p. Gand: Van Rysselverghe & Rombaut, 1923. [CB 16/314]

WINTER, Max. La méthode dans la philosophie des mathématiques. iii, 200 p. Paris: Alcan, 1912.

Bkk logic and foundations (including symbolic logic)

ACKERMANN, W. Solvable cases of the decision problem. viii, 114 p. (Studies in Logic and the Foundations of Mathematics) Amsterdam: North-Holland Publishing Co., 1954.

BECKER, Oskar. Mathematische Existenz. Untersuchungen zur Logik und Ontologie mathematischer Phänomene. viii, 369 p. (*Jahrbuch für Philosophie und phänomenologische Forschung,* 8) Halle a. S.: Max Niemeyer, 1927. [CB 23/235]

BEHMANN, H. Mathematik und Logik. 59 p. (Mathematisch-physikalische Bibliothek, 71) Leipzig: B.G. Teubner, 1927.

BETH, Evert Willem. Les fondements logiques des mathématiques. 222 p. (Collection de Logique Mathématique, 1) Paris: Gauthier-Villars, 1950.
2nd ed. 1955.

BETH, Evert Willem. The foundations of mathematics. A study in the philosophy of science. xxvi, 741 p. (Studies in Logic and the Foundations of Mathematics) Amsterdam: North Holland Publishing Company, 1959.
Based on the author's "Wisbegeerte der Wiskunde" [Philosophy of mathematics. (In Dutch)] Antwerp: 1948 and "Les fondements logiques des mathématiques", *see* above.

BETSCH, Christian. Fiktionen in der Mathematik. xxiv, 372 p. Stuttgart: Fr. Fromann, 1926. [CB 22/256]

BLACK, Max. The nature of mathematics. A critical survey. xiv, 219 p. London: Kegan Paul, 1934.

BOULIGAND, Georges; DESGRANGES, Jean. Le déclin des absolus mathématico-logiques. 270 p. (Collection "Esprit et Méthode") Paris: Société d'Edition d'Enseignement Supérieur, 1949.
Reviewed by Hugues Leblanc, *Isis,* 1951, 42: 71.

BRAND, Walther; DEUTSCHBEIN, Marie. Einführung in die philosophischen Grundlagen der Mathematik. 4, 96 p. Frankfurt a. M.· Diesterweg, 1929.

BURALI-FORTI, Cesare. Logica matematica. 2nd rev. ed. xxxii, 483 p. Milano: Hoepli, 1919.

CARNAP, Rudolf. Formalization of logic. xviii, 159 p. (Studies in Semantics, 2) Cambridge: Harvard University Press, 1943. [CB 64/450]

CARNAP, Rudolf. Foundations of logic and mathematics. viii, 71 p. (International Encyclopedia of Unified Science, 1: no. 3) Chicago: University of Chicago Press, 1939.

CARRUCCIO, Ettore. I fini dei 'calculus ratiocinator' di Leibniz, e la logica matematica del nostro tempo. *Boll. Unione Mat.Ital.,* 1948, 3: 1-16.

CARUGO, Adriano. Cio che resta vivo del "programma hilbertiano" nell'attuale situazione degli studi sui fondamenti della matematica. *Atti Conv.Naz.Logica* (1961), p. 177-88. Torino: Levrotto, 1961.

CASSINA, Ugo. Critica dei principi della matematica e questioni di logica. viii, 520 p. Rome: Edizioni Cremonese, 1961.
Reviewed by Fulvia Skof, *Physis,* 1962, 4: 167-70.

CAVAILLÈS, Jean. Méthode axiomatique et formalisme. 3 vol. 194 p. (Le Progrès de l'Esprit, 9-11; Actualités Scientifiques et Industrielles, 608-10) Paris: Hermann, 1938.
Reviewed by P. Schrecker, *Thalès,* 1937-39, 4: 278-80.

CHEVALLEY, Claude; DANDIEU, Arnaud. Logique hilbertienne et psychologie. *Rev.Phil.,* 1932, 57: 99-111.

COUTURAT, Louis. The algebra of logic. Transl. by L.G. Robinson, with a preface by Ph.E.B. Jourdain. xv, 98 p. Chicago/London: Open Court, 1914.
First published Paris: 1905.

DIECK, W. Der Widerspruch im Richtigen. Gemeinverständliche mathematische Kritik der geltenden Logik. 154 p. Sterkrade: W. Osterkamp, 1926. [CB 22/254]

DINGLER, Hugo. Philosophie der Logik und Arithmetik. 198 p. München: Reinhardt, 1931.

FRAENKEL, Abraham Adolf. On modern problems in the foundations of mathematics. *Scr.Math.,* 1933, 1: 222-7. [CB 39/447]

FRAENKEL, Abraham Adolf. On the crisis of the principle of the excluded middle. *Scr.Math.,* 1951, 17: 5-16.

FRAENKEL, Abraham Adolf. The recent controversies about the foundation of mathematics. *Scr.Math.,* 1947, 13: 17-36.

FREGE, Gottlob. The basic laws of arithmetic; exposition of the system. Transl., ed., and introd. by Montgomery Furth. lxiii, 142 p., bibliogr., app. Berkeley/Los Angeles: University of California Press, 1964.
Translation of: Grundgesetze der Arithmetik (Jena: 1893, 1903).

FREGE, Gottlob. The foundations of arithmetic. A logico-mathematical enquiry into the concept of number. English translation by J.L. Austin. xii, xii, xi, xi, 119, 119 p. New York: Philosophical Library, 1950. [CB 76/361]
The German original text with the English translation on opposite pages.
For German original *see* below.

FREGE, Gottlob. Die Grundlagen der Arithmetik. Eine logisch-mathematische Untersuchung über den Begriff der Zahl. xi, 119 p. Breslau: Marcus, 1934.
Reprint of 1884 edition.

FREYTAG, Bruno. Philosophical problems of mathematics. Translated from the German by Amethe Countess von Zeppelin. 88 p. New York: Philosophical Library, 1951.
Reviewed by Eugene C. Holmes, *Amer.J.Phys.*, 1952, 20: 317-18.
German original: Die ontologischen Grundlagen der Mathematik. Halle/Saale: Niemeyer, 1937.

FRY, Thornton C. A mathematical theory of rational inference. *Scr.Math.*, 1933-34, 2: 205-21.

GERLACH, J.E. Kritik der mathematischen Vernunft. 162 p. Bonn: Friedr. Cohen, 1922.
Reviewed by H. Wieleitner, *Isis*, 1923, 5: 470-1.

GÖDEL, Kurt. On formally undecidable propositions of "Principia mathematica" and related systems. Transl. from the German by B. Meltzer. 72 p. New York: Basic Books, 1962.

GOODSTEIN, R.L. The significance of incompleteness theorems. *Brit.J.Phil.Sci.*, 1963, 14: 208-20.

GOUDGE, Thomas A. Science and symbolic logic. *Scr.Math.*, 1943, 9: 69-80.

HENKIN, Leon. Are logic and mathematics identical? An old thesis of Russell's is reexamined in the light of subsequent developments in mathematical logic. *Science*, 1962, 138: 788-94.

HERBRAND, Jacques. Les bases de la logique hilbertienne. *Rev.Métaphys.Morale*, 1930, 37: 243-55.

HERMES, H. Aufzählbarkeit, Entscheidbarkeit, Berechenbarkeit. Einführung in die Theorie der rekursiven Funktionen. 246 p. (Die Grundlehren der mathematischen Wissenschaften, 109) Berlin/Göttingen/Heidelberg: Springer, 1961.

HEYTING, Arend. Mathematische Grundlagenforschung: Intuitionismus, Beweistheorie. iv, 73 p. (Ergebnisse der Mathematik und ihrer Grenzgebiete, 3) Berlin: Springer, 1934.

HILBERT, David; ACKERMANN, W. Grundzüge der theoretischen Logik. viii, 120 p. (Die Grundlehren der mathematischen Wissenschaften, 27) Berlin: Springer, 1928.
Reviewed by J. Herbrand, *Rev.Gén.Sci.*, 1928, 39: 614; by Heinrich Scholz, *Deut.Lit.Zeitung*, 1930, 1: 137-42.
2nd ed. 1938.

JOURDAIN, Philip E.B. Mathematicians and philosophers. *Monist*, 1915, 25: 633-8. [CB 8/363]
A contrast between the attitudes of mathematicians and philosophers towards logic.

KÖNIG, J. Neue Grundlagen der Logik, Arithmetik und Mengenlehre. 260 p., ill. Leipzig: L. Veit, 1914.

LANGER, Susanne K. An introduction to symbolic logic. 363 p. London: Allen and Unwin, 1937.
Reviewed by Amethe von Zeppelin, *Nature*, 1938, 142: 413-15.

LASKER, Emanuel. On the definition of logic and mathematics. *Scr.Math.*, 1935, 3: 247-9.

LEONARD, Henry S.; GOODMAN, Nelson. The calculus of individuals and its uses. *J.Symbolic Logic*, 1940, 5: 45-55.

LÉVY, Paul. Le raisonnement et l'expérience dans les fondements des mathématiques. *Scientia*, 1930, 47: 325-34.

LEWIS, Clarence Irving. A survey of symbolic logic. vi, 406 p. Berkeley: University of California Press, 1918.
Extensive bibliography.

LEWIS, Clarence Irving; LANGFORD, Cooper Harold. Symbolic logic. xii, 506 p. (Century Philosophy Series) New York: Century, 1932.
Reviewed by Henry Bradford Smith, *Phil.Sci.*, 1934, 1: 239-46.

LIETZMANN, Walther. Aufbau und Grundlage der Mathematik. 6, 89 p., map. (Mathematische Unterrichtswerke. Ergänzungsheft 3) Leipzig: Teubner, 1927. [CB 29/292]

LUSCHEI, Eugene C. The logical systems of Lesniewski. Studies in logic and the foundations of mathematics. Edited by L.E.J. Brouwer, E.W. Beth, and A. Heyting. vii, 361 p., fig., notes, bibliogr. Amsterdam: North-Holland Publishing Company, 1962.

NAGEL, Ernest. "Impossible numbers": a chapter in the history of modern logic. In: Studies in the history of ideas, (3), p. 429-74. New York: Columbia University Press, 1935.

NELSON, Leonard. Beiträge zur Philosophie der Logik und Mathematik. With prefaces and notes by Wilhelm Ackermann, Paul Bernays, and David Hilbert. 128 p. Frankfurt am Main: Verlag Öffentliches Leben, 1959.
Reviewed by Charles Parsons, *J.Phil.*, 1962, 59: 242-6.

NIDDITCH, P. The development of mathematical logic. 88 p. (Monographs in Modern Logic) New York: Free Press of Glencoe, 1962.

PASCH, Moritz. Mathematik am Ursprung. 149 p. (Gesammelte Abhandlungen über Grundfragen der Mathematik, 4) Leipzig: Felix Meiner, 1927. [CB 23/238]

PASCH, Moritz. Mathematik und Logik: vier Abhandlungen. *Arch. Gesamte Psychol.*, 1919, 38: 269-315.
Reprinted Leipzig: Engelmann, 1919. For critical comments *see* Study, Eduard, *below*.

QUINE, Willard Van Orman. Mathematical logic. xiii, 348 p. New York: Norton, 1940.
Reviewed by Bernard Friedman, *Isis*, 1941, 33: 289-91.

QUINE, Willard Van Orman. A system of logistic. x, 204 p. Cambridge: Harvard University Press, 1934. [CB 42/581]
Reviewed by Henry S. Leonard, *Isis*, 1935, 24: 168-72.

QUINE, Willard Van Orman; GOODMAN, Nelson. Elimination of extra-logical postulates. *J.Symbolic Logic*, 1940, 5: 104-9.

RAMSEY, Frank Plumpton. The foundations of mathematics, and other logical essays. Edited by R.B. Braithwaite. With a preface by G.E. Moore. xviii, 292 p. London: Kegan Paul, 1931.

REICHENBACH, Hans. Nomological statements and admissible operations. 140 p., ill. (Studies in Logic and the Foundations of Mathematics) Amsterdam: North-Holland Publishing Co., 1954.

RUSSELL, Bertrand. Introduction to mathematical philosophy. viii, 208 p. London: Allen; New York: Macmillan, 1919.
German translation München: Drei Masken Verlag, 1923 [CB 16/313]; French translation Paris: Payot, 1928.

RUSSELL, Bertrand. On the importance of the logical form. In: International Encyclopedia of Unified Science, no. 1, p. 39-41. Chicago: University of Chicago Press; Cambridge University Press, 1938.

RUSSELL, Bertrand. The philosophical importance of mathematical logic. *Monist*, 1913, 23: 481-93.
Translation of the article "L'importance philosophique de la logistique" in *Rev.Metaphys.Morale*, 1912, vol. 20.

RUSSELL, Bertrand. The principles of mathematics. 2nd ed. xxxix, 534 p. New York: Norton, 1938.
Reviewed by H.T. Davis, *Isis*, 1939, 30: 298-302.

SCHOLZ, H.; HASENJAEGER, G. Grundzüge der mathematischen Logik. xvi, 504 p. (Die Grundlehren der mathematischen Wissenschaften, 106) Berlin: Springer-Verlag, 1961.
Reviewed by E.W. Beth, *Synthese*, 1962, 14: 226-8.

SCHÜTTE, K. Beweistheorie. x, 355 p. (Die Grundlehren der mathematischen Wissenschaften, 103) Berlin: Springer-Verlag, 1960.
Reviewed by J.N. Crossley, *Brit.J.Phil.Sci.*, 1962, 13: 251-3.

SCHWEITZER, A.R. Les idées directrices de la logique génétique des mathématiques. *Rev.Métaphys.Morale*, 1914, 22: 174-96.

SKOLEM, Thoralf. Über einige Grundlagenfragen der Mathematik. 49 p. (*Skr.Norske Vidensk.Akad.Mat.Natur.Kl.*, 1929, no. 4) Oslo: Dybwad, 1929.

STUDY, Eduard. Denken und Darstellung. Logik und Werte, Dingliches und Menschliches in Mathematik und Naturwissenschaft. 4, 43 p. (Sammlung Vieweg, 59) Braunschweig: F. Vieweg u. Sohn, 1921.
Reply to Pasch's "Mathematik und Logik", *see* above.

WAVRE, Rolin. Is there a crisis in mathematics? With reference to the notion of existence and a doubtful application of the law of excluded mean. *Amer.Math.Mon.*, 1934, 41: 488-99.

WAVRE, Rolin. Y a-t-il une crise des mathématiques? A propos de la notion d'existence et d'une application suspecte du principe du tiers exclu. *Rev.Métaphys.Morale,* 1924, 31: 435-70. [CB 16/174]
Apropos of the views of Brouwer and Weyl opposed to those of Hilbert.

WEISSMAN, A. Remarks on the foundation of logic, particularly on the law of excluded middle. *Act.VIIe Congr.Int. Hist.Sci.* (Jerusalem, 1953), p. 629-32. Paris: Hermann, [n.d.]

WHITEHEAD, Alfred North; RUSSELL, Bertrand. Principia mathematica. 2nd ed. 3 vol. Cambridge University Press; New York: Macmillan, 1925-27.
Reviewed in *Isis,* 1926, 8: 226-31 (H.M. Sheffer); 1928, 10: 513-19 (C.H. Langford).

WITTGENSTEIN, Ludwig. Remarks on the foundations of mathematics. Edited by G.H. Wright, R. Rhees and G.E.M. Anscombe. German text and English translation by G.E.M. Anscombe. xix, 204 p. New York: Macmillan, 1956. [CB 82/203]

ZAREMBA, Stanislaw. La logique des mathématiques. 52 p. (Mémorial des Sciences Mathématiques, 15) Paris: Gauthier-Villars, 1926.

Bkk-bv

CHURCH, Alonzo. A bibliography of symbolic logic. *J.Symbolic Logic,* 1936, 1: 121-218. Additions and corrections to same, *J.Symbolic Logic,* 1938, 3: 178-212. [CB 58/567]

STEGMÜLLER, Wolfgang. Neuere Publikationen zur logisch-mathematischen Grundlagenforschung. *Kant-Stud.,* 1963, 54: 317-34. [CB 89/499]

WEISS, Paul. A preliminary draft of a bibliography of contributions to modern logic and the foundations of mathematics (1918 to May 1928). 12 p. Also a supplement dated May 1929. 6 p. Distributed by the author, 690 Widener Library, Cambridge, Mass. Cambridge, Mass.: [1928-29].
Mimeographed. These lists complete the extensive bibliography contained in C.I. Lewis' Survey of symbolic logic, 1918.

Bkk-c

BETH, Evert Willem. Une contribution à l'histoire de la logique mathématique. *Act.VIIIe Congr.Int.Hist.Sci.* (Florence, 1956), p. 1104-6. Paris: Hermann, 1958.

GONSETH, F. Les fondements des mathématiques. De la géométrie d'Euclide à la relativité générale et à l'intuitionisme. Préface de Jacques Hadamard. xvi, 244 p. Paris: Albert Blanchard, 1926. [CB 22/258]

Bkk-mzCAmc for the relation of symbolic logic and time and space *see* CAmc-mzBkk

Bkk-mzWT for the relation of symbolic logic and calculating machines *see* WTmz-Bkk

Bkm/kz other philosophical aspects

Bkm

BRUNSCHVICG, Léon, *et al.* L'idée de la vérité mathématique. *Bull.Soc.Franç.Phil.,* 1913, 13: 46.

Bkn

BENTLEY, Arthur F. Linguistic analysis of mathematics. 311 p. Bloomington, Ind.: Principia Press, 1932.
Reviewed by V.F. Lenzen, *Isis,* 1934, 20: 491-2.

BROUWER, L.E.J. Mathematik, Wissenschaft und Sprache. *Monatsh.Math.Phys.,* 1929, 36: 153-64.

KEYSER, Cassius Jackson. Mathematics and the science of semantics. *Scr.Math.,* 1933-34, 2: 247-60.

Bks

BOULIGAND, Georges. Epistémologie dualiste et analyse historique de quelques théories. *Thalès,* 1949-50, 6: 1-23.
A discussion of some mathematical theories from an epistemological point of view.

BOULIGAND, Georges. Le rôle de l'épistémologie dans l'histoire des mathématiques. *Arch.Int.Hist.Sci.,* 1957, 10: 105-11.

BOULIGAND, Georges. Sur une doctrine de la connaissance mathématique et ses incidences historiques. *Arch.Int.Hist. Sci.,* 1948-49, 2: 291-302.

GREENWOOD, Thomas. Etudes sur la connaissance mathématique. viii, 112 p. Ottawa: University of Ottawa, 1942.
Reviewed by E.T. Whittaker, *Nature,* 1944, 153: 268-9.

HAHN, Hans. Logik, Mathematik und Naturerkennen. 33 p. (Einheitswissenschaft, 2) Wien: Gerold, 1933.
French translation Paris: Hermann, 1935. [CB 44/513]

STUDY, Eduard. Mathematik und Physik. Eine erkenntnistheoretische Untersuchung. 31 p. (Sammlung Vieweg, 65) Braunschweig: F. Vieweg, 1923. [CB 15/229]

WEYL, Hermann. Die heutige Erkenntnislage in der Mathematik. ii, 32 p. (*Symposion,* 1925, no. 3) Erlangen: Weltkreis-verlag, 1926. [CB 21/569]

Bkt

CASANOVA, Gaston. Mathématiques et matérialisme dialectique. Préface de J. Chapelon. 196 p. Paris: Editions Sociales, 1947.
Reviewed by G. Bouligand, *Arch.Int.Hist.Sci.,* 1948-49, 2: 503-5.

Bkv

BOULIGAND, Georges. La causalité mathématique. *Thalès,* 1935, 2: 23-9.

Bkz

LORIA, Gino. Quo vadimus? *Atti III° Congr.Int.Mat.* (Bologna, 1928), (6), p. 421-6. Bologna: Zanichelli, 1932.

Bm fundamental concepts

BETH, Evert Willem. The problem of the existence of mathematical entities. Abstract of paper read on 2nd March 1951. *Bull.Brit.Soc.Hist.Sci.,* 1951, 1: 165.

KEYSER, Cassius Jackson. Three great synonyms: relation, transformation, function. *Scr.Math.,* 1935, 3: 301-16.

MILLER, George Abram. Five fundamental concepts of pure mathematics. *Sci.Mon.,* 1924, 19: 496-501.

MILLER, George Abram. Histoire de cinq concepts fondamentaux des mathématiques. *Enseign.Math.,* 1925, 24: 59-69. [CB 18/606]

MILLER, George Abram. Twelve fundamental mathematical concepts. *Tôhoku Math.J.,* 1931, 34: 230-5.

NEHLBERG, Josephine J. A classification of mathematical concepts. *Synthese,* 1962, 14: 78-86.

NESS, Wilhelm. Über den Mittelwert. *Praxis Math.,* 1962, 4: 156-7.

TANNER, R.C.H. On the role of equality and inequality in the history of mathematics. *Brit.J.Hist.Sci.,* 1962, 1: 159-69.

Bmd

NEVILLE, E.H. Time and the mathematician. *Scr.Math.,* 1938, 5: 171-5.

WINDRED, G. History of mathematical time. *Isis,* 1933, 19: 121-53; 20: 192-219. [CB 39/451]
Reviewed in *Nature,* 1934, 133: 388.

WINDRED, G. The interpretation of imaginary mathematical time. *Math.Gaz.,* 1935, 19: 280-90.
Historical outline with references.

Bmf

BOWES, Julian. Dynamic symmetry. *Scr.Math.,* 1933, 1: 236-45, 5 fig., 3 facs.; 309-14, 1 pl.

SHAW, James Byrnie. Occult symmetry. *Scr.Math.,* 1943, 9: 129-38.

WEYL, Hermann. Symmetry. iii, 168 p., 72 fig. Princeton, N.J.: Princeton University Press, 1952. [CB 79/171]

Bmz relation with other scientific subject fields

for the application of mathematics to other subject fields *see* INDEX

BmzA for relations of mathematics and science *see* AmzB

BmzAF

KENNEDY, E.S. Interrelations between mathematics and philosophy in the last three centuries. *Nat.Math.Mag.*, 1942, 16: 9 p.

BmzC for relations of mathematics and physics *see* CmzB

BmzD for relations of mathematics and chemistry *see* *see* DmzB

BmzN for relations of mathematics and medicine *see* NmzB

BmzOF for relations of mathematics and physiology *see* OFmzB

BmzTP

NILSSON, Nils Gustaf. [The measurement of ships and mathematics. An historical survey. (In Swedish, with English summary)]. *Lychnos*, 1936, 1: 235-47, 248-50. [CB 48/567]
Regarding the way in which the need to determine the size of a ship has influenced the development of mathematics.

Bn means of communication

Bnb

CAJORI, Florian. Empirical generalizations on the growth of mathematical notations. *Isis*, 1924, 6: 391-4. [CB 16/311]

CAJORI, Florian. A history of mathematical notations. 2 vol. 1. Notation in elementary mathematics. xvi, 451 p., 106 fig.; 2. Notations mainly in higher mathematics. xvii, 367 p., 20 fig. Chicago: Open Court Publishing Co., 1928-29.
Reviewed by George Sarton, *Isis*, 1929, 12: 332-6; 13: 129-30.

CAJORI, Florian. History of symbols for *n*-factorial. *Isis*, 1921, 3: 414-18. [CB 9/465]

CAJORI, Florian. Mathematical signs of equality. *Isis*, 1923, 5: 116-25. [CB 15/227]

CAJORI, Florian. The origin of the symbols for degrees, minutes and seconds. *Amer.Math.Mon.*, 1923, 30: 65-6.

CAJORI, Florian. The St. Andrews Cross (x) as a mathematical symbol. *Math.Gaz.*, 1922, 11: 136-43.

CAJORI, Florian. The unification of mathematical notations in the light of history. *Math.Teacher*, 1924, 17: 87-93.

CAJORI, Florian. Varieties of minus sign. *Math.Teacher*, 1923, 16: 295-301. [CB 15/227]

PEANO, G. Importanza dei simboli in matematica. *Scientia*, 1915, 18: 165-73.

PELSENEER, Jean. A propos de notations mathématiques. *Isis*, 1932, 17: 259.

WIELEITNER, Heinrich. Über das x der Mathematiker. *Arch. Gesch.Math.Naturwiss.Tech.*, 1929-30, 12: 93-100.

Bnc

BALL, W.W. Rouse. String figures. 2nd ed. 69 p. Cambridge: Heffer, 1921.
Republ. in collected monographs New York: Chelsea Publishing Co., 1960.

GANDZ, Solomon. Die Harpedonapten oder Seilspanner und Seilknüpfer. *Quellen Stud.Gesch.Math.Abt.A.*, 1930, 1: 255-77. [CB 30/466]

HADDON, Kathleen. Artists in string: string figures, their regional distribution and social significance. x, 174 p., bibliogr. London: Methuen; New York: Dutton, 1930.

Bng

ANDRÉE, Richard V. Cryptanalysis. *Scr.Math.*, 1952, 18: 5-16, bibliogr., pl.

KUNOW, Amelie Deventer von. Kryptographie oder Geheimschriftkunde. *Arch.Gesch.Math.Naturwiss.Tech.*, 1928, 11: 215-18.

LANGIE, André. Cryptography. Translated from the French by James Cruickshank Henderson Macbeth. viii, 192 p. London: Constable, 1922.

PRATT, Fletcher. Secret and urgent: the story of codes and ciphers. 282 p. Indianapolis: Bobbs-Merrill, 1939.
Reviewed by Howard H. Peckham, *Amer.Hist.Rev.*, 1940, 45: 606-7.

Bng-ce-bv

A BIBLIOGRAPHY of cryptography. *Amer.Math.Mon.*, 1943, 50: 345-6.

Bnh

CAJORI, Florian. Origin of the name "mathematical induction". *Amer.Math.Mon.*, 1918, 25: 197-201. [CB 9/489]

KASNER, Edward. New names in mathematics. *Scr.Math.*, 1938, 5: 5-14, 8 fig.

LORIA, Gino. Les noms et les choses. Remarques sur la nomenclature mathématique. *Enseign.Math.*, 1919, 20: 237-44. [CB 8/363]

LORIA, Gino. Sulla funzione euristica del linguaggio matematico. *Archeion*, 1941, 23: 360-3.

SCHIRMER, A. Der Wortschatz der Mathematik nach Alter und Herkunft untersucht. ix, 80 p. (*Zeitschrift für deutsche Wortforschung*, vol. 14, Supplement) Strassburg: Trübner, 1912.

SIMONS, Lao Genevra. Mathematical terms in the supplement to the Oxford English Dictionary - 1933. *Scr.Math.*, 1935, 3: 38-43.

SMITH, David Eugene. Changes in elementary mathematical terms in the last three centuries. *Scr.Math.*, 1935, 3: 291-300.

Bnh-be

JAMES, Glenn; JAMES, Robert C.; ed. Mathematics dictionary. Giving the meaning of the basic mathematical words and phrases, including an exhaustive covering of the terms from Arithmetic through the Calculus and the technical terms commonly used in the applications of these subjects. Rev. ed. 9, 273 p; tables, 46 p. Van Nuys, Calif.: Digest Press, 1943.
Reviewed by Marguerite D. Darkow, *Scr.Math.*, 1944, 10: 186-8.

Bo study and teaching

BRANFORD, Benchara. A study of mathematical education including the teaching of arithmetic. 2nd ed. xii,420 p. Oxford: Clarendon Press, 1921.
First published 1908. German translation 1913 (Leipzig: Teubner).

CAJORI, Florian. Mathematics in liberal education. A critical examination of the judgments of prominent men of the ages. 169 p. Boston: Christopher Publishing House, 1928. [CB 25/411]
This is essentially a collection of quotations from the writings of philosophers and scientists of all times dealing with the educational value of mathematics.

LORIA, Gino. Durante quarant' anni di insegnamento, confessioni e ricordi. *Boll.Mat.*, *Sez.Stor.Bibliogr.*, 1926, ser. 2, 5: lxv-lxxvii.

MURNAGHAN, Francis D. Teaching of mathematics in high school and college. *Bull.Phil.Soc.Wash.*, 1962, 16: 103-20.

REEVE, William David. The place of mathematics in modern education. *Scr.Math.*, 1938, 5: 23-31, 111-16.

SMITH, David Eugene. Mathematics in the training for citizenship. *Teach.Coll.Rec.*, 1917, 18: 15.

Bo-ce-bv

SMITH, David Eugene; GOLDZIEHER, Ch. Bibliography of the teaching of mathematics, 1900-1912. 95 p. Washington, D.C.: Bureau of education, 1912.

Bo-cj

L'Enseignement Mathématique. Organe officiel de la Commission Internationale de l'Enseignement Mathématique. *Isis*, 1913, 1: 257.

Bo-mzAFo

GREBE, W. Mathematischer und philosophischer Unterricht in ihrer gegenseitigen Befruchtung. *Z.Math.Naturwiss.Unterricht*, 1923, 54: 193-201. [CB 17/589]

WERNICKE, A. Mathematik und philosophische Propädeutik. 138 p. Leipzig: Teubner, 1913.

Bo-qx

CONFÉRENCE INTERNATIONALE DE L'ENSEIGNEMENT MATHÉMATIQUE, Paris, 1914. Compte rendu. *Enseign.Math.*, 1914, 16: 165-226, 245-356. [CB 6/453]

Boc

BIRKEMEIER, Wilhelm. Ueber den Bildungswert der Mathematik. Ein Beitrag zur philosophischen Pädagogik. vi, 191 p. (Wissenschaft und Hypothese, 25) Leipzig: Teubner, 1923. [CB 15/226]

CARVER, W.B. Thinking versus manipulation. *Amer.Math.Mon.*, 1937, 44: 359-63. [CB 51/251]

JONES, Samuel Isaac. Mathematical wrinkles; a handbook for teachers and private learners. Rev. ed. x, 361 p. Nashville, Tenn.: The author, [1929].
First published 1912.

LOEFFLER, Eugen. Ueber den Bildungswert der mathematischen Wissenschaften. *Jahresh.Ver.Math.Naturwiss.Ulm*, 1907-8, 14: 21.

Bod

LIETZMANN, Walter. Methodik des mathematischen Unterrichts. 3 vol. 1. Allgemeine Methodik. viii, 387 p. 1919. 2. Didaktik der einzelnen Unterrichtsgebiete. xii, 440 p. 1916. 3. Didaktik der angewandten Mathematik. xii, 234 p. 1924. Leipzig: Quelle u. Meyer, 1916-24. [CB 17/590]
2nd ed. of vol. 2 1923.

Bom

DIJKSTERHUIS, E.J. De Wiskunde op het "Gymnasium". [Mathematics in the Grammar School. (In Dutch)]. *Euclides*, 1952, 209-26.

KARPINSKI, Louis C. Lectures on the history of secondary school mathematics. In: Proceedings of the Mathematics conference arranged by the Head Mistresses' Association and the Secondary Education Board, Exeter, N.H., September 6th to 11th, 1936, p. 20-2.
Mimeographed.

LIETZMANN, Walter. Erkenntnislehre im mathematischen Unterricht der Oberklassen. 68 p. Charlottenburg: Mundus-Verlag, 1921. [CB 17/590]

LORIA, Gino. La préparation théorique et pratique des professeurs de mathématiques de l'enseignement secondaire dans les divers pays. Rapport général. *Enseign.Math.*, 1933, 32: 5-20.

REEVE, William David. The teaching of mathematics in the schools. *Scr.Math.*, 1935, 3: 138-42.

Bop

KARPINSKI, Louis C. The origin of the mathematics as taught to freshmen. *Scr.Math.*, 1939, 6: 133-40, 3 fig.

SEIDLIN, Joseph. A critical study of the teaching of elementary college mathematics. x, 108 p. New York: Teachers College Bureau of Publications, 1931.
Reviewed by Roger A. Johnson, *Amer.Math.Mon.*, 1932, 39: 114-15.

Bov

DEFRISE, Pierre. Visages de la mathématique: essai de semi-vulgarisation de quelques aspects fondamentaux de la pensée mathématique. 126 p. Brussels: Office de Publicité, [194-?]. [CB 73/167]
Reviewed by J.M. Feld, *Scr.Math.*, 1948, 14: 275.

KARPINSKI, Louis C. The obligations of a university teacher who writes popular science. Illustrated by "Mathematics for the million" [by Lancelot Hogben]. *Sch.Soc.*, 1938, 48: 338-40.

LORIA, Gino. La volgarizzazione delle scienze di ragionamento. *Scientia*, 1948, 42: 33-8.

Bp/r organizational and professional aspects

Bpw

SERGESCU, Pierre. Sur les relations mathématiques franco-roumaines. *Bull.Sci.Roumain*, 1952, 1: 5-17.

VETTER, Quido. Relations mathématiques entre les pays Tchèques et les pays de la Péninsule Ibérique, l'Amérique et l'Extrême Orient. *Act.IIIe Congr.Int.Hist.Sci.* (Portugal, 1934), 8 p. Lisbon: 1936.

Bqd

SPARN, Enrique. Las sociedades matemáticas con el mayor número de socios. *Bol.Mat.*, 1930, 3: 117-20.

Bqx

BOULIGAND, Georges. Quelques aspects des conférences internationales des sciences mathématiques (Genève, 1933-37). *Rev.Sci.*, 1938, 76: 221-6.

INTERNATIONAL CONGRESS OF MATHEMATICIANS, Strasbourg, 1920. Comptes rendus. xlvii, 670 p. Toulouse: Edouard Privat, 1921.
Section 4 (p. 613-64) contains papers on the philosophy, history and teaching of mathematics.
All later congresses (held every 4th year until 1936 and in 1954, 1958 and 1963) have a section covering the history and philosophy of mathematics.

Brd

SMITH, David Eugene. Religio Mathematici. *Amer.Math.Mon.*, 1921, 28: 339-49; also *Teachers Coll.Rec.*, 1921. [CB 12/640]

Brk-jd

LORIA, Gino. Matematici nella vita pubblica. Contributi storici alla psicologia dell' uomo di scienzia. *Arch.Stor.Sci.*, 1923, 4: 144-55. [CB 15/228]

Bs relations with society

CARMICHAEL, Robert D. The larger human worth of mathematics. *Sci.Mon.*, 1922, 14: 447-68.

FORSYTH, Andrew Russell. Mathematics in life and thought. 34 p. Cardiff: University of Wales Press Board, 1929.
Lecture delivered at the University College of Swansea on November 14, 1928.

JACKSON, Dunham. The human significance of mathematics. *Amer.Math.Mon.*, 1928, 35: 406-11.

KOKOMOOR, Franklin Wesley. Mathematics in human affairs. xi, 754 p. New York: Prentice-Hall, 1942.
Reviewed by G. Baley Price, *Science*, 1943, 97: 94.

Bsb

FETTWEIS, Ewald. Ethnologie und Geschichte der Mathematik. *Anthropos*, 1937, 32: 277-83.

FETTWEIS, Ewald. Parallelerscheinungen auf mathematischem Gebiet bei jetzt lebenden Naturvölkern und bei Kulturvölkern vergangener Zeiten. *Scientia*, 1931, 39: 423-36; French transl.suppl. 186-98.

STRUIK, D.J. Concerning mathematics. *Sci.Soc.*, 1936, 1: 81-101.

STRUIK, D.J. On the sociology of mathematics. *Sci.Soc.*, 1942, 6: 58-70.

WHITE, Leslie A. The locus of mathematical reality: an anthropological footnote. *Phil.Sci.*, 1947, 14: 289-303.

Bsc

KEYSER, Cassius Jackson. Man and men. *Scr.Math.*, 1943, 9: 232-6.

KLINE, Morris. The role of mathematics in civilization. *Confluence*, 1954, 3: 196-206.

Bsk

COLMAN, E. The present crisis in the mathematical sciences and general outlines for their reconstruction. 15 p. (Science at the Cross Roads) London: Kniga, 1931. [CB 38/592]

Bsm

DRESDEN, Arnold. The migration of mathematicians. *Amer. Math.Mon.*, 1942, 49: 415-29.

Bsp

MORSE, Marston. Mathematics and the maximum scientific effort in total war. *Sci.Mon.*, 1943, 56: 50-5.

Bst

LORIA, Gino. Mathematics and law. *Scr.Math.*, 1933, 1: 276.

Bt relations with the humanities

HOYLAND, Geoffrey. The tyranny of mathematics. An essay in the symbiosis of science, poetry and religion. 52 p. London: Student Christian Movement Press, 1945.

KEYSER, Cassius Jackson. Mathematics as a culture clue. *Scr. Math.*, 1933, 1: 185-203.

KEYSER, Cassius Jackson. Mathematics as a culture clue, and other essays. vii, 277 p. New York: Scripta Mathematica, 1947.
Reviewed by Carl B. Boyer, *Isis*, 1948, 38: 256-7.

KEYSER, Cassius Jackson. The rôle of mathematics in the tragedy of our modern culture. *Scr.Math.*, 1939, 6: 81-7.

KLIEM, Fritz. Humanismus und Mathematik. 60 p., 1 pl. (Sammlung Neudeutscher Humanismus, 7) Breslau: Trewendt & Grenier, 1929.
Reviewed by H. Wieleitner, *Mitt.Gesch.Med.*, 1930, 29: 71.

SCHAAF, William L., ed. Mathematics: our great heritage. Essays on the nature and cultural significance of mathematics. xi, 291 p. New York: Harper, 1948. [CB 73/167]

SULLIVAN, John William N. Mathematics and culture. *Math. Gaz.*, 1932, 16: 243-53.

WEBER, Maurice. La valeur "culturelle" des mathématiques. *Enseign.Sci.*, 1934, 8: 45-50.

Btd

GRANVILLE, W.A. The fourth dimension and the Bible. 119 p. Boston, Mass.: Badger, 1922.
Reviewed by David Eugene Smith, *Amer.Math.Mon.*, 1927, 34: 152.

Bth

ARCHIBALD, Raymond Clare. Mathematicians, and poetry and drama. *Science*, 1939, 89: 19-26, 46-50. [CB 57/237]

Btk

ARCHIBALD, Raymond Clare. Poems about mathematicians. *Scr. Math.*, 1933, 1: 364.

BUCHANAN, Scott. Poetry and mathematics. 197 p. New York: John Day, 1929. [CB 27/538]

Btp

BIRKHOFF, George D. Aesthetic measure. xiii, 225 p. Cambridge: Harvard University Press, 1933.
Reviewed by Derrick N. Lehmer, *Scr.Math.*, 1933, 2: 55-9.

KRULL, Wolfgang. Über die ästhetische Betrachtungsweise in der Mathematik. *Sitzungsber.Phys.-Med.Soz.Erlangen*, 1929, 61: 207-20.

SCHILLINGER, Joseph. The mathematical basis of the arts. Part one, Science and esthetics. Part two, Theory of regularity and coordination. Part three, Technology of art production. xii, 696 p. New York: Philosophical Library, 1948.
Reviewed by R.C. Archibald, *Isis*, 1949, 40: 293-5.

SMITH, David Eugene. The poetry of mathematics and other essays. iv, 90 p. (Scripta Mathematica Library, 1) New York: Scripta Mathematica, 1934.
Reviewed by E.T. Bell, *Amer.Math.Mon.*, 1935, 42: 558-62.

Btq

ALTSHILLER-COURT, Nathan. Art and mathematics. *Scr.Math.*, 1935, 3: 103-11, portr.

LIETZMANN, Walther. Mathematik und bildende Kunst. 150 p. Breslau: Hirt, 1930.
Reviewed by David Eugene Smith, *Amer.Math.Mon.*, 1931, 38: 224-5.

MONTEL, Paul. L'art et les mathématiques. *Sciences*, 1949, 76: 61-80, 5 fig.

SMITH, David Eugene. Mathematica Gothica. 30 p. Paris: Presses Universitaires de France, 1925. [CB 18/607]

WOLFF, Georg. Mathematik und Malerei. 2nd ed. 85 p., ill. (Mathematisch-physikalische Bibliothek, 20/21) Leipzig: B.G. Teubner, 1925. [CB 18/609]
1st edition Leipzig: Teubner, 1916.

Btt

ARCHIBALD, Raymond Clare. Mathematicians and music. *Amer. Math.Mon.*, 1924, 31: 1-25. [CB 16/311]
Reprints distributed by the author contain a typewritten page of corrigenda et addenda.

ARCHIBALD, Raymond Clare. Mathematics and music. *Argosy* (Sackville, N.B.), 1924, 50: 135-42.

SMITH, David Eugene. The relation of music to mathematics. *Teachers Coll.Rec.*, March 1927, 28: 664-8.

Bv ethnic groups

Bvf

SEVERI, Francesco. Peut-on parler d'un esprit latin même dans les mathématiques? *Rev.Sci.*, 1935, 73: 581-9.

Bvm

FRAENKEL, Abraham A. Jewish mathematics and astronomy. *Scr. Math.*, 1960, 25: 33-47.

FRAENKEL, Abraham A. [The Jewish contribution to mathematics and astronomy. (In Hebrew)]. 32 p. Tel-Aviv: 1947.
Reviewed in *Scr.Math.*, 1947, 13: 78.

Bw in different countries

LORIA, Gino. Les contributions des différents peuples au développement des mathématiques. 1re partie. Evénements mémorables et hommes représentatifs dans l'histoire des mathématiques. 2me partie. Le caractère international de la pensée mathématique. *Scientia*, 1921, 29: 169-84, 235-62. [CB 11/444]

Bw-o

VETTER, Quido. Nové směry v matematickém vyučování v cizině. [New trends in mathematical education abroad. (In Czech)]. *Střední Škol.*, [1936?], 16: 258-70.

Bwa North and Latin America

Bwa-ce-bv

KARPINSKI, Louis C. Bibliography of mathematical works printed in America through 1850. With the coöperation for Washington libraries of Walter F. Shenton. xxvi, 697 p., 908 fig. Ann Arbor: University of Michigan Press, 1940.
Reviewed by George Sarton, *Isis*, 1941, 33: 293-4.

KARPINSKI, Louis C. Supplement to the bibliography of mathematical works printed in America through 1850. *Scr.Math.*, 1941, 8: 233-6.
Supplement to the book published in Ann Arbor in 1940, *see* above.

Bwb North America

BIRKHOFF, G.D. Fifty years of American mathematics. In: American Mathematical Society. Semicentennial addresses, p. 270-315. (Semicentennial Publications, 2) New York: American Mathematical Society, 1938. [CB 57/190]
Part also published in *Science*, 1938, 88: 461-7.

MILLER, George Abram. American mathematics during three quarters of a century. Address of vice-president and chairman of Section A. Mathematics, American Association for the Advancement of Science (Cincinnati, Ohio, December 1923) *Science*, 1924, 59: 1-7.

MILLER, George Abram. Background of mathematics in America. *Science*, 1934, 80: 356-7.

SLAUGHT, H.E. Retrospect and prospect for mathematics in America. *Amer.Math.Mon.*, 1920, 27: 443-51.
An excellent summary of the progress of the serious study of mathematics in the United States and Canada in the period from 1910 to 1920.

SMITH, David Eugene; GINSBURG, Jekuthiel. A history of mathematics in America before 1900. x, 209 p. (Carus Mathematical Monographs, 5) Chicago: Open Court, 1934.
Reviewed by Frederick E. Brasch, *Isis*, 1935, 22: 553-6.

Bwb-ce-bx

MICHIGAN UNIVERSITY. Mathematica Americana. A guide to an exhibition in the William L. Clements Library at the University of Michigan, [by Karpinski, Louis C.] set up particularly for the meeting of the American Institute of Statisticians, the Mathematical Association of America, and the American Mathematical Society. 7 p., ill. Ann Arbor: 1935.

Bwb-cj

KARPINSKI, Louis C. *The American Mathematical Monthly*. *Isis*, 1920, 3: 490-1.

Bwb-nb

CAJORI, Florian. American contributions to mathematical symbolism. *Amer.Math.Mon.*, 1925, 32: 414-16.

Bwb-om

CAIRNS, S.S. Mathematics and the educational octopus. *Sci. Mon.*, 1953, 76: 231-40.
An appraisal of anti-intellectualism in the public secondary schools.

Bwb-op

BROWN, Kenneth E. General mathematics in American colleges. 167 p. New York: Teachers College Bureau of Publications, 1943. [CB 69/226]
Reviewed by Moses Richardson, *Scr.Math.*, 1944, 10: 189-90.

COOLIDGE, Julian Lowell. The story of mathematics at Harvard. *Harvard Alumni Bull.*, 1924, 26: 372-8.

Bwb-qd

AMERICAN MATHEMATICAL SOCIETY. The semicentennial celebration of the Society, Sept. 6-9, 1938. By the secretaries. *Bull. Amer.Math.Soc.*, 1939, 45: 1-46, pl.

ARCHIBALD, Raymond Clare, ed. A semi-centennial history of the American Mathematical Society, 1888-1938. 262 p. (Semi-centennial Publication, 1) New York: American Mathematical Society, 1938.
Reviewed by Mina Rees, *Scr.Math.*, 1940, 7: 121-5; by I. Bernard Cohen, *Isis*, 1940, 31: 473-5.

MEDER, Albert E., Jr. The American Mathematical Society, 1888-1938. *Science*, 1938, 88: 230-2.

Bwc Latin America

LORIA, Gino. Le matematiche in Ispagna e in Argentina. 24 p. (Union Matemática Argentina publicaciones, 1) Buenos Aires: 1938.

Bwc-ce

KARPINSKI, Louis C. Mathematics in Latin America. A brief survey of their publications to 1850. *Scr.Math.*, 1947, 13: 59-63.

Bwd Europe

SULLIVAN, John William Navia. The history of mathematics in Europe from the fall of Greek science to the rise of the conception of mathematical rigour. 109 p. London: Oxford University Press, 1925. [CB 18/607]

Bwd-qx

VETTER, Quido. Le deuxième Congrès des mathématiciens des pays slaves, Prague, 23-28, Septembre 1934. *Enseign.Math.*, 1934, 33: 367-71.

Bwe British Isles

GIBSON, G.A. Sketch of the history of mathematics in Scotland to the end of the 18th century. *Proc.Edinb.Math.Soc., ser. 2*, 1927-29, 1: 1-18, 71-93. [CB 23/237 and CB 24/525]

GUNTHER, Robert William Theodore. Early science in Oxford. Pt. 2. Mathematics. 101 p. London: Oxford University Press, 1922.
Bound up with Parts 1, 3-4 as volume 1.
Reviewed by George Sarton, *Isis*, 1924, 6: 449-53.

LE LIONNAIS, F. La contribution de la Grande Bretagne au développement des sciences mathématiques depuis un siècle. *Osiris*, 1954, 11: 40-9.

LORIA, Gino. Le glorie matematiche della Granbretagna. *Isis*, 1914, 1: 637-54.

Bwe-cj

ARCHIBALD, Raymond Clare. Notes on some minor English mathematical serials. *Math.Gaz.*, 1929, 18: 379-400. [CB 27/537]

LORIA, Gino. Il *Philosophical Magazine* e la storia delle matematiche. *Riv.Stor.Crit.Sci.*, 1916, 7: 1-5. [CB 8/362]

Bwe-da

PIAGGIO, H.T.H. Three Sadleirian professors: A.R. Forsyth, E.W. Hobson and G.H. Hardy. *Math.Gaz.*, 1931, 15: 461-5. [CB 35/275]

Bwe-o

WILSON, Duncan K. The history of mathematical teaching in Scotland to the end of the eighteenth century. viii, 99 p. London: University of London Press, 1935.
Reviewed by A. Inglis, *Math.Gaz.*, 1936, 20: 164-5.

Bwe-om

SIDDONS, A.W. Progress. *Math.Gaz.*, 1936, 20: 7-26.
Progress in the teaching of mathematics in English schools during the last hundred years.

Bwe-qg

LE LABORATOIRE mathématique de l'Université d'Édimbourg. [Notice of its founding.] *Isis*, 1913, 1: 257.

Bwf France

PICARD, Emile. Les sciences mathématiques en France depuis un demi-siècle. vi, 25 p. Paris: Gauthier-Villars, 1917.
Originally published in: Un demi-siècle de civilisation française, 1870-1915, par M. Baillaud [*et al.*] 472 p. Paris: Hachette, 1916.

SERGESCU, Petre. Essais scientifiques, 1941-1943. 264 p. Timisoara: Tipografia Romanesca, 1944.
Mainly on French mathematics of various periods.
Reviewed by R. Taton, *Arch.Int.Hist.Sci.*, 1949, 2: 497-8.

SERGESCU, Petre. Les sciences mathématiques. In: Sergescu, P.; Rostand, J.; Boutaric, A. Les sciences. 182 p. (Collection "Tableau du XXe siècle, 2) Paris: Denoël et Steele, 1933. [CB 51/539]
In France.

SERGESCU, Petre. Quelques dates remarquables dans l'évolution des mathématiques en France. 32 p. (Monografii Matematice, Publicate sub Ingrijirea Profesorilor de la Sectiunea de Matematici a Universitătii din Clujj, 4) Timisoara: "Tipografia Românească", 1941. [CB 62/74]

SMITH, David Eugene. Historical mathematical Paris. 48 p. Paris: Les Presses Universitaires de France, 1924.
On the many places in Paris of special interest to mathematicians. Most of this essay first appeared in *Amer.Math.Mon.*, 1923, 30: 107-13, 166-74.

Bwf-da

LEBESQUE, Henri. Les professeurs de mathématiques du Collège de France: Humbert et Jordan; Roberval et Ramus. *Rev.Sci.*, 1922, 60: 249-62.

Bwf-k

BOCKSTAELE, Paul. Het intuïtionisme bij de franse wiskundigen. [Intuitionism in French mathematics. (In Dutch)]. 123 p. (*Verhandel.Vlaam.Acad.Wetensch.Lett.Schone Kunsten Belg.Kl.Wetensch.*, 11: no. 32) Brussels: Paleis der Academiën, 1949. [CB 76/394]

Bwf-pw

SERGESCU, Pierre. Sur les relations mathématiques francoroumaines. *Bull.Sci.Roumain*, 1952, 1: 5-17.

Bwg/wh Central Europe

Bwg-br

Deutsche Mathematik. Im Auftrage der Deutschen Forschungsgemeinschaft. Vol. 1-7. Leipzig: Hirzel, 1936-44.

Bwg-cj

ARCHIBALD, R.C. The Hamburg mathematical society publications. *Scr.Math.*, 1932, 1: 85-6.

Bwg-k

DUBISLAW, Walter. Les recherches sur la philosophie des mathématiques en Allemagne. 1. Les problèmes mathématiques; 2. Les problèmes épistémologiques. *Rech.Phil.*, 1932, 1: 299-311.

Bwg-o

COURANT, Richard. Mathematical education in Germany before 1933. *Amer.Math.Mon.*, 1938, 45: 601-7.

WIELEITNER, Heinrich. Die Entwicklung des mathematischen und naturwissenschaftlichen Unterrichts in Bayern. *Festschrift des Deutschen Vereins zur Förderung des mathematischen und naturwissenschaftlichen Unterrichts*, p. 53-64. Würzburg: 1930.

Bwg-om

GRUNDEL, Friedrich. Die Mathematik an den deutschen höheren Schulen. 1. Von der Zeit Karls des Grossen bis zum Ende des 17. Jahrhunderts. vi, 110 p.; 2. Vom Anfang des 18. Jahrhunderts bis zum Anfang des 19. Jahrhunderts. vi, 148 p. (*Z.Math.Naturwiss.Unterricht* - Beihefte 12 and 13) Leipzig: Teubner, 1928-29. [CB 27/540]

Bwg-op

LOREY, Wilhelm. Das Studium der Mathematik an den deutschen Universitäten seit Anfang des 19. Jahrhunderts. xii, 431 p., 13 fig., 4 tables. (*Abhandlungen über den mathematischen Unterricht in Deutschland*, 3: no. 9) Leipzig: Teubner, 1916.

Bwh

DIANNI, Jadwiga; WACHULKA, Adam. Z dziejów polskiej mysli matematycznej. [Pages in the history of Polish mathematical thought. (In Polish)]. 140 p., 64 ill. Warsaw: Panstwowe Zaklady Wydawnictw Szkolnych, 1957.
Reviewed by S. Dobrzycki, *Arch.Int.Hist.Sci.*, 1958, 11: 201-2.

JELITAI, József. The history of mathematics in Hungary before 1830. Translated by G. Waldo Dunnington. *Nat.Math.Mag.*, 1937, 12: 125-30.

JELITAI, József. Zur Geschichte der Mathematik in Ungarn. *Archeion*, 1936, 18: 350-4.

MARCZEWSKI, Edward. [Le développement des mathématiques en Pologne. (In Polish with summary in French)]. 47 p. (Polska Akademia Umiejetności, Historia Nauki Polskiej w Monografiach, 1) Cracow: 1948.

SZÜCS, Adolphe. L'histoire des mathématiques en Hongrie. (7th International Congress of Historical Sciences, Warsaw, 1933). *Bull.Int.Comm.Hist.Sci.*, 1933, 5: 284-91.

VETTER, Quido. La Boemia nella storia della matematica. Supplemento alla "Guida allo studio della storia delle matematiche", del Prof. Gino Loria (Milano: Hoepli, 1916). *Boll.Mat.*, 1924, 31 p.

VETTER, Quido. The development of mathematics in Bohemia. *Amer.Math.Mon.*, 1923, 30: 47-58.

VETTER, Quido. Kratkii obzor razvitiia matematiki v cheshskikh zemliakh do Belogorskoi bitvy. [A sketch of the progress of mathematics in Bohemian territory up to the battle of Biela Gora. (In Russian)]. *Ist.-Mat.Issled.*, 1958, 11: 461-514.

VETTER, Quido. Matematické vědy v klášterech jezovitských na půdě republiky Československé. [The mathematical sciences in Jesuit monasteries in the territory of the Czechoslovak Republic. (In Slovak)] *Compt.Rend.IIe Congr.Math.Pays Slaves* (Prague, 1934), p. 263-4. Praha: 1935.

VETTER, Quido. Sullo sviluppo della matematica in Boemia. *Period.Mat.*, Nov. 1921, 1: 380-2.

Bwh-da

GOLAB, Stanislaw. O dorobku matematyków polskich w nauce swiatowej. [On the achievements of Polish mathematicians. (In Polish)]. *Zycie Nauk.*, 1947, 3: 79-91.

Bwh-om

VETTER, Quido. O českých matematicích z řad profesorstva středoškolského. [On Czech mathematicians in secondary education. (In Czech)] 7 p. Prag: 1925.

Bwh-oq

VETTER, Quido. Šest století matematického a astronomického učeni na universitě Karlově v Praze. [Six centuries of the teaching of mathematics and astronomy at the Karlově University of Prague. (In Czech, with Russian summary)] *Vestník Královské České Společnosti Nauk, Třida Mat.Přírodovědecká*, 1952, 14: 1-40.

Bwh-pw

VETTER, Quido. Relations mathématiques ... *See* Bpw

Bwi/wj Southern Europe

Bwi

AMODEO, Federico. Vita matematica napoletana; studio storico, biografico, bibliografico. 2 vol. Napoli: 1905, 1924. [CB 17/588]

AMODEO, Federico. Vita matematica napoletana del 1650 al 1860. *Atti Accad.Pontaniana*, 1902-23, passim.
Reviewed, with list of the 17 papers, by Aldo Mieli, *Arch.Stor.Sci.*, 1923, 4: 286.
Also published as above.

BOMPIANI, Enrico. Italian contributions to modern mathematics. *Amer.Math.Mon.*, 1931, 38: 83-95.

BORTOLOTTI, Ettore. Il primato dell'Italia nel campo della matematica. *Atti Soc.Ital.Progr.Sci.XXVII Riunione* (Bologna, 1938), (3), p. 596-617. Roma: 1939.

LORIA, Gino. Contributi dati dall'Italia alle matematiche pure, dai tempi più remoti ai giorni nostri. *Mathematica*, 1938, 14: 155-79.

LORIA, Gino. L'ininterrotta continuità del pensiero matematico italiano. *Period.Mat.*, 1932, 4: 1-16.

Bwi-cj

ARCHIBALD, Raymond Clare. Italian mathematical periodicals. *Scr.Math.*, 1933, 1: 275.

Bwi-da

LORIA, Gino. Matematici liguri dei secoli XV-XVIII. *Boll. Mat.*, 1943, 39: i-iii.
Notes concerning L.B. Alberti, G.B. Baliani, V. Rainieri, G.D. Cassini, G.F. Maraldi and G. Saccheri.

Bwi-oq

BORTOLOTTI, Ettore. L'école mathématique de Bologne. Aperçu historique. 75 p., portr. Bologna: Zanichelli, 1928. [CB 27/538]
Presented to the delegates at the 3rd International Mathematical Conference at Bologna, September 1928. Also Italian edition: Cenno storico su la Scuola Matematica di Bologna.

BORTOLOTTI, Ettore. La storia della matematica nella Università di Bologna. 226 p. Bologna: Zanichelli, 1947.
Reviewed by A. Natucci, *Arch.Int.Hist.Sci.*, 1951, 4: 208-10.

Bwi-or

AGOSTINI, Amedeo. Gli obblighi dei lettori di matematica nell'antico studio bolognese. *Period.Mat.*, 1923, 3: 1-4. [CB 14/550]
The professors of mathematics at the University of Bologna were obliged to compile an astrological almanac.

Bwj

AMADO LÓRIGA, Santiago. Tres siglos de influencia del ejército en el progreso y divulgación de las matemáticas en España. *Rev.Acad.Cienc.Exact.Fis.-Quim.Nat.Zaragoza*, 1964, *ser.* 2, 19: 9-27.

GOMES TEIXEIRA, Francisco. História das matemáticas em Portugal. vi, 300 p. Lisbon: Academia das Ciências, 1934.
Reviewed by Aldo Mieli, *Archeion*, 1935, 17: 291-5.

GOMES TEIXEIRA, Francisco. Les mathématiques en Portugal. *Enseign.Math.*, 1924, 23: 137-42.

GUIMARAES, Rodolphe. Les mathématiques en Portugal. 2nd ed. 2 vol. 659 p. (including Appendice I). Appendice II. La période 1909-10. 107 p. Coimbre: Imprimerie de l'Université; Paris: Gauthier-Villars, 1909, 1911.

LORIA, Gino. Le matematiche in Ispagna e in Argentina. 24 p. (Union Matemática Argentina publicaciones, 1) Buenos Aires: 1938.

LORIA, Gino. Le matematiche in Ispagna ieri ed oggi. Parte I[a]. Dal secolo XVI alla metà del XIX. Parte II[a]. I matematici moderni. *Scientia*, 1919, 25: 353-9, 441-9.

LORIA, Gino. Le matematiche in Portogallo. Ciò che furono, ciò che sono. *Scientia*, 1919, 26: 1-9.

Bwj-da

RIBEIRO DOS SANCTOS, Antonio. Memorias historical sobre alguns mathematicos Portuguezes, e estrangeiros domiciliarios em Portugal, ou nas conquistas. *Mem.Litt.Port. Acad.Cienc.Lisboa*, 1812, 8: 148-229.

Bwk/wm Northern Europe

Bwk

ALLIAUME, Maurice. Esquisse de l'histoire des mathématiques et de l'astronomie en Belgique depuis 1830. *Rev.Quest.Sci.*, 1930, 18: 267-305; also in *Histoire de la Belgique contemporaine, 1830-1914*, 3: p. 373-402. Bruxelles: A. Dewit, 1930.

BOCKSTAELE, P. De geschiedschrijving der wiskunde in Vlaanderen. [The historiography of mathematics in Flanders. (In Dutch)] *Euclides*, 1948, 23: 204-8.

ERRERA, Alfred; GODEAUX, Lucien. Les mathématiques en Belgique de 1830 à 1930. *Mathésis* (Gand), 1932, 46: suppl., 17 p.

GODEAUX, Lucien. Esquisse d'une histoire des sciences mathématiques en Belgique. 60 p., front. (Collection Nationale, 4me série, 39) Bruxelles: Office de Publicité, 1943. [CB 69/226]

GODEAUX, Lucien. L'état actuel des recherches mathématiques en Belgique. *Bull.Soc.Sci.Liége*, 1950, 19: 514-24.

GODEAUX, Lucien. Les sciences mathématiques dans le Hainaut. *Bull.Soc.Sci.Liége*, 1946, 15: 152-62.

Bwk-da

BELFROID, J. Notes sur les fastes de la mathématique belge. *Études Cl.*, 1939, 8: 367-78.
Short notes on Simon Stevin, Godefroid Wendelin, René François de Sluse, Adolphe Quetelet, Joseph Plateau, Paul Mansion, Constantin Le Paige.

GLODEN, Albert. La vie et l'oeuvre scientifique de neuf mathématiciens belges d'origines luxembourgeoise. *Hémecht*, 1949, 2: 12-36. [CB 42/367]

Bwk-k

BETH, Evert Willem. Exact-wetenschappelijke wijsbegeerte in Nederland. [The philosophy of the exact sciences in the Netherlands. (In Dutch)]. *Nieuw Tijdschr.Wisk.*, 1947-48, 35: 100-4.

Bwm-ce

NIELSEN, N. Matematiken i Danmark, 1528-1800. Bidrag til en bibliografiskhistorisk oversigt. [Mathematics in Denmark, 1528-1800. A contribution to a review of bibliographical history. (In Danish)] 2 vol. 1. 1528-1800; 2. 1801-1908. Kjøbenhavn: Gyldendal, 1912, 1910.

Bwn Russia

GNEDENKO, B.V. Ocherki po istorii matematiki v Rossii. [A sketch of the history of mathematics in Russia. (In Russian)]. 247 p. Moskva-Leningrad: OGIZ, Gosudarstvennoye izdatelsvo Tekniko-teoriticheskoi literatury, 1946. [CB 79/170]
Reviewed by Q. Vetter, *Arch.Int.Hist.Sci.*, 1953, 6: 105-6; in *Scr.Math.*, 1949, 15: 231.

GNEDENKO. B.V.; *et al.* O problemakh istorii matematiki v Rossi v SSSR i o rabotakh v etoĭ oblasti za 1956-1961. [On problems in the history of mathematics in Russia and in the U.S.S.R. and on works in this field between 1956-1961. (In Russian)]. *Ist.-Mat.Issled.*, 1963, 15: 11-36.

GUSEINOV, A.I.; AGAEV, G.N. K istorii razvitiya matematicheskikh issledovaniya v Azerbaidzhane. [History of mathematical research in Azerbaidzhan. (In Russian)]. *Isv.Akad. Nauk Azerbaidzh.SSSR, Ser.Fiz.Tekh.Mat.Nauk*, 1964, no. 3, 3-18.

SALTYKOW, N. [The Russian creative effort in mathematics. (In Russian)]. *Compt.Rend.1er Congr.Math.Pays Slaves*, (Warsaw, 1929), p. 81-91. Warszawa: 1930.

Bwn-ce-bv

AKADEMIIA NAUK SSSR. Matematika v īzdanīyakh Akademii Nauk, 1728-1935. Bībliograficheskiĭ ukazatel'. (Les mathématiques dans les publications de l'Académie des Sciences, 1728-1935. Repertoire bibliographique). [Compiled by O.V. Dinze and K.I. Shafranovski, edited by V.I. Smirnov. In Russian and French]. xx, 315 p., portr. Leningrad: Akademiia Nauk, 1936. [CB 60/145]

LUKOMSKAYA, A.M. Bibliografiia otechestvennoi literatury po matematike i fizike. Obzor bibliograficheskikh istochnikov. [Bibliography of Russian literature of mathematics and physics. Survey of bibliographical sources. (In Russian)] Pod redaktsiei V.I. Smirnova. 155 p. Moscow: Izdatel'stvo Akademii Nauk S.S.S.R., 1961.

Bwn-oq

ALEKSANDROV, P.S. [Mathematics in Moscow University during the first half of the 20th century. (In Russian)]. *Ist. -Mat.Issled.*, 1955, 8: 9-54.

ALEKSANDROV, P.S.; GNEDENKO, B.V.; STEPANOV, V.V. [Mathematics in Moscow University during the 20th century (to 1940). (In Russian)] *Ist.Mat.Issled.*, 1948, 1: 9-42.

BELOZEROV, S.E. [Mathematics at Rostov University. (In Russian)] *Ist.Mat.Issled.*, 1953, 6: 247-352, portr.

IUSHKEVICH, A.P. L'École Mathématique de Pétersbourg. *Proc. 10th Int.Congr.Hist.Sci.*(Ithaca, 1962), (2), p. 675-9. Paris: Hermann, 1964.

IUSHKEVICH, A.P. [Mathematics in Moscow University during the first hundred years of its existence. (In Russian)] *Ist.Mat.Issled.*, 1948, 1: 43-140.

LAPTEV, B.L. [Mathematics at the University of Kazan from 1917-1957. (In Russian)] *Ist.Mat.Issled.*, 1959, 12: 11-58.

Bwn-pw

GLIVICH, A.N. Is istorii rumynskogo matematicheskogo obshchestva - Sviasi mezhdu matematikami Rumynii i SSSR. [On the history of the Mathematical Society of Rumania. The contacts between Rumanian and Soviet mathematicians. (In Russian)] *Ist.-Mat.Issled.*, 1958, 11: 563-82.

Bwn-qd

ALEKSANDROV, P.S.; GOLOVIN, O.N. Moskovskoe matematicheskoe obshchestvo. [Moscow Mathematical Society. (In Russian)] *Usp.Mat.Nauk*, 1957, 12: (6), 9-46.

DEPMAN, I. S. Peterburgskoe Matematicheskoe Obshchestvo. [St. Petersburg Mathematical Society. (In Russian)] *Ist.Mat.Issled.*, 1960, 13: 11-106.

LEIBMAN, E.B. Matematicheskoe otdelenie Novorossiĭskovo obshchestva estestvoispytateleĭ (1876-1928). [The mathematical section of the Novorossisk Society of Natural Scientists. (In Russian)] *Ist.Mat.Issled.*, 1961, 14: 393-441.

Bwn-qv

KIRO, S.N. Matematika na s'ezdakh russkikh estestvoispytatelei i vrachei. [Mathematics at congresses of Russian natural scientists and medical men. (In Russian)] *Ist.-Mat.Issled.*, 1958, 11: 133-58.
Lists papers presented.

LAPKO, A.F.; LIUSTERNIK, L.A. Matematicheskie c'ezy i konferentsii v SSSR. [Mathematical congresses and conferences in the USSR. (In Russian)]. *Usp.Mat.Nauk*, 1957, 12: no. 6, 47-130; 1958, 13: no. 5, 121-66.

Bwn-sc

VUCINICH, Alexander. Mathematics in Russian culture. *J.Hist. Ideas*, 1960, 21: 161-79.

Bwo South Eastern Europe

POPA, Ilie. Is istorii matematiki v Rumynii. [Contributions to the history of mathematics in Roumania. (In Russian)] *Ist.-Mat.Issled.*, 1958, 11: 533-62.

SERGESCU, Petre. Aperçu sur les mathématiques en Roumanie au XXe siècle. *Compt.Rend.IIe Congr.Math.Pays Slaves* (Prague, 1934), p. 257-62. Prague: 1935.

SERGESCU, Petre. Le développement des sciences mathématiques en Roumanie. 61 p. In: Academia Română. La vie scientifique en Roumanie. Sciences pures. Bucarest: 1937. [CB 53/259]

SERGESCU, Petre. Matematica la români. [Mathematics in Rumania. (In Rumanian)] Conferinţă ţinută la "Liga Culturală" din Braşov. 40 p. Vălenii-de-Munte: Asezamântul tipografic Datina Românească, 1934.

Bwo-oq

BYCHKOV, V.P. Iz istorii matematiki v Rumynii (matematika v Iasskom universitete). [From the history of mathematics in Rumania (mathematics at Jassy University) (In Russian)] *Tr.Inst.Ist.Est.Tekh.*, 1961, 43: 290-350.

MYLLER, A. [Le développement de l'enseignement mathématique à l'Université de Iasi. (In Rumanian)] *Rev.Ştiinţ.Adamachi*, 1935, 22: 3-9.

POPA, Ilie. Matematica in ultimul pàtrar de veac la universitatea din Iaşi. [Mathematics at the University of Jassy during the last quarter of the century. (In Roumanian)] *Natura*(Bucharest), 1936, 25: 35-9.

POPA, Ilie. 25 de ani de activitate a Seminarului Matematic din Iaşi. [25 years of the activities of the mathematics seminar at Jassy. (In Roumanian)] *Rev.Stiint.Adamachi*, 1935, 21: 104-11.

Bwo-pw

GLIVICH, A.N. *See* Bwo-qd

SERGESCU, Pierre. Sur les relations mathématiques franco-roumaines. *Bull.Sci.Roumain*, 1952, 1: 5-17.

Bwo-qd

GLIVICH, A.N. Is istorii rumynskogo matematicheskogo obshchestva - Sviasi mezhdu matematikami Rumynii i SSSR. [On the history of the Mathematical Society of Rumania. The contacts between Rumanian and Soviet mathematicians. (In Russian)] *Ist.-Mat.Issled.*, 1958, 11: 563-82.

Bwt Far East

Bwt-ce-bv

YUAN T'UNG-LI. Bibliography of Chinese mathematics, 1918-1960. x, 154 p. Washington, D.C.: The Author, 1963. [CB 89/579]
A list of publications on modern mathematics by scientists of Chinese descent.

Bx techniques and instruments

Bxf-BO

LORIA, Gino. Le rôle de la représentation géométrique des grandeurs aux différentes époques de l'histoire des mathématiques. *Rev.Métaphys.Morale*, 1939, 46: 57-64.
From a lecture given at the 4th International History of Science Conference, Prague, 1937.

Bxk mathematical instruments

see also BCxk, BFza-xk, XP

MADDISON, Francis. Early astronomical and mathematical instruments. A brief survey of sources and modern studies. *Hist.Sci.*, 1963, 2: 17-50, bibliogr.

MICHEL, Henri. Les instruments anciens de mathématiques des Musées d'art et d'histoire. *Bull.Mus.Roy.Art Hist.*, 1935, no. 2, 26-34, 12 fig.

MICHEL, Henri. Introduction à l'étude d'une collection d'instruments anciens de mathématiques. 111 p., 15 pl. Anvers: De Sikkel, 1939. [CB 59/468]

Bxk-bw

SMITH, David Eugene. Catalogue of mathematical instruments. *Ind.Mus.N.Y.*, 1930, 1: 58-69.

Bxk-by

THE DAVID EUGENE SMITH gift of historical-mathematical instruments to Columbia University. *Science*, 1936, 83: 79.

WIJK, W.E. van. Antieke draagbare mathematische instrumenten in het Museum van Onderwijs te 's-Gravenhage. [The old portable mathematical instruments in the Museum of Education at the Hague. (In Dutch)] *Natuur*, 1942, 62: 12-20, 4 fig.; 39-42, 2 fig.; 61-70, 4 fig.

BA ARITHMETIC

for higher arithmetic (number theory) *see* BH

DEPMAN, I. Ia. Istoriia arifmetiki. [The history of arithmetic. (In Russian)]. 424 p. Moscow: Uchpedgiz, 1959.
Main emphasis is on the history of the teaching of arithmetic.
Reviewed by Iu. M. Gaiduk, *Vop.Ist.Est.Tekh.*, 1962, 13: 164-5.

KARPINSKI, Louis C. The history of arithmetic. xii, 200 p., ill. New York: Rand McNally, 1925.
Reviewed by Florian Cajori, *Isis*, 1926, 8: 231-2.

LARSEN, Harold D. Arithmetic for colleges. ix, 275 p. New York: Macmillan, 1950. [CB 76/394]
Includes an introduction on the history of numerals, numerology, etc. and various historical notes.

SMITH, David Eugene. Number stories of long ago. vii, 136 p., ill. Boston: Ginn, 1919. [CB 7/142]
Stories on the history of arithmetic written for children.

SMITH, David Eugene. On the origin of certain typical problems. *Amer.Math.Mon.*, 1917, 24: 64-71.
Historical discussion of the cistern problem, the Josephsspiel, the testament problem involving posthumous twins, and the hare and the hound or couriers, with variants.

TATON, René. Le calcul mental. 134 p. (Collection "Que Sais-Je?) Paris: Presses Universitaires de France, 1953.
Reviewed by M. Kraitchik, *Arch.Int.Hist.Sci.*, 1954, 7: 78-9.

VETTER, Quido. Z minulosti počtarských základů. [The history of elementary arithmetic. (In Czech)] 16 p. Brno: 1928.
Offprint from series of lectures, Počtarské Profily.

BAce

KARPINSKI, Louis C. Arithmetic centenarians: textbooks with a long life. *Scr.Math.*, 1933-34, 2: 34-40. [CB 40/399]

BAj

FETTWEIS, Ewald. Streitfragen aus der Geschichte der Arithmetik in ethnologischer und psychologischer Beleuchtung. *Scientia*, 1953, 88: 235-49.

THORNDIKE, Edward Lee. The psychology of arithmetic. xvi, 314 p. New York: Macmillan, 1923.

BAkk

DINGLER, Hugo. Philosophie der Logik und Arithmetik. 198 p. München: Reinhardt, 1931.

FREGE, Gottlob. *See* Bkk

HALSTED, George Bruce. On the foundation and tecnic of arithmetic. 133 p. Chicago: Open Court, 1912.

HÖLDER, Otto. Die Arithmetik in strenger Begründung. 2nd ed. iv, 73 p. Berlin: Springer, 1929.
First publ. Leipzig: Teubner, 1914.
Reviewed by Johann v. Neumann, *Deut.Lit.Zeitung*, 1930, 1: 285-6.

KOPPELMANN, W. Ist die Arithmetik ein logisch korrektes Lehrgebäude? *Ann.Phil.*, 1927, 6: 28 *et seq.*

PADOA, Alessandro. D'où convient-il de commencer l'arithmétique? *Atti IVo Congr.Int.Fil.* (Bologna, 1911), (2), p. 350-6. Genoa: Formiggini, 1913.

PETRONIEVICS, B. Les lois fondamentales de l'addition arithmétique et le principe de l'induction mathématique. *Rev. Gén.Sci.*, 1924, 35: 358-65.

STAMMLER, Gerhard. Der Begriff der Null und der negativen ganzen Zahlen. Ein Beitrag zur Grundlegung der Arithmetik. Im Anschlusz an den Aufsatz von W. Koppelmann: "Ist die Arithmetik ein logisch korrektes Lehrgebäude?". [*See* above]. *Ann.Phil.*, 1928, 7: 146-64. [CB 25/413]

WASCHE, Hans. Grundzüge zu einer Logik der Arithmetik. 43 p. (Bibliothek für Philosophie, 29; *Arch.Syst.Phil.Soziol.*, 30: no.1-2, suppl.) Berlin: Carl Heymann, 1926.

BAnb

CAJORI, Florian. Recent symbolisms for decimal fractions. *Math.Teacher*, 1923, 16: 183-7.

GINSBURG, J. Predecessors of Magini. *Scr.Math.*, 1932, 1: 168-89.
Apropos of symbols used as a decimal separatrix.

BAo

DEPMAN, I.Ia. *See* BA

YELDHAM, Florence A. The teaching of arithmetic through 400 years, 1535-1935. 143 p., front., facs. London: Harrap, 1936.
Reviewed by Louis C. Karpinski, *Isis*, 1937, 27: 92-4.

BAsb

FETTWEIS, Ewald. Arithmetik, Rasse und Kultur. *Archeion*, 1935, 17: 64-73.

BAwh-nb

VETTER, Quido. Notation of decimal fractions in Bohemia. *Amer.Math.Mon.*, 1932, 39: 511-14. [CB 38/594]

BAz

CASSINA, Ugo. Storia del triangolo aritmetico. *Boll.Mat.*, 1923, 19: xxxiii-xxxix.

BB NUMERALS; NUMERICAL SYSTEMS

AGOSTINI, Amedeo. La numerazione posizionale. *Archimede*, 1952, 4: 213-14.

BAEKELMANS, Willem. Het cijfer zeven. [The number seven. (In Dutch)] 127 p. Antwerpen: Gust Janssen, 1917.
The number seven in history, folklore and literature.

BOSTEELS, G. La vie des nombres. 141 p. Namur: Ad. Wesmael-Charlier, 1960.
On the history of the first twenty numerals and mathematical operations.

BOYER, Carl B. Fundamental steps in the development of numeration. *Isis*, 1944, 35: 153-68, 5 fig.

BOYER, Carl B. Zero: the symbol, the concept, the number. *Nat.Math.Mag.*, 1944, 18: 323-30.

CAJORI, Florian. The controversy of the origin of our numerals. *Sci.Mon.*, 1919, 9: 458-64. [CB 9/489]

CARRA DE VAUX. Sur l'origine des chiffres. *Scientia*, 1917, 21: 273-82. [CB 7/141]

DECOURDEMANCHE, J.A. Sur la filiation des chiffres européens modernes et des chiffres modernes des arabes. *Rev.Ethnogr. Sociol.*, 1912, 3: 138-48.

ESSIG, Jean. Douze, notre dix futur. Essai sur la numération duodécimale et un système métrique concordant. Prefacé de M. Albert Caquot. 169 p. Paris: Dunod, 1955. [CB 81/265]
A new defense of duodecimal numeration.

GOLDSCHMIDT, Victor. Die Entstehung unserer Ziffern. 51 p. (Heidelberger Akten der von Portheim-Stiftung, 19) Heidelberg: Winter, 1932.

HAGSTROEM, K.G. Sagan om de 10 tecknen. [History of our ten numerals. (In Swedish)]. 145 p., 30 pl. Uppsala: Almqvist & Wiksell, 1931.

HARTNER, Willy. Zahlen und Zahlensysteme bei Primitiv- und Hochkulturvölkern. *Paideuma*, 1943, 2: 268-326, ill.
Elaborate study of number words and symbols as revealed by the language and writing of many nations.

HILL, George Francis. The development of Arabic numerals in Europe, exhibited in 64 tables. 125 p. Oxford: Clarendon Press, 1915.

LEMOINE, Jean-Gabriel. Les gestes de nombres et leur importance ethnographique et linguistique. *Ethnographie*, 1935, no. 31, 107-9.

LOEFFLER, Eugen. Der Stellenwert in der Ziffernschrift. *Braunschweiger G.-N.-C.Monatsschr.*, January 1920, 540-8.

LOEFFLER, Eugen. Zahlwörter und Zahlzeichen bei den wichtigsten Kulturvölkern. Ueber die Entstehung und Ausbreitung unserer Ziffern. 59 p. (*Mitt.Ver. Math.Naturwiss.Ulm*, 1908-9, no. 15) Ulm: 1912.

LOEFFLER, Eugen. Ziffern und Ziffernsysteme. 2nd ed. 2 vol. 54 p.; 60 p. (Mathematische-physikalische Bibliothek 1; 34) Leipzig: Teubner, 1918-19. [CB 9/490]
First published 1912 in one volume as "Ziffern und Ziffernsysteme der Kulturvölker in alter und neuer Zeit".

MENNINGER, Karl. Kulturgeschichte der Zahlen. Aus der Entwicklung unserer Zahlsprache, unserer Zahlschrift und des Rechenbrettes. x, 365 p., 170 fig. Breslau: Hirt, 1934.

MENNINGER, Karl. Zahlwort und Ziffer. Eine Kulturgeschichte der Zahl. 2 vol. 1. Zahlreihe und Zahlsprache. 218 p., 39 fig.; 2. Zahlschrift und Rechnen. xii, 314 p., 255 fig. Göttingen: Verlag Vandenhoeck & Ruprecht, 1957, 1958.
Reviewed by J.E. Hofmann, *Arch.Int.Hist.Sci.*, 1957, 10: 255; 1958, 11: 199-200; by Howard F. Fehr, *Amer.Math.Mon.*, 1959, 66: 437.

SANFORD, Vera. Roman numerals. *Math.Teacher*, Jan. 1931, 24: 22-7.

SARTON, George. Decimal systems early and late. *Osiris*, 1950, 9: 581-601, 2 fig.

SERGESCU, Pierre. Histoire du nombre. 44 p. (Conférences du Palais de la Découverte, D, no. 23) Paris: Université de Paris, 1953.
Reviewed by M. Kraitchik, *Arch.Int.Hist.Sci.*, 1955, 8: 78.

SHIRLEY, John William. Binary numeration before Leibniz. *Amer.J.Phys.*, 1952, 19: 452-4, 2 fig. [CB 79/123]

SMELTZER, Donald. Man and number. An account of the development of man's use of number through the ages. viii, 114 p., ill., bibliogr. New York: Emerson Books, 1958. [CB 84/308]

SMITH, David Eugene. The Roman numerals. 1. Problems of their origin; 2. Other problems of their history. *Scientia*, 1926, 40: 1-8, 69-78; French transl., suppl., 1-8, 17-26. [CB 21/568]

SOLOMON, Bernard S. "One is no number" in China and the West. *Harvard J.Asiatic Stud.*, 1954, 17: 253-60.

TERRY, G.S. Duodecimal arithmetic. 407 p. London: Macmillan, 1938. [CB 59/468]

THUREAU-DANGIN, F. Sketch of a history of the sexagesimal system. Transl. into English by Solomon Gandz. *Osiris*, 1939, 7: 95-141.
Revised version of "Esquisse d'une histoire du système sexagésimal" (Paris: Geuthner, 1932).

WRIGHT, G.G. Neill. The writing of Arabic numerals. xxii, 424 p., 81 fig., 69 tables. London: University of London Press, 1952.

BBce

SÁNCHEZ PÉREZ, José A. Sobre las cifras rûmîes. *Al-Andalus*, 1935, 3: 97-125, facs. [CB 45/278]
Important paper on numerals, including edition and analysis of a Moroccan MS in the Escorial.

BBht

VOWLES, Hugh P. Introduction of Hindu-Arabic numerals into Western Europe. *Nature*, 1934, 134: 1008. [CB 43/270]

BBmzNwg-u

MARX, Otto. Die Zahlen in der Volksheilkunde des schlesischen Raumes. viii, 51 p. (Diss., Breslau) Breslau: 1934.

BBnb

GANGULI, Sāradākānta. The Indian origin of the modern place-value arithmetical notation. *Amer.Math.Mon.*, 1932, 39: 251-6.

HALCRO-JOHNSTON, J. The reverse notation. Introducing negative digits with twelve as base. x, 74 p. Glasgow: Blackie, 1938.
Reviewed by F.G.W.B., *Nature*, 1938, 142: 775.

KAYE, G.R. L'origine de notre notation numérique. *Scientia*, 1918, 24: 53-5. [CB 9/490]

SLOCUM, S.E. The romantic aspect of numbers. *Sci.Mon.*, 1918, 7: 68-79.
Slocum shows the important rôle played by number symbolism in the development of mankind.

BBnh

BORTOLOTTI, Ettore. Sul nome "Algoritmo". *Boll.Bibliogr.Stor. Sci.Mat.*, 1913, 15: 97-8; 1914, 16: 33-8.

MILLER, George Abram. Meaning of the word billion. *Sch.Soc.*, 1931, 33: 591.

VILLIERS, Melius de. The numeral words, their origin, meaning, history and lesson. 124 p. London: H.F. and G. Witherby, 1923. [CB 17/593]

BBvp-n

CARNOY, A. Symbolisme des mains et noms de nombres en indo-européen. *Muséon*, 1946, 59: 557-70.

NEHRING, A. Zahlwort und Zahlbegriff im Indogermanischen. *Wörter Sachen*, 1929, 12: 253-88.

BBwe

RÖSLER, Margarete. Die Vigesimalzählung im Englischen und Anglo-romanischen. *Engl.Stud.*, 1925, 59: 161-72.

BBwj-nb

CAJORI, Florian. On the Spanish symbol U for "thousands". *Bibl.Math.*, 1911-12, 12: 133-4.

CAJORI, Florian. Spanish and Portuguese symbols for "thousands". *Amer.Math.Mon.*, 1922, 29: 201-2.

GINSBURG, J. Spanish symbol for "thousand". *Scr.Math.*, 1932-33, 1: 264-5.

BBzn NUMEROLOGY

BELL, Eric Temple. The magic of numbers. viii, 418 p., front. New York: Whittlesey House, 1946. [CB 70/252]

BELL, Eric Temple. Numerology. viii, 188 p. Baltimore: Williams & Wilkins, 1933.

GIBSON, Walter B. The science of numerology: what numbers mean to you. xiv, 177 p. London: Rider, 1927.

HANCOCK, Harris. The "mystic" numeral 7. *Amer.Math.Mon.*, 1927, 34: 293-6.

LORIA, Gino. Eccentricità e misteri dei numeri. *Atti III Congr. Mathesis* (Genoa, 1912), p. 49-69. Roma: Manuzio, 1913.
French translation, Excentricités et mystères des nombres, in *Enseign.Math.*, 1913, 15: 193-201.

BC ARITHMETICAL OPERATIONS; NUMERICAL MATHEMATICS

BORTOLOTTI, Ettore. La propagazione della scienza attraverso i secoli. *Scientia*, 1932, 52: 273-86; French transl. suppl. 133-46.
The calculation of unit fractions from the Egyptians onwards.

CAJORI, Florian. Absurdities due to division by zero. *Math. Teacher*, 1929, 22: 366-8.

CAJORI, Florian. A history of the arithmetical methods of approximation to the roots of numerical equations of one unknown quantity. *Colo.Coll.Publ.Sci.Ser.*, 1910, 12: 171-215.

GILLINGS, R.J. Tests of divisibility. *Scr.Math.*, 1956, 22: 294-6.

IONIDES, Stephen A. Multiplication is vexation but 'rithmetic was also hated 2,000 years ago. *Eng.Bull.* (Denver), May 1938, 2 p.

IONIDES, Stephen A. Division is as bad. *Eng.Bull.* (Denver), July 1938, 2 p.

NORDGAARD, Martin Andrew. The origin and development of our present method of extracting the square and cube roots of numbers. *Math.Teacher*, 1924, 17: 223-38.

RICHTMYER, F.K. The romance of the next decimal place. *Science*, 1932, 75: 1-5.

ROMIG, H.G. Early history of division by zero. *Amer.Math. Mon.*, 1924, 31: 387-9.

SERGESCU, Petre. Istoria calculului numeric. [The history of numerical calculation. Resumé of lecture. (In Rumanian)] Resumatul lectiei facute la Universitatea Populara "N. Iorga" din Valenii-de-Munte la 16 Iulie 1932. 7 p. (Cuget Clar, 11-12) Valenii-de-Munte: 1933.

SIMONS, Lao Genevra. A note on the chain rule. *Scr.Math.*, 1935, 3: 93-4.

TATON, R. L'évolution d'une opération: la multiplication. *La Nature*, 1948, 76: 268-71.

TATON, R. Histoire du calcul. 128 p. (Collection Que Sais-Je?, 198) Paris: Presses Universitaires, 1946. [CB 73/167]
Reviewed by P. Sergescu, *Arch.Int.Hist.Sci.*, 1947, 1: 182.

UHLER, Horace Scudder. Miscellaneous hints for and experiences in computation. *Scr.Math.*, 1950, 16: 31-42.

VETTER, Quido. O počítání. [On reckoning. (In Czech)]. *Věda Život*, July 1942, 4 p.

BCsb

FETTWEIS, Ewald. Das Rechnen der Naturvölker. iv, 96 p., map. Leipzig: B.G. Teubner, 1927. [CB 23/258]

RÖCK, Fritz. Neunmalneun und Siebenmalsieben. *Mitt.Anthropol.Ges.Wien*, 1930, 60: 320-30.

SEIDENBERG, A. The ritual origin of counting. *Arch.Hist. Exact Sci.*, 1962, 2: 1-40.

BCwb-qk

LOWAN, Arnold N. The Computation Laboratory of the National Bureau of Standards. *Scr.Math.*, 1949, 15: 33-63, 2 pl.
Appendices contain lists of tables prepared by the Laboratory.

BCwh

DICKSTEIN, S. Sopra gli studi relativi alla storia delle matematiche compiuti in Polonia. *Boll.Mat.Sez.Stor.Bibliogr.*, 1926, 5: i-vi.

VETTER, Quido. Finden sich in Böhmen noch Spuren der alten Mediatio und Duplatio? 8 p. (*Cahiers Scientifiques*, no. 1. Cluj. 1 March 1930) Cluj: Institutul de Arte Grafice "Ardealul", 1930.
Also in *Cas.Pěstovani Mat.Fys.*, 1926, 55: 165-71.

BCwm

VANÄS, Erik. Divisionens historia i Sverige. [The history of division in Sweden. (In Swedish)]. *Lychnos*, 1954-55, 141-64.

BCwn

SPASSKII, I.G. [The origin and history of Russian reckoning. (In Russian)]. *Ist.-Mat.Issled.*, 1952, 5: 269-420.

BCxk aids to computation

for calculating machines *see* WT

BARNARD, Francis Pierrepont. The casting-counter and the counting board. A chapter in the history of numismatics and early arithmetic. 357 p., 63 pl. Oxford: Clarendon Press, 1916.

CAJORI, Florian. A history of the logarithmic slide rule. vi, 136 p., fig. In: Ball, W.W. Rouse. String figures and other monographs. New York: Chelsea Publishing Co., 1960.

GARVAN, Anthony N.B. Slide rule and sector. A study in science, technology and society. *Proc.10th Int.Congr.Hist.Sci.* (Ithaca, 1962), (1), p. 397-400. Paris: Hermann, 1964.

HOC, Marcel. Le calcul par les jetons. *Rev.Belge Numismatique*, 1935, 87: 88-90.

SMITH, David Eugene. Computing jetons. 70 p., 25 pl. (Numismatic Notes and Monographs, 9) New York: American Numismatic Society, 1921. [CB 14/553]

THOMPSON, James Edgar. A manual of the slide rule: its history, principle and operation. vii, 220 p. London: Chapman and Hall, 1931.
Reviewed in *Nature*, 1931, 128: 563.

BCxk-bx

HORSBURGH, E.M., ed. Modern instruments and methods of calculation. A handbook of the Napier tercentenary exhibition. viii, 343 p., ill. London: Bell, [1914]. [CB 7/141]

BCxk-nh

SOREAU, Rodolphe. Sur l'origine et les sens du mot "abaque". *Compt.Rend.Acad.Sci.*, 1918, 166: 67-9. [CB 11/445]

BCxt graphical methods; nomography

LALLEMAND, Charles. Sur la genèse et l'état actuel de la science des abaques. *Compt.Rend.Acad.Sci.*, 1922, 174: 82-8. Résumé by R.S., L'histoire de la nomographie, *Rev.Sci.*, 1922, 60: 197-8.

LUCKEY, Paul. Zur älteren Geschichte der Nomographie. *Unterrichtsbl.Math.Naturwiss.*, 1923, 29: 54-9.

LUCKEY, Paul. Zur Geschichte der Nomographie. *Z.Math.Naturwiss.Unterricht.*, 1927, 58: 455-65, 3 text fig. [CB 24/525]

OCAGNE, Maurice d'. A propos de l'histoire de la nomographie. *Rev.Gén.Sci.*, 1922, 33: 620-3.
Réponse à l'article de Rodolphe Soreau, *ibid.*, 518-23.

OCAGNE, Maurice d'. Résumé synthétique des principes fondamentaux de la nomographie. *Rev.Gén.Sci.*, 1929, 40: 325-9.

SOREAU, Rodolphe. Nomographie ou, Traité des abaques. 2nd ed. 2 vol. Paris: É. Chiron, 1921.

SOREAU, Rodolphe. Pour servir à l'histoire de la nomographie. *Rev.Gén.Sci.*, 1922, 33: 518-23.
The author argues that d'Ocagne does not pay sufficient homage to the work of others, particularly to that of Lallemand.

BCxt-wf-cd

OCAGNE, Maurice d'. Les archives nomographiques de l'École des Ponts et Chaussées. *Rev.Gén.Sci.*, 1928, 39: 625.

BD LOGARITHMS

AGOSTINI, Amedeo. L'invenzione dei logaritmi. *Period.Mat.*, *4th ser.*, 1922, 2: 135-50.

MILLER, George Abram. Group theory and the history of logarithms. *J.Indian Math.Soc.*, 1931-32, 19: 169-72.

BDxb

ADAMS, C.W. When was logarithmic paper first used? Answer to *Query* no. 80. (*Isis*, 1939, 30: 95-6). *Isis*, 1940, 31: 429-30.

BEATTY, Lewis B. When was logarithmic paper first used? Who introduced it? *Query* no. 80. Answer by George Sarton. *Isis*, 1939, 30: 95-6.
For other answers *see* above Adams, C.W. and below Durand, W.F.

DURAND, W.F. Invention of logarithmic paper. Answer to *Query* 80. (*Isis*, 1939, 30: 95). *Isis*, 1947, 32: 117.
Letter dated 3 April 1939 from W.F. Durand concerning his part in the development of logarithmic paper.

SAUSSURE, René de. Le papier logarithmique. *Rev.Sci.*, 1894, *4th ser.*, 2: 743-50.

BE TABLES

ANDOYER, H. Nouvelles tables trigonométriques fondamentales. *Compt.Rend.Acad.Sci.*, 1914, 158: 241-3. [CB 5/285]

ARCHIBALD, Raymond Clare. Tables of trigonometric functions in non-sexagesimal arguments. *Math.Tables Aids Comput.*, 1943, 1: 33-44.

SIMONS, Lao Genevra. Two reckoning tables. *Scr.Math.*, 1933, 1: 305-8, 3 fig. [CB 39/449]

BEc-br

Mathematical Tables and Aids to Computation. A quarterly journal edited on behalf of the Committee on Mathematical Tables and Aids to Computation. Vol. 1, no. 1- Washington, D.C.: National Research Council, 1943- [CB 64/450]

BEcg

DAVIS, Harold T. Tables of the higher mathematical functions, computed and compiled under the direction of Harold T. Davis, Indiana University and the Cowles Commission for research in economics. Vol. 1. xiii, 377 p., 2 pl. (Published as a contribution of the Waterman Institute for scientific research, Indiana University). Bloomington, Ind.: Principia, 1933.
Reviewed by George Sarton, *Isis*, 1934, 21: 330-4.

POLETTI, Luigi. L'atlante di oltre 60000 numeri primi fra 10 milioni e 3 viliardi (et ultra); estratti da serie quadratiche. *Atti Accad.Ital.Mem.Cl.Sci.Fis.Mat.Natur.*, 1940, 11: 725-51.
Report on this work in *Boll.Mat.*, 1938, 34: lx noted in *Isis*, 1939, 30: 281.

BEcg-bv

FLETCHER, A.; MILLER, J.C.P.; ROSENHEAD, L. An index of mathematical tables. viii, 451 p. London: Scientific Computing Service, 1946.
Reviewed by A.C. Aitken, *Nature*, 1946, 158: 252-3; by R.C. Archibald, *Math.Tables Aids Comput.*, 1946, 2: 13-18.

HENDERSON, James. Bibliotheca tabularum mathematicarum. Being a descriptive catalogue of mathematical tables. 1. Logarithmic tables, A. Logarithms of numbers. 208 p. (Tracts for Computers, 13) Cambridge University Press, 1926.

LEHMER, Derrick Henry. Guide to tables in the theory of numbers. xiv, 177 p. (Bulletin of the National Research Council, 105. Division of Physical Sciences, Committee on Mathematical Tables and Aids to Computation. Report I, Report of the Subcommittee on Section F: Theory of Numbers) Washington, D.C.: National Research Council, National Academy of Sciences, 1941. [CB 62/74]

LOWAN, Arnold N. *See* BCwb-qk

BEda

ARCHIBALD, Raymond Clare. Mathematical table makers. Portraits, paintings, busts, monuments, bio-bibliographical notes. 82 p., portr. (Scripta Mathematica Studies, 3) New York: Scripta Mathematica, 1948. [CB 73/166]
Also published in *Scr.Math.*, 1945, 11: 213-45; 1946, 12: 15-51.

BEwb

ARCHIBALD, Raymond Clare. The New York mathematics tables project. *Science*, 1942, 96: 294-6. [CB 63/260]

BEwb-qk

ARCHIBALD, Raymond Clare. The National Research Council committee on mathematical tables and aids to computation. *Science*, 1940, 92: 129-31.

BF ALGEBRA

AGOSTINI, Amedeo. Il teorema fondamentale dell'algebra. *Period.Mat.*, 1924, *ser. 4*, 4: 307-27. [CB 18/604]

BASHMAKOVA, I.G. Le théorème fundamental de l'algèbre et la construction des corps algèbraiques. *Arch.Int.Hist.Sci.*, 1960, 13: 211-22.

BORTOLOTTI, Ettore. L'algebra nella storia e nella preistoria della scienza. *Osiris*, 1936, 1: 184-230. [CB 46/587]

FINE, Henry Burchard. The number system of algebra treated theoretically and historically. x, 131 p. New York: Hafner, 1937.
A photo-offset edition of a work originally published in 1890.

FLECKENSTEIN, J.O. Eine dreihundertjährige Etappe der Entwicklung der Algebra von Tartaglia bis Galois (1546-1846). *Experientia*, 1946, 2: 321-3, 1 fig.

KARPINSKI, Louis C. The origin and development of algebra. *Sch.Sci.Math.*, 1923, 23: 54-64.
French translation in *Scientia*, 1919, 26: 89-101.

LUR'E, S. Ia. K voprosu o vozniknovenii algebraicheskogo myshleniia. [On the question of the development of algebraic thought. (In Russian)]. *Usp.Mat.Nauk*, 1946, 1: 248-57.

SANFORD, Vera. The history and significance of certain standard problems in algebra. viii, 102 p. (Contributions to Education, 251) New York: Teachers College, Columbia University, 1927. [CB 23/239]

SEGRE, Beniamino. The rise of algebra and the creation of algebraic geometry. *Cah.Hist.Mond.*, 1963, 7: 383-406.

WIELEITNER, Heinrich. Die sieben Rechnungsarten mit allgemeinen Zahlen. iv, 70 p. Leipzig: Teubner, 1912.

WIELEITNER, Heinrich. Zur Geschichte der gebrochenen Exponenten. *Isis*, 1924, 6: 509-20; 1925, 7: 490-1. [CB 16/315]

BFce

KARPINSKI, Louis C. Algebraical works to 1700. *Scr.Math.*, 1944, 10: 149-69.

VIVANTI, Giulio. I principali trattati di algebra dalle origine della stampa al 1800. *Period.Mat.*, 1924, *4th ser.*, 4: 277-306. [CB 16/314]

BFj

THORNDIKE, Edward Lee; *et al.* The psychology of algebra. xi, 483 p. New York: Macmillan, 1923.

BFk

VUILLEMIN, Jules. La philosophie de l'algèbre. 1. Recherches sur quelques concepts et methodes de l'algèbre moderne. 582 p. (Épiméthée. Essais Philosophiques) Paris: Presses Universitaires de France, 1962.

BFmzC

WHITTAKER, E.T. The new algebras and their significance for physics and philosophy. *Nature*, 1943, 152: 603.

BFnb

SARTON, George. Extreme slowness of the introduction of elementary algebraic symbols. *Isis*, 1937, 27: 328.

BFnh

GANDZ, Solomon. The origin of the term "algebra". *Amer.Math.Mon.*, 1926, 33: 437-40. [CB 22/258]

MILLER, George Abram. The word algebra. *Science*, 1932, 76: 14-15.

BFwb

BELL, Eric Temple. Fifty years of algebra in America, 1888-1938. In: American Mathematical Society. Semicentennial publications. 2. Semicentennial addresses, p. 1-34. New York: The Society, 1938.

BFwg

VOGEL, Kurt. 500 Jahre deutsche Algebra. *Praxis Math.*, 1962, 4: 89-90.

BFwi-da

BORTOLOTTI, Ettore. Italiani scopritori e promotori di teorie algebriche. *Annu.Univ.Modena*, 1918-19, 48-148.

BFwn

SUSHKEICH, A.K. [Materials for the history of algebra in Russia in the 19th and the beginnings of the 20th centuries. (In Russian)]. *Ist.-Mat.Issled.*, 1951, 4: 237-451.

BFza ALGEBRAIC EQUATIONS

AGOSTINI, Amedeo. Le funzioni simmetriche delle radici delle equazioni algebriche. *Period.Mat.*, 1925, *ser. 4*, 5: 321-36.
Brief historical survey from Cardano to Lagrange.

BOYER, Carl B. Early graphical solutions of polynomial equations. *Scr.Math.*, 1945, 11: 5-19, 8 fig. [CB 62/225]

FOULKES, H.O. The algebraic solution of equations. *Sci.Progr.*, 1932, 26: 601-8.
Equations of 5th,6th and 7th degrees from 1771 to 1931, with full references.

FUNKHOUSER, H. Gray. A short account of the history of symmetric functions of roots of equations. *Amer.Math.Mon.*, 1930, 37: 357-65.

GLODEN, A. Aperçu sur le développement des méthodes de résolution des équations algébriques. *Janus*, 1958, 47: 73-8.

KARPINSKI, Louis C. Linear and quadratic, straight and square. *Sch.Sci.Math.*, 1933, 34-9. [CB 38/593]

KIEFFER, Lucien. Sur la résolution des systèmes d'équations linéaires. *Arch.Inst.Grand Ducal Luxemb.Sect.Sci.*, 1959, 26: 105-24.

LORIA, Gino. Remarques sur les équations algébriques nonrationnelles. *Mathesis* (Gand), 1938, 52: 129-31.

NORDGAARD, Martin Andrew. A historical survey of algebraic methods of approximating the roots of numerical higher equations up to the year 1819. vi, 64 p. New York: Teachers College, Columbia University, 1922.

TROPFKE, Johannes. Zur Geschichte der quadratischen Gleichungen über dreieinhalb Jahrtausend. *Jahresber.Deut.Math.Ver.*, 1934, 44: 26-119, 43 fig.

VETTER, Quido. Sur l'équation du quarante-cinquième degré d'Adriaan van Roomen. *Bull.Sci.Math.*, 1930, 54: 277-83.

VOGEL, Kurt. Zur Geschichte der linearen Gleichungen mit mehreren Unbekannten. *Deut.Math.*, 1940, 5: 217-40.

BFza-xk

FRAME, J.S. Machines for solving algebraic equations. *Math. Tables Aids Comput.*, 1945, 1: 337-53. [CB 69/226]

BFzd DETERMINANTS

KOWALEWSKI, Gerhard. Einführung in die Determinantentheorie einschliesslich der Fredholmschen Determinanten. 2nd ed. viii, 304 p. Berlin/Leipzig: Walter de Gruyter, 1925. [CB 17/589]

LECAT, Maurice. Le déterminant supérieur, qu'est-il exactement? Les conceptions de Cayley, A. de Gasparis, Rice et autres. *Rev.Gén.Sci.*, 1929, 40: 231-41.

MILLER, George Abram. On the history of determinants. *Amer. Math.Mon.*, 1930, 37: 216-19.

MUIR, Thomas. Contributions to the history of determinants, 1900-1920. xxiv, 408 p. London: Blackie and Son, 1930.
Contains subject index to Muir's The theory of determinants.
Reviewed by A.C.A., *Nature*, 1930, 126: 839.

MUIR, Thomas. The theory of determinants in the historical order of development. 4 vol. 1. 1693 to 1841. 2nd ed. 475 p. 1906; 2. 1841 to 1860. 503 p. 1911; 3. 1861 to 1880. 491 p. 1920; 4. 1881 to 1900. 508 p. 1923. London: Macmillan, 1906-23. [CB 16/312]
1st ed. of volume 1 published 1890. For subject index to the complete work *see* above: Contributions to the history of determinants.

BFzg GROUPS

LITWAK, Barry. History of group theory leading to the development of infinite Abelian groups. *Math.Teacher*, 1964, 57: 30-2, bibliogr.

MILLER, George Abram. The collected works. 2 vol. 475 p.; 537 p. Urbana: University of Illinois, 1935-38. [CB 50/392 and CB 56/357]
Vol. I reviewed by W. Benjamin Fite, *Isis*, 1936, 26: 210-11; contains historical account of group theory.

MILLER, George Abram. Early mastery of the group concept. *Science*, 1943, 97: 90-1.

MILLER, George Abram. Easy group theory. *Sci.Mon.*, 1923, 15: 512-19.

MILLER, George Abram. Elements of the generality of the group concept. *Science*, 1943, 98: 362-3.

MILLER, George Abram. Group theory and the history of logarithms. *J.Indian Math.Soc.*, 1931-32, 19: 169-72.

MILLER, George Abram. A group theory dilemma of Sophus Lie and Felix Klein. *Science*, 1942, 95: 353-4.

MILLER, George Abram. The group-theory element of the history of mathematics. *Sci.Mon.*, 1921, 12: 75-82. [CB 12/634]

MILLER, George Abram. Salient theorems of the theory of groups and their history. *Sci.Mon.*, 1933, 36: 146-7.

MILLER, G.H. The evolution of group theory. *Math.Teacher*, 1964, 57: 26-30.
Brief and elementary summary from Euler to the present day.

BFzg-ce

MILLER, George Abram. Errors in the literature on groups of finite order. *Amer.Math.Mon.*, 1913, 20: 14-20.

BFzg-nh

MILLER, George Abram. Bits of history about two common mathematical terms. *Amer.Math.Mon.*, 1919, 26: 290-1.
Discussion of the terms "indicator" and "simple group".

MILLER, George Abram. On the introduction of the word group as a technical mathematical term. *Bibl.Math.*, 1912, 13: 62-4.

BFzg-wb-ce

MILLER, George Abram. The first articles on group theory published in America. *Science*, 1939, 90: 234.

BG SET THEORY

BERNAYS, P.; FRAENKEL, Abraham A. Axiomatic set theory. With a historical introduction by Abraham A. Fraenkel. 226 p. (Studies in Logic and the Foundations of Mathematics) Amsterdam: North Holland Publishing Company, 1958.

BRIDGMAN, P.W. A physicist's second reaction to Mengenlehre. *Scr.Math.*, 1933-34, 2: 224-34.

CAVAILLÈS, Jean. Remarques sur la formation de la théorie abstraite des ensembles. 2 vol. 145 p. (Le Progrès de l'Esprit, 7-8; Actualités Scientifiques et Industrielles, 606-7) Paris: Hermann, 1938.
Reviewed by P. Schrecker, *Thalès*, 1937-39, 4: 278-80.

FRAENKEL, Abraham Adolf. Natural numbers as cardinals. *Scr. Math.*, 1939, 6: 69-79, portr.

FRAENKEL, Abraham Adolf. Natural numbers as ordinals. *Scr. Math.*, 1940, 7: 9-20.

FRÉCHET, Maurice. L'analyse générale et les ensembles abstraits. *Rev.Métaphys.Morale*, 1925, 32: 1-30. [CB 18/575]

GLODEN, A. Introduction sommaire à la théorie des ensembles. Quelques problèmes de la théorie des nombres à la lumière des mathématiques modernes. *Bull.Mens.Soc.Natur.Luxembourg.*, 1948, 42: 107-16.

JOURDAIN, Philip E.B. The development of the theory of transfinite numbers. *Arch.Math.Phys.*, 1901, 10: 254-81; 1905, 14: 289-311; 1910, 16: 21-43; 1913, 22: 1-21.

SCHRECKER, Paul. On the infinite number of infinite orders. A chapter of the pre-history of transfinite numbers. *Studies and Essays offered to George Sarton*, p. 359-73. New York: Schuman, 1947. [CB 71/117]

BGce

MEDVEDEV, F.A. [The first textbooks on set theory. (In Russian)] *Tr.Inst.Ist.Est.Tekh.*, 1959, 28: 237-49.

BGkk

DIAMOND, R.J. Each and all. *Brit.J.Phil.Sci.*, 1962-63, 13: 278-86.

DINGLER, Hugo. Ueber die logischen Paradoxien der Mengenlehre und eine paradoxienfreie Mengendefinition. *Z.Positivistische Phil.*, 1913, 1: 143-50.

FRAENKEL, Abraham Adolf. Zehn Vorlesungen über die Grundlegung der Mengenlehre. Gehalten in Kiel auf Einladung der Kant-Gesellschaft, Ortsgruppe Kiel, vom 8.-12. Juni 1925. x, 182 p. (Wissenschaft und Hypothese, 31) Leipzig: B.G. Teubner, 1927. [CB 22/257]

FRAENKEL, Abraham Adolf; BAR-HILLEL, Y. Foundations of set theory. x, 415 p. (Studies in Logic and the Foundations of Mathematics) Amsterdam: North Holland Publishing Company, 1958.

RICHARD, J. Considérations sur la logique et les ensembles. *Rev.Métaphys.Morale*, 1920, 27: 355-69. [CB 13/290]

BH NUMBER THEORY (HIGHER ARITHMETIC)

ARCHIBALD, Ralph G. Goldbach's theorem. *Scr.Math.*, 1935, 3: 44-50. [CB 43/222]

ARCHIBALD, Ralph G. Quadratic Diophantine equations. *Scr. Math.*, 1933, 2: 27-33.

ARCHIBALD, Raymond Clare. Perfect numbers. *Amer.Math.Mon.*, 1921, 28: 140-53.

DICKSON, Leonard Eugene. History of the theory of numbers. 1. Divisibility and primality. xii, 486 p.; 2. Diophantine analysis. xxv, 803 p.; 3. Quadratic and higher forms. 313 p. Washington: Carnegie Institution, 1919-23.
Reviewed by J.M. Child, *Isis*, 1920, 3: 446-8; 1921, 4: 107-9; 1924, 6: 96-8.

DICKSON, Leonard Eugene. Perfect and amicable numbers. *Sci. Mon.*, 1921, 12: 349-54.

DICKSON, Leonard Eugene. The theory of numbers; its principal branches. *Scientia*, June 1922, 31: 421-31; French translation, suppl., 43-55. [CB 13/291]

ENESTRÖM, G. Ueber die ältere Geschichte der Zerfällung ganzer Zahlen in Summen kleinerer Zahlen. *Bibl.Math.*, 1913, 13: 352.

ESCOTT, Edward Brind. Amicable numbers. *Scr.Math.*, 1946, 12: 61-72.

FRAENKEL, Abraham Adolf. Problems and methods in modern mathematics. 1. Prime numbers and their distribution. 2. Division of the circle into a number of equal parts and other problems. 3. Fermat's simple and last theorems. The concept of congruence. 4. Perfect numbers and amicable numbers. 5. Algebraic and ideal numbers. *Scr.Math.*, 1943, 9: 5-18, 81-4, 162-8, 244-55.

GLODEN, A. Introduction sommaire à la théorie des ensembles. Quelques problèmes de la théorie des nombres à la lumière des mathématiques modernes. *Bull.Mens.Soc.Natur.Luxemb.*, 1948, 42: 107-16.

HARDY, Godfrey Harold. Some famous problems of the theory of numbers and in particular Waring's problem. (Inaugural lecture). 35 p. Oxford: Clarendon Press, 1920.

HECKE, Erich. Vorlesungen über die Theorie der algebraischen Zahlen. 266 p. Leipzig: Akademische Verlagsanstalt, 1923. [CB 17/589]

HOFMANN, J. Zur Geschichte des sogenannten Sechsquadrateproblems. *Math.Nachr.*, 1958, 18: 152-67.
The work of Euler and others.

HOLZER, Ludwig. Eulers Forschungen in seiner Anleitung zur Algebra vom Standpunkt der modernen Zahlentheorie. *Sammelband zu Ehren des 250. Geburtstages Leonhard Eulers*, p. 209-23. Berlin: Akademie-Verlag, 1959.
Reviewed by O. Ore, *Math.Rev.*, 1962, 23: 4, A36.

ITARD, Jean. Arithmétique et théorie des nombres. 128 p. Paris: Presses Universitaires de France, 1963.
Reviewed by René Taton, *Rev.Hist.Sci.*, 1964, 17: 168-9.

LEHMER, Derrick Henry. Guide to the tables ... *See* BEcg-bv

LEHMER, Derrick Henry. History of the problem of separating a number into its prime factors. *Sci.Mon.*, 1918, 7: 227-34.

LEHMER, Derrick Henry. Hunting big game in the theory of numbers. *Scr.Math.*, 1933, 1: 229-35. [CB 39/409]

MORDELL, L.J. The present state of some problems in the theory of numbers. *Nature*, 1928, 121: 138-40.

MOUY, P. Note sur la méthode de récurrence et l'idée de nombre entier. *Rev.Métaphys.Morale*, 1926, 33: 77-83.
Critique de l'interprétation donnée par H. Poincaré du raisonnement par récurrence.

ORE, Oystein. Number theory and its history. x, 370 p., 22 fig. New York: McGraw-Hill, 1948. [CB 75/88]

UHLER, Horace S. A brief history of the investigations on Mersenne numbers and the latest immense primes. *Scr.Math.*, 1952, 18: 122-31.

UHLER, Horace S. On the 16th and 17th perfect numbers. *Scr.Math.*, 1953, 19: 128-31. [CB 80/123]

VASIL'EV, Aleksandr Vasil'evich. Tseloe chislo. [Integers. (In Russian)] iv, 268 p. Leningrad: 1922.
Reviewed by D. Mirimanoff, *Enseign.Math.*, 1925, 24: 160.

BHda

GLODEN, A.; PALAMA, G. Bibliographie des multigrades avec quelques notices biographiques. 64 p. Luxembourg: 1948.
Reviewed by P. Sergescu, *Arch.Int.Hist.Sci.*, 1947-48, 1: 732.

BHwk

GLODEN, A. Esquisse d'une histoire de la théorie des nombres en Belgique. *IIIe Congr.Nat.Sci.* (Bruxelles, 1950), (2), p. 31-3. [Liége: 1951].

BHzf FERMAT'S PROBLEM

BACHMANN, Paul. Das Fermatproblem in seiner bisherigen Entwicklung. viii, 160 p. Berlin: Vereinigung Wissenschaftlicher Verleger, 1919.

BELL, Eric Temple. The last problem. 306 p. New York: Simon & Schuster; London: Victor Gollancz, 1962.
The history of Fermat's problem, from Babylonian mathematics to the 17th century.

BRICARD, Raoul. Sur un théorème célèbre d'arithmétique. *Enseign.Sci.*, 1936, 9: 240-2.
Fermat's problem.

LIETZMANN, W. Der Pythagoreische Lehrsatz: mit einem Ausblick auf das Fermatsche Problem. 4th rev. ed. iv, 71 p. (Mathematisch-physikalische Bibliothek, 3) Leipzig: Teubner, 1930.

NOGUÈS, R. Théorème de Fermat. Son histoire. 177 p. Paris: Vuibert, 1932.
Reviewed by L.P., *Rev.Gén.Sci.*, 1932, 43: 482.

BHzm MAGIC SQUARES

CAZALAS, E. Carrés magiques au degré *n* séries numérales de G. Tarry... Avec un aperçu historique et une bibliographie des figures-magiques. 192 p., pl., portr., bibliogr. Paris: Hermann, 1934. [CB 44/515]

KLETHER, Bruno. Magische Zahlenquadrate: Mechanische gemeinverständliche Lösungen für alle Arten von Quadraten. vii, 55 p. Wien: Braumüller, 1930.

KOWALEWSKI, Gerhard. Magische Quadrate und magische Parkette. 78 p. (Scientia Delectans, 2) Leipzig: Koehler, 1937.

KRAITCHIK, Maurice. Traité des carrés magiques. 108 p. Paris: Gauthier-Villars, 1930.
Reviewed by P.J. Richard, *Rev.Gén.Sci.*, 1931, 42: 121.

McCOY, John Calvin. The anatomy of magic squares. *Scr.Math.*, 1943, 9: 278-84.

BI CONCEPT OF NUMBER

BOYER, Carl B. Fractional indices, exponents, and powers. *Nat.Math.Mag.*, 1943, 18: no. 2, 6 p.

DANTZIG, Tobias. Number, the language of science. A critical survey written for the cultured non-mathematician. 4th rev. ed. ix, 340 p., fig. New York: Macmillan Company, 1954. [CB 81/265]
This edition consists of two parts, the first a revision of the author's standard work (first publ. 1930 and reviewed by George Sarton, *Isis*, 1931, 16: 455-9; 1934, 20: 592 and 1940, 31: 475-6); the second part is "an integrated story of the development of method and argument in the field of number". A French translation of the 1930 edition was publ. Paris: Payot, 1931.

DU PASQUIER, Louis Gustave. Le développement de la notion de nombre. 190 p. (Mémoires de l'Université de Neuchâtel, 3) Paris: Attinger, 1921.

GOUSSINSKY, B. Continuity and number. 31 p. Israel: Government Printing Press, 1959.

MILLER, George Abram. Historical note on negative numbers. *Amer.Math.Mon.*, 1933, 40: 4-5.

NATUCCI, Alpinolo. Il concetto di numero e le sue estensioni; studi storico-critici intorno ai fondamenti dell' aritmetica generale. viii, 474 p., bibliogr. Torino: Bocca, 1923.

NATUCCI, Alpinolo. Lo sviluppo dell' aritmetica generale. *Rass.Mat.Fis.*, 1924, 4: 161-75; 1925, 5: 183-98; 1926, 6: 25-33.

NATUCCI, Alpinolo. Sviluppo storico ... *See* Bc-bm

STAMMLER, Gerhard. Der Zahlbegriff seit Gauss. Eine erkenntnistheoretische Untersuchung. xvi, 192 p. Halle S.: Max Niemeyer, 1925. [CB 20/193]

BIzc COMPLEX NUMBERS

COURT, Nathan Altshiller. Imaginary elements in pure geometry - what they are and what they are not. *Scr.Math.*, 1951, 17: 55-64.

LORIA, Gino. L'enigma dei numeri immaginari attraverso i secoli. *Scientia*, 1917, 21: 101-21.

LORIA, Gino. Lo spettro dell'immaginario in geometria. *Scientia*, 1917, 22: 3-15.

UHLER, Horace S. On the numerical value of i . *Amer.Math. Mon.*, 1921, 28: 114-16.

WIELEITNER, Heinrich. Zur Frühgeschichte des Imaginären. *Jahresber.Deut.Math.Ver.*, 1927, 36: 74-88.
Survey of work, particularly by Cardano and Bombelli, with special reference to publications of E. Bortolotti, 1923-25.

WINDRED, G. History of the theory of imaginary and complex quantities. *Math.Gaz.*, 1929, 14: 533-41.

BIzc-xt

CAJORI, Florian. Historical note on the graphic representation of imaginaries before the time of Wessel. *Amer.Math. Mon.*, 1912, 19: 167-71.

BIzi IRRATIONAL NUMBERS

AUDISIO, Fausta. Il numero π. *Period.Mat.*, 1931, 11: 11-42, 149-50.

BORTOLOTTI, Ettore. La scoperta dell' irrazionale e le frazioni continue. *Period.Mat.*, 1931, 4th ser., 11: 133-48.

BORTOLOTTI, Ettore. Sul numero π. *Period.Mat.*, 1931, 11: 110-13.

MITCHELL, U.G.; STRAIN, Mary. The number *e*. *Osiris*, 1936, 1: 476-96. [CB 46/588]

ROSENFELD, L. Le problème logique de la définition des nombres irrationnels. *Isis*, 1927, 9: 345-58. [CB 24/526]

STRAUSS, Alfred. Die Weltzahl Pi. 325 p. Leipzig: Hummel, 1931.

UHLER, Horace S. Humorous epithets as applied to the calculation of $\sqrt{2}$. *Scr.Math.*, 1953, 19: 78-9.

WEAVER, James H. The duplication problem. *Amer.Math.Mon.*, 1916, 23: 106-13.
Brief account of the duplication problem, largely following Pappus for its ancient history.

WHITROW, G.J. Continuity and irrational number. *Math.Gaz.*, 1933, 17: 151-7.
An historical sketch of these concepts from Pythagoras to Cantor.

BJ ANALYSIS

BABINI, José. Las grandes etapas del análisis infinitesimal. *Imago Mundi* (Buenos Aires), 1953, no. 1, 23-41.

BOUTROUX, Pierre. Les principes de l'analyse mathématique: exposé historique et critique. 2 vol. xi, 548 p.; 516 p. Paris: Hermann, 1914-19.
Vol. 1 reviewed in *Isis*, 1913, 1: 734-42 (by E. Turrière) and 577-89 (by G. Sarton in the course of an article on the history of mathematics); vol. 2, *ibid.* 1921, 4: 96-107 (by J.M. Child).

BOYER, Carl B. Analysis: notes on the evolution of a subject and a name. *Math.Teacher*, 1954, 47: 450-62.
Traces briefly the historical rise of one of the three main divisions of mathematics, with particular reference to changes in the use of the term 'analysis'.

CAJORI, Florian. History of the exponential and logarithmic concepts. 1. From Napier to Leibniz and John Bernoulli I, 1614-1712. 2. From Leibniz and John Bernoulli I, 1712-1747. 3. The creation of a theory of logarithms of complex numbers by Euler, 1747-1749. 4. From Euler to Wessel and Argand, 1749 to about 1800. 5. Generalizations and refinements effected during the nineteenth century. *Amer.Math.Mon.*, 1913, 20: 5-38, 38-47, 75-84, 107-17, 148-51, 173-82, 205-10.

DELACHET, André. L'analyse mathématique. 118 p. (Que sais-je?) Paris: Presses Universitaires de France, 1949.

EVANS, Melbourne G. Aristotle, Newton and the theory of continuous magnitude. *J.Hist.Ideas*, 1955, 16: 548-57.

GEYMONAT, Ludovico. Storia e filosofia dell'analisi infinitesimale. 352 p. (Facolta di Scienze dell'Università di Torino, Corso di Storia delle Matematiche, Anno Accademico 1947-48) Torino: Levrotto & Bella, 1947.

MORDUKHAI-BOLTOVSKOI, Dimitri. Genese und Geschichte der Limestheorie. *Archeion*, 1933, 15: 45-72. [CB 39/449]

PEANO, Giuseppe. Sulla definitione di limite. *Atti Accad. Sci.Torino*, 1913, 48: 750-72.

RYBNIKOV, K.A. On the role of algorithms in the history of mathematical analysis. *Act.VIIIe Congr.Int.Hist.Sci.* (Florence, 1956), p. 142-5. Paris: Hermann, 1958.

RYBNIKOV, K.A. [On the so-called creative and critical periods in the history of mathematical analysis. (In Russian)] *Ist.Mat.Issled.*, 1954, 7: 643-65.

SERGESCU, Petre. Les recherches sur l'infini mathématique jusqu'à l'établissement de l'analyse infinitésimale. 32 p. (Actualités Scientifiques et Industrielles, 1083) Paris: Hermann, 1949. [CB 76/394]
Reviewed by H.J. Heymann, *Lychnos*, 1952, 388-9.

VETTER, Quido. A vyvojí názoru na analyzu a syntezu v matematice. [On the development of ideas concerning analysis and synthesis in mathematics. (In Czech)]. *Ceská Myšl*, 1923, 19: 147-58.

WIELEITNER, Heinrich. Das Fortleben der Archimedischen Infinitesimalmethoden bis zum Beginn des 17. Jahrh., insbesondere über Schwerpunktbestimmungen. *Quellen Stud.Gesch. Math.Abt.B*, 1930, 1: no. 2, 201-20, 8 fig.
Reviewed by A. Rome, *Rev.Quest.Sci.*, 1930, 18: 344-50.

WREN, F.L.; GARRETT, J.A. The development of the fundamental concepts of infinitesimal analysis. *Amer.Math.Mon.*, 1933, 40: 269-81.

BJk

BOUTROUX, Pierre. L'objet et la méthode de l'analyse mathématique. *Rev.Métaphys.Morale*, 1913, 21: 307-28.

BJmh

BELL, Eric Temple. Finite or infinite? *Phil.Sci.*, 1934, 1: 30-49.

BERGMANN, Hugo. Das Unendliche und die Zahl. 88 p. Halle: Max Niemeyer, 1913.

BURGER, D. L'évolution des idées de l'infini de Platon à Cantor. *Act.VI Congr.Int.Hist.Sci.* (Amsterdam, 1950), p. 145-50. Paris: Hermann, 1951.

ENRIQUES, Federigo. L'infinito nella storia del pensiero. *Scientia*, 1933, 54: 381-401; French transl. suppl., 163-81.

ENRIQUES, Federigo. I numeri e l'infinito. *Atti IV° Congr. Int.Fil.* (Bologna, 1911), (2), p. 357-78. Genoa: Formiggini, [1913].

KAUFMANN, Felix. Das Unendliche in der Mathematik und seine Ausschaltung. x, 203 p. Leipzig: Deuticke, 1930.
Reviewed by Orrin Frink, *Bull.Amer.Math.Soc.*, 1931, 37: 149-50.

LORIA, Gino. L'infinito e l'infinitesimo secondo i matematici moderni anteriori al secolo XVIII. *Scientia*, 1916, 19: 1-18.

MORDUKHAI-BOLTOVSKOI, Dimitri. The concept of infinity. Historical and critical notes. *Scr.Math.*, 1933, 1: 132-4, 252-3.

WEYL, Hermann. Die Stufen des Unendlichen. Vortrag, gehalten am 27. Oktober 1930 bei der Eröffnung der Gästetagung der Mathematischen Gesellschaft an der Universität Jena im Abbeanum. 1, 19 p. Jena: Fischer, 1931.

WINTER, M. Note sur l'infini en mathématiques. *Atti.IV° Congr.Int.Fil.* (Bologna, 1911), (5), p. 455-60. Genoa: Formiggini, 1913.

BJwi

TENCA, Luigi. Inizio dell'uso della nuova analisi infinitesimale in Italia. *Act.VIIIe Congr.Int.Hist.Sci.* (Florence, 1956), p. 3-9. Paris: Hermann, 1958.

BK SERIES AND FUNCTIONS

BOYER, Carl B. Proportion, equation, function: three steps in the development of a concept. *Scr.Math.*, 1946, 12: 5-13.

BURKHARDT, H.; KLEEBERG, R. Zur Geschichte der Interpolation durch Exponentialfunktionen. *Bibl.Math.*, 1913, 13: 150-3.

CHIRIKOV, M.V. [On the history of asymptotic series. (In Russian)] *Ist.Mat.Issled.*, 1960, 13: 441-72.

DAVIS, Harold T. *See* BEcg

DE CICCO, John. Survey of polygenic functions. *Scr.Math.*, 1945, 11: 51-6.

FELLMANN, Emil A. Ueber den Zusammenhang der Lemniskaten-Rektifikation mit speziellen Gammafunctionen. *Janus*, 1964, 51: 291-4.

GLODEN, A. Aperçu historique sur les séries. *Arch.Inst. Grand Ducal Luxemb.Sect.Sci.*, 1947, 17: 113-20.

GLODEN, A. Le développement de la théorie des séries depuis le début du 19e siècle jusqu'à nos jours. *Arch.Inst.Grand Ducal Luxemb.Sect.Sci.*, 1950, 19: 205-20.

GLODEN, A. Le développement des procédés de sommation des séries divergentes. *Act.VIe Congr.Int.Hist.Sci.* (Amsterdam, 1950), p. 178-86. Paris: Hermann, 1951.

GUSAK, A.A. Predystoriia i nachalo razvitiio teorii priblizleniia funktsiĭ. [The prehistory and early development of the theory of approximating functions. (In Russian)]. *Ist.-Mat.Issled.*, 1961, 14: 289-348.

MEDVEDEV, F.A. [On the development of the idea of a measurable function. (In Russian)] *Ist.Mat.Issled.*, 1959, 12: 481-92.

PAPLAUSKAS, A.B. Iz istorii trigonometricheskikh riadov. [From the history of trigonometric series. (In Russian)]. *Vop.Ist.Est.Tekh.*, 1963, 14: 72-5.

PAPLAUSKAS, A.B. Problema edinstvennosti v teorii trigonometricheskikh viadov. [The problem of uniqueness in the theory of trigonometric functions. (In Russian)]. *Ist. Mat. Issled.*, 1961, 14: 181-210.

PAPLAUSKAS, A.B. Voprosy summiruemosti i raskhodimost' trigonometricheskikh viadov. [Questions of the integrability and divergence of trigonometric series. (In Russian)] *Ist. Mat.Issled.*, 1963, 15: 129-70.

PASTORI, Maria. Le serie divergenti. *Period.Mat.*, 1928, *4th ser.*, 7: 302-20.

RAVETZ, J.R. Vibrating strings and arbitrary functions. *The logic of personal knowledge. Essays presented to Michael Polanyi on his 70th birthday*, p. 71-88. London: Routledge & Kegan Paul, 1961.

SINGH, A.N. The theory and construction of non-differentiable functions. In: Hobson, E.W., *et al.* Squaring the circle and other monographs. 110 p. New York: Chelsea, 1953. [CB 80/123]
 Reviewed by N.T. Gridgeman, *Sci.Mon.*, 1954, 78: 47-8.

STIPANIĆ, Ernest. Uno sguardo sull' evoluzione storica del concetto di funzione nella matematica. *Act.VIIIe Congr. Int.Hist.Sci.* (Florence, 1956), p. 115-19. Paris: Hermann, 1958.

WINTER, M. Les principes du calcul fonctionnel. *Rev.Métaphys. Morale*, 1913, 21: 462-510.

BKce-bv

LECAT, Maurice. Bibliographie des séries trigonométriques, avec un appendice sur le calcul des variations. 169 p. Bruxelles: The author, 1921. [CB 11/444]

BKfpx

L'HISTOIRE des fonctions elliptiques. Concours de l'Académie de Bologne. *Isis*, 1913, 1: 245.
 Details of prize offered by the Accademia delle Scienze dell'Istituto di Bologna on this subject.

BKnh

ARCHIBALD, Raymond Clare. Lambda functions. (Query no. 20) *Scr.Math.*, 1934, 2: 300.
 Enquiry on the origin of the name.

BKwi

FICHERA, Gaetano. L'analyse fonctionelle en Italie. *Cah. Hist.Mond.*, 1963, 7: 407-17.

LAURICELLA, G. L'opera dei matematici italiani nei recenti progressi della teoria delle funzioni di variabile reale e delle equazioni integrali. *Atti.Soc.Ital.Progr.Sci.*, V Riunione (Rome, 1911), p. 217-36. Rome: Bertero, 1912.

BKwn

GUSSOV, V.V. [The development of the theory of cylindrical functions in Russia and the U.S.S.R. (In Russian)]. *Ist. Mat.Issled.*, 1953, 6: 355-475.

LIKHIN, V.V. [Jacques Bernoulli's theory of functions and numbers and its development in Russia and the USSR. (In Russian)] *Ist.Mat.Issled.*, 1959, 12: 59-134.

BKxt

KRAZER, Adolf. Zur Geschichte der graphischen Darstellung von Funktionen. *Jahresber.Deut.Math. Ver.*, 1915, 24: 340-63. [CB 10/138]

WIELEITNER, Heinrich. Zur Geschichte der graphischen Darstellung von Funktionen. *Jahresber.Deut.Math.Ver.*, 1916, 25: 66.

BL CALCULUS

ALBRECHT, B. Vom Problem der Brachistochrone. Eine geschichtliche Skizze. 25 p. (Beilage zum Schulprogramm der Augusta-Schule zu Frankfurt a. O.) Frankfurt a. O.: Vogel & Neuber, 1912.

ALEXANDROVA, N.V. [On the history of calculus of variations. (In Russian)]. *Tr.Inst.Ist.Est.Tekh.*, 1959, 28: 219-36.

AUBRY, A. Le calcul infinitésimal avant Descartes et Fermat. *Ann.Sci.Acad.Polytech.Porto*, 1912, 7: 160-85.

BOYER, Carl B. The concepts of the calculus. A critical and historical discussion of the derivative and the integral. With a foreword by R. Courant. 346 p. New York: Hafner, 1949. [CB 75/87]
 First publ. New York: Columbia University Press, 1939. Reprinted as "The history of the calculus and its conceptual development" (New York: Dover, 1959).
 Reviewed by I. Bernard Cohen, *Isis*, 1947, 32: 205-10; for other reviews *see* CB 88/538.

BOYER, Carl B. History of the derivative and integral of the sine. *Math.Teacher*, 1947, 40: 267-75, 4 fig.

CAJORI, Florian. Grafting of the theory of limits on the calculus of Leibniz. *Amer.Math.Mon.*, 1923, 30: 223-34. [CB 15/227]

CAJORI, Florian. A history of the conceptions of limits and fluxions in Great Britain, from Newton to Woodhouse. viii, 299 p., ill. Chicago/London: Open Court, 1919.
 Reviewed by Pierre Boutroux, *Isis*, 1923, 5: 156-7.

CAJORI, Florian. Indivisibles and "ghosts of departed quantities" in the history of mathematics. *Scientia*, 1925, 37: 301-6. [CB 18/605]

CASTELNUOVO, Guido. Le origini del calcolo infinitesimale nell'era moderna. 166 p. (Per la Storia e Filosofia delle Matematiche, 12) Bologna: Zanichelli, 1938.
 2nd edition by Umberto Forti (234 p.), Milan: Feltrinelli, 1962.

COOLIDGE, Julian L. The story of tangents. *Amer.Math.Mon.*, 1951, 58: 449-62.

DOROFEEVA, A.V. Razvitie variatsionnogo ischisleniia kak ischisleniia variiatsiĭ. [The development of the calculus of variations. (In Russian)]. *Ist.-Mat.Issled.*, 1961, 14: 101-80.

FLECKENSTEIN, J.O. The line of descent of the infinitesimal calculus in the history of ideas. *Arch.Int.Hist.Sci.*, 1950, 3: 542-5, ill.

GUÉNON, René. Les principes du calcul infinitésimal. 144 p. (Tradition, 2) Paris: Gallimard, 1946.

HIGGINS, Thomas James. A note on the history of mixed partial derivatives. *Scr.Math.*, 1940, 7: 59-62.

KONDO, Yoitsu. [Formation of differential and integral calculus. (In Japanese)]. *J.Hist.Sci.Japan*, 1951, no. 19, 1-10; no. 20, 8-15.

LEBESQUE, Henri. Sur le développement de la notion d'intégrale. *Rev.Métaphys.Morale*, 1927, 34: 149-67.

McSHANE, Edward James. Integration. viii, 392 p. Princeton, N.J.: Princeton University Press, 1944. [CB 66/262]

MEDVEDEV, F.A. Vklad A.M. Liapunova v teoriiu integrala Stilt'esa. [The contributions of A.M. Liapunov to the integral theory of Stieltjes. (In Russian)] *Ist.Mat.Issled.*, 1961, 14: 211-34.

MUSSOTTER, R. Eine Skizze der Geschichte der Infinitesimal Rechnung. 21 p. (*Programm*) Wien: 1912.

RYBNIKOV, K.A. [First stages in the development of the calculus of variations. (In Russian)]. *Ist.Mat.Issled.*, 1949, 2: 355-498.

TOEPLITZ, Otto. The calculus: a genetic approach. Translated by Luise Lange. 192 p. Chicago: University of Chicago Press, 1963.
Translation of "Die Entwicklung der Infinitesimalrechnung" *see* below.

TOEPLITZ, Otto. Die Entwicklung der Infinitesimalrechnung. Eine Einleitung in die Infinitesimalrechnung nach der genetischen Methode. Aus dem Nachlass herausgegeben von Dr. Gottfried Köthe. ix, 181 p. (Die Grundlehren der mathematischen Wissenschaften in Einzeldarstellungen mit besonderer Berücksichtigung der Anwendungsgebiete, 56) Berlin/Göttingen/Heidelberg: Springer-Verlag, 1949.
Reviewed by Olaf Schmidt, *Centaurus*, 1951, 1: 378-80; by Arthur Rosenthal, *Scr.Math.*, 1952, 18: 149-50.

VOLTERRA, Vito. L'évolution des idées fondamentales du calcul infinitésimal. *Rev.Mois*, 1912, 13: 257-75.

WIELEITNER, Heinrich. Die Geburt der modernen Mathematik. Historisches und Grundsätzliches. 2. Die Infinitesimalrechnung. 72 p. (Wissen und Wirken, 13) Karlsruhe: 1925.

BLce-bv

LECAT, M. Bibliographie du calcul des variations. 115 p. Paris: Hermann, 1913.

BLk

ITARD, Jean. Quelques remarques sur la similitude et les méthodes infinitésimales. *Congr.Int.Phil.Sci.* (Paris, 1949), (8), p. 79-81. (Actualités Scientifiques et Industrielles, 1166) Paris: Hermann, 1952.

TIMERDING, H.E. Die Methoden der Infinitesimalrechnung. *Math.Naturwiss.Unterr.*, 1912, 43: 343-7, 347-50.

BLnb

CAJORI, Florian. The spread of Newtonian and Leibnizian notations of the calculus. *Bull.Amer.Math.Soc.*, 1921, 27: 453-8. [CB 12/633]

BLo

MENGER, Karl. Calculus 1950 - Geometry 1880. *Scr.Math.*, 1956, 22: 89-97.
On teaching the calculus.

BLwn

ZUBOV, V.P. Les "indivisibles" et le continu dans l'ancienne littérature russe (XI-XVII siècles). *Act.VIIIe Congr.Int.Hist.Sci.* (Florence, 1956), p. 89-102. Paris: Hermann, 1958.

BM DIFFERENTIAL AND INTEGRAL EQUATIONS

ARCHIBALD, Raymond Clare. History and bibliography of numerical integration of differential equations. *Scr.Math.*, 1934, 2: 188-9.

CAJORI, Florian. The early history of partial differential equations and of partial differentiation and integration. *Amer.Math.Mon.*, 1928, 35: 459-67. [CB 26/227]
For Spanish translation *see Rev.Mat.Hispano-Amer.*, 1929, 81-95.

DAVIS, Harold Thayer. The theory of linear operators from the standpoint of differential equations of infinite order. xiv, 628 p. (Monograph of the Waterman Institute of Indiana University, 72) Bloomington, Ind.: Principia Press, 1936. [CB 49/172]

DAVIS, Harold Thayer. The theory of the Volterra integral equation of second kind. 76 p., portr., bibliogr. (Indiana University Studies, 17: no. 88, 89, 90) Bloomington, Ind.: Indiana University Book Store, 1930. [CB 31/547]

DENJOY, Arnaud. Les équations différentielles périodiques. *Actes du Symposium International R.J. Bošković 1961*, p. 39-41. Beograd: 1962.

BMwn

LA SALLE, Joseph P.; LEFSHETZ, Solomon. Recent Soviet contributions to ordinary differential equations and nonlinear mechanics. *J.Math.Anal.Appl.*, 1961, 2: 651-60.
Reviewed by H.A. Antosiewcz, *Math.Rev.*, 1962, 23: 433, A2300.

BN VECTORS AND TENSORS

BURALI-FORTI, C.; MARCOLONGO, R.A. Analyse vectorielle générale. 2 vol. 1. Transformations linéaires; 2. Applications à la mécanique et à la physique. Pavia: Mattei, 1912-13.
For a lengthy summary (in Italian) of these volumes by the authors *see Isis*, 1914, 2: 174-82. This is preceded by a short review by G. Sarton, *ibid.*, 173.

CARUS, Edward Hegeler. Invariants as products and a vector interpretation of the symbolic method. viii, 44 p. Chicago: Open Court, 1927. [CB 23/236]

TONOLO, Angelo. Sulle origine del calcolo di Ricci. *Ann.Mat. Pura Appl.*, 1961, 53: no. 4, 189-207.
Reviewed by D.J. Struik, *Math.Rev.*, 1962, 23: 5, A37.

TRUESDELL, C. The physical components of vectors and tensors. *Z.Angew.Math.Mech.*, 1953, 33: 345-56.
One section of this article is devoted to the nature and history of the subject.

BO GEOMETRY

BOc general history

AGOSTINI, Amedeo. I problemi geometrici elementari e i problemi classici. In: Enciclopedia delle matematiche elementari, (2), p. 485-539, 9 fig. Milano: Hoepli, 1936.

ARCHIBALD, Raymond Clare. Remarks on Klein's "Famous problems of elementary geometry". *Amer.Math.Mon.*, 1914, 21: 247-59. [CB 9/465]

BALLY, Emile. Principes et premiers développements de géométrie générale synthétique moderne. viii, 218 p. Paris: Gauthier Villars, 1922.

BLASCHKE, Wilhelm. Reden und Reisen eines Geometers. 2nd enl. ed. 153 p. Berlin: VEB Deutscher Verlag der Wissenschaften, 1961.
Reviewed by G.R. MacLane, *Math.Rev.*, 1962, 23: 135, A765.

BOPP, Karl. Entwicklungslinien in der Geometrie. *Isis*, 1923, 5: 406-8, 2 fig. [CB 15/226]

CANDIDO, G. Pappo, Fagnano, Stewart, Chasles (coincidenze, priorità, generalizzazioni). *Period.Mat.*, 1935, 15: 58-62. [CB 44/514]

COLEMAN, Robert. The development of informal geometry. 12, 178 p. New York: Bureau of Publications, Teachers College, Columbia University, 1942.
Reviewed by E.R. Stabler, *Scr.Math.*, 1943, 9: 56-8.

COOLIDGE, Julian L. A history of geometrical methods. xviii, 451 p. Oxford: Clarendon Press, 1940; New York: Dover, 1963.
Reviewed by I. Bernard Cohen, *Isis*, 1941, 33: 347-50; by R. Taton, *Rev.Hist.Sci.*, 1949, 2: 195-6.

DEHN, Max. Die Grundlegung der Geometrie in historischer Entwicklung. In: Pasch, Moritz. Vorlesungen über neuere Geometrie, p. 185-275. 2nd ed. Berlin: Springer, 1926.

DEPMAN, I. IA. ["Practical geometry". (In Russian)] *Ist. Mat.Issled.*, 1955, 8: 620-9.

GODEAUX, Lucien. Les géométries. 215 p. (Collection Armand Colin, Section de Mathématiques, 206) Paris: Colin, 1937.

GOMÈS TEIXEIRA, Francisco. Sur les problèmes célèbres de la géométrie élémentaire non résolubles avec la règle et le compas. 132 p. Coïmbre: Université, 1915.

KLEIN, Felix. Famous problems of elementary geometry. The duplication of the cube, the trisection of an angle, the quadrature of the circle. An authorized translation of F. Klein's "Vorträge über ausgewählte Fragen der Elementargeometrie" ausgearbeitet von F. Tägert, by Wooster Woodruff Beman and David Eugene Smith. 2nd ed. rev and enl. with notes by Raymond Clare Archibald. xi, 92 p. New York: Stechert, 1930. [CB 37/547]

KUBOTA, T. [On the history of problems of elementary geometry. (In Japanese)] *J.Math.Ass.Japan for Secondary Educ.*, 1932, 14: 151-60.

LORIA, Gino. Il passato e il presente delle principali teorie geometriche. Storie e bibliografia. 4th rev. ed. xxiii, 467 p. Padova: Cedam, 1931.
  Reviewed by R. C. Archibald, *Isis*, 1933, 19: 229-31.

VERA, Francesco. Breve historia de la geometria. 200 p. Buenos-Aires: Losada, 1948.

BOdaj

WIELEITNER, Heinrich, ed. Analytische und synthetische Geometrie. vii, 90 p., 22 ill. (Mathematische Quellenbücher, 3) Berlin: O. Salle, 1928. [CB 25/413]

WIELEITNER, Heinrich, ed. Geometrie und Trigonometrie. viii, 68 p., fig. (Mathematische Quellenbücher, 2) Berlin: Otto Salle, 1927. [CB 23/240]

BOj psychological aspects

GREENWOOD, Thomas. Essais sur la pensée géométrique. 100 p. Ottawa: University of Ottawa, 1943.
  Reviewed by E.T. Whittaker, *Nature*, 1944, 153: 268-9.

PIAGET, Jean; INHELDER, Bärbel; SZEMINSKA, Alina. La géométrie spontanée de l'enfant. 516 p. Paris: Presses Universitaires de France, 1948.

ROSSIER, Paul. L'histoire des axiomes géométriques et l'évolution psychologique de l'enfant. *Arch.Int.Hist.Sci.*, 1948, 1: 363-4. Also in *Act.Ve Congr.Int.Hist.Sci.* (Lausanne, 1947), p. 93-4. Paris: Hermann, 1948.

STROHAL, Richard. Die Grundbegriffe der reinen Geometrie in ihrem Verhältnis zur Anschauung. Untersuchungen zur psychologischen Vorgeschichte der Definitionen, Axiome und Postulate. iv, 137 p. (Wissenschaft und Hypothese, 27) Leipzig: Teubner, 1925. [CB 21/569]

BOk philosophy and methodology

RICHARD, J. La géométrie au point de vue concret. *Rev.Métaphys.Morale*, 1927, 34: 337-51.

BOkb

HILBERT, D.; COHN-VOSSEN, S. Geometry and the imagination. Translated by P. Nemenyi. ix, 357 p. New York: Chelsea Publishing Company, 1950.
  Reviewed by Nathan Altshiller Court, *Scr.Math.*, 1953, 19: 145-6.

BOkk

BERGHUYS, Johannes Jacobus Wilhelmus. Grondslagen van de aanschouwelijke meetkunde. [The foundations of intuitive geometry. (In Dutch with summary in French and in English)] 231 p. (Thesis, Amsterdam) Groningen-Djakarta: Noordhoff, 1952.
  Includes a historical outline.

BOTTEMA, O. Zur Geschichte der Grundlagen der Geometrie. *Math.-Phys.Semesterber.*, 1962-63, 9: 164-8.
  In reply to Freudenthal, Hans, *see* below.
  Reviewed by S. Jáskowski, *Math.Rev.*, 1964, 27: 16.

BOULIGAND, Georges. *See* BOod

DINGLER, Hugo. Die Grundlagen der Geometrie: ihre Bedeutung für Philosophie, Mathematik, Physik und Technik. vii, 76 p. Stuttgart: Enke, 1933.

FREUDENTHAL, Hans. Die Grundlagen der Geometrie um die Wende des 19. Jahrhunderts. *Math.-Phys.Semesterber.*, 1960, 7: 2-25.

FREUDENTHAL, Hans. Zur Geschichte der Grundlagen der Geometrie. Zugleich eine Besprechung der 8. Aufl. von Hilberts "Grundlagen der Geometrie". *Nieuw Arch.Wisk.*, 1957, 5: 105-42.
  For Hilbert's work *see* below.

GOE, George. Kästner, forerunner of Gauss, Pasch, Hilbert. *Proc.10th Int.Congr.Hist.Sci.*(Ithaca, 1962), (2), p. 659-62. Paris: Hermann, 1964.

HILBERT, David. Grundlagen der Geometrie. 8th ed. by Paul Bernays. vii, 251 p. Stuttgart: Teubner, 1956.
  For review *see* Freudenthal, Hans above. 7th edition (Leipzig: Teubner, 1930) reviewed by Kurt Reidemeister, *Deut.Lit.Zeitung*, 1931, 2: 90-2.

JAKOBI, Robert. Äquidistante Punkte auf Parallelen. *Prax. Math.*, 1962, 4: 185.

NAGEL, Ernest. The formation of modern conceptions of formal logic in the development of geometry. *Osiris*, 1939, 7: 142-224.
  This paper discusses developments in pure geometry during the 19th century and their incidence upon some central ideas of modern logic.

NICOD, Jean. Foundations of geometry and induction. Containing geometry in the sensible world, and the logical problem of induction. Prefaces by Bertrand Russell and André Lalande. Translated by Philip Paul Wiener. iv, 286 p. (International Library of Psychology, Philosophy and Scientific Method) London: Kegan Paul; New York: Harcourt, Brace, 1930.
  Reviewed by T.G., *Nature*, 1931, 128: 430; by Arnold Dresden, *Bull.Amer.Math.Soc.*, 1931, 37: 152-3.

POINCARÉ, Henri. Des fondements de la géométrie. 65 p. Paris: Chiron, 1921.
  First published in *The Monist*, 1898, in English.

RUSSELL, Bertrand. An essay on the foundations of geometry. 201 p. New York: Dover Publications, 1956.
  An unaltered republication of the first edition of 1897.

BOks

SJÖSTEDT, C.E. Zur Erkenntnistheorie der Geometrie. *Adolf Phalén in memoriam; philosophical essays*, p. 75-120. Uppsala/Stockholm: Almqvist & Wiksell, 1937.

BOkv

BOULIGAND, Georges. Relations d'incertitude en géométrie et en physique. Préface de L. de Broglie. 28 p. Paris: Hermann, 1934.

BOm fundamental concepts

GORDIN, H.M. Infinity and the part-and-whole axiom. Definitions of the fundamental entities of geometry. *Monist*, 1919, 29: 1-11.

NUVOLI, Lidia. Il principio di dualita in geometria. *Physis*, 1960, 2: 101-20.

BOme space

CAJORI, Florian. Early "proofs" of the impossibility of a fourth dimension of space. *Arch.Stor.Sci.*, 1926, 7: 25-8. [CB 21/567]

CAJORI, Florian. Origins of fourth dimension concepts. *Amer. Math.Mon.*, 1926, 33: 397-406. [CB 22/256]

DUPONT, Paul. Les géométries euclidiennes et non-euclidiennes, et l'espace physique. *Rev.Phil.*, 1927, 52: 74-102.

FAVARD, J. Espace et dimension. 302 p. Paris: Michel, 1950.
  Reviewed by F. Russo, *Rev.Quest.Sci.*, 1951, 12: 440-1.

FREUDENTHAL, Hans. Der orientierte Raum des Mathematikers. *Naturwissenschaften*, 1963, 50: 199-205. [CB 89/501]
  A discussion of the views of Newton, Leibniz, Kant and others.

GONSETH, Ferdinand. La géométrie et le problème de l'espace. 6 vol. Neuchâtel: Editions du Griffon, 1945-55.
  Vol. 1, 2, 3 reviewed by P. Grésy, *Arch.Int.Hist.Sci.*, 1949, 2: 509-10; vol. 6 by G. Hirsch, *ibid.*, 1956, 9: 62-3.

LAURÈS, Clément. Les bases de la géométrie et de la physique. L'invariance de l'espace euclidien. 125 p., ill. Paris: A. Blanchard, 1928. [CB 24/525]

LIBOIS, P. De l'espace métrique à l'espace projectif. *Compt. Rend. IIe Congr. Nat. Sci.* (Bruxelles, 1935), p. 96-104. Brussels: 1935. [CB 47/282]

SCHLEIER, -. Inwieweit werden die Kantischen Ansichten vom Raume durch die moderne mathematische Forschung bestätigt? *Z. Positivistische Phil.*, 1914, 2: 136-45. [CB 6/446]

STUDY, Eduard. Die realistische Weltansicht und die Lehre vom Raume. Geometrie, Anschauung und Erfahrung. 2nd rev. ed. 1. Das Problem der Aussenwelt. xi, 85 p. (Die Wissenschaft, 54) Braunschweig: F. Vieweg u. Sohn, 1922.
1st edition of complete work published Braunschweig: Vieweg, 1914 (ix, 145 p.).

TIETJEN, Cl. H. Raum oder Zahl? 51 p., ill. (Schule im Aufbau aus völkischer Wirklichkeit, 6) Leipzig: Brandstetter, 1936. [CB 54/529]

TUMMERS, J.H. La géométrie et le problème de l'espace. *Dialectica*, 1962, 16: 56-60.

VRIES, Hendrik de. Die vierte Dimension. Eine Einführung in das vergleichende Studium der verschiedenen Geometrien. Übersetzt nach der 2. Auflage von Ruth Struik. ix, 167 p., 35 fig. (Wissenschaft und Hypothese, 29) Leipzig/Berlin: B.G. Teubner, 1926.
Reviewed by H. Hopf, *Deut. Lit. Zeitung*, 1928, 1230-1.

WEITZENBÖCK, Roland. Der vierdimensionale Raum. vii, 142 p. (Die Wissenschaft, 80) Braunschweig: Vieweg, 1929.
Reviewed by L. Bieberbach, *Arch. Gesch. Math. Naturwiss. Tech.*, 1929, 12: 112.

WIELEITNER, Heinrich. Zur Frühgeschichte der Räume von mehr als drei Dimensionen. *Isis*, 1925, 7: 486-9.
Brief historical account of the notion of hyperspace (space of more than three dimensions). Additional note by R.C. Archibald.

BOmzB relation with other mathematical fields

BOmzBFzg

REY PASTOR, J. La systématisation de la géométrie au moyen de la théorie des groupes. *Scientia*, 1918, 23: 413-22.

SCHUBARTH, E. Der Gruppenbegriff in der Geometrie. *Experientia*, 1947, 3: 385-93, 5 fig. [CB 72/270]

BOmzBIzc

LORIA, Gino. Lo spettro dell'immaginario in geometria. *Scientia*, 1917, 22: 3-15.

BOn/o communication; teaching

BOnh

KARPINSKI, Louis C. The terminology of elementary geometry. *Sch. Sci. Math.*, 1924, 24: 162-7. [CB 16/312]

BOo

STAMPER, A.W. A history of the teaching of elementary geometry, with reference to present day problems. x, 163 p. (Teachers College Series, 23) [New York: Columbia University, 1906].

BOod

BOULIGAND, Georges. Sur la répercussion de quelques courants d'idées géométriques en matière de logique et d'enseignement. *Rev. Gén. Sci.*, 1936, 47: 581-8.

BOUTROUX, Pierre. L'édifice géométrique et la démonstration. *Enseign. Math.*, 1913, 15: 298-305. [CB 3/562]

BOt relations with the humanities

BOtp

MORITZ, Robert E. On the beauty of geometrical forms. *Scr. Math.*, 1936, 4: 25-35, 2 pl., 1 fig.

BOtq

IVINS, William M.J. Art and geometry. A study in space intuitions. x, 135 p. Cambridge, Mass.: Harvard University Press, 1946. [CB 70/253]

SHEPARD, Anna O. The symmetry of abstract design. With special reference to ceramic decoration. (Contributions to American Anthropology and History, 47) *Publ. Carnegie Inst. Wash.*, 1948, 574: 209-93, ill. [CB 75/88]

BOw in different countries

BOwg-o

WOLFF, G. The development of the teaching of geometry in Germany. *Math. Gaz.*, 1937, 21: 82-98.

BOwi

AMALDI, U. Sullo sviluppo della geometria in Italia durante l'ultimo cinquantennio. *Atti Soc. Ital. Progr. Sci.*, V Riunione (Rome, 1911), p. 981-7. Rome: Bertero, 1912.

SEGRE, Beniamino. La geometria in Italia, dal Cremona ai giorni nostri. *Ann. Mat. Pura Appl.*, 1932, 11: 1-16.

BOwk

GODEAUX, Lucien. Les recherches de géometrie dans ces dernières années en Belgique. *Rev. Gén. Sci.*, 1959, 66: 6-16.

BOx techniques and instruments

BOxg

VUIBERT, Henri. Les anaglyphes géometriques. 32 p., ill. Paris: Vuibert, 1912.
Stereoscopic representation of 3-dimensional concepts. Reviewed in *Isis*, 1913, 1: 492-3.

BOxh

ARCHIBALD, Raymond Clare. Geometrography and other methods of measurement of geometrical constructions. *Amer. Math. Mon.*, 1918, 25: 37-8. [CB 10/153]
Short bibliographical note on geometrography, that is, the art of geometrical constructions, invented by Émile Lemoine.

GEPPERT, Harald. Sulle costruzioni geometriche che si eseguiscono colla riga ed un compasso ad apertura fissa. *Period. Mat.*, 1929, 9: 292-319. [CB 28/542]

PETERSEN, J. Methods and theories for the solution of problems of geometrical construction. 102 p. In: Ball, W.W. Rouse. String figures and other monographs. New York: Chelsea Publishing Co., 1960.

BOxk

HUDSON, H.P. Ruler and compass. In: Hobson, E.W., *et al.* Squaring the circle and other monographs. 143 p. New York: Chelsea, 1953.

BOxt

TATON, René. L'influence des techniques graphiques sur le développement de la géométrie. *Hommage à Gaston Bachelard*, p. 93-101. Paris: Presses Universitaires de France, 1957.

TATON, René. Les techniques graphiques et le développement de la géométrie. *Act. VIIIe Congr. Int. Hist. Sci.* (Florence, 1956), p. 18-24. Paris: Hermann, 1958.

BP EUCLIDIAN GEOMETRY
(plane, solid and higher dimensional)

for conic sections *see under* BQ

ARCHIBALD, Raymond Clare. Historical note on centers of similitude of circles. *Amer. Math. Mon.*, 1916, 23: 159-61.

COXETER, H.S.M. Regular polytopes. xi, 321 p., pl., diagr. London: Methuen, 1948.

FISCHER, Theodor. Zwei Vorträge über Proportionen. 102 p., 43 fig. München: Oldenbourg, 1934.

HILL, M.J.M. The theory of proportion. xx, 108 p. London: Constable, 1914.
Reviewed by P. Jourdain, *Isis*, 1920, 3: 307.

KIEFFER, Lucien. Les notions de congruence et d'équivalence en géométrie élémentaire (Aperçu historique). *Arch. Inst. Grand-Ducal Luxemb. Sect. Sci.*, 1957, 24: 161-71.

LINDEMANN, F. Zur Geschichte der Polyeder. *Sitzungsber. Bayer. Akad. Wiss. Math. Naturwiss. Abt.*, 1934, 265-75. [CB 44/516]

LIUSTERNIK, L.A. Convex figures and polyhedra. Transl. from the Russian by T. Jefferson Smith. 176 p., fig. New York: Dover Publications, 1963.

POLACHEK, Harry. The structure of the honeycomb. *Scr. Math.*, 1940, 7: 87-98, 6 fig.

STRUIK, D.J. Het probleem "De impletione loci". [The problem "De impletione loci". (In Dutch)] *Nieuw Arch.Wisk.*, 1925, 15: 121-37.
Space filling regular solids from Plato to modern times.

TOGLIATTI, Eugenio G. Sul volume della sfera (Esposizione storico-comparativa). *Period.Mat.*, 1922, 4: no. 2, 305-26.
Reviewed by H. Bosmans, *Rev.Quest.Sci.*, 1924, 4: 1-4.

WEAVER, J.H. Some extensions of the work of Pappus and Steiner on tangent circles. *Amer.Math.Mon.*, 1920, 27: 2-11.

WHITLOCK, W.P. Rational right triangles with equal areas. *Scr.Math.*, 1943, 9: 155-61, 265-7, ill.

WIELEITNER, Heinrich. Ueber den Rauminhalt der Pyramide. *Unterrichtsbl.Math.Naturwiss.*, 1925, 31: 91-2.

BPce-bv

NEUBERG, J. Bibliographie des triangles spéciaux. 54 p. Bruxelles: Hayez, 1924.

BPk

BECKER, Oskar. Die Rolle der euklidischen Geometrie in der Protophysik. *Phil.Natur*, 1964, 8: 49-64.

BPkk

COURT, N.A. Plane geometry and plain logic. *Sci.Mon.*, 1956, 83: 28-37.

BPnh

GANDZ, Solomon. On three interesting terms relating to area. *Amer.Math.Mon.*, 1927, 34: 80-6.
Philological discussion of the terms meshihah, chroia (Greek) and takṣîr (thishboreth) and derivatives.

SARTON, George. When did the term "golden section" or its equivalent in other languages originate? (Query no. 130) *Isis*, 1951, 42: 47.

BPwi

CAVALLARO, Vincenzo G. Storia della geometria del triangolo in Italia. *Boll.Mat.*, Settembre 1938, 34: xli-xliv, lxi-lxvii.

BPxd

BEUMER, M.G. Enkele grepen uit de geschiedenis der trisectie. [A few examples from the history of trisection. (In Dutch)]. *Euclides*, 1947-48, 23: 230-6.

BREIDENBACH, W. Die Dreiteilung des Winkels. iv, 38 p., 43 fig. (Mathematische-Physikalische Bibliothek, 78) Leipzig: Teubner, 1933. [CB 39/447]

COURT, N.A. Notes on inversion. *Math.Teacher*, 1962, 55: 655-7.
A short history of the geometrical transformation, with emphasis on the nineteenth century, but with mention of earlier adumbrations.

EMCH, Arnold. Some points in the history of the catacaustica and a clarifying representation of the curve. *Scr.Math.*, 1952, 18: 31-5, 3 fig.

GOLDENRING, Robert. Die elementargeometrischen Konstruktionen des regelmässigen Siebzehnecks. Eine historisch-kritische Darstellung. 69 p., 51 fig. Leipzig: Teubner, 1915.
Reviewed by R. C. Archibald, *Bull.Amer.Math.Soc.*, 1916, 22: 239-46.

KEMPE, A.B. How to draw a straight line; a lecture on linkages. In: Hobson, E.W., *et al.* Squaring the circle and other monographs. 51 p. New York: Chelsea, 1953. [CB 80/123]
Reviewed by N.T. Gridgeman, *Sci.Mon.*, 1954, 78: 47-8.

MITZSCHERLING, A. Das Problem der Kreisteilung. Ein Beitrag zur Geschichte seiner Entwicklung. 214 p., 210 fig. Leipzig: Teubner, 1913.

PATTERSON, Boyd C. The origins of the geometric principle of inversion. *Isis*, 1933, 19: 154-80. [CB 39/388]
Dandelin; Quetelet; Steiner; Magnus; Plücker; Belavitis.

TANDBERG, J. Vinkelns tredelning. [The trisection of the angle. (In Swedish)] *Tidskr.Elem.Mat.Fys.Kem.*, 1935, 85-94; 1936, 145-59.
Historical introduction.

WEISS, E.A. Die geschichtliche Entwicklung der Lehre von der Geraden-Kugeltransformation. *Deut.Math.*, 1936, 1: 23-37, 15 fig.

BPxd-bv

ARCHIBALD, Raymond Clare. Bibliography of the theory of linkages. *Scr.Math.*, 1934, 2: 293.

BPzc SQUARING THE CIRCLE

BEUTEL, E. Die Quadratur des Kreises. iv, 75 p., 15 fig. Leipzig: Teubner, 1913.

HOBSON, E.W. Squaring the circle. viii, 58 p. Cambridge University Press, 1914.

HOBSON, E.W., *et al.* Squaring the circle and other monographs. 361 p., ill. New York: Chelsea, 1953. [CB 80/123]
Facsimile reprint of 4 works by different authors.
Reviewed by N.T. Gridgeman, *Sci.Mon.*, 1954, 78: 47-8.

WIELEITNER, Heinrich. Zur Geschichte der quadrierbaren Kreismonde. Aus dem handschriftlichen Nachlass von Dr. Heinrich Wieleitner. Hrsg. von Jos. E. Hofmann. 74 p., 33 fig. (*Wissenschaftliche Beilage zum Jahresbericht des Neuen Realgymnasiums München für das Schuljahr 1933-34)* [München: 1934]. [CB 41/600]

BPzc-wh

DIANNI, Jadwiga. The problem of circle's quadrature in Polish mathematics. (Summary of a communiqué.) *Act.VIIIe Congr.Int.Hist.Sci.* (Florence, 1956), p. 132-3. Paris: Hermann, 1958.

BQ ANALYTICAL AND DIFFERENTIAL GEOMETRY

AMODEO, Federico. Sintesi storico-critica della geometria delle curve algebriche. 420 p., 30 portr. Napoli: Conte, 1945.

BOYER, Carl B. Cartesian geometry from Fermat to Lacroix. *Scr. Math.*, 1947, 13: 133-53, 5 fig.

BOYER, Carl B. Early contributions to analytic geometry. *Scr.Math.*, 1953, 19: 93-108, 230-8.
A chapter of "The history of analytic geometry", *see* below.

BOYER, Carl B. Historical stages in the definition of curves. *Nat.Math.Mag.*, 1945, 19: 294-310.

BOYER, Carl B. History of analytic geometry. ix, 291 p. (Scripta Mathematica Studies, 6 and 7) New York: *Scripta Mathematica*, 1956.
Reviewed by René Taton, *Isis*, 1959, 50: 489-92; by B.A. Rozenfel'd, *Vop.Ist.Est.Tekh.*, 1959, 8: 165-7.

BOYER, Carl B. The invention of analytic geometry. *Sci. Amer.*, Jan. 1949, 180: (1), 40-5, ill.

BOYER, Carl B. Post-Cartesian analytical geometry. *Scr. Math.*, 1955, 21: 101-35, 24 fig.

CAJORI, Florian. Generalizations in geometry as seen in the history of developable surfaces. *Amer.Math.Mon.*, 1929, 36: 431-7, 1 fig. [CB 28/541]

COOLIDGE, Julian L. A history of the conic sections and quadric surfaces. xi, 214 p. Oxford: Clarendon Press, 1945. [CB 70/253]
This is a companion volume to the author's previous work "A history of geometrical methods", *see* BOc.

COOLIDGE, Julian L. The origin of analytic geometry. *Osiris*, 1936, 1: 231-50. [CB 46/587]

DIJKSTERHUIS, E.J. De Versiera. [The witch of Agnesi curve. (In Dutch)] *Euclides*, 1932-33, 9: 233-65, 18 fig.

HILL, L.S.; DARKOW, M.D. An algebraic treatment of geometry on a spherical surface. *Scr.Math.*, 1935, 3: 234-46, 1 pl.

KIEFFER, Lucien. La construction des axes en axonométrie orthogonale. (Aperçu historique) *Sci.Hist.*, 1964, 6: 185-91.

LORIA, Gino. Curve piane speciali algebriche e trascendenti. Teoria e storia. 2 vol. 1. Curve algebriche. xvi, 574 p., fig.; 2. Curve trascendenti; curve dedotte da altre. xi, 439 p., fig. Milano: Hoepli, 1930. [CB 28/542 and CB 30/467]

LORIA, Gino. Curve sghembe speciali, algebriche e trascendenti. 2 vol. Bologna: Nicola Zanichelli, 1925.

LORIA, Gino. Da Descartes e Fermat a Monge e Lagrange. Contributo alla storia della geometria analitica. *Atti Accad. Naz.Lincei Mem.Cl.Sci.Fis.Mat.Natur., 5th ser.*, 1923, 14: 777-845. [CB 18/606]

LORIA, Gino. Perfectionnements, évolution, métamorphoses du concept de "coordonnées". *Mathematica*, 1942, 18: 125-45.

LORIA, Gino. Perfectionnements, évolution, métamorphoses du concept de "coordonnées". Contribution à l'histoire de la géometrie analytique. *Osiris*, 1948, 8: 218-88. [CB 75/87]

LYSENKO, V.I. Iz ustorii voprosa o tochkakh vozvrata ploskoĭ krivoĭ. [Historical questions relating to the turning point of a plane curve. (In Russian)] *Ist. Mat.Issled.*, 1961, 14: 517-26.

MILNE, John J. The story of a problem and its solution. *Math. Gaz.*, 1930, 15: 142-4.
The 'locus ad tres et quatuor lineas' problem in the third book of the "Conics" of Apollonius and its discussion by Pappus, Descartes and Newton.

MORDUKHAI-BOLTOVSKOI, D.D. [From the past of analytical geometry. (In Russian)]. *Tr.Inst.Ist.Est.*, 1952, 4: 216-35.

ROSENBLATT, A. Postepy teoryi powierzchni algebraicznych. [Development of the theory of algebraic surfaces. (In Polish)] *Prace Mat.Fiz.*, 1912, 23: 51-192.

SEGRE, Beniamino. The rise of algebra and the creation of algebraic geometry. *Cah.Hist.Mond.*, 1963, 7: 383-406.

STRUIK, D.J. Outline of a history of differential geometry. *Isis*, 1933, 19: 92-120; 20: 161-91. [CB 39/450 and CB 40/397]

STRUIK, D.J. Ueber die Entwicklung der Differentialgeometrie. Antrittsvorlesung Utrecht, 1923. *Jahresber.Deut.Math.Ver.*, 1925, 34: 14-25.

VRIES, H. de. How analytic geometry became a science. *Scr. Math.*, 1948, 14: 5-15.

WAERDEN, B.L. van der. The foundation of algebraic geometry. A very incomplete historical survey. *Studies and essays presented to R. Courant*, p. 437-9. New York: Interscience, 1948.

WHITMAN, E.A. Some historical notes on the cycloid. *Amer. Math.Mon.*, 1943, 50: 309-15, fig.

WIELEITNER, Heinrich. Die Geburt der modernen Mathematik. Historisches und Grundsätzliches. 2 vol. 1. Die analytische Geometrie; 2. Die Infinitesimalrechnung. (Wissen und Wirken, 12 & 13) Karlsruhe in Baden: Braun, 1924-25. [CB 17/593]

WILCZYNSKI, E.J. Some remarks on the historical development and the future prospects of the differential geometry of plane curves. *Bull.Amer.Math.Soc.*, 1916, 22: 317-29. [CB 8/362]

BQk

STAECKEL, Paul. Beiträge zur Kritik der Differentialgeometrie. 27 p. (*Sitzungsber.Heidelb.Akad.Wissensch.Math.Naturwiss. Kl.Abt.A Math.Phys.Wiss.*, 1914, vol. 5) Heidelberg: 1914.

BQnh

CAJORI, Florian. What is the origin of the name "Rolle's Curve"? *Amer.Math.Mon.*, 1918, 25: 290-2.

BQxk

ARTOBOLEVSKII, I.I. To the development of the theory of mechanisms for the reproduction of algebraic curves. *Arch. Int.Hist.Sci.*, 1960, 13: 87-93.

BR PROJECTIVE AND DESCRIPTIVE GEOMETRY

AMODEO, Federigo. Orígine e sviluppo della geometria proiettiva. 176 p. Naples: Pellerano, 1939.
Reviewed by José Babini, *Archeion*, 1940, 22: 99-100.

CASSINA, Ugo. Sur l'histoire des concepts fondamentaux de la géométrie projective. 36 p., 3 fig. (Les Conférences du Palais de la Découverte, D, 50) Paris: Université de Paris, 1957.

COOLIDGE, J.L. The rise and fall of projective geometry. *Amer.Math.Mon.*, 1934, 41: 217-28. [CB 42/582]

LORIA, Gino. Storia della geometria descrittiva dalle origini sino ai giorni nostri. xxiv, 584 p. Milano: Hoepli, 1921.
Reviewed by L.C. Karpinski, *Isis*, 1923, 5: 181-2.

TATON, René. L'histoire de la géométrie descriptive. 25 p., 6 fig. (Les Conférences du Palais de la Découverte, D, 32) Paris: Université de Paris, 1954.

BRce-bv

ARCHIBALD, Raymond Clare. Bibliographies of projective differential geometry. *Scr.Math.*, 1932, 1: 171.

BRwf-op

OCAGNE, Maurice d'. Notions sommaires de géométrie projective à l'usage des candidats à l'Ecole Polytechnique. 24 p. Paris: Gauthier-Villars, 1923.

BRzp PERSPECTIVE

DOESSCHATE, G. ten. Uit de geschiedenis der oudste stadia van de perspectiefleer. [Concerning the early study of perspective. (In Dutch)] *Bijdr.Gesch.Geneesk.*, 1938, 18: 116-28, 129-40, 5 fig.

FLOCON, Albert; TATON, René. La perspective. 128 p., fig. (Que Sais-Je?, 1050) Paris: Presses Universitaires de France, 1963.
Reviewed by Jean Itard, *Rev.Hist.Sci.*, 1964, 17: 169-70.

SULZBERGER, Suzanne. La perspective est-elle une science ou un art? *Alumni*, 1950, 19: 358-65, 2 fig.

BS TRIGONOMETRY

AGOSTINI, Amedeo. Le funzioni circolari e le funzioni iperboliche - trigonometria piana e sferica. In: Enciclopedia delle matematiche elementari, (2), p. 545-615. Milan: Hoepli, 1936.

AGOSTINI, Amedeo. Sulla trigonometria. *Period.Mat.*, 1952, 30: 164-6.

ANDOYER, H. *See* BE

ARCHIBALD, Raymond Clare. *See* BE

DIJKSTERHUIS, E.J. Van koorde tot sinus, van umbra tot tangens. [From string to sine, from shadow to tangent. (In Dutch)] *Euclides*, 1953-54, 29: 271-85.

KARPINSKI, Louis C. The place of trigonometry in the development of mathematical ideas. *Scr.Math.*, 1945, 11: 268-72.

KASNER, Edward. The recent theory of the horn angle. *Scr. Math.*, 1945, 11: 263-7.

PREWAZNIK, Franz. Trigonometrie ohne Winkelfunktionen. *Praxis Math.*, 1963, 5: 240-2.
A brief discussion of Snell, Ozanam, and Mansion's computation of the angles in a triangle from the length of the sides.

WIELEITNER, Heinrich. *See* BOc

BSce-bv

KARPINSKI, Louis C. Bibliographical check list of all works on trigonometry published up to 1700 A.D. *Scr.Math.*, 1946, 12: 267-83, 5 fig.
Supplemented by: Richeson, A.W. Additions to Karpinski's trigonometry list. *Scr.Math.*, 1952, 18: 94.

BSnh

PESCI, G. A proposito di una etimologia [sinus]. *Period.Mat.*, 1912, 15: Suppl., 43-5.

BT NON-EUCLIDIAN GEOMETRY

BARBARIN, Paul. La géométrie non euclidienne. 3e éd. suivie de notes sur la géométrie non euclidienne dans ses rapports avec la physique mathématique, par A. Buhl. 176 p., 7 pl. (Scientia, 15) Paris: Gauthier-Villars, 1928.
First and second editions, 1902 and 1907.

BONOLA, Roberto. Non-Euclidean geometry. A critical and historical study of its developments. English transl. by H.S. Carslaw. With a supplement containing the George Bruce Halsted translation of "The science of absolute space", by John Bolyai, and "The theory of parallels", by Nicholas Lobachevski. xii, 268, 71, 50 p., ill., diagr., bibliogr. New York: Dover Publications, 1955.
Carslaw's translation from the Italian original (Bologna: 1906) first published 1912.

CARSLAW, H.S. Non-Euclidean plane geometry and trigonometry. x, 179 p. In: Ball, W.W. Rouse. String figures and other monographs. New York: Chelsea Publishing Co., 1960.

ENRIQUES, Federigo. Conferenze sulla geometria non euclidea, per cura del Dott. Olegario Fernandez. 46 p. Bologna: N. Zanichelli, 1918.

GRÉGOIRE, A. Les géométries non-euclidiennes. *Rev.Quest.Sci.*, 1932, 21: 361-400.

KLEIN, Felix. Vorlesungen über nicht-euklidische Geometrie. Für den Druck neu bearb. von W. Rosemann. xii, 326 p. (Die Grundlehren der mathematischen Wissenschaften, 26) Berlin: Springer, 1928.
Reviewed by K. Reidemeister, *Deut.Lit.Zeitung*, 1928, 5: 2071-2.

LIEBMANN, Heinrich. Nichteuklidische Geometrie. 3rd rev.ed. 150 p., 40 fig. Berlin: de Gruyter, 1923.

MacLEOD, Andries. Introduction à la géométrie non-euclidienne. 433 p. Paris: Hermann, 1922. [CB 14/552]

NORDEN, A.P. 125 let neevklidovoi geometrii. [125 years of non-Euclidean geometry. (In Russian)] *Usp.Mat.Nauk*, 1951, 6: no. 3, 3-9.

ROSENFELD, B.A. New researches in the prehistory of Lobachevsky's geometry and in the history of its interpretations. *Act. VIIIe Congr.Int.Hist.Sci.* (Florence, 1956) p. 138-41. Paris: Hermann, 1958.

SIMON, Max. Nichteuklidische Geometrie in elementarer Behandlung. Bearb. und hrsg. von Kuno Fladt. xviii, 115 p., 125 fig. (Beihefte zur *Zeitschrift für mathematischen und naturwissenschaftlichen Unterricht*, 10) Leipzig: B.G. Teubner, 1925. [CB 18/607]
Includes many historical notes.

ZACHARIAS, Max. Das Parallelenproblem und seine Lösung. Eine Einführung in die hyperbolische nichteuklidische Geometrie. 44 p., 27 fig. (Mathematisch-physikalische Bibliothek, 92) Leipzig: Teubner, 1937.
Reviewed by R.M. Winger, *Amer.Math.Mon.*, 1938, 45: 541.

BThd

HALSTED, G.B. Non-Euclidean geometry in the Encyclopaedia Britannica. *Science*, 1912, 35: 736-40.

BTj

BERGFELD, Emil. Zur Psychologie des Parallelenaxioms. *Z. Psychol.*, 1933, 130: 103-7.

BU TOPOLOGY

ERRERA, Alfred. Exposé historique du problème des quatre couleurs. *Period.Mat.*, 1927, 7: 20-41.

HUREWICZ, Witold; WALLMAN, Henry. Dimension theory. viii, 165 p. (Princeton Mathematical Series, 4) Princeton: Princeton University Press, 1941. [CB 62/74]

KERÉNYI, Karl. Labyrinth-Studien. 72 p., 30 fig. (Albae Vigiliae, 10) Zürich: Rhein-Verlag, 1950. [CB 77/383]

MATTHEWS, W.H. Mazes and labyrinths, a general account of their history and development. xviii, 254 p. London: Longmans, 1922.

PIER, Jean-Paul. Genèse et évolution de l'idée de compact. *Rev.Hist.Sci.*, 1961, 14: 169-79.

SMALE, S. A survey of some recent developments in differential topology. *Bull.Amer.Math.Soc.*, 1963, 69: 131-45.
A review of work done in the last decade, touching briefly on some major points of development since Poincaré. Includes bibliography.

STEIN, Sherman K. The mathematician as an explorer. *Sci. Amer.*, 1961, 204: no. 5, 149-58.
Account of how a memory word used by drummers in ancient India led to the classic problem of the traveling salesman's route.

TUCKER, Albert W.; BAILEY, Herbert S. Topology. A fascinating and important branch of modern mathematics. *Sci.Amer.*, 1950, 182: no. 1, 18-24.

WINN, C.E. Sur l'historique du problème des quatre couleurs. *Bull.Inst.Egypte*, 1937-38, 20: 191-2.

BUkb

FRANKLIN, Philip. What is topology? *Phil.Sci.*, 1935, 2: 39-47, 5 fig.

BUu

GARDNER, Martin. Topology and magic. *Scr.Math.*, 1951, 17: 75-83.

BV PROBABILITY AND STATISTICS

BVc general history

BATEN, William Dowell. Recent interests in probability and mathematical statistics. *Scr.Math.*, 1938, 5: 165-70.

BIRŽIŠKA, Victorias. [On the development of the theory of probability. (In Lithuanian)]. *Kosmos* (Kaunas), 1931, 12: 81-104.

BOREL, Emile. Allocution prononcée en séance publique annuelle du 17 décembre 1934. *Compt.Rend.Acad.Sci.*, 1934, 199: 1456-77.
Dealing with the theory of probabilities, p. 1473-7.

BOREL, Emile. Le hasard. 311 p. (Nouvelle Collection Scientifique) Paris: Alcan, 1914.

CRAMÉR, Harald. A.I. Khinchin's work in mathematical probability. *Ann.Math.Statist.*, 1962, 33: 1227-37.

DANTZIG, D. van. Laplace, probabiliste et statisticien, et ses précurseurs. *Arch.Int.Hist.Sci.*, 1955, 8: 27-37.

DAVID, F.N. Games, gods and gambling. The origins and history of probability and statistical ideas from the earliest times to the Newtonian era. xvi, 275 p., pl., fig. New York: Hafner, 1962.
Reviewed by Christoph J. Scriba, *Isis*, 1964, 55: 217-18.

DU PASQUIER, Louis Gustave. Le calcul des probabilités, son évolution mathématique et philosophique. xxi, 304 p. Paris: J. Hermann, 1926.
Reviewed by P.J. Richard, *Rev.Gén.Sci.*, 1927, 38: 83-4; by F.A. Foraker, *Amer.Math.Mon.*, 1928, 35: 31-2.

FISHER, Ronald. Expansion of statistics. *Amer.Scient.*, 1954, 42: 275-82.
Brief history of the growth of statistics.

FRÉCHET, Maurice. Une remarque d'ordre historique sur le classement des probabilités nulles (ou de la raréfaction). *Compt.Rend.Acad.Sci.*, 1964, 258: 4877-8.

GNEDENKO, B.V. [A.M. Liapunov and the theory of probabilities. (In Russian)] *Ist.Mat.Issled.*, 1959, 12: 135-60.

GNEDENKO, B.V. The main stages in the history of the theory of probability. *Act.VIIIe Congr.Int.Hist.Sci.* (Florence, 1956), p. 128-31. Paris: Hermann, 1958.

IRWIN, J.O. Some aspects of the development of modern statistical method. *Math.Gaz.*, 1935, 19: 18-30.
A summary of the history of probability from Pascal in 1650, and of statistical theory from Quetelet in 1835.

KING, Amy C.; READ, Cecil B. Pathways to probability; history of the mathematics of certainty and chance. 139 p., ill., bibliogr. New York: Holt, Rinehart, and Winston, 1963.

KOREN, John, ed. The history of statistics. Their development and progress in many countries. Memoirs to commemorate the seventyfifth anniversary of the American Statistical Association. xii, 773 p. New York: Macmillan, 1918.
Reviewed by George Sarton, *Isis*, 1922, 4: 387-9.

MISES, Richard von. *See* BVk

MROČEK, V.R. [The origin and development of probability theory. (In Russian)]. *Arkh.Ist.Nauk.Tekh.*, 1934, 2: 45-60.

PEARSON, Karl. Historical note on the origin of the normal curve of errors. *Biometrika*, Dec. 1924, 16: 402-4. [CB 17/550]
Pearson has discovered that De Moivre published a treatment of the probability integral some time before the work of Laplace and Gauss.

PENGLAOU, Charles. Les pourfendeurs de statistiques. *J.Soc. Statist.Paris*, 1949, 90: 34-51.

SASULY, Max. Trend analysis of statistics. xiii, 421 p. Washington, D.C.: Brookings Institution, 1934.
The problem goes back more than a century.
Reviewed by H.T. Davis, *Isis*, 1936, 25: 491-3.

TODHUNTER, Isaac. History of the mathematical theory of probability from the time of Pascal to that of Laplace. xvi, 624 p. New York: Stechert, 1931.
Reprint of the work originally published in London in 1865.

VARBERG, Dale E. The development of modern statistics. *Math. Teacher*, 1963, 56: 252-7, 344-8.
An elementary account of some aspects from Pearson to Wald.

WESTERGAARD, Harald. Contributions to the history of statistics. vii, 280 p. London: King, 1932.

WOLFENDEN, Hugh H. The fundamental principles of mathematical statistics. With special reference to the requirements of actuaries and vital statisticians and an outline of a course in graduation. xv, 379 p. New York: Macmillan (for the Actuarial Society of America), 1942. [CB 63/271]
The historical section in 19 chapters covers 26 pages and the historical bibliography from 1657 to 1940 includes 190 items.

BVc-br

Metron. International review of statistics. Vol. 1-, no. 1- Rovigo (Veneto): Industrie grafiche italiane, 1920- [CB 10/214]

BVce-bv

DEMING, Lola S. Selected bibliography of statistical literature [covering the years 1930-1960]. 1. Correlation and regression theory; 2. Time series; 3. Limit theorems; 4. (with D. Gupta) Markov chains and stochastic processes; 5. Frequency functions, moments and graduation; 6. Theory of estimating and testing of hypotheses, sampling distributions, and theory of sample surveys; 7. Supplement, 1958-60. *J.Res. Nat.Bur.Stand.*, 1960, 64B: 55-68, 69-76, 175-98; 1961, 65B: 61-93; 1962, 66B: 15-28, 109-51; 1963, 67B: 91-139.

BVk philosophy and methodology

for statistical aspects in the philosophy of science or the sciences *see* INDEX

BACHELIER, L. Le jeu, la chance, le hasard. 320 p. (Bibliothèque de Philosophie Scientifique) Paris: E. Flammarion, 1914.

FRÉCHET, Maurice. The diverse definitions of probability. *J.Unified Sci.*, 1939, 8: 7-23.

HADAMARD, Jacques. Les principes du calcul des probabilités. *Rev.Métaphys.Morale*, 1922, 29: 289-94. [CB 14/551]

MISES, Richard von. Probability, statistics and truth. 2nd rev. ed. English ed. prepared by Hilda Geiringer. ix, 244 p. New York: Macmillan, 1957.
For original *see* below.

MISES, Richard von. Wahrscheinlichkeit, Statistik und Wahrheit. Einführung in die neue Wahrscheinlichkeitslehre und ihre Anwendung. 3rd ed. 278 p. Wien: Springer, 1951. [CB 78/182]
Preface contains a brief history of probabilities from the seventeenth century on. First publ. 1928.
Reviewed by Paul Flaskämper, *Deut.Lit.Zeitung*, 1929, 6: 1741-6.

NAGEL, Ernest. Principles of the theory of probability. vii, 80 p. (International Encyclopedia of Unified Science, 1: no. 6) Chicago: University of Chicago Press, 1939.

PENGLAOU, Charles. La statistique existe-t-elle en tant que discipline autonome? *J.Soc.Statist.Paris*, 1937, 78: 130-62.

WILLCOX, Walter F. Definitions of statistics. *Rev.Inst.Int. Statist.*, 1935, 3: 388-99.

BVkk

CARNAP, Rudolf. Logical foundations of probability. 2nd ed. xxii, 613 p. Chicago: University of Chicago Press, [1962].
Reviewed by R.H. Vincent, *Dialogue*, 1963, 2: 97-101.

CZUBER, Emanuel. Die philosophischen Grundlagen der Wahrscheinlichkeitsrechnung. viii, 343 p. (Wissenschaft und Hypothese, 24) Leipzig: B.G. Teubner, 1923.

FRÉCHET, Maurice. On some contributions to the foundations of the calculus of probability. *Scr.Math.*, 1940, 7: 110-12.

HACKING, Ian. On the foundations of statistics. *Brit.J.Phil. Sci.*, 1964, 15: 1-26.

LUKASIEWICZ, Jan. Die logischen Grundlagen der Wahrscheinlichkeitsrechnung. 75 p. Krakau: Akademie der Wissenschaften, 1913.

STRUIK, D.J. On the foundations of the theory of probabilities. *Phil.Sci.*, 1934, 1: 50-70. [CB 40/399]

BVks

HAGSTROEM, K.G. Connaissance et stochastique. *Dialectica*, 1949, 3: 153-72.

BVn means of communication

BVn-be

KURTZ, Albert K.; EDGERTON, Harold A. Statistical dictionary of terms and symbols. xi, 191 p. New York: Wiley, 1939. [CB 59/469]

BVw in different countries

BVwb-qd

WALKER, Helen M. The role of the American Statistical Association. *J.Amer.Statist.Ass.*, 1945, 40: 1-10.
Presidential Address at the 104th annual meeting of the Association, Washington, D.C., Dec. 27, 1944.

BVwe-qd

ASHTON, Thomas Southcliffe. Economic and social investigations in Manchester 1833-1933. A centenary history of the Manchester Statistical Society. With an index of reports and papers of the Society. xii, 179 p. London: King, 1934.

ROYAL STATISTICAL SOCIETY. Annals of the Society, 1834-1934. xii, 308 p., 8 pl. London: The Society, 1934.

BVwh

FABIAN, František. Mathematische Statistik in der Tschechoslowakischen Republik. *Wiss.Z.Humboldt-Univ.Berlin Math. Naturwiss.Reihe*, 1959-60, 5: 699-703.

VETTER, Quido. L'évolution de la statistique en Bohême. *Arch.Int.Hist.Sci.*, 1948, 1: 684-96. Also in *Act.Ve Congr. Int.Hist.Sci.* (Lausanne, 1947), p. 231-43. Paris: Hermann, 1948.

BVwi

GINI, Corrado, *et al.* I contributi italiani al progresso della statistica. 153 p. Roma: Società Italiana per il Progresso delle Scienze, 1939. [CB 59/469]
An offprint from Un secolo di progresso scientifico italiano: 1838-1939, vol. 1.

BVwn

GNEDENKO, B.V. [The development of the theory of probability in Russia. (In Russian)]. *Tr.Inst.Ist.Est.*, 1948, 2: 390-425.

BVx techniques and instruments

JOHNS, Victor. On the mechanical handling of statistics. *Amer.Math.Mon.*, 1926, 33: 495-501.

BVxt

FUNKHOUSER, H. Gray. Historical development of the graphical representation of statistical data. *Osiris*, 1937, 3: 269-404. [CB 53/260]
Reviewed by J.M. Keynes, *Econ.J.*, 1938, 48: 281-2; by J.M. Thompson, *Amer.Math.Mon.*, 1938, 45: 541-2; by H.M. Walker, *Scr.Math.*, 1938, 5: 257-9.

BVz special topics

CHEBOTAREV, A.S. Iz istorii razvitiia sposoba naimen'shikh kvadratov. [The history of the development of the method of least squares. (In Russian)]. *Vop.Ist.Est.Tekh.*, 1961, 11: 20-8.

HUNTINGTON, Edward V. Mathematics and statistics, with an elementary account of the correlation coefficient and the correlation ratio. *Amer.Math.Mon.*, 1919, 26: 421-35.

BW APPLIED STATISTICS

for statistics applied to special scientific subject fields *see* INDEX

DAVIS, Harold T.; NELSON, W.F.C. Elements of statistics, with applications to economic data. xi, 424 p., 50 fig. Bloomington, Ind.: Principia Press, 1935. [CB 45/279]
Appendices contain mathematical notes and tables, and biographies of the early mathematical economists and the text includes valuable historical notes on index numbers, analysis of time series, harmonic analysis.

DODD, Stuart C. The scientific measurement of fitness for self-government. *Sci.Mon.*, 1954, 78: 94-9.
Statistical indices used to decide when a dependent people becomes fit for self-government.

LANGE, Oskar. Introduction to econometrics. Prepared ... on the basis of lectures delivered at the University of Warsaw. Transl. from the Polish. 2nd ed. 433 p. Oxford/New York: Pergamon Press, 1962.
Italian translation of Polish original published Turin: Boringhieri, 1962 and reviewed by Franca Casali, *Physis*, 1964, 6: 239-41.

NEYMAN, Jerzy. Statistics - servant of all sciences. *Science*, 1955, 122: 401-6.

NICEFORO, Alfredo. Il metodo statistico, teorie e applicazioni alle scienze e all'arte. 3rd ed. 813 p. Messina: G. Principato, 1932.
2nd edition 1923; French translation. Paris: 1925.
First published as: La misura della vita, *see* below.

NICEFORO, Alfredo. La misura della vita. Applicazioni del metodo statistico alle scienze naturali, alle scienze sociali e all'arte. xii, 515 p., 112 tables, 29 diagr. Torino: Bocca, 1919.
Introduction to this work published in *Riv.Antropol.*, 1912, vol. 17.
Later editions entitled: Il metodo statistico, *see* above.

SPENGLER, Joseph J. On the progress of quantification in economics. *Isis*, 1961, 52: 258-76.

WALKER, Helen M. Studies in the history of statistical method. With special reference to certain educational problems. viii, 229 p., 12 ill. Baltimore: Williams and Wilkins, 1929.
Reviewed by George Sarton, *Isis*, 1930, 13: 382-3.

BWwf-qk

HUBER, Michel. Quarante années de la Statistique Générale de la France (1896-1936). *J.Soc.Statist.Paris*, 1937, 78: 179-213.

HUBER, Michel. La Statistique Générale de la France. *Rev. Gén.Sci.*, 1914, 25: 553-9, 7 fig. [CB 6/454]

BWwk

HOUTZAGER, Dirk. Hollands lijf- en losrenteleningen voor 1672. (In Dutch). 203 p., ill. Schiedam: Roelants, 1950. [CB 77/367]
Thesis dealing with early insurance and actuarial matters, chiefly in Holland up to 1672.

BX MERCANTILE AND INDUSTRIAL MATHEMATICS

GARCÍA DE ZÚÑIGA, Eduardo. Orígenes del cálculo mercantil. Interés simple. Interés compuesto. 7 p. Montevideo: 1941.

MURRAY, David. Chapters in the history of bookkeeping, accountancy and commercial arithmetic. vi, 519 p. Glasgow: Jackson, 1930. [CB 29/293]

ROOVER, Raymond de. Aux origines d'une technique intellectuelle. La formation et l'expansion de la comptabilité à partie double. *Ann.Hist.Écon.Soc.*, 1937, no. 44-5, 171-93, 270-98. [CB 52/580]

ROOVER, Raymond de. Early accounting problems of foreign exchange. *Account Rev.*, 1944, 19: 381-407. [CB 68/42]

BXwb-ce-bv

BENTLEY, Harry C.; LEONARD, Ruth S. Bibliography of works on accounting by American authors. 2 vol. 1. Books published 1796-1900. xxii, 197 p.; 2. Books published 1901-1934. x, 408 p. Boston, Mass.: Published by the author, 1934-35. [CB 44/514]

BY RECREATIONAL MATHEMATICS

AHRENS, Wilhelm. Mathematische Unterhaltungen und Spiele. 2nd ed. 2 vol. viii, 400 p., 200 fig.; x, 455 p., 128 fig. Leipzig: B.G. Teubner, 1918. [CB 17/588]
Revised reprint of volume 1 published 1921 (3rd ed.).

BALL, W.W. Rouse. Mathematical recreations and essays. Revised by H.S.M. Coxeter. 11th ed. xvi, 418 p. New York: Macmillan, 1939.
Reviewed by Lao G. Simons, *Scr.Math.*, 1941, 8: 120-1.

CARROLL, Lewis. Mathematical recreations. 2 vol. 1. Symbolic logic and The game of logic. 295 p.; 2. Pillow problems and A tangled tale. 261 p. New York: Dover, 1958.

DUDENEY, Henry Ernest. Amusements in mathematics. viii, 258 p. London: Nelson, 1917.

DUDENEY, Henry Ernest. Modern puzzles and how to solve them. 190 p., ill. London: Pearson, 1926.

HARGRAVE, Catherine Perry. A history of playing cards and a bibliography of cards and gaming. Compiled and illustrated from the old cards and books in the collection of the United States Playing Card Company in Cincinnati. xxiv, 468 p. New York: Houghton Mifflin, 1930.

HEFFTER, Lothar. Was ist Mathematik? Unterhaltungen während einer Seereise. 160 p. Freiburg i. Br.: Th. Fisher, 1922. [CB 15/228]

JONES, Samuel Isaac. Mathematical clubs and recreations. xiv, 236 p. Nashville: Jones, 1940.
Reviewed by Mildred T. Lawton, *Scr.Math.*, 1941, 8: 118-19.

JONES, Samuel Isaac. Mathematical nuts for lovers of mathematics. x, 340 p. Nashville, Tenn.: The author, 1932.

KOWALEWSKI, Gerhard. Alte und neue mathematische Spiele: eine Einführung in die Unterhaltungsmathematik. vi, 145 p. Leipzig: Teubner, 1930.

KOWALEWSKI, Gerhard. Boss-puzzle und verwandte Spiele. 72 p., 24 fig. (Scientia Delectans, 1) Leipzig: Engelmann, 1921.

KRAITCHIK, Maurice. Mathematical recreations. 328 p. New York: Norton, 1942.
Reviewed by H.S.M. Coxeter, *Scr.Math.*, 1944, 10: 181-3.

KRAITCHIK, Maurice. La mathématique des jeux ou récréations mathématiques. vii, 566 p., 965 fig. Bruxelles: Stevens, 1930. [CB 32/576]

MacMAHON, P.A. New mathematical pastimes. x, 116 p. Cambridge University Press, 1921.

NORTHROP, Eugene P. Riddles in mathematics. 7, 226, 36 p. New York: Van Nostrand, 1944.
Reviewed by Howard Eves, *Scr.Math.*, 1943, 9: 269-71.

PÉTARD, H. A contribution to the mathematical theory of big game hunting. *Amer.Math.Mon.*, 1938, 45: 446-7.

SCHAAF, William L. Mathematical curiosities and hoaxes. *Scr. Math.*, 1939, 6: 49-55.

THÉBAULT, Victor. Recreational geometry. *Scr.Math.*, 1952, 18: 151-61, 8 fig.

THÉBAULT, Victor. Les récréations mathématiques (parmi les nombres curieux). Avec des notes de A. Buquet. 197 p. Paris: Gauthier-Villars, 1952.
Reviewed by P. Dubarle, *Rev.Quest.Sci.*, 1952, 13: 284.

BYc-bq

CONGRÈS INTERNATIONAL DE RÉCRÉATION MATHÉMATIQUE, (Paris, 1937). Comptes-rendus du deuxième Congrès International de Récréation Mathématique. 103 p., ill. Bruxelles: Librairie du Sphinx, 1937.

CONGRÈS INTERNATIONAL DE RÉCRÉATION MATHÉMATIQUE, (Brussels, 1935). Comptes-rendus du premier Congrès International de Récréation Mathématique. 131 p., ill. Bruxelles: Librairie du Sphinx, 1935.

BYce-bv

SCHAAF, William L. Recreational mathematics. List of works on mathematical recreations. *Scr.Math.*, 1944, 10: 192-200.

BZ PHYSICAL SCIENCES

C PHYSICS

Cc general history

Cc-be *encyclopaedias; systematic compendia*

GLAZEBROOK, Richard Tetley, ed. A dictionary of applied physics. 5 vol., ill. London: Macmillan, 1922-23. [CB 16/325]

THEWLIS, J., ed. The encyclopaedic dictionary of physics. 9 vol. London: Pergamon; New York: Macmillan, 1961-64.
Reviewed by F. Villars, *Science*, 1963, 141: 1025-6.

Cc-bm *large scale works*

AKADEMIIA NAUK SSSR. INSTITUT ISTORII ESTESTVOZNANIIA I TEKHNIKI. Ocherki razvitiia osnovnykh fizicheskikh ideĭ. [Development of the basic ideas in physics. (In Russian)] Ed. by A.T. Grigorian and L.S. Polak. 510 p. Moskva: Izdvo Akademii Nauk SSSR, 1959.
Reviewed by M. Wong, *Arch.Int.Hist.Sci.*, 1959, 12: 317-18.

AUERBACH, Felix. Entwicklungsgeschichte der modernen Physik, zugleich eine Uebersicht ihrer Tatsachen, Gesetze und Theorien. viii, 344 p., 115 ill. Berlin: Springer, 1923.
Reviewed by F. Otto Koenig and F. Dannemann, *Isis*, 1924, 6: 444-7.

AUERBACH, Felix. Physik in graphischen Darstellungen. xii, 257 p., 29 pl. Leipzig: Teubner, 1925.

BLIN-STOYLE, R.J., *et al.* Turning points in physics: a series of lectures given at Oxford University in Trinity Term, 1958. With an introduction by A.C. Crombie. 192 p. Amsterdam: North-Holland Publishing Co.; New York: Interscience, 1959.
Reprinted 1961 (New York: Harper). Dutch translation Utrecht/Antwerp: Spectrum, 1961.

BLÜH, Otto; ELDER, Joseph Denison. Principles and applications of physics. 886 p., 730 ill. New York: Interscience Publishers, 1955.
An exposition of contemporary physics.
Reviewed by Gerald Holton, *Isis*, 1956, 47: 431-3.

BORN, Max. Physics in my generation. viii, 232 p., 16 fig. London: Pergamon Press, 1956.
Reviewed by H. Dopp, *Rev.Quest.Sci.*, 1956, 17: 604-5.

BORN, Max. Physik im Wandel meiner Zeit. 252 p. Braunschweig: Friedr. Vieweg & Sohn, 1957.
Reviewed by R. Bruce Lindsay, *Phys.Today*, 1958, 11: 28.

BROGLIE, Louis de. Matter and light. The new physics. Translated by W.H. Johnston. 300 p. New York: Norton, 1939.
Translation of "Matière et lumière" (Paris: Michel, 1937). Reprinted New York: Dover, 1955.
Reviewed by I. Bernard Cohen, *Isis*, 1949, 32: 378-80.

BROGLIE, Louis de. New perspectives in physics. Translated by A.J. Pomerans. xii, 291 p. New York: Basic Books, Inc., 1962. [CB 88/542]
One section of the book is devoted to various aspects of the history of science. Translation of "Nouvelles perspectives en microphysique" (Paris: A. Michel, 1956).

BROGLIE, Louis de. Physics and microphysics. With a foreword by A. Einstein. Translated by Martin Davidson. 286 p. New York: Pantheon Books, 1955. [CB 82/264]
Translation of "Physique et microphysique" (Paris: A. Michel, 1947). Reprinted New York: Harper, 1960.

BROGLIE, Louis de, *et al.* Conférences d'actualités scientifiques et industrielles, (no. 1-9), faites au Conservatoire National des Arts et Métiers en 1929. viii, 272 p., ill. Paris: Hermann, 1930. [CB 29/258]
Series of lectures on contemporary physics.

BUCKLEY, H. A short history of physics. xi, 263 p. London: Methuen, 1927.
Reviewed by A.G.C., *Nature*, 1928, 121: 823-4.

CAJORI, Florian. A history of physics in its elementary branches: including the evolution of physical laboratories. Rev. and enl. ed. xiii, 424 p. New York: Macmillan, 1929.

CHALMERS, T.W. Historic researches. Chapters in the history of physical and chemical discovery. vi, 288 p., 85 fig. London: Morgan, 1949.
Reviewed by Eduard Farber, *Isis*, 1951, 42: 67.

CHASE, Carl Trueblood. The evolution of modern physics. ix, 203 p. New York: Van Nostrand, 1947. [CB 73/169]

CHASE, Carl Trueblood. A history of experimental physics. 195 p., 15 pl. New York: Van Nostrand, 1932. [CB 57/240]

COHEN, I. Bernard. The birth of a new physics. 200 p., ill. (Science Study Series) Garden City, N.Y.: Doubleday, 1960.
Reviewed by Stillman Drake, *Isis*, 1960, 51: 578; by Howard Laster, *Science*, 1960, 131: 219-20; by Alfred Romer, *Amer.J.Phys.*, 1960, 28: 822-3.

CREW, Henry. General physics. 4th ed. xii, 674 p. New York: Macmillan, 1927. [CB 23/243]
Includes a number of historical references.

CREW, Henry. The rise of modern physics. 2nd ed. xix, 434 p. Baltimore: Williams & Wilkins, 1935. [CB 24/530]
First published 1928.
Reviewed by V.F. Lenzen, *Isis*, 1936, 24: 449-50.

D'ABRO, A. The decline of mechanism in modern physics. x, 982 p. New York: Van Nostrand, 1939.
Reviewed by I. Bernard Cohen, *Isis*, 1949, 32: 380-2.

D'ABRO, A. The rise of the new physics: its mathematical and physical theories. 2 vol. vii, 982 p., 36 portr. New York: Dover Publications, 1951.
Corrected and enlarged edition of "Decline of mechanism in modern physics", *see* above.
Reviewed by V.F. Lenzen, *Isis*, 1952, 43: 292-3.

DARROW, Karl Kelchner. Introduction to contemporary physics. ix, 453 p. New York: Van Nostrand, 1926. 24
Reviewed by W.H. Westphal, *Naturwissenschaften*, 1927, 188.

EINSTEIN, Albert; INFELD, Leopold. The evolution of physics. The growth of ideas from early concepts to relativity and quanta. x, 320 p. New York: Simon and Schuster, 1938.
Spanish translation "La fisica aventura del pensamiento" (Buenos Aires: Losada, 1939).
Reviewed by V.F. Lenzen, *Isis*, 1939, 30: 124-5.

FIERZ, M.; WEISSKOPF, V.F.; ed. Theoretical physics in the twentieth century: a memorial volume to Wolfgang Pauli. x, 328 p. New York: Interscience Publishers, 1960.
Reviewed by E.M. Hafner, *Amer.J.Phys.*, 1962, 30: 232-3.

FRASER, Charles C. Half-hours with the great scientists. The story of physics. xx, 527 p., 342 ill. New York: Reinhold; 1948. [CB 75/89 and CB 77/370]

GAMOW, George. Biography of physics. viii, 338 p., ill. New York: Harper & Brothers, 1961; Harper & Row, 1964.
Reviewed by William F. Meggers, *Phys.Today*, 1962, 15: no. 3, 76-8.

GAMOW, George. Matter, earth and sky. xi, 593 p. Englewood Cliffs, N.J.: Prentice-Hall, 1958; London: Macmillan, 1959.
Reviewed by G.R. Noakes, *Nature*, 1959, 184: 214.

GERLAND, E. Geschichte der Physik, von den ältesten Zeiten bis zum Ausgange des achtzehnten Jahrhunderts. x, 762 p. München/Berlin: R. Oldenbourg, 1913.
Reviewed by George Sarton, *Isis*, 1913, 1: 527-8.

GLIOZZI, Mario; GIUA, Michele; ed. Storia della fisica. 481 p., ill., pl. (Storia delle Scienze, coordinata da Nicola Abbagnano, 2) Torino: Unione Tipografico-Editrice Torinese, 1962.
Reviewed by Desiderio Papp, *Isis*, 1963, 54: 492-4.

GRAETZ, Leo. Alte Vorstellungen und neue Tatsachen der Physik. Drei Vorlesungen. viii, 120 p., 11 ill. Leipzig: Akademische Verlagsgesellschaft, 1925.

GUAYDIER, Pierre. Les étapes de la physique. 127 p. (Que Sais-Je?) Paris: Presses Universitaires de France, 1950. [CB 78/183]

GUAYDIER, Pierre. Les grandes découvertes de la physique moderne. 264 p. (Les Grandes Découvertes Scientifiques) Paris: Corrêa, 1951.
Reviewed by A. Delorme, *Rev.Hist.Sci.*, 1952, 5: 282.

HAAS, Arthur. Das Naturbild der neuen Physik. 130 p., 8 fig. Berlin: De Gruyter, 1932.
First publ. 1920 [CB 14/520]. Based on a series of popular lectures.
Reviewed by Edmund O. von Lippmann, *Chem.-Zeitung*, 1932, 56: 198.

HAAS, Arthur. The new physics. Lectures for laymen and others. Authorized transl. by Robert W. Lawson. 3rd ed. rev. and enl. xi, 172 p. London: Methuen, 1930.
First published 1923. German original "Das Naturbild der neuen Physik" *see* above.

HESSE, Mary B. Science and the human imagination. Aspects of the history and logic of physical science. 171 p. New York: Philosophical Library, 1955.
Reviewed by V.F. Lenzen, *Isis*, 1956, 47: 190-1.

HOPPE, Edmund. Geschichte der Physik. viii, 536 p. Braunschweig: Friedr. Vieweg, 1926. [CB 21/571]
Reviewed by George Sarton, *Isis*, 1927, 9: 571-2.
French translation Paris: Payot, 1928.

HOPPE, Edmund. Geschichte der Physik. In: Scheel, Karl, ed. Geschichte der Physik. Vorlesungstechnik, p. 1-179. (Handbuch der Physik, 1) Berlin: Springer, 1926. [CB 25/416]

JEANS, James Hopwood. The growth of physical science. x, 264 p., 9 pl., 39 fig. Cambridge University Press; New York: Macmillan, 1948. 2nd rev. ed. Cambridge/New York: Cambridge University Press, 1951.
Reviewed by V.F. Lenzen, *Isis*, 1949, 40: 81; in *Science*, 1951, 114: 219.

JEANS, James Hopwood. The new background of science. viii, 301 p. Cambridge University Press; New York: Macmillan, 1933.
Reviewed by H.T. Davis, *Isis*, 1934, 21: 326-8.
Second edition 1934.

KHVOL'SON, Orest Danilovich. Die Evolution des Geistes der Physik 1873-1923. Aus dem Russischen übersetzt von V.R. Bursian. vi, 197 p. Braunschweig: Vieweg, 1925.
Reviewed by G. Mie, *Deut.Lit. Zeitung*, 1929, 6: 2122-30.

KHVOL'SON, Orest Danilovich. Die Physik 1914-1926. 17 ausgewählte Kapitel. Uebersetzt von Georg Kluge. ix, 696 p. Braunschweig: Vieweg, 1927.

KISTNER, A. Geschichte der Physik. 2nd ed. 2 vol. 1. Bis Newton. 126 p.; 2. Von Newton bis zur Gegenwart. 149 p. (Sammlung Göschen, 293-4) Berlin: W. de Gruyter, 1919.
First publ. 1906

KUDRIAVTSEV, P.S. [History of physics. Vol. 1. From ancient physics to Mendeleev. Vol. 2. 1870-1900. (In Russian)] Moscow: 1948, 1956-
Volume 1 reviewed by B. Kedrov, *Culture Life*, February 1950, no.5; extracts reprinted in *Occasional Pamphlets no. 10 of the Society for Freedom in Science*, p. 3-4. Oxford: 1950.

KUZNETSOV, Boris G. Printsipy klassicheskoi fiziki. [Principles of classical physics. (In Russian)] 323 p. Moskva: Izd-vo Akademii Nauk SSSR, 1958.

KUZNETSOV, Boris G. Razvitie fizicheskikh idei ot Galileya do Einshteina v svete sovremennoi nauki. [Development of physical ideas from Galileo to Einstein in the light of modern science. (In Russian)]. 511 p. Moscow/Leningrad: Izd-vo Akademii Nauk SSSR, 1963.
Reviewed by U.I. Frankfurt, *Priroda*, 1963, no. 9, 118-19.

KUZNETSOV, Boris G., ed. Razvitie sovremennoi fiziki. [The development of contemporary physics. (In Russian)] 331 p. Moscow: Izdatel'stvo "Nauka", 1964. [CB 90/626]
A collection of articles on the development of modern physics which includes several on the work of Niels Bohr.

LAGEMANN, Robert T. Physical science. Origins and principles. xviii, 458 p., bibliogr., fig., ill., app., index. Boston, Toronto: Little, Brown and Co., 1963. [CB 89/502]

LANGE, Heinrich. Geschichte der Grundlagen der Physik. 2 vol. 1. Die formalen Grundlagen. Zeit-Raum-Kausalität. x. 356 p.; 2. Die materialen Grundlagen. Impuls-Energie-Wirkung. 416 p. (Orbis, 2: no. 7 and no. 13) Freiburg/München: Karl Alber, 1954, 1961.
Vol. 1 reviewed by Gottfried Martin, *Kant-Stud.*, 1954-55, 46: 368-74; by R. Hooykaas, *Arch.Int.Hist.Sci.*, 1957, 10: 261-5; by Adolf Meyer-Abich, *Sudhoffs Arch.*, 1960, 44: 374-5; vol. 2 by H. Degen, *Naturwiss.Rundsch.*, 1962, 15: 411-12.

LANGEVIN, Paul. La physique depuis vingt ans. 456 p., 14 fig. (Encyclopédie Scientifique) Paris: Gaston Doin, 1923. [CB 15/185]

LAUE, Max von. Geschichte der Physik. 176 p. (Geschichte der Wissenschaften, 2. Naturwissenschaften) Bonn: Universitäts-Verlag, 1946. [CB 73/169]
2nd ed. 1947. For English translation *see* below.
Reviewed by Ilse Rosenthal-Schneider, with note by I.B. Cohen, *Isis*, 1948, 38: 258-60.

LAUE, Max von. History of physics. Translated from the German edition of 1947 by Ralph E. Oesper. viii, 150 p. New York: Academic Press, 1950.
Reviewed by Duane Roller, *Scr.Math.*, 1952, 18: 271-3.

LORENTZ, Hendrik Antoon. Problems of modern physics. A course of lectures delivered in the California Institute of Technology. Ed. by H. Bateman. vi, 312 p. Boston: Ginn, 1927.

MILLIKAN, Robert Andrews; GALE, Henry Gordon; EDWARDS, Charles William. A first course in physics for colleges. xiii, 676, xlii p., 538 fig., ill. Boston: Ginn, 1928. [CB 25/416]
Much historical information is included.

MILLIKAN, Robert Andrews; ROLLER, Duane; WATSON, Earnest Charles. Mechanics, molecular physics, heat, and sound. xiv, 498 p., 55 pl. Boston: Ginn, 1937.
A textbook that contains much historical material.
Reviewed by V.F. Lenzen, *Isis*, 1937, 27: 527-8.

THE NATURAL philosopher: a series of volumes containing papers devoted to the history of physics and to the influence of physics on human thought and affairs through the ages. 3 vol. 155 p.; 125 p.; 111 p. New York: Blaisdell, 1963-64. [CB 89/501]
Ceased publication with vol. 3.
Reviewed by L. Marton, *Phys.Today*, 1964, 17: no. 6, 56-8 (vol. 1); no. 9, 70-2 (vol. 2).

OMER, G.C., *et al.* Physical science: men and concepts. viii, 601 p. London: G.C. Harrap; Boston: D.C. Heath, 1962.
Reviewed by R. Harré, *Hist.Sci.*, 1963, 2: 173.

PAPP, Desiderio. Historia de la física: desde la antigüedad hasta los umbrales del siglo XX. 2nd ed. 441 p., fig., portr. Madrid: Espasa-Calpe, S.A., 1961.
Reviewed by Carl B. Boyer, *Isis*, 1963, 54: 292-3.

PELSENEER, Jean. L'évolution de la notion de phénomène physique des primitifs à Bohr et Louis de Broglie. Leçons sur l'histoire de la pensée scientifique professées à l'Université libre de Bruxelles. 177 p. Bruxelles: 1947.
Reviewed by P. Sergescu, *Arch.Int.Hist.Sci.*, 1948, 1: (27), 531-5; by Gino Loria, ibid., 623-9; by V.F. Lenzen, *Isis*, 1948, 39: 194-6.

PITONI, Rinaldo. Storia della fisica. 405 p. (Storia delle Scienze, 3) Torino: Società tipografico-editrice nazionale, 1913.
Reviewed by Aldo Mieli, *Isis*, 1913, 1: 742-4.

PLA, Cortés. Algunos aspectos de la física moderna. 191 p., pl., fig. Rosario, Argentina: 1939. [CB 70/256]

PLANCK, Max. A survey of physics. A collection of lectures and essays. Transl. by R. Jones and D.H. Williams. vii, 184 p. London: Methuen, 1925.
German original Physikalische Rundblicke. Leipzig: Hirzel, 1922.

POINCARÉ, Lucien. La physique moderne, son évolution. Ed. refondue et augmentée de trois chapitres, par Maurice de Broglie. 292 p. (Bibliothèque de Philosophie Scientifique) Paris: E. Flammarion, 1925. [CB 18/575]

PUCCIANTI, Luigi. Storia della fisica. 141 p., bibliogr. (Cultura Viva, 10) Firenze: Le Monnier, 1951. [CB 83/198]
Reviewed by A. Natucci, *Arch.Int.Hist.Sci.*, 1952, 5: 395.

RAMAN, C.V. The new physics. With an introduction by Francis Low. ix, 144 p. New York: Philosophical Library, 1951. [CB 78/183]

RAMSAUER, Carl. Grundversuche der Physik in historischer Darstellung. Von den Fallgesetzen bis zu den elektrischen Wellen. vii, 189 p., 129 ill. Berlin/Göttingen/Heidelberg: Springer Verlag, 1953. [CB 81/268]
Reviewed by E.J. Dijksterhuis, *Arch.Int.Hist.Sci.*, 1953, 6: 512-13; by Anna Beckman, *Lychnos*, 1953, 407-8.

REICHEN, Charles-Albert. A history of physics. 111 p., ill. (The New Illustrated Library of Science and Invention, 8) New York: Hawthorn, 1963.
Essentially a picture book. French and German editions also.

REY, Abel. La théorie de la physique chez les physiciens contemporains. 2e éd., revue et augmentée d'un aperçu sur l'évolution actuelle de la physique. xii, 346 p. Paris: Félix Alcan, 1923.
Reviewed by L. Guinet, *Isis*, 1923, 5: 484-5.

RICHTMYER, Floyd Karker; KENNARD, E.H. Introduction to modern physics. 4th ed. xvii, 759 p. (International Series in Pure and Applied Physics) New York: McGraw-Hill Book Co., 1947. [CB 73/169]
Chapters I-III are historical.
2nd edition, 1934; reviewed by George Sarton, *Isis*, 1935, 24: 172-4.

ROGERS, Eric M. Physics for the inquiring mind. ix, 778 p., fig. Princeton, N.J.: Princeton University Press, 1960. [CB 86/462]
A work rich in historical material.

SCHURMANN, Paul F. Historia de la física. 2nd ed. 2 vol. xxiv, 381 p.; 672 p. Buenos Aires: Editorial Nova, 1946.
First edition. Montevideo: 1936; reviewed by Mary Elvira Weeks, *Isis*, 1938, 29: 172-6.

SHAMOS, Morris H., ed. Great experiments in physics. viii, 370 p., fig., tables. New York: Henry Holt, 1959.
Reviewed by Erwin N. Hiebert, *Isis*, 1962, 53: 516-17; for other reviews *see* CB 86/462.

SPASSKII, B.I. Istoriia fiziki. [The history of physics. (In Russian)] 2 vol. ill., portr. Moscow: Izd-vo Moskovskogo Universiteta, 1963-64.

SWANENBURG, B.D. De verovering der materie. De groei van het wereldbeeld der natuurkunde van de Grieken tot heden. [The conquest of matter. The growth of the world picture of physics from the Greeks to the present day. (In Dutch)]. 332 p., 100 fig. Utrecht: de Haan, 1950.
Reviewed by R. Hooykaas, *Arch.Int.Hist.Sci.*, 1951, 4: 790-1.

TAYLOR, Lloyd William. Physics, the pioneer science. [With the collaboration, in the chapters on modern physics, of Forrest Glenn Tucker.] xii, 847, xliv p. Boston: Houghton-Mifflin, 1941.
Reviewed by I. Bernard Cohen, *Isis*, 1943, 34: 378-9.

VOLKRINGER, H. Les étapes de la physique. ix, 217 p. (Encyclopédie Gauthier-Villars) Paris: Gauthier-Villars, 1929.

WARBURG, E., ed. Physik. viii, 762 p. (Kultur der Gegenwart, 3: i) Leipzig: Teubner, 1915.

WIEN, W. Vorträge über die neuere Entwicklung der Physik und ihrer Anwendungen. Gehalten im Baltenland im Frühjahr 1918 auf Veranlassung des Oberkommandos der achten Armee. iv, 116 p. Leipzig: Barth, 1919.

WILSON, William. A hundred years of physics. 319 p., ill. (100 Years Series) London: Duckworth; New York: Macmillan Co., 1950.
Reviewed by I. Bernard Cohen, *Isis*, 1951, 42: 272-3; by G.R. Noakes, *Nature*, 1951, 167: 1043.

ZIMMER, Ernst. Umsturz im Weltbild der Physik, gemeinverständlich dargestellt. Mit einem Geleitwort von Max Planck. 338 p., ill. Munich: C. Hanser, 1961.

Cc-bn *essays; articles*

ANDRADE, E.N. da C. Physics from 1850 to 1900. *Nature*, 1951, 168: 622-5.

BORN, Max. Physics in the last fifty years. *Nature*, 1951, 168: 625-30.

BROGLIE, Maurice de. L'oeuvre de la physique moderne. *Rev. Gén.Sci.*, 1932, 43: 73-6.
Discours prononcé au Congrès de Nancy de l'Association Française pour l'Avancement des Sciences.

BUMSTEAD, Henry Andrews. The history of physics. *Sci.Mon.*, 1921, 12: 289-309.
Tabloid summary.

DINGLER, Hugo. Zur Entstehung der sogenannten theoretischen Physik. *Z.Gesamte Naturwiss.*, 1939, 4: 329-41.

DIRAC, P.A.M. The evolution of the physicist's picture of nature. *Sci.Amer.*, 1963, 208: no. 5, 45-53

GANS, Richard. Die Physik der letzten dreissig Jahre. 19 p. (Königsberger Universitätsreden, 7) Königsberg: Gräfe und Unzer, 1930.

GÉRARD, Louis. Sur le problème de Malfatti, le pendule de Foucault et autres questions d'analyse et de physique. 64 p. Paris: Vuibert, 1929.

HOLTON, Gerald. On the recent past of physics. *Amer.J.Phys.*, 1961, 29: 805-10.
Opening remarks made at the symposium "Topics in the history of modern physics" held in New York in February 1961.

HULL, Gordon Ferrie. Fifty years of physics - a study in contrasts. *Science*, 1946, 104: 238-44.

JEANS, James Hopwood. The new world-picture of modern physics. Presidential address delivered at Aberdeen on September 5, 1934. *Nature*, 1934, 134: 355-65; *Science*, 1934, 80: 213-22.

LAMB, Horace. The evolution of mathematical physics. Being the Rouse Ball Lecture for 1924. 48 p. Cambridge University Press, 1924.

LENAIZAN, Beaulard de. Sur l'évolution de loi physique. *Rev. Int.Enseign.*, 1922, 42: 146-61, 193-205. [CB 14/566]

LEVI CIVITA, T. Extension et évolution de la physique mathématique au cours des cinquante dernières années. *Scientia*, 1912, 11: 275-92.

LODGE, Oliver. A century's progress in physics. An address delivered at University College, on Monday, March 14, 1927. 36 p. London: University of London Press, 1927.

LORENTZ, Hendrik Antoon. Vue générale de la physique moderne. Discours prononcé au Congrès International de Physique, Como, 1927. *Period.Mat., ser. 4*, 1928, 8: 229-38.

MILLIKAN, Robert Andrews. Conceptions in physics changed in our generation. *Scientia*, 1927, 41: 255-64; French transl. suppl., 107-16.

MILLIKAN, Robert Andrews. Twentieth century physics. *Proc. Amer.Inst.Elect.Eng.*, Sept. 1917. Reprinted in *Annu.Rep. Smithsonian Inst.for 1918*, p. 169-84. Washington, D.C.: 1920.

NOWAK, K. Rückschau über 20 Jahre. *Neue Phys.*, 1964, 4: 12-32.
Recollections of various aspects of the history of modern physics.

PAPANASTASSIOU, Ch. E. L'évolution de la théorie physique. *Thalès*, 1935, 2: 228-33.

SATTERLY, John. Reminiscences in physics from 1894 onward. *Amer.J.Phys.*, 1957, 25: 288-300.

SMYTH, H.D. From X-rays to nuclear fission. *Amer.Scient.*, 1947, 35: 485-501.
A brief history of physics during the last fifty years.

SPASSKI, B.I. M.V. Lomonosov i razvitie fiziki. K 250-letiiu so dnia rozhdeniia M.V. Lomonosova. [M.V. Lomonosov and the development of physics, on the 250th anniversary of his birth. (In Russian)] *Usp.Fiz.Nauk*, 1961, 75: 397-410; English transl. in *Soviet Phys.Usp.*, 1962, 4: 841-9.

THOMSON, J.J. Reminiscences of physics and physicists. *Science*, 1934, 80: 169-73.

TOLL, John S. Recent development in physics. *Sci.Teacher*, 1958, 25: 25-6, 48-51.
Partial survey of fundamental discoveries reported from 1955 to 1957 with references to the original papers.

WILSON, William. Physical phenomena as interpreted in recent times. *Amer.Scient.*, 1955, 43: 298-306.

Cc-br *periodicals*

Advances in Physical Sciences. [Translation of back issues of *Uspekhi Fizicheskikh Nauk* from vol. 61, 1957.] Publ. for the National Science Foundation and the Atomic Energy Commission by the Israel Program for Scientific Translations. Washington, D.C.: 1960- [CB 87/633]

Cc-bv/cj bibliography; literature; sources

Cc-bx

VEIGA, A. Botelho da Costa. Exposição de física, Abril de 1930. (Biblioteca Nacional) Catalogo. 92 p. Lisbon: Oficinas Graficas, 1930

Ccb

NIELS BOHR LIBRARY OF PHYSICS. *Isis*, 1961, 52: 417

Cce

SCHEEL, Karl. Physikalische Literatur. In: Scheel, Karl, ed. Geschichte der Physik. Vorlesungstechnik, p. 180-6. (Handbuch der Physik, 1) Berlin: Springer, 1926. [CB 25/416]

Cce-bv

American Journal of Physics. Cumulative index, vol. 1-20, 1933-52; vol. 21-30, 1953-62. *Amer.J.Phys.*, 1953, 21: no. 9, pt. 2, 189 p.; 1963, 31: extra no., 266 p. [CB 80/125]

DARROW, Karl Kelchner. Classified list of published bibliographies in physics, 1910-1922. v, 102 p. (*Bulletin of the National Research Council*, 8: part 5) Washington, D.C.: 1924.

SARTON, G. La nouvelle physique. *Isis*, 1914, 2: 193-8.
A brief review of the literature of modern physics.

Ccj

ROLLER, Duane. The periodical literature of physics: some of its history, characteristics and trends. *Amer.J.Phys.*, 1946, 14: 300-8, portr.

Ccm

WATSON, E.C. Reproductions of prints, drawings, and paintings of interest in the history of physics. 1-76. *Amer. J.Phys.*, 1938, vol. 6 - 1956, vol. 24.

Cd biography

Cd-bv

HIGGINS, Thomas James. Book-length biographies of physicists and astronomers. *Amer.J.Phys.*, 1944, 12: 31-9, 234-6.

Cda

BARR, E. Scott. Anniversaries in 1957 (-1964) of interest to physicists. *Amer.J.Phys.*, 1957, 25: 370-9; 1958, 26: 104-21; 1959, 27: 209-33; 1960, 28: 462-75; 1961, 29: 234-48; 1962, 30: 347-62; 1963, 31: 75-88; 1964, 32: 285-305.
Biographical notes.

HART, Ivor B. The great physicists. vi, 138 p. London: Methuen, 1927.

HERMANN, A. Grosse Physiker. Vom Werden des neuen Weltbildes. 178 p., 66 pl. Stuttgart: Ernst Battenberg Verlag, 1959.
About one page each given to the work of sixty-six selected physicists from Galileo to Taung-Dao Lee.
Reviewed by Gerald Holton, *Isis*, 1962, 53: 564; by H. Degen, *Naturwiss.Rundsch.*, 1960, 5: 196.

HUNTRESS, Ernest R. Biographical digests. I-IV. Centennials and polycentennials during 1949-1952 with interest for chemists and physicists. *Proc.Amer.Acad.Arts Sci.*, 1948-49, 77: 33-54; 1949-50, 78: 3-35; 1950-51, 79: 3-44; 1951-52, 81: 35-97.
Title varies.

LAGMANN, Robert. Pseudonyms of physicists. *Sci.Mon.*, 1956, 83: 130-4, 2 fig.

McKIE, Douglas. Personalities in physics. *Nature*, 1936, 137: 419-21.

PODOLSKY, Edward. Physician physicists. *Ann.Med.Hist.*, 1913, 3: 300-7.

Cda-py

AUGER, Pierre, *et al.* Les prix Nobel de physique et de chimie. 506 p., pl. Monaco: Union Européenne d'Éditions, 1962.
Reviewed by René Taton, *Rev.Hist.Sci.*, 1964, 17: 180-1.

HEATHCOTE, Niels H. de V. Nobel prize winners in physics, 1901-1950. 473 p. (Pathbreakers in 20th Century Science. Life of Science Library, 30) New York: Henry Schuman, 1953.
Reviewed by I. Bernard Cohen, *Isis*, 1954, 45: 407-8. /25

NOBELSTIFTELSEN, Stockholm. Nobel lectures including presentation speeches and laureates' biographies. Physics 1942-1962. 621 p. Amsterdam/London/New York: Elsevier for the Nobel Foundation, 1964.
Reviewed in *Times Sci.Rev.*, autumn 1964, 17; by Robert Weber, *Phys.Today*, 1964, 17: no. 12, 55-6.

Cdae

CREW, Henry. Portraits of famous physicists. With biographical accounts. [52] p., ill. New York: Scripta Mathematica, 1942.
Consists of thirteen leaflets in portfolio.
Reviewed by Aldo Mieli, *Archeion*, 1942, 24: 254-5.

Cdaj

CLARKE, Norman, ed. A physics anthology. x, 323 p. London: Chapman and Hall, 1960.
Reviewed by Anna Beckman, *Lychnos*, 1960-61, 338-9.

MAGIE, William Francis. A source book in physics. xiv, 620 p., ill. Cambridge, Mass.: Harvard University Press, 1963.
An unaltered reprint of the 1935 edition (New York: McGraw-Hill). [CB 49/176]

MASSAIN, R. Physique et physiciens. 2nd ed. 399 p. Paris: Editions de l'Ecole, [1948]. First publ. 1939. [CB 75/89]
An anthology of texts with short biographical notes.

Cf history of physics as a study

BLÜH, Otto. The history of physics and the old humanism. *Amer.J.Phys.*, 1950, 18: 308-11.

HIROSIGE, Tetu. Studies of history of physics in Japan. *Jap.Stud.Hist.Sci.*, 1962, 1: 26-34.

KING, W. James. The 'History of recent physics' project of the American Institute of Physics. *Arch.Int.Hist.Sci.*, 1962, 15: 127-36.

KLINCKOWSTROEM, Carl von. Die Anfänge der physikhistorischen Forschung. *Arch.Stor.Sci.*, 1923, 4: 113-22. [CB 15/236]

KONDO, Herbert. History and the physicist. *Amer.J.Phys.*, 1955, 23: 430-6.

Cfd

FOR biographies and bibliographies of individual historians of physics (20th century) *see* volumes 1 and 2 under:-

Cajori, Florian; Hoppe, Edmund; Laue, Max Theodor Felix von; Mach, Ernst; Whittaker, Edmund Taylor; and under the names mentioned in Afd and Bfd

Cg teaching the history of physics

BLÜH, Otto. On the history and philosophy of science. A reply. *Amer.J.Phys.*, 1956, 24: 178-9.
A reply to Holton's comments "On the history and philosophy of physics", *see* below.

BLÜH, Otto. Physics and culture. *Amer.J.Phys.*, 1955, 23: 161-8.
A review of Sarton's "Ancient science through the Golden Age of Greece" and "A guide to the history of science" with added reflections on the teaching of the history of physics.

HOLTON, Gerald. On the history and philosophy of physics. *Amer.J.Phys.*, 1955, 23: 389-90.
On the teaching of the subject apropos of Blüh's article "Physics and culture", *see* above.

SEEGER, Raymond J. On teaching the history of physics. (American Association of Physics Teachers address, 1964). *Amer.J.Phys.*, 1964, 32: 619-25.

Cgp

HANSON, Norwood Russell. History and philosophy of science in an undergraduate physics course. *Phys.Today*, 1955, 8: no. 8, 4-9.

HENSHAW, Clement L. Do students find history interesting in physical science courses? *Amer.J.Phys.*, 1950, 18: 373-7.

JOHNSON, E.H. Courses on the history of physics in American college and universities. *Science*, 1931, 74: 435-7.

Cgt

HAAS, Arthur Eric. Der Wert der geschichtlichen Methode im physikalischen Unterricht. *Z.Math.Naturwiss.Unterricht*, 1914, 45: 281-6.

KISTNER, Adolf. Physikalische Experimente auf historischer Grundlage. *Pädagog.Arch.*, 1913, 55: 296-307.

Ch historiography and particular aspects of the history of physics

Chd

AGASSI, Joseph. The confusion between physics and metaphysics in the standard histories of sciences. *Proc.10th Int.Congr. Hist.Sci.* (Ithaca, 1962), (1), p. 231-50. Paris: Hermann, 1964.
Reviewed by Charles C. Gillispie, *Isis*, 1964, 55: 97-9; by L. Pearce Williams, *Arch.Int.Hist.Sci.*, 1963, 16: 437-9.

Chf

ANGLAS, Jules. D'Euclide à Einstein. Relativité et connaissance. 121 p., 21 fig. Paris: Stock, 1926.

KUZNETSOV, I.V. History of physics and the problem of truth. *Act.VIIIe Congr.Int.Hist.Sci.* (Florence, 1956), p. 261-4. Paris: Hermann, 1958.

MALISOFF, William Marias. Physics: the decline of mechanism. *Phil.Sci.*, 1940, 7: 400-14.

Chg

BAUER, E.; *et al.* L'évolution de la physique et la philosophie. x, 151 p. Paris: Alcan, 1935. [CB 51/247]

HARDIE, C.D. Professor Whittaker and the history of physics. *Isis*, 1943, 34: 344-6.
A critical review of Whittaker's address, *see* below.

WHITTAKER, E.T. Aristotle, Newton, Einstein. Address of the President at the Annual Statutory Meeting, October 27, 1942. *Proc.Roy.Soc.Edinb.Sect.A*, 1941-43, 61: 231-46.
Summary in *Nature*, 1943, 151: 59.
Essay review by C.D. Hardie, *Isis*, 1943, 34: 344-6.

Chj

FLEURY, Hippolyte de. En relisant Lucrèce. "Le livre de la nature" et la physique moderne. 66 p. Paris: Larose, 1929.
Reviewed by P.J. Richard, *Rev.Gén.Sci.*, 1929, 40: 123.

ROSEN, Edward. The debt of classical physics to Renaissance astronomers, particularly Kepler. *Proc.10th Int. Congr. Hist.Sci.*(Ithaca, 1962), (1), p. 81-92. Paris: Hermann, 1964.
With comments by Wm. Stahlman, R.S. Cohen and D. Papp.

SADOUN-GOUPIL, Michelle. L'oeuvre de Pascal et la physique moderne. *Rev.Hist.Sci.*, 1963, 16: 23-52.

Cj psychological aspects

STEVENS, Blamey. The psychology of physics. xvi, 282 p. Manchester: Sherratt & Hughes, 1939. [CB 58/570]

Ck philosophy and methodology

AGASSI, Joseph. Between micro and macro. *Brit.J.Phil.Sci.*, 1963, 14: 26-31.

BLAIR, G.W. Scott. Some aspects of the search for invariants. *Brit.J.Phil.Sci.*, 1950, 1: 230-44.

BOLL, Marcel. La philosophie physique. *Rev.Positiviste Int.*, 1913, 13: 162-85.

BORN, Max. Physics and metaphysics. *Sci.Mon.*, 1956, 82: 229-35.
The Joule Memorial Lecture of the Manchester Literary and Philosophical Society, delivered in 1950.

BORN, Max. Physik und Metaphysik. *Naturwiss.Rundsch.*, 1956, 9: 295-301.

BORN, Max. Some philosophical aspects of modern physics. (Inaugural lecture as Tait Professor of Natural Philosophy, University of Edinburgh). *Proc.Roy.Soc.Edinb.*, 1936-37, 57: 1-18.

BRIDGMAN, Percy Williams. Permanent elements in the flux of present-day physics. *Science*, 1930, 71: 19-23.
Address to the American Association for the Advancement of Science, Des Moines, Iowa, December, 1929.

BRIDGMAN, Percy Williams. Philosophical implications of physics. *Bull.Amer.Acad.Arts Sci.*, 1950, 3: 2-6.

BRIDGMAN, Percy Williams. Reflections of a physicist. xii, 392 p. New York: Philosophical Library, 1950. [CB 77/365]

BRIGHT, Laurence. Whitehead's philosophy of physics. 48 p. London/New York: Sheed and Ward, 1958.
Reviewed by H. Dopp, *Rev.Quest.Sci.*, 1959, 20: 320.

BROGLIE, Louis de. L'individualité dans le monde physique. *Arch.Inst.Int.Sci.Théor.Sér.A Bull.Acad.Int.Phil.Sci.*, 4. Problèmes de philosophie des sciences. Problèmes de connaissance en physique moderne, p. 61-73. Discussion, p. 74-80. (Actualités Scientifiques et Industrielles, 1066) Paris: Hermann, 1949.

BROWN, G. Burniston. The unification of macroscopic physics. *Sci.Progr.*, 1958, 46: 15-29.

BRUNSCHVICG, Léon. La physique du vingtième siècle et la philosophie. 30 p. Paris: Hermann, 1936.

CAPEK, Milic. The philosophical impact of contemporary physics. xvii, 414 p. Princeton, N.J.: Van Nostrand, 1961; London: Van Nostrand, 1962.
For reviews *see* CB 89/576.

EDDINGTON, Arthur Stanley. The philosophy of physical science. (Tarner Lectures, 1938) ix, 230 p. London: Cambridge University Press; New York: Macmillan, 1939.
Reviewed by E. Schrödinger, *Nature*, 1940, 145: 402-3; by V.F. Lenzen, *Isis*, 1941, 33: 79-80.

FRANK, Philipp. Between physics and philosophy. 238 p. Cambridge, Mass.: Harvard University Press, 1941.
Rev. ed. 1949 under the title "Modern science and its philosophy" (324 p.) [CB 77/365]
Reviewed by V.F. Lenzen, *Isis*, 1942, 34: 180.

HAERING, Th. L. Philosophie der Naturwissenschaft. Versuch eines einheitlichen Verständnisses der Methoden und Ergebnisse der (anorganischen) Naturwissenschaft. Zugleich eine Rehabilitierung des vorwissenschaftlichen Weltbildes. 788 p. München: Rösl, 1923. [CB 18/603]
Concerns the philosophy of physics.

HEISENBERG, Werner. The physicist's conception of nature. Transl. from the German by Arnold J. Pomerans. 192 p. New York: Harcourt, Brace, 1958.
For reviews *see* CB 85/381 and CB 88/521.
Translation of: Das Naturbild der heutigen Physik (Hamburg: Rowohlt, 1955).

HEISENBERG, Werner. Physics and philosophy: the revolution in modern science. 206 p. (World Perspectives, 19) New York: Harper, 1958; London: Allen & Unwin, 1959. (176 p.).
Reviewed by James MacLachlan, *Phys.Today*, 1958, 11: 36-8; by D.M. Bose, *Sci.Cult.*, 1960, 25: 678-86.

HOUSTON, W.V. The philosophy of physics. *Science*, 1937, 85: 413-19.

HUJER, Karel. Problems in the philosophy of modern physics. *Physis*, 1964, 6: 5-14.

HUTTEN, Ernest H. The language of modern physics. An introduction to the philosophy of science. 278 p. London: George Allen & Unwin Ltd.; New York: Macmillan Co., 1956.
Reviewed by Erich M. Harth, *Phys.Today*, 1957, 10: no. 2, 38-40.

JEANS, James Hopwood. Physics and philosophy. vii, 222 p. Cambridge University Press, 1942.
Reviewed by E.A. Milne, *Nature*, 1943, 151: 62-4; by Philip P. Wiener, *J.Hist.Ideas*, 1943, 4: 484-9.

JOERGENSEN, Joergen. Remarques sur les principales implications métaphysiques des théories et des idées récentes de la physique. *Rev.Métaphys.Morale*, 1932, 39: 323-51.

JORDAN, Pascual. Physics of the 20th century. Transl. by Eleanor Oshry. xii, 185 p. New York: Philosophical Library, 1944.
Reviewed in *Nature*, 1944, 154: 751.
Translation of: Die Physik des 20. Jahrhunderts. Einführung in den Gedankeninhalt der modernen Physik. 5th ed. Braunschweig: F. Vieweg, 1943. First publ. 1936.

KATTSOFF, Louis O. Physical science and physical reality. viii, 311 p. The Hague: Martinus Nijhoff, 1957.

KORNMÜLLER, Alois Eduard. Zur Beziehung zwischen Psyche, Gehirn und Natur im Zusammenhang mit dem Naturbild der modernen Physik. *Naturwiss.Rundsch.*, 1955, 8: 140-5.

LECLERC, Ivor. Whitehead and the problem of extension. *J. Phil.*, 1961, 58: 559-65.

LE CORBEILLER, Ph. Positions philosophiques impliquées par la physique classique. (Communication faite au Séminaire de Léon Brillouin au Collège de France le 16 mars 1939). *Thalès*, 1939, 4: 95-9. [CB 70/256]

LODGE, Oliver. Beyond physics, or the idealisation of mechanism: being a survey and attempted extension of modern physics in a philosophical and psychical direction. 172 p. London: Allen and Unwin, 1930.
Reviewed by A.D. Ritchie, *Nature*, 1930, 126: 268-70.

LUPASCO, Stéphane. La physique macroscopique et sa portée philosophique. 109 p. Paris: Vrin, 1935. [CB 45/275]

MACH, Ernst. Popular scientific lectures. 5th ed. viii, 411 p. La Salle, Ill.: Open Court, 1943.
5th rev.ed. of German original Leipzig: J.A. Barth, 1923.

MARGENAU, Henry. The nature of physical reality. A philosophy of modern physics. vii, 479 p., 13 fig. New York: McGraw Hill, 1950.
Reviewed by V.F. Lenzen, *Isis*, 1951, 42: 69-70.

MILNE, E.A. Some points in the philosophy of physics: time, evolution, and creation. *Annu.Rep.Smithsonian Inst.for 1933*, p. 219-38. Washington, D.C.: 1935.
An address delivered to the British Institute of Philosophy on Oct. 17, 1933. Reprinted from *Philosophy*, 1934, 9: 1-20.

NIRO, Pío. Einstein, el einsteinismo y una física consistente. 15 p. Buenos Aires: Héctor Gatti, 1951.

PETROVIĆ, Mikhail. Mécanismes communs aux phénomènes disparates. v, 279 p. (Nouvelle Collection Scientifique) Paris: Alcan, 1922.

PLANCK, Max. The new science: where is science going? The universe in the light of modern physics. The philosophy of physics. 328 p. New York: Meridian Books, 1959. [CB 85/465]
A reprint of three works in one volume.

PLANCK, Max. The philosophy of physics. Transl. by W.H. Johnston. 128 p. New York: W.W. Norton, 1963.
First publ. in English London: Allen and Unwin, 1936.

PLANCK, Max. Das Weltbild der neuen Physik. *Monatsh.Math. Phys.*, 1929, 36: 387-410.

REY, Abel. Les idées directrices de la physique mécaniste. *Rev.Phil.*, 1912, ler semestre, 327-66, 493-513.

REY, Abel. Le retour éternel et la philosophie de la physique. 320 p. Paris: Flammarion, 1927.
Reviewed by George Sarton, *Isis*, 1927, 9: 477-9.

RIDEAU, Emile. Philosophie de la physique moderne. 98 p. Paris: Cerf, 1939.
Reviewed by A.B., *Rev.Gén.Sci.*, 1940-41, 51: 165.

RUSSELL, Bertrand. The analysis of matter. viii, 408 p. London: Kegan Paul; New York: Harcourt Brace, 1927.

SAGUI, Cornelio L. L'atomo, l'universo e l'infinito. *Humanitas* (Brescia), 1953, 8: 141-66.

SAMUEL, Herbert Louis Samuel, *Viscount*. Essay in physics. With a letter from Albert Einstein. vi, 154 p. Oxford: Blackwell, 1951.
Also published New York: Harcourt, Brace, 1952.
Reviewed by F.I.G. Rawlins, *Nature*, 1951, 168: 215.

STARK, J. The pragmatic and the dogmatic spirit in physics. *Nature*, 1938, 141: 770-2.

WHITEHEAD, Alfred North. The concept of nature. Tarner Lectures delivered in Trinity College, Nov. 1919. x, 202 p. Cambridge University Press, 1920. [CB 10/212]
A companion book to the author's "Enquiry concerning the principles of natural knowledge", *see* below.

Ck

WHITEHEAD, Alfred North. An enquiry concerning the principles of natural knowledge. 2nd ed. xiv, 207 p. Cambridge University Press, 1925.
First publ. 1919.

WHYTE, L.L. The growth and implications of modern physics: a philosophical view. (Abstract of address). *Bull.Brit. Soc.Hist.Sci.*, 1955, 2: 13-14.

WHYTE, L.L. One-way processes in physics and biophysics. *Brit.J.Phil.Soc.*, 1955, 6: 107-21.

Ck-c

DINGLE, Herbert. Philosophy of physics, 1850-1950. *Nature*, 1951, 168: 630-6.

HOLTON, Gerald. Johannes Kepler et les origines philosophiques de la physique moderne. 26 p. (Conférences du Palais de la Découverte, D 78) Paris: Université de Paris, 1961.

LE LIONNAIS, F. Descartes et Einstein. *Rev.Hist.Sci.*, 1952, 5: 139-54, 3 fig.

WALLACE, William A. St. Thomas Aquinas, Galileo, and Einstein. *Thomist*, 1961, 24: 1-22.

Ck-o

SEEGER, Raymond J. On teaching the philosophy of physics. *Amer.J.Phys.*, 1960, 28: 384-93.

Ckb the nature of physics

ANDRADE, E.N. da C. Physics for the modern world. viii, 100 p., fig. New York: Barnes & Noble, 1963.

BRAGG, William Henry. Concerning the nature of things. Six lectures delivered at the Royal Institution. xi, 231 p., ill. London: Bell, 1925.
Reprinted 1954 (New York: Dover Publications).

CAMPBELL, Norman Robert. Physics: the elements. vii, 565 p. Cambridge University Press, 1920. [CB 11/452]
French translation of the first part of this work entitled "Les principes de la physique". (xx, 200 p.). Paris: Alcan, 1923. [CB 16/339]

CHAMBADAL, Paul. La physique moderne et son interprétation. 202 p. Paris: Armand Colin, 1956. [CB 83/198]

DINGLE, Herbert. The new outlook in physics. In: Dingle, Herbert. The scientific adventure, p. 256-62. London: Pitman, 1952.
Broadcast talk originally published in *The Listener*, 18 November 1948.
German translation, Die neuen Anschauungen in der Physik, *Phil.Natur.*, 1950, 1: 76-83.

EDDINGTON, Arthur Stanley. The nature of the physical world. (Gifford Lectures, 1927) xix, 361 p. Cambridge University Press, 1928.
Reviewed by E.T. Whittaker, *Nature*, 1929, 123: 4-5.
French translation (Paris: Payot, 1932) [CB 35/298].
German translation (Braunschweig: Vieweg, 1931) reviewed by C.G. Hempel, *Deut.Lit.Zeitung*, 1931, 2: 2339-46.

EDDINGTON, Arthur Stanley. New pathways in science. 333 p., 4 pl. (Messenger Lectures, 1934) Cambridge University Press, 1935; reprinted, Ann Arbor: University of Michigan Press, 1959.
Reviewed by Herbert Dingle, *Nature*, 1935, 135: 451-4; in *Phys.Today*, 1960, 13: 47.

FRANK, Philipp. Modern physics and common sense. *Scr.Math.*, 1939, 6: 5-16.

HAAS, Arthur Erich. Objective and human physics. *Science*, 1927, 66: 463-9.

HEISENBERG, Werner. The representation of nature in contemporary physics. *Daedalus Amer.Acad.Arts Sci.*, 1958, no. 3, 95-108.

HESSE, Mary B. On what there is in physics. *Brit.J.Phil.Sci.*, 1962, 13: 234-44.

HOBSON, Ernest William. The ideal aim of physical science. A lecture delivered on November 7, 1924, before the University of London at King's College. iv, 34 p. Cambridge University Press, 1925.

HOLTON, Gerald. Introduction to concepts and theories in physical science. xx, 650 p. Cambridge, Mass.: Addison-Wesley Press, 1952.
Reviewed in *Scr.Math.*, 1953, 19: 175-6.

LITTLE, Noel C. A unified approach to physics. *Amer.J.Phys.*, 1951, 19: 351-3. [CB 78/183]

LUHR, Overton. Physics tells why. ix, 318 p. Lancaster, Pa.: Jaques Cattell Press, 1943. [CB 65/80]

POINCARÉ, Henri. Principles of mathematical physics. *Sci. Mon.*, 1956, 82: 165-75.
Translation of an article that appeared first in *The Monist* in January, 1905.

REICHENBACH, Hans. Atom and cosmos: the world of modern physics. Transl. and rev. by Edward S. Allen. 300 p. New York: Macmillan, 1933.
Reviewed by Cassius Jackson Keyser, *Scr.Math.*, 1933, 1: 327-41.
German original (Berlin: Deutsche Buchgemeinschaft, 1930) reviewed by Maurice Lecat, *Rev.Quest.Sci.*, 1931, 19: 467-80; 20: 237-61.

SEEGER, Raymond J. On understanding physical phenomena. *Physis*, 1964, 6: 245-68.

STALLO, J.B. The concepts and theories of modern physics. Ed. by P.W. Bridgman. xxix, 325 p. Cambridge, Mass.: Harvard University Press, 1960.
Reviewed by Stillman Drake, *Isis*, 1962, 53: 275-6.

WATSON, W.H. On understanding physics. xii, 146 p. Cambridge University Press, 1938.
Reprinted New York: Harper Bros., 1959.
Reviewed by V.F. Lenzen, *Isis*, 1940, 31: 469-71.

WATSON, W.H. Understanding physics today. xiii, 219 p. Cambridge University Press, 1963.
Reviewed by E. Nagel, *Sci.Amer.*, 1963, 209: no. 4, 145-6.

WEIZSÄCKER, Carl Friedrich von. Zum Weltbild der Physik. 7th rev. ed. 378 p. Stuttgart: S. Hirzel Verlag, 1958.
First published Leipzig: 1943. English translation from 4th German edition, 1949 "The world view of physics" (London: Routledge & Kegan Paul, 1952). French translation "Le monde vu par la physique" (Paris: Flammarion, 1956).
Reviewed by R. Bruce Lindsay, *Phys.Today*, 1958, 11: no. 11, 52.

Ckd hypotheses and theories; explanation

BORN, Max. Experiment and theory in physics. iv, 44 p. Cambridge University Press; New York: Macmillan Co., 1943. [CB 66/261 and 263]
Reprinted New York: Dover, 1956.

BRIDGMAN, Percy Williams. The nature of physical theory. 138 p. Princeton, N.J.: Princeton University Press, 1936.
Paperback edition New York: Wiley, 1964.
Reviewed by William Marias Malisoff, *Phil.Sci.*, 1936, 3: 360-4.

BROWN, G. Burniston. Have we abandoned the physical theory of nature? *Sci.Progr.*, 1956, 44: 619-34.

BUCHDAHL, Gerd. Theory construction: the work of Norman Robert Campbell. *Isis*, 1964, 55: 151-62.
For Campbell, Norman Robert. Physics: the elements, *see* Ckb

DESTOUCHES-FÉVRIER, Paulette. Le réel et la théorie physique. *Arch.Inst.Int.Sci.Théor.Sér.A Bull.Acad.Int.Phil.Sci.*, 2. Problèmes de philosophie des sciences. 2. Les sciences et le réel, p. 61-79. Discussion, p. 80-94. (Actualités Scientifiques et Industrielles, 1061) Paris: Hermann, 1948.

DESTOUCHES-FÉVRIER, Paulette. La structure des théories physiques. 423 p. Paris: Presses Universitaires de France, 1951.
Reviewed by F. Russo, *Rev.Hist.Sci.*, 1952, 5: 117-18.

DINGLE, Herbert. The laws of nature. (Halley Lecture, 1944) *Nature*, 1944, 153: 731-6, 758-63.

DINGLER, Hugo. Physik und Hypothese. Versuch einer induktiven Wissenschaftslehre nebst einer kritischen Analyse der Fundamente der Relativitätstheorie. xi, 200 p. Berlin/Leipzig: Vereinigung wissenschaftlicher Verleger, 1921.
Reviewed by H.M. Sheffer, *Isis*, 1922, 4: 385.

DUHEM, Pierre. The aim and structure of physical theory. Transl. by Philip P. Wiener. xiii, 344 p. Princeton: Princeton University Press, 1954.
Reviewed by Robert E. Schofield, *Isis*, 1956, 47: 67-8.
Translation of: La théorie physique: son objet, sa structure. 2nd edition. 1914.

FEIGL, Herbert. Theorie und Erfahrung in der Physik. iv, 142 p. (Wissen und Wirken, 58) Karlsruhe: Braun, 1929. [CB 28/546]

FINE, Arthur. Physical geometry and physical laws. *Phil. Sci.*, 1964, 31: 156-62.

FRANK, Philipp. Der Charakter der heutigen physikalischen Theorie. *Scientia*, 1931, 49: 183-96; French transl., suppl., 74-84.

HESSE, Mary B. Operational definition and analogy in physical theories. *Brit.J.Phil.Sci.*, 1952, 2: 281-94.

LANCZOS, Cornelius. Albert Einstein and the role of theory in contemporary physics. *Amer.Scient.*, 1959, 47: 41-59.

LENZEN, Victor F. The nature of physical theory. A study in the theory of knowledge. xii, 301 p. New York: Wiley, 1931.
Reviewed by H.T. Davis, *Isis*, 1934, 20: 488-91; by Leigh Page, *Science*, 1932, 76: 145-6; by Norman R. Campbell, *Nature*, 1932, 130: 40-1; by Heinrich Scholz, *Deut.Lit. Zeitung*, 1933, 4: 2250-2.

LENZEN, Victor F. The significance of physical theory. *Science*, 1954, 119: 517-22.
Article occasioned by publication of English translation of Duhem's La théorie physique, *see* above.

LOWINGER, Armand. The methodology of Pierre Duhem. 184 p. New York: Columbia University Press, 1941.
Contains translations of portions of Duhem's "The aim and structure of physical theory".
Reviewed by Benjamin Ginzburg, *Isis*, 1942, 34: 33-4.

PAP, Arthur. The a priori in physical theory. xi, 102 p. New York: King's Crown Press, 1946. [CB 70/252]

PEIERLS, R.E. The laws of nature. 284 p. New York: Scribner's, 1956. [CB 83/198]

REY, Abel. La théorie de la physique chez les physiciens contemporains. 3rd ed. 345 p. (Bibliothèque de Philosophie Contemporaine) Paris: Alcan, 1930.
Reviewed by P.J. Richard, *Rev.Gén.Sci.*, 1930, 41: 282-3.

VOUILLEMIN, Charles Ernest. Qu'est-ce, au fond, que la science? Réflexions sur les théories de la physique. 404 p. (Bibliothèque des Sciences Modernes et Sociales) Paris: Albin Michel, 1924.

WALKER, Marshall J. An orientation toward modern physical theory. *Sci.Mon.*, 1955, 81: 27-37.

ZILSEL, Edgar. The genesis of the concept of physical law. *Phil.Rev.*, 1942, 51: 245-79.

Cke method

AUERBACH, Felix. Die Methoden der theoretischen Physik. x, 436 p., 150 fig. Leipzig: Akademische Verlagsgesellschaft, 1925. [CB 17/597]

BENDER, Wm. The method of physical coincidences and the scale coordinate. *Phil.Sci.*, 1934, 1: 253-72.

BRADDICK, H.J.J. The physics of experimental method. 404 p. London: Chapman & Hall, 1954.
Reviewed by A. Sellerio, *Scientia*, 1955, 49: 38.

BRIDGMAN, P.W. Dimensional analysis. 112 p. New Haven: Yale University Press, 1922.

CORNÉLISSEN, Christian. Les hallucinations des Einsteiniens, ou les erreurs de méthode chez les physiciens-mathématiciens. xiii, 86 p. Paris: Blanchard, 1923.

DADOURIAN, H.M. The principle of the unobservable. *Sci.Mon.*, 1944, 59: 293-5

DINGLER, Hugo. Die Methode der Physik. 422 p. München: Reinhardt, 1938.
Reviewed by V.F. Lenzen, *Isis*, 1947, 32: 203-5.

DUGAS, René. La méthode physique au sens de Duhem devant la mécanique des quanta. *Rev.Gén.Sci.*, 1937, 48: 68-71.

EWING, Alfred. Some modern aspects of physical research. Presidential address delivered before the Royal Society of Edinburgh at the annual meeting on October 26, 1925. *Nature*, 1925, 116: 713-15.

FOX, Russell. The science of science; methods of interpreting physical phenomena, by scientists of the Westinghouse Research Laboratories: Russell Fox, Max Garbuny and Robert Hooke. xi, 243 p. (A Westinghouse Search Book) New York: Walker, 1964.

FREUDENTHAL, Hans. De begrippen axiom en axiomatiek in de wis- en natuurkunde. [The concepts axiom and axiomatics in mathematics and physics. (In Dutch)] *Simon Stevin*, 1955-56, 30: 156-75.

HESSE, Mary B. Models in physics. *Brit.J.Phil.Sci.*, 1953, 4: 198-214

JAMMER, Max. Models and physical theory. *Proc.10th Int. Congr.Hist.Sci.* (Ithaca, 1962), (2), p. 691-4. Paris: Hermann, 1964.

KÖRNER, S.; PRYCE, M.H.L.; ed. Observation and interpretation. A symposium of philosophers and physicists. Proceedings of the ninth Symposium of the Colston Research Society held in the University of Bristol, 1-4 April 1957. xiv, 218 p., front. (Colston Papers, 9) London: Butterworths Scientific Publications; New York: Academic Press, Inc., 1957.
Reviewed by Arthur Smullyan, *Isis*, 1959, 50: 488-9; by George Weiss, *Phys.Today*, 1958, 11: no. 9, 48; by S.S. Schweber, *Amer.Scient.*, 1959, 47: 78A-84A.

MARGENAU, Henry. Methodology of modern physics. *Phil.Sci.*, 1935, 2: 48-72, 164-87.

SARANGOV, TZ. S.; SPASSKII, B.I. O metode modelei i analogii v razvitii fiziki. [On the method of models and analogies in the development of physics. (In Russian)]. *Vestnik Moskovskogo Gos.Univ.Fiz.Astron.*, 1963, no. 5, 96-103.

SEAMAN, Francis. Mach's principle of continuity. *Proc.10th Int.Congr.Hist.Sci.*(Ithaca, 1962), (1), p. 333-5. Paris: Hermann, 1964

VASSILIEV, S.F. [On the problem of the principle of observability. (In Russian with English summary)]. *Arkh.Ist. Nauk.Tekh.*, 1935, 6: 1-31. [CB 45/276]

Cke-mzMGke

HARTSHORNE, Charles. The parallel development of method in physics and psychology. *Phil.Sci.*, 1934, 1: 446-59.

Ckg

DARWIN, C.G. Logic and probability in physics. *Nature*, 1938, 142: 381-4.
From the presidential address to the British Association, Cambridge, 1938.

GILLISPIE, Charles C. Les fondements intellectuels de l'introduction des probabilités en physique. 23 p. (Conférence donnée au Palais de la Découverte, Dec. 1, 1962, D 88) Paris: Université de Paris, 1962.

MENDELSSOHN, K. Probability enters physics. *Amer.Scient.*, 1961, 49: 37-49.

Ckk logic and foundations

BRIDGMAN, Percy Williams. The logic of modern physics. xiv, 228 p. New York: Macmillan, 1927.
Reviewed by Harold Jeffreys, *Nature*, 1928, 121: 86-7.
German translation (Munich: Hueber, 1932) reviewed by E.O. von Lippmann, *Chem.Zeitung*, 1932, 56: 875.

BRIDGMAN, Percy Williams. P.W. Bridgman's "The logic of modern physics" after thirty years. *Daedalus Amer.Acad. Arts Sci.*, 1959, 88: 518-26.

DINGLE, Herbert. The Doppler effect and the foundations of physics. *Brit.J.Phil.Sci.*, 1960, 11: 11-31, 113-29.

DINGLER, Hugo. Die Grundlagen der Physik. Synthetische Prinzipien der mathematischen Naturphilosophie. xiv, 336 p. Berlin: Walter de Gruyter, 1923.
Reviewed by Henry M. Sheffer, *Isis*, 1924, 6: 572-3.

EINSTEIN, Albert. Considerations concerning the fundaments of theoretical physics. *Science*, 1940, 91: 487-92
Address before the 8th American Scientific Congress, Washington, D.C., 15 May 1940.

EVE, A.S. Foundations of physics. *Nature*, 1938, 142: 857-9.

FAGGIANI, D. La struttura logica della fisica. 318 p., 12 fig. (Biblioteca di Cultura Scientifica, 40) Torino: Edizioni Scientifiche Einaudi, 1957.
Reviewed in *Scientia*, 1958, 93: Supplement, 5.

FRANK, Philipp. Foundations of physics. v, 78 p. (International Encyclopedia of Unified Science, 1) Chicago: University of Chicago Press, 1946.
Reviewed by Victor F. Lenzen, *Isis*, 1947, 37: 104.

FREUDENTHAL, Hans. De begrippen axiom en axiomatiek in de wis- en natuurkunde. [The concepts axiom and axiomatics in mathematics and physics. (In Dutch)] *Simon Stevin*, 1955-56, 30: 156-75.

HESSE, Mary B. *See* Cc-bm

HOLTON, Gerald; ROLLER, Duane H.D. Foundations of modern physical science. 782 p. Reading, Mass.: Addison-Wesley Publishing, 1958.
Reviewed by James MacLachlan, *Phys.Today*, 1958, 11: no. 12, 44-8.

KUZNETSOV, Boris G. [Paths of development of quanto-relativistic logic. (In Russian)]. *Tr.Inst.Ist.Est.Tekh.*, 1959, 22: 69-105.

LAURÈS, Clément. Les bases de la géométrie et de la physique. L'invariance de l'espace euclidien. 125 p., ill. Paris: A. Blanchard, 1928. [CB 24/525]

LINDSAY, Robert Bruce; MARGENAU, Henry. Foundations of physics. xiii, 537 p. London: Wiley, 1936.
Reviewed by William Marias Malisoff, *Phil.Sci.*, 1936, 3: 371-2.

SCHREBER, Karl Edmund. Die Grundlagen und Grundbegriffe der Physik der Vorgänge. Versuch einer Fortbildung der Gedanken Robert Mayers. 312 p. Leipzig: Noske, 1933.

TISZA, Laszlo. The logical structure of physics. *Synthese*, 1962, 14: 110-31.

WALLER, I. Grundfankar i modern fysik. [Principes fondamentaux de la physique moderne. (In Swedish, with French summary)]. *Lychnos*, 1936, 1: 272-8. [CB 48/570]

Ckm verification and falsification

WHYTE, L.L. Some thoughts on certainty in physical science. *Brit.J.Phil.Sci.*, 1963, 14: 32-8.

Cks epistemological aspects

BRÜLL, Erhard. Erkenntniskritische Grundprobleme der Relativitätstheorie, Quanten- und Wellenmechanik. 66 p. Breslau: Borgmeyer, 1929.

FRANK, Philipp. Théorie de la connaissance et physique moderne. Trad. de l'allemand par E. Vouillemin, revue et mise à jour par l'auteur. Introd. de Marcel Boll. 54 p. (Actualités Scientifiques et Industrielles, 97) Paris: Hermann, 1934.
First published in *Erkenntnis*.

GEHRCKE, E. Physik und Erkenntnistheorie. 119 p. (Wissenschaft und Hypothese, 22) Leipzig: Teubner, 1921. [CB 12/637]

GORGÉ, Viktor. Philosophie und Physik. Die Wandlung zur heutigen erkenntnistheoretischen Grundhaltung in der Physik. Foreword by Andre Mercier. 137 p. Berlin: Duncker & Humblot, 1960.

MANNEBACK, Charles. La connaissance de la nature chez les physiciens contemporains. *Rev.Quest.Sci.*, 1950, 121: 481-93.

PLANCK, Max. Wege zur physikalischen Erkenntnis. 280 p. Leipzig: Hirzel, 1933.

ROSENTHAL-SCHNEIDER, Ilse. Limits in modern physics and their epistemological implications. *Australian J.Sci.*, 1952, 15: 77-81.

STUDY, Eduard. Mathematik und Physik. Eine erkenntnistheoretische Untersuchung. 31 p. (Sammlung Vieweg, 65) Braunschweig: F. Vieweg, 1923. [CB 15/229]

Ckt philosophical systems

BACHELARD, Gaston. L'activité rationaliste de la physique contemporaine. 223 p. (Bibliothèque de Philosophie Contemporaine) Paris: Alcan, 1951.
Reviewed by M. De Tollenaere, *Rev.Quest.Sci.*, 1951, 12: 426; by Bernard Rochot, *Rev.Hist.Sci.*, 1952, 5: 186-7.

BACHELARD, Suzanne. La conscience de la rationalité. Étude phénoménologique sur la physique mathématique. 212 p. (Bibliothèque de Philosophie Contemporaine) Paris: Presses Universitaires de France, 1958.
Reviewed by F. Russo, *Rev.Hist.Sci.*, 1959, 12: 370.

BANDYOPADHYAY, Pratul. Physics today: a new phase of scepticism. *Sci.Cult.*, 1963, 29: 177-82.

MOSCHETTI, Luigi. Fenomenismo e relativismo nel pensiero di E. Mach. 102 p. Genova: Francesco Perella, 1923. [CB 16/340]

NEUSCHLOSZ, Simon M. El irracionalismo en la física contemporánea. *Minerva* (Buenos Aires), 1944, 1: 44-9.

PACOTTE, Julien. Le physicalisme dans le cadre de l'empirisme intégral. 54 p. (Actualités Scientifiques et Industrielles, 343) Paris: Hermann, 1936.

TONNELAT, Marie Antoinette. Idéalisme et réalisme dans l'évolution de la physique contemporaine. *Actes du Symposium International R.J. Bošković 1961*, p. 43-53. Beograd: Štampa Izdaračka Ustanova "Naučno delo", 1962.

Ckv causality; determinism and indeterminism

BERGMANN, Hugo. Der Kampf um das Kausalgesetz in der jüngsten Physik. 78 p. Braunschweig: Vieweg, 1929.
Reviewed by Edmund O. von Lippmann, *Chem.Zeitung*, 1929, 53: 615.

BOHM, David. Causality and chance in modern physics. xi, 170 p. London: Routledge & Kegan Paul; Princeton, N.J.: D. Van Nostrand Company, 1957.
Reprinted New York: Harper Bros., 1961.
Reviewed by James R. Newman, *Sci.Amer.*, January 1958, 198: 111-12, 114-16; by L. Rosenfeld, *Nature*, 1958, 181: 658.

BOHR, Niels. Causality and complementarity. *Phil.Sci.*, 1937, 4: 289-98.

BORN, Max. Natural philosophy of cause and chance. Being the Waynflete Lectures delivered in the College of St. Mary Magdalen, Oxford, in Hilary term 1948. viii, 216 p. Oxford: Clarendon Press, 1949.

BOULIGAND, Georges. Relations d'incertitude en géométrie et en physique. Préface de L. de Broglie. 28 p. Paris: Hermann, 1934.

BRADLEY, R.D. Determinism or indeterminism in microphysics. *Brit.J.Phil.Sci.*, 1962, 13: 193-215.

BROGLIE, Louis de. Déterminisme et causalité dans la physique contemporaine. *Rev.Métaphys.Morale*, 1929, 36: 433-43.

BROGLIE, Louis de. La représentation simultanée des possibilités dans la nouvelle physique. *Rev.Métaphys.Morale*, 1932, 39: 149-52.

BRUNSCHVICG, Léon. L'expérience humaine et la causalité physique. lxvi, 625 p. (Bibliothèque de Philosophie Contemporaine) Paris: Alcan, 1922.
Reviewed by H. Metzger, *Isis,* 1923, 5: 479-83; *see also* Weber, Louis, below.

CASSIRER, Ernst. Determinism and indeterminism in modern physics. Historical and systematic studies of the problem of causality. Transl. by O. Theodor Benfey. With a preface by Henry Margenau. xxiv, 227 p. New Haven: Yale University Press; London: Oxford University Press, 1956. [CB 83/197]
Translation of: Determinismus und Indeterminismus in der modernen Physik. (Göteborg: 1936).

DANZER-VANOTTI, Hedwig. "Atmen im luftleeren Raum". *Phil. Natur.,* 1964, 8: 198-200.
A quotation from Einstein regarding determinism. Apropos of the article by Weissmann, M.A. (*see* below).

DESTOUCHES, J.L. Déterminisme et indéterminisme en physique moderne. *Arch.Inst.Int.Sci.Théor.Sér.A Bull.Acad.Int.Phil. Sci.,* 4. Problèmes de philosophie des sciences, 4. Problèmes de connaissance en physique moderne, p. 7-42. Discussion p. 43-60. (Actualités Scientifiques et Industrielles, 1066) Paris: Hermann, 1949.

FERGUSON, Allan. Prof. Planck and the principle of causality in physics. *Nature,* 1932, 130: 45-8.
A discussion of the Seventeenth Guthrie Lecture delivered by Max Planck before the Physical Society on June 17, *see* below.

GOTTESMANN, Benjamin. Das Kausalproblem im Lichte des modernen Wissens. (Die Ergebnisse der Physik.) *Atti IV. Congr.Int.Fil.* (Bologna, 1911), (2), p. 85-98. Genoa: Formiggini, 1913.

HÖNIGSWALD, Richard. Kausalität und Physik. Eine methodologische Überlegung. *Sitzungsber.Preuss.Akad.Wiss.Phys.Math. Kl.,* 1933, 568-78.

LANGEVIN, Paul. La física actual y el determinismo. [Translated by] Fernando Carbonell. 75 p. Colección Cultura. Montevideo: Claudio García, 1944.
Reviewed by M.B., *Minerva* (Buenos Aires), 1944, 1: 184-5. Includes articles previously published in "El Siglo", "El Pais" and "La Mañana" of Montevideo.

MEURERS, Joseph. Das Problem der Kausalität im Bereich der grossen Massen und Räume. *Phil.Natur.,* 1957, 4: 209-22.

PAULI, W. Die philosophische Bedeutung der Idee der Komplementarität. *Experientia,* 1950, 5: 72-5. [CB 76/393]

PLANCK, Max. The concept of causality. The seventeenth Guthrie lecture delivered on June 17, 1932. *Proc.Phys.Soc.,* 1932, 44: 529-39.
For discussion of this lecture *see* Ferguson, Allan, above.

PLANCK, Max. Die Kausalität im Naturgeschehen. *Scientia,* 1933, 53: 153-64; French transl., suppl., 52-62. [CB 39/445]

PLANCK, Max. Der Kausalitätsbegriff in der Physik. 26 p. Leipzig: Barth, 1932.
Reviewed by E. O. von Lippman, *Chem.Zeitung,* 1932, 56: 435.

POPPER, Karl R. Indeterminism in quantum physics and in classical physics. *Brit.J.Phil.Sci.,* 1950, 1: 117-33, 173-95. [CB 77/366]

ROIG-GIRONELLA, Juan. El indeterminismo físico y la noción filosófica de causalidad. *Act.IIe Congr.Int.Phil.Sci.* (Zurich, 1954), p. 82-5. Neuchâtel: Editions du Griffon, 1955.

SCHRÖDINGER, Erwin. Über Indeterminismus in der Physik. Ist die Naturwissenschaft milieubedingt? Zwei Vorträge zur Kritik der naturwissenschaftlichen Erkenntnis. 62 p., 5 fig. Leipzig: Barth, 1932.

WEBER, Louis. L'expérience humaine et la causalité physique. *Rev.Métaphys.Morale,* 1923, 30: 59-95.
Critical review of Léon Brunschvicg's book, *see* above.

WEISSMANN, M.A. Der Determinismus A. Einsteins. *Phil. Natur.,* 1960-61, 6: 479-84.

WOJCIECHOWSKI, Jerzy A. Remarques sur la notion de cause dans la physique contemporaine. *Dialogue,* 1962, 1: 81-92.

Ckw positivism

NEIDORF, Robert. Discussion: Is Einstein a positivist? *Phil. Sci.,* 1963, 30: 173-88.

Ckz the future of physics

LINDSAY, R.B. The future of theoretical physics. *Phil.Sci.,* 1938, 5: 452-71.

Cmz relations with other scientific disciplines

CmzB

ALEXANDER, Jerome. Mathematical imagery and physical phenomena. *Scr.Math.,* 1936, 4: 139-45, ill.

BIRKHOFF, George D. The mathematical nature of physical theories. *Amer.Scient.,* 1943, 31: 281-310, portr.

BOCHNER, Salomon. The significance of some basic mathematical conceptions for physics. *Isis,* 1963, 54: 179-205.

BOHR, Niels. Mathematics and natural philosophy. *Sci.Mon.,* 1956, 82: 80-8.

BURGER, D.; VOLLGRAFF, J.A. De uitvinding van de natuurkundige formule. [The discovery of formulae expressing physical phenomena. (In Dutch)]. *Faraday,* 1948, 17: 93-7.

DIRAC, P.A.M. The relation between mathematics and physics. *Proc.Roy.Soc.Edin.,* 1938-39, 59: part 2, 122-9.

SIDDIQI, M. Raziuddin. Mathematical methods for the unification of physical theories. *Stud.Hyderabad Acad.,* 1940, no. 2, 121-8.

CmzBF

WHITTAKER, E.T. The new algebras and their significance for physics and philosophy. *Nature,* 1943, 152: 603.

CmzBT

BARBARIN, Paul. La géométrie non euclidienne. 3e éd. suivie de notes sur la géométrie non euclidienne dans ses rapports avec la physique mathématique, par A. Buhl. 176 p., 7 pl. (Scientia, 15) Paris: Gauthier-Villars, 1928.
First and second editions, 1902 and 1907.

CmzCD

HOOYKAAS, R. Das Verhältnis von Physik und Mechanik in historischer Hinsicht. 22 p. Wiesbaden: Franz Steiner Verlag, 1963.

ROELANTS, H. De verhouding van fysika en mechanika. [The relations between physics and mechanics. (In Dutch. Résumé in French)]. *Sci.Hist.,* 1964, 6: 30-44.

CmzDD

LANGMUIR, Irving. Modern concepts in physics and their relation to chemistry. *Annu.Rep.Smithsonian Inst. for 1930,* p. 219-41. Washington, D.C.: 1932.
First publ. *Gen.Elec.Rev.,* 1929, 32: 649-59.

CmzDY for relations of physics with alchemy *see* DYmzC

CmzJ for relations of physics with biology *see* JmzC

CmzN

MUNTNER, Suessman. [The influence of modern physics on medical thought. (In Hebrew with English summary)] *Koroth,* 1957, 1: 357-77.

NORTHROP, F.S.C. The history of modern physics in its bearing upon biology and medicine. *Yale J.Biol.Med.,* 1938, 10: 209-32.

WOODGER, J.H. Physics, psychology and medicine: a methodological essay. 145 p. Cambridge University Press, 1956.

Cn communication

Cnb

COPLEY, G.N. William Stroud and quantity calculus. *Nature,* 1960, 188: 254.
Symbols for representing physical quantities.

ROLLER, Duane. A proposed procedure for selecting and using symbols for physical units. *Amer.J.Phys.,* 1953, 21: 293-6.

Cnm

MECKE, R.; LAMBERTZ, A. Vorlesungstechnik. In: Scheel, Karl, ed. Geschichte der Physik. Vorlesungstechnik, p. 209-399. (Handbuch der Physik, 1) Berlin: Springer, 1926. [CB 25/416]

Co study and teaching

THOMSON, J.J. The growth in opportunities for education and research in physics during the past fifty years. *Science*, 1931, 74: 317-24.

TIMERDING, H.E. Forschung und Unterricht. In: Scheel, Karl, ed. Geschichte der Physik. Vorlesungstechnik, p. 187-208. (Handbuch der Physik, 1) Berlin: Springer, 1926. [CB 25/416]

Cof/og

BLÜH, Otto. Physics examinations and the new curriculum. *Amer.J.Phys.*, 1948, 16: 20-4.

Cop

BLÜH, Otto. Physics in premedical education. *Amer.J.Phys.*, 1949, 17: 156-63.
Sketches course in use at the University of British Columbia, Vancouver.

DODD, L.E. The new and the old in elementary physics teaching. *Amer.J.Phys.*, 1955, 23: 386-7.

TAYLOR, Lloyd W. Physics in the Liberal Arts College. *Amer. Phys.Teacher*, 1938, 6: 315-17.

Cq/r organizational and professional aspects

Cqg

JAFFE, George. Recollections of three great laboratories. *J. Chem.Educ.*, 1952, 29: 230-8.
Jaffe studied in the laboratories of Ostwald, J.J. Thompson, and the Curies.

Cqx

BROGLIE, Maurice de. Les premiers congrès de physique Solvay et l'orientation de la physique depuis 1911. 126 p., 40 pl. (Cahiers de la Collection Sciences d'Aujourd'hui) Paris: Albin Michel, 1951.
Reviewed by P.W. Bridgman, *Isis*, 1954, 45: 314-15.

PELSENEER, Jean. Cinquantenaire du premier conseil de physique Solvay, 1911-1961. 12 p., 11 pl. Bruxelles: Institut International de Physique Solvay, 1962. [CB 87/633]

Cqy

INSTITUT INTERNATIONAL DE PHYSIQUE, fondé par E. Solvay. [Notice of its organization and aims] *Isis*, 1913, 1: 258.

PELSENEER, Jean. Note sur un historique inédit des Instituts Internationaux de Physique et de Chimie Solvay. *IIIe Congr. Nat.Sci.* (Bruxelles, 1950), vol. 1, p. 36. Liège: Desoer, 1951.

Cr

CZERNY, Marianus. Der Physiker als Beobachter und Gestalter von Naturerscheinungen. 15 p. (*Sitzungsberichte der wissenschaftlichen Gesellschaft an der Johann Wolfgang Goethe-Universität* Frankfurt/Main, 1) Wiesbaden: Franz Steiner Verlag, 1962.

Crd

SMYTH, H.D. The new responsibilities of physicists. *Phys. Today*, 1955, 8: no. 5, 10-11.

Cs relations with society

BENDA, Julien. L'humanité et la nouvelle physique. *Hellên. Contemp.*, 1950, 4: 356-61.

CAUDWELL, Christopher, [pseud. of Christopher St. John Sprigg]. The crisis in physics. With an introduction by H. Levy. xvi, 245 p. London: Lane, 1939. [CB 60/143]

KHVOL'SON, Orest Danilovich. Die Physik und ihre Bedeutung für die Menschheit. Aus dem Russischen übersetzt von Georg Kluge. viii, 277 p. Braunschweig: Vieweg, 1924.

SCHRÖDINGER, Erwin. Science and humanism. Physics in our time. ix, 68 p. Cambridge University Press, 1951.
Reviewed by F.I.G. Rawlins, *Nature*, 1952, 169: 984.

Csb

MEYERSON, Emile. Le physicien et le primitif: extraits d'un livre intitulé "Du cheminement de la pensée" à paraître prochainement. *Rev.Phil.*, 1930, 109: 321-58, bibliogr.
For the complete work *see* Ák-c

ZILSEL, Edgar. Physics and the problem of historico-sociological laws. *Phil.Sci.*, 1941, 8: 567-79.

Cse

DINGLE, Herbert. Physics and the public mind. *Nature*, 1934, 133: 818-20

Csk

BORN, Max. Physics and politics. Foreword by Dame Kathleen Lonsdale. 86 p. New York: Basic Books, 1962.

KOL'MAN, Ernest. Lenin i noveishaia fizika. [Lenin and modern physics. (In Russian)] 150 p. Moskva: Gos. Izd-vo Polit. Lit-ry, 1959. [CB 88/622]

MATTICK, Paul. Marxism and the new physics. *Phil.Sci.*, 1962, 29: 350-64.

Csy

COMPTON, Arthur H. Physics and the future. *Science*, 1938, 88: 115-21.

Ct relations with the humanities

DIETZ, David. Cultural values of physics. *Annu.Rep.Smithsonian Inst.for 1940*, p. 139-54. Washington, D.C.: 1941.

LAMPA, Anton. Die Physik in der Kultur. 84 p. München: Georg D.W. Callwey, 1925.

OPPENHEIMER, J. Robert. Science and the common understanding. 120 p. London: Oxford University Press; New York: Simon and Schuster, 1954. [CB 80/203]
The 1953 Reith Lectures.

Ctc

SEARS, Paul B. The steady state: physical law and moral choice. *Phi Beta Kappa Key Rep.*, Jan. 1959, 24: 2-3, 8.

Cw in different countries

CREW, Henry. The scientific leadership of the world. *Method. Rev.*, Jan. 1920, 95-102.
List of 233 main achievements in physics during the last 300 years, the purpose being to ascertain the part played by each nation in the progress of physics.

REY, Abel. La contribution que les divers pays ont donnée aux progrès de la physique. 1. Physique Newtonnienne et physique de Fresnel, Maxwell, Clausius. 2. Physique énergetique et physique électronique. *Scientia*, May and June 1921, 29: 345-60, 429-42.

Cwb North America

HARRISON, George R. Karl Compton and American physics. *Phys.Today*, 1957, 10: no. 11, 19-22.

VAN VLECK, J.H. American physics comes of age. *Phys.Today*, 1964, 17: no. 6, 21-6.

Cwb-br

Physics in Canada 1949- Toronto: Canadian Association of Physicists, 1949-

Cwb-ch

MACKWORTH, M.L. Dissertations in physics. An indexed bibliography of all doctoral theses accepted by American universities, 1861-1959. Palo Alto, Calif.: Stanford University Press, 1961.

Cwb-oq

DAVIS, Tenney L.; GOODWIN, H.M. A history of the Departments of Chemistry and Physics at the Massachusetts Institute of Technology (1865-1933). 35 p., ill. Cambridge, Mass.: The Institute, 1933.
Reviewed by Hélène Metzger, *Archeion*, 1933, 15: 466.

Cwb-qd for physical societies in North America *see* Franklin Institute, 2: 694

Cwb-rc

BELL, Raymond M. Origins and ages of American physicists. *Amer.J.Phys.*, 1946, 14: 396-8, 1 fig.

Cwb-sp

COHEN, I. Bernard. American physicists at war. From the Revolution to the World Wars. From the First World War to 1942. *Amer.J.Phys.*, 1945, 13: 223-35, 333-46, 2 fig.

Cwe/wt British Isles; France

Cwe-qg for research institutes in physics in the British Isles
see Cavendish Laboratory, 2: 678
National Physical Laboratory, 2: 728

Cwf

FABRY, Charles. Histoire de la physique. In: Histoire de la nation française. Vol. XIV. Histoire des sciences en France, Part 2, p. 167-418. Paris: Plon, 1924.
Reviewed by George Sarton, *Isis*, 1925, 7: 514-16.

Cwf-oq

MUSÉUM NATIONAL D'HISTOIRE NATURELLE. Célébration du centenaire de la chaire de physique du Muséum National d'Histoire Naturelle. *Rev.Gén.Sci.*, 1939, 50: 120-32.

Cwf-qd

SOCIÉTÉ FRANÇAISE DE PHYSIQUE. Le livre du cinquantenaire de la Société. 160 p., fig., pl. Paris: Editions de la Revue d'Optique Théorique et Expérimentale, 1925.

Cwf-qg

BROGLIE, Louis de. L'activité du Centre de théories physiques de l'Institut Henri Poincaré pendant les dernières années. *Experientia*, 1946, 2: 33-6.

Cwg/wh Central Europe

Cwg

DORNER, O.; HAMACHER, J. Vom deutschen Anteil an der physikalischen Forschung. Begründer und Führer der Klassischen Physik. vi, 71 p. Leipzig: Teubner, 1930.
Reviewed by H. Wieleitner, *Mitt.Gesch.Med.*, 1931, 30: 94.

Cwg-cj

SCHIMANK, Hans. Ludwig Wilhelm Gilbert und die Anfänge der *Annalen der Physik*. *Sudhoffs Arch.*, 1963, 47: 360-72.

Cwg-o

TÖPFER, Erich, ed. Ernst Grimsehl und seine Bedeutung für den Physikunterricht; Festschrift zur 100. Wiederkehr seines Geburtstages am 6. August 1961. 72 p., ill., portr. Hamburg: Kommissionsverlag Cram, De Gruyter, 1961.

Cwg-oq

DEUBNER, Alexander. Die Physik an der Berliner Universität von 1910 bis 1960. *Wiss.Z.Humboldt Univ.Berlin Math.Naturwiss.Reihe*, 1960, 9: 85-9.

Cwg-qd

AUS der Geschichte der Berliner Physik. Bildnis-Sammlung zur Feier des 90jährigen Bestehens der Berliner Physikal. Gesellschaft, hrsg. von der Bild- und Filmsammlung Deutscher Physiker. 24 p., 24 portr. Leipzig: Barth, 1935. [CB 45/281]

BRÜCHE, E. Aus der Vergangenheit der Physikalischen Gesellschaft. 1. Vom Magnus-Koloquium und Vereinsgründung. 2. Die ersten 25 Jahre. 3. Die Epoche von Hermann von Helmholtz. 4. An der Schwelle des Jahrhunderts. 5. Die alten Gesellschaftszeitschriften. 6. Die Jahre zwischen Quanten- und Relativitätstheorie. *Phys.Bl.*, 1960, 16: 499-505, 616-20; 1961, 17: 27-33, 120-7, 225-32, 400-10.

FESTSCHRIFT zur Jahrhundertfeier des Physikalischen Vereins dargeboten von den Dozenten seiner Institute. 159 p., ill. Frankfurt a.M.: C. Naumann's Druckerei, 1924.

Cwg-qg

BIERMANN, L. 50 Jahre physikalische Grundlagenforschung in der Kaiser-Wilhelm-Gesellschaft und der Max-Planck-Gesellschaft. *Naturwissenschaften*, 1961, 48: (1), 2-10.

RITSCHL, Rudolf. Überblick über die Forschungsarbeit des 1. Physikalischen Instituts der Humboldt Universität seit 1949. *Wiss.Z.Humboldt Univ.Berlin Math.Naturwiss.Reihe*, 1960, 9: 91-7.

Cwg-vm

STARK, Johannes; MÜLLER, Wilhelm. Jüdische und deutsche Physik. Vorträge zur Eröffnung des Kolloquiums für theoretische Physik an der Universität München. 56 p. Leipzig: Helingsche Verlagsanstalt, 1941.
Reviewed by Zaunick, *Mitt.Gesch.Med.*, 1940, 39: 319.

Cwh

PIECH, Tadeusz. [Histoire du développement de la physique en Pologne. (In Polish with summary in French)]. 45 p. (Polska Akademia Umiejetności, Historia Nauki Polskiej Monografiach, 3) Cracow: 1948.

POGÁNY, Bela. Le développement de la physique en Hongrie. (7th International Congress of Historical Sciences, Warsaw, 1933). *Bull.Int.Comm.Hist.Sci.*, 1933, 5: no. 19, 292-7.

ZEMPLÉN, Jolán M. A magyarországi fizika története 1711-ig. [History of physics in Hungary up to 1711. (In Hungarian)] 317 p., notes. Budapest: Akadémiai Kiadó, 1961.
Reviewed by L. Vekerdi, *Isis*, 1963, 54: 488-90.

Cwi Italy

IVANENKO, D.D. Fizicheskaia nauka Italii. [Physical science in Italy. (In Russian)]. *Usp.Fiz.Nauk*, 1957, 62: 523-7. English transl. in *Advances Phys.Sci.*, 1960, 62: 645-72.

Cwk Low Countries

Cwk-oq

JACKSON, L.C. The University of Leyden. Contributions to physics and chemistry. *Nature*, 1941, 147: 163-4.

Cwk-qd

NEVE DE MEVERGNIES, M. La Société Belge de Physique (1950-1960). *Mouvement Sci.Belg.*, 1961, 4: 285-6.

Cwk-qg

BURGER, D. Het natuurkundig laboratorium van Philips bestaat veertig jaar. [Forty years of the Philips physics laboratory. (In Dutch)] *Faraday*, 1953-54, 23: 132.

CASIMIR, H.B.G. Some main lines of 50 years of Philips research in physics. *Philips Tech.Rev.*, 1962-63, 24: 341-52.

Cwn Russia

IVANENKO, D.D. Early years of Soviet physics. *Act.VIIIe Congr.Int.Hist.Sci.* (Florence, 1956), p. 265-8. Paris: Hermann, 1958.

SHPOL'SKII, E.V. Sorok let sovetskoi fiziki. [Forty years of Soviet physics. (In Russian)]. *Usp.Fiz.Nauk*, 1957, 63: 461-501. English transl. in *Advances Phys.Sci.*, 1960, 63: 625-77. [CB 88/644]
Review of the progress of physics in Russia, 1917-1957.

Cwn-ce-bv

LUKOMSKAYA, A.M. Bibliografiia otechestvennoi literatury po matematike i fizike. Obzor bibliograficheskikh istochnikov. [Bibliography of Russian literature of mathematics and physics. Survey of bibliographical sources. (In Russian)] Pod redaktsiei V.I. Smirnova. 155 p. Moscow: Izdatel'stvo Akademii Nauk S.S.S.R., 1961.

Cwn-cj

RADOVSKII, M.I. V.K. Lebedinskii - redaktor fizicheskikh zhurnalov (k 25-letiiu so dnia smerti). [V.K. Lebedinskii - editor of physics journals (on the twentyfifth anniversary of his death). (In Russian)] *Usp.Fiz.Nauk*, 1962, 73: 345-51.

Cwn-qg

SKOBEL'TSYN, D.V.; FRANK, I.M. Fizicheskii Institut imeni P.N. Lebedeva Akademii S.S.S.R. [The P.N. Lebedev Physical Institute of the U.S.S.R. Academy of Sciences, 1934-1957. (In Russian)] *Usp.Fiz.Nauk,* 1957, 63: 503-25; English translation in *Advances Phys.Sci.,* 1960, 63: 678-712.

Cx techniques and instruments

PACOTTE, Julien. La pensée technique. ii, 156 p. (Bibliothèque de Philosophie Contemporaine) Paris: Alcan, 1931. [CB 33/396]

Cxb

CAJORI, Florian. A history of physics in its elementary branches: including the evolution of physical laboratories. Rev. and enl. ed. xiii, 424 p. New York: Macmillan, 1929.

Cxd

ALPERT, Daniel. Ultrahigh vacuum: a survey. *Phys.Today,* 1963, 16: no. 8, 22-31.

BRIDGMAN, Percy Williams. The physics of high pressure. New impression with supplement. vii, 398 p. (International Textbooks of Exact Sciences) London: Bell, 1949.
First published 1931.

PAUL, William; WARSCHAUER, Douglas M.; ed. Solids under pressure. With a chapter by P.W. Bridgman. xvii, 478 p., ill., bibliogr. New York: McGraw-Hill, 1963. [CB 89/582]

Cxk

GUNTHER, Robert William Theodore. Early science in Oxford. Pt. 3 and 4. Physics and surveying. 222 p., ill. Oxford: Privately printed, 1923.
Bound up with Parts 1 and 2 as Volume 1.
Reviewed by G. Sarton, *Isis,* 1924, 6: 449-53.

WHITE, Frederick A. The role of instrumentation in the evolution of modern physics. *Proc.10th Int.Congr.Hist.Sci.* (Ithaca, 1962), (1), p. 457-9. Paris: Hermann, 1964.

Cxk-by

BELL, Raymond A. Apparatus of historical interest. *Amer.J. Phys.,* 1950, 18: 53.
Apropos of physics apparatus (chiefly from 19th cent.) at Washington and Jefferson College, Washington, Pa.

TANDBERG, J.G. Die Triewaldsche Sammlung am physikalischen Institut der Universität zu Lund und die Originalluftpumpe Guerickes. *Lunds Univ.Årsskr.Avd. 2, new ser.,* 1920, 16: no. 9, 31 p. [CB 11/415]

Cxm

RUSSO, François. La définition des grandeurs physiques. *Rev. Quest.Sci.,* 1956, 17: 485-96.

Cxq

GLIOZZI, Mario. Le origini della fisica sperimentale: la determinazione del peso specifico dell'aria. *Period.Mat.,* 1931, 11: 1-10. [CB 40/401]

IRVING, H. The applications of floating equilibrium to the determination of density. *Sci.Progr.,* 1937, 31: 654-5.
Historical review.

CA FUNDAMENTAL PHYSICS

BLOCH, Léon. Les théories newtoniennes et la physique moderne. *Rev.Métaphys.Morale,* 1928, 35: 41-54.

EDDINGTON, Arthur Stanley. Fundamental theory. viii, 292 p. Cambridge University Press, 1946.
Reviewed by E.A. Milne, *Nature,* 1947, 159: 486-8; by A.J. Coleman, *Science,* 1947, 106: 226.

FLÜGGE, S. Beugungsprobleme der Physik. *Scientia,* 1952, 87: 165-9; French transl., suppl., 83-7.

GRIGORIAN, A.T., ed. Einshtein i razvitie fiziko-matematicheskoi mysli. Sbornik statei. [Einstein and the development of physico-mathematical thought. A collection of articles.] 239 p. Moscow: Izdatel'stvo Akademii Nauk SSSR, 1962. [CB 88/642]
Includes English and Russian summaries.

HOOYKAAS, R. The discrimination between "natural" and "artificial" substances and the development of corpuscular theory. *Arch.Int.Hist.Sci.,* 1948, 1: 640-51. Also in *Act.Ve Congr. Int.Hist.Sci.* (Lausanne, 1947), p. 113-24. Paris: Hermann, 1948.

INFELD, Leopold. The world in modern science. Matter and quanta. Transl. from the Polish by Louis Infield. With an introduction by Albert Einstein. 287 p., front., 25 fig. London: Gollancz; New York: Putnam, 1934.
Original Polish edition 1933.

KUZNETSOV, Boris G. Osnovy teorii otnositelnosti i kvantovoi mekhaniki v ikh istorischeskom razvitii. [Fundamentals of the theory of relativity and quantum mechanics in historical development. (In Russian)]. 327 p., fig. Moskva: Izdatelstvo Akademii Nauk SSSR, 1957.

LORENTZ, Hendrik Antoon. Lectures on theoretical physics, delivered at the University of Leiden. Authorised transl. by L. Silberstein and A.P.H. Trivelli. 3 vol. 1. Aether theories and aether models; kinetical problems; 2. Thermodynamics. Entropy and probability. The theory of radiation. The theory of quanta; 3. Maxwell's theory. The principle of relativity for uniform translations. London: Macmillan, 1927-31.
Translation of: Lessen over theoretische natuurkunde. 8 vol. Leiden: Brill, 1919-25.

OPPENHEIMER, J. Robert. The flying trapeze: three crises for physicists. x, 65 p. (Whidden Lectures for 1962) London: Oxford University Press, 1964. [CB 90/622] 438
Three lectures two of which deal with the conceptual transpositions associated with relativity and quantum theory.

ROUGIER, Louis. La matérialisation de l'énergie. Essai sur la théorie de la relativité et sur la théorie des quanta. xii, 148 p., bibliogr. Paris: Gauthier-Villars, 1919.
Summary of the latest physical theorier

SIVADJIAN, Joseph. Oppositions et incompatibilités entre certains principes de la physique relativiste et quantique. *Act.IIe Congr.Int.Phil.Sci.* (Zurich, 1954), (2), p. 86-90. Neuchâtel: Éditions du Griffon, 1955.

WHITTAKER, E.T. A history of the theories of aether and electricity. 2 vol. Rev. ed. 1. The classical theories. xiv, 434 p.; 2. The modern theories, 1900-1926. xii, 319 p. London: Nelson, 1951, 1953; New York: Philosophical Library, 1951, 1954.
First published 1910. Revised edition reprinted by Harper Torchbooks, 1960.
Reviewed in *Isis,* 1914, 2: 222-4 (S. Magrini); 1952, 43: 293-4 (V.F. Lenzen); 1956, 47: 428-30 (P.W. Bridgman); by V.C.A. Ferraro, *Observatory,* 1952, 72: 40-1.

WIEN, W. Vorlesungen über neuere Probleme der theoretischen Physik. Gehalten an der Columbia University in New York im April 1913. iv, 76 p., ill. Leipzig: Teubner, 1913. [CB 5/289]

ZINZEN, A. Die sogenannten Erhaltungssätze der Physik. *Kant-Stud.,* 1954-55, 46: 333-43.

CAkk

KUZNETSOV, Boris G. [Paths of development of quanto-relativistic logic. (In Russian)]. *Tr.Inst.Ist.Est.Tekh.,* 1959, 22: 69-105.

CAks

BRÜLL, Erhard. Erkenntniskritische Grundprobleme der Relativitätstheorie, Quanten- und Wellenmechanik. 66 p. Breslau: Borgmeyer, 1929.

CAm fundamental concepts

BRIDGMAN, Percy Williams. The nature of some of our physical concepts. 64 p. New York: Philosophical Library, 1952. [CB 79/168]
Three lectures first printed in *Brit.J.Phil.Sci.,* 1951, 1: 257-72; 2: 25-44, 142-60.
Reviewed by G.J. Whitrow, *Bull.Brit.Soc.Hist.Sci.,* 1950, 1: 101-4.

HEYL, Paul R. Fundamental concepts in physics in the light of recent discoveries. Abstracts of a series of three public lectures at the Carnegie Institute of Technology on January 6, 7, and 8 [1925]. *Science,* 1925, 61: 221-5.

HOLTSMARK, J. Die Wandlungen des Kontinuumbegriffes in der Physik im Laufe der Zeiten. *Actes du Symposium International, R.J. Bošković* (1961), p. 97-102. Beograd: Stampa Izdaračka Ustanova "Naucno delo", 1962.

JOHNSON, E.H. The evolution of physical concepts. *Sch.Sci. Math.*, 1930, 30: 283-91.

KEMBLE, Edwin C. The philosophical concepts in modern physics. Operational reasoning, reality, and quantum mechanics. *J. Franklin Inst.*, 1938, 225: 263-75.

LODGE, Oliver. Continuity. Address to the British Association for the Advancement of Science. 40 p. Birmingham: 1913.

MILNE, E.A. The fundamental concepts of natural philosophy. *Proc.Roy.Soc.Edinb.*, 1943, 62: 10-24.
James Scott Lecture delivered on May 3, 1943.

REY, Abel. La notion d'objet et l'évolution de la physique contemporaine. *Rev.Phil.*, 1922, 201-42.

WERNICK, Georg. Der Begriff des physikalischen Körpers nach Mach. *Vierteljahrsschr.Wiss.Phil.*, 1915, 5: (39), 82-97.

WHITROW, G.J. Operational analysis and the nature of some physical concepts. *Bull.Brit.Soc.Hist.Sci.*, 1950, 1: 101-4.
Review of Bridgman, Percy Williams. The nature of some of our physical concepts, *see* above.

CAmc time and space

see also under CB RELATIVITY

BENEDICKS, Carl. Space and time: an experimental physicist's conception of these ideas and of their alteration. With an introduction by Sir Oliver Lodge. xiv, 98 p. London: Methuen, 1924.

BOREL, Emile. Space and time. xiv, 234 p. London: Blackie, 1926.

BURGER, D. Mogmaals over ruimte en tijd. [Once again on space and time. (In Dutch)]. *Faraday*, 1954-55, 24: 93-8, 2 fig.

COHN, F. Physikalisches über Raum und Zeit. 2nd ed. 24 p. (*Naturwissenschaftliche Vorträge und Schriften*, hrsg. von der Berliner *Urania*, 6) Leipzig: Teubner, 1913

COSTA DE BEAUREGARD, Olivier. La notion du temps: équivalence avec l'espace. 208 p. (Actualités Scientifiques et Industrielles, 1300) Paris: Hermann, 1963.
Reviewed by W. Voisé, *Arch.Int.Hist.Sci.*, 1964, 16: 75-6.

GRÜNBAUM, Adolf. Philosophical problems of space and time. xii, 448 p., bibliogr. (Borzoi Books in the Philosophy of Science) New York: Knopf, 1963.
Reviewed by Heinz R. Post, *Isis*, 1964, 55: 449-50; by Stephen Toulmin, *N.Y.Rev.Books*, 1964, 2: no. 3, 8-9; by O. Costa de Beauregard, *Arch.Int.Hist.Sci.*, 1964, 17: 311-14.

HOLMES, Eugene C. The main philosophical considerations of space and time. *Amer.J.Phys.*, 1950, 18: 560-70.

LAPAN, Arthur. On space and time as attributes of nature and forms of experience. *Phil.Sci.*, 1936, 3: 9-18.

MÜLLER, Georg. Seinszeit und Gegenwartszeit, Zeitraum und Weltraum. *Phil.Natur.*, 1964, 8: 90-108.

PETROVIĆ, Mikhail. Durées physiques indépendantes des dimensions spatiales. 28 p. Zurich: Jean Frey, 1924.

POIRIER, René. Essai sur quelques caractères des notions d'espace et de temps. 387 p. Paris: Vrin, 1931.
Reviewed by A. Koschewnikoff, *Deut.Lit.Zeitung*, 1933, 4: 12-17.

REICHENBACH, Hans. The philosophy of space and time. Transl. by Maria Reichenbach and John Freund: with introductory remarks by Rudolf Carnap. xvi, 295 p., fig. New York: Dover Publications, 1957; reprinted 1959. 464
Reviewed by H. Dopp, *Rev.Quest.Sci.*, 1959, 20: 617-18.
Translation of: Philosophie der Raum-Zeit-Lehre. Berlin/Leipzig: Walter de Gruyter, 1928; reviewed by Albert Einstein, *Deut.Lit.Zeitung*, 1928, 19-20.

REISER, Oliver L. Time, space and "Gestalt". *Phil.Sci.*, 1934, 1: 197-223.

ROBB, Alfred Arthur. A theory of time and space. vi, 373 p. Cambridge University Press, 1914.

CAmc-c

GENT, Werner. Die Philosophie des Raumes und der Zeit. Historische, kritische und analytische Untersuchungen. Die Geschichte der Begriffe des Raumes und der Zeit von Aristoteles bis zum vorkritischen Kant (1768). xii, 273 p. Bonn: Cohen, 1926. [CB 22/261]

GENT, Werner. Die Raum-Zeit-Philosophie des 19. Jahrhunderts. Historische, kritische und analytische Untersuchungen. Die Geschichte der Begriffe des Raumes und der Zeit vom kritischen Kant bis zur Gegenwart. xii, 397 p. Bonn: Cohen, 1930.

SCHNEIDER, Ilse. Das Raum-Zeit-Problem bei Kant und Einstein. iii, 75 p. Berlin: Springer, 1921. [CB 70/255]

CAmc-mzBkk

BURKE, John Butler. The emergence of life. Being a treatise on mathematical philosophy and symbolic logic by which a new theory of space and time is evolved. viii, 396 p. London: Oxford University Press, 1931.
Reviewed by H.T. Davis, *Isis*, 1933, 19: 214-17.

CAmd time

COSTA DE BEAUREGARD, Olivier. La part de la convention dans la définition physique et la mesure du temps. *Rev.Quest. Sci.*, 1948, 9: 481-95.

DINGLE, Herbert. The function of time measurement in modern physics. (With French summary) *Arch.Inst.Int.Sci.Théor. Sér.A Bull.Acad.Int.Phil.Sci.*, 3. Problèmes de philosophie des sciences 3. Théories nouvelles de relativité, p. 32-56. Discussion, p. 57-69. (Actualités Scientifiques et Industrielles, 1065) Paris: Hermann, 1949.

GUILLAUME, Edouard. La question du temps d'après M. Bergson. *Rev.Gén.Sci.*, 1922, 33: 573-82.
Apropos of Bergson's "Durée et simultanéité", *see* CBze-k.

SCHLEGEL, Richard. Time and the physical world. xii, 211 p. East Lansing: Michigan State University Press, 1961.
Reviewed by G.J. Whitrow, *Isis*, 1963, 54: 407-8; and in *Sci.Amer.*, 1962, 206: no. 6, 196.

CAme space

BACHELARD, Gaston. L'expérience de l'espace dans la physique contemporaine. 141 p. Paris: Alcan, 1937.

CARNAP, Rudolf. Der Raum. Ein Beitrag zur Wissenschaftslehre. 87 p., bibliogr. (*Kant Stud.* Ergänzungshefte, 56) Berlin: Reuther und Reichard, 1922.

DESTOUCHES, Jean Louis. Les récent progrès dans la notion d'espace physique. *Thalès*, 1936, 3: 85-9.

DINGLER, Hugo. Das Problem des absoluten Raumes in historisch-kritischer Behandlung. 50 p. Leipzig: Hirzel, 1923.

FREUDENTHAL, Hans. De ruimteopvatting in de exacte wetenschappen van Kant tot heden. [Conceptions of space in the exact sciences from Kant to the present. (In Dutch)]. *Euclides*, 1955-56, 31: 165-82.

GOULD, James A. The concept of absolute space. *J.Hist.Ideas*, 1961, 22: 119-20.

JAMMER, Max. Concepts of space. The history of theories of space in physics. With a foreword by Albert Einstein. xvi, 196 p. Cambridge, Mass.: Harvard University Press, 1954.
Reviewed by V.F. Lenzen, *Isis*, 1955, 46: 287-9; by Jean Itard, *Scr.Math.*, 1955, 21: 289-90; by Per Collinder, *Lychnos*, 1956, 395.
Reprinted with addition of preface and appendix. New York: Harper Torchbooks, 1960 [CB 86/462].

JAMMER, Max. Des Problem des Raumes. Die Entwicklung der Raumtheorien. 220 p. Darmstadt: Wissenschaftliche Buchgesellschaft, 1960.
German translation of "Concepts of space", *see* above.
Reviewed by N. Stuloff, *Sudhoffs Arch.*, 1963, 47: 83-4.

KAPP, Reginald O. Space. *Brit.J.Phil.Sci.*, 1959, 37: 1-15.

KAULBACH, Friedrich. Das Raumproblem bei Kant und in der modernen Physik. *Phil.Natur.*, 1961, 6: 349-63.

MEYER, Heinrich. Raumstrukturen und Erkenntnisfragen. *Stud. Gen.*, 1958, 11: 237-53.

NICOD, Jean. La géométrie des sensations de mouvement. *Rev. Métaphys.Morale*, 1921, 28: 537-43. [CB 13/290]

POPPOVICH, Nikola M. Die Lehre vom diskreten Raum in der neueren Philosophie. 89 p. Wien: Braumüller, 1922. [CB 14/559]

SCHOPPER, H. Symmetrieprinzipien und Naturgesetze. *Naturwissenschaften*, 1963, 50: 205-11. [CB 89/582]
General review of discussions connected with symmetry principles and the related question of the structure of physical space.

SHAPERE, Dudley. The causal efficacy of space. *Phil.Sci.*, 1964, 31: 111-21.

WAERDEN, B.L. van der. Over de ruimte. [Concerning space. (In Dutch)]. 18 p. Groningen-Djakarta: Noordhoff, 1950.
Inaugural lecture of the professorship in mathematics at the University of Amsterdam. Historical discussion of the concept of space.

WHITROW, G.J. Why physical space has three dimensions. *Brit. J.Phil.Sci.*, 1955-56, 6: 13-31.

CAmj forces and fields

DUGAS, René. Vicissitudes de la notion de force. *Rev.Sci.*, 1946, 84: 456-61.

HESSE, Mary B. Forces and fields. The concept of action at a distance in the history of physics. x, 318 p. Edinburgh: Thomas Nelson and Sons, Ltd., 1961; New York: Philosophical Library, 1962.
For reviews *see* CB 88/542 and CB 89/501.

LANDAU, L.D.; LIFSHITZ, E.M. The classical theory of fields. Transl. by Morton Hamermesh. Rev. 2nd ed. 404 p. London: Pergamon Press, 1962.
Reviewed by B.E.J. Pagel, *Observatory*, 1963, 83: 84.
Translation from Russian of: Teorii polia. 2nd edition 1948; first published Moscow: 1941; 4th edition 1962.

STROMBACH, Werner. Der Kraftbegriff. *Phil.Natur.*, 1964, 8: 307-47.
Its interpretations from antiquity to the end of the 17th century.

TONNELAT, Marie-Antoinette. De l'idée de milieu à la notion de champ. *Arch.Int.Hist.Sci.*, 1959, 12: 337-56.

TONNELAT, Marie-Antoinette. L'évolution de la notion de force du 17e au 20e siècle. *Act.VIIe Congr.Int.Hist.Sci.* (Jerusalem, 1953), p. 610-14. Paris: Hermann, [n.d.].

TRUESDELL, C.; TOUPIN, R.A. The classical field theories. In: Handbuch der Physik, Encyclopedia of Physics, ed. by S. Flügge. Vol. 3, part 1. Principles of classical mechanics and field theory, p. 226-793. Berlin: Springer Verlag, 1960. [CB 86/463]

ULLMO, Jean. Les prolongements modernes de l'histoire de la notion de force. 21 p. (Les Conférences du Palais de la Découverte, D 13) Paris: Université de Paris, 1952.

CAmk mass, energy and momentum

BELL, A.E. The concept of energy. *Nature*, 1943, 151: 519-23, 3 fig.

BROWN, G. Burniston. Gravitational and inertial mass. *Amer. J.Phys.*, 1960, 28: 475-83. [CB 86/462]

BRUNOLD, Charles. Histoire abrégée des théories physiques concernant la matière et l'énergie. 48 p. Paris: Masson, 1952.
Reviewed by Madeleine Courtin, *Rev.Hist.Sci.*, 1952, 5: 281-2.

DUNGEN, F.H. van den. Sur la notion de masse. *Bull.Acad.Roy. Belg.Cl.Sci.*, 1947, 31: 666-8.

FLASCHNER, Ludwig. Zur ontologischen Begründung der Massbegriffe und Gesetze in Mechanik und Elektrizitätslehre. *Phil.Natur.*, 1952, 2: 137-77, 2 tables.

HOPPE, Edmund. Der Begriff Masse. *Arch.Gesch.Math.Naturwiss. Tech.*, 1929, 11: 351-63.

HORN, Carl. Goethe als Energetiker, verglichen mit den Energetikern Robert Mayer, Ottomar Rosenbach, Ernst Mach. 91 p. Leipzig: J.A. Barth, 1914.

JAMMER, Max. Concepts of mass in classical and modern physics. x, 230 p. Cambridge, Mass.: Harvard University Press, 1961.
Reviewed by C. Truesdell, *Isis*, 1963, 54: 290-1; for other reviews *see* CB 88/543 and CB 89/501.

PIGGOTT, H.E. Some ideas on energy and momentum. *Math.Gaz.*, 1934, 18: 228-44. [CB 44/516]

SCHIMANK, H. Geschichte des Energieprinzips. *Beitr.Gesch. Tech.Ind.*, 1930, 20: 31-46, 5 fig.

SCHURUPOW, A. Masse und Energie. *Deut.Z.Phil.*, 1960, 8: no. 7, 880-2.

WALDEN, Paul. Materie und Energie. *Chem.Zeitung*, 1933, 57: 813-14.

CAmk-nh

HUNTINGTON, Edward V. Bibliographical note on the use of the word mass in current textbooks. *Amer.Math.Mon.*, 1918, 25: 1-15.

CAmk-op

BARTON, Vola P. The presentation of mass to the undergraduate. *Amer.J.Phys.*, 1946, 14: 328-31.

CB RELATIVITY

AMADUZZI, Lavoro. Le principe de relativité. *Scientia*, 1918, 24: 239-43, 321-36. [CB 9/491]

BECQUEREL, Jean. Exposé élémentaire de la théorie d'Einstein et de sa généralisation; suivi d'un appendice à l'usage des mathématiciens. 260 p., 17 fig. Paris: Payot, 1922. [CB 13/292]

BERGMAN, Peter G. Fifty years of relativity. *Science*, 1956, 123: 487-94, portr.
A history.

BIRKHOFF, George David. The origin, nature and influence of relativity. Lowell Institute Lectures, Boston, and Los Angeles Lectures, University of California, Southern Branch. ix, 185 p. New York: Macmillan, 1925.

BIRKHOFF, George David; LANGER, R.E. Relativity and modern physics. xi, 283 p. Cambridge, Mass.: Harvard University Press, 1923.
Reviewed by H.P. Manning, *Amer.Math.Mon.*, 1925, 32: 185-201.

BOLTON, Lyndon. An introduction to the theory of relativity. xi, 177 p. London: Methuen, 1921.

BORN, Max. Einstein's theory of relativity. Translated by H.L. Brose. 135 diagr., portr. London: Methuen, 1924.
Revised edition, prepared with the collaboration of Gunther Leibfried and Walter Biem. New York: Dover; London: Constable, 1962.
1st ed. Publ. 1920. 2nd German ed. Berlin: Springer, 1921.

BOUASSE, H. La question préalable contre la théorie d'Einstein. *Scientia*, 1923, 33: 13-25. [CB 14/554]

BRIDGMAN, Percy Williams. A sophisticate's primer of relativity. Prologue and epilogue by Adolf Grünbaum. vii, 191 p. Middletown, Conn.: Wesleyan University Press, 1962.

BROSE, Henry L. The theory of relativity. An introductory sketch based on Einstein's original writings. 32 p. Oxford: Blackwell, 1919.

BURALI-FORTI, Cesare; BOGGIO, Tommaso. Espaces courbes. Critique de la relativité. xxiv, 255 p. Torino: Sten, 1924.

CAMPBELL, Norman Robert. Modern electrical theory. Supplementary chapters. 16. Relativity. 124 p. Cambridge: 1923.

RELATIVITY

CARLEBACH, J. *See* CDzi

CARMICHAEL, Robert D. The theory of relativity. 2nd ed. rev. and enl. 112 p. (Mathematical Monographs, 12) New York: Wiley, 1920.

CARMICHAEL, Robert D., *et al.* A debate on the theory of relativity. With an introduction by William Lowe Bryan. viii, 154 p. Chicago: Open Court, 1927. [CB 23/241]

COLEMAN, James A. Relativity for the layman. A simplified account of the history, theory, and proofs of relativity. 131 p., 24 fig. New York: William-Frederick Press, 1954; also published New York: New American Library, 1958; reprinted 1962.

CUNNINGHAM, Ebenezer. The principle of relativity. xiv, 221 p. Cambridge University Press, 1914.

CUNNINGHAM, Ebenezer. Relativity, the electron theory and gravitation. 2nd ed. of 'Relativity and the electron theory' (1914). vii, 148 p. (Monographs on Physics) London: Longmans, Green, 1921.

DONDER, Théophile de. Au-delà de la relativité. *Flambeau,* July 1929, 14 p.

EDDINGTON, Arthur Stanley. The mathematical theory of relativity. ix, 247 p. Cambridge University Press, 1923.
2nd ed. ix, 270 p. Cambridge University Press, 1924.
1st ed. reviewed by Philip Franklin, *Amer.Math.Mon.,* 1924, 31: 444-7.

EDDINGTON, Arthur Stanley. Relativitätstheorie in mathematischer Behandlung. Transl. and ed. by Alex. Ostrowski and Harry Schmidt with appendix: Eddingtons Theorie und Hamiltonsches Prinzip von Albert Einstein. xiv, 377 p. Berlin: Springer, 1925.
Reviewed by H. Thirring, *Deut.Lit.Zeitung,* 1926, 2058-60.
Translation of: The mathematical theory of relativity, *see* above.

EDDINGTON, Arthur Stanley. Space, time and gravitation. An outline of the general relativity theory. vii, 218 p. Cambridge University Press, 1920. [CB 10/199]
Reprinted New York: Harper Brothers, 1959.
German translation Braunschweig: F. Vieweg, 1923.

EDDINGTON, Arthur Stanley. The theory of relativity and its influence on scientific thought. (Romanes Lectures, 1922) 32 p. Oxford: Clarendon Press, 1922.

EDDINGTON, Arthur Stanley. Vues générales sur la théorie de la relativité. Traduction autorisée accompagnée d'une étude sur l'oeuvre d'Eddington et de notes par Thomas Greenwood. xxiv, 102 p. Paris: Gauthier-Villars, 1924.

FUBINI, Guido. Sul valore della teoria di Einstein. *Scientia,* 1924, 35: 85-92; French translation, ibid., suppl., 21-8. [CB 16/316]

FÜNFZIG Jahre Relativitätstheorie. Cinquantenaire de la Théorie de la Relativité. Jubilee of Relativity theory. Proceedings [of Conference at Berne, 11-16 July 1955] ed. by André Mercier and Michel Kervaire. 286 p. (*Helv.Phys. Acta,* Suppl. 4) Basel: Birkhauser Verlag, 1956.
Reviewed by W.H. McCrea, *Nature,* 1955, 176: 330; by Banesh Hoffmann, *Scr.Math.,* 1959, 24: 164.

GRAEF FERNANDEZ, Carlos. My tilt with Albert Einstein [as related to Samuel Kaplan]. *Amer.Scient.,* 1956, 44: 204-11.
A letter from Professor Graef Fernandez describing a discussion he had with Einstein concerning Birkhoff's theory of relativity.

GUILLAUME, Edouard. Les bases de la théorie de la relativité. *Rev.Gén.Sci.,* 1920, 31: 200-10.
(I) La mécanique newtonienne; (II) La théorie limitée; (III) La théorie générale.

HALDANE, Richard Burdon, *Viscount.* The reign of relativity. xxiii, 430 p. London: Murray, 1921.
French translation Paris: Gauthier-Villars, 1922.

HENDERSON, Archibald; HOBBS, Allan Wilson; LASLEY, John Wayne. The theory of relativity: studies and contributions. xiii, 99 p., 7 fig. Chapel Hill, N.C.: The University of North Carolina Press, 1924.

HOROVITZ, Karl. Die geschichtliche Entwicklung des physikalischen Relativitätsgedanken. *Arch.Gesch.Naturwiss.Tech.,* 1914, 5: 251-65.

KATSH, Abraham I. Einstein's theory of relativity. [In Hebrew] 60 p., portr. Tel Aviv: 1936.
Reviewed by Daniel Norman, *Isis,* 1938, 29: 132-3.

KOTTLER, Friedrich. Considérations de critique historique sur la théorie de la relativité. 1. De Fresnel à Lorentz; 2. Henri Poincaré et Albert Einstein. *Scientia,* 1924, 36: 231-42, 301-16.

LAUE, Max von. Einstein und die Relativätstheorie. *Naturwissenschaften,* 1956, 43: 1-8; reprinted in *Abhandl.Fritz Haber Inst.Max Planck Ges.,* 1956, vol. 33.
Reviewed by L. Marton, *Phys.Today,* 1958, 11: no. 5, 39-40.

LAUE, Max von. Die Relativitätstheorie. 2 vol. 1. Das Relativititätsprinzip der Lorentz-transformation. 4th enl. ed. xiii, 302 p., ill. 2. Die allgemeine Relativitätstheorie und Einsteins Lehre von der Schwerkraft. 2nd rev. ed. xii, 290 p. (Die Wissenschaft, 38, 68) Braunschweig: Vieweg, 1921, 1923.
French translation Paris: 1924.

LORENTZ, Hendrik Antoon. The Einstein theory of relativity, a concise statement. 64 p. New York: Brentano, 1920.
First published in *Nieuwe Rotterdamsche Courant,* 19 Nov. 1919.

LYNCH, Arthur. The case against Einstein. xxx, 275 p. London: Allan, 1932.
Reviewed by T.G., *Nature,* 1933, 131: 260.

MERCIER, André. Fifty years of the theory of relativity. *Nature,* 1955, 175: 919-21.

MILNE, E.A. Kinematic relativity. vi, 238 p. (International Series of Monographs on Physics) Oxford: Clarendon Press, 1948.

MILNE, E.A. Kinematic relativity. (With French summary) *Arch. Inst.Int.Sci.Théor.Sér.A Bull.Acad.Int.Phil.Sci.,* 3. Problèmes de philosophie des sciences, 3, Théories nouvelles de relativité, p. 7-32. Discussion, p. 57-69. (Actualités Scientifiques et Industrielles, 1065) Paris: Hermann, 1949.

MILNE, E.A. Relativity, gravitation and world structure. viii, 365 p. Oxford University Press, 1935. 552
Reviewed by H.T. Davis, *Isis,* 1936, 26: 215-18.

MOCH, Gaston. La relativité des phénomènes. 370 p., ill. Paris: Flammarion, 1922. [CB 13/294]

MÜLLER, Aloys. Der Gegenstand der Mathematik mit besonderer Beziehung auf die Relativitätstheorie. vi, 94 p., ill. Braunschweig: Vieweg, 1922.

PALATINI, Attilio. La teoria di relatività nel suo sviluppo storico. *Scientia,* 1919, 26: 195-207, 277-89.

PAULI, Wolfgang. Relativitätstheorie. In: *Encyklopädie der mathematischen Wissenschaften,* vol. 5, pt. 2, no. 19, p. 539-775. Leipzig: Teubner, 1921.
Reviewed by J. Einstein, *Naturwissenschaften,* 1922, 184.

PAULI, Wolfgang. Theory of relativity. Transl. by G. Field [from the article "Relativitätstheorie" in *Encyklopädie der mathematischen Wissenschaften,* vol. V19. (Leipzig: Teubner, 1921)] with supplementary notes by the author. xiv, 241 p. London/New York: Pergamon Press, 1958.
Reviewed by Banesh Hoffmann, *Scr.Math.,* 1959, 24: 244-5; for other reviews *see* CB 85/467 and CB 86/503.

RELATIVITY. (*Nature* Special Number). *Nature,* 1921, 106: 781-813. [CB 10/200]

RICE, James. Relativity, a systematic treatment of Einstein's theory. 389 p. London: Longmans, Green, 1923.
Reviewed by James Pierpont, *Amer.Math.Mon.,* 1924, 31: 395-8.

ROBINSON, L.; SCHILD, A.; SCHUCKING, E. *See* CDzg

RUSSELL, Bertrand. The ABC of relativity. Revised edition ed. by Felix Pirani. 144 p., fig. New York: New American Library of World Literature, Inc., 1959
An unaltered reprint of the revised edition of 1958.
First published London/New York: 1925. German translation Munich: 1928.

RUSSELL, Henry Norris. Modifying our ideas of nature: the Einstein theory of relativity. (Princeton Lectures, 2) Princeton, N.J.: 1920; reprinted, *Annu.Rep.Smithsonian Inst. for 1921*, p. 197-211. Washington, D.C.: U.S. Government Printing Office, 1922.

SCHAFFERS, V. La relativité comme théorie physique. *Rev. Quest.Sci.*, 1925, 88: 343-98.

SESMAT, Augustin. Les systèmes privilégiés de la physique relativiste. Exposé méthodique et critique des théories d'Einstein. 449 p. (Actualités Scientifiques et Industrielles, 7) Paris: Hermann, 1936.
Reviewed by Jules Géhéniau, *Isis*, 1940, 31: 478-9.

SILBERSTEIN, Ludwik. The theory of relativity. 2nd ed. enl. x, 563 p. London: Macmillan, 1924. [CB 18/610]
First published 1914.
Reviewed in *Nature*, 1925, 115: 409.

STAROSSELSKAIA-NIKITINA, O.A. La contribution de Paul Langevin à la théorie rélativiste et sa portée historique. *Act.VIIIe Congr.Int.Hist.Sci.*(Florence, 1956), (1), p. 178-82. Paris: Hermann, 1958

STEINMETZ, Charles Proteus. Four lectures on relativity and space. x, 126 p., ill. New York: McGraw-Hill, 1923.

TOLMAN, Richard Chace. Relativity, thermodynamics and cosmology. xv, 502 p. (International Series of Monographs on Physics) Oxford: Clarendon Press, 1934.
Reviewed by Enos E. Witmer, *Phil.Sci.*, 1935, 2: 262-5.

TOLMAN, Richard Chace. The theory of the relativity of motion. ix, 225 p. Berkeley: University of California Press, 1917.
Historical survey at the beginning.

TONINI, V. La relatività a cinquant'anni dalla prima formulazione einsteiniana. *Scientia*, 1955, 49: 283-90.

WHITEHEAD, Alfred North. The principle of relativity with applications to physical science. xii, 190 p. Cambridge University Press, 1922.

CBc-bv

COMBRIDGE, J.T., comp. Bibliography of relativity and gravitation theory, 1921 to 1937. 1707 items, unpaged. London: King's College, 1965.
Mimeographed.

CBdaj

LORENTZ, Hendrik Antoon, et al. The principle of relativity: a collection of original memoirs on the special and general theory of relativity, by H.A. Lorentz, A. Einstein, H. Minkowski and H. Weyl. With notes by A. Sommerfeld. Transl. by W. Perrett and G.B. Jeffery. viii, 216 p., 7 diagr. London: Methuen, 1923.
Reprinted, New York: Dover, 1952.

CBhd

LAFUMA, Henri. Florilège Einsteinien. *Merc.France*, 1 janv. 1924, 33-59; 15 janv. 1924, 329-52. [CB 16/316]
A critical study of popular French accounts of Einstein's theories.

CBhf

CARR, H. Wildon. The general principle of relativity in its philosophical and historical aspect. x, 165 p. London: Macmillan, 1920.

CARUS, Paul. The principle of relativity as a phase in the development of science. *Monist*, 1913, 23: 417-22

HOLTON, Gerald. On the thematic analysis of science: the case of Poincaré and relativity. *Proc.10th Int.Congr.Hist.Sci.* (Ithaca, 1962), (2), p. 797-800. Paris: Hermann, 1964.

McCREA, W.H. The evolution of theories of space-time and mechanics. *Phil.Sci.*, 1939, 6: 137-62.

CBj

GEHRCKE, Ernst. Die Massensuggestion der Relativitätstheorie. Kulturhistorisch-psychologische Dokumente. viii, 108 p., ill. Berlin: Hermann Meusser, 1924.
Extracts dealing with Einstein and his theory from newspapers of various countries.

CBk philosophy and methodology

BARNETT, Lincoln. The universe and Dr. Einstein. 127 p., 4 pl., fig. New York: William Sloane Associates, 1948. [CB 75/89]

CASSIRER, Ernst. Substance and function and Einstein's theory of relativity. Authorized translation by William C. and Marie C. Swabey. xii, 465 p. Chicago: Open Court, 1923.
Reviewed by Henry M. Sheffer, *Isis*, 1924, 6: 439-40.
Reprinted, New York: Dover, 1953. [CB 80/117]

DRIESCH, Hans. Relativitätstheorie und Weltanschauung. 2nd ed. viii, 106 p. Leipzig: Quelle und Meyer, 1930.
First publ. 1924 under the title "Relativitätstheorie und Philosophie".

FEUER, Lewis S. Philosophy and the theory of relativity. *Sci. Soc.*, 1947, 11: 259-69.
Apropos of Philipp Frank's biography of Einstein (New York: 1947).

FRANK, Philipp. Relativity, a richer truth. xvi, 142 p. Boston: Beacon Press, 1950. [CB 79/168]

GUILLAUME, Édouard. La théorie de la relativité et sa signification. *Rev.Métaphys.Morale*, 1920, 27: 423-69. [CB 13/293]

HÖFFDING, Harald. La relativité philosophique. Traduit du danois par J. de Coussange. vii, 293 p. Paris: Alcan, 1924.

LIPSIUS, Friedrich Reinhard. Wahrheit und Irrtum in der Relativitätstheorie. v, 154 p. Tübingen: J.C.B. Mohr, 1927. [CB 24/527]
Reviewed by Kurt Grelling, *Deut.Lit.Zeitung*, 1927, 2564-8.

MÜLLER, Aloys. Die philosophischen Probleme der Einsteinschen Relativitätstheorie. 2nd rev. ed. of "Das Problem des absoluten Raumes". viii, 224 p., fig. (Die Wissenschaft, 39) Braunschweig: Vieweg, 1922.

CBke

CORNÉLISSEN, Christian. Les hallucinations des Einsteiniens, ou les erreurs de méthode chez les physiciens-mathématiciens. xiii, 86 p. Paris: Blanchard, 1923.

WRINCH, Dorothy. The theory of relativity in relation to scientific method. *Nature*, 1922, 109: 381-2.

CBkg

MEYERSON, Emile. La déduction relativiste. xvi, 396 p. Paris: Payot, 1925.
Reviewed by Hélène Metzger, *Isis*, 1925, 7: 517-20.

CBkk

DINGLER, Hugo. Physik und Hypothese. Versuch einer induktiven Wissenschaftslehre nebst einer kritischen Analyse der Fundamente der Relativitätstheorie. xi, 200 p. Berlin/ Leipzig: Vereinigung wissenschaftlicher Verleger, 1921.
Reviewed by H.M. Sheffer, *Isis*, 1922, 4: 385.

KOPFF, A. I fondamenti della relatività einsteiniana. Edizione italiana per cura di R. Contu e T. Bembo, aggiuntivi due studi di G. Castelnuovo e T. Levi-Civita, scritti sul valore e le interpretazioni della teoria di Aliotta, ecc. xxx, 476 p. Milano: Hoepli, 1923.

MOHOROVIČIĆ, Stjepan. Die Einsteinsche Relativitätstheorie und ihr mathematischer, physikalischer und philosophischer Charakter. 77 p. Berlin: W. de Gruyter, 1923. [CB 16/317]

SEVERI, F. Elementi logici e psicologici dei principi di relatività. Esame delle obiezioni d'ordine generale contro la relatività del tempo. *Scientia*, 1925, 37: 1-10, 77-86; French transl. suppl., 1-10, 15-24.

CBks

ELSBACH, Alfred C. Kant und Einstein. Untersuchungen über das Verhältnis der modernen Erkenntnistheorie zur Relativitätstheorie. viii, 374 p. Berlin: Walter de Gruyter, 1924. [CB 18/610]
Reviewed by Henry M. Sheffer, *Isis*, 1924, 6: 573-4.

WIEN, Wilhelm. Die Relativitätstheorie vom Standpunkte der Physik und Erkenntnislehre. Vortrag. 36 p. Leipzig: Barth, 1921.

CBmc

CASTELNUOVO, G. L'espace-temps des relativistes a-t-il un contenu réel? *Scientia*, 1923, 33: 169-81. [CB 14/554]

METZ, André. Temps, espace, relativité. 211 p. (Science et Philosophie) Paris: Gabriel Beauchesne, 1928. [CB 25/414]

SCHOUTEN, J.A. Ueber die Entwicklung der Begriffe des Raumes und der Zeit und ihre Beziehungen zum Relativitätsprinzip. Transl. from the 2nd Dutch ed. vi, 39 p. Leipzig: Teubner, 1924.
German translation of: Over de ontwikkeling der begrippen ruimte en tijd, in verband met het relativiteitsbeginsel. First Dutch edition 1920.

CBmd

DINGLE, Herbert. The function of time measurement in modern physics. (With French summary) *Arch.Inst.Int.Sci.Théor. Sér.A Bull.Acad.Int.Phil.Sci.*, 3. Problèmes de philosophie des sciences, 3. Théories nouvelles de relativité, p. 32-56. Discussion, p. 57-69. (Actualités Scientifiques et Industrielles, 1065) Paris: Hermann, 1949.

ESCLANGON, Ernest. La notion de temps: temps physique et relativité, la dynamique du point matériel. iv, 77 p. Paris: Gauthier-Villars, 1938.
Reviewed by A. v. Z., *Nature*, 1938, 142: 595.

INFELD, Leopold. The fourth dimension and relativity. *Scr. Math.*, 1940, 7: 79-85.

CBme

DÖHLEMANN, Karl. Gibt es eine Geometrie als Wissenschaft vom Raume? Geometrie und Relativitätstheorie. *Ann.Phil.*, 1924, 4: 369-84.

STEINMETZ, Charles Proteus. Four lectures on relativity and space. x, 126 p., ill. New York: McGraw-Hill, 1923.

CBs/y other special aspects

CBsc

PETZOLDT, Joseph. Die Stellung der Relativitätstheorie in der geistigen Entwicklung der Menschheit. 2nd enl. ed. vii, 98 p. Leipzig: 1923.

CBwn

MÜLLER-MARKUS, Siegfried. Zur Diskussion der Relativitätstheorie in der Sowjetwissenschaft. *Phil.Natur.*, 1961, 6: 327-48.

CByBT

ROUGIER, L. L'utilisation de la géométrie non-euclidienne dans la physique de la relativité. *Enseign.Math.*, 1914, 16: 5-18. [CB 5/287]

CBze EINSTEIN'S SPECIAL THEORY

BAUER, E. Critique des notions d'éther, d'espace et de temps. Cinématique de la relativité. 32 p. Paris: Hermann, 1932. [CB 39/451]

BRONOWSKI, J. The clock paradox. *Sci.Amer.*, 1963, 208: no. 2, 134-44.

DEBYE, P. Arnold Sommerfeld und die Überlichtgeschwindigkeit. *Phys.Bl.*, 1960, 16: (11), 568-70.

DINGLE, Herbert, *et al.* Relativity and space travel. [Letters to the Editor] *Nature*, 1956, 177: 782-5; 178: 680-2; 1957, 179: 1242; 180: 499-500; 1959, 183: 1761; 1962, 195: 985; 1963, 197: 1287-8.

DINGLE, Herbert. The special theory of relativity. vii, 94 p. (Methuen's Monographs on Physical Subjects) London: Methuen, 1940. [CB 61/398]

GILBERT, Leo. Das Relativitätsprinzip, die jüngste Modenarrheit der Wissenschaft. 124 p. (Wissenschaftliche Satyren, vol. 1) Brackwede i. W.: W. Breitenbach, 1913.
Extracts from this work were published in English translation in *Monist*, 1914, 24: 288-309.

HOLTON, Gerald. On the origins of the special theory of relativity. *Amer.J.Phys.*, 1960, 28: 627-36.

KAHAN, T. Sur les origines de la théorie de la relativité restreinte. *Rev.Hist.Sci.*, 1959, 12: 159-65.

KUZNETSOV, Boris G. [Basic ideas of the special theory of relativity. (In Russian)]. In: Akademiia Nauk SSSR, Institut istorii estestvoznaniia i tekhniki. Ocherki razvitiia osnovnykh fizicheskikh ideĭ, p. 263-87. Moskva: Izd-vo Akademii Nauk SSSR, 1959.

LA VALLÉE POUSSIN, Charles Jean de. Le temps et la relativité restreinte. *Rev.Quest.Sci.*, 1924, 85: 321-69.

McCREA, W.H. The Fitzgerald-Lorentz contraction: some paradoxes and their resolution. *Sci.Proc.Roy.Dublin Soc.*, 1952, 26: (1), 27-36.

McCREA, W.H. Relativity physics. 4th ed. rev. vii, 87 p., 8 ill. (Methuen's Monographs on Physical Subjects) London: Methuen; New York: Wiley, 1954. [CB 77/341]
First published 1935.

McMILLAN, Edwin M. The "clock paradox" and space travel. *Science*, 1957, 126: 381-4.

METZ, André. Les équations de la relativité restreinte à partir de l'expérience. *Rev.Sci.*, 1923, 61: 266-70. [CB 16/230]

MORE, Louis Trenchard. The units of measure and the principle of relativity. *Monist*, 1914, 24: 225-58.

PERRIN, Francis. La dynamique relativiste et l'inertie de l'énergie. 20 p. (Actualités Scientifiques et Industrielles, 41) Paris: Hermann, 1932.

PETZOLDT, Joseph. Die Relativitätstheorie der Physik. *Z. Positivistische Phil.*, 1914, 2: 1-56, bibliogr.

PLA, Cortés. Velocidad de la luz y relatividad. Con un apéndice conteniendo las memorias originales de Arago, Fizeau y Foucault. 295 p. Buenos Aires: Espasa-Calpe, 1947. [CB 75/89]
Reviewed by Aldo Mieli, *Arch.Int.Hist.Sci.*, 1948, 1: 740-1.

POINCARÉ, Henri. La mécanique nouvelle. Conférence, mémoire et note sur la théorie de la relativité. Introduction de M. Edouard Guillaume. xvi, 81 p., diagr. Paris: Gauhier-Villars, 1924.

SCRIBNER, Charles, Jr. Henri Poincaré and the principle of relativity. *Amer.J.Phys.*, 1964, 32: 672-8.

SPEISER, D. L. Euler, the principle of relativity and the fundamentals of classical mechanics. *Nature*, 1961, 190: 757-9.

TÖRNEBOHM, Håkan. The clock paradox and the notion of clock retardation in the special theory of relativity. *Theoria*, 1963, 29: 79-90.

ULEGLA, I. Istoriia paradoksa chasov i kosmicheskie puteshestviia. [The history of the clock paradox and space travel. (In Russian)] *Vop.Ist.Est.Tekh.*, 1962, 12: 184-9.

WHITROW, G.J. The Fitzgerald-Lorentz contraction phenomenon and theories of the relativity of Galilean frames. *Sci. Proc.Roy. Dublin Soc.*, 1952, 26: (1), 37-44.

CBze-k

BERGSON, Henri. Durée et simultanéité. À propos de la théorie d'Einstein. 2nd enl. ed. x, 289 p. Paris: Alcan, 1923.
First published 1922.
Reviewed by Henry M. Sheffer, *Isis*, 1924, 6: 570-1; by H. Wildon Carr, *Nature*, 1922, 110: 503-5.

BONSACK, F. Réponse à M. Evans et à quelques autres. *Dialectica*, 1962, 16: 82-91.
A discussion of Evans' "Relativity of simultaneity", *see* below.

CARUS, Paul. The principle of relativity in the light of the philosophy of science. 109 p. Chicago: Open Court, 1913.

DINGLE, Herbert. Reason and experiment in relation to the special relativity theory. *Brit.J.Phil.Sci.*, 1964, 15: 41-61.

EVANS, Melbourne G. The relativity of simultaneitv: a critical analysis. *Dialectica*, 1962, 16: 61-82.

GRÜNBAUM, Adolf. The relevance of philosophy to the history of the special theory of relativity. *J.Phil.*, 1962, 59: 561-74.

LAUE, Max von. Das Relativitätsprinzip. *Jahrb.Phil.*, 1913, 1: 99-128, 369.

TÖRNEBOHM, Håkan. The Lorentz-formulae and the metrical principle. *Phil.Sci.*, 1962, 29: 269-78.

TÖRNEBOHM, Håkan. On the concepts of distance and length in the special theory of relativity. *Theoria*, 1963, 29: 283-9.

TÖRNEBOHM, Håkan. Two concepts of simultaneity in the special theory of relativity. *Theoria*, 1963, 29: 147-53.

CBze-kk

GRÜNBAUM, Adolf. Logical and philosophical foundations of the special theory of relativity. *Amer.J.Phys.*, 1955, 23: 450-64, 1 fig.

CBze-kv

KAR, Robert. Kausalistische Erklärung der relativistischen Paradoxa. *Phil.Natur.*, 1964, 8: 250-4.

CBze-mc

MINKOWSKI, Hermann. Time and space. *Monist*, 1918, 28: 288-301.
Originally published in German, 1908.

CBze-wn

MÜLLER-MARKUS, Siegfried. Einstein und die Sowjetphilosophie. 1. Die Grundlagen und die spezielle Relativitätstheorie. xvi, 481 p. Dordrecht: D. Reidel, 1960.
Reviewed by David Dinsmore Comey, *J.Phil.*, 1962, 59: 809-15.

CBzg GENERAL THEORY

AMES, J.S. Einstein's law of gravitation. *Science*, 1920, 51: 253-61.

BIRD, J. Malcolm, ed. Einstein's theory of relativity and gravitation. A selection of material from the essays submitted in the competition for the Eugen Higgins prize. xiv, 345 p. New York: Scientific American Publishing Company, 1921.

CUNNINGHAM, Ebenezer. Einstein's relativity theory of gravitation. *Nature*, 1919, 104: 354-6, 374-6, 394-5.

EDDINGTON, Arthur Stanley. Can gravitation be explained? *Scientia*, 1923, 33: 313-25; French transl. suppl., 51-63.
Considerations on the homogeneity and isotropy of the curvature of space-time in Einstein's theory.

FOCK, V.A. The researches of A.A. Fridman on the Einstein theory of gravitation. Transl. by W.H. Furry. *Soviet Phys. Usp.*, 1964, 6: 473-4.

FOCK, V.A. O roli printsipov otnositel'nosti i ekvivalentnosti v teorii tiagoteniia einshteina. [On the principles of relativity and of equivalence in the Einsteinian gravitation theory. (In Russian)] *Actes du Symposium International R.J. Boskovic 1961*, p. 27-37. Beograd: 1962.

LEVINSON, Horace C.; ZEISLER, Ernest Bloomfield. The law of gravitation in relativity. 2nd ed. 128 p. Chicago: University of Chicago Press, 1931. [CB 33/395]

McVITTIE, G.C. Distance and relativity. *Science*, 1958, 127: 501-5.

METZ, André. Le temps, l'espace et la matière dans la théorie de la relativité généralisée. *Rev.Quest.Sci.*, 1924, 86: 277-315.

RAINICH, G.Y. Mathematics of relativity. vii, 173 p. New York/London: Wiley, 1950. [CB 77/368]

SAMPSON, Ralph Allen. On gravitation and relativity. 24 p. (Halley Lecture) Oxford: Clarendon Press, 1920.

SCHLICK, Moritz. Space and time in contemporary physics. An introduction to the theory of relativity and gravitation. Transl. by Henry L. Brose. Introduction by F.A. Lindemann. xi, 89 p. Oxford: Clarendon Press, 1920.
2nd German edition Berlin: 1919.

SCHRÖDINGER, Erwin. Space-time structure. viii, 119 p. Cambridge University Press, 1950. [CB 77/368]

VASILIEV, Aleksandr Vasilievich. Space, time, motion: an historical introduction to the general theory of relativity. Translated from the Russian by H.M. Lucas and C.P. Sanger. With an introduction by Bertrand Russell. 256 p. London: Chatto and Windus, 1924.

WEYL, Hermann. Space, time, matter. Lectures on the general theory of relativity. Transl. by Henry L. Brose. xi, 330 p. London: Methuen, 1922.
Reviewed by A.S. Eddington, *Nature*, 1922, 109: 634-6.
5th German edition Berlin: 1923.
French translation of 4th German edition, Paris: Blanchard, 1922; reviewed by R. Thiry, *Rev.Gén.Sci.*, 1922, 33: 404-6.

WHITTAKER, E.T. The outstanding problems of relativity. From the presidential address to Section A (Mathematical and Physical Sciences) of the British Association delivered at Leeds on Sept. 5. *Nature*, 1927, 120: 368-71; also in *Science*, 1927, 66: 223-9.

WILSON, Edwin B. Space, time and gravitation. *Sci.Mon.*, 1920, 10: 217-35.

CBzg-k

BUCHEL, Wolfgang. Metrisches Feld, Kraftfeld, Feldquanten - zur Interpretation der allgemeinen Relativitätstheorie. *Phil.Natur.*, 1964, 8: 22-48.

CBzg-kk

FREUNDLICH, Edwin. The foundations of Einstein's theory of gravitation. Transl. by Henry L. Brose. xvi, 61 p. Cambridge University Press, 1920.

CBzg-me

GRÜNBAUM, Adolf. The philosophical retention of absolute space in Einstein's general theory of relativity. *Phil. Rev.*, 1957, 66: 525-35.

CBzt TESTS OF RELATIVITY
see also COze ETHER

ALLIAUME, Maurice. Astronomie et relativité, 1923. *Rev.Quest. Sci.*, 1924, 86: 471-508. [CB 16/284]

BOUTARIC, Augustin. Lumière, masse et gravitation. *Rev. Quest.Sci.*, 1925, 87: 168-81. [CB 18/612]

BRASCH, Frederick E. Einstein's appreciation of Simon Newcomb. *Science*, 1929, 49: 248-9.
Letter by Einstein concerning Newcomb's contributions to the study of perturbations in the three-body problem and the effect of relativity on the results.

CHAZY, Jean. La théorie de la relativité et la mécanique céleste. viii, 261 p. Paris: Gauthier-Villars, 1930.

DARMOIS, G. La théorie einsteinienne de la gravitation; les vérifications expérimentales. 30 p. Paris: Hermann, 1932.

DYSON, Frank, et al. The deflection of light by gravitation and the Einstein theory. *Sci.Mon.*, 1920, 10: 79 et seq.
Reprint of the report of the joint eclipse meeting of the Royal Society and the Royal Astronomical Society, 1919 Nov. 6, Sir Joseph Thomson presiding. *Observatory*, 1919, 42: 389-98.

EVE, A.S. Tests of relativity theory. *Nature*, 1926, 117: 520-2.

FORBES, Eric Gray. A history of the solar red shift problem. *Ann.Sci.*, 1961, 17: 129-64

KOPFF, A. La déviation des rayons lumineux au voisinage du soleil et la théorie de la relativité. *Scientia*, 1924, 35: 397-416. [CB 16/316]

LANGEVIN, Paul. L'oeuvre d'Einstein et l'astronomie. *Astronomie*, 1931, 45: 277-97.

LANGEVIN, Paul. L'oeuvre d'Einstein et l'astronomie. *Enseign. Sci.*, 1932, 5: 193-202, 225-9.

LA ROSA, M. Prove astronomiche contrarie alla relatività. 1. Le stelle variabili; 2. Una nuova teoria delle stelle variabili. *Scientia*, 1924, 36: 1-11, 69-80; French transl. suppl., 1-11, 21-32. [CB 16/286]

LARMOR, Joseph. Newtonian time essential to astronomy. *Nature*, April 9, 1927, 119: suppl. 49-60

LEMAÎTRE, Georges. La théorie de la relativité et l'expérience. *Rev.Quest.Sci.*, 1926, 89: 346-74.

LUNN, A.C. Experimental science and world geometry. *Science*, 1926, 63: 579-86.

MIKAILOV, A.A. The deflection of light by the gravitational field of the sun. *Mon.Not.Roy.Astron.Soc.*, 1959, 119: 593-608.

PICARD, Emile. La théorie de la relativité et ses applications à l'astronomie. iv, 27 p. Paris: Gauthier-Villars, 1922.

POOR, Charles Lane. The motions of the planets and the relativity theory. *Science*, 1921, 54: 30-4.

SAUGER, Maurice. L'expérience de Dayton Clarence Miller et les limitations de la théorie de la relativité. *Rev.Gén.Sci.*, 1926, 37: 230-4.

TRUMPLER, Robert. Historical note on the problem of light deflection in the sun's gravitational field. *Science*, 1923, 58: 161-3. [CB 15/231]
Apropos of the claim that Einstein had plagiarized J. Soldner.

CC QUANTUM THEORY

ADAMS, Edwin P. The quantum theory. 2nd ed., rev. and enl. 109 p. (*Bull.Nat.Res.Council*, 7: part 3. November, 1923) Washington, D.C.: 1923. [CB 16/325]
First published 1920 as *Bull.Nat.Res.Council*, 1: part 5.

ALLEN, Herbert Stanley. The quantum and its interpretation. xiii, 274 p. London: Methuen, 1928.
Reviewed by G.P. Thomson, *Nature*, 1928, 121: 977-8.

ALLEN, Herbert Stanley. The quantum theory. *Nature*, 1928, 122: 887-91

ARIYAMA, Kanetaka. [50 years of the quantum theory. 1. Theory of the assembly of molecular systems. (In Japanese)]. *J.Hist.Sci.Japan*, 1952, no. 21, 1-4.
For part 2 *see* Sakata, Syôichi, below.

BIRTWISTLE, George. The new quantum mechanics. xiii, 290 p. Cambridge University Press, 1928.
Reviewed by L.M. Milne-Thomson, *Nature*, 1928, 122: 527.

BLIGH, Neville M. The evolution and development of the quantum theory. 112 p. London: Arnold, 1926.

BLOCH, Eugène. L'ancienne et la nouvelle théorie des quanta. 418 p., 42 fig. Paris: Hermann, 1930. [CB 29/256]

BOHM, David. Quantum theory. 646 p. New York: Prentice-Hall, 1951. [CB 78/183]

BOHR, Niels. On the application of the quantum theory to atomic structure. Part I. The fundamental postulates of the quantum theory. Translated by L.F. Curtiss. 42 p. (*Proc.Cambridge Phil.Soc.. Suppl.*) Cambridge University Press, 1924.
From *Z.Phys.*, 1923, 13: 117-65. No more published.

BOLL, Marcel. L'idée générale de la mécanique ondulatoire et de ses premières applications; atome d'hydrogène; phénomènes chimiques; conduction électrique. 74 p. Paris: Hermann, 1932. [CB 38/594]

BRILLOUIN, Léon. Notions de mécanique quantique; les méthodes d'approximation. 36 p. (Exposés sur la Théorie des Quanta, 1. Actualités Scientifiques et Industrielles, 39) Paris: Hermann, 1932.

BROGLIE, Louis de. Le dualisme des ondes et des corpuscles dans l'oeuvre de Albert Einstein. Lecture faite en la séance annuelle des prix du 5 décembre 1955. 35 p., portr. Paris: Institut de France, Académie des Sciences, 1955.

BROGLIE, Louis de. Introduction à la mécanique ondulatoire. xvi, 292 p., ill., portr. Paris: Hermann, 1930. [CB 29/258]

BROGLIE, Louis de. Recueil d'exposés sur les ondes et les corpuscules. 82 p., portr. Paris: Hermann, 1930. [CB 29/258]

BROGLIE, Louis de. Théorie de la quantification dans la nouvelle mécanique. xxviii, 250 p. Paris: Hermann, 1932. [CB 38/575]

BROGLIE, Louis de. Waves and corpuscles in modern physics. *Annu.Rep.Smithsonian Inst. for* 1930, p. 243-53, 2 pl. Washington, D.C.: U.S. Government Printing Office, 1931.
Lecture delivered at a conference at the Bureau of Arts and Measures, 26 Jan. 1930. Translated from *Rev.Gén.Sci.*, 1930, 41: 101-8.

CONDON, Edward U. Evolution of the quantum theory. *Sci. Mon.*, 1951, 72: 217-22.

CONDON, Edward U. Sixty years of quantum physics. *Bull.Phil. Soc.Wash.*, 1962, 16: 83-102.

DARROW, Karl K. The quantum theory. *Sci.Amer.*, 1952, 186: no. 3, 47-54, ill.

DELORME, Albert. Mécanique ondulatoire et théorie des quanta. *Rev.Syn.*, 1958, 79: 131-4.

DIRAC, P.A.M. The principles of quantum mechanics. 4th ed. xii, 312 p. Oxford: Clarendon Press, 1958.
First published 1930; second edition 1935; reviewed by H.T. Davis, *Isis*, 1936, 25: 493-6.

EINSTEIN, Albert. The advent of the quantum theory. *Science*, 1951, 113: 82-4.

EISENMANN, J.; ROCARD, Y. Le principe de correspondance et l'état actuel de la théorie des quanta. *Rev.Métaphys. Morale*, 1926, 33: 183-200.

GEIGER, Hans. Quanten. Bearb. von W. Bothe [et al]. x, 782 p., 225 fig. (Handbuch der Physik, 23) Berlin: Springer, 1926.
Reviewed in *Nature*, 1928, 121: 7-8.

GLEBOV, L.A. [The history of the growth of quantum mechanics. (In Russian)] *Tr.Inst.Ist.Est.Tekh.*, 1959, 28: 421-50.

HAAS, Arthur. Wave mechanics and the new quantum theory. Transl. from the German ed. "Materiewellen und Quantenmechanik" [Leipzig: 1928] by L.W. Codd. xviii, 124 p. London: Constable, 1928.
Reviewed by R.H.F., *Nature*, 1929, 123: 362.

HEISENBERG, Werner. Die Entwicklung der Quantenmechanik. In: Die moderne Atomtheorie. [Nobel prize lectures 1933] 45 p. Leipzig: Hirzel, 1934.

HEISENBERG, Werner. The physical principles of the quantum theory. Transl. by Carl Eckart and Frank C. Hoyt. xii, 186 p. (University of Chicago Science Series) Chicago, Ill.: 1930.
German original Die physikalischen Prinzipien der Quantentheorie. Leipzig: Hirzel, 1930.

HOFFMANN, Banesh. The strange story of the quantum. An account for the general reader of the growth of the ideas underlying our present atomic knowledge. xi, 239 p. New York: Harper, 1947.
Reviewed by G. Wyllie, *Nature*, 1947, 160: 692.

HUND, F. Das Problem der Stoffe und seine Lösung. *Naturwissenschaften*, 1963, 50: 344-8.
Discussion of the role of quantum theory in fusing together virtually unrelated notions of the constituents of matter which developed within classical physics and chemistry.

HUND, F. Vor fünfzig Jahren - Der Schritt zur Quantentheorie des Atombaues und der Spektrallinien. *Phys.Bl.*, 1963, 19: 494-502

HYLLERAS, Egil A. Reminiscences from early quantum mechanics of two-electron atoms. *Rev.Mod.Phys.*, 1963, 35: 421-31. [CB 89/581]
The author studied under Max Born at Göttingen.

JEANS, James Hopwood. Report on radiation and the quantum theory. 2nd ed. iv, 86 p. London: Fleetway Press (for the Physical Society of London), 1924.
First published in 1914; considerable additions.

KLEIN, Martin J. Einstein and the wave-particle duality. *Natur.Phil.*, 1964, 3: 1-49.

KLEIN, Martin J. Einstein's first paper on quanta. *Natur. Phil.*, 1963, 2: 57-86.

KLEIN, Martin J. Max Planck and the beginnings of the quantum theory. *Arch.Hist.Exact.Sci.*, 1962, 1: 459-79.

KLEIN, Martin J. Planck, entropy, and quanta, 1901-1906. *Natur.Phil.*, 1963, 1: 83-108.

KUZNETSOV, Boris G. [Basic ideas of quantum physics. (In Russian)]. In: Akademiia Nauk SSSR, Institut istorii estestvoznaniia i tekhniki. Ocherki razvitiia osnovnykh fizicheskikh ideĭ, p. 390-421. Moskva: Izd-vo Akademii Nauk SSSR, 1959.

LINDEMANN, F.A., *Viscount* Cherwell. The physical significance of the quantum theory. vi, 148 p. Oxford: Clarendon Press, 1932.

LORENTZ, Hendrik Antoon. Max Planck und die Quantentheorie. *Naturwissenschaften*, 1925, 13: 1077-82.

NATANSON, Wladyslaw. Pierwsze zasady mechaniki undulacyjnej. [First principles of wave mechanics. (In Polish)] 76 p. *Prace Mat.Fiz.*, 37: no. 1) Warszawa: 1930.

PLANCK, Max. Leçons de thermodynamique, avec une conférence sur Le théorème de Nernst et l'hypothèse des quanta. *See* CH

PLANCK, Max. Zur Geschichte der Auffindung des physikalischen Wirkungsquantums. *Naturwissenschaften*, 1943, 31: 153-9.

POLAK, L.S. [Die optisch-mechanische Analogie bei Schrödinger. (In Russian with German summary)] *Arkh.Ist.Nauk.Tekh.*, 1936, no. 8, 29-73.

POLAK, L.S. [The origins of quantum physics. (In Russian)]. In: Akademiia Nauk SSSR, Institut istorii estestvoznaniia i tekhniki. Ocherki razvitiia osnovnykh fizicheskikh ideĭ, p. 323-89. Moskva: Izd-vo Akademii Nauk SSSR, 1959.

POLAK, L.S. Pervye shagi kvantovoi fiziki. [The first steps of quantum physics. (In Russian)] *Vop.Ist.Est.Tekh.*, 1958, no. 6, 56-72.

POLIKAROV, A. Über die Deutung der Quantenmechanik. *Wiss.Z. Humboldt-Univ.Berlin, Math.Naturwiss.Reihe.*, 1962, 11: 1-24.

PRZIBRAM, K., ed. Schrödinger - Planck - Einstein - Lorentz. Briefe zur Wellenmechanik. 69 p., 4 portr. Vienna: Springer Verlag, 1963.

REICHE, Fritz. Die Quantentheorie. Ihr Ursprung und ihre Entwicklung. vi, 231 p. Berlin: Springer, 1921.
Reviewed by George Sarton, *Isis*, 1922, 4: 375-6.

ROSENFELD, L. Le dualisme entre ondes et corpuscules. *Archeion*, 1937, 19: 74-7.

ROSENFELD, L. Early history of quantum mechanics. *Nature*, 1950, 166: 883-4.

ROSENFELD, L. La première phase de l'évolution de la théorie des quanta. *Osiris*, 1936, 2: part 6, 149-96, 4 portr.

ROSENFELD, L. L'univers à cinq dimensions et la mécanique ondulatoire. *Bull.Acad.Roy.Belg.Cl.Sci.*, 1927, *5th ser.*, 13: 304-25.

SAKATA, Syôichi. [50 years of the quantum theory. 2. Theory of elementary particles. (In Japanese)]. *J.Hist.Sci.Japan*, 1952, no. 21, 5-9.
Part 1 by Ariyana, K., *see* above.

SCHROEDINGER, Erwin. Collected papers on wave mechanics. Transl. from the second German edition by F.J. Shearer and W.M. Deans. xiii 146 p. London/Glasgow: Blackie, 1928.
German original Abhandlungen zur Wellenmechanik. 2nd edition. Leipzig: Barth, 1929. (First published 1927)

SCHROEDINGER, Erwin. Four lectures on wave mechanics. viii, 53 p. London/Glasgow: Blackie, 1928.
German translation Berlin: Springer, 1928.

SCHROEDINGER, Erwin. Die gegenwärtige Situation in der Quantenmechanik. *Naturwissenschaften*, 1935, 23: 807-12, 844-9.

SCHROEDINGER, Erwin. Der Grundgedanke der Wellenmechanik. In: Die moderne Atomtheorie. [Nobel prize lectures 1933] 45 p. Leipzig: Hirzel, 1934.

SEEGER, Raymond J. A critique of recent quantum theories. *Proc.Nat.Acad.Sci.*, 1931, 17: 301-10; 1932, 18: 303-10.

SOMMERFELD, A.; BOPP, F. Fifty years of quantum theory. Transl. from the German. *Science*, 1951, 113: 85-92.
Discusses the consequences of Planck's discovery.

ULLMO, Jean. La crise de la physique quantique. 45 p. (Actualités Scientifiques et Industrielles, 1231) Paris: Hermann, 1955.

CCk philosophy and methodology

ALBERGAMO, Francesco. La teoria dei quanti nella interpretazione fenomenistica del Reichenbach. *Act. VIIIe Congr.Int. Hist.Sci.*(Florence, 1956), (1), p. 254-60. Paris: Hermann, 1958.

DUGAS, René. Sur le problème de la réalité en mécanique quantique. *Thalès*, 1936, 3: 125-35.

EISENMANN, J.; ROCARD, Y. Le principe de correspondance et l'état actuel de la théorie des quanta. *Rev.Métaphys.Morale*, 1926, 33: 183-200.

HALDANE, J.B.S. Quantum mechanics as a basis for philosophy. *Phil.Sci.*, 1934, 1: 78-98.

HANSON, Norwood Russell. Copenhagen interpretation of quantum theory. *Amer.J.Phys.*, 1959, 27: 1-15. [CB 85/466]
Concerns the Bohr-Heisenberg philosophy.

KEMBLE, Edwin C. The philosophical concepts in modern physics. Operational reasoning, reality, and quantum mechanics. *J. Franklin Inst.*, 1938, 225: 263-75.

LANDÉ, Alfred. The case against quantum duality. *Phil.Sci.*, 1962, 29: 1-6.

LANDÉ, Alfred. From dualism to unity in quantum mechanics. *Brit.J.Phil.Sci.*, 1959, 37: 16-24.

LANDÉ, Alfred. From dualism to unity in quantum physics. xvi, 114 p., app., bibliogr. Cambridge University Press, 1960.
Reviewed by V.F. Lenzen, *Phil.Sci.*, 1962, 29: 213-17.

LANDÉ, Alfred. Vom Dualismus zur einheitlichen Quantentheorie. *Phil.Natur.*, 1964, 8: 232-41.

LOSEE, John. The use of philosophical arguments in quantum physics. *Phil.Sci.*, 1964, 31: 10-17

MALISOFF, William Marias. An examination of the quantum theories. *Phil.Sci.*, 1934, 1: 71-7, 170-5, 398-408; 1935, 2: 334-43. [CB 42/580]

MARGENAU, Henry. Advantages and disadvantages of various interpretations of the quantum theory. *Phys.Today*, 1954, 7: no. 10, 6-13, 1 fig.

MARGENAU, Henry. Measurements and quantum states. *Phil.Sci.*, 1963, 30: 1-16, 138-57.

MARIANI, Jean. La signification philosophique de la théorie des quanta. *Thalès*, 1934, 1: 85-93. [CB 45/281]

OMELIANOVSKII, M.E. Filosofskaia evoliutsiia Kopengagenskoi shkoly fizikov. [Philosophical evolution of the Copenhagen school of physicists. (In Russian)] *Vestnik Akad.Nauk SSSR*, 1962, 32: (9), 86-96.

QUANTA and reality. A symposium. 96 p., ill. London: Hutchinson; Larchmont, N.Y.: American Research Council, 1962. [CB 88/530]
Most of the material formed B.B.C. radio series broadcast in 1961.

SCHILLER, Ralph. Interpretations of the quantum theory. *Synthese*, 1962, 14: 5-16.

CCke

DUGAS, René. La méthode de la mécanique des quanta. Axiomatique, déterminisme et représentation. 60 p. (Exposés de Philosophie des Sciences) Paris: Hermann, 1935.

SIEGEL, Armand. Operational aspects of hidden-variable quantum theories with a postscript on the impact of scientific trends on art. *Synthese,* 1962, 14: 171-88.

CCkh

ALBERTSON, James. The statistical nature of quantum mechanics. *Brit.J.Phil.Sci.,* 1962, 13: 229-33.

KLEIN, Martin J. Ehrenfest's contributions to the development of quantum statistics. *Proc.Ned.Akad.Wetensch. Ser.B,* 1959, 62: 41-62.

CCkk

HANSON, N.R. The logic of the correspondence principle. *Scientia,* 1958, 93: 64-70.

LANDÉ, Alfred. Foundations of quantum theory. A study in continuity and symmetry. viii, 106 p. New Haven: Yale University Press; London: Oxford University Press, 1955. [CB 81/341]

RAINOV, T.I. [Schrödinger and the theoretical foundations of quantum mechanics. (In Russian)] *Sorena,* 1936, no. 4, 9-27.
A discussion of Schrödinger's Die gegenwärtige Situation in der Quantenmechanik, see CC

REICHENBACH, Hans. Philosophic foundations of quantum mechanics. x, 182 p. Berkeley: University of California Press, 1944.
Reviewed by Edmund T. Whittaker, *Nature,* 1946, 158: 356-7.

RICHTER, Ewald. Bemerkungen zur Quantenlogik. *Phil.Natur.,* 1964, 8: 225-3]

ROSENFELD, L. Foundations of quantum theory and complementarity. *Nature,* 1961, 190: 384-8.

STRAUSS, M.D.H. Quantum theory and logic. *Bull.Brit.Soc. Hist.Sci.,* 1950, 1: 99-101.

CCkv

BRIDGMAN, Percy Williams. The new vision of science. *Harper's Mag.,* March 1929, 443-51. [CB 26/225]
A discussion of the uncertainty principle.

MEYERSON, Emile. Réel et déterminisme dans la physique quantique. 50 p. (Exposés de Philosophie des Sciences, 1) Paris: Hermann, 1933.

OMELIANOVSKYI, M.E. Determinismus und Quantenmechanik. *Act. IIe Congr.Int.Phil.Sci.* (Zurich, 1954), (2), p. 74-81. Neuchâtel: Éditions du Griffon, 1955.

CCmc

BROGLIE, Louis de. L'espace et le temps dans la physique quantique. *Proc.10th Int.Congr.Phil.* (Amsterdam, 1948), p. 806-15. Amsterdam: North Holland Publishing Co., 1949.

CCq/y other special aspects

CCqx

BOHR, Niels. The Solvay meetings and the development of quantum physics. *La Theorie quantique des champs, 12ème Conseil de Physique*(Bruxelles, 1961), p. 13-36. New York/London: Interscience; Bruxelles: R. Stoops, 1962.

CCyBFzg

WEYL, Hermann. Gruppentheorie und Quantenmechanik. 288 p. Leipzig: Hirzel, 1928.
Reviewed by A. Hammerstein, *Arch.Gesch.Math.Naturwiss. Tech.,* 1929, 11: 444-5.

CCyCB

BROGLIE, Louis de. Conséquences de la relativité dans le développement de la mécanique ondulatoire. 14 p. Paris: Hermann, 1932.

CD MECHANICS IN GENERAL; SOLID MECHANICS

CDc general history

BELL, A.E. Early work on periodic motion. *Nature,* 1941, 147: 78-80.

BOREL, Emile. L'évolution de la mécanique. 227 p., 26 ill. (Bibliothèque de Philosophie Scientifique) Paris: Flammarion, 1943.

DIJKSTERHUIS, Eduard Jan. Val en Worp. Een bijdrage tot de geschiedenis der Mechanica van Aristoteles tot Newton. [Falling bodies and projectiles. A contribution to the history of mechanics from Aristotle to Newton. (In Dutch)]. viii, 466 p. Groningen: P. Noordhoff, 1925.
Reviewed by H. Wieleitner, *Isis,* 1926, 8: 378-9.

DUGAS, René. Histoire de la mécanique. Préface de Louis de Broglie. 649 p., 110 fig. (Bibliothèque Scientifique, 16. Philosophie et Histoire) Neuchâtel: Griffon; Paris: Dunod, 1950.
See English translation below.
Reviewed by I. Bernard Cohen, *Isis,* 1951, 42: 271-2; by Pierre Costabel, *Rev.Hist.Sci.,* 1953, 6: 72-4.

DUGAS, René. A history of mechanics. Translated by J.R. Maddox. 671 p., ill. Neuchâtel: Griffon; New York: Central Book Company, 1955; London: Routledge and Kegan Paul, 1957. [CB 83/198]
For reviews *see* CB 83/198, CB 85/389 and CB 86/462.
For reviews of French original *see* above.

DUNGEN, F.H. van den. Lois et postulats. *Rev.Univ.Bruxelles,* 1934-35, 40: 214-30.
A brief outline of the development of mechanics since Newton.

GIRVIN, Harvey F. A historical appraisal of mechanics. With a foreword by A.A. Potter. ix, 275 p. Scranton, Pa.: International Textbook Co., 1948. [CB 73/168]

GRIGORIAN, A.T. Appraisal of Newton's mechanics and of Einstein's 'autobiography'. *Arch.Int.Hist.Sci.,* 1961, 14: 13-22.

HAAG, J. Sur les principes de la mécanique. *Rev.Gén.Sci.,* 1915, 26: 75-85.

HAAS, Arthur Erich. Die Grundgleichungen der Mechanik dargestellt auf Grund der geschichtlichen Entwicklung. 216 p. Leipzig: Veit, 1914.

HÖNL, Helmut. Galilei - Newton - Einstein. Von der klassischen zur Relativitätsmechanik. *Naturwiss.Rundsch.,* 1964, 17: 300-5.

HOLTON, Gerald. Science and the changing allegory of motion. *Scientia,* 1963, 98: 191-200.

IVASHKEVICH, V.IU. K istorii razvitiia osnovnykh predposylok invariantnoi teorii mekhaniki. [On the history of the development of the basic premises of the invariant theory of mechanics. (In Russian)]. *Tr.Inst.Ist.Est.Tekh.,* 1961, 43: 378-405.

JOUGUET, Emile. Lectures de mécanique. La mécanique enseignée par les auteurs originaux. Nouveau tirage avec notes et additions. 2 vol. 1. La naissance de la mécanique. x, 237 p.; 2. L'organisation de la mécanique. 330 p. Paris: Gauthier-Villars, 1924.
Reviewed by George Sarton, *Isis,* 1925, 7: 156-8.

MACH, Ernst. Die Mechanik in ihrer Entwicklung. Historisch-kritisch dargestellt. 9th ed. xii, 493 p., ill. Leipzig: F.A. Brockhaus, 1933.
2nd edition of English translation, The science of mechanics, Chicago: Open Court, 1902.

MacLEAN, J. De historische ontwikkeling der stootwetten van Aristoteles tot Huygens. [The historical development of laws of impact from Aristotle to Huygens. (In Dutch)]. 69 p. Amsterdam: Vrije Universiteit (Dissertation), 1959. [CB 85/390]
Another edition. 72 p., fig. Rotterdam: Van Sijn, 1959; Amsterdam: Vrije Universiteit, 1960.
Reviewed by Serge Moscovici, *Rev.Hist.Sci.,* 1960, 13: 274.

MOTT-SMITH, Morton. Principles of mechanics simply explained. Ill. by Emil Kosa. xiv, 171 p., bibliogr. New York: Dover Publications, Inc., 1963. [CB 89/502]
Previously publ. as "This mechanical world" (New York: Appleton, 1931). This book sets forth the basic ideas of physics in the historical context from which they emerged.

POLAK, L.S. The development of the principles of the dynamics of system in the 19th and 20th centuries. *Act.VIIIe Congr. Int.Hist.Sci.* (Florence, 1956), p. 174-7. Paris: Hermann, 1958.

POLAK, L.S. Nekotorye tendentsii razvitiya printsipov dinamiki sistemy v XIX v. i pervoi chetverti XX v. [Certain trends in the development of the system of dynamics in the 19th and the first quarter of the 20th century. (In Russian)]. *Tr.Inst.Ist.Est.Tekh.*, 1957, 19: 538-43.

RAINOV, T.I. [On the history of constructing a system of "mechanics without forces". (In Russian)]. *Sotsialist.Rekonstruktsiia Nauk.*, 1933, 3: no. 1, 57-80.

RIEPPEL, A. von; FREYTAG, L. Beiträge zur Entwicklungsgeschichte der technischen Mechanik. *Beitr.Gesch.Tech.Ind.*, 1917, 7: 25-40. [CB 10/201]

SESMAT, Augustin. Systèmes de référence et mouvements. 2 vol. 1. Physique classique. 690 p., ill.; 2. Physique relativiste. 450 p., ill. (Actualités Scientifiques et Industrielles, 479-92) Paris: Hermann, 1937. [CB 51/254]

TOULMIN, Stephen; GOODFIELD, June. The fabric of the heavens. The development of astronomy and dynamics. 285 p., ill. London: Hutchinson; New York: Harper and Brothers, 1961. [CB 88/541]
For reviews *see* CB 87/564, CB 88/541 and CB 89/500.

TRUESDELL, C. Recent advances in rational mechanics. *Science*, 1958, 127: 729-39.
"Follows closely the Sigma Xi initiation lecture delivered on 16 May 1956 at the State University of Iowa."

CDf

TRUESDELL, C. Neuere Anschauungen über die Geschichte der allgemeinen Mechanik. *Z.Angew.Math.Mech.*, 1958, 38: 148-57, 4 fig.

TRUESDELL, C. Reactions of the history of mechanics upon modern research. *Proc.4th U.S.Nat.Congr.Appl.Mech.* (Berkeley, 1962), (1), p. 35-47. New York: American Society of Mechanical Engineers, 1962.

CDhd

CHILD, J.-M. Archimedes' principle of the balance and some criticisms upon it. In: Singer, Charles, ed. Studies in the history and method of science, vol. 2, p. 450-520, 25 fig. Oxford: Clarendon Press, 1921.
Elaborate criticism of Mach's interpretation of Archimedian statics.

JOURDAIN, Philip E.B. Remarks on some passages in Mach's Mechanics. *Monist*, 1912, 22: 285-304.
Reprinted in the author's: The principle of least action, Chicago: Open Court, 1913.

REIMANN, Dora. Historische Studie über Ernst Machs Darstellung der Entwicklung des Hebelsatzes. *Quellen Stud.Gesch. Math.Abt.B.*, 1936, 3: 554-92, fig. [CB 50/395]

CDhj

JAMMER, Max. [Physical thought of the 14th century, and its contribution to the foundation of modern mechanics. (In Hebrew, summary in English)] *Koroth*, 1953, 1: [3-4].

NAZĪF BEY, Mustafā. [The views on motion of the Islamic philosophers and their influence on modern dynamics. (In Arabic)] 33 p. Cairo: Al-matba a al-amīrīya, 1943.
This is the fourth Ibn al-Haitham lecture delivered at the University Fu'ād al-Awwal in Cairo.

SLICHTER, C.S. The "Principia" and the modern age. *Amer. Math.Mon.*, 1937, 44: 433-44, 2 fig.

CDk philosophy and methodology

CDkk

GRIGOR'IAN, A.T. [Concerning the question of the foundation of axioms and basic concepts of classical mechanics. (In Russian)]. *Vop.Ist.Est.Tekh.*, 1960, 9: 78-82.

HUNTINGTON, Edw. V. The logical skeleton of elementary dynamics. *Amer.Math.Mon.*, 1917, 24: 1-16.

JAMMER, Max. Concepts of force: a study in the foundations of dynamics. x, 269 p. Cambridge, Mass.: Harvard University Press; London: Oxford University Press, 1957.
Reviewed by R.T. Weidner, *Phys.Today*, 1958, 11: no. 5, 30; by Mary B. Hesse, *Brit.J.Phil.Sci.*, 1959, 10: 69-73; by Roger Martin, *Arch.Int.Hist.Sci.*, 1959, 12: 318.

PAINLEVÉ, Paul. Les axiomes de la mécanique. Examen critique. Note sur la propagation de la lumière. xvii, 112 p. (Les Maîtres de la Pensée Scientifique) Paris: Gauthier-Villars, 1922. [CB 14/554]

PESCI, Gustavo. Le false leggi sul moto le quali servivano finora come fondamento delle scienze naturali e le vere leggi sul moto. *Atti IV° Congr.Int.Fil.* (Bologna, 1911), (2), p. 378-403. Genoa: Formiggini, 1913.

SPEISER, D. L. Euler, the principle of relativity and the fundamentals of classical mechanics. *Nature*, 1961, 190: 757-9.

WHITROW, G.J. The foundations of dynamics. *Brit.J.Phil.Sci.*, 1950, 1: 92-107.

WOLF, Rudolf. Ueber die Konsequenzen der Mehrfachdefinition von Grundbegriffen in der Theorie der klassischen Mechanik. *Phil.Natur.*, 1952, 2: 238-50.

CDkv

ETTLINGER, H.J. Some mathematical aspects of motion and causality. *Scr.Math.*, 1939, 6: 141-8, 4 fig.

CDmj

ELLIS, Brian. Universal and differential forces. *Brit.J. Phil.Sci.*, 1963, 14: 177-94.

SAUNDERS, L.R. Rational deduction in physics: the parallelogram of forces. *Brit.J.Phil.Sci.*, 1964, 14: 265-73.

CDmk

DUGAS, René. L'énergie cinétique à travers l'histoire de la mécanique. *Rev.Sci.*, 1946, 84: 67-74.

CDmzC

HOOYKAAS, R. Das Verhältnis von Physik und Mechanik in historischer Hinsicht. 22 p. Wiesbaden: Franz Steiner Verlag, 1963.

ROELANTS, H. De verhouding van fysika en mechanika. [The relations between physics and mechanics. (In Dutch. Résumé in French)]. *Sci.Hist.*, 1964, 6: 30-44.

CDo teaching

CDod

HENDERSON, James B. The Stroud system of teaching dynamics. *Math.Gaz.*, 1924, 12: 99-105.

CDom

WEINREICH, H. Ausgewählte Fragen des Mechanikunterrichtes auf der Oberstufe. Drei Vorträge, gehalten gelegentlich des mathematisch-naturwissenschaftlichen Ferienkurses an der Universität Göttingen von 8. bis 17. Juli 1924. 65 p. (Beihefte zur *Zeitschrift für mathematischen und naturwissenschaftlichen Unterricht*, 9) Leipzig: B.G. Teubner, 1925.
Includes many historical comments.

CDw in different countries

CDwi

SIGNORINI, Antonio. Contributions italiennes à la mécanique théorique de Leonardo de Vinci à Levi-Cività. *Cah.Hist. Mond.*, 1963, 7: 419-33.

CDwn

GRIGOR'IAN, A.T. The main trends in the development of mechanics in the U.S.S.R. *Arch.Int.Hist.Sci.*, 1962, 15: 267-79.

LA SALLE, Joseph P.; LEFSHETZ, Solomon. Recent Soviet contributions to ordinary differential equations and nonlinear mechanics. *J.Math.Anal.Appl.*, 1961, 2: 651-60.
Reviewed by H.A. Antosiewcz, *Math.Rev.*, 1962, 23: 433, A2300.

CDwn-oq

GOLUBEV, V.V. [Mechanics in Moscow University before the great October socialist revolution and during the Soviet period. (In Russian)]. *Ist. Mat.Issled.*, 1955, 8: 77-126.

CDwo

VALCOVICI, V. Le développement de la mécanique en Roumanie. *Rev.Gén.Sci.*, 1947, 54: 38-41.

CDxk instruments

PERRY, John. Spinning tops. Rev. ed. 155 p. (Romance of Science Series) London: 1919.

RICHARDSON, K.I.T. The gyroscope applied. 384 p., many fig., pl. New York: Philosophical Library, 1954.
A short section is devoted to the history of the gyroscope.

CDyB application of mathematics

BOCHNER, S. The role of mathematics in the rise of mechanics. *Amer.Scient.*, 1962, 50: 294-311.

CDyBL

GRIGORIAN, A.T. [History of the integral calculus in mathematical functions relating to mechanics. (In Russian)]. *Vop. Ist.Est.Tekh.*, 1956, 1: 24-7.

CDyBTwn

GRIGOR'IAN, A.T. Les travaux sur la mécanique non-Euclidienne en Russie. *Scientia*, 1960, 95: 347-50.

GRIGOR'IAN, A.T. Raboty po neevklidovoi mekhanike v Rossii. [Works on non-Euclidian mechanics in Russia. (In Russian)]. *Tr.Inst.Ist.Est.Tekh.*, 1961, 43: 363-77.

CDz special topics

CLARINVAL, André. Esquisse historique de la courbe de poursuite. *Arch.Int.Hist.Sci.*, 1957, 10: 25-37, 7 fig.

FRADLIN, B.N. K istorii dinamiki negolonomnykh sistem. [On the history of the dynamics of non-holonomic systems. (In Russian)]. *Vop.Ist.Est.Tekh.*, 1961, 11: 61-8.

FRADLIN, B.N. Ob odnoi oshibke v negolonomnoi mekhanike. [On one error in non-holonomic mechanics. (In Russian)] *Tr.Inst.Ist.Est.Tekh.*, 1961, 43: 470-7.

FRADLIN, B.N. Ob odnoi zabytoi rabote I.V. Meshcherskogo. [Concerning a forgotten work of I.V. Meshcherskii.] *Vop.Ist. Est.Tekh.*, 1962, 13: 75-6.
A forgotten priority, in dynamics, that belongs to I.V. Meshcherskii. It has so far been ascribed to Paul-Émile Appell.

FRADLIN, B.N. Petr Vasil'evich Voronets - Odin iz osnovopolozhnikov negolonomnoi mekhaniki. [Peter Vasil'evich Voronets - one of the founders of non-holonomic mechanics. (In Russian)] *Tr.Inst.Ist.Est.Tekh.*, 1961, 43: 422-69.

GODITSKII-TSVIRKO, A.M. [An outline of the history of the funicular polygon. (In Russian)] 26 p., 23 ill. (*Sb.Inst. Inzh.Putei Soobshch.*, 101) Leningrad: 1929. [CB 29/295]

TABOR, David. A propos du frottement de roulement: une controverse oubliée. *Rev.Hist.Sci.*, 1961, 14: 13-18.

WILLIAMS, E. Some observations of Leonardo, Galileo, Mariotte and others relative to size effect. *Ann.Sci.*, 1957, 13: 23-9.

CDzb BALLISTICS

CHARBONNIER, Prosper. Essais sur l'histoire de la balistique. Extrait du "Mémorial de l'artillerie française". 334 p., ill. Paris: Société d'éditions géographiques, maritimes et coloniales, 1928.
Reviewed by L. Guinet, *Isis*, 1931, 15: 376-80.

OCAGNE, Maurice d'. Coup d'oeil sur l'histoire de la balistique. *Rev.Quest.Sci.*, 1928, 94: 239-53.
Apropos of Prosper Charbonnier's "Essais sur l'histoire de la balistique", *see* above.

SEEGER, Raymond John. On aerophysics research. *Amer.J.Phys.*, 1951, 19: 459-69. [CB 79/174]
An outline review of the history of ballistics.

CDzg GRAVITATION

x for the General Theory of Relativity *see* CBzg

ARMITAGE, Angus. The deviation of falling bodies. *Ann.Sci.*, 1947, 5: 342-51.

BLAIR, George A. Notes on falling bodies. *Sky Telesc.*, 1962, 23: 310. [CB 88/540]

CARRINGTON, Hereward. Earlier theories on gravitation. *Monist*, 1913, 23: 445-58.

COSTABEL, Pierre. Centre de gravité et équivalence dynamique. 19 p. (Les Conférences du Palais de la Découverte, D, no. 34) Paris: Université de Paris, 1955.

FRANÇOIS, Charles. La théorie de la chute des graves. Evolution historique du problème. *Ciel Terre*, 1913, 34: 135-7, 167-9, 261-73.

HECKSCHER, A. Historische Herleitung der Pendelgesetze. *Arch. Gesch.Naturwiss.Tech.*, 1914-15, 5: 155-82, 266-81, 315-51, 398-419.

HESSE, Mary B. Action at a distance in classical physics. *Isis*, 1955, 46: 337-53.

HEYL, Paul R. Gravitation - still a mystery. *Sci.Mon.*, 1954, 78: 303-6, 1 fig.

HEYL, Paul R. Old and new ideas regarding gravitation. *J. Chem.Educ.*, 1932, 9: 1897-1907. [CB 37/590]

HEYL, Paul R. What is gravitation? *Sci.Mon.*, 1938, 47: 114-23.

MacKAYE, James. The dynamic universe. x, 308 p. New York: Scribner, 1931.
A modern version of Le Sage's theory of gravitation.
Reviewed by H.T. Davis, *Isis*, 1931, 16: 158-61.

PICARD, Émile. Le problème des trois corps. À propos des recherches récentes de M. Sundmann. *Rev.Gén.Sci.*, 1913, 24: 722-5.

PITONI, R. Cenni storici sulle leggi della caduta dei gravi. *Period.Mat.*, 1913, 16: 53-6.

ROBINSON, L.; SCHILD, A.; SCHUCKING, E. Relativistic theories of gravitation. *Phys.Today*, 1963, 16: no. 8, 17-20.

TANGL, Karl. Eötvös zum 70. Geburtstage. Seine Untersuchungen über die Gravitation. *Naturwissenschaften*, 1918, 6: 445-7.

THÜRING, Bruno. Studien über die sog. Gravitationskonstante. *Ann.Acad.Sci.Fennicae*, ser. A, 3. (*Geologica-Geographica*), 1961, no. 61, 269-83.

CDzg-k

DINGLER, Hugo. Ueber das Gravitationsgesetz. *Z.Positivistische Phil.*, 1913, 1: 220-6.

THÜRING, Bruno. Die Axiome der Wirkfähigkeit oder das Gravitations-Axiom. *Phil.Natur.*, 1964, 8: 153-63.

WEISHEIPL, J. Athanasius. Nature and gravitation. 124 p. River Forest, Ill.: Albertus Magnus Lyceum, 1955. [CB 84/311]

CDzi INERTIA

CARLEBACH, J. Die Geschichte des Trägheitssatzes im Lichte des Relativitätsprinzips. Programm. 24 p. Berlin: Weidmannsche Buchhandlung, 1912.

COHEN, I. Bernard. *'Quantum in se est'*: Newton, Kepler, Galileo, Descartes, and Lucretius. *Proc.Amer.Cath.Phil.Ass.*, 1964, 38: 36-46.

COHEN, I. Bernard. *'Quantum in se est'*: Newton's concept of inertia in relation to Descartes and Lucretius. *Notes Roy. Soc.Lond.*, 1964, 19: 131-55.

COSTABEL, Pierre. Histoire du moment d'inertie. *Rev.Hist. Sci.*, 1950, 3: 315-36.

DESHAYES, M. La découverte de l'inertie. Essai sur les lois générales du mouvement de Platon à Galilée. 82 p. Paris: Les Presses Modernes, 1930.

METZ, André. Le principe d'inertie: son histoire et son interprétation d'après Émile Meyerson. *Rev.Gen.Sci.*, 1927, 37: 209-12.

CDzi-k

HANSON, Norwood Russell. The law of inertia: a philosopher's touchstone. *Phil.Sci.*, 1963, 30: 107-21.

STÉPHANIDÈS, Michel. Inertie polymorphe, essai d'une extension du principe de l'inertie. 2nd ed. 42 p. Paris: Maisonneuve, 1929. [CB 30/465]

CDzv VARIATIONAL PRINCIPLES

ABELÉ, Jean. Introduction à la notion d'action et au principe de l'action stationnaire. *Rev.Quest.Sci.*, 1948, 119: 25-42. [CB 73/168]

BRUNET, Pierre. Etude historique sur le principe de la moindre action. 113 p. (Actualités Scientifiques et Industrielles, 693) Paris: Hermann, 1938.
Essay review by Paul Schrecker, *Isis*, 1941, 33: 329-34.

JOURDAIN, Philip E.B. The nature and validity of the principle of least action. *Monist*, 1913, 23: 277-93.
Note by author, *Isis*, 1913, 1: 278-9.
Reprinted in the author's "The principle of least action", *see* below.

JOURDAIN, Philip E.B. The principle of least action. 83 p. Chicago: Open Court Publishing Co., 1913.
Note by author, *Isis*, 1913, 1: 527. Three articles reprinted from *The Monist*, 1912-13.

KNESER, Adolf. Das Prinzip der kleinsten Wirkung von Leibniz bis zur Gegenwart. ii, 70 p. (Wissenschaftliche Grundfragen: Philosophische Abhandlungen, 9) Leipzig: Teubner, 1929.

LANCZOS, Cornelius. The variational principles of mechanics. xii, 307 p. Toronto: University Press; London: Oxford University Press, 1949.

SCHRECKER, Paul. Notes sur l'évolution du principe de la moindre action. *Isis*, 1941, 33: 329-34.
Essay review of Pierre Brunet's "Étude historique sur le principe de la moindre action", *see* above.

CE FLUID MECHANICS

BOYS, C.V. Soap bubbles and the forces which mould them. 156 p., front., fig. (Science Study Series, S 3) Garden City, N.Y.: Doubleday Anchor Books, 1959.
First published London/New York: 1890.
Reviewed by Charles Hellman, *Science*, 1959, 130: 616-17; in *Sci.Amer.*, 1959, 201: no. 5, 222-3.

DAUJAT, Jean. Note sur les origines de l'hydrostatique. *Thalès*, 1934, 1: 53-6.

DEDEBANT, G.; WEHRLÉ, Ph. La mécanique des fluides turbulents fondée sur des concepts statistiques. *Thalès*, 1939, 4: 151-67.

DRYDEN, H.L. Fifty years of boundary-layer theory and experiment. *Science*, 1955, 121: 375-80.

DURAND, W.F. The development of our knowledge of the laws of fluid mechanics. *Science*, 1933, 78: 343-51.

GANDILLOT, Maurice. Note sur une illusion de relativité. iv, 88 p. Paris: Gauthier-Villars, 1913.
Resistance of fluids.

GERONIMUS, Ia.L. Sergej Alexejewitsch Tschaplygin, 1869 bis 1942; von der hydrodynamischen Forschung zur Gasdynamik. Transl. by Heinrich Koch. 88 p., ill. Berlin: Verlag Technik, 1954. [CB 90/599]

GIACOMELLI, R.; PISTOLESI, E. Historical sketch of aviation theory. In: Durand, W.F., ed. Aerodynamic theory, (1), p. 305-95. Berlin: Springer, 1934. [CB 59/470]

HARDY, William B. Properties of thin films. *Nature*, 1926, 118: 700-1.

MAGNAN, A.; SAINTE-LAGUË, A. Le vol au point fixe. 32 p., ill. (Actualités Scientifiques et Industrielles, 60. Exposés de Morphologie Dynamique et de Mécanique du Mouvement, 4) Paris: Hermann, 1933.
On the aerodynamics of flight of insects and birds.

NEMÉNYI, P.F. The main concepts and ideas of fluid dynamics in their historical development. *Arch.Hist.Exact Sci.*, 1962, 2: 52-86.

POWELL, Ralph W. History of Manning's formula. *J.Geophys. Res.*, 1960, 65: 1310-11. [CB 86/462]

RABUT, Charles. Charles Louis Weyher et la synthèse expérimentale des tourbillons. *Rev.Gén.Sci.*, 1923, 34: 141-8, 10 fig. [CB 15/178]

TANNERY, Paul. Sur l'histoire de la pression hydrostatique. Note inédite de Paul Tannery. *Archeion*, 1937, 19: 67-9.

TRUESDELL, C. The mechanical foundations of elasticity and fluid dynamics. *J.Ration.Mech.*, 1952, 1: 125-300. Corrections and additions to the above, *ibid.*, 1953, 2: 593-616.
A review of the subject which contains a number of historical notes, as well as a list of references beginning with Hooke and ending with 1953.

TRUESDELL, C. Zur Geschichte des Begriffes "innerer Druck". *Phys.Bl.*, 1956, 12: 315-26.

VÉRONNET, Alexandre. Les figures d'équilibre d'un liquide en rotation. Travaux anciens et recherches récentes. *Rev. Gén.Sci.*, 1921, 32: 325-30.

CEce-bx

TRUESDELL, C. Notes on the history of the general equations of hydrodynamics. *Amer.Math.Mon.*, 1953, 60: 445-58.
A description of volumes in an exhibit in the Indiana University of Mathematics Library commemorating the two-hundredth anniversary of the general equations of fluid dynamics.

CEdaj

BEYER, Robert T., ed. Foundations of high speed aerodynamics. Facsimiles of nineteen fundamental studies as they were originally reported in the scientific journals. With a bibliography compiled by George F. Carrier. xi, 286 p. New York: Dover Publications, 1951. [CB 79/143]

CEke

TRUESDELL, C. Experience, theory, and experiment. *(Proc.6th Hydraul.Conf.) Bull.State Univ.Iowa Stud.Eng.*, 1956, no. 36, 3-18, 5 fig.
A discussion of method, illustrated by examples drawn from the history of fluid mechanics, including the author's own research.

CEod

MARSHALL, J. Stanley. On behalf of Archimedes. *Sci.Teacher*, 1957, 24: 390-2, 2 fig.
A strong plea is made for the retention of Archimedes' principle in the teaching of physics in schools.

CEwf

JOUGUET, René. Histoire des études hydrodynamiques en France. *Rev.Sci.*, 1925, 63: 345-60.

CEwn

GRIGORIAN, A.T. The contribution of Russian scientists to the development of aerodynamics. *Proc.10th Int.Congr.Hist.Sci.* (Ithaca,1962), (2), p. 793-6. Paris: Hermann, 1964.
French translation in *Scientia*, 1963, 98: 46-50.

CEyB

SAUER, Robert. Die Aufgabe des Mathematikers in der Aerodynamik (Siebente Ludwig-Prandtl-Gedächtnis-Vorlesung, Karlsruhe, 19 April 1963). *Z.Flugwiss.*, 1963, 11: 349-56.

CF ELASTICITY AND PLASTICITY

TRUESDELL, C. The mechanical foundations of elasticity and fluid dynamics. *See* CE

VACCA, Giovanni. Sulle origini della scienza dell' elasticità. *Atti Accad.Naz.Lincei Rendic.Cl.Sci.Fis.Mat.Natur.*, 1916, 25: 29-37.

CFn

THÉORIES du potentiel et de l'élasticité: unification par voie d'entente internationale des notations et de la terminologie. *Isis*, 1913, 1: 491-2.

CG ACOUSTICS; VIBRATIONS

BARBOUR, J. Murray. Tuning and temperament. A historical survey. xiv, 228 p., 9 ill, front. East Lansing: Michigan State College Press, 1953.
Reviewed by W. Paul Gilbert, *Isis*, 1956, 47: 66-7; by Arnold Dresden, *Scr.Math.*, 1952, 18: 292-4.

BRAGG, William. The world of sound. Six lectures delivered before a juvenile auditory at the Royal Institution, Christmas, 1919. viii, 196 p. London: Bell, 1920.

DYMENT, S.A. The Laplace correction. *Sci.Progr.*, 1931, 26: 231-40.
Theories of propagation of sound from 1660 to 1851.

HENDERSON, M.C. Sound in air: absorption and dispersion. *Sound*, 1963, 2: 28-36. [CB 90/626]

ILIOVICI, G. Résumé historique du repérage par le son. *Enseign.Sci.*, 1935, 8: 140 *et seq.*, 208-13.

MILLER, Dayton Clarence. Anecdotal history of the science of sound to the beginning of the 20th century. xii, 114 p., ill. New York: Macmillan, 1935. [CB 48/569]

CGxd

PLA, Cortés. Las experiencias realizadas para determinar la velocidad del sonido en el aire. 12 p. (Publicaciones del Instituto de Matemática, 6) Rosario: Republica Argentina, 1945. [CB 70/256]

CGxx

FUCHS, Franz. Der Aufbau der technischen Akustik im Deutschen Museum. 59 p. (*Abhandl.Ber.Deut.Mus.*, 31: no. 2) München: Deutsches Museum, 1963.

CGyBD

BARBOUR, J. Murray. Musical logarithms. *Scr.Math.*, 1940, 7: 21-31, 1 facs.
A historical study of logarithms used in acoustics for representing musical intervals.

CH HEAT; THERMODYNAMICS

CHc general history

BACHELARD, Gaston. Etude sur l'évolution d'un problème de physique: la propagation thermique dans les solides. 184 p. Paris: J. Vrin, 1927. [CB 25/415]

BARNETT, Martin K. The development of the concept of heat. From the fire principle of Heraclitus through the caloric theory of Joseph Black. *Sci.Mon.*, 1946, 62: 165-72, 247-57.

BOUTARIC, Augustin. La chaleur et le froid. 284 p., 68 fig. Paris: Flammarion, 1927. [CB 23/242]

BRUNOLD, Charles. L'entropie, son rôle dans le développement historique de la thermodynamique. v, 222 p. Paris: Masson, 1930.
Reviewed by F.M., *Rev.Gén.Sci.*, 1932, 43: 58-9.

BURR, Alex. C. Notes on the history of the concept of thermal conductivity. *Isis*, 1933, 20: 246-59; 1934, 21: 169-86. [CB 40/401 and CB 41/602]

GLEBOV, L.A. K razvitiiu teorii adiabaticheskikh invariantov Erenfesta. [On the development of the theory of adiabatic invariants by Ehrenfest. (In Russian)] *Vop.Ist.Est.Tekh.*, 1961, 11: 57-60.

HIEBERT, Erwin N. Historical roots of the principle of conservation of energy. 118 p., ill., bibliogr. Madison: The State Historical Society of Wisconsin (for the Department of History, University of Wisconsin), 1962.
Reviewed by P. Bockstaele, *Sci.Hist.*, 1962, 4: 207-8; by S.C. Brown, *Amer.J.Phys.*, 1963, 31: 146-7; by I. Bernard Cohen, *Amer.Hist.Rev.*, 1963-64, 69: 810-11.

HIEBERT, Erwin N. Theoretical backgrounds to the development of thermodynamics: the development of the concept of mechanical work to 1750. *Isis*, 1954, 45: 200.
Title of doctoral dissertation presented to the University of Wisconsin.

KLEIN, Martin J. The origins of Ehrenfest's adiabatic principle. *Proc.10th Int.Congr.Hist.Sci.*(Ithaca, 1962), (2), p. 801-4. Paris: Hermann, 1964.

KUZNETSOV, B.G.; FRANKFURT, U.I. [History of the law of conservation and transmutation of energy. (In Russian)] *Tr. Inst.Ist.Est.Tekh.*, 1959, 28: 339-76.

MACH, Ernst. Die Prinzipien der Wärmelehre. Historisch-kritisch entwickelt. 4th ed. xii, 484 p., 150 fig., 6 portr. Leipzig: Barth, 1923.

MENDOZA, E. A sketch for a history of early thermodynamics. *Phys.Today*, 1961, 14: no. 2, 32-42

NERNST, Walther. The new heat theorem; its foundations in theory and experiment. Transl. from the 2nd German ed. by Guy Barr. xvi, 281 p., ill. London: Methuen, 1926.
English translation of: Die theoretischen und experimentellen Grundlagen des neuen Wärmesatzes, Halle (Saale): W. Knapp, 1924; first published 1918.

PARTINGTON, J.R. Advances in thermodynamics. *Nature*, 1952, 170: 730-2.

PLANCK, Max. Leçons de thermodynamique, avec une conférence sur Le théorème de Nernst et l'hypothèse des quanta. Traduit sur la 3e éd. allem. par R. Chevassus. 311 p. Paris: A. Hermann, 1913.
French translation of Vorlesungen über die Theorie der Wärmestrahlung, *see* below, with additional matter.

PLANCK, Max. Das Prinzip der Erhaltung der Energie. 5th ed. xvi, 278 p. (Wissenschaft und Hypothese, 6) Leipzig: Teubner, 1924.
First published 1887.

PLANCK, Max. Treatise on thermodynamics. Transl. by A. Ogg. 3rd ed. transl. from the 7th German ed. xiv, 297 p. London: Longmans, 1927.
7th German edition of Vorlesungen über Thermodynamik Berlin: de Gruyter, 1922; reviewed in *Nature*, 1922, 110: 207.

PLANCK, Max. Vorlesungen über die Theorie der Wärmestrahlung. 5th rev.ed. x, 221 p., 6 ill. Leipzig: J.A. Barth, 1923.

ROSENFELD, L. La genèse des principes de la thermodynamique. *Bull.Soc.Sci.Liège*, 1941, 10: no. 3, 199-212.

SCHURMANN, Pablo F. Evolución de las teorías de la naturaleza de la luz. El nacimiento de la termodinámica. 91 p. Montevideo: Monteverde, 1938.
Revision of three lectures delivered by the author.

SIMON, Francis. The third law of thermodynamics: an historical survey. (40th Guthrie Lecture). *Year Book Phys. Soc.Lond.*, 1956, 1-22, 14 fig.

WATANABE, Masao. [On the establishment of the law of conservation of energy - especially in relation to a certain preceding historical conception. (In Japanese, with English summary)]. *Essays Stud.Tokyo Wom.Christ.Coll.*, 1953, 4: 45-56; 1954, 5: 1-16.

WITZ, Aimé. Les chaleurs spécifiques des gaz et des vapeurs. *Rev.Gén.Sci.*, 1923, 34: 425-35.
Includes a history of the subject.

CHda

COHEN, I. Bernard. Pioneers in the theory of heat. *Sci. Amer.*, 1954, 191: 60-3, 5 fig.

CHk philosophy and methodology

BONSACK, François. Information, thermodynamique, vie et pensée. Préface de Louis Couffignal. 191 p. Paris: Gauthier-Villars, 1961.
Reviewed by Michel Ambacher, *Dialogue*, 1962, 1: 227-8.

BRIDGMAN, Percy W. The nature of thermodynamics. xii, 229 p. Cambridge, Mass.: Harvard University Press, 1941. [CB 62/75]
1961 reprint (New York: Harper) contains as an appendix, the author's essay of 1953, entitled "Reflections on thermodynamics", and a brief, new introduction (2 pages).

GABIUS, P. Denkökonomie und Energieprinzip. xiii, 208 p. Berlin: Karl Curtius, 1913.
Reviewed by Ernst Bloch, *Isis*, 1913, 1: 542.

ROTHSTEIN, Jerome. Thermodynamics and some undecidable physical questions. *Phil.Sci.*, 1964, 31: 40-8.

CHm

DUKOV, V.M. Rol' poniatiia konvektsionnogo toka v razvitii fiziki. [The role of the concept of the convection current in the development of physics. (In Russian)]. *Tr.Inst.Ist. Est.Tekh.*, 1961, 43: 112-39.

CHmd

COSTA DE BEAUREGARD, Olivier. Le second principe de la science du temps (entropie - information - irréversibilité). 158 p. Paris: Éditions du Seuil, 1963.
Reviewed by W. Voisé, *Arch.Int.Hist.Sci.*, 1964, 16: 75-6.

GRÜNBAUM, Adolf. Time and entropy. *Amer.Scient.*, 1955, 43: 550-72.

CHx techniques and instruments

CHxb

BRAGG, William Henry. History of the vacuum flask. *Nature*, 1940, 145: 408-10, 2 fig.

CHxk-by

SCIENCE MUSEUM. Handbook of the collection relating to heat and cold. By J.A. Chaldecott. Part II. Catalogue of exhibits with descriptive notes. 64 p., 6 pl. London: H.M. Stationery Office, 1954. [CB 82/204]
Reviewed by A. Armitage, *Bull.Brit.Soc.Hist.Sci.*, 1955, 2: 37.

CHxm measurement

for clinical thermometry *see* QDxp

BARNETT, Martin K. The development of thermometry and the temperature concept. *Osiris*, 1956, 12: 269-341.

BOYER, Carl B. History of the measurement of heat. *Sci. Mon.*, 1943, 57: 442-51, 546-54.

GLIOZZI, Mario. Idea de temperatura et historia de thermometro. *Schola Vita*, 1931, 6: 21-4.

GUILLAUME, Ch.Ed. Pierre Chappuis et le développement moderne de la thermométrie. *Rev.Gen.Sci.*, 1916, 27: 204-8.

MALININ, Dorothy R.; YOE, John H. Development of the laws of calorimetry. *J.Chem.Educ.*, 1961, 38: 129-31.

MEYER, Kirstine. Die Entwicklung des Temperaturbegriffes im Laufe der Zeiten. Uebersetzt aus dem Dänischen von Irmgard Kolde und mit einem Vorwort von Eilhard Wiedemann. vi, 160 p. (Die Wissenschaft, 48) Braunschweig: Vieweg, 1913.

NEGRETTI and ZAMBRA, London. Story of temperature measurement. With the help of J.A. Chaldecott. 20 p., 36 ill., bibliogr. London: [1958].
Reviewed by R.J. Forbes, *Janus*, 1958, 47: 259.

POWELL, R.W.; WOLEDGE, G. History of the British thermal unit. *Nature*, 1942, 149: 525-6, 613.

CHxm-by

SCIENCE MUSEUM. Handbook of the collection illustrating temperature measurement and control. By J.A. Chaldecott. Part II. Catalogue of exhibits with descriptive notes. vi, 57 p., 6 pl. London: H.M. Stationery Office, 1955. [CB 81/268 and 82/191]
Reviewed by A. Armitage, *Bull.Brit.Soc.Hist.Sci.*, 1955, 2: 37.

CHxp

ARMSTRONG, George T. The calorimeter and its influence on the development of chemistry. *J.Chem.Educ.*, 1964, 41: 297-307.

BOYER, Carl B. Early principles in the calibration of thermometers. *Amer.J.Phys.*, 1942, 10: 176-80. [CB 64/450]

BUESS, H. Zur Frühgeschichte des Thermometers. *Experientia*, 1946, 2: 194-5, ill.

TAYLOR, F. Sherwood. The origin of the thermometer. *Ann. Sci.*, 1942, 5: 129-56, 14 fig.

VOLLMANN, R. The story of the thermometer. *Discovery*, 1959, 20: 378-84.

VOLLMANN, R. Das Thermometer. *Ciba-Z.*, 1957, 8: 2882-910, 23 fig. [CB 84/303]

CHxu control instruments

RAMSEY, A.R.J. The thermostat or heat governor. An outline of its history. *Trans.Newcomen Soc.*, 1950, 25: 53-72, 19 fig.

CHzl LOW TEMPERATURES

ADWENTOWSKI, Karol; PASTERNAK, Antoni; WOJTASZEK, Zdzislaw. Who of the two: Dewar or Olszewski? A polemic in England about the priority in liquefaction of permanent gases. *Kwart.Hist.Nauk.Tech.*, 1957-58 (special issue), 77-95.

PICARD, Emile. Les basses températures et l'oeuvre de M. Kamerlingh Onnes. Lecture faite en la séance publique annuelle du 18 décembre 1939. Notice historique. *Mém.Acad. Sci., 2nd ser.*, 1936-39, 24 p., portr.

SCIENCE MUSEUM. Very low temperatures, their attainment and uses. A survey of the physical principles underlying the attainment of extremely low temperatures and of their technical and scientific applications, as illustrated in a special exhibition held in the Science Museum, March-May, 1936. 3 vol. by T.C. Crawhall. 1. 31 p.; 2. An illustrated descriptive account of the exhibits. 59 p., fig.; 3. A symposium of lectures [by various authors]. 75 p. London: H.M. Stationery Off., 1936-37. [CB 53/261]

CI KINETIC THEORY; STATISTICAL MECHANICS

BRUSH, Stephen G. Development of kinetic theory of gases. 1. Herapath. 2. Waterston. 3. Clausius. 4. Maxwell. 5. The equation of state. 6. Viscosity. *Ann.Sci.*, 1957, 13: 188-98, 273-82; 1958, 14: 185-96, 243-55; *Amer.J.Phys.*, 1961, 29: 593-605; 1962, 30: 269-81.

CONFERENCE ON IRREVERSIBLE THERMODYNAMICS AND THE STATISTICAL MECHANICS OF PHASE TRANSITIONS. Proceedings of the Conference held at Brown University in June 1962. Ed. by T. Shedlovsky and E. Montroll. *J.Math.Phys.*, 1963, 4: (2), 147-322. [CB 89/581]
The conference was held to mark the 30th anniversary of the publication of Onsager's paper on irreversible thermodynamics and the reciprocal relations.

DUGAS, René. La théorie physique au sens de Boltzmann et ses prolongements modernes. Préface de Louis de Broglie. 310 p. (Bibliothèque scientifique, 33) Neuchâtel: Éditions de Griffon, 1959.
Reviewed by Anna Beckman, *Lychnos*, 1960-61, 348-50; by R. Bruce Lindsay, *Phys.Today*, 1960, 13: 52.

GOSIEWSKI, Wladyslaw. Róznych teoryj o ciśnenu w gazach. [Various theories of pressure in gases. (In Polish)]. *Tow. Nauk Scislych Paryzu Tam.*, 1874, 5: no. 2, 1-15. English translation published by Lawrence Radiation Laboratory, University of California, document UCRL-Trans-885 (L), 1962. [CB 88/621]

JEANS, James Hopwood. The dynamical theory of gases. 3rd ed. viii, 442 p. Cambridge University Press, 1921.
First published 1904.

JEANS, James Hopwood. An introduction to the kinetic theory of gases. vi, 311 p. Cambridge University Press, 1940. [CB 62/76]
The book begins with a short historical survey of the subject.

KIPNIS, A.Ia. K istorii ustanovleniia uraveniia sostoianiia ideal'nogo gaza. [On the history of the establishment of the equation of state of an ideal gas. (In Russian)] *Vop. Ist.Est.Tekh.*, 1962, 13: 91-4.

MENDOZA, E. A sketch for a history of the kinetic theory of gases. *Phys.Today*, 1961, 14: no. 3, 36-9.

MENDOZA, E. The surprising history of the kinetic theory of gases. *Mem.Manchester Lit.Phil.Soc.*, 1963, 105: 15-28.

CIkk

EHRENFEST, Paul; EHRENFEST, Tatiana. The conceptual foundations of the statistical approach in mechanics. Transl. by Michael J. Moravcsik. xvi, 114 p., bibliogr. Ithaca, N.Y.: Cornell University Press, 1959. [CB 87/632]
The original "Begriffliche Grundlagen der statistischen Auffassung in der Mechanik" was published in 1912.

ROSEN, Robert. The Gibbs paradox and the distinguishability of physical systems. *Phil.Sci.*, 1964, 31: 232-6.

CIwh

PIECH, Tadeusz, ed. Wkład polskich uczonych do fizyki statystyczno-molekularnej. [Polish scholarly contributions to statistical molecular physics. (In Polish with summary in English and Russian)] xxv, 279 p. (Sources of the History of Science and Technology, 3) Wrocław: Zaklad Narodowy im Ossolińskich, 1962.
The papers divide into two groups: purely thermodynamical from 1880-1890; thermodynamical-statistical, from the beginning of the 20th century.

CJ OPTICS

see also CN ELECTROMAGNETISM;
CO ELECTROMAGNETIC WAVES; RADIATION
CP SPECTROSCOPY
OQzv VISION

CJc general history

BRAGG, William Henry. The universe of light. x, 283 p., ill. London: Bell; New York: Macmillan, 1933.

BROGLIE, Louis de. Coup d'oeil sur l'histoire de l'optique. *Thalès*, 1934, 1: 3-8.

BROGLIE, Louis de. Un exemple des synthèses successives de la physique: les théories de la lumière. *Thalès*, 1935, 2: 9-22; also in *Enseign.Sci.*, 1936, 10: 65-79.

BROGLIE, Louis de. Voies anciennes et perspectives nouvelles en théorie de la lumière. *Rev.Métaphys.Morale*, 1934, 41: 445-57.

COURTINES, Marcel. La lumière, principe du monde, à propos de Jean Perrin, prix Nobel de physique 1926. 61 p. (*Cah. Quinzaine, 18th ser.*, no. 4) Paris: Artisan du Livre, 1927.
Reviewed by P.J. Richard, *Rev.Gén.Sci.*, 1928, 39: 24.

FORTI, Umberto. Le concezioni della luce da Democrito a Cartesio. *Period.Mat.*, 1928, 8: 90-102, 3 fig.

FORTI, Umberto. Gli ultimi tentativi di una concezione meccanica della luce, e la teoria elettromagnetica. *Period. Mat.*, 1930, 10: 189-203.

FRANKFURT, U.I.; FRENK, A.M. Ocherki razvitiia optiki dvizhushchikhsia tel. [Essays on the development of the optics of moving bodies. (In Russian)]. *Tr.Inst.Ist.Est. Tekh.*, 1961, 43: 3-49.

HARVEY, E. Newton. A history of luminescence from the earliest times until 1900. xxiii, 692 p., 50 pl. (*Mem. Amer.Phil.Soc.*, 44) Philadelphia: American Philosophical Society, 1957.
Reviewed by Conway Zirkle, *Isis*, 1959, 50: 68-9; for other reviews *see* CB 83/185, CB 84/314 and CB 85/392.

HOPPE, Edmund. Geschichte der Optik. vi, 263 p. (J.J. Webers Illustrierte Handbücher) Leipzig: J.J. Weber, 1926.

IVES, Herbert E. Adventures with standing light waves. (The Rumford Medal Lecture.) *Proc.Amer.Acad.Arts Sci.*, 1951, 81: 1-32. [CB 79/174]

LOHNE, Johannes. Zur Geschichte des Brechungsgesetzes. *Sudhoffs Arch.*, 1963, 47: 152-72.

LORIA, Stanislaw. Die Lichtbrechung in Gasen als physikalisches und chemisches Problem. 92 p. Braunschweig: Vieweg, 1914.

MacDONALD, H.M. Theories of light. *Science*, 1934, 80: 233-8.
Address to the British Association for the Advancement of Science, Aberdeen, 1934.

MACH, Ernst. The principles of physical optics: an historical and philosophical treatment. Transl. by John S. Anderson and A.F.A. Young. xi, 324 p., 10 pl. London: Methuen, 1926.
German original (Leipzig: J.A. Barth, 1921) reviewed by Ernst Bloch, *Isis*, 1921-22, 4: 560-2.

MALLIK, D.N. Optical theories. Based on lectures delivered before Calcutta University. 181 p. Cambridge University Press, 1917.

MERRITT, Ernest; NICHOLS, Edward L.; CHILD, C.D. Selected topics in the field of luminescence. 126 p. (*Bull.Nat. Res.Counc.*, 5: part 5, no. 30) Washington, D.C.: 1923. [CB 16/294]

MICHELSON, Albert Abraham. Studies in optics. xxv, 176 p. (Phoenix Science Series) Chicago, Ill.: University of Chicago Press, 1962.
A re-issue of the 1927 edition.

NEURATH, Otto. Prinzipielles zur Geschichte der Optik. *Arch.Gesch.Naturwiss.Tech.*, 1915, 5: 371-89.

NIKITENKO, G.I. [The rise of the quantum theory of light. (In Russian)]. *Tr.Inst.Ist.Est.Tekh.*, 1959, 28: 405-20.

OPITZ, H.R.G. Über das erste Problem der Dioptrik. 2 parts. 1. 26 p.; 2. Materialien zu einer kritischen Geschichte des Problems. 23 p. (Programme) Berlin: Weidmann, 1903-12.

PAINLEVÉ, Paul. Les axiomes de la mécanique. Examen critique. Note sur la propagation de la lumière. xvii, 112 p. (Les Maîtres de la Pensée Scientifique) Paris: Gauthier-Villars, 1922. [CB 14/554]

PAPANASTASSIOU, Ch.E. Les théories sur la nature de la lumière de Descartes à nos jours et l'évolution de la théorie physique. 162 p. Paris: Jouve, 1935. [CB 45/282]

PICARD, Émile. L'évolution des idées sur la lumière et l'oeuvre d'Albert Michelson. *Rev.Sci.*, 1936, 74: 33-48.

PICARD, Émile. L'évolution des idées sur la lumière et l'oeuvre d'Albert Michelson. Lecture faite en la séance annuelle du 16 décembre 1935. Notice historique. 35 p., portr. (*Mém. Acad.Sci., 2nd ser.*, 62) Paris: Gauthier-Villars, 1935.

PLA, Cortes. El enigma de la luz. With a foreword by George Sarton. 328 p., 15 pl., 48 fig. Buenos Aires: Kraft, 1949.
Reviewed by H.J.J. Winter, *Isis*, 1951, 42: 164; by Jean Itard, *Arch.Int.Hist.Sci.*, 1950, 3: 706-8.

POLAK, L.S. Iz istorii volnovoi teorii sveta. [History of the wave theory of light. (In Russian)]. *Vop.Ist.Est.Tekh.*, 1956, 2: 76-80.

PRAT, Roland. L'optique. 187 p. Paris: Éditions du Seuil, 1962.
Reviewed by Vasco Ronchi, *Arch.Int.Hist.Sci.*, 1963, 16: 87.

RONCHI, Vasco. Classical optics is a mathematical science. *Arch.Hist.Exact Sci.*, 1961, 1: 160-71.

RONCHI, Vasco. Classical optics is a mathematical science. *Atti Fond.Ronchi*, 1964, 19: 635-50.
Includes a short history of classical optics. The paper is similar to the above.

RONCHI, Vasco. L'evoluzione dell'ottica negli ultimi venticinque anni. *Atti Fond.Ronchi*, 1952, 7: 1-12.

RONCHI, Vasco. Histoire de la lumière. Traduit de l'italien par Juliette Taton. 292 p., 83 fig. (Bibliothèque de l'École Pratique des Hautes Études, VIe section) Paris: Armand Colin, 1956. [CB 83/199]
French translation of the second edition of "Storia della luce", *see* below.
Reviewed by Fredrik Berg, *Lychnos*, 1957-58, 432; by Maurice Daumas, *Arch.Int.Hist.Sci.*, 1958, 11: 60-3; by Jean Itard, *Rev.Hist.Sci.*, 1958, 11: 365.

RONCHI, Vasco. Optics, the science of vision. Transl. from the Italian and rev. by Edward Rosen. ix, 360 p., ill. New York: New York University Press, 1957. [CB 83/199]
Italian original Bologna: Zanichelli, 1955.
Reviewed by Lawrence Kruger, *Bull.Hist.Med.*, 1958, 32: 482.

RONCHI, Vasco. Storia della luce. 2nd ed. 285 p., 84 fig. (Fondazione "Giorgio Ronchi") Bologna: N. Zanichelli, 1952.
First publ. 1939 and reviewed by I. Bernard Cohen, *Isis*, 1941, 33: 294-6. 2nd ed. reviewed in *Rev.Hist.Sci.*, 1952, 5: 127 (A. Biot) and 1953, 6: 74-5 (R. Taton).

RONCHI, Vasco. Ventiquattr' anni dopo. *Atti Fond.Ronchi*, 1951, 6: 3-8.

RUNGE, I. Zur Farbenlehre. *Z.Tech.Phys.*, 1927, 8: 289-99.

SABRA, A.I. Explanation of optical reflection and refraction: Ibn al-Haytham, Descartes, Newton. *Proc.10th Int.Congr.Hist.Sci.* (Ithaca, 1962), (1), p. 551-4. Paris: Hermann, 1964.

SABRA, A.I. A note on a suggested modification of Newton's corpuscular theory of light to reconcile it with Foucault's experiment of 1850. *Brit.J.Phil.Sci.*, 1954-55, 5: 149-51.

SCHURMANN, Pablo F. Evolución de las teorías de la naturaleza de la luz. El nacimiento de la termodinámica. 91 p. Montevideo: Monteverde, 1938.
Revision of three lectures delivered by the author.

THOMSON, J.J. The structure of light. xii, 38 p. (Fison Memorial Lecture) Cambridge University Press, 1925.
French translation (Paris: Blanchard, 1929) reviewed by G. Beck, *Deut.Lit.Zeitung*, 1929, 6: 1600-2.

TONNELAT, M.A. Quelques exemples comparés "d'expériences cruciales" choisis dans l'histoire des théories de la lumière. *Act.VIIIe Congr.Int.Hist.Sci.* (Florence, 1956), p. 109-14. Paris: Hermann, 1958.

VOLKRINGER, H. Les théories sur la nature de la lumière (sommaire des conférences). *Thalès*, 1934, 1: 57-8.

CJc-br

Forschungen zur Geschichte der Optik. (Supplement to *Zeitschrift für Instrumentenkunde*) Vol. 1-3. 1928-35; 1936-38; 1939-43. Berlin: Julius Springer, 1928-43.

CJce-bu

POLLARD, A.F.C. The decimal bibliographical classification of the Institut international de bibliographie. Partly translated for the formation and use of a universal bibliographical repertory concerning optics, light and cognate subjects. vii, 110 p. Cambridge University Press, 1926.
Abridged translation of the classification tables contained in the *Manuel du Répertoire bibliographique universel* ... intended to serve as a guide to the Subject Index of the Transactions of the Optical Society.

CJce-bv

Transactions of the Optical Society. Subject Index of the Transactions of the Optical Society by A.F.C. Pollard. Vol. 1-25. iv, 90 p. Cambridge University Press, 1926. [CB 21/573]

CJhd

ROHR, Moritz von. Über Geschichtstabellen für die technische Optik. *Naturwissenschaften*, 1932, 20: 937-40.

CJk/w special aspects

CJkb

BROGLIE, Louis de. Deux conceptions adverses sur la nature de la lumière et leur synthèse possible. *Scientia*, 1927, 47: 128-34.

PLANCK, Max. Das Wesen des Lichts. Vortrag. 2nd ed. 22 p. Berlin: Springer, 1920.
French translation Paris: Blanchard, 1927.

CJsc

RONCHI, Vasco. The development of optics and its impact on society. *Impact*, 1959, 9: 123-36.

CJwn

CHENAKAL, V.L. [Optics in pre-revolutionary Russia. (In Russian)]. *Tr.Inst.Ist.Est.*, 1947, 1: 121-67.

CJxk optical instruments

see also FAxk TELESCOPES
ORzs SPECTACLES
WU OPTICAL INSTRUMENTS: TECHNOLOGY
XF PHOTOGRAPHY

AHLSTRÖM, Otto. Synverktyg från äldre tider. [Optical instruments in olden times. (In Swedish)] 168 p., 167 ill. Stockholm: Stockholms Förenade Specialoptiker, 1943.
Catalogue of an exhibition covering 1600-1900.
Reviewed by Fredrik Berg, *Lychnos*, 1943, 424-5.

CLAY, Reginald S. The photographic lens from the historical point of view. (25th annual Traill-Taylor Memorial Lecture) *Photogr.J.*, 1922, 46: 459-76. Summary in *Nature*, 1922, 110: 739-40.

FELLMANN, Emil A. Ueber asphaerische Linsen, ein Beitrag zur Problemgeschichte der Optik. *Physis*, 1963, 5: 166-72.

JACOB, G. Die Erwähnungen der Schattenstheater und der Zauberlaternen bis zum Jahre 1700. 18 p., bibliogr. Berlin: Mayer & Müller, 1912.

KISCH, Arnold I. Predecessors of the glass micrometer. *J. Roy.Microscop.Soc.*, 1951, 71: 181-5, 3 pl. [CB 79/174]

LAUFER, Berthold. Optical lenses. *T'oung Pao*, 1915, 16: 169-228. [CB 7/147]

MIDDLETON, W.E. Knowles. Archimedes, Kircher, Buffon, and the burning-mirrors. *Isis*, 1961, 52: 533-43.

PARISELLE, H. Les instruments d'optique. vi, 218 p. Paris: Colin, 1923. [CB 14/561]

PAUSCHMANN, G. Zur Geschichte der linsenlosen Abbildung. *Arch.Gesch.Naturwiss.Tech.*, 1922, 9: 86-103.

PERGENS, Ed. Optotypes. *Janus*, 1917, 22: 406-13. [CB 11/447]

RAYLEIGH, Robert John Strutt, *4th baron*. Vision in nature and vision aided by science; science and warfare. *Science*, 1938, 88: 175-81, 204-8.

ROHR, Moritz von. Der Astigmatismus in sprachlicher und sachlicher Hinsicht. *Naturwissenschaften*, 1932, 20: 847-50.

ROHR, Moritz von. Die Erkenntnis von dem wahren Wesen des Lichtbildes und ihr Einfluss auf das Verständnis für die optischen Geräte im allgemeinen. *Naturwissenschaften*, 1932, 20: 496-501, 514-20.

ROHR, Moritz von. Die optischen Instrumente. Brille, Lupe, Mikroskop, Fernrohr, Aufnahmelinse und ihnen verwandte Vorkehrungen. 4th ed. vi, 130 p., 91 fig. Berlin: Springer, 1930.

RONCHI, Vasco. Forty years of history of a grating interferometer. *Appl.Opt.*, 1964, 3: 437-51.

RONCHI, Vasco. Les lentilles de verre du moyen âge à l'époque moderne. 17 p. (Conférences du Palais de la Découverte, Série D, 52) Paris: Université de Paris, 1957.

RONCHI, Vasco. Storia delle lenti. *Atti Fond.Ronchi*, 1947, 2: 1-24.

SINGER, Charles. Steps leading to the invention of the first optical apparatus. In: Singer, Charles, ed. Studies in the history of science, vol. 2, p. 385-413, 533-4. Oxford: Clarendon Press, 1921. [CB 11/449]

VOSKUIL, J. De afstamming van de tooverlantaarn. [Development of the magic lantern. (In Dutch)] *Faraday*, 1946-47, 16: 45-55, ill.
Lecture delivered in Leiden, 26 Oct., 1946.

WUERSCHMIDT, J. Zur Geschichte, Theorie und Praxis der Camera Obscura. *Z.Math.Naturwiss.Unterricht*, 1915, 46: 466-76.

CJxk-tq

REVEL, J.-F. Les instruments d'optique à l'aide des grands maîtres. *Connaiss.Arts*, 1961, no. 114, 70-7.

CJxkm microscopes

for microscopy *see* JA

ALLEN, Roy Morris. The microscope. viii, 286 p. London: Chapman and Hall, 1940.
Reviewed in *Nature*, 1941, 147: 129.

CLAY, Reginald S.; COURT, Thomas H. The history of the microscope, compiled from original instruments and documents, up to the introduction of the achromatic microscope. xiv, 266 p., 164 fig. London: Griffin, 1932.
Reviewed by C.A. Kofoid, *Isis*, 1934, 21: 227-30.

DEUTSCH, Karl. Some notes on the development of electron microscopy. *NTM Z.Gesch.Naturwiss.Tech.Med.*, [1963], 1: no. 4, 45-9.

DISNEY, Alfred N. Origin and development of the microscope, as illustrated by catalogues of the instruments and accessories, in the collections of the Royal Microscopical Society, together with bibliographies of original authorities. In collaboration with Cyril F. Hill and Wilfred E. Watson Baker. Preceded by an historical survey on the early progress of optical science by the editor. xi, 303 p., 36 fig., 30 pl. London: Royal Microscopical Society, 1928. [CB 25/415]
Reviewed by C.A. Kofoid, *Isis*, 1934, 20: 495-7.

FORD, William W. Development of our early knowledge concerning magnification. *Science*, 1934, 79: 578-81.

FREUNDLICH, Martin M. Origin of the electron microscope. The history of a great invention and of a misconception concerning the inventors is renewed. *Science*, 1963, 142: 185-8.

FRISON, Edward. The belated construction of water-immersion objectives in Britain. *J.Quekett Microscop.Club*, 1961, 5: 349-57.

FRISON, Edward. Historical survey of the use of divergent and correcting lenses in the microscope. *Microscope*, 1951, 8: 115-20.

GENUNG, Elizabeth F. The development of the compound microscope. *Bull.Hist.Med.*, 1942, 12: 575-94.

HINTZSCHE, E. Das Mikroskop. *Ciba Z.*, 1949, 10: 4310-40, ill.

NEVIANI, Antonio. Appunti per una storia intorno ai foraminiferi dall'antichità al secolo XVIII. Con appendice sugli antichi microscopi dell'Istituto di Bologna venduti all'esterno nel 1886. *Mem.Pontif.Accad.Sci.Nuovi Lincei*, 1935, *ser. 3*, 2: 131-210. [CB 48/577]

POLICARD, A. La merveilleuse histoire du microscope. *Rev. Univ.Lyon*, 1932, 3: 203-31.

RONCHI, Vasco. De la microscopie optique à la microscopie électronique. *Scientia*, 1950, 44: 17-22.

RONCHI, Vasco. Nuovi rilievi circa l'invenzione del microscopio. *Atti Fond.Ronchi*, 1949, 4: 38-44, 2 fig.

SOBOL, S.L. On the history of the invention of the achromatic microscope. *Act.VIIIe Congr.Int.Hist.Sci.* (Florence, 1956), p. 800-3. Paris: Hermann, 1958.

USHER, Abbott Payson. The development of the microscope and its application to medicine and public health. *Amer.J. Pharm.Educ.*, 1951, 15: 319-38.

WREDDEN, J.H. The microscope: its theory and applications. With an historical introduction by W.E. Watson-Baker. xxiv, 296 p. London: Churchill, 1947. [CB 73/174]

CJxkm-by

CITTERT, P.H. van. Descriptive catalogue of the collection of microscopes in charge of the Utrecht University Museum. With an introductory historical survey of the resolving power of the microscope. 110 p., ill. Groningen: Noordhoff, 1934.
Reviewed by M.A. Van Andel, *Bijdr.Gesch.Geneesk.*, 1935, 15: 68.

KLAAUW, C.J. van der. Oude microtemen in het Nederlandsch Historisch Natuurwetenschappelijk Museum te Leiden. [Old microscopes in the Dutch Natural History Museum in Leiden. (In Dutch)] *Bijdr.Gesch.Geneesk.*, 1934, 14: 187-95, 1 pl.

RIJKSMUSEUM VOOR DE GESCHIEDENIS DER NATUURWETENSCHAPPEN. Descriptive catalogue of the simple microscopes in the Rijksmuseum voor de Geschiedenis der Natuurwetenschappen at Leyden. By P. van der Star. 86 p., 8 pl., ill. (Communication, 87) Leiden: 1953. [CB 80/131]
Reviewed by Ed. Frison, *Arch.Int.Hist.Sci.*, 1953, 32: 513-14.

CJxkm-wb

CESVET, Helen. Some early American microscopes in the Dittrick Museum. *Bull.Cleveland Med.Libr.*, 1963, 10: (2), 23-8.

LEIKIND, Morris. The microscope collection of the Medical Museum, Armed Forces Institute of Pathology. *What's New*, Dec. 1952, 17-22, pl.

LEWIS, Frederic T. The advent of microscopes in America. With notes on their earlier history. *Sci.Mon.*, 1943, 57: 249-59.

RICHARDS, Oscar W. American microscope makers and introduction to the collection. *J.Roy.Microscop.Soc.*, 1964, 83: 123-6.
The collection is that of more than 500 instruments in the Medical Museum of the Armed Forces Institute of Pathology in Washington.

CJzv VELOCITY OF LIGHT

BOYER, Carl B. Early estimates of the velocity of light. *Isis*, 1941, 33: 24-40.

DORSEY, N. Ernest. The velocity of light. *Trans.Amer.Phil. Soc.*, 1944, 34: 1-110. [CB 68/53]

ESSEN, I. The velocity of light. *Endeavour*, 1956, 15: 87-91, 3 fig., 1 table.

GHEURY DE BRAY, M.E.J. Published values of the velocity of light. *Nature*, 1927, 120: 404-5.

GHEURY DE BRAY, M.E.J. The velocity of light. *Nature*, 1927, 120: 602-4.

GHEURY DE BRAY, M.E.J. The velocity of light. History of its determination from 1849 to 1933. *Isis*, 1936, 25: 437-48. [CB 49/175]

GHEURY DE BRAY, M.E.J. La vitesse de la lumière. *Ciel Terre*, 1928, 44: 23-9, 107-18, 202-8, 403-10; 1929, 45: 3-11, 82-8, 187-91; 1930, 46: 216-23; 1931, 47: 110-24; 1934, 50: 132-4.

JAFFE, Bernard. Michelson and the speed of light. 197 p., ill. (Anchor Books; Science Study Series) Garden City, N.Y.: Doubleday, 1960.
Reviewed by Mark Graubard, *Science*, 1961, 133: 1472-3; by R. Siegfried, *Isis*, 1962, 53: 426-8; by R. Bruce Lindsay, *Phys.Today*, 1962, 15: no. 1, 72-4.

O'DELL, C.R. The velocity of light. *Leafl.Astron.Soc. Pacific*, no. 402, Dec. 1962, 9: 8 p.
Lists the various methods used in determining the velocity of light during 1676-1958.

PLA, Cortés. Sobre la constancia de la velocidad de la luz. *Rev.Cienc.*, 1948, 50: 21-6.

PLA, Cortés. Velocidad de la luz y relatividad. Con un apéndice conteniendo las memorias originales de Arago, Fizeau y Foucault. 295 p. Buenos Aires: Espasa-Calpe, 1947. [CB 75/89]
Reviewed by Aldo Mieli, *Arch.Int.Hist.Sci.*, 1948, 1: 740-1.

CK COLOUR SCIENCE

BIRREN, Faber. Color; a survey in words and pictures, from ancient mysticism to modern science. 223 p., ill., bibliogr. New Hyde Park, N.Y.: University Books, 1963.

BIRREN, Faber. The story of color from ancient mysticism to modern science. 338 p. Westport, Conn.: Crimson Press, 1941.

BORN, Max. Betrachtungen zur Farbenlehre. *Naturwissenschaften*, 1963, 50: 29-39. [CB 89/562]
Includes a criticism of Heimendahl, *see* below.

FRANKLIN, Christine Ladd. Colour and colour theories. xv, 287 p. London: Kegan Paul, 1929.

HALBERTSMA, K.T.A. A history of the theory of colour. 267 p. Amsterdam: Swets and Zeitlinger, 1949. [CB 79/173]
Reviewed by R. Hooykaas, *Arch.Int.Hist.Sci.*, 1951, 30: 791-3; by E.J. Dijksterhuis, *Rev.Hist.Sci.*, 1952, 5: 187-9.

HEIMENDAHL, Eckart. Licht und Farbe: Ordnung und Funktion der Farbwelt. 284 p. Berlin: De Gruyter, 1961.

NATUCCI, A. Ipotese antiche e moderne sulla formazione dei colori. *Act.VIIIe Congr.Int.Hist.Sci.* (Florence, 1956), p. 225-36. Paris: Hermann, 1958.

RONCHI, Vasco. Storia del colore. *Atti VIIe Giornate Int. Colore* (Florence, 1963), p. 3-14. Firenze: Baccini e Chiappi, [1964?].

TONNELAT, M.-A. L'évolution des idées sur la nature des couleurs. 23 p. (Conférence du Palais de la Découverte le 3 mars 1956) Paris: Université de Paris, 1956.

CKth

SKARD, Sigmund. The use of color in literature. A survey of research. *Proc.Amer.Phil.Soc.*, 1946, 90: 163-249.

CL MAGNETISM

ANDRADE, E.N. da C. The early history of the permanent magnet. *Endeavour*, 1958, 17: 22-30, 14 fig.

BITTER, Francis. Magnets: the education of a physicist. 155 p., fig. (Science Study Series, S2) Garden City, N.Y.: Doubleday Anchor Books, 1959.
Reviewed by Charles Hellman, *Science*, 1959, 130: 616-17.

DARWIN, C.G. Recent developments in the theory of magnetism. Discourse delivered at the Royal Institution on Friday, May 15, 1925. *Nature*, 1925, 116: 403-5.

DORFMAN, J.G. L'évolution de la théorie du magnétisme au XXme siècle. *Act.VIIIe Congr.Int.Hist.Sci.* (Florence, 1956), p. 250-3. Paris: Hermann, 1958.

KRAMER, John B. The early history of magnetism. *Trans.Newcomen Soc.*, 1933-34, 14: 183-200.

QUIMBY, S.L.; *et al.* Theories of magnetism. 261 p. (*Bull. Nat.Res.Counc.*, 3: no. 18) Washington: 1922. [CB 16/326]
German translation: Theorien des Magnetismus. x, 309 p. (Die Wissenschaft, 74) Braunschweig: Vieweg, 1925.

STILL, Alfred. Soul of lodestone: the background of magnetical science. 233 p. New York: Murray Hill, 1946.
A companion volume to the author's Soul of amber: the background of electrical science, *see* CMc

VAN VLECK, John Hasbrouck. Landmarks in the theory of magnetism. *Amer.J.Phys.*, 1950, 18: 495-509.

WEISS, Pierre; FOËX, Gabriel. Le magnétisme. viii, 216 p., 69 fig. Paris: A.Colin, 1926. [CB 21/573]

CM ELECTRICITY
including electricity and magnetism (combined)

CMc general history

CAMPBELL, Norman Robert. Modern electrical theory. 2nd ed. xii, 400 p. (Cambridge Physical Series) Cambridge University Press, 1913.
Supplementary chapters 15-17 on Series spectra, Relativity and The structure of the atom, published as monographs 1921-23.

CANBY, Edward T. A history of electricity. 105 p. (The New Illustrated Library of Science and Invention, 6) New York: Hawthorn Books, 1963; London: Leisure Arts, 1964. [CB 90/517]
French and German editions Lausanne: Rencontre und Erik Nitsche, 1963.

CHAUFFOUR, Hubert. Les origines du galvanisme. 96 p. (Thesis) Paris: Impr. Jouve, 1913.

DAUJAT, Jean. Origines et formation de la théorie des phénomènes électriques et magnétiques. 530 p., 40 fig. Paris: Hermann, 1945.
Reviewed by René Taton, *Rev.Sci.*, 1947, 85: 633-4.

DEVAUX, Pierre. Histoire de l'électricité. 128 p., ill. ("Que Sais-Je?", 7) Paris: Presses Universitaires de France, 1941.

GOODMAN, Herman. Story of electricity and a chronology of electricity and electrotherapeutics. With an introduction by Victor Robinson. 62 p., ill. New York: Medical Life Press, 1928.
First publ. in *Med.Life*, 1927, 34: 576-626, 12 ill.

HENRY, P.S.H. Static: its occurrence and effects. *Ciba Rev.*, 1959, 11: 2-8.
Discusses the history of static electric charges from Thales to the present.

INTERNATIONAL ELECTRICAL CONGRESS. Compte rendu du Congrès International d'Electricité, Paris, 1932. 13 vol. Paris: Gauthier-Villars, 1933. [CB 41/602]
Volume 12 (11th and 13th Sessions) contains a number of papers on the history of electricity.

LANGEVIN, Paul. Cinquante ans d'évolution de la science électrique. *Atomes*, 1947, no. 11, 57-60.
Written in 1933.

MANN, Martin. The revolution in electricity. 171 p., 125 photos., 12 diagr. New York: Viking Press, 1962.
This book recounts the major historical developments in electrical sciences and describes the rapidly growing science of solid state physics.

MILLER, Dayton C. Sparks, lightning, cosmic rays. An anecdotal history of electricity. xvii, 192 p. New York: Macmillan, 1939.
Reviewed by I. Bernard Cohen, *Isis*, 1949, 32: 382-3.

NATIONAL ELECTRICAL MANUFACTURERS ASSOCIATION. Chronological history of electrical development from 600 B.C. 106, 37 p. New York: The Association, 1946.
Reviewed by Mario Gliozzi, *Arch.Int.Hist.Sci.*, 1949, 2: 761-3.

PLANCK, Max. Einführung in die Theorie der Electrizität und des Magnetismus. iv, 208 p., 12 ill. Leipzig: Hirzel, 1922.

ROBINSON, Myron. A history of the electric wind. *Amer.J. Phys.*, 1962, 30: 366-72.

ROLLER, Duane; ROLLER, Duane H.D. The development of the concept of the electric charge. Electricity from the Greeks to Coulomb. ix, 97 p., 11 fig. (Harvard Case Histories in Experimental Science, 8) Cambridge, Mass.: Harvard University Press; London: Oxford University Press, 1954.
Reviewed by V.F. Lenzen, *Isis*, 1955, 46: 369-70; for other reviews *see* CB 81/269 and CB 82/204.

ROLLER, Duane; ROLLER, Duane H.D. Prenatal history of electrical science. *Amer.J.Phys.*, 1953, 21: 343-56, 2 fig. [CB 80/125]

SANFORD, Fernando. Some early theories regarding electrical forces. The electric emanation theory. *Sci.Mon.*, 1921, 12: 544-50. [CB 12/638]

SKILLING, Hugh Hildreth. Exploring electricity. Man's unfinished quest. viii, 277 p., 20 ill. (Humanizing Science Series) New York: Ronald Press, 1948. [CB 75/90]

SOIXANTENAIRE de l'École Supérieure d'Électricité (Malakoff), 1894-1954. Exposés prononcés au cours des séances des 10-13 mai 1954. 244 p., portr., maps, fig. Paris: Imp. Chaix, 1955.
Reviewed by F. Russo, *Rev.Hist.Sci.*, 1958, 11: 96.

STILL, Alfred. Soul of amber: the background of electrical science. xiii, 274 p. New York: Murray Hill, 1944.

THOMSON, J.J. Electricity and matter. 162 p. (Mrs. Hepsa Ely Silliman Memorial Lecture) New York: Scribner, 1904.
French translation Paris: Gauthier-Villars, 1922.

TURPAIN, Albert. Le nouveau domaine de l'électricité; l'évolution des théories électriques. x, 72 p. Paris: Gauthier-Villars, 1924.

VERSCHAFFELT, J.E. Hoe onze voorstelling van de dielectrische polarisatie der materie zich ontwikkelde. [How our conception of the dielectrical polarisation of matter developed. (In Dutch)]. *Wis Natuurk.Tijdschr.*, 1940, 10: 45-56.

VILLARD, P. Le courant électrique et la ligne droite. *Rev. Sci.*, 1912, 50: 2e semestre, 545-8. [CB 3/564]

WINDRED, G. Early electrical science. *Discovery*, 1937, 18: 123-6.

WINDRED, G. The relation between pure and applied electrical theory: with special reference to mathematical methods. *Isis*, 1932, 18: 184-90. [CB 36/438]

WITZ, A. L'électricité. Ses hypothèses et ses théories successives. 173 p. Louvain: Ceuterick, 1921. [CB 14/561]
Originally published in *Rev.Quest.Sci.*, 1920, 78: 65-101, 305-26; 1921, 79: 72-95, 367-99.

CMc-bv

MOTTELAY, Paul Fleury. Bibliographical history of electricity and magnetism chronologically arranged. xx, 673 p., ill. London: Griffin, 1922.
Reviewed by George Sarton, *Isis*, 1924, 6: 104-7.

CMc-bx

STAR, P. van der. Catalogus. Uit de kinderjaren van de elektriciteit, de geschiedenis van de elektriciteit van 1600 tot ca. 1831. 28 p. (Rijksmuseum voor de Geschiedenis der Natuurwetenschappen, Mededeling, 116) Leiden: Rijksmuseum voor de Geschiedenis der Natuurwetenschappen, 1961.
Reviewed by Paul Bockstaele, *Sci.Hist.*, 1961, 3: 203.

CMce-bv

AMERICAN INSTITUTE OF ELECTRICAL ENGINEERS. Catalogue of the Wheeler gift of books, pamphlets and periodicals in the Library. Ed. by William D. Weaver. With introd., descriptive and critical notes by Brother Potamian. 2 vol. 504; 475 p., ill. New York: The Institute, 1909.
The library of electricity and magnetism collected by Latimer Clark (1822-98), acquired by Schuyler Skaats Wheeler (1860-1923) and presented to the Institute in 1901. Reviewed by George Sarton, *Isis*, 1924, 6: 104-7.

CMda

DIBNER, Bern. Ten founding fathers of the electrical science. 48 p., 21 ill. (Burndy Library Publications in the History of Science and Technology, 11) Norwald, Conn.: Burndy Library, 1954.
This brief history of electricity contains biographies of Gilbert, Guericke, Franklin, Volta, Ampère, Ohm, Gauss, Faraday, Henry, and Maxwell.

SCHAEFER, G.; NAUMANN, W. Medical men as investigators of magnetism and electricity. *Ciba Symp.* (Summit, N.J.), 1941, 3: 1037-42.

TURNER, Dorothy M. Makers of science. Electricity and magnetism. xv, 184 p., 65 ill. London: Oxford University Press, 1927. [CB 22/266]

CMdaj

DANNEMANN, Friedrich, ed. Die Entdeckung der Elektrizität. 108 p., 25 ill. (Voigtländers Quellenbücher, 75) Leipzig: R. Voigtlander, 1914. [CB 6/456]

CMk/x special aspects

CMkh

KING, W. James. The quantification of the concepts of electric charge and electric current. Part I. *Natur.Phil.*, 1963, 2: 107-27.

CMnh

KORN, A. Terminologie du potentiel et de l'électricité. *Isis*, 1914, 2: 183-90.

CMsc

SIEGEL, G. L'électricité comme facteur de civilisation. *Rev.Sci.*, 1912, 50: 2e semestre, 331-6.

CMwn

MITKEWICH, W.Th. Faraday and electrical science in Russia and the U.S.S.R. *Nature*, 1931, 128: 359-62.

SOKOLOV, V.A. K istorii issledovaniia fizicheskikh svoistv dielektrikov. [On the history of investigation of the physical properties of dielectrics. (In Russian)]. *Vop. Ist.Est.Tekh.*, 1963, 15: 96-101.
A review of the work of Russian physicists in this area at the end of the nineteenth and beginning of the twentieth centuries.

CMxk

SCHIMANK, Hans. Geschichte der Elektrisiermaschine bis zum Beginn des 19. Jahrhunderts. *Z.Tech.Phys.*, 1935, 16: 245-54.

CMxm electrical measurement

HUMPHREYS, A.W. The development of the conception and measurement of electric current. *Ann.Sci.*, 1937, 2: 164-78.

JAEGER, Wilhelm. Die Entstehung der internationalen Masse der Elektrotechnik. v, 101 p. (*Gesch.Einzeldarstell.Elektrotech.*, 4) Berlin: Springer, 1932.

KENNELLY, A.E. Recent developments in electrical units. *Elec.Eng.*, Feb. 1939, 58: 78-80. [CB 57/241]

KOKUBU, Yujiro; KOSHIO, Takabumi. [Problems on unification of unit-system from the historical point of view. (In Japanese)]. *J.Hist.Sci.Japan*, 1952, no. 22, 12-15.

RUTENBERG, D. The early history of the potentiometer system of electrical measurement. *Ann.Sci.*, 1939, 4: 212-43, 33 fig., 1 pl.

CMxm-nh

BARR, E. Scott. Concerning the naming of the "practical" electrical units. *Amer.J.Phys.*, 1961, 29: 532-9.

CMzs SUPERCONDUCTIVITY

BERLINCOURT, T.G. Type II superconductivity. *Rev.Mod.Phys.*, 1964, 6: 19-26.

GINSBERG, D.M. Resource letter Scy-1 on superconductivity. *Amer.J.Phys.*, 1964, 32: 85-9.

GORTER, C.J. Superconductivity until 1940 in Leiden and as seen from there. *Rev.Mod.Phys.*, 1964, 36: 3-7.

MENDELSSOHN, K. Prewar work on superconductivity as seen from Oxford. *Rev.Mod.Phys.*, 1964, 36: 7-12.

CN ELECTROMAGNETISM; ELECTRODYNAMICS

BAUER, Edmond. L'electromagnétisme hier et aujourd'hui. 348 p., 15 fig. (Sciences d'Aujourd'hui) Paris: Albin Michel, 1949. [CB 79/173]

BJERKNES, V.K.F. Dynamical aspects of electromagnetism. *Nature*, 1931, 128: 369-71.

BRAGG, William Henry. The story of electromagnetism. 64 p. London: Bell, 1941.
Reviewed in *Nature*, 1942, 149: 425.

COTTON, Aimé. Discours prononcé à l'Académie des Sciences de Paris, séance publique annuelle du lundi 19 décembre, 1938. *Compt.Rend.Acad.Sci.*, 1938, 207: 1269-79.
Includes account of the Laboratoire de Bellevue which houses the electro-magnet of the Académie des Sciences.

KENNELLY, A.E. The development of electromagnetism during the last hundred years. *Annu.Rep.Amer.Hist.Ass.for 1920*, p. 275-81. Washington, D.C.: 1925.

KENNELLY, A.E. The modern electric age in relation to Faraday's discovery of electromagnetic induction. *Nature,* 1931, 128: 356-9.

KUZNETSOV, B.G. Elektrodinamika Maksvella, ee istoki, razvitie i istoricheskoe znachenie. (k 75-letiiu so dnia smerti Maksvella.) [Maxwell's electrodynamics, its origin, growth and historical significance - on the 75th anniversary of Maxwell's death. (In Russian)] *Tr.Inst.Ist.Est.Tekh.,* 1955, 5: 136-80, portr.

KUZNETSOV, B.G. Origines historiques de l'électrodynamique de Maxwell. *Act.VIIIe Congr.Int.Hist.Sci.* (Florence, 1956), p. 286-8. Paris: Hermann, 1958.

McLAREN, Samuel Bruce. Scientific papers, Mainly on electrodynamics and natural radiation, including the substance of an Adams Prize Essay in the University of Cambridge. viii, 112 p., portr. Cambridge University Press, 1925. [CB 18/575]

MAGRINI, Silvio. I fenomeni magnetici nelle varie teorie elettromagnetiche. Note storico-critiche. 166 p., 27 fig. Bologna: Zanichelli, 1912.
Reviewed by A. Mieli, *Isis,* 1919, 2: 427-8.

MOON, Parry; SPENCER, Domina Eberle. Electromagnetism without magnetism: an historical sketch. *Amer.J.Phys.,* 1954, 22: 120-4.

ROY, Louis. L'électrodynamique des milieux isotropes en repos, d'après Helmholtz et Duhem. 94 p. Paris: Gauthier-Villars, 1923.

SWANN, W.F.G., *et al.* Electrodynamics of moving media. 172 p. (*Bull.Nat.Res.Counc.,* no. 24) Washington, D.C.: 1922.

CNmj

HIROSIGE, Tetu. Lorentz's theory of electrons and the development of the concept of electromagnetic field. *Jap. Stud.Hist.Sci.,* 1962, 1: 101-10.

CNmj-bv

SCOTT, William T. Resource letter FC-1 on the evolution of the electromagnetic field concept. *Amer.J.Phys.,* 1963, 31: 819-26.
Bibliographical guide.

CNze ELECTRON PHYSICS; IONIZATION

see also UX ELECTRONICS TECHNOLOGY
see CR for the discovery of the electron

AUGER, Pierre. L'effet photo-électrique des rayons X dans les gaz. 28 p. Paris: Hermann, 1931.
Lecture given at the Conservatoire des Arts et Métiers on 23 April, 1931.

CADY, Walter Guyton. Piezoelectricity. An introduction to the theory and applications of electromechanical phenomena in crystals. xxiii, 806 p., 164 fig. (International Series in Pure and Applied Physics) New York: McGraw Hill, 1946. [CB 75/89]
This book contains much historical information.

DEUTSCH, Karl. Some notes on the development of electron microscopy. *NTM Z.Gesch.Naturwiss.Tech.Med.,* [1963], 1: no. 4, 45-9.

FREUNDLICH, Martin M. Origin of the electron microscope. The history of a great invention and of a misconception concerning the inventors is renewed. *Science,* 1963, 142: 185-8.

JOHNSON, J.B. Contribution of Thomas A. Edison to thermionics. *Amer.J.Phys.,* 1960, 28: 763-73.

THOMSON, George. Early work in electron diffraction. *Amer. J.Phys.,* 1961, 29: 821-5.

THOMSON, J.J. Cathode rays. Lecture at the Royal Institution, April 30, 1897. *Amer.J.Phys.,* 1947, 15: 458-64, 10 fig. [CB 72/255]
Originally published *Proc.Roy.Inst.,* 1897, 15: 419-32. Lecture reprinted to celebrate the jubilee of the electron.

TIMPANARO, Sebastiano. Le richerche del Righi sul fenomeno foto elettrico. *Arduo,* 1922, 2: 66-75.

TOWNSEND, John S.E. Motion of electrons in gases. Being an address given at the centenary celebration of the Franklin Institute in Philadelphia, September 1924. 35 p. Oxford: Clarendon Press; New York: Oxford University Press, 1925.

VOROB'EV, A.A. Razvitie predstavlenii ob udarnoi ionizatsii v tverdykh dielektrikakh i poluprovodnikakh. [The development of concepts concerning impact ionization in solid dielectrics and semiconductors. (In Russian)]. *Vop.Ist.Est. Tekh.,* 1963, 14: 37-48.

WINDRED, G. Review of the theory and applications of photoelectric effects. *J.Telev.Soc.,* 1934, 1: 329-38, 8 fig., bibliogr.
A historical review.

CNze-wb-qd

MARTON, L. APS Division of Electron Physics. The first twenty years. *Phys.Today,* 1964, 17: no. 10, 44-50.

CO ELECTROMAGNETIC WAVES; RADIATION

BOUTARIC, Augustin. La lumière et les radiations invisibles. 284 p., 55 fig. Paris: Ernest Flammarion, 1925. [CB 20/194]

BRUSH, S.G. History of the Lenz-Ising model. 61 p., portr., bibliogr. (Lawrence Radiation Laboratory, Report UCRL-7940) Livermore, Calif.: University of California (for the U.S. Atomic Energy Commission, Technical Information Division), 1964.

GULLI, Luciano. Alcune considerazioni sulla propagazione delle onde a frequenze elevate ed ultraelevate. *Act.VIIIe Congr.Int.Hist.Sci.* (Florence, 1956), (1), p. 237-44. Paris: Hermann, 1958.

JEANS, James Hopwood. *See* CC

LEBEDEV, Petr Nikolaevich. Die Druckkräfte des Lichtes. Zwei Abhandlungen, hrsg. von P. Lasareff. 58 p., 25 fig., portr. (Ostwald's Klassiker, 188) Leipzig: W. Engelmann, 1913. [CB 3/559]
Reprinted from *Ann.Phys.,* 1901, 6: 433-58 and 1910, 32: 411-38.
French edition, Pression de la lumière, Paris: Blanchard, 1926.

LEBEDEV, Petr Nikolaevich. An experimental investigation of the pressure of light. *Annu.Rep.Smithsonian Inst.* for 1902, p. 177-8. Washington, D.C.: 1903.
Reprinted from *Astrophys.J.,* 1902.

SÜSSKIND, Charles. Observations of electromagnetic-wave radiation before Hertz. *Isis,* 1964, 55: 32-42.

SÜSSKIND, Charles. Some observations of electromagnetic-wave radiation before Hertz. *Proc.10th Int.Congr.Hist.Sci.*(Ithaca, 1962), (2), p. 785-8. Paris: Hermann, 1964.

COxm

SMITH, R.D. Recent development in the detection and measurement of infra-red radiation. *Sci.Mon.,* 1956, 82: 3-19.

COze ETHER

CERASOLI, Ercole. Il problema dell'etere cosmico dalla sua origine ai tempi nostri. *Archeion,* 1937, 19: 71-4.

DIRAC, P.A.M. Is there an aether? *Nature,* 1951, 168: 906-7.

DOPP, H. L'expérience classique de Michelson. *Rev.Quest. Sci.,* 1931, 50: 106-26. [CB 34/525]

IVES, Herbert E. Genesis of the query "Is there an ether?" *J.Opt.Soc.Amer.,* 1953, 43: 217-18.

LA ROSA, Michele. Der Aether. Geschichte einer Hypothese. Lecture given in the Biblioteca Filosofica di Palermo. Transl. from the Italian manuscript by K. Muth. 116 p. Leipzig: Barth, 1912.
Published in Italian: Storia di un'ipotesi. L'"etere". *Annu.Bibl.Fil.,* 1912, vol. 1.

LÉMERAY, E.M. L'éther actuel et ses précurseurs. 142 p. (Actualités Scientifiques) Paris: Gauthier-Villars, 1922.

LENARD, Philipp. Ueber Aether und Uraether. 2nd enl. ed. 66 p. Leipzig: Hirzel, 1922.
First published 1921.

LODGE, Oliver. Ether and reality: a series of discourses on the many functions of the ether of space. 179 p. (Broadcast Library) London: Hodder and Stoughton, 1925.
German translation Braunschweig: Friedr. Vieweg, 1928.

LODGE, Oliver. Matter and energy. *Scientia*, 1925, 37: 11-14; French transl., suppl. 11-14. [CB 18/613]
On the ether of space.

LODGE, Oliver. My philosophy, representing my views on the many functions of the ether of space. 318 p. London: Benn, 1933.

LODGE, Oliver. On Prof. Miller's ether drift experiment. *Nature*, 1926, 117: 854. [CB 21/570]

MATHIAS, Oskar. Die Geschichte des Michelson-Versuches und seine Bedeutung für die moderne Physik. *Z.Phys.Chem.Unterricht*, 1931, 44: 168-75.

MILJANIĆ, Pavle. À propos de la tendance de divers physiciens modernes à ne pas reconnaître l'existence effective d'un milieu connectif et transmetteur universel. *Actes du Symposium International R.J. Bošković 1961*, p. 143-50. Beograd: Stampa Izdaračka Ustanova "Naučno delo", 1962.

MILLER, Dayton C. Ether drift experiments. *Nature*, 1926, 117: 890.

MILLER, Dayton C. Significance of the ether-drift experiments of 1925 at Mount Wilson. *Science*, 1926, 63: 433-44.

POLAK, L.S. [On the history of the problem of the ether. (In Russian with English summary)] *Arkh.Ist.Nauk.Tekh.*, 1936, no. 9, 1-22.

PROKHOVNIK, S.J. The case for an aether. *Brit.J.Phil.Sci.*, 1963, 14: 195-207.

SANFORD, Fernando. The ether theories of electrification. *Sci.Mon.*, 1922, 14: 547-59.

SAUGER, Maurice. L'expérience de Dayton Clarence Miller et les limitations de la théorie de la relativité. *Rev.Gén.Sci.*, 1926, 37: 230-4.

SCHÜTZ, Alexander von. Ueber eine Theorie der Aetherstrahlung. *Ann.Natur.Kulturphil.*, 1913, 12: 187-205.

SHANKLAND, Robert S. Michelson-Morley experiment. *Amer.J.Phys.*, 1964, 32: 16-35.

SHANKLAND, Robert S. The Michelson-Morley experiment. *Sci.Amer.*, 1964, 210: no. 11, 107-14, portr.

SHANKLAND, Robert S., *et al.* A new analysis of the interferometer observations of Dayton C. Miller. 32 p. Cleveland: Case Institute of Technology, 1954.

SYNGE, J.L. Effects of acceleration in the Michelson-Morley experiment. *Sci.Proc.Roy.Dublin Soc.*, 1952, 26: 45-54.

WHITTAKER, E.T. The aether: past and present. *Endeavour*, 1943, 2: 117-20, 3 ill.

WHYTE, Lancelot Law. A forerunner of twentieth century physics: a re-view of Larmor's "Aether and matter". *Nature*, 1960, 186: 1010-14.

ZEHNDER, Ludwig. Der Aether im Lichte der klassischen Zeit und der Neuzeit. 76 p. Tübingen: Laupp, 1933.

COzx X-RAYS

see also CX X-RAY CRYSTALLOGRAPHY
QE RADIOLOGY

AUGER, Pierre. *See* CNze

BLEICH, Alan Ralph, ed. The story of X-rays from Roentgen to isotopes. 186 p., ill. New York: Dover Publications, 1961.
Reviewed by P. de Plaen, *Rev.Quest.Sci.*, 1962, 23: 275; by F.A. Tubbs, *Med.Hist.*, 1963, 7: 291.

BROGLIE, Maurice de. X-rays. Transl. by J.R. Clarke. xiii, 204 p., ill. London: Methuen, 1925.
French original Paris: Presses Universitaires de France, 1922.

COMPTON, Arthur H. The scattering of X-ray photons. *Amer.J.Phys.*, 1946, 14: 80-4.

COMPTON, Arthur H. The scattering of X-rays as particles. *Amer.J.Phys.*, 1961, 29: 817-20.

COMPTON, Arthur H. Secondary radiations produced by X-rays, and some of their applications to physical problems. 56 p. (*Bull.Nat.Res.Counc.*, 4: no. 20) Washington, D.C.: 1922.

GLASSER, Otto. The genealogy of the Roentgen rays. *Amer.J.Roentgenol.*, 1933, 30: 180-200, 349-67.

GLASSER, Otto. Wilhelm Conrad Röntgen and the early history of the roentgen rays. With a chapter "Personal reminiscences of W.C. Röntgen" by Margret Boveri. xii, 494 p., ill. Springfield, Ill.: Thomas, 1934.
Reviewed by George Sarton, *Isis*, 1934, 22: 256-9.
2nd edition of German original Berlin/Heidelberg: 1959 (first publ. 1931). Reviewed by H. Degen, *Naturwiss. Rundsch.*, 1960, 13: 325.

KAYE, G.W.C. X rays, an introduction to the study of Roentgen rays. xix, 252 p., ill. London/New York: Longmans, Green, 1914.

QUEVRON, Louis. Cinquante ans d'études sur les rayons X. *France-Illus.*, 1946, 25: 303-5, 3 photo., 4 fig.

RUTHERFORD, Ernest. Moseley's work on X-rays. *Nature*, 1925, 116: 316-17, portr.

WEBSTER, David L. Problems of X-ray emission. *Bull.Nat.Res.Counc.*, 1920, 1: 427-55.

COzx-wb-qg

HULL, A.W. Thirty years of X-ray research at the General Electric Research Laboratory. *Amer.J.Phys.*, 1946, 14: 71-9, 17 fig.

COzx-wk-qg

DORGELO, H.B.; LANGE, J.J. de; GOPPEL, J.M. Doel, organisatie en resultaten van het Röntgeninstituut der Technische Hoogeschool en van de Röntgenafdeeling van den Technisch-Physischen Dienst T.N.O. en T.H. te Delft. [Aim, organization and results of the x-ray institute of the Technical University and of the x-ray department of the Technical-Physical service T.N.O. and the Technical University of Delft. (In Dutch)] *Ingenieur*, 1946, 58: Sect. O, 21-8, 12 fig.

COzx-xb

GLASSER, Otto. What kind of tube did Röntgen use when he discovered the X-ray? *Radiology*, 1936, 27: 138-40.

COzx-xe-wb

BROWN, Percy. American martyrs to science through the Roentgen rays. xv, 276 p. Springfield, Ill.: Thomas, 1936.
Reviewed by M.F. Ashley-Montagu. *Isis*, 1936, 26: 219-20.

CP SPECTROSCOPY

BABCOCK, H.D. Beyond the red in the spectrum. *Annu.Rep. Smithsonian Inst. for 1930*, p. 165-76, 2 pl. Washington, D.C.: 1931.
A lecture delivered before the Carnegie Institution at Washington, D.C., Dec. 10, 1929; and at Pasadena, Calif., Feb. 20, 1930. Reprinted from *Publ.Astron.Soc.Pacific*, 1930, 42: 83-98.

BARR, E. Scott. Historical survey of the early development of the infrared spectral region. *Amer.J.Phys.*, 1960, 28: 42-54.

BRUCHE, E. 100 Jahre Spektralanalyse. *Phys.Bl.*, 1960, 16: no. 6, 320-3.

COBLENTZ, W.W. Early history of infrared spectroradiometry. *Sci.Mon.*, 1949, 68: 102-7.

DINGLE, Herbert. A hundred years of spectroscopy. The fifty-third Robert Boyle Lecture, delivered before the Oxford University Scientific Club, Trinity Term, 1951. 23 p. Oxford: Blackwell, Scientific Publications, 1951.

DINGLE, Herbert. A hundred years of spectroscopy. *Brit.J.Hist.Sci.*, 1963, 1: 199-216.

FOWLER, Alfred. Report on series in line spectra. vii, 183 p. London: Physical Society, 1922.

HARRISON, George R. New methods in spectroscopy. *Science*, 1940, 91: 225-8.
Address on the occasion of the award of the Rumford Medals of the Academy of Arts and Sciences, Boston, October 11, 1939.

LODGE, Oliver. The history of Zeeman's discovery, and its reception in England. *Nature*, 1922, 109: 66-9.

LYMAN, Théodore. The spectroscopy of the extreme ultraviolet. 2nd ed. vii, 160 p. (Monographs on Physics) London: Longmans, 1928
First published 1913.
French translation, L'ultraviolet. Paris: Alcan, 1924. [CB 16/326]

RUNGE, I. Zur Geschichte der Spektroskopie von Balmer bis Bohr. *Z.Phys.Chem.Unterricht*, 1939, 3: 103-13, 1 fig.

SHPOL'SKII, E.V. Stoletie spektral'nogo analiza. [A century of spectrum analysis. (In Russian)]. *Usp.Fiz.Nauk*, 1959, 69: 657-78, portr. English translation in *Soviet Phys.Usp.*, 1959, 2: 958-73, portr.

WATSON, E.C. The discovery of the Zeeman effect. *Amer.J. Phys.*, 1954, 22: 633-5, 3 fig.

ZEEMAN, P. Les lignes spectrales et les théories modernes de la physique. *Scientia*, 1921, 29: 13-21.
The progress of spectrum analysis since Newton.

ZEEMAN, P. Optical effects of motion. *Nature*, 1924, 113: 796, 838-9.

ZEEMAN, P. Researches in magneto-optics with special reference to the magnetic resolution of spectrum lines. xiv, 219 p., 74 fig. (Macmillan's Science Monographs) London: Macmillan, 1913.

ZEEMAN, P. Verhandelingen over magneto-optische verschijnselen. [Treatises on magneto-optical phenomena. (In Dutch)] xv, 34] p., portr. Leiden: Eduard Ijdo, 1921. [CB 13/239]
Memorial volume to celebrate the 25th anniversary of Zeeman's discovery.

CPda

BARR, E. Scott. The infrared pioneers. *Infrared Phys.*, 1963, 3: 195-206.

CPkk

DINGLE, Herbert. The Doppler effect and the foundations of physics. *Brit.J.Phil.Sci.*, 1960, 11: 11-31, 113-29.

CPxk

RAEVSKII, I.P. Evoliutsiia predstavlenii o roli pribora v spektral'noi razlo-henii. [The evolution of concepts concerning the role of the apparatus in spectral dispersion. (In Russian)]. *Vop.Ist.Est.Tekh.*, 1962, 13: 73-5. [CB 88/623]

CPyCC

BOHR, Niels. Ueber die Quantentheorie der Linienspektren. Übersetzt von P. Hertz. iv, 168 p. Braunschweig: F. Vieweg, 1923.

CAMPBELL, Norman Robert. Modern electrical theory. Supplementary chapters. 15. Series spectra. 119 p. Cambridge: 1921.

CAMPBELL, Norman Robert. Théorie quantique des spectres. La relativité. Supplément à l'ouvrage: La théorie électrique moderne. Transl. from the English by A. Corvisy. 230 p. Paris: Hermann, 1924.
French translation of: Modern electrical theory. Supplementary chapters 15, Series spectra, 16, The structure of the atom, *see* above.

HUND, F. Vor fünfzig Jahren - Der Schritt zur Quantentheorie des Atombaues und der Spektrallinien. *Phys.Bl.*, 1963, 19: 494-502.

SILBERSTEIN, Ludwik. Report on the quantum theory of spectra. iv, 42 p. London: Hilger, 1920.

VAN VLECK, John Hasbrouck. Quantum principles and line spectra. 316 p. (*Bull.Nat.Res.Counc.*, 10: no. 54) Washington, D.C.: 1926.

CPyCOzx

DUANE, William. Data relating to X-ray spectra. With a brief statement of their bearing on theories of the structure of atoms and the mechanism of radiation. *Bull.Nat. Res.Counc.*, 1920, 1: 383-408.

SIEGBAHN, Manne. The spectroscopy of X-rays. Transl. with the author's additions by George A. Lindsay. xii, 287 p., fig. London: Humphrey Milford; New York: Oxford University Press, 1925. [CB 18/614]
German original first published Berlin: 1924.

CQ THE STRUCTURE OF MATTER

CQc general history

ABBOT, C.G. The architecture of atoms and a universe built of atoms. *Annu.Rep.Smithsonian Inst.for 1922*, p. 157-66. Washington, D.C.: 1924.

ANDRADE, E.N. da C. An approach to modern physics. ix, 232 p. London: Bell, 1956.
2nd edition 1959; 3rd edition 1962. Based on the author's "The mechanism of nature", *see* below.

ANDRADE, E.N. da C. The birth of the nuclear atom. Rutherford was unaware that his discovery of the nucleus would change the world. *Sci.Amer.*, November 1956, 195: 93-104, 4 ill.

ANDRADE, E.N. da C. The mechanism of nature: being a simple approach to modern views on the structure of matter and radiation. Rev. enl. ed. xii, 188 p. London: Bell, 1936.
First published 1930.

ANDRADE, E.N. da C. The structure of the atom. 3rd ed., rev. and enl. xviii, 750 p., diagr. London: G. Bell, 1927.
First published 1923.
Reviewed in *Nature*, 1927, 119: 554-5.

BERTHOUD, Alfred. Les nouvelles conceptions de la matière et de l'atome. v, 314 p. (Encyclopédie Scientifique: Bibliothèque d'Histoire et de Philosophie des Sciences) Paris: Doin, 1923. [CB 14/544]
English translation by Eden and Cedar Paul (London: Allen and Unwin, 1924).

BOHR, Niels. Atomic theory and the description of nature. Four essays, with an introductory survey. vi, 119 p. Cambridge University Press, 1934.
Reviewed by Herbert Dingle, *Nature*, 1934, 133: 962-4.
German edition (77 p. Berlin: Springer, 1931) reviewed by A. Sommerfeld, *Deut.Lit.Zeitung*, 1931, 2: 2105-6.
French translation (120 p. Paris: Gauthier-Villars, 1932) reviewed by J. Pelseneer, *Rev.Univ.Bruxelles*, 1933-34, 39: 3-9.

BOHR, Niels. On the constitution of atoms and molecules; papers of 1913 reprinted from the *Philosophical Magazine*. Introd. by L. Rosenfeld. liii, 77 p., facs., portr. Copenhagen: Munksgaard; New York: W.A. Benjamin, 1963.

BOHR, Niels. The structure of the atom. Lecture delivered at Stockholm, December 11, 1922, on the occasion of the receipt of the Nobel prize in physics for the year 1922. English translation by Dr. Frank C. Hoyt. *Nature*, 1923, 112: 29-44.

BORN, Max. The constitution of matter: modern atomic and electron theories. Transl. from the 2nd German ed. by E.W. Blair and T.S. Wheeler. vii, 80 p. London: Methuen, 1923.
Second German edition Berlin: Springer, 1922.

BORN, Max. The mechanics of the atom. Transl. by J.W. Fisher and rev. by D.R. Hartree. xvi, 317 p. (International Text-books of Exact Science) London: G. Bell, 1927.
Reviewed in *Nature*, 1927, 120: 324-5.

BORN, Max. Problems of atomic dynamics. Two series of lectures on 1. The structure of the atom; 2. The lattice theory of rigid bodies. xiv, 200 p., ill. Cambridge, Mass.: Massachusetts Institute of Technology, 1926.
German edition (Berlin: Springer, 1926) reviewed by H.S. Allen, *Nature*, 1927, 119: 77-9.

BOUTARIC, Augustin. La vie des atomes. 248 p., ill. (Bibliothèque de Philosophie Scientifique) Paris: Flammarion, 1923.
Reviewed by F. Beaulard de Lenaizan, *Rev.Gén.Sci.*, 1923, 34: 152.

BRAGG, William, *et al.* Science lifts the veil. A series of broadcast talks on the conquest of the sub-visible universe. vi, 61 p., ill. London: Longmans Green, 1942. [CB 69/222]

CAMPBELL, Norman Robert. Modern electrical theory. Supplementary chapters. 17. The structure of the atom. 171 p. Cambridge: 1923.

CLARK, C.H. Douglas. The basis of modern atomic theory. xx, 292 p. London: Methuen, 1926.
Reviewed by J.A. Crowther, *Nature*, 1926, 118: 365-6.

COMPTON, Karl Taylor. Recent discoveries and theories relating to the structure of matter. (Reprinted from Princeton Lectures No. 10, Princeton University, June, 1922). *Annu.Rep.Smithsonian Inst.for 1922*, p. 145-56. Washington, D.C.: 1924.

DAMPIER, William Cecil. Matter and change. An introduction to physical and chemical science. viii, 280 p., 3 pl. Cambridge University Press, 1924.

DARWIN, Charles Galton. The new conceptions of matter. viii, 192 p., 6 pl. London: Bell, 1931.
Reviewed by Herbert Dingle, *Nature*, 1932, 130: 183-5.

DARWIN, Charles Galton. Recent developments in atomic theory. The twenty-eighth Robert Boyle Lecture delivered before the Junior Scientific Club of the University of Oxford on June 4, 1926. 15 p., 1 pl. London: Oxford University Press, 1927.

DAVIDSON, Martin. The mid-twentieth century atom. 127 p., 16 fig. London: Hutchinson, 1946.

DUKOV, V.M. [Concerning the origins of electronic theory. (In Russian)]. *Vop.Ist.Est.Tekh.*, 1960, 9: 71-7.

DIE ERSTEN zehn Jahre der Theorie von Niels Bohr über den Bau der Atome. *Naturwissenschaften*, 1923, 533-624. [CB 15/185]
Whole number devoted to Bohr.

GAMOW, G. Mr. Tompkins explores the atom. x, 97 p. New York: Macmillan Co.; Cambridge University Press, 1944. [CB 66/263]

GLIOZZI, Mario. I modelli atomici. *Arch.Int.Hist.Sci.*, 1957, 10: 329-39.

HAAS, Arthur Erich. Atomic theory: an elementary exposition. Transl. by T. Verschoyle. New ed. with summary concerning advances in atomic physics, 1926-1935. li, 222 p. London: Constable, 1936.
First published 1927.

HAAS, Arthur Erich. Die Elektronenhypothese in ihrem Verhältnis zu älteren physikalischen Theorien. *Arch.Gesch. Naturwiss.Tech.*, 1913, 6: 144-9.

HARTREE, D.R. The calculation of atomic structure. 181, xiii p. New York: John Wiley and Sons, 1957.
The first chapter contains a brief historical introduction to atomic theory.
Reviewed by Frank J. Blatt, *Amer.J.Phys.*, 1958, 26: 135-6.

HESSE, Mary B. Changing views of matter. *Hist.Sci.*, 1964, 3: 79-84.
An essay review of McMullin "The concept of matter", *see* below.

HIROSIGE, Tetu; NISIO, Sigeo. Formation of Bohr's theory of atomic constitution. *Jap.Stud.Hist.Sci.*, 1964, 3: 6-28.

HOOYKAAS, R. Het ontstaan van de chemische atoomleer. [The origin of the chemical atomic theory. (In Dutch)]. *Tijdschr. Phil.*, 1947, 9: 63-136.
Beginning with Empedocles and Democritos and ending with Dalton.

HOULLEVIGUE, Louis. La matière. Sa vie et ses transformations. Préface de Ed. Bouty. xxxii, 319 p. Paris: Armand Colin, 1913. [CB 2/314]

JAEGER, F.M. Elementen en Atomen eens en thans. Schetsen uit de ontwikkelingsgeschiedenis der elementenleer en atomistiek. [Elements and atoms then and now. Sketches from the history of the development of the knowledge of the elements and of atomism. (In Dutch)]. 2nd ed. viii, 312 p., ill. Groningen: Wolters, 1920.
First published 1918.
Reviewed by George Sarton, *Isis*, 1921, 4: 83.

JOHNSON, Edgar N. Atoms, fire, waves or what? *J.Chem.Educ.*, 1960, 37: 267-70.

JONES, G.O.; ROTBLAT, J.; WHITROW, G.J. Atoms and the universe. An account of modern views on the structure of matter and the universe. 2nd ed. 275 p. London: Eyre & Spottiswoode, 1962; New York: Scribner, 1963.
First published London: 1956 (New York: 1957). [CB 83/279]

THE JUBILEE of the nuclear atom. *Endeavour*, 1962, 21: 3-4.

KIRCHBERGER, Paul. Die Entwicklung der Atomtheorie. Gemeinverständlich dargestellt. 2nd ed. xii, 294 p., 31 fig., 10 pl. Karlsruhe: Müller, 1929.
French translation Paris: Payot, 1930.

LAGOWSKI, J.J. The structure of atoms. vii, 120 p., 44 fig. (Classic Researches in General Chemistry) Boston, Mass.: Houghton Mifflin, 1964.

LANGMUIR, Irving. Phenomena, atoms, and molecules; an attempt to interpret phenomena in terms of mechanisms or atomic and molecular interactions. xi, 436 p., ill. New York: Philosophical Library, 1950.
Includes a bibliography of papers by the author.
Reviewed by A.R. Miller, *Endeavour*, 1951, 10: 222.

LASSWITZ, Kurd. Geschichte der Atomik vom Mittelalter bis Newton. 2nd ed. 2 vol. xii, 518 p.; viii, 609 p. Leipzig: Leopold Voss, 1926.
Reviewed by Hugo Dingler, *Isis*, 1927, 9: 465-7.

LIEBEN, Fritz. Vorstellungen vom Aufbau der Materie im Wandel der Zeiten. Eine historische Übersicht. x, 384 p. Wien: Franz Deuticke, 1953. [CB 81/270]
Reviewed by Arne Fredga, *Lychnos*, 1956, 406-7.

LODGE, Oliver. Atoms and rays: an introduction to modern views on atomic structure and radiation. 4th ed. 222 p. London: Ernest Benn, 1932.
First published 1924.

LORING, F.H. Atomic theories. ix, 218 p., 66 fig. London: Methuen, 1921. [CB 13/285]

LOWRY, T.M. Electrons, atoms and molecules. *Nature*, 16 Jan. 1926, 117: suppl. 33-40.

McMULLIN, Ernan, ed. The concept of matter. xi, 624 p. Notre Dame, Ind.: University of Notre Dame Press, 1963.
Record of the conference of philosophers, physicists, and historians of science, held at University of Notre Dame in 1961.
Essay review by Mary Hesse, *Hist.Sci.*, 1964, 3: 79-84.

MELDRUM, Andrew Norman. The development of the atomic theory. ii, 13 p. London: Oxford University Press, 1919.

MELDRUM, Andrew Norman. The development of the atomic theory. 1. Berthollet's doctrine of variable proportions; 2. The various accounts of the origin of Dalton's theory; 3. Newton's theory and its influence in the eighteenth century; 4. Dalton's physical atomic theory; 5. Dalton's chemical theory; 6. The reception accorded to the theory advocated by Dalton; 7. The rival claims of William Higgins (d. 1825) and John Dalton. *Mem.Manch.Lit.Phil.Soc.*, 1909-10, 54: no. 7, 16 p.; 1910-11, 55: no. 3, 12 p.; no. 4, 15 p.; no. 5, 22 p.; no. 6, 18 p.; no. 19, 10 p.; no. 22, 11 p.

MELSEN, Andrew G. van. From atomos to atom: the history of the concept atom. Translated by Henry J. Kasen. 240 p. Pittsburgh: Duquesne University Press, 1952.
Reprinted New York: Harper, 1960. Dutch original "Van atomos naar atoom: de geschiedenis van het begrip atoom" (Amsterdam: Meulenhoff, 1949).
German translation "Atom Gestern und heute" (Freiburg/ München: Karl Alber, 1957) reviewed by R. Bruce Lindsay, *Phys.Today*, 1959, 12: no. 2, 44-6.

METZGER, Hélène. Projet d'article pour un vocabulaire historique. Atome. *Rev.Hist.Sci.*, 1947, 1: 51-2.

NASH, Leonard K. The atomic-molecular theory. vi, 115 p. (Harvard Case Histories in Experimental Science, 4) Cambridge, Mass.: Harvard University Press, 1951.
Reviewed by V.F. Lenzen, *Isis*, 1951, 42: 65.

PAULI, Wolfgang. Remarks on the history of the exclusion principle. *Science*, 1946, 103: 213-15.

PERRIN, Jean. Atoms. Authorised transl. by D.Ll. Hammick. 2nd Engl. ed. rev. xv, 231 p. London: Constable, 1923.
First published in English 1916. First French edition Paris: 1913. Third edition of German translation Dresden: 1923.

RICE, Francis Owen; TELLER, Edward. The structure of matter. xiii, 361 p. New York: Wiley, 1949. [CB 74/387]

RICHARDSON, Owen Willans. The electron theory of matter. 2nd ed. vi, 631 p., ill. Cambridge University Press, 1916.
First published 1914.

ROSHDESTVENSKI, D. [Evolution of ideas concerning the structure of atoms and molecules. (In Russian)]. *Arkh.Ist. Nauk.Tekh.*, 1933, 1: 1-20.

RUSSELL, Bertrand. The ABC of atoms. 175 p. London: Kegan Paul; New York: Dutton, 1923.

RUTHERFORD, Ernest. The electrical structure of matter. Inaugural address delivered to the British Association at Liverpool on September 12, 1923. *Nature*, 1923, 112: 409-19.

SETH, Rajani Kanta. Ether, electron and matter. 83 p. Calcutta: The Author, 1945. [CB 69/227]

SMITH, William Benjamin. The electronic theory of matter. *Monist*, 1917, 27: 321-51.
Paper read (in Spanish) at the 1st Pan-American Scientific Congress, Santiago de Chile, December 1908-January 1909.

SODDY, Frederick. The interpretation of the atom. xviii, 355 p., 20 pl. London: Murray, 1932.

SVEDBERG, The. Die Materie. Ein Forschungsproblem in Vergangenheit und Gegenwart. Transl. into German by H. Finkelstein. iii, 162 p., ill. Leipzig: Akademische Verlagsgesellschaft, 1914.

THOMSON, J.J. The atomic theory. 39 p. (Romanes Lecture) Oxford: Clarendon Press, 1914.

TOULMIN, Stephen; GOODFIELD, June. The architecture of matter. 339 p., pl. London: Hutchinson, 1962; New York: Harper & Row, 1962.
Reviewed by L. Pearce Williams, *Isis*, 1964, 55: 102-4; by H.J.S., *Ambix*, 1962, 10: 153-4; by D.J. Montgomery, *Phys. Today*, 1963, 16: no. 10, 68-70.

VELDE, A.J.J. van de. Het atoom in de geschiedenis tot John Dalton. [The atom in history up to John Dalton. (In Dutch)]. 70 p. (*Mededeel.Vlaams.Acad.Wetensch.*, *Lett.Schoone Kunsten België*, 19) Antwerp: 1948. [CB 73/171]

VOL'FKOVICH, S.I. [Survey of N.A. Morozov, D.P. Konovalov and W. Crookes on "Periodic system of the structure of matter". (In Russian)] *Tr.Inst.Ist.Est.*, 1949, 3: 200-8.

WEBSTER, David L.; PAGE, Leigh. A general survey of the present status of the atomic structure problem. *Bull.Nat. Res.Counc.*, 1921, 2: 335-95.

WILSON, William. The microphysical world. vii, 216 p. New York: Philosophical Library, 1954. [CB 80/204]

YAGI, Eri. On Nagaoka's Saturnian atomic model. *Jap.Stud. Hist.Sci.*, 1964, 3: 29-47.

CQk philosophy and methodology

BACHELARD, Gaston. Les intuitions atomistiques (Essai de classification). 164 p. Paris: Boivin, 1932. [CB 39/443]

BUCHDAHL, Gerd. Sources of scepticism in atomic theory. *Brit. J.Phil.Sci.*, 1959, 10: 120-34.

GORMAN, Mel. Philosophical antecedents of the modern atom. *J.Chem.Educ.*, 1960, 2: 100-4.

HANSON, Norwood Russell. The dematerialization of matter. *Phil.Sci.*, 1962, 29: 27-46.

HUTTEN, Ernest H. On the Pauli principle. *Act.IIe Congr.Int. Phil.Sci.*(Zurich, 1954), (2), p. 12-18. Zurich: Éditions du Griffon, 1955.

KOLMAN, E. On the problem of a unified physical theory of matter. *Phil.Sci.*, 1935, 2: 400-12.

MALFITANO, G. La notion de matière au Centre International de Synthèse. *Rev.Gén.Sci.*, 1940, 51: 32-41.

RUSSELL, Bertrand. Analysis of matter. viii, 408 p. London: Kegan Paul, Trench, Trübner; New York: Harcourt Brace, 1927.
German translation "Philosophie der Materie" (Leipzig: Teubner, 1929) reviewed by Edmund O. von Lippmann, *Chem. Zeitung*, 1929, 53: 559.

WEYL, Hermann. Was ist Materie? Zwei Aufsätze zur Naturphilosophie. 88 p., 8 fig. (*Naturwissenschaften*, 1924, vol. 12) Berlin: Julius Springer, 1924. [CB 17/597]

WHYTE, Lancelot Law. The atomic problem: a challenge to physicists and mathematicians. 56 p. London: George Allen & Unwin, 1961.
Reviewed by B.C. Brookes, *Brit.J.Phil.Sci.*, 1962, 13: 180-1.

CQkt

GREGORY, Joshua C. A short history of atomism: from Democritus to Bohr. vi, 258 p. London: Black, 1931.

HARRISON, Charles T. Bacon, Hobbes, Boyle, and the ancient atomists. *Harv.Stud.Philol.Lit.*, 1933, 15: 191-218.

JASINOWSKI, Bogumil. La renaissance de l'atomisme au début du XIXe siècle et ses prémisses historiques. *Archeion*, 1942, 24: 164-7.

KARGON, Robert. William Rowan Hamilton, Michael Faraday, and the revival of Boscovichean atomism. *Amer.J.Phys.*, 1964, 32: 792-5.

STONES, G.B. The atomic view of matter in the 15th, 16th, and 17th centuries. *Isis*, 1928, 10: 445-65.

VIRIEUX-REYMOND, A. Quelques remarques à propos de l'atomisme antique et des atomismes modernes et contemporains. *Act. VIIe Congr.Int.Hist.Sci.* (Jerusalem, 1953), p. 620-4. Paris: Hermann, [n.d.].

WHYTE, Lancelot Law. Essay on atomism. From Democritus to 1960. ix, 108 p. London: Nelson; Middletown, Conn.: Wesleyan University Press, 1961. [CB 88/531]
For reviews see CB 88/531 and CB 89/491.

CQkt-j

PIAGET, Jean. A propos de la psychologie de l'atomisme. *Thalès*, 1948, 5: 3-7.

CQmc

COX, Richard T. Time, space and atoms. 154 p. Baltimore: Williams & Wilkins, 1933.
Reviewed by V.F. Lenzen, *Isis*, 1934, 20: 484.

DESTOUCHES, Jean-Louis. Les notions d'espace et de temps dans leurs rapports avec les théories atomiques. *Thalès*, 1935, 2: 136-41.

CQs/y special aspects

CQs

MØLLER, Christian; RASMUSSEN, Ebbe. The world and the atom. Foreword by Niels Bohr. Transl. from the second Danish edition by Gerald C. Wheeler and Bernard Miall. 200 p. London: Allen and Unwin, 1940.
Reviewed by J.A. Crowther, *Nature*, 1941, 147: 689-90.

CQyCC

BOHR, Niels. Chemistry and the quantum theory of atomic constitution (Faraday lecture, May 8th, 1930). *J.Chem.Soc.*, 1932, 349-84. [CB 36/413]

BOHR, Niels. On the application of the quantum theory to atomic structure. Part I. The fundamental postulates of the quantum theory. Translated by L.F. Curtiss. 42 p. (*Proc.Cambridge Phil.Soc.*, *Suppl.*) Cambridge University Press, 1924.
From *Z.Phys.*, 1923, 13: 117-65. No more published.

BRILLOUIN, Léon. La théorie des quanta et l'atome de Bohr. 181 p. (*Recueil des Conférences-Rapports de Documentation sur la Physique,* 2: 1re *série,* conférences, 4, 5, 6) Paris: Les Presses Universitaires de France, 1922.

HUND, F. Das Problem der Stoffe und seine Lösung. *Naturwissenschaften,* 1963, 50: 344-8.
Discussion of the role of quantum theory in fusing together virtually unrelated notions of the constituents of matter which developed within classical physics and chemistry.

HUND, F. Vor fünfzig Jahren - Der Schritt zur Quantentheorie des Atombaues und der Spektrallinien. *Phys.Bl.,* 1963, 19: 494-502.

HYLLERAS, Egil A. Reminiscences from early quantum mechanics of two-electron atoms. *Rev.Mod.Phys.,* 1963, 35: 421-31. [CB 89/581]
The author studied under Max Born at Göttingen.

JEANS, James Hopwood. Atomicity and quanta. 64 p. (The Rouse Ball Lecture, 1925) Cambridge University Press, 1926.

JEANS, James Hopwood. Electric forces and quanta. The sixteenth Kelvin Lecture, delivered on February 5 at the Institution of Electrical Engineers. *Nature,* 1925, 115: 361-8.

POLAK, L.S. Vozniknovennie kvantovoi teorii atoma. Model atoma Rezerforda-Bora. [The origin of the quantum theory of the atom. Rutherford and Bohr's model of the atom. (In Russian)] *Tr.Inst.Ist.Est.Tekh.,* 1957, 19: 431-49.

CQyCL

STONER, Edmund Clifton. Magnetism and atomic structure. xiii, 371 p., ill. London: Methuen, 1926.
Reviewed by Walther Gerlach, *Naturwissenschaften,* 1927, 20-1.

CQyCP

BOHR, Niels. Les spectres et la structure de l'atome; trois conférences. Traduit par A. Corvisy. 150 p. Paris: Hermann, 1923.

BOHR, Niels. The theory of spectra and atomic constitution: three essays. x, 126 p. Cambridge: University Press, 1922. 2nd ed., 1924.
Reviewed by R.H. Fowler, *Nature,* 1923, 111: 523-6.

BUTAVAND, F. L'harmonie tourbillonnaire de l'atome. Les spectres et les éléments. 54 p., ill. Paris: Gauthier-Villars, 1914. [CB 6/456]

SOMMERFELD, Arnold. Atomic structure and spectral lines. Transl. from the 5th German ed. by Henry L. Brose. 3rd ed. rev. 687 p. London: Methuen, 1934.
First published in English 1923. 5th German edition Braunschweig: Vieweg, 1931. (First published 1919). French translation Paris: 1923.

CR SUBATOMIC PARTICLES

CRc general history

ANDERSON, C.D. Early work on the positron and muon. *Amer.J. Phys.,* 1961, 29: 825-30.

ANDERSON, David Leonard. The discovery of the electron: the development of the atomic concept of electricity. 138 p., ill. Princeton, N.J.: Van Nostrand, 1964.
Reviewed by Leonard M. Rieser, *Science,* 1964, 144: 691-2; by L. Marton, *Phys.Today,* 1964, 17: no. 8, 44-5.

BARTLETT, Albert Allen. Compton effect: historical background. *Amer.J.Phys.,* 1964, 32: 120-7.

BOUTARIC, Augustin. La physique moderne et l'électron. 268 p., 45 fig. (Nouvelle Collection Scientifique) Paris: Alcan, 1927. [CB 24/530]

BYKOV, G.V. K istorii otkrytiia elektrona. [On the history of the discovery of the electron. (In Russian)] *Vop.Ist.Est. Tekh.,* 1963, no. 15, 25-9.
An examination of the contributions of J.J. Thomson, E. Wiechert, and W. Kaufmann.

CHADWICK, James. Some personal notes on the search for the neutron. *Proc.10th Int.Congr.Hist.Sci.*(Ithaca, 1962), (1), p. 159-62. Paris: Hermann, 1964.

CHEN NING YANG. Elementary particles. A short history of some discoveries in atomic physics. x, 68 p., ill. Princeton: Princeton University Press, 1962.
Reviewed by Madeleine Courtin, *Arch.Int.Hist.Sci.,* 1962, 15: 193.

CURIE, Irène; JOLIOT, Frédéric. La projection de noyaux atomiques par un rayonnement très pénétrant: l'existence du neutron. 22 p. (Exposés de Physique Théorique, 11) Paris: Hermann, 1932.

DIRAC, P.A.M. Theorie der Elektronen und Positronen. In: Die moderne Atomtheorie. [Nobel prize lectures 1933] 45 p. Leipzig: Hirzel, 1934.

ELLIS, T.D. The light-quantum theory. *Nature,* 1926, 117: 895-7.

FEATHER, Norman. The experimental discovery of the neutron. *Proc.10th Int.Congr.Hist.Sci.*(Ithaca, 1962), (1), p. 135-47. Paris: Hermann, 1964.
With comments by G.J. Whitrow and Théo Kahan.

HANSON, Norwood Russell. Discovering the positron. *Brit.J. Phil.Sci.,* 1961, 12: 194-214, 1962, 12: 299-313.
A study of the Anderson particle, the Dirac particle and the Blackett-Occhialini particle.

HEISENBERG, Werner. Die Entwicklung der einheitlichen Feldtheorie der Elementarteilchen. *Naturwissenschaften,* 1963, 50: 3-7. [CB 89/580]

HUGHES, Donald J. The neutron story. 158 p., fig. (Science Study Series, S1) Garden City, N.Y.: Doubleday Anchor Books, 1959.
Reviewed by Charles Hellman, *Science,* 1959, 130: 616-17; in *Sci.Amer.,* 1959, 201: no. 5, 222-3.

MILLIKAN, Robert Andrews. The electron; its isolation and measurement and the determination of some of its properties. Ed. and introd. by Jesse W.M. DuMond. lxii, 268 p., ill. (Phoenix Science Series) Chicago: University of Chicago Press, 1963.
Facsimile of the original 1917 edition.
Reviewed by Alfred M. Bork, *Isis,* 1964, 55: 400-1.
For French translation of second edition (Paris: Alcan, 1926) *see* CB 21/572.

MILLIKAN, Robert Andrews. Electrons (+ and -), protons, photons, neutrons, mesotrons, and cosmic rays. Rev. ed. x, 642 p., 124 fig. Chicago: University of Chicago Press, 1947. [CB 71/118]

OWEN, G.E. The discovery of the electron. *Ann.Sci.,* 1955, 11: 173-82.

PEIERLS, R.E. Fundamental particles. *Nature,* 1946, 158: 773-5. [CB 70/224]

SAKATA, Syôichi. [50 years of the quantum theory. 2. Theory of elementary particles. (In Japanese)]. *J.Hist.Sci.Japan,* 1952, no. 21, 5-9.

SEGRÈ, Emilio. The consequences of the discovery of the neutron. *Proc.10th Int.Congr.Hist.Sci.*(Ithaca, 1962), (1), p. 149-58. Paris: Hermann, 1964.

SHEBALIN, S.F. Otkrytiiu Neitrona - 30 let. [Discovery of the neutron - 30th anniversary. (In Russian)] *Priroda,* 1962, no. 10, 83-4.

SPRING, K.H. Photons and electrons. 108 p., 38 diagr. (Methuen's Monographs on Physical Subjects) New York: Wiley, 1950. [CB 79/174]

THOMSON, J.J. Beyond the electron. A lecture given at Girton College on March 3, 1928. 44 p. Cambridge University Press, 1928.

WEINTROUB, S. Jubilee of the discovery of the electron. *Nature,* 1947, 160: 776-8.

WEISSKOPF, V.F. The place of elementary particle research in the development of modern physics. *Phys.Today,* 1963, 16: no. 6, 26-34.

CRc-bx

INSTITUTE OF PHYSICS. The electron jubilee exhibition, held at the Science Museum, London, Sept. 1947-Jan.1948, to illustrate the discovery of the electron in 1897, phenomena in which the electron plays a major part, and the scientific and industrial developments and applications arising from those phenomena. By D.H. Follett. 48 p., front., 7 fig. London: The Institute, 1947.

CRk/y special aspects

CRk

BLOKHINTSEV, D.I. Kniga V.I. Lenina "Materializm i empiriokrititsizm" i sovremennye predstavleniya o strukture elementarnykh chastits. [Lenin's book "Materialism and empiriocriticism" and modern notions concerning the structure of elementary particles. (In Russian)] *Usp.Fiz.Nauk*, 1959, 69: 3-12.

FLEMING, John J. Sub-quantum entities. *Phil.Sci.*, 1964, 31: 271-4.

HANSON, Norwood Russell. The concept of the positron. A philosophical analysis. 225 p., fig., ill. London/New York: Cambridge University Press, 1962.
Reviewed by J.C. Ward, *Isis*, 1964, 55: 250-1; for other reviews *see* CB 89/576 and CB 90/626.

SCHRÖDINGER, E. What is an elementary particle? *Endeavour*, 1950, 9: 109-16.

STERNGLASS, Ernest J. The elementary particle concept in modern physical theory. *Proc.10th Int.Congr.Hist.Sci.* (Ithaca, 1962), (1), p. 355-8. Paris: Hermann, 1964.

STERNGLASS, Ernest J. Particle interference and the causal space-time description of atomic phenomena. *Horizons of a philosopher, Essays in honor of David Baumgardt*, p. 422-32. Leiden: E.J. Brill, 1963.

WHYTE, L.L. Fundamental physical theory. An interpretation of the present position of the theory of particles. *Brit. J.Phil.Sci.*, 1951, 1: 303-27.

CRmzCQkt

WHYTE, Lancelot Law. Boscovich and particle theory. *Nature*, 1957, 179: 284-5.

WHYTE, Lancelot Law. Boscovich's atomism and the particles of 1961. *Actes du Symposium International R.J. Bošković* (1961), p. 85-8. Publ. 1962.

CRs/t

COMPTON, Karl T. The electron: its intellectual and social significance. *Science*, 1937, 85: 27-37.
Address of the retiring president of the American Association for the Advancement of Science, Atlantic City, December 28, 1936.

CRxm

WEISS, Pierre. Le magnéton. *Rev.Gén.Sci.*, 1914, 25: 12-24.

CRzc COSMIC RAYS

AUGER, Pierre. What are cosmic rays? Revised and enlarged American edition. Translated from the French by Maurice M. Shapiro. vii, 128 p., 22 pl. Chicago: University of Chicago Press, 1945. [CB 69/202]
Revised translation brought up to date of the author's "Rayons cosmiques" (Paris: 1941).

GENTNER, W. Einige Rückblicke auf die Anfänge der 50 jährigen Forschung über die kosmische Strahlung. *Naturwissenschaften*, 1963, 50: 317-18. [CB 89/580]

LEPRINCE-RINGUET, Louis. Cosmic rays. Transl. from the French by Fay Ajzenberg. xii, 290 p., ill. New York: Prentice-Hall, 1950.
French revised edition Paris: Michel, 1948.

MILLER, Dayton C. *See* CMc

MILLIKAN, Robert A. Bemerkungen zur Geschichte der kosmischen Strahlung. *Phys.Z.*, 1930, 31: 241-7.
Translated by Alexander Goetz. A shortened English version, translated from the *Phys.Z.*, appeared in *Science*, 1930, 71: 640-1.

MILLIKAN, Robert A. History of research in cosmic rays. *Nature*, 1930, 126: 14-16, 29-30.

PERSICO, E. I raggi cosmici. *Scientia*, 1931, 49: 81-94. French transl., suppl., 29-40.

SWANN, W.F.G. The history of cosmic rays. *Amer.J.Phys.*, 1961, 29: 811-16.

CS NUCLEAR AND ATOMIC PHYSICS

for atomic structure *see* CQ
atomic energy *see* UR

BAVINK, Bernhard. Grundriss der neueren Atomistik. vi, 130 p., ill. Leipzig: Hinzel, 1922.
French translation 'L'atomistique'. Paris: Gauthier-Villars, 1923. [CB 16/292]

BURGSTALLER, S. Die Entwicklung der Atomistik. *Lotos*, 1912, 60: 211-18, 229-34.

CAMPI, Plinius; RUSCONI, Aldo. Fisica nucleare: della pila di Volta alla pila atomica. viii, 215 p., ill. Milan: Hoepli, 1946.
Reviewed by Franco Rasetti, *Science*, 1947, 105: 455.

CASTELFRANCHI, Gaetano. Fisica moderna atomica e nucleare. 10th ed. xi, 710 p., ill. Milano: Hoepli, 1959.
1st published as: Fisica moderna. Visione sintetica della fisica d'oggi. ix, 588 p. Milano: Hoepli, 1929. French translation, Physique moderne. 660 p. Paris: Blanchard, 1930. [CB 30/469]. 3rd French edition. Edited by M. Boll. 2 vol. Paris: Dunod, 1949-50.

CASTELFRANCHI, Gaetano. Recent advances in atomic physics. Transl. by W.S. Stiles and J.W.T. Walsh. 2 vol. London: Churchill, 1932.
Translation, with some omissions and abridgements, from 3rd Italian edition of: Fisica moderna atomica e nucleare.

COCKCROFT, John. The Rutherford Memorial Lecture. [Canterbury University College, Christchurch, N.Z., 20 September 1952] *Proc.Roy.Soc.Ser.A*, 1953, 217: 1-8.
Gives a brief account of the development of nuclear physics in the hands of Rutherford and of the applications of nuclear energy which derive from his work.

EIDINOFF, Maxwell Leigh; RUCHLIS, Hyman. Atomics for the millions. Ill. by Maurice Sendak. With an introduction by Harold C. Urey. xiv, 281 p. New York: McGraw-Hill, 1947.
English edition entitled 'Atomics'. London: Harrap, 1950.

HARKINS, William Draper. The neutron, the intermediate or compound nucleus, and the atomic bomb. *Science*, 1946, 103: 289-302.

HEISENBERG, Werner. Nuclear physics. ix, 225 p., ill. New York: Philosophical Library, 1953. [CB 80/204]

LAPP, Ralph E. Roads to discovery. 191 p., ill. New York: Harper & Brothers, 1960.
A history of nuclear physics.

LEPRINCE-RINGUET, Louis. The coming of age of the atom. *J.Franklin Inst.*, 1956, 261: 47-53.

MIELI, Aldo. Il periodo atomico moderno. 1. I dati del problema; 2. Tentativi di soluzione del problema; 3. La risoluzione del problema. *Scientia*, 1917, 22: 178-88, 417-25; 1918, 23: 23-35.

NUCLEONICS; what everybody should know about atomic physics. 38 p., 46 fig. Washington, D.C.: Progress Press, 1946. [CB 70/224]
Summary based on materials prepared for the U.S. Navy. The final chapter is a chronology.

PERRIN, Jean. La recherche scientifique. Atomistique. 24 p. (Actualités Scientifiques et Industrielles, 58) Paris: Hermann, 1933.

POLLARD, Ernest C.; DAVIDSON, William L. Applied nuclear physics. 2nd ed. ix, 352 p., fig., pl. New York/London: Wiley, 1951. [CB 79/174]
One of the appendices lists the dates of important developments in this field from 1904 to 1948.

PURCELL, Edward M. Nuclear physics without the neutron: clues and contradictions. *Proc.10th Int.Congr.Hist.Sci.* (Ithaca, 1962), (1), p. 121-33. Paris: Hermann, 1964.
With comments by S.A. Goudsmit.

RASETTI, Franco. Elements of nuclear physics. xiv, 327 p. New York: Prentice-Hall, 1936.
Original Italian edition Bologna: Zanichelli, 1936.

ROMER, Alfred. The development of atomic physics. ii, 75 p., 24 fig. Canton, N.Y.: 1949. [CB 76/368]
Lithoprinted.

RUBENS, H. Die Entwicklung der Atomistik. Festrede. 40 p. Berlin: Aug. Hirschwald, 1913.

SOMMERFELD, Arnold. Three lectures on atomic physics. Transl. by Henry L. Brose. iv, 70 p. London: Methuen, 1926.

CSdaj

BEYER, Robert T. Foundations of nuclear physics. Facsimiles of thirteen fundamental studies as they were originally reported in the scientific journals. vi, 272 p., ill., bibliogr. New York: Dover, 1949.
Reviewed by I. Bernard Cohen, *Isis*, 1951, 42: 272-3.

CSk/t special aspects

CSk

BOHR, Niels. Atomic physics and human knowledge. viii, 101 p. New York: John Wiley and Sons, Inc., 1958.
Reviewed by W.H. McCrea, *Nature*, 1959, 183: 1218-19.

BOHR, Niels. Essays 1958-1962 on atomic physics and human knowledge. x, 100 p. New York/London: Interscience, 1963.
Reviewed by R.B. Lindsay, *Phys.Today*, 1964, 17: no. 12, 55.

MUDRY, J. Philosophy of atomic physics. 136 p. New York: Philosophical Library, 1958.
Reviewed by Norwood Russell Hanson, *Amer.J.Phys.*, 1960, 28: 410-11.

CSpw

BOHR, Niels. Atomic physics and international cooperation. *Proc.Amer.Phil.Soc.*, 1947, 91: 137-8.

CSs

EINSTEIN, Albert. Only then shall we find courage. *Sci.Cult.*, 1947, 13: 46-8.
First published in *N.Y.Times Mag.*

HARRISON, George Russell. Atoms in action. The world of creative physics. Rev. ed. xii, 401 p. New York: Morrow, 1941. [CB 62/76]
First published 1939. Third edition London: Allen and Unwin, 1948; New York: Morrow, 1949.

KROPP, Gerhard. Das Aussenweltproblem der modernen Atomphysik. 72 p. (Probleme der Wissenschaft in Vergangenheit und Gegenwart, 7) Berlin: Wissenschaftliche Editionsgesellschaft, 1948. [CB 73/149]

PRINCETON BICENTENNIAL CONFERENCE ON THE FUTURE OF NUCLEAR SCIENCE, Princeton University, 1946. Physical science and human values, a symposium. vii, 181 p. Princeton: Princeton University Press, 1947.

SECRECY in science. *Amer.Scient.*, 1947, 35: 525-35.
A discussion at the Princeton Bicentennial Conference on "The future of nuclear science" based on a paper "The uses and hopes of science societies" presented by Harlow Shapley. *See also* above: Princeton Bicentennial Conference.

CSsk

MOOREHEAD, Alan. The traitors. The double life of Fuchs, Pontecorvo, and Nunn May. 222 p. London: Hamish Hamilton, 1952. [CB 79/145]

CStq

MARTI IBÁÑEZ, Félix. The psychological impact of atomic science on modern art. An experiment in correlation. *J. Clin.Exp.Psychopathol.*, 1952, 13: 40-67.

CSw in different countries

CSwb-qk

KOMONS, Nick A.; BUSHNELL, David. The Air Force and nuclear physics. A history of the Air Force Office of Scientific Research Nuclear Physics Program. v, 142 p. Washington, D.C.: Office of Aerospace Research, 1963.

CSwt-sb

HIROSIGE, Tetu. Social conditions for the researches of nuclear physics in pre-war Japan. *Jap.Stud.Hist.Sci.*, 1963, no. 2, 80-93.

CSx techniques and instruments

CSxb

COCKCROFT, John. High-energy particle accelerators. *Endeavour*, 1955, 14: 61-70.

LAWRENCE, E.O. High-current accelerators. *Science*, 1955, 122: 1127-32.
An illustrated history of cyclotrons, etc.

VOROB'EV, A.A. [History of the development of electron accelerators. (In Russian)]. *Vop.Ist.Est.Tekh.*, 1959, 8: 33-47.

CSxb-cd

DEE, P.I.; WORMELL, T.W. An index to C.T.R. Wilson's laboratory records and notebooks in the library of the Royal Society. *Notes Roy.Soc.Lond.*, 1963, 18: 54-66.

CSxp

GREINACHER, H. The evolution of particle counters. *Endeavour*, 1954, 13: 190-7.

KREBS, A.T. Early history of the scintillation counter. *Science*, 1955, 122: 17-18.

CSxx museums

ALTHIN, Torsten Karl Vilhelm. The Cranbrook Atomarium. 29 p., ill. Bloomfield Hills, Mich.: Cranbrook Institute of Science, 1964.

SCIENCE MUSEUM. Handbook of the collection illustrating atomic physics. By F.A.B. Ward. 60 p., ill. London: Her Majesty's Stationery Office, 1963.

CT NUCLEUS

GOUDSMIT, S.A. Pauli and nuclear spin. *Phys.Today*, 1961, 14: 18-21.

JENSEN, J. Hans D. Zur Geschichte der Theorie des Atomkerns. (Nobelvortrag) *Angew.Chem.*, 1964, 76: 69-75.

KONDO, Atsushi. [Concerning the criticism on the resonance theory by Pauling. (In Japanese)] *J.Hist.Sci.Japan*, 1953, no. 25, 6-11.

PRESTON, M.A. Resource letter NS-1 on nuclear structure. *Amer.J.Phys.*, 1964, 32: 820-4.

PROCTOR, W.G. Recuerdos de los primeros días de la resonancia magnética nuclear en la Universidad de Stanford. *Afinidad*, 1964, 21: 247-52.

PURCELL, E.M. Nuclear magnetism. *Amer.J.Phys.*, 1954, 22: 1-9, 6 fig.

WIGNER, Eugene P. On the development of the compound nucleus model. *Amer.J.Phys.*, 1955, 23: 371-80.

CU NUCLEAR PROCESSES AND RADIOACTIVITY

see also UR ATOMIC ENERGY

BECQUEREL, Jean. La radioactivité et les transformations des éléments. 206 p. Paris: Payot, 1924. [CB 16/292]

BECQUEREL, Jean; CROWTHER, J.A. Discovery of radioactivity. *Nature*, 1948, 161: 609.

BIQUARD, Pierre. Frédéric Joliot-Curie et l'énergie atomique. 255 p., ill. (Savants du Monde Entier, 3) Paris: Seghers, 1961.
Reviewed by F. Moreau, *Rev.Syn.*, 1962, 83: 426-31.

BRAGG, William Henry. Radioactivity as a kinetic theory of a fourth state of matter. (Weekly evening meeting, January 27, 1911) *Proc.Roy.Inst.*, 1911-13, 20: 1-10; French transl. *Rev. Sci.*, 1912, 50: 2e semestre, 769-75.

BROGLIE, Maurice de. Atomes, radio-activité, transmutations. 269 p. (Bibliothèque de Philosophie Scientifique) Paris: Flammarion, 1939.
Reviewed by D. Danic, *Thalès*, 1939, 4: 281.

BROGLIE, Maurice de. Les récents progrès de la désintégration artificielle des éléments par bombardement de rayons. 32 p., 1 pl. Paris: Hermann, 1931.
Conférence faite au Conservatoire des Arts et Métiers le 29 avril 1931.

BRUNNGRABER, Rudolf. Radium. [A novel.] 250 p. New York: Random House, 1937. [CB 52/562]
German original: "Radium: Roman eines Elementes" (Stuttgart: Ruwohlt, 1936). A novel which deals with the exploitation of radium following its discovery by the Curies.

CHALMERS, T.W. A short history of radioactivity. 78 p. London: The Engineer, 1951. [CB 80/192]
Reprinted from a series of articles in *The Engineer* in 1950.
Reviewed by S. Weintroub, *Nature*, 1952, 169: 213.

DARROW, Karl. Nuclear fission. *Annu.Rep.Smithsonian Inst. for 1940*, p. 155-9. Washington, D.C.: 1941.

DEWING, Stephen B. Modern radiology in historical perspective. 200 p. Springfield, Ill.: Charles C. Thomas, 1962.

FERMI, Enrico. Physics at Columbia University. The genesis of the nuclear energy project. *Phys.Today*, 1955, 8: no. 11, 12-16.
Verbatim transcript of address to the American Physical Society, 30 January 1954.

GEORGE, André. Lord Rutherford ou l'alchimiste. *Rev.France*, 1938, 525-33.

GOLDANSKII, V.I. Plody velikogo otkrytiya; k 30-letiyu otkrytiya iskusstvennoi radioaktivnosti. [Fruits of an important discovery; on the 30th anniversary of the discovery of artificial radioactivity. (In Russian)] *Vestnik Akad. Nauk SSSR*, 1964, no. 7, 31-5.

GRAETZER, Hans G. Discovery of nuclear fission. *Amer.J.Phys.*, 1964, 32: 9-15.
Includes an English translation of Hahn and Strassmann's original paper on the radiochemical evidence for the fission of uranium.

HAHN, Otto. New atoms, progress and some memories. Edited by W. Gaade. 184 p. New York: Elsevier, 1950.
Reviewed by I. Bernard Cohen, *Isis*, 1951, 42: 272-3.

HAHN, Otto. Von Radiothor zur Uranspaltung. Eine wissenschaftliche Selbstbiographie. 159 p., app. 47 p., ill. Braunschweig: F. Vieweg, 1962.
Reviewed by Heinz Degen, *Naturwiss.Rundsch.*, 1963, 16: 284.

HENRI BECQUEREL 1896. Conférences prononcées à l'occasion du cinquantième anniversaire de la découverte de la radioactivité. 55 p., 5 portr., 6 pl., 3 fig. Paris: Muséum National d'Histoire Naturelle et École Polytechnique, 1946. [CB 81/330]

JAUNCEY, G.E.M. The early years of radio-activity. *Amer.J. Phys.*, 1946, 14: 226-41, 3 fig.
Discusses the work of Becquerel, the Curies, Rutherford, Soddy and Bragg.

JOLIOT-CURIE, M.F. L'énergie atomique. *Experientia*, 1946, 2: 60-2.
Historical sketch beginning with Henri Becquerel, Pierre and Marie Curie. Very brief and general.

LANGEVIN, Paul. L'ère des transmutations. *Pensée* (Paris), 1945, *new ser.* no. 4, 3-16.

LODGE, Oliver. The discovery of radioactivity, and its influence on the course of physical science. (Becquerel Memorial Lecture, 1912) *Mem.Lect.Chem.Soc.*, 1910-13, 2: 217-54.

MARCARD, René. De la pierre philosophale à l'atome. 392 p., ill. Paris: Librairie Plon, 1959.
Reviewed by G. Heym, *Ambix*, 1960, 8: 51.

MEITNER, Lise. Lise Meitner looks back. *Advance Sci.*, 1964, 20: no. 88, 39-46. [CB 90/627]

MEITNER, Lise. Looking back. *Bull.Atom.Sci.*, 1964, 20: no. 3, 2-7. [B 90/601]

MILLIKAN, Robert A. Present status of theory and experiment as to atomic disintegration and atomic synthesis. *Nature*, 1931, 127: 167-70.
Retiring presidential address to the American Association for the Advancement of Science, delivered at Cleveland on Dec. 29, 1930.

NOYES, William Albert; NOYES, W. Albert, Jr. Modern alchemy. ix, 207 p., ill. Springfield, Ill.: Thomas, 1932.

OSGOOD, Thomas H.; HIRST, H. Sim. Rutherford and his alpha particles. *Amer.J.Phys.*, 1964, 32: 681-6.

PANETH, Fritz. Ancient and modern alchemy. *Science*, 1926, 64: 409-17.

RANC, Albert. Henri Becquerel et la découverte de la radioactivité. 101 p. (Sciences et Savants, 3) Paris: Éditions de la Liberté, 1946. [CB 76/373]
Reviewed by R. Lennuier, *Rev.Quest.Sci.*, 1948, 9: 599.

RASSENFOSSE, André de; GUÉBEN, G. Des alchimistes aux briseurs d'atomes. 2nd ed. 182 p. (Bibliothèque Scientifique Belge) Paris: Hermann, 1936.
First published 1928.
Reviewed by Hélène Metzger, *Archeion*, 1936, 18: 281.

REBOUL, G. La pierre philosophale et la constitution de la matière. *Rev.Sci.*, 1923, 61: 659-75.
Comparison of current theories concerning the structure of matter and those of the alchemists.

ROMER, Alfred. The restless atom. 198 p., fig. (Science Study Series, S 12) Garden City, N.Y.: Doubleday, 1960. Also publ. London: Heinemann, 1962, 99 p., ill. [CB 87/565]
A short history of experiments in atomic transmutation at the end of the 19th and early years of the 20th centuries.

ROMER, Alfred. The transformation theory of radioactivity. *Isis*, 1958, 49: 3-12.

RUTHERFORD, Ernest, *Lord Rutherford*. The artificial transmutation of the elements. Thirty-fifth Robert Boyle lecture delivered before the Oxford University Junior Scientific Club on 2nd June 1933. 12 p. London: Oxford University Press, 1933. [CB 43/274]

RUTHERFORD, Ernest, *Lord Rutherford*. The life history of an α-particle. Discourse delivered at the Royal Institution on Friday, June 15, 1923. [With addendum] *Nature*, 1923, 112: 305-12.

RUTHERFORD, Ernest, *Lord Rutherford*. Radioactive substances and their radiations. vii, 699 p., ill., pl., diagr. Cambridge University Press; New York: Putnam, 1913.
German translation Radioaktive Substanzen und ihre Strahlungen. Leipzig: Akademische Verlagsgesellschaft, 1913.

RUTHERFORD, Ernest, *Lord Rutherford*. Transmutation of matter. *Nature*, 1938, 141: 58-61. [CB 53/238]

SODDY, F. The interpretation of radium. 4th ed., rev. and enl. xvi, 260 p., ill. London: John Murray, 1920.
First published 1909.
French translation of 3rd English edition Le radium. Paris: Alcan, 1919.

SOLOMON, Arthur K. Why smash atoms? Ill. by Katherine R. Campbell. Rev. ed. xii, 204 p. Cambridge, Mass.: Harvard University Press, 1946. [CB 60/149]
First published 1940.

SPARBERG, Esther B. A study of the discovery of fission. *Amer.J.Phys.*, 1964, 32: 2-8.

STAROSEL'SKAYA-NIKITINA, O.A. Istoriya radioaktivnosti i vozniknoveniya yadernoi fiziki. [History of radioactivity and the origin of nuclear physics.] 428 p. Moscow: Izd-vo Akademii Nauk SSSR, 1963.
Reviewed by A.R. Pozner, *Priroda*, 1964, no. 9, 122-3.

VALADARES, Manuel. The discovery of artificial radioactivity. *Impact*, 1964, 14: 83-8.

CUcd

ZAITSEVA, L.L. Nekotorye neopublikovannye materialy, otnosiashchiesia k istorii ucheniia o radioaktivnosti. [Some unpublished materials relating to the history of studies of radioactivity. (In Russian)]. *Tr.Inst.Ist.Est.Tekh.*, 1961, 35: 149-66. [CB 87/633]

CUdaj

GRAETZER, Hans G. Discovery of nuclear fission. *Amer.J.Phys.*, 1964, 32: 9-15.
Includes an English translation of Hahn and Strassmann's original paper on the radiochemical evidence for the fission of uranium.

ROMER, Alfred, ed. The discovery of radioactivity and transmutation. xi, 233 p., 7 ill. (Classics of Science, 2) New York: Dover, 1964.
Papers by Becquerel, Rutherford, Pierre and Marie Curie, etc. from 1896 to 1905.

CUs

BERNAL, J.D.; BUTT, D.K. The technical and social consequences of the discovery of artificial radioactivity in 1934. *Impact*, 1964, 14: 89-100.

CUw

LAWSON, R.W. The part played by different countries in the development of the science of radioactivity. *Scientia*, 1921, 30: 257-70; French transl., suppl. 39-50. [CB 12/598]
Particular emphasis is laid on the part played by the geologist Suess in providing the Curies with the industrial residues from which they isolated radium.

CUwg

GOUDSMIT, Samuel A. Alsos. The failure in German science. xiv, 260 p. London: Sigma Books; New York: Schuman, 1947.
Reviewed by Henry Guerlac, *Isis*, 1950, 41: 224-7; by N.F. Mott, *Nature*, 1948, 162: 3-4.

CUwj

COSTANZO, Giovanni. A radioactividade em Portugal no seu inicio. Notas historicas. *Petrus Nonius*, 1949, 7: 13-22.

CUxd radiocarbon dating

ARNOLD, J.R.; LIBBY, W.E. Radiocarbon dates. *Science*, 1951, 113: 111-20. [CB 77/380]

JOHNSON, Frederick. Radiocarbon dating. A report on the program to aid in the development of the method of dating. 65 p., 2 fig. (Memoirs of the Society for American Archaeology, 8) Salt Lake City: The Society, 1951.

KAMEN, Martin David. The early history of carbon-14. *J.Chem. Educ.*, 1963, 40: (5), 234-42.
A detailed and personal account by one of the leading participants.

KAMEN, Martin David. Early history of carbon-14. *Science*, 1963, 140: 584-90.

LIBBY, Willard F. Radiocarbon dating. vii, 124 p. Chicago: University of Chicago Press, 1952. [CB 79/185]
2nd ed. ix, 175 p. Chicago: University of Chicago Press, 1955. [CB 83/200]

LIBBY, Willard F. Radiocarbon dating. *Amer.Scient.*, 1956, 44: 98-112. [CB 82/218]
A history of the technique invented by the author.

LIBBY, Willard F. Radiocarbon dating. *Endeavour*, 1954, 13: 5-16.

ZUMBERGE, J.H.; POTZGER, J.E. Pollen profiles, radiocarbon dating and geologic chronology of the Lake Michigan basin. *Science*, 1955, 121: 309-11.

CUxd-wb

RALPH, E.K. University of Pennsylvania radiocarbon dates. *Science*, 1955, 121: 149-50.

RUBIN, M.; SUESS, Hans E. U.S. Geological Survey radiocarbon dates. *Science*, 1954, 120: 467-73; 1955, 121: 481-8.

SUESS, Hans E. Natural radiocarbon measurements by acetylene counting. *Science*, 1954, 120: 5-7.
For some measurements by this technique *see* above, Rubin, M.; Suess, Hans E.

CV MOLECULES

BROGLIE, Louis de. La réalité des molécules et l'oeuvre de Jean Perrin. Lecture faite en la séance annuelle des prix du 17 décembre 1945. *Mém.Acad.Sci.*, 1949, 67: 29 p., portr.

BUSSE, W.F. Two decades of high-polymer physics, a survey and forecast. *Phys.Today*, 1964, 17: no. 9, 32-41.

COULSON, C.A. Interatomic forces: Maxwell to Schrödinger. *Nature*, 1962, 195: 744-9.

MILLINGTON, E.C. Studies in cohesion from Democritus to Laplace. *Lychnos*, 1944-45, 55-78, ill.

SOCIÉTÉ FRANÇAISE DE PHYSIQUE, Paris. Les progrès de la physique moléculaire. Conférences faites en 1913-1914 par Mme P. Curie, MM. J. Becquerel, De Broglie, A. Cotton, Ch. Fabry, P. Langevin, Ch. Mauguin, H. Mouton. iv, 243 p., 2 pl. (Collection de Mémoires Relatifs à la Physique, 2e série) Paris: Gauthier-Villars, 1914 [appeared 1918].

SVEDBERG, The. Die Existenz der Moleküle. Experimentelle Studien. viii, 244 p., ill. Leipzig: Akademische Verlagsgesellschaft, 1912.

CVyCC

ARIYAMA, Kanetaka. [50 years of the quantum theory. 1. Theory of the assembly of molecular systems. (In Japanese)]. *J.Hist.Sci.Japan*, 1952, no. 21, 1-4.

CVyCP

CABANNES, Jean. Anisotropie des molécules. Effet Raman. Conférence faite au Conservatoire national des Arts et Métiers les 2 et 3 mai 1930. 65 p., ill., bibliogr. Paris: Hermann, 1930.

RUTHERFORD, Ernest. Recent reactions between theory and experiment. The Raman effect: the constitution of hydrogen gas. *Nature*, 1929, 124: 878-80.
From the presidential address delivered at the anniversary meeting of the Royal Society on 30 November.

CW CRYSTALLOGRAPHY

EWALD, P.P. International status of crystallography, past and future. *Nature*, 1944, 154: 628-31.

HEY, Max H. History of the 'Widmanstätten' structure. *Nature*, 1939, 143: 764.

LE CORBEILLER, Philippe. Crystals and the future of physics. *Sci.Amer.*, 1953, 188: 50-6, 7 fig.

METZGER, Hélène. La genèse de la science des cristaux. 248 p. Paris: Alcan, 1918.
Reviewed by L. Guinet, *Isis*, 1920, 3: 445-6.

NEVIANI, Antonio. Le più antiche osservazioni sulla geometria e struttura dei cristalli da Plinio a Stenone. *Riv.Stor. Sci.*, 1935, 17: 24-35.

NOWACKI, Werner. Cinquante ans de théorie générale de la structure des cristaux. *Ann.Guébhard-Séverine*, 1936, 12: 120-39, 25 fig.

PABST, Adolf. The development of crystallography. *Mineralogist*, 1936, 4: no. 1, 3-4, 54-9; no. 2, 7-8, 22-5.

PHILLIPS, F.C. An introduction to crystallography. ix, 302 p., 500 diagr. London: Longmans, Green, 1946. [CB 75/94]
This treatise includes historical information, e.g., very brief biographical sketches of the founders.

RINNE, Friedrich. Crystals and the fine-structure of matter, with a drawing by A. Dürer, and portraits of the leading investigators in the study of fine-structure. Transl. by Walter S. Stiles. ix, 195 p., ill. London: Methuen; New York: Dutton, 1924.
Translation of: Das feinbauliche Wesen der Materie nach dem Vorbilde der Kristalle. 2nd-3rd ed. Berlin: 1922.

TERTSCH, H. Das Geheimnis der Kristallwelt. 391 p., 12 pl., 48 fig. Wien: Gerlach & Wiedling, 1947.
Reviewed by W. Nowacki, *Experientia*, 1949, 5: 170.

TUTTON, Alfred Edwin Howard. The natural history of crystals. xii, 287 p., ill. London: Kegan Paul, 1924.

CWwn

BOKII, G.B.; SHAFRANOVSKII, I.I. [Russian crystallography. (In Russian)]. *Tr.Inst.Ist.Est.*, 1947, 1: 81-120.

SHAFRANOVSKII, I.I. Istoriia kristallografi v Rossii. [The history of crystallography in Russia. (In Russian)]. 415 p., ill. Moscow/Leningrad: Izdatel'stvo Akademii Nauk SSSR, 1962.
A survey of crystallography in Russia, from earliest times to 1917.
Reviewed by Loren Graham, *Isis*, 1964, 55: 248-9.

CWxh

BURMESTER, L. Geschichtliche Entwicklung des kristallographischen Zeichnens und dessen Ausführung in schräger Projection. *Z.Kristallogr.*, 1922, 57: 1-47, 1 pl. [CB 15/222]

CX X-RAY CRYSTALLOGRAPHY

BRAGG, William Henry. An introduction to crystal analysis. vii, 168 p., 8 pl. London: Bell, 1928.

BRAGG, William Henry; BRAGG, William Lawrence. X-rays and crystal structure. 5th ed. xi, 324 p., ill. London: Bell, 1925.
First published 1915.
German translation Die Reflexion von Röntgenstrahlen an Kristallen: Grundlegende Untersuchungen in den Jahren 1913 und 1914. Leipzig: Voss, 1928.

BRAGG, William Lawrence. The history of X-ray analysis. iv, 24 p., 4 pl. (Science in Britain) London: Longmans, Green (for the British Council), 1943. [CB 69/203]
Reviewed by F. Ian G. Rawlins, *Nature*, 1943, 152: 463.

DAVIS, Bergen. Intensity of emission of X-rays and their reflection from crystals. *Bull.Nat.Res.Counc.*, 1920, 1: 410-26.

DELONE, B.N. Rentgenovy luchi i kristally [50 let otkrytiia Maksa Laue]. [Roentgen rays and crystals. 50th anniversary of Max von Laue's discovery. (In Russian)] *Priroda*, 1962, no. 12, 85-7.

EWALD, Peter Paul. William Henry Bragg and the new crystallography. *Nature*, 1962, 195: 320-5.

EWALD, Peter Paul. Zur Entdeckung der Röntgeninterferenzen vor zwanzig Jahren und zu Sir W. Braggs siebzigsten Geburtstag. *Naturwissenschaften*, 1932, 20: 527-30.

EWALD, Peter Paul, ed. Fifty years of X-ray diffraction. Dedicated to the International Union of Crystallography. ix, 720 p., pl. Utrecht: A. Vosthoek's Uitgeversmij (for the International Union of Crystallography), 1962.
Reviewed by Malcolm Barlow, *Phys.Today*, 1963, 16: no. 10, 70-2; by I. Fankuchen, *Science*, 1962, 138: 1254-5.

FIFTY years of X-ray crystal analysis. (Editorial.) *Endeavour*, 1962, 21: 123-4.

LAUE, Max von. Address before the First Congress of the International Union of Crystallography at Harvard University... August 1948. Mount Vernon, N.Y.: North American Philips Company Inc., Research and Control Instruments Division, [1948?].
Autobiographical reminiscences concerning the discovery of X-ray interference in crystals in 1912.

LEHMANN, O. Die Beweise für die Existenz von Molekülen und die Sichtbarmachung der Molekularstruktur von Kristallen durch Röntgenstrahlen. 58 p. Karlsruhe: Braun, 1913.

LONSDALE, Kathleen. L'analyse des cristaux au moyen des rayons X et problèmes chimiques. 26 p., ill. (Les Conférences du Palais de la Découverte, 9 mai 1946) Alençon: 1949.

NIGGLI, A. Fünfzig Jahre Röntgeninterferenzen. *Naturwissenschaften*, 1963, 50: 461-2. [CB 89/581]

RADCHENKO, I.V. 45 let rentgenografii shidkostei. [45 years of X-ray study of liquids. (In Russian)]. *Ukrain.Fiz.Zh.*, 1962, 7: 820-6.

ROBERTSON, J.M. Origins and historical development of X-ray analysis. *Brit.J.Appl.Phys.*, 1963, 14: 635-42.

ZEHN Jahre Laue-Diagramm. *Naturwissenschaften*, 1922, 10: no. 16, 361-416, portr. [CB 13/244]
The whole of this number is devoted to the history of that discovery.

CXdaj

LAUE, Max von, *et al.* Die Interferenz der Röntgenstrahlen. 111 p., 4 pl. (Ostwald's Klassiker, 204) Leipzig: Akademische Verlagsgesellschaft, 1923. [CB 14/526]

CXhj

GLASER, Otto C.; WRINCH, Dorothy. Diffraction patterns in nineteenth-century astronomy and twentieth-century X-ray crystallography. *Science, Medicine and History. Essays in honour of Charles Singer*, (2), p. 197-202, 2 pl. London: Oxford University Press, 1953.

CXwe-bx

PHILLIPS, D.C. Exhibition on "the development of x-ray crystal analysis in Great Britain". *Proc.Roy.Inst.*, 1962, 39: 246-51.

CXwg

GERLACH, Walther. Münchener Erinnerungen. Aus der Zeit von Max von Laues Entdeckung vor 50 Jahren. *Phys.Bl.*, 1963, 19: 97-103.

CXxd

GUINIER, André. X-ray crystallographic technology. Engl. transl. by T.L. Tippell. xiii, 330 p., ill. London: Hilger & Watts, 1952.

CXyB

ALEXANDER, Jerome. Mathematics in the service of chemistry. *Scr.Math.*, 1944, 10: 201-12, 15 fig.
The use of mathematics in analysing the results of X-ray crystallography.

CY SOLID STATE

BORN, Max. Atomtheorie des festen Zustandes (Dynamik der Kristallgitter). 2nd ed. vi, 527-781 p., ill. (Encyklopädie, 5: part 3, no. 4) Leipzig: Teubner, 1923.

MANN, Martin. *See* CMc

NERNST, Walther. The theory of the solid state. viii, 104 p. London: Hodder & Stoughton, 1914.
Based on four lectures delivered at University College, London, in March 1913.

CYyCM

DIMAROVA, E.N. K istorii izucheniia poluprovodnikovykh svoistv zakisi medi. [On the history of the study of the semiconductor properties of cuprous oxide. (In Russian)]. *Tr.Inst.Ist.Est.Tekh.*, 1961, 43: 165-81.

DUKOV, V.M. Razvitie klassicheskoi teorii metallicheskoi provodimosti. [Development of the classical theory of the conductivity of metals. (In Russian)]. *Vop.Ist.Est.Tekh.*, 1962, 13: 64-9.

FRANKFURT, U.I. Uchenie o termoelektrichestve s momenta vozniknoveniia elektronnoi teorii metallov (1900-1925). [The concept of thermoelectricity from the appearance of the electron theory of metals, 1900-1925. (In Russian)]. *Vop.Ist.Est.Tekh.*, 1962, 13: 69-73.

PEARSON, G.L.; BRATTAIN, W.H. History of semiconductor research. *Proc.Inst.Radio Eng.*, 1955, 43: 1794-1806.

CYyCMwn

SOKOLOV, V.A. K istorii issledovaniia fizicheskikh svoistv dielektrikov. [On the history of investigation of the physical properties of dielectrics. (In Russian)]. *Vop. Ist.Est.Tekh.*, 1963, 15: 96-101.
A review of the work of Russian physicists in this area at the end of the nineteenth and beginning of the twentieth centuries.

CZ LIQUID AND GASEOUS STATES; PLASMA

TRILLAT, J.J. L'état liquide et les états mésomorphes. 24 p., ill. (Conférences d'Actualités Scientifiques et Industrielles, 26) Paris: Hermann, 1931.
Conférence faite au Conservatoire des arts et métiers le 5 mai 1931.

D CHEMISTRY

see also SB AGRICULTURAL CHEMISTRY
VU CHEMICAL INDUSTRY

Dc general history

Dc-bm *large scale works*

AKADEMIIA NAUK SSSR. INSTITUT ISTORII ESTESTVOZNANIIA I TEKHNIKI. Ocherki po istorii khimii. [Sketches in the history of chemistry. (In Russian). Edited by Iu. I. Solovev.] 427 p. Moskva: Izdatel'stvo Akademii Nauk SSSR, 1963.
Reviewed by Henry M. Leicester, *Arch.Int.Hist.Sci.*, 1964, 17: 327-8.

ARMSTRONG, E.F., ed. Chemistry in the twentieth century: an account of the achievement and the present state of knowledge in chemical science. Prepared under the guidance of a committee representing the scientific societies. 281 p. London: Ernest Benn, 1924.

BÄUMLER, Ernst. Ein Jahrhundert Chemie. 392 p., ill. Düsseldorf: Econ-Verlag, 1963.
With two articles by Gustav Ehrhart and Volkmar Muthesius.
Reviewed by Eduard Farber, *Technol.Cult.*, 1964, 5: 440-1.

BEALE, Harriett Blaine. The beginnings of chemistry: a story book of science for young people. x, 243 p., ill. New York: Coward, McCann, 1929.

BERRY, A.J. From classical to modern chemistry. Some historical sketches. xii, 251 p. New York/Cambridge: Cambridge University Press, 1954.
Reviewed by Aaron J. Ihde, *Isis*, 1955, 46: 369; by Lucius W. Elder, *Sci.Mon.*, 1955, 81: 147-8; by Charles C. Gillispie, *Arch.Int.Hist.Sci.*, 1955, 8: 196-8.

BERRY, A.J. Modern chemistry. Some sketches of its historical development. x, 240 p. Cambridge University Press, 1946; reprinted 1948. [CB 79/175]
Reviewed by H.W. Melville, *Nature*, 1947, 159: 3.

BRITTON, Hubert Thomas Stanley. Chemistry, life and civilization: a popular account of modern advances in chemistry. vii, 248 p., 29 pl. London: Chapman and Hall, 1931.

BROWN, James Campbell. A history of chemistry from the earliest times till the present day. xxix, 543 p. London: J. & A. Churchill, 1913.
Reviewed by E. Bloch, *Isis*, 1913, 1: 279-80.

CEUILLERON, Jean. Histoire de la chimie. 128 p. ("Que Sais-Je?" Le Point de Connaissances Actuelles, 35) Paris: Presses Universitaires de France, 1957. [CB 83/199]
Reviewed by A. Bruylants, *Rev.Quest.Sci.*, 1958, 19: 444-5.

CHALMERS, T.W. Historic researches. Chapters in the history of physical and chemical discovery. vi, 288 p., 85 fig. London: Morgan, 1949.
Reviewed by Eduard Farber, *Isis*, 1951, 42: 67.

DELACRE, M. Histoire de la chimie. xvi, 632 p. Paris: Gauthier-Villars, 1920.
Reviewed by L. Guinet, *Isis*, 1921, 4: 84.

DOBBIN, Leonard. Occasional fragments of chemical history. 85 p. Edinburgh: priv. print., 1942.

EKECRANTZ, Thor. Geschichte der Chemie. Kurzgefasste Darstellung. viii, 232 p. Leipzig: Akademische Verlagsgesellschaft, 1913. [CB 4/778]

FARBER, Eduard. The evolution of chemistry: a history of its ideas, methods, and materials. ix, 349 p., 30 fig. New York: Ronald Press, 1952.
Reviewed by Aaron J. Ihde, *Isis*, 1953, 44: 83; by R.J. Forbes, *Arch.Int.Hist.Sci.*, 1954, 7: 81-2.

FARBER, Eduard. Die geschichtliche Entwicklung der Chemie. xii, 312 p., 4 tables. Berlin: Julius Springer, 1921.
Reviewed by Ernst Bloch, *Isis*, 1923, 5: 465-6.

FERCHL, Fritz; SÜSSENGUTH, A. Kurzgeschichte der Chemie. v, 217 p., 200 fig. Mittenwald (Bayern): Nemayer (for Gesellschaft für Geschichte der Pharmacie), 1936. [CB 51/262]

FERCHL, Fritz; SÜSSENGUTH, A. A pictorial history of chemistry. viii, 214 p., 186 fig. London: Heinemann, 1939. [CB 70/257]
Translation of the above.

FIERZ-DAVID, H.E. Die Entwicklungsgeschichte der Chemie. Eine Studie. xv, 425 p., 106 fig., 4 tables. Basel: Birkhäuser, 1945.
Reviewed by Eduard Farber, *Isis*, 1947, 37: 105-6; 2nd rev. ed. 1952 reviewed by R.J. Forbes, *Arch.Int.Hist.Sci.*, 1953, 6: 514-15.

FINDLAY, Alexander. A hundred years of chemistry. 352 p., 11 fig. London: Duckworth; New York: Macmillan, 1937.
2nd ed. 318 p. (100 Years Series) London: Duckworth, 1948.
Reviewed by Mary Elvira Weeks, *Isis*, 1938, 29: 176-9; by John Read, *Nature*, 1948, 162: 946.

FOSTER, William. The romance of chemistry. xvi, 468 p., 31 pl. London: Allen and Unwin, 1927.

GIUA, Michele. Storia della chimica dall' alchimia alle dottrine moderne. iv, 392 p. Torino: Chiantore, 1946.
Reviewed by Aldo Mieli, *Arch.Int.Hist.Sci.*, 1948, 1: 726-8; by W. Hubicki, *Kwart.Hist.Nauk.Tech.*, 1956, 1: 818-19.

HERZ, Walter G. Grundzüge der Geschichte der Chemie. Richtlinien einer Entwicklungsgeschichte der allgemeinen Ansichten in der Chemie. 142 p. Stuttgart: Enke, 1916.

HOLMYARD, E.J. Chemistry to the time of Dalton. 128 p., ill. (Chapters in the History of Science, 3) New York: Oxford University Press, 1925. [CB 18/616]

IHDE, Aaron J. The development of modern chemistry. xii, 851 p., ill. New York: Harper and Row, 1964.

ISTORIA khimicheskikh nauk. [The history of chemistry. (In Russian)] 351 p., bibliogr. (*Tr.Inst.Ist.Est.Tekh.*, 30) Moskva: Izdatel'stvo Akademii Nauk SSSR, 1960.
Whole volume; contents listed in CB 86/463.

JAFFE, Bernard. Crucibles: the story of chemistry from ancient alchemy to nuclear fission. xii, (2), 480, 2 p. New York: Simon & Schuster, 1948.
Spanish translation "Crisoles" by Leon Mirias publ. Buenos Aires: Antonio Zamora, 1948.
Reviewed by Denis Duveen, *Isis*, 1950, 41: 133.

JAFFE, Bernard. New world of chemistry. xi, 692 p. New York: Silver Burdett, 1940. [CB 61/400]

KENDALL, James. Great discoveries by young chemists. xii, 231 p., 34 pl. London/New York: Nelson, 1953. [CB 81/269-70]
Lectures delivered at the Royal Institution in 1938 and published as Young chemists and great discoverers, London: Bell, 1939.
Reviewed by John Read, *Nature*, 1940, 145: 123-4.

KOPP, H. Geschichte der Chemie. 2 vol., 4 parts. 455 p., 426 p., 372 p., 448 p. Leipzig: Lorentz, 1931.
First publ. 1843-47.

LADENBURG, A. [Lectures on the history of the development of chemistry from Lavoisier to our time. (In Russian)]. Transl. from the 4th ed., [1907], and ed. by E.C. Elchaninov. With the addition of [An outline of the history of chemistry in Russia, by P.I. Walden. (In Russian)]. viii, 695 p. Odessa: Mathesis, 1917. [CB 27/548]
Russian translation of Vorträge über die Entwicklungsgeschichte der Chimie von Lavoisier.

LEICESTER, Henry M. The historical background of chemistry. viii, 260 p., 2 fig. New York: John Wiley and Sons; London: Chapman & Hall Ltd., 1956.
Reviewed by Erwin N. Hiebert, *Isis*, 1958, 49: 88-9; for other reviews *see* CB 83/200 and CB 85/391.

LETTS, E.A. Some fundamental problems in chemistry, old and new. xiii, 235 p., 44 fig. London: Constable, 1914.
Reviewed by G. Sarton, *Isis*, 1920, 3: 443.

LOCKEMANN, Georg. Geschichte der Chemie in kurzgefasster Darstellung. 2 vol. 1. Vom Altertum bis zur Entdeckung des Sauerstoffs. 142 p., 4 pl.; 2. Von der Entdeckung des Sauerstoffs bis zur Gegenwart. 151 p., 16 pl. (Sammlung Göschen, 264, 265/265a) Berlin: de Gruyter, 1950-55.
Reviewed by J.R. Partington, *Nature*, 1951, 168: 716; by W. Hubicki (in Polish), *Kwart.Hist.Nauk.Tech.*, 1956, 1: 181-2.
For English translation *see* below; French translation (Paris: Dunod, 1962) [CB 88/545] reviewed by A. Delorme, *Rev.Syn.*, 1963, 84: 619.

LOCKEMANN, Georg. The story of chemistry. 277 p. New York: Philosophical Library; London: Peter Owen, 1960.
Reviewed by Frank Greenaway, *Isis*, 1961, 52: 593-4; for other reviews *see* CB 86/463 and CB 87/565.

LOWRY, Thomas Martin. Historical introduction to chemistry. 3rd ed. xv, 581 p., 57 fig. London: Macmillan, 1936. [CB 7/129]
First publ. 1915.

MARCARD, René. De la pierre philosophale à l'atome. 392 p., ill. Paris: Librairie Plon, 1959.
Reviewed by G. Heym, *Ambix*, 1960, 8: 51.

MARSH, J.E. The origins and growth of chemical science. x, 161 p., ill. London: Murray, 1929. [CB 27/548]

MASSAIN, R. Chimie et chimistes. Preface by Louis de Broglie. xiii, 392 p., ill. Paris: Éditions de l'École, 1952. [CB 83/200]
Reviewed by E.R. Webster, *Arch.Int.Hist.Sci.*, 1953, 6: 122; by Maurice Daumas, *Rev.Hist.Sci.*, 1953, 6: 75-7.

MASSON, Irvine. Three centuries of chemistry: phases in the growth of a science. vii, 191 p. London: Ernest Benn, 1925.

MENSHUTKIN, B.N. [Chemistry and the ways of its development. (In Russian)] 352 p., 140 ill. Moskva: Akademiia Nauk SSSR, 1937. [CB 53/263]

MENSHUTKIN, B.N. [The most important milestones in the development of chemistry during the last one hundred and fifty years. (In Russian)]. 116 p. Leningrad: Akademiia Nauk SSSR, 1932. [CB 39/454]

METZGER, Hélène. La chimie. 170 p. (Histoire du Monde, 4) Paris: De Boccard, 1930.
Reviewed by L. Guinet, *Isis*, 1931, 15: 188-90.

MEYER, Ernst von. Geschichte der Chemie von den ältesten Zeiten bis zur Gegenwart, zugleich Einführung in das Studium der Chemie. 4th ed. xiv, 616 p. Leipzig: Veit, 1914.
First publ. 1889.
Reviewed by Ernst Bloch, *Isis*, 1922, 4: 360-1.

MEYER, Richard. Vorlesungen über die Geschichte der Chemie. viii, 467 p. Leipzig: Akademische Verlagsgesellschaft, 1922.

MIELI, Aldo. Pagine di storia della chimica. xxiii, 254 p., 16 ill. Roma: Casa Editrice Leonardo da Vinci, 1922.
Reviewed by G. Sarton, *Isis*, 1923, 5: 173-4.

MOORE, Forris Jewett. A history of chemistry. 3rd rev. ed. by William T. Hall. xxi, 447 p., ill. New York: McGraw-Hill, 1939.
First publ. 1918. 2nd ed. 1931 [CB 34/501]
Reviewed by Tenney L. Davis, *Isis*, 1949, 32: 384.

MOUREU, Ch. Discours et conférences sur la science et ses applications. 372 p. Paris: Gauthier-Villars, 1927.
Deals chiefly with chemistry and many historical aspects of the subject.
Reviewed by F. Michel, *Rev.Gén.Sci.*, 1928, 39: 151.

NAKASEKO, Rokuro. Sekai Kwagaku-shi. [History of world chemistry. (In Japanese)] v, 571 p., 31 photographs. Kyôto: Kaniya Shôten, 1927.
Reviewed by Marcello Muccioli, *Archeion*, 1928, 9: 379-82.

NAKESEKO, Rokuro. [History of recent chemistry. (In Japanese)] 3, 561 p., 16 portr. Kyoto: Kaniya Book Store, 1927. [CB 27/549]

PARTINGTON, J.R. Everyday chemistry. viii, 668 p. London: Macmillan, 1929. [CB 37/592]
3rd edition, 1952. The book contains a survey of the history of chemistry.

PARTINGTON, J.R. A history of chemistry. Vol. 2-4. 2. xxiv, 795 p. 1961. 3. xxiii, 854 p. 1962. 4. xxxi, 1007 p. 1964. London: Macmillan; New York: St. Martin's Press, 1961-64.
Volume 2 reviewed by Marie Boas Hall, *Isis*, 1963, 54: 495-7; for other reviews *see* CB 87/565, CB 88/545, CB 89/503.
Volume 3 reviewed by H.M. Leicester, *Isis*, 1964, 55: 106-7; for other reviews *see* CB 89/551 and CB 90/518.
Volume 4 reviewed by G. Kersaint, *Arch.Int.Hist.Sci.*, 1964, 17: 323; by L. Pearce Williams, *Science*, 1964, 145: 1288-9.

PARTINGTON, J.R. A short history of chemistry. xiii, 415 p., 127 fig., bibliogr. New York: Harper (Harper Torchbook), 1960.
Reprint of 3rd ed. publ. London: Macmillan, 1957. The book was first publ. 1937 and reviewed by Tenney L. Davis, *Isis*, 1938, 29: 179-81.

PICTET, Amé. Souvenirs et travaux d'un chimiste. 228 p., 2 portr. Neuchâtel: Éditions de la Baconnière, 1941.
Reviewed by Marc Cramer, *Isis*, 1943, 34: 415-17.

RAMSAY, William. Vergangenes und Künftiges aus der Chemie. Biographische und chemische Essays transl. by Wilhelm Ostwald. 2nd ed. vii, 296 p. Leipzig: Akademische Verlagsgesellschaft, 1913. [CB 4/778]
German translation of "Essays, biographical and chemical" (London: Constable, 1908).

READ, John. Humour and humanism in chemistry. xxiii, 388 p., 90 ill. London: Bell, 1947. [CB 73/171]

READ, John. Through alchemy to chemistry. A procession of ideas and personalities. xvii, 206 p., 51 ill. London: G. Bell and Sons, Ltd., 1957. [CB 83/200]
For reviews *see* CB 84/312.

REICHEN, Charles Albert. A history of chemistry. 104 p., ill. (The New Illustrated Library of Science and Invention, 10) New York: Hawthorn Books, 1963.
French and German editions Lausanne: Rencontre and Erik Nitsche, 1963. Essentially a picture book.

RUSKA, Julius, ed. Studien zur Geschichte der Chemie. Festgabe Edmund O. v. Lippmann, zum siebzigsten Geburtstage dargebracht aus Nah und Fern und im Auftrage der Deutschen Gesellschaft für Geschichte der Medizin und der Naturwissenschaften. vi, 242 p., portr. Berlin: Springer, 1927. [CB 22/268]

SCIENCE MUSEUM. Pure chemistry ... by A. Barclay. 3rd impression with amendments. 2 vol. 1. Historical review. 72 p., 14 pl.; 2. Handbook of the collections illustrating pure chemistry. Descriptive catalogue. 76 p., 13 pl., 3 fig. London: H.M. Stationery Off., 1962.

STERN, Rose. A short history of chemistry. 2nd ed. 160 p., ill. London: Dent, 1926.
First edition 1924.

STILLMAN, John Maxson. The story of early chemistry. xiii, 566 p. New York/London: D. Appleton and Company, 1924. [CB 16/295]
Reviewed by Tenney L. Davis, *Isis*, 1925, 7: 511-14.

THORPE, Edward. Storia della chimica. Versione dall' inglese, introduzione e note di Rinaldo Pitoni. 325 p. Torino: Società Tipografico-editrice Nazionale, 1911. [CB 3/565]
Italian translation, with additional notes on Italian chemistry, of "History of chemistry". 2 vol. (London: Watts, 1909-10).

TILDEN, William A. Chemical discovery and invention in the twentieth century. 6th ed. rev. by S. Glasstone. xvi, 492 p., ill. London: Routledge, 1936.
First publ. 1917. [CB 7/119]

TILDEN, William A. The progress of scientific chemistry in our own times, with biographical notices. 2nd ed. xii, 366 p. London: Longmans, Green, 1913.

TIMMERMANS, Jean. Histoire de la chimie. 121 p., 26 pl. Bruxelles: Presses Universitaires de Bruxelles, 1948.
Reviewed by Paul Erculisse, *Arch.Int.Hist.Sci.*, 1948, 2: 743; by Maurice Daumas, *Rev.Hist.Sci.*, 1953, 6: 75.

TING, Su-Hien. [A history of chemistry for general reference. (In Chinese)]. 420 p. Peking: National University of Peking, 1925.

VALERDI, Agustin Muruay. Compendio de historia de la quimica y de la farmacia. 201 p. Madrid: E. Raso, 1912.

WALDEN, Paul. Geschichte der Chemie. 2nd rev. ed. 127 p. (Geschichte der Wissenschaften, 2) Bonn: Athenäum-Verlag, 1950.
First published 1947.
Reviewed by Arne Fredga, *Lychnos*, 1952, 405-6. French translation (Paris: Lamarre, 1953) reviewed by Maurice Daumas, *Rev.Hist.Sci.*, 1956, 9: 185-6.

WINDERLICH, Rudolph. Lehrbuch der Chemie für höhere Lehranstalten. 2 vol. 1. Unterstufe. 6th rev. ed. 154 p., 72 fig., 4 portr.; 2. Oberstufe. 4th rev. ed. viii, 291 p., 198 fig. Braunschweig: Vieweg, 1948, 1949. [CB 73/171 and CB 74/387]
This textbook is remarkable because of the attention it pays to the history of chemistry.

Dc-bn *essays; articles*

ADAMS, Roger. Chemical research in the war and post-war periods. *Chem.Eng.News*, 1946, 24: 1643-7, 1755.
Reviewed by Winslow H. Hartford, *Sci.Mon.*, 1946, 63: 261.

BEDEL, Charles. L'avènement de la chimie moderne. *Rev.Hist. Sci.*, 1951, 4: 324-33.

BLOKH, M.A. 150-letie so dnya otkrȳtiya kisloroda. [150 years from the day of the discovery of oxygen. (In Russian)] *Přiroda*, 1923, no. 7-12, 107-8.

BRUNOLD, Ch. Les grands courants d'organisation rationnelle dans la chimie moderne. *Thalès*, 1935, 2: 30-3.

FARBER, Eduard. Geschichtliche Vorbilder chemischen Arbeitens. *Proteus* (Bonn), 1937, 2: 65-73.

FARBER, Eduard. Die geschichtliche Entwicklung der Chemie. *Beitr.Gesch.Tech.Ind.*, 1924, 14: 50-64.

FIGUROVSKII, N.A. Einleitung zum kurzen Abriss der allgemeinen Geschichte der Chemie. *NTM Z.Gesch.Naturwiss.Tech. Med.*, [1962], 1: no. 3, 1-10.

HOCHWALT, Carnall A. The impact of chemistry on the world of science. *Sci.Mon.*, 1953, 77: 48-53.

HURD, Charles B. The progress of chemistry. *Fac.Pap.Union Coll.*, 1931, 2: 103-13.

IHDE, Aaron J. The pillars of modern chemistry. *J.Chem. Educ.*, 1956, 33: 107-10, 1 fig.

JOB, André. Les progrès des théories chimiques: thèse. Discussion: Mm. Boll, Meyerson. *Bull.Soc.Franç.Phil.*, 1913, 13: 47-62.

JOHNSTON, John. The history of chemistry. *Sci.Mon.*, 1921, 13: 5-23, 130-43.
A sketch of that history.

KUZNETSOV, V.I.; FAERSHTEIN, M.G.; ZHDANOV, IU.A. Voznikovenie sovremennoi khimii. [The rise of modern chemistry. (In Russian)]. *Vop.Ist.Est.Tekh.*, 1963, 15: 3-24. [CB 90/518]
Three papers given at a conference in the Institute of the History of Science and Technology, April 1962.

LAMB, Arthur B. A century of progress in chemistry. *Science*, 1933, 78: 371-6.
The President's Address at a meeting of the American Chemical Society at the Century of Progress Exposition in Chicago, September 14, 1933.

MIELI, Aldo. I periodi della storia chimica. *Rendic.Soc. Chim.Ital.*, 1914, fasc. 8, 8 p.

ROTH, W. Die Entwicklung der Chemie zur Wissenschaft. 32 p., 6 fig. (Werdegang der Entdeckungen, 9) München: Oldenbourg, 1922.
Popular account of the development of chemistry.

RUSKA, Julius. Über die Anfänge der wissenschaftlichen Chemie. *Forsch.Fortschr.*, 1937, 13: 380-1.

SPETER, Max. Historiochemisches Allerlei. *Studien zur Geschichte der Chemie; Festgabe Edmund O. v. Lippmann*, p. 218-27. Berlin: Springer, 1927. [CB 22/268]

UREY, Harold C. Chemistry and the future. *Science*, 1938, 88: 133-9.
Includes a list of main discoveries from 1899 to 1935.

WILLSTÄTTER, Richard. A chemist's retrospects and perspectives. *Science*, 1933, 78: 271-4.

Dc-br *periodicals*

Annual Report on the Progress of Chemistry for 1904- London: Chemical Society, 1905-

Chymia: Annual studies in the history of chemistry. Published under the auspices of the Edgar F. Smith Memorial Collection. Vol. 1- Philadelphia: University of Pennsylvania Press; London: Oxford University Press, 1948- [CB 77/371]
Vol. 5 reviewed by J.R. Partington, *Nature*, 1959, 184: 1900-1; by W.A. Smeaton, *Arch.Int.Hist.Sci.*, 1959, 12: 435; vol. 7 reviewed in *Pharm.Hist.*, 1962, 7: 53.

Jahrbuch der Chemie für 1891-1918. Bericht über die wichtigsten Fortschritte der reinen und angewandten Chemie. 28 vol. Frankfurt/Braunschweig: Vieweg, 1892-1920.

Dc-bt *charts*

KLICKSTEIN, Herbert S. Outline of the history of chemistry. Single sheet fold. St. Louis, N.Y.: Mallinckrodt Chemical Works, 1950. [CB 78/184]
Reviewed by Maurice Daumas, *Rev.Hist.Sci.*, 1952, 5: 283-4.

MEISSNER, W. Walter. Chemischer Grundatlas. Ein Handbuch für den Unterricht in geschichtlicher, technischer, anorganischer und allgemeiner Chemie einschliesslich der Mineralogie auf 30 (grösstenteils vielfarbigen) Karten, nebst 15 Tabellen. xvi, 95 p., 345 fig. Leipzig: Noske, 1935. [CB 51/263]

WALDEN, Paul. Chronologische Übersichstabellen zur Geschichte der Chemie von den ältesten Zeiten bis zur Gegenwart. xi, 118 p. Berlin: Springer-Verlag, 1952.
Reviewed by Arne Fredga, *Lychnos*, 1953, 412-13.

Dc-bu/ct bibliography; literature; sources

Dc-bu

PIETSCH, Erich. Bericht über den Stand der Arbeiten an der Zentralkartei für die Geschichte der Chemie in der Redaktion des Gmelin-Handbuches. *Angew.Chem.*, 1938, 51: 648-9.
Reviewed by Zaunick, *Mitt.Gesch.Med.*, 1939, 38: 93-4.

Dc-bv

BLOKH, M.A. [Literature on the history of chemistry for recent years. (In Russian)] *Arkh.Ist.Nauk.Tekh.*, 1934, 2: 305-13; 4: 427-48.

HISTORY, education, and literature (of chemistry). *Bibliogr. Rev.Chem.*, 1963, 5: 1-6.

MIELI, Aldo. Etudes anciennes et récentes d'histoire de la chimie. *Scientia*, 1917, 21: 432-40.

Dcd-ai

CARBONELLI, Giovanni. Sulle fonti storiche della chimica e dell'alchimia in Italia tratte dallo spoglio dei manoscritti delle Biblioteche con speciale riguardo ai Codici 74 di Pavia e 1166 Laurenziano. Opera corredata di 242 riproduzioni fotografiche. xxii, 220 p. Roma: Istituto Nazionale Medico Farmacologico, 1925.
Reviewed by E.O. von Lippmann, *Isis*, 1926, 8: 465-76; by Aldo Mieli, *Arch.Stor.Sci.*, 1925, 6: 245-60; by K. Sudhoff, *Mitt.Gesch.Med.*, 1927, 26: 261-2.

LIPPMANN, Edmund O. von. Quellen zur Geschichte der Chemie und Alchemie in Italien. *Isis*, 1926, 8: 465-76.
Review of G. Carbonelli, Sulle fonti storiche della chimica e dell'alchimia in Italia, 1925, *see* above.

Dce

MELLON, Melvin Guy. Chemical publications: their nature and use. viii, 253 p. (Chemical Series) New York: McGraw, 1928.
Reviewed by A.A.E., *Nature*, 1929, 123: 636.

OSTWALD, Wilhelm. Die chemische Literatur und die Organisation der Wissenschaft. iv, 120 p. Leipzig: Fock, 1919.

Dce-bu

PEAKES, Gilbert L.; KENT, Allen; PERRY, James; ed. Progress report in chemical literature retrieval. 217 p. (Advances in Documentation and Library Science, 1) New York: Interscience, 1957.
Reviewed by Saul Herner, *Science*, 1958, 127: 967-8.

Dce-bv

CRANE, Evan Jay; PATTERSON, Austin M. A guide to the literature of chemistry. ix, 438 p., ill. New York: John Wiley, 1927.

DUVEEN, Denis Ian. Bibliotheca alchemica et chemica. An annotated catalogue of printed books on alchemy, chemistry and cognate subjects in the library of Denis I. Duveen. vii, 669 p., 16 pl. London: Weil, 1949. [CB 74/387]
The Duveen Collection is now at the University of Wisconsin.

DYSON, G. Malcolm. A short guide to chemical literature. 144 p. London: Longmans, 1951.
Reviewed in *Nature*, 1951, 168: 355.

FERGUSON, John. Bibliotheca chemica. A catalogue of the alchemical, chemical and pharmaceutical books in the collection of the late James Young of Kelly and Durris. 2 vol. London: Holland Press, 1957.
Reviewed in the *Times Lit.Suppl.*, 7 June, 1957, 356.

NEDERLANDSE CHEMISCHE VERENIGING. Catalogus van de historische boeken der Koninklijke Chemische Vereniging in bruikleen geplaatst in het Rijksmuseum voor de Geschiedenis der Natuurwetenschappen te Leiden. Bijgewerkt tot 1 Augustus 1954. [Catalogue of the historical books of the Royal Netherlands Chemical Society ... (In Dutch)] 43 p. Amsterdam: 1954.

PELSENEER, Jean. Catalogue sommaire des manuscrits du Fonds Stas de l'Université Libre de Bruxelles. *Bull.Soc.Chim. Belg.*, 1937, 46: 367-76.

Dce-by

DUVEEN, Denis Ian. The Duveen Alchemical and Chemical Collection. [Wisconsin University] *Book Collect.*, 1956, 5: 331-42. [CB 85/391]

GLASGOW. UNIVERSITY. Library. Catalogue of the Ferguson Collection of books, mainly relating to alchemy, chemistry, witchcraft and gipsies, in the Library of the University. 2 vol. xv, 820 p. (Publications) Glasgow: Robert Maclehose, 1943. [CB 66/263]

IVES, Samuel A.; IHDE, Aaron J. The Duveen library. *J.Chem. Educ.*, 1952, 29: 244-7.
Description of the Duveen Collection now at the University of Wisconsin.
see also Edgar Fahs Smith Memorial Library, 2: 690.

Dcg

RÖMPP, Hermann. Chemische Fundgrube. Eine Auslese von 250 unbekannten chemischen Patenten und Erfindungen aus allen Ländern. 193 p. Stuttgart: Franckh, 1941.
First published 1938.
Reviewed by Zaunick, *Mitt.Gesch.Med.*, 1941-42, 40: 122.

Dcp

FRY, Harry Shipley. An outline of the history of chemistry symbolically represented in a Rookwood fountain. *J.Ind. Eng.Chem.*, 1922, 14: 868.

Dcs

MILES, Wyndham D.; KLICKSTEIN, Herbert. Chemistry and numismatics. Paper presented to the 115th meeting, American Chemical Society, San Francisco, California, March 29, 1949. 5 p.
Typescript.

Dct

KLICKSTEIN, Herbert S.; LEICESTER, Henry M. Philately - a chapter in the history of chemistry. *J.Hist.Med.*, 1947, 2: 337-78, 2 pl.

Dd biography

Dd-bv

HIGGINS, Thomas James. Book-length biographies of chemists. *Sch.Sci.Math.*, October 1944, 650-65.

Dda

BLOKH, M.A. Biograficheskii spravochnīk. Vijdaīushchiesīa khīmikī ī uchenye xix i xx stoletii, rabotavshie v smezhnijkh s khīmīeyu oblastyakh naukī. [Biographical handbook: leading chemists and scholars of the 19th and 20th centuries working in sciences related to chemistry. (In Russian)]. 2 vol. xliv, 512 p.; 513-832 p. Leningrad: Chemical-Technical Press, 1929-31.
Reviewed by A. Pogo, *Isis*, 1930, 13: 383-6.

BUGGE, Günther, ed. Das Buch der grossen Chemiker. 2 vol. 1. Von Zosimos bis Schönbein. xii, 496 p., 62 fig.; 2. Von Liebig bis Arrhenius. x, 559 p., 78 fig. Berlin: Verlag Chemie, 1929, 1930. Reprinted Weinheim: Verlag Chemie, 1955. [CB 29/298, CB 31/552, CB 34/500 and CB 83/199]
Reviewed by Friedrich Klemm, *Sudhoffs Arch.*, 1956, 40: 96; by Sten Lindroth, *Lychnos*, 1956, 405-6.

CHEMICAL SOCIETY memorial lectures delivered before the Chemical Society. 4 vol. 1. 1893-1900; 2. 1900-1913; 3. 1914-1932; 4. 1933-1942. London: 1901-51.
Later lectures included in the *Journal* of the Society.
Volume 3 reviewed by Tenney L. Davis, *Isis*, 1934, 22: 251.

FARBER, Eduard, ed. Great chemists. xxvi, 1642 p., portr. New York/London: Interscience Publishers, 1961. [CB 88/544]
Reviewed by F. Greenaway, *J.Roy.Inst.Chem.*, 1962, 86: 470-1; by L. Pearce Williams, *Science*, 1962, 136: 501-2; in *Sci.Amer.*, 1962, 206: no. 5, 191.

FERCHL, Fritz. Von Libau bis Liebig: Chemikerköpfe und Laboratorien. 48 leaves. Mittenwald: Nemayer, 1930. [CB 34/501]

FERCHL, Fritz, ed. Chemisch-Pharmazeutisches Bio- und Bibliographikon. Im Auftrage der Gesellschaft für Geschichte der Pharmazie. 2 vol. 603 p. Mittenwald: Nemayer, 1937-38.
Reviewed by Max Speter, *Isis*, 1939, 30: 125-7.

HARROW, Benjamin. Eminent chemists of our time. xvi, 248 p., ill. New York: Van Nostrand, 1920. [CB 10/156]

HOLMYARD, E.J. The great chemists. vi, 137 p., front. London: Methuen, 1928. [CB 25/417]

HOLMYARD, E.J. Makers of chemistry. xv, 314 p., 98 ill. Oxford: Clarendon Press, 1931. [CB 32/581]

HUNTRESS, Ernest R. Biographical digests. I-IV. Centennials and polycentennials during 1949-1952 with interest for chemists and physicists. *Proc.Amer.Acad.Arts Sci.*, 1948-49, 77: 33-54; 1949-50, 78: 3-35; 1950-51, 79: 3-44; 1951-52, 81: 35-97.
Title varies.

JAFFE, Bernard. Crucibles; the lives and achievements of the great chemists. vii, 377 p., ill. New York: Simon & Schuster; London: Jarrolds, 1930; rev. ed. vii, 385 p., ill. Cleveland: World Publishing Company, 1942.

MORGAN, Bryan. Men and discoveries in chemistry. xii, 176 p., ill. London: John Murray, 1962.

RAY, Prafulla Chandra. Makers of modern chemistry. viii, 111 p. Calcutta: Chuckervertty, Chatterjee; London: Probsthain, 1925. [CB 21/574]

SACHTLEBEN, R.; HERMANN, A. Grosse Chemiker. Von der Alchemie zur Grosssynthese. 178 p. Stuttgart: E. Battenberg, 1960.
Reviewed by H. Schimank, *Sudhoffs Arch.*, 1962, 46: 271-3.

SMITH, Edgar F. Forgotten chemists. *J.Chem.Educ.*, 1926, 3: 29. [CB 19/803]

SMITH, Henry Monmouth. Torchbearers of chemistry. Portraits and brief biographies of scientists who have contributed to the making of modern chemistry. With bibliography of biographies by Ralph E. Oesper. 270 p., 253 ill. New York: Academic Press, 1949. [CB 75/90]

TILDEN, William A. Famous chemists. The men and their work. vi, 296 p., ill. London: Routledge, 1921. [CB 12/628]

Dda-py

AUGER, Pierre, *et al.* Les prix Nobel de physique et de chimie. 506 p., pl. Monaco: Union Européenne d'Éditions, 1962.
Reviewed by René Taton, *Rev.Hist.Sci.*, 1964, 17: 180-1.

BONIN, W. von. Die Nobelpreisträger der Chemie. 89 p., ill. (Forum Imaginum, 9) Munich: Heinz Moos Verlag, 1963.
Reviewed by H. Degen, *Naturwiss.Rundsch.*, 1964, 17: 452.

FARBER, Eduard. Nobel prize winners in chemistry, 1901-1950. 219 p. (Pathbreakers in 20th Century Science. Life of Science Library, 31) New York: Henry Schuman, 1953.
Reviewed by I. Bernard Cohen, *Isis*, 1954, 45: 407-8.

FARBER, Eduard. Nobel prize winners in chemistry 1901-1961. vii, 341 p., fig., photographs. (Life of Science Library, 41) London/Toronto/New York: Abelard-Schuman, 1963.
An enlarged revised edition of the volume first published in 1953.
Reviewed by L. Pearce Williams, *Science*, 1963, 140: 623; by Denis Duveen, *Technol.Cult.*, 1964, 5: 114.

SACHTLEBEN, Rudolf. Nobel prize winners descended from Liebig. Translated and annotated by Ralph Oesper. A table of academic genealogy. *J.Chem.Educ.*, 1958, 35: 73-5.

Ddae

NEWELL, Lyman C. Caricatures of chemists as contributions to the history of chemistry. *J.Chem.Educ.*, 1931, 8: 2138-55, 28 fig.

Ddaj

LEICESTER, Henry M.; KLICKSTEIN, Herbert S. A source book in chemistry 1400-1900. xvi, 544 p., fig. (Source Books in the History of the Sciences) New York: McGraw-Hill, 1952.
Reviewed by Aaron J. Ihde, *Isis*, 1953, 44: 84; by R. Hooykaas, *Lychnos*, 1953, 413-14.

Df history of chemistry as a study

DAVIS, Tenney L. Catching up with chemistry. Remarks on the value of historical studies. *Rep.New Engl.Ass.Chem.Teachers*, May 1930, 8 p.

FARBER, Eduard. How practical is the study of the history of chemistry? *Chemist*, 1952, 29: 525-7.

PIETSCH, Erich. Sinn und Aufgaben der Geschichte der Chemie. 33 p. Berlin: Verlag Chemie, 1937. [CB 53/264]

RUSKA, Julius. Aufgaben der Chemiegeschichte. Nach einem auf Einladung der Rheinischen Gesellschaft für Geschichte der Naturwissenschaften, der Medizin und der Technik am 26. November 1928 zu Leverkusen gehaltenen Vortrage. *Jahresber. ForschungsInst.Gesch.Naturwiss.Berlin*, 1929, 2: 11-38.

TESTI, Gino. Gli studi storici della chimica in Italia. Comunicazione alla Sociedade de Pharmacia e Chimica di São Paulo, Brasile. 14 p. Città della Pieve: Tip. Dante, 1932.

Dfd

VELDE, A.J.J. van de. Het aandeel der laboratoriumonderzockers in de geschiedenis der chemie. [The contribution of practical chemists to the history of chemistry. (In Dutch)] *Mededeel.Vlaam.Chem.Ver.*, 1946, 8: 66-73.
Short biographical notes concerning the practical chemists who wrote books or papers on the history of chemistry.

FOR biographies and bibliographies of individual historians of chemistry (20th century) *see* volumes 1 and 2 under:-
Bauer, Alexander; Darmstädter, Ernst; Davis, Tenney Lombard; Heinrich, Ferdinand; Holmyard, Eric John; Jacques, Jean; Lippman, Edmund O. von; Lockemann, Georg Theodor Louis Wilhelm; Menshutkin, Boris Nikolaevich; Metzger, Hélène; Mieli, Aldo; Mittasch, Paul Alwin; Moore, Forris Jervert; Newell, Lyman Churchill; Ostwald, Wilhelm; Patterson, Thomas Stewart; Read, John; Ruska, Julius, Smith, Edgar Fahs; Taylor, Frank Sherwood.

Dfpx

DEXTER CHEMICAL CORPORATION AWARD in the history of chemistry. *Isis*, 1956, 47: 55; 1960, 51: 570.

Dfqd

NEWELL, Lyman C. Historical sketch of the division of history of chemistry, American Chemical Society. *J.Chem.Educ.*, 1932, 9: (4), 667-9.

Dfsk

FIGUROVSKII, N.A. [Problem of the Soviet historians of chemistry in the struggle with the servile attitude toward Western science. (In Russian)] *Tr.Inst.Ist.Est.*, 1949, 3: 28-44.

Dg

BLOCH, Ernst. Die Fortschritte des chemisch-historischen Unterrichts in Oesterreich. *Isis*, 1913, 1: 478-9.

FIGUROVSKII, N.A. Principes fondamentaux d'un cours contemporain d'histoire générale de la chimie. *Act.VIIIe Congr. Int.Hist.Sci.* (Florence, 1956), p. 539-43. Paris: Hermann, 1958.

SMITH, Edgar F. Observations on teaching the history of chemistry. *J.Chem.Educ.*, 1925, 2: 533-55.

Dgd

NEWELL, Lyman C. A tested method of teaching the history of chemistry. *J.Chem.Educ.*, 1926, 3: 166-9.

SOLOVEICHIK, Solomon. Teaching the history of chemistry with the aid of a perfect model. Paper presented at the 124th meeting of the American Chemical Society, 1958. 8 p. [Yeshiva University, New York: The author, 1958].
Mimeographed.

Dgp

MIELI, Aldo. Programma del corso di storia della chimica tenuto nell'Università di Roma 1913-1914. 25 p. Chiusi: Stab. Tip. Cerere, 1914. [CB 6/458]

Dgt

DE MILT, Clara. The value of the history and philosophy of science in the training of graduate students in chemistry. *J.Chem.Educ.*, 1952, 29: 340-4.

WINDERLICH, R. Geschichte der Chemie, ein notwendiger Bestandteil des chemischen Unterrichts. 28 p. (Oberrealschule Programm) Oldenburg i. Gr.: Ad. Littmann, 1913.

Dh historiography and particular aspects of the history of chemistry

BUGGE, Günther. Some problems relating to history of science and technology. *J.Chem.Educ.*, 1932, 9: 1567-75.
Deals in particular with the history of chemistry.

CHAKHPARONOV, M.I. L'histoire de la chimie et les problèmes qu'elle suscite. *Fil.Nauk.*, 1961, no. 1, 165-74.

FIGUROVSKII, N.A. General problems of history of chemistry. *Kwart.Hist.Nauk.Tech.*, 1962, 6: (Special issue), 79-89.

Dhd

DIERGART, Paul. Vorschläge zu einer planmässigen Gestaltung chemiegeschichtlicher Arbeit. *Proteus* (Bonn), 1937, 2: 74-83.

IHDE, Aaron J. Are there rules for writing history of chemistry? *Sci.Mon.*, 1955, 81: 183-6.

RUSKA, Julius. Methods of research in the history of chemistry. *Ambix*, 1937, 1: 21-9.

SCHNEIDER, W. Probleme der Chemiegeschichtsforschung. *Angew. Chem.*, 1961, 73: 779.

Dhd-db

DUVEEN, Denis I. Personalized bibliography: an approach to the history of chemistry. *J.Chem.Educ.*, 1961, 38: 418-21.
A well considered plea for more interpretative bibliographies of important figures in the history of chemistry.

Dhg

BLOCH, Ernst. Einfluss und Schicksal der mechanistischen Theorien in der Chemie. *Studien zur Geschichte der Chemie; Festgabe Edmund O. von Lippmann*, p. 204-17. Berlin: Springer, 1927.

CALDIN, E.F. Theories and the development of chemistry. *Brit.J.Phil.Sci.*, 1959, 10: 209-22.

FARBER, Eduard. Alte Gedanken und neue chemische Theorien. *Isis*, 1937, 26: 99-126. [CB 50/396]

FARBER, Eduard. Are there rules in the historical development of chemistry? *J.Chem.Educ.*, 1940, 17: 309-11.

FARBER, Eduard. Chemical discoveries by means of analogies. *Isis*, 1950, 41: 20-6.

FARBER, Eduard. Coppernicanische Umkehrungen in der Geschichte der Chemie. *Osiris*, 1938, 5: 478-98. [CB 57/243]

FARBER, Eduard. Der Stetigkeits-Gedanke und seine Verwirklichung. *Osiris*, 1937, 3: 47-68.

LEICESTER, Henry M. Chemistry, chemical technology, and scientific progress. *Technol.Cult.*, 1961, 2: 352-6.

Dhj

WALDEN, Paul. Ancient natural-philosophical ideas in modern chemistry. *J.Chem.Educ.*, 1952, 29: 386-91.

WALDEN, Paul. Aus der Naturgeschichte chemischer Ideen. Modernes im Spiegel der Vergangenheit. *Z.Angew.Chem.*, 1927, 40: 637-44.
Reviewed by Paul Diergart, *Mitt.Gesch.Med.*, 1928, 27: 20-1.

Dhm

LENNARD-JONES, John. New ideas in chemistry. *Sci.Mon.*, 1955, 80: 175-84.

Djg

WALDEN, Paul. The role of chance in chemical discoveries. *J.Chem.Educ.*, 1951, 28: 304-8.

Djj

BLOKH, M.A. Über einige Gesetzmässigkeiten im Schaffen hervorragender Chemiker. 55 p. Berlin: Verlag Chemie, 1931.

KENDALL, James. *See* Dc-bm

LEHMAN, Harvey C. The chemist's most creative years. The 2500 ablest of the world's chemists attained their maximum production rate at ages 30 through 34. *Science*, 1958, 127: 1213-22.

Dk philosophy and methodology

BACHELARD, Gaston. Le pluralisme cohérent de la chimie moderne. 235 p. Paris: Vrin, 1932.
Reviewed by H. Metzger, *Isis*, 1933, 19: 233-5.

BOHM, Walter. Die Naturwissenschaftler und ihre Philosophie; Geistesgeschichte der Chemie. 315 p., bibliogr. Vienna: Herden, 1961.

BOLL, Marcel. La philosophie chimique. *Rev.Positiviste Int.*, 1913, 13: 269-89.

BRADLEY, John. On the operational interpretation of classical chemistry. *Brit.J.Phil.Sci.*, 1955-56, 6: 32-42.

BREDIG, Georg. Denkmethoden der Chemie. 54 p. Leipzig: J.A. Barth, 1923.

CALDIN, E.F. The structure of chemistry in relation to the philosophy of science. v, 49 p. (Newman History and Philosophy of Science Series, 8) London/New York: Sheed and Ward, 1961.
Reviewed by W.A. Smeaton, *J.Roy.Inst.Chem.*, 1962, 86: 286; by Mary B. Hesse, *Hist.Sci.*, 1962, 1: 115-17; by W.F. Coulson, *Brit.J.Phil.Sci.*, 1962, 13: 184-5.

DAUMAS, Maurice. L'acte chimique. Essai sur l'histoire de la philosophie chimique. 208 p. (L'Humanisme Scientifique) Bruxelles: Editions du Sablon, 1946.
Reviewed by Pierre Brunet, *Rev.Hist.Sci.*, 1947, 1: 94-5.

DELACRE, Maurice. Essai de philosophie chimique. 170 p. Paris: Payot, 1923.

MEISSNER, W. Walter. Chymia perennis. Eine ganzheitliche Betrachtung naturphilosophischer Prägung des stetig-ständigen Kreislaufes einer "immerwährenden Chemie". xvi, 1012 p. Bielefeld-Bethel: Deutscher Heimat-Verlag, 1954.
Reviewed by G. Heym, *Ambix*, 1957, 6: 113-14.

URBAIN, G. Les disciplines d'une science: la chimie. 325 p. Paris: Gaston Doin, 1921.
Reviewed by L. Guinet, *Isis*, 1922, 4: 545-8.

Dke

RENAUD, Paul. Essai sur les définitions expérimentales des opérations chimiques. 40 p. (Actualités Scientifiques et Industrielles, 359) Paris: Hermann, 1936.

Dkh

GUERLAC, Henry. Quantification in chemistry. *Isis*, 1961, 52: 194-214.

Dm

HOOYKAAS, R. The concepts of "individual" and "species" in chemistry. *Centaurus*, 1958, 5: 307-22.

MADRAS, Samuel. The historical approach to chemical concepts. *J.Chem.Educ.*, 1955, 32: 593-8.

RABINOWITSCH, Eugen. Grundbegriffe der Chemie. 151 p. (Sammlung Göschen, 804) Berlin: de Gruyter, 1930.

THIESSEN, Peter A. Stoffe, Kräfte und Gedanken als Träger chemischer Gestaltung. 27 p. (Preussische Akademie der Wissenschaften; Vorträge und Schriften, 7) Berlin: de Gruyter, 1941.
Reviewed by R. Zaunick, *Mitt.Gesch.Med.*, 1941/42, 40: 120.

TIMMERMANS, Jean. La notion d'espèce en chimie. iii, 134 p. Paris: Gauthier-Villars, 1928.
Reviewed by T.M. Lowry, *Nature*, 1929, 123: 308-10.

WALDEN, Paul. Mass, Zahl und Gewicht in der Chemie der Vergangenheit: ein Kapitel aus der Vorgeschichte des sogenannten quantitativen Zeitalters der Chemie. 106 p. (Sammlung chemischer und chemisch-technischer Vorträge. New ser., 8) Stuttgart: Enke, 1931.
Reviewed by E.O. von Lippmann, *Chem.Zeitung*, 1931, 55: 927; by Charles Albert Browne, *Ind.Eng.Chem.*, 1932, 24: 596.

DmzB

MEZGER, Chr. Die Chemie als mathematisches Problem. 108 p., diagr. Metz: G. Scriba, 1913.

DmzN

ABEL, John J. Chemistry in relation to medicine. *J.Chem. Educ.*, 1929, 6: 1045-64.

POYNTER, F.N.L., ed. Chemistry in the service of medicine. 207 p. London: Pitman; Philadelphia: Lippincott, 1963. [CB 90/519]
Reviewed by J.D. Whittet, *Med.Hist.*, 1963, 7· 386-7.

STIEGLITZ, Julius, ed. Chemistry in medicine. A cooperative treatise intended to give examples of progress made in medicine with the aid of chemistry. xxi, 757 p., 23 ill. New York: Chemical Foundation, 1928. [CB 26/233]

Dn communication

Dnb

CAVEN, Robert Martin; CRANSTON, J.A. Symbols and formulae in chemistry: an historical study. ix, 220 p. (Manuals of Pure and Applied Chemistry) London: Blackie, 1928.

CORDIER, Victor. Die chemische Zeichensprache einst und jetzt. xii, 220 p., 11 fig., 3 pl. Graz: Leykam-Verlag, 1929.

CROSLAND, M.P. Historical studies in the language of chemistry. xvii, 406 p., ill., bibliogr. London: Heinemann; Cambridge, Mass.: Harvard University Press, 1962.
Reviewed by Henry M. Leicester, *Isis*, 1963, 54: 492; for other reviews *see* CB 88/544 and CB 89/502.

LESPIEAU, Robert. Sur les notations chimiques. *Rev.Mois*, 1913, 16: 257-78.

McKIE, Douglas. Some early chemical symbols. *Ambix*, 1937, 1: 75-7.

PARTINGTON, J.R. The origin of modern chemical symbols and formulae. *J.Soc.Chem.Ind.*, 1936, 55: 759-62.

SMITH, Edward H. Some early chemical symbols. *Ind.Eng.Chem.*, 1924, 16: 406.

WALDEN, Paul. Zur Entwicklungsgeschichte der chemischen Zeichen. *Studien zur Geschichte der Chemie; Festgabe Edmund O. von Lippmann*, p. 80-105. Berlin: Springer, 1927. [CB 22/269]

WALKER, James. Chemical symbols and formulae. *Nature*, 1923, 111: 883-6.
Presidential address delivered at the annual general meeting of the Chemical Society on March 22, 1923.

Dnf

GUYE, Philippe A. Rapport sur l'unification des abréviations bibliographiques dans les mémoires de chimie. (Abstract of the Proceedings of the third Session of the Council of the "Association internationale des Sociétés chimiques" held at the Institut Solvay, Parc Léopold, Brussels, September 19th -23rd, 1913) 12 p. Genève: Imprimerie Albert Kündig, 1914.

Dnh

AMERICAN CHEMICAL SOCIETY. Chemical nomenclature. A collection of papers comprising the Symposium on Chemical Nomenclature, presented before the Division of Chemical Literature, American Chemical Society, Sept. 1951. 112 p., ill. (Advances in Chemistry Series, 8) Washington, D.C.: American Chemical Society, 1953.

COUCH, James F. The evolution of chemical terminology. 1. Coagulation. 2. Phototropism-organotropism. 3. The "micella". 4. The therm. 5. Some alchemical terms. 6. Hydroxide. 7. Electrolyte. 8. Toxin. 9. Pectization and peptization. *Amer.J.Pharm.*, 1922, 94: 92-7, 343-7, 469-76; 1923, 95: 150-4, 227-32, 533-54, 806-12; 1924, 96: 746-51; 97: 858-61.

WINDERLICH, Rudolf. Chemie und Sprache. *Proteus* (Bonn), 1937, 2: 58-65.

Dnh-be

HACKH, Ingo Waldemar Dagobert. A chemical dictionary: containing the words generally used in chemistry and many of the terms used in the related sciences of physics, astrophysics, mineralogy, pharmacy, and biology, with their pronunciations; based on recent chemical literature. viii, 790 p. London: Churchill, 1930.
Reviewed by C.S. Gibson, *Nature*, 1930, 125: 593-4.

MAYER, A.W. Chemical technical dictionary. lv, 872 p. New York: Chemical Publishing Co., 1942. [CB 64/451]
This is an American reprint of the Russian edition of the translation made specifically for Russian and English readers by B.N. Menshutkin and M.A. Blokh of Mayer's "Chemisches Fachwörterbuch" (Deutsch-Englisch-Französich) and published at Leningrad.

Dnj-be

BALLENTYNE, D.W.G.; LOVETT, D.R.A. A dictionary of named effects and laws in chemistry, physics and mathematics. 2nd ed. v, 243 p. London: Chapman & Hall, 1961.

WAGNER, Kurt G. Autoren-Namen als chemische Begriffe, ein alphabetisches Nachschlagebuch. 264 p. Weinheim: Verlag Chemie, 1951. [CB 83/200]
Reviewed by R.J. Forbes, *Arch.Int.Hist.Sci.*, 1952, 5: 402-3; in *Pharm.Hist.*, 1962, 7: 11-12.

Do/r study and teaching; organizational and professional aspects

Do

BAILAR, John C. Chemical education - then and now. *J.Chem. Educ.*, 1961, 38: 434-7.

DAINS, Frank B. Advances in the teaching of chemistry since 1914. (Edgar Fahs Smith Memorial Number). *J.Chem.Educ.*, 1932, 9: 745-50.

GUARESCHI, Icilio. Etat comparatif de la science en 1800-1811 et en 1900-1911. Notions historiques sur l'enseignement de la chimie. *Rev.Sci.*, 1912, 50: 1er sem., 449-57.
French Summary of the Inaugural Address to the 2o Congresso Nazionale di Chimica applicata.

HILDEBRAND, Joel H. A philosophy of teaching. *J.Chem.Educ.*, 1949, 26: 450-5.
Mainly on the teaching of chemistry.

TAYLOR, J.N. A half-century in chemical education. A chronological record of the scientific contributions of Charles Edward Munroe. *Gen.Sci.Quart.*, March and May 1926. [CB 20/172]

Dp

OSTWALD, Wilhelm. Die chemische Literatur und die Organisation der Wissenschaft. iv, 120 p. Leipzig: Fock, 1919.

Dpw

BROWNE, Charles Albert; BROWNE, Louise McD. American influences on chemical research and education in the Near East. *J.Chem.Educ.*, 1931, 8: 1681-702, ill.

MUSABEKOV, IU. S. Iz istorii nauchnykh sviazci russkikh i frantsuzskikh khimikov. [On the history of scientific ties between Russian and French chemists. (In Russian)]. *Vop. Ist.Est.Tekh.*, 1961, 11: 89-91.

Dqx

IIe CONGRÈS de l'Association Internationale des Sociétés de Chimie, Berlin, 1912. *Isis*, 1913, 1: 113.

Dqy

NICLOUX, Maurice. Projet de fondation d'un Institut International de Chimie. *Rev.Gén.Sci.*, 1912, 23: 814-17.

OSTWALD, Wilhelm. Berzelius' "Jahresbericht" and the international organization of chemists. Translated by Ralph Oesper. *J.Chem.Educ.*, 1955, 32: 373-5.

OSTWALD, Wilhelm. Denkschrift über die Gründung eines internationalen Institutes für Chemie. 31 p. Leipzig: Akademische Verlagsgesellschaft, 1912.

OSTWALD, Wilhelm. Die Internationale Organisation der Chemiker *Ann.Natur.Kulturphil.*, 1913, 12: 217-33.

OSTWALD, Wilhelm. Memorial on the foundation of an international chemical institute. *Science,* 1914, 40: 147-58.
Projected idea for an International Chemical Institute to be founded in connection with the International Association of Chemical Societies.

PELSENEER, Jean. Cinquantenaire de l'Institut International de Chimie fondé par Ernest Solvay, 1913-1963, Bruxelles. 12 p., 13 pl. Bruxelles: Institut International de Chimie Solvay, 1963.

PELSENEER, Jean. Note sur un historique inédit des Instituts internationaux de physique et de chimie Solvay. *IIIe Congr. Nat.Sci.* (Bruxelles, 1950), p. 36. Liège: Desoer, 1950.

SEIDELL, Atherton. The Berthelot centenary and the resulting international efforts to advance chemistry. *Science,* 1928, 67: 497-9.

Dr

CHAPMAN, A. Chaston. The growth of the profession of chemistry during the past half-century (1877-1927). 23 p. London: The Institute of Chemistry of Great Britain and Ireland, 1927.

Drd

PHILIP, J.C. Chemistry and the modern state. *Nature,* 1936, 138: 492-5. [CB 49/177]
From the presidential address entitled "The training of the chemist for the service of the community" to Section B (chemistry) of the British Association, September 1936.

Ds/t social and humanistic relations

Ds

ARRHENIUS, Svante. Die Chemie und das moderne Leben. Deutsche Ausgabe von B. Finkelstein. xii, 373 p., 20 ill. Leipzig: Akad. Verlagsgesellschaft, 1922.

FINDLAY, Alexander. Chemistry in the service of man. 8th ed. xx, 326 p., 36 pl., with a new preface by the author. London/New York/Toronto: Longmans, Green and Co., 1957. [CB 83/199]
First published 1916.

Dsg

BALKE, S. Über die Wahlverwandschaft von Wissenschaft, Technik und Wirtschaft in der Chemie. *Angew.Chem.,* 1961, 73: 779.

FARRELL, Hugh. What price progress? The stake of the investor in the development of chemistry. 102 p. New York: The Chemical Foundation, Inc., 1925.

JACQUES, Jean. Influence des facteurs économiques sur l'évolution de la chimie. *Pensée* (Paris), 1945, no. 4, 84-8.

Dsp

MOUREU, Charles. La chimie et la guerre. Science et avenir. iii, 384 p. (Les Leçons de la Guerre) Paris: Masson, 1920.

STINE, Charles M.A. Molders of a better destiny. *Science,* 1942, 96: 305-11.
On chemical progress due to the last war.

Dsy

JONES, Thomas William. Hermes: or the future of chemistry. 88 p. (To-day and To-morrow Series) London: Kegan Paul, 1928.

PAULING, Linus C. Chemical achievement and hope for the future. *Annu.Rep.Smithsonian Inst.for 1950,* p. 225-41. Washington, D.C.: 1951.

Dt

MELDRUM, A.N. Chemistry as a liberal study. Presidential address. Section of Chemistry. *Proc.10th Indian Sci.Congr.* (Calcutta, 1924), p. 86-100. Calcutta: 1924. [CB 16/294]

WINDERLICH, R. Chemie und Kultur. vi, 139 p., ill. Leipzig: Leopold Voss, 1927.

Dw in different countries

VANIZETTI, B.L. De la contribution des divers pays au développement de la chimie. *Scientia,* 1921, 30: 85-103.

Dwb North America

BROWNE, Charles Albert; *et al.* Our chemical heritage. 54 p., fig. New York: American Chemical Society, 1935. [CB 44/518]

BROWNE, Charles Albert; BROWNE, Louise McD. *See* Dpw

NEWELL, Lyman C. The earlier and later days of chemistry in New England. In: Report of twenty-fifth anniversary of the New England Association of Chemistry Teachers, Boston, March 15, 1924. [Boston?: 1924?]
Part reprinted in *J.Chem.Educ.,* 1925, 2: 161-4.

SMITH, Edgar F. The American spirit in chemistry. *J.Ind. Eng.Chem.,* 1919, 11: 405-10. [CB 13/285]

SMITH, Edgar F. Chemistry in America. Chapters from the history of the science in the United States. xiv, 356 p., ill. New York: Appleton, 1914.

SMITH, Edgar F. Fragments relating to the history of chemistry in America. *J.Chem.Educ.,* 1926, 3: 629-37.

SMITH, Edgar F. Old chemistries. xi, 89 p., 31 pl. New York: McGraw-Hill, 1927.
This book lays stress on American chemists and influences on American chemistry.
Reviewed by George Sarton, *Isis,* 1927, 9: 479-80.

WARRINGTON, C.J.S.; NICHOLLS, R.V.V. A history of chemistry in Canada. x, 502 p., 13 pl. Toronto: Pitman, 1949.

Dwb-ce

SIEGFRIED, Robert. A study of chemical research publications from the United States before 1880. (Wisconsin thesis, 1952)
Completion noted in *Isis,* 1954, 45: 200; 1955, 46: 56.

Dwb-da

COLUMBIA UNIVERSITY. Symposium on pioneers in chemistry at Columbia. *J.Chem.Educ.,* 1955, 32: 498-517, ill. [CB 82/255]

NEWELL, Lyman C. The founders of chemistry in America. *J. Chem.Educ.,* 1925, 2: 48.

NEWELL, Lyman C.; DAVIS, Tenney L. Notable New England chemists. 16 p., portr. Boston: 1928. [CB 25/417]

Dwb-o

HALE, Harrison. The history of chemical education in the United States from 1870 to 1914. (Edgar Fahs Smith Memorial Number) *J.Chem.Educ.,* 1932, 9: 729-44.

NEWELL, Lyman C. Chemical education in America from the earliest days to 1820. (Edgar Fahs Smith Memorial Number) *J. Chem.Educ.,* 1932, 9: 677-95.

Dwb-om

ROSEN, Sidney. The rise of high-school chemistry in America (to 1920). *J.Chem.Educ.,* 1956, 33: 627-33, 3 fig.

Dwb-oq

DAVIS, Tenney L.; GOODWIN, H.M. A history of the Departments of Chemistry and Physics at the Massachusetts Institute of Technology (1865-1933). 35 p., ill. Cambridge, Mass.: The Institute, 1933.
Reviewed by Hélène Metzger, *Archeion,* 1933, 15: 466.

GORMAN, Mel. Chemistry at the University of San Francisco, 1863-1906. *J.Chem.Educ.,* 1964, 41: 627-9.

KANSAS. UNIVERSITY. History of the chemistry department of the University. 64 p. (*Kan.Univ.Sci.Bull.,* 26) Lawrence, Kan.: 1925. [CB 19/774]
From 1866 to 1923.

KLICKSTEIN, Herbert S. David Hosack on the qualifications of a professor of chemistry in the medical department. With a short history of the Professorship of Chemistry at Columbia College Medical Department (1776-1876), College of Physicians and Surgeons of New York (1807-1860), and Rutgers Medical College (1826-1830). *Bull.Hist.Med.,* 1954, 28: 212-36.

MILES, Wyndham D. The development of chemical education in Columbia, Princeton, Rutgers and Pennsylvania. *Isis*, 1955, 46: 284.
Note on completion of doctoral thesis.

SIEGFRIED, Robert; IHDE, Aaron J. Beginnings of chemical education in Beloit, Lawrence and Ripon Colleges. *Trans. Wis.Acad.Sci.Arts Lett.*, 1953, 42: 25-38, 6 portr.

SMITH, Edgar F. The history of chemistry in America with reference to Yale. *Science*, 1923, 57: 425-9.
Address at the dedication exercises of the Sterling Chemistry Laboratory at Yale University, April 4, 1923.

Dwb-qd

BROWNE, Charles Albert; WEEKS, Mary Elvira. A history of the American Chemical Society. Seventy-five eventful years. xi, 526 p. Washington, D.C.: American Chemical Society, 1952.
Reviewed by Aaron J. Ihde, *Isis*, 1954, 45: 101-2; by Eric K. Rideal, *Nature*, 1953, 171: 536-7.

MILES, Wyndham. Early American chemical societies. 1. The 1789 Chemical Society of Philadelphia; 2. The Chemical Society of Philadelphia. *Chymia.*, 1950, 3: 95-113.

Dwb-qk

KOMONS, Nick A. A decade of chemical research. History of the Air Force Office of Scientific Research Chemistry Program. viii, 134 p. Washington, D.C.: Office of Aerospace Research, 1962.

Dwb-r

STRAUSS, Anselm L.; *et al.* The professional scientist; a study of American chemists. 282 p., ill. (Social Research Studies in Contemporary Life) Chicago: Aldine Publishing Co., 1962.

Dwb-vx

GEISER, Samuel Wood. The Negro in American chemistry. *Opportunity*, Feb. 1935, 3 p.

Dwe British Isles

GUNTHER, Robert William Theodore. Early science in Oxford. Pt. 1. Chemistry. vi, 91 p. Oxford: Oxford Science Laboratories, 1920.
Bound up with parts 2-4 as Volume 1.
Reviewed by G. Sarton, *Isis*, 1924, 6: 449-53; by E. Thorpe, *Nature*, 1921, 107: 13-15.

TAYLOR, F. Sherwood. A century of British chemistry. 40 p., 11 ill. London: Longmans, Green, 1947.
Reviewed by R.J. Forbes, *Arch.Int.Hist.Sci.*, 1949, 2: 777.

Dwe-da

FINDLAY, Alexander; MILLS, William Hobson; ed. British chemists. 432 p., 16 pl. London: Chemical Society, 1947. [CB 73/170]
Reviewed by John Read, *Nature*, 1947, 160: 657-8.

REILLY, Desmond. Irish chemical pioneers of 150 years. *J. Chem.Educ.*, 1950, 27: 237-40. [CB 76/397]

REILLY, Desmond, ed. Three centuries of Irish chemists. ii, 30 p. (Historical and Archaeological Papers, 2) Cork: University Press, 1941.
Reviewed by T.L. Davis, *Isis*, 1948, 38: 260; by John Read, *Nature*, 1941, 148: 633.

Dwe-oq

COCKER, Wesley; WHEELER, T.S. Chairs of chemistry in Ireland. *Nature*, 1952, 169: 575. [CB 79/131]

FINDLAY, Alexander. Chairs of chemistry in Great Britain. *Nature*, 1952, 169: 160. [CB 79/131]

FINDLAY, Alexander. The teaching of chemistry in the Universities of Aberdeen. viii, 92 p., 19 ill., bibliogr. (Aberdeen University studies, 112) Aberdeen: University Press, 1935. [CB 45/282]

GUNTHER, Robert Theodore. The Daubeny laboratory register, 1849-1923. Complete in one vol. A history of the Daubeny Laboratory, Magdalen College, Oxford. To which is appended a list of the writings of Dr. Daubeny, and a register of the names of persons who have attended the chemical lectures of Dr. Daubeny from 1822 to 1867 as well as those who have received instruction in the Laboratory up to the present time. With a pref. by the President of Magdalen. xxv, 532 p., pl. London: Oxford University Press, 1904-1924. [CB 24/481]
The third (final) part of this volume (p. 297-532) was reviewed in *Isis*, 1925, 7: 561.

MACKENZIE, John E. The chair of chemistry in the University of Edinburgh in the XVIIIth and XIXth centuries. *J.Chem. Educ.*, 1935, 12: 503-11. [CB 45/283]

TODD, A.R. Chairs of chemistry in Great Britain. *Nature*, 1952. 169: 292. [CB 79/128]

Dwe-qb

BERRY, A.J.; MOELWYN-HUGHES, E.A. Chemistry at Cambridge from 1901 to 1910. *Proc.Chem.Soc.*, 1963, 357-63.
Based on the unpublished minute book of the Cambridge University Chemical Club.

Dwe-qd

TOMPKINS, F.C. The Faraday Society, 1903-1953. *Nature*, 1953, 171: 671-4.

see also Chemical Society, London, 2: 679.

Dwf France

COLSON, Albert. Histoire de la chimie. In: Histoire de la Nation Française. Vol. XIV. Histoire des sciences en France, (1), part 3, p. 421-610. Paris: Plon, 1924.
Reviewed by George Sarton, *Isis*, 1925, 7: 514-16.

MUSABEKOV, Iu.S. *See* Dpw

Dwf-cc

DAVIS, Tenney L. What a student of the history of chemistry may see and do in Paris. *J.Chem.Educ.*, 1934, 11: 211-16, 12 fig. [CB 42/586]

Dwf-qd

CENTENAIRE de la Société Chimique de France, 1857-1957. viii, 252 p. Paris: Masson, 1957.
Reviewed by J. Lang, *Rev.Quest.Sci.*, 1959, 20: 298-9.

Dwg/wh Central Europe

Dwg-cj

HARFF, Horst. Die Entwicklung der deutschen chemischen Fachzeitschrift. Ein Beitrag zur Wesensbestimmung der wissenschaftlichen Fachzeitschrift. 144 p., 20 pl. Berlin: Verlag Chemie, 1941.
Reviewed by Arne Fredga, *Lychnos*, 1943, 391.

VAN KLOOSTER, H.S. The story of Liebig's *Annalen der Chemie*. *J.Chem.Educ.*, 1957, 34: 27-30.

Dwg-da-py

ZEKERT, Otto. Österreichische Nobelpreisträger für Medizin, Physiologie und Chemie. 86 p., ill. (HMW-Jahrbuch, 1961) Wien: Heilmittelwerke, 1961.
Reviewed by Nils von Hofsten, *Lychnos*, 1960-61, 417.

Dwg-oq

CHEMNITIUS, Fritz. Die Chemie in Jena von Rolfinck bis Knorr (1629-1921). 192 p., ill. Jena: Diedermann, 1921. [CB 32/500]

FREUDENBERG, Karl. The study of chemistry at Heidelberg: a glimpse of an historic home of research. *J.Chem.Educ.*, 1927, 4: 441-6.

Dwg-qg

PRANDTL, Wilhelm. Das chemische Laboratorium der Bayerischen Akademie der Wissenschaften in München. *Chymia*, 1949, 2: 81-97, 19 ill.

PRANDTL, Wilhelm. Die Geschichte des chemischen Laboratoriums der Bayerischen Akademie der Wissenschaften in München. vi, 141 p., 73 ill. Weinheim: Verlag Chemie, 1952.
Reviewed by R. Hooykas, *Arch.Int.Hist.Sci.*, 1952, 5: 403-4.

RUSKA, Julius. Forschungsinstitut für Geschichte der Naturwissenschaften in Berlin. Zweiter Jahresbericht. Mit einer wissenschaftlichen Beilage. Aufgaben der Chemiegeschichte nach einem von dem Direktor des Forschungsinstituts am 26. November 1928 zu Leverkusen gehaltenen Vortrage. 38 p. Berlin: Springer, 1929.

Dwh

DRUCE, Gerald. The Mendeléeff-Brauner tradition in Czech chemistry. *Nature*, 1943, 150: 623-4.

LAMPE, Wiktor. [Historical sketch of the development of chemistry in Poland. (In Polish with French summary)]. 64 p. (Polska Akademia Umiejetności, Historia Nauki Polskiej w Monografiach, 4) Cracow: 1948.

SZABADVÁRY, Ferenc. The early history of chemistry in Hungary. *J.Chem.Educ.*, 1963, 40: 46-8.

VRANÝ, Adalb. Geschichte der Chemie und der auf chemischer Grundlage beruhenden Betriebe in Böhmen bis zur Mitte des 19. Jahrhunderts. vii, 397 p. Prague: 1902.

Dwh-qg

WOJTASZEK, Zdzisław. [Old printing shop building as headquarters of Jagellonian University's Chemical Institute. (In Polish)] *Kwart.Hist.Nauk.Tech.*, 1964, 9: 229-41.

Dwi/wj Southern Europe

Dwi

TESTI, Gino. Storia della chimica con particolare riguardo all'opera degli italiani. 352 p., ill. (Istituto Italiano di Storia della Chimica, Roma) Roma: Casa Editrice Mediterranea, 1940.
Reviewed by Aldo Mieli, *Archeion*, 1940, 22: 414-22; by Sten Lindroth, *Lychnos*, 1942, 399.

THORPE, Edward. *See* Dc-bm

Dwi-da

PROVENZAL, Giulio Cesare. Profili bio-bibliografici di chimici italiani, sec. xv-sec. xix. xxiv, 301 p., portr. Roma: Istituto Nazionale Medico Farmacologico "Serono", 1938.

Dwj

PEREIRA SALGADO, José. A história da química em Portugal. *Act.IIIe Congr.Int.Hist.Sci.* (Portugal, 1934), p. 11-19. Lisbon: 1936.

Dwj-ce

STEVENS, Leo J. The chemical and related literature of Spain. *J.Chem.Educ.*, 1955, 32: 412-16.

Dwk/wm Northern Europe

Dwk

MUND, Walter. L'histoire des sciences en Belgique: la chimie. In: Histoire de la Belgique contemporaine, (3), p. 413-30. Bruxelles: Dewit, 1930.

Dwk-oq

JACKSON, L.C. The University of Leyden. Contributions to physics and chemistry. *Nature*, 1941, 147: 163-4.

Dwk-qd

FASCICULE consacré à la commémoration du 50e anniversaire de la fondation de la Société Chimique de Belgique, 1887-1937. *Bull. Soc.Chim.Belg.*, 1937, 46: Numéro jubilaire, no. 8-9.

Dwm

VEIBEL, Stig. Kemien i Danmark. I. Kemiens historie i Danmark. 250 p. Copenhagen: Busch, 1939.
Reviewed by Sten Lindroth, *Lychnos*, 1940, 452-3.

Dwn Russia

BLOKH, M.A. [The course of modern chemistry. (In Russian)] *Příroda*, 1923, no. 1-6, 74-6; 1925, no. 4-6, 97-102.
On the history of chemistry in Russia.

BLOKH, M.A. Die Entwicklung der russischen Chemie im zwanzigsten Jahrhundert. *Beitr.Gesch.Tech.Ind.*, 1929, 19: 147-50.

BLOKH, M.A. Khimiia v SSSR za desiat' let, 1917-1927 gg. [Chemistry in the USSR in the decade 1917-1927. (In Russian)] 148 p. (*Zh.Russ.Fiz.Khim.Obschchest.A.Khim.Otd.*, vol. 60, supplement) Moskva: 1928.

IPATIEFF, Vladimir Nikolaevich. The life of a chemist. Memoirs. Ed. by Xenia Joukoff Eudin, Helen Dwight Fisher and Harold H. Fisher. Transl. by Vladimir Haensel and Mrs. Ralph H. Lusher. xv, 658 p., portr., 7 ill. (Hoover Library on War, Revolution and Peace. Publication no. 21) Stanford University, Calif.: Stanford University Press; London: Oxford University Press, 1946. [CB 78/156]
Throws light on the history of chemistry in Russia.

KAPUSTINSKII, A.F. Ocherki po istorii neorganicheskoi i fizicheskoi khimii v Rossii, ot Lomonosova do Velikoi Oktyabrskoi Sotsialisticheskoi Revolyutsii. [On the history of inorganic and physical chemistry in Russia. From Lomonosov to the Great October Revolution. (In Russian)]. 166 p., 19 ill. (Seriya Itogi i problemy sovremennoi nauki, Akademiia Nauk SSSR, Institut Istorii Estestvoznaniia) Moskva-Leningrad: Izd. Akademii Nauk SSSR, 1949. [CB 83/264]

LEICESTER, Henry. The history of chemistry in Russia prior to 1900. *J.Chem.Educ.*, 1947, 24: 438-43.

LEICESTER, Henry. Some aspects of the history of chemistry in Russia. *J.Chem.Educ.*, 1963, 40: 108-9.

MUSABEKOV, Iu.S. *See* Dpw

OVCHARENKO, F.D. Sostoianie khimicheskoi nauki na Ukraine. [The condition of chemical science in the Ukraine. (In Russian)]. *Vop.Ist.Est.Tekh.*, 1963, 14: 61-5.

WALDEN, Paul. [Outline of the history of chemistry in Russia. (In Russian)]. In: Ladenburg, A. [Lectures on the history of the development of chemistry from Lavoisier to our time. (In Russian)], p. 361-95. Odessa: Mathesis, 1917.

Dwn-cg

FIGUROVSKII, N.A. [On an old Russian collection of chemical recipes. (In Russian)] *Tr.Inst.Ist.Est.*, 1948, 2: 239-68.

Dwn-da

BLOKH, M.A. [Russian chemist Academicians. (In Russian)] *Příroda*, 1925, no. 7-9, 205-14. [CB 28/460]

KOMPPA, Gust. Über ältere finnische Chemiker. *Z.Angew.Chem.*, 1927, 40: 1431-4.
Reviewed by Paul Diergart, *Mitt.Gesch.Med.*, 1928, 27: 162.

Dwn-oq

FIGUROVSKII, N.A. Khimiya v Moskovskom Universitete za 200 let (1755-1955). [Chemistry at Moscow University the last 200 years. (In Russian)] [Lecture at the All-Union Society for the Propagation of Political and Scientific Knowledge.] 32 p. Moscow: Izdatelsvo "Znanie", 1955.

POGODIN, S.A. Khimiia v Petersburgskoi Akademii nauk do M.V. Lomonosova. [Chemistry at the St. Petersburg Academy of Sciences before M.V. Lomonosov. (In Russian)] *Tr.Inst.Ist. Est.Tekh.*, 1962, 39: 3-23.

Dwn-qd

KROTIKOV, V.A. K istorii organizatsii russkogo khimicheskogo obshchestva. [On the history of the Russian Chemical Society (In Russian)] *Vop.Ist.Est.Tekh.*, 1962, 13: 83-8.

Dwn-sg

VOL'FKOVICH, S.I. [Chemistry and the socialized industrialization of the U.S.S.R. (In Russian)]. *Tr.Inst.Ist.Est.*, 1952, 4: 31-45.

Dwp/wt Africa; Asia

Dwp

BROWNE, Charles Albert; BROWNE, Louise McD. *See* Dpw

Dws

RAY, Prafulla Chandra. Life and experiences of a Bengali chemist. 2 vol. viii, 257 p.; viii, 469 p. Calcutta: Chuckervertty, Chatterjee, 1932. [CB 39/431]
Volume 2 reviewed by Tenney L. Davis, *Isis*, 1937, 27: 515-16.

Dwt

TANAKA, Minoru. Hundert Jahre der Chemie in Japan. 1. Studien über den Prozess der Verpflanzung und Selbständigung der Naturwissenschaften als wesentlicher Teil des Werdegangs modernen Japans; 2. Die Art und Weise der Selbständigung chemischer Forschungen während der Periode, 1901-30. *Jap. Stud.Hist.Sci.*, 1964, 3: 89-107; 1965, 4: 162-72.

YUAN HAN-TSING. [History of chemistry in China. (In Chinese)] 301 p. Peking: 1956.
Reviewed by P. Huard and M. Wong, *Arch.Int.Hist.Sci.*, 1957, 10: 113-15.
Contains some chapters on modern chemistry in China.

Dx techniques and instruments; experimentation

Dxb

BILTZ, H. Zur Geschichte des Bunsenbrenners. *Z.Angew.Chem.*, 1928, 41: 112.

KOHN, Moritz. Remarks on the history of laboratory burners. *J.Chem.Educ.*, 1950, 27: 514-16, 6 ill.

PARTINGTON, J.R. Evolution of the chemical laboratory. *Endeavour*, 1942, 1: 145-50, 9 fig.

SCHELENZ, Hermann. Ueber Pressen. Ein Beitrag zur Geschichte der chemischen Geräte. *Chem.Zeitung*, 1912, 36: 397-401, ill.

SCHINDLER, Hans. Notes on the history of the separatory funnel. *J.Chem.Educ.*, 1957, 34: 528-30, 8 fig. [CB 83/265]

WINDERLICH, R. Brenngläser als Hilfsmittel chemischen Forschens. *Chymia*, 1949, 2: 37-43, 2 pl.

Dxb-wb

CHILD, Ernest. The tools of the chemist, their ancestry and American evolution. 220 p., ill. New York: Reinhold, 1940.
Reviewed by E. Farber, *Isis*, 1941, 33: 80-1.

Dxe

SOLOVEICHIK, Samuel. Toxicity: killer of great chemists? *J.Chem.Educ.*, 1964, 41: (5), 282-4.
Casual discussion of work with toxic chemicals by Scheele, Davy, Cruickshank, and Woodhouse.

Dxk

BACKER, H.-J. Oude chemische werktuigen en laboratoria van Zosimos tot Boerhaave. [Old chemical instruments in laboratories from Zosimos to Boerhaave. (In Dutch)] 68 p., 51 ill. Groningen: Wolters, 1918. [CB 11/440]

Dxp

MULTHAUF, Robert P. On the use of the balance in chemistry. *Proc.Amer.Phil.Soc.*, 1962, 106: 210-27.

RHEINBOLDT, Heinrich. Balança e pesagens na epoca preclassica da química. 167 p., ill. (*Selec.Quím.*, 3) São Paulo: 1945. [CB 70/257]

Dxq

LIPPMANN, Edmund O. von. Zur Geschichte der Volumgewichtsermittlung. *Chem.Zeitung*, 1915, 39: 985-6.
Criticism of article by H. Schelenz, *see* below.

SCHELENZ, Hermann. Zur Geschichte der Volumgewichtsermittlung. *Chem.Zeitung*, 1915, 39: 913.

Dxx museums

GREENAWAY, Frank. Chemistry at the Science Museum [London]. *Roy.Inst.Chem.*, 1961, 85: 126-31, ill. [CB 87/617]

SCIENCE MUSEUM. Catalogue of the collections with descriptive notes and illustrations. Chemistry. Compiled by A. Barclay. 76 p., 13 pl. London: H.M. Stationery Office, 1927.
Revised ed., 1962.

DA THEORY OF THE ELEMENTS AND CONSTITUTION

see also CQ STRUCTURE OF MATTER
DJ STRUCTURAL CHEMISTRY

BAUMGÄRTNER, F. Die Geschichte der Entdeckung künstlicher Elemente. *Naturwissenschaften*, 1964, 51: 1-7.

BLIGH, N.M. The progress of the chemical theory and practice. Newly discovered chemical elements. *Scientia*, 1928, 43: 229-36; French transl. suppl. 86-92.

DAVIS, Helen Miles. The chemical elements. With revisions by Glenn T. Seaborg. 198 p., tables. Washington, D.C.: Science Service, 1959.

FARBER, Eduard. Variants of preformation theory in the history of chemistry. *Isis*, 1963, 54: 443-60.

FRIEND, J. Newton. Man and the chemical elements, from stone-age hearth to the cyclotron. ix, 354 p., 4 pl. London: Charles Griffin, 1951. [CB 79/175]
Reviewed by John Read, *Nature*, 1952, 169: 209; 2nd ed. (ix, 354 p., ill. London: Charles Griffin, 1961) reviewed by Douglas McKie, *Ann.Sci.*, 1960, 16: 274.

HOOYKAAS, R. Die Elementenlehre der Iatrochemiker. *Janus*, 1937, 41: 1-28.

HOOYKAAS, R. Het begrip element in zijn historisch-wijsgeerige ontwikkeling. [The concept of "element" in its historical philosophical development. (In Dutch with French summary)]. (Thesis, Utrecht). 238 p. Utrecht: Fa. Schotanus & Jens, 1933.

HOOYKAAS, R. De wet van elementenbehoud. [The law of conservation of elements. (In Dutch)]. *Chem.Weekbl.*, 1947, 43: 526-31. [CB 72/271]

JAEGER, Frans Maurits. De ontdekkingsgeschiedenis der chemische elementen. [The history of the discovery of the chemical elements. (In Dutch)] 191 p. Antwerp: Het Kompas; Amsterdam: De Spieghel, 1935.

PARTINGTON, J.R. The concepts of substance and chemical element. *Chymia*, 1948, 1: 109-21.

RAMSAY, William. Ancient and modern views regarding the chemical elements. Presidential address. *Rep.Brit.Ass. Advance.Sci.*, 1911, 80: 3-22; reprinted in *Annu.Rep.Smithsonian Inst.for* 1911, p. 183-97. Washington, D.C.: 1912.

WEEKS, Mary Elvira. Discovery of the elements. With illustrations collected by F.B. Dains. 5th rev. ed. xiv, 578 p. Easton, Pa.: *Journal of Chemical Education*, 1945. [CB 69/227]
The first edition (*see* CB 39/455) was based on a series of articles in *J.Chem.Educ.*, 1932, 9: 3-30, 215-35, 459-85, 863-4, 1034-57, 1231-43, 1386-1434, 1593-1619, 1751-73, 1915-39. Spanish translation Barcelona: Marin, 1949. [CB 78/185]; Chinese translation Shanghai: Commercial Press, 1940. [CB 35/264]

DAks

PANETH, F.A. The epistemological status of the chemical concept of element. *Brit.J.Phil.Sci.*, 1962, 13: 1-14, 144-60.

DAmzDY

DAVIS, Tenney L. Neglected evidence in the history of phlogiston together with observations on the doctrine of forms and the history of alchemy. *Ann.Med.Hist.*, 1924, 6: 280-7.

DAnh

HAUBEN, Saul S. The derivations of the names of the elements. *J.Chem.Educ.*, 1933, 10: 227-34.

DAu

BESANT, Annie; LEADBETTER, Charles W. Occult chemistry. Clairvoyant observations on the chemical elements. Rev. ed. by A.P. Sinnett. 110 p. London: Theosophical Publishing House, 1919.
Part reprint of first edition 1908. Reprinted from *The Theosophist*.

DAxq ATOMIC WEIGHTS

DAMBIER, P. Sur l'intervention du nombre π dans les relations entre poids atomiques. *J.Chim.Phys.*, 1913, 11: 260-6.
Reviewed by G. Sarton, *Isis*, 1914, 1: 709-10.

FORBES, George Shannon. Investigations of atomic weights by Theodore William Richards. *J.Chem.Educ.*, 1932, 9: 453-8.

GUYE, Philippe A. Coup d'oeil rétrospectif sur les déterminations du poids atomique du chlore. Poids atomique de l'argent. Considérations générales sur la détermination des poids atomiques. *J.Chim.Phys.*, 1913, 11: 275-318.
Reviewed by G. Sarton, *Isis*, 1914, 1: 709-10.

HEPBURN, Joseph Samuel. Atomic weights - an historical sketch. *Med.Life*, 1936, 43: 163-8.

SARTON, George. Sur la détermination des poids atomiques. *Isis*, 1914, 1: 709-10.
Reviewing articles by P. Dambier and P.A. Guye, *see* above.

DAzi ISOTOPES

ANDERS, Oswald U. The place of isotopes in the periodic table: the 50th anniversary of the Fajans-Soddy displacement law. *J. Chem.Educ.*, 1964, 41: no. 10, 522-5.

ASTON, F.W. Isotopes. viii, 152 p., ill. London: Arnold, 1922.
French translation Paris: Hermann, 1923; German translation Leipzig: Hirzel, 1923.
2nd English edition. xi, 182 p., ill. London: Arnold, 1924.

ASTON, F.W. Mass spectra and isotopes. Being the twenty-sixth Robert Boyle Lecture delivered before the Junior Scientific Club of the University of Oxford. 16 p. London: Oxford University Press, 1924.

ASTON, F.W. The story of isotopes. *Science*, 1933, 78: 5-6.

ASTON, F.W. The story of isotopes. *Science*, 1935, 82: 235-40.
Address to the British Association for the Advancement of Science, Norwich, September 1935.

CURIE, Marie. L'isotopie et les éléments isotopes. 210 p. (*Rec.Conf.Rapp.Doc.Phys.*, 9: 2e sér., 1-3) Paris: Presses Universitaires de France, 1924.

ISOTOPES - a fiftieth anniversary. *Proc.Chem.Soc.*, 1963, 325-31.

THOMSON, J.J. Rays of positive electricity and their application to chemical analyses. x, 237 p., 9 pl. (Monographs on Physics) 2nd ed. London: Longmans, 1921.
First published 1913.

DAzi-wb

KING, Harold S. Pioneering research on isotopes at Harvard. *J.Chem.Educ.*, 1959, 36: 225-7.

DAzp PERIODIC SYSTEM

ANTROPOFF, Andreas von. Les formes usuelles du système périodique des éléments. (In French, with English summary). *Ann. Guébhard-Séverine*, 1937, 13: 161-74, 6 fig., 1 pl.

RABINOWITSCH, Eugen; THILO, Erich. Periodisches System. Geschichte und Theorie. xi, 302 p., 50 fig., 49 pl. Stuttgart: Enke, 1930.
Reviewed by Zaunick, *Mitt.Gesch.Med.*, 1930, 29: 147-8; by L. Meitner, *Deut.Lit.Zeitung*, 1930, 1341-4.

SARTON, George. Moseley. The numbering of the elements. *Isis*, 1927, 9: 96-111, portr., bibliogr.

SCHMIDT, Curt. Das periodische System der chemischen Elemente. viii, 144 p., ill. Leipzig: Barth, 1917.

SHCHUKAREV, S.A.; MAKARENIA, A.A. Razvitie predstavlenii o vtorichnoi periodichnosti. [The development of concepts of secondary periodicity. (In Russian)] *Vop.Ist.Est.Tekh.*, 1962, 13: 76-9.

VAN SPRONSEN, Jan W. The prehistory of the periodic system of the elements. *J.Chem.Educ.*, 1959, 36: 565-7.

DC ANALYTICAL CHEMISTRY

CURTMAN, Louis J. Introduction to semi-micro qualitative chemical analysis. Rev. ed. xvi, 391 p., front., 39 fig. New York: Macmillan, 1950.
1st edition, 1942.

GREENAWAY, F. The early development of analytical chemistry. *Endeavour*, 1962, 21: 91-7.

LONGO, Rafael E. Historia del microanálisis. *Cienc.Tecnol.*, 1956, 6: 101-47.

MADSEN, E. Rancke. The development of titrimetric analysis till 1806. 239 p., 10 fig. Copenhagen: G.E.C. Gad, 1958. [CB 84/312]
From Robert Boyle to F.A.H. Descroizilles.
Reviewed by F.W. Gibbs, *Ambix*, 1958, 6: 157-9; by Eduard Farber, *Science*, 1958, 127: 1235; by Arne Olander, *Lychnos*, 1960-61, 351-2.

NIERENSTEIN, M. The early history of the first chemical reagent [gallnuts]. *Isis*, 1931, 16: 439-46.

SOLOVYOV, YU. I. Ocherki istorii fiziko-chimicheskogo analiza. [The history of physico-chemical analysis. (In Russian)] 222 p., 15 fig., 13 portr. Moskva: Izdatelstvo Akademii Nauk SSSR, 1955. [CB 83/265]

DCcj

BOIG, Fletcher S.; HOWERTON, Paul W. History and development of chemical periodicals in the field of analytical chemistry: 1877-1950. *Science*, 1952, 115: 555-60.

DCwb

HILLEBRAND, William Francis. Our analytical chemistry and its future. 36 p. (The Chandler Lecture, 1916) New York: Columbia University Press, 1917.

OLSEN, J.C. Historical aspects of analytical chemistry in the United States for the last fifty years. *J.Chem.Educ.*, 1927, 4: 506-11.

DCwf

JOUNIAUX, A. Les origines françaises de la chimie analytique. 62 p. (Actualités Scientifiques et Industrielles, 707) Paris: Hermann, 1938.

DCxd

BAKER, A. Albert. A history of indicators. *Chymia*, 1964, 9: 147-67.
A detailed survey, from Boyle to 1920, of materials and theory.

SZABADVÁRY, Ferenc. Indicators. A historical perspective. *J.Chem.Educ.*, 1964, 41: 285-7.

DCzc CHROMATOGRAPHY

FARRADANE, J. History of chromatography. *Nature*, 1951, 167: 120.

HESSE, Gerhard; WEIL, Herbert. Michael Tswett's first paper on chromatography. 35 p., 2 pl. Eschwege: M. Woelm, 1954.
Includes an English translation of Tswett's earliest paper on the subject.
Reviewed by Aaron J. Ihde, *Isis*, 1956, 47: 93-4.

WEIL, Herbert. Die Anfänge der Chromatographie. *Chem.Zeitung*, 1954, 78: 419-24, 496-9.

WEIL, Herbert. History of chromatography. *Nature*, 1950, 166: 1000-1. [CB 77/342]

WEIL, Herbert; WILLIAMS, Trevor I. Early history of chromatography. *Nature*, 1951, 167: 906.

WILLIAMS, Trevor I. The elements of chromatography. 90 p., front., 30 fig., 7 pl. New York: Philosophical Library; London/Glasgow: Blackie, 1954.
Reviewed by Aaron J. Ihde, *Isis*, 1956, 47: 93-4.

ZECHMEISTER, L. Early history of chromatography. *Nature*, 1951, 167: 405-6.

ZECHMEISTER, L. History, scope, and methods of chromatography. *Ann.N.Y.Acad.Sci.*, 1948, 49: 145-60.

ZECHMEISTER, L. Mikhail Tswett - the inventor of chromatography. *Isis*, 1946, 36: 108-9; 1948, 38: 243.

DCzm MASS SPECTROSCOPY

ASTON, F.W. Mass spectra and isotopes. *See* DAzi

DEMPSTER, Arthur J. Thirty years of mass spectroscopy. *Sci.Mon.*, 1948, 67: 145-53.

DCzs SPECTROCHEMISTRY

CENTURY of spectrochemistry. *Endeavour*, 1959, 18: 171-2.

GILLIS, J. Honderd jaar na de opkomst van de Kwalitatieve Spectrochemie. [A hundred years since the rise of qualitative spectrochemistry. An historical survey. (In Dutch)]. *Brug*, 1960, 4: 228-33.

URBAIN, G. Introduction à l'étude de la spectrochimie. iii, 248 p. Paris: Hermann, 1911.
German translation Dresden: Steinkopf, 1913.

DD PHYSICAL CHEMISTRY

for physical inorganic chemistry *see* DSyDF, DSyDJ, DSyDK, DTyDD, DTyDL
physical organic chemistry *see* DUyDD

BAUME, Georges. La chimie physique en 1912. *J.Chim.Phys.*, 1913, 11: 327-404.

GUYE, Charles Eugène. Physico-chemical evolution. Translated by J.R. Clarke. xii, 172 p. London: Methuen, 1925.
English translation of "L'évolution physico-chimique" (Paris: Chiron, 1922); German translation,Bern: Paul Haupt, 1925.

LEMOINE, Georges. L'évolution de la chimie physique. *Rev.Sci.*, 1912, 50: 2e semestre, 673-80.

SCHWAB, Georg-Maria. Die Stellung der physikalischen Chemie in der heutigen Naturwissenschaft. *Naturwiss.Rundsch.*, 1959, 12: 125-8.

DDmzC

LANGMUIR, Irving. Modern concepts in physics and their relation to chemistry. *Annu.Rep.Smithsonian Inst.for 1930*, p. 219-41. Washington, D.C.: 1932.
Presidential address before the 78th meeting of the American Chemical Society, Minneapolis, 1929. First published *Gen.Elec.Rev.*, 1929, 32: 649-59.

DDwb-oq

HILDEBRAND, Joel H. Fifty years of physical chemistry in Berkeley. *Annu.Rev.Phys.Chem.*, 1963, 14: 1-4.

DDwg-da

HARTECK, Paul. Physical chemists in Berlin, 1919-1933. *J. Chem.Educ.*, 1960, 37: 462-6.

DDwh-oq

STROŃSKI, Ignacy. Pierwszy zaklad chemii fizycznej w Polsce. [The first department of physical chemistry in Poland. (In Polish, with English summary)] *Stud.Mater.Dziej.Nauk.Pol., ser. C*, 1964, 9: 107-33.
This department was organized by Ludwik Bruner at the Jagellonian University.

DDwn-ce-bv

STOGOV, V.V., ed. Ukazatel' soderzhania *Zhurnala Russkogo Fiziko-Khimicheskogo Obshchestva* 1873-1930. Chast' fizicheskaia. [Index to the contents of the *Journal of the Russian Physical-Chemical Society*, 1873-1930. Physics section. (In Russian)] 207 p. Moskva: Izdatel' stvo Akademii Nauk SSSR, 1960.

DDyCH CHEMICAL THERMODYNAMICS

HIEBERT, Erwin N. The concept of chemical affinity in thermodynamics. *Proc.10th Int.Congr.Hist.Sci.* (Ithaca, 1962), (2), p. 871-3. Paris: Hermann, 1964.

KIPNIS, A.I. Ocherk istorii vozniknoveniia khimicheskoi termodinamiki. [Sketch of the history of the rise of chemical thermodynamics. (In Russian)]. *Tr.Inst.Ist.Est.Tekh.*, 1961, 35: 39-107, bibliogr.
From Carnot through van't Hoff and Gibbs.

DDyCHwn

KIPNIS, A.I. [History of chemical thermodynamics in Russia. (In Russian)] *Vop.Ist.Est.Tekh.*, 1960, 9: 125-8.

KIPNIS, A.I. Razvitie khimicheskoĭ termodinamiki v Rossii. [Development of chemical thermodynamics in Russia. (In Russian)]. 345 p., portr. Leningrad: Nauka [Leningradskoe otd-nie], 1964.

DE CHEMICAL STATICS AND DYNAMICS

CLIBBENS, Douglas A. The principles of the phase theory. Heterogeneous equilibria between salts and their aqueous solutions. xx, 382 p. London: Macmillan, 1920.

EMANUEL', N.M. Khimicheskaia kinetika i perspektivy ee razvitiia v XX veke. [Chemical kinetics and the prospects of its development in the 20th century. (In Russian)]. *Vop.Ist.Est.Tekh.*, 1963, 14: 3-36.

FARBER, Eduard. The proportionality between rates of transformation and the transformable entity. *Proc.10th Int.Congr.Hist.Sci.* (Ithaca, 1962), (2), p. 903-5. Paris: Hermann, 1964.

HOOYKAAS, R. De wet van massabehoud. [The law of conservation of mass. (In Dutch)] *Chem.Weekbl.*, 1947, 43: 244-8.
History of the law of conservation of mass in chemical transformations.

KONDRATEV, V.N. Ocherk istorii razvitiya kinetiki khimicheskikh reaktsii. [The history of the development of kinetic chemical reactions. (In Russian)] *Vop.Ist.Est.Tekh.*, 1956, 2: 9-49.

KUZNETSOV, V.I. Nekotorye vyvody iz istorii ucheniia o dvoistvennoi reaktsionnoi sposobnosti. [Some conclusions from the history of the doctrine of double reaction capacity. (In Russian)] *Vop.Ist.Est.Tekh.*, 1962, 13: 19-25.

LINDAUER, Maurice W. The evolution of the concept of chemical equilibrium from 1775 to 1923. *J.Chem.Educ.*, 1962, 39: 384-90.
A survey of the high points from Geoffroy and Bergman to Gibbs and G.N. Lewis.

RENAUD, Paul. Nouvelle conception de l'inertie chimique. *Rev.Gén.Sci.*, 1938, 49: 375-82.

SOLOV'EV, IU. I.; STAROSEL'SKII, P.I. Iz istorii fizicheskoi khimi; printsip maksimal'noi raboty. [From the history of physical chemistry; the principle of maximum work. (In Russian)] *Tr.Inst.Ist.Est.Tekh.*, 1962, 39: 24-48.

DEdaj

BENFEY, O. Theodor, ed. Classics in the theory of chemical combination. xii, 191 p., ill. (Classics of Science, 1) New York: Dover, 1963.
Reviewed by G.V. Bykov, *Arch.Int.Hist.Sci.*, 1964, 17: 324-6; by L. Rosenfeld, *Centaurus*, 1964, 10: 212.

DEmd

BENFEY, O. Theodor. Concepts of time in chemistry. *J.Chem. Educ.*, 1963, 40: 574-7.
Contains suggestions of a new approach to the history of chemical kinetics.

FARBER, Eduard. Early studies concerning time in chemical reactions. *Chymia*, 1961, 7: 135-48.

DEmj

FAJANS, Kasimir. The development of views regarding the nature of chemical forces. *Science*, 1930, 72: 99-107, 7 fig.

DEzc CATALYSIS

LIPPMANN, Edmund O. von. Beitrag zur Geschichte der Katalyse. *Chem.Zeitung*, 1929, 53: 22.
Tracing the history of catalysis back to Apuleius through St. Augustine, Bartholomew the Englishman, and Albert the Great.

MÉTADIER, Jacques. La théorie de la catalyse. Vue d'ensemble et essai de synthèse. 101 p. (Actualités Scientifiques et Industrielles, 1005) Paris: Hermann, 1946.
Reviewed by H.W. Melville, *Nature*, 1947, 159: 791.

MITTASCH, Alwin. Kurze Geschichte der Katalyse in Praxis und Theorie. viii, 139 p. Berlin: Springer, 1939.
Reviewed by Eduard Farber, *Isis*, 1949, 32: 389-90.

MITTASCH, Alwin. Über katalytische Verursachung im biologischen Geschehen. x, 126 p. Berlin: Springer, 1935.
Essay review by Eduard Farber, *Isis*, 1938, 29: 398-402.

DEzc-k

FARBER, Eduard. A philosophy of catalysis. *Isis*, 1938, 29: 398-402.

DEzc-kv

MITTASCH, Alwin. Katalyse und Determinismus: ein Beitrag zur Philosophie der Chemie. ix, 203 p., 10 fig. Berlin: Springer, 1938.
Essay review by Eduard Farber, *Isis*, 1938, 29: 398-402.

DEzd DISTILLATION

see also SWza ALCOHOLIC BEVERAGES

DAVIDSSON, J.A. Die Erfindung der Destillation. Transl. from the Swedish by Eugenie Hoffmann. *Int.Monatsschr.Erforsch. Alkoholismus*, 1912, 22: no. 8, 294-303.

EGLOFF, Gustav; LOWRY, C.D. Distillation methods, ancient and modern. *Ind.Eng.Chem.*, 1929, 21: 920-3, 11 fig. [CB 29/298]

FORBES, R.J. La distillation à travers les âges. 12 p., 21 fig. Bruxelles: Société belge pour l'Etude du Pétrole, 1947.

GILDEMEISTER, Eduard; HOFFMANN, Friedrich. Geschichte der Destillierweisen und -geräte. In their: Die aetherischen Oele. 3rd ed. (1), p. 221-62, ill. Leipzig: L. Staackmann, 1928. [CB 25/438]

LEJEUNE, Fritz. Betrachtungen zur Destillierkunst. *Pharm. Ind.*, 1941, 8: 66-74.
Reviewed by P. Diergart, *Mitt.Gesch.Med.*, 1940, 39: 328.

LIEBMANN, A.J. History of distillation. *J.Chem.Educ.*, 1956, 33: 166-73, 9 fig.

SCHREINER, Oswald. History of the art of distillation and of distilling apparatus. 59 p., 65 fig. Milwaukee: Pharmaceutical Review Publishing Co., 1901.

SUDHOFF, Karl. Weiteres zur Geschichte der Destillationstechnik. *Arch.Gesch.Naturwiss.Tech.*, 1914, 5: 282-8, 4 fig.

DEzd-wh

IVANYÍ, Béla. [The "burning" of water in Western Hungary in the 16th-18th centuries. (In Hungarian. Summaries in Russian and German)]. *Országos Orv.Könyvtar Közleményei*, 1956, no. 4, 5-34. [CB 84/361]

DEzd-xb

COLVERD, Owen. The Forbes mystillery. (Letter to the Editor.) *Proc.Chem.Soc.*, 1962, 378-9.
Apropos of the introduction of steam heating mentioned in R.J. Forbes: The evolution of the still, *see* below.

FESTER, G.A. Zur Geschichte des Gegenstromkühlers. *Sudhoffs Arch.*, 1961, 45: 341-50.
Development of this chemical apparatus (mostly in connection with distillation) largely due to Lavoisier.

FORBES, R.J. The evolution of the still. *Proc.Chem.Soc.*, 1962, 237-42. [CB 88/544]
From earliest times to 1857 A.D. For supplementary note concerning the introduction of steam-heating in the 19th century by Owen Colverd, *see* above.

LEVEY, Martin. The earliest stages in the evolution of the still. *Isis*, 1960, 51: 31-4.

TAYLOR, F. Sherwood. The evolution of the still. *Ann.Sci.*, 1945, 5: 185-202, 14 fig.

DF TYPES OF REACTIONS

DFzc COMBUSTION

GREGORY, Joshua Craven. Combustion from Heracleitos to Lavoisier. vii, 231 p. London: Arnold, 1934.
Reviewed by E.F.A., *Nature*, 1934, 134: 892; by Hélène Metzger, *Archeion*, 1934, 16: 235-7.

LIPPMANN, Edmund O. von. Weiteres über Herkunft und Rolle der pflanzlichen Aschen-Bestandteile. *Chem.Zeitung*, 1932, 56: 2.

PARTINGTON, J.R. Some milestones in the study of hydrocarbon flames. *Ann.Sci.*, 1945, 5: 229-52.

SCOTT, Wilson L.; FARBER, Eduard. Complementary views on oxidation and reduction. *Proc.10th Int.Congr.Hist.Sci.* (Ithaca, 1962), (2), p. 887-90. Paris: Hermann, 1964.

VASSAILS, Gérard. Le poids du feu. *Rev.Hist.Sci.*, 1950, 3: 222-41. [CB 77/371]

DG THERMOCHEMISTRY

WOLFENDEN, J.H. The dawn of hot atom chemistry. *J.Chem. Educ.*, 1955, 32: 276.

DGxq

ARMSTRONG, George T. The calorimeter and its influence on the development of chemistry. *J.Chem.Educ.*, 1964, 41: 297-307.

DH ELECTRO- AND MAGNETOCHEMISTRY

BERRY, A.J. Some aspects of early electro-chemistry. *Bull. Brit.Soc.Hist.Sci.*, 1952, 1: 205-10.

BROCKMAN, C.J. Fused electrolytes - an historical sketch. *J.Chem.Educ.*, 1927, 4: 512-23.

BROCKMAN, C.J. Primary cells - a brief historical sketch. *J.Chem.Educ.*, 1927, 4: 770-80.

DEUEL, H.; HOSTETTLER, F. Hundert Jahre Ionenaustausch. *Experientia*, 1950, 6: 445-56.

EBERT, A. The theory of hydrogen ion concentration. *Ciba Rev.*, 1955, no. 112, 4046-52, 8 portr.

FINK, Colin G. Electrochemistry's debt to Edgar Fahs Smith. Cathode film control in electrometal deposition. *Science*, 1935, 82: 1-5.

GEBHARDT, Otto. Ein Beitrag zur Untersuchung der exakten Grundlagen der Elektrolyse mit besonderer Berücksichtigung der Ueberführungszahlen. *Arch.Gesch.Naturwiss.Tech.*, 1916, 7: 207-19, 404-19.

KISTIAKOVSKII, V.A. [Arrhenius' theory of electrolytic dissociation and the evolution of modern chemistry. (In Russian)] 15 p. *(Tr.Kom.Ist.Znanii*, 6) Leningrad: Akademiia Nauk, 1929. [CB 29/252]

LYLE, Robert E.; LYLE, Gloria G. A brief history of polarimetry. *J.Chem.Educ.*, 1964, 41: 308-13.

MÜLLER, Otto H. The development of polarography and polarographic instruments. *J.Chem.Educ.*, 1964, 41: 320-8.

PIONTELLI, R. I progressi dell' elettro-chimica negli ultimi cinquantanni. *Scientia*, 1958, 93: 136-9.

SCHIFF, Julius. Zur Geschichte der konstanten galvanischen Elemente. *Arch.Gesch.Naturwiss.Tech.*, 1916, 7: 288-98.

SOLOV'EV, IU. I. Sull'origine della teoria dell'idratazione ionica. *Act.VIIIe Congr.Int.Hist.Sci.* (Florence, 1956), p. 590-3. Paris: Hermann, 1958.

SZABADVÁRY, Ferenc. Development of the pH concept. *J.Chem. Educ.*, 1964, 41: 105-7.

DI RADIO-, RADIATION AND PHOTOCHEMISTRY

BERTHOUD, A. Lois et principes fondamentaux de la photochimie. *Scientia*, 1930, 48: 9-18.

BURTON, Milton. Development of current concepts of elementary processes in radiation chemistry. *J.Chem.Educ.*, 1959, 36: 273-8.

GLOCKLER, George. Early contributions by S.C. Lind to the radiation chemistry of gases. *J.Chem.Educ.*, 1959, 36: 262-6.

HART, Edwin J. Development of the radiation chemistry of aqueous solutions. *J.Chem.Educ.*, 1959, 36: 266-72.

IREDALE, T. Photochemistry in retrospect. *Nature*, 1944, 154: 326-7.

NITTA, Isamu. [The development of X-ray chemistry in the last half century. (In Japanese)] *Kagaku Kōgyō*, 1963, 16: 1077.
Other articles in the same issue on similar subjects.

RAYLEIGH, Robert John Strutt, 4th Baron. The glow of phosphorus. *Nature*, 1924, 114: 612-14.

SHEPPARD, S.E. Photo-chemistry. ix, 461 p. (Textbooks of Physical Chemistry) London: Longmans, Green, 1914.

DJ STRUCTURAL CHEMISTRY

for the structure of matter *see also* CQ
crystal structure *see* CW

ACHALME, Pierre Jean. Les édifices physico-chimiques. 3 vol. 1. L'atome, sa structure, sa forme. 244 p., 15 pl., 63 ill.; 2. La molécule. 234 p.; 3. La molécule minérale. 350 p. Paris: Payot, 1921-24.
Reviewed by L. Guinet, *Isis*, 1922, 4: 544; 1923, 5: 464-5; 1925, 7: 292.

BENFEY, O. Theodor. From vital force to structural formulas. xi, 115 p., fig. (Classic Researches in Organic Chemistry) Boston: Houghton Mifflin, 1964.

BOLL, Marcel. L'atomistique. Les atomes et les molécules, structures électroniques, capillarité et osmose, les colloides, la catalyse. Exposé élémentaire. 136 p., 82 ill. (Collection Hippocrate) Paris: Le François, 1934.
Reviewed by Hélène Metzger, *Archeion*, 1934, 16: 238-9.

BRADLEY, John. The classical molecular and atomic theory of chemistry. *Sch.Sci.Rev.*, 1957-58, 39: 11-18, 200-10. [CB 84/374]

BYKOV, G.V. Istoriia klassicheskoi teorii khimicheskogo stroeniia. [The history of the classical theory of chemical structure. (In Russian)] 311 p. Moscow: Izdatel'stvo Akademii Nauk SSSR, 1960.
Reviewed by Edmund Trepka, *Kwart.Hist.Nauk.Tech.*, 1961, 6: 140-1.

BYKOV, G.V. Razrabotka v SSSR istorii teorii khimicheskogo stroeniia i nauchnogo nalediia A.M. Butlerova. [Work in the USSR on the history of the theory of chemical structure and the scientific legacy of A.M. Butlerov. (In Russian)] *Vop. Ist.Est.Tekh.*, 1962, 12: 165-9.

BYKOV, G.V. The rise and development of the classical theory of chemical structure. *Act.VIIIe Congr.Int.Hist.Sci.* (Florence, 1956), p. 573-6. Paris: Hermann, 1958.

CAMPAIGNE, E. The contributions of Fritz Arndt to resonance theory. *J.Chem.Educ.*, 1959, 36: 336-9.

CANNIZZARO, Stanislao. Historische Notizen und Betrachtungen über die Anwendung der Atomtheorie in der Chemie und über die Systeme der Konstitutionsformeln von Verbindungen. Aus dem Italienischen mit einer biographischen Einleitung von B. Lino Vanzetti und M. Speter. 166 p. Stuttgart: F. Enke, 1913.
First appeared in *Gazetta Chimica Italiana*, 1871.

COHEN, Ernst. Fünfzig Jahre aus der Geschichte einer Theorie (1874-1924). Ihre Grundleger. Vortrag am 25. Oktober 1924 in der Aula der Universität Amsterdam. *Naturwissenschaften*, 1925, 13: 284-90.
Theory of the asymmetrical carbon atom put forward by Le Bel and Van't Hoff separately in 1874.

COPLEY, George Novello. The law of Avogadro-Gerhardt (?) and 'Van der Waals' forces'. *Sch.Sci.Rev.*, 1939, 21: 869.

GIUA, Michele. Sviluppo storico dell' atomistica e della dottrina della valenza. In: Nuova enciclopedia di chimica, vol. 12, P. 3a, p. 459-635, 15 ill. Torino: Unione tipogr. editrice torinese, 1926. [CB 22/267]

KENDALL, James. At home among the atoms: a first book of congenial chemistry. xv, 270 p., 16 pl. London: Bell, 1929.
Reviewed by John Read, *Nature*, 1930, 125: 155-7.

LANSDOWN, Brenda. The chemical background of the atom. 68 p., fig. (Workbook of Scientific Thinking, 1) New York: Dalton Book Shop, 1950.

LESPLEAU, R. La molécule chimique. 286 p. Paris: Alcan, 1920.
Reviewed by L. Guinet, *Isis*, 1920, 3: 426-8.

MENSHUTKIN, B.N. [Particle and atom in chemistry. (In Russian)] 144 p. Moscow: Novaya Derevnya, 1929.

MIELI, Aldo. La teoría atómica química moderna. xiii, 243 p. Buenos Aires: Espasa-Calpe, 1947.
Reviewed by Pierre Brunet, *Arch.Int.Hist.Sci.*, 1947, 1: 172-6.

MUSABEKOV, Iu. S.; KOSHKIN, L.V. Vozniknovenie i razvitie ucheniia o radikalakh. [Origin and development of the concept of radicals. (In Russian)] *Tr.Inst.Ist.Est.Tekh.*, 1961, 35: 245-92.
A substantial history of the concept from 1782 to 1929. Bibliography of 130 items.

OKAMOTO, Y. [Technical background of the formation of high-molecule chemistry. (In Japanese)] *J.Hist.Sci.Japan*, 1955, no. 33, 22-9.

PARTINGTON, J.R. The origins of the atomic theory. *Ann.Sci.*, 1939, 4: 245-82, 5 fig.

TANAKA, Minoru. Ein Beitrag zur Geschichte der Atomistik. Über die Rolle der chemischen Forschung beim Werdegang der modernen Atomistik. *Jap.Stud.Hist.Sci.*, 1962, 1: 111-16.

THOMSON, J.J. The electron in chemistry: being five lectures delivered at the Franklin Institute, Philadelphia. v, 144 p. Philadelphia: The Franklin Institute; London: Chapman & Hall, 1923.

DJwi

GIUA, Michele. L'apport italien à l'étude des molecules et des macromolecules après Avogadro. *Cah.Hist.Mond.*, 1963, 7: 485-501.

DJwn

GRAHAM, Loren R. A Soviet marxist view of structural chemistry: the theory of resonance controversy. *Isis*, 1964, 55: 20-31.

DJyCJ

KOLRAUSCH, K.W.F. Ramaneffekt und Chemie. *Scientia*, 1932, 51: 335-47.

DJza AFFINITY

BLOCH, Ernst. Das chemische Affinitaetsproblem geschichtlich betrachtet. *Isis*, 1926, 8: 119-57. [CB 21/573]

BRUNOLD, Charles. Le problème de l'affinité chimique et l'atomistique: étude du rapprochement actuel de la physique et de la chimie. v, 118 p. Paris: Masson, 1930.
Reviewed in *Nature*, 1931, 127: 300-1.

FARBER, Eduard. Zur Geschichte der Zuordnung von Stoff und Eigenschaft. *Isis*, 1931, 16: 425-38.

HIEBERT, Erwin N. The concept of chemical affinity in thermodynamics. *Proc.10th Int.Congr.Hist.Sci.* (Ithaca, 1962), (2), p. 871-3. Paris: Hermann, 1964.

NORSKE VIDENSKAP-AKADEMI I OSLO. Law of mass action. A centenary volume, 1864-1964. 194 p. Oslo: Universitetsforlaget, 1964. [CB 90/518]
Reviewed in *Curr.Sci.*, 1964, 33: 580.

DJzb BONDS; VALENCY

AMIEL, Jean. Quelques nouvelles théories de la valence chimique. *Thalès*, 1934, 1: 155-60.

BYKOV, G.V. Vozniknovenie poniatiia o kovalentnoi sviazi v khimii. [The origin of the concept of covalent bonds in chemistry. (In Russian)] *Vop.Ist.Est.Tekh.*, 1961, 11: 11-19.

KAUFFMANN, Hugo. Die Valenzlehre. x, 557 p. Stuttgart: Enke, 1911.
Reviewed by E. Bloch, *Isis*, 1913, 1: 280-1.

LEWIS, Gilbert Newton. Valence and the structure of atoms and molecules. 172 p., ill. (American Chemical Society. Monograph series) New York: Chemical Catalogue Company, 1923.
Reviewed by Eugène Bloch, *Rev.Gén.Sci.*, 1924, 35: 151.

PALMER, W.G. Valency: classical and modern. x, 242 p., 59 fig. Cambridge University Press, 1945. [CB 70/257]

SIDGWICK, Nevil Vincent. The electronic theory of valency. xii, 310 p. Oxford: Clarendon Press, 1927.
Reviewed by T.M. Lowry, *Nature*, 1928, 121: 527-31.

DK STEREOCHEMISTRY

BLOKH, M.A. K 50-letiyu stereokhimii. [On the 50th anniversary of stereochemistry. (In Russian)] *Priroda*, 1925, 14: (10-12), 95-102. [CB 29/252]

BLOKH, M.A. K pyatidesyatiletiyu stereokhimii. [On the 50th anniversary of stereochemistry. (In Russian)] *Tekh.Ékon. Vestnik*, 1925, 5: no.8-9, 646-50. [CB 29/252]

BOUTARIC, Augustin. Sur l'histoire de l'acide racémique et du mot racémique. *Rev.Sci.*, 1941, 79: 384-5.

CERASOLI, Ercole. Sulla origine della stereochimica. *Archeion*, 1935, 17: 401-4.

DELÉPINE, Marcel. La théorie du carbone asymétrique. Conférence faite devant la Société chimique de France le 22 décembre 1924 à l'occasion du cinquantenaire de cette théorie. *Bull.Soc.Chim.France*, février 1925, 197-236. [CB 18/563]

IHDE, Aaron J. The unraveling of geometric isomerism and tautomerism. *J.Chem.Educ.*, 1959, 36: 330-6.

PATTERSON, T.S.; BUCHANAN, Charles. Historical and other considerations regarding the crystal form of sodium-ammonium *d*- and *l*- tartrate, potassium *d*- and *l*- tartrate, potassium-ammonium *d*- and *l*- tartrate, and potassium racemate. *Ann. Sci.*, 1947, 5: 288-95, 317-24, 14 fig.

WALDEN, Paul. Fünfzig Jahre stereochemischer Lehre und Forschung. Vortrag in der Deutschen Chemischen Gesellschaft am 22.November 1924. *Ber.Deut.Chem.Ges.*, 1925, 58: 237-65.

WALDEN, Paul. Stereochemie und Technik. *Z.Angew.Chem.*, 1925, 38: 429-39.

WALDEN, Paul. Vergangenheit und Gegenwart der Stereochemie. (Nach einem am 25. Sept. 1924 in der Amsterdamer Universitäts-Aula gehaltenen Vortrage.) *Naturwissenschaften*, 1925, 13: 301-12, 331-6, 352-9, 376-84.

DL STATES OF MATTER

DM SURFACE CHEMISTRY; ADSORPTION

HARDY, W.B. Historical notes upon surface energy and forces at short range. *Nature*, 1922, 109: 375-8. [CB 13/300]
For comments *see Nature*, 1922, 109: 518.

VEIL, Suzanne. L'oeuvre de Langmuir dans le domaine de l'adsorption. *Rev.Sci.*, 15 juil. 1938, 271-6.

DN SOLUTIONS

ARRHENIUS, Svante. Theories of solutions. 247 p. New Haven: Yale University Press, 1912.

FEIJFER, F.M.G. de. Uit de geschiedenis van de osmotische verschijnselen. [From the history of osmotic phenomena. (In Dutch)]. *Bijdr.Gesch.Geneesk.*, 1921, 1: 293-9, 3 fig.

MIALL, Stephen. The problem of solution: a tavern talk between certain chymists and others. With an introduction by H.E. Armstrong, and critical letters by T.M. Lowry, A. Findlay, and others. 33 p. London: Benn, 1923.

SOLOV'YEV, Iu. I. [History of the theory of solutions. (In Russian)] 580 p., bibliogr. Moscow: Izdatel'stvo Akademii Nauk SSSR, 1959. [CB 86/463]

STRADIN', IA. P. [From the history of the first theories of the electrical conductivity of solutions. (In Russian)]. *Vop.Ist.Est.Tekh.*, 1959, 8: 122-7.

TYRRELL, H.J.V. The origin and present status of Fick's diffusion law. *J.Chem.Educ.*, 1964, 41: 397-400.

DO COLLOID CHEMISTRY

BOUTARIC, A. Les colloïdes et l'état colloïdal. 258 p., ill. (Nouvelle Collection Scientifique) Paris: Alcan, 1931. [CB 35/298]

FREUNDLICH, Herbert. Kapillarchemie. Eine Darstellung der Chemie der Kolloide und verwandter Gebiete. 2nd ed. xv, 1181 p., ill. Leipzig: Akademische Verlagsgesellschaft, 1922.
Reviewed by Alfred Coehn, *Naturwissenschaften*, 1923, 275.

SVEDBERG, Theodor. Colloid chemistry. Wisconsin lectures. 2nd ed., rev. and enl. in collaboration with Arne Tiselius. 302 p., ill. (American Chemical Society. Monograph series [16]) New York: Chemical Catalog Company, 1928.
First published 1924.

SVEDBERG, Theodor. Die Methoden zur Herstellung kolloider Lösungen anorganischer Stoffe: ein Hand- und Hilfsbuch für die Chemie und Industrie der Kolloide. xii, 508 p., ill. Dresden: 1909; reprinted 1922.

DOmzN

HILLE, Hermann. A history of colloids in medicine. *Med.Life*, 1925, 32: 419-53; 1930, 37: 111-63, 24 ill.

DR INORGANIC CHEMISTRY

for inorganic chemicals *see also* VQ

BULLOFF, Jack J. Inorganic chemistry in the nuclear age; a historical perspective. *J.Chem.Educ.*, 1959, 36: 465-8.

HÄGG, Gunnar. Oorganisk kemi förr och nu. [Inorganic chemistry, past and present. (In Swedish with English summary)]. *Lychnos*, 1937, 2: 227-35.
Sketch of the history of inorganic chemistry with special reference to the determination of the structure of molecules.

MAZZA, L. I progressi della chimica inorganica negli ultimi cinquant'anni. *Scientia*, 1959, 94: 139-48.

MEISSNER, W. Walter. Chemischer Handatlas: anorganische Chemie unter besonderer Berücksichtigung von Atomphysik und Atomchemie. Graphische Darstellung der Eigenschaften chemischer Elemente und ihrer Verbindungen nach der Anordnung des natürlichen Systems der Elemente auf 60 vielfarbigen Karten mit Beschriftung in deutscher, englischer, französischer, italienischer, spanischer Sprache nebst ausführlichem, erläuterndem Texte. xi, 137 p. Braunschweig: Westermann, 1931.
Reviewed in *Nature*, 1932, 129: 851-2.

PANETH, F.A. Trend of inorganic and physical chemistry since 1850. *Nature*, 1951, 168: 371.

PARTINGTON, J.R. A text-book of inorganic chemistry. 6th ed. x, 996 p., 394 fig. New York: Macmillan, 1950. [CB 77/371]
First published 1921. Includes many historical references.

PHILBRICK, F.A.; HOLMYARD, E.J. A text book of theoretical and inorganic chemistry. viii, 803 p. London: Dent, 1932. [CB 37/592]
Contains a historical introduction (56 p.).

WERNER, A. Neuere Anschauungen auf dem Gebiete der anorganischen Chemie. 3rd ed. xx, 419 p. (Die Wissenschaft, 8) Braunschweig: Vieweg, 1913.

DRdaj

GOLDBLATT, Leo Arthur, ed. Collateral readings in inorganic chemistry. 2 vol. [1st series]. v, 225 p. Second series. viii, 198 p. New York: Appleton-Century, 1937, 1942.
2nd series reviewed by E.F. Armstrong, *Nature*, 1942, 150: 475.

DRo

SBORGI, Umberto. Quelques aspects de l'enseignement de la chimie inorganique basés sur le développement de la chimie depuis Mendeleïeff jusqu'à la découverte de la structure de l'atome. *Ann.Guébhard-Séverine*, 1953, 29: 93-7.

DRwb

SMITH, Edgar F. A half century of mineral chemistry in America 1876-1926. Reprinted from the Golden Jubilee Number "A half century of chemistry in America". *J.Amer. Chem.Soc.*, 1926, 48: 69-88.

DRws

MEHTA, S.M. India's contribution to inorganic chemistry. *Sci. Cult.*, 1957, 23: 5-11, 2 fig.

DRyDD PHYSICAL INORGANIC CHEMISTRY
see DSy and DTy

DS NON-METALS AND NON-METALLIC COMPOUNDS

ABBOT, C.G. The discovery of helium and what came of it. *Annu.Rep.Smithsonian Inst.for 1918*, p. 121-6. Washington, D.C.: 1920.
Popular account including the application to ballooning.

BEDEL, Charles. Histoire de la découverte des halogènes. 23 p. (Les Conférences du Palais de la Découverte, Sér. D, 18) Paris: Université de Paris, 1953.

CHERNICK, Cedric L. "Compounds" (?) of the noble gases prior to 1962. *J.Chem.Educ.*, 1964, 41: 185-6.

CHEVALLIER, Paul. La table d'émeraude, secret de la préparation de l'acide sulfurique. *Biol.Méd.*, 1948, 37: suppl., i-lix.

COOK, Gerhard A., ed. Argon, helium, and the rare gases. The elements of the helium group. 1. History, occurrence, and properties. xxii, 394, 33 p. New York: Interscience, 1961.
Reviewed by Aaron J. Ihde, *Science*, 1962, 135: 308.

GUARESCHI, Icilio. La vita dell' idrogeno nell' armonia della natura. *Ind.Chim.Mineraria Met.*, 1914, *new ser.*, 1: 33-44.

HYMAN, Herbert H. Noble-gas compounds. xiii, 404 p., charts, graphs. Chicago/London: University of Chicago Press, 1963.
This volume contains two articles of historical interest, E.N. Hiebert's Historical remarks on the discovery of argon: the first noble gas, and D.M. Yost's A new epoch in chemistry.

KEESOM, W.H. Helium. xx, 494 p. Amsterdam: Elsevier Publishing Co., 1942.
Reviewed by F.E. Simon, *Nature*, 1947, 160: 382-3.

LIPPMANN, Edmund O von. Zur Geschichte der angeblichen Entstehung von Wasser aus Luft. *Chem.Zeitung*, 1931, 55: 681.

PARTINGTON, J.R. The composition of water. viii, 106 p., 10 fig., 6 pl. (Classics of Scientific Method, 4) London: G. Bell, 1928. [CB 25/418]

RAMSAY, William. The gases of the atmosphere. The history of their discovery. 4th ed. xiii, 306 p., 9 portr. London: Macmillan, 1915.
First published 1896.

RUSKA, Julius. Der Salmiak in der Geschichte der Chemie. *Z.Angew.Chem.*, 1928, 41: 1321-4.

RUTHERFORD, Ernest, Lord Rutherford. The new hydrogen. *Nature*, 1934, 133: 481-4. [CB 41/578]

RUTHERFORD, Ernest, Lord Rutherford. The new hydrogen. *Science*, 1934, 80: 21-5.
Lecture before the Royal Institution of Great Britain, March 23, 1934.

SCHROETER, J. Discovery of chlorine and the beginnings of the chlorine industry. The story of chlorine down to the present. *Ciba Rev.*, 1960, 12: no. 139, 5-23.

TRAVERS, Morris W. The discovery of argon. *Nature*, 1925, 115: 121-2.

TRAVERS, Morris W. The discovery of the rare gases. vii, 128 p. London: Arnold, 1928.
Reviewed by Irvine Masson, *Nature*, 1929, 123: 195-7.

TRAVERS, Morris W. Ramsay and helium. *Nature*, 1935, 135: 619.

WERTIME, Theodore A. The discovery of the element carbon. *Osiris*, 1954, 11: 211-20.

DSnh

GIBBS, F.W. On "nitre" and "natron". *Ann.Sci.*, 1938, 3: 213-16.

RUSKA, Julius. Sal ammoniacus, Nushâdir und Salmiak. 23 p. (*Sitzungsber.Heidelb.Akad.Wiss.Phil.Hist.Kl.*, 1923, vol. 5) Heidelberg: 1923. [CB 15/216]

DSyDF

HABER, Fritz. Fünf Vorträge aus den Jahren 1920-1923. 92 p. Berlin: Springer, 1924. [CB 16/248]
The first of these is the author's Nobel prize lecture on the synthetic manufacture of ammonia.

MITTASCH, Alwin. Geschichte der Ammoniaksynthese. 196 p., 4 ill., 12 pl. Weinheim (Bergstrasse): Verlag Chemie, 1951.
Reviewed by E. Farber, *Isis*, 1952, 43: 79-80; by Eric K. Rideal, *Nature*, 1952, 169: 385.

DSyDJzb

GORMAN, Mel. The evidence from infrared spectroscopy for hydrogen bonding. A case history of the correlation and interpretation of data. *J.Chem.Educ.*, 1957, 34: 304-6.

GORMAN, Mel. Some aspects of hydrogen bonding in inorganic chemistry. *J.Chem.Educ.*, 1956, 33: 468-72, bibliogr.
A portion of the article is devoted to the history of this concept.

DSyDK

DARMOIS, Eugène. L'hydrogène est un mélange: ortho et parahydrogène. 24 p. Paris: Hermann, 1931.
Lecture given at the Conservatoire des Arts et Métiers, May, 1931.

WECKERING, R. Histoire des recherches sur la stéréoélectronic des composés du bore. *Act.IIIe Congr.Bénélux Hist.Sci.*, (Luxembourg, 1960), p. 203-13. Leiden: E.J. Brill, 1960; also *Janus*, 1960, 49: 203-14.

DT METALS AND METALLIC COMPOUNDS

see also DY ALCHEMY
VC METALLURGY

DUBRISAY, René. Le développement historique de la chimie des métaux et de ses applications. *Rev.Sci.*, 1933, 71: 1-3.

DUFRENOY, Marie Louise; DUFRENOY, Jean. The significance of antimony in the history of chemistry. *J.Chem.Educ.*, 1950, 27: 595-7.

FARBER, Eduard. The development of metal hydride chemistry. *Chymia*, 1962, 8: 165-80. [CB 90/599]

HILLER, Joh. E. Die Kalisalze in Geschichte und Wissenschaft. *Mitt.Gesch.Med.*, 1940, 39: 356-7.

HOMMEL, W. Zur Geschichte des Zinks. Ursprung des Namens Zink. Erkennung des Zinks als Metall. *Chem.Zeitung*, 1912, 36: 905-6, 918-20.

HOWARD-WHITE, F.B. Nickel. An historical review. xiv, 350 p., ill. New York: Van Nostrand, 1963.
Reviewed by Earl R. Parker, *Science*, 1963, 142: 218; by H.J.S., *Ambix*, 1963, 11: 99-100.

IRVING, H. An historical account of Pharaoh's serpents. *Sci. Progr.*, 1935, 30: 62-6.
History of mercury thiocyanate.

KENNA, B.T. The search for technetium in nature. *J.Chem. Educ.*, 1962, 39: 436-42.

KENT, Andrew. On the early chemistry of gold. *Proc.Roy.Phil. Soc.Glasgow*, 1931-32, 101-12. [CB 48/571]

KIRCHHEIMER, Franz. Das Uran und seine Geschichte. 372 p., ill., pl. Stuttgart: E. Schweizerbart'sche, 1963.
The early history of uranium up to the discovery of radium in 1898.
Reviewed by H. Seper, *Bl.Technikgesch.*, 1964, 26: 147.

KRONMAN, E.S. Reniĭ. (Opyt monografii elementa no. 75) [Rhenium. (An attempt at a monograph on element no. 75) (In Russian)] 86 p. Moskva/Leningrad: Tsvetmetizdat, 1932.
History of element no. 75, discovered in 1925 by Walter Noddack and his wife, Ida Tacke.
Reviewed by J.G.F. Druce, *Nature*, 1933, 131: 224.

LIBMAN, Ed. P.; PLOTKIN, S. Ya. U istokov nauchnykh rabot po redkim metallam. [The origin of scientific work on rare metals. (In Russian)] *Priroda*, 1964, no. 12, 81-3.
Mostly *circa* 1918-1920.

LIPPMANN, Edmund O. von. Die Geschichte des Wismuts zwischen 1400 und 1800. Ein Beitrag zur Geschichte der Technologie und der Kultur. 42 p. Berlin: Springer, 1930. [CB 29/299]

LIPPMANN, Edmund O. von. Nachträge zur Geschichte des Wismuts. *Chem.Zeitung*, 1933, 57: 4.

MARCHAL, Germaine. Le glucinium. L'historique de sa découverte, sa préparation et ses propriétés. *Rev.Gén.Sci.*, 1928, 39: 271-6.

QUILL, Lawrence L. Illinium - element number 61. *J.Chem. Educ.*, 1928, 5: 561-8.

RHOUSOPOULOS, O.A. Zur Geschichte der Quecksilberverbindungen. *Mitt.Gesch.Med.*, 1915, 14: 406.

SCHROETER, J. Quecksilber und Quecksilberverbindungen im Wandel der Zeit. *Ciba-Z.*, 1959, 8: 3202-6.

TRIFONOV, D.N. K istorii shest'desiat pervogo elements. [On the history of the sixty-first element. (In Russian)] *Tr. Inst.Ist.Est.Tekh.*, 1961, 35: 126-42.

DTce-bv

POTRATZ, Herbert A.; EKELEY, John B. A bibliography of indium, 1863-1933. *Univ.Colo.Stud.Ser.A*, 1934, 21: 151-87.

DTnh

LIPPMAN, Edmund O von. Noch einmal "Caput mortuum". *Chem. Zeitung*, 1921, 45: 801.
The red iron oxide was often called "Caput mortuum" and "colcothar". The origin of the first phrase is Egyptian-Greek; of the second, Greek-Syriac.

LIPPMANN, Edmund O. von. Wie ist der Ausdruck "Caput mortuum" für Eisenoxyd zu erklären. (Nachtrag). *Chem.Zeitung*, 1906, 30: 323-4, 925.

DTwn-nh

FIGUROVSKII, N.A. O proiskhozhdenii drevnerusskikh nazvanii metallov. [On the development of Old Russian metals terminology.] Materialy po istorii otechestvennoi khimii. Ottisk doklada na pervom vsesoyuznom soveshchanii po istorii otechestvennoi khimii, 12-14 maya 1948. [Materials on the history of national chemistry. Excerpt from the report of the First All-Union Assembly on the history of national chemistry, 12-14 May, 1948. (In Russian)] Academy of Sciences of the U.S.S.R., Section of Chemical Sciences, Commission on the History of Chemistry, p. 251-67. Moscow: Izd. Akad. Nauk SSSR, 1950.

DTyCU

MATIGNON, Camille. L'industrie du radium. *Rev.Sci.*, 1925, 63: 524-32. English transl.: The manufacture of radium. *Annu. Rep.Smithsonian Inst.for 1925*, p. 221-34, 4 pl. Washington, D.C.: 1926.

SILVERMAN, Alexander. Pittsburgh's contribution to radium recovery. *J.Chem.Educ.*, 1950, 27: 303-8, 5 ill. [CB 77/341]
At Pittsburgh was located the laboratory of the Standard Chemical Company which produced the first commercial radium in the world.

WALLMANN, J.C. The first isolations of the transuranium elements. A historical survey. *J.Chem.Educ.*, 1959, 36: 340-3.

DTyDD

VAN KLOOSTER, H.S. Three centuries of Rochelle Salt. *J.Chem. Educ.*, 1959, 36: 314-18.

DTyDL

WINDERLICH, R. Les avatars d'une expérience de chimie. *Ann. Guébhard-Séverine*, 1930, 6: 111-18. [CB 39/455]
Apropos of the preparation of iron sulphide used to illustrate the difference between a physical mixture and a chemical combination of iron and sulphur.

DU ORGANIC CHEMISTRY

GRAEBE, Carl. Geschichte der Organischen Chemie. Vol. 1. x, 416 p. Berlin: Springer, 1920.
Continued by Paul Walden, *see* below.
Reviewed by Arthur John Hopkins, *Isis*, 1922, 4: 361-5.

HJELT, Edv. Geschichte der organischen Chemie von ältester Zeit bis zur Gegenwart. xii, 556 p. Braunschweig: Vieweg, 1916.
Reviewed by G. Sarton, *Isis*, 1920, 3: 440-3.

KEKULÉ-Couper Centennial Symposium on the development of theoretical organic chemistry. (American Chemical Society, Division of the History of Chemistry, Chicago, September, 1958.) *J.Chem.Educ.*, 1959, 36: 319-39.
Introduction by O.T. Benfey (p. 319-20).

LIPPMANN, Edmund O. von. Zeittafeln zur Geschichte der organischen Chemie. Ein Versuch. ix, 67 p. Berlin: Julius Springer, 1921.
Reviewed by G. Sarton, *Isis*, 1922, 4: 458.

THORPE, Jocelyn Field. The scope of organic chemistry. Address of the president of Section B - Chemistry - British Association for the Advancement of Science. Oxford, August 1926. *Science*, 1926, 64: 211-16, 236-40.

TODD, A.R. A hundred years of organic chemistry. *Nature*, 1951, 168: 326.

TODD, A.R. Organic chemistry: a view and a prospect. *Annu. Rep.Smithsonian Inst. for 1961*, p. 373-80. Washington, D.C.: 1962.

WALDEN, Paul. Geschichte der organischen Chemie seit 1880. xiii, 946 p. Berlin: Springer, 1941.
Continuation of Carl Graebe's work, *see* above.
Reviewed by Arne Fredga, *Lychnos*, 1942, 401-2.

WUYTS, Henri. Aspects imprévus de l'évolution de la chimie organique. *Bull.Acad.Roy.Belg.Cl.Sci.*, 1941, 27: 379-93.

DUcj

BOIG, Fletcher S.; HOWERTON, Paul W. History and development of chemical periodicals in the field of organic chemistry: 1877-1949. *Science*, 1952, 115: 25-31, 5 fig.

DUnb

MASON, Howard S. History of the use of graphic formulas in organic chemistry. *Isis*, 1943, 34: 346-54, 23 fig.

DUnh

LIPPMANN, Edmund O. von. Zur Frage nach dem Alter des Ausdrucks "Organische Chemie". *Chem.Zeitung*, 1932, 56: 501.

WALDEN, Paul. Von der Iatrochemie zur "organischen Chemie". Historisches über Entstehung und Namenbildung der "organischen Chemie". *Z.Angew.Chem.*, 1927, 40: 1-16.
Reviewed by Paul Diergart, *Mitt.Gesch.Med.*, 1927, 26: 182.

DUwn-sg

SERGIENKO, S.R. [The role of the Russian school of organic chemistry in the development of industry. (In Russian)] *Tr.Inst.Ist.Est.*, 1949, 3: 209-35.

DUyDD PHYSICAL ORGANIC CHEMISTRY

see also DVyDF

DUyDEzc

ESAFOV, V.I. K istorii otkrytiia organicheskikh reaktsii v prisutstvii bezvodnykh galogenidov aliuminiia. [On the history of the detection of organic reactions in the presence of anhydrous halides of aluminum. (In Russian)] *Tr.Inst.Ist.Est.Tekh.*, 1962, 39: 104-40.

PUZITSKII, K.V.; EIDUS, Ia.T. Raboty E.I. Orlova v oblasti organicheskogo sinteza i kataliza. [Works of E.I. Orlov in the field of organic synthesis and catalysis. (In Russian)] *Tr.Inst.Ist.Est.Tekh.*, 1961, 35: 185-96.

SABATIER, Paul. La catalyse en chimie organique. 255 p. Paris: C. Béranger, 1913.

DUyDEzc-wn

KUZNETSOV, V.I. [Major steps in the development of organic catalysis in the USSR. (In Russian)] *Vop.Ist.Est.Tekh.*, 1960, 9: 51-61.

DUyDFnj

RHEINBOLDT, Heinrich. Fifty years of the Grignard reaction. *J.Chem.Educ.*, 1950, 27: 476-88, 17 ill. [CB 77/337]

SEMENTSOV, A. S.N. Reformatskii and his reaction. *J.Chem. Educ.*, 1957, 34: 530-2.

SURREY, Alexander R. Name reactions in organic chemistry. 192 p. New York: Academic Press, 1954.
Reviewed in *Pharm.Hist.*, 1962, 7: 11-12.

DUyDJ

BYKOV, G.V. [On the evolution of quantitative theories of electronic construction of organic molecules. (In Russian)] *Tr.Inst.Ist.Est.Tekh.*, 1959, 28: 477-521.

BYKOV, G.V. [The primary stages in the development of the electronic theory of organic chemistry. (In Russian)] *Vop. Ist.Est.Tekh.*, 1959, 7: 43-57.

KOSHKIN, L.V.; MUSABEKOV, IU. S. Evoliutsiia metodov issledovaniia svobodnykh organicheskikh radikalov. [The evolution of methods of investigating free organic radicals. (In Russian)] *Tr.Inst.Ist.Est.Tekh.*, 1962, 39: 141-75.

DUyDJwn

BYKOV, G.V. Elektronnye teorii organicheskoi khimii v SSSR. [Electron theories of organic chemistry in the U.S.S.R. (In Russian)] *Tr.Inst.Ist.Est.Tekh.*, 1961, 35: 293-329. [CB 87/632]

DV ORGANIC COMPOUNDS

for organic chemicals *see also* VR

BEDEL, Charles. Quelques étapes dans la connaissance des substances organiques. *Proc.10th Int.Congr.Hist.Sci.* (Ithaca, 1962), (2), p. 867-9. Paris: Hermann, 1964.

DARMSTAEDTER, Ernst. Zur Geschichte des Äthers (Diäthyläthers). *J.Prakt.Chem.*, 1928, 120: 74-88. [CB 26/168]

DOBBIN, Leonard. The history of the discovery of phosgene. *Ann.Sci.*, 1945, 5: 270-87.

FARBER, Eduard. The glycol centenary. *J.Chem.Educ.*, 1956, 33: 117.

GORMAN, Mel. The history of acetone, 1600-1850. *Chymia*, 1962, 8: 97-104.

GORMAN, Mel; DOERING, Charles. History of the structure of acetone. *Chymia*, 1959, 5: 202-8.

HEUSER, Emil. The high points in the development of cellulose chemistry since 1876. *J.Chem.Educ.*, 1952, 29: 449-53.

KAUFFMAN, George B. Frédéric Swarts: pioneer in organic fluorine chemistry. *J.Chem.Educ.*, 1955, 32: 301-3.

KURZER, Frederick; SANDERSON, Phyllis M. Urea in the history of organic chemistry. Isolation from natural sources. *J. Chem.Educ.*, 1956, 33: 452-9, 4 fig.

MARSHALL, A. Histoire de l'acide picrique. *Monit.Sci.*, 1926, 15: 114-15. [CB 22/268]

PATTERSON, T.S. Note on Blaise de Vigenère, John Ferguson, and benzoic acid. *Ann.Sci.*, 1939, 4: 61-4, 1 pl.

DVwn

VORONENKOV, V.V.; MUSABEKOV, Iu.S. Osnovnye etapy i napravleniia razvitiia khimii terpenov v Rossii. [The principal stages and directions of the development of terpene chemistry in Russia. (In Russian)] *Tr.Inst.Ist.Est.Tekh.*, 1962, 39: 195-211.

DVyCW

PHILIPSBORN, Hellmut von. Calciumoxalat. 275 Jahre mikroskopischer Forschung. *Sudhoffs Arch.*, 1954, 38: 336-66, 41 ill.

DVyCX

TRILLAT, J.J. Les applications des rayons X à l'étude des composés organiques. 22 p., ill. (Conférences d'Actualités Scientifiques et Industrielles, 25) Paris: Hermann, 1931.
Conférence faite au Conservatoire des arts et métiers le 4 mai 1931.

DVyDF

STRADIN', Ia. P. [On the history of the discovery of analytical reactions of rhodanids with salts of duovalentic cobalt and trivalentic iron. (In Russian)] *Vop.Ist.Est.Tekh.*, 1959, 7: 146-8.

TEIKH, M. K istorii sinteza mocnevoi kisloty. [On the history of the synthesis of uric acid. (In Russian)] *Tr.Inst. Ist.Est.Tekh.*, 1961, 35: 212-44.
From Scheele through Gorbachevskii.

DW NATURAL PRODUCTS AND BIOCHEMICAL SUBSTANCES

ANDRÉ, Emile. Histoire du développement de la chimie des corps gras. *Bull.Soc.Chim.France*, 1932, 1-29, 145-70.

BEYLER, Roger E. Some recent advances in the field of steroids. *J.Chem.Educ.*, 1960, 37: 491-4.
1930-1960.

DUFRENOY, Jean; DUFRENOY, Marie Louise. De la genèse à la bombe atomique. *Rev.Pathol.Comp.*, 1949, 49: 22-38, bibliogr. [CB 75/92]
Mainly a history of melanin.

DUFRENOY, Marie Louise; DUFRENOY, Jean. Four centuries of the history of melanin. *Scientia*, 1950, 88: 272-7; French transl., suppl., 119-23.

FARBER, Eduard. The development of protein chemistry. *J. Chem.Educ.*, 1938, 15: 434-44, 2 fig.

GILDEMEISTER, Eduard; HOFFMANN, Friedrich. Die aetherischen Oele. 3rd ed. Vol. 1. xvi, 864 p., 2 maps, ill. Leipzig: L. Staackmann, 1928. [CB 25/438]
Contains historical introduction (p. 1-262).
English translation of 2nd edition: The volatile oils. 3 vol. London: Longmans, 1913-22.

GINZBURG, O.F. Razvitie predstavlenii o stroenii trifenilmetanovykh krasitelei. [The development of conceptions about the structure of triphenylmethyl pigments. (In Russian)] *Tr.Inst.Ist.Est.Tekh.*, 1962, 39: 176-94.

MÖLLER, Hans Jacob. *Lignum nephreticum.* 62 p., 2 pl. Copenhagen: 1912.

NIERENSTEIN, M. The natural organic tannins. History: chemistry: distribution. viii,319 p. London: Churchill, 1934. [CB 42/587]

PARTINGTON, J.R. Lignum nephriticum. *Ann.Sci.*, 1955, 11: 1-26.

RETI, L. Cactus alkaloids and some related compounds. *Fortschr.Chem.Organischer Naturst.*, 1950, 6: 242-89.
Includes historical summary, p. 243-6.

SAFFORD, William E. *Lignum nephreticum.* Its history and an account of the remarkable fluorescence of its infusion. *Annu.Rep.Smithsonian Inst.for 1915*, p. 271-98, 7 pl. Washington, D.C.: 1916. [CB 7/106]

SAFFORD, William E. Nature's magic. Rediscovery of a remarkable wood, first known in the sixteenth century (as lignum nephriticum), which produces with water a beautiful opalescence not yet explained by science. *Amer.Mus.J.*, 1918, 18: 48-54, ill.
Eysenhardtia polystachya of Mexico and *Pterocarpus indicus* of the Philippines.

SAHYUN, Melville, ed. Outline of the amino acids and proteins. 251 p., ill. New York: Reinhold, 1944. [CB 68/53]
Contains much historical material.

STREET, H.E.; TREASE, G.E. The discovery of asparagine. *Ann. Sci.*, 1951, 7: 70-6, 2 pl.

VICKERY, Hubert Bradford; SCHMIDT, Carl L.A. The history of the discovery of the amino acids. *Chem.Rev.*, 1931, 9: 169-318. [CB 37/593]

WILLSTÄTTER, R.; STOLL, A. Untersuchungen über Chlorophyll. 424 p. Berlin: J. Springer, 1913.

DY ALCHEMY

DYc general history

ATWOOD, Mary Anne. A suggestive inquiry into the hermetic mystery, with a dissertation on the more celebrated of the alchemical philosophers, being an attempt towards the recovery of the ancient experiment of nature. New ed., with an introd. by W.L. Wilmshurst. Also an appendix containing the memorabilia of M.A. Atwood ... 597 p. Belfast: William Tait, 1918; reprinted New York: Julian Press, 1960.
First published 1850.

BERNUS, Alexander von. Das Geheimnis der Adepten. [With an appendix including articles by Gambriel, Erich Sopp and others.] 67 p. Württemberg: Osiris Verlag, 1956.
Reviewed by G. Heym, *Ambix*, 1958, 6: 161-2.

BOCKSTAELE, Paul. De oorsprong van de alchemie. [The origin of alchemy. (In Dutch)] *Sci.Hist.*, 1962, 4: 39-40.

BURCKHARDT, Titus. Alchemie: Sinn und Weltbild. 230 p., ill. Olten/Freiburg i. Br.: Walter Verlag, 1960.
Reviewed by G. Heym, *Ambix*, 1960, 8: 177-80.

CARON, M.; HUTIN, S. Les alchimistes. 187 p., ill., bibliogr. ("Le Temps Qui Court", 16) Paris: Editions du Seuil, 1959.
Reviewed by H.J. Sheppard, *Ambix*, 1960, 8: 50; by J. Payen, *Rev.Hist.Sci.*, 1960, 13: 159; by Suzanne Colnort-Bodet, *Arch.Int.Hist.Sci.*, 1962, 15: 202.

CEZARD, Pierre. L'alchimie et les recettes techniques. *Métaux Civilisations*, 1945, 1: 5-10, 41-5, fig.

COCHREN, A. Alchemy rediscovered and restored. 158 p. Philadelphia: McKay, [1941]. [CB 62/76]

DARMSTAEDTER, Ernst. Die Alchemie. *Z.Krit.Okkultismus.*, 1925, 1: 13-21.

DAVIS, Tenney L. Primitive science, the background of early chemistry and alchemy. *J.Chem.Educ.*, 1935, 12: 3-10, 12 fig. [CB 44/518]

DAVIS, Tenney L. The problem of the origins of alchemy. *Sci. Mon.*, 1936, 43: 551-8.

DUBS, Homer H. The origin of alchemy. *Ambix*, 1961, 9: 23-36.

ELIADE, Mircea. Forgerons et alchimistes. 209 p., 8 pl. ("Homo Sapiens") Paris: Flammarion, 1956.
Reviewed by Seyyed Hossein Nasr, *Isis*, 1958, 49: 451-3; by G. Heym, *Ambix*, 1957, 6: 109-11.

FOOTE, Paul Darwin. The alchemist. *Sci.Mon.*, 1924, 19: 239-62.

FRIESER, Rudolf. Alchemists - forefathers of modern chemists. *Interchem.Rev.*, 1957, 16: 17-28, 6 fig.

GANZENMÜLLER, Wilhelm. Beiträge zur Geschichte der Technologie und der Alchimie. 389 p., 26 ill. Weinheim/Bergstr.: Verlag Chemie, GMBH., 1956.
Reviewed by W. Pagel, *Isis*, 1958, 49: 84-6; for other reviews *see* CB 82/205, CB 83/185 and CB 84/295.

GOLLAN, Josué. La alquímia. 361 p., ill. Santa Fé, Argentina: Librería y Editorial Castellví S.A., 1956.
Reviewed by G.H., *Ambix*, 1957, 6: 54-5.

GRAUBARD, Mark. Astrology and alchemy: two fossil sciences. xi, 382 p. New York: Philosophical Library, 1953. [CB 81/285]
Reviewed by Rufus Suter, *Scr.Math.*, 1954, 20: 190-2; by Frank K. Edmondson, *Sci.Mon.*, 1954, 78: 396.

GRILLOT DE GIVRY, Émile Angelo. Witchcraft, magic and alchemy. Translated by J. Courtenay Locke. 395 p., 10 pl. London: Harrap, 1931.
Reviewed in *Nature*, 1932, 130: 792-4.

HAMMER-JENSEN, Ingeborg. Die älteste Alchemie. 159 p. (Danish Academy of Sciences) Copenhagen: 1921.
Reviewed by A.J. Hopkins, *Isis*, 1922, 4: 523-30.

HARTLAUB, G.F. Der Stein der Weisen. Wesen und Bildwelt der Alchemie. 52 p., ill. Munich: Prestel Verlag, 1959.
Reviewed by H.J. Sheppard, *Ambix*, 1960, 8: 49.

HOLMYARD, E.J. Alchemy. The story of the fascination of gold and the attempts of chemists, mystics, and charlatans to find the Philosophers' Stone. 281 p., ill. Harmondsworth, Middlesex: Penguin Books, 1957.
Reviewed by Seyyed Hossein Nasr, *Isis*, 1958, 49: 451-3; for other reviews *see* CB 83/213, CB 84/328 and CB 86/475.

HOPKINS, Arthur John. Alchemy, child of Greek philosophy. xi, 262 p. New York: Columbia University Press, 1934.
Reviewed by W.J. Wilson, *Isis*, 1935, 24: 174-7. [CB 43/274]

HOPKINS, Arthur John. Earliest alchemy. *Sci.Mon.*, 1918, 6: 530-7. [CB 7/129]

HOPKINS, Arthur John. A modern theory of alchemy. *Isis*, 1925, 7: 58-76. [CB 19/802]

HUNNIUS, Curt. Dämonen, Ärzte, Alchemisten. 347 p., ill. Stuttgart: Wissenschaftliche Verlagsgesellschaft, 1962.
Reviewed by H. Schadewaldt, *Naturwiss.Rundsch.*, 1962, 15: 487; by R. Niederhuemer, *Bl.Technikgesch.*, 1964, 26: 150.

HUTIN, Serge. A history of alchemy. Transl. by Tamara Alferoff. 143 p., ill. (A Sun Books History, SB-7) New York: Walker, 1963.
Translation of "L'alchimie" (Paris: Presses Universitaires de France, 1952).

JOLLIVET-CASTELOT, François. La fabrication chimique de l'or. [With English, German and Spanish translations.] 126 p. Douai: The Author, 1928.
French text, p. 1-30.
Reviewed by A.A.E., *Nature*, 1928, 121: 981.

JOLLIVET-CASTELOT, François. La révolution chimique et la transmutation des métaux. 370 p. Paris: Chacornac, 1925.

KOPP, Hermann. Die Alchemie in älterer und neuerer Zeit. 2 vol. xvii, 260 p.; vi, 425 p. Hildesheim: Georg Olms, 1962.
A reprint of the 1886 edition published in Heidelberg.
Reviewed by W.P., *Ambix*, 1963, 11: 97-8.

LIPPMANN, Edmund O. von. Der böse Geist Barrabas, ein Feind der Alchemisten. *Naturwissenschaften*, 1936, 24: 416.

LIPPMANN, Edmund O. von. Entstehung und Ausbreitung der Alchemie. 3 vol. xvi, 742 p.; vi, 257 p.; 166 p. Berlin: Springer, 1919, 1931 (vol. 1 and 2); Weinheim: Verlag Chemie, 1954 (vol. 3).
Vol. 1 and 2 reviewed by George Sarton, *Isis*, 1919, 3: 302-5; 1931, 16: 462-3; vol. 3 by J.R. Partington, *Arch. Int.Hist.Sci.*, 1954, 7: 366-7.

LIPPMANN, Edmund O. von. Über einige neuere Beiträge zur Geschichte der Alchemie. *Essays on the history of medicine presented to Karl Sudhoff*, p. 89-98. Zürich: 1924. [CB 16/294]

LIPPMANN, Edmund O. von. Zur Geschichte der Alchemie. *Z. Angew.Chem.*, 1922, 35: 529-31. Also in: Lippmann, Edmund O. von. Beiträge zur Geschichte ... (1), p. 33-43. Berlin: J. Springer, 1923.
A study of "Die älteste Alchemie" by Ingeborg Hammer-Jensen, *see* above.

MAHDIHASSAN, S. Alchemy as descending from herbalism or kimiya versus soma. *Scientia*, 1964, 99: 132-6; French transl. suppl. 77-81.

MAHDIHASSAN, S. Significance of the four elements in alchemy. *Janus*, 1964, 51: 303-13.

MERCER, J.E. Alchemy. Its science and romance. x, 245 p., 4 ill. London: Society for Promoting Christian Knowledge, 1921. [CB 12/628]

MILES, Wyndham. The gold seekers: an outline of the ancient art of alchemy. *Armed Forces Chem.J.*, 1956, 10: 24-44, portr., 5 fig.

PANETH, Fritz. Ancient and modern alchemy. *Science*, 1926, 64: 409-17.

PARTINGTON, J.R. History of alchemy and early chemistry. *Nature*, 1947, 159: 81-5.

POCE, Mario. Alchimia e alchimisti. Tredici secoli di follie scientifiche e filosofiche. 266 p., ill. Rome: 1930.
Reviewed by Gino Testi, *Archeion*, 1933, 15: 278.

READ, John. Alchemy and alchemists. *Nature*, 1951, 168: 759-62.

READ, John. Prelude to chemistry. An outline of alchemy, its literature and relationship. xxvi, 328 p. New York: Macmillan, 1937.
Reviewed by Tenney L. Davis, *Isis*, 1937, 27: 528-31.

REBOUL, G. La pierre philosophale et la constitution de la matière. *Rev.Sci.*, 1923, 61: 659-75.
Comparison of current theories concerning the structure of matter and those of the alchemists.

RUSKA, Julius. Turba philosophorum. Ein Beitrag zur Geschichte der Alchemie. x, 368 p., 1 pl. (*Quellen Stud. Gesch.Naturwiss.Med.*, 1) Berlin: Springer, 1931.
Reviewed by Max Meyerhof, *Orient.Lit.Zeitung*, 1933, 36: 12-15.

SCHMIEDER, Karl Christoph. Geschichte der Alchemie. (1832) Herausgegeben und mit einer Einleitung versehen von Franz Strunz. 28, x, 613 p. München-Planegg: Barth, 1927.

SINGER, Dorothea Waley. L'alchimie. *Compt.Rend.IVe Congr. Int.Hist.Méd.* (Brussels, 1923), p. 28-36. Anvers: 1927.

STAPLETON, H.E. The antiquity of alchemy. *Ambix*, 1953, 5: 1-43, ill.

STAPLETON, H.E. The antiquity of alchemy. *Act.VIe Congr.Int. Hist.Sci.* (Amsterdam, 1950), p. 56-60. Paris: Hermann, 1951. Also in *Arch.Int.Hist.Sci.*, 1951, 4: 35-8.

STILLMAN, John Maxson. The story of alchemy and early chemistry. xiii, 566 p. New York: Dover Publications, 1960.
Reviewed by D. Geoghegan, *Ambix*, 1961, 9: 50; by A. Bruylants, *Rev.Quest.Sci.*, 1961, 22: 559-60; by Suzanne Colnort-Bodet, *Arch.Int.Hist.Sci.*, 1962, 15: 202.

STRUNZ, Franz. Astrologie, Alchemie, Mystik: ein Beitrag zur Geschichte der Naturwissenschaften. 351 p. München-Planegg: Otto Wilhelm Barth, 1928.

TAYLOR, F. Sherwood. The alchemists: founders of modern chemistry. x, 246 p., 15 pl., 27 fig. (Life of Science Library) New York: Schuman, 1949; London: Heinemann, 1951.
Also published New York: Collier Books, 1962.
Reviewed by Wyndham Miles, *Isis*, 1950, 41: 237; by E.J. Holmyard, *Nature*, 1952, 170: 725-6.

THOMPSON, C.J.S. The lure and romance of alchemy. 249 p. (Simple Guide Series) London: Harrap, 1932. [CB 39/455]
Reviewed by E.J. Holmyard, *Nature*, 1933, 132: 152-3.

VELDE, A.J.J. van de. Uit de geschiedenis der alchemie. [From the history of alchemy. (In Dutch)]. *Verslagen Mededeel.Vlaam.Acad.Taal.Letterk.*, March 1942, 165-216, bibliogr.

WAITE, Arthur Edward. The secret tradition in alchemy: its development and records. xxii, 415 p. London: Kegan Paul; New York: Alfred A. Knopf, 1926.
Reviewed by E.J. Holmyard, *Nature*, 1926, 118: 869-70.

WIEDEMANN, Eilhard. Zur Geschichte der Alchemie. *J.Prakt. Chem.*, 1912, 85: 391-2.

DYc-br *periodicals*

Ambix. The Journal of the Society for the Study of Alchemy and Early Chemistry. Vol. 1, no. 1, May 1937- London: The Society, 1937-
For May 1937, no. 1 *see* CB 51/262 and CB 71/119.

DYc-bu/cv bibliography; literature; sources

DYc-bv

FRICK, K. Einführung in die alchemiegeschichtliche Literatur. *Sudhoffs Arch.*, 1961, 45: 147-63.

HEYM, Gerard. An introduction to the bibliography of alchemy. *Ambix*, 1937, 1: 48-60.

SHEPPARD, H.J. Alchemy: its part in the cultural heritage of chemistry. *Sch.Sci.Rev.*, 1957, 38: 204-11.
A brief over-view of the subject with a reading list of 39 books appended.

DYcd-bv

WILSON, William Jerome. Catalogue of Latin and vernacular alchemical manuscripts in the United States and Canada. *Osiris*, 1939, 6: 1-836. [CB 76/397 and CB 59/471]
Reviewed by Tenney L. Davis, *Isis*, 1949, 32: 385-6; by A. Delatte, *Bull.Acad.Roy.Belg.Cl.Lett.*, 1939, 326-7.

DYce

BEIN, Willy. Das Stein der Weisen und die Kunst Gold zu machen. Irrtum und Erkenntnis in der Wandlung der Elemente, mitgeteilt nach den Quellen der Vergangenheit und Gegenwart. 174 p., ill. (Voigtländers Quellenbücher, 88) Leipzig: Voigtländer, 1915.
An anthology of alchemy from the earliest times to our days.

RUSKA, Julius. Quelques problèmes de littérature alchimiste. Traduit par Ad. Kuenzi. *Ann.Guébhard-Séverine*, 1931, 7: 156-73. [CB 37/439 and CB 37/592]

DYce-bv

DUVEEN, Denis Ian. Bibliotheca alchemica et chemica. An annotated catalogue of printed books on alchemy, chemistry and cognate subjects in the library of Denis I. Duveen. vii, 669 p., 16 pl. London: Weil, 1949. [CB 74/387]
The Duveen Collection is now at the University of Wisconsin.

FERGUSON, John. Bibliotheca chemica. A catalogue of the alchemical, chemical and pharmaceutical books in the collection of the late James Young of Kelly and Durris. 2 vol. London: Holland Press, 1957.
Reviewed in the *Times Lit.Suppl.*, 7 June, 1957, 356.

GLASGOW. UNIVERSITY. Library. Catalogue of the Ferguson Collection of books, mainly relating to alchemy, chemistry, witchcraft and gipsies, in the Library of the University. 2 vol. xv, 820 p. (Publications) Glasgow: Robert Maclehose, 1943. [CB 66/263]

DYce-by

DUVEEN, Denis Ian. The Duveen Alchemical and Chemical Collection. [Wisconsin University] *Book Collect.*, 1956, 5: 331-42. [CB 85/391]

IVES, Samuel A.; IHDE, Aaron J. The Duveen library. *J.Chem. Educ.*, 1952, 29: 244-7.
Description of the Duveen Collection now at the University of Wisconsin.

DYcm

DAVIS, Tenney L. Pictorial representations of alchemical theory. *Isis*, 1938, 28: 73-86, 8 fig.

HEYM, Gerard. Some alchemical picture books. *Ambix*, 1937, 1: 69-75, 5 fig.

TAYLOR, F. Sherwood. Alchemical illustrations. *Nature*, 1952, 170: 12-13.
Substance of an address given at the opening of an Exhibition of alchemical books at the Science Museum, London(*see Nature*, 21 June 1952, 169: 1041).

DYcm-by

READ, John. The [Sir William Jackson] Pope collection of alchemical paintings and engravings. *Nature*, 1941, 147: 243.

DYdaj

BARRETT, Francis. The lives of alchemystical philosophers. With a critical catalogue of books in occult chemistry, and a selection of the most celebrated treatises on the theory and practice of the hermetic art. 382 p. London: Watkins. 1955.
Facsimile reprint of first edition, 1815.
Reviewed by D.G., *Ambix*, 1957, 6: 53-4.

DYf history of alchemy as a study

GANZENMÜLLER, W. Zukunftsaufgaben der Geschichte der Alchemie. *Chymia*, 1953, 4: 31-6.

GANZENMÜLLER, W. Wandlungen in der geschichtlichen Betrachtung der Alchemie. *Chymia*, 1950, 3: 143-54.

MOND, Robert. The study of alchemy. *Ambix*, 1937, 1: 1-2.

RUSKA, Julius. Über den gegenwärtigen Stand der Alchemiegeschichte. *Chem.Zeitung*, 1936, 60: 735-6.

DYj psychological aspects

JUNG, Carl Gustav. Mysterium coniunctionis. An inquiry into the separation and synthesis of psychic opposites in alchemy. Ed. by Herbert Read, Michael Fordham and Gerhard Adler. Transl. by R.F.C.Hull. xix, 704 p. (Bollingen Series 20. Collected Works of C.G. Jung, 14) New York: Pantheon Books, 1963. [CB 89/519]
German original: Mysterium coniunctionis. Unter Mitarbeit von M.-L. v. Franz. 3 vol. (Vol. 3. Aurora consurgens. By M.-L. v. Franz.) Zürich: Rascher Verlag, 1955-57. Reviewed by G. Heym, *Ambix*, 1957-58, 6: 47-51.

JUNG, Carl Gustav. Psychology and alchemy. xxiv, 563 p. (Bollingen Series, 20. Collected works of C.G. Jung, 12) New York: Pantheon Books, 1953. [CB 82/218]
German original: Psychologie und Alchemie. 696 p., 270 ill. Zürich: Rascher, 1944. [CB 70/257]
Essay review by Walter Pagel, *Isis*, 1948, 39: 44-8.

SECRÉTAN, Claude. Alchimie, psychologie et pensée scientifique. *Ann.Guébhard-Séverine*, 1951-52, 27-8: 97-111.

DYmz relation with scientific subject fields

MAHDIHASSAN, S. Alchemy and its connection with astrology, pharmacy, magic and metallurgy. *Janus*, 1957, 46: 81-103.

DYmzC

HALLOPEAU, L.A. Les théories des alchimistes et leur influence sur les premières doctrines physiques. *Rev.Gén.Sci.*, 1918, 29: 246-50.

DYmzD

JOLLIVET-CASTELOT, François. Chimie et alchimie. 288 p. Paris: E. Nourry, 1928.

PARTINGTON, J.R. Chemistry as rationalised alchemy. Presidential address. *Bull.Brit.Soc.Hist.Sci.*, 1951, 1: 129-35.

DYmzDA

DAVIS, Tenney L. Neglected evidence in the history of phlogiston together with observations on the doctrine of forms and the history of alchemy. *Ann.Med.Hist.*, 1924, 6: 280-7.

DYmzN

ALLENDY, R. L'alchimie et la médecine. Etude sur les théories hermétiques dans l'histoire de la médecine. 157 p. (Thesis) Paris: Charcornac, 1912.

BERNUS, Alexander von. Alchimie et médecine. [Introduction and short bibliography by Prof. H. Hunwald and an appendix by Dr. R.A.B. Oosterhuis.] 191 p. Paris: Editions Dangles, 1960.
Reviewed by H.J.S., *Ambix*, 1960, 8: 118.

DYmzVC

ELIADE, Mircea. Metallurgy, magic and alchemy. *Zalmoxis*, 1938, 1: 85-129.

DYmzVY

FORBES, R.J. Alchemy and colour. (Modern chemistry and alchemy. Alchemy, dye and colour. The pots of Gerber's cooks.) *Ciba Rev.*, 1961, no. 5, 2-32.

DYn/t other special aspects

DYnb

DUVEEN, Denis I. Some symbols used by the alchemist. *Endeavour*, July 1948, 7: 116-21, ill.

LUEDY, F. Alchemistische und chemische Zeichen. 57 p., 127 pl. Berlin: Gesellschaft für Geschichte der Pharmazie, 1928. [CB 26/232]

PARTINGTON, J.R. The origins of the planetary symbols for the metals. *Ambix*, 1937, 1: 61-4.

SHEPPARD, H.J. Egg symbolism in alchemy. The origins of egg symbolism. *Ambix*, 1958, 6: 140-8, 2 fig.

SHEPPARD, H.J. The ouroboros and the unity of matter in alchemy. A study in origins. *Ambix*, 1962, 10: 83-96.

SHEPPARD, H.J. A survey of alchemical and hermetic symbolism. *Ambix*, 1960, 8: 35-41.

WIRTH, Oswald. Le symbolisme hermétique dans ses rapports avec l'alchimie et la franc-maçonnerie. 2nd ed. 229 p. Paris: Le Symbolisme, 1931.

DYnb-be

SCHNEIDER, Wolfgang. Lexikon alchemistisch-pharmazeutischer Symbole. 140 p., pl. Weinheim: Verlag Chemie, 1962.
For reviews *see* CB 88/564.

DYnh

MAHDIHASSAN, S. Alchemy in the light of its names in Arabic, Sanskrit and Greek. *Janus*, 1961, 49: 79-100.

RUSKA, Julius. Sal Alembroth. *Georg Jacob zum 70. Geburtstag*, p. 234-40. Leipzig: Harrassowitz, 1932.
Attempt to explain the origin of the old alchemical name of the double chloride of ammonium and mercury (al-ṭabarzad, al-barūd?).

DYnh-be

TESTI, Gino. Dizionario di alchimia e di chimica antiquaria. 201 p. ("Le Vie del Sapere", Biblioteca Economica di Cultura Varia, 4) Rome: Casa Editrice Mediterranea, 1950. [CB 78/184]

DYt

READ, John. The alchemist in life, literature and art. xii, 100 p., 30 pl. London: Nelson, 1947.
Reviewed by T.I.W., *Nature*, 1948, 161: 787.

READ, John. Alchemy: instrument of culture. *Mem.Manchester Lit.Phil.Soc.*, 1962, 104: 14-20.

DYtd

HARTLAUB, G.F. Alchemisten und Rosenkreuzer. Sittenbilder von Petrarca bis Balzac, von Breughel bis Kubin. 36 p., 30 pl. Heidelberg: Heidelberger Verlagsanstalt und Druckerei, 1947.

LANGEVELD, L.A. Alchemisten en Rozekruisers. [Alchemists and Rosicrucians. (In Dutch)]. 7, 228, 10 p. s'Gravenhage: Van Stockum, 1927.
Reviewed by F.M.G. de Feyfer, *Bijdr.Gesch.Geneesk.*, 1928, 8: 75.

DYtq

NICHOLSON, Douglas G. The alchemist in art - relation to current science. *J.Chem.Educ.*, 1950, 27: 117-20, 7 ill.
The article shows 7 illustrations from the Fisher collection of alchemical and historical pictures.

READ, John. Alchemy and art. *Nature*, 1952, 169: 479-81.

SARTON, George. Ancient alchemy and abstract art. *J.Hist.Med.*, 1954, 9: 157-73.

DYtt

PARTINGTON, J.R. Alchemy and music. *Nature*, 1935, 136: 107.

DYw in different countries

DYwb-da

WILKINSON, Ronald Sterne. New England's last alchemists. *Ambix*, 1962, 10: 128-38.

DYwe

READ, John. Alchemy in Scotland. *Chem.Drug.*, 1938, 128: 742-5, ill.

DYwe-th

FISCH, Harold. Alchemy and English literature. *Proc.Leeds Phil.Lit.Soc.*, 1953, 7: 123-36. [CB 82/218]

DYwf-daj

D'YGÉ, Claude. Nouvelle assemblée des philosophes chymiques. 233 p. Paris: Dervy Livres, 1954.
Reviewed by G. Heym, *Ambix*, 1957, 6: 56-7.

DYwg-cd

DUVEEN, Denis; OFFENBACHER, Emil. An alchemical correspondence in Germany under the Nazi regime. 29 p. Long Island City, N.Y.: Reinitz Soap Corp., 1951.

DYwh-ce

BENCZE, J. [Two unknown Hungarian manuscripts on alchemy. (In Hungarian)]. *Orv.Hétil.*, 1964, 105: 1712-14.

CSILLAG, István. [The only book on alchemy in the Hungarian language. (In Hungarian)]. *Orv.Hétil.*, 1964, 105: 1040-2.

DYwi-th

ZOCCOLI, Federico Gambigliani. Alcune poesie alchemiche ritenute inedite. *Riv.Stor.Sci.*, 1937, 28: 273-82, 1 facs.

DYwj

RUSKA, Julius. Über Spaniens Anteil an der Entwicklung der Alchemie. *Forsch.Fortschr.*, 1933, 9: 389-90.

F ASTRONOMY

Fc general history

Fc-bm *large scale works*

ABETTI, Giorgio. Esplorazione dell'universo. 334 p., fig., 16 pl. Bari: Laterza, 1959.
Reviewed by M.G. Fracastoro, *Scientia*, 1960, 95: 99-100.

ABETTI, Giorgio. The history of astronomy. Transl. from the Italian by Betty Burr Abetti. xii, 338 p., 32 pl. New York: Henry Schuman, 1952.
For Italian original *see* below.
Reviewed by C. Doris Hellman, *Isis*, 1953, 44: 298-300; by Joseph Ashbrook, *Scr.Math.*, 1954, 20: 192-3.

ABETTI, Giorgio. Storia dell'astronomia. 370 p., 32 pl. Florence: Vallecchi, 1949.
Reviewed by L. Jacchia, *Isis*, 1951, 42: 72.
For English translation *see* above; Spanish translation (Mexico/Buenos Aires: 1956) reviewed by M.L. Bonelli, *Physis*, 1959, 1: 52-3.

ARMITAGE, Angus. A century of astronomy. xvi, 256 p., 44 pl. London: Low; New York: Macdonald, 1950. [CB 59/369]

BECKER, Friedrich. Histoire de l'astronomie. 2nd ed. Suivi de Astronomie moderne, par Ernest Esclangon. 174 p. Paris: Lamarre, 1954.
Reviewed by R. Taton, *Rev.Hist.Sci.*, 1958, 11: 364.
Translation of 2nd German edition of Becker's "Geschichte der Astronomie", *see* below.

BECKER, Friedrich. Geschichte der Astronomie. 2nd ed. 95 p. (Geschichte der Wissenschaften, 2) Bonn: Universitäts Verlag, 1947.

BERRY, Arthur. A short history of astronomy from earliest times through the nineteenth century. xxi, 440 p. New York: Dover Publications, Inc., 1961.
An unabridged re-issue of the edition of 1898.
Reviewed by Colin A. Ronan, *Sky Telesc.*, 1963, 25: 46, 48.

BOQUET, F. Histoire de l'astronomie. 510 p. Paris: Payot, 1924. [CB 18/611]

BORK, Ferdinand. Die Geschichte des Weltbildes. iv, 150 p. 18 fig. (Ex Oriente Lux, 3) Leipzig: Pfeiffer, 1930.

DANNEMANN, Friedrich. Wie unser Weltbild entstand. Die Entwicklung der Vorstellungen über den Bau des Kosmos von den Anfängen bis zur Einstein'schen Relativitätstheorie. 25th ed. 101 p. (Kosmos Bändchen) Stuttgart: Frankh, 1930.
First published 1912.
A popular and well illustrated account of the development of astronomy.

DOIG, Peter. A concise history of astronomy. vi, 320 p. London: Chapman & Hall, 1950; New York: Philosophical Library, 1951.
Reviewed by John W. Streeter, *Isis*, 1951, 42: 73-5; by Carl Boyer, *Scr.Math.*, 1952, 18: 268-71.

DOUBLET, E. Histoire de l'astronomie. 572 p. Paris: Gaston Doin, 1922.
Reviewed by L. Guinet, *Isis*, 1923, 5: 172-3.

DREYER, J.L.E. A history of astronomy from Thales to Kepler. Formerly titled, History of the planetary systems from Thales to Kepler. 2nd rev. ed. x, 438 p., fig. New York: Dover, 1953.
Reviewed by William D. Stahlman, *Isis*, 1953, 44: 396-7.

ERNST, Br.; VRIES, Tj. E. de. Atlas of the universe. Transl. by D.R. Welsh. 227 p. London/Edinburgh: Nelson, 1961.
Reviewed by Douglas McKie, *Ann.Sci.*, 1961, 17: 197.

FLAMMARION, Camille. The Flammarion book of astronomy. An entirely new edition of the original work prepared under the direction of Gabrielle Camille Flammarion and of André Danjon ... Translated into English by Annabel and Bernard Pagel. 670 p. New York: Simon and Schuster, 1964.
The new edition of "Astronomie populaire" was published in Paris: Flammarion, 1955.
Reviewed by Harry Woolf, *Science*, 1964, 146: 1153.

HALE, George Ellery. The depths of the universe. xvi, 98 p., 45 ill. New York: Scribner, 1924.
Includes historical sketch of each problem discussed.
Reviewed by George Sarton, *Isis*, 1925, 7: 152.

HALE, George Ellery. The new heavens. xv, 88 p. New York/London: Scribner, 1922.
3 essays: The new heavens; Giant stars; Cosmic crucibles.

HOYLE, Fred. Astronomy. 320 p. Garden City, N.Y.: Doubleday and Co., 1962.
Reviewed by Owen Gingerich, *Sky Telesc.*, 1963, 26: 41.

HUMBERT, Pierre. Histoire des découvertes astronomiques. 272 p. Paris: Revue des Jeunes, 1948.

IONIDES, Stephen A.; IONIDES, Margaret L. Stars and men. 460 p., 74 ill. New York: Bobbs-Merrill, 1939. [CB 78/398]
Contains many historical references.

JEANS, James Hopwood. Astronomy and cosmogony. 2nd ed. x, 428 p., 16 pl. Cambridge University Press, 1929.
First published 1928.
Reviewed by H.D., *Nature*, 1929, 123: 937-8.

JOFFE, M. La conquista delle stelle. Astrolatria, astrologia, astronomia, astrofisica. A cura di G. De Florentiis. 730 p., ill. Milano: Mondadori, 1958.
Reviewed by G. Abetti, *Scientia*, 1959, 94: 237.

KING, Henry Charles. The background of astronomy. 254 p. London: Watts, 1957.
Reviewed in *Sch.Sci.Rev.*, 1957, 38: 511-12; by M.W. Burke-Gaffney, *Arch.Int.Hist.Sci.*, 1957, 10: 378-9; by Wilhelm Norlind, *Lychnos*, 1957-58, 424-5.

KING, Henry Charles. Exploration of the universe; the story of astronomy. 304 p., ill. London: Secker and Warburg, 1964.
Publ. in paperback New York: Signet.

LEY, Willy. Watchers of the skies. An informal history of astronomy from Babylon to the space age. xiii, 528 p., ill. New York: Viking Press, 1963.
Reviewed by C. Doris Hellman, *Isis*, 1964, 55: 376-7; by Owen Gingerich, *Sky.Telesc.*, 1964, 28: 164-5.

MACPHERSON, Hector. Modern astronomy. Its rise and progress. 196 p., 26 fig. London: Oxford University Press, 1926. [CB 22/263]

MOORE, Patrick. The picture history of astronomy. 253 p. New York: Grosset & Dunlap, 1961.
Reviewed in *Sky Telesc.*, 1962, 23: 344; *ibid.*, 1963, 25: 45-6 (by Patrick V. Rizzo).

NEW ASTRONOMY. By the editors of *Scientific American*. 243 p. New York: Dover, 1955.

OPPENHEIM, S. Das astronomische Weltbild im Wandel der Zeit. 2nd ed. 134 p. Leipzig: Teubner, 1912.

PANNEKOEK, Antonie. De groei van ons wereldbeeld. Een geschidenis van de sterrekunde. [The growth of our world picture. A history of astronomy. (In Dutch)] 440 p. Amsterdam-Antwerpen: Wereldbibliotheek, 1951. [CB 79/172]
Reviewed by E.J. Dijksterhuis, *Rev.Hist.Sci.*, 1952, 5: 278-9.

PANNEKOEK, Antonie. A history of astronomy. 521 p., fig. ill. London: Allen & Unwin; New York: Interscience Publishers, 1961.
Reviewed by Morton Grosser, *Isis*, 1963, 54: 494-5; for other reviews *see* CB 88/541 and CB 89/500.

PFEIFFER, John. The changing universe. The story of the new astronomy. xi, 244 p., ill. London: Victor Gollancz, 1956.
Reviewed by F.G. Smith, *Nature*, 1958, 181: 980.

ROUSSEAU, Pierre. Man's conquest of the stars. 356 p. London: Jarrold, 1959.
Reviewed by Steadman Thompson, *Sky Telesc.*, 1959, 33: 698.

RUDAUX, Lucien; VAUCOULEURS, Gérard de. Astronomie; les astres, l'univers. viii, 486 p., 866 ill. Paris: Larousse, 1948.
Reviewed by P. Humbert, *Arch.Int.Hist.Sci.*, 1948, 2: 228.

SAGERET, J. Le système du monde des Chaldéens à Newton. 280 p., 20 fig. (Nouvelle Collection Scientifique) Paris: Alcan, 1913.

STRUVE, Otto; ZEBERGS, Velta. Astronomy of the 20th century. 544 p., ill. New York: Macmillan, 1962.
Reviewed by Thornton Page, *Science*, 1962, 138: 1321-2; by E.J. Oepik, *Phys.Today*, 1964, 17: no. 2, 56.

THOMAS, Oswald. Astronomie. Tatsachen und Probleme. 7th ed. 1011 p., ill. Salzburg: "Das Bergland-Buch", 1956.
Reviewed by Jos. E. Hofmann, *Arch.Int.Hist.Sci.*, 1957, 10: 258.

TOULMIN, Stephen; GOODFIELD, June. The fabric of the heavens. The development of astronomy and dynamics. 285 p., ill. London: Hutchinson; New York: Harper and Brothers, 1961. [CB 88/541]
For reviews *see* CB 87/564, CB 88/541 and CB 89/500.

TURNER, Hubert Hall. Astronomical discovery. Introd. by Dirk Brouwer. xiv, 222 p., ill. Gloucester, Mass.: Peter Smith, 1963.
Paperback edition by the University of California Press, 1963.

VAUCOULEURS, Gérard de. Discovery of the universe. An outline of the history of astronomy from the origins to 1956. 328 p. New York: Macmillan; London: Faber, 1957.
Reviewed by C.C. Kiess, *Phys.Today*, 1957, 10: no. 10, 38-40; *Sch.Sci.Rev.*, 1957, 39: 178; by Sarah Lee Lippincott, *Sci. Mon.*, 1957, 85: 327.

WATERFIELD, Reginald L. A hundred years of astronomy. 526 p. New York: Macmillan, 1938.
Reviewed by N.T. Bobrovnikoff, *Isis*, 1939, 31: 109-12.

WOLF, Rudolf. Geschichte der Astronomie. xiv, 815 p. Leipzig: Koehler, 1933. [CB 42/584]
A reprint of the 1877 edition (Munich: Oldenbourg).

ZINNER, Ernst. Astronomie. Geschichte ihrer Probleme. xii, 404 p. (Orbis Academicus. Problemsgeschichten der Wissenschaft in Dokumenten und Darstellungen, Naturwissenschaftliche Abteilung, 2: no. 1) Freiburg/München: Karl Alber, 1951.
Reviewed by J.W. Abrams, *Isis*, 1952, 43: 291-2; by O. Neugebauer, *Centaurus*, 1953, 2: 367-8.

ZINNER, Ernst. Die Geschichte der Sternkunde von den ersten Anfängen bis zur Gegenwart. xi, 673 p., 54 ill., 13 pl. Berlin: Springer, 1931.
Reviewed by A. Pogo, *Isis*, 1931, 16: 161-7; by P. Kirchberger, *Deut.Lit.Zeitung*, 1931, 2: 1815-20.

Fc-bn *essays; articles*

ABBOT, C.C. Accomplishments of modern astronomy. *Proc.Amer. Phil.Soc.*, 1927, 66: (Bicentenary volume), 231-50.

ABBOT, C.G. Astronomy in Shakespeare's time and in ours. *Annu.Rep.Smithsonian Inst.for 1936*, p. 109-22, 6 pl. Washington: U.S. Government Printing Office, 1937.

ABETTI, Giorgio. Astronomia moderna. *Scientia*, 1961, 96: 42-6, 71-6.

ADAMS, Walter S. Recent scientific progress in astronomy. *News Serv.Bull.Carnegie Inst.Wash.*, 1936, 4: 63-72, ill.
Includes history of the telescope.

EDDINGTON, Arthur Stanley. A century of astronomy. *Nature*, 1922, 109: 815-17. [CB 13/237]

GUYOT, E. Le système du monde de Ptolémée à Einstein. A propos du quatrième centenaire de la mort de Copernic (19 février 1473 - 24 mai 1543). *Scientia*, 1946, 79: 77-82.

PANNEKOEK, Antonie. The origin of astronomy. *Mon.Not.Roy. Astron.Soc.*, 1951, 111: 347-56.
George Darwin Lecture.

SPITZER, Lyman. Horizons in astronomy. *Amer.Scient.*, 1955, 43: 323-30.

STRUVE, Otto. Astronomy in 1900. *Sky Telesc.*, 1961, 22: 64-9.

ZINNER, Ernst. Untersuchungen zur Geschichte der Sternkunde. *Ber.Naturforsch.Ges.Bamberg*, 1932, 26: 1-62, 2 fig. [CB 38/596]

Fc-br *periodicals*

Eudemus. An international journal devoted to the history of mathematics and astronomy. Published by Brown University, Providence, Rhode Island, U.S.A. Vol. 1. Copenhagen: Einar Munksgaard, for Brown University, 1941.
No more published.

The Heavens. Tenkai. (In Japanese) Vol. 1- Kyoto: Oriental Astronomical Association, 1920-
Historical articles in vol. 13, no. 142, February 1933, listed in CB 39/453.

Istoriko-Astronomicheskie Issledovaniia. [Historico-astronomical researches. (In Russian)] Vol. 1- Moscow: Gosudarstvennoe Izdatel'stvo Fiziko-Matematicheskoi Literatury, 1955-
For contents list of Vol. 6 (1960) *see* CB 86/461.
Vol. 7 (1961) reviewed in *Sky Telesc.*, 1962, 23: 223.

Meddelanden från Lunds Astronomiska Observatorium
Historical articles in English from this periodical are published from time to time in a numbered series: Historical Notes and Papers.

Vistas in Astronomy. Ed. by A. Beer. Vol. 1- London/New York: Pergamon Press, 1955-
Vol. 1 reviewed by William D. Stahlman, *Isis*, 1958, 49: 447-9.

Fc-bu/cv bibliography; literature; sources

Fc-bv

Bibliography of books and papers on the history of astronomy published in 1960-. Moscow: Commission 41 (History of Astronomy), International Astronomical Union, 1962-
Annual list of about 300 items.

INTERNATIONAL ASTRONOMICAL UNION. Eleventh General Assembly, Berkeley, 15-24 August 1961. Proceedings. xii, 532 p. New York: Academic Press, 1962.
The report of Commission 41 (Histoire de l'Astronomie) is followed by a bibliography of recent works concerning the history of astronomy, particularly in China, Poland, U.S.S.R. and Japan.

NAKAYAMA, Shigeru. Japanese studies in the history of astronomy. *Jap.Stud.Hist.Sci.*, 1962, 1: 14-22.

[SELECTED bibliography of the literature on the history of astronomy issued in the USSR and other countries. (In Russian)] *Ist.Astron.Issled.*, 1955, 1: 359-67.
This survey covering the literature of the preceding year(s) appears in each volume of the periodical; it was edited by Iu.G. Perel in vol. 4-8.

Fcb

COLLARD, Auguste. Une bibliothèque belge centenaire. La Bibliothèque de l'Observatoire Royal et de l'Institut Royal Météorologique de Belgique - 1833-1933. *Arch.Bibl.Mus.Belg.*, 1935, 12: 78-109.

KEMP, D. Alasdair. The Crawford Library of the Royal Observatory, Edinburgh. *Isis*, 1963, 54: 481-3.

MUNSTERBERG, Margaret. The Bowditch collection in the Boston Public Library. *Isis*, 1942, 34: 140-2.

Fcd-bv

ZINNER, Ernst. Aus alten Handschriften. *Ber.Naturforsch.Ges. Bamberg*, 1962, 38: 8-57.
Listing of astronomical manuscripts in European libraries.

Fce

WOOLARD, Edgar W. Great astronomical treatises of the past. *J.Wash.Acad.Sci.*, 1942, 32: 189-216.

Fce-bu

INTERNATIONAL ASTRONOMICAL UNION. [Resolutions of Commission 5 (concerned with bibliography) adopted at the 6th General Assembly, Stockholm, August 1938.] *Isis*, 1939, 30: 281.

LAVROVA, N.B. [Notes on the history of astronomical bibliography. (In Russian)] *Ist.Astron.Issled.*, 1959, 5: 83-196.

Fce-bv

Astronomischer Jahresbericht. Vol. 1-68. Enhaltend die Litteratur des Jahres 1899-1968. Berlin: 1900-69.
No more published.
Vol. 12-43, 1912-1944 were published by the Königliches Astronomisches Rechen-Institut zu Berlin; vol. 44-68, 1947-1969, by the Astronomisches Rechen-Institut in Heidelberg.

COLLARD, Auguste. L'astronomie et les astronomes. Répertoire des ouvrages à consulter. Collection créée pour l'avancement des sciences, des lettres et des arts en Belgique. viii, 120 p. Bruxelles: Van Oest, 1921. [CB 11/438]
A list of 758 items supplementing Houzeau and Lancaster's Bibliographie générale de l'astronomie.

HOUZEAU, J.C.; LANCASTER, A. Bibliographie générale de l'astronomie jusqu'en 1880. New ed. with introd. and author index by D.W. Dewhirst. Preface by A. Beer. 2 vol. in 3. xxiv, viii, 858 p.; vii, 859-1727 p.; lxxxviii, 2225 p. London: Holland Press, 1964.
A reprint of the 1880-1889 edition with some additional material by D.W. Dewhirst.

LAVROVA, N.B. Bibliografiia astronomicheskikh bibliografī. [Bibliographie de bibliographies astronomiques. (In Russian with table of contents and preface in French)] vi, 110 p Moscow: 1962.

NISSEN, Claus. Alte Astronomie. *Börsenbl.Deut.Buchhandel*, 1952, 8: no. 24, 114-15.

Fce-bx

THE WONDERFUL planetary machine. An extensive library exhibit marks the second restoration of the Rittenhouse orrery. *Princeton Alumni Weekly*, 1954, 54: 10-11, 4 fig.

Fck

HESS, Wilhelm. Die Einblattdrucke des 15. bis 18. Jahrhunderts unter besonderer Berücksichtigung ihres astronomischen und meteorologischen Inhaltes. Rede. 38 p. Bamberg: J.M. Reindl, 1913.

Fcn

BROWN, Basil J.W. Astronomical atlases, maps and charts. An historical and general guide. 200 p., 19 pl., front. London: Search, 1932. [CB 41/601]

FAVARO, G.A. Un grande esempio di collaborazione scientifica: il catalogo e la carta fotografica del cielo. *Scientia*, 1927, 41: 173-80, French transl. suppl., 71-8.
History of the catalogue of star photographs and of the photographic map of the sky.

HOULLEVIGUE, L. La carte du ciel. *Rev.Paris*, 1913, 20: 799-813.

MOREUX, Th. Les progrès de la cosmographie depuis son origine. *Scientia*, 1917, 22: 405-17.

Fd biography

Fd-bv

HIGGINS, Thomas James. Book-length biographies of physicists and astronomers. *Amer.J.Phys.*, 1944, 12: 31-9, 234-6.

Fda

BORN, Max. Astronomical recollections. *Vistas Astron.*, 1955, 1: 41-4.

EVERSHED, Mary Acworth. Who's who in the moon. Notes on the names of all lunar formations adopted in 1935 by the International Astronomical Union. *Mem.Brit.Astron.Ass.*, 1938, 34: part 1, 3-130, 2 pl.
Contains brief biographical notes on all persons whose names have been applied to lunar formations.

GINGERICH, Owen. A spiral galaxy of astronomers. *Sky Telesc.*, 1963, 25: 132-4. [CB 89/499]

MACPHERSON, Hector. Makers of astronomy. viii, 244 p., 9 ill. London: Oxford University Press, 1933.
Reviewed by Aldo Mieli, *Archeion*, 1933, 15: 277-8; in *Nature*, 1933, 132: 804.

NOYES, Alfred. The torch-bearers. xi, 281 p. (1. Watchers of the sky). London: Blackwood; New York: Stokes, 1922.
Sketch of the history of astronomy in verse. Prologue, epilogue and seven chapters devoted respectively to Copernicus, Tycho Brahe, Kepler, Galileo, Newton, William and John Herschel.

RONAN, Colin A. The astronomers. 232 p., ill., 25 pl. New York: Hill and Wang, 1964. [CB 90/516]

SCHOUTEN, W.J.A. Grote sterrenkundigen van Ptolemaeus tot De Sitter. [Great astronomers from Ptolemy to De Sitter. (In Dutch)] vii, 285 p. Rijswijk: Leidsche Uitgeversmaatschappij, 1950.
Reviewed by E.J. Dijksterhuis, *Rev.Hist.Sci.*, 1951, 4: 195.

TASS, A.M., ed. Porträt Gallerie der Astronomischen Gesellschaft. 2nd ed. 85 p., portr. Budapest: Ungarische Universitätsdruckerei, 1931.
First edition edited by C.V.L. Charlier and F.A. Engström, 1904.
Both editions reviewed by R.C. Archibald, *Scr.Math.*, 1934, 2: 176-8.

WILLIAMS, H.S. Great astronomers. xix, 618 p., ill. New York: Simon and Schuster, 1930.

Fdaj

SHAPLEY, Harlow; HOWARTH, Helen E.; ed. A source book in astronomy, 1500-1900. xvi, 412 p., ill. New York: McGraw-Hill Book Company, 1929.
Reviewed by George Sarton, *Isis*, 1929, 13: 130-4.

SHAPLEY, Harlow, ed. Source book in astronomy, 1900-1950. xv, 423 p., front., pl., fig., tables. Cambridge, Mass.: Harvard University Press, 1960.
Reviewed by Otto Struve, *Isis*, 1962, 53: 430-1; for other reviews *see* CB 87/563.

Ff history of astronomy as a study

KULIKOVSKII, P.G., ed. [On some problems of studying the history of astronomy. (In Russian)] *Ist.Astron.Issled.*, 1960, 6: 13-28.

McCOLLEY, Grant. Humanism and the history of astronomy. *Studies and Essays offered to George Sarton*, p. 321-57. New York: Schuman, 1947. [CB 71/117]

SARTON, George. The study of the history of astronomy in Bamberg. *Isis*, 1935, 22: 530-31.
Includes extract from Ernst Zinner's report on the Observatory.

VERNET, Juan. En torno a la historia de la astronomia. *Urania Soc.Astrôn.Españ.*, 1951, no. 225, 1-7.

ZINNER, Ernst. Astronomiegeschichtliche Forschungen in Moskau und Leningrad. *Forsch.Fortschr.*, 1959, 3: 104-6.

ZINNER, Ernst. Wege und Ziele der Geschichte der Sternkunde. *Sterne*, 1925, 5: 149-56.

Ffd

FOR biographies and bibliographies of historians of astronomy *see* Volume 1 under :-
Berry, Arthur; Idel'son, Naum Il'ich.

Ffqx

INTERNATIONAL ASTRONOMICAL UNION. Commission 41 - History of Astronomy. [The Commission was founded in 1948 and published its first report in *Transactions of the International Astronomical Union*, vol. 8, 1954.]

Fh/v special aspects

Fhj

WOOLARD, Edgar W. The impress of past ages in modern astronomy. *Pop.Astron.*, 1949, 57: 363-72.

Fhm

ROUGIER, Louis. L'astronomie et l'histoire des idées. *Rev. Paris*, 1929, 36: 855-85.

Fjg

IRWIN, John B. Serendipity in astronomy. *Sky Telesc.*, 1964, 28: 192-5.

Fk

ARMELLINI, G. I fondamenti scientifici della astronomia. xv, 320 p., 44 ill. Milan: Hoepli, 1947.
Reviewed by E. v. d. Pahlen, *Experientia*, 1947, 3: 380-1.

CHARLIER, C.V.L. La loi des grands nombres. *Scientia*, 1921, 30: 433-9. [CB 12/633]

MOREUX, Théophile. Où en est l'astronomie. vi, 294 p. (Collection des Mises au Point) Paris: Gauthier-Villars, 1920.
Reviewed by L. Guinet, *Isis*, 1921-22, 4: 325.

Fnb

HORN D'ARTURO, G. Numeri arabici e simboli celesti. *Pubbl. Osserv.Astron.Univ.Bologna*, 1925, 1: 187-204. [CB 18/606]

Fnh

MICHEL, Henri. A propos de terminologie. *Ciel Terre*, 1951, 67: no. 5-6, 97-100.
Coordonnées sphériques; gnomon; jour artificiel.

Fnh-be

SPITZ, Armand; GAYNOR, Frank. Dictionary of astronomy and astronautics. vi, 439 p., 16 pl. New York: Philosophical Library, 1959.
More than 2200 terms and concepts, from ancient astronomy to modern astronautics, are precisely defined.

Fnh-m

WOOLARD, Edgar W. The evolution of fundamental astronomical concepts as reflected in the terminology of astronomy. *Pop. Astron.*, 1949, 57: 482-8.

Fpw

HEINDEL, R. Heathcote. Americans and the Royal Astronomical Society. *Science*, 1938, 87: 575.

PEREL, Iu. G.; RADOVSKY, M.L. [From the history of the scientific relations between Russian and American astronomers. (In Russian)] *Ist.Astron.Issled.*, 1960, 6: 212-50.

Fr

FROST, Edwin Brant. An astronomer's life. xi, 300 p., 8 pl. Boston: Houghton Mifflin, 1933.
Reviewed in *Nature*, 1933, 132: 950.

Fse

RUMRILL, H.B. The revival of popular interest in astronomy. *Pop.Astron.*, 1937, 45: 310-17.

Ft

DAVIDSON, Martin. The stars and the mind. A study of the impact of astronomical development on human thought. x, 210 p., 8 pl. London: Watts, 1947. [CB 74/386 and CB 75/88]
2nd ed. 1948.
Reviewed by H.D. Anthony, *Nature*, 1947, 159: 521; by Jean Pelseneer, *Ciel Terre*, 1947, 63: 174-6.

MOREHOUSE, D.W. Astronomy's contribution to the stream of human thought. *Science*, 1932, 75: 27-32.

Ftd

DAISOMONT, M. Le clergé catholique devant l'astronomie, suivi d'un Essai sur le conflit entre l'astronomie et l'église romaine au XVIIe siècle. 50 p., 3 pl. Bruges: De Tempel, 1950.

DAVIDSON, Martin. The heavens and faith. xv, 162 p. London: Watts, 1936.
Reviewed by J.C.H., *Nature*, 1936, 138: 227.

INGE, William Ralph. God and the astronomers: containing the Warburton lectures 1931-33. xiii, 308 p. London: Longmans, Green, 1933.
Reviewed by R.A.S., *Nature*, 1933, 132: 619-20.

MONOD, Victor. Dieu dans l'univers. Essai sur l'action exercée sur la pensée chrétienne par les grands systèmes cosmologiques depuis Aristote jusqu'à nos jours. 360 p. Paris: Fischbacher, 1933.

WHITTAKER, Edmund. Space and spirit. Theories of the universe and the arguments for the existence of God. vii, 150 p. London: Nelson, 1946.
Reviewed by J.C. Hardwick, *Nature*, 1947, 159: 418.

Fth

HUMBERT, Pierre. Les erreurs astronomiques des littérateurs. *Rev.Quest.Sci.*, 1928, 13: 396-418.

Fvm

FRAENKEL, Abraham A. [The Jewish contribution to mathematics and astronomy. (In Hebrew)]. 32 p. Tel-Aviv: 1947.
Reviewed in *Scr.Math.*, 1947, 13: 78.

FRAENKEL, Abraham A. Jewish mathematics and astronomy. *Scr. Math.*, 1960, 25: 33-47.

Fw in different countries

Fwb North America

GUDDE, Erwin G. A century of astronomy and geodesy in California. In: A century of progress in the natural sciences, 1853-1953, p. 65-74. San Francisco: California Academy of Sciences, 1955.

HEINDEL, R. Heathcote. *See* Fwe-qd

PEREL, Iu.G.; RADOVSKY, M.L. *See* Fpw

Fwb-p

NATIONAL RESEARCH COUNCIL. Ground-based astronomy: a ten-year program. A report prepared by the Panel on Astronomical Facilities for the Committee on Science and Public Policy of the National Academy of Sciences. xii, 105 p., ill. (National Research Council. Publication 1234) Washington: 1964. [CB 90/627]

Fwb-qd

BILLINGS, Cecil M. History of the Rittenhouse Astronomical Society, 1888-1960. 123 p. Philadelphia, Pa.: 1961. [CB 88/532]
Reviewed by Joseph Ashbrook, *Sky Telesc.*, 1962, 23: 44-5.

YERKES OBSERVATORY. *Science*, 1947, 106: 195-220, ill. [CB 72/257]
A series of articles to celebrate the 50th anniversary of the founding of the Yerkes Observatory and the American Astronomical Society.

Fwc Latin America

CAJORI, Florian. The mathematical sciences in the Latin colonies of America. *Sci.Mon.*, 1923, 16: 194-204. [CB 15/206]
Brief account of astronomical work done in Latin America between 1492 and 1800.

Fwe British Isles

GUNTHER, Robert William Theodore. Early science in Oxford. 2. Astronomy. xv, 408 p. Oxford: Printed for the subscribers, 1923.
Reviewed by G. Sarton, *Isis*, 1924, 6: 449-53.

Fwe-qd

DREYER, J.L.E., et al. History of the Royal Astronomical Society, 1820-1920. vii, 258 p., 12 pl. London: Wheldon and Wesley (for the Society), 1923.

HEINDEL, R. Heathcote. Americans and the Royal Astronomical Society. *Science*, 1938, 87: 575.

Fwf France

BIGOURDAN, G. [Various notes on French astronomy.] *Compt. Rend.Acad.Sci.*, 1918, vol. 166 and 167.

DOUBLET, E. L'astronomie française. *Rev.Sci.*, 1923, 61: 234-40. [CB 15/206]

Fwg/wh Central Europe

Fwg

ANZ, Heinrich, ed. Gotha und sein Gymnasium. Bausteine zur Geistesgeschichte einer deutschen Residenz. Zur 400-Jahrfeier des Gymnasium Ernestinum. Stuttgart: 1924.
The great geographical establishment of Justus Perthes is situated in Gotha. This volume contains a chapter by Hermann Wagner entitled "Gothas Bedeutung für die Pflege der Astronomie und Geographie".

KUIPER, Gerard P. German astronomy during the war. *Pop. Astron.*, 1946, 54: 263-87.

Fwg-cd-bv

ZINNER, Ernst. Verzeichnis der astronomischen Handschriften des deutschen Kulturgebietes. ii, 544 p. München: C.H. Beck, 1925. [CB 19/801]

ZINNER, Ernst. Die Vorarbeiten zu einem Handschriftenverzeichnis der deutschen Sternforschung. *Sitzungsber.Bayer. Akad.Wiss.Math.Phys.Kl.*, 1922, 121-6.

Fwg-oq

KNOPF, Otto. Die Astronomie an der Universität Jena von der Gründung der Universität im Jahre 1558 bis zur Entpflichtung des Verfassers im Jahre 1927. 14, 226 p. (*Z.Ver.Thüringische Altertumskunde Beih.*, 1937, 7) Jena: G. Fischer, 1937.

Fwg-qd

TASS, A.M., ed. Porträt Gallerie der Astronomischen Gesellschaft. 2nd ed. 85 p., portr. Budapest: Ungarische Universitätsdruckerei, 1931.
First edition edited by C.V.L. Charlier and F.A. Engström, 1904.
Both editions reviewed by R.C. Archibald, *Scr.Math.*, 1934, 2: 176-8.

Fwh

BIRKENMAJER, A. Roboczy konspekt zespołowej historii astronomii w Polsce. [A working outline of a collective history of astronomy in Poland. (In Polish with Russian and English summaries)] *Stud.Mater.Dziej.Nauk.Pol.Sér.C*, 1959, 2: 7-27.

FISCHER, Charles. The history of astronomy in Slovakia through the 19th century. *Proc.10th Int.Congr.Hist.Sci.* (Ithaca, 1962), (2), p. 769-71. Paris: Hermann, 1964.

KELÉNYI, Béla Ottó. Geschichte der ungarischen Astronomie. 106 p., 14 fig. (Astronomische Abhandlungen des K. Ungarischen Astrophysikalischen Observatoriums von Konkoly's Stiftung in Budapest-Svábhegy, 1: no. 2) Budapest: 1930.
Reviewed by E. Zinner, *Vierteljahrsschr.Astron.Ges.*, 1931, 66: 17-18.

RYBKA, E. Krótki rys dziejów astronomii we Lwowie. [A short outline of the history of astronomy in Lwow. (In Polish with summaries in Russian and English)]. *Stud.Mater.Dziej. Nauk.Pol.Ser.C*, 1959, 2: 53-68.

SLOUKA, Hubert, *et al.* Astronomie v Ceskoslovensku: od dob nejstarších di dneška. [Astronomy in Czechoslovakia: from the earliest times to today. (In Czech)] 346 p. Prague: Osveta, 1952.
Reviewed by Quido Vetter, *Isis*, 1954, 45: 100-1.

TASS, Anton. Die Sternkunde in Ungarn. (*7th Int.Congr.Hist. Sci.*, Warsaw, 1933). *Bull.Int.Comm.Hist.Sci.*, 1933, 5: no. 19, 298-311.

WOSZCZYK, A. L'astronomie en Pologne (depuis Copernic jusqu'à nos jours). *Ciel Terre*, 1959, 75: 108-22.

Fwh-da

BANACHIEWICZ, T. The rôle of Cracovians in astronomy. *Vistas Astron.*, 1955, 1: 200-6.

MERGENTALER, Jan. [The scientific achievements of Polish astronomers. (In Polish with summary in English)] *Życie Nauk.*, 1946, 2: 226-35, 316-18.

Fwh-oq

VETTER, Q. Šest století matematického a astronomického učení na universitě Karlově v Praze. [Six centuries of the teaching of mathematics and astronomy at the Karlově University of Prague. (In Czech, with Russian summary)] *Věstník Královské České Společnosti Nauk, Třída Mat.Přírodovědecká*, 1952, 14: 1-40.

Fwi/wj Southern Europe

Fwi-da

ABETTI, Giorgio. Italian pioneers in the physics of the universe: astronomy. *Cah.Hist.Mond.*, 1963, 7: 435-52.

Fwj-u

LEHMANN-NITSCHE, Robert. Astronomía popular Gallega. 26 p. Buenos Aires: Coni, 1924.
Reprinted from *Humanidades* (Buenos Aires), vol. 8, p. 371-94.

Fwk Low Countries

ALLIAUME, Maurice. Esquisse de l'histoire des mathématiques et de l'astronomie en Belgique depuis 1830. *Rev.Quest.Sci.*, 1930, 18: 267-305; also in *Histoire de la Belgique Contemporaine, 1830-1914*, (3), p. 373-402. Bruxelles: A. Dewit, 1930.

LE MAIRE, Octave. L'astronomie à Malines, 1246-1904. *Folklore Brabançon*, 1936, 16: 18-75.

STROOBANT, Paul. Histoire de l'astronomie en Belgique de 1830 à 1930. *Compt.Rend.Ier Congr.Nat.Sci.* (Bruxelles, 1930), 9 p. Bruxelles: Secrétaire Général, [1931].

Fwk-da

CORT, J.H. Jongere Nederlandsche sterrenkundigen op belangrijke posten in het buitenland. [Young Dutch astronomers in important posts abroad. (In Dutch)] *Hemel Dampkring*, 1941, 39: 355-63, 3 portr. [CB 71/117]

Fwk-qd

SOCIÉTÉ BELGE D'ASTRONOMIE, DE MÉTÉOROLOGIE ET DE PHYSIQUE DU GLOBE. Cinquantenaire de la Société, 27 octobre 1945. Memorial. 32 p., 6 pl. Bruxelles: 1945.

Fwn/wo Russia; Finland; South Eastern Europe

Fwn

MOORE, Patrick. Astronomy in the Soviet Union. *Discovery*, 1961, 22: 69-70.

PEREL, Iu.G.; RADOVSKY, M.L. *See* Fpw

STRUVE, Otto. G.A. Shajn and Russian astronomy. *Sky Telesc.*, 1958, 17: 272-3.

T'UMANYAN, B.E. Hay astgagitut'yan patmut'yun. Hnaguyn žamanakneric minčeu XIX dari skizbě. [History of Armenian astronomy. From earliest times to the beginning of the 19th century. (In Armenian, with English and Russian summaries)] 415 p., ill. Yerevan: "MITK" Publishing House, 1964.

YARNEFELT, G. Astronomiya v Finlyandii. [Astronomy in Finland. (In Russian)] *Ist.Astron.Issled.*, 1962, 8: 241-67.

Fwn-ce

VYSSOTSKY, A.N. Astronomical records in the Russian chronicles from 1000 to 1600 A.D. (as collected by D.O. Sviatsky). 51 p., map. (Historical Notes and Papers, 22) Lund: Lund Observatory, 1949.
Also published in series: *Medd.Lunds Astron.Observ., ser. 2*, 126.

Fwn-sk

STRUVE, Otto. Astronomy in the manner of 1984. *Science*, 1952, 116: 206-7.
Apropos of the views of P.P. Parenago, professor of astronomy at Moscow University, expressed in his book "The world of the stars" which contains an attack on "capitalist science".

Fwo

NIKOLITCH, Georges. Histoire de l'astronomie yougoslave. (Thesis) Montpellier: 1946.
Typescript.
Reviewed by P. Humbert, *Arch.Int.Hist.Sci.*, 1948, 1: 529-31.

Fwr/wy Asia; Africa

Fwt

YAMAMOTO, Issei. Japanese astronomy in past and present. Lecture delivered on July 24, 1931, at Kyoto. *Isis*, 1932, 17: 425-7.
Synopsis.

Fwv

KUIPER, Gerard P. Astronomy in the Netherlands Indies. In: Honig, Pieter; Verdoorn, Frans; ed. Science and scientists in the Netherlands Indies, p. 22-6. New York: 1945.

Fwy

EVANS, David S. Astronomy in South Africa. *Endeavour*, 1950, 9: 45-50.

Fxg planetaria

BÉVENOT, Hugh G. The Weingarten planetarium. *Isis*, 1926, 8: 300-12, 2 pl.
Description, explanation and reconstruction of the planetarium painted on one of the walls of the late-Gothic cloister of Weingarten Abbey, near the Lake of Constance.

COUDERC, Paul. Le planétarium du Palais de la Découverte. 30 p., 14 fig. (Conférence du Palais de la Découverte) Paris: Université de Paris, 1952.

CROMMELIN, C.A. Planetaria. A historical survey. (Communication from the National Museum for the History of Science at Leyden, 94) *Antiq.Horology*, 1955, 1: 70-8, 8 fig.

CROMMELIN, C.A. Planetaria. An historical survey (including the 20th century). *Bull.Nat.Ass.Watch Clock Collect.*, 1956, 7: 132-40, 9 fig.

FELDHAUS, Franz M. Zur Geschichte der Planetarien. *Geschichtsbl.Tech.Ind.*, 1927, 11: 89-91.

FOX, Philip. Adler Planetarium and Astronomical Museum. Operated and maintained by Chicago Park District. An account of the Optical Planetarium and a brief guide to the Museum. 4th ed. 63 p., 72 fig., 3 pl. Chicago, Ill.: Ringley, 1937. [CB 64/450]

KING, H.C. The planetarium. *Endeavour*, 1959, 18: 35-44. [CB 85/388]

MARSHALL, Roy K. The planetarium. Parts I-III. *Sky Telesc.*, 1943, 3: no. 1, 3-5, 19, ill.; no. 2, 12-13, ill.; no. 3, 8-10, ill.
Part I reviewed in *Nature*, 1944, 153: 191.

MICHEL, Henri. Les ancêtres du planetarium. *Ciel Terre*, 1955, 71: 78-88, 8 fig.

PRZYPKOWSKI, Tadeusz. Astronomiczna geneza aparatu projekcyjnego. [Astronomical origin of a projecting apparatus. (In Polish with summaries in Russian and English)] *Kwart. Hist.Nauk.Tech.*, 1961, 6: 225-55.

RICE, Howard C., Jr. The Rittenhouse orrery, Princeton's eighteenth-century planetarium, 1767-1954. A commentary on an exhibition held in the Princeton Library. xi, 88 p., 16 pl. Princeton, N.J.: Princeton University Press, 1954.
Reviewed by Harry Woolf, *Isis*, 1955, 46: 76-7.

WARBURG, A. Eine astronomische Himmelsdarstellung in der alten Sakristei von S. Lorenzo in Florenz (1911). In: Warburg, A., Die Erneuerung der Heidnischen Antike, p. 169-72, 366, 1 pl. Leipzig: 1932.

Fxk astronomical instruments

for telescopes *see* FAxk
astrolabes *see* FDxp
armillary spheres *see* FFxg
sundials *see* FVxp

AMBRONN, L. Beiträge zur Geschichte der Feinmechanik. *Beitr. Gesch.Tech.Ind.*, 1919, 9: 1-40, 29 ill., bibliogr.
A history of astronomical instruments.

GUNTHER, N. Fernoptische Beobachtungs- und Messinstrumente. vi, 100 p., ill., tables. (Optik und Feinmechanik in Einzeldarstellungen, 2) Stuttgart: Wissenschaftliche Verlagsgesellschaft, 1959.
Reviewed by V. Ronchi, *Scientia*, 1960, 95: 363.

HALE, George E. The possibilities of instrumental development. *Annu.Rep.Smithsonian Inst.for 1923*, p. 187-93. Washington, D.C.: 1925.
Reprinted from *Pop.Astron.*, Nov. 1923, 31: no. 9.

MADDISON, Francis. Early astronomical and mathematical instruments. A brief survey of sources and modern studies. *Hist.Sci.*, 1963, 2: 17-50.

MICHEL, H. Quatre instruments anciens de l'Observatoire Royal de Belgique. *Ciel Terre*, 1937, 53: 129-34, ill.

PRICE, Derek J. The early observatory instruments of Trinity College, Cambridge. *Ann.Sci.*, 1952, 8: 1-12, 4 pl.

TURRIÈRE, Emile. Optique industrielle. 2 vol. in 1. 1. Verres et verreries d'optique. Objectifs photographiques. (Petzval, Steinheil, Goerz, Taylor, Zeiss) Téléobjectifs. 264 p. [2]. Appendice. Calcul des objectifs astronomiques de Fraunhofer. 2e éd. 112 p. (Travaux du Bureau d'Etudes d'optique du Service géographique de l'Armée, fasc. 1) Paris: Delagrave, 1920.

Fxk-bv

ZINNER, Ernst. Die Bücher über astronomische Instrumente. *Börsenbl.Deut.Buchhandel*, 1952, 8: no. 24, 113-14.

Fxk-by

BIGOURDAN, G. Coordonnées et instruments de l'Observatoire de la Marine. *Compt.Rend.Acad.Sci.*, 1919, 168: 1137-41.

KAYE, G.R. Astronomical instruments in the Delhi Museum. 25 p., pl. (*Mem.Archaeol.Surv.India*, 12) Calcutta: Superintendent Government Printing, India, 1921.

MICHEL, Henri. Les instruments anciens de mathématiques des Musées d'art et d'histoire. *Bull.Mus.Roy.Art Hist.*, 1935, no. 2, 26-34, 12 fig.
Chiefly sundials and astrolabes.

MORTENSEN, Harald. Den astronomiske Samling i Rundetaarn. [The astronomical collection at Rundetaarn. (In Swedish)] *Natur. Verden*, 1934, 192-236, 2 portr., 4 fig.

PRICE, Derek J. de Solla. A collection of armillary spheres and other scientific instruments. *Ann.Sci.*, 1954, 10: 172-87, 10 pl.

ZINNER, E. Kunsthistorisches Museum. Sonderschau in der neuen Burg. Bildteppiche und astronomisches Gerät. 15 p., 18 ill. Wien: 1940. [CB 71/118]
Description of the tapestries and astronomical instruments in the Kunsthistorisches Museum of Vienna.

ZINNER, E. Die Sternkundliche Abteilung des deutschen Museums von Meisterwerken der Naturwissenschaft und Technik zu München. *Sterne*, 1925, 5: 125-33, 3 fig.

Fxk-wd

ZINNER, Ernst. Deutsche und niederländische astronomische Instrumente des 11.-18. Jahrhunderts. x, 680 p., 13 fig., 80 pl. München: C.H. Beck, 1956.
Reviewed by Derek J. Price, *Isis*, 1958, 49: 87-8; for other reviews *see* CB 83/191 and 197, CB 84/310 and CB 86/458.

Fxk-wn

T'UMANYAN, B.E. Haykakan norahayt astğagitakan gorcik. [Recently discovered Armenian astronomical instruments. (In Armenian)] 32 p., ill. Yerevan: Haypethrat, 1958.

FyB use of mathematics

FyBC

BOCCARDI, Jean. La science et l'art des calculs numériques. *Rev.Gén.Sci.*, 1931, 42: 457-61.
Its importance in astronomy.

FyBV

BELOT, Emile. Le danger de l'application du calcul des probabilités aux sciences de la nature et en particulier à l'astronomie. *Scientia*, 1919, 26: 242-6. [CB 9/496]

FyCB effect of relativity

see CBzt tests of relativity

FA OPTICAL ASTRONOMY

BLACKWELL, D.E. The future of optical astronomy. 20 p. Oxford: Clarendon Press, 1962.
Reviewed by P.A. Wayman, *Observatory*, 1963, 83: 85-6.

BOCCARDI, Jean. La valeur des anciennes observations dans l'astronomie. *Rev.Gén.Sci.*, 1927, 38: 699-702.

MILLOSEVICH, E. Dalla torre di Babele al laboratorio di Groninga. *Scientia*, 1912, 12: 192-201; French transl. suppl. 80-90.

SAYILI, A. The "observation well". *Act.VIIe Congr.Int.Hist. Sci.* (Jerusalem, 1953), p. 542-50. Paris: Hermann, [n.d.].

FAqg

CAJORI, Florian. Four old astronomical observatory buildings. *Sci.Mon.*, 1928, 26: 372-6.
The Observatory at Bogota, 1803 (the earliest permanent observatory building in America), the Copenhagen Observatory, 1642, the Paris Observatory, 1667, the Greenwich Observatory, 1675.

STROOBANT, Paul, *et al.* Les observatoires astronomiques et les astronomes. 2nd ed. 314 p. Tournai/Paris: 1931. Supplément. 106 p. Gembloux: J. Duculot, 1936.

FAwb-qg

BAILEY, Solon I. The history and work of Harvard Observatory, 1839 to 1927. An outline of the origin, development and researches of the Astronomical Observatory of Harvard College, together with brief biographies of its leading members. xiii, 301 p., 23 pl. (Harvard Observatory Monographs, 4) New York: McGraw-Hill, 1931.
Reviewed by Frederick E. Brasch, *Science*, 1931, 74: 598-9.

BUSHNELL, David. The Sacramento Peak Observatory, 1947-1962. v, 77 p. Washington, D.C.: Historical Division, Office of Information, Office of Aerospace Research, 1962.

CENTENNIAL of the Observatory of the University of Cincinnati. *Science*, 1943, 98: 359.

HALE, George E. The astrophysical observatory of the California Institute of Technology. *Astrophys.J.*, 1935, 82: 111-39, 11 pl.

HARVARD UNIVERSITY. Observatory. Harvard College Observatory; the first century, a review of the past and a preview of the future. 94 p., ill. Cambridge, Mass.: The Observatory, 1946.

MEHLIN, Theodore G. Williams College renovates Hopkins Observatory. *Sky Telesc.*, 1962, 23: 67-9.
A brief history of this 125-year-old observatory.

STRUVE, Otto. The birth of McDonald Observatory. *Sky Telesc.*, 1962, 24: 316-20.

WALTERS, Raymond. The centenary of the Cincinnati Observatory. *Science*, 1943, 98: 551-3.

YERKES OBSERVATORY. *Science*, 1947, 106: 195-220, ill. [CB 72/257]
A series of articles to celebrate the 50th anniversary of the founding of the Yerkes Observatory and the American Astronomical Society.

FAwe-qg

DYSON, Frank W. Histoire de l'Observatoire de Greenwich. *Rev. Sci.*, 1931, 69: 1-13, 27 fig.

KNOX-SHAW, H. The Radcliffe Observatory. *Vistas Astron.*, 1955, 1: 144-9.

LAURIE, P.S. The old Royal Observatory. 17 p. Greenwich: National Maritime Museum, 1961.
Reviewed by J.O. Hill, *Mariner's Mirror*, 1962, 48: 147-8.

THE NORMAN LOCKYER OBSERVATORY. Unveiling of a portrait medallion of the founder. *Nature*, 1922, 110: 192-5.

SPENCER JONES, Harold. The Cape Observatory and its work. *Sci.Progr.*, 1933, 28: 1-16, 2 pl.

SPENCER JONES, Harold. The Royal Observatory, Greenwich. 44 p., ill. (Science in Britain) London: Longmans Green, 1944.

SPENCER JONES, Harold. The Royal Observatory, Greenwich. *Endeavour*, 1948, 7: 9-14.
A short history of the Observatory apropos of its moving to new quarters.

STRATTON, F.J.M. The history of the Cambridge Observatories. 26 p., 8 pl. (Annals of the Solar Physics Observatory, Cambridge, 1) Cambridge University Press, 1949.
Reviewed by R.A. Lyttleton, *Observatory,* 1950, 70: 38.

FAwf

BIGOURDAN, G. Histoire de l'astronomie d'observation et des observations en France. 2 vol. 184 p.; 198 p. Paris: Gauthier-Villars, 1918, 1931.

FAwf-qg

BAILLAUD, Benjamin. L'Observatoire de Paris et les observatoires français. *Rev.Sci.,* 1927, 65: 257-67, 293-302.

BIGOURDAN, G. Les élèves et les astronomes passagers de l'Observatoire de la Marine. *Compt.Rend.Acad.Sci.,* 1919, 169: 49-53.

BIGOURDAN, G. L'observatoire de l'Hôtel de Cluny, plus tard Observatoire de la Marine. *Compt.Rend.Acad.Sci.,* 1919, 168: 1025-30.

BIGOURDAN, G. L'Observatoire du Palais Mazarin, aujourd'hui Palais de l'Institut. *Compt.Rend.Acad.Sci.,* 1919, 169: 264-9.

BIGOURDAN, G. Sur quelques anciennes stations astronomiques du Sud-Est de la France, entre les Alpes et le Rhône. *Compt. Rend. 58e Congrès des Sociétés Savantes,* p. 21-37. Paris: 1925.

BIGOURDAN, G. Travaux de l'Observatoire de la Marine. *Compt. Rend.Acad.Sci.,* 1919, 168: 1174-8.

LE CENTENNAIRE de G. Rayet, fondateur de l'Observatoire de Bordeaux. *Astronomie,* 1940, 54: 145-7, portr.

DOUBLET, E. Les observatoires du Parc de Montsouris. *Rev. Sci.,* 1932, 70: 20-2. [CB 38/566]

FLAMMARION, C. L'entourage de l'Observatoire de Paris. *Astronomie,* 1913, 27: 157-63.

LES OBSERVATOIRES astronomiques et les astronomes. *Isis,* 1914, 2: 191.
To announce the preparation of a new edition of the book bearing this title, first published in 1907 (*see* Stroobant, Paul, FAqg).

FAwg-nh

ZINNER, E. Die Herkunft des Wortes "Sternwarte". *Vierteljahrsschr.Astron.Ges.,* 1937, 72: 132.

FAwg-qg

GUYOT, Edmond. L'Observatoire Cantonal de Neuchâtel 1858-1938. *Bull.Soc.Neuchâteloise Sci.Natur.,* 1938, 63: 5-36, 21 fig.

OBERGUGGENBERGER, Viktor. 50 Jahre Sternwarte Innsbruck. 15 p., ill. Innsbruck: Universität Sternwarte, 1954.

ZINNER, E. Die Remeis-Sternwarte von 1889-1953. *Ber.Naturforsch.Ges.Bamberg,* 1954, 34: 1-8.

ZINNER, E. Die Remeis-Sternwarte zu Bamberg in den Jahren 1940-49. *Ber.Naturforsch.Ges.Bamberg,* 1950, 32: 1-12, bibliogr.

ZINNER, E. Die Remeis-Sternwarte zu Bamberg. 96 p. (*Veröffentl.Remeis-Sternwarte Bamberg,* 4) Bamberg: 1939.

FAwh-qg

KAMIENSKI, M. Zarys dziejów Obserwatorium Warszawskiego 1815-1945. [History of the Observatory of Warsaw. (In Polish)] *Stud.Mater.Dziej.Nauk.Pol., sér. C.,* 1959, 2: 69-116.

KEPIŃSKI, F. Zaklad i obserwatorium astronomiczne Politechniki warszawskiej (1925-1955). [The Institute and Observatory of the Warsaw Polytechnic. (In Polish)] *Stud.Mater. Dziej.Nauk.Pol., sér. C.,* 1959, 2: 117-39.

FAwi-qg

RIGHINI, Guglielmo. La tradizione astronomica fiorentina e l'Osservatorio di Arcetri. *Physis,* 1962, 4: 133-50.

FAwk-qg

SITTER, Willem de. Early astronomy and the Observatory of Leyden. *Nature,* 1933, 132: 771-2.
The Observatory of Leyden had really two founders, Golius in 1633 and Kaiser in 1861.

STROOBANT, Paul. Aperçu de l'histoire de l'Observatoire Royal de Belgique. *Bull.Astron.Observ.Belg.,* 1935, 2: 5-11.

FAwm-qg

NIELSEN, Axel V. Ole Rømer-Observatoriet - dets oprindelse og dets første leder. [The Ole Romer Observatory - its origin and its first director. (In Danish with English summary)] *Arhus Stifts Arboger,* 1962, 55: 35-87.

NIELSEN, Axel V. Hundreds års astronomi på Østervold. [A hundred years of astronomy at Østervold. (In Danish, with English summary)] 53 p. Copenhagen: 1962.

FAwn-qg

BAIKOV, A.A. [Pulkovo Observatory from 1901 to 1907. (In Russian)] *Ist.Astron.Issled.,* 1959, 5: 445-56.

DZIEUWULSKI, W. Historia obserwatorium astronomicznego Uniwersytetu St. Batorego w Wilnie (1919-1939). [History of the observatory of Stefan Batory University in Vilnius. (In Polish with summaries in English and Russian)] *Stud.Mater. Dziej.Nauk.Pol., sér.C,* 1959, no. 2, 29-52.

NOVOKSHANOVA, Z.K. [The astronomical observatory of the Military Topography Department of the General Staff. (In Russian)] *Ist. Astron.Issled.,* 1958, 4: 491-8. [CB 85/451]

SHCHEGLOV, V.P. Iz istorii Tashkentskoi astronomicheskoi observatorii. [From the history of the Tashkent Astronomical Observatory. (In Russian)] *Ist.Astron.Issled.,* 1962, 8: 363-71.

STRUVE, Otto. The Poulkovo Observatory (1839-1941). *Sky Telesc.,* 1941, 1: (4), 3-4, 1 ill.

TSERASKII, V.K. [Note on the Moscow observatory. (In Russian)] *Ist. Astron.Issled.,* 1958, 4: 573-80.

VYSSOTSKY, Alexander N. Reminiscences of Pulkova Observatory. *Sky Telesc.,* 1962, 24: 12-15.

FAwy-qg

SPENCER JONES, Harold. The Cape Observatory ... *See* FAwe

FAxf-XF astronomical photography

see also FSxf-XF

FAVARO, G.A. Un grande esempio di collaborazione scientifica: il catalogo e la carta fotografica del cielo. *Scientia,* 1927, 41: 173-80, French transl. suppl., 71-8.
History of the catalogue of star photographs and of the photographic map of the sky.

FREIESLEBEN, H.C. Max Wolf. Der Bahnbrecher der Himmelsphotographie 1863-1932. 241 p., ill. (Grosse Naturforscher, 26) Stuttgart: Wissenschaftliche Verlagsgesellschaft, 1962.
Reviewed by H. Elsasser, *Naturwiss.Rundsch.,* 1963, 16: 75.

NORMAN, Daniel. The development of astronomical photography. *Osiris,* 1938, 5: 560-94, 9 fig. on 4 pl.
Brief but elaborate study, followed by a chronological outline 1839-1932, including cross references to the text.

RITCHEY, George Willis. L'évolution de l'astrophotographie et les grands télescopes de l'avenir. (The development of astrophotography and the great telescopes of the future.) Introduction de L. Delloye. 62 p., ill. Paris: Société astronomique de France, 1929.
In French and English.
Reviewed by R.A.S., *Nature,* 1930, 125: 169.

SLIPHER, Earl C. *See* FN

VAUCOULEURS, Gérard de. Astronomical photography. From the daguerreotype to the electron camera. Transl. by R. Wright. 94 p., ill., pl. New York: Macmillan, 1961. [CB 87/619]
Reviewed by Charles H. Smiley, *Science,* 1962, 136: 520.

FAxk telescopes

BAROCAS, V. Large telescopes and their use. *Scientia,* 1959, 94: 311-15.

BELL, Louis. The telescope. x, 287 p., 190 fig. New York: McGraw-Hill, 1922.
A popular account.

BOWEN, I.S. Telescopes. *Astron.J.,* 1964, 69: 816-25.

COURT, Thomas H.; ROHR, Moritz von. A history of the development of the telescope from about 1675 to 1830 based on documents in the Court collection. *Trans.Opt.Soc.,* 1928-29, 30: 207-60, 27 fig.

EISLER, Robert. The polar sighting-tube. *Arch.Int.Hist.Sci.,* 1949, 2: 312-32, 10 fig.
Prehistory of the telescope.

HALE, George Ellery. Signals from the stars. xx, 138 p., front., 56 fig. New York: Scribner, 1931. [CB 35/297]
Four essays, two dealing with solar research and two with large telescopes.

KING, Henry C. Early development of the reflecting telescope. *Refractionist,* 1939, 28: 340-55.

KING, Henry C. The history of the telescope. xvi, 456 p., ill. London: Charles Griffin; Cambridge, Mass.: U.S.A. Sky Publishing Company, 1955.
Reviewed by I. Bernard Cohen, *Isis,* 1957, 48: 357-8; for other reviews *see* CB 82/203 and CB 83/197.

KRUDY, E. von; BRUNN, A. von. Das Spiegelteleskop in der Astronomie. Geschichtliche Darstellung der wissenschaftlichen Wertung und technischen Herstellung der Spiegelteleskope sowie leichtfassliche Anleitung zur Selbstherstellung kleinerer Spiegelteleskope für Liebhaberastronomen. 2nd rev. ed. vii, 120 p., 60 fig., 3 pl. Leipzig: Barth, 1930.

LOCKYER, William J.S. The growth of the telescope. *Nature,* 1923, 112: 284-8, 4 fig.

LOCKYER, William J.S. The growth of the telescope. *Sci.Mon.,* 1924, 18: 92-104.

PEASE, F.S. Astronomical telescopes. *Annu.Rep.Smithsonian Inst.for 1928,* 201-11, 7 pl. Washington, D.C.: 1929. [CB 28/545]
A lecture delivered on Dec. 15, 1927, at the Public Library, Los Angeles. Reprinted with additional illustrations from the *Publ.Astron.Soc.Pacific,* February 1928, 40: no. 233.

RIEKHER, R. Fernrohre und ihre Meister. Eine Entwicklungsgeschichte der Fernrohrtechnik. 444 p., 262 ill. Berlin: VEB Verlag Technik, 1957.
Reviewed by Ernst Zinner, *Deut.Lit.Zeitung,* 1957, 78: (1 p.); by H. Degen, *Naturwiss.Rundsch.,* 1959, 12: 359-60.

RIEMER, Marvin F. The telescope and the world of astronomy. 211 p., ill. Stamford, Conn.: Herman, 1964.

STRAND, K. Aa. The new 61-inch astrometric reflector. *Sky Telesc.,* 1964, 27: 204-9, 232-3.
Parallax measurements since the 17th century and a new instrument to improve them.

FAxk-th

NICOLSON, Marjorie. The telescope and imagination. *Mod. Philol.,* 1935, 32: 233-60.

FAxk-wg

VHINK, W. Eine historische Bemerkung über das Fernrohr mit Fokussierlinse (Werkstätten v. F.W. Breithaupt & Sohn, Kassel). *Z.Instrumentenk.,* 1931, 51: 91-3.

FB RADIO ASTRONOMY; INFRA-RED AND RADAR ASTRONOMY

BOK, Bart J. New science of radio astronomy. *Sci.Mon.,* 1955, 80: 333-45.

HACK, M. La radioastronomia alla scoperta di un nuovo aspetto dell'Universo. 268 p., 35 fig. Bari: Edizioni Laterza, 1960.
Reviewed by G. Abetti, *Scientia,* 1961, 15: 61.

JANSKY, C.M., Jr. The discovery and identification by Karl Guthe Jansky of electromagnetic radiation of extra-terrestrial origin in the radio spectrum. *Proc.Inst.Radio Eng.,* 1958, 46: 13-15. [CB 85/469]

JANSKY, Karl Guthe. Electrical phenomena that apparently are of interstellar origin. *Pop.Astron.,* 1933, 41: 548-55.

SOUTHWORTH, George C. Early history of radio-astronomy. *Sci. Mon.,* 1956, 82: 55-66.

FC SPACE RESEARCH AND EXPLORATION

EMME, Eugene M. Aeronautics as astronautics: an American chronology of science and technology in the exploration of space, 1915-1960. xi, 240 p. Washington, D.C.: National Aeronautics and Space Administration, 1961.

LAPP, Ralph E. Man and space. 184 p. New York: Harper, 1961.
Reviewed in *Science,* 1961, 134: 42.

LEHNER, Ernst; LEHNER, Johanna. Lore and lure of outer space. 192 p., ill. New York: Tudor, 1964.

MÜLLER, Wolfgang D. Man among the stars. Translated from "Du wirst die Erde sehn als Stern". 307 p., pl. New York: Criterion, 1957.
Reviewed by Thomas S. Gardner, *Science,* 1957, 126: 1120.

SPITZER, L. The beginnings and future of space astronomy. *Amer.Scient.,* 1962, 50: 473-84.

FCda

THOMAS, Shirley. Men of space: profiles of the leaders in space research, development and exploration. Vol. 1-6. Philadelphia: Chilton, 1960-63.
Sub-title varies.

FD SPHERICAL ASTRONOMY AND ASTROMETRY

FDc general history

ALLEN, C.W. Representative measurements in astronomy. *Mon. Not.Roy.Astron.Soc.,* 1963, 125: 529-41.

BODA, Karl. 100 Jahre Parallaxenforschung (Vortragsauszug). *Jahresber.Phys.Ver.Frankfurt a.M.,* 1937-38, 29-32.

BRINTON, Henry. Measuring the universe. 100 p., ill., bibliogr. London: Methuen, 1962.

HOGG, Helen Sawyer. The historical importance of astrometry. *J.Roy.Astron.Soc.Can.,* 1963, 57: 155-62.

MICHEL, Henri. Exercices d'astronomie spherique. 29 p. Bruxelles: L'Avenir, 1952. [CB 79/172]
This booklet may be considered an elementary supplement to the author's "Traité de l'astrolabe", *see* FDxp.

NORDLINGER, H.H. Some modern methods of measuring the sidereal universe. *Scr.Math.,* 1935, 3: 317-25.

WOOLARD, Edgar W. The historical development of celestial co-ordinate systems. *Publ.Astron.Soc.Pacific,* 1942, 54: 3-16.

FDc-bx

STICKER, Bernhard; KIRCHVOGEL, P.A. Documenta astronomica; eine Ausstellung historischer Instrumente und Dokumente aus der Entwicklung der astronomischen Messkunst im Museum für Völkerkunde und Vorgeschichte, Hamburg, 23. August - 5. September 1964. 80 p., 9 pl. Wiesbaden: Franz Steiner Verlag, 1964.

FDmzYC

DINSMOOR, William Bell. Archaeology and astronomy. *Proc. Amer.Phil.Soc.,* 1939, 80: 95-173, 10 fig.

FDqx

CONGRÈS International des Éphémérides Astronomiques. Paris: 1911. *Isis*, 1913, 1: 496-7.
Account of the resolutions adopted by the Congress.

FDwm

ERLANDSSON, Hans. The orientation of the Cathedral of Lund. A lecture held at the Observatory of Lund in Samfundet för Astronomisk Historieforskning, at its meeting 23 May 1946. 19 p., ill. (Historical Notes and Papers, 21) Lund: Lund Observatory, 1948.
Also published in series: Meddelande från Lunds Astronomiska Observatorium, *ser. 2*, 123.

FDxp astrolabes and other measuring instruments

CITTERT, P.H. van. Astrolabes. A critical description of the astrolabes, noctilabes and quadrants in the care of the Utrecht University Museum. iii, 50 p., 13 fig., 27 pl. Leiden: E.J. Brill, 1954.
For reviews *see* CB 82/203, CB 83/197 and CB 84/310.

DONALDSON, Dwight M. The nomenclature and common uses of the astrolabe. *Islamic Cult.*, 1945, 19: 49-53, 5 fig.

FRANK, Josef. Zur Geschichte des Astrolabs. [Extract from thesis.] 33 p. Erlangen: 1920. [CB 10/190]

GINSBURG, Jekuthiel. The astrolabe. *Ind.Mus.N.Y.*, 1930, 1: 1-14, 5 fig.

GUNTHER, Robert William Theodore. The astrolabe: its uses and derivatives. *Scot.Geogr.Mag.*, 1927, 43: 135-47. [CB 24/529]

GUNTHER, Robert William Theodore. The astrolabes of the world. Based upon the series of instruments in the Lewis Evans Collection in the Old Ashmolean Museum at Oxford, with notes on astrolabes in the collections of the British Museum, Science Museum, Sir J. Findlay, Mr. S.V. Hoffman, the Mensing Collection, and in other public and private collections. 2 vol. 1. The Eastern astrolabes. xvii, iii, 304 p., 139 fig., 68 pl.; 2. The Western astrolabes. viii, p. 305-610, 83 pl., fig. Oxford University Press, 1932.
Reviewed by A. Pogo, *Isis*, 1933, 20: 310-16; 1934, 20: 492-5.

GUNTHER, Robert William Theodore. The mariner's astrolabe. *Geogr.J.*, 1928, 72: 342-4.

IONIDES, Stephen A. Astrolabes. *Eng.Bull.* (Denver), Jan. 1938, 2 p.

LATHAM, Marcia. The astrolabe. *Amer.Math.Mon.*, 1917, 24: 162-8.
Explains the principles and use of the astrolabe.

MICHEL, Henri. Traité de l'astrolabe. viii, 202 p., 24 pl. Paris: Gauthier-Villars, 1947.
Reviewed by G. Van Biesbroeck, *Isis*, 1948, 39: 194.

RENAUD, H.P.J. Sur une tablette d'astrolabe appartenant à Henri Terrasse. *Hespéris*, 1939, 26: 157-69, 3 pl.

SOTTAS, Jules. L'astrolabe-quadrant du Musée de Rouen. *Astronomie*, 1912, 26: 422-9.

ZINNER, Ernst. Über die früheste Form des Astrolabs. *Ber. Naturforsch.Ges.Bamberg*, 1947, 30: 9-21, 2 fig. [CB 72/271]

FDxp-bw

GARCÍA FRANCO, Salvador. Catálogo crítico de astrolabios existentes en España. vii, 446 p., 84 fig. Madrid: Instituto Histórico de Marina, 1945. [CB 73/168]

PRICE, Derek J. de Solla. An international checklist of astrolabes. *Arch.Int.Hist.Sci.*, 1955, 8: 243-63, 363-81.

FE THE HEAVENLY BODIES

FEu

MENZEL, Donald H. Flying saucers. xii, 319 p., ill. Cambridge, Mass.: Harvard University Press, 1953. [CB 80/145]

FEu-bv

JOBES, Gertrude; JOBES, James. Outer space: myths, name meanings and calendars from the emergence of history to the present day. 479 p. New York: Scarecrow Press, 1964.
Reviewed by Jay K. Lucker, *Libr.J.*, Nov. 1964, 4510.

FEyGD

STROOBANT, Paul. Sur l'agrandissement apparent des constellations, du soleil et de la lune à l'horizon. (Troisième note) *Bull.Acad.Roy.Belg.Cl.Sci.*, 1928, 14: 91-108. [CB 28/545]

FEyJ

SPENCER, Harold Jones. Life on other worlds. xiv, 259 p., 17 pl. London: English Universities Press, 1940.
Reviewed by J.H. Jeans, *Nature*, 1940, 146: 211-12.

FEyX

MORRISON, Philip. Interstellar communication. *Bull.Phil.Soc. Wash.*, 1962, 16: 59-81.

FF SOLAR SYSTEM (including the planets in general)

CHAMBERLIN, Thomas Chrowder. The genesis of planets. Study of fundamental problems of geology. *Year Book Carnegie Inst. Wash.*, 1924, no. 23, 268-80.

CHAMBERLIN, Thomas Chrowder. The two solar families: the sun's children. xxi, 311 p., ill. Chicago: University of Chicago Press, 1928.

CORTESE, Emilio. Planetologia. vii, 387 p., ill. (Manuali Hoepli, 397-8) Milano: Hoepli, 1913. [CB 3/567]

FRISCHAUF, Johannes. Grundriss der theoretischen Astronomie und der Geschichte der Planetentheorie. 3rd enl. ed. xvi, 248 p., 22 fig. Leipzig: Engelmann, 1922.
2nd edition 1903.

LAFLEUR, L.J. Cranks and scientists. *Sci.Mon.*, 1951, 73: 284-9.
Apropos of Velikovsky's "Worlds in collision", *see* below.

MALISOFF, William Marias. Some new laws for the solar system. *Science*, 1929, 70: 328-9. [CB 27/545]
Apropos of A.E. Caswell's suggested law, namely, the mean distances of the planets from the sun are proportional to the squares of simple integral numbers, made in a letter to *Science*, 1929, 69: 384. See also Caswell's reply to the above article, ibid. 70: 538.

PANNEKOEK, Antonie. Planetary theories. *Pop.Astron.*, 1947, 55: 422-38; 1948, 56: 2-13, 63-75, 177-92, 300-12.

PRICE, Derek J. de S. Contra-Copernicus: a critical re-estimation of the mathematical planetary theory of Ptolemy, Copernicus and Kepler. In: Clagett, Marshall, ed. Critical Problems in the History of Science, p. 197-218. Madison, Wis.: University of Wisconsin Press, 1959.

RYBKA, Eugeniusz. Four hundred years of the Copernican heritage. Transl. by Marianna Abrahamowicz. 235 p., 50 ill., bibliogr. (Jagellonian University Jubilee Publications, 18) Cracow: Jagellonian University of Cracow, 1964. [CB 90/516]

STIMSON, Dorothy. The gradual acceptance of the Copernican theory of the universe. 147 p., 3 pl. New York: Baker and Taylor Co., 1917. [CB 11/439]

VELIKOVSKY, Immanuel. Worlds in collision. xiv, 401 p. New York: Macmillan, 1950. [CB 78/183]
Reviewed by Otto Neugebauer, *Isis*, 1950, 41: 245-6.

WATANABE, Masao; OGAWA, Sekiko. [A comparison of heliocentric and geocentric systems by models. (In Japanese)] *J.Hist.Sci.Japan*, 1961, no. 58, 34-7.

FFcg

MEEUS, Jean. Tables of the moon and sun. 273 p. Kessel-Lo, Belgium: Kesselberg Sterrenwacht, 1962.
Reviewed by Raynor L. Duncombe, *Sky Telesc.*, 1963, 26: 42-3.

SCHOCH, Karl. Planeten-Tafeln für Jedermann. Zur Berechnung der geozentrischen Oerter und Helligkeiten der grossen Planeten (und des Mondes) für den Zeitraum von 3400 v. Chr. bis 2600 n. Chr. ohne Anwendung der Logarithmen und trigonometrischen Funktionen bis auf ein Zehntel Grad unter besonderer Berücksichtigung der Babylonischen Astronomie. Mit über 100 leicht verständlichen, vollständig durchgeführten Beispielen für alle astronomischen Vorgänge von Hammurabi bis zum Jahre 1927. 14, 15 p. Berlin-Pankow: Linser-Verlag, 1927.

STAHLMAN, William D.; GINGERICH, Owen. Solar and planetary longitudes for years - 2500 to + 2000 by 10-day intervals. xxix, 566 p. Madison: University of Wisconsin Press, 1963.
Reviewed by E.S. Kennedy, *Isis*, 1964, 55: 221-2; for other reviews *see* CB 89/500 and CB 90/516.

TUCKERMAN, Bryant. Planetary, lunar, and solar positions, A.D. 2 to A.D. 1649 at five-day and ten-day intervals. 842 p. (American Philosophical Society Memoirs, 59) Philadelphia: The Society, 1964. [CB 90/516]

FFnb

PARTINGTON, J.R. The origins of the planetary svmbols ror the metals. *Ambix*, 1937, 1: 61-4.

FFth

PROCTOR, Mary. Legends of the sun and moon. 159 p. London: Harrap, 1926.

FFwh

ZEMPLÉN, Jolán M. [Copernicus and Hungary. (In Polish)] *Kwart.Hist.Nauk.Tech.*, 1962, 7: 259-84.

FFwm

SANDBLAD, Henrik. [The Copernican system of the universe in Sweden. (In Swedish, with English summary)] *Lychnos*, 1943, 149-88; 1944-45, 79-131.

FFwn

RABINOVICH, I.M.; APINIS, A.A. [On the history of the heliocentric theory in Latvia. (In Russian)] *Ist.Astron.Issled.*, 1960, 6: 194-211.

FFwt

SZCZEŚNIAK, Boleslaw. Notes on the penetration of the Copernican theory into China (17th-19th centuries). *J.Roy.Asiat. Soc.*, 1945, 30-8, 3 pl.

SZCZEŚNIAK, Boleslaw. The penetration of the Copernican theory into China and Japan (17th-19th centuries). *Bull.Pol.Inst. Arts Sci.Amer.*, 1945, 3: 699-717.

SZCZEŚNIAK, Boleslaw. The penetration of the Copernican theory into feudal Japan. *J.Roy.Asiat.Soc.*, 1944, 52-61, 2 pl.

FFxg mechanical models

NOLTE, Friedrich. Die Armillarsphäre. 50 p. (*Abhandl.Gesch. Naturwiss.Med.*, 2) Erlangen: 1922. [CB 14/541]

PRICE, Derek J. de Solla. A collection of armillary spheres and other scientific instruments. *Ann.Sci.*, 1954, 10: 172-87, 10 pl.

FFxg-wf

POULLE, Emmanuel. L'horloge astronomique de la cathédrale de Bourges. *Bull.Soc.Nat.Antiquair.Fr.*, 1961, 168-75.

SENAC, E.J. La pendule astronomique. 16 p., 8 fig. (Les Conférences du Palais de la Découverte) Paris: Université de Paris, 1948. [CB 84/310]

UNGERER, Alfred. L'horloge astronomique de la cathédrale de Strasbourg. *Compt.Rend.Ie Congr.Int.Math.* (Strasbourg, 1920), p. 656-63. Toulouse: E. Privat, 1921. [CB 14/567]

UNGERER, Alfred. L'horloge astronomique de la cathédrale de Strasbourg. Avec la collaboration de A. Danjon et G. Rougier. 60 p. Paris: Société astronomique de France, 1922.

FFyX interplanetary communications

VOROB'EV, B.N. Nachalo rabot K.E. Tsiolkovskogo po mezhplanetnym soobshcheniiam. [Early work of K.E. Tsiolkovskii on interplanetary communications. (In Russian)] *Vop.Ist. Est. Tekh.*, 1958, no. 6, 30-8.

FFyXwn-qd

KRAMAROV, G.M. Obshchestvo izucheniia meshplanetnykh soobshchenii. [The Society for the Study of Interplanetary Communication. (In Russian)] *Tr.Inst.Ist.Est.Tekh.*, 1962, 45: 107-14.

FG ORIGIN OF THE SOLAR SYSTEM

for cosmogony in general *see* FU

BELOT, E. Essai de cosmogonie tourbillonnaire. 28 p. Paris: 1911.
Reviewed by G. Sarton, *Isis*, 1913, 1: 30.

BELOT, E. L'origine dualiste de la terre et des mondes. *Rev. Quest.Sci.*, 1925, 7: 33-52.
A summary of the hypothesis outlined in the book above.

DAUVILLIER, Alexandre. L'origine des planètes: essai de cosmogonie. 221 p. Paris: University of France Press, 1956.
Reviewed by S.A. Korff, *Phys.Today*, 1957, 10: 40.

DINGLE, Herbert. The origin of the solar system. *Nature*, 1932, 129: 333-5.

FAIRCHILD, Herman L. Our world in the making. *Science*, 1926, 64: 365-71.
Synoptic comparison of the nebular or Laplacian hypothesis and of the planetesimal theory defended by T.C. Chamberlin and F.R. Moulton.

GIFFORD, A.C. The origin of the solar system. 1. From the Chaldeans to Chamberlin and Moulton; 2. From Jeans to the present day. *Scientia*, 1932, 52: 141-56, 203-22.

JEANS, James Hopwood. The origin of the solar system. *Nature*, 1924, 113: suppl. March 1, 329-40.
Discourse delivered at the Royal Institution on February 15.

MOULTON, Forest Ray. The planetesimal hypothesis. *Science*, 1928, 68: 549-59.

SAUSSURE, Léopold de. La série septénaire cosmologique et planétaire. *J.Asiatique*, 1924, 204: 333-70. [CB 22/263]

SKILLING, Wm. T. A continued search for the beginning. *Sci.Mon.*, 1949, 68: 84-90.
Brief description of the hypothetical origin of the solar system arranged chronologically.

SPENCER JONES, Harold. The origin of the solar system. *Endeavour*, 1951, 10: 119-25.

UREY, Harold C. The planets. Their origin and development. xvii, 245 p., 16 fig. New Haven: Yale University Press, 1952. [CB 79/173]

FH MOTIONS; CELESTIAL MECHANICS

AITON, E.J. The vortex theory of the planetary motions. *Ann. Sci.*, 1957, 13: 249-64; 1958, 14: 132-47, 157-72.

BIRKHOFF, George D. Recent advances in dynamics. *Science*, 1920, 51: 51-5.
Progress of celestial mechanics with special reference to Jacobi, G.W. Hill, Burns, Poincaré, Levi-Civita and Sundman.

BOYER, Carl B. Note on epicycles and the ellipse from Copernicus to Lahire. *Isis*, 1947, 38: 54-6.

FOTHERINGHAM, John K. Trepidation. *Mon.Not.Roy.Astron.Soc.*, 1926-27, 87: 142-67, 182-96. [CB 28/544]

MICHEL, Henri. Sur l'origine de la théorie de la trépidation. *Ciel Terre*, 1950, 66: 227-34.

PICART, Luc. Calcul des orbites et des éphémérides. 306 p. (Encyclopédie Scientifique) Paris: Doin, 1913.

PLUMMER, H.C. The present position of celestial mechanics. *Scientia*, 1921, 29: 1-12, French transl. suppl., 1-11

SESMAT, Augustin. Le système absolu classique et les mouvements réels. Etude historique et critique. 688 p. (Actualités Scientifiques et Industrielles, 479-85) Paris: Hermann, 1936.
Reviewed by Jules Géhéniau, *Isis*, 1940, 31: 476-8.

TOULMIN, Stephen; GOODFIELD, June. *See* Fc-bm

VINCENT, Maxime. Les dépressions sidérales. Nouvelles hypothèses sur la constitution de la matière et la mécanique céleste. 2nd ed. 108 p. Paris: Fischbacher, 1913.

WILLIAMS, Kenneth P. *See* FO

WINTNER, Aurel. The analytical foundations of celestial mechanics. xii, 448 p. (Princeton Mathematical Series, 5) Princeton: Princeton University Press, 1941.
Reviewed by I.B. Cohen, *Isis*, 1943, 34: 230.

WODETZKY, Joseph. Über die Definition der Syzygien. *Jubilee volume in honour of Edward Mahler*, p. 374-8. Budapest: Mahler Ede Jubileumi Emlékbizottsag, 1937.

FHyCB

CHAZY, Jean. La théorie de la relativité et la mécanique céleste. viii, 261 p. Paris: Gauthier-Villars, 1930.

POOR, Charles Lane. The motions of the planets and the relativity theory. *Science*, 1921, 54: 30-4.

FJ ECLIPSES, TRANSITS AND OCCULTATIONS

FOTHERINGHAM, John K. Historical eclipses. Being the Halley lecture delivered May 17, 1921. 32 p. Oxford: Clarendon Press, 1921.

GINZEL, F.-K. Beiträge zur Kenntnis der historischen Sonnenfinsternisse und zur Frage ihrer Verwendbarkeit. 43 p., 2 pl. (*Abhandl.Preuss.Akad.Wiss.Phys.Math.Kl.*, 1918, no. 4) Berlin: 1918. [CB 11/438]

LOCKYER, W.J.S. Total solar eclipses in the British Isles. *Nature*, 1927, 119: 87-90. [CB 22/263]
Historical summary with special reference to the eclipse of June 29, 1927.

MITCHELL, Samuel Alfred. Eclipses of the sun. 4th rev. ed. xviii, 520 p., 9 fig., 80 pl. New York: Columbia University Press, 1935.
First publ. 1923. [CB 16/286]
Reviewed by Alexander Pogo, *Isis*, 1936, 25: 496-504.

POGO, Alexander. The saros cycle ending with the partial eclipse of January 5, 1935. *Pop.Astron.*, 1935. 43: 7-14, 2 fig., 2 maps. [CB 44/517]
The first of a series of papers dealing with the periodicity of eclipses.

POGO, Alexander. The eclipse of February 3, 1935 - a partial eclipse visible in Central America. *Pop.Astron.*, 1935, 43: 95-9, 3 fig. [CB 44/517]
The second of a series of papers dealing with the periodicity of eclipses.

POGO, Alexander. Lunar saros series. *Pop.Astron.*, 1935, 43: 207-13, 2 fig. [CB 44/517]
The third of a series of papers dealing with the periodicity of eclipses.

POGO, Alexander. Solar saros series. *Pop.Astron.*, 1935, 43: 335-44, 1 fig. [CB 45/280]
The fourth of a series of papers dealing with the periodicity of eclipses.

POGO, Alexander. Calendar years with five solar eclipses. *Pop.Astron.*, 1935, 43: 412-23, 2 diagr. [CB 46/589]
The fifth of a series of papers dealing with the periodicity of eclipses.

POGO, Alexander. Calendar years with three lunar eclipses. *Pop.Astron.*, 1935, 43: 549-57, 2 diagr. [CB 46/590]
The sixth of a series of papers dealing with the periodicity of eclipses.

POGO, Alexander. The eclipse of 1935 December 25 - an umbral eclipse of the midnight sun in the Antarctic. *Pop.Astron.*, 1935, 43: 617-27, 2 diagr. [CB 46/590]
The seventh of a series of papers dealing with the periodicity of eclipses.

POGO, Alexander. Classification of solar and lunar eclipses. *Pop.Astron.*, 1937, 45: 540-9.

POGO, Alexander. The eclipse of 1938 November 22 - a partial solar eclipse visible in the tropics. *Pop.Astron.*, 1938, 46: 565-7.

POGO, Alexander. The four penumbral lunar eclipses of 1944. *Pop.Astron.*, 1943, 51: 129-33, 4 fig.

POGO, Alexander. Limits of umbral runs in lunar saros series. *Pop.Astron.*, 1938, 46: 456-61.

POGO, Alexander. The lunar appulse of 1936 December 28. *Pop. Astron.*, 1936, 44: 79-81, 481-3, 2 fig.

POGO, Alexander. The lunar appulses of 1882 and their exeligmos returns in 1936. *Publ.Astron.Soc.Pacific*, 1935, 47: 187-90.

POGO, Alexander. The lunar eclipse of 1938 May 14 and its saros series. *Pop.Astron.*, 1938, 46: 385-9.

POGO, Alexander. The lunar saros series of the Columbus eclipse of 1504 February 29 - March 1. *Pop.Astron.*, 1936, 44: 353-63.

POGO, Alexander. On the visibility of lunar appulses. *Pop. Astron.*, 1937, 45: 83-6, 2 fig.

POGO, Alexander. The penumbral lunar eclipses of 1940. *Pop. Astron.*, 1940, 48: 125-7, 3 fig.

POGO, Alexander. The solar eclipse of 1938 May 29 - the first umbral eclipse of its saros series. *Pop.Astron.*, 1938, 46: 256-9.

ROME, A. Sur une loi empirique des éclipses de lune. *Ann. Soc.Sci.Bruxelles*, 1931, 51: 94-103. [CB 35/298]

SCHROETER, J. Fr. Spezieller Kanon der zentralen Sonnen- und Mondfinsternisse welche innerhalb des Zeitraumes von 600 bis 1800 n. Chr. in Europa sichtbar waren. xxiv, 305 p., maps, tables. Kristiania: Jacob Dybwad, 1923. [CB 15/208]

TSU WEN SHION. A statistical survey of solar eclipses in Chinese history. *Pop.Astron.*, 1934, 42: 136-41.
Of the 920 eclipses recorded, 174 were partial, 335 total, 343 annular, 61 annular-total, and 7 eclipses were "in error and did not take place".

FK SUN

ABETTI, Giorgio. Il sole. 2nd ed. xix, 562 p., ill. Milano: Hoepli, 1952.
First publ. 1934.
Reviewed by A. Natucci, *Arch.Int.Hist.Sci.*, 1953, 6: 117.

FLEMING, John Ambrose. The sun and the earth's magnetic field. *Annu.Rep.Smithsonian Inst.for 1942*, p. 173-208, ill. Washington, D.C.: 1943.

FORBES, Eric Gray. A history of the solar red shift problem. *Ann.Sci.*, 1961, 17: 129-64.

FORTI, Umberto. Nulla e molto di nuovo intorno al sole. *Nuova Antologia, 7th ser.*, 1931, 275: 512-22.

GAMOW, George. The birth and death of the sun. Stellar evolution and subatomic energy. xix, 219 p., 60 fig. (Pelican Books) New York: Penguin Books, 1945.
First published by Viking Press, New York, in 1940; second edition, 1945.

HALE, George Ellery. Signals from the stars. xx, 138 p., front., 56 fig. New York: Scribner, 1931. [CB 35/297]
Four essays, two dealing with solar research and two with large telescopes.

KHAN, Mohd. A.R. The zodiacal light. *Stud.Hyderabad Acad.*, 1939, 1: 1-13.
Historical and theoretical account of zodiacal light and more briefly of the counterglow.

MIKAILOV, A.A. The deflection of light by the gravitational field of the sun. *Mon.Not.Roy.Astron.Soc.*, 1959, 119: 593-608.

ST. JOHN, Charles E. Growth in our knowledge of the sun. *Annu.Rep.Smithsonian Inst.for 1930*, p. 177-89, 7 pl. Washington, D.C.: 1931.
Reprinted, with the author's alterations and additions, from *Publ.Astron.Soc.Pacific*, June 1929, 41: 133-44.

SANDIG, H.-U. Zur Beobachtungsgeschichte des Zodiakallichtes. *Ber.Naturforsch.Ges.Bamberg*, 1947, 30: 23-31. [CB 72/271]

SARTON, George. Early observations of the sunspots? (Query no. 111) *Isis*, 1947, 37: 69-71.

SCHOVE, D. Justin. The earliest dated sunspot. *J.Brit. Astron.Ass.*, 1950, 61: 22-5.

SCHOVE, D. Justin. Sunspot epochs 188 A.D. to 1610 A.D. *Pop.Astron.*, 1948, 56: 247-52, 2 fig.

SCHOVE, D. Justin. Sunspots and aurorae. *J.Brit.Astron.Ass.*, 1948, 58: 178-90, 1 fig.
A historical review.

SCHOVE, D. Justin. Sunspots, aurorae and blood rain: the spectrum of time. *Isis*, 1951, 42: 133-8.

SHALER, Amos J. Solar physics (origin to 1875). 40 p. (Actualités Scientifiques et Industrielles, 777) Paris: Hermann, 1939.

STETSON, Harlan True. Sunspots and their effects. xv, 201 p., 15 fig., front. New York: McGraw-Hill, 1937. [CB 53/260]

TRUMPLER, Robert. Historical note on the problem of light deflection in the sun's gravitational field. *Science*, 1923, 58: 161-3. [CB 15/231]

TURNER, H.H. On an unsuccessful search for the 9.2-year magnetic period in sunspot records, with a new analysis of those records back to 1610. *Mon.Not.Roy.Astron.Soc.*, 1925-26, 86: 119-30. [CB 28/545]

ZINNER, Ernst. Ältere Beobachtung von Sonnenflecken. *Ber. Naturforsch.Ges.Bamberg*, 1952, 33: 36-7.

FKqy

CONGRÈS (Ve) de l'Union Internationale pour les Recherches Solaires. Bonn: 1913. *Isis*, 1913, 1: 493-5.
Account of Congress and work of its seven Commissions.

FKwb-qg

ADAMS, W.S. Early solar research at Mount Wilson. *Vistas Astron.*, 1955, 1: 619-23.

HALE, George Ellery. Ten years' work of a mountain laboratory: a brief account of the Mount Wilson solar observatory of the Carnegie Institution of Washington. 99 p., 65 fig. Washington: Carnegie Institution, 1915.

FKwe

EVERSHED, J. Recollections of seventy years of scientific work. *Vistas Astron.*, 1955, 1: 33-40, 5 fig.

FKwi-qg

ABETTI, Giorgio. Thirty years of solar work at Arcetri. *Vistas Astron.*, 1955, 1: 624-30, 2 fig.

FKxf-CP

HALE, George Ellery. Some new possibilities in solar research. *Nature*, 3 July 1926, 118: suppl., 1-8.
Describing the use of a spectroheliscope.

FKyG

RAMOS DA COSTA, A. A influência da actividade solar na meteorologia. Historia da sua evolução. *Petrus Nonius*, 1939, 2: 97-103.

FL EARTH AS A PLANET

for geophysics *see* GI
tides *see* GYzt
geodesy *see* HB

BEGHIN, Henri. Les preuves de la rotation de la terre. 22 p., 17 fig. (Les Conférences du Palais de la Découverte, 23 avril 1955, A-207) Paris: Université de Paris, 1955.

CHAMBERLIN, Thomas Chrowder. The genesis of planets. Study of fundamental problems of geology. *Year Book Carnegie Inst. Wash.*, 1924, no. 23, 268-80.

CHAMBERLIN, Thomas Chrowder. The growth of the earth. *Scientia*, 1927, 42: 117-27, 181-92; French transl. suppl., 47-57, 81-91.

CHAMBERLIN, Thomas Chrowder. The two solar families: the sun's children. xxi, 311 p., ill. Chicago: University of Chicago Press, 1928.

COHEN, I. Bernard. The theory of concentric spheres again. *Isis*, 1944, 35: 333-4.
Discusses Edna Kenton's The book of earths, 1928 and her account of various concave cosmogonies, *see below*.

DUNGEN, F.H. van den; COX, J.F.; MIEGHEM, J. van. Les fluctuations de la rotation de la terre. *Scientia*, 1957, 92: 269-72.

DUNGEN, F.H. van den; COX, J.F.; MIEGHEM, J. van. Sur quelques astronomes qui n'ont pas postulé implicitement l'uniformité de la rotation de la terre. *Bull.Acad.Roy. Belg.Cl.Sci.*, 1950, 36: 801-10.

GUYOT, Edmond. La rotation de la terre et ses variations. *Ann.Guébhard-Séverine*, 1953, 29: 117-41.

KENTON, Edna. The book of earths. xxv, 290 p., ill. New York: W. Morrow, 1928.
Reviewed by I.B. Cohen, *Isis*, 1944, 35: 333-4.

McCOLLEY, Grant. The theory of the diurnal rotation of the earth. *Isis*, 1937, 26: 392-402. [CB 51/257]

NORMAN, Daniel; SARTON, George. The fantastic theory of concentric spheres. *Isis*, 1942, 34: 29-30.

PARSON, George. Discovery of the earth. vi, 232 p. Boston: J.W. Luce, 1929. [CB 27/545]

SMART, W.M. The origin of the earth. vi, 239 p., 8 pl., 42 fig. Cambridge University Press, 1951. [CB 79/173]

STETSON, Harlan T. Modern evidences for differential movement of certain points on the earth's surface. *Science*, 1944, 100: 87-93, 113-17.

WOOLARD, Edgar William. Historical note on the deflecting influence of the rotation of the earth. *J.Franklin Inst.*, 1942, 233: 465-70.

FM MOON

BOTH, Ernst E. A history of lunar studies. 34 p. Buffalo, N.Y.: Buffalo Museum of Science, 1962.
Reviewed in *Sky Telesc.*, 1962, 23: 284.

FAUTH, Hermann. Philipp Fauth and the moon. *Sky Telesc.*, 1959, 19: 21-4.

FLECKENSTEIN, J.O. 300 Jahre Mondforschung. *Experientia*, 1947, 3: 83-4, 1 fig.

FOTHERINGHAM, J.K. The longitude of the moon from 1627 to 1918. *Mon.Not.Roy.Astron.Soc.*, 1919-20, 80: 289-307.

GÜTTLER, A.; PETRI, W. Der Mond. Kulturgeschichte und Astronomie des Erdtrabanten. 71 p., ill. Heidelberg: Heinz Moos Verlag, 1962.
Reviewed by Heinz Degen, *Naturwiss.Rundsch.*, 1963, 16: 118.

SLAVENAS, P. [The motion of the moon. A review of the problem from antiquity to the present. (In Lithuanian)] *Kosmos* (Kaunas), 1931, 12: 165-81.

YAMPOLSKY, Philip. The origin of the twenty-eight lunar mansions. *Osiris*, 1950, 9: 62-83.

FMcn

CALLATAY, Vincent de. Atlas de la lune. xi, 144 p. Paris: Gauthier-Villars, 1962.
Reviewed by G. Fielder, *Observatory*, 1963, 83: 86.

FAUTH, Philipp. Grosser Mondatlas [with explanatory text in German. 2nd ed.] 38 p., ill., portr., 31 maps; portfolio of 25 maps. Bremen: Olbers-Gesellschaft, 1964.

LE MORVAN, C. Grande carte photographique et systématique de la lune, avec introduction. 48 pl. in 8 fasc., 1 suppl. fasc. Paris: G. Thomas, 1914.

MOORE, Patrick. Selenography: mapping the moon. *Discovery*, 1959, 20: 420-7.

FMnh

HUMBERT, Pierre. Les premiers essais de nomenclature lunaire. *Sphinx* (Brussels), 1938, 8: 93-4.

WANDERS, A.J.M. Het ontstaan van de tegenwoordige maannomenclatuur. [The creation of the modern lunar nomenclature. (In Dutch)] *Hemel Dampkring*, 1944, 42: 1-5, 21-7, 2 ill. [CB 71/118]

FMnj

EVERSHED, Mary Acworth. Who's who in the moon. Notes on the names of all lunar formations adopted in 1935 by the International Astronomical Union. *Mem.Brit.Astron.Ass.*, 1938, 34: part 1, 3-130, 2 pl.

FMu

BELLAMY, Hans Schindler. Moons, myths and man. A reinterpretation. 358 p., ill. London: Faber, 1936.

DERCHAIN, P., *et al.* La lune. Mythes et rites. 373 p., 2 maps. Paris: Editions du Seuil, 1962.
Reviewed by A.S. Tritton, *J.Roy.Asiatic Soc.*, 1963, 116.

FMwg-u

WOLF, Werner. Der Mond im deutschen Volksglauben. 91 p., 11 fig. (Bausteine zur Volkskunde und Religionswissenschaft, 2) Bühl: Konkordia, 1929.
Reviewed by L. Mackensen, *Deut.Lit.Zeitung*, 1930, 1: 158-60; by Marzell, *Mitt.Gesch.Med.*, 1932, 31: 245.

FMwn

T'UMANYAN, B.E. Lunnyĭ ukazatel. [Lunar index. (In Russian)]. *Ist.Astron.Issled.*, 1960, 6: 256-62.
A page from the history of practical astronomy in Armenia.

FMyCU

FORBES, V.S. The moon and radioactivity. *Annu.Rep.Smithsonian Inst.for 1930*, p. 207-17. Washington, D.C.: 1931.
Reprinted, with author's alterations and additions, from the *Geol.Mag.*, February 1929, 66: 57-65.

FMyFCth

NICOLSON, Marjorie Hope. Voyages to the moon. 297 p. New York: Macmillan, 1949.
Reviewed by Mark Graubard, *Isis*, 1949, 40: 286.

FMyFCwb

STREETER, John W. Twenty Americans on the moon. *Sky Telesc.*, 1947, 6: no. 8, 11.

FMyGG

SPURR, J.E. Geology applied to selenology. The Imbrian Plain region of the moon. viii, 112 p., 4 pl., 23 fig. Lancaster, Pa.: Science Press, 1944. [CB 68/53]

FN OTHER PLANETS AND SATELLITES

ABETTI, Giorgio. La interpretazione delle configurazioni del pianeta Marte. *Atti Fond.Ronchi*, 1957, 12: 400-3, 5 pl.

ALEXANDER, A.F. O'D. The planet Saturn. A history of observation, theory and discovery. 474 p., fig., pl. London: Faber; New York: Macmillan, 1962.
For reviews *see* CB 88/540 and CB 89/499.

ANTONIADI, E.M. Le planète Mars: étude basée sur les résultats obtenus avec la grande lunette de l'Observatoire de Meudon et exposé analytique de l'ensemble des travaux exécutés sur cet astre depuis 1659. ix, 240 p., 10 pl. Paris: Hermann, 1930. [CB 32/578]
Reviewed by A.V., *Rev.Gén.Sci.*, 1930, 41: 584; in *Nature*, 1931, 127: 51-3.

ANTONIADI, E.M. La planète Mercure et la rotation des satellites: étude basée sur les résultats obtenus avec la grande lunette de l'Observatoire de Meudon. 76 p., 36 fig., 3 pl. Paris: Gauthier-Villars, 1934.
Reviewed by Pierre Brunet, *Archeion*, 1935, 17: 299.

ASHBROOK, Joseph. Astronomical scrapbook: W.H. Pickering and the satellites of Jupiter. *Sky Telesc.*, 1963, 26: 335-6.

FAYET, G. Les petites planètes. 146 p., 16 fig., tables. (*Annu.Bur.Longitudes* (Paris), 1932, notice B) Paris: Gauthier-Villars, 1932. [CB 38/595]

GOLDSCHMIDT, Victor. Der Planet Pluto und die Harmonie der Sphären. 22 p. Heidelberg: Winter, 1932.
Reviewed by J. Ruska, *Deut.Lit.Zeitung*, 1933, 4: 185-6.

GROSSER, Morton. The search for a planet beyond Neptune. *Isis*, 1964, 55: 163-83.
History of the discovery of Pluto.

LUYTEN, Willem J. Pluto not a planet? *Science*, 1956, 123: 896-7. [CB 82/203]

MAGGINI, Mentore. Le macchie e i "canali" di Marte. *Scientia*, 1930, 47: 304-14; French transl. suppl., 125-32.

MAUDERLI, S. Die Welt der kleinen Planeten. *Experentia*, 1946, 2: 204-10.
Includes historical survey of the discovery of the small planets.

NICHOLSON, Seth B. The satellites of Jupiter. *Annu.Rep.Smithsonian Inst.for 1940*, p. 131-8, 1 pl. Washington, D.C.: 1941.

SLIPHER, Earl C. The photographic story of Mars. 168 p. Cambridge, Mass.: Sky Publishing Corporation; Flagstaff, Ariz.: Northland Press, 1962.
From 1905 to 1960 Slipher photographed every opposition of Mars. This work is summarized.
Reviewed by Audouin Dollfus, *Sky Telesc.*, 1963, 25: 165-6.

TOMBAUGH, Clyde William. Reminiscences of the discovery of Pluto. *Sky Telesc.*, 1960, 19: 264-70.

VAUCOULEURS, Gérard de. The planet Mars. Translated from the French by Patrick A. Moore. 87 p., ill. London: Faber, 1950.
French edition: Le problème Martien (Paris: Elzévir, 1946) reviewed by P.L. Dupont, *Ciel Terre*, 1947, 63: 61.

WOOLARD, Edgar. Comparison of the observations of Uranus previous to 1781 with theoretical positions obtained by numerical integration. *Astron.J.*, 1952, 57: 35-8.

FNnh

BARTON, Samuel G. The names of the satellites. *Pop.Astron.*, 1946, 44: 1-10.

FNp

PROJET d'organisation pour l'observation des astéroïdes. *Isis*, 1913, 1: 260, 497.

FO COMETS AND METEORS

ASHBROOK, Joseph. Astronomical scrapbook: harvester of the skys. *Sky Telesc.*, 1963, 25: 198-9.
William R. Brooks, discoverer of comets.

BOCCARDI, Jean. Les idées modernes relativement aux comètes. *Rev.Gén.Sci.*, 1928, 39: 69-71.

HUJER, Karel. On the history of Biela's comet and the origin of periodic meteors. *Proc.10th Int.Congr.Hist.Sci.* (Ithaca, 1962), (2), p. 773-6. Paris: Hermann, 1964.

KHAN, Mohd. A.R. Meteoric showers, past and present. 13 p. [Begumpet, Deccan, India: The author, 1944.]
Reprinted from the *Journal of the Osmania University*, 1935, vol. 3, with numerous notes and additional historical matter.

OLIVIER, Charles P. Comets. 246 p., ill. Baltimore: Williams & Wilkins, 1930. [CB 31/551]

PROCTOR, Mary. The romance of comets. xiii, 210 p., 16 pl. New York: Harper, 1926.

PROCTOR, Mary; CROMMELIN, A.C.D. Comets. Their nature, origin, and place in the science of astronomy. xi, 204 p. London: Technical Press, 1937.
Reviewed by C. Doris Hellman, *Isis*, 1938, 28: 513-14.

ROMIG, Mary F.; LAMAR, Donald L. Strange sounds from the sky. *Sky Telesc.*, 1964, 28: 214-15.
Discussion of certain meteors from 1783 to the present, in an effort to explain the sounds.

SCHOVE, D. Justin. Halley's comet: 1930 B.C. to A.D. 1986. The comet of David and Halley's comet. Halley's comet and Kamienski's formula. *J.Brit.Astron.Ass.*, 1955, 65: 285-90; 1956, 66: 131-9.

WILLIAMS, Kenneth P. The calculation of the orbits of asteroids and comets. vii, 214 p., 18 fig. Bloomington, Ind.: Principia Press, 1934. [CB 43/271]

FOc-bw

BIGOURDAN, G. Les comètes. Liste chronologique de celles qui ont paru de l'origine à 1900, ou éléments d'une statistique cométaire. 76 p. (*Annu.Bur.Longitudes* (Paris), 1927, Appendice A) Paris: Gauthier-Villars, 1927.

YAMAMOTO, A.S. Preliminary general catalogue of comets. 37 p. (Publications of the Kwasan Observatory, 1) Kyoto: 1936. [CB 51/259]
Revised edition of general catalogue of comets by Issei Yamamoto, 1931.

FOce

ROMIG, Mary F.; LAMAR, Donald L. Anomalous sounds and electromagnetic effects associated with fireball entry. 67 p. (RM-3724-ARPA) Santa Monica, Calif.: Rand Corporation, 1963.
Surveys 19th and 20th century astronomical literature on the subject.

FOzm METEORITES

BEYER, H. Otley. Philippine tektites and the tektite problem in general. *Annu.Rep.Smithsonian Inst.for 1942*, p. 253-9. Washington, D.C.: 1943.

BRITISH MUSEUM. The preservation of the Cranbourne meteorite. *Natur.Hist.Mag.*, 1936, 5: 381-93, ill., map.
History of discovery and preservation of the largest meteorite in any European collection.

HENDERSON, E.P. American meteorites and the national collection. *Annu.Rep.Smithsonian Inst.for 1948*. p. 257-68, 6 pl. Washington, D.C.: 1949.

HENDERSON, E.P.; PERRY, Stuart H. Meteorites and their metallic constituents. *Annu.Rep.Smithsonian Inst.for 1942*, p. 235-51, 2 fig., 6 pl. Washington, D.C.: 1943.
Including historical data.

MERRILL, George P. The composition and structure of meteorites compared with that of terrestrial rocks. *Annu.Rep. Smithsonian Inst. for 1917*, p. 175-88, 9 pl. Washington, D.C.: 1919.

NININGER, H.H. Out of the sky. An introduction to meteoritics. viii, 336 p., pl., fig. Denver: University of Denver Press, 1952; reprinted 1959 (New York: Dover).

NININGER, H.H. A résumé of researches at the Arizona meteor's crater. *Sci.Mon.*, 1951, 72: 75-86.

RAYLEIGH, Robert John Strutt, *4th Baron*. Meteorites and some of the problems which they present. *Endeavour*, 1944, 3: 127-34, 8 fig.

FOzm-bw

PRIOR, George Thurland. Catalogue of meteorites. With special reference to those represented in the collection of the British Museum (Natural History). 196 p. London: The Museum, 1923.
Appendix (48 p.) publ. 1927; 2nd appendix (136 p.) publ.

FOzm-ce

HOGG, Helen Sawyer. Out of old books. *J.Roy.Astron.Soc. Can.*, 1962, 56: 174-9, 215-21, 257-61; 1963, 57: 41-8. 81-8, 129-36, 269-75.
Relates reports of meteorites.

FP STARS AND STAR CLUSTERS

AITKEN, Robert Grant. The binary stars. 2nd ed. xii, 309 p., 4 pl., 13 fig., 3 portr. New York: McGraw-Hill, 1935. [CB 45/280]
First edition 1918.

ARRHENIUS, Svante. The destinies of the stars. Transl. from the Swedish by J.E. Fries. xvii, 256 p. New York: Putnam, 1918.
Swedish original: Stjarnernes öden. 1915.
French translation: Le destin des étoiles. Paris: Alcan, 1921. [CB 11/437]

ARRHENIUS, Svante. Die Sternenwelt. Nach hinterlassenen Aufzeichnungen bearbeitet und ergänzt von Knut Lundmark. Übers. von Alexis Finkelstein. x, 359 p., 1 pl., 61 fig. Leipzig: Akademische Verlagsgesellschaft, 1931.
Translation of "Stjärnwärlden", the second part of an enlarged edition of "Världarnas utveckling", 1906.
Reviewed by P. Kirchberger, *Deut.Lit.Zeitung*, 1932, 3: 1288-90.

ASHBROOK, Joseph. Astronomical scrapbook: "Not observed or existing". *Sky Telesc.*, 1963, 26: 80-1.
The article deals with stars catalogued but probably not existing, including stars listed by Flamsteed, Baily, and others.

BOBROVNIKOFF, N.T. The discovery of variable stars. *Isis*, 1942, 33: 687-9.

CHOU, Kyong Chol. Algol - still a demon star! *Sky Telesc.*, 1964, 27: 24-6.
Observations of this variable star from the 17th to the 20th centuries.

EDDINGTON, Arthur Stanley. The internal constitution of the stars. viii, 407 p. Cambridge University Press, 1926.
German translation: Der innere Aufbau der Sterne (Berlin: 1928).
Reviewed by Svein Rosseland, *Nature*, 1927, 119: 111-13.

EDDINGTON, Arthur Stanley. Stars and atoms. 127 p., 6 pl. New Haven: Yale University Press, 1927.
German translation: Sterne und Atome. (Berlin: 1928).
Reviewed by Friedrich Hund, *Deut.Lit.Zeitung*, 1929, 6: 1407-8.
French translation from 3rd English edition: Etoiles et atomes. (Paris: 1930). [CB 33/395]

JEANS, James Hopwood. Cosmogony and stellar evolution. *Nature*, 1921, 107: 557-60, 588-90; reprinted in *Annu.Rep.Smithsonian Inst.for 1921*, p. 153-64. Washington, D.C.: 1922.

JEANS, James Hopwood. The motions of the stars. *Scientia*, 1923, 33: 181-95. [CB 14/540]

JEANS, James Hopwood. The stars in their courses. xi. 188 p., 47 pl. Cambridge University Press, 1931.
French translation: Les étoiles dans leurs courses. (Paris: 1932). [CB 36/436]

LA ROSA, M. Prove astronomiche contrarie alla relatività. 1. Le stelle variabili; 2. Una nuova teoria delle stelle variabili. *Scientia*, 1924, 36: 1-11, 69-80; French transl. suppl., 1-11, 21-32. [CB 16/286]

LUNDMARK, Knut. Was the Crab Nebula formed by a supernova in 1054 A.D.? *Festskrift tillägnad Osten Bergstrand*, p. 89-106. Uppsala: Almqvist & Wiksell, 1938.

MILNE, Edward Arthur. The white dwarf stars; being the Halley lecture delivered on 19 May 1932. 32 p., 3 fig. Oxford: Clarendon Press, 1932. [CB 37/590]

MINEUR, H. Histoire de l'astronomie stellaire jusqu'à l'époque contemporaine. 57 p. (Actualités Scientifiques et Industrielles, 115) Paris: Hermann, 1934.

NIELSEN, Axel V. Contributions to the history of the Hertzsprung-Russell diagram. *Centaurus*, 1964, 9: 219-53.

NIELSEN, Axel V. Hertzsprung-Russell diagrammet. [In Danish, with English summary] *Nord.Astron.Tidsskr.*, 1963, 3: 78-113. [CB 90/627]

PETRIE, R.M. The *B* stars and galactic exploration. *Sky Telesc.*, 1963, 26: 330-4.

SALET, Pierre. La vie des étoiles. *Rev.Gén.Sci.*, 1923, 34: 358-62. [CB 15/208]

SMART, W.M. Some famous stars. iv, 220 p., 60 fig., 14 pl. London: Longman, Green, 1950.
Reviewed by H. Dopp, *Rev.Quest.Sci.*, 1951, 12: 449.

STRAND, K. Aa. The double star 61 Cygni. *Sky Telesc.*, 1941, 1: no. 3, 6-8, fig.

STRUVE, Otto. Milestones in double star astronomy. *Sky Telesc.*, 1962, 24: 17-19.

STRUVE, Otto. Stellar radial velocities and their observation. *Sky Telesc.*, 1961, 22: 132-5.
An historical survey.

STRUVE, Otto. The story of Epsilon Aurigae. *Sky Telesc.*, 1962, 23: 127-9.

THOMAS, H.L. U Scorpii as a recurrent nova. *Bull.Astron. Observ.Harvard Univ.*, 1940, no. 912, 10-12, 2 fig.

WAERDEN, B.L. van der. Die Sichtbarkeit der Sterne in der Nähe des Horizontes. *Vierteljahrsschr.Naturforsch.Ges. Zürich*, 1954, 99: 20-39, 5 fig.

WORLEY, Charles E. Visual observing of double stars. *Sky Telesc.*, 1961, 22: 73-6.
An historical survey.

ZINNER, Ernst. Alte Beobachtungen des Sternes o Ceti. *Ber.Naturforsch.Ges.Bamberg*, 1946, 29: 40-2.

ZINNER, Ernst. Sprunghafte Änderungen der Sterne. *Ber. Naturforsch.Ges.Bamberg*, 1946, 29: 42-7.

ZINNER, Ernst. Zur Erklärung des Lichtwechsels der vermissten Sterne. *Ber.Naturforsch.Ges.Bamberg*, 1952, 33: 1-35.

FPc-bw

KOPFF, A. Star catalogues, especially those of fundamental character. *Mon.Not.Roy.Astron.Soc.*, 1936, 96: 714-30.

FPcn

LOVI, George. Star charts of former days. *Sky Telesc.*, 1964, 27: 222-5, ill.

FPnh

KUNITZSCH, Paul. Arabische Sternnamen in Europa. 240 p. Wiesbaden: Verlag Otto Harrassowitz, 1959.
Reviewed by George A. Davis, *Sky Telesc.*, 1960, 20: 294-5; by E. Zinner, *Naturwissenschaften*, 1960, 16: 1-2; by W. Petri, *Naturwiss.Rundsch.*, 1960, 13: 242.

RUMRILL, H.B. Star name pronunciation. *Publ.Astron.Soc. Pacific*, 1936, 48: 139-54.

FPth

DREWS, Arthur. Der Sternhimmel in der Dichtung und Religion der alten Völker und des Christentums. Eine Einführung in die Astralmythologie. 316 p., ill. Jena: Diederichs, 1923.

FPu

ARRHENIUS, Svante. Ueber den Ursprung des Gestirnkultus. *Atti IV° Congr.Int.Fil.* (Bologna, 1911), (1), p. 160-74. Genoa: Formiggini, 1912.

LASSALLY, Oswald. Von der Entstehung des Aberglaubens an Sterne und Steine. *Geisteskultur*, 1931, 40: 87-92.

ZINNER, Ernst. The stars above us or the conquest of superstition. xiv, 141 p., ill., bibliogr. New York: Scribner, 1957. [CB 84/310]
Translation of "Sternglaube und Sternforschung" *see* below.
Reviewed by C. Doris Hellman, *Science*, 1958, 127: 243-4.

ZINNER, Ernst. Sternglaube und Sternforschung. xiv, 172 p., ill. Freiburg i. B./München: K. Alber, 1953. [CB 80/145]
Reviewed by Bernhard Sticker, *Sudhoffs Arch.*, 1954, 38: 192.

FPvp-nh

SCHERER, Anton. Gestirnnamen bei den indogermanischen Völkern. 276 p., 8 pl. (Indogermanische Bibliothek: Forschungen zum Wortschatz der indogermanischen Sprachen, 1) Heidelberg: Winter 1953.
Reviewed by E. Zinner, *Theol.Lit.Zeitung*, 1957, no. 9, 674-6.

FPwg-qg

STROHMEIER, W. The Bamberg search for bright variable stars. *Sky Telesc.*, 1963, 26: 264-5.

FPxm

JEANS, James Hopwood. The survey of the stars. *Nature*, 1927, 119: 394-6.
From an address delivered to the Royal Astronomical Society on Feb. 11, referring to the award of the Gold Medal of the Society to Frank Schlesinger for his work on stellar parallax and astronomical photography.

LUNDMARK, Knut. The estimates of stellar magnitudes by Ptolemaios, Al Sûfi and Tycho Brahe. *Vierteljahrsschr.Astron. Ges.*, 1926, 61: 230-6.

SEARES, Frederick H. Magnitudes again. *Science*, 1938, 87: 1-8.

VAUCOULEURS, G. de. Histoire de la photométrie stellaire. *Bull.Soc.Astron.Pop.Toulouse*, 1943, no. 242, 11 p.

FPyBWwm

HUMBERT, Pierre. La statistique stellaire et les travaux de l'école suédoise. *Rev.Quest.Sci.*, 1928, 13: 244-55.
D'après les travaux de C.W.L. Charlier, directeur de l'observatoire de l'université de Lund, et ses collaborateurs.

FQ CONSTELLATIONS

BRONSART, Huberta von. Kleine Lebensbeschreibung der Sternbilder. 164 p., ill. Stuttgart: Kosmos-Verlag, 1963.
Illustrated history of constellation lore up to the present time.
Reviewed by Joseph Ashbrook, *Sky Telesc.*, 1964, 28: 287-300.

DINGLER, Hugo. Die Entstehung der Sternbilder und die Zahl Sieben. *Arch.Gesch.Math.Naturwiss.Tech.*, 1929, 11: 265-71.

FAGAN, Cyril. Zodiacs old and new. 60 p. London: Anscombe, 1951.
Reviewed by D.M., *Observatory*, 1951, 71: 164-5.

FLAMMARION, Camille. Les signes du zodiaque, les planètes et les jours de la semaine. *Astronomie*, 1912, 26: 1-3.

GUNDEL, Wilhelm. Dekane und Dekansternbilder. Ein Beitrag zur Geschichte der Sternbilder der Kulturvölker. Mit einer Untersuchung über die altägyptischen Sternbilder und Gottheiten der Dekane von S. Schott. x, 452 p., 33 pl. (Studien der Bibliothek Warburg, 19) Glückstadt: Augustin, 1936.
Reviewed by Willy Hartner, *Isis*, 1937, 27: 344-8.

GUNDEL, Wilhelm. Sterne und Sternbilder im Glauben des Altertums und der Neuzeit. viii, 353 p. Bonn: Kurt Schroeder, 1922.

HARTNER, Willy; ETTINGHAUSEN, Richard. The conquering lion, the life cycle of a symbol. *Oriens*, 1964, 17: 161-71. [CB 90/512]

LEHMANN-NITSCHE, Robert. Astronomia popular española 1. Un bronce antiguo con la representación de las Pléyadas, hallado en Monte Pindo (Galicia). *Bol.Real Acad.Gallega,* 1923, 18: 81-6.

LEHMANN-NITSCHE, Robert. Der apokaliptische Drache. *Z. Ethnol.,* 1933, 65: 193-230.
Constellation of Scorpio.

LEHMANN-NITSCHE, Robert. La constelación de la Osa Mayor y su concepto como huracán o dios de la tormenta en la esfera del Mar Caribe. *Rev.Mus.Plata,* 1924, 28: 103-45.

LEHMANN-NITSCHE, Robert. Das Sternbild der Bärenjagd (Vorläufige Mitteilung). Der Ziegenmelker und die beiden Grossgestirne in der südamerikanischen Mythologie. *Verhandl.24.Inter.Amer.Kongr.* (Hamburg, 1930), p. 225-7, 221-4. Hamburg: De Gruyter, 1934.

LEHMANN-NITSCHE, Robert. Das Sternbild des Bohrers. *Geschichtsbl.Tech.Ind.,* 1927, 11: 92-3.

LEHMANN-NITSCHE, Robert. Das Sternbild des Orkans. *Iberica* (Hamburg), 1925, 3: 41-4.

LEHMANN-NITSCHE, Robert. Das Sternbild des Siebes. *Mém. Soc.Finn.Ougrienne,* 1933, 67: 224-32.

WAERDEN, B.L. van der. History of the zodiac. *Arch.Orientforsch.,* 1953, 16: 216-30, 9 fig., 4 pl.

FQth

HÄFKER, Hermann. Etwas von den Märchen und Sagen der Sternbilder. *Weltall,* 1931, 31: 28-9.

FQtq

OHLMARKS, Åke. Quelques aspects de l'identification de constellations sur les rochers sculptés par rapport à l'histoire des religions. 6 p. (Historical Notes and Papers, 9) Lund: Lund Observatory, 1937. Also published in *Medd.Lunds Astron.Observ., ser. 2,* 1937, no. 85.

ROUCH, Jules. Les signes du zodiaque dans l'art décoratif. *Rev.Gén.Sci.,* 1928, 39: 101-5.

SVENONIUS, Björn. Quelques essais d'identification de constellations sur les rochers sculptés en ostrogothie (Suède). 16 p., 5 fig. (Historical Notes and Papers, 7) Lund: Lund Observatory, 1937. Also published in series: *Medd.Lunds Astron.Observ., ser. 2,* 83. [CB 51/259]

FR INTERSTELLAR MATTER

HAGEN, J.G. The history of cosmic clouds. *Scientia,* 1932, 51: 133-6; French transl. suppl., 81-5. [CB 35/297]

STRUVE, Otto. Interstellar gas clouds. *Sky Telesc.,* 1961, 21: 269-71.
A survey of the theories on this subject since 1904.

FS THE GALAXY (MILKY WAY)

ASHBROOK, Joseph. Astronomical scrapbook: the visual Milky Way. *Sky Telesc.,* 1963, 26: 204-6.

COX, J.F. Un siècle d'étude de la voie lactée. *Bull.Tech. Ass.Ing.,* 1935, 157-67.

LINDBLAD, Bertil. The rotation of the galaxy. *Scientia,* 1932, 51: 325-34.
A general account by a pioneer.

FSxf-XF

LYNDS, Beverly T. The plan of selected areas. *Leafl.Astron. Soc.Pacif.,* Oct. 1963, 9: no. 412, 8 p., 2 fig. [CB 89/581]
The plan was inaugurated by J.C. Kapteyn in 1906.

STRUVE, Otto. E.E. Barnard and milky way photography. *Sky Telesc.,* 1961, 22: 14-18.

FT GALAXIES AND GALACTIC CLUSTERS

ARRHENIUS, Svante. Das Milchstrassen Problem. *Scientia,* 1914, 15: 349-63.

CURTIS, H.D. The spiral nebulae and the constitution of the universe. *Scientia,* 1924, 35: 1-9; French transl. suppl., 1-8. [CB 16/285]

HALE, George Ellery. Beyond the Milky Way. xv, 105 p., 43 ill. New York: Scribner, 1926. [CB 21/570]

HOYLE, Fred. Of men and galaxies. vii, 73 p. (John Danz Lectures) Seattle: University of Washington Press, 1964.

HUBBLE, Edwin. The nature of the nebulae. *Annu.Rep.Smithsonian Inst.for 1938,* p. 137-48, 1 pl. Washington, D.C.: 1939.

HUBBLE, Edwin. The realm of the nebulae. xiii, 210 p., 15 pl. (Yale University: Silliman Memorial Lectures, 1935) New Haven: Yale University Press; London: Oxford University Press, 1936.
Reprinted New York: Dover, 1958.
Reviewed by J.H.J., *Nature,* 1936, 138: 859-60.

ORUS, Juan J. de. Teorías sobre los brazos de las nebulosas espirales. *Arch.Int.Hist.Sci.,* 1954, 7: 141-60.

SALET, Pierre. Les univers-îles. *Rev.Gén.Sci.,* 1926, 37: 168-76. [CB 20/194]

SHAPLEY, Harlow. The clouds of Magellan: a gateway to the sidereal universe. *Amer.Scient.,* 1956, 44: 73-97.
A brief history of our knowledge of our galaxy and others.

STRUVE, Otto. A historic debate about the universe. *Sky Telesc.,* 1960, 19: 398-401.
An account of the 1920 debate between Harlow Shapley and Heber D. Curtis.

FTmd

BLÜH, Otto. The galaxies and time. *J.Roy.Astron.Soc.Can.,* 1949, 43: 169-80.

FU THE UNIVERSE; COSMOLOGY AND COSMOGONY

for the origin of the solar system *see* FG

FUc general history

FUc-bm *large scale works*

BAVINK, B. Weltschoepfung in Mythos and Religion, Philosophie und Naturwissenschaft. Aus dem Nachlass hrsg. und mit einem Anhang versehen von Al. Wenzl. 126 p. Basel: Reinhardt, 1950.

BELL, Eric Temple. The search for truth. x, 279 p. Baltimore: Williams and Wilkins, 1934; London: Allen and Unwin, 1935.
Reviewed by Oliver L. Reiser, *Phil.Sci.,* 1935, 2: 118-20.
A history of general cosmological ideas.

BROMS, Allan. Our emerging universe. xiv, 296 p. Garden City, N.Y.: Doubleday, 1961.

EDDINGTON, Arthur Stanley. The expanding universe. viii, 182 p. New York: Macmillan; Cambridge University Press, 1933.
Reviewed by H.T. Davis, *Isis,* 1934, 21: 322-6.

GAMOW, George. Matter, earth and sky. xi, 593 p. Englewood Cliffs, N.J.: Prentice-Hall, 1958; London: Macmillan, 1959.
Reviewed by G.R. Noakes, *Nature,* 1959, 184: 214.

GOLDBECK, Ernst. Der Mensch und sein Weltbild. Gesammelte kosmologische Abhandlungen. viii, 330 p. Leipzig: Quelle & Meyer, 1925. [CB 20/191]

HAAS, Arthur. Die kosmologischen Probleme der Physik. vii, 124 p. Leipzig: Akademische Verlagsgesellschaft, 1934.
Reviewed in *Nature,* 1934, 134: 125.

HILLEBRAND, Karl. Die Entwicklung kosmischer Systeme. Versuch einer gemeinverständlichen Darstellung der gegenwärten Anschauungen über die Entwicklung von Weltsystemen und ihrer wissenschaftlichen Grundlagen. 90 p. Graz: Leuschiner und Lubensky, 1926.
Reviewed by H. Wieleitner, *Mitt.Gesch.Med.,* 1926, 25: 227.

HOYLE, Fred. The nature of the universe. A series of broadcast lectures. v, 121 p., 6 pl. Oxford: Blackwell, 1950.

HUBBLE, Edwin. The observational approach to cosmology. ix, 68 p., ill. Oxford: Clarendon Press, 1937.

HUBBLE, Edwin. The realm of the nebulae. xiii, 210 p., ill. London: Oxford University Press, 1936.

JEANS, James Hopwood. Eos: or The wider aspects of cosmogony. 88 p., 6 pl. (To-day and To-morrow Series) London: Kegan Paul, 1928.
Reviewed by H.D., *Nature*, 1929, 123: 937-8.

JEANS, James Hopwood. The mysterious universe. ix, 154 p., 2 pl. Cambridge University Press, 1930.
French translation: Le mystérieux univers. Paris: Hermann, 1931. [CB 35/294]; German translation: Der Weltenraum und seine Rätsel. Stuttgart: Deutsche Verlaganstalt, 1931.
Reviewed by Herbert Dingle, *Nature*, 1930, 126: 799-800.

JEANS, James Hopwood. Problems of cosmogony and stellar dynamics. vii, 293 p., 5 pl., diagr. Cambridge University Press, 1919.

JEANS, James Hopwood. The universe around us. 4th ed. x, 297 p., 32 pl. Cambridge University Press, 1944; reprinted 1960.
First published 1929.
French translation: L'univers. Paris: Payot, 1930. [CB 33/395]; German translation: Sterne, Welten und Atome. Stuttgart: Deutsche Verlagsanstalt, 1931.
Reviewed by R.A.S., *Nature*, 1929, 124: 903-5; by H. Spencer Jones, *Endeavour*, 1944, 3: 163.

JONES, G.O.; ROTBLAT, J.; WHITROW, G.J. Atoms and the universe. An account of modern views on the structure of matter and the universe. 2nd ed. 275 p. London: Eyre & Spottiswoode, 1962; New York: Scribner, 1963.
First publ. London: 1956 (New York: 1957). [CB 83/279]

KOYRÉ, Alexandre. From the closed world to the infinite universe. xii, 313 p. (Hideye Noguchi Lectures, 7) Baltimore, Md.: Johns Hopkins Press, 1957; New York: Harper & Bros., 1958.
French translation Paris: Presses Universitaires de France, 1962.
Reviewed by Marie Boas, *Isis*, 1958, 49: 363-6; for further reviews *see* CB 83/186, CB 84/347, CB 87/552 and CB 88/522.

KUZNETSOV, B.G. Évoliutsiia kartiny mira. [The evolution of the world picture. (In Russian)] 350 p. Moskva: Akademiia Nauk SSSR, Institut Istorii Estestvozvaniia i Tekhniki, 1961.

LEMAÎTRE, Georges. The primeval atom. An essay on cosmogony. Translated by Betty H. and Serge A. Korff. ix, 186 p. New York: Van Nostrand, 1950.
Reviewed by T.G. Cowling, *Nature*, 1951, 168: 259.
For French original "L'hypothèse de l'atome primitif" (Neuchâtel: Griffon; Paris: Dunod, 1946) *see* CB 72/270.

LEMAÎTRE, Georges. L'univers. 73 p. Louvain: Nauwelaerts, 1950.
Reviewed by T.G. Cowling, *Nature*, 1951, 168: 259.

LOVELL, A.C.B. The individual and the universe. 111 p., ill. (B.B.C. Reith Lectures) London: Oxford University Press; New York: Harper, 1959; republished New York: New American Library of World Literature (Mentor Book), 1961.
Reviewed by R.A. Lyttleton, *Nature*, 1959, 183: 1624-5; by Anna Beckman, *Lychnos*, 1959, 361-2; by G. Abetti, *Scientia*, 1960, 95: 266-8.

MACPHERSON, Hector. Modern cosmologies: a historical sketch of researches and theories concerning the structure of the universe. vii, 131 p., 12 pl. London: Oxford University Press, 1929.

MAILLARD, Louis. Quand la lumière fut. 2 vol. 1. Les cosmogonies anciennes. 214 p., 6 pl., 49 fig.; 2. Les cosmogonies modernes. 280 p., 36 pl. Paris: Presses Universitaires de France, 1922-23.

MILNE, E.A. Kinematic relativity. vi, 238 p. (International Series of Monographs on Physics) Oxford: Clarendon Press, 1948.

MILNE, E.A. Relativity, gravitation and world-structure. viii, 365 p. Oxford University Press, 1935.
Reviewed by H.T. Davis, *Isis*, 1936, 26: 215-18.

MOREUX, Th. Le ciel et l'univers. 626 p., ill. Paris: Doin, 1928. [CB 26/229]

MUNITZ, Milton K., ed. Theories of the universe from Babylonian myth to modern science. x, 437 p. Glencoe, Ill.: Free Press & Falcon's Wing Press, 1957.
Reviewed by Gerald Holton, *Isis*, 1959, 50: 160-1; for other reviews *see* CB 84/309, CB 85/389 and CB 88/541.

ÖPIK, Ernst J. The oscillating universe. 144 p. New York: New American Library of World Literature, 1960.

PAPP, Desiderio. El problema del órigen de los mundos. 2nd ed. 159 p. (Colección Austral) Buenos Aires-Mexico: Espasa Calpe Argentina, 1951.
Reviewed by R. Taton, *Rev.Hist.Sci.*, 1954, 7: 289-90.

REICHENBACH, Hans. Von Kopernikus bis Einstein: der Wandel unseres Weltbildes. 122 p. (Wege zum Wissen, 85) Berlin: Ullstein, 1927.

RONAN, Colin A. Changing views of the universe. 206 p. London: Eyre and Spottiswoode; New York: Macmillan, 1961.
Reviewed by John B. Irwin, *Science*, 1961, 134: 275; by George A. Blair, *Sky Telesc.*, 1961, 22: 225-6; by A. Armitage, *Hist.Sci.*, 1962, 1: 118-19.

SCHMEIDLER, F. Alte und moderne Kosmologie. Erfahrung und Denken. 99 p. (Schriften zur Förderung der Beziehungen zwischen Philosophie und Einzelwissenschaften, 9) Berlin/Munich: Duncker & Humblot, 1962.
Reviewed by Heinz Degen, *Naturwiss.Rundsch.*, 1963, 16: 204.

SCIAMA, D.W. The unity of the universe. xvii, 213 p., fig., pl. Garden City, N.Y.: Doubleday Anchor, 1961. [CB 87/563]

SHAPLEY, Harlow. Flights from chaos: a survey of material systems from atoms to galaxies. Adapted from lectures at the College of the City of New York, class of 1872 Foundation. vii, 168 p. New York: McGraw-Hill, 1930.

SHAPLEY, Harlow. Of stars and men. The human response to an expanding universe. vi, 157 p. Boston: Beacon Press, 1958.
Reviewed by G.C. McVittie, *Science*, 1958, 128: 295; for other reviews *see* CB 84/310, CB 85/389, CB 86/461.

SINGH, Jagjit. Great ideas and theories of modern cosmology. 276 p. New York: Dover Publications, 1961.
For the scientifically informed layman.

SITTER, Willem de. Kosmos. A course of six lectures on the development of our insight into the structure of the universe, delivered for the Lowell Institute in Boston, November 1931. viii, 138 p., ill. Cambridge, Mass.: Harvard University Press, 1932.
Reviewed by N.T. Bobrovnikoff, *Isis*, 1933, 20: 316-18.

STRUVE, Otto. The universe. ix, 159 p., ill. Cambridge, Mass.: Massachusetts Institute of Technology Press, 1962.
Reviewed by G. de Vaucouleurs, *Science*, 1962, 138: 675-6.

TOLMAN, Richard Chace. Relativity, thermodynamics and cosmology. xv, 502 p. (International Series of Monographs on Physics) Oxford: Clarendon Press, 1934.
Reviewed by Enos E. Witmer, *Phil.Sci.*, 1935, 2: 262-5.

TROELS-LUND, Troels Frederik. Himmelsbild und Weltanschauung im Wandel der Zeiten. Autorisierte vom Verfasser durchgesehene Übersetzung von Leo Bloch. 5th ed. v, 276 p. Leipzig: Teubner, 1929. [CB 29/296]
Danish original first publ. 1901.

VÉRONNET, Alexandre. Constitution et évolution de l'univers. 480 p., 29 fig. Paris: G. Doin, 1926. [CB 22/263]

WHITROW, G.J. The structure and evolution of the universe. 212 p. London: Hutchinson and Co., Ltd.; New York: Harper & Brothers, 1959.
Reviewed by Stanley P. Wyatt, *Sky Telesc.*, 1959, 33: 697-8; in *Sci.Amer.*, 1960, 202: no. 1, 181-2; by P. Bockstaele, *Sci.Hist.*, 1960, 2: 24-6.

WHITROW, G.J. The structure of the universe. An introduction to cosmology. 171 p. (Hutchinson's University Library, 29) London: Hutchinson & Co., 1949. [CB 76/395]

WHITTAKER, Edmund. From Euclid to Eddington. A study of conceptions of the external world. 212 p. New York: Dover Publications, Inc., 1959.
An unaltered re-issue of the author's Tarner Lectures of 1947 originally published by Cambridge University Press. [CB 79/167]
Reviewed by H. Dopp, *Rev.Quest.Sci.*, 1959, 20: 617.

FUc-bn *essays; articles*

BONDI, H. Science and the structure of the universe. (Joule-Memorial Lecture) *Mem.Manchester Lit.Phil.Soc.*, 1958-59, 101: 58-71.

BOUTARIC, A. La cosmologie dualiste et tourbillonnaire. *Scientia*, 1926, 40: 345-56.

CAJORI, Florian. Are the heavens full or are they void? A history of hypotheses. *Sci.Mon.*, 1926, 23: 346-55. [CB 22/262]

COSTA DE BEAUREGARD, Oliver. Vitesse et univers relativiste. Souvenir du R.P. Abelé. *Arch.Int.Hist.Sci.*, 1962, 15: 333-6.

DAUVILLIER, Alexandre. Les hypothèses cosmogoniques et la theorie des cycles cosmiques. *Scientia*, 1963, 98: 121-6.

DEPRIT, André. Une géométrie de l'univers. Le petit monde du Chanoine Lemaître. *Rev.Gén.Belge*, mars 1960, 96: 37-51.

HAAR, D. ter. The age of the universe. *Sci.Mon.*, 1953, 77: 173-81. [CB 80/124]

HUANG SU-SHU. Jeans' criterion of gravitational instability. *Sky Telesc.*, 1963, 26: 77-9. [CB 89/500]

HUBBLE, Edwin. The problem of the expanding universe. *Science*, 1942, 95: 212-15.

JEANS, James Hopwood. The astronomical horizon. 23 p., pl. (The Philip Maurice Deneke Lecture, 1944) London: Oxford University Press, 1945.

JEANS, James Hopwood. The nebular hypothesis and modern cosmogony. 31 p., 4 pl. (Halley Lecture, 1922) Oxford: Clarendon Press; New York: Oxford University Press, 1923.
Reviewed by Harold Jeffreys, *Nature*, 1923, 111: 662.

JEANS, James Hopwood. The physics of the universe. (Henry Herbert Wills Memorial Lecture of the University of Bristol, delivered Oct. 30) *Nature*, 1928, 122: 689-700.

JEANS, James Hopwood. Recent developments of cosmical physics. *Nature*, Dec. 4, 1926, 118: suppl., 29-40.

JEANS, James Hopwood. The size and age of the universe. *Nature*, 1936, 137: 17-24, 3 fig.
Discourse delivered at the Royal Institution on November 29, 1935. Reprinted in *Annu.Rep.Smithsonian Inst.for 1936*, p. 123-36. Washington, D.C.: 1937.

JEANS, James Hopwood. The wider aspects of cosmogony. *Nature*, 1928, 121: 463-70, 3 fig.

KAPTEYN, J.C. On the structure of the universe. *Scientia*, 1913, 14: 345-57.

KIENLE, H. Das Weltsystem des Kopernikus und das Weltbild unserer Zeit. *Naturwissenschaften*, 1943, 31: 1-12.

KOYRÉ, Alexandre. Newton, Galilée et Platon. *Act.IXe Congr. Int.Hist.Sci.* (Barcelona, 1959), (1), p. 111-33. Paris: Hermann, 1960.

KOYRÉ, Alexandre; COHEN, I. Bernard. Newton, Galilée et Platon. *Act.IXe Congr.Int.Hist.Sci.* (Barcelona, 1959), (1), p. 165-97. Paris: Hermann, 1960.

LAUE, Max von. Von Kopernikus bis Einstein. *Naturwiss. Rundsch.*, 1957, 10: 83-9.

LEMAÎTRE, Georges. L'hypothèse de l'atome primitif. *Rev. Quest.Sci.*, 1948, 9: 321-39.

McCREA, W.H. Cosmology - a brief review. *Quart.J.Roy.Astron. Soc.*, 1963, 4: 185-202.

MACMILLAN, William Duncan. The structure of the universe. *Science*, 1920, 52: 67-74.

MINEUR, Henri. L'univers en expansion. 42 p., ill. (Exposés de Physique Théorique, 8) Paris: Hermann, 1933. [CB 39/453]

PAMYATI A.A. Fridman (k 75-letiyu so dnya rozhdeniya). [In memory of A.A. Fridman (on the 75th anniversary of his birth). (In Russian)] *Usp.Fiz.Nauk*, 1963, 80: 345-453; English transl. in *Soviet Phys.Usp.*, 1963, 6: (4), 467-94.
Includes Russian translations of Friedmann's paper and Einstein's comments originally published in *Zeitschrift für Physik*, 1922, 1923 and 1924.

POLIKAROV, A. Zum heutigen Stand des kosmologischen Problems. *Actes du Symposium International R.J. Bošković (1961)*, p. 195-204. Beograd: 1962.

ROSEN, Edward. A full universe. *Sci.Mon.*, 1946, 63: 213-17.

SCHLEGEL, Richard. Steady-state theory at Chicago. *Amer.J. Phys.*, 1958, 26: 601-4.

SHAPLEY, Harlow; CURTIS, Heber D. The scale of the universe. *Bull.Nat.Res.Counc.*, 1921, 2: 171-217.

VÉRONNET, Alexandre. Étude critique des hypothèses cosmogoniques modernes. *Rev.Gén.Sci.*, 1926, 37: 572-81, 604-12. [CB 22/264]
From Kant to Véronnet.

VOGT, H. Probleme der Kosmogonie. *Naturwissenschaften*, 1923, 11: 957-62.

WHITTAKER, Edmund. The beginning and end of the world. 64 p. (Riddell Memorial Lectures, ser. 14) London: Oxford University Press, 1942.
French translation: Le commencement et la fin du monde (Paris: 1953); reviewed by B. Rochot, *Rev.Hist.Sci.*, 1954, 7: 93.

ZEL'DOVICH, Ya.B. The theory of the expanding universe as originated by A.A. Fridman. Transl. by W.H. Furry. *Soviet Phys.Usp.*, 1964, 6: (4), 475-94.

FUda collective biography

BRUNNER, William. Pioniere der Weltallforschung. 296 p., ill. Zürich: Büchergilde Gutenberg, 1951.
Reviewed by N.V.E. Nordenmark, *Lychnos*, 1953, 404-5.

FUk philosophy and methodology

BRIDGMAN, P.W. Significance of the Mach principle. *Amer.J. Phys.*, 1961, 29: 32-6.

DAVIDSON, W. Philosophical aspects of cosmology. *Brit.J.Phil. Sci.*, 1962, 13: 120-9.

DELEVSKY, J. Cosmogonie et philosophie de l'histoire. *Rev. Phil.*, 1933, 116: 239-73.

DELEVSKY, J. Note sur la possibilité des répétitions cosmologiques. *Isis*, 1945, 36: 19-21.

DINGLE, Herbert. Cosmology and science. A historical epilogue to this issue. The argument: in earlier times the search for knowledge was handicapped by presupposed cosmological principles. Modern cosmologists must guard against the same tendency. *Sci.Amer.*, 1956, 195: no. 3, 224-36, fig.

DINGLE, Herbert. Philosophical aspects of cosmology. *Vistas Astron.*, 1955, 1: 162-6.

DINGLE, Herbert. Science and modern cosmology. *Mon.Not.Roy. Astron.Soc.*, 1953, 113: 393-407.

FINLAY-FREUNDLICH, E. Cosmology. iii, 59 p. (International Encyclopedia of Unified Science, 1: no. 8) Chicago: University of Chicago Press, 1951.

GINZBURG, Benjamin. The finite universe and scientific extrapolation. *J.Phil.*, 1935, 32: 85-92. [CB 43/271]

HARRÉ, R. Philosophical aspects of cosmology. *Brit.J.Phil. Sci.*, 1962, 13: 104-19.

HENDERSON, Archibald. Is the universe finite? *Amer.Math. Mon.*, 1925, 32: 213-23.

KAPP, Reginald O. Towards a unified cosmology. 303 p., fig. New York: Basic Books, 1960. [CB 86/461]
Reviewed by V.F. Lenzen, *Phil.Sci.*, 1962, 29: 216-17.

KONINCK, Charles de. The hollow universe. xi, 127 p. London/Toronto: Oxford University Press, 1960.
Reviewed by R.F.J. Withers, *Brit.J.Phil.Sci.*, 1962, 13: 183; by Jerzy A. Wojciechowski, *Dialogue*, 1962, 1: 96-7.

LOT, Ferdinand. L'origine du monde. 75 p. Paris: Société Parisienne d'Editions, 1950.

MEURERS, Joseph. Die wissenschaftstheoretische Position einer evolutiven Welterklärung. *Phil.Natur.*, 1964, 8: 9-21.

MUNITZ, Milton K. Kantian dialectic and modern scientific cosmology. *J.Phil.*, 1951, 48: (10), 327-8.

MUNITZ, Milton K. The logic of cosmology. *Brit.J.Phil.Sci.*, 1962, 13: 34-50.

MUNITZ, Milton K. One universe or many? *J.Hist.Ideas*, 1951, 12: 231-55.

MUNITZ, Milton K. Space, time and creation. Philosophical aspects of scientific cosmology. x, 182 p. Glencoe, Ill.: Free Press & Falcon's Wing Press, 1957.
Reviewed by Gerald Holton, *Isis*, 1959, 50: 159-60; for other reviews *see* CB 84/301, CB 85/382 and CB 88/530.

POPPEI, Gerhard. Zur philosophischen Deutung der elementaren Synthese- und Zerfallsprozesse im Kosmos. *Wiss.Z.Humboldt-Univ.Berlin Math.Naturwiss.Reihe*, 1962, 11: 233-41.

REISER, Oliver L. The evolution of cosmologies. *Phil.Sci.*, 1952, 19: 93-107. [CB 79/172]

VÉRONNET, Alexandre. Notre univers est-il fini ou infini? *Rev.Gén.Sci.*, 1923, 34: 568-76. [CB 16/287]

WHITEHEAD, Alfred North. Process and reality: an essay in cosmology. xii, 544 p., indices. (The Academy Library) New York: Harper Torchbooks, 1960. [CB 86/457]
Reprint of 1929 edition by MacMillan of the Gifford Lectures, 1927-28.

WHITROW, G.J. Is the physical universe a self-contained system? *Monist*, 1962, 47: 77-93.

WHITROW, G.J. The limits of the physical universe. *Stud. Gen.*, 1952, 5: 329-37.

FUks

BUSCO, Pierre. Les cosmogonies modernes et la théorie de la connaissance. 435 p. Paris: Félix Alcan, 1924.
Reviewed by L. Guinet, *Isis*, 1926, 8: 233.

FUkv

WHITTAKER, Edmund. Chance, freewill and necessity, in the scientific conception of the universe. (Guthrie Lecture) *Proc.Phys.Soc.*, 1943, 55: 459-71.
French translation published with: Le commencement et la fin du monde (Paris: 1953), a translation of the author's The beginning and end of the world (*see* FUc-bn).

FUmc

JEANS, James Hopwood. Space, time and the universe. *Nature*, 1926, 117: 308-11.
Presidential address delivered before the Royal Astronomical Society on February 12 1926.

FUmzFB

RYLE, Martin. Radio astronomy and cosmology. *Nature*, 1961, 190: 852-4.

FUt/w other special aspects

FUtd

COHEN, Chapman. God and the universe: Eddington, Jeans, Huxley and Einstein. With a reply by A.S. Eddington. 133 p. London: Pioneer Press, [n.d.].
Reviewed by T.G., *Nature*, 1931, 127: 811.

COLLIER, Katherine Brownell. Cosmogonies of our fathers. 500 p. New York: Columbia University Press, 1934.
Reviewed by Robert K. Merton, *Isis*, 1935, 24: 167-8.

DAVIDSON, Martin. Modern cosmology and the theologians. *Vistas Astron.*, 1955, 1: 166-72.

MEYER, Heinrich. The age of the world. A chapter in the history of enlightenment. 132 p. Allentown, Pa.: Muhlenberg College, 1951. [CB 78/183]
Mimeographed.

FUwn-sk

MIKULAK, Maxim W. Soviet cosmology and communist ideology. *Sci.Mon.*, 1955, 81: 167-72.

FV ASTRONOMICAL CHRONOLOGY

for time measurement *see* Axm
clocks *see* WS

BAEHR, U. Tafeln zur Behandlung chronologischer Probleme. Parts 1-3. 76 p. (Veröffentlichungen des Astronomischen Rechen-Instituts zu Heidelberg, 3) Karlsruhe: G. Braun, 1955.
Reviewed by Willy Hartner, *Gnomon*, 1959, 31: 177-8.

BIGOURDAN, G. L'origine et le progrès de l'astronomie en relation avec la mesure du temps et avec le problème des longitudes. *Scientia*, 1916, 19: 427-34.

BIGOURDAN, G. Le problème de l'heure: son évolution et son état actuel. *Annu.Bur.Longitudes* (Paris), 1924, *C*, 1-17.
Speech delivered at the Congrès national chronométrique, 22 October 1923.

COLSON, F.H. The week: an essay on the origin and development of the seven-day cycle. vii, 126 p. Cambridge University Press, 1926.
Reviewed by Martin P. Nilsson, *Deut.Lit.Zeitung*, 1926, 2463-5.

ENDER, F. Über die Inkonsequenz unserer Zeitrechnung. *Experientia*, 1951, 7: 114-16. [CB 78/182]

GINZEL, F.K. Handbuch der mathematischen und technischen Chronologie. Das Zeitrechnungswesen der Völker. 3 vol. Leipzig: Hinrichs, 1906-14.

LINTON, Olof. [L'année, le mois et le jour de la création. Contribution à l'histoire de la chronologie chrétienne. (In Swedish with French summary)]. *Lychnos*, 1937, 2: 271-312. [CB 51/289]

MAKEMSON, Maud W. Ephemeris time and universal time. *Leafl. Astron.Soc.Pacific*, 1963, 9: no. 407, 8 p.
Discusses time measurements used by astronomers.

NEUGEBAUER, Paul Victor. Astronomische Chronologie. 2 vol. 1. Text. xii, 190 p., 17 fig.; 2. Tables. 136 p. Berlin: De Gruyter, 1929.
Reviewed by A. Pogo, *Isis*, 1930, 14: 450-4.

SCHOVE, D. Justin. Chronology of natural phenomena in east and west. *Arch.Int.Hist.Sci.*, 1960, 13: 263-8.

SCHOVE, D. Justin. The so-called "Spectrum of Time". *Act. VIIIe Congr.Int.Hist.Sci.* (Florence, 1956), (1), p. 432. Paris: Hermann, 1958.

SITTER, W. de. On the rotation of the earth and astronomical time. *Nature*, 1928, 121: 99-106.

FVqy

BIGOURDAN, G. Le jour et ses divisions. Les fuseaux horaires et la Conférence internationale de l'Heure. 107 p. (*Annu.Bur.Longitudes*, Notice B) Paris: 1914. [CB 5/287]

BUREAU DES LONGITUDES. Conference internationale de l'heure (Paris, octobre 1912) Les comptes rendus. iv, 286 p., 21 fig. Paris: Gauthier-Villars, 1912. [CB 4/776]

LALLEMAND, Ch. Projet d'organisation d'un service international de l'heure. *Rev.Sci.*, 1912, 2e semestre, 50: 513-16.

LECOINTE, G. La Conférence Internationale de l'Heure de Paris et l'unification de l'heure. *Vie Int.*, 1912, 2: 43-60.

LECORNU, L. Sur un projet de monument de l'heure. *Compt.Rend. Acad.Sci.*, 1914, 158: 18-19. [CB 5/287]

SARTON, G. Conférence Internationale de l'heure. (Paris, 1912, 1913) *Isis*, 1913, 1: 495-6; 1914-19, 2: 190-1.

FVxs sundials and other astronomical time-measuring instruments

BIGOURDAN, G. Gnomonique ou Traité théorique et pratique de la construction des cadrans solaires, suivi de tables auxiliaires relatives aux cadrans et aux calendriers. 214 p., 104 fig. Paris: Gauthier-Villars, 1922.
With brief history of the subject.

CAFMEYER, M. Zonnewijzers op Jezuïetengoed. [Sun-dials of the Jesuits. (In Dutch)] *Biekorf,* 1959, 60: 12-14.

DRECKER, Joseph. Die Theorie der Sonnenuhren. xi, 112 p., 14 pl. (Die Geschichte der Zeitmessung und der Uhren, 1: Part E) Berlin: de Gruyter, 1925. [CB 23/241]
Reviewed by E. Zinner, *Vierteljahrsschr.Astron.Ges.,* 1933, 68: 39-46.

FINDLAY, John R. Obsolete methods of reckoning time. *Scot. Geogr.Mag.,* May 16, 1927, 43: 129-35.
On the reckoning of hours on sundials, and on instruments for converting hours of one type into those of another.

HELBIG, Jean. A propos de nos cadrans solaires. *Bull.Mus. Roy.Art.Hist.,* 1939, 11: 50-64, 20 fig.

HIGGINS, Kathleen. The classification of sundials. *Ann.Sci.,* 1953, 9: 342-58, 4 pl.

MAYALL, R. Newton. Making portable sundials. *Sky Telesc.,* 1964, 28: 9-12.
Illustrations are of sundials of the 16th century and later. Directions are given both for making and for using sundials.

ROQUET, D. Le cadran solaire de l'Observatoire de Juvisy et les cadrans solaires en général. *Astronomie,* 1912, 26: 441-64.

TERPSTRA, P. Zonnewijzers. [Sundials. (In Dutch)] 148 p., 68 text ill. Groningen/Djakarta: J.B. Wolters, 1953.

YALDEN, J. Ernest G. Dialling. *Ind.Mus.N.Y.,* 1930, 19-57, 6 pl., 5 fig.

ZINNER, Ernst. Alte Sonnenuhren an Gebäuden sind bedroht. *Forsch.Fortschr.,* 1957, 31: 364-7, 2 fig.

ZINNER, Ernst. Tidsmaaling ved Hjaelp af Sol- og Stjerneure. [Time measurement with the help of sun and star clocks. (In Norwegian)] *Nord.Astron.Tidsskr.,* 1928, 9: 123-30, 5 fig.

FVxs-bw

MICHEL, Henri. Catalogue des cadrans solaires du Musée de la Vie Wallonne. 1. Montres solaires. 47 p. Liège: Éditions du Musée Wallon, 1953.
Reviewed by C.A. Crommelin, *Arch.Int.Hist.Sci.,* 1953, 6: 328-9.

FVxs-by

KÖRBER, Hans-Gunther. Über die Hillmannsche Sammlung von Sonnenuhren und Kompassen im Geomagnetischen Institut Potsdam. *Monatsber.Deut.Akad.Wiss.Berlin,* 1963, 5: 641-50. [CB 89/493]
The collection consists of 41 sundials, 12 compasses, and 10 calendars.

FVxs-wd

ZINNER, Ernst. Alte Sonnenuhren an europäischen Gebäuden. viii, 233 p., 24 pl. (Boethius, 3) Wiesbaden: Steiner Verlag, 1964.
Survey of about 5,000 European sundials dating from before A.D. 1800.
Reviewed by Henri Michel, *Arch.Int.Hist.Sci.,* 1964, 17: 336-7.

ZINNER, Ernst. Europäische Sonnenuhren. *Ber.Naturforsch.Ges. Bamberg,* 1960, 37: 14-16.

FVxs-we

GREEN, Arthur Robert. Sundials; incised dials or mass-clocks, a study of the time-markers of medieval churches, containing descriptions, photographs, diagrams and analyses of dials, chiefly in Hampshire, but also in various other counties. xx, 203 p., ill. London: Society for Promoting Christian Knowledge, 1926.

FVxs-wg

ZINNER, Ernst. Alte Sonnenuhren an Bamberger Gebäuden. *Ber. Naturforsch.Ges.Bamberg,* 1929, 25: 58-62.

ZINNER, Ernst. Die moderne Sonnenuhr, eine deutsche Erfindung. *Forsch.Fortschr.,* 1939, 15: 171-3.

ZINNER, Ernst. Schutz den Sonnenuhren an alten Kirchen. *Deut.Kunst- Denkmalpflege,* 1936, 58-62, ill.

ZINNER, Ernst. Tiroler Sonnenuhren. *Z.Deut.Alpenver.,* 1939, 70: 132-7.

FVxs-wi

ZINNER, Ernst. Forschungen in Italien. *Physis,* 1961, 3: 20-36.
On sundials in Italy.

ZINNER, Ernst. Die italienische Sonnenuhr. *Ber.Naturforsch. Ges.Bamberg,* 1962, 38: 1-4.

FW CALENDAR

FWc general history

ACHELIS, Elisabeth. The calendar for everybody. xii, 141 p. [Explanatory note inserted]. New York: Putnam, 1943. [CB 66/262]

ACHELIS, Elisabeth. The world calendar: addresses and occasional papers chronologically arranged on the progress of calendar reform since 1930. 189 p. New York: Putnam, 1937.

BIDEZ, J. Le nom et les origines de nos almanachs. *Mélanges Émile Boissacq,* p. 77-85. Bruxelles: Secrétariat des Editions de l'Institut de Philologie et d'Histoire orientales et slaves, 1937.

BLACK, Frederick Alexander. The calendar and its reform. viii, 80 p., 3 pl. London: Gall and Inglis, 1932.
Reviewed in *Nature,* 1933, 131: 859.

BORK, Ferdinand. Vorstufen unseres Kalenders in der Volkskunde und im Kalender. *Weltall,* 1930, 30: 9-11.

CAJORI, Florian. Comparison of methods of determining calendar dates by finger reckoning. *Archeion,* 1928, 9: 31-42, 5 fig. [CB 24/529]

CHAILAN, E. La réforme du calendrier. *Rev.Sci.,* 1912, 2e sem., 50: 326-31.

CHAUVE-BERTRAND, -, *Abbé.* Le début de l'année à travers les siècles et chez divers peuples. *Ann.Franç.Chronom.,* 1957, 27: 188-92.

FOTHERINGHAM, David Ross. The date of Easter and other Christian festivals. With a preface by Lord Desborough. xv, 56 p. London: Society for Promoting Christian Knowledge, 1928.

FOTHERINGHAM, John K. The Metonic and Callippic cycles. *Mon. Not.Roy.Astron.Soc.,* 1923-24, 84: 383-92.

FRICK, Bertha M.; IVES, S.A. Calendar reform across eighteen centuries. As shown by source materials available in the Columbia University Library. *J.Cal.Reform,* 1943, 13: 130-8, 181-5.

GREIFF, Günther. Verschollenes Wissen. 104 p., 16 pl. Berlin: De Gruyter, 1934.
Concerning calendar and zodiac lore and terminology.
Reviewed by E. Zinner, *Deut.Lit.Zeitung,* 1934, 5: 1722-4.

JACOBOWITZ, Abraham Leib. [The calendar and its use for chronological purposes, including a Jewish-Christian-Moslem calendar from the creation to the year 6000 A.M., by A.A. Akavia. (In Hebrew)] 182 p. [Jerusalem: 1953].

JERPHANION, Guillaume de. D'où vient l'écart entre la Pâque des Orientaux et celle des Latins? Brève histoire du comput pascal. (Etudes, 20 avril 1924) In: La voix des monuments. Notes et études d'archéologie chrétienne, p. 296-321. Paris/Bruxelles: Van Oest, 1930. [CB 32/579]

LEAGUE OF NATIONS. Report on the reform of the calendar submitted to the Advisory and technical committee for communications and transit of the League of Nations by the Special committee of enquiry into the reform of the calendar. 163 p. (Publications of the League of Nations, VIII. Transit, 1926, VIII. 6) Geneva: Imprimerie Kundig, 1926.

LITHBERG, Nils. *Computus* med särskild hänsyn till runstaven och den borgerliga kalendern. [*Computus* with particular reference to runic staves and popular almanacs. (In Swedish with German summary)] 326 p. (Nordiska Museets Handlingar, 29) Stockholm: Norstedt, 1953.
Reviewed by W.E. van Wijk, *Isis*, 1954, 45: 212-13.

PHILIP, Alexander. The calendar. Its history, structure and improvement. xi, 104 p. Cambridge University Press, 1921.

PHILIP, Alexander. The improvement of the Gregorian calendar. 30 p. London: Routledge, 1918.

PHILIP, Alexander. The reform of the calendar. 127 p. London: Kegan Paul, 1914.

POGO, Alexander. Uncommon Easter dates. *Pop.Astron.*, 1943, 51: 254-6.

POGO, Alexander. Unusual Easter dates. *Science*, 1940, 91: 292. [CB 59/470]

PRZYBYLLOK, Erich. Unser Kalender in Vergangenheit und Zukunft. 94 p. (Morgenland, 22) Leipzig: Hinrich, 1930.

SANFORD, Vera. September hath XIX days. *Math.Teacher*, May 1952, 45: 336-9.

TEMPLE, R.C. A fixed Easter and the reform of the Christian calendar. *Indian Antiq.*, 1924, 53: 212-19, 235-40. [CB 18/612]

THOMPSON, J. Eric. A correlation of the Mayan and European calendars. 22 p. (Field Museum of Natural History, publication 241, anthropological series, 17: no. 1) Chicago: 1927. [CB 27/564]

WALKER, George W. Easter reckoning made easy. *Pop.Astron.*, 1944, 52: 173-83, 3 fig. [CB 66/263]

WALKER, George W. Rare dates for Easter. *Pop.Astron.*, 1944, 52: 139-42. [CB 66/263]
Additions and corrections to A. Pogo's paper "Uncommon Easter dates" *see* above.

WALLACE, Lewis A.R. The luni-solar calendar. 11 p., 2 fig. (Historical notes and papers, 14) Lund: Lund Observatory, 1938. Also published in *Medd.Lunds Astron.Observ., ser. 2*, 1938, no. 102.

WARREN, Howard C. A common sense calendar. *Science*, 1918, 47: 375-7.

WATKINS, Harold. Time counts. The story of the calendar. xi, 274 p., ill. London: Neville Spearman; New York: Philosophical Library, 1954.
A study in calendar form, rather than a history of methods of year reckoning.

WIJK, W.E. van. De Gregoriaansche kalender. Een technisch-tijdrekenkundige studie. [The Gregorian calendar: a technical chronological study. (In Dutch)] x, 76, 1 p., 13 fig. Maastricht: A.A.M. Stols, 1932.
Reviewed by A. Pogo, *Isis*, 1938, 28: 140-2; by E.J. Dijksterhuis, *Euclides*, 1932-33, 9: 276.

WIJK, W.E. van. Onze Kalender. [Our calendar. (In Dutch)] 165 p. Amsterdam-Anvers: Wereld Bibliothek, 1955. [CB 82/204]
Reviewed by Henri Michel, *Arch.Int.Hist.Sci.*, 1957, 36: 138-9.

WILSON, Philip Whitwell. The romance of the calendar. 351 p., 13 fig. London: Allen and Unwin; New York: Norton, 1937.
Reviewed by A. Pogo, *Isis*, 1938, 29: 169-72; by Marian Lockwood, *Natur.Hist.*, 1937, 39: 371.

ZINNER, Ernst. Kalender. In: Merker-Stammler. Reallexikon der deutschen Literaturgeschichte, 2nd ed., vol. 1, p. 806-8. Berlin: Walter de Gruyter, 1955-58.

ZINNER, Ernst. Ein Kalendervorschlag. *Ber.Naturforsch.Ges. Bamberg*, 1946, 29: 1-6.

FWcj

GETAZ, E. *Le Messager Boiteux de Berne et de Vevey. Papyrus*, 1926, 7: 403-8. [CB 21/526]
A study of the history of the almanac.

FWp/u special aspects

FWpw

UNIFICATION internationale du calendrier. *Vie Int.*, 1913, 3: 334-40.

FWqy-br

Journal of Calendar Reform. Vol. 1-25. New York: World Calendar Association, 1931-56.

FWr

WEHRLI, G.A. Der Arzt als Kalenderschreiber. *Festschrift zur Feier seines 60. Geburtstages Max Neuburger gewidmet*, p. 308-15. Wien: Verlag des Fest-Komitees, 1928.

FWw in different countries

FWwb-ph

NATIONAL COMMITTEE ON CALENDAR SIMPLIFICATION FOR THE UNITED STATES. Report ... submitted to the Secretary of State, Washington, August 1929. 119 p. Rochester, N.Y.: National Committee on Calendar Simplification, 1929.
Reviewed by H.C.P., *Nature*, 1929, 124: 977-8.
Supplementary report ... submitted to the Secretary of State, Washington, May, 1931. 112 p. Rochester, N.Y.: Office of the Chairman, 1931.

FWwe

SCHNIPPEL, Emil. Die englischen Kalenderstäbe. 111 p. (Beiträge zur englischen Philologie, 5) Leipzig: B. Tauchnitz, 1926.
Reviewed by F. Holthausen, *Deut.Lit.Zeitung*, 1928, 624.

WRIGHT, Arthur Robinson. British calendar customs: England. Ed. by T.E. Lones. 3 vol. 1. Movable festivals; 2. Fixed festivals, January-May, inclusive; 3. Fixed festivals, June-December, inclusive. (Publications of the Folklore Society, 97, 102, 106) London: Glaisher, 1936-41.
Reviewed in *Nature*, 1936, 137: 970.

FWwf-u

LECLERC, J. Les fêtes du soleil. *Astronomie*, 1940, 59: 156-8, ill.

FWwm

LITHBERG, Nils. Almanackan. Från astrologisk rådgivare till svensk kalender. [Almanacks. From the astrological guide to the Swedish calendar. (In Swedish)] 64 p., 15 fig. (Svenska Humanistiska Förbundet, 40) Stockholm: Norstedt, 1933.
Reviewed by R. Zaunick, *Mitt.Gesch.Med.*, 1934, 33: 62.

FWwn

MAISTROV, L. Ye.; PROSVIRKINA, S.K. [Russian wooden calendars. (In Russian)] *Ist.Astron.Issled.*, 1960, 6: 279-98.

FWwp-nh

KOWALSKI, Tadeusz. Zu den türkischen Monatsnamen. *Arch. Orient.*, 1930, 2: 3-26, 2 pl.

FWwx

CHAÎNE, Marius. La chronologie des temps chrétiens de l'Egypte et de l'Ethiopie. Historique et exposé du calendrier et du comput de l'Egypte et de l'Ethiopie depuis les débuts de l'ère chrétienne à nos jours, accompagnés de tables donnant pour chaque année, avec les caractéristiques astronomiques du comput alexandrin, les années correspondantes des principales ères orientales, suivis d'une concordance des années juliennes, grégoriennes, coptes et ethiopiennes avec les années musulmanes, et de plusieurs appendices. xv, 344 p. Paris: Geuthner, 1925.

FY ASTROLOGY

FYc general history

BARBAULT, André. Défense et illustration de l'astrologie. 295 p. Paris: Grasset, 1955.
Reviewed by F. Mathis, *Rev.Quest.Sci.*, 1956, 17: 633-4.

BOK, Bart J.; MAYALL, Margaret W. Scientists look at astrology. *Sci.Mon.*, 1941, 52: 233-44, ill.

BOLL, Franz. Sternglaube und Sterndeutung. Die Geschichte und das Wesen der Astrologie unter Mitwirkung von Carl Bezold. Hrsg. von W. Gundel. 4th ed. xiv, 230 p., 24 pl., 2 star charts. Leipzig: Teubner, 1931.
First publ. 1917; for 2nd ed. *see* CB 9/482; 3rd ed. reviewed by George Sarton, *Isis*, 1927, 9: 476-7; 4th ed. by H. Wieleitner, *Mitt.Gesch.Med.*, 1932, 31: 22.

BROGDEN, Stanley. Superstition is returning. *Discovery*, 1938, 1: 403-6.
Circumstances which caused a revival of astrology in England in 1930-38.

BUTLER, Hiram E. Solar biology. A scientific method of discerning character, diagnosing disease, determining mental, physical and business qualifications, conjugal adaptability, etc., from date of birth. 23rd ed., ill. xl, 288, 206 p. Applegate, Calif.: Esoteric Publishing Co., 1920.
First published 1887; 29th edition 1931.
Reviewed by G. Sarton, *Isis*, 1920, 3: 449-50.

CARTER, Charles E.O. The principles of astrology, theoretical and applied. 200 p. London: Theosophical Publishing House, 1925.

CLASSEN, Johannes. Naturwissenschaftliche Astrologie. 44 p., ill. Düsseldorf: Zenit-Verlag, 1931.

CONNOR, Elizabeth. Astrology is not extinct. *Publ.Astron. Soc.Pacific*, Oct. 1943, 55: 12-18.

DAISOMONT, M. Où en est l'astrologie? 51 p., 11 fig. Bruges: De Tempel, 1947.

DIELS, Hermann, Zur Geschichte und Bedeutung der Astrologie. *Deut.Lit.Zeitung*, 1918, 39: 275-82.
Apropos of Boll's "Sternglaube und Sterndeutung", *see* above.

DRECKER, Joseph. Zeitmessung und Sterndeutung in geschichtlicher Darstellung. 188 p., 67 ill. Berlin: Borntraeger, 1925.
Summary of present knowledge on chronology and horology (with historical notes) followed by an explanation of astrology.

EISLER, Robert. The royal art of astrology. 296 p., front., 16 pl., 48 ill., 5 diagr. London: Michael Joseph, 1946.
Reviewed by N.T. Bobrovnikoff, *Isis*, 1949, 40: 79-81.

GRAUBARD, Mark. Astrology and alchemy: two fossil sciences. xi, 382 p. New York: Philosophical Library, 1953. [CB 81/285]
Reviewed by Rufus Suter, *Scr.Math.*, 1954, 20: 190-2; by Frank K. Edmondson, *Sci.Mon.*, 1954, 78: 396.

GUNDEL, W. Sternglaube, Sternreligion und Sternorakel. Aus der Geschichte der Astrologie. 2nd rev. ed. 168 p. Heidelberg: Quelle & Meyer, 1959.
First publ. Leipzig: 1933.
Reviewed by H. Werner, *Naturwiss.Rundsch.*, 1960, 5: 200.

KEIL, Gundolf. Die verworfenen Tage. *Sudhoffs Arch.*, 1957, 41: 27-58. [CB 83/213]

KLÖCKLER, Herbert von. Astrologie als Erfahrungswissenschaft. xiii, 384 p., 37 fig. (Metaphysik und Weltanschauung) Leipzig: Reinicke, 1927.

KOCH, Walter; KNAPPICH, Wilhelm. Horoskop und Himmelshäuser. 2 vol. 1. Grundlagen und Altertum. 144 p., fig., tables; 2. Regiomontanus und das Häusersystems des Geburtsortes. 160 p., 24 fig., 16 pl. Göppingen: Siriusverlag Dr. Koch, 1959, 1960.

KRAUSE, Arthur. Die Astrologie. Entwicklung, Aufbau und Kritik. vii, 319 p., 50 fig. Leipzig: J.J. Weber, 1927.
Reviewed by W. Gundel, *Deut.Lit.Zeitung*, 1928, 783-4.

LASSALLY, Oswald. Von der Entstehung des Aberglaubens an Sterne und Steine. *Geisteskultur*, 1931, 40: 87-92.

SAINTYVES, P., pseud. of Émile Nourry. L'astrologie populaire étudiée spécialement dans les doctrines et les traditions relatives à l'influence de la lune. Essai sur la méthode dans l'étude du folklore des opinions et des croyances. 464 p. Paris: Nourry, 1937. [CB 56/387]

STEIGER, A.L. von. Der "königliche" Mensch. Nach einem Vortrag über den objektiven Wahrheitskern der geburtsastrologischen Tradition. 16 p. Bern: A.L. von Steiger, 1941.
Reviewed by R. Zaunick, *Mitt.Gesch.Med.*, 1940, 39: 326-7.

STRAUSS, Heinz Artur. Astrologie. Grundsätzliche Betrachtungen. 76 p. München: Kurt Wolff, 1927.
Reviewed by K. Sudhoff, *Mitt.Gesch.Med.*, 1927, 26: 253-4.

STRUNZ, Franz. Astrologie, Alchemie, Mystik: ein Beitrag zur Geschichte der Naturwissenschaften. 351 p. München-Planegg: Otto Wilhelm Barth, 1928.

TALLMADGE, G. Kasten. De l'influence des astres sur la naissance de l'homme. *Petrus Nonius*, 1939, 2: 169-75, 2 facs.

TALLMADGE, G. Kasten. On the influence of the stars on human birth. *Bull.Hist.Med.*, 1943, 13: 251-67, 4 pl.

THORNDIKE, Lynn. The true place of astrology in the history of science. *Isis*, 1955, 46: 273-8.

WARBURG, A. Orientalisierende Astrologie (1926). In: A. Warburg. Die Erneuerung der heidnischen Antike, p. 559-65, 657. Leipzig: 1932.

ZINNER, Ernst. Die astrologische Treffsicherheit. *Gesundheitslehrer Ausg.* A, 1932, 35: 170-3. [CB 38/596]

ZINNER, Ernst. Die Horoskope der Weltentstehung. *Forsch. Fortschr.*, 1943, 19: 99-101, ill.

ZINNER, Ernst. Der Mensch und die Sterne. *Fortschr.Med.*, 1933, 51: 128-32, 175-9.

FYc-be

DE VORE, Nicholas. Encyclopedia of astrology. xii, 435 p. New York: Philosophical Library, 1947.
Reviewed by N.T. Bobrovnikoff, *Isis*, 1949, 40: 79-81.

FYcj

AGOSTINI, Amedeo. Gli obblighi dei lettori di matematica nell'antico studio bolognese. *Period.Mat.*, 1923, 3: 1-4. [CB 14/550]
The professors of mathematics at the University of Bologna were obliged to compile an astrological almanac.

FYm/w special aspects

FYmzDY

MAHDIHASSAN, S. Alchemy and its connection with astrology, pharmacy, magic and metallurgy. *Janus*, 1957, 46: 81-103.

FYmzN

CARTER, Charles E.O. A concise encyclopaedia of psychological astrology. Together with observations of the astrological characteristics of about fifty diseases and an introductory essay on the zodiacal signs from the standpoint of biology and psychology. 159 p. London: Foulsham, 1924.

MERCIER, Charles Arthur. Astrology in medicine. The Fitzpatrick lectures delivered before the Royal College of Physicians ... 1913. With addendum on saints and signs. 100 p. London: Macmillan, 1914.

RICHTER, Erwin. Einwirkung medicoastrologischen Volksdenkens auf Entstehung und Formung des Bärmutterkrötenopfers der Männer im geistlichen Heilbrauch. *Sudhoffs Arch.*, 1958, 42: 326-49.

WICKERSHEIMER, Ernest. La médecine astrologique dans les almanachs populaires du XXe siècle. *Paris Méd.*, 1912, partie paramédicale, p. 371-7. Also in *Bull.Soc.Franç.Hist.Méd.*, 1911, 10: 26-39.

FYmzPW

PEIPER, Albrecht. Das Neugeborene in der Sterndeutung (Astrologie). *Kinderärztl.Prax.*, 1964, 32: 329-33.

FYnb-ce

STRYCKER, É. de. La baleine, l'aveugle et le chat dans un texte astrologique. *Rev.Belg.Philol.Hist.*, 1938, 17: 222-5.

FYtq

WARBURG, A. Italienische Kunst und internationale Astrologie im Palazzo Schifanoja zu Ferrara (1912). In: A. Warburg, Die Erneuerung der heidnischen Antike, p. 459-81, 627-44, 13 pl. Leipzig: 1932.

FYwg

STRAUSS, Heinz Artur. Der astrologische Gedanke in der deutschen Vergangenheit. 104 p., ill. München: Oldenbourg, 1926.

FZ EARTH SCIENCES

FZc

HAAS, Hippolyt. Was uns die Steine erzählen! Altes und Neues aus den Gebieten der Geologie und Geographie. 314 p., ill. Berlin: Alfred Schall, 1912.

HÖLDER, Helmut. Geologie und Paläontologie in Texten und ihrer Geschichte. xviii, 565 p., fig., pl., bibliogr. (Orbis Academicus, 2: 11) Freiburg/Munich: Verlag Karl Alber, 1960.
Reviewed by Albert V. Carozzi, *Isis*, 1962, 53: 398-400; by K. Mägdefrau, *Naturwiss.Rundsch.*, 1961, 5: 202; by Gerhard Regnéll, *Lychnos*, 1962, 478-80.

VALLAUX, Camille. La géologie et la géographie physique. *Géographie*, 1923, 39: 145-64. [CB 16/305]

ZITTEL, Karl von. History of geology and palaeontology. To the end of the nineteenth century. xiii, 562 p. (Historiae Naturalis Classica, 12) Codicote, Herts: Wheldon & Wesley; New York: Hafner Publishing Company, 1962.
An unaltered reprint of the edition which first appeared in London in 1901.

FZc-bv

[DISSERTATIONS on the history of geology, geography, mining, and metallurgy published 1944-1954. (In Russian)] *Tr.Inst. Ist.Est.Tekh.*, 1955, 3: 232-7.

FZke

GLANGEAUD, Louis. L'expérience et la recherche opérationnelle dans les sciences de la terre et de la nature. *Rev.Syn.*, 1963, 34: 125-70.

FZsc

MERRIAM, John C. Earth sciences as the background of history. *Bull.Geol.Soc.Amer.*, 1920, 31: 233-46; reprinted in *Sci. Mon.*, 1921, 12: no. 1, 15-17.

FZwb

PARKS, William Arthur. The development of stratigraphic geology and palaeontology in Canada. *Proc.Roy.Soc.Can.*, 1922, 16: Sect. 4, 1-46.

FZwb-qk

MERRILL, George P., ed. Contributions to a history of American state geological and natural history surveys. xviii, 549 p., ill. (*Bull.U.S.Nat.Mus.*, 109) Washington, D.C.: 1920. [CB 10/158]

FZwg-oq

PENCK, Albrecht. Die erdkundlichen Wissenschaften an der Universität Berlin. Rede zur Gedächtnisfeier des Stifters der Berliner Universität König Friedrich Wilhelms III in der Aula am 3. August 1918. 44 p. Berlin: 1918.

FZwn

ISTORIIA ESTESTVOZNANIIA V ROSSII. 3. Geologo-geograficheskie i biologicheskie nauki. [History of natural science in Russia. 3. Geological-geographical and biological sciences. Ed. by S.R. Mikulinskii. (In Russian)] 603 p., ill. Moscow: Izdatel'stvo Akademii Nauk SSR, 1962.

MOSCOW. UNIVERSITET. Rol russkoi nauki v razvitii mirovoi nauki i kultury. [The role of Russian science in the development of world science and culture. (In Russian)] Vol. 2. 103 p. (*Uch.Zap.Moskovskogo Gos.Univ.*, no. 104) Moskva: Izdanie MGU, 1946.
This volume contains articles on earth sciences in Russia; contents listed in CB 80/127-8.

FZzc NATURAL CALAMITIES

for earthquakes and volcanic eruptions *see* GP; epidemics QN; floods and winds GFA.

JEANSELME, Édouard. Inondations, famines et tremblements de terre sont les avant-coureurs de la peste. *Proc.3rd Int. Congr.Hist.Med.*(London, 1922), p. 37-41. Antwerp: De Vlijt, 1923.

Matériaux pour l'Etude des Calamités. (Société de Géographie de Genève) No. 1-40. Genève: 1924-37. [CB 21/589]

FZzc-we

TAYLOR, E.G.R. The early literature of natural calamities in Britain: with a bibliography. *Scot.Geogr.Mag.*, 1932, 48: 83-9.

G METEOROLOGY

Gc general history

BETTONI, Pio. La meteorologia nella sua origine e nel suo sviluppo. *Meteorol.Prat.*, 1925, 6: no. 2, 50-7.
Brief sketch of the development of meteorology from the earliest times.

BJERKNES, J. Half a century of change in the "meteorological scene". *Bull.Amer.Met.Soc.*, 1964, 45: 312-15.

DUFOUR, Louis. Les grandes époques de l'histoire de la météorologie. *Ciel Terre*, 1943, 59: 355-9.

DUFOUR, Louis. Quelques considérations sur le développement de la météorologie. *Act.Ve Congr.Int.Hist.Sci.* (Lausanne, 1947), p. 108-12. Paris: Hermann, 1948. Also in *Arch.Int. Hist.Sci.*, 1948, 1: 286-90.

GAUTHIER, Henri. Questions de géophysique contemporaine. *Rev.Quest.Sci.*, 1924, 86: 5-25, 345-68.
The position of problems of practical and theoretical meteorology during the last twenty years.

HELLMANN, Gustav. Beiträge zur Geschichte der Meteorologie. 3 vol. 148 p.; vi, 340 p.; ii, 102 p. (Veröffentlichungen des Königlich Preussischen Meteorologischen Instituts, 273, 296, 315) Berlin: Behrend, 1914-17, 1922. [CB 10/190 and CB 16/285]

HELLMANN, Gustav. Die Entwicklung der meteorologischen Beobachtungen bis zum Ende des XVIII. Jahrhunderts. 48 p. (*Abhandl.Preuss.Akad.Wiss.Phys.Math.Kl.*, 1) Berlin: 1927.

A METEOROLOGICAL cross section: the Köppen birthday volumes. *Geogr.Rev.*, 1933, 23: 472-8.

RAMOS DA COSTA, A. Um capítulo da história da meteorologia. Desde os fins do século passado até hoje. *Petrus Nonius*, 1937, 1: 52-60.

ROUCH, Jules. Coup d'oeil sur l'histoire de la météorologie. *Rev.Sci.*, 1931, 69: 530-3.

SHAW, William Napier. A century of meteorology. *Nature*, 1931, 128: 925-6.

SHAW, William Napier. The drama of weather. xiv, 269 p., 92 fig. New York: Macmillan; Cambridge University Press, 1933. [CB 58/579]
2nd ed. 1939. First two chapters are a summary of the origin and progress of meteorology.
Reviewed by C.A. Kofoid, *Isis*, 1935, 24: 186-8.

SHAW, William Napier. Manual of meteorology. With the assistance of Elaine Austin. 2 vol. 1. Meteorology in history. xx, 339 p., 18 pl.; 2. Comparative meteorology. xl, 466 p., 225 ill. Cambridge University Press, 1926-28.
Volume 1 reviewed by W.H. Dines, *Nature*, 1927, 119: 915-17; volume 2 reviewed by Alexander McAdie, *Science*, 1928, 67: 632; by V. Bjerknes, *Nature*, 1928, 121: 931-2.

SHAW, William Napier. The meteorology of yesterday, today and tomorrow. *Scientia*, 1932, 51: 393-404.

SIMPSON, G.C. The new ideas in meteorology. From the presidential address delivered at Southampton on August 28, before Section A (Mathematical and physical science) of the British Association. *Nature*, 1925, 116: 361-5.

SMITH, H.T. Marine meteorology, history and progress. 1. Early history; 2. Middle period; 3. Present day. *Mar.Observ.*, 1925, 2: 33-5, 90-2, 173-5, 5 fig. [CB 18/631]

SUTTON, O.G. The development of meteorology as an exact science. *Nature*, 1954, 173: 1112-14.

TANNEHILL, Ivan Ray. Weather around the world. xi, 200 p., 55 fig. Princeton, N.J.: Princeton University Press, 1943. [CB 65/83]

WALTER, Emil J. Technische Bedingungen in der historischen Entwicklung der Meteorologie. *Gesnerus*, 1952, 9: 55-66, 4 fig.
With a chronology from Hippocrates to 1906.

ZINSZER, Harvey A. Meteorological mileposts. *Sci.Mon.*, 1944, 58: 261-4.
A brief list of outstanding contributions to meteorology from Aristotle to the twentieth century.

Gc-bu/cv bibliography; literature; sources

Gc-bx

SCIENCE MUSEUM. The science of weather: an exhibition held at the ... Museum to mark the 100th birthday of the Royal Meteorological Society in 1950. By D. Chilton. 32 p., ill. London: H.M. Stationery Off., 1950.

Gcb

BULL, G.A. The Library of the Royal Meteorological Society. *Weather*, 1963, 18: 346-7. [CB 89/492]

COLLARD, Auguste. Une bibliothèque belge centenaire. La Bibliothèque de l'Observatoire Royal et de l'Institut Royal Météorologique de Belgique - 1833-1933. *Arch.Bibl.Mus.Belg.*, 1935, 12: 78-109.

Gcd

DEPT, Gaston Gérard. Quelques documents météorologiques inédits. *Rev.Quest.Sci.*, 1931, 50: 460-73. [CB 37/602]

Gce-bv

AMERICAN METEOROLOGICAL SOCIETY. A selective bibliography in meteorology. *Weatherwise*, 1957, 10: 47-9, 95-7; 1959, 12: 73-5; 1961, 14: 187-91, 199-205; 1963, 16: 175-87. [CB 89/583]

Bibliography of Meteorological Literature. Prepared by the Royal Meteorological Society with the collaboration of the Meteorological Office. Vol. 1-6, no. 6 (1920-48). London: Royal Meteorological Society, 1922-50.

Gck

HESS, Wilhelm. Die Einblattdrucke des 15. bis 18. Jahrhunderts unter besonderer Berücksichtigung ihres astronomischen und meteorologischen Inhaltes. Rede. 38 p. Bamberg: J.M. Reindl, 1913.

Gcn

BLASCHKE, M. Zur Geschichte der Wetterkarte. *Weltall*, 1928, 28: 24-6.

CAHILL, B.J.S. Projections for world maps. *Mon.Weather Rev.*, 1929, 57: 128-33, 6 fig. [CB 27/560]

VANDEVYVER, L.M. Les nouvelles cartes synoptiques du Weather Bureau de Washington. *Ciel Terre*, 1914, 35: 169-72. [CB 6/455]

Gk/u special aspects

Gk

BERGET, Alphonse. Où en est la météorologie. vii, 300 p., ill. (Collection des Mises au Point) Paris: Gauthier-Villars, 1920.

BJERKNESS, V. La météorologie considérée comme science exacte. *Rev.Sci.*, 1913, 51: 1er semestre, 432-4.

Go-ce

HELLMANN, Gustav. Entwicklungsgeschichte des meteorologischen Lehrbuches. In his: Beiträge zur Geschichte der Meteorologie, vol. 2, no. 6, p. 3-133. Berlin: Behrend, 1917. [CB 10/190]

Gqy

CANNEGIETER, Hendrik Gerrit. The history of the International Meteorological Organization 1872-1951. 280 p. (*Ann.Meteorol.*, 1) Offenbach a.M.: Deutscher Wetterdienst, 1963. [CB 89/504]
The International Meteorological Organization became the World Meteorological Organization in 1951.

Gt

HUMPHREYS, W.J. Ways of the weather: a cultural survey of meteorology. v, 400 p. Lancaster, Pa.: J. Cattell Press, 1942. [CB 64/453]

Gtd-ce

HELLMANN, Gustav. Die theologisch-meteorologische Literatur. In his: Beiträge zur Geschichte der Meteorologie, vol. 1, no. 4, p. 113-38. Berlin: Behrend, 1914. [CB 10/190]

Gth

DUFOUR, Louis. Météorologie et littérature. 31 p. (Conférences du Palais de la Découverte, D75) Paris: Université de Paris, 1961.

Gu

DUFOUR, Louis. Le folklore météorologique de la lune. *Ciel Terre*, 1941, 57: 49-66, 1 pl.

DUFOUR, Louis. Questionnaire sur le folklore météorologique. *Ciel Terre*, 1941, 57: 265-8.

HELLMANN, Gustav. Ueber den Ursprung der volkstümlichen Wetterregeln (Bauernregeln). *Sitzungsber.Preuss.Akad.Wiss. Phys.Math.Kl.*, 1923, 148-70.
Followed by a list of books on popular weather rules, classified by countries (p. 162-9).

HUMPHREYS, W.J. Weather proverbs and paradoxes. viii, 125 p. Baltimore: Williams and Wilkins, 1923.
Reviewed by Henry Crew, *Science*, 1924, 59: 301.

INWARDS, R. Weather lore ... Ed. and amplified for the Royal Meteorological Society by E.L. Hawke. 251 p. 4th ed. London: Rider, 1950.
First published 1869.
Reviewed by Louis Dufour, *Arch.Int.Hist.Sci.*, 1951, 4: 225-6.

Gu-th

DUFOUR, Louis. Quelques remarques sur les relations entre la littérature et le folklore météorologique. *Ciel Terre*, 1960, 76: 221-5.

Gw in different countries

Gwb

ABBE, Truman. Professor Abbe and the isobars. The story of Cleveland Abbe, America's first weatherman. xi, 259 p., 14 pl. New York: Vantage Press, Inc., 1955.
Reviewed by O.G. Sutton, *Nature*, 1956, 178: 110-11.

ALDREDGE, Robert Croom. Weather observers and observations at Charleston, South Carolina, 1670-1871. Reprinted from Historical appendix of the Year Book of the City of Charleston for the year 1940, p. 190-257. 68 p. [n.p.: 1940].
Reviewed by I.E. Drabkin, *Bull.Hist.Med.*, 1943, 13: 116.

HUME, Edgar Erskine. The foundation of American meteorology by the United States Army Medical Department. *Bull.Hist. Med.*, 1940, 8: 202-38, 14 fig.

STUPART, Frederic. History of meteorology in North America since 1848. *Bull.Amer.Meteorol.Soc.*, 1924, 5: 1-6.

Gwb-ce

HUMPHREYS, William J. A review of papers on meteorology and climatology published by the American Philosophical Society prior to the twentieth century. *Proc.Amer.Phil.Soc.*, 1942, 86: 29-33.

Gwb-daj

LOWE, A.B. Weathermen of early Canada. *Weather*, 1963, 18: 354-9.
Observations by early explorers and traders (Hudson's Bay Co.) from Martin Frobisher (1578) to Peter Fidler's Observations from the Canadian northwest (1790-1819).

Gwb-q

MILLER, Eric R. The evolution of the meteorological institutions in the United States. *Mon.Weath.Rev.*, 1931, 59: 1-6.
An outline of the growth of the organizations that have dealt with climate and weather in the United States of America.

Gwb-qg

STONE, Robert G. Die Entwicklung der amerikanischen Bergobservatorien und das derzeitige Netz von Bergstationen in den Vereinigten Staaten von Amerika. *Jahresber.Sonnblick-Ver.*, 1934, 43: 11-30, 2 fig.

STONE, Robert G. The history of mountain meteorology in the United States and the Mount Washington Observatory. *Trans. 15th Amer.Geophys.Union*(1934), p. 124-33. Washington, D.C.: 1934.

Gwc

LEBRIJA CELAY, Manuel. A brief history of meteorology in Mexico and the present organization of the services. *Weatherwise*, 1963. 16: 208-11, 236. [CB 89/505]

Gwe-qd

ROYAL METEOROLOGICAL SOCIETY. *Nature*, 1925, 115: 657-8. [CB 18/566]
Brief account of the history of the Society and of its predecessors.

Gwf

DOUBLET, E. La météorologie en France et en Allemagne. *Rev. Philomath.Bordeaux*, 1911, vol. 14; 1912, vol. 15, 81 p.

Gwg

DOUBLET, E. La météorologie en France et en Allemagne. *Rev. Philomath.Bordeaux*, 1911, vol. 14; 1912, vol. 15, 81 p.

GÜNTHER, S. Die Meteorologie in Bayern. *Meteorol.Z.*, 1912, 29: 353-66.

HELLMANN, Gustav. Die Entwicklung der meteorologischen Beobachtungen in Deutschland von den ersten Anfängen bis zur Einrichtung staatlicher Beobachtungsnetze. 25 p. (*Abhandl. Preuss.Akad.Wiss.Phys.Math.Kl.*,1926, no. 1) Berlin: 1926.

Gwh

STEINER, L. Die meteorologischen Beobachtungen und Forschungen in Ungarn. (Seventh *Int.Congr.Hist.Sci.*, Warsaw, 1933) *Bull.Int.Comm.Hist.Sci.*, 1933, 5: no. 19, 312-18.

Gwk

DUFOUR, Louis. Esquisse d'une histoire de la météorologie en Belgique. *Ciel Terre*, 1945, 61: 1-10, 1 pl.

DUFOUR, Louis. Esquisse d'une histoire de la météorologie en Belgique. 55 p., fig. (Institut Royal Météorologique de Belgique, miscellanées, fasc. 40) Bruxelles: 1950.

DUFOUR, Louis. Notes pour servir à l'histoire de la météorologie en Belgique (2e série). 20 p. (Institut Royal Météorologique de Belgique, miscellanées, fasc. 31) Bruxelles: 1947.

DUFOUR, Louis. Points à élucider dans l'histoire de la météorologie en Belgique. *Rev.Belg.Philol.Hist.*, 1948, 26: 568-75.

DUFOUR, Louis. Sketch history of meteorology in Belgium. *Weather*, 1951, 6: 359-64, 5 fig.

VANDERLINDEN, E. Chronique des événements météorologiques en Belgique jusqu'en 1834. 329 p. Bruxelles: Hayez, 1924.
Reviewed by G.G. Dept, *Rev.Quest.Sci.*, 1931, 50: 460-73.

Gwk-qd

SOCIÉTÉ BELGE D'ASTRONOMIE, DE MÉTÉOROLOGIE ET DE PHYSIQUE DU GLOBE. Cinquantenaire de la Société, 27 octobre 1945. Memorial. 32 p., 6 pl. Bruxelles: 1945.

Gwk-qg

BURGER, D. Het honderdjarig feest van het Koninklijk Nederlands Meteorologisch Institut, 1854-1954. [The centennial of the Royal Netherlands Meteorological Institute. (In Dutch)] *Faraday*, 1953-54, 23: 129-130.

Gwk-u

DUFOUR, Louis. La météorologie populaire en Belgique. 123 p., front. (Collection Nationale, 4me série, 43) Bruxelles: Office de Publicité, 1943. [CB 69/232]

DUFOUR, Louis. Quelques dictons météorologiques. *Folklore Brabançon*, 1939-40, 19: 263-5.
Heard in Brabant.

Gwn

KHRGIAN, A. Kh. Historia meteorologii v Rossii. [History of meteorology in Russia. (In Russian)] *Tr.Inst.Ist.Est.*, 1948, 2: 71-104.

KHRGIAN, A.H. The history of meteorology in Russia. *Act.VIIIe Congr.Int.Hist.Sci.* (Florence, 1956), p. 445-8. Paris: Hermann, 1958.

Gws

BANERJI, S.K. Progress of meterology in India. *Sci.Cult.*, 1962, 28: 197-204.

Gwx

VANDENPLAS, A. Esquisse d'une histoire de la météorologie au Congo Belge. *IIIe Congr.Nat.Sci.* (Bruxelles, 1950), (1), p. 148-9. Liége: 1951.

Gxk instruments

HELLMANN, Gustav. Beiträge zur Erfindungsgeschichte der meteorologischen Instrumente. 60 p. (*Abhandl.Preuss.Akad. Wiss.Phys.Math.Kl.*, 1920, no. 1) Berlin: 1920.
Contributions to the history of the thermometer, barometer, pluviometer, vane and compass card.

MULTHAUF, Robert P. The introduction of self-registering meteorological instruments. 20 p., ill. (*Bull.U.S.Nat. Mus.*, 225) Washington, D.C.: Smithsonian Institution, 1961.

Gxx museums

SCIENCE MUSEUM. Catalogue of the collections with descriptive and historical notes and illustrations: meteorology. 107 p., 6 pl. London: H.M. Stationery Off., 1922.

GyFK effect of SUN

RAMOS DA COSTA, A. A influência da actividade solar na meteorologia. Historia da sua evolução. *Petrus Nonius*. 1939, 2: 97-103.

Gzm WEATHER MODIFICATION

HUMPHREYS, William J. Rain-making and other weather vagaries. 150 p. Baltimore: Williams and Wilkins, 1926.
Reviewed by Alexander McAdie, *Science*, 1926, 64: 625.

HUSCHKE, Ralph. A brief history of weather modification since 1946. *Bull.Amer.Meteorol.Soc.*, 1963, 44: 425-9.

McADIE, Alexander George. Making the weather. x, 88 p. New York: Macmillan, 1923.

GA THE ATMOSPHERE IN GENERAL

APPLETON, Edward. Sir Joseph Larmor and the ionosphere. (Larmor Memorial Lecture). *Proc.Roy.Irish Acad.*, 1961, 61: sect. A, 55-66.

BESSON, Louis. Aperçu historique sur la classification des nuages. 20 p. (Memorial de l'Office National Météorologique de France, 1re année, no. 2) Paris: 1923. [CB 17/556]

BOTLEY, C.M. The air and its mysteries. xv, 296 p., ill. London: Bell, 1938. American edition arranged by H.A. Webb. xvi, 302 p., ill. New York: Appleton Century, 1940.
Reviewed by E.L. Hawke, *Nature*, 1938, 142: 375.

DEDEBANT, G.; WEHRLÉ, Ph. La mécanique de l'atmosphère et des grands milieux fluides fondée sur les concepts d'échelle et de probabilité. *Thalès*, 1935, 2: 53-81.

KEMPF, Nikolaus. Die Entwicklung der Theorien über den Höhenrauch. *Arch.Gesch.Naturwiss.Tech.*, 1914, 5: 303-14, 415-50; 1916, 7: 26-55, 141-62, bibliogr.

SHAW, William Napier. The air and its ways. The Rede Lecture, 1921, in the University of Cambridge, with other contributions to meteorology for schools and colleges. xix, 237 p. Cambridge University Press, 1923.

GAsr

HOOVER, C.F. The significance of the scientific conquest of the air for intellectual freedom. *Ann.Med.Hist.*, 1930, *new ser.*, 2: 651-9.
A discussion of science, superstition and intellectual freedom with special reference to atmospheric phenomena.

GAwk

DUFOUR, Louis. Les débuts de l'aérologie en Belgique. *Misc. Inst.Météorol.Belg.*, 1947, 31: 18-20; also in *Ciel Terre*, 1948, 64: 108-10.

GAxm

LAGRANGE, E. Propositions de la Commission Internationale pour l'Etude Scientifique de la Haute Atmosphère. *Ciel Terre*, 1913, 34: 176-7.
Discusses suggestion that atmospheric pressures should be stated in millibars.

GAxq

BARRESI, Giovanni. A proposito di una storia del barometro. Risposta al prof. Aldo Mieli. 62 p. Palermo: Edizioni Sandron, 1929.

BARRESI, Giovanni. Riflessioni i ricerche su la storia del barometro e la sua denominazione. 105 p. Palermo: R. Sandron, 1908; reprinted 1928.
Reviewed by A. Mieli, *Archeion*, 1928, 9: 377.

BERT, Paul. Barometric pressure. xxxii, 1055 p. Columbus, Ohio: College Book Co., 1943.
Reviewed by M.F.A. Montagu, *Isis*, 1944, 35: 35-6.

MIDDLETON, W.E. Knowles. The history of the barometer. xx, 489 p., ill. Baltimore: Johns Hopkins Press, 1964.
Reviewed by Louis P. Harrison, *Isis*, 1964, 55: 450-1; by Silvio A. Bedini, *Science*, 1964, 144: 727; by Sanborn C. Brown, *Phys.Today*, 1964, 17: no. 9, 68-70.

WAARD, Cornelis de. L'expérience barométrique, ses antécédents et ses explications. Etude historique. 198 p. Thouars, Deux-Sèvres: Imprimerie Nouvelle, 1936.
Reviewed by George Sarton, *Isis*, 1936, 26: 212-15, 1 fig.

GAxq-wk

MICHEL, Henri. Le baromètre liégeois. *Physis*, 1961, 3: 205-12.

GB WINDS

AUBERT DE LA RUE, E. Man and the winds. Translated by Madge E. Thompson. 206 p. New York: Philosophical Library, 1955.

CLINE, Isaac Monroe. Tropical cyclones, comprising an exhaustive study ... of ... features observed and recorded in sixteen tropical cyclones which have moved on gulf and south Atlantic coasts during the twenty five years 1900-1924 inclusive. xii, 13, 301 p., maps, diagr., bibliogr. New York: Macmillan, 1926.
Reviewed by Oliver L. Fassig, *Geogr.Rev.*, 1928, 18: 175-6.

HELLMANN, Gustav. Die ältesten Untersuchungen über Windhosen. In his: Beiträge zur Geschichte der Meteorologie, vol. 2, p. 329-34. Berlin: Behrend, 1917. [CB 10/191]

HOBBS, W.H. Some curious early accounts of the Greenland foehn. *Bull.Amer.Meteorol.Soc.*, 1928, 9: 79-81.

HOBBS, W.H. Exploring about the North Pole of the winds. viii, 376 p., ill., maps. London: Putnam, 1930.

LAUGHTON, Carr; HEDDON, V. Great storms. viii, 251 p., 13 pl. London: Philip Allan, 1927.
Reviewed by E. Taylor, *Nature*, 1928, 121: 490-1.

LUDLUM, David M. Early American hurricanes, 1492-1870. xii, 198 p., maps, charts. Boston: American Meteorological Society, 1963.
Gives available meteorological data for the situations historically surrounding the occurrence of hurricanes in the Atlantic and Gulf coastline regions.
Reviewed by Arnold Court, *Geogr.Rev.*, 1964, 54: 150.

MIEGHEM, J. van. Le premier exemple d'analyse d'un cyclone dans l'espace et dans le temps. 20 p. (*Inst.Météorol.Belg. miscellanées*, fasc. 2) Bruxelles: 1939.

TANNEHILL, Ivan Ray. Hurricanes: their nature and history - particularly those of the West Indies and the southern coasts of the United States. 2nd ed. x, 265 p. Princeton N.J.: Princeton University Press, 1942.
First publ. 1938 and reviewed in *Nature*, 1938, 142: 663.
Reviewed by Conway Zirkle, *Isis*, 1944, 35: 195-6.

WALTER, Emil. Der Schweizerföhn. 40 p., 39 fig. (*Neujahrsbl. Naturforsch.Ges.Zürich*, 1938, no. 140) Zürich: Fretz, 1938. [CB 57/255]

GBnh

GOLD, E. Origin of the word 'geostrophic'. *Bull.Amer. Meteorol.Soc.*, 1963, 44: 249. [CB 89/583]
Introduced by Sir Napier Shaw.

OCKENDEN, C.V. Origins of "geostrophic" and "cyclostrophic". *Bull.Amer.Meteorol.Soc.*, 1963, 44: 778. *See also* Gold, E., above.

TALLQVIST, Knut. Himmelsgegenden und Winde. *Stud.Orient.*, 1928, 2: 105-85. [CB 25/428]
A study on the names of celestial directions and winds in many languages.

GBu

DUFOUR, Louis. Les origines de la météorologie étudiées dans le folklore du vent. *Ciel Terre,* 1943, 59: 156-71, ill.

GC PRECIPITATIONS; FLOODS

for rain making *see* Gzm WEATHER MODIFICATION

BROOKS, Charles Ernest Pelham; GLASSPOOLE, J. British floods and droughts. With an introductory note by Hugh Robert Mill. 119 p., 2 pl. London: Benn, 1928.
Reviewed by L.C.W. Bonacina, *Nature,* 1929, 123: 403-4.

CHURCH, James Edward. Seeking snow in the Himalaya ("Home of Snow"). *Sci.Cult.,* 1947, 13: 82-6.
Autobiographical notes of the snow specialist, Dr. Church, adviser of the Himalaya snow project.

FISCHER, Hanns. Weltwenden: die grossen Fluten in Sage und Wirklichkeit. 2nd rev. ed. xii, 230 p., 53 ill. Leipzig: R. Voigtländer, 1925.
Reviewed by R. Zaunick, *Mitt.Gesch.Med.,* 1926, 25: 167.

GRUAU, -, Colonel. La théorie de la grêle de Ch. Weyer. *Rev. Gén.Sci.,* 1916, 27: 573-5, 2 fig.

HOBBS, William H. The snow of outstanding mountain peaks. (*Transactions of the Meetings of the International Commissions of Snow and Glaciers,* Edinburgh, September 1936) *Bull.Ass.Int.Hydrol.Sci.,* 1938, 23: 715-18, 2 fig.

HOYT, William G.; LANGBEIN, Walter B. Floods. x, 469 p., ill. Princeton: Princeton University Press, 1955.
An appendix contains the history of floods in America, beginning with 1543, followed by a history of floods by streams.

RIEM, Johannes Karl Richard. Die Sintflut in Sage und Wissenschaft. 194 p., ill., map. (Natur und Bibel in der Harmonie ihrer Offenbarungen, 4) Hamburg: Agentur des Rauhen Hauses, 1925.
Reviewed by R. Zaunick, *Mitt.Gesch.Med.,* 1926, 25: 166-7.

SCHOVE, D. Justin. Chinese "raininess" through the centuries. *Meteorol.Mag.,* 1949, 78: 11-16, 4 fig.

THOMSON, M.T., *et al.* Historical floods in New England. iv, 105 p. (Water-Supply Paper 1779-M) Washington, D.C.: U.S. Geological Survey, 1964.
A summary of the history of floods in New England from 1635 through 1955.

YAO SHAN-YU. The chronological and seasonal distribution of floods and droughts in Chinese history, 206 B.C.-A.D. 1911. *Harvard J.Asiatic Stud.,* 1942, 6: 273-312.

GCnh

DUFOUR, Louis. Quelques considérations historiques et lexicologiques sur le sens météorologique des termes brume et brouillard. *Ciel Terre,* 1964, 80: 38-52.
Traces the definitions of these meteorological terms from van Musschenbroek to the modern usage.

DUFOUR, Louis. Quelques considérations historiques sur le sens du terme grésil. *Ciel Terre,* 1963, 79: 25-35.
Traces the meaning of the word grésil (hail) from Aristotle to modern usage.

GD ELECTRICAL AND OPTICAL PHENOMENA

BOYER, Carl B. The rainbow: from myth to mathematics. 376 p., pl., fig., bibliogr. New York/London: Thomas Yoseloff, 1959.
Reviewed by Peter Diamandopoulos, *Isis,* 1964, 55: 219-20; by Robert P. Multhauf, *Science,* 1960, 131: 29; and in *Sci.Amer.,* 1960, 202: 221.

BOYER, Carl B. The tertiary rainbow: an historical account. *Isis,* 1958, 49: 141-54.

CHAUVEAU, B. Electricité atmosphérique. 3 vol. 1. Introduction historique. xii, 92 p.; 2. Le champ électrique de l'atmosphère. x, 264 p., 29 fig., 11 pl.; 3. xi, 240 p. Paris: G. Doin, 1922-25.
Vol. 1 reviewed by L. Guinet, *Isis,* 1923, 5: 193-4; for vol. 2 and 3 *see* CB 16/284 and CB 18/631.

DOPP, H. L'électricité atmosphérique. *Rev.Quest.Sci., 4th ser.,* 1926, 10: 5-47. [CB 22/286]

ELTERMAN, L. Rayleigh and extinction co-efficients to 50 km for the region 0.27u to 1.55u. *Appl.Opt.,* 1964, 3: 1139-47.

HUGHES, J.V. Sky brightness as a function of altitude. *Appl.Opt.,* 1964, 3: 1135-8.
The paper discusses Rayleigh's contributions to scattering theories.

MIDDLETON, W.E. Knowles. The early history of the visibility problem. *Appl.Opt.,* 1964, 3: 599-602.
Chiefly apropos of the work of Pierre Bouguer and Johann Heinrich Lambert.

A RE-EXAMINATION of Lord Rayleigh's data on the airglow 5577A(OI) emission. *Planetary Space Sci.,* 1964, 12: 97-112. [CB 90/602]

REMILLARD, W.J. The history of thunder research. *Weather,* 1961, 16: 245-53.
A brief review of the nature of thunder from Aristotle to recent times, with 32 references.

SCHONLAND, B.F.J. The flight of thunderbolts. 152 p., 6 pl., ill. Oxford: Clarendon Press, 1950. [CB 79/174]

STEKOL'NIKOV, I.S. Razvitie ucheniia o molnii i dlinnoi iskre. [The development of the study of lightning and long sparks. (In Russian)] *Vop.Ist.Est.Tekh.,* 1962, 12: 75-92.

STÖRMER, Carl. Über die Probleme des Polarlichtes. 86 p., diagr., ill. (Ergebnisse der kosmischen Physik, 1: 1-86) Leipzig: Akademische Verlagsgesellschaft, 1931.
Reviewed by H.D. Harradon, *Geogr.Rev.,* 1932, 22: 344-5.

TWERSKY, Victor. Rayleigh scattering. *Appl.Opt.,* 1964, 3: 1150-62.

GDu

DUFOUR, Louis. Le folklore de la foudre. *Ciel Terre,* 1940, 56: 95-104.

DUFOUR, Louis. L'optique atmosphérique par les dictons. *Ciel Terre,* 1937, 53: 331-45.

GDwh

SEYDL, Otto. A list of 402 northern lights observed in Bohemia, Moravia and Slovakia from 1013 till 1951. (In English, summary in Czech and Russian.) *Geofys.Sb.,* 1954, 159-94.

GDwn

SVIATSKII, D.O. [Aurora borealis in Russian literature and science from the 10th to the 18th century. (In Russian)] *Arkh.Ist.Nauk.Tekh.,* 1934, 4: 47-67, 2 pl., 1 fig. [CB 43/282]

GDyFE

STROOBANT, Paul. Sur l'agrandissement apparent des constellations, du soleil et de la lune à l'horizon. (Troisième note) *Bull.Acad.Roy.Belg.Cl.Sci.,* 1928, 14: 91-108. [CB 28/545]

GE WEATHER FORECASTING

BILANCINI, R. I moderni metodi di previsione del tempo. *Scientia,* 1962, 97: 202-8.

DUFOUR, Louis; MIEGHEM, J. van. Historique de la prévision du temps par l'analyse des cartes météorologiques. *Ciel Terre,* 1946, 62: 111-14.

GEORGII, Walter. Wettervorhersage: die Fortschritte der synoptischen Meteorologie. viii, 114 p. (Wissenschaftliche Forschungsberichte: Naturwissenschaftliche Reihe, 11) Dresden: Theodor Steinkopff, 1924.

ROUCH, Jules. L'atmosphère et la prévision du temps. 208 p., 35 fig. (Collection Colin, 36) Paris: Colin, 1923. [CB 16/287]

ROUCH, Jules. Les méthodes de prévision du temps. 280 p. (Nouvelle Collection Scientifique) Paris: Alcan, 1924.

ROUCH, Jules. La prévision du temps à longue échéance. *Rev. Sci.*, 1922, 60: 185-95. [CB 13/281]

SHAW, William Napier. Forecasting weather. 2nd rev. ed. xliii, 584 p. London: Constable, 1923.

GEda

HELLMANN, Gustav. Wetterpropheten des 19. und 20. Jahrhunderts. In his: Beiträge zur Geschichte der Meteorologie, vol. 2, no. 9, p. 233-314. Berlin: Behrend, 1917. [CB 10/215]

GEwb-qk

HUMPHREYS, William J. Origin and growth of the Weather Service of the United States, and Cincinnati's part therein. *Sci. Mon.*, 1924, 18: 372-82.

McGUIRE, James K. History of the Weather Bureau office in New York City. *Weatherwise*, 1961, 14: 50-2, 71. [CB 87/620]
A brief history from the establishment of the U.S. signal office (Nov. 1, 1870), to recent times.

MANLEY-BENDALL, M.; PERROTIN, Henri. Organisation et fonctionnement du service météorologique des Etats-Unis. *Rev.Gén. Sci.*, 1914, 25: 113-18.
Account of U.S. Weather Bureau.

WHITNAH, Donald R. A history of the United States Weather Bureau. ix, 267 p., pl., bibl. Urbana, Ill.: University of Illinois Press, 1961.
Reviewed by Walter B. Hendrickson, *Isis*, 1962, 53: 422-3; by M.F. Harris, *Amer.Hist.Rev.*, 1961-62, 67: 226-7.

GEySC

SHAW, William Napier. Agricultural meteorology: a brief historical review. *Conf.Empire Meteorol.Agr.Sect.* (London, 1929), (2), p. 3-13. London: H.M. Stationery Off., 1929.
Development of weather forecasting for agricultural purposes.

GEySCwg-u

HALDY, Bruno. Die deutschen Bauernregeln, gesammelt und herausgegeben. Mit Monatsbildern von Josua Leander Gampp. 126 p., ill. Jena: Diederichs, 1923.

GF CLIMATOLOGY

for the effect of climate on life *see* JO
trees *see* KXyJO

BROOKS, Charles Ernest Pelham. Climate in everyday life. 314 p. New York: Philosophical Library, 1951.

BROOKS, Charles Ernest Pelham. Climate through the ages: study of climatic factors and their variations. Rev. ed. 395 p., ill. London: Benn; New York: McGraw-Hill, 1949.
First published London: Benn, 1926.

EUWING, Maurice; DUNN, William L. Theory of ice ages. *Science*, 1956, 123: 1064-6.

KISS, Edmund. Die oft verlästerte, von vielen gepriesene, von manchem schon vernichtete, aber zäh und kampfbereit weiterlebende Welt- Eis- Lehre, allen Gelehrten und Ungelehrten, vorzüglich aber allen unbefangenen und jugendlichen Gemütern, so diesen Wahnsinn selbst verdammen wollen, oder aber diese neue Offenbarung ehrfürchtig und dankbar in sich aufzunehmen trachten, nach Hanns Hörbigers Lehre dargestellt. 117 p., pl. Leipzig: Koehler & Amelang, [1933]. [CB 43/281]
Belongs to a series devoted to the 'glacial theory' and its applications to the interpretation of history, and the elucidation of world mysteries.

KRAINER, N.P. P.A. Kropotkin o proiskhozhdenii valunov (po neopublikovannoi rukopisi vtorogo toma "Issledovaniia o lednikovom periode"). [P.A. Kropotkin about the origin of detritus (on the basis of an unpublished manuscript of the second volume of "Research about the ice age"). (In Russian)] *Tr.Inst.Ist.Est.Tekh.*, 1962, 42: 195-211.

MASCART, Jean. Notes sur la variabilité des climats. Documents lyonnais, études de climatologie. Première partie Introduction générale historique. 383 p. Lyon: Audin, 1925.

OLIVEIRA BOLÉO, José de. Aspectos do estudo das variações climatológicas. *Petrus Nonius*, 1944, 5: 74-82, 3 fig.

PLASS, Gilbert N. Carbon dioxide and the climate. *Amer. Scient.*, 1956, 44: 302-16.
Concerning a possible cause of the Ice Ages, particularly the "greenhouse" effect of carbon dioxide in the air.

SCHWARZBACH, Martin. Climates of the past. An introduction to paleoclimatology. 340 p. New York: Van Nostrand, 1963.
Reviewed by Hans Boesch, *Geogr.Helv.*, 1963, 19: 126.

SIMPSON, G.L. Climatic changes. In: Huntington, Ellsworth. The pulse of progress. viii, 341 p. London: Scribner, 1926.

ZINNER, Ernst. Alte Wetterbeobachtungen. *Meteorol.Z.*, 1935, 52: 443-4.

GFmzF

MILANKOVITCH, M. Ausbau und gegenwärtiger Stand der astronomischen Theorie der erdgeschichtlichen Klimate. *Experientia*, 1948, 4: 413-18. [CB 74/386]

GFmzHV

DEEVEY, Edward S. Pollen analysis and history. *Amer.Scient.*, 1944, 32: 39-53.
A discussion of the contribution of the pollen analysis of bogs to our knowledge of postglacial climate.

GFo-ce-bv

HELLMANN, Gustav. Bibliographie des klimatologischen Lehrbuches. In his: Beiträge zur Geschichte der Meteorologie, vol. 3, p. 8-14. Berlin: Behrend, 1922.
From J.F. Schouw, Copenhagen, 1827, to Eugen Alt, Leipzig, 1916.

GFsc

HUNTINGTON, Ellsworth. Changes of climate and history. *Amer. Hist.Rev.*, 1913, 18: 213-32.

GFwb

LANDSBERG, H.E. Early stages of climatology in the United States. *Bull.Amer.Meteorol.Soc.*, 1964, 45: 268-78. [CB 90/605]

GFA REGIONAL CLIMATOLOGY

CLAYTON, Henry Helm, ed. World weather records, collected from official sources by Felix Exner, Sir Gilbert Walker, G.C. Simpson, H. Helm Clayton, Robert C. Mossman. Published under grant from John A. Roebling. vi, 1199 p. Washington: Smithsonian Institution, 1927.
Reviewed in *Nature*, 1927, 120: 747.

GFB

HOYT, William G.; LANGBEIN, Walter B. Floods. x, 469 p., ill. Princeton: Princeton University Press, 1955.
An appendix contains the history of floods in America, beginning with 1543, followed by a history of floods by streams.

LUDLUM, David M. Early American hurricanes, 1492-1870. xii, 198 p., maps, charts. Boston: American Meteorological Society, 1963.
Gives available meteorological data for the situations historically surrounding the occurrence of hurricanes in the Atlantic and Gulf coastline regions.
Reviewed by Arnold Court, *Geogr.Rev.*, 1964, 54: 150.

TANNEHILL, Ivan Ray. Hurricanes: their nature and history - particularly those of the West Indies and the southern coasts of the United States. 2nd ed. x, 265 p. Princeton N.J.: Princeton University Press, 1942.
First publ. 1938 and reviewed in *Nature*, 1938, 142: 663.
Reviewed by Conway Zirkle, *Isis*, 1944, 35: 195-6.

THOMSON, M.T., *et al.* Historical floods in New England. iv, 105 p. (Water-Supply Paper 1779-M) Washington, D.C.: U.S. Geological Survey, 1964.
A summary of the history of floods in New England from 1635 through 1955.

GFD

EASTON, C. Les hivers dans l'Europe occidentale: étude statistique et historique sur leur température, discussion des observations thermométriques 1852-1916 et 1757-1851, tableaux comparatifs, classifications des hivers 1205-1916, notices historiques sur les hivers remarquables, bibliographie. iv, 210 p. Leyde: Brill, 1928.
Reviewed by C.E.P.B., *Nature*, 1928, 122: 917-18.

GFDce

WEIKINN, C. Quellentexte zur Witterungsgeschichte Europas von der Zeitwende bis zum Jahre 1850. Hydrographie. 4 vol. 1. Zeitwende-1500. 539 p.; 2. 1501-1600. 486 p.; 3. 1601-1700. 492 p.; 4. 1701-1750. 592 p. (Quellensammlung zur Hydrographie und Meteorologie, 1) Berlin: Akademie Verlag, 1958-63.
Parts 1 and 2 reviewed by Franz Baur, *Naturwiss.Rundsch.*, 1961, 14: 284.

GFE

BROOKS, Charles Ernest Pelham; GLASSPOOLE, J. British floods and droughts. With an introductory note by Hugh Robert Mill. 119 p., 2 pl. London: Benn, 1928.
Reviewed by L.C.W. Bonacina, *Nature*, 1929, 123: 403-4.

GFG

WALTER, Emil. Der Schweizerföhn. 40 p., 39 fig. (*Neujahrsbl. Naturforsch.Ges.Zürich*, 1938, no. 140) Zürich: Fretz, 1938. [CB 57/255]

ZINNER, Ernst. Das Wetter von Bamberg. *Ber.Naturforsch. Ges.Bamberg*, 1929, 25: 1-57; Nachtrag zum "Wetter von Bamberg". *ibid.*, 1946, 29: 14-27.

GFK

LAHR, E. Un siècle d'observations météorologiques appliquées à l'étude du climat luxembourgeois. xv, 284 p. Luxembourg: Bourg-Bourger, 1950.
Reviewed by Louis Dufour, *Arch.Int.Hist.Sci.*, 1951, 4: 226.

GFT

SCHOVE, D. Justin. Chinese "raininess" through the centuries. *Meteorol.Mag.*, 1949, 78: 11-16, 4 fig.

YAO SHAN-YU. The chronological and seasonal distribution of floods and droughts in Chinese history, 206 B.C.-A.D. 1911. *Harvard J.Asiatic Stud.*, 1942, 6: 273-312.

GFW

MEINIG, Donald W. Goyder's line of rainfall. The role of a geographic concept in south Australian land policy and agricultural settlement. *Agr.Hist.*, 1961, 35: 207-14.

GFZ

HOBBS, W.H. The climate of the Arctic as viewed by the explorer and the meteorologist. *Science*, 1948, 108: 193-201.
A very condensed history of Arctic meteorology.

HOBBS, W.H. Some curious early accounts of the Greenland foehn. *Bull.Amer.Meteorol.Soc.*, 1928, 9: 79-81.

GG GEOLOGY

GGc general history

ADAMS, Frank Dawson. The birth and development of the geological sciences. 506 p., ill. Baltimore: Williams & Wilkins, 1938; New York: Dover, 1954.
Reviewed by William H. Hobbs, *Isis*, 1947, 32: 218-20.

BERGBAU und Bergleute. Neue Beiträge zur Geschichte des Bergbaus und der Geologie. 294 p., ill. (Freiberger Forschungshefte. Kultur und Technik, D 11) Berlin: Akademie-Verlag, 1955. [CB 84/312]
Reviewed by Felix F. Strauss, *Isis*, 1962, 53: 521-3.

BERINGER, Carl Christoph. Geschichte der Geologie und des geologischen Weltbildes. vii, 158 p. Stuttgart: Ferdinand Enke Verlag, 1954.
Reviewed by Cecil J. Schneer, *Isis*, 1957, 48: 358-9; by Axel Garboe, *Centaurus*, 1955, 4: 169-71; by M. Gortani, *Scientia*, 1955, 49: 302-3.

BREWSTER, Edwin Tenney. This puzzling planet. The earth's unfinished story; how men have read it in the past, and how the wayfarer may read it now. 328 p., ill. Indianapolis: Bobbs-Merrill, 1928.
Reviewed by George Sarton, *Isis*, 1929, 12: 341-3.

CAILLEUX, A. Histoire de la géologie. 126 p., fig. (Collection Que Sais-Je?) Paris: Presses Universitaires de France, 1961.
Reviewed by P. de Béthune, *Rev.Quest.Sci.*, 1962, 23: 144.

DALY, Reginald Aldworth. Our mobile earth. xxii, 342 p., ill. New York: Scribner, 1926.
Reviewed by Charles Schuchert, *Science*, 1926, 64: 624; by E.B. Bailey, *Nature*, 1927, 119: 421-2.

FAIRCHILD, Herman Leroy. The development of geologic science. *Sci.Mon.*, 1924, 19: 77-101.

GREGORY, Herbert A. History of geology. *Sci.Mon.*, 1921, 12: 97-126. [CB 12/632]

GREGORY, J.W. A century of geology. *Nature*, 1931, 128: 857-60.

HÖLDER, Helmut. Geologie und Paläontologie in Texten und ihrer Geschichte. xviii, 565 p., fig., pl., bibliogr. (Orbis Academicus, 2: 11) Freiburg/Munich: Verlag Karl Alber, 1960.
Reviewed by Albert V. Carozzi, *Isis*, 1962, 53: 398-400; by K. Mägdefrau, *Naturwiss.Rundsch.*, 1961, 5: 202; by Gerhard Regnéll, *Lychnos*, 1962, 478-80.

HOTCHKISS, W.O. The story of a billion years. x, 137 p., 8 fig. (Century of Progress Series) New York: Century 1932. [CB 39/462]
Includes a summary of important geological discoveries in the last century.

HUMMEL, K. Geschichte der Geologie. 123 p. (Sammlung Göschen, 899) Berlin: De Gruyter, 1925. [CB 34/629]

LAUNAY, L. de. La science géologique. Ses méthodes, ses résultats, ses problèmes, son histoire. 2nd rev. ed. 776 p., 53 fig., 5 pl. Paris: Colin, 1913.

MARGERIE, Emmanuel de. Critique et géologie. Contribution à l'histoire des sciences de la terre (1882-1942). 4 vol. lxxix, 2108 p., 768 fig. Paris: Colin, 1943-48.
Reviewed by G. Sarton, *Isis*, 1945, 36: 74-5; 1948, 38: 263-4 and CB 74/390; by A. Renier, *Ann.Soc.Géol.Belg.*, 1944, 68: B19-39.

MOLENGRAAFF, Gustav-Adolf-Frederik. Een blik op den snellen opbloei der geologische wetenschap in de laatste 50 jaren. Rede uitgesproken bij gelegenheid van zijn aftreden als Hoogleeraar op 1 April 1930. [A glance at the rapid revival of geological science in the last fifty years: speech delivered on the occasion of his retirement as Professor on 1 April 1930. (In Dutch)] 20 p. Delft: Waltman, 1930.

MOORE, Ruth. The earth we live on. The story of geological discovery. Drawings by Sue Allen. xiv, 416, x p., ill. New York: Alfred A. Knopf, 1956; London: Jonathan Cape, 1957.
Reviewed by Cecil J. Schneer, *Isis*, 1957, 48: 479-81; by Jan Lundquist, *Lychnos*, 1957-58, 444-5.

SARTON, George. La synthèse géologique de 1775 à 1918. *Isis*, 1919, 2: 357-94, 2 pl. [CB 6/487]

SCHWARZBACH, Martin. Fortschritte der Geologie im letzten Jahrzehnt. *Naturwiss.Rundsch.*, 1956, 9: 291-6.

STRAELEN, V. van. Une vieille histoire. *Bull.Acad.Roy.Belg. Cl.Sci.*, 1950, 36: 1002-9.
Geological theories since Constant Prévost.

TERMIER, Pierre. À la gloire de la terre, souvenirs d'un géologue. 2nd ed. 431 p. Paris: Nouvelle Librairie Nationale, 1924.
1st edition reviewed by L. Guinet, *Isis*, 1924, 6: 95-6.

TIKHOMIROV, V.V.; CHAIN, V.E. Kratkii ocherk istorii geologii. [Short outline of the history of geology. (In Russian)] 260 p., ill. Moscow: Gosgeoltekhizdat, 1956.

WOODWARD, H.B. History of geology. vi, 154 p., 14 portr. (History of Science Series) London: Watt, 1912.

ZITTEL, Karl von. History of geology and palaeontology. To the end of the nineteenth century. xiii, 562 p. (Historiae Naturalis Classica, 12) Codicote, Herts: Wheldon & Wesley; New York: Hafner Publishing Company, 1962.
An unaltered reprint of the edition which first appeared in London in 1901.

GGc-be

CHALLINOR, John. A dictionary of geology. xvi, 235 p. Cardiff: University of Wales Press; New York: Oxford University Press, 1962. [CB 88/546]

MEUNIER, Stanislas. Dictionnaire de géologie. 716 p. Paris: Dunod, 1926.

GGc-br

Ocherki po Istorii Geologicheskikh Znanii. [Contributions to the history of the geological sciences. (In Russian)] (Akademiia Nauk SSSR, Institut Geologicheskich Nauk) Vol. 1- Moskva: 1953-
Contents of vol. 5 (1956) listed in CB 84/312; of vol. 6, 7 and 8 in CB 85/391.

GGc-bv

GORDEEV, D.I. [Monographs and handbooks on the history of geology. (In Russian)] *Tr.Inst.Ist.Est.Tekh.*, 1961, 37: no. 2, 345-9.

WHITE, George W. Reference books for history of geology. *Stechert-Hafner Book News*, 1963, 18: no. 3, 29-30.

GGce

EYLES, V.A. Bibliography and the history of science. *J.Soc. Bibliogr.Natur.Hist.*, 1955, 3: 63-71, front.
Illustrated from the history of geology.

GGce-bv

SMIRNOVA, O.K., *et al.* Geologiia v izdaniiakh Akademii nauk. [Geology in the publications of the Academy of Sciences. (In Russian)] 2 vol. 1. 1728-1928. 471 p.; 2. 1929-1937. 656 p. Leningrad: Akademiia Nauk SSSR, 1938-41. [CB 60/157]

GGcn

MARGERIE, Emmanuel de. Une nouvelle carte géologique du monde? *Ann.Géogr.*, 1922, 31: 109-31.
Criticism of Henry B. Milner's Geological map of the world (London: Stanford, 1921), *see* below.

MARGERIE, Emmanuel de. La carte géologique du monde. Historique. État actuel. Projets d'avenir. Rapport présenté au 12e *Congrès Géologique International* (Toronto, 1913). *Géographie*, 1913, 28: 375-89. [CB 6/464]

MILNER, Henry B. A geological map of the world. 1060 x 620 mm. London: Stanford, 1921.

SHEPPARD, T. The evolution of topographical and geological maps. *Rep.Brit.Ass.Advance.Sci.*, 1920, 391-8. [CB 10/195]

GGd-bv

WELLS, John W. A list of books on the personalities of geology. *Ohio J.Sci.*, 1947, 47: 192-200.

GGda

FENTON, Carroll Lane; FENTON, Mildred Adams. Giants of geology. xvi, 333 p., ill. Garden City, N.Y.: Doubleday, 1952.
Revised and enlarged edition of "The story of the great geologists", a popular biographical history of geology for the general reader.

WELLS, John W.; WHITE, George W. Biographies of geologists. *Ohio J.Sci.*, 1958, 58: 285-98. [CB 84/313]
Thumb-nail biographical notes, with bibliographical references, of 142 famed geologists of all lands, from Alexander Agassiz to Joseph Dwight Whitney.

GGdaj

MATHER, Kirtley F.; MASON, Shirley L. A source book in geology. xxii, 702 p. New York: McGraw-Hill, 1939. [CB 58/578]

GGfd

TIKHOMIROV, V.V. Istoriya i filosofiya geologii v trudakh N. S. Shatskogo. [History and philosophy of geology in the papers of N.S. Shatskii. (In Russian)] *Ocherki Ist.Geol. Znanii*, 1962, no. 10, 90-109.

GGg

UNKLESBAY, A.G. Teaching the history of geology. *J.Geol. Educ.*, 1953, 1: 51-9.

GGhm

CANNON, Walter F. The uniformitarian-catastrophist debate. *Isis*, 1960, 51: 38-55.

GGk philosophy and methodology

BUBNOFF, Serge von. Grundprobleme der Geologie; eine Einführung in geologisches Denken. viii, 237 p. Berlin: Borntraeger, 1931.
Reviewed in *Nature*, 1932, 129: 420.

HAARMANN, Erich. Um das geologische Weltbild. Malleo et mente. xi, 108 p., ill., map. Stuttgart: Enke, 1935. [CB 43/281]

HAUG, Emile. Les disciplines de la geologie. *Rev.Gén.Sci.*, 1921, 32: 101-11, 165-75, 229-38.
1. Géologie descriptive; 2. G. dynamique; 3. G. historique; 4. G. régionale; 5. G. appliquée.

LAUNAY, Louis de. Où en est la géologie? x, 206 p. (Collection des Mises au Point) Paris: Gauthier-Villars, 1921. [CB 12/632]
Reviewed by L. Guinet, *Isis*, 1921, 4: 325.

TOMKEIEFF, S.I. The anatomy of geology. *Bull.Brit.Soc.Hist. Sci.*, 1950, 1: 87-9.

GGk-bv

ALBRITTON, Claude C. Philosophy of geology: a select bibliography and index. 168 p. Dallas: Southern Methodist University, 1963. Also published in Fabric of geology, ed. by C.C. Albritton, p. 202-363. Reading, Mass.: Addison-Wesley, 1963. Second bibliography and index for the philosophy of geology. *J.Grad.Res.Center*, 1964, 33: 73-114. [CB 90/519]

GGkd

KITTS, David B. Historical explanation in geology. *J.Geol.*, 1963, 71: 297-313.
Discussion of historical methodology applied to geologic concepts.

GGke

PAULCKE, W. Das Experiment in der Geologie. x, 108 p. Karlsruhe: J. Langs Buchdruckerei, 1912.

VYSSOTSKI, B.P. [The problem of actualism and of uniformism and the system of methods in geology. (In Russian)] *Vop. Fil.*, 1961, 15: no. 3, 134-45.

GGkq

SPARN, Enrique. La differenciación de las ciencias geologicas de acuerdo con el título de suas revistas. *Bol.Acad.Nac. Cienc.*, 1927, 30: 341-7.
Reviewed by R. Zaunick, *Mitt.Gesch.Med.*, 1928, 27: 165.

GGm/t other special aspects

GGmzYC

BURKITT, M.C. Correlation of the archaeological and geological records. *Nature*, 1930, 126: 509-10.
Including a table of correlation.

GGnh

ADAMS, Frank D. Earliest use of the term geology. *Bull.Geol. Soc.Amer.*, 1932, 43: 121-3. [CB 40/406]
Earliest appearance in English work in Robert Lovell: Pammineralogicon, or An universal history of minerals, 1661.

ADAMS, Frank D. Further note on the earliest use of the word "geology". *Bull.Geol.Soc.Amer.*, 1933, 44: 821-6.
Apropos of its use by Mickel Pederson Escholt (1657) and by Ulyssus Aldrovandus (1605).

BURT, Frederick A. Origin of geological terms. *Sci.Mon.*, 1949, 69: 20-1.

GGnh-be

CISSARZ, Arnold; JONES, William R. German-English geological terminology: an introduction to German and English terms used in geology, including mineralogy, petrology, mineral deposits, etc. xvii, 250 p. London: Murby, 1931.

DAVIES, George MacDonald. A French-English vocabulary in geology and physical geography. ix, 140 p. London: Murby, 1932.

HOWELL, J.V., ed. Glossary of geology and related sciences. A cooperative project. x, 325 p. (NAS-NRC Publication 501) Washington: American Geological Institute, 1957.
Reviewed by George W. White, *Isis*, 1959, 50: 269-70.

GGo

MERRIAM, John C. The teaching of historical geology as a factor conditioning research. *Bull.Geol.Soc.Amer.*, 1920, 31: 339-49.

GGod

RUSKA, Julius. Methodik des mineralogisch-geologischen Unterrichts. viii, 520 p., 35 ill., 1 pl. Stuttgart: Enke, 1920.
Reviewed by G. Sarton, *Isis*, 1921, 3: 443-4.

GGqx

BIGOT, A. La session du XIIe Congrès Géologique International au Canada [août 1913]. *Rev.Gen.Sci.*,1914, 25: 479-88.

GGs

SHERLOCH, Robert Lionel. Man as geological agent: an account of his actions on inanimate nature. 372 p. London: Witherby, 1922.
Reviewed by Grenville A.J. Cole, *Nature*, 1923, 111: 352-4.

GGsc

DAVIDSON, C.F. Geology in the service of mankind. *Sci.Cult.*, 1962, 28: 448-56.

LAUNAY, Louis de. L'orogénie de la péninsule Balkanique. Les contrecoups de la géologie sur l'histoire. *Rev.Gén.Sci.*, 1912, 23: 817-26.

GGt

Eranos Jahrbuch, 22. Mensch und Erde. 494 p. Zurich: Rhein-Verlag, 1954.
Whole number; for contents *see* CB 80/144-5.

HAMSHAW THOMAS, H. The rise of geology and its influence on contemporary thought. *Ann.Sci.*, 1947, 5: 325-41.

PARKS, W.A. Cultural aspects in geology. *Nature*, 1925, 116: 432-5.

GGtd

HOOYKAAS, R. Natural law and divine miracle. A historical-critical study on the "principle of uniformity" in geology, biology, and theology. xiv, 237 p. Leiden: Brill, 1959.
Reviewed by P.H. Van Laer, *Janus*, 1961, 50: 72-4.

MILLHAUSER, Milton. The scriptural geologists. An episode in the history of opinion. *Osiris*, 1954, 11: 65-86.

GGtp

HALLOWES, Kenneth Knight. The poetry of geology. xii, 61 p. London: Murby, 1933.

GGw in different countries

GREGORY, J.-W. National contributions to geology. *Scientia*, 1921, 30: 1-12; French transl. suppl., 1-12. [CB 11/443]

GGwb

CHAMBERLIN, Thomas Chrowder. Seventy-five years of American geology. An address before the Section of Geology and Geography of the A.A.A.S., on December 28, 1923. *Science*, 1924, 59: 127-35.

LANDES, Henry. History of geology in the state of Washington. *Wash.Hist.Quart.*, 1928, 19: 243-9.

MERRILL, George Perkins. The first one hundred years of American geology. xxi, 773 p., 36 pl., 130 ill. New Haven: Yale University Press, 1924.
Reviewed by George Sarton, *Isis*, 1925, 7: 498-501.
Reprinted New York: Hafner, 1964. [CB 90/605]

PERKINS, George Henry. History and summary of geological work in Vermont, 1810-1923. *Rep.State Geol.Mineral Ind. Vermont*, 1921-22, 13: 1-70.

WHITE, George W. Early American geology. *Sci.Mon.*, 1953, 76: 134-40, bibliogr.
An account of geological observations by the explorers of the United States up to the nineteenth century.

GGwb-da

CRONEIS, Carey. Geographic environment and geological leadership: the Cincinnati Arch area. *J.Geol.Educ.*, 1963, 11: 81-90. [CB 89/566]
Short sketches of 15 outstanding geologists and paleontologists who secured their early training and enthusiasm in the Cincinnati area.

BROWNING, William. Medical men as early American geologists. *Med.Life*, 1929, 36: 137-44.

GGwb-or

FRYXELL, Fritiof. National Association of Geology Teachers. *Geo Times*, 1961, 7: 17-23, 43.

GGwb-ov

PANGBORN, Mark W. A history of the popularization of geology in America. A bibliographic survey. *J.Wash.Acad.Sci.*, 1959, 49: 224-7.

GGwb-qd

BETZ, Frederick, Jr. The Geological Society of America. *Geo Times*, 1961, 5: 18-23, 46-7.

CRAIG, G.Y. The Geological Society of America, 1888-1963. *Nature*, 1963, 200: 738-9.

FAIRCHILD, Herman Le Roy. The Geological Society of America, 1888-1930. A chapter in earth science history. xvii, 232 p., 18 portr. New York: Geological Society, 1932.

MATHER, Kirtley F. Geology, geologists, and the AAAS. *Science,* 1959, 129: 1106-11.

TUCKERMAN, Frederick. Edward Hitchcock and the origin of the Association of American Geologists. *Science,* 1924, 60: 134-5.

GGwc

PASTORE, Franco. Nuestra mineralogía y geología durante los ultimos cincuenta años (1872-1922). Cincuentenario de la Sociedad Cientifica Argentina (1872-1922). 47 p. (Evolución de las Ciencias en la Republica Argentina, 6) Buenos Aires: 1925. [CB 22/205]

GGwe-ce

CHALLINOR, J. The early progress of British geology. 1. From Leland to Woodward, 1538-1728. 2. From Strachey to Michell, 1719-1788. 3. From Hutton to Playfair, 1788-1802. *Ann.Sci.,* 1953, 9: 124-53, 1 pl.; 1954, 10: 1-19, 107-48.
A survey of the early literature.

GGwe-qd

RUDWICK, M.J.S. The foundation of the Geological Society of London. Its scheme for co-operative research and its struggle for independence. *Brit.J.Hist.Sci.,* 1963, 1: 325-55.

SMITH, W. Campbell. The Geological Society of London. *Nature,* 1958, 181: 149-51.

GGwf

MARGERIE, Emmanuel de. La géologie. In: La Science française. 2nd ed., p. 199-267, bibliogr. Paris: Larousse, 1933.
History of French geology.

MARGERIE, Emmanuel de. Une mission d'enseignement géologique aux Etats-Unis. Livre jubilaire, publié à l'occasion du cinquantenaire de la fondation de la Société Géologique de Belgique, p. 215-26. Liége: 1924. [CB 20/173]
A course of lectures on the history of French geology during the last 100 years.

GGwf-o

KILIAN, W.; GIGNOUX, M. L'enseignement de la géologie en France. *Rev.Gén.Sci.,* 1913, 24: 831-44.

GGwf-oq

DUBOIS, Georges. L'enseignement de la géologie à l'Université de Strasbourg avant 1870. *Rev.Alsace,* 1938, 85: 60 p.

PRUVOST, Pierre. Coup d'oeil sur l'enseignement de la géologie à la Sorbonne, depuis ses origines. *Rev.Quest.Sci.,* 1951, 122: 91-111.

GGwf-qd

MARGERIE, Emmanuel de. La Société Géologique de France de 1880 à 1929. 81 p., 20 pl. Extrait du Livre jubilaire publié à l'occasion du centenaire de la Société Géologique de France, 1830-1930. Paris: 1930. [CB 31/559]

GGwh

KOŘAN, Jan. K počátkům české geologie. [The beginnings of Czech geology. (In Czech with summary in German)] *Sb.Dějiny Přírodn.Věd Tech.,* 1963, 8: 53-73. [CB 90/519]

SAMSONOWICZ, Jan. [Histoire de la géologie en Pologne. (In Polish with summary in French)] 43 p. (Polska Akademia Umiejętności, Historia Nauki Polskiej w Monografiach, 6) Cracow: 1948.

GGwi-da

GORTANI, Michele. Italian pioneers in geology and mineralogy. *Cah.Hist.Mond.,* 1963, 7: 503-19.

GGwk-oq

PANNEKOEK, A.J. Geological research at the universities in the Netherlands, 1877-1962. *Geol.Mijnbouw,* 1962, 41: 161-74. [CB 88/546]

GGwm

GARBOE, Axel. Geologiens historie e Danmark. 2 vol. 1. Fra myte til videnskab. 284 p., ill.; 2. Forskereog resultater fra 1835 til nutiden. 522 p., ill. København: C.A. Reitzels Forlag, 1959; 1961.
Reviewed by Poul Graff-Petersen, *Isis,* 1963, 54: 414-15; by Jan Lundquist, *Lychnos,* 1960-61, 356-8; 1962, 480-2.

GGwn-da

TIKHOMIROV, V.V.; VOSKRESENSKAIA, N.A. Iz istorii geologicheskikh nauk. Pamiatn'ie dat'i na ianvar' - mart 1961. Odzor 29. [From the history of the geological sciences. Commemorative dates from January - March 1961. No. 29. (In Russian)] *Sovet.Geol.,* 1961, no. 1, 142-5.
This is one of the series of short biographies of Russian geologists which appeared in *Seria Geologicheskaia* and later in *Sovetskaia Geologiia* from 1953. T.A. Sofiano was the joint author up to no. 24.

GGx techniques and instruments

GGxd

BASCOM, Willard. A hole in the bottom of the sea. The story of the Mohole Project. 352 p., pl., fig. London: Weidenfeld and Nicolson; New York: Doubleday, 1961.
Reviewed in *Science,* 1961, 134: 42-3; in *Sci.Amer.,* 1961, 205: no. 2, 162; by Edward Bullard, *Endeavour,* 1962, 21: 196.

LANDEN, David. Impact of the development of photogrammetry upon geology. *J.Wash.Acad.Sci.,* 1959, 49: 234-52.

LEWIS, Hamilton M. A history of well logging. *Geophysics,* 1962, 27: 507-27. [CB 88/546]

GGxx museums

FISCHER, Walther. *See* GTwg

MAZZINI, Giuseppe. Il museo civico imolese. *Arch.Stor.Sci.,* 1924, 5: 131-8. [CB 16/282]
Contains mostly geological exhibits.

GH REGIONAL GEOLOGY

GHce-bv

Bibliography and Index of Geology exclusive of North America, 1933 - Washington: Geological Society of America, 1934 -

GHB geology of North America

BASSLER, Ray S. Glacial varved clay concretions of New England. *Annu.Rep.Smithsonian Inst.for 1948,* p. 269-76, 12 pl. Washington, D.C.: 1949.

FRIEDMAN, Jules. Development of geologic thought concerning Ulster County, New York. *J.Wash.Acad.Sci.,* 1959, 49: 252-5.

GOULD, Charles Newton. Covered wagon geologist; an autobiography. xiii, 282 p., ill., maps. Norman: University of Oklahoma Press, 1959.
Reviewed by V.L. Vanderhoof, *Science,* 1960, 131: 407-8.

JOHNSON, Douglas. The origin of the Carolina Bays. xi, 341 p., 18 ill. (Columbia Geomorphic Studies, 4) New York: Columbia University Press, 1942. [CB 63/274]

LAFORGE, Laurence. Geology of the Boston area, Massachusetts. v, 105 p., 15 pl., 6 fig., maps. (*Bull.U.S.Geol.Survey,* 839) Washington, D.C.: U.S. Govt. Print. Off., 1932.
Historical sketch (p. 4-7) and reproduction of the earliest geologic map of the Boston district, 1818.

MARGERIE, Emmanuel de. Etudes américaines. 1 vol. in 2. 1. Géologie et géographie. xii, 294 p., 39 fig.; 2. Paysages, régions, explorateurs et cartes. 295-812 p. Paris: Colin, 1952-54. [CB 79/182]
Reviewed by George Sarton, *Isis,* 1954, 45: 387-8.

MARGERIE, Emmanuel de. La méthode des courbes structurales et la tectonique du Colorado. *Zbior Prac poświecony przez Towarzystwo Geograficzne we Lwowie Eugenjuszowi Romerowi,* p. 617-43, map. Lwow: 1934. [CB 45/290]

WELLS, John West. *See* GRwb

ZUMBERGE, J.H.; POTZGER, J.E. Pollen profiles, radiocarbon dating and geologic chronology of the Lake Michigan basin. *Science,* 1955, 121: 309-11.

GHBce-bv

BIBLIOGRAPHY of North American geology [covering the years 1919-65]. 12 vol. (U.S. Geological Survey Bulletins) Washington: 1931-69.
Continuation of: Nickles, John Milton. Geologic literature, *see* below.

NEVERS, George M.; SALKER, Richard D. Annotated bibliography of Indiana geology through 1955. 486 p. (Indiana Geological Survey, Bulletin, 24) Bloomington: Indiana Department of Conservation, 1962. [CB 88/546]
Contains "all significant references on Indiana geology between the years 1776 and 1955".

NICKLES, John Milton. Geologic literature of North America, 1785-1918. 2 vol. 1. Bibliography. 1167 p. 2. Index. 685 p. (U.S. Geological Survey. Bulletin, 746, 747) Washington: U.S. Govt. Print. Off., 1923-24.
Continued by: Bibliography of North American geology, *see* above.

RUTTEN, L.M.R. Bibliography of West Indian geology. vii, 103 p. (*Geogr.Geol.Mededeel.Physiogr.Geol.Reeks,* 16) Utrecht: Oosthoek, 1938.
Reviewed by R. Zaunick, *Mitt.Gesch.Med.,* 1939, 38: 316.

GHBqk

MERRILL, George P., ed. Contributions to a history of American state geological and natural history surveys. xviii, 549 p., ill. (*Bull.U.S.Nat.Mus.,* 109) Washington, D.C.: 1920. [CB 10/158]

NOLAN, Thomas B. The United States Geological Survey and the advancement of geology in the public service. *J.Wash.Acad. Sci.,* 1959, 49: 209-14.

PRICE, Paul H. Evolution of the geological survey. *West Virginia Hist.,* 1951, 13: 20-32.
History of geological surveys in the U.S.

RABBITT, John C.; RABBITT, Mary C. The U.S. Geological Survey. 75 years of service to the nation, 1879-1954. *Science.* 1954, 119: 741-58.

THE WEST VIRGINIA GEOLOGICAL AND ECONOMIC SURVEY. Its accomplishments and outlook. Centennial ed. 207 p., 65 fig. Morgantown, Pa.: 1963. [CB 89/567]
An history of geological investigations by the West Virginia Geological Survey, established in 1897.

GHC geology of Latin America

BRANNER, John Casper. Outlines of the Geology of Brazil to accompany the geologic map of Brazil (1:5,000,000). *Bull. Geol.Soc.Amer.,* 1919, 30: 189-338, 3 pl., col. map. [CB 8/361]

GHD geology of Europe

GHEcn

DAVIS, A.G. Notes on Griffith's geological maps of Ireland. *J.Soc.Bibliogr.Natur.Hist.,* 1950, 2: 209-11.

EYLES, V.A.; EYLES, Joan M. On the different issues of the first geological map of England and Wales. *Ann.Sci.,* 1938, 3: 190-212, 4 pl., 3 fig.

NORTH, F.J. Geological maps. Their history and development with special reference to Wales. vi, 133 p., 10 pl., 16 fig., map. (Amgueddfa Genedlaethol Cymru. National Museum of Wales) Cardiff: 1928. [CB 27/539]

GHEqk

BAILEY, Edward. Geological Survey of Great Britain. xii, 278 p., 4 pl. London: Thomas Murby, 1952.
Reviewed by A.E. Trueman, *Nature,* 1953, 171: 96, by V.A. Eyles, *Ann.Sci.,* 1955, 11: 101-2.

FLETT, John Smith. The first hundred years of the Geological Survey of Great Britain. 280 p., 13 pl. London: H.M. Stationery Office, 1937.
Reviewed by W.W. Watts, *Nature,* 1937, 140: 915-17.

NORTH, F.J. The Ordnance Geological Survey. Its first memoir. *Nature,* 1939, 143: 1052-4.

GHF

DIDIER, L. Histoire du bassin de Bruay. *Bull.Soc.Géol.France,* 1928, *4th ser.,* 28: 493-8.

GHFc-bv

MARGERIE, Emmanuel de. Le Jura. 2 vol. 1. Bibliographie sommaire du Jura français et suisse. Orographie, tectonique et morphologie. xii, 642 p., and atlas.; 2. Commentaire de la carte structurale. Description tectonique du Jura français. 898 p. (Mémoires pour servir à l'explication de la carte géologique détaillée de la France) Paris: Imprimerie Nationale, 1922-36.
Part 1 reviewed by G. Sarton, *Isis,* 1923, 5: 468-9.

GHFcn

MARGERIE, Emmanuel de. Le service de la carte géologique de la France dans les Pyrénées. In: Critique et géologie, (3), p. 1381-404. Paris: Colin, 1946.
Extract from the monumental work reviewed by George Sarton, *Isis,* 1945, 36: 74-5; 1948, 38: 263-4.

GHFqk

EYLES, V.A. The first national geological survey. *Geol.Mag.,* 1950, 87: 373-82. [CB 77/377]
The National Geological Survey of France planned in 1822.

GHG

BRAUNS, Reinhard. Die geologisch-mineralogische Durchforschung des Laacher Seegebietes in ihrer geschichtlichen Entwicklung dargestellt. *Proteus,* 1937, 2: 83-92.

FREYBERG, Bruno von. Die geologische Erforschung Thüringens in älterer Zeit: ein Beitrag zur Geschichte der Geologie biz zum Jahre 1843. xi, 160 p., 8 pl. Berlin: Bornträger, 1932.
Reviewed in *Nature,* 1933, 131: 531.

MARGERIE, Emmanuel de. Three stages in the evolution of Alpine geology: De Saussure-Studer-Heim. *Quart.J.Geol.Soc. Lond.,* 1946, 102: pt. 3, xcvii-cxiv, bibliogr.

MARGERIE, Emmanuel de. Trois moments dans l'histoire de l'étude des Alpes suisses: de Saussure, Studer, Alb. Heim. *Bull.Sect.Geogr.Comité Trav.Hist.Sci.,* 1943, 58: 1-39, 31 fig.

GHK

LERICHE, Maurice. L'histoire de la géologie dans la région gallo-belge. *Rev.Univ.Bruxelles,* 1928-29, 34: 132-57.

GHN

BATIUSHKOVA, I.V. Regional'nye geologicheskie issledovaniia Akademii nauk v period vosstanovleniia narodnogo khoziaistva (1917-1925). [Regional geological studies of the Academy of Sciences during the recovery of the national economy (1917-1925). (In Russian)] *Tr.Inst.Ist.Est.Tekh.,* 1962, 42: 212-27.

KUROCHKIN, G.D. K istorii izucheniia russkimi puteshestvennikami XVII-XX vv. geografii, geologii i poleznykh iskopaemykh Tuvy. [On the history of the study by Russian travelers of the 17th through 20th centuries of the geography, geology and useful minerals of Tuva. (In Russian)] *Tr.Inst. Ist.Est.Tekh.,* 1962, 42: 247-51.

OBRUČEV, V.A. Istoriia geologiceskogo issledovaniia Sibiri. [History of geological research in Siberia. (In Russian)] 5 vol. 1. XVII and XVIII centuries. 153 p.; 2. 1801-1850. 25 p.; 3. 1851-1888. 354 p.; 4. 1889-1917. 787 p.; 5. 1918-1940. (Pts. 1-5, 9). Leningrad: Akademiia Nauk SSSR, 1931-49, 1959-.
Volumes 1-4 reviewed by S.I.T., *Geogr.J.,* 1939, 93: 445-6.

VILENKIN, V.L. K istorii geologo-geograficheskogo issledovaniia Kavkaza (vtoraia polovina XIX v. - 1917 g). [On the history of geological and geographical study of the Caucasus (the second half of the 19th century and up to 1917). (In Russian)] *Tr.Inst.Ist.Est.Tekh.,* 1962, 42: 63-79.

GHNqk

KLECPOV, I.L. Geologicheskii Komitet, 1882-1929 gg. [Geological Committee, 1882-1929. (In Russian)] 175 p. Moscow: Izd-vo Nauka, 1964. [CB 90/605]
An account of the growth of the state geological service in Russia from the foundation of the Geological Committee in 1882 to its reorganization in 1929.

GHO

NOPCSA, Ferencz. Geographie und Geologie Nordalbaniens. Mit einem Anhang: Zur Geschichte der Kartographie des Gebietes. 1. Beiträge zur Kartographie Albaniens nach orientalischen Quellen von H. von Mzik. 2. Zur Geschichte der okzidentalen Kartographie Nordalbaniens von F. Nopcsa. xiv, 703, 35 p. (*Geol.Hung.Ser.Geol.*, 3) Budapest: Institutum Regni Hungariae Geologicum, 1929.
Reviewed by J.W. Gregory, *Nature*, 1930, 125: 8-9.

GHR geology of Asia

BERKEY, Charles P.; MORRIS, Frederick K. Geology of Mongolia: a reconnaissance report based on the investigations of the years 1922-23. xxxi, 475 p., 44 pl., 6 maps. (Central Asiatic Expeditions of the American Museum of Natural History. Natural History of Central Asia, 2) New York: The Museum, 1927.
Reviewed by J.W.G., *Nature*, 1928, 122: 303-4.

GHRwb-qh

OSBORN, Henry Fairfield. Arrest of geologic, archeologic and paleontologic work in Central Asia. *Science*, 1931, 74: 139-42.
The Central Asiatic Expedition organised by the American Museum of Natural History refused permission by the Peiping Commission for the Preservation of Antiquities to continue its geological and palaeontological work.

GHSce-bv

LA TOUCHE, Thomas Henry Digges. Bibliography of Indian geology and physical geography with annotated index of minerals of economic value. Published by order of the government of India. Calcutta: Geological Survey of India, 1917-1923.

GHSqk

A BRIEF history of the Geological Survey of India and its activities. *Sci.Cult.*, 1964, 30: 213-6.

FERMOR, Lewis. Centenary celebrations of the Geological Survey of India. *Nature*, 1951, 167: 10-12, 584-6.

FOX, Cyril S. The Geological Survey of India, 1846 to 1947. *Nature*, 1947, 160: 889-91.

GHOSH, A.K. Geological survey of India (1851-1951). *Sci. Cult.*, 1951, 16: 307-13.

GHOSH, A.K. A short history of the Geological Survey of India. *Sci.Cult.*, 1946, 11: 331-3.

GHT

TAKAI, Fuyuji, ed. Geology of Japan, compiled on the occasion of the sixtieth birthday of Professor Teiichi Kobayashi. 279 p., 30 fig., 14 charts. Tokyo: University of Tokyo Press, 1963. [CB 90/520]

WATANABE, Mitsuaki. [Chronological table of the geology and mineralogy of modern Japan. (In Japanese)] *J.Hist.Sci. Japan*, 1953, no. 25, 17-22.

GHTqk

ANDERSSON, J.-G. The National Geological Survey of China. *Natur.Hist.*, 1921, 21: 4-12. [CB 11/424]

CHANG HUNG-CHAO. The Geological Survey of China. *Science*, 1922, 56: 233-7.

INOUYE, Kinosuke. Imperial Geological Survey of Japan: its history, organization, and work. *J.Geogr.* (Tokyo), 1924, 36: 11-22. [CB 16/276]

GHTth

CHANG HUNG-CHAO. [Lapidarium sinicum. A study of the rocks, minerals, fossils and metals as known in Chinese literature. (In Chinese with title page, preface and table of contents in English)] 2, 4, 8, 348, 2, ix p., 11 pl. (Memoirs of the Geological Survey of China, Ser. B, no. 2) Peking: Geological Survey of China, 1921.
Reviewed by P. Demiéville, *Bull.École Franç.Extrême-Orient*, 1924, 24: 276-301.
2nd revised edition 1927.

GHV

UMBGROVE, J.H.F. Structural history of the East Indies. xi, 62 p., 10 pl., 68 fig., map. Cambridge University Press, 1949. [CB 75/84]

GHX geology of Africa

RENIER, Armand. Jules Cornet (1865-1929), fondateur de la géologie du Congo. *Rev.Zool.Bot.Africaines*, 1935, 27: (*Suppl. Bull.Cercle Zool.Congolais*, vol. 12), (20)-(31).
Discours prononcé à l'occasion de l'inauguration du Mémorial Cornet au Musée du Congo belge, le 4 mai 1935.

GI GEOPHYSICS

for the earth as a planet *see* FL
geodesy *see* HB

AMERICAN GEOPHYSICAL UNION. A survey of research problems in geophysics prepared by Chairmen of sections. *Proc.Nat. Acad.Sci.*, 1920, 6: 545-601. [CB 12/624]

GIcd

ODISHAW, Hugh. What shall we save in the geophysical sciences? *Isis*, 1962, 53: 80-6.

GIpw

KELLNER, L. Alexander von Humboldt and the organization of international collaboration in geophysical research. *Contemp.Phys.*, 1959, 1: 35-48.

PERRIER, Georges. La coopération internationale en géodésie et en géophysique. Troisième assemblée générale de l'Union Géodésique Internationale à Prague, Septembre 1927. 120 p. (*Annu.Bur.Longitudes*, 1928. Annexe C) Paris: Gauthier Villars, [1927]. [CB 24/537]

SPECIAL COMMITTEE OF THE INTERNATIONAL GEOPHYSICAL YEAR. Annals of the International Geophysical Year, 1957-1958. Vol. 1. The histories of the international polar years and the inception and development of the International Geophysical Year. Foreword by Sydney Chapman. xi, 446 p., tables, pl., maps, fig. London/New York/Paris: Pergamon Press, 1959.

TERMINATION of the International Geophysical Year. *Endeavour*, 1959, 18: 3-4.

WATERMAN, Alan T. International geophysical year. *Amer. Scient.*, 1956, 44: 130-3. [CB 82/265]

GIwi-da

CALO, Pietro. Italian pioneers in the physics of the universe: geophysics. *Cah.Hist.Mond.*, 1963, 7: 453-69.

GIwi-qg

OSSERVATORIO GEOFISICO DELLA R. UNIVERSITÀ DI MODENA. Nel primo centenario della fondazione dell'Osservatorio. 1827-1927. xlii, 192 p., fig., pl. (Publicazione, 39) Modena: Società Tipografica Modenese, Antica Tipografia Soliani, 1927.
Reviewed by Sebastiano Timpanaro, *Archeion*, 1928, 9: 527-8.

GIwk

COMITÉ NATIONAL BELGE DE GÉODÉSIE ET DE GÉOPHYSIQUE. Aperçu historique de l'activité scientifique de la Belgique en géodésie et en géophysique, publié à l'occasion de la 9e Assemblée générale de l'Union Géodésique et Géophysique Internationale, tenue à Bruxelles du 21 août au 1er septembre 1951. 103 p., fig., pl. Bruxelles: 1951.
Reviewed by R. Taton, *Rev.Hist.Sci.*, 1953, 6: 91.

GIwk-qd

SOCIÉTÉ BELGE D'ASTRONOMIE, DE MÉTÉOROLOGIE ET DE PHYSIQUE DU GLOBE. Cinquantenaire de la Société, 27 octobre 1945. Memorial. 32 p., 6 pl. Bruxelles: 1945.

GIwt

YUASA, Mitsutomo. [Chronological table of geophysics of modern Japan. (In Japanese)] *J.Hist.Sci.Japan*, 1951, no. 18, 29-39.

GJ GRAVITATIONAL FIELD; ISOSTASY

BORN, Axel. Isostasie und Schweremessung. Ihre Bedeutung für geologische Vorgänge. iv, 160 p., ill. Berlin: Springer. 1923.

BOWIE, William. Isostasy. xv, 275 p., 39 ill. New York: E.P. Dutton, 1927. [CB 24/252]

BOWIE, William. Isostasy and the size and shape of the earth. *Science*, 1914, 39: 697-707. [CB 6/455]

BOWIE, William. The yielding of the earth's crust. *Annu. Rep.Smithsonian Inst.for 1921*, p. 235-47. Washington, D.C.: 1922.
An account of isostatic compensation.

PERRIER, Georges. Les raisons géodésiques de l'isostasie terrestre. 131 p., bibliogr. (*Annu.Bur.Longitudes*(Paris), 1926, Not. B) Paris: Gauthier-Villars, 1926.

WOOLARD, Edgar William. Historical note on the deflecting influence of the rotation of the earth. *J.Franklin Inst.*, 1942, 233: 465-70.
Includes review of William Ferrel's investigations.

GJce-bv

KNOPF, Adolph. Bibliography of isostasy. 2 p., 39 leaves. Washington: National Research Council, 1924.
Mimeographed. Based on bibliography in William Bowie's Investigations of gravity and isostasy, 1917.

GJwn

MEDUNIN, A.E. Izuchenie v Rossii deformatsii Zemli, vyzvannykh lunno-solnechnym pritiazheniem (1892-1920). [The study in Russia of the deformation of the earth caused by lunar and solar attraction (1892-1920). (In Russian)] *Tr.Inst.Ist.Est. Tekh.*, 1961, 43: 151-64.

GJxm-we

BULLARD, E.C.; JOLLY, H.L.P. Gravity measurements in Great Britain. *Mon.Not.Roy.Astron.Soc.Geophys.Suppl.*, 1936, 3: 443-77.

GK TERRESTRIAL HEAT

GEILER, Heinz. Zur Geschichte der geothermischen Tiefenstufe. *Arch.Gesch.Math.Naturwiss.Tech.*, 1931, 13: 352-8.

GL GEOMAGNETISM

for the compass *see* GLxp
the use of the compass in navigation *see* HCxk

BALMER, Heinz. Beiträge zur Geschichte der Erkenntnis des Erdmagnetismus. 892 p., 45 fig. (*Veröffentl.Schweiz.Ges. Gesch.Med.Naturwiss.*, 20) Aarau: Verlag H.R. Sauerländer, 1956.
Reviewed by E.J. Dijksterhuis, *Arch.Int.Hist.Sci.*, 1957, 10: 49-50; by E.C. Bullard, *Endeavour*, 1957, 16: 174-5; by Stig Ekelöf, *Lychnos*, 1957-58, 432-3.

BALMER, Heinz. Beiträge zur Geschichte der Erkenntnis des Erdmagnetismus. *Gesnerus*, 1956, 13: 65-81.

CHAPMAN, Sydney; BARTELS, Julius. Geomagnetism. 2 vol. (xxviii, x, 1049 p.) 1. Geomagnetic and related phenomena; 2. Analysis and physical interpretation of the phenomena. (International Series of Monographs on Physics) Oxford: Clarendon Press, 1940.
The history of the subject is treated fully.
Reviewed by G.C. Simpson, *Geogr.J.*, 1941, 97: 383-5.

COMMEMORATION of the life and work of Alexander Dallas Bache and Symposium on Geomagnetism. *Proc.Amer.Phil.Soc.*, 1941. 84: no. 2, 125-351, portr., fig.

FLEMING, John Ambrose. L'exploration magnétique et électrique de la terre: ses aspects physiques et cosmiques, et ses progrès. *Rev.Gén.Sci.*, 1926, 37: 454-67.

FLEMING, John Ambrose. The sun and the earth's magnetic field. *Annu.Rep.Smithsonian Inst.for 1942*, p. 173-208, ill. Washington, D.C.: 1943.

HAZARD, Daniel L. Terrestrial magnetism in the twentieth century. *Annu.Rep.Smithsonian Inst. for 1925*, p. 243-56. Washington, D.C.: 1926. Reprinted from *J.Wash.Acad.Sci.*, 1925, 15: no. 6.
Address of the retiring president of the Philosophical Society of Washington, presented at the meeting on Jan. 10, 1925.

KONCHEV, S.K. [On the history of the Kursk magnetic anomaly. (In Russian)] *Vop.Ist.Est.Tekh.*, 1959, 7: 67-74.

LOUIS AGRICOLA BAUER. *Terrestr.Magnet.Atmos.Elec.*, Sept. 1932, 37: no. 3.
Includes some historical articles in the field of terrestrial magnetism.

MITCHELL, A. Crichton. Chapters in the history of terrestrial magnetism. 1. On the directive property of a magnet in the earth's field and the origin of the nautical compass. 2, 3. The discovery of the magnetic declination. *Terrest. Magnet.Atmos.Elect.*, 1932, 37: 105-46; 1937, 42: 241-8; 1939, 44: 77-80. [CB 37/602 and CB 53/261]

NIPPOLDT, A. Ein Beitrag zur Frage der Ausrichtung der Kirchenachsen mit dem Magneten. *Arch.Gesch.Naturwiss.Tech.*, 1916, 7: 109-14, 236-44.
An interesting contribution to the history of magnetic declination.

SMITH, F.E. Theories of terrestrial magnetism. *Nature*. 1930, 126: 402-5.

WINTER, Heinrich. Die Erkenntnis der magnetischen Missweisung und ihr Einfluss auf die Kartographie. *Compt.Rend.Congr. Int.Géogr.* (Amsterdam, 1938), (2), p. 55-80, 4 pl. Leiden: E.J. Brill, 1938.
Elaborate study of the development of knowledge on magnetic declination from the first half of the thirteenth century to the end of the seventeenth century.

GLwb-qg

COHEN, I. Bernard. The one hundredth anniversary of the establishment of the Alexander Dallas Bache Magnetic Observatory. *Isis*, 1941, 33: 336-7.

FRENCH, C.A. Magnetic work of the Dominion Observatory, Ottawa, Canada, 1907-32. *Terrestr.Magnet.Atmos.Elec.*. 1932, 37: 335-42.

GLwf

MAURAIN, Charles. Les observations magnétiques en France jusqu'en 1921. *Ann.Inst.Phys.Globe Univ.Paris*, 1923, 1: 9-18. [CB 15/207]

GLxp compass

for the use of the compass in navigation *see* HCxk

BUSCH, W. Die Entwicklung des Schiffskompasses in Sage und Geschichte. *Ann.Hydrogr.Marit.Meteorol.*, 1926, 54: 120-6, 169-74.

CITTERT, P.H. van. Proportionaalpassers. [Proportional compasses. (In Dutch)] *Ned.Tijdschr.Natuurk.*, 1947, 13: 1-22, 15 fig.
Notes illustrating ancient specimens.

HASHIMOTO, Masukichi. Origin of the compass. *Mem.Res.Dep. Toyo Bunko*, 1926, no. 1, 69-92. [CB 28/525]

HENNIG, Richard. Die Frühkenntnis der magnetischen Nordweisung. *Beitr.Gesch.Tech.Ind.*, 1932, 21: 25-42.

HENNIG, Richard. Ein Zusammenhang zwischen der Magnetberg-Fabel und der Kenntnis des Kompasses. *Arch.Kulturgesch.*. 1930, 20: 350-69.

MICHEL, Henri. Notes sur l'histoire de la boussole. *Commun. Acad.Mar.Belg.*, 1950, 5: 1-11.

MITCHELL, A. Crichton. *See* GL

PRICE, Derek J. de Solla. On the origin of clockwork, perpetual motion devices and the compass. (*Contrib.Mus.Hist. Technol.*, Paper 6) *Bull.U.S.Nat.Mus.*, 1959, 218: 82-112.
Reviewed by Henri Michel, *Ciel Terre*, 1960, 76: 64.

SAUSSURE, Léopold de. L'origine de la rose des vents et l'invention de la boussole. 68 p. (*Arch.Sci.Phys.Natur.*, 5: no. 3-4) Genève: Kündig, 1923. [CB 15/208]

SCHÜCK, Albert. Der Kompass. 3 vol. Hamburg: 1911-17. [CB 11/438]

SCHÜCK, Albert. Die Vorgänger des Kompasses. *Zentralzeitung Opt.Mech.*, 1911, 32: 103-5, 121-2, 138-40, 156-8, 171-2, 185-6, ill.

WINTER, Heinrich. What is the present stage of research in regard to the development of the use of the compass in Europe? *Res.Progr.*, 1936, 2: 225-33, 3 fig.

GLxp-by

KÖRBER, Hans-Gunther. Über die Hillmannsche Sammlung von Sonnenuhren und Kompassen im Geomagnetischen Institut Potsdam. *Monatsber.Deut.Akad.Wiss.Berlin*, 1963, 5: 641-50. [CB 89/493]
The collection consists of 41 sundials, 12 compasses, and 10 calendars.

GM GEOCHEMISTRY

VERNADSKII, Vladimir Ivanovich. Ocherki geochimii. [Outlines of geochemistry. (In Russian)] 4th (2nd Russian) ed. 380, 2 p. Moskva: 1934. [CB 51/274]
The 1st edition (in French) was based on the lectures delivered by Vernadskii at the Sorbonne, in 1923-24 and appeared under the title: La géochimie (Paris: Alcan, 1924). [CB 16/307]
Includes a history of the subject.

GMwb-qd

INGERSON, Earl. The Geochemical Society. *Geo Times*, 1962, 6: 8-14, 39. [CB 88/646]

GN GEOCHRONOLOGY; HISTORY OF THE EARTH

BURKITT, M.C. Correlation of the archaeological and geological records. *Nature*, 1930, 126, 509-10.
Including a table of correlation.

CHAMBERLIN, T.C.; *et al.* The age of the earth. *Proc.Amer. Phil.Soc.*, 1922, 61: 247-88. Reprinted in *Annu.Rep.Smithsonian Inst.for 1922*, p. 241-73. Washington, D.C.: 1924.

DE GEER, Gerard. Geochronology, as based on solar radiation, and its relation to archeology. *Annu.Rep.Smithsonian Inst. for 1928*, p. 687-96. Washington, D.C.: 1929. Reprinted from *Antiquity*, 1928, 11: no. 7.

HABER, Francis C. The age of the world, Moses to Darwin. xi, 303 p. Baltimore: Johns Hopkins Press, 1959.
Reviewed by Walter F. Cannon, *Isis*, 1960, 51: 213-15; for other reviews *see* CB 85/391, CB 86/464 and CB 87/566.

HOBBS, William H. Earth evolution and its facial expression. xviii, 178 p. London/New York: Macmillan, 1922.
Reviewed in *Nature*, 1922, 110: 270-2.

HURLEY, Patrick M. How old is the earth? 160 p., ill., bibliogr. (Science Study Series) New York: Doubleday, 1959.
Reviewed by Charles Hellman, *Science*, 1959, 130: 616-17; in *Sci.Amer.*, 1959, 201: no. 5, 222-3.

LOUGEE, Richard J. A chronology of post-glacial time in eastern North America. *Sci.Mon.*, 1953, 76: 259-76.

MERRIAM, John C. The living past. xi, 144 p., 16 pl. New York: Scribner, 1930.
Reviewed by George Sarton, *Isis*, 1930, 14: 456-8.

PATTERSON, C.; TILTON, G.; INGHRAM, M. Age of the earth. *Science*, 1955, 121: 69-74.
The history and correlation of different methods of determining the age of the earth.

RAYLEIGH, John William Strutt, *3rd Baron*, *et al.* The age of the earth. *Nature*, 1921, 108: 279-84. Reprinted in *Annu. Rep.Smithsonian Inst.for 1921*, p. 249-60. Washington, D.C.: 1922.
Discussion at the Edinburgh meeting of the B.A.A.S. between Rayleigh, W.J. Sollas, J.W. Gregory and Harold Jeffreys.

SPARKS, John B. The histomap of evolution. With foreword, bibliography, and recommended books. 12 p., chart. Chicago: Rand, McNally, 1932. [CB 37/602]
Shows the sequence of events in the geological evolution of the earth and the palaeontological sequences of organisms.

WILMARTH, M. Grace. The geologic time classification of the United States Geological Survey compared with other classifications. Accompanied by the original definitions of era, period and epoch terms. A compilation. 138 p., 1 chart. (Department of the Interior, United States Geological Survey: Bulletin, 769) Washington, D.C.: Government Printing Office, 1925. [CB 20/202]

ZEUNER, Frederick E. Dating the past: an introduction to geochronology. 2nd ed. xviii, 474 p. New York: Longmans, Green, 1951. [CB 77/380]
Reviewed by E.C. Bullard, *Nature*, 1951, 168: 48.
First publ. London: Methuen, 1946 and reviewed by V.G. Childe, *Geogr.J.*, 1946, 108: 227-9.

GNc-br

Die Eiszeit. Zeitschrift für allgemeine Eiszeitforschung. Organ des Instituts für Eiszeitforschung in Wien. Vol. 1-4. Leipzig: 1924-27.
Continued as *Eiszeit und Urgeschichte*.

GNmzLG

HOOYKAAS, R. The parallel between the history of the earth and the history of the animal world. *Arch.Int.Hist.Sci.*, 1957, 10: 3-18. [CB 83/269]

GNwm-u

OLSSON, Bror. Mundus senescens. En skiss om tron på en åldrande värld i svenskt folkliv och litteratur. [Mundus senescens. The belief in an ageing world in Swedish popular belief and literature; an outline. (In Swedish)] *Lychnos*, 1954-55, 66-81.

GNxf-CU

see also CUxd radiocarbon dating

FLINT, Richard Foster. Pin-pointing the past with the cosmic clock. *Natur.Hist.*, 1951, 60: 200-6, ill.

JOLY, John. Radioactivity and the surface history of the earth; being the Halley Lecture delivered on May 28, 1924. 40 p. Oxford: Clarendon Press, 1924.

MUENCH, O.B. Determining geological age from radioactivity. *Sci.Mon.*, 1950, 71: 298-301.

ZUMBERGE, J.H.; POTZGER, J.E. Pollen profiles, radiocarbon dating and geologic chronology of the Lake Michigan basin. *Science*, 1955, 121: 309-11.

GO SEISMOLOGY AND VULCANOLOGY

BOUASSE, H. Séismes et sismographes. 394 p. Paris: Delagrave, 1927.

HOBBS, William H. The cause of earthquakes, especially those of the eastern United States. Reprinted from papers of the Michigan Academy of Science, Arts and Letters, vol. 5, 1925. *Annu.Rep.Smithsonian Inst.for 1926*, p. 257-77, 5 fig. Washington, D.C.: 1927.
Contains a brief history of earthquake theories.

MONTESSUS DE BALLORE, Fernand, *comte de*. La géologie sismologique: les tremblements de terre. xiv, 488 p., 16 pl. Paris: Armand Colin, 1924.
Reviewed by L. Guinet, *Isis*, 1926, 8: 217-19.

MONTESSUS DE BALLORE, Fernand, *comte de*. Histoire de la sismologie. *Rev.Quest.Sci.*, 1921, 29: 29-57, 320-50. [CB 18/629]

MONTESSUS DE BALLORE, Fernand, *comte de*. La sismologie moderne, les tremblements de terre. xx, 284 p., ill. Paris: Colin, 1911.

PASTOR, Alfonso Rey. Las teorias sismogénicas a través de la historia. *Iberica,* 1924, 11: 234-8, 248-52, 9 fig.

ROTHÉ, Edmond. Le tremblement de terre. xxxiv, 248 p., 51 fig. Paris: Alcan, 1925. [CB 20/202]
The introduction gives an account of the development of seismology from Alexis Perrey.

SAPPER, Karl. Vulkankunde. viii, 424 p. Stuttgart: Engelhorn, 1927.
The volume concludes with a history of volcanological research from the earliest times.
Reviewed by H.H. Read, *Geogr.J.,* 1931, 77: 185-6.

WARTNABY, J. Seismology. A brief historical survey and a catalogue of exhibits in the Seismological Section of the Science Museum. v, 47 p., front., 6 pl., 8 fig. (Geophysics Handbook, 1) London: H.M.S.O., 1957. [CB 83/201]

GOc-br

Zeitschrift für Vulkanologie. Volcanological Review. Revue Vulcanologique. Vol. 1-17. Berlin: 1914-38. [CB 6/464]

GOce-bv

Bibliography of Seismology. (Publications of the Dominion Observatory Ottawa) Ottawa: 1929.

GOda

DAVISON, Charles. The founders of seismology. xiv, 240 p. Cambridge University Press, 1927. [CB 23/254]

GOqg-bd

WOOD, Harry O. A list of seismologic stations of the world. *Bull.Nat.Res.Counc.,* 1921, 2: 397-538.

GOqy

INSTITUT VULCANOLOGIQUE INTERNATIONAL, par E.L. *Ciel Terre,* 1913, 34: 208.

GOu

MONTESSUS DE BALLORE, Fernand, *comte de.* Ethnographie sismique et volcanique, ou les tremblements de terre et les volcans dans la religion, la morale, la mythologie et le folklore de tous les peuples. viii, 206 p. Paris: Champion, 1923.
Reviewed by L. Guinet, *Isis,* 1924, 6: 437-9.

GOwk-qg

GILS, J.M. van. La genèse des stations séismologiques belges. *IIIe Congr.Nat.Sci.* (Bruxelles, 1950), p. 45-7. [Liège: 1951]

GOyFM

STETSON, Harlan T. Correlation of frequencies of seismic disturbances with the hour angle of the moon. *Publ.Bur.Cent. Séismol.Int.Sér.A.Trav.Sci.,* 1937, 15: 244-57. Also published in *Proc.Amer.Phil.Soc.,* 1938, 78: 411-24.

GP VOLCANIC ERUPTIONS; EARTHQUAKES

BULLARD, Fred M. Volcanoes: in history, in theory, in eruption. xvi, 441 p., pl., fig., bibliogr. Austin: University of Texas Press, 1962.
Only p. 16-30 devoted to historical aspects.

DAVISON, Charles. Great earthquakes. xii, 286 p. London: Murby, 1936.
A summary account of eighteen earthquakes between 1755 and 1931.
Reviewed by P. Lake, *Geogr.J.,* 1937, 89: 284-5.

DAVISON, Charles. Studies on the periodicity of earthquakes. ix, 107 p. London: Murby, 1938.
Reviewed by S.C., *Nature,* 1938, 142: 689.

HECK, Nicholas Hunter. Earthquakes. xi, 222 p., maps, ill. Princeton: Princeton University Press, 1936.
Reviewed by Ernest A. Hodgson, *Geogr.Rev.,* 1937, 27: 346-7.

HOBBS, William H. New volcanoes and a new mountain range. *Science,* 1944, 99: 287-90, 2 maps.
Including chronological list of new volcanoes from 1538 to 1943.

GPbw

SAPPER, Karl. Katalog der geschichtlichen Vulkanausbrücke. xi, 358 p. (Schriften der wissenschaftlichen Gesellschaft in Strassburg, 27) Strassburg: Teubner, 1917. [CB 10/196]

GPce-bv

MONTESSUS DE BALLORE, Fernand, *comte de.* Bibliografia general de temblores y terromotos. 7 pt. in 3 vol. (1516 p.) Santiago de Chile: Imprenta Universitaria for Sociedad Chilena de Historia y Geografia, 1915-19.

GPA REGIONAL SEISMOLOGY AND VULCANOLOGY

GPB

HECK, N.H. Earthquake history of the United States. 2 pt. 1. Continental United States (Exclusive of California and western Nevada) and Alaska. 85 p., map.; 2. California and western Nevada. 25 p. (U.S. Department of Commerce, Coast and Geodetic Survey, 609) Washington: Govt. Print. Off.. 1938-39. [CB 57/253]

HOBBS, William H. The cause of earthquakes, especially those of the eastern United States. Reprinted from papers of the Michigan Academy of Science, Arts and Letters, vol. 5, 1925. *Annu.Rep.Smithsonian Inst.for 1926,* p. 257-77, 5 fig. Washington, D.C.: 1927.
Contains a brief history of earthquake theories.

GPC

BAILEY, Willis. Studies in comparative seismology: earthquake conditions in Chile. With contributions by Perry Byerly, Johannes Felsch, Eric Jordan, J.B. Macelwane, Lu Sierra Vera, and Henry S. Washington. xi, 178 p., 75 pl., maps., 19 fig. (Carnegie Institution of Washington, Publication 382) Washington: 1929. [CB 27/538]
Includes the historical record of the earthquake activity of Atacama, a province of northern Chile and the geology of the region in so far as it bears on the cause of earthquakes.

LASTRES, Juan B. Terremotos, hospitales y epidemias de la Lima colonial. *Archeion,* 1940, 22: 141-53. Also in *An.Soc. Peruana Hist.Med.,* 1940, 30-41.

ORDOÑEZ, Ezequiel. El volcán de Parícutin. 15 p., ill. Mexico: 1943.

PUTTE, Jean van de. Etude sur l'origine des tremblements de terre, raz de marée et eruptions volcaniques (Phénomènes séismiques et volcaniques au Guatémala). ii, 139 p., 24 cartes et figures. Bruxelles: Larcier, 1924. [CB 16/307]
Records observations in Guatemala from 1541. First publ in *Ciel et Terre.*

GPE

DAVISON, Charles. A history of British earthquakes. xviii, 416 p., 100 fig. Cambridge Unitersity Press, 1924. [CB 18/628]

GPF

DE BEER, Gavin. The volcanoes of Auvergne. *Ann.Sci.,* 1962, 18: 49-61.

PERRET, Frank A. The volcano-seismic crisis at Montserrat. 1933-1937. xi, 76 p., 51 ill. (Carnegie Institution of Washington, Publication 512) Washington: 1939. [CB 58/578]

GPG

GIESSBERGER, Hans. Die Erdbeben Bayerns. 2 vol. 1. 72 p. (*Abhandl.Bayer.Akad.Wiss.,* 29: no. 6) München: 1922; 2. 69 p. München: R. Pflaum, 1924.

GPGce-bv

GIESSBERGER, Hans. Das Schrifttum zur Erdbebenkunde Bayerns. 16 p. Nürnberg: Carl Koch, 1926.

GPH

BATIUSHKOVA, I.V. Iz istorii izucheniia zemletriasenii v Pol'she. [From the history of the study of earthquakes in Poland. (In Russian)] *Tr.Inst.Ist.Est.Tekh.,* 1962, 42: 228-46.

BATIUSHKOVA, I.V. K iz istorii izucheniia zemletriasenii v Chechoslovakii. [On the history of the study of earthquakes in Czechoslovakia. (In Russian)] *Vop.Ist.Est.Tekh.*, 1959, 8: 134-7.

GPI

ALFANO, G.B.; FRIEDLAENDER, I. Die Geschichte des Vesuv. 71 p. Berlin: D. Reimer, 1929.

CHEVALLIER, R. Les coulées anciennes de l'Etna. Chronologie et topographie. *Rev.Gén.Sci.*, 1924, 35: 230-6, 267-80.

DE FIORI, O. Le cruzioni sottomarine, i fenomeni vulcanici secondari nelle Eolie a le cruzioni storiche di Lipari. *Z.Vulcanol.*, 1922, 6: 114-54; 1923, 7: 1-54. [CB 17/586]

PERRET, Frank A. The Vesuvius eruption of 1906. Study of a volcanic cycle. 152 p., 25 pl., 98 text fig. Washington, D.C.: Carnegie Institution, 1924. [CB 16/307]

GPJtk

MIRANDA, Raul de. A influencia dos fenomenos sismicos no espirito poético portuguès. *Petrus Nonius*, 1949, 7: 23-8.

GPKce

GILS, J.M. van. La chronique séismologique en Belgique, du début de l'ère chrétienne jusqu'au XXe siècle. *Ciel Terre*, 1950, 66: 218-21.

GPP

WILLIS, Bailey. Earthquakes in the Holy Land. *Bull.Seismol. Soc.America*, 1928, 18: 73-103. [CB 38/580]
For corrections to this paper *see Nature*, 1933, 131: 550 and *Science*, 1933, 77: 351.

WILSON, Arnold T. Earthquakes in Persia. *Bull.Sch.Orient. Stud.*, 1930, 6: 103-31, 1 pl.
Including list of earthquakes from 550 A.D. to 1930, and map.

GPQ

ROUX, Georges. Notes sur les tremblements de terre ressentis au Maroc avant 1933. *Mém.Soc.Sci.Natur.Maroc*, 1934, no. 39, 41-71.
List of earthquakes in Morocco from 211 B.C. to 1932 (161 items), with brief introduction and bibliography.

GPT

DAVISON, Charles. The Japanese earthquake of 1923. xii. 127 p., 6 pl. London: Murby, 1931.

HECK, N.H. Japanese earthquakes. *Annu.Rep.Smithsonian Inst. for 1945*, p. 201-17, 3 pl., 4 fig. Washington, D.C.: 1946.
Including list of 63 destructive earthquakes from 1596 to 1944.

HOANG, Pierre. Catalogue des tremblements de terre signalés en Chine d'après les sources chinoises (1767 av. J.-C. - 1895 après J.-C.). 2 vol. xxviii, 423 p., map. (Variétés Sinologiques, 28) Chang Hai: Imprimerie de la mission catholique, 1909, 1913. [CB 6/436]

GPV

SELGA, Miguel. Apuntes históricos sobre temblores de Filipinas. *Archeion*, 1940, 22: 71-85.

WICHMANN, Arthur. Die Erdbeben des indischen Archipels bis zum Jahre 1857. 193 p. (*Verhandel.Akad.Wetensch.Afd. Natuur.*, 2. sectie, 20: no. 4) Amsterdam: 1918. [CB 10/196]

GQ TECTONICS; STRUCTURAL GEOLOGY

AMERICAN ASSOCIATION OF PETROLEUM GEOLOGISTS. Theory of continental drift: a symposium on the origin and movement of land masses, both intercontinental and intra-continental, as proposed by Alfred Wegener. By W.A.J.M. van Waterschoot van der Gracht, Bailey Willis, Rollin T. Chamberlin, [*et al.*] x, 240 p. Tulsa, Okla.: The Association; London: T. Murby, 1928.
Reviewed by Arthur Holmes, *Nature*, 1928, 122: 431-3.

ARGAND, Emile. La tectonique de l'Asie. *Compt.Rend.XIIIe Congr.Géol.Int.* (Bruxelles, 1922), (1), p. 171-372, 27 fig. Liège: Imprimerie H. Vaillant-Carmanne, 1924. [CB 18/628]

BAILEY, E.B. Tectonic essays, mainly Alpine. xii, 200 p. Oxford: Clarendon Press, 1935.
A history of the development of tectonic ideas.
Reviewed by A.M. Davies, *Geogr.J.*, 1936, 87: 561-2.

BELUSOV, V.V. Basic problems in geotectonics. (Editor of English edition, John C. Maxwell; principal translator, Paul T. Broneer). 809 p., fig. New York: McGraw-Hill, 1962. [CB 88/545]
Translation of the Russian edition of 1954. Includes a history of geotectonics from classical times to the present.

DIVE, P. La dérive des continents et les mouvements intratelluriques. Préface de Emile Picard. 58 p., ill. Paris: Dunod, 1933.

DU TOIT, Alexander Logie. A geological comparison of South America with South Africa. With a palaeontological contribution by F.R. Cowper Reed. viii, 158 p., 16 pl., map. (Carnegie Institution, Publication 381) Washington, D.C.: 1927. [CB 24/542]

DU TOIT, Alexander Logie. Our wandering continents; an hypothesis of continental drifting. xiii, 366 p. London: Oliver & Boyd, 1937.

FELD, Jacob. History of the development of lateral earth pressure theories. *Brooklyn Eng.Club Proc.*, 1928, 26: 61-104. [CB 25/414]

GOLDER, Hugh Q. The history of earth pressure theory. *Arch. Int.Hist.Sci.*, 1953, 6: 209-19; also published *Act.VIe Congr.Int.Hist.Sci.* (Amsterdam, 1950), p. 545-54. Paris: Hermann, 1953. [CB 80/127]

HAPGOOD, Charles H. Earth's shifting crust. A key to some basic problems of earth science. With the collaboration of James H. Campbell. Foreword by Albert Einstein. 438 p., 15 fig. New York: Pantheon Books, 1958.

HERITSCH, Franz. Die Deckentheorie in den Alpen (Alpine Tektonik, 1905-1925). *Fortschr.Geol.Paläontol.*, 1927, 6: no. 17, 75-210.
Reviewed by P.G.H. Boswell, *Nature*, 1928, 121: 412-14.

HOLLAND, Thomas H. The permanence of oceanic basins and continental masses. 22 p., bibliogr. London: Macmillan, 1937.
The Huxley memorial lecture for 1937, giving a historical synopsis of the subject.

JACOB, Charles. Les théories tectoniques nouvelles: E. Argand, A. Wegener. *Ann.Géogr.*, 1925, 34: 97-112.

KAISIN, F. La cause générale des déformations de l'écorce terrestre et la dérive des continents. *Rev.Quest.Sci.*, 1926, 9: 67-98. [CB 20/202]

MARGERIE, Emmanuel de. La méthode des courbes structurales et la tectonique du Colorado. *Zbior Prac poświecony przez Towarzystwo Geograficzne we Lwowie Eugenjuszowi Romerowi*, p. 617-43, map. Lwow: 1934. [CB 45/290]

MASCART, Jean. A propos du déplacement des continents. *Rev. Gén.Sci.*, 1929, 40: 101-14.

SCHUCHERT, Charles. The hypothesis of continental displacement. *Annu.Rep.Smithsonian Inst.for 1928*, p. 249-82. Washington, D.C.: 1929.
From: American Association of Petroleum Geologists. Theory of continental drift. 1928, *see* above.

WEGENER, Alfred. Die Entstehung der Kontinente und Ozeane. 4th ed. x, 231 p. (Die Wissenschaft, 66) Braunschweig: Vieweg, 1929. [CB 13/289]
First publ. 1915. French translation "La genèse des continents et des océans" (Paris: Blanchard, 1924) reviewed by Maurice Gignoux, *Rev.Gén.Sci.*, 1925, 36: 139-42.
For English translation *see* below.

WEGENER, Alfred. The origin of continents and oceans. Translated from the third German edition by J.G.A. Skerl. With an introduction by J.W. Evans. xx, 212 p. London: Methuen, 1924.

WEGENER, Alfred. Die geophysikalischen Grundlagen der Theorie der Kontinentenverschiebung. *Scientia*, 1927, 41: 103-16; French transl., suppl., 49-61. [CB 23/254]

ZVORJKINE, A.A. Sur l'histoire de l'examen de la pression de terrain. *Act.VIIIe Congr.Int.Hist.Sci.* (Florence, 1956), p. 1073-7. Paris: Hermann, 1958.

GR STRATIGRAPHY; PETROLOGY AND PETROGRAPHY

for meteorites *see* FUzm

BASSLER, Ray S. Glacial varved clay concretions of New England. *Annu.Rep.Smithsonian Inst. for 1948*, p. 269-76, 12 pl. Washington, D.C.: 1949.

CROOK, Thomas. *See* GS

FISCHER, W. Gesteins- und Lagerstättenbildung im Wandel der wissenschaftlichen Anschauung. 592 p., ill. Stuttgart: E. Schweizerbart, 1961.
Reviewed by Joh. E. Hiller, *Naturwiss.Rundsch.*, 1961, 14: 359.

HOLMES, Arthur. Natural history of granite. *Nature*, 1945, 155: 412-15.

MERRILL, George P. The composition and structure of meteorites compared with that of terrestrial rocks. *Annu.Rep. Smithsonian Inst.for 1917*, p. 175-88, 9 pl. Washington, D.C.: 1919.

OULIANOFF, N. Réflexions sur le métamorphisme des roches. *Scientia*, 1959, 94: 57-61.

READ, H.H. Metamorphism and igneous action. *Advance.Sci.*, 1940, 1: 223-51.
Historical discussion of concept of metamorphism.

RÜGER, Ludwig. Die Geröllgneise von Obermittweida (Erzgebirge) und die Entwicklung der Lehre vom Metamorphismus. *Aus Heimat*, 1931, 44: 106-16, 5 fig.
Reviewed by R. Zaunick, *Mitt.Gesch.Med.*, 1932, 31: 30.

SMITH, W. Campbell. A remarkable septarium from South Wales. *Natur.Hist.Mag.*, 1930, 2: 262-6.
Historical notes on attempted explanations of septaria from Paracelsus to the present day.

GRnh

HOLMES, Arthur. The nomenclature of petrology: with references to selected literature. 2nd ed. v, 284 p. London: Murby, 1928.
First publ. 1920.

TOURTELOT, Harry A. Origin and use of the word "shale". *Amer.J.Sci.*, 1960, 258-A: 335-43. [CB 90/520]

GRwb

PARKS, William Arthur. The development of stratigraphic geology and palaeontology in Canada. *Proc.Roy.Soc.Can.*, 1922, 16: Sect. 4, 1-46.

WELLS, John West. Early investigations of the Devonian system in New York, 1656-1836. 74 p., pl., fig., tables. New York: Geological Society of America, 1963.

GRwn

LAPIN, V.V. [The creation and development of technical petrography in the Soviet Union. (In Russian)] *Tr.Inst.Ist.Est.*, 1952, 4: 381-93.

GS MINERAL DEPOSITS

ADAMS, Frank Dawson. Origin and nature of ore deposits. An historical study. *Bull.Geol.Soc.Amer.*, 1934, 45: 375-424, portr. [CB 42/595]

AMERICAN INSTITUTE OF MINING AND METALLURGICAL ENGINEERS. Seventy-five years of progress in the mineral industry, 1871-1946, including Proceedings of the 75th anniversary of the ... Institute ... and World Conference on Mineral Resources, March 1947, ed. by A.B. Parsons. xii, 817 p., 111 portr., 58 fig. New York: The Institute, 1947.
Reviewed by L. Don Leet, *Isis*, 1949, 40: 82-3.

AMSTUTZ, G.C. Some basic concepts and thoughts on the space-time analysis of rocks and mineral deposits in orogenic belts. *Geol.Rundsch.*, 1960, 50: 165-89. [CB 87/567]
Contains a brief historical summary of classification of mineral deposits.

BATEMAN, Alan M. The growth of geologic knowledge in the discovery of metallic and nonmetallic mineral resources. *Cah.Hist.Mond.*, 1955, 2: 979-90.

BOYD, M.L.; MONTGOMERY, D.S. A study of the Athabasca bitumen from the Abasand Quarry, Alberta, Canada. 1. Early history, analysis of the bituminous sand, and isolation and structural analysis of the asphaltene fraction. 67 p. (Mines Branch Research Report, R 78) Ottawa: Department of Mines and Technical Surveys, 1961.
A summary of the observations and investigations from 1778 to the present.

CROOK, Thomas. History of the theory of ore deposits: with a chapter on the rise of petrology. 163 p. London: Murby, 1933.
Reviewed by V.A.E., *Nature*, 1934, 134: 988-9.

DICKEY, Parke A. 100 years of oil geology. *Geo Times*, 1959, 3: no. 6, 6-9, 24-5; no. 7, 6-7, 24-5, bibliogr.

GSsk

LEITH, C.K. World minerals and world politics: a factual study of minerals in their political and international relations. xii, 213 p. New York: Whittlesey House, 1931.
Reviewed by A.C. Veatch, *Geogr.Rev.*, 1931, 21: 334-6.

GSwb

JILLSON, Willard Rouse. Early mineral explorations in the Mississippi valley (1540-1840). (*Publ.Ill.State Hist.Libr.*, 31) *Trans.Ill.State Hist.Soc.*, 1924, 41-57.

OWEN, Edgar W. Remarks on the history of American petroleum geology. *J.Wash.Acad.Sci.*, 1959, 49: 256-60.

GSwb-qd

DOTT, Robert H. The American Association of Petroleum Geologists. *Geo.Times*, 1961, 6: 12-16, 35-9. [CB 88/645]

ROVE, Olaf N. Society of Economic Geologists. *Geo Times*, 1962, 7: 8-13, 36-7.

GSwh-qd

TEICH, Mikuláš. Královská česká společnost nauk a počátky vědeckého průzkumu přírody v Čechách. [The Royal Bohemian Society of Sciences and the beginnings of scientific surveys of natural resources in Bohemia. (In Roumanian, with English summary)] 77 p. Praha: 1959.

GSx

SCIENCE MUSEUM. Applied geophysics. A brief survey of the development of apparatus and methods employed in the investigations of subterranean structural conditions and the location of mineral deposits. 102 p., 10 pl. London: H.M. Stationery Off., 1936. [CB 49/183]
First edition appeared in 1931 [with catalogue of exhibits in the National Collection]. By H. Shaw. 3rd edition.

GSxf-GI

PETROVSKII, A.A. [Evolution of geophysical methods of prospecting. (In Russian)] *Arkh.Ist.Nauk.Tekh.*, 1934, 2: 61-80, 12 fig.

GT MINERALOGY

see also CW CRYSTALLOGRAPHY
RS PHARMACO-MINERALOGY

GTc general history

BROMEHEAD, C.E.N. Aetites or the eaglestone. *Antiquity*, 1947, 21: 16-22, 2 pl. [CB 73/176]

ERDMANNSDÖRFFER, Ott Heinrich. Mineralogie einst und jetzt. 17 p. (Heidelberger Universitätsreden, 15) Heidelberg: Winter, 1931.
Reviewed by R. Zaunick, *Mitt.Gesch.Med.*, 1932, 31: 274.

GROTH, Paul. Entwicklungsgeschichte der mineralogischen Wissenschaften. iv, 262 p., 5 fig. Berlin: Springer, 1926.
Reviewed by Arrien Johnsen, *Arch.Gesch.Math.Naturwiss. Tech.*, 1927, 10: 367-8.

HURLBUT, Cornelius S.; WENDEN, H.E. The changing science of mineralogy. x, 117 p., ill. Boston: Heath, 1964.

MULTHAUF, Robert. The beginning of mineralogical chemistry. *Isis*, 1958, 49: 50-3.

SCHROETER, Joachim. George Agricolas Mineralsystem und sein Nachleben bis ins 18. Jahrhundert. *Schweiz.Mineral.Petrogr. Mitt.*, 1957, 37: 19 p.

GThc

BROMEHEAD, C.E.N. Flavus or blavus: a difficulty in understanding early descriptions of minerals. *Mineral.Mag.*, 1947, 28: 104-7.

GTj/u special aspects

GTj

SCHUHL, Pierre Maxime. Imagination et science des cristaux ou platonisme et minéralogie. *J.Psychol.Norm.Pathol.*, 1949, 42: 27-34.

GTk

NIGGLI, Paul. Probleme der Naturwissenschaften, erläutert am Begriff der Mineralart. 252 p., 100 fig. (Wissenschaft und Kultur, 5) Basel: Birkhäuser, 1949.

GTod

RUSKA, Julius. Methodik des mineralogisch-geologischen Unterrichts. viii, 520 p., 35 ill., 1 pl. Stuttgart: Enke, 1920.
Reviewed by G. Sarton, *Isis*, 1921, 3: 443-4.

GTu

CLARENCE, E.W. Sympathie, Mumia, Amulette, okkulte Kräfte der Edelsteine und Metalle. 2 vol. 1. Sympathie und Mumia. xi, 322 p.; 2. Okkulte Kräfte der Edelstein und Metalle. iii, 224 p., ill. Berlin-Pankow: Linser-Verlag, 1927.

LASSALLY, Oswald. Von der Entstehung des Aberglaubens an Sterne und Steine. *Geisteskultur*, 1931, 40: 87-92.

GTw in different countries

GTwb

KRAUS, Edward. The future of mineralogy in America. *Science*, 1921, 53: 219-26. [CB 10/158]

GTwb-qd

FISHER, Jerome D. Mineralogical Society of America. *Geo Times*, 1963, 7 8-12.

GTwc

PASTORE, Franco. Nuestra mineralogía y geología durante los ultimos cincuenta años (1872-1922). Cincuentenario de la Sociedad Cientifica Argentina (1872-1922). 47 p. (Evolución de las Ciencias en la Republica Argentina, 6) Buenos Aires: 1925. [CB 22/205]

GTwf-oq

LACROIX, Alfred. Notice historique sur le troisième fauteuil de la section de minéralogie (lue à la séance publique annuelle de l'Académie des Sciences le 17.12.1928). 88 p. Paris: Gauthier-Villars, 1928. [CB 27/559]

GTwf-qd

WALLERANT, Fred. La Société Française de Minéralogie de 1878 à 1928. *Bull.Soc.Franç.Minéral.*, 1930, 53: 3-21, portr.

GTwg

FISCHER, Walther. Mineralogie in Sachsen von Agricola bis Werner. Die ältere Geschichte des Staatlichen Museums für Mineralogie und Geologie zu Dresden (1560-1820). viii, 347 p., 18 fig., 24 pl. Dresden: Heinrich, 1939.
Reviewed by Nils Zenzén, *Lychnos*, 1941, 398-403.

GTwg-oq

KLEBER, Will. Die Entwicklung der Mineralogie an der Berliner Universität während der ersten Hälfte des 20. Jahrhunderts. *Wiss.Z.Humboldt Univ.Berlin Math.Naturwiss.Reihe*, 1960, 9: 99-105.

GTwh

TOKARSKI, Julian. [Mineralogy in Poland. (In Polish with summary in French)] 38 p. (Polska Akademia Umiejetności, Historia Nauki Polskiej w Monografiach, 5) Cracow: 1948.

WRANÝ, Adalbert. Die Pflege der Mineralogie in Böhmen. Ein Beitrag zur vaterländischen Geschichte der Wissenschaften. viii, 421 p. Prag: Dominicus, 1896.

GTwi

RODOLICO, Francesco. Lineamenti di storia della mineralogia toscana. *Riv.Stor.Sci.*, 1953, 44: 187-93.

GTwi-da

D'ACHIARDI, Giovanni. I mineralogisti pisani dei tempi passati. 16 p. (Conferenza tenuta alla R. Scuola normale sup. di Pisa il 28 marzo 1931) Pisa: Lischi, 1931.
Reviewed by R. Zaunick, *Mitt.Gesch.Med.*, 1932, 31: 275.

GORTANI, Michele. Italian pioneers in geology and mineralogy. *Cah.Hist.Mond.*, 1963, 7: 503-19.

GTwj

OLIVEIRA MACHADO E COSTA, Alfredo Augusto de. As triadas constituintes de mineralogia portuguesa. Communicação apresentada ao XX Congresso Luso-Espanhol reunido em San Sebastian em abril de 1947. *Petrus Nonius*, 1951, 7: 106-16.

GTwk

DENAYER, Marcel. Les sciences minérales en Belgique de 1830 à 1930. In: Livre d'or du Centenaire de l'Indépendance belge, p. 248-51. Bruxelles/Anvers: Leclercq, De Ridder et De Haas, 1931.

GTwn

SHCHERBAKOV, D.I. V.I. Vernadskii i sovetskaya mineralogiya. [V.I. Vernadskii and Soviet mineralogy. (In Russian)] *Vop. Ist.Est.Tekh.*, 1956, no. 2, 138-45.

GTxx museums

THE ADAM SEYBERT mineral collection. *Science*, 1936, 83: 49. [CB 46/547]

FISCHER, Walther. *See* GTwg

GTyGN CHRONOLOGY

POVARENNYKH, A.S. K voprosu o periodizatsii mineralogii. [On the problem of periodization in mineralogy. (In Russian)] *Ocherki Ist.Geol.Znanií*, 1962, 10: 65-89.

GU GEM STONES

ABBOTT, Mary. Jewels of romance and renown. 217 p. London: Laurie, 1933.

Bernstein-Forschungen. Amber Studies. Ed. by Karl Andrée. Pt. 1-4. Berlin: De Gruyter, 1929-39.

BROMEHEAD, C.E.N. The forgotten uses of selenite. *Mineral. Mag.*, 1943, 26: 325-33.

EVANS, Joan. Magical jewels of the Middle Ages and the Renaissance particularly in England. 261 p., 4 pl. Oxford: Clarendon Press, 1922. [CB 15/222]

FARRINGTON, Oliver Cummings. Famous diamonds. 27 p., 5 pl. (Geology Leaflet 10) Chicago: Field Museum of Natural History, 1929.

KOZMINSKY, Isidore. The magic and science of jewels and stones. xv, 434 p., ill. New York: Putnam, 1922.

KUNZ, George Frederick. The curious lore of precious stones: being a description of their sentiments and folk lore, superstitions, symbolism, mysticism, use in medicine, protection, prevention, religion, and divination, crystal gazing, birthstones, lucky stones and talismans astral, zodiacal and planetary. xiv, 406 p., ill. Philadelphia: Lippincott, 1913.

KUNZ, George Frederick. Magic of jewels and charms. xv, 422 p., 90 ill. Philadelphia: Lippincott, 1915.

LA TOUCHE, Theo. W. Diamonds of Golconda. *Asiatic Rev.*, 1945, 41: 280-4.

POGUE, Joseph-E. The turquois. A study of its history, mineralogy, geology, ethnology, archaeology, mythology, folk-lore and technology. 162 p., 22 pl. (*Mem.Nat.Acad. Sci.*, 12: part 2) Washington, D.C.: 1915. [CB 11/443]

WHITLOCK, Herbert Percy. The story of the gems: a popular handbook. vi, 206 p., 34 pl. New York: Furman, 1936.
Reviewed by B.W.A., *Nature*, 1937, 140: 703.

WILLIAMS, Alpheus Fuller. The genesis of the diamond. 2 vol. xv, 352, vi p., 89 pl.; xii, iv p., 132 pl. London: Benn, 1932.
Reviewed by A.E.H. Tutton, *Nature*, 1933, 131: 255-7.

WILLIAMSON, George Charles. The book of amber. With a foreword by Edward Heron-Allen. 268 p., 5 pl. London: Benn, 1932.
Reviewed in *Nature*, 1932, 130: 44.

WOLLASTON, T.C. Opal: the gem of the never never. xi, 164 p., 15 pl. London: Murby, 1924.

GUce-bv

DENMAN, Carolyn. Jade: a comprehensive bibliography. *J.Amer. Orient.Soc.*, 1945, 65: 118-26.

GUwn

IAKOVLEVA, O.A. [On the question of so-called semi-precious stones in Muscovite Russia. (In Russian)] *Tr.Inst.Ist.Est. Tekh.*, 1955, 3: 211-15.

GUxx

UNITED STATES NATIONAL MUSEUM. Handbook and descriptive catalogue of the collections of gems and precious stones in the United States National Museum. By George P. Merrill. viii, 225 p., 26 fig., 14 pl. (*Bull.U.S.Nat.Mus.*, 118) Washington: Govt. Print. Off., 1922.

GV GEOMORPHOLOGY; EXTERNAL GEODYNAMICS

GVc

ALMAGIÀ, Roberto. Il rapporto quantitativo fra l'area delle terre emerse e quella degli spazi acquei sul globo. Breve sguardo al problema. *Act.VIIIe Congr.Int.Hist.Sci.* (Florence, 1956), p. 463-6. Paris: Hermann, 1958.

BUESS, H. Geschichtliches zur Lehre von der Talbildung durch fliessendes Wasser. *Experientia*, 1946, 2: 229-30.

CHORLEY, Richard J. Diastrophic background to twentieth-century geomorphological thought. *Bull.Geol.Soc.Amer.*, 1963, 74: 953-70.
Traces the rise and fall of the eustatic theory of Eduard Suess.

CHORLEY, Richard J.; DUNN, Antony J.; BECKINSALE, Robert P. The history of the study of landforms; or, the development of geomorphology. 1. Geomorphology before Davis. xvi, 678 p., 131 ill. London: Methuen; New York: Wiley, 1964.
The first volume of a projected two- or three- volume series.
Reviewed by J. Hoover Mackin, *Science*, 1964, 146: 1665-6.

DAVIS, William Morris. The coral reef problem. vi, 596 p., 227 fig. (American Geographical Society, Special Publication, 9, Shaler Memorial Series) New York: The Society, 1928.
First part devoted to criticism of all previous theories, beginning with that of Darwin.
Reviewed by George Sarton, *Isis*, 1928, 11: 399-401.

DAVIS, William Morris. The framework of the earth. *Amer.J. Sci.*, 1919, 48: 225-41.
Discussion of Suess's work.

HENDERSON, Junius. Geology in its relation to landscape. vii, 152 p., 30 pl. Boston: Stratford, 1925.

KRÄMER, Augustin. Die Entstehung und Besiedlung der Koralleninseln. Nach neuen Gesichtspunkten auf Grund eigener Untersuchungen. 53 p., 6 fig., 4 pl. Stuttgart: Schweizerbart, 1927.

LADD, H.S.; TRACY, J.I. The problem of coral reefs. *Sci.Mon.*, 1949, 69: 297-305.

PETTERSSON, H. The accretion of cosmic matter to the earth. *Endeavour*, 1960, 19: 142-6.
Deep sea and Arctic snow evidence of 1872-1876 and recent investigations of deep sea caves and air samples.

ROVERETO, Gaetano. Forme delle terra. Trattato di geologia morfologica (Geomorfologia). 2 vol. 1. Basi e generalità. xvi, 1-641 p. 2. Tipi regionali. viii, 648-1187 p. Milano: Hoepli, 1923-25. [CB 18/630]

TIETZE, Emil. Einige Seiten über Eduard Suess. Ein Beitrag zur Geschichte der Geologie. *Jahrb.Geol.Reichsanst.*, 1916, 66: (3-4), 333-556.

VAUGHAN, Thomas Wayland. Corals and the formation of coral reefs. *Annu.Rep.Smithsonian Inst.for 1917*, p. 189-238, 37 pl. Washington, D.C.: 1919.

WRIGHT, John K. The heights of mountains: "an historical notice". *Spec.Libr.Ass.Geogr.Map Div.Bull.*, 1958, no. 31, 4-15, 1 map.
Mimeographed.

GVwh

MOSCHELES, J. Résultats des recherches géomorphologiques dans la République tchécoslovaque. *Géographie*, 1923, 40: 294-303, bibliogr.

GVwm-qd

GERZ, Otto. Kungl. Fysiografiska Sällskapet i Lund, 1772-1940. Historisk överblick och personförteckningar. [The Royal Physiographical Society in Lund. A historical survey and list of members. (In Swedish)] 463 p. Lund: Gleerup, 1940.
Reviewed by Aldo Mieli, *Archeion*, 1941, 23: 476-9.

GVyGL

KOHN, Heinrich. Die Entstehung der heutigen Oberflächenformen der Erde und deren Beziehungen zum Erdmagnetismus. *Ann. Natur.Kulturphil.*, 1913, 12: 88-130.

GVyGN

JOLY, John. The surface-history of the earth. 2nd ed. xxi, 211 p. Oxford: Clarendon Press, 1930.
First published 1925.

GVA REGIONAL GEOMORPHOLOGY

GVB

BRETZ, J. Harlen. The Grand Coulee. x, 89 p., 53 fig., 1 map, 8 stereoscopic views. (American Geographical Society, Special Publication, 15) New York: The Society, 1932.
Description and discussion of the Grand Coulee; includes history of the earlier interpretations, 1835, etc. (p. 39-43).

GVC

JAGUARIBE DE MATTOS, F. Les idées sur la physiographie sud-américaine. *Act.IIIe Congr.Int.Hist.Sci.* (Portugal, 1934), p. 391-440. Lisbon: 1936. [CB 51/272]

GVK

BEEKMAN, A.A. De zoogenaamde afdamming van het Kreekrak en de Belgen. [The supposed erection of the dyke of the Kreekrak and the Belgians. (In Dutch)] *Tijdschr.Ned.Aardrijksk. Genoot.*, 1928, 45: 965-70, 1 map.
It is argued that the dyke is a natural barrier.

GVR

MARGERIE, Emmanuel de. L'oeuvre de Sven Hedin et l'orographie du Tibet. 139 p., 28 fig., 1 portr. (*Bull.Sec.Géogr. Comité Trav.Hist.Sci.*, 1928) Paris: Imprimerie Nationale, 1929. [CB 29/276]

GW GLACIOLOGY

MANSON, Marsden. The unsatisfactory status of the glacial controversy. *Science*, 1925, 62: 212-14.

MEUNIER, Stanislas. Les glaciers et les montagnes. 262 p. (Bibliothèque de Philosophie Scientifique) Paris: Flammarion, 1920.

WICHMANN, Artur. Aus den Kindheitstagen der Glazialgeologie. *Geologe*, February 1914, 223-9.

GWk

GIEHM, Gerhardt. Welterkenntnis und Weltenbau. Philosophisches zur Glazialkosmogonie. viii, 181 p. Leipzig: Voigtländer, 1928.
Reviewed by R. Zaunick, *Mitt.Gesch.Med.*, 1930, 29: 77.

GWke

WESTGATE, Lewis G. Errors in scientific method - glacial geology. *Sci.Mon.*. 1940, 51: 299-309.

GWwb

THWAITES, Fredrik Turville. The development of the theory of multiple glaciation in North America. *Trans.Wis.Acad. Sci.Arts Lett.*, 1927, 23: 41-164.
Reviewed by R. Zaunick, *Mitt.Gesch.Med.*, 1932, 31: 30.

GWwm

THORARINSSON, Sigurdur. Glaciological knowledge in Iceland before 1800, a historical outline. *Jökull*, 1960, 10: 1-17. [CB 88/547]

GWA REGIONAL GLACIOLOGY

GWB

HOBBS, William H. The glacial anticyclone and the continental glaciers of North America. *Proc.Amer.Phil.Soc.*, 1943, 86: 368-402, 35 fig., 12 maps.
Includes history of the subject.

GWG

THORINGTON, J. Monroe. The Oetzthal glaciers in history and cartography before 1800. *Geogr.J.*, 1930, 75: 233-41.

GWM

REKSTAD, J. Om variasjoner av isbreene paa Vestlandet. [On the variations of glaciers in western Norway. (In Norwegian)] *Naturen*, 1928, 25-31, 1 map.

GWMce-bv

HOEL, Adolph; NORVIK, Johannes. Glaciological bibliography of Norway. 242 p. (*Skr.Norsk Polarinst.*, 126) Oslo: Norsk Polarinstitutt, 1962. [CB 90/519]

GWR

DAINELLI, Giotto. Budhists and glaciers of Western Tibet. The account of a visit to the largest glacier in the world, and of adventures on the way there and back. xiv,304 p., pl., map. London; Kegan Paul, 1933.

GX HYDROLOGY AND HYDROGRAPHY

ADAMS, Frank Dawson. The origin of springs and rivers: an historical review. 16 p., 1 pl. (*Fennia*, 50, no. 1) Helsingfors: 1928. [CB 26/236, 241]

FEDOSEEV, I.A. Znachenie rabot M.A. Rykacheva v razvitii gidrologii sushi. [The significance of the works of M.A. Rykachev in the development of inland hydrology. (In Russian)] *Vop.Ist.Est.Tekh.*, 1962, no. 12, 197-200.

HALBFASS, W. Der gegenwärtige Stand der Seenforschung. 1. Topographie, Hydrographie, Geologie der aussereuropaïschen Seen; 2. Topographie, Hydrographie, Geologie der europaïschen Seen; 3. Die Thermik der Seen. *Fortschr.Naturwiss.Forsch.*, 1912, 6: 1-66; 1913, 7: 1-72; 1913, 9: 1-54.

JONES, P.B.; *et al.* The development of the science of hydrology. 35 p., bibliogr. (*Tex.Water Comm.Circ.*, 63-03) Austin: 1963.
A summary of history of hydrologic observations and theories from the earliest times to the present.

PARIZEK, Richard R. The hydrologic cycle concept. *Mineral Ind.*, 1963, 32: no. 7, 1-8, bibliogr.
A review of the history of ideas of the hydrologic cycle from classical times to the present.

GXwf-da

ROLLET DE L'ISLE, Maurice. Étude historique sur les ingénieurs hydrographes et le Service Hydrographique de la Marine (1814-1914). *Ann.Hydrogr.*, 1950, 1 (bis), 378 p., 22 pl.
Work written in 1914.
Reviewed in *Imago Mundi*, 1953, 10: 136.

GXwn

ALEKSEEV, A.I. Russkaia morskaia gidrograficheskaia nauka v XIX - nachale XX veka. [Russian marine hydrographic science in the 19th and early 20th century. (In Russian)] *Tr.Inst. Ist.Est.Tekh.*, 1962, 42: 80-102.

FEDOSEYEV, I.A. Development of hydrology of the land in prerevolutionary Russia. *Proc.10th Int.Congr.Hist.Sci.* (Ithaca, 1962), (2), p. 1023-6. Paris: Hermann, 1964.

GORDEEV, D.I. Istoriia paleogidrogeologii i nekotorykh smezhnykh otraslei znaniia v SSSR za poslevoennye gody (1946-1960 gg.). [History of paleohydrogeology and some related fields of knowledge in the USSR in the postwar years, 1946-1960. (In Russian)] *Vop.Ist.Est.Tekh.*, 1961, 11: 29-39.

GXxp

FRAZIER, Arthur H. Daniel Farrand Henry's cup type 'telegraphic' river current meter. *Technol.Cult.*, 1964, 5: 541-65.

GXyCE

THORADE, Hermann. Probleme der Wasserwellen. viii, 220 p. Hamburg: Grand, 1931.
Bibliography from Leonardo da Vinci to 1930, with 329 references.
Reviewed by D.J. Matthews, *Geogr.J.*, 1932, 79: 148.

GXA REGIONAL HYDROLOGY

GXB

HOUGH, Jack L. The prehistoric Great Lakes of North America. *Amer.Scient.*, 1963, 51: 84-109. [CB 89/504]

LAMBART, Helen H.; RIGBY, G.R. Submerged history of the Long Sault. *Canad.Geogr.J.*, 1963, 67: 147-57.

WELLS, John W. Early hydrographic work on an American lake. *Science*, 1943, 98: 562.

WILLIAMS, Howel. Crater Lake, the story of its origin. xii, 101 p. Berkeley: University of California Press, 1941. [CB 62/80]

GXD

LAUTERBORN, Robert. Der Rhein. Naturgeschichte eines deutschen Stromes. Die erd- und naturkundliche Erforschung des Rheins und der Rheinlande vom Altertum bis zur Gegenwart. 1. Die Zeit vom Altertum bis zum Jahre 1800. 1st sect. *Ber.Naturforsch.Ges.Freiburg*, 1930, 30: 1-311; 2. Die Zeit von 1800 bis 1930. 1st sect. *Ibid.* 1933, 33: 1-324; 2nd sect. viii, 439 p. Ludwigshafen: Lauterborn, [1938]. [CB 61/377]

GXE

WALTERS, R.C. Skyring. The ancient wells, springs, and holy wells of Gloucestershire: their legends, history, and topography. xiv, 194 p., 62 pl. Bristol: St. Stephen's Press, 1928.

GXF

COMPIN, Paul. Essais sur les origines et l'antiquité des thermes de Bourbon Lancy. 63 p. Paris: Jules Rousset, 1913.

GXG

HÄBERLE, Daniel. Die Mineralquellen der Rheinpfalz und ihre nächsten Nachbargebiete in geologisch-historischer Beziehung. 103 p., 11 pl. Kaiserslautern: 1912.

REINDL, Jos. Die bayerische Seenforschung in ihrer geschichtlichen Entwicklung. *Arch.Gesch.Naturwiss.Tech.*, 1912, 4: 132-47.

GXK

BEEKMAN, A.A. De wateren van Nederland aardrijkskundig en geschiedkundig beschreven. [The waters of the Netherlands described geographically and from the point of view of history. (In Dutch)] viii, 283 p. S'Gravenhage: Nijhoff, 1948.

GY OCEANOGRAPHY

for sea travel *see* HO
marine and cave biology *see* JNzm

GYc general history

BERGET, A. Les problèmes de l'océan. 330 p. (Bibliothèque de Philosophie Scientifique) Paris: Flammarion, 1920.
Reviewed by A. Loir and H. Legangneux, *Rev.Gén.Sci.*, 1921, 32: 344-5.

BIGELOW, Henry Bryant. A developing view-point in oceanography. *Science*, 1930, 71: 84-9.

BIGELOW, Henry Bryant. Oceanography: its scope, problems, and economic importance. vi, 263 p. Boston: Houghton Mifflin, 1931.
Reviewed by H.A. Marmer, *Geogr.Rev.*, 1931, 21: 703-4.

CARRUTHERS, J.N. Some oceanography from the past. *J.Inst. Navigation*, 1963, 16: 180-8.

COWEN, Robert C. Frontiers of the sea: the story of oceanographic exploration. 307 p., pl. London: Victor Gollancz; Garden City, N.Y.: Doubleday, 1960.
Reviewed by K.F. Bowden, *Nature*, 1961, 190: 202.

DEACON, George E.R. Oceanography in the International Geophysical Year. *Advance.Sci.*, 1961, 17: 410-14.

DEACON, George E.R. Oceans. An atlas history of man's exploration of the deep. 297 p., ill., maps, charts London: Hamlyn, 1962.

DEACON, George E.R. Scientific exploration of the oceans. *Mem.Manchester Lit.Phil.Soc.*, 1959-60, 102: 41-64.

FOWLER, G. Herbert, ed. Science of the sea: an elementary handbook of practical oceanography for travellers, sailors and yachtsmen. Prepared for the Challenger Society for the Promotion of the Study of Oceanography. 2nd ed. by E.J. Allen. xxiii, 502 p. Oxford: Clarendon Press, 1928.
First published 1912.

McEWEN, George F. The science of oceanography. *Proc.1st Pan. Pacific Sci.Conf.* (Honolulu, 1920), p. 597-607. (Bernice P. Bishop Museum. Special Publication, 7) Honolulu: Honolulu Star, 1921.

MANTEN, A.A. The origin of marine geology. *Mar.Geol.*, 1964, 2: 1-28. [CB 90/522]

NORLIND, Arnold. Okeanos. [In Swedish with German summary] *Svensk Geogr.Årsbok*, 1927, 9-21, 3 maps, 1 pl.
Short sketch of the history of various concepts that have been held since the time of the early Greeks regarding the encircling stream of Ocean, and later, regarding the oceans.

PLAKHOTNIK, A.F. [History of the study of the oceans and seas. Early history of oceanographical research from antiquity up to the last decades of the 19th century. (In Russian)] *Tr.Inst.Ist.Est.Tekh.*, 1961, 37: 52-79.

ROTSCHI, H. Man discovers the sea. *Impact*, 1960, 10: 79-103.

RUSSELL, R.C.H.; MACMILLAN, D.H. Waves and tides. 348 p., ill. New York: Philosophical Library, 1953.
An attempt to present the development of the oceanographic sciences to the layman and in a form useful to the professional seaman.

THE SEA: ideas and observations on progress in the study of the seas. General editor: M.N. Hill. 3 vol. 1. Physical oceanography. xv, 864 p.; 2. The composition of sea-water. Comparative and descriptive oceanography. xiv, 554 p.; 3. The earth beneath the sea. History. xvi, 963 p., ill. New York: Wiley; London: Interscience, 1962-63.
Volume 3 reviewed by E.L. Hamilton, *Science*, 1963, 142: 215-16; by G.E.R. and Margaret B. Deacon, *Geogr.J.*, 1964, 130: 120-3.

THOMPSON, Thomas G. A short history of oceanography with emphasis on the role played by chemistry. (Symposium on chemistry of the sea.) *J.Chem.Educ.*, 1958, 35: 108-12, 1 fig.

THOULET, J. L'océanographie. x, 288 p. (Science et Civilisation, 3) Paris: Gauthier-Villars, 1922. [CB 13/288]

VON ARX, William S. An introduction to physical oceanography. x, 422 p., ill. Reading, Mass.: Addison-Wesley, 1962.
Includes an introductory chapter and an appendix on the history of oceanography.
Reviewed by James Crease, *Science*, 1962, 136: 515.

GYda

HERDMANN, William Abbott. Founders of oceanography and their work. xii, 340 p., 29 pl. London: Arnold, 1923.
Reviewed by George Sarton, *Isis*, 1924, 6: 91-5.

GYhh

PLAKHOTNIK, A.F. Istochniki i printsipy periodizatsii istorii okeanografii. [The origins and principles of the periodization of the history of oceanography. (In Russian)] *Tr. Inst.Ist.Est.Tekh.*, 1962, 42: 103-29.

GYq/t special aspects

GYqh

BUEN, Rafael de. Lista cronológica de las campañas y navegaciones a las que se deben observaciones científicas de caracter oceanográfico. 62 p. (Memorias del Consejo Oceanográfico Ibero-Americano, 5) Madrid: 1930.

GUBERLET, Muriel L. Explorers of the sea. Famous oceanographic expeditions. 234 p., ill. New York: Ronald, 1964.

WUST, Georg. Repräsentative Tiefsee-Expeditionen und Forschungsschiffe 1873-1960. (Aus der "Denkschrift zur Lage der Meereskunde" der Deutschen Forschungsgemeinschaft 1962.) *Naturwiss.Rundsch.*, 1963, 16: 211-14.

GYth

HENNIG, Richard. Liegen der Erzählung vom "Geronnenen Meer" geographische Tatsachen zugrunde? *Geogr.Z.*, 1926, 32: 62-73. [CB 20/200]

GYw in different countries

GYwb-qh

CARNEGIE INSTITUTION OF WASHINGTON. Scientific results of Cruise VII of the "Carnegie" during 1928-1929 under command of Captain J.P. Ault. Oceanography. 4. The work of the "Carnegie" and suggestions for future scientific cruises. vii, 111 p., fig., maps. (Carnegie Institution of Washington, Publication 571) Washington, D.C.: 1946. [CB 70/223]

PAUL, J. Harland. The last cruise of the "Carnegie". With a foreword by John A. Fleming. xvii, 331 p., 198 ill. Baltimore: Williams & Wilkins, 1932.
Reviewed by George Sarton, *Isis*, 1933, 20: 300-2.
The programme included oceanographic investigations.

GYwj

RAMOS DA COSTA, Augusto. Alguns dados para a história da oceanografia em Portugal. *Act.IIIe Congr.Int.Hist.Sci.* (Portugal, 1934), p. 440-6. Lisbon: 1936.
History of oceanography in Portugal.

GYwj-qg

BELLÓN, Luis. Premiers travaux du Laboratoire océanographique des Canaries. *Rev.Gén.Sci.*, 1931, 42: 599.

GYwm-qh

HEDGPETH, Joel W. The steamer "Albatross". *Sci.Mon.*, 1947, 65: 17-22, ill. [CB 72/255]

GYwn

SHULEIKIN, Vasilii Vladimirovich. Of days gone by. Transl from the Russian by J. Guralsky. 493 p., ill. Moscow: Foreign Languages Publishing House, 1960. [CB 86/513]
Autobiography of the first important Russian oceanographer.

GYx techniques and instruments

GYxm

ABBOT, C.G. How deep is the ocean? *Annu.Rep.Smithsonian Inst.for 1922*, p. 275-84. Washington, D.C.: 1924.

BENCKER, H. The bathymetric soundings of the oceans. *Hydrogr. Rev.*, 1930, 7: 64-97.
Contains chronological list of ocean explorations from the year 1800.

DRUBBA, Helmut. On the first echo-sounding experiment. *Ann. Sci.*, 1954, 10: 28-32, 1 pl.

DRUBBA, Helmut; RUST, Hans Heinrich. Die Entwicklung der akustischen Meerestiefenmessung. *Z.Angew.Phys.*, 1953, 5· 388-400, 7 fig.

SCHULZ, Bruno. Stand und Bedeutung der Echolotfrage. *Tijdschr. Ned.Aardrijkskundig Genoot., 2nd ser.*, 1925, 42: 85-103, 5 fig.
Discussion of the German, French, British and American methods of echo-sounding.

GYxp

DRUBBA, Helmut; RUST, Hans Heinrich. Historische Geräte für die Meerestiefenbestimmung. *Hansa*, 1955, 92: 1601-5, 5 fig.

MULTHAUF, Robert P. The line-less sounder: an episode in the history of scientific instruments. *J.Hist.Med.*, 1960, 15: 390-8.

ROUCH, Jules. Les machines à sonder par grandes profondeurs. *Rev.Sci.*, 1922, 60: 624-8, ill.

GYxt-bt

UNITED STATES HYDROGRAPHIC OFFICE. Graphic representation of soundings taken by *U.S.S. Stewart* with sonic depth finder. Mediterranean Sea. 3 sheets. Scale 1: 1,550,000. Washington: 1923. [CB 16/304]
These maps show the results of practical investigations made by the United States Navy into the serviceability of the newly perfected sonic depth finder.

UNITED STATES HYDROGRAPHIC OFFICE. Graphic representation of soundings taken by *U.S.S. Stewart* with sonic depth finder [Newport, R.I. to Gibralter]. Pilot chart of the north Atlantic ocean, January, 1923. Scale 1: 6,000,000. Washington: 1923.

UNITED STATES HYDROGRAPHIC OFFICE. San Francisco to Port Descanso. Bathymetrical chart (Scale 1: 850,000) compiled from data obtained with sonic depth finder by *U.S.S. Cony* and *U.S.S. Hull*, 1922 (No. 5194). Washington: 1923.

VIGLIERI, A. Carte génerale bathymétrique des océans. *Scientia*, 1959, 94: 103-11.

GYxx museums

MARGERIE, Emmanuel de. L'inauguration du Musée Océanographique de Monaco. *Géographie*, 1910, 21: 6 p.

GYzc CURRENTS

ENDRÖS, A. Zum Problem des Euripus. *Sitzungsber.Bayer.Akad. Wiss.Math.Phys.Kl.*, 1914, 99-139.
A scientific study of the irregular currents taking place between the isle of Euboea and the Greek mainland.

MARMER, H.A. The Gulf Stream and its problems. *Geogr.Rev.*, 1929, 19: 457-78, 6 fig. Reprinted in *Annu.Rep.Smithsonian Inst.for 1929*, p. 285-307, fig. Washington, D.C.: 1930.
Including history of our knowledge of it, from the time of its discovery in 1513 by Ponce de Leon. The first to chart it was Franklin, 1786.

STOMMEL, Henry. The Gulf Stream. *Sci.Mon.*, 1950, 70: 242-53. [CB 85/392]
A brief history of its discovery and an evaluation of its causes.

GYzt TIDES

AITON, E.J. The contributions of Newton, Bernoulli and Euler to the theory of the tides. *Ann.Sci.*, 1955, 11: 206-23, 6 fig.

BURSTYN, Harold L. Theory and practice in man's knowledge of the tides. *Proc.10th Int.Congr.Hist.Sci.* (Ithaca, 1962), (2), p. 1019-22. Paris: Hermann, 1964.

FICHOT, E. L'influence de la rotation terrestre sur la physionomie des marées. 71 p. (*Annu.Bur.Longitudes*, 1925, *Notice A*) Paris: Gauthier-Villars, 1925.

LARMOR, Joseph. The dynamical theory of tides. Historical origins. Letter to the Editor. *Times* (London), June 10, 1932, 15.

MARMER, Harry Aaron. The tide. xii, 282 p., 60 ill. New York: Appleton, 1926. [CB 20/199]

THORADE, Hermann. Ebbe und Flut in der Nordsee; ein geschichtlicher Rückblick. *Petermanns Mitt.Ergänzungsheft*, 1930, 209: 195-206.

GYzt-ce

GERNEZ, D. Les indications relatives aux marées dans les anciens livres de mer. *Arch.Int.Hist.Sci.*, 1949, 1: 671-91. [CB 75/93]

GYzt-xk

BENCKER, Henri Lucien Georges. Les machines à prédire les marées. 110 p., ill. (Bureau Hydrographique International, Publication Spéciale, 13) Monaco: 1926.
Describing about fifteen types of tide-predicting machines from Sir William Thomson's first one, 1872, to the Liverpool machine of 1925.

GYA REGIONAL OCEANOGRAPHY

DEACON, G.E.R. The Sargasso Sea. *Geogr.J.*, 1942, 99: 16-28.
A review of the literature from James Rennell, 1832 to 1939.

LE DANOIS, Edouard. L'Atlantique, histoire et vie d'un océan. 290 p., ill. (Science d'aujourd'hui) Paris: A. Michel, 1938.
Spanish edition (Buenos Aires: 1940) reviewed by Gustavo Fester, *Archeion*, 1940, 22: 440-1.

McEWEN, George F. The status of oceanographic studies of the Pacific. *Proc.1st Pan-Pacific Sci.Conf.* (Honolulu, 1920), p. 487-97. (Bernice P. Bishop Museum, Special Publication, 7) Honolulu: Honolulu Star, 1921.
Historical sketch, p. 487-9.

OUTHWAITE, Leonard. The Atlantic: a history of an ocean. 479 p., ill. New York: Coward-McCann, 1957. [CB 84/313]

PETTERSSON, O.; DRECHSEL, C.F. Memorandum on investigations in the Atlantic with programme for same. 21 p., 2 pl. (*Rapp.Procès Verbaux Cons.Perma.Int.Explor.Mer*, 16) Copenhagen: Host, 1913.
Text in English and German.

TOWLE, Edward L. The myth of the open north polar sea. *Proc. 10th Int.Congr.Hist.Sci.* (Ithaca, 1962), (2), p. 1037-41. Paris: Hermann, 1964.

GYAnh

SAUSSURE, Léopold de. L'origine des noms de mer Rouge, mer Blanche et mer Noire. *Globe*, 1924, 63: 23-36. [CB 20/201]

GYAwg-qh

DEUTSCHE ATLANTISCHE EXPEDITION, 1925-27. Deutsche atlantische Expedition auf dem Forschungs- und Vermessungsschiff "Meteor", 1925-1927. Wissenschaftliche Ergebnisse. 16 vol. Berlin: De Gruyter, 1932- .
Some of the volumes are not yet complete.
Vol. 1 reviewed by D.J. Matthews, *Geogr.J.*, 1934, 83: 242-3; vol. 10 by J.S. Gardiner, *ibid.* 1932, 80: 349-50.

GYAwn

AKADEMIIA NAUK SSSR. The Pacific: Russian scientific investigations. 192 p., 2 fig., 13 maps, 1 table, 11 pl. Leningrad: Publishing Office of the Academy, 1926. [CB 22/253]

GZ WATER DIVINING

AIGNER, Eduard. Die neuesten Ergebnisse der Wünschelrutenforschung in Praxis und Theorie. Zum zehnjährigen Bestehen des Verbands zur Klärung der Wünschelrutenfrage. 32 p. (Schriften des Verbands, 9) Stuttgart: K. Wittwer, 1922.

BARRETT, William; BESTERMAN, Theodore. The divining-rod: an experimental and psychological investigation. xxiii, 336 p., 12 pl. London: Methuen, 1926.
Reviewed by Hugh Robert Mill, *Nature*, 1927, 119: 309-12.

DURVILLE, Gaston. Les merveilles de la baguette divinatoire. *Aesculape*, 1913, 3: 122-6, 11 fig.

ELLIS, Arthur J. The divining rod: a history of water witching. 59 p., 4 ill. (United States Geological Survey, Water-Supply paper 416) Washington, D.C.: 1917. [CB 10/215]

FRANCE, Henry de. The modern dowser: a guide to the use of the divining rod and pendulum. Translated by A.H. Bell. xvii, 139 p. London: Bell, 1936.
Reviewed in *Nature*, 1937, 139: 352.

GREGORY, J.W. Water divining. *Annu.Rep.Smithsonian Inst.for 1928*, p. 325-48, 16 fig. Washington, D.C.: 1929. [CB 28/560]
Read at the session of the British Waterworks Association, Public Works, Roads, and Transport Congress, 1927.

HAENEL, H. Zur physiologischen Mechanik der Wünschelrute. Mit einem Anhang: Beobachtungen an dem Rutengänger Donath. 42 p., ill. (Schriften des Verbands zur Klärung der Wünschelrutenfrage) Stuttgart: Wittwer, 1918. [CB 10/215]

KLINCKOWSTROEM, Carl von. Die Wünschelrute als wissenschaftliches Problem. Mit Anhang: Geophysikalische Aufschlussmethoden. 40 p., 3 ill. Stuttgart: Wittwer, 1922.

KLINCKOWSTROEM, Carl von; MALTZAHN, Rudolf von. Handbuch der Wünschelrute; Geschichte, Wissenschaft, Anwendung. 321 p., ill. München: Oldenbourg, 1931. [CB 32/602]

LE BON, Gustave. Programme d'expériences permettant de résoudre d'une manière définitive le problème de la baguette divinatoire. *La Nature*, 1913, 41: 1er semestre, 379-80.

MAGER, Henri. Les baguettes des sourciers et les forces de la nature. Pourquoi se meuvent les baguettes. Elles obéissent aux lois d'Ampère. Services que peuvent rendre les baguettes et les pointes rectangulaires reliées au sol par deux conducteurs. xi, 423 p., ill. Paris: Dunod, 1920.

MAGER, Henri. Les sourciers et leurs procédés. 4th ed. xx, 390 p. Paris: Dunod, 1930.
First published 1913.

MAGER, Henri. Water diviners and their methods. Translated from the fourth edition of "Les sourciers et leurs procédés", by A.H. Bell. xi, 308 p., 8 pl. London: Bell, 1931.

MALTZAHN, Rudolf von; MARQUARDT, E. Professor Zunker und die Wünschelrute. *Arch.Klärung Wünschelrutenfrage*, 1931, 1: 48-58, 3 fig.

MILL, Hugh Robert. Belief and evidence in water divining. *Nature*, 1927, 120: 882-4.

PROKOP, Otto, ed. Wünschelrute, Erdstrahlen und Wissenschaft. viii, 183 p., 39 fig. Stuttgart: Enke, 1955.
Reviewed by Johannes Steudel, *Sudhoffs Arch.*, 1956, 40: 91.

REGNAULT, Jules. Les sourciers. Comment se détermine la profondeur à laquelle se trouvera la nappe d'eau. *Hydrologica*, 1913, 2: 288-91.

ROCAL, Georges. La baguette des baguettisants. *Mer.France*, 15 February 1924, 59-88. [CB 16/345]

DER VERLAUF einer Wünschelruten-Bohrung 1918-1920. Aus den Akten des Bayer. Landesamtes für Wasserversorgung. *Arch. Klärung Wünschelrutenfrage*, 1931, 1: 59-68, 1 fig. [CB 35/307]

VIRÉ, Armand. L'art de découvrir les sources. Les sourciers et la baguette divinatoire. *La Nature*, 1913, 41: 1er semestre, 328-33.

ZUNKER, Ferdinand. Über die Wünschelrutendränung. *Kulturtechniker*, 1929, no. 5/6, 428.

ZUNKER, Ferdinand. Zum Verfahren der Wasseradern-Querdränung. *Kulturtechniker*, 1927, no. 3, 184.

GZce-bv

KLINCKOWSTROEM, Carl von. Bibliographie der Wünschelrute seit 1910 u. Nachträge (1610-1909). 53 p. (Schriften des Verbandes zur Klärung der Wünschelrutenfrage, 1: 3) Stuttgart: K. Wittwer, 1912.

GZqx

NOËL, E. Le Congrès de la baguette divinatoire à Halle sur la Saale. *La Nature*, 1914, 42: 1er semestre, 102.

GZwb

VOGT, Evon Z.; HYMAN, Ray. Water witching U.S.A. ix, 248 p., front., bibliogr. Chicago: University of Chicago Press, 1959.

GZwg

BROWNE, Charles Albert. Observations upon the use of the divining rod in Germany. *Science*, 1931, 73: 84-6, fig.

KRANZ, Walter. Wünschelrutenversuche am Gebirgsbau der Blattgebiete Leonberg und Weissach NW Stuttgart, mit Beitrag zur Baugrundgeologie. *Arch.Klärung Wünschelrutenfrage*, 1931, 1: 3-42, 8 fig., 2 pl.

H GEOGRAPHY

Hc general history

AHMAD, Kazi S. Geography through the ages. *Pakistan Geogr. Rev.*, 1964, 19: 1-30.

ALMAGIÀ, Roberto. Scritti geografici (1905-1957). xii, 652 p. Rome: Edizioni Cremonese, 1961.
Reviewed by E. Migliorini, *Scientia*, 1963, 98: 73-5.

BAKER, John Norman Leonard. The history of geography. xxviii, 266 p., maps. portr. Oxford: Blackwell, 1963.
Publications by Baker, collected by his students, to honor his retirement from the Bursarship of Jesus College, Oxford.

BANSE, Ewald. Lexikon der Geographie. 2 vol. 786 p.; 785 p. Braunschweig: G. Westermann, 1923.

CRONE, Gerald R. Background to geography. 224 p. London: Museum Press, 1964.
Reviewed by M.J. Wise, *Geogr.J.*, 1964, 130: 399-400.

DICKINSON, R.E.; HOWARTH, O.J.R. The making of geography. iv, 264 p., 5 pl., fig. Oxford: Clarendon Press, 1933.
Reviewed by C.A. Kofoid, *Isis*, 1935, 23: 294; by E.G.R. Taylor, *Geogr.J.*, 1934, 83: 66-7.

FITZGERALD, Walter. Progress in geographical method. *Nature*, 1944, 153: 481-3.
Historical outline from Montesquieu, 1748, to present day.

FREEMAN, T.W. A hundred years of geography. 335 p. London: Duckworth, 1961; Chicago: Aldine, 1962.
A historical and biographical survey of geography as a developing science.
Reviewed by Sheldon Judson, *Amer.Scient.*, 1963, 51: 64A; by Ronald H. Buchanan, *Science*, 1963, 141: 800; by A. Meynier, *Rev.Hist.*, 1964, 232: 236-7.

HETTNER, Alfred. Die Geographie; ihre Geschichte, ihr Wesen und ihre Methoden. viii, 463 p. Breslau: Ferd. Hirt, 1927.
Reviewed by N. Krebs, *Deut.Lit.Zeitung*, 1927, 2265-8.

KELTIE, J. Scott. A half century of geographical progress. *Scot.Geogr.Mag.*, 1915, 31: 617-36; also *Annu.Rep.Smithsonian Inst.for 1916*, p. 501-21, 2 pl. Washington, D.C.: 1917.

KREBS, Norbert. Die Entwicklung der Geographie in den letzten fünfzehn Jahren. *Frankf.Geogr.Hefte*, 1925-27, 1: 19 p. [CB 24/484]

KRETSCHMER, Konrad. Geschichte der Geographie. 2nd ed. 163 p. (Sammlung Göschen, 624) Berlin/Leipzig: 1923. First published 1912.

PATTISON, William D. The four traditions of geography. *J. Geogr.*, 1964, 63: 211-16.

REEVES, Edward Ayearst. The recollections of a geographer. 224 p., 8 pl. London: Seeley, Service, 1935.

TABERNER, Fernando Valls; REPARAZ, Gonzalo de. Historia de la geografía. In: Geografia universal; descripción moderna del mundo, (1). El espacio y la tierra, p. 532-62, ill. Barcelona: Instituto Gallach, 1931.
Brief, semi-popular sketch of the outlines of the history of geography illustrated with reproductions of early maps and with maps illustrating the progress of exploration.

TAYLOR, Griffith, ed. Geography in the twentieth century. A study of growth, fields, techniques, aims and trends. A symposium by twenty-two authors from Canada, the United States, England, Czechoslovakia, and Poland. 2nd ed. xi, 661 p., 57 maps and diagr., 15 pl. New York: Philosophical Library; London: Methuen, 1953. [CB 77/343 and CB 80/128]

Hc-bq

CONGRESSO GEOGRAFICO ITALIANO. Atti. [1st, 1892-] Rome, *etc.*: 1892- [CB 16/300 and CB 26/238]
No conferences held between 1910 and 1921 and between 1934-47. The conference proceedings contain many contributions in the field of historical geography and the history of geography.

INTERNATIONAL GEOGRAPHICAL CONGRESS. [Proceedings. 1st Congress, Antwerp, 1871 -] Antwerp, *etc.*: 1872- 20th Congress, London, 1964.
The proceedings of these conferences contain many papers on the history of geography and on historical geography. For an account of the 11th Congress, *see* Baulig, H. The International Geographical Congress at Cairo. *Geogr.Rev.*, 1925, 15: 470-4; of the 16th Congress, *see* *Imago Mundi*, 1939, 3: 100-2.

Hc-br

Geographisches Jahrbuch. Vol. 1-, 1866- Gotha: 1866-
For contents of volumes for 1919-23 and 1924-25 *see* CB 16/301 and CB 20/201; for 1926 *see* CB 22/285; for 1929 *see* CB 29/307.

Hc-bv/cv bibliography; literature; sources

Hc-bv

Bibliographie Géographique Internationale, 1891- Paris: 1891- [CB 17/585 and CB 20/200]
Includes historical section. Title varies. Now published under the auspices of the International Geographical Union.

CONGRESSO GEOGRAFICO ITALIANO. Indice degli Atti dei Congressi Geografici Italiani dal primo al decimo (1892-1927) a cura del dott. Elio Migliorini. 125 p. Roma: Presso la R. Societa Geografica Italiana, 1934.
The proceedings contain many papers on the history of geography and historical geography.

DEPT, Gaston G. Chronique de géographie. (Revue des recueils périodiques) *Rev.Quest.Sci.*, 1928, 94: 468-79; 1929, 96: 276-89; 1931, 99: 127-41; 1931, 100: 305-21; 1935, 117: 420-46; 1936, 110: 117-43; 1937, 112: 103-42; 1938, 114: 115-32, 278-98; 1939, 116: 266-99. [CB 56/396]
Includes sections on the history of geography.

GOBLET, Y.M. La géographie historique et l'histoire de la géographie au IIIe Congrès de l'Union Géographique Internationale (Paris, Sept. 1931). *Rev.Hist.*, 1932, 170: 32-45.

HAKLUYT SOCIETY. A list of the publications of the Hakluyt Society. 16 p. London: Quaritch, 1946. [CB 70/263]

Hce-bv

AUROUSSEAU, M. Recent contributions to urban geography: a review. *Geogr.Rev.*, 1924, 14: 443-55. [CB 16/299]

BROOKS, Arthur A. Index to the *Bulletin of the American Geographical Society*, 1852-1915. xii, 242 p. New York: American Geographical Society, 1918.

Geographical Journal. Index to supplements to the *Geographical Journal.* Recent geographical literature supplements, vol. 1-4, no. 1-41, 1918-1932. 469 p. London: Royal Geographical Society, 1936.
Reviewed by William H. Jesse, *Pap.Bibliogr.Soc.Amer.*, 1938, 32: 102-5.

WRIGHT, John Kirtland; PLATT, Elizabeth T. Aids to geographical research: bibliographies, periodicals, atlases, gazeteers and other reference books. 2nd ed. xii, 331 p. (American Geographical Society, Research series, 22) New York: Columbia University Press, 1947.
For first edition (New York: American Geographical Society, 1923) *see* CB 15/221.

Hf history of geography as a study

BESCHORNER, H. Stand der geographisch- historischen Forschung in Deutschland. *Geisteswissenschaften*, 1913, 1: 45-8.

WRIGHT, John Kirtland. The history of geography: a point of view. *Ann.Ass.Amer.Geogr.*, 1925, 15: 192-201.

WRIGHT, John Kirtland. A plea for the history of geography. *Isis*, 1926, 8: 477-91. [CB 21/582]

Hfqd

COVILLE, Alfred. The French committee for historical geography and history of geography. *Imago Mundi*, 1937, 2: 54.

THE HUMBOLDT SOCIETY for the study of the history of geography and cartography. *Imago Mundi*, 1937, 2: 22.

MULLETT, Charles F. The Hakluyt Society: its first hundred years. *Sci.Mon.*, 1946, 63: 423-7.

Hk/s special aspects

Hk

DE GEER, Sten. On the definition, method, and classification of geography. *Geogr.Ann.*, 1923, 5: 1-37. [CB 16/300]

ESAKOV, V.A. [The role and significance of D.N. Anuchin in the development of the theory of geographical knowledge. (In Russian)] *Tr.Inst.Ist.Est.Tekh.*, 1955, 3: 85-103.

HARTSHORNE, Richard. The nature of geography. A critical survey of current thought in the light of the past. vi, 482 p., 1 fig. Lancaster, Penn.: Association of American Geographers, 1939.
Reviewed by John K. Wright, *Isis*, 1941, 33: 298-300.

KERP, Heinrich. Auf der Suche nach einem philosophischen Einheitsbegriff der Erdkunde. *Proteus*, 1937, 2: 104-12.

KIRK, William. Problems of geography. *Geography*, 1963, 48: 357-71.

VALLAUX, Camille. Les sciences géographiques. viii, 414 p. Paris: Felix Alcan, 1925. [CB 17/585]

Hkd

LEWIN, J. A review of recent ideas on geographical explanation. *Wessex Geogr.*, 1964, no. 5, 21-8.

Hke

HETTNER, Alfred. Methodische Zeit- und Streitfragen. *Geogr. Z.*, 1923, 29: 37-59.
Discussion of recent tendencies in geographical methodology particularly in Germany.

SAUER, Carl O. The survey method in geography and its objectives. *Ann.Ass.Amer.Geogr.*, 1914, 14: 17-33. [CB 16/304]

SVIATLOVSKY, E.E.; EELLS, Walter Crosby. The centrographical method and regional analysis. *Geogr.Rev.*, 1937, 27: 240-54, 8 fig.
With historical résumé.

Hkq

HERBERTSON, A.J. The higher units. A geographical essay. *Scientia*, 1913, 14: 199-212, French transl. suppl., 113-28.
A classification by type of the earth's surface into natural regions.

HmzMP

BOWMAN, Isaiah. Geography in relation to the social sciences. Geography in the schools of Europe by Rose B. Clark. xxii, 382 p., 17 ill. (Report of the American Historical Association Commission on the Social Studies, part 5) New York: Scribner's, 1934. [CB 42/594]

HmzNC

SCHWIND, Martin. Das Verhältnis des Menschen zu seiner Umwelt als geographisches Problem. *Abhandlungen zur Wissenschaftsgeschichte und Wissenschaftslehre*, p. 25-41. (Veröffentlichungen der Gesellschaft für Internationale Wissenschaftsgeschichte, 1952, no. 2) Bremen: Carl Schünemann, [n.d.].

Hnh

AUROUSSEAU, M. Revision of the R.G.S.II system. *Geogr.J.*, 1941, 97: 318-21.
Official rules of the Royal Geographical Society for the spelling and pronunciation of place-names.

BÖTTCHER, Joh. Ed. Geographische Benennungen nach kirchlichen Festen. *Arch.Gesch.Naturwiss.*, 1920, 9: 39-44.

SAUSSURE, Léopold de. L'origine des noms de mer Rouge, mer Blanche et mer Noire. *Globe*, 1924, 63: 23-36. [CB 20/201]

Ho

HODGSON, H.B. Notes on the history of the teaching of geography. *Geography*, 1937, 22: 44-8.
Place of geography in European education in medieval and modern times.

Hp

ACKERMAN, Edward A. Where is a research frontier? *Ann.Ass.Amer.Geogr.*, 1963, 53: 429-40.

Hsc

REPARAZ, Gonzalo de. Veinticinco lecciones de historia naturalista. 277 p. (Colección Gonzalo de Reparaz, 2) Barcelona: Mentora, 1929. [CB 31/558]
The essays deal with the interaction of geography with history and politics.

Hsg

STAMP, Josiah. Geography and economic theory. *Geography*, 1937, 22: 1-14.
A review of opinions on extent of common content of the two subjects.

Hw in different countries

for regional geography *see* HK

Hwb North America

DAVIS, W.M. The progress of geography in the United States. *Ann.Ass.Amer.Geogr.*, 1924, 14: 159-215.
Broad survey of the progress of scientific geographical studies in the United States.

WARNTZ, William. Geography now and then. Some notes on the history of academic geography in the United States. xii, 162 p., ill. New York: American Geographical Society, 1964.
Reviewed by George F. Carter, *Science*, 1964, 145: 147; by G.R. Crone, *Geogr.J.*, 1964, 130: 554.

Hwb-da

GEISER, Samuel Wood. Geographers of early Texas: a bibliographic note. *Tex.Geogr.Mag.*, 1943, 7: 37-8. [CB 66/221]

Hwb-o

DEPT, Gaston G. L'étude et l'enseignement de la géographie aux Etats-Unis. *Bull.Soc.Belge Géogr.*, 1926, 50: 119-32.

DRYER, Charles Redway. A century of geographic education in the United States. *Ann.Ass.Amer.Geogr.*, 1924, 14: 117-49.

Hwb-ph

ALPERT, Harry. Geography, social science, and the National Science Foundation. *Prof.Geogr.*, 1957, 9: no. 6, 7-9.

Hwb-qd

BRIGHAM, Albert Perry. The Association of American Geographers, 1903-1923. *Ann.Ass.Amer.Geogr.*, 1924, 14: 109-16.

WRIGHT, John Kirtland. The American Geographical Society, 1852-1952. *Sci.Mon.*, 1952, 74: 121-31.

WRIGHT, John Kirtland. Geography in the making. The American Geographical Society, 1851-1951. xxi, 437 p., 30 pl., front., maps. New York: American Geographical Society, 1952. [CB 79/182]

Hwd Europe

JOERG, W.L.G. Recent geographical work in Europe. *Geogr.Rev.*, 1922, 12: 431-84, 1 fig. [CB 15/220]

Hwd-om

CLARK, Rose B. Geography in the schools of Europe. In: Bowman, Isaiah. Geography in relation to the social sciences. xxii, 382 p., 17 ill. (Report of the American Historial Association Commission on the Social Studies, part 5) New York: Scribner's, 1934. [CB 42/594]

Hwe

CRONE, Gerald R. British geography in the twentieth century. *Geogr.J.*, 1964, 130: 197-220.

MACKINDER, Halford John. Progress of geography in the field and in the study during the reign of His Majesty King George the Fifth. *Geogr.J.*, 1935, 86: 1-12. [CB 45/241]

Hwe-qd

BASCHIN, Otto. Royal Geographical Society, 1830-1930. *Naturwissenschaften*, 1930, 18: 659-62.

BRIGHAM, Albert Perry. The centenary of the Royal Geographical Society. *Geogr.Rev.*, 1931, 142-5.

CLOSE, Charles. Addresses on the history of the Royal Geographical Society at the centenary meeting, Oct. 21st. *Geogr.J.*, 1930, 76: 455-76.

MILL, Hugh Robert. The record of the Royal Geographical Society, 1830-1930. Published at the celebration of the Society's centenary, Oct. 1930. xvi, 288 p., 35 pl. London: Royal Geographical Society, 1930.
Reviewed by R.N.R.B., *Nature*, 1930, 126: 679-80.

Hwf

FEBVRE, Lucien. L'école géographique française et son effort de synthèse. *Rev.Syn.Hist.*, 1928, 45: 26-41.

MARGERIE, Emmanuel de. L'oeuvre des géographes français depuis cent ans. *Bull.Soc.Roy.Belg.Geogr.*, 1926, 50: 199-215.
Brief critique, with useful footnote references, of the work of French geographers in descriptive geography, cartography, and explanatory or interpretative geography.

MARTONNE, Emmanuel de. Geography in France. vii, 70 p. (American Geographical Society Research Series, 4a) New York: 1924.
Discussion of the work of Vidal de La Blache, his disciples and followers.
Reviewed by J.K. Wright, *Isis*, 1925, 7: 153-5.

PERPILLOU, A. Geography and geographical studies in France during the war and the occupation. *Geogr.J.*, 1946, 107: 50-7.

Hwg-cj

EDER, Herbert M. The biography of a periodical: *Geographische Zeitschrift*, 1895-1963. *Prof.Geogr.*, 1964, 16: part 3, 1-5.

Hwg-o

ANZ, Heinrich, ed. Gotha und sein Gymnasium. Bausteine zur Geistesgeschichte einer deutschen Residenz. Zur 400-Jahrfeier des Gymnasium Ernestinum. Stuttgart: 1924.
The great geographical establishment of Justus Perthes is situated in Gotha. This volume contains a chapter by Hermann Wagner entitled "Gothas Bedeutung für die Pflege der Astronomie und Geographie".

Hwg-oq

HAEFKE, Fritz. 150 Jahre Geographie an der Berliner Universität. *Wiss.Z.Humboldt Univ.Berlin Math.Naturwiss.Reihe*, 1961, 10: 5-12.

HOFMAN, Robert. Die Geographie an der Universität Würzburg. v, 93 p. Dettelbach (Unterfranken): Konrad Triltsch, 1912.

Hwg-qg

FIECHTER, Alfredo. L'Istituto Geografico Militare di Vienna: origine, attività, fine. *Universo*, 1924, 5: 793-808, 1 pl. [CB 21/492]
The Austrian K.K. Militärgeographisches Institut had its origins in northern Italy in surveys undertaken during the Napoleonic era. Since the dissolution of the Austro-Hungarian Empire the work of the Institute has been broken up.

Hwh

BUJAK, Franciszek. Studja geograficzno-historyczne. [Studies in history of geography. (In Polish)] xi, 299 p. Warszawa/Krakow: 1924.
A collection of essays on geographical studies in Poland during and since the fifteenth century. Brief analysis of contents in *Bibliogr.Géogr.*, 1924, 34: 13.

Hwi

BERTACCHI, Cosimo. Conversazioni geografiche. Per la storia della geografia in Italia. 262 p. Torino: Fratelli Bocca, 1925. [CB 21/580]

Hwi-bv

ALMAGIA, Roberto. La geografia. x, 109 p. (ICS, Profili bibliografici de L'Italia che scrive) Roma: Istituto per la Propaganda della Cultura italiana, 1919. [CB 8/360]
The first of a series of little books to be devoted to bibliographical sketches of the Italian contributions to science and civilization.

Hwi-da

BERTACCHI, Cosimo. Geografi ed esploratori italiani contemporanei. 460 p. Milan: Agostini, 1929.

Hwi-qd

AGOSTINI, Enrico de. La Reale Società Geografica Italiana e la sua opera dalla fondazione ad oggi (1867-1936). 153 p., 14 fig. Rome: Reale Società Geografica Italiana, 1937.

Hwi-qg

LOPERFIDO, Antonio. L'opera scientifica dell'Istituto Geografico Militare. *Boll.Soc.Geogr.Ital., 5th ser.*, 1923, 12: 426-39.

Hwn

BERG, L.S. Ocherk istorii russkoĭ geograficheskoi nauki (uplot' do 1923 goda). [Outline of the history of Russian geographical science (prior to 1923). (In Russian)] 154 p., ill. (*Tr.Kom.Ist.Znaniĭ*, 4) Leningrad: Akademiia Nauk, 1929. [CB 27/556]

FRENCH, R.A. Geography and geographers in the Soviet Union. *Geogr.J.*, 1961, 127: 158-67.

Hwn-oq

BARKOV, A. [The Moscow school of geographers. Moscow State University. (In Russian)] *Uch.Zap.Moskovskogo Gos.Univ.*, 1946, no. 104, 17-23.

HyBW use of statistics

GREGORY, S. Statistical methods and the geographer. 240 p. London: Longmans, 1963.
Reviewed by M.H. Westmacott, *Geogr.J.*, 1964, 130: 304-5.

HB GEODESY; SURVEYING

HBc general history

ABRAMS, John W.; COHEN, I.B. Proof of the sphericity of the earth. What is the earliest appearance of the proof of the sphericity of the earth based on the fact that the masts of a distant ship are visible above the horizon when the body of the ship is no longer visible? (Query no. 125) *Isis*, 1950, 41: 198.

BOCCARDI, Jean. Un coup d'oeil sur l'évolution de la géodésie. *Rev.Gén.Sci.*, 1925, 36: 390-7. [CB 19/806]

COHEN, I. Bernard. Proof of the sphericity of the earth. (Query no. 125) *Isis*, 1951, 42: 47.

DEHALU, M. La figure de la terre déduite des mesures géodésiques. *Bull.Cercle Géogr.Liégeois*, 1930, 2: 14-27.

DE L'ISLE, Rollet. Historic notes on the difference of longitude between Paris and Greenwich. *Hydrogr.Rev.*, 1926, 3: 177-81. [CB 22/283]

GÜNTHER, Siegmund. Die indirekten Ortsbestimmungsmethoden in der Entwicklung der mathematischen Geographie. *Sitzungsber. Bayer.Akad.Wiss.Math.Phys.Kl.*, 1919, 299-351. [CB 11/438]

GÜNTHER, Siegmund. Zur Entwicklungsgeschichte der Lehre von der Erdgestalt. *Arch.Gesch.Naturwiss.Tech.*, 1912, 3: 451-64.

HEISKANEN, W.A. New era in geodesy. *Science*, 1955, 121: 48-51.

HELBRONNER, Paul. La genèse de l'opération de la jonction geodésique directe de la Corse à la chaîne méridienne des Alpes. *Rev.Gén.Sci.*, 1931, 42: 359-66, 499-507, 676-81, 703-13.

HINKS, Arthur R. Maps and survey. 3rd ed. xiv, 284 p., 28 pl. Cambridge University Press, 1933. [CB 40/406]

HORSTINK, J.Th. Enkele bladzijden uit de geschiedenis der geometrie. [A few pages from the history of geometry. (In Dutch)] *Indische Gids*, 1925, 47: 112-23.
Brief review of the history of mathematical geography and cartography.

LAMB, Horace. The figure and constitution of the earth. Inaugural address delivered to the British Association at Southampton on August 26. *Nature*, 1925, 116: 333-9.

LAMBERT, Walter D. The figure of the earth and the new international ellipsoid of reference. *Science*, 1926, 63: 242-8.

MAKEMSON, Maud W. Old and new beliefs about the earth's figure. *Proc.10th Int.Congr.Hist.Sci.* (Ithaca, 1962), (2), p. 1027-9. Paris: Hermann, 1964.

MATHIESON, John. Geodesy: a brief historical sketch. *Scot. Geogr.Mag.*, 1926, 42: 328-47. [CB 26/236]

MÜLLER, Franz Joh. Studien zur Geschichte der theoretischen Geodäsie. viii, 203 p. Augsburg: 1918.
Collected essays on the history of geodesy, formerly published in the *Zeitschrift des bayerischen Geometervereins*, 1906-9.
Reviewed by G. Sarton, *Isis*, 1920, 3: 438-9.

NIKOLIĆ, Dorde. Rudjer Bošković et la géodésie moderne. *Actes du Symposium International R.J. Bošković* (1961), p. 175-89. Beograd: Štampa Izdaračka Ustanova "Naučno delo", 1962.

PERRIER, Georges. Historique sommaire de la géodésie. *Thalès*, 1935, 2: 117-29.

PERRIER, Georges. Petite histoire de la géodésie. Comment l'homme a mesuré et pesé la terre. 188 p. (Nouvelle Collection Scientifique) Paris: Alcan, 1939. [CB 69/231]
German translation, Kurze Geschichte der Geodäsie (Bamberg: Bamberger Verlagshuis, 1950) reviewed by Per Collinder, *Lychnos*, 1952, 375.

TAYLOR, Eva G.R. Ideas on the shape, size and movements of the earth. 19 p. (Historical Association Pamphlet, 126) London: 1943.

WAVRE, Rolin. La figure du monde. Préfacé par Jean Piajet. 172 p., portr. Neuchâtel: La Baconnière, 1950.
A posthumous publication which develops "le problème de l'espace des Grecs à nos jours".
Reviewed by P. Rossier, *Rev.Hist.Sci.*, 1953, 6: 181.

WEBB, R. Stretton. Notes on the history of geodesy. *S.Afr. Surv.J.*, 1930, 286-91.

HBce-by

DOWSON, Ernest. Collection of cadastral survey and land records. *Geogr.J.*, 1932, 80: 93-4.
Concerning plans to build up, at the Royal Geographical Society in London, a collection from all parts of the world.

HBk/q special aspects

HBk

LALLEMAND, Charles. Discours prononcé à la Séance publique annuelle du lundi 13 décembre 1926 par le Président de l'Académie des sciences. *Compt.Rend.Acad.Sci.*, 1926, 183: 1145-60.
Reflections on the general problems of geodesy.

HBmzGJ

PERRIER, Georges. Les raisons géodésiques de l'isostasie terrestre. 131 p., bibliogr. (*Annu.Bur.Longitudes* (Paris), 1926, Not. B) Paris: Gauthier-Villars, 1926.

HBpw

PERRIER, Georges. La coopération internationale en géodésie et en géophysique. Troisième assemblée générale de l'Union Gódésique Internationale à Prague, Septembre 1927. 120 p. (*Annu.Bur.Longitudes*, 1928. Annexe C) Paris: Gauthier Villars, [1927]. [CB 24/537]

HBqx

SARTON, George. La XVIIe Conférence générale de l'Association Géodésique Internationale, Hambourg, 1912. *Isis*, 1914, 2: 191-2.
With a short history of the previous conferences.

HBw in different countries

HBwb

ARNESON, Edwin P. The early art of terrestrial measurement and its practice in Texas. *Southwest.Hist.Quart.*, 1925, 24: 79-97. [CB 20/200]

BOWIE, William. Geodetic operations in the United States, Jan. 1st, 1933 to Dec. 31st, 1935. 25 p. (Special Publication, 207. Division of Geodesy, U.S. Coast and Geodetic Survey) Washington, D.C.: Gov.Print.Off., 1936.
Reviewed by J. de G. Hunter, *Geogr.J.*, 1937, 89: 85.

CAJORI, Florian. A century of American geodesy. *Isis*, 1930, 14: 411-16, 7 fig.

GUDDE, Erwin G. A century of astronomy and geodesy in California. In: A century of progress in the natural sciences, 1853-1953, p. 65-74. San Francisco: California Academy of Sciences, 1955.

HBwb-cd

REINGOLD, Nathan. Records of the Coast and Geodetic Survey. v, 83 p. (National Archives Publication, 59:3) Washington, D.C.: National Archives and Records Service, 1958. [CB 84/314]
An inventory of the National Archives holdings.

REINGOLD, Nathan. Research possibilities in the U.S. Coast and Geodetic Survey records. *Arch.Int.Hist.Sci.*, 1958, 11: 337-46.

HBwb-qk

CAJORI, Florian. Swiss geodesy and the United States coast survey. *Sci.Mon.*, August 1921, 117-29. [CB 11/419]
The United States coast survey owes its foundation to Ferdinand Rudolf Hassler.

U.S. COAST AND GEODETIC SURVEY. Centennial celebration, April 5 and 6, 1916. 196 p., 45 fig. Washington, D.C.: Government Printing Office, 1916.

HBwe

GUNTHER, Robert William Theodore. Early science in Oxford. Pt. 3 and 4. Physics and surveying. 222 p., ill. Oxford: Privately printed, 1923.
Bound up with Parts 1 and 2 as Volume 1.
Reviewed by G. Sarton, *Isis*, 1924, 6: 449-53.

HBwf-qk

SARTON, G. Le monument des missions géodésiques françaises à Quito. *Isis*, 1914, 2: 163-4.
The monument unveiled on 10th August 1913 to the memory of the two French geodetic missions, 1735-43 and 1899-1906.

HBwh-nh

SKOLIMOWSKI, Henryk. Ewolucja zakresów terminów "geodezja" i "geodeta" w świetle polskich podręczników geodezyjnych wieków XVI-XVIII. [The evolution of the meaning of the terms "geodesy" and "geodesist" in the light of Polish textbooks of land surveying from the 16th to the 18th century. (In Polish)] *Kwart.Hist.Nauk. Tech.*, 1963, 8: 245-55.

HBwi-da

MARUSS, Antonio. Italian pioneers in the physics of the universe: geodesy. *Cah.Hist.Mond.*, 1963, 7: 471-82

HBwk

COMITÉ NATIONAL BELGE DE GÉODÉSIE ET DE GÉOPHYSIQUE. Aperçu historique de l'activité scientifique de la Belgique en géodésie et en géophysique, publié à l'occasion de la 9e Assemblée générale de l'Union Géodésique et Géophysique Internationale, tenue à Bruxelles du 21 août au 1er septembre 1951. 103 p., fig., pl. Bruxelles: 1951.
Reviewed by R. Taton, *Rev.Hist.Sci.*, 1953, 6: 91.

HBwm

ANDERSEN, Einar. 200 års videnskabelig geodaetisk virksomhed i Danmark, 1757-25 Februar 1957. [200 years of scientific geodetic work in Denmark, 1757-25 February 1957. (In Danish with a French translation)] 63 p., ill. (Geodaetisk Institut, Meddelelse, 32) Copenhagen: 1957.

HBwn

MARTONNE, Edmond de. La géodésie en Russie soviétique. *Rev. Sci.*, 1930, 68: 737-45.

HBwn-hd

FEL', S.E. Kritika nekotorykh istochnikov po istorii russkoi geodezii i kartografii. [A critique of several sources on the history of Russian geodesy and cartography. (In Russian)] *Tr.Inst.Ist.Est.Tekh.*, 1962, 42: 172-81. [CB 88/525]

HBwn-qd

NOVOKSHANOVA, Z.K. Deiatel'nost' Otdeleniia matematicheskoi geografii Russkogo geograficheskogo obshchestva. [The activity of the mathematical geography section of the Russian Geographic Society. (In Russian)] *Tr.Inst.Ist.Est.Tekh.*, 1962, 42: 151-71.

HBwn-qg

HEISKANEN, W.; *et al.* Finnisches Geodätisches Institut 1918-1938. 128 p. (*Veröffentl.Finn.Geod.Inst.*, 26) Helsinki: 1939.
Reviewed by H.L.P. Jolly, *Geogr.J.*, 1939, 93: 538.

HBwn-qk

NOVOKSHANOVA, Z.K. Mekanicheskaya masterskaya Glavnogo Shtaba. [The mechanical shop of the Military Topography Department of the General Staff. (In Russian)] *Ist.Astron.Issled.*, 1962, no. 8, 351-60.

HBwx-qk

WILLIAMS, J.H. Historical outline and analysis of the work of the Survey Department of Kenya Colony, 1 April 1903 to 30 September 1929. vi, 118 p. Nairobi: Government Printer, 1931.
Reviewed by E.M. Jack, *Geogr.J.*, 1932, 79: 513-14.

HBx techniques and instruments

HBxd-wf

LALLEMAND, Ch.; PRÉVOT, E. Le nivellement général de la France de 1878 à 1927. xxxiv, 664 p. Paris: Ministère des Travaux Publiques, 1927.
Reviewed by C.F. Close, *Geogr.J.*, 1932, 80: 164-5. The review deals with some points in the history of precise levelling.

HBxd-ws

DAWSON, A.H.G. The geodetic levelling of Ceylon (1928-1929). 2 vol. 22, xxxii p.; vi, 138 p. Colombo: Ceylon Government Press, 1932.
The first volume opens with the history of levelling in Ceylon prior to 1924.
Reviewed by T.H. Laby, *Geogr.J.*, 1933, 82: 79-9.

HBxf-XF photogrammetry

CORBIN, Paul. La stéréoautogrammetrie. *Rev.Gén.Sci.*, 1914, 25: 223-52, ill.

CORBIN, Paul; CROUZET, E. A propos de la stéréoautogrammétrie. *Rev.Gén.Sci.*, 1914, 25: 463-4, 541-3, 621-2.
Correspondence concerning P. Corbin's article, *see* above.

LANDEN, David. Impact of the development of photogrammetry upon geology. *J.Wash.Acad.Sci.*, 1959, 49: 234-52.

HBxf-XFwk

BAETSLE, P.-L. La photogrammétrie et son développement en Belgique. *Mouvement Sci.Belg.*, 1961, 4: 276-84.

LETROYE, A. Précurseurs de la photogrammétrie en Belgique. *Bull.Soc.Belg.Photogram.*, 1952, no. 28, 27-34, 7 fig.

HBxf-XFwn

SMIRNOV, A.A. Kratkii istoricheskii ocherk razvitiia nazemnoi stereofotogrammetrii v Sovetskom Soiuze. [A brief historical essay about the development of surface stereophotogrammetry in the Soviet Union. (In Russian)] *Tr.Inst.Ist.Est.Tekh.*, 1962, 42: 182-94.

HBxk instruments

BREITHAUPT, G. Zur Geschichte der Dosenlibelle. *Z.Instrumentenk.*, 1931, 51: 256-9.

DAUMAS, Maurice. Le carré des ombres sur les instruments occidentaux. *Act.VIIe Congr.Int.Hist.Sci.* (Jerusalem, 1953), p. 252-7, 2 fig. Paris: Hermann, [n.d.].

KIELY, Edmond Richard. Surveying instruments - their history and classroom use. xiii, 411 p. (19th Yearbook of the National Council of Teachers of Mathematics) New York: Teachers College, Columbia University, Bureau of Publications, 1947.

LÜDEMANN, Karl. Zur Geschichte der Dosenlibelle. (Beiträge zur Geschichte des geodätischen und markscheiderischen Messungswesens und der vermessungstechnischen Instrumentenkunde, 12) *Z.Instrumentenk.*, 1931, 51: 136-44.

HBxk-wb

SMART, Charles E. The makers of surveying instruments in America since 1700. xxiv, 182 p., ill. Troy, N.Y.: Regal Art Press, 1962.
A catalogue of instruments and the men who made them.
Reviewed by Silvio A. Bedini, *Technol.Cult.*, 1964, 5: 260-1.

HBxm

CAJORI, Florian. History of determinations of the heights of mountains. *Isis*, 1929, 12: 482-514, 13 fig. [CB 29/297]

HC NAVIGATION

for charting the seas *see* HH
sea travel *see* HO
ships and shipbuilding *see* TP

HCc general history

BEAUJOUAN, Guy; POULLE, E. Les origines de la navigation astronomique au XIVe et XVe siècles. In: Mollat, Michel, ed. Le navire et l'économie maritime du XVe au XVIIIe siècles, p. 103-17. (Bibliothèque Générale de l'École Pratique des Hautes Études, VIe section, no. 7) Paris: S.E.V.P.E.N., 1957.
Reviewed by M. Destombes, *Arch.Int.Hist.Sci.*, 1960, 13: 144-5.

BLEWITT, Mary. Celestial navigation for yachtsmen. 3rd ed. 64 p., 26 fig. London: Iliffe; New York: Philosophical Library, 1955.
First publ. 1950.

COLLINDER, Per. A history of marine navigation. Translated from the Swedish by Maurice Michal. 195 p., 50 fig. New York: St. Martin's Press, 1955. [CB 81/271]

COTTER, Charles H. An historical review of the ex-meridian problem. *J.Inst.Navigation*, 1964, 17: 72-82.

CURTIS, Heber D. Navigation near the Pole. *Proc.U.S.Nav.Inst.*, 1939, 65: 9-19, 5 fig.

CURTISS, R.H. An account of the rise of navigation. *Pop.Astron.*, 1918, 26: 217-28; also in *Annu.Rep.Smithsonian Inst.for 1918*, p. 127-38. Washington, D.C.: 1920

FREIESLEBEN, H.C. Der Polarstern in der Navigation. *Sudhoffs Arch.*, 1955, 39: 157-61.

HARDING, Louis Allen. A brief history of the art of navigation. An outline and background of the methods employed by navigators for finding their way around the seas. 142 p., 10 tables, 58 fig. New York: William-Frederick Press, 1952.

HEWSON, J.B. A history of the practice of navigation. 270 p. Glasgow: Brown, Son and Ferguson, 1951.
Reviewed by S.E. Morison, *Isis*, 1953, 44: 301-2.

MARGUET, F. Histoire générale de la navigation du XVe au XXe siècle. 301 p., ill. Paris: Société d'Editions Géographiques, Maritimes et Coloniales, 1931. [CB 39/601]
Reviewed by L. Sapin, *Isis*, 1933, 19: 235-7; by E.G.R. Taylor, *Geogr.J.*, 1932, 79: 244.

MEIGS, John Forsyth. The story of the seaman. Being an account of the ways and appliances of seafarers and of ships from the earliest time until now. 2 vol. x, 356 p.; 357-675 p., ill. Philadelphia/London: J.B. Lippincott, 1924.

ROUCH, J. Un coup d'oeil sur l'histoire de la navigation. *Rev.Gén.Sci.*, 1932, 43: 599-612.

STEVENSON, D. Alan. The world's lighthouses before 1820. xxiv, 310 p., pl., fig., tables, maps. New York: Oxford University Press, 1959.
Reviewed by John Haskell Kemble, *Isis*, 1961, 52: 110-11; by H.P. Mead, *Mariner's Mirror*, 1961, 45: 66-8.

TAYLOR, E.G.R. The haven-finding art. A history of navigation from Odysseus to Captain Cook. With a foreword by Commodore K. St. B. Collins, R.N. xii, 295 p., front., 25 pl., 28 fig. London: Hollis and Carter, 1956; New York: Abelard-Schuman Ltd., 1957.
Reviewed by S.E. Morison, *Isis*, 1958, 49: 352-3; by Per Collinder, *Lychnos*, 1956, 372-3; by Trevor I. Williams, *Endeavour*, 1958, 17: 54.

WHALL, W.B. The romance of navigation. Edited by Francis E. McMurtrie. xii, 292 p. London: Sampson Low, 1925.

HCce

WROTH, Lawrence C. The way of a ship: an essay on the literature of navigation science. xii, 92 p. Portland, Me.: Southworth-Anthoensen Press, 1937.
Reviewed by E.G.R. Taylor, *Geogr.J.*, 1938, 92: 89.

HCr

TAYLOR, E.G.R. The early navigator. *Geogr.J.*, 1949, 113: 58-61, 4 pl.

HCw in different countries

HCwb-cj

HOOGEWERFF, J.A. Publication of the "American Ephemeris and Nautical Almanac" for 1916. *Science,* 1914, 39: 945-6. [CB 6/455]

HCwf-cj

MARGUET, F. La "Connaissance des temps" et son histoire. *Rev. Gén.Sci.,* 1912, 23: 133-40.

HCwj

FONTOURA DA COSTA, A. A marinharia dos descobrimentos. Bibliografia náutica portuguesa, até 1700. 512, x p. Lisboa: Impressa da Armada, 1933.
Taking each basic process of navigation, the author traces its development as exhibited in the sources under examination.
Reviewed by E.H.G. Dobby, *Geogr.J.,* 1935, 86: 374-6.

HCwj-bv

FONTOURA DA COSTA, A. Bibliografia náutica portuguesa até 1700. Rev. ed. 157 p., ill. Lisboa: Divisão de publicações e biblioteca, Agência geral da Colónias, 1940.
First published in 1934 as an appendix to the author's "A marinharia dos descobrimentos".

REPARAZ, Gonçal de. Catalunya a les mars. Navegants, mercaders i cartògrafs catalans de l'edat mitjana i del renaixement. Contribució a l'estudi de la història del comerç i de la navegació de la Mediterrània. Pròleg de Gonçal de Reparaz. [In Catalan, with Spanish preface] 252 p. Barcelona: Mentora, 1930.
Reviewed by A. Pogo, *Isis,* 1931, 16: 173-4.

HCxk instruments

for astrolabes *see* FDxp
the history of the compass *see* GLxp

BEMMELEN, W. van. De kompaswaarnemingen der oude zeevaarders en de verplaatsing der Magnetische Pool. [The compass observations of the old seafarers and the change in the magnetic pole. (In Dutch)] *Tijdschr.Ned.Aardrijksk.Genoot., 2nd ser.,* 1925, 42: 508-19, 4 fig.

BROMEHEAD, C.E.N. Ships' loadstones. *Mineral.Mag.,* 1948, 28: 429-37.

BUSCH, W. Die Entwicklung des Schiffskompasses in Sage und Geschichte. *Ann.Hydrogr.Marit.Meteorol.,* 1926, 54: 120-6, 169-74.

HORSBURGH, Ellice M. The cross-staff and its use in navigation. *Scot.Geogr.Mag.,* 1930, 46: 92-100, 7 ill.

HUTCHINS, H.L.; MAY, W.E. From lodestone to gyro-compass. 211 p., 19 pl., 33 fig. New York: Philosophical Library, 1953.
Reviewed by Duane H.D. Roller, *Isis,* 1953, 44: 303.

MOERMAN, H.J. Zeylsteen en kompas. [Lodestone and compass. (In Dutch)] *Tijdschr.Ned.Aardrijksk.Genoot.,* 1931, 48: 200-20.

SAUSSURE, Léopold de. L'origine de la rose des vents et l'invention de la boussole. 68 p. (*Arch.Sci.Phys.Natur.,* 5: no. 3-4) Genève: Kündig, 1923. [CB 15/208]

SCHÜCK, Albert. Zur Einführung des Kompasses in die nordwesteuropäische Nautik. *Arch.Gesch.Naturwiss.Tech.,* 1912, 4: 40-78.

TAYLOR, E.G.R.; RICHEY, M.W. The geometrical seaman, a book of early nautical instruments. viii, 112 p., 37 ill. London: Hollis & Carter for the Institute of Navigation, 1962.

HCxs

CROMMELIN, C.A. The introduction of the marine chronometer into naval and mercantile use. *J.Suisse Horlogerie,* 1950, 75: 294-7.

GOULD, Rupert T. The marine chronometer. Its history and development. xvi, 287 p., 39 pl., 85 fig. London: J.D. Potter, Admiralty Agent for Charts, 1923.
Reviewed by George Sarton, *Isis,* 1924, 6: 122-9.
Reprint published London: Holland Press, 1960.
Reviewed by Rolf Du Rietz, *Lychnos,* 1962, 409-10; by Susanna Fisher, *Mariner's Mirror,* 1962, 48: 148-9.

SPENCER JONES, Harold. The history of the marine chronometer. *Endeavour,* 1955, 14: 212-19, 9 fig.

HCxt

MAY, W.E. The compass rose. *Typographica,* December 1964, 10: 12-29.

THOMPSON, Silvanus P. The rose of the winds. The origin and development of the compass-card. 31 p., 6 pl. (*Proc.Brit. Acad.,* 6) London: Oxford University Press, 1914.

HCxx museums

BREWINGTON, Marion V. The Peabody Museum collection of navigating instruments, with notes on their makers. 154 p., pl. Salem, Mass.: Peabody Museum, 1963. [CB 90/509]
Reviewed by D.W. Waters, *Mariner's Mirror,* 1964, 50: 334; by David Pingree Wheatland, *Amer.Neptune,* 1964, 24: 217-19; by Silvio A. Bedini, *Technol.Cult.,* 1964, 5: 640-1.

HD AIR NAVIGATION

HUGHES, Arthur J. History of air navigation. 154 p. London: Allen and Unwin, 1946.
Reviewed by J.S.B., *Geogr.J.,* 1946, 108: 150-1.

WEEMS, Philip Van Horn. Celestial navigation. *Proc.Amer. Phil.Soc.,* 1954, 98: 270-2. [CB 82/207]

HDr

MURCHIE, Guy. Song of the sky. vii, 438 p., ill. Boston: Houghton Mifflin, 1954. [CB 81/344]
An air navigator's description of his occupation.

HF CARTOGRAPHY

HFc general history

ALMAGIÀ, Roberto. Rassegna su alcune questioni dibattute di storia della cartografia. *Archeion,* 1940, 22: 361-71.

BAGROW, Leo. Geschichte der Kartographie. 383 p., fig., 120 pl. Berlin: Safari-Verlag, 1951.
Reviewed by Em. Janssens, *Arch.Int.Hist.Sci.,* 1952, 5: 440-1.
The revised English translation (*see* below) was translated back into German and published in 1963 under the title "Meister der Kartographie".

BAGROW, Leo. History of cartography. English trans. from the German by D.L. Paisey; ed., rev., and enlarged by R.A. Skelton. 312 p., ill., maps. Cambridge, Mass.: Harvard University Press; London: Watts, 1964.
Reviewed by Louis Barron, *Libr.J.,* 1964, 89: 4508.

BARKER, W.H. The history of cartography. *J.Manchester Geogr. Soc.,* 1923-24, 39-40: 1-17. [CB 22/281]

BROWN, Lloyd A. The story of maps. 397 p., maps, ill. Boston: Little, Brown, 1949.
Reviewed by Erwin Raisz, *Isis,* 1950, 41: 243.

CRAWFORD, O.G.S. How to use old maps. *Antiquity,* 1950, 24: 202-3.

CRONE, G.R. Maps and their makers. An introduction to the history of cartography. 180 p., 23 maps. London: Hutchinson's University Library, 1953.
Reviewed by B.H., *Imago Mundi,* 1954, 11: 179.

CURNOW, I.J. The world mapped: being a short history of attempts to map the world from antiquity to the twentieth century. vi, 104 p., 10 pl. London: Sifton Praed, 1930.
Reviewed by E.G.R. Taylor, *Geogr.J.,* 1931, 77: 485.

DEBENHAM, Frank. The world is round. The story of man and maps. 100 p. London: Macdonald, in association with Rathbone Books, 1959.
Reviewed by M. Caradine, *Nature,* 1960, 185: 67.

DELORME, Albert. Sur quelques atlas. *Rev.Syn.,* 1960, 81: 411-13.

FEAD, Margaret Irene. Notes on the development of the cartographic representation of cities. *Geogr.Rev.,* 1933, 23: 441-56, 11 fig.

FISCHER, Joseph. Resultados de mis investigaciones cartográficas. *Iberica,* Nov. 1913.

FORDHAM, Herbert George. Maps, their history, characteristics and uses: a handbook for teachers. xii, 83 p., 8 pl. Cambridge University Press, 1923.
Reviewed in *Geogr.Rev.,* 1924, 14: 656-7.

GOODE, J. Paul. The map as a record of progress in geography. *Ann.Ass.Amer.Geogr.,* 1927, 17: 1-14.

HINKS, Arthur R. Maps and survey. 3rd ed. xiv, 284 p., 28 pl. Cambridge University Press, 1933. [CB 40/406]

HOLMAN, Louis A. Old maps and their makers considered from the historical and decorative standpoints. A survey of a huge subject in a small space, 60 p., 15 maps, 4 ill. Boston: Charles E. Goodspeed, 1926.

JERVIS, W.W. The world in maps: a study in map evolution. 208 p., 24 pl. London: Philip, 1936.
Reviewed in *Imago Mundi,* 1937, 2: 98; by G.R. Crone, *Geogr.J.,* 1937, 90: 85-6.

JOERG, W.L.G. Post-war atlases: a review. *Geogr.Rev.,* 1923, 13: 583-98. [CB 16/302]

LIBAULT, A. Histoire de la cartographie. 86 p. Paris: Chaix, 1959.
Reviewed by E.C., *Bull.Soc.Belg.Géogr.,* 1960, 84: 140.

LYNAM, Edward. The mapmaker's art: essays on the history of maps. xii, 140 p., 52 fig. London: Batchworth; New York: British Book Centre, 1953.
Reviewed by Sonia S. Wohl, *Isis,* 1954, 45: 102-3; and in *Imago Mundi,* 1954, 11: 179.

RAISZ, Erwin. General cartography. 2nd ed. xv, 354 p. New York: McGraw-Hill, 1948.
First published 1938.

RAISZ, Erwin. Time charts of historical cartography. *Imago Mundi,* 1937, 2: 9-16, maps.

REEVES, Edward A. The mapping of the earth. Past, present and future. *Rep.Brit.Ass.Advance.Sci.,* 1916, 421-33.

ROSSIER, Paul. Les cartes géographiques et leur histoire. 25 p., 4 fig. (Conférences du Palais de la Découverte, Série D, 31) Paris: Université de Paris, 1954.

SALISHCHEV, K.A. Osnovy kartovedeniya. Istoricheskaya chast. [Foundations of cartographic knowledge. Historical section. (In Russian)] 238 p., ill. Moscow: Geodesisdat, 1943.
Chapters 1-3, history of maps outside Russia; chapter 4, history of maps in Russia from late XV century to present. Reviewed by E.H.M., *Geogr.J.,* 1945, 105: 213.

SMITH, Glenn S. A review of topographic mapping. *Mil.Engineer,* 1924, 16: no. 86, 108-15, 7 ill.

SOUKHOV, V.I. [On the history of cartography and its scientific tasks. (In Russian)] *Tr.Inst.Ist.Est.Tekh.,* 1961, 37: no. 2, 186-208.

TOOLEY, Ronald Vere. Maps and mapmakers. viii, 128 p., ill. London: Batsford, 1949.

HFc-br

Imago Mundi. A review of early cartography. Founded by Leo Bagrow. Vol. 1- Amsterdam: 1935- [CB 56/181]
Sub-title and place of publication vary in early volumes. Volume 2 reviewed by E. Heawood, *Geogr.J.,* 1938, 91: 83-5.

HFc-bv/cv bibliography; literature; sources

HFc-bv

RISTOW, W.W.; LEGEAR, C.E. A guide to historical cartography. A selected annotated list of references on the history of maps and map making. 18 p. Washington: Library of Congress, Reference Department, Map Division, 1954.
Mimeographed.
Reviewed in *Imago Mundi,* 1955, 12: 184.

HFce

FORDHAM, Herbert George. Studies in carto-bibliography British and French, and in the bibliography of itineraries and road books. vii, 180 p. Oxford: Clarendon Press, 1914.

SARTON, George. Phillip Lee Philips' contributions to the bibliography of cartography. *Isis,* 1921, 4: 40-3.

HFce-bv

WOLKENHAUER, W. Aus der Geschichte der Kartographie. Kartographische Bibliographie, 1840-1917. *Deut.Geogr.Bl.,* 1917, 38: 157-201. [CB 10/158]

HFcn maps

BRITISH MUSEUM. Six early printed maps selected from those exhibited at the British Museum on the occasion of the International Geographical Congress, 1928. 4 p., 6 folded pl. London: Oxford University Press, 1928. [CB 26/236]

FONCIN, Myriem. Some manuscript maps recently acquired by the Département des Cartes et Plans of the Bibliothèque Nationale, Paris. *Imago Mundi,* 1960, 15: 40-5.

GALLO, Rodolfo. Some maps in the Correr Museum in Venice. *Imago Mundi,* 1960, 15: 46-51.

HUMPHREYS, Arthur Lee. Old decorative maps and charts: with illustrations from engravings in the Macpherson collection, and a catalogue of the atlases, etc. in the collection, by Henry Stevens. xliii, 51 p., 79 maps (plates), 2 ill. London: Halton and Truscott Smith, 1926. [CB 24/541]
Reviewed in *Geogr.Rev.,* 1928, 339-40.

HUMPHREYS, Arthur Lee; SKELTON, R.A. Decorative printed maps of the 15th to 18th centuries. A revised edition of Old decorative maps and charts. 80 p., 84 pl. London/New York: Staples Press, 1952.
Reviewed in *Imago Mundi,* 1953, 10: 130-1.

RAISZ, Erwin. Atlas of global geography. 63 p., maps, fig. New York: Harper, 1944. [CB 66/267]

SKELTON, R.A. *See* HJcn

STEVENSON, Edward L. A description of (15) early maps. Originals and facsimiles (1452-1611). Being a part of the permanent wall exhibition of the American Geographical Society. With a partial list and brief references to the reproductions of others which may be consulted in the Society's Library. 21 p. New York: American Geographical Society, 1921.

STEVENSON, Edward L. Maps reproduced as glass transparencies, selected to represent the development of map-making from the first to the seventeenth century. 44 p., ill. New York: American Geographical Society, 1913.

WIEDER, F.C. Oude kaarten in Italië. [Old maps in Italy. (In Dutch)] *Tijdschr.Ned.Aardrijksk.Genoot.,* 1923, *2nd ser.,* 40: 397-409.
Notes of investigations by the author of fifteenth, sixteenth, and seventeenth century maps in libraries in Padua, Venice, Florence, and Rome.

HFcn-bw

BAGROW, Leo. Old inventories of maps. *Imago Mundi,* 1948, 5: 18-20.

CATALOGO ragionato delle pubblicazioni cartografiche estere conservate nella Biblioteca e Cartoteca dell' Istituto Geografico Militare. *Universo,* 1926, 7: 60-2, 141-7, 228-36, 310-27, 399-406, 490-8, 596-606, 673-81, 763-75, 868-72, 929-31, 1025-8; 1927, 8: 87-91, 213-15, 309-13. [CB 22/284]
Cartobibliographic notes on maps of other parts of the world than Italy arranged by countries.

EDWARDS, Francis, Firm, booksellers, London. Ancient geography; a catalogue of atlases and maps of all parts of the world from XV century to present day ... [Catalogue including 852 items.] 144 p., ill. London: F. Edwards, 1929.

FORDHAM, Herbert George. Hand-list of catalogues and works of reference relating to carto-bibliography and kindred subjects for Great Britain and Ireland, 1720-1927. 26 p. Cambridge University Press, 1928.

ISTITUTO GEOGRAFICO MILITARE. Catalogo ragionato delle carte esistenti nella cartoteca dell'Istituto. 3 vol. Firenze: Istituto Geografico Militare, 1932-34.
Reviewed in *Imago Mundi,* 1937, 2: 103.

TOOLEY, R.V. Geographical oddities. 22 p., 20 ill. (Map Collectors' Series, 1) London: Map Collectors' Circle, 1963.

WARSAW. Bibljoteka Narodowa. [Catalogue de l'exposition des collections cartographiques de la Bibliothèque Nationale à Varsovie. (In Polish)] 112 p. Warsaw: 1934.
Reviewed in *Imago Mundi*, 1935, 1: 75.

WARSAW. Politechnika. Catalogus mapparum geographicarum ad historiam pertinentium, quae curante collegio historico-geographorum adiuvantibus viris congressui ordinando in polytechnico Varsoviensi exponuntur. xv, 296 p. Warsaw: 1933.
Reviewed in *Imago Mundi*, 1935, 1: 76.

YONGE, Ena L. Facsimile atlases and related material: a summary survey. *Geogr.Rev.*, 1963, 53: 440-6.

HFcn-bx

BALTIMORE. MUSEUM OF ART. The world encompassed. An exhibition of the history of maps held at the Baltimore Museum of Art 7 October to 23 November 1952. Organized by the Peabody Institute Library, the Walters Art Gallery, the John Work Garrett Library of the Johns Hopkins University in cooperation with the Baltimore Museum of Art. [A catalogue by Lloyd Arnold Brown. 60 pl.] Baltimore: Trustees of the Walters Art Gallery, 1952.

VICTORIA UNIVERSITY OF MANCHESTER; MANCHESTER GEOGRAPHICAL SOCIETY. Loan exhibition of old maps (facsimiles of manuscript maps and globes, early printed maps, etc.) to be held in the Whitworth Hall of the Manchester University (25-31 January 1923). Catalogue of exhibits with descriptive notes. 42 p. Manchester: 1923. [CB 20/200]
Also printed as an Appendix to *J.Manchester Geogr.Soc.*, 1923-24, 34-40.

HFcn-by

ALMAGIA, Roberto. Planisferi, carte nautichè e affini dal secolo XIV al XVII esistenti nella Biblioteca Apostolica Vaticana. 156 p., 56 maps. Vaticano: Monumenta Cartografica Vaticana, 1944.
Reviewed by Angela Codazzi, *Imago Mundi*, 1948, 5: 15-17.

FISCHER, Norbert. Die grossen Kartensammlungen in ihrem Werden und Aufbau. *Zentralbl.Bibl.*, 1931, 48: 269-88.

KARPINSKI, Louis C. Cartographical collections in America. *Imago Mundi*, 1935, 1: 62-4.

KOEMAN, C. Collections of maps and atlases in the Netherlands; their history and present state. x, 301 p., ill. (*Imago Mundi*: Supplement 3) Leiden: E.J. Brill, 1961.
Reviewed by G.R. Crone, *Imago Mundi*, 1962, 16: 164.

LIBRARY OF CONGRESS. DIVISION OF MAPS. Noteworthy maps. 3 vol. [1]. Accessions for the fiscal year ending June 30, 1926. 28 p. 2. ... for the fiscal year ending June 30, 1927. vi, 36 p. 3. Accessions 1927-28. v, 33 p. Washington: U.S. Govt. Print. Off., 1927-30. [CB 27/557 and CB 30/474]

NEWBERRY LIBRARY. List of manuscript maps in the Edward E. Ayer Collection. Compiled by Clara A. Smith. Chicago: The Library, 1927.

RUGE, W. Aelteres kartographisches Material in deutschen Bibliotheken. Fünfter Bericht über die Jahre 1910-1913. 128 p. (*Nachr.Ges.Wiss.Göttingen, Philol.Hist.Kl.*, 1916, Beiheft) Göttingen: 1916.

SMITH, Thomas R.; THOMAS, Bradford L. Maps of the 16th to 19th centuries in the University of Kansas Libraries. An analytical carto-bibliography. 137 p. (Library Series, 16) Lawrence, Kan.: University of Kansas Libraries, 1963.

WARECKA, Daniela. [The cartographic collection in the Central Archives of Poland. (In Polish with summary in Russian)] *Kwart.Hist.Kult.Material.*, 1955, 3: 435-44.

WRIGHT, John Kirtland. Early topographical maps. Their geographical and historical value as illustrated by the maps of the Harrison collection of the American Geographical Society. 38 p., 8 fig. New York: American Geographical Society, 1924.

HFco globes

BOGGS, S.W. Globen, Teilgloben und durchsichtige sphärische Flächen. (With English summary.) *Globusfreund*, 1955, no. 4, 20-9.
Apropos of the research and development programme of the U.S. Committee on Construction and Use of Precise Globes and Spherical Maps.

CORONELLI World League ... *See* HFqx

HAARDT, Robert. Wie alte Globen in Österreich, Deutschland und in der Schweiz den letzten Krieg überstanden haben. *Erdkunde*, 1954, 7: 156-8, 1 pl.

HAARDT, Robert. The world's ancient globes. *Compt.Rend.XVIe Congr.Int.Geogr.* (Lisbon, 1949), p. 258-63. Lisbon: 1952.

MURIS, Oswald; SAARMANN, Gert. Der Globus im Wandel der Zeiten. Eine Geschichte der Globen. 288 p., ill. Berlin/Beutelsbach bei Stuttgart: Columbus Verlag Paul Oestergaard, 1961.
Reviewed by Herman Richter, *Lychnos*, 1962, 408-9.

OBERHUMMER, Eugen. The history of globes: a review. *Geogr. Rev.*, 1924, 14: 101-12. [CB 15/220]
A critical review of E.L. Stevenson's book, *see* below.

STEVENSON, Edward Luther. Terrestrial and celestial globes. Their history and construction including a consideration of their value as aids in the study of geography and astronomy. 2 vol. xxvi, 218 p., 87 ill.; xii, 291 p., 143 ill. (Publications of the Hispanic Society of America, 86) New Haven: Yale University Press, 1921.
Reviewed by George Sarton, *Isis*, 1922, 4: 549-53.

HFco-bv

BONACKER, Wilhelm. Das Schrifttum zur Globenkunde. *Janus*, 1959, 48: 81-132.
660 works on globes are cited and arranged chronologically, from medieval manuscripts to contemporary journal articles.

HFco-bw

HAARDT, Robert. The contribution of the "Coronelli-World League of Friends of the Globe" to the development of the international catalogue of early globes. *Act. VIIIe Congr. Int.Hist.Sci.* (Florence, 1956), p. 468-472. Paris: Hermann, 1958.

YONGE, Ena L. An international catalogue of early globes. *Imago Mundi*, 1956, 13: 184-5.

HFco-by

HILL, H.O. A short account of some of the globes in the National Maritime Museum, Greenwich. *Globusfreund*, 1955, no. 4, 12-13.

HFda collective biography

FORDHAM, Herbert George. Some notable surveyors and mapmakers of the sixteenth, seventeenth, and eighteenth centuries and their work. A study in the history of cartography. xii, 100 p., 9 ill. Cambridge University Press, 1929.

HARMS, Hans. Künstler des Kartenbilds. 246 p., ill., portr. Oldenburg: Ernst Völker, 1962.

HFk/u special aspects

HFk

ECKERT, Max. Die Kartenwissenschaft: Forschung und Grundlagen zu einer Kartographie als Wissenschaft. 2 vol. xvi, 640 p., 10 ill., 1 map; xiv, 880 p., 35 ill. Berlin: Walter de Gruyter, 1921-25.
Reviewed by J.K. Wright, *Isis*, 1926, 8: 517-19.

HINKS, A.R. The science and the art of map-making. From the presidential address delivered at Southampton on August 27 before Section E. (Geography) of the British Association. *Nature*, 1925, 116: 715-19.

HFnb

LYNAM, Edward. Ornament, writing and symbols on maps, 1250-1800. *Geogr.Mag.*, 1945-46, 18: 323-6, 365-8, 35 ill. [CB 70/263]

MAY, W.E. *See* HCxt

TALMAN, C.F. "Wind-blowers". (Query no. 22) *Isis*, 1933, 19: 503.

HFpw

OLSZEWICZ, Boleslaw. Stosunki Między Krajami Shandynawskimi a Polska w Zakresie Kartografii (od Epoki Odrodzenia po Wiek XIX). [Intercourse between Scandinavian countries and Poland in the domain of cartography. From the Renaissance to the nineteenth century. (In Polish, with summaries in Russian and English)] *Kwart.Hist.Nauk.Tech.*, 1961, 6: 17-24.

OLSZEWICZ, Boleslaw. Les rapports entre les Pays Scandinaves et la Pologne dans le domaine de la cartographie, depuis la Renaissance jusqu'au XIXe siècle. *Przegl.Geogr.*, 1960, 32: suppl., 15-20.

HFqx

CORONELLI World League of Friends of the Globe. [Notice of the organization of the League] *Isis*, 1956, 47: 56.

MARGERIE, Emmanuel de. La Carte internationale du monde au millionième, et la Conférence de Paris (10-18 décembre 1913). *Ann.Géogr.*, 1914, 23: 97-108. [CB 6/462]
Second meeting of the International Map Committee.

HFse

BOGGS, S.W. Cartohypnosis. *Libr.J.*, 1947, 72: 433-5, 446-7. [CB 71/123]

HFu

MARINUS, Albert. Que peut-on attendre de la cartographie folklorique? 11 p. *XVIe Congr.Int.Anthrop.* (Bruxelles, 1935). Bruxelles: Imprimerie médicale et scientifique, 1937.

HFw in different countries

for the cartography of different countries *see* HG

HFwb-cn

JOERG, W.L.G. Recent American wall maps: a review. *Geogr. Rev.*, 1924, 14: 456-64. [CB 16/302]

HFwc

RUIZ MORENO, Adrián. La evolución de la cartografia argentina: su importancia actual y futura. *Gaea*, 1925, 1: 165-82.

HFwe

LYNAM, Edward. British maps and map-makers. 48 p. London: Collins, 1945.
Reviewed by G.H.T. Kimble, *Geogr.J.*, 1945, 106: 223-4.

HFwe-ns

ONE hundred years of map making. The story of W. and A.K. Johnston. 20 p., 3 pl. Edinburgh: Printed by W. and A.K. Johnston, [1925] [CB 21/533]
Brief historical sketch of one of the leading map publishing houses in Great Britain.

PHILIP, George. The story of the last hundred years. A geographical record, 1834-1934. 108 p., pl. London: G. Philip & Son, 1934.

HFwg-da

NISCHER VON FALKENHOF, Ernst. Oesterreichische Kartographen, ihr Leben, Lehren und Wirken. 192 p., 14 maps, 9 portr. Wien: Oesterreichischer Bundesverlag für Unterricht, Wissenschaft und Kunst, 1925. [CB 21/582]

HFwh

OLSZEWICZ, Boleslaw. *See* HFpw

HFwi

CARACI, Giuseppe. Ancora a proposito di antiche rappresentazioni cartografiche a stampa di Firenze. *Geografia*, 1927, 15: 31-8.

HFwj

REPARAZ, Gonzalo de. *See* HCwj

HFwj-cn

CORTESÃO, Armando; TEIXEIRA DA MOTA, A. Portugaliae monumenta cartographica. 6 vol. pl., fig. Coimbra: Coimbra University Press; Lisbon: Comissao Executiva do V Centenário da Morte do Infante D. Henrique, 1960-62.
Reviewed by C.R. Boxer, *Imago Mundi*, 1962, 16: 163; by C.R. Boxer, *J.Roy.Asiatic Soc.*, 1962, 165-6.

REPARAZ, Gonzalo de. Els mapes catalans de la Bibliothèque Nationale de Paris. *Estud.Univ.Catalans*, 1928, 13: 18 p.
Notes on 24 maps of the 14th to 17th centuries.

HFwk

DENUCÉ, Jan. De geschiedenis van de Vlaamsche kaartsnijkunst. [History of Flemish map engraving. (In Dutch)] Antwerp: Nederlandsche Boekhandel, 1941.

SELIGMANN, A.E.M. La cartographie en Belgique. In: *Grande Encyclopédie de la Belgique et du Congo*, (4), p. 25-31. Bruxelles: 1938.
From Mercator to the present.

WEEMAELS, Frans. Leuven als cartografisch centrum. [Louvain as a cartographic centre. (In Dutch)] *Brabant*, 1962, 14: no. 6, 32-5.

WIEDER, Frederik Caspar. Nederlandsche historisch-geographische Documenten in Spanje ... met een inleiding tot de studie der Oud-nederlandsche Cartographie. [Dutch historico-geographical documents in Spain ... with an introduction to the study of ancient Dutch cartography. (In Dutch)]. viii, 348 p., maps. Leiden: Brill, 1915.

HFwk-bx

ANTWERP. EXPOSITION DE LA CARTOGRAPHIE BELGE, 1926. Exposition de la cartographie belge aux XVIe,XVIIe et XVIIIe siècles, organisée au Musée Plantin-Moretus à l'occasion du Cinquantenaire de la Société Royale de Géographie d'Anvers. lx, 59 p., 28 pl. Antwerp: Impr. J.E. Buschmann, 1926.
An illustrated catalogue of an exhibition of books, atlases, and maps, preceded by biographical and bibliographical notes on the outstanding Belgian cartographers of the sixteenth, seventeenth and eighteenth centuries.

TIBERGHIEN, Albert. Liste sommaire des documents cartographiques exposés, en novembre 1926, au Palais d'Egmont, à l'occasion du Cinquantenaire de la Société Royale Belge de Géographie, à Bruxelles. *Bull.Soc.Belg.Géogr.*, 1926, 50: 322-44.
This list will serve as a cartobibliography of maps of Belgium and of the work of Belgian cartographers from the sixteenth century to the present.

HFwk-co

CROMMELIN, C.A. Over nederlandsche, in het bijzonder Amsterdamsche, globes uit de XVIe, XVIIe en XVIIIe eeuw. [Concerning Dutch, in particular Amsterdam, globes of the 16th, 17th and 18th centuries. (In Dutch)] *Natuur Mensch*, 1934, no. 2, 2 p.

HFwm

KARTOGRAFISKA SÄLLSKAPET. Sveriges kartläggning: en översikt. [Swedish cartography: a review. (In Swedish)] viii, 318 p., 3 maps. Stockholm: Generalstabens Litografiska Anstalts Förlag, 1922.

OLSZEWICZ, Boleslaw. *See* HFpw

HFwn

CHURKIN, V.G. [Lenin and Soviet cartography. (In Russian)] *Izv.Vses.Geogr.Obshchest.*, 1960, 92: no. 3, 205-15, bibliogr.

HFwp

TURKISH maps in the Topkapu Saray Museum. *Imago Mundi*, 1949, 6: 92.

HFx techniques and instruments

HFxf-GL

WINTER, Heinrich. Die Erkenntnis der magnetischen Missweisung und ihr Einfluss auf die Kartographie. *Compt.Rend.Congr. Int.Géogr.* (Amsterdam, 1938), (2), p. 55-80, 4 pl. Leiden: E.J. Brill, 1938.
Elaborate study of the development of knowledge on magnetic declination from the first half of the thirteenth century to the end of the seventeenth century.

HFxh

CHAURAND DE ST. EUSTACHE, Enrico de. Per un migliore illuminamento obliquo nelle rappresentazioni cartografiche. *Universo,* 1923, 4: 909-14. [CB 16/299]
Methods of representing relief on topographical maps.

DEETZ, Charles H. Cartography. A review and guide for the construction and use of maps and charts. Revised edition 1943. vi, 84 p., 30 fig. (U.S. Department of Commerce, Coast and Geodetic Survey, Special Publication 205) Washington, D.C.: U.S. Gov. Print. Off., 1943.

WOLKENHAUER, W. Zeitliche Entwicklung und Eigenschaften der Kartenprojektionen. *Kartographische Schulgeogr.Z.,* 1917, 6: 185-7.
Chronological summary of the development of map projection with a few bibliographical notes.

HFxp

NECTOUX, A. Un nouvel instrument de topographie: le tachéomètre graphique. *Rev.Sci.,* 12 avril 1924, 62: 207-12.
The instrument is due to Jules Gaultier.

HFxx museums

BOCKSTAELE, Paul. Het Mercator-Muzeüm te Sint-Niklaas. Met enkels beschouwingen over de geschiedenis der wetenschappen in Vlaanderen. [The Mercator Museum at St. Niklaas. With a brief view of the history of science in Flanders. (In Dutch)] *Toerist,* 1962, 41: 548-51.

BOCKSTAELE, Paul. De Mercatorverzameling te Sint Niklaas. [The Mercator collection at Sint Niklaas. (In Dutch)] *Oost-Vlaanderen,* 1962, 11: 34-5. [CB 88/591]

HG REGIONAL CARTOGRAPHY

ENQUÊTE sur les atlas historiques en préparation et sur la documentation cartographique. *Bull.Int.Comm.Hist.Sci.,* 1928, 1: 497-523. [CB 24/537]
Information on sources relative to the historical geography of different countries.

HGB NORTH AMERICA

FITE, Emerson D.; FREEMAN, Archibald. A book of old maps, delineating American history from the earliest days down to the close of the Revolutionary War. xv, 299 p., 74 maps. Cambridge: Harvard University Press, 1927.
Each map is accompanied by descriptive text and bibliographical references.
Reviewed by James A. Robertson, *Amer.Hist.Rev.,* 1928, 33: 408-10; and in *Geogr.Rev.,* 1928, 18: 339-40.

GANONG, W.F. Crucial maps in the early cartography and place-nomenclature of the Atlantic Coast of Canada. *Proc.Roy.Soc. Can.,* Sect. 2, 1929, *3rd ser.,* 23: 135-75, 14 fig.

KARPINSKI, Louis C. The evolution of the map of the world: errors in early maps lead to the discovery of America. How the Great Lakes were placed on the map. Mapping out America: how the Mayflower's arrival was anticipated. Mapping the Mississippi Valley. Mapping the Great Northwest: fake records made by unscrupulous cartographers claiming new lands. Mapping the Northwest Passage: how hundreds of brave souls succumbed to the lure of pathfinding. *Dearborn Independ.,* 1924, May 31, July 19; 1925, March 7, May 2. August 1, 8.

LAYNG, Theodore F. The first line in the cartography of Canada. *Can.Surveyor,* 1964, 18: 67-74.

RAISZ, Erwin. Outline of the history of American cartography. *Isis,* 1937, 26: 373-91, 2 charts, 5 fig. [CB 51/273]

TRUE, David O. Some early maps relating to Florida. *Imago Mundi,* 1954, 11: 73-84, 2 pl., 4 fig.

WAGNER, Henry Raup. The cartography of the Northwest coast of America to the year 1800. 2 vol. xi, 270 p.; v, p. 271-543. Berkeley: University of California Press, 1937.
Reviewed by Charles A. Kofoid, *Isis,* 1939, 30: 543-5; by Hunter Miller, *Amer.Hist.Rev.,* 1938, 44: 132-4; by E. Heawood, *Geogr.J.,* 1938, 91: 374-6.

WHEAT, Carl I. Mapping the American West, 1540-1857. A preliminary study. *Proc.Amer.Antiq.Soc.,* 1954, 64: 19-194, 1 pl. [CB 82/207]

WHEAT, Carl I. Mapping the Transmississippi West, 1540-1861. 6 vol. 1. The Spanish Entrada to Louisiana Purchase 1540-1804. 1957; 2. From Lewis and Clark to Fremont 1804-1845. 1958; 3. From the Mexican War to the Boundary Survey 1846-1854. 1959; 4. From the Pacific Railroad Surveys to the onset of the civil war 1855-1860. 1960; 5. From the civil war to the geological survey. 2 vol. 1963. San Francisco: Institute of Historical Cartography, 1957-63.
Volumes 1 and 2 reviewed by V.S. Pritchett, *Sci.Amer.,* 1959, 201: no. 2, 166-7; by John E. Sunder, *Amer.Hist.Rev.,* 1960, 40: 328-9; by Robert E. Riegel, *Amer.Hist.Rev.,* 1959, 65: 139-40; 1960, 66: 233. Volume 5 reviewed by Walker D. Wyman, *Amer.Hist.Rev.,* 1963, 69: 865.

HGBcn

PAULLIN, Charles O. Atlas of the historical geography of the United States. Edited by John K. Wright. xiv, 162 p., 166 pl. Washington, D.C.: Carnegie Institution and American Geographical Society, 1932.
Reviewed by Louis C. Karpinski, *Isis,* 1934, 22: 305-8; by John K. Wright, *Geogr.Rev.,* 1932, 22: 353-60, map.

HGBcn-bw

PHILLIPS, Philip Lee. A descriptive list of maps and views of Philadelphia in the Library of Congress, 1683-1865. 91 p., 2 ill. (Special Publication, 2) Philadelphia: Geographical Society of Philadelphia, 1926. [CB 22/285]

HGC LATIN AMERICA

APENES, Ola. Mapas antiguos del Valle de Mexico. 31 p., 43 maps in half-tone. Mexico: Instituto de Historia, Universidad Nacional Autónoma, 1947.

BOGGS, S.W. The map of Latin America by treaty. *Proc.Amer. Phil.Soc.,* 1938, 79: 399-410, 4 fig.

BOWMAN, Isaiah. The millionth map of Hispanic America. *Science,* 1946, 103: 319-23.

BURLAND, C.A. The map as a vehicle of Mexican history. *Imago Mundi,* 1960, 15: 11-18.

MEDINA, José Toribio. Cartografia Hispano-Colonial de Chile. Texto con noticias históricas. 44 p. Santiago de Chile: Impr. Universidad (for Ministerio de Industria y Obras Públicas: Dirección de Obras Publicas: Inspección General de Geografia), 1924. [CB 18/627]
Atlas consisting of 33 photographic reproductions of maps.

OUTES, Félix F. Cartas y planos inéditos de los siglos XVII y XVIII y del primer decenio del XIX, conservados en el archivo de la dirección de geodesía, catastro y mapa de la Provincia de Buenos Aires. Con una regesta y observaciones críticas. 45 p., 50 pl. (Publicaciones del Instituto de Investigaciones Geográficas de la Facultad de Filosofía y Letras, serie B, Documentos Cartográficos, Planimétricos e Iconográficos, 3) Buenos Aires: Peuser, 1930.

HGD EUROPE

ALMAGIÀ, Roberto. Per una collezione sistematica di riproduzioni di carte antiche delle diverse regioni europee. *Proc.Int.Geogr.Congr.* (Cambridge, 1928), p. 406-8. Cambridge University Press, 1930.

FORDHAM, Herbert George. Les guides-routiers, itinéraires et cartes-routières de l'Europe 1500-1850. Conférence faite le 20 avril 1926, au 167e dîner de la Société Le Vieux Papier. 45 p., maps, ill., bibliogr. Lille: Imprimerie Lefebvre-Ducrocq, 1926.
A strictly carto-bibliography study, valuable as establishing a basis for further researches into the history of travel in Europe.

HGE BRITISH ISLES

CLOSE, Charles Frederick. The map of England, or about England with an ordnance map. x, 166 p., 8 ill. London: Davies, 1932.
Reviewed by O.G.S.C., *Antiquity*, 1932, 6: 509; in *Nature*, 1933, 131: 260.

COWAN, William. The maps of Edinburgh, 1544-1929. 2nd ed. revised with census of copies in Edinburgh libraries, by Charles B. Boog Watson. 136 p. Edinburgh: Public Libraries, 1932.

ESSEX. RECORD OFFICE. The art of the mapmaker in Essex, 1566-1860. [By F.G. Emmison.] xv, 30 p., pl. (Essex Record Office Publications, 4) Chelmsford: Essex County Council, 1947. [CB 72/274]
Introduction to the catalogue of maps and all the coloured and half-tone plates, *see* HGEcn-bw.

FORDHAM, Herbert George. The evolution of the maps of the British Isles. Address delivered in the Whitworth Hall of the University of Manchester, January 26, 1923. 20 p. Manchester: University Press, 1923.

GIMSON, Basil L.; RUSSELL, Percy. Leicestershire maps: a brief survey. viii, 40 p. Leicester: Backus, 1947.

MacLEOD, M.N. The evolution of British cartography. *Endeavour*, 1944, 3: 62-7, 5 maps.

WINTERBOTHAM, H.S.L. Mapping of the Colonial Empire. *Advance. Sci.*, 1936, 101-16.
Historical sketch as regards British Empire.

HGEcn-bw

CHUBB, Thomas. A descriptive list of the printed maps of Norfolk, 1574-1916, with biographical notes and a tabular index by T. Chubb, and a descriptive list of Norwich plans, 1541-1914, by George A. Stephen. xvi, 289 p., maps, ill., pl., plans. Norwich: Jarrold, 1928.

CHUBB, Thomas. The printed maps in the atlases of Great Britain and Ireland. A bibliography, 1597-1870. With an introduction by F.P. Sprent, and biographical notes on the map makers, engravers, and publishers. 479 p. London: Homeland Association, 1927.

ESSEX RECORD OFFICE. Catalogue of maps in the Essex Record Office, 1566-1855. Ed. by F.G. Emmison. xx, 106 p., 30 pl. Chelmsford: Essex County Council, 1947.
The introduction to this catalogue and all the colored and half-tone plates have been published separately under the title "The art of the map maker in Essex, 1566-1860", *see* HGE

FORDHAM, Herbert George. The road-books and itineraries of Great Britain, 1570-1850: a catalogue with an introduction and a bibliography. xvi, 72 p. Cambridge University Press. 1924.

PALMER, Margaret. Maps of the isles of Scilly. 16 p., 8 ill. (Map Collectors' Series, 3) London: Map Collectors' Circle, 1963.

SHARP, Henry A. An historical catalogue of Surrey maps. 56 p. Croydon: The Central Library, 1929.

SKELTON, R.A. County atlases of the British Isles: a new bibliography. Part 1. 40 p. (Map Collectors' Series, 9) London: Map Collectors' Circle, 1964.

WHITAKER, Harold. A descriptive list of the printed maps of Yorkshire and its ridings, 1577-1900. xiii, 261 p., 23 pl. (Yorkshire Archaeological Society record series, 86) Leeds: The Society, 1933.

HGEcn-by

ROYAL GEOGRAPHICAL SOCIETY. English county maps in the collection of the Royal Geographical Society. With introduction and notes by Edward Heawood. ii, 14 p., 21 maps. (Reproductions of Early Engraved Maps, 2) London: The Society, 1932.
Reviewed in *Nature*, 1933, 131: 530.

WHITAKER, Harold. The Harold Whitaker Collection of County atlases, road-books and maps presented to the University of Leeds. 143 p. Leeds: Brotherton Library, 1947.

HGEqk

CLOSE, Charles Frederick. The Ordnance Survey. *Antiquity*, 1931, 5: 149-60.
Article on the British National Survey, from the late 16th century through the foundation of the Ordnance Survey Board in 1791 to the 19th century.

HGF FRANCE

BURAT, -, *Colonel*. La carte de France. *Bull.Soc.Topogr.France*, 1925, 49: 49-60.
Historical sketch of the topographic mapping of France from the eighteenth century to the present.

FERRAND, H. La région du Queyras (Dauphiné), d'après les anciens géographes. *Bull.Sect.Géogr.Comité Trav.Hist.Sci.*, 1922, 37: 67-79. [CB 15/219]

HELBRONNER, Paul. Histoire sommaire de la représentation cartographique de la Corse. *Rev.Gén.Sci.*, 1930, 41: 509-18; 1931, 42: 335-43.

VALLOT, J. Evolution de la cartographie de la Savoie et du Mont Blanc. Fasc. 1. 32 p., with atlas. Paris: Barrère, 1922. [CB 18/627]

HGG/HGH CENTRAL EUROPE

HGG

BORGEAUD, Marc-Aug. Cartographie genèvoise du XVIe au XIXe siècle. *Arch.Int.Hist.Sci.*, 1949, 2: 363-75, 4 pl.

DÖRRIES, Hans. Studien zur älteren bremischen Kartographie. *Bremisches Jahrb.*, 1928, 31: 335-7; 1929, 32: 243-70.

FLÜCKIGER, Otto. Die Schweiz aus der Vogelschau. xliii, 172 p., 258 ill. Erlenbach-Zürich/München/Leipzig: Eugen Rentsch, 1924. [CB 16/300]
A collection of 243 airplane photographs of Switzerland. In the introductory part there are also 15 reproductions of interesting "bird's-eye views" of Switzerland dating from the sixteenth century onward.
Reviewed in *Geogr.Rev.*, 1924, 14: 645.

HANKE, Michael. Geschichte der amtlichen Kartographie Brandenburg-Preussens bis zum Ausgang der friderizianischen Zeit. Bearbeitet von Hermann Degner. Mit einem Vorwort von Albrecht Penck. 403 p., 1 map. (Geographische Abhandlungen, 3rd ser., 7) Stuttgart: Engelhorn, 1935.
Reviewed by Eugen Oberhummer, *Deut.Lit.Zeitung*, 1937, 58: 1665-8.

HENSCHEL, Gerh. Literatur und Karten zur Geographie der Oberlausitz für die Zeit von 1560-1833. *Neues Lausitzisches Mag.*, 1932, 108: 114-46; 1934, 110: 82-122; 1935, 111: 185-223.

MÜHLBERGER, Josef. Die Entwicklung der österreichischen Staatskartographie. *Mitt.Reichsamts Landesaufn.*, 1929, 5: 193-213.

NETZSCH, Hermann. Deutsches topographisches Kartenwesen mit besonderer Berücksichtigung der bayerischen Verhältnisse. 30 p., 37 pl., 3 fig. München: Verlag des Topographischen Büro, 1927.
Reviewed by Albrecht Penck, *Deut.Lit.Zeitung*, 1930, 1: 35-40.

SWITZERLAND. LANDESTOPOGRAPHIE. Hundert Jahre Eidgenössische Landestopographie, ehemaliges Eidgenössisches Topographisches Bureau 1838-1938. 1. Historische Berichte. Geschichtlicher Streifzug durch die ersten hundert Jahre Eidg. Landestopographie, 1838-1938 von K. Schneider. Die Landestriangulation, I-III Ordnung der Schweiz, von H. Zölly. Le nivellement fédéral, par A. Charles. Topographische Arbeiten von R. Tank. Die geschichtliche Entwicklung der Kartenreproduktion von M. Simon. 68 p., 6 maps, 5 fig. Bern: 1938.
Reviewed in *Mitt.Gesch.Med.*, 1940, 39: 337.

THORINGTON, J. Monroe. The Oetzthal glaciers in history and cartography before 1800. *Geogr.J.*, 1930, 75: 233-41.

WEISZ, Leo. Die Schweiz auf alten Karten. 232 p. Zürich: Verlag der *Neuen Zürcher Zeitung*, 1945.

WOLKENHAUER, W. Deutschland im Kartenbilde. Uebersicht der ältesten und einer Auswahl neuerer und neuesten Karten von (Gesamt-) Deutschland. *Deut.Geogr.Bl.*, 1919, 39: 19-32. [CB 10/195]

HGGwm

CURSCHMANN, Fritz. Die schwedischen Matrikelkarten von Vorpommern und ihre wissenschaftliche Auswertung. *Imago Mundi,* 1935, 1: 52-7, maps.

HGH

CHALUBINSKA, A. [The oldest economic maps of Poland. (In Polish, with French summary)] *Stud.Mater.Dziej Nauk.Pol.,* 1963, *ser. C.,* 6: 56-96.

EPERJESSY, Kálmán. Kézirati térképek Magyaroszágról a bécsi levéltárakban. [Manuscript maps of Hungary in the archives of Vienna. (In Hungarian with German summary)] 56 p., 20 pl. Szeged: Collegium Hungaricum, 1928.

OLSZEWICZ, Boleslaw. Polska kartografja wojskowa: zarys historyczny. [Polish military cartography: historical sketch. (In Polish)] 199, lxxx p., maps. (Wojskowy Instytut Naukowo-Wydawniczy) Warsaw: Glówna Ksiegarnia Wojskowa, 1921.
History of Polish military cartography from the fifteenth century to the present time, with a twelve-page résumé in French.

HGI/HGJ SOUTHERN EUROPE

HGI

ALMAGIÀ, Roberto. Monumenta Italiae cartographica: riproduzioni di carte generali e regionali d'Italia del secolo XIV al XVII. vi, 88 p., 65 pl. Florence: Istituto Geografico Militare, 1929.

ALMAGIÀ, Roberto. Presentazione dell'opera "Monumenta cartographica Italiae". *Rep.Proc.12th Int.Geogr.Congr.* (Cambridge, 1928), p. 396-400. Cambridge University Press, 1930.

BIASUTTI, Renato. Lo sviluppo della cartografia dell'Italia nei secoli XIV-XVII. *Universo,* 1930, 11: 549-57.

CAPELLO, Carlo F. Studi sulla cartografia Piemontese. 1. Il Piemonte nella cartografia pre moderna (con particolare riguardo alla cartografia Tolemaica). 157 p., 90 pl. (Università degli Studi di Torino, facoltà di magistero. Scritti vari, 3: facs. 1) Torino: 1952.
Reviewed in *Imago Mundi,* 1955, 12: 185.

CIULLINI, Rodolfo. Di una raccolta di antiche carte e vedute della città di Firenze. *Universo,* 1924, 5: 589-94, 13 facs. of maps. [CB 16/299]

MORI, Attilio. La cartografia dell'Italia dal secolo XIV al XVIII. *Boll.Soc.Geogr.Ital.,* 1930, 7: 205-18.

MORI, Attilio. La cartografia ufficiale in Italia e l'Istituto Geografico Militare. Notizie storiche raccolte e ordinate da Attilio Mori. (Nel cinquantenario dell'Istituto Geografico Militare: 1872-1922.) viii, 425 p., 75 pl. Rome: Stabilimento Poligrafico per l'Amministrazione della Guerra, 1922. [CB 16/302]

REVELLI, Paolo. Figurazioni cartografiche di Genova (1435-1935). 79 p., 24 pl., portr. Genoa: Comune di Genova, 1936.
Reviewed by Aldo Mieli, *Archeion,* 1936, 18: 277-8.

HGJ

BLAZQUEZ, Antonio. Cartografía de la península ibérica. Noticia de mapas interesantes para la geografía de España. *Rev.Geogr.Colon.Merc.,* 1924, 21: 281-300. [CB 18/625]

BLAZQUEZ, Antonio. Noticias de mapas de España de los siglos XVI al XVIII. *Rev.Geogr.Colon.Merc.,* 1923, 20: 96-109.
A list of 163 sixteenth, seventeenth, and eighteenth century charts, maps and collections of maps of Spain, compiled by D. José Luis Velazquez toward the close of the eighteenth century.

HGK/HGM NORTHERN EUROPE

HGK

FOCKEMA, Andreae. Geschiedenis der kartografie van Nederland van den Romeinschen tijd tot het midden van de 19de eeuw. [History of the cartography of the Netherlands from the time of the Romans until the middle of the 19th century. (In Dutch)] viii, 128 p., 25 pl. The Hague: Nijhoff, 1947.
Reviewed by R.J. Forbes, *Isis,* 1950, 41: 136.

KOEMAN, C. De betekenis van de waterschapskaarten van Delfland voor de geschiedenis van de kartografie van Nederland. [The significance of the polder maps of Delfland for the history of the cartography of the Netherlands. (In Dutch)] *Tijdschr. Ned.Aardrijksk.Genoot.,* 1960, *2nd ser.,* 77: 132-4.

HGKcn-bw

TOOLEY, R.V. Leo Belgicus: an illustrated list of variants. 16 p., 24 pl. (Map Collectors' Series, 7) London: Map Collectors Circle, 1963.
The Leo Belgicus, or map of Belgium in the form of a lion, is used in its older connotation, Belgium including the whole of the Netherlands.

HGM

BRATT, Einar. En krönika om kartor över Sverige. [A chronicle of maps of Sweden. (In Swedish)] 131 p., 11 pl. Stockholm: Generalstabens Litografiska Anstalt, 1958.
Reviewed by Åke Davidsson, *Lychnos,* 1957-58, 408-9.

HERMANNSSON, Halldór. The cartography of Iceland. vii, 81 p., 27 pl. (Islandica, 21) Ithaca, N.Y.: Cornell University Press, 1931.
Reviewed by Hans Kuhn, *Deut.Lit.Zeitung,* 1932, 3: 947-51.

SÄLLSKAPET FÖR UTGIVANDE AV LANTMÄTERIETS HISTORIA. Svenska Lantmäteriet 1628-1928: Historisk skildring utgiven av Sällskapet för utgivande av Lantmäteriets Historia. [Swedish Topographic Survey. Historic description edited by the Society for publishing the history of the Swedish topographic survey. (In Swedish)] 3 vol. viii, 629 p., maps, diagr., ill.; 614 p., map, ill.; 41 maps. Stockholm: Norstedt, 1928.
Brief notice by Ernst Antevs, *Geogr.Rev.,* 1929, 19: 352.

HGMwk

WIEDER, Frederik Caspar, ed. The Dutch discovery and mapping of Spitsbergen 1596-1829, edited by order of the Netherland Minister of Foreign Affairs. 124 p., 45 pl. and maps. Amsterdam: Netherland Ministry of Foreign Affairs and Royal Dutch Geographic Society, 1919.

HGN RUSSIA

KÖHLIN, H. Some remarks on maps of the Crimea and the Sea of Azov. *Imago Mundi,* 1960, 15: 84-8.

PREOBRAZHENSKY, A.I. Russkiye ekonomicheskiye karty i atlasy. [Russian economic maps and atlases. (In Russian)] 329 p., ill. Moskva: 1953.
Reviewed in *Imago Mundi,* 1954, 11: 180.

SALISHCHEV, K.A. *See* HF

HGO SOUTH EASTERN EUROPE

MŽIK, Hans von. Beiträge zur Kartographie Albaniens nach orientalischen Quellen. In: Nopcsa, Ferencz. Geographie und Geologie Nordalbaniens ... Anhang: Zur Geschichte der Kartographie des Gebietes, 1. (*Geol.Hung.Ser.Geol.,* 3) Budapest: Institutum Regni Hungariae Geologicum, 1929.

NOPCSA, Ferencz. Zur Geschichte der okzidentalen Kartographie Nordalbaniens. In his: Geographie und Geologie Nordalbaniens ... Anhang: Zur Geschichte der Kartographie des Gebietes, 2. p. 625-703, 7 pl., 39 ill. (*Geol.Hung.Ser.Geol.,* 3) Budapest: Institutum Regni Hungariae Geologicum, 1929.
Reviewed by O.W., *J.Roy.Asiatic Soc.,* 1929, 684.

ROMANIA. SERVICIUL GEOGRAFIC AL ARMATEI. Serviciul geografic al armatei Române. 50 ani de activitate 1874-1924. 104 p., 18 maps, 16 ill. Bucarest: 1924.
A sketch of the work of the geographical service of the Rumanian army during its first fifty years of activity, with specimens of topographical sheets and diagrammatic maps showing the progress of triangulation.

HGQ NORTH AFRICA

BELLOT, A. La carte d'Algérie, 1830-1930. iv, 162, 104 p. Paris: Service Géographique de l'Armée, 1930.
Reviewed by H.S.L. Winterbotham, *Geogr.J.,* 1932, 79: 233-4.

JONDET, Gaston. Atlas historique de la ville et des ports d'Alexandrie. 56 p., map, diagr., table, 37½ cm. (Mémoires présentés à la Société Sultanieh de Géographie, 2) Le Caire: Imprimerie de l'Institut Français d'Archéologie Orientale, 1921.
Fifty-four photographic reproductions of maps, charts, and birdseye views, dating from the 15th century to 1920; accompanied by explanatory text.

YŪSUF KAMĀL, prince. *See* HGX

HGR ASIA

STEIN, Aurel. Memoir on maps of Chinese Turkistan and Kansu, from the surveys made during Sir Aurel Stein's explorations, 1900-1901, 1906-1908, 1913-1915. With appendices by Major Kenneth Mason and James de Graaff Hunter. xv, 208 p., 30 pl. (48 maps, 12 charts, separate) (Records of the survey of India, 17) Dehra Dun: Trigonometrical Survey Office, 1923.

HGT

BERNARD, Henri. Les étapes de la cartographie scientifique pour la Chine et les pays voisins depuis le XVIe jusqu'à la fin du XVIIIe siècle. *Monumenta Serica*, 1935, 1: 428-77, 2 maps. [CB 48/544]

BREITFUSS, L. Early maps of North-Eastern Asia and of the lands around the North Pacific. Controversy between G.F. Müller and N. Delisle. *Imago Mundi*, 1939, 3: 87-99, 19 fig., 3 maps.

CHINA. NATIONAL GEOLOGICAL SURVEY. [A new atlas of China. (In Chinese)] 53 maps, 180 p. Shanghai: Shen Pao Press, 1934.
Review by G.B. Barbour, *Geogr.J.*, 1936, 87: 177-8.

CHINESE gazetteers. *Isis*, 1942, 34: 29.
Refers to modern works.

DAHLGREN, Erik Wilhelm. Les débuts de la cartographie du Japon. 65 p. (*Arch.Etudes Orient.*, 4) Upsala: Appelberg: 1911. [CB 27/517]

DINGLE, Edwin John, ed. The new atlas and commercial gazetteer of China. A work devoted to its geography and economic and commercial development. Comp. and transl. from the latest and most authoritative surveys and records. 25 maps, ill. Shanghai: North China Daily News and Herald, [1917].

STANFORD, Edward. Complete atlas of the Chinese Empire containing separate maps of the ... provinces and ... dependencies ... v, 16 p., 23 maps. London/Philadelphia: China Inland Mission, 1917.
First published 1908 (London/Philadelphia: Morgan and Scott).

HGV

DAVIS, Charles J. Stick charts of Micronesia. *Navigation* (Los Angeles), 1964, 11: 32-7.

HGW AUSTRALIA

HGWcn-bw

TOOLEY, R.V. The printed maps of Tasmania. 36 p., 14 ill. (Map Collectors' Series, 5) London: Map Collectors' Circle, 1963.

HGX AFRICA

YŪSUF KAMAL, *prince*. Monumenta cartographica Africae et Aegypti par Youssouf Kamal. 5 vol. in 16, ill., pl., portr., maps, diagr., facs. 1. Époque avant Ptolemée. 107 fol.; 2. Ptolemée et époque gréco-romaine, fasc. 1-3, fol. 108-480; fasc. 4, Atlas antiquus et index, 130 fol.; 3. Époque arabe, fasc. 1-5, fol. 481-1072; 4. Époque des portulans, suivie par l'époque des découvertes, fol. 1073-484; 5. Additamenta (naissance et evolution de la cartographie moderne), fasc. 1-2, fol. 1484-653. [Le Caire]: 1926-51.
Vol. 1, 2 and 3, fasc. 1-2, reviewed in *Geogr.Rev.*, 1934, 24: 175.

YŪSUF KAMAL, *prince*. Quelques éclaircissements épars sur mes Monumenta cartographica Africae et Aegypti. 215 p. Leiden: priv. print., 1935.
Reviewed by Dana B. Durand, *Isis*, 1936, 24: 453-5.

HGYcn-bw

TOOLEY, R.V. Early maps and views of the Cape of Good Hope. 16 p., 35 ill. (Map Collectors' Series, 6) London: Map Collectors' Circle, 1963.

HGZ ARCTIC REGIONS

BAGROW, Leo. Eskimo maps. *Imago Mundi*, 1948, 5: 92, 2 pl.

HGZcn-bw

TOOLEY, R.V. Maps of Antarctica: a list of early maps of the South Polar regions. 26 p., 20 ill. (Map Collectors' Series, 2) London: Map Collectors' Circle, 1963.

HGZyGD

HOBBS, William H. Conditions of exceptional visibility within high latitudes, particularly as a result of superior mirage. *Ann.Ass.Amer.Geogr.*, 1937, 27: 229-40.
This is important for the history of cartography, as it reveals a cause of error which has distorted many maps of Arctic regions.

HOBBS, William H. Visibility and the discovery of Polar lands. *Geogr.Ann.*, 1933, 15: 217-24, 6 fig. [CB 40/406]

HH CHARTING THE SEAS

ALMAGIA, Roberto. Quelques questions au sujet des cartes nautiques et des portulans d'après les recherches récentes. *Act.Ve Congr.Int.Hist.Sci.* (Lausanne, 1947), p. 140-9. Paris: Hermann, 1948.

GROLL, M. Alte und neue Seekarten. *Mar.Rundsch.*, 1912, 23: 601-16.

GUILLEN, J. Hacia el origen de la cartografía maritima. *Act. IXe Congr.Int.Hist.Sci.* (Barcelona, 1959), p. 145-63. Paris: Hermann, 1960.

SHALOWITZ, Aaron L. Nautical charting (1807-1957). *Sci.Mon.*, 1957, 84: 290-301, 11 ill.

SOMERVILLE, Henry Boyle Townshend. The chart makers. 302 p. London: Blackwood, 1928.

WINTER, Heinrich. The origin of the sea chart. *Imago Mundi*, 1956, 13: 39-44, 4 fig.

WROTH, Lawrence C. The early cartography of the Pacific. *Pap.Bibliogr.Soc.Amer.*, 1944, 38: 87-268, 22 pl. [CB 68/57]

HHcn-bw

DESTOMBES, Marcel. Catalogue des cartes nautiques manuscrites sur parchemin, 1300-1700. Cartes hollandaises. La cartographie de la Compagnie des Indes Orientales, 1593-1743. 99 p., front., 4 pl. Saigon: 1941.
Reviewed by G. Sarton, *Isis*, 1948, 38: 262.

HHwb

WROTH, Lawrence C. Some American contributions to the art of navigation 1519-1802. 47 p. Providence: 1947.
Reviewed in *Imago Mundi*, 1949, 6: 102.

HHwe

ROBINSON, A.H.W. Marine cartography in Britain: a history of the sea chart to 1855. 222 p., fig., pl., bibliogr. Leicester: Leicester University Press, 1962.
Reviewed by Helen Wallis, *Mariner's Mirror*, 1964, 50: 75-7.

HI AIR CHARTING

RISTOW, Walter W. Aviation cartography, a historico-bibliographic study of aeronautical charts. 114 p. Washington, D.C.: Library of Congress, 1956.
Reviewed by Antoine de Smet, *Arch.Int.Hist.Sci.*, 1958, 11: 69-70.

HIcn

MILLER, O.M. An experimental air navigation map. *Geogr.Rev.*, 1933, 23: 48-60, 1 map. [CB 38/603]

RISTOW, Walter W. Aviation cartography, a historico-bibliographic study of aeronautical charts. 114 p. Washington, D.C.: Library of Congress, 1956.
Reviewed by Antoine de Smet, *Arch.Int.Hist.Sci.*, 1958, 11: 69-70.

HIqy

COMMISSION Internationale de la Carte Aéronautique. Réunion de Bruxelles, 1913. *Vie Int.*, 1913, 4: 472-5.

HJ TRAVEL AND EXPLORATION

HJc general history

BAKER, John Norman Leonard. A history of geographical discovery and exploration. 544 p., 51 fig. (Harrap's New Geographical Series) London: Harrap, 1931. [CB 37/601]

BECKMAN, Leif Olof; OHLMARKS, Åke. Vår väg genom världen; de geografiska upptäckternas historia, under vetenskapligt medarbetarskap av Carl Skottsberg och Oscar Wieselgren. [Our way through the world. The history of geographical exploration. With scientific collaboration by C.S. and O.W. (In Swedish)] 3 vol., ill., portr., maps, bibliogr. 1. Antiken och den äldre medeltiden [Antiquity and the early middle ages], av Å. Ohlmarks; 2. Europeiska färder och forskningar fram till 'upptäckternas tidevarv'. Det väldiga Asien och vägarna dit [European journeys and exploration until the 'age of discovery'. Asia and the long roads to the large continent], av Å. Ohlmarks; Den amerikanska dubbelkontinenten [The American double continent], av L. Beckman; 3. Amerikas senare upptäcktshistoria. Afrikas upptäcktshistoria efter 1500. Australien och Oceanien. Arktis och Antarktis [Later exploration in America. Exploration in Africa after 1500. Australia and Oceania. The Arctic and Antarctic], av L. Beckman. Stockholm: H. Geber, 1947-51. [CB 80/128]
Vol. 3 reviewed by Erik Gren, *Lychnos*, 1952, 375-8.

BETTEX, Albert. The discovery of the world. 379 p., ill. New York: Simon and Schuster, 1960. [CB 86/465]

BUCHAN, John. The last secrets. The final mysteries of exploration. 303 p., 12 pl., 10 maps. London: Nelson, 1922.
Popular narratives of certain explorations of the last two or three decades.

BUTZE, Herbert. Die Entdeckung der Erde; 5000 Jahre Abenteuer, Reisen und Forschen. 367 p., ill., portr., maps, facs. Gütersloh: C. Bertelsmann, 1962.
Reviewed by E. Baumberger, *Geogr.Helv.*, 1964, 19: 122.

CARBONERA, G. Il giro del mondo. 118 p. (I Grandi Viaggi di Scoperta, 2) Milano: Federazione Italiana delle Biblioteche Popolari, 1921.

DÉPREZ, Eugène. Les grands voyages et les grandes découvertes jusqu'à la fin du XVIIIe siècle. Origines, développement, conséquences. *Bull.Int.Comm.Hist.Sci.*, 1930, 2: 555-614.

GILLESPIE, James Edward. A history of geographical discovery, 1400-1800. viii, 111 p. New York: Holt, 1933. [CB 39/461]

HENNIG, Richard. Unfreiwillege Seefahrten in ihrer Bedeutung für die Kenntnis und Besiedlung des Erdballs. *Petermanns Mitt.*, 1924, 70: no. 9-10, 210-13; no. 11-12, 263-8.

KELTIE, John Scott; GILMOUR, Samuel Carter. Adventures of exploration. 5 vol. 1. Finding the continents. iv, 128 p., 4 pl.; 2. Central and South America. iv, 156 p., 4 pl.; 3. Asia. iv, 164 p.; 4. Africa. iv, 180 p.; 5. Australia and New Zealand. iv, 204 p. London: George Philip and Son, 1925-26.

KEY, Charles E. The story of twentieth-century exploration. 286 p. London: Harrap, 1937.
Reviewed by J.M. Scott, *Geogr.J.*, 1937, 90: 576.

MAḤMŪD MURĀD. [Geographical discoveries of four thousand years. (In Arabic)] 140 p., ill. Cairo: An-Nahḍah, 1340 [1922]. [CB 42/595]

MARTINEAU, Alfred; MAY, L. Ph. Tableau de l'expansion européenne à travers le monde de la fin du XIIe au début du XIXe siècle. 369 p. Paris: Société de l'histoire des colonies françaises, 1935.
Reviewed by Aldo Mieli, *Archeion*, 1935, 17: 319.

OLSEN, Ørjan. De store opdagelser. [The great discoveries. (In Norwegian)] 6 vol. 1950 p., ill. Oslo: Nasjonalforlaget, 1929-31.
Reviewed by Willy Hartner, *Isis*, 1937, 27: 532-4.
For French translation of this work *see* below.

OLSEN, Ørjan. La conquête de la terre. Histoire des découvertes et des explorations des origines à nos jours. 6 vol. 280 p.; 259 p.; 271 p.; 272 p.; 291 p.; 329 p. Paris: Payot, 1933-37.
Reviewed by Pierre Brunet, *Archeion*, 1934, 16: 241-2; 1935, 17: 318-19; 1937, 19: 437-8.

OUTHWAITE, Leonard. Unrolling the map. The story of exploration. With drawings of ships by Gordon Grant. xiv, 351 p., 56 maps. London: Constable, 1935.
Reviewed in *Imago Mundi*, 1937, 2: 99.

REPARAZ, Gonçal de. Historia de la colonización. 2 vol. Barcelona: Editorial Labor, 1933-35. [CB 38/609]

SCHADENDORF, W. The story of travel. *Ciba Rev.*, 1962, no. 3, 2-11.

SYKES, Percy. A history of exploration from the earliest times to the present day. 3rd ed. (with appendix). xiv, 426 p., ill., 24 pl., 17 maps. London: Routledge & Kegan Paul, 1950.
First publ. London: Routledge; New York: Macmillan, 1934 [CB 48/580]
Reviewed by E.D. Maclagan, *J.Roy.Asiatic Soc.*, 1937, 383-4; by Erik Gren, *Lychnos*, 1952, 378-9.

THOMAS, Lowell. The untold story of exploration. With illustrations by Kurt Wiese. xii, 333 p., 12 ill. New York: Dodd, Mead, 1935. [CB 52/599]

WOOD, H.J. Exploration and discovery. 192 p. London: Hutchinson's University Library, 1952.

HJc-bx

EXPLORERS HALL. (A continuing exhibition at the headquarters of the National Geographic Society in Washington, D.C.) *Sci. Teacher*, 1957, 24: 120-1, 5 ill.

HJcn

SKELTON, R.A. Explorers' maps. Chapters in the cartographic record of geographical discovery. xi, 337 p., front., ill. New York: Frederick A. Praeger; London: Routledge and Kegan Paul, 1958.
Reviewed by George Kish, *Isis*, 1960, 51: 96-7; in *Sci.Amer.*, 1959, 201: no. 4, 212.

HJda

BANSE, Ewald. Grosse Forschungsreisende. Ein Buch von Abenteurern, Entdeckern und Gelehrten. 284 p., 62 fig. München: Lehmann, 1933.
Reviewed by Karl Sapper, *Deut.Lit.Zeitung*, 1933, 4: 1807-9.

LES EXPLORATEURS célèbres. 367 p., ill. Paris: Mazenot, 1947.
Reviewed by Pierre Brunet, *Rev.Hist.Sci.*, 1948, 1: 374.

LA RONCIÈRE, Ch. de. Histoire de la découverte de la terre. Explorateurs et conquérants. viii, 304 p., 8 pl., 586 ill. Paris: Larousse, 1938.

MITCHELL, J. Leslie. Earth conquerors. The lives and achievements of the great explorers. 370 p., 9 portr. New York: Simon and Schuster, 1934. [CB 44/520]

HJdaj

CZIBULKA, Alfons von. Berühmte Weltfahrer von Marco Polo bis Sven Hedin, mit ihren Reiseberichten. vii, 485 p., ill. München: Drei Masken Verlag, [1926]
Selections from notable works of travel for the general reader, each preceded by a brief introduction.

LOOKER, Samuel J., ed. Travel old and new; a selection from the literature of travel in both hemispheres. xxx, 473 p. London: Daniel O'Connor, 1922.

STEFANSSON, Vilhjalmur, ed. Great adventures and explorations. From the earliest times to the present, as told by the explorers themselves. Edited with an introduction and comments. With the collaboration of Olive Rathbun Wilcox. Maps designed by Richard Edes Harrison. 788 p., ill., maps. New York: Dial Press, 1947. [CB 71/124]

HJh

WRIGHT, John Kirtland. Some broader aspects of the history of exploration. A review. *Geogr.Rev.*, 1935, 25: 317-20.

HJs/v special aspects

HJs

BOWMAN, Isaiah. The pioneer fringe. ix, 361 p., 249 fig. (American Geographical Society, special publication, 13) New York: 1931. [CB 36/445]
A study of the pioneer or "experimental" zones all over the world.

HJth

FIRESTONE, Clark Barnaby. The coasts of illusion, a study of travel tales. Drawings by Ruth Hambidge. x, 410 p. London: Harper, 1924.

GOVE, Philip Babcock. The imaginary voyage in prose fiction. xiii, 445 p. New York: Columbia University Press, 1941. [CB 61/407]

HJvm

ADLER, Elkan Nathan. Jewish travellers. Edited with an introduction by Elkan Nathan Adler. xxiv, 391 p. London: Routledge, 1930.

HJw by different countries

for the exploration of different countries *see* HK

HJwb-qd

GROSVENOR, Gilbert. Earth, sea and sky. Twenty years of exploration by the National Geographic Society. *Sci.Mon.*, 1954, 78: 296-302.

HJwe

SEERS, A. Waddingham. The story of early English travel and discovery. 240 p., 8 ill., 9 maps. London: Harrap, 1923.

HJwf

FOURNIER, P. Voyages et découvertes scientifiques des missionaires naturalistes français à travers le monde pendant cinq siècles (XVe à XXe siècles). 258 p., 2 fig., 30 portr. (Encyclopédie Biologique, 10: contribution à l'histoire des sciences naturelles) Paris: Lechevalier, 1932.
Reviewed by C.A. Kofoid, *Isis*, 1934, 22: 303-5.

SOUTHWORTH, Constant. The French colonial venture. xi, 204 p., ill. London: King, 1931.
Reviewed by Mark Jefferson, *Geogr.Rev.*, 1932, 22: 339-40.

HJwi-da

ALMAGIÀ, Roberto; MORI, Attilio; ed. Il nuovo repertorio bio-bibliografico dei viaggiatori italiani. *Boll.Soc.Geogr. Ital., ser. 6*, 1924, 1: 461-86. [CB 18/625]

DONAZZOLO, Pietro. I viaggiatori veneti minori. Studio bio-bibliografico. 412 p. (Memorie della Reale Società Geografica Italiana, 16) Rome: [1929]. [CB 32/590]
Supplements the great work of Amat Di S. Filippo, *Studi biografici e bibliografici sulla storia della geografia in Italia*, 2 vol. 2nd ed. Rome: 1882. Brief sketches and full bibliographical details are given regarding 392 travelers.
Reviewed by G.R.C., *Geogr.J.*, 1930, 76: 82.

HJwj

CORDEIRO, Luciano. Questões historico-coloniais. 3 vol. 424 p.; 314 p.; 386 p. Lisbôa: Agência geral das Colónias, divisão de publicações e biblioteca, 1935-36.
Collected articles mainly concerning the great figures of Portugal's age of expansion.
Reviewed in *Geogr.J.*, 1938, 91: 568-9.

HJwk

OLBRECHTS, Frans M. Vlaanderen zendt zijn Zonen uit! [Flanders sent her sons out. (In Flemish)] 2nd ed. 284 p., ill. Antwerp: Standaard-Boekhandel, 1947. [CB 75/94]
First publ. Leuven: 1942.

HJwn

GOLDENBERG, L.A.; NOSOV, S.P. [The first scientific expeditions after the setting up of the Soviet régime. (In Russian)] *Tr.Inst.Ist.Est.Tekh.*, 1961, 37: no. 2, 311-29.

NOZIKOV, N. Russian voyages round the world. Edited and with an introduction by M.A. Sergeyev. Transl. from the Russian by Ernst and Mira Lesser. xx, 165 p. London: Hutchinson, 1945. [CB 70/214]

HJyRA FIRST AID

BURROUGHS WELLCOME & CO. The romance of exploration and emergency first-aid from Stanley to Byrd. 160 p., 59 ill. New York/London: Burroughs Wellcome, 1934. [CB 46/595]
An illustrated handbook of an exhibit at the Century of Progress Fair at Chicago.

HK TRAVEL AND EXPLORATION: BY REGION (including area studies)

for the exploration of mountains *see* HM

HERBERTSON, A.J.; HOWARTH. O.J.R., *et al.* The Oxford survey of the British Empire. 6 vol. ill, pl., maps, diagr. 1. The British Isles and Mediterranean territories; 2. Asiatic territories; 3. African territories; 4. American territories; 5. Australasian territories; 6. General survey. Oxford: Clarendon Press, 1914.

HKA NORTH AND SOUTH AMERICA

FRIEDERICI, Georg. Der Charakter der Entdeckung und Eroberung Amerikas durch die Europäer: Einleitung zur Geschichte der Besiedlung Amerikas durch die Völker der alten Welt. 3 vol. 1. Die Kolonisationsschauplätze. Die Eingeborenen. Die Spanier; 2. Die Portugiesen. Die Deutschen. Die Irokesen. Die Franzosen; 3. Die Niederländer. Die Skandinavier. Engländer und Anglo-Amerikaner. Die Russen. Verzeichnis der benutzten Quellen. (Allgemeine Staatengeschichte; Geschichte der Aussereuropäischen Staaten) Stuttgart-Gotha: Friedrich Andreas Perthes, 1925-36. [CB 24/540]

HKAnh

ADAMS, Edward Dean. America and Americans. The name and its significance. 56 p., 8 ill. New York: Bartlett Orr Press, 1926.
On the origin of the name "America".

HKB NORTH AMERICA

for Greenland *see* HLP

BURPEE, Lawrence J. The discovery of Canada. x, 280 p. Toronto: Macmillan, 1944.
Reviewed by J.N.L. Baker, *Nature*, 1947, 159: 182.

BURPEE, Lawrence J. The search for the Western sea. The story of the exploration of North-western America. New rev. ed. 2 vol. Toronto: Macmillan, 1935.
First publ. 1908.

CLINE, Gloria Griffen. Exploring the Great Basin. xviii, 254 p., maps, ill., notes, bibliogr. Norman: University of Oklahoma Press, 1963.
Reviewed by A.P. Nasatir, *Miss.Val.Hist.Rev.*, 1964, 50: 702-3.

CROUSE, Nellis M. In quest of the western ocean. xiii, 480 p., maps, bibliogr. New York: William Morrow, 1928.

FREEMAN, Lewis Ransome. Down the Grand Canyon. 371 p. New York: Dodd, Mead, 1924.

JOERG, W.L.G. The geography of North America: a history of its regional exposition. *Geogr.Rev.*, 1936, 26: 640-63.

MARGERIE, Emmanuel de. Etudes américaines. 1 vol. in 2. 1. Géologie et géographie. xii, 294 p., 39 fig.; 2. Paysages, régions, explorateurs et cartes. 295-812 p. Paris: Colin, 1952-54. [CB 79/182]
Reviewed by George Sarton, *Isis*, 1954, 45: 387-8.

PAIN, S.A. The way north: men, mines and minerals. vi, 249 p., ill. Toronto: Ryerson, 1964.
An account of the curious history of the ancient route between North Bay and Hudson Bay in Ontario as collected and recollected by the author.

POWELL, John Wesley. The exploration of the Colorado River. xii, 176 p. Garden City, N.Y.: Doubleday, 1961.

VANDIVEER, Clarence A. The fur trade and early western exploration. 316 p., front., pl., portr. Cleveland: Clark, 1929.
Reviewed by Wayne E. Stevens, *Amer.Hist.Rev.*, 1929, 35: 173.

WARKENTIN, John. The western interior of Canada. A record of geographical discovery, 1617-1917. 310 p., 4 maps, bibliogr. Toronto: McClelland and Stewart, 1964.

WHEELER, Olin D. The trail of Lewis and Clark, 1804-1904; a story of the great exploration across the continent in 1804-1806. With a description of the old trail, based upon actual travel over it, and of the changes found a century later. New ed. 2 vol. xxiv, 377 p.; xv, 419 p., ill. New York: Putnam, 1927.

WILLIAMS, Samuel Cole. Early travels in the Tennessee country, 1540-1800. xi, 540 p. Johnson City: Watauga Press, 1928.
Reviewed by Solon J. Buck, *Amer.Hist.Rev.*, 1929, 34: 605-6.

WOOLLEN, William Watson. The inside passage to Alaska, 1792-1920, with an account of the North Pacific Coast from Cape Mendocine to Cook Inlet, from the accounts left by Vancouver and other early explorers, and from the author's journals of exploration and travel in that region. Ed. from the author's original manuscripts by Paul Leland Haworth. 2 vol. Cleveland, Ohio: Arthur H. Clark, 1924.

HKBce

DOERR, Arthur H. The United States in professional geographic literature: a recent view. *Prof.Geogr.*, 1964, 16: no. 1, 11-15.

HOWAY, F.W. The early literature of the northwest coast. *Proc.Roy.Soc.Can.*, 1924, *ser. 3*, 18: sect. 2, 1-31.

HKBce-bv

HUBACH, Robert R. Early midwestern travel narratives: an annotated bibliography, 1634-1850. x, 149 p. Detroit: Wayne State University Press, 1961.
Reviewed by Harvey L. Carter, *William Mary Quart.*, *3rd ser.*, 1962, 19: 315-16.

KNOX COLLEGE. Library. An annotated catalogue of books belonging to the Finley collection on the history and romance of the Northwest. Collected and presented to the Library by Edward Caldwell of New York City. Supplemented by a bibliography of the discovery and exploration of the Mississippi Valley, by Appleton P.C. Griffin. x, 67 p., bibliogr. Galesburg, Ill.: 1924.

WAGNER, Henry R. The Spanish southwest, 1542-1794. An annotated bibliography. 302 p., facs. Berkeley, Calif.: James J. Gillick, 1924. [CB 21/582]

WICKERSHAM, James. A bibliography of Alaskan literature 1724-1924. Containing the titles of all histories, travels, voyages, newspapers, periodicals, public documents, etc., relating to, descriptive of, or published in Russian America or Alaska, from 1724 to and including 1924. xxvii, 635 p. (Alaska Agricultural College and School of Mines, miscellaneous publications, 1) Cordova: Cordova Daily Times Print, 1927.

HKBcn

PAULLIN, Charles O. Atlas of the historical geography of the United States. Edited by John K. Wright. xiv, 162 p., 166 pl. Washington, D.C.: Carnegie Institution and American Geographical Society, 1932.
Reviewed by Louis C. Karpinski, *Isis*, 1934, 22: 305-8; by John K. Wright, *Geogr.Rev.*, 1932, 22: 353-60, map.

HKBda

BREBNER, John Bartlet. The explorers of North America, 1492-1806. xvi, 502 p. London: Black; New York: Macmillan, 1933. [CB 43/280]
Reviewed by E.W. Gilbert, *Geogr.J.*, 1934, 83: 156-7.
Reprinted London: Black; New York: Meridian Books, 1964.

KONJIAS, Helen T. Physicians as explorers in the new world. *Ciba Symp.* (Summit, N.J.), 1940, 2: 643-52.

HKBnh

ADAMS, Edward Dean. America and Americans. The name and its significance. 56 p., 8 ill. New York: Bartlett Orr Press, 1926.
On the origin of the name "America".

HKBth

DONDORE, Dorothy Anne. The prairie and the making of middle America: four centuries of description. xiii, 472 p., ill., bibliogr. Cedar Rapids, Iowa: Torch Press, 1926.
Reviewed in *Geogr.Rev.*, January 1928, 18: 163-4.

HKBwk-da

SMET, Antoine de. Voyageurs Belges aux États-Unis du XVIIe siècle à 1900: notices bio-bibliographiques. 201 p. Brussels: Bibliothèque Royale de Belgique, 1959.
Reviewed by Wilbur R. Jacobs, *Amer.Hist.Rev.*, 1961-62, 67: 793-4.

HKC LATIN AMERICA

AGOSTINI, Alberto M. de. I miei viaggi nella Terra del Fuoco. 296 p., ill. Torino: Agostini, 1923.
German translation: Zehn Jahre im Feuerland (Leipzig: Brockhaus, 1924).

GANN, Thomas William Francis. Mystery cities: exploration and adventure in Lubaantun. 252 p. London: Duckworth, 1925.

HAGEN, Victor Wolfgang von. Ecuador and the Galápagos Islands. ix, 290 p., pl. Norman: University of Oklahoma Press, 1949. [CB 74/382]

OGILVIE, Alan G. Geography of the Central Andes. A handbook to accompany the La Paz sheet [S E 19] of the map of Hispanic America on the millionth scale. With an introduction by Isaiah Bowman. xi, 240 p. New York: The American Geographical Society, 1922. [CB 16/303]

SPENCER, Baldwin. Spencer's last journey: being the journal of an expedition to Tierra del Fuego by the late Sir Baldwin Spencer; with a memoir. Ed. by R.R. Marett and T.K. Penniman. With contributions by Sir James Frazer and H. Balfour. xii, 153 p., 14 pl., portr., map. Oxford: Clarendon Press, 1931.

STEFFEN, Hans. Beiträge zur Entdeckungs- und Erforschungsgeschichte der südamerikanischen Kordilleren. *Ibero-Amer. Arch.*, 1930, 4: 173-233, 5 maps.

HKCwb

HOVEY, Edmund Otis. The Porto Rico survey. *Science*, 1914, 39: 896-8.
Exploration of Puerto Rico under the auspices of the New York Academy of Sciences.

HKCwb-da

MARTIN, Lawrence. Early explorers of southern South America from the United States. *Nature*, 1940, 146: 238-9.
Abstract of a paper presented to section VIII (History and geography) of the Eighth American Scientific Congress.

HKCwj

HISTÓRIA da colonizacão portuguesa do Brasil. Edição monumental commemorativa do primeiro centenario da indipendência do Brasil. 3 vol. cxxxii, 276 p.; 458, lxiv p.; 396 p., pl., maps, ill. Pôrto: Litografia nacional, 1921-26.
Reviewed by Aldo Mieli, *Archeion*, 1936, 18: 272-7.

HKCwn

BOGORAS, Waldemar. Le centième anniversaire des expéditions russes à l'Amérique du Sud. *Atti XXII Congr.Int.Amer.* (Roma, 1926), 2: 607-17, 5 fig. Rome: R. Garroni, 1928. [CB 29/248]

LUKIN, B.V. K 50-letiyu Russkoi nauchnoi ekspeditsii v Latinskuyu Ameriku. [On the 50th anniversary of the Russian scientific expedition to Latin America. (In Russian)] *Vestnik Akad.Nauk SSSR.*, 1964, 34: no. 6, 107-9.

HKD EUROPE

for the exploration of the Alps *see* HM

EAST, William Gordon. An historical geography of Europe. 4th ed. xx, 492 p., maps. London: Methuen, 1962.
First publ. 1935 [CB 53/269] and reviewed in *Geogr.Rev.*, 1936, 26: 520.

HKE

DARBY, Henry Clifford. Historical geography from the coming of the Anglo-Saxons to the industrial revolution. In: Watson, J.W.; Sissons, J.B.; ed. The British Isles, p. 198-200. Edinburgh: Nelson (for the 20th International Geographical Congress), 1964.

DARBY, Henry Clifford. An historical geography of England before A.D. 1800: fourteen studies. xii, 566 p., maps. Cambridge University Press, 1936.
Reviewed in *Geogr.Rev.*, 1936, 26: 696-8.
Reprinted, with corrections, 1948.

FITZGERALD, Walter. The historical geography of early Ireland. With an introduction by Percy M. Roxby. vii, 100 p., ill. (*Geographical Teacher*, Supplement 1) London: George Philip, 1926.

HERBERTSON, A.J.; HOWARTH. O.J.R., *et al.* The Oxford survey of the British Empire. 6 vol. ill, pl., maps, diagr. 1. The British Isles and Mediterranean territories; 2. Asiatic territories; 3. African territories; 4. American territories; 5. Australasian territories; 6. General survey. Oxford: Clarendon Press, 1914.

HKEnh

EKWALL, Eilert. English river names. xcii, 488 p. Oxford: Clarendon Press, 1928.

MAWER, Allen. Problems of place-name study. xi, 140 p. Cambridge University Press, 1929.
Reviewed by Karl Luick, *Deut.Lit.Zeitung*, 1930, 1: 1898-9.

MAWER, Allen; STENTON, F.M.; ed. Introduction to the survey of English place names. 2 vol. Cambridge University Press, 1924.

HKFnh

DAUZAT, Albert. Les noms de lieux, origine et évolution. viii, 264 p., ill. Paris: Delagrave, 1926.

DAUZAT, Albert. La toponymie française. 338 p., 8 maps. Paris: Payot, 1939.
Reviewed by George Sarton, *Isis*, 1942, 34: 186-7, map.

LONGNON, Auguste. Les noms de lieu de la France; leur origine, leur signification, leurs transformations. Résumé des conférences de toponomastique générale faites à l'École pratique des Hautes-Études, publié par Paul Marichal et Léon Mirot. 5 fasc., xiii, 831 p. Paris: Champion, 1920-29.
Reviewed by H. Stein, *Moyen Age*, 1921, 32: 178-80; 1923, 34: 264-6; by Albert Dauzat, *Larousse Mens.*, 1930, 8: 311-12.

HKG

BESCHORNER, Hans. Die sächsische Landschaft im Wandel der geschichtlichen Jahrhunderte. *Mitt.Ver.Erdk.Dresden*, 1913, 2: 749-82.

HKH

POSEWITZ, Theod. Aus alten Zeiten in der Tátra. *Jahrb.Ungar. Karpathenver.*, 1913, 40: 1-39.

HKHnh

NÉMETH, Julius. Magna Hungaria. *Beiträge zur historischen Geographie, Kulturgeographie, Ethnographie und Kartographie, vornehmlich des Orients, Festband Eugen Oberhummer*, p. 92-8. Leipzig: Deuticke, 1929.
Traces the origin of the name "Magyar".

HKI

RODOLICO, Francesco. L'explorazione naturalistica dell'Appennino. 403 p., ill. Florence: Le Monnier, 1964.
Reviewed by Mario Loria, *Physis*, 1964, 6: 237-9.

HKJ

REPARAZ-RUIZ, G. de. Essai sur l'histoire de la géographie de l'Espagne. *Ann.Midi*, 1940, 5: 280-341.

HKJce-bv

SCHÜTZ, Julius Franz. Bausteine zu einer Bibliographie der Canarischen, Madeirischen und Capverdischen Inseln und der Azoren (bis einschl. 1920). iv, 144 p. (Bücherkunde in Einzeldarstellungen, 2) Graz: Moser, 1929.

HKK

AMERYCKX, J.; VERHULST, A. Enkele historisch-geografische problemen in verband met de oudste geschiedenis van de Vlaamse Kustvlakte. Een Colloquium van bodemkundigen en historici. Quelques problèmes de géographie historique se rapportant à l'histoire la plus ancienne de la côte flamande. Un colloque de pédologistes et d'historiens. 24 p., maps. (Voorlichtingsreeks, 22) Gent: Oostvlaams Verbond van de Kringen voor Geschiedenis, 1958.

HKKnh

VINCENT, Auguste. Que signifient nos noms de lieux? 91 p. (Collection Nationale, 82) Bruxelles: Office de Publicité, 1947. [CB 72/277]
Regarding our knowledge of Belgian place names.

HKM

MORRILL, R.L. The development of spatial distributions of towns in Sweden: an historical-predictive approach. *Ann. Ass.Amer.Geogr.*, 1963, 53: 1-14.

STEFANSSON, Vilhjalmur. Iceland: the first American Republic. xxxviii, 275 p., front., ill. New York: Doubleday, Doran, 1939.
Reprinted 1943.
Reviewed by George Sarton, *Isis*, 1943, 34: 379-80.

HKMce-bv

KLOSE, Olaf. Islandkatalog der Universitätsbibliothek Kiel und der Universitäts- und Stadtbibliothek Köln, hrsg. v.d. Univ.-Bibl. Kiel. xii, 423 p. (Kataloge d. Univ.-Bibl. Kiel, hrsg. v. Christoph Weber, 1) Kiel: Univ.-Bibl., 1931.
Reviewed by Andreas Heusler, *Deut.Lit.Zeitung*, 1932, 3: 928-9.

HKN

BERG, L.S. Istoria geograficheskogo oznakomleniya s Yakutskim kraem. [History of the geographical exploration of the Yakutsk region. (In Russian)] In: Yakoutiia: sbornik statei pod redaktsiei Vittenbourga [Collection of articles edited by P. Vittenbourg], p. 1-38. Leningrad: Akademiia Nauk SSSR, 1927.
Reviewed by N. Transehe, *Isis*, 1928, 11: 398-9.

JITKOV, B. K istorii issledovanii Russkogo Severa. [On the history of the exploration of the Russian North. (In Russian, with French summary)] *Zemlevedenie*, 1924, 26: 159-80. [CB 21/538]
The expedition of A.V. Juravski between the northern Ural Mountains and the Pechora River 1904-8 is described in detail.

LUBIMENKO, Inna. Le rôle comparatif des différents peuples dans la découverte et la description de la Russie. *Rev.Syn. Hist.*, 1929, 48: 37-56.

NANSEN, Fridtjof. L'Arménie et le proche orient. 364 p., ill., 3 maps. Paris: Imprimerie Massis, 1928. [CB 42/501]

NANSEN, Fridtjof. Through the Caucasus to the Volga. Transl. by G.C. Wheeler. 255 p. London: Allen and Unwin, 1931.

UMURAZAKOV, S.U. Kratkii ocherk istorii geograficheskogo izuchenia Kirgizii. [A brief essay on the history of the geographic study of Kirghizia. (In Russian)] *Tr.Inst.Ist. Est.Tekh.*, 1962, 42: 3-39.

YAKOUTIIA: sbornik statei pod redaktsiei Vittenbourga. [Yakoutiia: collection of articles edited by P. Vittenbourg. (In Russian)] xxvi, 745 p., ill. Leningrad: Akademiia Nauk SSSR, 1927.
Results of exploration in 1925.

HKO

ARGENTI, P.P.; KYRIAKIDIS, S.P.; ed. Chios according to the geographers and travellers. 3 vol. xvi, 1944 p., 78 pl. Athens: Estia Press, 1946. [CB 76/401]
Reviewed by T.J.D., *Geogr.J.*, 1949, 113: 106.
In ten European languages.

IORGA, Nicolae. Istoria Românilor prin călători. [History of Rumania from the writings of travellers. (In Rumanian)] 4 vol. 1. Până la jumatatea sec. al XVII-ea. [Up to middle of 17th century] 287 p.; 2. Până la 1800. [Up to 1800] 250 p.; 3. Până în zilele noastre. [Up to our own day] 269 p.; 4. Şi adause. [Supplement] 86 p. Bucureşti: 1919-22.
2nd edition Văleni: 1928-29.

KURZ, Marcel. Le Mont Olympe (Thessalie). x, 232 p., 14 pl., 3 panoramas, 2 maps. Paris: Victor Attinger, 1923. [CB 18/584]

NOPCSA, Ferencz. Geographie und Geologie Nordalbaniens. Mit einem Anhang: Zur Geschichte der Kartographie des Gebietes. 1. Beiträge zur Kartographie Albaniens nach orientalischen Quellen von H. von Mzik. 2. Zur Geschichte der okzidentalen Kartographie Nordalbaniens von F. Nopcsa. xiv, 703, 35 p. (*Geol.Hung.Ser.Geol.*, 3) Budapest: Institutum Regni Hungariae Geologicum, 1929.
Reviewed by J.W. Gregory, *Nature*, 1930, 125: 8-9.

HKOda

IORGA, Nicolae. Une vingtaine de voyageurs dans l'Orient européen. *Rev.Hist.Sud-Est Europé.*, 1928, 5: 288-354. [CB 26/238]

HKOwf-da

IORGA, Nicolae. Les voyageurs français dans l'Orient européen (du XVe au XVIIIe siècle). 128 p. Paris: J. Gamber, 1928.

HKP ASIA MINOR

BRAWER, A.J. Le progrès et les changements dans la géographie de la Palestine depuis 1914. *Compt.Rend.Congr.Int.Géogr.* (Cairo, 1925), (5), p. 37-45, 1 map. Le Caire: 1926. [CB 22/282]

BURCHARDT, Hermann. Aus dem Jemen. Hermann Burchardts letzte Reise durch Südarabien. Bearbeitet von Eugen Mittwoch. [In Arabic and German] iv, 75 p. Leipzig: Deutsche Morgenländische Gesellschaft, 1926.
Reviewed by R. Levy, *J.Roy.Asiatic Soc.*, 1929, 394.

DE GAURY, Gerald. Arabian journey and other desert travels. 190 p., 31 pl., 3 maps. London: Harrap, 1950.

DEUTSCHES ARCHÄOLOGISCHES INSTITUT. ABTEILUNG ISTANBUL. Wegweiser für wissenschaftliche Reisen in der Türkei. 68, 5 p., 1 plan. Istanbul: 1930.
2nd edition. vii, 68 p. Istanbul: Buchhandlung Kapps, 1933.
Reviewed by U. Kahrstedt, *Orient.Lit.Zeitung*, 1932, 35: 271.

GLUECK, Nelson. The river Jordan. Being an illustrated account of earth's most storied river. xvi, 268 p., ill. Philadelphia: Westminster Press, 1946. [CB 70/239]

GRANT, Christina Phelps. The Syrian desert. Caravans, travel and exploration. xv, 410 p., 16 pl., 4 maps. London: Black, 1937; New York: Macmillan, 1938. [CB 53/250]
Reviewed by George Sarton, *Isis*, 1938, 29: 143-5.

HARTMANN, Richard. Im neuen Anatolien. Reiseeindrücke. iv, 148 p., 65 fig. Leipzig: Hinrichs, 1928.
Reviewed by Theodor Menzel, *Deut.Lit.Zeitung*, 1930, 1: 1337-9.

IKBĀL 'ALI SHĀH, Sirdar. Westward to Mecca: a journey of adventure through Afghanistan, bolshevik Asia, Persia, Iraq and Hijaz to the cradle of Islam. 224 p., 12 pl. London: Witherby, 1928.
Reviewed by H.L.C., *Nature*, 1929, 124: 539.

KAMMERER, Albert. La mer Rouge. L'Abyssinie et l'Arabie depuis l'antiquité. Essai d'histoire et de géographie historique. 3 vol. (*Mém.Soc.Géogr.Egypte*, 15-17) Le Caire: 1929-52.

KIERNAN, Reginald Hugh. The unveiling of Arabia. The story of Arabian travel and discovery. 360 p., 31 ill., maps. London: Harrap, 1937.
Reviewed by George Sarton, *Isis*, 1938, 29: 143-5.

MUSIL, Alois. Arabia Deserta, a topographical itinerary. xvii, 631 p., ill., maps. (American Geographical Society, Oriental Explorations and Studies, 2) New York: 1927. [CB 22/250]

MUSIL, Alois. The middle Euphrates, a topographical itinerary. xv, 426 p., ill. (American Geographical Society. Oriental Explorations and Studies, 3) New York: 1927.

MUSIL, Alois. The northern Heǧâz, a topographical itinerary. xii, 374 p., ill., maps. (American Geographical Society, Oriental Explorations and Studies, 1) New York: 1926. [CB 22/249]

MUSIL, Alois. Northern Neǧd, a topographical itinerary. xiii, 368 p., ill. (American Geographical Society. Oriental Explorations and Studies, 5) New York: 1928.

MUSIL, Alois. Palmyrena, a topographical itinerary. xiv, 367 p., ill. (American Geographical Society. Oriental Explorations and Studies, 4) New York: 1928.

MŽIK, Hans von, ed. Beiträge zur historischen Geographie, Kulturgeographie und Kartographie, vornehmlich des Orients. Festband Eugen Oberhummer. viii, 202 p., 4 pl., 7 fig., 6 maps, facs. Leipzig: Deuticke, 1929.

NANSEN, Fridtjof. *See* HKN

PETRIE, William Matthew Flinders. Eastern exploration, past and future. (Royal Institution Lectures) vi, 118 p. London: Constable, 1918.

PHILBY, Harry St. John B. Arabia. xx, 364 p. London: Benn, 1930.
Reviewed by H.A.R. Gibb, *Bull.Sch.Orient.Stud.*, 1931, 6: 794-5.

PHILBY, Harry St. John B. Arabian days: an autobiography. xvi, 336 p., ill. London: R. Hale, 1948.
Reviewed by S.M. Zwemer, *Muslim World*, 1948, 38: 298-300.

PHILBY, Harry St. John B. The empty quarter; being a description of the Great South Desert of Arabia known as Rub'al Khali. xxiv, 432 p., maps, ill. New York: Holt, 1933.
Reviewed in *Geogr.Rev.*, 1934, 24: 510-12.

PHILBY, Harry St.J.B. The heart of Arabia: a record of travel and exploration. 2 vol. xxiii, 386 p.; vii, 354 p. London: Constable, 1922.

RATHJENS, Carl; WISSMANN, Hermann von. Rathjens-von Wissmannsche Südarabien-Reise. [Reports] 3. Landeskundliche Ergebnisse. xvi, 229 p., maps, ill. (Hamburgische Universität. Abhandlungen aus dem Gebiet der Auslandskunde, 40. Series B. Völkerkunde, Kulturgeschichte und Sprachen, 20) Hamburg: De Gruyter, 1934.
Reviewed in *Geogr.Rev.*, 1935, 25: 521.

RIHANI, Ameen. Arabian peak and desert: travels in al-Yaman. ix, 280 p., 14 pl. London: Constable, 1930.
Reviewed by D.S.M., *J.Roy.Asiatic Soc.*, 1931, 675-6.

THOMAS, Bertram Sidney. Alarms and excursions in Arabia. With a preface by Arnold T. Wilson. 296 p. London: Allen and Unwin, 1931.

THOMAS, Bertram Sidney. Arabia Felix: across the empty quarter of Arabia with an appendix by Sir Arthur Keith. xxix, 397 p., 48 pl. London: Cape, 1932.

VAN DER MEULEN, D. Aden to the Hadhramaut. A journey in South Arabia. With foreword by Sir Bernard Reilly. xvi, 254 p., front., ill., map. London: Murray, 1947. [CB 73/162]

HKPda

GALDSTON, Iago. Medical explorers of Arabia. *Bull.N.Y.Acad.Med.*, 1937, 13: 512-38.

SEIDE, J. Doctors and naturalists as pilgrims and travellers to the Holy Land. *Janus*, 1959, 48: 53-61.

HKPvm

EISENSTEIN, J.D., ed. Ozar Massaoth, a collection of itineraries by Jewish travellers to Palestine, Syria, Egypt and other countries ... with maps, notes and index. (In Hebrew) Vol. 1. 352 p. New York: Priv. print., 1926.
Reviewed by Joshua Finkel, *Isis*, 1928, 11: 147-9.

HKPwb

BUTLER, Howard Crosby; NORRIS, Frederick A.; STOEVER, Edward Royal. Geography and itinerary [of the Expedition]. ix, 114 p., maps, 57 ill. (Syria: publications of the Princeton University archaeological expeditions to Syria in 1904-1905 and 1909. Division 1) Leyden: Brill, 1930.
Reviewed by Louis Jalabert, *J.Savants*, 1931, 199-207.

HKPwf-da

DEHÉRAIN, Henri. [Lecture at the closing session of the 58th Congress of Learned Societies, Paris, April 18, 1925] *Bull. Sect.Géogr.Comité Trav.Hist.Sci.*, 1925, 40: xlvi-lx.
On geographical contributions of French travelers, consuls, and officers in the army, navy, and merchant marine in the Levant during the 17th-19th centuries.

HKQ NORTH AFRICA

BAGNOLD, Ralph A. Libyan sands. Travel in a dead world. xi, 351 p., portr., pl., maps. London: Hodder and Stoughton, 1935.

BAZIN, René. Charles de Foucauld, explorateur du Maroc, ermite au Sahara. 478 p., portr., map. Paris: Plon-Nourrit, 1921. [CB 13/242]

DUMREICHER, André von. Fahrten, Pfadfinder und Beduinen in den Wüsten Ägyptens. 244 p., 31 fig. München: Drei Masken, 1931.
Reviewed by M. Meyerhof, *Orient.Lit.Zeitung*, 1932, 35: 133.

GHISLERI, A. La Libia nella storia e nei viaggiatori dai tempi Omerici all'occupazione italiana. viii, 171 p., front., pl., maps. Torino: G.B. Paravia, 1928.

HAARDT, Georges Marie; AUDOUIN-DUBREUIL, Louis. Le raid Citroën. La première traversée du Sahara en automobiles. De Touggourt à Tombouctou par l'Atlantide. 307 p., ill., 2 maps. Introd. de André Citroën; illustrations de Bernard Boutet de Monvel. Paris: Plon, 1923.
English translation: Across the Sahara by motor car (London: Fisher Unwin, 1924).

INSTITUT DES HAUTES ETUDES MAROCAINES. Initiation au Maroc. 2nd ed. xiv, 357 p. Paris: Les Editions d'Art et d'Histoire, 1937. [CB 54/523]

LUDWIG, Emil. The Nile: the life-story of a river: from the source to Egypt. Translated by Mary H. Lindsay. 352 p., 34 pl. London: Allen, 1936.
Reviewed by H.E. Hurst, *Nature*, 1937, 139: 351.

MORI, Attilio. L'esplorazione geografica della Libia. Rassegna storica e bibliografica. 112 p., map. (Governo della Cirenaica, Ufficio Studi: Rapporti e Monografie Coloniale, Serie 2a, no. 5) Florence: Tipografia Mariano Ricci, 1927.

SLOUSCHZ, Nahum. Travels in North Africa. ix, 488 p. Philadelphia: Jewish Publication Society of America, 1927.
Reviewed in *Jew.Quart.Rev.*, 1929, 19: 439

'UMAR TUSŪN, *prince*. Mémoire sur l'histoire du Nil. 3 vol. 1. v, 264 p., ill.; 2. p. 265-543, 52 tables; 3. 5 pl., 17 maps. (Mémoires présentés à l'Institut d'Egypte, 8, 9, 10) Cairo: Imprimerie de l'Institut français d'archéologie orientale, 1925. [CB 18/627 and CB 16/304]

HKQnh

CRONE, Gerald R. The origin of the name *Antillia*. *Geogr.J.*, 1938, 91: 260-2.
Argues, with reproductions from charts, that *Antillia* was derived by a series of copyists' blunders, from *Getulia*, the classical name for the western region of Mediterranean Africa.

HKQwf-da

LEBEL, Roland. Les voyageurs français du Maroc. L'exotisme marocain dans la littérature de voyage. 406 p. (Bibliothèque de culture et de vulgarisation nord-africaines) Paris: Larose, 1936.
Reviewed by Pierre Brunet, *Archeion*, 1936, 18: 409.

HKR ASIA IN GENERAL; CENTRAL ASIA

for the exploration of the Himalayas
see HM and HN

ANDREWS, Roy Chapman. New expedition to Central Asia. *Natur. Hist.*, 1920, 20: 349-55. [CB 10/210]

ANDREWS, Roy Chapman, *et al.* The new conquest of Central Asia: a narrative of the explorations of the Central Asiatic expeditions in Mongolia and China, 1921-1930. With chapters by Walter Granger, Clifford H. Pope, Nels C. Nelson; and summary statements by others. 679 p., 128 pl. (Central Asiatic Expeditions: Natural history of Central Asia, 1) New York: American Museum of Natural History, 1932.
Reviewed in *Nature*, 1933, 132: 81-3; and by C.E.A.W. Oldham, *J.Roy.Asiatic Soc.*, 1934, 825-8.

BELL, Charles. Tibet, past and present. xiv, 326 p., 93 ill. Oxford: Clarendon Press, 1924.
German translation by Karl Hans Pollogg (Leipzig: 1925)
Reviewed by Friedrich Weller, *Asia Major*, 1927, 4: 462-4.

BERGER, A. Mit Sven Hedin durch Asiens Wüsten. 383 p. Berlin: Wegweiser-Verlag, 1932.

BOSSHARDT, Walter. Durch Tibet und Turkistan. Reisen im unberührten Asien. xv, 246 p., ill., maps. Stuttgart: Strecker & Schröder, 1930.

BURNHAM, John Bird. The rim of mystery. A hunter's wanderings in unknown Siberian Asia. xv, 281 p., 60 ill., map. New York: Putnam, 1929.
Reviewed by C. Mabel Rickmers, *J.Roy.Asiatic Soc.*, 1930, 184-6.

CABLE, Mildred; FRENCH, Francesca. The Gobi desert. 303 p., ill. London: Hodder and Stoughton, 1942; New York: Macmillan, 1944. [CB 65/74]
Reviewed by M.F.A.M., *Isis*, 1945, 36: 71.

CABLE, Mildred; FRENCH, Francesca. Through Jade Gate and central Asia: an account of journeys in Kansu, Turkestan, and the Gobi Desert. xvi, 304 p., 12 pl. London: Constable, 1927.

CHARPENTIER, Jarl. Some additional remarks on vol. 1 of Sven Hedin's "Southern Tibet". *Geogr.Ann.*, 1919, 269-89.
For the book cited *see* Hedin, Sven Anders, et al. below.

DABBS, Jack A. History of the discovery and exploration of Chinese Turkestan. 225 p., 4 maps. (Central Asiatic Studies, 8) The Hague: Mouton, 1963.

DAVID-NEEL, Alexandra. Voyage d'une Parisienne à Lhassa. A pied et en mendiant de la Chine à l'Inde à travers le Thibet. xii, 332 p., ill. Paris: Plon, 1927.
Reviewed by George Sarton, *Isis*, 1930, 14: 441-4.
English translation: My journey to Lhasa (New York/London: Harper, 1927) reviewed by H. Less Shuttleworth, *J.Roy. Asiatic Soc.*, 1928, 160-3. German translation: Arjopa (Leipzig: Brockhaus, 1928) reviewed by A.H. Francke, *Deut. Lit.Zeitung*, 1929 6: 1785-6.

DAVID-NEEL, Alexandra. Grand Thibet: au pays des brigands gentilshommes. 356 p., ill. Paris: Plon, 1933.
German translation: Mönche und Strauchritter. (Leipzig: Brockhaus, 1933). English translation: Tibetan journey. (London: Lane, 1936).
Reviewed by J. Bacot, *J.Asiatique*, 1933, 222: 103.

FILCHNER, Wilhelm. My central Asian expedition, 1925-8. *J.Roy. Asiat.Soc.*, 1929, 685-91.

FILCHNER, Wilhelm. Om Mani Padme Hum. Meine China- und Thibet-Expedition 1925-28. ix, 352 p., 103 ill., map. Leipzig: Brockhaus, 1929.
Reviewed by C. Mabel Rickmers, *J.Roy.Asiatic Soc.*, 1929, 932-4; by Aug. Herm. Francke, *Deut.Lit.Zeitung*, 1929, 6: 2316-18.

GLINKA, G.B.; TKHORSHCHEVSKI, I.I.; TSETKOV, M.A.; ed. [Asiatic Russia. (In Russian)] 3 vol. 1 & 2. Text. viii, 576 p., 638 p., numerous ill.; 3. Index. xcv p., 1 atlas, 71 maps, 4 p., introductory text, 23 p., index. St. Petersburg: Emigration Bureau of the General Office for Land Improvement and Agriculture, 1914. [CB 18/587]

HEDIN, Sven Anders. Across the Gobi desert. Transl. from the German by H.J. Cant. xxi, 402 p., 114 ill., 3 maps. London: Routledge, 1931.
Reviewed by C.E.A.W.O., *J.Roy.Asiat.Soc.*, 1932, 1021-4.
German edition Auf grosser Fahrt (Leipzig: Brockhaus, 1929) reviewed by Albrecht Penck, *Deut.Lit.Zeitung*, 1929, 6: 733-4; in *Geogr.Rev.*, 1929, 19: 694-6.

HEDIN, Sven Anders. Jehol, city of emperors. Transl. from the Swedish by E.J. Nash. xiv, 278 p., 65 ill., map. London: Kegan Paul, 1932.
Reviewed by T.C. Hodson, *J.Roy.Asiat.Soc.*, 1933, 480-2; in *Nature*, 1933, 131: 184-5.
German translation (Leipzig: Brockhaus, 1932) reviewed by T.C. Hodson, *J.Roy.Asiat.Soc.*, 1933, 208.

HEDIN, Sven Anders. Riddles of the Gobi desert. Transl. from the Swedish by Elizabeth Sprigge and Claude Napier. x, 382 p., 24 pl. London: Routledge, 1933.
Reviewed in *Nature*, 1934, 133: 159.
German translation Rätsel der Gobi (Leipzig: Brockhaus, 1931) reviewed by Vorwahl, *Mitt.Gesch.Med.*, 1931, 30: 294.

HEDIN, Sven Anders. Tibet. *Open Court*, 1933, 47: 67-95, 3 ill.

HEDIN, Sven Anders, et al. Southern Tibet; discoveries in former times compared with my own researches in 1906-1908. 9 vol., 2 folders of maps, atlas of Tibetan panoramas, maps, ill. Stockholm: Lithographic Institute of the General Staff of the Swedish Army, 1916-22. [CB 15/188]

HEIM, Arnold. Minya Gongkar: Forschungsreise ins Hochgebirge von chinesisch Tibet. 244 p., maps, ill. Bern: Huber, 1933.
Reviewed by H. de Terra, *Geogr.Rev.*, 1935, 25: 169.

KINGDON-WARD, Francis. The riddle of the Tsangpo gorges. xv, 328 p. With contributions by the Earl Cawdor. London: Arnold, 1926.

KINGDON-WARD, Jean. My hill so strong. 240 p. London: Cape, 1952.

LOPATIN, I.A. Russian Asia. *Open Court*, 1933, 47: 120-44, 1 ill.

McGOVERN, W. Montgomery. To Lhasa in disguise: an account of a secret expedition through mysterious Tibet. 352 p. London: Thornton Butterworth, 1924.

MARGERIE, Emmanuel de. L'oeuvre de Sven Hedin et l'orographie du Tibet. 139 p., 28 fig., 1 portr. *(Bull.Sec.Géogr. Comité Trav.Hist.Sci.*, 1928) Paris: Imprimerie Nationale, 1929. [CB 29/276]

PELLIOT, Paul. La Haute Asie. 37 p., 21 ill. (Brochure publiée à l'occasion de la Mission Citroen Centre-Asie) Paris: Edition Artistique, [1936?].
Reviewed by Henri Bernard, *Monumenta Serica*, 1935-36, 1: 203.

RICKMERS, Willi Rickmer. Alai! Alai! Arbeiten und Erlebnisse der Deutsch-Russischen Alai-Pamir-Expedition. 300 p., 90 fig., 52 diagr., map. Leipzig: Brockhaus, 1930.
Reviewed by Fritz Machatschek, *Deut.Lit.Zeitung*, 1931, 2: 754-5.

RICKMERS, Willi Rickmer. Travels in the Altai-Pamirs. *J.Roy. Asiat.Soc., 3rd ser.*, 1929, 691-6.

ROERICH, George Nicholas. Trails to inmost Asia: five years of exploration with the Roerich Central Asian expedition. xx, 504 p., 151 ill., 1 map. New Haven: Yale University Press; London: Oxford University Press, 1931.
Reviewed by C.E.A.W.O., *J.Roy.Asiatic Soc.*, 1932, 713-17.

ROERICH, Nicholas Konstantin. Altai-Himalaya. A travel diary. xix, 407 p. New York: Stokes, 1929; London: Jarrolds, 1930.
Written during the Roerich American expedition in Central Asia, 1924-28.

SHERAP, Paul. A Tibetan on Tibet: being the travels and observations of Mr. Paul Sherap (Dorje Zödba) of Tachienlu. With an introductory chapter on Buddhism, and a concluding chapter on the Devil Dance by G.A. Combe. xx, 212 p., portr., map, bibliogr. London: T. Fisher Unwin, 1926.

STEIN, Aurel. Innermost Asia. Detailed report of explorations in Central Asia, Kan-su and eastern Iran, carried out and described under the orders of H.M. Indian Government. 4 vol. 1. Text. xxxix, p. 1-547; 2. Text. xii, p. 549-1159; 3. Plates and plans. xi p., 137 pl., 59 plans; 4. Maps. Oxford: Clarendon Press, 1928.
Reviewed by F.W. Thomas, *J.Roy.Asiatic Soc.*, 1929, 944-51.

STEIN, Aurel. On ancient Central-Asian tracks. Brief narrative of three expeditions in innermost Asia and northwestern China. xxiv, 342 p., 102 pl. London: Macmillan, 1933.
Reviewed by Arthur W. Hummel, *Amer.Hist.Rev.*, 1933, 39: 360; in *Nature*, 1933, 131: 415-17; by O. Stein, *Deut.Lit. Zeitung*, 1934, 5: 274-6; by C.E.A.W. Oldham, *J.Roy.Asiatic Soc.*, 1935, 822-5.

STEIN, Aurel. Serindia: detailed report of explorations in Central Asia and Westernmost China, carried out and described under the orders of H.M. Indian Government. 1580 p., 345 ill., 59 plans, 175 pl., 96 maps. Vol. 1-3, text; vol. 4, plates; vol. 5, maps. Oxford: Clarendon Press, 1921.
Reviewed by Lionel Giles, *J.Roy.Asiatic Soc.*, 1924, 141-6.

TEICHMAN, Eric. Travels of a consular officer in Eastern Tibet. Together with a history of the relations between China, Tibet and India. xxiv, 248 p., 64 pl., 8 maps. Cambridge University Press, 1922.

VISSER, Ph.C. Zwischen Kara-Korum und Hindukusch. Eine Reise nach dem unbekannten Herzen Asiens. 288 p., ill. Leipzig: Brockhaus, 1928.
Reviewed by A. Herrmann, *Orient.Lit.Zeitung*, 1930, 33: 794-6.

WADDELL, Laurence Austine. Lhasa and its mysteries: with a record of the expedition of 1903-4. 4th ed. 534 p. London: Methuen, 1930.
First published 1905.

WILLFORT, Fritz. Turkestanisches Tagebuch. Sechs Jahre in Russisch-Zentralasien. Unter Mitarbeit von Hans Prager. viii, 327 p., 27 fig., 2 maps. Wien: Braumüller, 1930.
Reviewed by H. Jansky, *Orient.Lit.Zeitung*, 1932, 35: 487-9.

HKRda

ROBINSON, Victor. The physician as explorer in Asia. *Ciba Symp.* (Summit, N.J.), 1940, 2: 626-32.

HKRnh

BENVENISTE, Emile. Mots voyageurs en Asie centrale. *J.Asiatique*, 1948, 236: 177-88.

HKRwi

DE FILIPPI, Filippo. The Italian expedition of the Himalaya, Karakoram and Eastern Turkestan, 1913-1914. xvi, 528 p., pl. London: Arnold, 1932.

DE FILIPPI, Filippo. Relazioni scientifiche della spedizione italiana De Filippi, nell'Himàlaia, Caracorùm e Turchestàn Cinese, 1913-1914. Ser. 1. Geodesia e geofisica. 3 vol.; Ser. 2. Resultati geologici e geografici. 12 vol. Bologna: Nicola Zanichelli, 1925, 1922-35. [CB 24/484]

TUCCI, Giuseppe. Santi e briganti nel Tibet ignoto. (Diario della spedizione nel Tibet occidentale 1935). xv, 190 p., 268 fig., 154 pl., 1 map. Milan: Hoepli, 1937.

TUCCI, Giuseppe; GHERSI, E. Cronaca della missione scientifica Tucci nel Tibet occidentale (1933). 2 pl., 272 fig. (Reale Accademia d'Italia, Viaggi di Studio ed Esplorazioni, 2) Rome: 1934.

HKRwn

KOZLOV, Petr Kuz'mich. Mongolei, Amdo und die tote Stadt Chara Choto. Die Expedition der Russischen Geographischen Gesellschaft, 1907-1909. Mit einem Geleitwort von Dr. Sven von Hedin, herausgegeben von Dr. Wilhelm Filchner. Autorisierte Uebersetzung aus dem Russischen von L. Breitfuss und P.G. Zeidler. xiii, 304 p., 129 ill., 4 maps. Berlin: Naufeld & Henius, 1925.

LOBANOV-ROSTOVSKY, A. Russia and Asia. viii, 334 p. New York: Macmillan, 1933.
Reviewed by G.F. Hudson, *Geogr.J.*, 1933, 82: 74-5.
A straightforward narrative of Russian exploration and expansion in Asia.

HKS SOUTH WESTERN ASIA

for Asia Minor *see* HKP

CHATTERJEE, S.P. Bengal in maps. A geographical analysis of resource distribution in West Bengal and Eastern Pakistan. Foreword by Syama Prasad Mockerjee. 105 p. Bombay: Orient Longmans, 1949.

FURON, Raymond. L'Afghanistan. Géographie, histoire, ethnographie, voyages. 133 p., ill., maps. Paris: Blanchard, 1926.
Reviewed by G. Regelsperger, *Rev.Gen.Sci.*, 1926, 37: 589.

MURRAY, John, publisher. A handbook for travellers in India, Burma and Ceylon. 9th ed. clxviii, 664 p., 79 maps, plans. London: Murray, 1913.
19th edition. cii, 634 p. London: Murray, 1962.
Reviewed by G. Sarton, *Isis*, 1919, 2: 402-3.

STARK, Freya. The valleys of the Assassins and other Persian travels. 365 p., 32 ill., 6 maps. London: Murray, 1934.

STEIN, Aurel. The Indo-Iranian borderlands: their prehistory in the light of geography and of recent explorations. *J. Roy.Anthropol.Inst.*, 1934, 64: 179-202, pl., 2 maps. [CB 42/566]

HKT FAR EAST

HANDEL-MAZZETTI, Heinrich. Naturbilder aus Südwest-China: Erlebnisse und Eindrücke eines österreichischen Forschers während des Weltkrieges. xiv, 380 p., 77 pl. Wien: Oesterreichischer Bundesverlag für Unterricht, Wissenschaft und Kunst, 1927.
Reviewed by A. Henry, *Nature*, 1927, 119: 667-8.

HEDIN, Sven. The silk road. Transl. from the Swedish by F.H. Lyon. viii, 322 p., 31 pl. London: Routledge, 1938.
Translation of: Sidenvägen. 405 p. Stockholm: 1936.

LICENT, Emile. Hoang ho - Pai ho. Comptes rendus de onze années (1923-1933) de séjour et d'exploration dans le bassin du Fleuve Jaune, du Pai Ho, et des autres tributaires du golfe du Pei Tcheu ly. 3 vol. 1061 p., 77 maps. (Publications du Musée Hoang Ho-Pai Ho, 38) Tientsin: Mission de Sienhsien, 1936.
Reviewed by Eugene A. Golomshtok, *J.Amer.Orient.Soc.*, 1937, 57: 449-51.

PEREIRA, George Edward. From Peking to Lhasa: the narrative of journeys in the Chinese Empire. Compiled by Sir Francis Younghusband from notes and diaries supplied by Major-General Sir Cecil Pereira. x, 293 p., 33 pl. London: Constable, 1926.

HKV SOUTH EASTERN ASIA

MURRAY, John, publisher. *See* HKS

SHARP, C. Andrew. The discovery of the Pacific islands. xiv, 259 p., maps. Oxford: Clarendon Press, 1960.
Reviewed by Mary Boyd, *Isis*, 1962, 53: 400.

HKW AUSTRALIA

DAVIES, Stephen H. Early discoveries in the northern territory. *Queensland Geogr.J.*, 1924-26, 40-41: 24-34.
Notes on explorations of the coast of the northern territory between Cape Wessel and the Western Australian border from the early seventeenth century to 1849.

JACK, Robert Logan. Northmost Australia. Three centuries of exploration, discovery and adventure in and around the Cape York Peninsula, Queensland. 2 vol. 381 p.; 415 p. London: Simpkin, 1922.

SCOTT, Ernest. Australian discovery. 2 vol., ill., maps. 1. By sea; 2. By land. London: Dent, 1929.
Reviewed in *Geogr.J.*, 1930, 75: 189.

HKWce

GARNIER, B.J. Geographical literature of New Zealand. *Geogr. J.*, 1947, 109: 271-5.

HKWda

ELDER, John Rawson. The pioneer explorers of New Zealand. 121 p., pl. London: Blackie, 1929.

HKWnh

RYAN, J. Australian place names - a neglected study. *Australian Geogr.*, 1964, 9: 218-22.

HKX AFRICA

for North Africa *see* HKQ

BECK, Hanno. Caput Nili - zur Geschichte des Problems der Quellen des Nils. *Naturwiss.Rundsch.*, 1964, 17: 183-8.

CARBONERA, G. L'esplorazione del continente nero. 151 p., ill. (I Grandi Viaggi di Scoperta, 4) Milano: Federazione Italiana delle Biblioteche Popolari, [n.d.]. [CB 20/209]

CHEESMAN, Robert Ernest. Lake Tana and the Blue Nile. An Abyssinian quest. xiv, 400 p., pl., map. London: Macmillan, 1936.

EYDOUX, Henri Paul. L'exploration du Sahara. 242 p. Paris: Gallimard, 1938.
Reviewed by W. Fitzgerald, *Geogr.J.*, 1939, 94: 247-8.

FONTOYNONT, Antoine; RAOMANDAHY, Emmanuel. La grande Comore. 105 p., 17 ill. (Mémoires de l'Académie Malgache, 23) Tananarive: Imprimerie moderne de l'Emyrne, 1937. [CB 58/561]

FROBENIUS, Leo. Und Afrika sprach. 3 vol. Berlin: Soc. Vita, 1912.
See essay review by Gradenwitz below.

GAUTIER, E.F. Les premiers résultats de la mission Frobenius. *Rev.Afr.*, 1921, 62: 47-61. [CB 12/623]

GILLIER, R.P.L. La pénétration en Mauritanie. Découverte - explorations - conquête. La police du désert et la pacification définitive, etc. xii. 360 p. Paris: Paul Geuthner, 1926. [CB 22/296]

GRADENWITZ, Alfred. L'art africain. *La Nature*, 1913, 2e sem., 229-32, 7 fig.
On Frobenius's expedition and his book, *see* above.

HAARDT, Georges Marie; AUDOUIN-DUBREUIL, Louis. Le raid Citroën. La première traversée du Sahara en automobiles. De Touggourt à Tombouctou par l'Atlantide. 307 p., ill., 2 maps. Introd. de André Citroën; illustrations de Bernard Boutet de Monvel. Paris: Plon, 1923.
English translation: Across the Sahara by motor car (London: Fisher Unwin, 1924).

KAMMERER, Albert. La mer Rouge. L'Abyssinie et l'Arabie depuis l'antiquité. Essai d'histoire et de géographie historique. 3 vol. (*Mém.Soc.Géogr.Egypte*, 15-17) Le Caire: 1929-52.

LANGENMEIER, Theodor. Lexikon zur alten Geographie des südöstlichen Aequatorialafrika. vii, 100 p., 50 ill. (*Abhandlungen des Hamburgischen Kolonialinstituts*, 39) Hamburg: Friederichsen, 1918.

WITTE, Jehan de. Un explorateur et un apôtre du Congo français. Monseigneur Augouard, archevêque titulaire de Cassiopée, vicaire apostolique du Congo français. Sa vie, ses notes de voyage et sa correspondance. x, 372 p., 71 ill., 1 pl., map. Paris: Emile-Paul frères, 1924.
Prosper Augouard's African career began in 1877.

HKXce-bv

PLATT, Elizabeth T. Madagascar: great isle, red isle. A bibliographical survey. *Geogr.Rev.*, 1937, 27: 301-8, 1 fig.

HKXda

HOWARD, C., ed. West African explorers. With an introduction by J.H. Plumb. ix, 598 p. (World's Classics, 523) London: Oxford University Press, 1951.
Reviewed by Erik Gren, *Lychnos*, 1953, 397.

ROBINSON, Victor. Medical explorers in Africa. *Ciba Symp.* (Summit, N.J.), 1940, 2: 633-42, fig.

HKXwb

AKELEY, Mary L. Jobe. Carl Akeley's Africa. The account of the Akeley-Eastman-Pomeroy African Hall Expedition of the American Museum of Natural History. Foreword by Henry Fairfield Osborn. xx, 322 p., ill., maps. London: Gollancz, 1931. [CB 33/371]
Reviewed by C.W. Hobley, *Geogr.J.*, 1931, 77: 573-4.

HKXwf-th

LEBEL, A. Roland. L'Afrique occidentale dans la littérature française (depuis 1870). ix, 277 p. Paris: Emile Larose, 1925. [CB 22/284]

HKYda

AXELSON, Erik, ed. South African explorers. xxv, 346 p., 1 map. London: Oxford University Press, 1954.
Reviewed by Erik Gren, *Lychnos*, 1956, 382-3.

HL POLAR EXPLORATION

CROFT, Andrew. Polar exploration. Epics of the twentieth century. x, 268 p. London: Black, 1939.
Reviewed by A. Courtauld, *Geogr.J.*, 1941, 97: 329-30.

DOBROWOLSKI, Antoni Boleslaw. Wyprawy polarne. [Polar expeditions. (In Polish)] xxviii, 359 p., 85 fig., 5 pl., 2 maps. Warsaw: 1925. [CB 24/539]
Reviewed by Stanislav Lencewicz, *Bibliogr.Géogr.*, 1926, 36: 561.

EASTON, C. Vijftig jaar poolonderzoek 1875-1925. [Fifty years of polar exploration. (In Dutch)] *Tijdschr.Ned. Aardrijksk.Genoot., 2nd ser.*, 1926, 43: 17-54, 5 maps.

ELIAS, Edith L. The book of polar exploration. 301 p., ill. London: Harrap, 1928.
French translation: Les explorations polaires (Pôle Nord, Pôle Sud) (Paris: Payot, 1930).

GREELY, A.W. The polar regions in the twentieth century: their discovery and industrial evolution. x, 270 p., maps, ill. Boston: Little, Brown & Co., 1928.
Reviewed in *Geogr.Rev.*, 1929, 19: 526.

HOBBS, William H. An explorer-scientist's pilgrimage. An autobiography. 222 p., ill. Ann Arbor, Mich.: Edwards, 1952.
Reviewed by George D. Hubbard, *Science*, 1952, 116: 490.

JOERG, W.L.G. Brief history of polar exploration since the introduction of flying. To accompany a physical map of the Arctic and a bathymetric map of the Antarctic. 49 p., 8 fig. (American Geographical Society, Special Publication 11) New York: American Geographical Society, 1930.

KIRWAN, L.P. A history of polar exploration. x, 374 p., maps, pl. New York: Norton, 1960.
English edition published under title: The white road (London: Hollis & Carter, 1959).
Reviewed by Erwin N. Hiebert, *Isis*, 1963, 54: 145-7; for other reviews *see* CB 86/465 and CB 87/567.

MARKHAM, Clements R. The lands of silence. A history of Arctic and Antarctic exploration. xii, 539 p., ill., maps. Cambridge University Press, 1921.
Reviewed by George Sarton, *Isis*, 1922, 4: 365-7.

MECKING, Ludwig. Die Polarwelt in ihrer kulturgeographischen Entwicklung besonders der jüngsten Zeit. 19 p. (Rede) Leipzig/Berlin: B.G. Teubner, 1925.

NORDENSKJÖLD, Otto. Le monde polaire. Traduit du suédois par G. Parmentier et M. Zimmermann. xi, 324 p. Paris: Colin, 1913.
French translation of Polarvärlden och dess grannländer (Stockholm: 1907).

ROUCH, Jules. Les régions polaires. 220 p. (Nouvelle Collection Scientifique) Paris: Alcan, 1927. [CB 24/542]

ROUVIER, G. La conquête des Pôles. 282 p. Paris: A. Lemerre, 1922. [CB 14/548]
History of polar expeditions from 1497 to 1922.

THOMAS, Lowell. Sir Hubert Wilkins (1888-1958). His world of adventure. An autobiography recounted by Lowell Thomas. 286 p., ill. London: Arthur Baker, 1962.
Reviewed by Michael Kelly, *Arch.Intern.Med.*, 1963, 112: (4), 626-7.

VERCEL, Roger. A l'assaut des pôles. 253 p., map. Paris: Michel, 1938.
Popular history of arctic and antarctic expeditions.

HLcd-by

SAVOURS, Ann. The Manuscript Collection of the Scott Polar Research Institute, Cambridge. *Archives*, Michaelmas 1959, no. 4, 102-8.

HLpw

NORDENSKJÖLD, Otto. Collaboration internationale pour l'exploration des contrées polaires. *Vie Int.*, 1913, 4: 179-84.

HLyHG

HOBBS, William H. Conditions of exceptional visibility within high latitudes, particularly as a result of superior mirage. *Ann.Ass.Amer.Geogr.*, 1937, 27: 229-40.
This is important for the history of cartography, as it reveals a cause of error which has distorted many maps of Arctic regions.

HOBBS, William H. Visibility and the discovery of Polar lands. *Geogr.Ann.*, 1933, 15: 217-24, 6 fig. [CB 40/406]

HLN NORTH POLE; the ARCTIC

AMUNDSEN, Roald; ELLSWORTH, Lincoln. Air pioneering in the arctic: the two polar flights of Roald Amundsen and Lincoln Ellsworth. 126 p., maps, ill. New York: National Americana Society, 1929.
Reviewed in *Geogr.Rev.*, 1929, 526.

AMUNDSEN, Roald; ELLSWORTH, Lincoln. The first flight across the polar sea. 274 p. London: Hutchinson, 1927.

BAIDUKOV, Georgii Filippovich. Over the North Pole. Translated from the Russian by Jessica Smith. Preface by Vilhjalmur Stefansson. xiv, 99 p., pl., portr. New York: Harcourt, Brace, 1938.
The story of the first trans-polar flight by one of the Soviet airmen who flew from Moscow to Portland, Oregon, in 1937.

CATONE, G. Otto Sverdrup nell'Artide inesplorata. vi, 228 p. Torino: G.B. Paravia, 1953.

COOK, Frederick Albert. Return from the Pole. Ed. with an introd. by Frederick J. Pohl. x, 335 p. New York: Pellegrini and Cudahy, 1951. [CB 79/146]

COOK, Frederick Albert. Zum Mittelpunkt der Arktis [My attainment of the Pole]: Reiseberichte ohne die Pol-Kontroverse. Verdeutscht und herausgegeben von Erwin Volckmann. 385 p. Braunschweig: Westermann, 1928.
Partial translation of the English text first published in New York, 1911.

CROUSE, Nellis M. The search for the Northwest passage. vi, 533 p., 4 pl., 1 map. New York: Columbia University Press, 1934.
Reviewed by C.A. Kofoid, *Isis*, 1935, 24: 185-6; by R.B., *Geogr.J.*, 1935, 86: 173-4.

FAIRLEY, T.C. Sverdrup's Arctic adventures. xii, 305 p., ill., pl. New York: Longmans, Green, 1960.
Reviewed by H.M. Dater, *Science*, 1960, 131: 1366.

FESS, Simeon Davidson. The North Pole aftermath. Speech in the House of Representatives, Congress of the United States, March 4, 1915. 27 p. Washington, D.C.: U.S. Govt. Print. Off., 1915.

FILICE, Francis P. Biography of the Gjøa. *Pacific Discovery*, 1962, 15: 2-9.
An account of Amundsen's exploration of the Northwest Passage.

GORDIENKO, P.A. The Arctic Ocean. *Sci.Amer.*, 1961, 204: no. 5, 88-102.
A historical account of arctic exploration from late medieval times.

HALL, Thomas F. Has the North Pole been discovered? An analytical and synthetical review of the published narratives of the two Arctic explorers Frederick A. Cook and Robert Peary, also of a review of the action of the U.S. government. 539 p., maps, charts. Boston: Badger, 1917.
Hall contends that neither Cook nor Peary reached the pole.

HAYES, James Gordon. The conquest of the North Pole. Recent Arctic exploration. 317 p., 16 pl., 11 maps. New York: Macmillan; London: Butterworth, 1934.
Reviewed by Charles A. Kofoid, *Isis*, 1939, 30: 538-9.

HOBBS, William H. Discovery and exploration within the area to the west of the Kane basin. *Bull.Geogr.Soc.Phila.*, 1937, 35: 26-30, 2 fig.

HOBBS, William H. The progress of discovery and exploration within the Arctic region. *Ann.Ass.Amer.Geogr.*, 1937, 27: 1-22, 4 maps.

LEWIN, Walter Henry. The great North Pole fraud. With a monograph by Thos. F. Hall on the murder of Professor Ross G. Marvin. vii, 192 p. London: Daniel, 1935.

MACMILLAN, Donald Baxter. Etah and beyond; or, Life within twelve degrees of the Pole. With illustrations from photographs by the author. xix, 287 p., pl., portr., maps. London: Chapman and Hall, 1927.

MACMILLAN, Donald Baxter. Four years in the white North. 428 p., ill. Boston: Hale, 1933.

MACMILLAN, Donald Baxter. How Peary reached the Pole. The personal story of his assistant. xii, 306 p., ill. Boston: Houghton, Mifflin, 1934.

MASON, Kenneth. Notes on the northern sea route. *Geogr.J.*, 1940, 96: 27-41.
History of the opening up of the route from the White Sea to Bering Strait.

MIRSKY, Jeannette. To the North! The story of Arctic exploration from the earliest times to the present. With an introduction by Vilhjalmur Stefansson. xx, 386 p., 16 pl., 13 maps, 9 fig. New York: Viking Press, 1934.
English edition published with title: Northern conquest (London: H. Hamilton, 1934); revised edition entitled: To the Arctic (London: Wingate, 1949).
Reviewed by C.A. Kofoid, *Isis*, 1935, 23: 483-5.

MOUNTEVANS, Edward R.G.R.E., *baron*. Arctic solitudes. 143 p., ill. London: Lutterworth Press; New York: Philosophical Library, 1953. [CB 80/129]

NOICE, Harold. With Stefansson in the Arctic. 269 p. New York: Dodd, Mead, 1924.

ROBINSON, J. Lewis. Conquest of the Northwest Passage by R.C.M.P. schooner "St. Roch". *Annu.Rep.Smithsonian Inst. for 1945*, p. 219-34, 12 pl., 1 map. Washington, D.C.: 1946. [CB 70/263]

ROUCH, Jules. Les expéditions aériennes au pole nord. *Rev. Gén.Sci.*, 1928, 39: 703-9; 1929, 40: 45-52, 175-7, 300-8.

ROUCH, Jules. Le Pôle Nord. Histoire des voyages arctiques. 250 p., 31 pl., 6 maps. Paris: Ernest Flammarion, 1923. [CB 16/303]

SEGAL, Louis. The conquest of the Arctic. 285 p., 31 pl., 2 maps. London: Harrap, 1939.
Reviewed by Charles A. Kofoid, *Isis*, 1949, 32: 398-9.

SHELESNYAK, M.C. Across the top of the world. A discussion of the Arctic. With an Arctic book list by Vilhjalmur Stefansson. vi, 71 p., ill. Washington, D.C.: Office of Naval Research, Navy Department, 1947.
Description of Arctic conditions, with an historical outline of Arctic discovery.

SHELESNYAK, M.C. The Navy explores its northern frontiers. *J.Amer.Soc.Nav.Eng.*, 1947, 59: 471-85, 8 ill.

STEFANSSON, Vilhjalmur. Adventures in error. viii, 299 p. New York: McBride, 1936.
Most of the stories refer to arctic conditions.
Reviewed by George Sarton, *Isis*, 1938, 29: 457-9, facs.

STEFANSSON, Vilhjalmur. The friendly Arctic: the story of five years in Polar regions. New ed., with new material. xxxvii, 812 p. New York: Macmillan, 1943. [CB 70/264]
First published 1921.

STEFANSSON, Vilhjalmur. Unsolved mysteries of the Arctic. xvii, 381 p. New York: Macmillan Co., 1939. [CB 58/577]
Reviewed by Francis R. Johnson, *Isis*, 1947, 32: 212-14.

STEFANSSON, Vilhjalmur. We're missing our future in the North. *Maclean's Mag.*, 1 August 1951, 7: 43-6, ill.

HLNc-br

Arktis Vierteljahrschrift der internationalen Studiengesellschaft zur Erforschung der Arktis mit dem Luftschiff. Vol. 1-4. Gotha: 1928-31.

HLNwb

CASWELL, John Edwards. The utilization of the scientific reports of United States Arctic expeditions, 1850-1909. (Under the direction of Edgar Eugene Robinson.) viii, 304 p. (Technical report II, Contract N6onr 25122 between the Office of Naval Research and Stanford University) Distributed by: Biology Branch, Office of Naval Research; Department of History, Stanford University, July 1951. [CB 78/155]
Mimeographed.

IVES, J.D.; SAGAR, R.B. Return to the Ice Age: Geographical Branch research in Baffin Island. *Can.Geogr.J.*, 1963, 67: 38-47.

HLNwe

GLEN, Alexander Richard. Young men in the Arctic. The story of the Oxford University expedition to Spitzbergen, 1933. 329 p., ill., pl. London: Faber and Faber, 1935.

GLEN, Alexander Richard; CROFT, N.A.C. Under the Pole Star. The Oxford University Arctic expedition, 1935-36. xv, 365 p., 48 pl., 22 maps, diagr. London: Methuen, 1937.

HOBBS, William H. The British Arctic Air Route Expedition. *Geogr.Rev.*, 1932, 22: 684-6.

SHACKLETON, Edward. Arctic journeys. The story of the Oxford University Ellesmere Land expedition, 1934-35. Preface by Lord Tweedsmuir. xv, 372 p. London: Hodder and Stoughton, 1937.

HLNwi

NOBILE, Umberto. In volo alla conquista del segreto polare. 500 p., 131 fig., maps, plans. Verona: A. Mondadori, 1928.

NOBILE, Umberto. "L'Italia" al Polo Nord. xi, xv, 475 p., ill. Milan: Mondadori, 1930.

NOBILE, Umberto. Die Vorbereitungen und die wissenschaftlichen Ergebnisse der Polarexpedition der "Italia". Übersetzt von W.J. van der Stay. 98 p., 5 pl., 39 fig. Gotha: 1929.

NOBILE, Umberto. With "Italia" to the North Pole. English transl. by Frank Fleetwood. 358 p., pl., portr., 2 maps. London: Allen and Unwin, 1930.

HLNwm

HOLM, Gustav. De Islandske Kursforskrifters Svalbarde. [Svalbard according to Icelandic sailing instructions. (In Danish)] *Meddelelser Grönland*, 1925, 59: 277-97. [CB 22/284]

HLNwn

ARMSTRONG, Terence E. The Russians in the Arctic. Aspects of Soviet exploration and exploitation of the Far North, 1937-1957. 182 p., pl., bibliogr. Fair Lawn, N.J.: Essential Books; London: Methuen, 1958.
Reviewed by Erwin N. Hiebert, *Isis*, 1963, 54: 513.

BRONTMAN, Lazar Konstantinovich. On the top of the world: the Soviet expedition to the North Pole, 1937. Ed. by O.J. Schmidt. xiii, 287 p., 25 pl., maps. London: Gollancz, 1938.
Reviewed by R.N. Rudmose Brown, *Nature*, 1938, 141: 995.

HLP GREENLAND

CARLSON, William S. Greenland lies north. viii, 306 p. New York: Macmillan, 1940. [CB 61/393]

DENMARK. KOMMISSIONEN FOR VIDENSKABELIGE UNDERSØGELSER I GRØNLAND. Greenland. 3 vol. 1. The discovery of Greenland, exploration and nature of the country. 575 p.; 2. The past and present population of Greenland. iv, 415 p.; 3. The colonization of Greenland and its history until 1929. v, 468 p. Copenhagen: Reitzel; London: Oxford University Press, 1928-29.
Volume 1 reviewed by William Hovgaard, *Geogr.Rev.*, 1929, 19: 338-40; by J.M. Wordie, *Nature*, 1929, 123: 439-40. Volume 2 reviewed by J.M. Wordie, *Nature*, 1930, 125: 442.

DUNBAR, M.J. Greenland - an experiment in human ecology. *Com. J.* (Toronto), March 1947, 69-109.

GABEL-JØRGENSEN, -. Dr. Knud Rasmussen's contribution to the exploration of the south-east coast of Greenland, 1931-1933. *Geogr.J.*, 1935, 86: 32-53, portr.

GEORGI, Johannes. Mid-ice: the story of the Wegener expedition to Greenland. Transl. (rev. and supplemented by the author) by F.H. Lyon. xiv, 247 p., 24 pl. London: Kegan Paul, 1934.

HOBBS, William H. The Wegener Greenland Expedition of 1930-1931. *Geogr.Rev.*, 1932, 22: no. 4, 3 p.

KRABBE, Th.N. Greenland: its nature, inhabitants and history. Transl. from the Danish by Annie I. Fausboll. xvi, 129, ix p., 170 pl. Copenhagen: Levin and Munksgaard, 1930.
Reviewed by R.N.R.B., *Nature*, 1930, 125: 379.

RASMUSSEN, Knud Johan Victor. Across Arctic America; narrative of the fifth Thule Expedition. xx, 388 p., portr., pl., maps. London: Putnam, 1927.
An abridged translation of "Fra Grønland til Stillehavet".

RASMUSSEN, Knud Johan Victor. Greenland by the Polar sea. The story of the Thule Expedition from Melville Bay to Cape Morris Jesup. Transl. from the Danish by Asta and Rowland Kenney. xxiv, 327 p. London: 1921.

ROUCH, J. Les voyages d'exploration au Groenland. *Rev.Sci.*, 1923, 61: 257-66, 295-8, 358-62.

SORBETS, Jacques. Avec Wegener au Groenland. *Rev.Hommes Mondes*, déc. 1949, 10: 570-9.

SPENDER, Michael. The sixth and seventh Thule expeditions of Knud Rasmussen. *Geogr.J.*, 1934, 83: 140-2, portr.

STEFANSSON, Vilhjalmur. Greenland. viii, 338 p., front., ill. New York: Doubleday, Doran, 1942.
Reviewed by George Sarton, *Isis*, 1943, 34: 379-80, 2 fig.

TVING, R. Traek af Grønlandsfartens historie. A thousand years of Greenland shipping. (In Danish with English summary) 224 p. (Det Grønlandske Selskabs Skrifter, 13) København: Munksgaard, 1944.
Reviewed by H. Richter, *Lychnos*, 1944-45, 417-18.

HLS ANTARCTIC

ANDERSSON, J.G. Antarctic. 308 p., ill. Stockholm: Saxon & Lindström, 1944.
Reviewed by Nils von Hofsten, *Lychnos*, 1944-45, 419.

BERNACCHI, L.C. Antarctic exploration past and present. *Geography*, 1935, 20: 176-90.

BYRD, Richard Evelyn. Little America: aerial exploration in the antarctic and the flight to the South Pole. xvi, 422 p., 58 pl. London: Putnam, 1931.
Reviewed in *Nature*, 1931, 127: 923.

CHERRY-GARRARD, Apsley George Benet. The worst journey in the world: Antarctic. 2 vol. lxiv, 300 p., 30 pl., 4 maps; viii, 301-585 p., 28 pl., 1 map. London: Constable, 1922. 2nd ed., 1929.
Reviewed by Hugh Robert Mill, *Nature*, 1923, 111: 386-8.

CHRISTENSEN, Lars. Recent reconnaissance flights in the Antarctic. *Geogr.J.*, 1939, 94: 192-203.
For map and notes to accompany paper *see* The Course of antarctic exploration, below.

CHRISTIE, E.W. Hunter. The Antarctic problem. An historical and political study. 336 p. London: Allen & Unwin, 1951.

THE COURSE of Antarctic exploration between longitudes 20°W. and 110°E. Notes on the map compiled to accompany the paper by Lars Christensen. *Geogr.J.*, 1939, 94: 204-8, map.
An elaborate map distinguishing the discoveries of some thirty-eight different expeditions, with names and dates of all known landings on the coast.

ELLSWORTH, Lincoln. The first crossing of Antarctica. *Geogr. J.*, 1937, 89: 193-213.
The crossing of 1935.

EVANS, Edward R.G.R. South with Scott. xiv, 284 p. London: Collins, 1921.

GAIN, M. Les explorations dans l'Antarctique de J.-B. Charcot et leurs résultats scientifiques. (Conférence faite au Palais de la Découverte le 24 mars 1945) 34 p., 6 fig. Paris: Palais de la Découverte, [n.d.]

HAWTHORNE, Roger. Exploratory flights of Admiral Byrd (1940). *Proc.Amer.Phil.Soc.*, 1945, 89: 398a-398e, 7 fig.

HAYES, James Gordon. Antarctica. A treatise on the Southern Continent. xv, 448 p., ill. London: Richards, 1928.

HAYES, James Gordon. The conquest of the South Pole. Antarctic exploration 1906-1931. 318 p., 24 pl. London: Butterworth, 1932.
Reviewed by J.M. Wordie, *Nature*, 1932, 130: 945.

HAYES, James Gordon. The exploration of Antarctica. *J.Manchester Geogr.Soc.*, 1923-24, 39-40: 18-48. [CB 22/283]
Reviewed in *Geogr.Rev.*, 1926, 16: 320-1.

HENRY, Thomas R. The white continent. The story of Antarctica. 212 p., ill. London: Eyre and Spottiswoode, 1951.

HINKS, Arthur Robert. The observations of Amundsen and Scott at the South Pole. *Geogr.J.*, 1944, 103: 160-80. [CB 69/205]

HOBBS, William H. The pack-ice of the Weddell Sea. *Ann.Ass. Amer.Geogr.*, 1939, 29: 159-70.

HURLEY, Frank. Argonauts of the South: being a narrative of voyagings and polar seas and adventures in the Antarctic with Sir Douglas Mawson and Sir Ernest Shackleton. xv, 290 p., 75 ill., maps. New York: Putnam, 1925.

JOERG, W.L.G. The work of the Byrd antarctic expedition, 1928-1930. 71 p., 16 maps. New York: American Geographical Society, 1930.

MILLER, Francis Trevelyan. The fight to conquer the ends of the earth; Byrd's great adventure: with the complete story of all polar explorations for one thousand years. 383 p., ill. Chicago: Winston, 1930.

OWEN, Russell. The Antarctic Ocean. xiii, 254 p., 15 ill., 12 maps. New York: Whittlesey House, 1941. [CB 62/80]

PONTING, Herbert George. The great white south. Being an account of experiences with Captain Scott's South Pole Expedition and of the nature life of the Antarctic. xxvi, 306 p., 175 ill. London: Duckworth, 1921.
A revised ed. was published in 1923.

ROUCH, Jules. La conquête aérienne du Pôle Sud. *Rev.Gén.Sci.*, 1931, 42: 210-16.
Deals with Wilkins's flights and Byrd's expedition.

ROUCH, Jules. Le Pôle Sud. Histoire des voyages antarctiques. 250 p., 88 pl., 14 maps. Paris: Flammarion, 1922. [CB 14/548]

TAYLOR, Griffith. Antarctic adventure and research. xi, 245 p., maps, ill. (Appleton New World of Science Series) New York: Appleton, 1930.
Reviewed by J.M. Wordie, *Geogr.Rev.*, 1931, 21: 171-2.

WALTON, E.W. Kevin. Two years in the Antarctic. 194 p., front., ill. New York: Philosophical Library, 1955. [CB 81/271]

HLSwb

UNITED STATES ANTARCTIC SERVICE EXPEDITION. Reports on scientific results of the Expedition, 1939-1941. Preface by R.E. Byrd. vi, 398 p., fig. (*Proc.Amer.Phil.Soc.*, vol. 89) Philadelphia: 1945. [CB 69/204]

HLSwe

COLEMAN-COOKE, John. Discovery II in the Antarctic. The story of British research in the southern seas. 255 p., 24 pl., map, bibliogr. London: Odhams, 1963.
Reviewed by Ann Savours, *Geogr.J.*, 1964, 130: 151.

DEACON, G.E.R. The Antarctic voyages of R.R.S. Discovery II and R.R.S. William Scoresby, 1935-37. *Geogr.J.*, 1939, 93: 185-209.

JOYCE, Ernest Edward Mills. The south polar trail. The log of the Imperial trans-Antarctic expedition. With an introd. by Hugh Robert Mill. 220 p., front., map, pl., portr. London: Duckworth, 1929.

MACKINTOSH, N.A. The fifth commission of the R.R.S. Discovery II. *Geogr.J.*, 1941, 97: 201-16. [CB 62/63]

RYMILL, John. Southern lights: the official account of the British Graham Land Expedition, 1934-37. With two chapters by A. Stephenson, and an historical introduction by Hugh Robert Mill. xvi, 296 p. London: Chatto & Windus, 1938.
Reviewed by R.E. Priestley, *Geogr.J.*, 1939, 93: 172-3.

HLSwg

DRYGALSKI, Erich von, ed. Deutsche Südpolar-Expedition, 1901-1903. 22 vol., 2 atlases. Berlin: De Gruyter, 1905-31. [CB 37/558]
Reviewed by H.R. Mill, *Geogr.J.*, 1932, 79: 506-8.

FILCHNER, Wilhelm. Zum sechsten Erdteil. Die zweite deutsche Südpolar Expedition unter Mitwirkung der Expeditionsteilnehmer Alfred King, Erich Przybyllok. xix, 410 p. Berlin: Ullstein, 1923.

HLSwk

BASTIN, F.E. Les expéditions antarctiques belges. *Bull.Soc. Géogr.Anvers*, 1961, 73: no. 1-2, 63-70.

DEROM, Guy. L'expédition antarctique belge 1960. *Bull.Soc. Géogr.Anvers*, 1962, 73: no. 3-4, 87-90

DOBROWOLSKI, A.B. Le voyage du Belgica considéré au point de vue de l'histoire du Pôle Sud. *Bull.Acad.Roy.Belg.Cl.Sci.*, 1947, 33: 453-62.

DOYEN, Paulette. Les expéditions antarctiques belges. *Mouvement Sci.Belg.*, 1961, 4: 241-6.

HLSwm

AAGAARD, Bjarne. Fangst og forskning i Sydishavet. [Fishing and research in the Antarctic. (In Norwegian)] 3 vol. 1. Svunne dager. [Past days]; 2. Nye tider. [Recent times]; 3. Antarktikas historie. [The history of the Antarctic] (Kommandør Chr. Christensens Hvalfangstmuseum, Publikasjon 9-11) Oslo: Gyldendal, 1930-34.
The story of Norwegian endeavour in the Antarctic as far as it was connected with Norwegian whalers and whaling.
Reviewed by R.N.R. Brown, *Geogr.J.*, 1931, 77: 386-7; 1935, 86: 370-1.

ISACHSEN, Gunnar. Norwegian explorations in the Antarctic, 1930-1931. *Geogr.Rev.*, 1932, 22: 83-96, map.

HLSwt

HAMRE, Ivar. The Japanese South Polar expedition of 1911-1912: a little-known episode in Antarctic exploration. *Geogr.J.*, 1933, 82: 411-23.

HLSww

SCHOLES, Arthur. Fourteen men. The story of the Australian Antarctic expedition to Heard Island. xii, 273 p., 21 pl. London: Allen and Unwin, 1951.
Reviewed by J.D.M. Blyth, *Nature*, 1952, 169: 682.

HM MOUNTAIN EXPLORATION; MOUNTAINEERING

CLARK, Ronald W. A picture history of mountaineering. 17 p., 351 ill. New York: Macmillan, 1956.
Reviewed in *Sci.Amer.*, 1957, 196: no. 1, 134.

ENGEL, Claire Eliane. History of mountaineering in the Alps. 296 p., ill. London: Allen & Unwin, 1950.

GREGORY, John Walter; GREGORY, C.J. To the Alps of Chinese Tibet: an account of a journey of exploration up to and among the snow-clad mountains of the Tibetan frontier. 321 p., ill., 16 pl., map, diagr. London: Seeley, Service, 1923.

HELBRONNER, Paul. Description géométrique détaillée des Alpes françaises. 9 vol. in 8. Paris: Gauthier-Villars, 1910-32. [CB 16/301]
Reviewed by George Sarton, *Isis*, 1924, 6: 90-1.

HYDE, Walter Woodburn. The Alps in history. *Proc.Amer.Phil. Soc.*, 1935, 75: 431-42.

LE BONDIDIER, L. Histoire de l'exploration des Pyrénées. *Isis*, 1926, 8: 492-6.
Two letters written by L. Le Bondidier, keeper of the Pyrenean Museum of Lourdes, describing the Salle d'Honneur of that Museum. Brief introduction by George Sarton.

LEHNER, Wilhelm. Die Eroberung der Alpen. xi, 727 p., 44 pl., 1 diagr., 2 maps, 2 fold. tables. München: Hochalpenverlag, 1924.
Volume devoted to the history of mountain exploration and of mountaineering as a sport not only in the Alps but in other parts of the world.

LUNN, Arnold. The Alps. 256 p. (Home University Library) London: Williams and Norgate, 1914.

MARGERIE, Emmanuel de. L'oeuvre d'Henri Beraldi, historien du Pyrénéisme. *Bull.Sect.Géogr.Comité Trav.Hist.Sci.*, 1943, 58: 71-91.

NISSON, Claude. La conquête du Mont-Blanc. 215 p., fig. Paris: Spes, 1930.
Reviewed by B.M., *Rev.Gén.Sci.*, 1930, 41: 482-3.

SARTON, George. Histoire de l'exploration des Pyrénées. *Isis*, 1926, 8: 492-3.
Includes an account of the Musée Pyrénéen at Lourdes.

SLEEN, Wicher Gosen Nicolaas van der. Four months camping in the Himalayas. Translated by M.W. Hoper. xiii, 213 p. London: Allan, 1929.
Translation of Dutch original: Vier maande kampeeren in den Himalaya (Rotterdam: Nijgh & Van Ditmar, 1927).
Reviewed by C. Mabel Rickmers, *J.Roy.Asiatic Soc.*, 1930, 951.

SORRE, Maximilien. Les Pyrénées méditerranéennes; étude de géographie biologique. 508 p., ill., maps. Paris: Colin, 1913.

STEINITZER, Alfred. Der Alpinismus in Bildern. 2nd ed. 492 p., 637 ill., 16 pl. Münich: R. Piper, 1924. [CB 22/285]

STOLZ, Otto. Anschauung und Kenntnis der Hochgebirge Tirols vor dem Erwachen des Alpinismus. *Z.Deut.Österr.Alpenver.*, 1927, 58: 8-36; 1928, 59: 14-66. [CB 26/240]

YOUNGHUSBAND, Francis. Wonders of the Himalaya. vii, 210 p. London: John Murray, 1924.
Reviewed by J.W.G., *Nature*, 1924, 114: 673-4.

HMce-bv

DREYER, A. Bücherverzeichnis der Alpenvereinsbücherei mit Verfasser- und Bergnamenverzeichnis. Hrsg. vom Hauptausschuss des deutschen und österreichischen Alpenvereins und vom Verein der Freunde der Alpenvereinsbücherei. xvi, 1358 p. München: K. Lindauer, 1927.
Reviewed by Eugen Weber, *Deut.Lit.Zeitung*, 1927, 1622-3.

HMda

BEER, G.R. de. Early travellers in the Alps. xx, 204 p. London: Sidgwick & Jackson, 1930. [CB 32/589]
Reviewed in *Geogr.J.*, 1930, 76: 559.

HMhm

KIRCHNER, Walther. Mind, mountain and history. *J.Hist. Ideas*, 1950, 11: 412-47.

HMqm

HYDE, Walter Woodburn. The great St. Bernard Pass and its Hospice. *Isis*, 1937, 27: 306-20.

HMwf-qb

CLUB ALPIN FRANÇAIS. Commission des Travaux Scientifiques. L'oeuvre scientifique du Club Alpin français. (1874-1922). vi, 518 p. Paris: 1936.
Reviewed by Dana B. Durand, *Isis*, 1938, 28: 143-4

HN MOUNT EVEREST

BRUCE, Charles Granville, et al. The assault on Mount Everest, 1922. xi, 339 p., 32 pl., 2 maps. London: Arnold, 1923.

BURRARD, Sydney. Mount Everest and its Tibetan names. A review of Sir Sven Hedin's book [*i.e.* "Mount Everest]. 19 p. (Survey of India. Professional paper, 26) Dehra Dun: Survey of India, Geodetic Branch Office, 1931.

CROSTHWAIT, H.L. Mount Everest. *Nature*, 1933, 131: 10-14, 1 fig.
Historical account of the efforts to climb it and of the results already obtained.

HEDIN, Sven Anders. Mount Everest. 193 p. Leipzig: F.A. Brockhaus, 1923.
Swedish original: Mount Everest, och andra asiatiska problem (Stockholm: 1922).
German translation Leipzig: F.A. Brockhaus. 1923.
For review *see* Burrard, Sydney above.

HUNT, John. The ascent of Everest. xx, 299 p., ill. London: Hodder & Stoughton, 1953; New York: Dutton, 1954.
American edition entitled: The conquest of Everest. With a chapter on the final assault by Edmund Hillary.

HUNT, John; HILLARY, Edmund. The ascent of Mount Everest. *Geogr.J.*, 1953, 119: 386-99, ill.

PUGH, L.G.C.E. Scientific aspects of the expedition to Mount Everest, 1953. *Geogr.J.*, 1954, 120: 183-92.

SOMERVELL, Theodore Howard. After Everest. The experiences of a mountaineer and medical missionary. xiii, 339 p. London: Hodder and Stoughton, 1936.

YOUNGHUSBAND, Francis. The epic of Mount Everest. 319 p., ill. London: Arnold; New York: Longmans, Green, 1926

HNwg

HEIM, Arnold; GANSSER, August. Thron der Götter. Erlebnisse der ersten Schweizerischen Himalaja-Expedition (1936.) 270 p., 238 fig., 2 pl., 1 map. Zürich: Morgarten-Verlag, 1938.

HO SEA TRAVEL

for charting the seas *see* HH
navigation *see* HC

BEAGLEHOLE, J.C. The exploration of the Pacific. 2nd ed. xv, 411 p., 4 maps. (The Pioneer Histories) London: Black, 1947. [CB 48/579]
First publ. 1934.
Reviewed by G.R. Crone, *Geogr.J.*, 1935, 85: 97-8.

BOXER, C.R. Mocambique Island as a way-station for Portuguese East India men. *Mariner's Mirror*, 1962, 48: 3-18.

CHABANIER, E. Connaissance de la Mer Rouge. *Géographie*, 1936, 65: 85-124. [CB 48/580]
Historical study.

DEHÉRAIN, Henri. Dans l'Atlantique. 243 p., 5 maps. Paris: Hachette, 1912.

HEYERDAHL, Thor. The Kon-Tiki expedition by raft across the South Seas. 235 p. London: Allen & Unwin, 1950. [CB 77/361]

IVES, Ronald L. The Manila galleons. *J.Geogr.*, 1964, 63: 5-19.

JANSSENS, É. Histoire ancienne de la Mer du Nord. 2e éd. 99 p., ill. (Collection Lebègue, 25) Bruxelles: Office de Publicité, 1946.
First edition 1943.
Reviewed by Erik Gren, *Lychnos*, 1952, 379-80.

LLOYD, Christopher. Pacific horizons: the exploration of the Pacific before Captain Cook. 188 p. London: Allen and Unwin, 1946.
Reviewed by A.H.C., *Geogr.J.*, 1947, 109: 128.

MÖRNER, Birger. Söderhavet. 1. De stora färderna. Vid rikets port. Polynesien. [The Southern Ocean. 1. The great voyages. At the gateway of the kingdom. Polynesia. (In Swedish)] xi, 230 p., ill., 1 map. Uppsala: J.A. Lindblads Förlag, 1923.

POUJADE, Jean. La route des Indes et ses navires. 304 p., 89 fig. Paris: Payot, 1946.
Reviewed by J. Sauvaget, *J.Asiatique*, 1948, 236: 325-8.

PRICE, A. Grenfell. The western invasions of the Pacific and its continents. A study of moving frontiers and changing landscapes, 1513-1958. 236 p. Oxford: Clarendon Press, 1963.
Reviewed by Andrew H. Clark, *Geogr.Rev.*, 1963, 54: 291-3.

ROSE, J. Holland. Man and the sea. Stages in maritime and human progress. xi, 288 p., 28 pl., 2 maps, 28 fig. Boston: Houghton Mifflin, 1936. [CB 48/586]

HOce-bx

LEHIGH UNIVERSITY. LIBRARY. The Great South Sea. An exhibition of rare books and watercolors. 11 p. Bethlehem, Pa.: 1962.

HOst

POTTER, Pitman Benjamin. The freedom of the seas in history, law, and politics. xvi, 299 p. New York: Longmans, Green, 1924.
Reviewed by Louise Fargo Brown, *Amer.Hist.Rev.*, 1924, 30: 113-15.

HOu

BASSETT, Wilbur. Wanderships. Folk-stories of the sea, with notes upon their origin. 136 p. Chicago: Open Court, 1917.

HOwe-sg

CORNFORD, Leslie Cope. A century of sea trading, 1824-1924. The General Steam Navigation Company, Limited. Ill. by W.L. Wyllie and J. Spurling. x, 182 p. London: Black, 1924.

HOwm

WORM-MÜLLER, Jacob Sternersen. Den Norske sjøfarts historie fra de aeldste tider til vore dage. [History of Norwegian shipping from the earliest times till the present day. (In Norwegian)] 6 vol. 7000 p., ill. Kristiania (Oslo): Steen, 1923-52.

HP IMAGINARY LANDS

BISHOP, C.W. The Isle of Gold and the Isle of Silver. *Geogr. Rev.*, 1934, 24: 671-2. [CB 42/594]

CHASSIGNEUX, Edmond. Rica de oro et rica de plata. *T'oung Pao*, 1933, 30: 37-84.
History of those real or imaginary islands.

DE CAMP, L. Sprague; LEY, Willy. Lands beyond. 327 p., 18 fig. New York: Rinehart, 1952. [CB 79/181]
The overall theme deals with the lands beyond the horizon. The authors trace the gradual displacement of imaginary realms brought about by the knowledge of geography

HENNIG, Richard. Von rätselhaften Ländern; versunkene Stätten der Geschichte. 326 p., 25 ill. München: Delphin-Verlag, 1925.
Reviewed by R. Zaunick, *Mitt.Gesch.Med.*, 1926, 25: 168-9.

SCHULTEN, Adolf. Die Inseln der Seligen. *Geogr.Z.*, 1926, 32: 229-47.
The author identifies the Island of the Blessed with Madeira and Plato's Atlantis with the region of Tartessus.

TAYLOR, E.G.R. Imaginary islands: a problem solved. *Geogr.J.*, 1964, 130: 105-19.

WAGNER, Henry R. Some imaginary California geography. *Proc. Amer.Antiq.Soc.*, 1926, 36: 83-129, ill. [CB 22/285]

HQ ATLANTIS

BESSMERTNY, Alexander. Das Atlantisrätsel. Geschichte und Erklärung der Atlantishypothesen. 212 p., 29 fig., 8 pl. Leipzig: Voigtländer, 1932.
Reviewed by Aldo Mieli, *Archeion*, 1933, 15: 123.
French translation, L'Atlantide (Paris: Payot, 1935) reviewed by Pierre Brunet, *ibid.*, 1935, 17: 469.

BJÖRKMAN, Edwin. The search for Atlantis: excursions by a layman among old legends and new discoveries. 127 p. London: Knopf, 1927.

BRAMWELL, James Guy. Lost Atlantis. 288 p. London: Cobden-Sanderson, 1937.

DE CAMP, L. Sprague. Lost continents. The Atlantis theme in history, science and literature. 362 p., front., 17 ill. New York: Gnome Press, 1954. [CB 80/144]

FILIPPOFF, L. Sur la détermination de l'époque de la disparition de l'Atlantide. *Compt.Rend.Acad.Sci.*, 1930, 191: 393. [CB 31/550]

GATTEFOSSÉ, R.M. La vérité sur l'Atlantide. 142 p. Lyon: Legendre, 1923.

KARST, Joseph. Atlantis und der Libi-äthiopische Kulturkreis. v, 115 p. Heidelberg: Winter, 1931.
Reviewed by T.G. Pinches, *J.Roy.Asiatic Soc.*, 1933, 135-7; by Max Pieper, *Orient.Lit.Zeitung*, 1934, 37: 351.

NAVARRO, Lucas Fernandez. L'état actuel du problème de l'Atlantide. *Rev.Gén.Sci.*, 1916, 27: 425-9, 459-66.

NEGRIS, Ph. L'Atlantide. *Rev.Sci.*, 1922, 60: 614-17. [CB 14/549]

RUTOT, A. L'Atlantide. *Bull.Acad.Roy.Belg.Cl.Sci.*, 1919, 907-59.

SCHUCHERT, Charles. Atlantis and the permanency of the North Atlantic Ocean. *Proc.Nat.Acad.Sci.*, 1917, 3: 65-72.
A reply to Termier's paper, *see* below.

SPENCE, Lewis. The problem of Atlantis. xi, 232 p., 16 pl. London: Rider, 1924.

TERMIER, Pierre. L'Atlantide. 22 p. (*Bull.Inst.Océanogr.*, 256) Monaco: 1913. Also in *Rev.Sci.*, 1913, 51: 1er semestre, 33-41.
English translation: Atlantis. *Annu.Rep.Smithsonian Inst. for 1915*, p. 219-34. Washington, D.C.: 1916.

ZUR Atlantisfrage. *Petermann's Mitt.*, 1927-28, vol. 73-4. [CB 26/199]

HQce-bv

BESNIER, M.; GERMAIN, Louis. Atlantide. [Critical bibliography]. *Bibliogr.Géogr.*, 1926, 36: 58.

GATTEFOSSÉ, Jean; ROUX, Claudius. Bibliographie de l'Atlantide et des questions connexes, (géographie, ethnographie et migrations anciennes. Atlantique et Méditerranée, Afrique et Amérique, fixité ou dérive des continents, déluges, traditions, etc.). 111 p., ill. Lyon: Bosc Riou, 1926.

HQmzL

GERMAIN, Louis. Le problème de l'Atlantide et la zoologie. *Ann.Géogr.*, 1913, 22: 209-26.

HQwj-u

WHISHAW, Ellen Mary. Atlantis in Andalucia: a study of folk memory. 284 p. London: Rider, 1929.

HU PALAEONTOLOGY

for human palaeontology *see* MB

HUc general history

BUGLER, G. Précisions pour une histoire des origines de la paléontologie. *Rev.Hist.Sci.*, 1949, 2: 270-4.

DE TERRA, Hellmut; MOVIUS, Hallam L. Research on early man in Burma. With supplementary reports upon the Pleistocene vertebrates and mollusks of the region by Edwin H. Colbert and J. Bequaert, and Pleistocene geology and early man in Java by Hellmut De Terra. *Trans.Amer.Phil.Soc.*, 1943, 32: 265-464.
Reviewed by M.F. Ashley Montagu, *Isis*, 1944, 35: 39-40.

DEVAUX, Emile. Les ralentissements de développement et l'interprétation des grands faits paléontologiques. *Rev.Gén.Sci.*, 1923, 34: 239-43. [CB 15/222]

ERBEN, Heinrich Karl. Fortschritte der Paläontologie im letzten Jahrzehnt. *Naturwiss.Rundsch.*, 1959, 12: 119-24.

FUNDAMENTALS of paleontology: a manual for paleontologists and geologists of the USSR. Chief editor: Yu A. Orlov. Translated from the Russian. Vol. 1. 490 p. Jerusalem: Israel Program for Scientific Translations for the National Science Foundation, Washington, 1962. [CB 88/546]
Translation of: Osnovy paleontologii. 1. Moskva: Izdatel'stvo Akademii Nauk SSSR, 1959.
Includes a summary of the history of paleontology from ancient times to the present.

HÖLDER, Helmut. Geologie und Paläontologie in Texten und ihrer Geschichte. xviii, 565 p., ill., bibliogr. (Orbis Academicus, 2: 11) Freiburg/Munich: Verlag Karl Alber, 1960.
Reviewed by Albert V. Carozzi, *Isis*, 1962, 53: 398-400; by K. Mägdefrau, *Naturwiss.Rundsch.*, 1961, 5: 202; by Gerhard Regnéll, *Lychnos*, 1962, 478-80.

HUTCHINSON, G. Evelyn. Marginalia. *Amer.Scient.*, 1954, 42: 300-8.
A history of (a) the dodo and solitaire, and (b) the Piltdown man.

KRUYTZER, E.M. Limburgs bodem en zijn rijkdom aan fossielen. [The soil of Limburg and its abundance of fossils. (In Dutch)] *Sci.Hist.*, 1960, 2: no. 3, 1-14.
The discovery and exploration of the fossil beds of Limburg.

PFIZENMAYER, E.W. Siberian man and mammoth. Translated from the German by Muriel D. Simpson. xii, 256 p. London: Blackie, 1939.
Translation of: Mammutleichen und Urwaldmenschen in Nordost-Sibirien (Leipzig: Brockhaus, 1926). A full account of the mammoth in all its aspects: twenty-one finds of mammoths are recorded in Siberia.
Reviewed by R.N.R. Brown, *Geogr.J.*, 1939, 94: 69.

SPARKS, John B. The histomap of evolution. With foreword, bibliography, and recommended books. 12 p., chart. Chicago: Rand, McNally, 1932. [CB 37/602]
Shows the sequence of events in the geological evolution of the earth and the palaeontological sequences of organisms.

WALCOTT, Charles D. Evidences of primitive life. *Annu.Rep. Smithsonian Inst.for 1915*, p. 235-55, ill. Washington, D.C.: 1916.

ZITTEL, Karl von. History of geology and palaeontology. To the end of the nineteenth century. xiii, 562 p. (Historiae Naturalis Classica, 12) Codicote, Herts.: Wheldon & Wesley; New York: Hafner Publishing Company, 1962.
An unaltered reprint of the edition which first appeared in London in 1901.

HUc-bx

BRITISH MUSEUM (NATURAL HISTORY). Guide to an exhibition illustrating the early history of palaeontology. 68 p., 4 pl. (Special guide, 8) London: British Museum, 1931.

HUcp-by

STERNBERG, Charles Hazelius. The life of a fossil hunter. With an introduction by Henry Fairfield Osborn. xiv, 286 p., 46 ill., portr. San Diego: Jensen Printing Co., 1931. [CB 40/365]
Originally published New York: H. Holt, 1909.

HUda-bv

LAMBRECHT, K.; QUENSTEDT, W.; QHENSTEDT, A. Palaeontologi catalogus bio-bibliographicus. xxii, 495 p. The Hague: Junk, 1939.

HUk/t special aspects

HUk

NEWELL, Norman D. The nature of the fossil record. *Proc.Amer. Phil.Soc.*, 1959, 103: 264-85.

RUDWICK, M.J.S. Problems in the recognition of fossils as organic remains. *Proc.10th Int.Congr.Hist.Sci.* (Ithaca, 1962), (2), p. 985-7. Paris: Hermann, 1964.

HUmzJ

WATSON, David Meredith Seares. Paleontology and modern biology. xii, 216 p., 77 ill. (Mrs Hepsa Ely Silliman Memorial Lectures) New Haven: Yale University Press, 1951. [CB 79/180]

HUmzJG

DUFRENOY, Jean; DUFRENOY, Marie-Louise. Les fossiles et la notion d'évolution. *Action Univ.*, 1948, 15: 4-26.

LULL, Richard Swann. Organic evolution. xviii, 729 p., 253 fig., 30 pl. New York: Macmillan, 1917.
Chiefly from a palaeontological point of view.

SIMPSON, George G. Evolutionary determinism and the fossil record. *Sci.Mon.*, 1950, 71: 262-7.

HUmzJH

JEPSEN, Glenn L.; MAYR, Ernst; SIMPSON, George Gaylord; ed. Genetics, paleontology, and evolution. Edited for the Committee on common problems of genetics, paleontology, and systematics, of the National Research Council. xiv, 474 p., fig., pl. Princeton: Princeton University Press, 1949. [CB 75/92]

HUnh

DAVITASHVILI, L. SH.; KHIMSHIASHVILI, N.G. K istorii termina "paleontologiya" i nekotorikh drugikh nazvanii nauki ob organizmakh proshlikh geologicheskikh vremen. [On the history of the term "paleontology" and certain other names of science in the organization of past geological time. (In Russian)] *Vop.Ist.Est.Tekh.*, 1956, 2: 176-81.

HUqh

OSBORN, Henry Fairfield. Arrest of geologic, archeologic and paleontologic work in Central Asia. *Science*, 1931, 74: 139-42.
The Central Asiatic Expedition organised by the American Museum of Natural History refused permission by the Peiping Commission for the Preservation of Antiquities to continue its geological and palaeontological work.

TOKUNAGA, Shigeyasu; NAORA, Nobuo. Report of diggings at Ho-chia-kou ... (In Japanese with resumé and bibliography in English) 2 pt. 119 p.; 7 p., ill. (Report of the first scientific expedition to Manchouquo, 1933, section 2, pt. 1) Tokyo: Waseda University, 1934. [CB 43/256]

HUs

HAWKINS, H.L. Palaeontology and humanity. *Nature*, 1936, 138: 534-7.
From the presidential address to Section C (Geology) of the British Association, delivered at Blackpool on September 14.

HUth

LAMONT, Archie. Palaeontology in literature. *Quarry Managers' J.*, 1947, 30: 432-41, 542-51, 4 fig.

HUw in different countries

HUwb

HOLLAND, F.D. The status of paleontology in North Dakota. *Proc.N.Dak.Acad.Sci.*, 1961, 15: 445-63. Reprinted as *North Dakota Survey Miscellaneous Series*, no. 16, Grand Forks, North Dakota: 1961.
A historical summary of geological explorations and investigations in North Dakota from 1738 to the present.

MERRIAM, John C. An outline of progress in palaeontological research on the Pacific Coast. *Univ.Calif.Publ.Bull.Dep.Geol.*, 1921, 12: 237-66.

HUwh

BIEDA, Franciszek. [Histoire de la paléontologie en Pologne. (In Polish with summary in French)] 39 p. (Polska Akademia Umiejetności, Historia Nauki Polskiej w Monografiach, 10) Cracow: 1948.

HUwn-mzJH

DAVITASHVILI, L.Sh. [The notion of heredity of acquired traits by organisms in Russian paleontology up to 1917. (In Russian)] *Tr.Inst.Ist.Est.*, 1953, 5: 51-92.

HUxx

NORTH, F.J. Type and figured fossils in the National Museum of Wales. 20 p. Cardiff: 1928.
The first chapter explains the origin and nature of the collections.

HV PALAEOBOTANY

ARBER, E-A. Newell. A sketch of the history of palaeobotany with special reference to the fossil flora of the British coal measures. In: Singer, Charles, ed. Studies in the History of Science, vol. 2, p. 472-89, ill. Oxford: Clarendon Press, 1921. [CB 11/440]

BERRY, Edward W. Paleobotany. A sketch of the origin and evolution of floras. *Annu.Rep.Smithsonian Inst.for 1918*, p. 289-407, 6 pl. Washington, D.C.: 1920.
Preceded by a short historical introduction.

ERDTMAN, G. An introduction to pollen analysis. Foreword by Roger P. Wodehouse. xv, 239 p., 28 pl., fig. (New series of plant science books, 12) Waltham, Mass.: Chronica Botanica, 1943. [CB 68/55]

GOLDRING, Winifred. The oldest known petrified forest. *Annu. Rep.Smithsonian Inst.for 1928*, p. 315-24, 9 pl. Washington, D.C.: 1929.
Reprinted with slight changes in the illustrations, from *Sci.Mon.*, June 1927, 24: 514-29.

SUDBURY, Louise. What is the first fossil collected by man? *Science*, 1928, 68: 135.
The *Cycadeoidea etrusca* in the Capellini Museum, Bologna.

WIELAND, G.R. A historic fossil. *Science*, 1925, 61: 541. [CB 18/558]

ZUMBERGE, J.H.; POTZGER, J.E. Pollen profiles, radiocarbon dating and geologic chronology of the Lake Michigan basin. *Science*, 1955, 121: 309-11.

HVc-br

Pollen Analysis Circular. Ed. by Paul Bigelow Sears. No. 1 (May 5, 1943) - Oberlin, Ohio: Oberlin College, Dept. of Botany, 1943-
Typescript.
For no. 7 (July 1, 1944) *see* CB 68/56.

HVmzGF

DEEVEY, Edward S. Pollen analysis and history. *Amer.Scient.*, 1944, 32: 39-53.
A discussion of the contribution of the pollen analysis of bogs to our knowledge of postglacial climate.

HVmzJG

SCOTT, Dukinfield Henry. Extinct plants and problems of evolution: founded on a course of public lectures delivered at the University College of Wales, Aberystwyth, in 1922. xiv, 240 p. London: Macmillan, 1924.
Reviewed by A.C. Seward, *Nature*, 1924, 113: 596-7.

HW PALAEOZOOLOGY

ADAMS, Frank D. Early references to fossil fishes. Answer to Query no. 97. (*Isis*, 1941, 33: 56-8) *Isis*, 1941, 33: 335.
See Sarton, George, below.

BROILI, F. Unser Wissen über die ältesten Tetrapoden. *Fortschr. Naturwiss.Forsch.*, 1913, 8: 51-93.

CARPENTER, F.M. A review of our present knowledge of the geological history of the insects. *Psyche* (Cambridge, Mass.), 1930, 37: 15-34, 1 pl.

COLBERT, Edwin H. Evolutionary growth rates in the dinosaurs. *Sci.Mon.*, 1949, 69: 71-9.

DIGBY, Bassett. The mammoth and mammoth-hunting in northeast Siberia. 224 p., photographs, map. London: Witherby, 1926. [CB 25/425]

EISLER, Robert. Early references to fossil fishes. Answer to Query no. 97. (*Isis*, 1941, 33: 56-8) *Isis*, 1943, 34: 363.
See Sarton, George, below.

GOODRICH, L. Carrington. Early mentions of fossil fishes. Answer to Query no. 97. (*Isis*, 1941, 33: 56-8) *Isis*, 1942, 34: 25.
See Sarton, George, below.

GUDGER, E.W. The earliest winged fish-catchers. *Sci.Mon.*, 1944, 59: 120-9, 13 fig.

JOLEAUD, L. Revue de paléontologie animale. *Rev.Gén.Sci.*, 1920, 31: 487-500.
Survey of recent progress.

OSBORN, Henry Fairfield. Proboscidea. A monograph on the discovery, evolution, migration and extinction of the mastodonts and elephants of the world. Edited by Mabel Rice Percy. 2 vol. 1. Moeitherioidea, Deinotherioidea, Mastodontoidea; 2. Stegodontoidea, Elephantoidea. New York: American Museum Press, 1936-42.
Volume 2 reviewed by D.M.S. Watson, *Nature*, 1944, 153: 5-7.

PEASE, Arthur Stanley. Fossil fishes again. Answer to Query no. 97. (*Isis*, 1941, 33: 56-8) *Isis*, 1942, 33: 689-90.
See Sarton, George, below.

PROSTOV, Eugene V. Early mentions of fossil fishes. Answer to Query no. 97. (*Isis*, 1941, 33: 56-8) *Isis*, 1942, 34: 24-5.
See Sarton, George, below.

SARTON, George. The earliest reference to fossil fishes (1253, 1309). Query no. 97. *Isis*, 1941, 33: 56-8.
For answers, *see* above: Adams, Frank D., Eisler, Robert, Goodrich, L.C., Pease, Arthur Stanley and Prostov, Eugene V.

SCOTT, William Berryman. A history of land mammals in the western hemisphere. xvii, 786 p., ill. New York: Macmillan, 1937.
First publ. 1913.

HWwb

SIMPSON, George Gaylord. The beginnings of vertebrate paleontology in North America. *Proc.Amer.Phil.Soc.*, 1942, 86: 130-88, 23 fig.

HWwn

BORISIAK, A.A. [Brief outline of the history of Russian paleozoology. (In Russian)] *Tr.Inst.Ist.Est.*, 1947, 1: 5-20.

HWwq-u

JOLEAUD, L. Le rôle des coquillages marins fossiles et actuels dans la magie berbère. *Homenagem à Martins Sarmento*, p. 150-74. Guimaraes (Portugal): 1933.
Reviewed by J. Herber, *Rev.Hist.Relig.*, 1934, 109: 234-5.

HWxx

COCKERELL, T.D.A. Fossil mammals at the Colorado Museum of Natural History. *Sci.Mon.*, 1923, 17: 271-7.

PARKS, W.A. Dinosaurs in the Royal Ontario Museum. *Univ. Toronto Quart.*, 1935, 4: 179-200, 6 pl.

HY NATURAL HISTORY

HYc

CHAPMAN, Abel. Retrospect: reminiscences and impressions of a hunter-naturalist in three continents, 1851-1928. Ill. by Joseph Crawhall, W.H. Riddell and rough sketches by the author. xix, 353 p., 56 pl. London: Gurney, 1928.
Reviewed by Herbert Maxwell, *Nature*, 1929, 123: 521.

HOFSTEN, Nils von. Zur älteren Geschichte des Diskontinuitätsproblems in der Biogeographie. *Zool.Ann.*, 1916, 7: 197-353. [CB 28/549]

PENNETIER, G. Discours sur l'évolution des connaissances en histoire naturelle. 1. L'antiquité et le moyen-âge. 56 p.; 2. Renaissance. 69 p.; 3. XVIIe siècle. 95 p.; 4. (1) XVIIIe-XIXe siècles. Aperçu général, doctrines biologiques. 80 p.; (2) Géologie. 319 p.; (3) Botanique. 368 p.; (4, 5) Zoologie. 927 p. (*Act.Mus.Hist.Natur.Rouen*, fasc. 14-30) Rouen: 1911-26.

HYcd

MERRILL, E.D. Microfilm records of the Linnean Society of London. *Science*, 1942, 96: 352.

HYce

SWANN, C. Kirke. Natural history books from a bookseller's point of view. *J.Soc.Bibliogr.Natur.Hist.*, 1956, 3: 117-26.

HYce-br

Journal of the Society for the Bibliography of Natural History. Vol. 1- London: The Society, 1936- [CB 68/54]

HYce-bv

BAY, J. Christian. Journeys and voyages to nature. A survey of one hundred books. 67 p. Chicago: John Crerar Library, 1951.

A CATALOGUE of papers concerning the dates of publication of natural history books. *J.Soc.Bibliogr.Natur.Hist.*, 1936, 1: 1-30. 1st-4th Supplements. *Ibid.*, 1943, 2: 1-18; 1953, 3: 5-12; 1957, 3: 165-74; 1962, 4: 1-19.

JUNK, Wilhelm. Rara historico-naturalia et mathematica. 3 pts. 1. (in 21 parts). iii, 121 p. 1900-13; 2. (in 3 parts). p. 123-240. 1926-36. Supplementum. p. 243-95. Berlin: W. Junk, 1900-29; The Hague: W. Junk, 1936-39.
Deals with the bibliography of rare books and periodicals on natural history, with detailed collations, prices, indications of the fall and rise of their value, etc.

Scientiae Naturalis Bibliographia. Annus 1, 1937 - annus 3, pt. 1, 1939. Den Haag: Junk, 1938-39. [CB 53/254]

HYce-by

SHERBORN, Charles Davies, comp. Where is the ——— collection? An account of the various natural history collections which have come under the notice of the compiler ... between 1880 and 1939. 148 p. Cambridge University Press, 1940. [CB 69/229]

HYcm

ARCHER, Mildred. Natural history drawings in the India Office Library. 116 p. London: H.M.S.O., 1962.

HYda

BEEBE, William, ed. The book of naturalists. xiv, 499 p. New York: Knopf, 1944. [CB 70/258]

MIALL, L.C. The early naturalists. Their lives and works (1530-1789). xi, 396 p. London: Macmillan, 1912.

OSBORN, Henry Fairfield. Impressions of great naturalists. xxviii, 216 p., 12 portr. New York: Charles Scribner, 1924.
Reviewed by Raoul M. May, *Isis*, 1926, 8: 188-9.

PEATTIE, Donald Culross. Green laurels. The lives and achievements of the great naturalists. xxiii, 368 p., 30 pl., 5 fig. New York: Simon and Schuster, 1936.
Reviewed by C.A. Kofoid, *Isis*, 1937, 27: 95.

TERRES, John K., ed. Discovery. Great moments in the lives of outstanding naturalists. xiii, 338 p. Philadelphia: Lippincott, 1961.
Reviewed by Lorus J. Milne and Margery Milne, *Science*, 1962, 136: 504.

HYdae

GARDNER, L.I.; WELLS, L.G. The Wolff-Leavenworth Collection of engraved portraits at Syracuse University. *Bull.Hist.Med.*, 1961, 35: 175-7.
This collection contains more than 5900 engravings of physicians and naturalists, European and American.

HYdaj

BOAS, Friedrich; MERKENSCHLAGER, Friedrich. Biologenbrevier. 119 p. Hamburg-Bergedorf: Stromverlag, 1947. [CB 77/372]
An anthology of sayings, chosen by biologists, from the writings of men of science, mainly naturalists.

WEST, Herbert Faulkner. The nature writers. A guide to richer reading. With a foreword by Henry Beston. 155 p. Brattleboro, Vt.: Daye, 1939. [CB 58/565]

HYkb

BATES, Marston. The nature of natural history. 309 p. New York: Scribner's, 1950.
Reviewed by Conway Zirkle, *Isis*, 1951, 42: 164.

HYtp

MERRIAM, John C. The garment of God. Influence of nature in human experience. xii, 162 p. New York: Scribner, 1943.
Reviewed by G. Sarton, *Isis*, 1943, 34: 375.

HYwb

SMALLWOOD, William Martin; SMALLWOOD, Mabel Sarah Coon. Natural history and the American mind. xvii, 445 p., 10 ill. (Columbia Studies in American Culture) New York: Columbia University Press, 1941. [CB 66/265]

HYwb-da

TRACY, Henry Chester. American naturists. viii, 282 p. New York: Dutton, 1931.
Reviewed by Charles A. Kofoid, *Isis*, 1932, 17: 445-6.

HYwb-qd

CREED, Percy R. The Boston Society of Natural History, 1830-1930. xii, 117 p. Boston, Mass.: The Society, 1930.
Reviewed by J. Stanley Gardiner, *Nature*, 1930, 126: 195-6.

HENDRICKSON, Walter B. The Arkites and other pioneer natural history organizations of Cleveland. vii, 56 p., ill. (Makers of Cleveland Series, 1) Cleveland: Press of Western Reserve University, 1962. [CB 88/532]

HENDRICKSON, Walter B. Culture in early Arkansas. The Antiquarian and Natural History Society of Little Rock. *Arkansas Hist.Quart.*, Spring 1958, 1-22.

HYwc

BELTRÁN, Enrique. Setenta y cinco años de ciencias naturales en México. *Rev.Soc.Mex.Hist.Natur.*, 1943, 4: 245-64.

HYwc-bv

BELTRÁN, Enrique. *La Naturaleza*, periodico cientifico de la Sociedad Mexicana de Historia Natural, 1869-1914. Reseña bibliográfica e indice general. *Rev.Soc.Mex.Hist.Natur.*, 1948, 9: 145-74.

HYwc-qd

IZQUIERDO, José Joaquín. Contactos y paralelos de la nueva Sociedad Mexicana de Historia Natural, con su precursora, y divergencias que convienen para su futuro. *Rev.Soc.Mex.Hist. Natur.*, 1950, 11: 1-20.

HYwe-da

RAVEN, Charles E. English naturalists from Neckam to Ray. A study of the making of the modern world. x, 379 p. Cambridge University Press, 1947. [CB 71/121]
Reviewed by Conway Zirkle, *Isis*, 1948, 39: 196-7.

HYwe-qd

ELWES, E.V. On local natural history societies. *J.Torquay Natur.Hist.Soc.*, 1912, 1: no. 4, 172-9.
Includes account of Torquay Natural History Society.

GODDARD, T. Russell. History of the Natural History Society of Northumberland, Durham and Newcastle-upon-Tyne, 1829-1929. xvi, 195 p., 12 pl. Newcastle-upon-Tyne: Reid, 1929.
Reviewed in *Nature*, 1930, 125: 487-8.

HYwf-da

FOURNIER, P. Voyages et découvertes scientifiques des missionaires naturalistes français à travers le monde pendant cinq siècles (XVe à XXe siècles). 258 p., 2 fig. 30 portr. (Encyclopédie Biologique, 10: contribution à l'histoire des sciences naturelles) Paris: Lechevalier, 1932.
Reviewed by C.A. Kofoid, *Isis*, 1934, 22: 303-5.

PENNETIER, G. Naturalistes normands (XVe-XXe siècles). Communication faite le 7 juin 1911 au Congrès du Millénaire Normand. 24 p. Rouen: Léon Gy, 1911.

HYwf-oq

MAYER, André. L'histoire naturelle et la physiologie au Collège de France. Collège de France. Livre jubilaire composé à l'occasion de son quatrième centenaire, p. 169-90, 5 pl. Paris: Presses Universitaires de France, 1932.

HYwh-br

Vesmír: Journal of the Czechoslovak Naturalists. (In Czech with English summaries) *New ser.*, vol. 1-. Prague: 1923-.
Founded in 1871.

HYwh-da

ZEMBRZUSKI, Louis. Participation des médecins et des naturalistes polonais au progrès de la science universelle. *Bull. Soc.Franç.Hist.Méd.*, 1939, 33: 241-54.

HYwi-da

CAPPARONI, Pietro. Profili bio-bibliografici di medici e naturalisti celebri italiani dal sec. XV° al sec. XVIII°. 2 vol. 132 p., 30 pl.; 138 p., 30 pl. Roma: Istituto nazionale medico farmacologico, 1925, 1928. [CB 20/196]

HYwk

AMSTERDAM natuurhistorisch gezien. Gedenkboek uitgegeven ter gelegenheid van het 40-jarig bestaan van de a fd. Amsterdam der Nederlandse Natuurhistorische Vereniging. 1901-26 Januari-1941. [View of natural history in Amsterdam. Memorial volume on the 40th anniversary of the Dutch Natural History Society in Amsterdam. (In Dutch)] xxii, 314 p. Amsterdam: Scheltema & Holkema. 1941.

HYwo-da

BOLOGA, Valeriu L. Les premiers naturalistes roumains. *Hommage à la mémoire du Professeur J. Cantacuzène*, p. 36-40. Paris: Masson, 1934.

HYwq

VOLUME Jubilaire de la Société des Sciences Naturelles du Maroc (1920-1945). L'évolution des sciences naturelles au Maroc de 1934-1947. 403 p., ill. Rabat: Institut Scientifique Chérifien, 1948.
Reviewed by M. Caullery, *Arch.Int.Hist.Sci.*, 1951, 4: 498.

HYxx museums

HYxx-wb

DITMARS, Raymond Lee. The making of a scientist. xiv, 258 p., ill. New York: Macmillan, 1936. [CB 54/238]
Includes an account of the early history of the American Museum of Natural History in New York.

GREGORY, W.K. Henry Fairfield Osborn and the American Museum of Natural History. *Nature,* 1942, 150: 513-15.

HANINGTON, Charles H. The Colorado Museum of Natural History: an historical sketch. *Proc.Colo.Mus.Natur.Hist.*, 1938, 17: 1-48, 13 pl., 4 fig.
An account of the foundation, organization, growth, exhibits, collections, and personnel of a museum concerned with the Rocky Mountain region.

OSBORN, Henry Fairfield. Fifty years of the American Museum of Natural History. *Science,* 1919, 49: 477-81.

REA, Paul M. One hundred fifty years of museum history. *Science,* 1923, 57: 677-81.
Describing the foundation of the Charleston Museum in 1773 and its progress. The museum was the earliest in America.

HYxx-we

BRITISH MUSEUM (NATURAL HISTORY). The history of the collections contained in the natural history departments of the British Museum. 2 vol. London: British Museum (Natural History), 1904, 1912.

BRITISH MUSEUM (NATURAL HISTORY). Jubilee quinquagenary celebration. *Nat.Hist.Mag.*, 1931, 3: 134-8.

BRITISH MUSEUM (NATURAL HISTORY). A short history of the collections. xi, 62 p. (Special guide, 9) London: British Museum, 1931.

HYxx-wf

LEMOINE, Paul. Le Muséum National d'Histoire Naturelle, Paris. *Natur.Hist.Mag.*, 1935, 5: 4-19, ill.
Historical sketch from 1626.

REGNIER, Robert. Le centenaire du Muséum de Rouen. xx, 31 p. Rouen: Imprimerie Administrative de la Ville, 1929.

REGNIER, Robert. L'Exposition du centenaire (1828-1928). Rouen: Muséum d'Histoire Naturelle, d'Ethnographie et de Préhistoire de Rouen, 1928.
Contains valuable information on the Rouen Museum.

ROULE, Louis. Les musées régionaux d'histoire naturelle et leur rôle dans l'enseignement public. *Rev.Sci.*, 1923, 61: 129-36. [CB 14/539]

HYxx-wg

ZIMMER, C. The Natural History Museum (Das Museum für Naturkunde), Berlin. *Natur.Hist.Mag.*, 1933, 4: 37-47.
Includes historical notes.

HYxx-wi

MEZZANA, Niccolo. Il Museo Civico di Storia Naturale in Savona. *Arch.Stor.Sci.*, 1925, 6: 206-12. [CB 19/823]
Founded by Armando David in 1851.

HYxx-wk

KRUYTZER, E.M. Le Musée d'Histoire Naturelle de Maastricht. *Janus,* 1961: 62-5.

HYxx-wm

LÖNNBERG, Einar. The Natural History Museum (Natur-Historiska Riksmuseum) Stockholm. *Natur.Hist.Mag.*, 1933, 4: 77-93.
Includes historical notes.

PEDERSEN, Johannes. The Carlsberg Foundation. The Carlsberg Laboratory; Scientific grants; The Museum of Natural History at Frederiksborg Castle, The new Carlsberg Foundation. 96 p., ill. Copenhagen: The Foundation, 1956.
Reviewed by Suzanne Colnort, *Rev.Hist.Sci.*, 1958, 11: 96.

HYxx-ws

PRASHAD, B. The Indian Museum, Calcutta. *Natur.Hist.Mag.*, 1931, 3: 33-8.
A history of the museum from 1784 to the present day, by the superintendent of the Zoological Survey of India.

HYxy

ADAMS, Charles C. The importance of establishing natural history reservations for research and education. *N.Y.State Mus.Bull.*, 1931, no. 288, 51-9.

CORNISH, Vaughan. National parks: and the heritage of scenery. xi, 139 p. London: Praed, 1930.
Reviewed by J.R., *Nature,* 1930, 126: 393-4.

SHANKLAND, Robert. Steve Mather of the national parks. With an introduction by Gilbert Grosvenor. viii, 326 p. New York: Knopf, 1951.
Reviewed by Ronald F. Lee, *Amer.Hist.Rev.*, 1952, 57: 540.

HYA/HYZ NATURAL HISTORY (REGIONAL)

HYA NORTH AND SOUTH AMERICA

BELTRÁN, Enrique. The naturalist in America in 1942 ± 75 years. *Amer.Natur.*, 1944, 78: 544-55.

GUYOT, Lucien. La découverte de l'Amérique et les sciences naturelles. In: Les conséquences de la découverte de l'Amérique par Christophe Colomb, p. 41-67, 5 fig. Paris: Université de Paris, 1951.

HYB

BRIMLEY, Herbert Hutchinson. A North Carolina naturalist. Selections from his writings, edited by Eugene P. Odum. 205 p., 44 ill. Chapel Hill: University of North Carolina Press, 1949.

COLLINS, Henry B., Jr.; CLARK, Austin H.; WALKER, Egbert H. The Aleutian Islands: their people and natural history (with keys for the identification of the birds and plants). iv, 131 p., 21 pl., 8 fig. (Smithsonian Institution, War Background Studies, 21) Washington, D.C.: 1945.

MERRIAM, John C. Crater Lake. A study in appreciation of nature. *Amer.Mag.Art,* 1933, 26: 357-61, ill.

MERRIAM, John C. The unity of nature as illustrated by the Grand Canyon. *Sci.Mon.*, 1931, 33: 227-34. [CB 40/407]

ROOSEVELT, Theodore. Theodore Roosevelt's America. Selections from the writings of the Oyster Bay naturalist. Ed. by Farida A. Wiley. xxiii, 418 p. (American Naturalist Series) New York: Devin-Adair, 1955.
Reviewed by L. Harrison Matthews, *Nature,* 1956, 177: 813.

HYBda

ALDEN, Roland H.; IFFT, John D. Early naturalists in the Far West. 59 p., pl. (Occasional Papers of the California Academy of Sciences, 20) San Francisco: 1943. [CB 65/81]

EWAN, Joseph. Rocky mountain naturalists. xv, 358 p., 9 ill. Denver, Col.: University of Denver Press, 1950. [CB 77/373]

HYBqk

MERRILL, George P., ed. Contributions to a history of American state geological and natural history surveys. xviii, 549 p., ill. (*Bull.U.S.Nat.Mus.*, 109) Washington, D.C.: 1920. [CB 10/158]

HYC

CUTRIGHT, Paul Russell. The great naturalists explore South America. xii, 340 p. New York: Macmillan, 1940. [CB 59/461]

HAGEN, Victor Wolfgang von, ed. South America. The green world of the naturalists. Five centuries of natural history in South America. Selected and annotated with biographical sketches and introduction. xvii, 398 p., ill. New York: Greenberg, 1948; London: Eyre & Spottiswoode, 1951. [CB 78/18

KERR, John Graham. A naturalist in the Gran Chaco. xi, 235 p. New York: Cambridge University Press, 1950. [CB 77/338]

RUSCONI, Carlos. Fauna y flora de las arenas puelchenses de Buen Aires. *Act.IIIe Congr.Int.Hist.Sci.* (Portugal, 1934), p. 194-9. Lisbon: 1936.

HYCda

CHARDON, Carlos E. Longevity and casualties among naturalists in tropical America. *Sci.Mon.*, 1947, 64: 108-207.
From Fernandez de Oviedo (1478-1557) to Ferdinand Nevermann (1881-1938).

HYD EUROPE

SORRE, Maximilien. Les Pyrénées méditerranéennes; étude de géographie biologique. 508 p., ill., maps. Paris: Colin, 1913.

HYE

FITTER, R.S.R. London's natural history. xii, 282 p. London: Collins, 1945. [CB 70/258]

GARDINER, J.S.; TANSLEY, A.G. The natural history of Wicken Fen. 6 pts. xii, 652 p. Cambridge: Bowes & Bowes, 1923-32.
Reviewed by W.H.T. Tams, *Natur.Hist.Mag.*, 1932, 3: 277-83.

PERRY, Richard. A naturalist on Lindisfarne. 248 p., 16 pl., bibliogr. London: Lindsay Drummond, 1946. [CB 73/173]
Includes historical introduction and history of the biological exploration of the island.
Reviewed by Frances Pitt, *Nature*, 1946, 158: 731.

HYI

RODOLICO, Francesco. L'esplorazione naturalistica dell'Appennino. 403 p., ill. Florence: Le Monnier, 1964.
Reviewed by Mario Loria, *Physis*, 1964, 6: 237-9.

HYP/HYX ASIA; AUSTRALIA; AFRICA

HYP

KLUNZINGER, Carl Benjamin. Erinnerungen aus meinem Leben als Naturforscher und Arzt zu Koseir am Roten Meere. *Zool.Ann.*, 1914, 6: 223-311.

HYPda

SEIDE, J. Doctors and naturalists as pilgrims and travellers to the Holy Land. *Janus*, 1959, 48: 53-61

HYQ

SERGENT, Edmond; SERGENT, Etienne. Histoire d'un marais algérien. 293 p., 4 maps, 18 pl., ill. Institut Pasteur d'Algérie, 1947. [CB 73/185]
The swamp of Mendil.

HYQqd

SEURAT, L.G. Historique de la fondation de la Société d'Histoire Naturelle de l'Afrique du Nord (27 mai 1909). *Bull. Soc.Hist.Natur.Afr.Nord*, 1935, 26(2): 10-17.

HYR

ANDREWS, Roy Chapman. New expedition to Central Asia. *Natur. Hist.*, 1920, 20: 349-55. [CB 10/210]

ANDREWS, Roy Chapman, *et al.* The new conquest of Central Asia: a narrative of the explorations of the Central Asiatic expeditions in Mongolia and China, 1921-1930. With chapters by Walter Granger, Clifford H. Pope, Nels C. Nelson; and summary statements by others. 679 p., 128 pl. (Central Asiatic Expeditions: Natural history of Central Asia, 1) New York: American Museum of Natural History, 1932.
Reviewed in *Nature*, 1933, 132: 81-3; and by C.E.A.W. Oldham, *J.Roy.Asiatic Soc.*, 1934, 825-8.

CARRUTHERS, Douglas. Beyond the Caspian. A naturalist in Central Asia. xx, 290 p., 22 pl. Edinburgh: Oliver and Boyd, 1949. [CB 76/379]

HEBER, A. Reeve; HEBER, Kathleen M. In Himalayan Tibet: a record of twelve years spent in the topsy-turvy land of lesser Tibet with a description of its cheery folk, their ways and religion, of the rigours of the climate and beauties of the country, its fauna and flora. 283 p. London: Seeley, Service, 1926.

KINGDON-WARD, Francis. The mystery rivers of Tibet: a description of the little-known land where Asia's mightiest rivers gallop in harness through the narrow gateway of Tibet: its peoples, fauna and flora. 316 p., 16 pl., 3 maps. London: Seeley, Service, 1923.

STEVENS, Herbert. Through deep defiles to Tibetan uplands. The travels of a naturalist from the Irrawaddy to the Yangtse. 250 p., ill. London: Witherby, 1934.

YOUNGHUSBAND, Francis Edward. The heart of nature; or The quest for natural beauty. xxviii, 235 p. London: Murray, 1921.
German translation Leipzig: Brockhaus, 1923.

HYV

BURKILL, I.H. The biogeographic division of the Indo-Australian Archipelago. A history of the divisions which have been proposed. *Proc.Linnean Soc.London*, 1941-42, 154: 127-38, 8 maps.

CRANDALL, Lee Saunders. Paradise quest; a naturalist's experiences in New Guinea. xvii, 226 p., front., ill., pl., portr. New York/London: C. Scribner, 1931.

HYW

BODENHEIMER, F.S. The uniqueness of Australia in biology. In: Keast, A.; Crocker, R.L.; Christian, C.S.; ed. Biogeography and ecology in Australia, p. 9-35. (Monographicae biologicae, 8) Den Haag: W. Junk, 1959.

HYX

WORTHINGTON, E.B. Science in Africa. A review of scientific research relating to tropical and southern Africa. xiii, 746 p., 5 maps, 8 pl. London: Oxford University Press, 1938. [CB 57/228]

HYXwk

LEBRUN, Jean. Les biologistes belges au Congo. (Un bilan scientifique.) *Bull.Acad.Roy.Belge.Cl.Sci.*, 1961, 47: 1183-218.

HYZ POLAR REGIONS

BROWN, Robert Neal Rudmose. A naturalist at the poles. The life, work and voyages of Dr William Speirs Bruce, the polar explorer. With 5 chapters by W.G. Burn Murdoch. 316 p., ill., portr., 3 maps. London: Seeley Service, 1923.

J BIOLOGY

Jc general history

Jc-bm *large scale works*

AMBARD, L. La biologie. 116 p. (Histoire du Monde, 5) Paris: De Boccard, 1930.
Reviewed by L. Guinet, *Isis*, 1931, 15: 188-90.

ANKER, Jean; DAHL, Svend. Werdegang der Biologie. Übersetzt von L. Johnsson. vii, 304 p., 8 pl., 21 fig. Leipzig: Hiersemann, 1938.

ASIMOV, Isaac. A short history of biology. ix, 183 p., fig. (American Museum Science Book) Garden City, N.Y.: Natural History Press of Doubleday, 1964.
Reviewed by Mark Graubard, *Science*, 1964, 144: 670.

BODENHEIMER, F.S. The history of biology: an introduction. 465 p., 19 pl., 38 fig. London: Dawson, 1958.
Reviewed by Leonard G. Wilson, *Isis*, 1961, 52: 421-3; for other reviews *see* CB 85/392, CB 86/465 and CB 87/567.

BOSCH, Franz. Die Begründung der neueren Biologie. vi, 190 p., 9 tables, 10 fig. Kempten/München: Jos. Kösel, 1914. [CB 460]

CAULLERY, Maurice. Les étapes de la biologie. 126 p., 12 fig. Paris: Presses Universitaires de France, 1941.

CHUN, Carl; JOHANNSEN, W.; ed. Allgemeine Biologie. xii, 691 p., 115 fig. (Die Kultur der Gegenwart, Pt. 3, 4th section, 1) Leipzig: Teubner, 1915.
The historical introduction, from Linné to Darwin, is contributed by Em. Radl (29 p.) and discussed by Hans Heller, *Mitt.Gesch.Med.*, 1919, 18: 161-5.

CLARK, Paul F.; CLARK, Alice Schiedt. Memorable days in medicine: a calendar of biology and medicine. 305 p., ill. Madison, Wisc.: University of Wisconsin Press, 1942.
Reviewed by O. Temkin, *Bull.Hist.Med.*, 1943, 13: 246.

CUNNINGHAM, J.T. Modern biology. A review of the principal phenomena of animal life in relation to modern concepts and theories. xii, 244 p. London: Kegan Paul, 1928.

DAWES, Ben. A hundred years of biology. 429 p., 25 fig. London: Gerald Duckworth, 1952.
Reviewed by Erwin H. Ackerknecht, *Isis*, 1953, 44: 301.

ENCYCLOPÉDIE française. Vol. 4. La vie. Edited by André Mayer. 582 p. Paris: Société de Gestion de l'Encyclopédie française, 1937.
Reviewed by Joseph Needham, *Nature*, 1937, 140: 664.

GABRIEL, Mordecai; SEYMOUR, Fogel. Great experiments in biology. xiii, 317 p. Englewood Cliffs, N.J.: Prentice Hall, 1955. [CB 82/207]
For reviews *see* CB 82/207 and CB 84/314.

GRAY, Peter, ed. The encyclopedia of the biological sciences. xxii, 1119 p., fig. London: Chapman and Hall; New York: Reinhold, 1961.
Reviewed by W.T. Stearn, *Brit.J.Hist.Sci.*, 1962, 1: 188-9; in *Sci.Amer.*, 1962, 206: no. 2, 185-6; by Mark Graubard, *Science*, 1961, 134: 93-4.

HUXLEY, Julian. Essays of a biologist. xv, 306 p. London: Chatto and Windus, 1923.

ISTORIA biologicheskikh nauk. [History of biology. (In Russian)] Pt. 1-10. *Tr.Inst.Ist.Est.Tekh.*, 1955, vol. 4; 1957, vol. 14, vol. 16; 1959, vol. 23; 1958, vol. 24; 1960, vol. 31, vol. 32; 1961, vol. 36; 1962, vol. 40; 1961, vol.41.
Whole volumes; contents of pt. 6 and 7 listed in CB 86/465.

LOCY, William A. Biology and its makers. 3rd rev. ed. xxvi, 477 p., 123 ill. New York: Holt, 1915.
First publ. 1908.

LOCY, William A. The growth of biology. xiv, 481 p. New York: Holt, 1925.
Reviewed by Stephen d'Irsay, *Isis*, 1926, 8: 513-14.

LYSENKO, Trofim Denisovich. The science of biology today. 62 p. New York: International Publishers, 1948. [CB 74/388]
Translation of the presidential address delivered by Academician Lysenko on 31 July 1948 at the V.I. Lenin Academy of Agricultural Sciences.

MIELI, Aldo. Breve historia de la biologia. 161 p. Buenos Aires: Espasa-Calpe, 1951. [CB 78/187]

MITCHELL, Peter Chalmers. My fill of days. 440 p. London: Faber and Faber, 1937. [CB 54/508]
The author was Secretary of the Zoological Gardens in London from 1903 to 1935. The volume includes anecdotes and comments on leaders in European biology in the late 19th and early 20th centuries.

MOORE, Ruth. The coil of life. The story of the great discoveries in the life sciences. xxvii, 418 p., ill. New York: Knopf, 1961.
Reviewed by Garrett Hardin, *Science*, 1961, 133: 1414.

NORDENSKIÖLD, Nils Erik. The history of biology. Translated from the Swedish by Leonard Bucknall Eyre. xi, 629, xv p., portr. New York: Knopf, 1928; London: Kegan Paul, 1929
Reviewed by George Sarton, *Isis*, 1929, 12: 332-40.
German translation, Jena: Gustav Fischer, 1926.

NOVIKOV, Mikhail Mikhailovich. Dejiny biologických teórií. [History of biological theory. (In Czech)] 167 p., pl. Turčiansky sv. Martin: Matica Slovenska, 1944.

NOVIKOV, Mikhail Mikhailovich (NOWIKOFF, Michael). Grundzüge der Geschichte der biologischen Theorien. Werdegang der abendländischen Lebensbegriffe. 222 p., 70 ill. München: Carl Hanser Verlag, 1949.
Reviewed by Jean Anker, *Centaurus*, 1951, 1: 276-7; and by Nils von Hofsten, *Lychnos*, 1952, 409-10.

RÁDL, Emanuel. Geschichte der biologischen Theorien in der Neuzeit. Part 1. 2nd ed. xiii, 351 p. Leipzig: Engelmann, 1913.
Reviewed by G. Sarton, *Isis*, 1914, 2: 224-9.
Part 2 first publ. 1909.

RÁDL, Emanuel. The history of biological theories. Translated and adapted from the German by E.J. Hatfield. xii, 408 p. London: Oxford University Press, 1930.
Condensation of Geschichte der biologischen Theorien. Part 2, 1909.
Reviewed by G. Sarton, *Isis*, 1931, 15: 195-6.

RIDLEY, G.N. Man studies life: the story of biology. x, 109 p. (Thinker's Library, 97) London: Watts, 1944.
Reviewed by T.H.H., *Nature*, 1944, 154: 503.

ROOK, Arthur, ed. The origins and growth of biology. 402 p., ill. Baltimore: Penguin Books, 1964.

ROSTAND, Jean. Esquisse d'une histoire de la biologie. 257 p., 14 ill. Paris: Gallimard, 1945.
Reviewed by Erwin H. Ackerknecht, *Bull.Hist.Med.*, 1947, 21: 269; and in *Nature*, 1947, 159: 420.
Italian translation (Torino: Einaudi, 1949) reviewed by Pietro Franceschini, *Riv.Stor.Sci.*, 1950, 41: 234.

ROSTAND, Jean. Aux sources de la biologie. 276 p. Paris: Gallimard, 1958.
Reviewed by A. Bauchau, *Rev.Quest.Sci.*, 1959, 20: 478; by Jean Théodoridès, *Rev.Hist.Sci.*, 1959, 12: 87.

SCHMUCKER, Theodor. Geschichte der Biologie. Forschung und Lehre. 296 p. Göttingen: Vandenhoeck & Ruprecht, 1936.
Reviewed by Nils von Hofsten, *Lychnos*, 1937, 2: 551.

SINGER, Charles. A history of biology to about the year 1900. A general introduction to the study of living things. 3rd rev. ed. xxxvi, 580 p., front., fig. London/New York: Abelard-Schuman, 1959.
Reviewed by Everett Mendelsohn, *Isis*, 1963, 54: 415-17; by A.R. Gemmell, *Nature*, 1960, 185: 492-3
First publ. Oxford: Clarendon Press, 1931 and New York: Harper, 1931 and reviewed by Dorothy Stimson, *Isis*, 1934, 22: 298-300; and by F.M.G. de Feyfer, *Bijdr.Gesch.Geneesk.*, 1931, 11: 256-7; 2nd edition (New York: Schumann, 1950) reviewed by Conway Zirkle, *Isis*, 1951, 42: 82. French translation of first edition reviewed by Pierre Brunet, *Archeion*, 1934, 16: 434-6. Spanish translation Buenos Aires, 1947.

SIRKS, M.J.; ZIRKLE, Conway. The evolution of biology. v, 376 p., 64 fig., bibliogr. New York: Ronald Press, 1964.

SIRKS, M.J. De ontwikkeling der biologie. [The development of biology. (In Dutch)] 184 p., 24 fig., 14 pl. Gorinchem: Noorduyn, 1947.
Reviewed by R. Hooykaas, *Arch.Int.Hist.Sci.*, 1949, 2: 530.

SNYDER, Emily Eveleth. Biology in the making. xii, 539 p. New York: McGraw-Hill, 1940. [CB 60/152]

TAYLOR, Gordon Rattray. The science of life: a picture history of biology. 368 p., ill., pl. New York: McGraw-Hill; London: Thames & Hudson, 1963.
Reviewed by Leonard G. Wilson, *J.Hist.Med.*, 1964, 19: 174-7.

WELLS, H.G.; HUXLEY, Julian; WELLS, G.P. The science of life. xvi, 896 p. London: Cassell, 1931.
Reviewed in *Nature*, 1931, 127: 477-9.

WOODRUFF, Lorande Loss. Foundations of biology. 6th ed. xvii, 773 p. New York: Macmillan, 1941. [CB 61/403]
The last chapter is devoted to biological history.
First publ. 1922. 5th ed. 1936 [CB 48/574] 7th ed. 1951.

Jc-bn *essays; articles*

BATESON, W. Progress in biology. Address delivered on March 12 in connection with the centenary of Birkbeck College. *Nature*, 1924, 113: 644-6.

BODENHEIMER, F.S. The transition from classical to new biology. *Act.IXe Congr.Int.Hist.Sci.* (Barcelona-Madrid, 1959), p. 131-44. Paris: Hermann, 1960.

CANGUILHEM, G., *et al.* Histoire de la biologie; du développment à l'évolution au XIXe siècle. *Thalès*, 1960, 11: 1-63.

GARRISON, Fielding Hudson. The history of research work in the biological sciences. *Bull.Sch.Med.Univ.Maryland*, 1933, 17: 93-108.

GRAUBARD, Mark. Guide to biological horizons. *Science*, 1961, 134: 93-4.
A review of The encyclopedia of the biological sciences, *see* Gray, Peter, ed. Jc-bm

HELLER, Hans. Bemerkungen zu einer geschichtlichen Entwicklung der vor-Darwinischen Biologie. *Mitt.Gesch.Med.*, 1919, 18: 161-5.
A propos of Radl's historical introduction to Chun, C.; Johannsen, W. Allgemeine Biologie, *see* Jc-bm

RABAUD, Etienne. La biologie. Son développement depuis le début du XXe siècle. *Larousse Mens.*, 1932, 9: 55-7, 3 portr.

[SOME aspects of the history of biological science.] 60p. *Botanica*, 1951, 2: no. 2. [CB 80/130]

THOMPSON, D'Arcy Wentworth. Magnalia naturae: or the greater problems of biology. *Annu.Rep.Smithsonian Inst.for 1911*, p. 379-93. Washington, D.C.: 1912.
Address to the British Association, 31 August 1911.

WOODRUFF, Lorande Loss. History of biology. *Sci.Mon.*, 1921, 12: 253-81.
A summary of this history.

YASUGI, R. [History and contemporary problems of biology. (In Japanese)] *J.Hist.Sci.Japan*, 1955, no. 33, 1-7.

Jc-bq *Symposia*

Biological Symposia: a series of volumes devoted to current symposia in the field of biology. (American Association for the Advancement of Science). 1- Lancaster, Pa.: Jaques Cattell Press, 1940-
Volumes 6, 7 and 9 reviewed by Charles A. Kofoid, *Isis*, 1943, 34: 418, 527-8, 525.

Jc-br *periodicals*

Biologen-Kalender. 1. Leipzig: Teubner, 1914.
No more published.

Jc-bv/cv bibliography; literature; sources

Jc-bv

OYE, Paul van. De geschiedenis der natuurwetenschappen in het *Biologisch Jaarboek*. [The history of the natural sciences in the *Biologisch Jaarboek*. (In Dutch)] *Sci.Hist.*, 1959, 1: 79-86.

THÉODORIDÈS, J. L'histoire des sciences biologiques au XIVe Congrès International d'Histoire de la Médecine (Rome-Salerne, 1954). *Rev.Gén.Sci.*, 1954, 61: 261-3.

Jcb

O'MALLEY, Charles D. The Barkan library of the history of medicine and natural science books; an account of its development. *Stanford Med.Bull.*, 1951, 9: 145-55.

Jce

COLE, F.J. Bibliographical reflections of a biologist. *Proc. Oxford Bibliogr.Soc.*, 1938, 169-86.
Reprinted in *Osiris*, 1948, 8: 289-315.

DRACHMAN, Julian M. Studies in the literature of natural science. xii, 487 p., 6 pl. New York: Macmillan, 1936.
Reviewed by C.A. Kofoid, *Isis*, 1937, 27: 89-90; by T.G., *Nature*, 1932, 129: 263.

Jd biography

Jd-bv

HUARD, Pierre; MONTAGNÉ, M. Index biographique concernant les sciences biologiques et médicales. *Trav.Inst.Anat.Fac.Méd. Indochine*, 1944, 9: 39-104.

HUARD, Pierre; MONTAGNÉ, M. Index biographique succinct des anatomistes, morphologistes, anthropologistes et naturalistes. *Trav.Inst.Anat.Fac.Méd.Indochine*, 1944, 9: 1-37.

Jda collective biography

ALMQUIST, Ernst. Grosse Biologen. Eine Geschichte der Biologie und ihrer Erforscher. 143 p., 23 portr. München: Lehmann, 1931.
Reviewed by Charles A. Kofoid, *Isis*, 1932, 18: 206-7.

MAY, Walther. Grosse Biologen. Bilder aus der Geschichte der Biologie. vi, 201 p. Leipzig: B.G. Teubner, 1914.

SCHIERBEEK, A. Van Aristoteles tot Pasteur. Leven en werken der groote biologen. [From Aristotle to Pasteur. Life and work of the great biologists. (In Dutch)] 479 p., 121 fig. Amsterdam: Versluys, 1923. [CB 15/211]

THOMSON, J. Arthur. The great biologists. viii, 176 p. (The Great Scientists Series) London: Methuen, 1932.

Jdaj

BODENHEIMER, F.S. Mekorot le-toldot ha-biyologiyah. [Sources for the history of biology. (In Hebrew)] Jerusalem: Kiryat Sepher, 1952.
Reviewed by Max Jammer, *Isis*, 1953, 44: 89-91.

BRÜCKNER, Gottfried. Aus der Entdeckungsgeschichte der lebendigen Substanz. 64 p. (Voigtländers Quellenbücher, 32) Leipzig: R. Voigtländer, 1913. [CB 3/566]

CLASSICS in biology. A course of selected reading by authorities. Introductory reading guide by S. Zuckerman. xxxii, 351 p. New York: Philosophical Library, 1960.
Reviewed by Bentley Glass, *Isis*, 1964, 55: 213-14; by S.F. Barker, *Phil.Sci.*, 1963, 30: 396

Jf history of biology as a study

STROHL, J. Vom Wesen und von der Bedeutung der Biologie-Historie. *Schweiz.Med.Wochenschr.*, 1923, 53: 185-8. [CB 14/543]

TEMPLADO, J. Una introducción a la historia de la biología. *Arbor*, 1961, 49: no. 187-8, 126-7.

VERDOORN, Frans. On the aims and methods of biological history and biography. With some notes for the collaborators of the "Index Botanicorum". *Chron.Bot.*, 1944, 8: 427-8, ill.

YASUGI, Ryuichi; TSUKUBA, Hisaharu. On the study of the history of biology in Japan. *Jap.Stud.Hist.Sci.*, 1962, 1: 35-7.

Jg teaching history of biology

SIMON, I. Avant-propos: l'enseignement de l'histoire de la médecine et de l'histoire de la biologie en Israël. *Rev. Hist.Méd.Hébraique*, 1957, 10: 3-18.

Jgt

SAITO, K. [History of science in education in biology. (In Japanese)] *J.Hist.Sci.Japan*, 1955, no. 33, 29-33.

Jh historiography and particular aspects of the history of biology

Jhd

GUTINA, V.N. Osnovnye printsipy osvesheniya istorii biologii, Konferentsiya v Moskve. [Basic principles in the interpretation of the history of biology, Moscow Conference. (In Russian)] *Vestnik.Akad.Nauk SSSR*, 1964, 34: no. 4, 167-8.

MEYER, Adolf. Wer soll Geschichte der Biologie schreiben? *Arch.Gesch.Med.*, 1937, 29: 357-62.

SAITŌ, Kazuo. [Method of description in the history of biology. (In Japanese)] *J.Hist.Sci.Japan*, 1953, no. 26, 37-9.

Jhf

HESSE, Peter G. Der Lebensbegriff bei den Klassikern der Naturforschung. Seine Entwicklung bei 60 Denkern und Forschern bis zur Goethezeit. viii, 180 p., 2 pl. Jena: Fischer, 1943.
Reviewed by Nils von Hofsten, *Lychnos*, 1943, 381.

MEYER, Adolf. Das Wesen der idealistischen Biologie und ihre Beziehungen zur modernen Biologie. *Arch.Gesch.Math.Naturwiss. Tech.*, 1928, 11: 149-78.

WAGNER, Richard. Zur geschichtlichen Entwicklung der Erkenntnis biologischer Regelung. *Naturwiss.Rundsch.*, 1961, 14: 65-8.

Jhg

MEYER, Adolf. Krisenepochen und Wendepunkte des biologischen Denkens. viii, 62 p. Jena: Fischer, 1935.
Reviewed by Aldo Mieli, *Archeion*, 1935, 17: 498-504.

MEYER, Adolf. Über historische Kontinuität und Epochenunabhängigkeit. Eine Antwort an Herrn Aldo Mieli. *Arch.Gesch. Med.*, 1936, 29: 196-202.
In reply to Aldo Mieli's review of his book, *see* above.

SCHOPFER, William Henri. L'évolution de la méthode en biologie, du point de vue de l'histoire des sciences. *Congr.Int. Phil.Sci.*(Paris, 1949), (8), p. 117-25. (Actualités Scientifiques et Industrielles, 1166) Paris: Hermann, 1952.

Jhj

HERRMANN, Heinz. The Aristotelian and the modern unification of the structural and functional aspect of living matter. *Bull.Hist.Med.*, 1943, 14: 391-4.

LINNAEUS tradition and our time. *Nature*, 1958, 181: 611-12.
A summary of the Presidential address given by Dag Hammarskjöld to the Royal Swedish Academy in December 1957.

MEYER, Adolf. The tradition of ancient biology and medicine in the vitalistic periods of modern biology and medicine. *Bull. Inst.Hist.Med.*, 1937, 5: 800-21.

MEYER, Adolf. Das Wesen der antiken Naturwissenschaft mit besonderer Berücksichtigung des Aristotelismus in der modernen Biologie. *Sudhoffs Arch.*, 1929, 22: 1-23, 1 fig.

Jhm

MEYER, Adolf. Ideen und Ideale der biologischen Erkenntnis. xiii, 202 p. (Bios, 1) Leipzig: Barth, 1934.
Reviewed by Ernst Wolf, *Isis*, 1935, 22: 546-8.

Jk philosophy and methodology

Jk-bm *large scale works*

ARBER, Agnes. The mind and the eye: a study of the biologist's standpoint. 126 p. New York: Cambridge University Press, 1953.
Reviewed by Conway Zirkle, *Isis*, 1953, 44: 300-1.

BECK, William S. Modern science and the nature of life. xix, 302 p. New York: Harcourt, Brace, 1957; London: Macmillan, 1958. Paperback edition. 316 p. (Pelican Books, A473) Harmondsworth, Mddx.: Penguin Books, 1961.
Reviewed by Alex Comfort, *Nature* 1958, 181: 1627-8; by Nils von Hofsten, *Lychnos*, 1962, 482-3.

BERTALANFFY, Ludwig von. Problems of life. An evaluation of modern biological thought. xi, 216 p. London: Watts, 1952.
Translation of: Das biologische Weltbild. 1. Die Stellung des Lebens in Natur und Wissenschaft. 202 p. Bern: Francke, 1949.
Reviewed by Joseph Needham, *Nature*, 1953, 172: 1119.

BOUNHIOL, Jean Paul. La vie. 332 p. (Bibliothèque de Philosophie Scientifique) Paris: E. Flammarion, 1927. [CB 24/534]

BOUNOURE, L. L'autonomie de l'être vivant. Essai sur les formes organiques et psychologiques de l'activité vitale. 224 p., 34 fig. (Bibliothèque de Philosophie Contemporaine) Paris: Presses Universitaires de France, 1949.
Reviewed by P. Chauchard, *Rev.Quest.Sci.*, 1949, 10: 303-5.

BRADLEY, John Hodgdon. Patterns of survival. 223 p. New York: Macmillan, 1938. [CB 57/235]

BUTLER, J.A.V. Man is a microcosm. xiii, 159 p. New York: Macmillan, 1951. [CB 78/187]

COLLIN, Rémy. Physique et métaphysique de la vie: esquisse d'une interprétation synthétique des phénomènes vitaux. vii, 104 p. Paris: Doin, 1925.

CUÉNOT, Lucien. Invention et finalité en biologie. 259 p., ill. (Bibliothèque de Philosophie Scientifique) Paris: Flammarion, 1941.
Reviewed by R. Furon, *Rev.Gén.Sci.*, 1942, 52: 57.

DRIESCH, Hans. Philosophie des Organischen. 2nd rev. ed. 608 p., 14 fig. Leipzig: Engelmann, 1921.
First edition, 1909.

GRASSET, Joseph. Devoirs et périls biologiques. 546 p. (Bibliothèque de Philosophie Contemporaine) Paris: Alcan, 1917.
Reviewed by L. Guinet, *Isis*, 1920, 3: 88.

GUILLEMINOT, Hyacinthe. La matière et la vie. 318 p. Paris: Flammarion, 1919.
Reviewed by L. Guinet, *Isis*, 1920, 3: 296-7.

HALDANE, John Scott. The philosophical basis of biology. x, 169 p. (Donnellan Lectures, University of Dublin, 1930) London: Hodder and Stoughton, 1931.
German translation Berlin: Prismen-Verlag, 1932.

HENDERSON, Lawrence Joseph. The fitness of the environment. An enquiry into the biological significance of the properties of matter. xv, 317 p. New York: Macmillan, 1913. Reprint with introd. by George Wald. xxiv, 317 p. (Beacon Paperback Edition) Boston: Beacon Press, 1958.

HOGBEN, Lancelot. The nature of living matter. ix, 316 p. London: Kegan Paul, 1930.
Reviewed by D.M.S. Watson, *Nature*, 1931, 127: 350-1.

IUGAI, G.A. Problema tselostnosti organizma; filosofskii analiz. [The problem of the wholeness of an organism; a philosophical analysis. (In Russian)] 248 p. Moscow: Izdatel'stvo Sotsial'no-ekonomicheskoi Literatury, 1962. [CB 88/647]

JELLINEK, S. Faradays Symbole als Grundlage einer neuen biologischen Forschungsrichtung. vii, 70 p., 14 pl. Wien: Urban & Schwarzenberg, 1949.

JOHNSTONE, James. The philosophy of biology. xv, 391 p. Cambridge University Press, 1914. [CB 6/461]

LE DANTEC, F. La science de la vie. 321 p. (Bibliothèque de Philosophie Scientifique) Paris: Flammarion, 1912.

LILLIE, Ralph S. General biology and philosophy of organism. 215 p. Chicago: University of Chicago Press, 1945.
A discussion of the nature of the living and non-living, body and mind, random and directed activity, stability and change.

NAGEOTTE, Jean. L'organisation de la matière dans ses rapports avec la vie. vi, 560 p. Paris: Félix Alcan, 1922. [CB 14/542]

NEEDHAM, Joseph. Order and life. x, 175 p. (The Terry lectures for 1935 delivered before Yale University) Cambridge University Press, 1936.
Reviewed by G.P., *Rev.Gen.Sci.*, 1936, 48: 80; by G.R. de Beer, *Nature*, 1936, 138: 863.

NEEDHAM, Joseph. The sceptical biologist. (Ten essays) v, 288 p. London: Chatto and Windus, 1929; New York: Norton, 1930.
Reviewed by A. Meyer, *Isis*, 1932, 17: 277-8; by W.J. Crozier, *J.Gen.Psychol.*, 1931, 5: 129-31; by A.D.R., *Nature*, 1930, 125: 374.

NICOLLE, Charles. La nature. Conception et morale biologiques. 134 p. Paris: Alcan, 1935.

OSTERHOUT, Winthrop John Van Leuven. The nature of life. vii, 117 p. (Brown University, the Clover Lectures, 1922) New York: Henry Holt, 1924.

RICHET, Charles. Apologie de la biologie. 100 p. (Collection des Apologies) Paris: Doin, 1929.

RIGNANO, Eugenio. Man not a machine: a study of the finalistic aspects of life. 77 p. (Psyche miniatures: General series, 3) London: Kegan Paul, 1926.

RIGNANO, Eugenio. Les manifestations finalistes de la vie. *Scientia*, 1925, 38: 229-48, 315-28, 379-409; 1926, 39: 19-38, 96-110. [CB 20/197]
Also publ. in book form Qu'est-ce que la vie, *see* below.

RIGNANO, Eugenio. La mémoire biologique. Essais d'une conception philosophique nouvelle de la vie. 248 p. Paris: Flammarion, 1923.
Reviewed by L. Guinet, *Isis*, 1924, 6: 564-5.

RIGNANO, Eugenio. The nature of life. Translated by N. Mallison. x, 168 p. (International Library of Psychology, Philosophy and Scientific Method) London: Kegan Paul, 1930.
Translation of Che cos'e la vita (Bologna: Zanichelli, 1926); for French translation *see* below.

RIGNANO, Eugenio. Qu'est-ce que la vie? Nouveaux essais de synthèse biologique. 208 p. Paris: Alcan, 1926.
First publ. in *Scientia*, *see* Les manifestations ... above, with one additional chapter.
Reviewed by Alphonse Labbé, *Rev.Gén.Sci.*, 1930, 41: 344-5.

RUSSELL, E.S. The study of living things. Prolegomena to a functional biology. xx, 139 p. London: Methuen, 1924.

SAULNIER, Claude. L'individualité biologique, essai scientifique et philosophique. 208 p. Paris: Expansion Scientifique Française, 1958.
Reviewed by P. Huard, *Rev.Syn.*, 1962, 83: 301-2.

SCHRÖDINGER, Erwin. What is life? The physical aspect of the living cell. Based on lectures delivered under the auspices of the Institute at Trinity College, Dublin, in February 1943. viii, 91 p. Cambridge University Press; New York: Macmillan, 1945. [CB 69/229]

SIEGEL, Carl. Grundprobleme der Philosophie organisch entwickelt. xi, 218 p. Wien: Braumüller, 1925.
Reviewed by F. Netolitzky, *Naturwissenschaften*, 1926, 739-40.

SMITH, Vincent Edward, ed. Philosophy of biology. 95 p. (St. John's University Studies. Philosophical Series, 3) New York: St. John's University Press, 1962.

STUDNITZ, Gotthilft von. Biologisches Brevier. 5 Vorträge. ix, 129 p. Bonn: Bouvier, 1948. [CB 77/373]
A series of five lectures on philosophical aspects of biology.

WALLACE, Alfred Russel. Le monde de la vie. Manifestation d'un pouvoir créateur, d'un esprit directeur et d'un but final. Transl. by C. Barbey-Boissier. Avant propos de Casimir de Candolle. 554 p., 110 fig. Genève: Kündig, 1914.
French translation of: The world of life (London: 1910).

WARTHIN, Alfred Scott. The creed of a biologist, a biologic philosophy of life. viii, 62 p. New York: Hoeber, 1930.
Reviewed by Francis R. Packard, *Ann.Med.Hist.*, *new ser.*, 1930, 2: 451.

WHEELER, William Morton. Essays in philosophical biology. Selected by G. H. Parker. xv, 261 p. Cambridge, Mass.: Harvard University Press, 1939. [CB 58/573]

WOLFF, Gustav. Leben und Erkennen. Vorarbeiten zu einer biologischen Philosophie. 442 p. München: Reinhardt, 1933.
Reviewed by Aldo Mieli, *Archeion*, 1933, 15: 287-9.

Jk-bn *essays; articles*

BECKNER, Morton. Metaphysical presuppositions and the descriptions of biological systems. *Synthese*, 1963, 15: 260-74.

BERTALANFFY, Ludwig von. Das Problem des Lebens. *Scientia*, 1927, 41: 265-74; French transl. suppl. 117-25. [CB 23/247]

BOUNOURE, Louis. La conception d' "être vivant" et le domaine de la biologie générale. *Rev.Gén.Sci.*, 1935, 46: 331-40, 495-504.

BRUNI, Giuseppe. Sintesi e natura. *Rendic.Ist.Lombardo Sci.Lett.Parte Gen.Atti Uffic.*, 1938, 71: 49-72.
Reviewed by R. Zaunick, *Mitt.Gesch.Med.*, 1941-42, 40: 120.

CUÉNOT, Lucien. La finalité en biologie. *Arch.Inst.Int.Sci. Théor.Sér.A. Bull.Acad.Int.Phil.Sci.* 5. Problèmes de philosophie des sciences. 5, Problèmes de bio-philosophie, p. 37-49, bibliogr., Discussion, p. 51-9. (Actualités Scientifiques et Industrielles, 1067) Paris: Hermann, 1948.

DONNAN, F.G. The mystery of life. *Nature*, 1928, 122: 512-14.
See also editorial, *ibid.*, 501-3.

DRIESCH, Hans. Der Begriff des "Standpunktes" in der Philosophie. *Sudhoffs Arch.*, 1934, 27: 213-22.

FARBER, Eduard. Forces and substances of life. *Osiris*, 1954, 11: 422-37.

GERARD, R.W. Higher levels of integration. *Science*, 1942. 95: 309-13.

GOLDSCHMIDT, Victor. Zur Mechanik des organischen Lebens. *Ann.Natur.Kulturphil.*, 1913, 12: 138-61.

LENOIR, Raymond. La philosophie devant la vie. *Rev.Métaphys. Morale*, 1927, 34: 177-237.

LILLIE, Ralph S. Directive action and life. *Phil.Sci.*, 1937, 4: 202-26.

LILLIE, Ralph S. The directive influence in living organisms. *J.Phil.*, 1932, 29: 477-91.

LILLIE, Ralph S. The living and the non-living. *Amer.Natur.*, 1934, 68: 304-32.

LILLIE, Ralph S. Living systems and non-living systems. *Phil. Sci.*, 1942, 9: 307-22. [CB 64/452]

LILLIE, Ralph S. The nature of organizing action. *Amer.Natur.*, 1938, 72: 389-415.

LILLIE, Ralph S. The problem of synthesis in biology. *Phil. Sci.*, 1942, 9: 59-71.

LILLIE, Ralph S. The problem of vital organization. *Phil.Sci.*, 1934, 1: 296-312.

LILLIE, Ralph S. The psychic factor in living organisms. *Phil.Sci.*, 1943, 10: 262-70. [CB 66/265]

LILLIE, Ralph S. Science and life. *J.Phil.*, 1930, 27: 421-30

LILLIE, Ralph S. The scientific view of life. *J.Phil.*, 1928, 25: 589-606.

LILLIE, Ralph S. Vital organization and the psychic factor. *Phil.Sci.*, 1944, 11: 161-70.

McCLUNG, C.E. The unity of life. *Science*, 1926, 64: 561-9.

METZ, A. La réaction universelle. *Rev.Sci.*, 1922, 60: 437-41. [CB 13/307]

MEYER, Adolf. Das Organische und seine Ideologien. *Sudhoffs Arch.*, 1934, 27: 3-19.

MEYER, Adolf. Das Problem des Lebens. *Verhandl.Deut.Wiss. Ver.Santiago Chile*, 1931, 1: 71-103.

MEYER, Adolf. Ueber organische Systeme. Erster Teil. *Verhandl.Deut.Wiss.Ver.Santiago Chile*, 1931, 1: 105-18.

MEYER, Adolf. Umwelt und Innenwelt organischer Systeme nebst Bemerkungen über ihre Simplifikation zu physischen Systemen. *Sudhoffs Arch.*, 1934, 27: 328-52.

NEEDHAM, Joseph. Recent developments in the philosophy of biology. *Quart.Rev.Biol.*, 1928, 3: 77-91. [CB 25/423]

RICHET, Charles. Les causes finales en biologie. *Rev.Deux Mondes*, *6th ser.*, 1913, 16: 799-829.

RIGNANO, Eugenio. The concept of purpose in biology. *Mind*, 1931, 40: 335-40.

RITTER, William E.; BAILEY, Edna W. The organismal conception, its place in science and its bearing on philosophy. *Univ. Calif.Publ.Zool.*, 1928, 31: 307-58. [CB 25/411]

ROSENTHAL-SCHNEIDER, Ilse. The laws of nature in the light of modern physics and biology. *Australian J.Sci.*, 1946, 8: 120-3.
Discussion suggested by Erwin Schrödinger: What is life?, *see* Jk-bm

RUSSO, Ph. La matière vivante. *Rev.Idées*, 1913, 10: 1er sem., 284-311.

SALMAN, D.H. La nature du vivant. *Arch.Inst.Int.Sci.Théor. Sér.A. Bull.Acad.Int.Phil.Sci.* 5. Problèmes de philosophie des sciences. 5, Problèmes de bio-philosophie, p. 7-24, Discussion, p. 25-36. (Actualités Scientifiques et Industrielles, 1067) Paris: Hermann, 1948.

SCHIERBEEK, A. De organische eenheid. [Organic unity. (In Dutch)] 36 p. In: Eenheid en opgang [Unity and progress]. Zeist: J. Ploegsma, 1937.

SCHLICHTING, TH. H. De leer der spiritus of levensgeesten. [The theory of "spiritus" or life spirit. (In Dutch)] *Bijdr. Gesch.Geneesk.*, 1939, 19: 41-54.

SCHULTZ, Julius. Die Philosophie des Organischen. *Jahrb. Phil.*, 1913, 1: 167-99, 371-3.

SZYMANSKI, J.S. Ueber eine Gesetzmässigkeit im Verhalten der Organismen. *Ann.Natur.Kulturphil.*, 1913, 12: 131-7.

Jkd/kn theories; method; logic

Jkd

CANFIELD, John. Teleological explanation in biology. *Brit.J. Phil.Sci.*, 1964, 14: 285-95.

CAULLERY, Maurice. La nature des lois biologiques. *Rev. Métaphys.Morale*, 1914, 22: 334-60. [CB 6/460]

SCHAXEL, Julius. Grundzüge der Theorienbildung in der Biologie vii, 221 p. Jena: Fischer, 1919.
Reviewed by F. Alverdes, *Deut.Lit.Zeitung*, 1921, 758.

WILKIE, J.S. Causation and explanation in theoretical biology. *Brit.J.Phil.Sci.*, 1951, 1: 273-90.

Jke

BONNER, John Tyler. Analogies in biology. *Synthese*, 1963, 15: 275-9.

COONEN, L.P. Evolution of method in biology. In: Smith, Vincent E., ed. Philosophy of biology, 22 p. (St. John's University Studies. Philosophical Series, 3) New York: St. John's University Press, 1962.

GLANGEAUD, Louis. L'expérience et la recherche opérationnelle dans les sciences de la terre et de la nature. *Rev.Syn.*, 1963, 34: 125-70.

JENNINGS, Herbert Spencer. Biology and experimentation. *Science*, 1926, 64: 97-105.

MUNTNER, Suessman. [Development of research methods in biology. (In Hebrew with English summary)] *Koroth*, 1962, 2: 503-13.

PILET, Paul-Emile. L'expérience en biologie. *Rev.Syn.*, 1963, 34: 171-98.

SOCIETY FOR EXPERIMENTAL BIOLOGY. Models and analogues in biology. 255 p. (Symposia, 14) Cambridge University Press; New York: Academic Press, 1960.
Reviewed by Marjorie Grene, *Brit.J.Phil.Sci.*, 1962, 13: 329-32.

STOLOWSKI, Joseph. Témoins et faux témoins en biologie. *Rev. Syn.*, 1962, 83: 209-36.
An examination of the sources of error in biological experimentation and of the perils of overly refined techniques.

WOODGER, J.H. Axiomatic method in biology. With appendices by A. Tarski and W.F. Floyd. x, 174 p. Cambridge University Press, 1937.

Jkh

BLACKWELDER, R.E.; HAYME, L.E. Statistics, experiment and the future of biology. *Sci.Mon.*, 1955, 80: 225-9.

GERARD, R.W. Quantification in biology. *Isis*, 1961, 52: 334-52.

GRMEK, Mirko Drazen. L'introduction de l'expérience quantitative dans les sciences biologiques. 38 p., fig. (Conférences du Palais de la Découverte, D83) Paris: Palais de la Découverte, 1962.

HOLMES, S.J. Micromerism in biological theory. *Isis*, 1948, 39: 145-58.
A history of the conception of biological units.

MACLEOD, Julius. The quantitative method in biology. 2nd ed., with a memoir of the author and a list of his scientific writings. xxiii, 228 p., ill. (Publication of the University of Manchester, Biological series, 2) Manchester: University Press, 1926.
First published 1919.

Jkk

MAINX, Felix. Foundations of biology. 86 p. (International Encyclopedia of Unified Sciences, 1: 9) Chicago: University of Chicago Press, 1955. [CB 81/272]

MEYER, Adolf. Geistesgeschichtliche Grundlagen der Biologie. 333 p., ill. Stuttgart: Gustav Fischer, 1963.
Reviewed by Bruno Endlich, *Naturwiss.Rundsch.*, 1964, 17: 324.

MEYER, Adolf. Logik der Morphologie: im Rahmen einer Logik der gesamten Biologie. vii, 290 p. Berlin: Springer, 1926.

MITCHELL, Peter Chalmers. Logic and law in biology. *Nature* 1927, 119: 748-50.
Huxley memorial lecture delivered at the Imperial College of Science and Technology, South Kensington, May 4, 1927.

Jkm

LECLERC DU SABLON, Mathieu. Les incertitudes de la biologie. 336 p., 24 fig. (Bibliothèque de Philosophie Scientifique) Paris: Flammarion, 1912.

ROSTAND, Jean. Error and deception in science. Essays on biological aspects of life. Trans. from the French by A.J. Pomerans. 196 p. New York: Basic Books, 1960.
Originally publ. 1945 (Columbia Studies in Philosophy, 9)
Reviewed by S.F. Barker, *Phil.Sci.*, 1963, 30: 406-7.

Jkn

WOODGER, J.H. Biology and language: an introduction to the methodology of the biological sciences including medicine. The Tarner lectures, 1949-50. 364 p. Cambridge University Press, 1952.

Jkq classification in biology

for plant taxonomy *see* KS
animal taxonomy *see* LS

BAUVERIE, J. La systématique des formes. Les grandes étapes du progrès de la classification naturelle, ses tendances actuelles. 64 p., ill. Paris: Les Editions du Cerf, [1932].

DOBZHANSKY, Theodosius. A critique of the species concept in biology. *Phil.Sci.*, 1935, 2: 344-55.

GILMOUR, J.S.L. The development of taxonomic theory since 1851. *Nature*, 1951, 168: 400-2.

GILMOUR, J.S.L. The species: yesterday and tomorrow. *Nature*, 1958, 181: 379-80.

GREGG, John R. The language of taxonomy. An application of symbolic logic to the study of classificatory systems. Preface by Jacques Barzun. 70 p. New York: Columbia University Press, 1954.

HUXLEY, Julian, ed. The new systematics. viii, 583 p. Oxford: Clarendon Press; New York: Oxford University Press. 1940. [CB 60/151]

TEILHARD DE CHARDIN, Pierre. L'histoire naturelle du monde. Réflexions sur la valeur et l'avenir de la Systématique. *Scientia*, 1925, 37: 15-24. [CB 18/621]

Jkt philosophical systems

BELTRÁN, Enrique. Problemas biológicos. Ensayo de interpretación dialectica materialista. Prólogo de Marcel Prenant. xxi, 179 p. Monterrey, N.L. (México): Ediciones del Instituto de Investigaciones Científicas de la Universidad de Nuevo León, 1945. [CB 69/228]

KAPP, Reginald O. Science versus materialism. vi, 280 p. London: Methuen, 1940.
Reviewed by F.G. Donnan, *Nature*, 1942, 149: 394-5.

MEYER, Adolf. Die Idee des Holismus. *Scientia*, 1935, 58: 18-29; French transl. suppl., 9-19.

NEEDHAM, Joseph. Organicism in biology. *J.Phil.Stud.*, January 1928, 3: 29-40. [CB 25/423]

SMUTS, Jan Christiaan. Die kausale Bedeutung des Holismus. *Arch.Gesch.Med.*, 1935, 27: 465-6.

Jkv causality; determinism and indeterminism

BOHN, G. Du déterminisme et de la finalité. *Rev.Idées*, 1913, 10: 117-48, 250-83.

GRAMONT-LESPARRE, A. de. Les inconnus de la biologie déterministe. 300 p. Paris: Alcan, 1914.

HERRICK, C. Judson. Fatalism or freedom. A biologist's answer. 96 p. New York: W.W. Norton, 1926. [CB 22/299]

LILLIE, Ralph S. Biological causation. *Phil.Sci.*, 1940, 7: 314-36.

LILLIE, Ralph S. Physical indeterminism and vital action. *Science*, 1927, 66: 139-44.

LILLIE, Ralph S. Types of physical determination and the activities of living organisms. *J.Phil.*, 1931, 28: 561-73.

NORTHROP, F.S.C. Causality in field physics in its bearing upon biological causation. *Phil.Sci.*, 1938, 5: 166-80.

PARKER, George Howard. Organic determinism. *Science*, 1924, 59: 517-21. [CB 16/290]

Jkx mechanism and vitalism

ANTHONY, Raoul. Sur le sens et la portée du vitalisme. *Scientia*, 1923, 33: 395-401. [CB 15/137]

BAYLISS, W.M. Vitalism. *Scientia*, 1922, 31: xxxi, 291-9; French transl. suppl., 24-35. [CB 13/282]

BLEULER, Eugen. Mechanismus-Vitalismus-Mnemismus. ii, 148 p. (Abhandlungen zur Theorie der organischen Entwicklung, 6) Berlin: Springer, 1931.

CHRISTMANN, Fritz. Biologische Kausalität. Eine Untersuchung zur Überwindung des Gegensatzes: Mechanismus - Vitalismus. iv, 111 p. (*Heidelb.Abhandl.Phil.*, 16) Tübingen: Mohr, 1928.
Reviewed by Adolf Meyer, *Deut.Lit.Zeitung*, 1929, 6: 1503-4.

DENDY, Arthur. Mécanisme et vitalisme. *Scientia*, 1923, 33: 325-33. [CB 15/209]

DRIESCH, Hans. Behaviorismus und Vitalismus. 10 p. (*Sitzungsber.Heidelb.Akad.Wiss.Phil.Hist.Kl.*, 1927-28, 1) Heidelberg: 1927.

DRIESCH, Hans. Geschichte des Vitalismus. 2nd ed. of first part of: Der Vitalismus als Geschichte und Lehre (1905). x. 214 p. Leipzig: Barth, 1922.
For English translation of whole work *see* below.

DRIESCH, Hans. The history and theory of vitalism. Translated by C.K. Ogden. Revised and partly rewritten for the English edition by the author. viii, 239 p. London: Macmillan, 1914.
Reviewed by G. Sarton, *Isis*, 1920, 3: 439-40.
Translation of Der Vitalismus als Geschichte und Lehre. 1905.

GREGORY, Joshua C. Mechanism and vitalism. *Sci.Progr.*, 1918, 13: 134-9.
Essay suggested by Loeb's work, *see* below.

GUILLEMINOT, Hyacinthe. Vitalisme ou physico-chimisme. *Scientia*, 1922, 32: 225-37, 301-13. [CB 14/541]

HALDANE, John Scott. Mechanism, life and personality. An examination of the mechanistic theory of life and mind. 2nd ed. vii, 152 p. London: Murray, 1921.
First edition 1914.

HARRIS, David Fraser. A defense of philosophic neo-vitalism. *Scientia*, 1924, 35: 259-68; French transl. suppl., 57-66. [CB 16/289]

HENDERSON, Lawrence Joseph. Mechanism from the standpoint of physical science. *Phil.Rev.*, 1918, 27: 571-6.

HOERNLÉ, R.F. Alfred. Mechanism and vitalism. *Phil.Rev.*, 1918, 27: 628-45.

JENKINSON, J.W. Vitalism. In: Singer, Charles, ed. Studies in the history of science, vol. 1, p. 59-78. Oxford: Clarendon Press, 1917.
Revised edition of a paper in *Hibbert J.*, 1911, 9: 545-59. History and criticism of the question.

JENNINGS, H.S. Mechanism and vitalism. *Phil.Rev.*, 1918, 27: 577-96.

JOAD, C.E.M. The future of life: a theory of vitalism. xiii, 168 p. London/New York: Putnam, 1928.

KOCH, Richard. Die Autobiographie von Wilhelm Roux als Dokument zum Mechanismus-Vitalismusstreit. *Sudhoffs Arch.*, 1929, 22: 114-50.

LILLIE, Ralph S. The nature of the vitalistic dilemma. *J. Phil.*, 1926, 23: 673-82.

LOEB, Jacques. The mechanistic conception of life. Biological essays. 230 p. Chicago: University of Chicago Press, 1912.
Reviewed by G. Sarton, *Isis*, 1914, 2: 232.
French translation Paris: Alcan, 1914.

LOEB, Jacques. Mechanistic science and metaphysical romance. *Yale Rev.*, 1915, 4: 766-85.

LOEB, Jacques. The organism as a whole from a physicochemical viewpoint. x, 379 p., ill. New York/London: Putnam, 1916.

LOSSKII, N. L'intuition, la matière et la vie. viii, 180 p. Paris: Alcan, 1928. [CB 27/536]
Collection of articles translated from the Russian.

LUGARO, E. Contre le vitalisme. *Scientia*, 1922, 32: 389-401. [CB 14/542]

MARVIN, Walter T. Mechanism versus vitalism as a philosophical issue. *Phil.Rev.*, 1918, 27: 616-27.

MAY, Eduard. Das Vitalismusproblem und die Erklärung der Lebensphänomene. *Phil.Natur.*, 1952, 2: 251-7.

MEYER, Adolf. El problema del vitalismo en la biología y en la medicina actual. *Anal.Univ.Chile, ser.* 2, 1929, 7: 1243-89. [CB 30/472]

MITCHELL, Peter Chalmers. Materialism and vitalism in biology: the Herbert Spencer lecture delivered at Oxford, June 3, 1930. 30 p. Oxford: Clarendon Press, 1930.

OLDEKOP, Ewald. Le principe de hiérarchie dans la nature et ses rapports avec le problème du vitalisme et du mécanisme. 100 p. Paris: Vrin, 1933.
Reviewed by Pierre Brunet, *Archeion*, 1933, 15: 454-5.

PIÉRON, H. Du rôle et de la signification du conflit scientifique entre mécanisme et vitalisme. *Scientia*, 1922, 31: 115-27. [CB 12/626]

PLATE, Ludwig. Vitalismus und Mechanismus in einer neuen biologischen Auffassung. *Scientia*, 1929, 46: 13-20; French transl. suppl., 1-8.

RABAUD, Etienne. Le vitalisme et la science. *Scientia*, 1923, 33: 195-214. [CB 14/542]

RIGNANO, Eugenio. Nè vitalismo nè mecanismo. Replica al Prof. Plate. *Scientia*, 1929, 46: 21-4; French transl. suppl. 9-20.
Reply to Plate, L., *see* above.

RUSSELL, E.S. Vitalism. *Atti IVo Congr.Int.Fil.* (Bologna. 1911), (2), p. 424-39. Genoa: Formiggini, 1913.

SCHUBERT-SOLDERN, Rainer. Mechanism and vitalism; philosophical aspects of biology. Ed. by Philip G. Fothergill. xviii, 244 p. Notre Dame, Ind.: University of Notre Dame Press, 1962.

SINGER, Edgar A. Beyond mechanism and vitalism. *Phil.Sci.* 1934, 1: 273-95.

SINGER, Edgar A. Logico-historical study of mechanism, vitalism, naturalism. In: Pennsylvania University. Studies in the history of science, p. 89-102. Philadelphia: University of Pennsylvania Press, 1941.

THOMSON, J.A. Vitalisme méthodologique. *Scientia*, 1923, 33: 26-37. [CB 14/543]

TISSOT, Robert. Zur Physiologie der Vitalreihe. *Z.Positivistische Phil.*, 1913, 1: 110-42.

TURNER, J.E. Vitalism or mechanism? Via media. *Sci.Progr.*, 1918, 13: 305-11.

WHEELER, Leonard Richmond. Vitalism: its history and validity. xii, 275 p. London: Witherby, 1939.
Reviewed by Aldo Mieli, *Archeion*, 1940, 22: 111-12.

Jkx-bv

SCHUSTER, Julius. Über neuere Schriften zur Geschichte und Philosophie des biologischen Streits um die vitale Kausalität. Ein kritischer Bericht. *Mitt.Gesch.Med.*, 1934, 33: 89-99.

Jkx-daj

NOLL, Alfred. Die Lebenskraft in den Schriften der Vitalisten und ihrer Gegner. 86 p. (Voigtlaenders Quellenbücher, 69) Leipzig: Voigtländer, [1914]. [CB 9/483]

Jmd time; rhythm

see also JGmd

FLATTELY, F.W. Rhythm in nature. *Sci.Progr.*, 1920, 14: 418-26; reprinted in *Annu.Rep.Smithsonian Inst.for 1920*, p. 389-97. Washington, D.C.: 1922. [CB 13/282]

KLAGES, Ludwig. Vom Wesen des Rhythmus. Auszug aus dem Vortrage. *Sudhoffs Arch.*, 1934, 27: 223-8.

LECOMTE DU NOUY, Pierre. Biological time. With foreword by Alexis Carrel. xiv, 150 p. New York: Macmillan, 1937. [CB 51/268]

PAGEL, Walter. J.B. van Helmont, "De tempore", and biological time. *Osiris*, 1948, 8: 346-417, 4 fig. [CB 75/66]
Deals in part with van Helmont and the concept of time of Bergson.

Jmz relation with other scientific subject fields

JmzA

BROCK, Friedrich. Stellung und Bedeutung der autonomen Biologie und Umweltforschung im Rahmen der hierarchischen Pyramide der Wissenschaften. *Sudhoffs Arch.*, 1935, 27: 467-79.

JmzC

JOHNSTONE, James. The mechanism of life in relation to modern physical theory. xii, 248 p. London: Arnold, 1921.

LUKOWSKY, Arthur. Leben und Physik. *Kant-Stud.*, 1958-59, 50: 409-15.

NORTHROP, F.S.C. The history of modern physics in its bearing upon biology and medicine. *Yale J.Biol.Med.*, 1938, 10: 209-32.

JmzCQkt

ROSTAND, Jean. L'atomisme en biologie. 280 p. Paris: Gallimard, 1956.
Reviewed by Suzanne Delorme, *Rev.Hist.Sci.*, 1956, 9: 372-3; by Jean Théoridès, *Arch.Int.Hist.Sci.*, 1957, 36: 159.

ROSTAND, Jean. Esquisse d'une histoire de l'atomisme en biologie. *Rev.Hist.Sci.*, 1949, 2: 241-65; 1950, 3: 156-69; 1951, 4: 41-59; 1952, 5: 155-70.

JmzCS

BOHR, Niels. Licht und Leben. *Naturwissenschaften*, 1933, 21: 245-50.
On some relations between atomic physics and biology.

BOHR, Niels. Licht und Leben - noch einmal. *Naturwissenschaften*, 1963, 50: 725-7. [CB 89/579]

JmzCW

PRZIBRAM, Hans. Die anorganischen Grenzgebiete der Biologie (insbesondere der Kristallvergleich). 240 p. (Sammlung Borntraeger, 10) Berlin: Borntraeger, 1926.
Reviewed by E.W.M., *Nature*, 1927, 119: 738-40.

Jn/o means of communications; teaching

Jnb

GOLDSMITH, Elizabeth Edwards. Life symbols as related to sex symbolism. A brief study into the origin and significance of certain symbols which have been found in all civilizations, such as the Cross, the Circle, the Serpent, the Triangle, the Tree of Life, the Swastika, and other solar emblems showing the unity and simplicity of thought underlying their use as religious symbols. xxviii, 455 p. London: Putnam, 1924.

Jnh

HUARD, Pierre. Origine de quelques termes de biologie. *Extrême-Orient Méd.*, 1951, 3: 213-16.

JAEGER, Edmund C. A source-book of biological names and terms. 3rd ed. 317 p., ill. Springfield, Ill.: Charles C. Thomas, 1955. [CB 81/272]
First publ. 1944. [CB 69/228]

LAMEERE, Aug. Histoire de l'expression "biologie". *Compt. Rend.IIe Congr.Nat.Sci.* (Bruxelles, 1935), p. 128-30. Brussels: 1935.

MONTAGU, M.F. Ashley. Bloody. The natural history of a word. *Psychiatry*, 1943, 6: 175-90.

SCHMIDT, Günther. Über die Herkunft der Ausdrücke Morphologie und Biologie. Geschichtliche Zusammenhänge. *Nova Acta Leopoldina*, 1935, 2: 597-620.

SCHMITT, Waldo L. Applied systematics: the usefulness of scientific names of animals and plants. *Annu.Rep.Smithsonian Inst.for 1953*, p. 323-37. Washington, D.C.: 1954.

WERNER, C.F. Wortelemente lateinisch-griechischer Fachausdrücke in der Biologie, Zoologie und vergleichenden Anatomie. 397 p. Leipzig: Akademische Verlagsgesellschaft Geest & Portig K.-G., 1956.
Reviewed by Erik Wiksen, *Lychnos*, 1957-58, 446.

Jnh-be

HENDERSON, I.F.; HENDERSON, W.D. A dictionary of scientific terms: pronunciation, derivation, and definition of terms in biology, botany, zoology, anatomy, cytology, embryology, physiology. 6th ed. by J.H. Kenneth. xvi, 532 p. Edinburgh: Oliver & Boyd, 1957.
First publ. 1920.

Jo

BELTRÁN, Enrique. Los maestros y los programas de ciencias biológicas. *Bol.Seminar.Estud.Pedagóg.*, 1944, 2: 209-35.

Jp/q organizational aspects; societies and institutions

Jp

CHEADLE, Vernon I. Administration of modern biology. *Plant Sci.Bull.*, 1962, 8: no. 4, 1-5.

SEBRELL, W.H. The support of biological research. *Amer. Scient.*, 1957, 45: 150-6.

STEBBINS, G. Ledyard. Toward better cooperation in the life sciences. *Plant Sci.Bull.*, 1962, 8: no. 3, 1-5.

Jqg

JACK, Homer A. Biological field stations of the world. *Chron. Bot.*, 1945, 9: 1-73. [CB 69/228 and CB 70/259]

Js relations with society

CARREL, Alexis. Man, the unknown. xv, 346 p. New York/London: Harper, 1935.

COOK, O.F. Biology in human progress. Urbanism the underlying cause of social fermentation and decay of civilization. *J. Hered.*, 1923, 14: 253-9. [CB 15/245]

CURTIS, Winterton C. Science and human affairs from the viewpoint of biology. vii, 330 p. London: Bell, 1922.

DENDY, Arthur. The biological foundations of society. x, 197 p. London: Constable, 1924.

HJORT, Johan. The human value of biology. xii, 241 p. Cambridge, Mass.: Harvard University Press, 1938.
Reviewed by H.T. Davis, *Isis*, 1939, 30: 302-4.

HORWOOD, Murray P. Biology and human affairs. *Sci.Mon.*, 1940, 51: 49-56.

HUXLEY, Julian. Man stands alone. x, 297 p. New York: Harper, 1941. [CB 61/409]

JENNINGS, H.S. Biology and social reform. *J.Soc.Phil.*, 1937, 2: 155-66.
Apropos of Alexis Carrel's book "Man the unknown".

PEARL, Raymond. Biology and human trends. *J.Wash.Acad.Sci.*, 1935, 25: 253-72.

RESHAPING man's heritage. Biology in the service of man. By J.S. Huxley, H.G. Wells, J.B.S. Haldane [and others]. 96 p., 7 pl. London: Allen and Unwin, 1944.
"A series of broadcast talks."
Reviewed by T.H. Hawkins, *Nature*, 1944, 154: 39-40.

Jsc

BREYSIG, Kurt. Aus meinen Tagen und Träumen. Memoiren, Aufzeichnungen, Briefe, Gespräche. xiii, 191 p. Berlin: Gruyter, 1962. [CB 90/500]
On biology and history.
Reviewed by Heinrich Schipperges, *Arch.Int.Hist.Sci.*, 1963, 16: 441.

Jsp

COLE, Leon J. Biological philosophy and the war. *Sci.Mon.*, 1919, 8: 247-57.

Jsy

VERDOORN, Frans. Future of biology in world affairs. *Nature*, 1944, 154: 595-9.

Jt relations with the humanities

JEANSELME, E. De l'introduction des notions biologiques dans le domaine de l'érudition et de l'histoire. *Presse Méd* 1934, 42: 243-4.

VERDOORN, F. Biohistory, its aims and scope. *Act.VIIIe Congr. Int.Hist.Sci.* (Florence, 1956), p. 762-9. Paris: Hermann, 1958.
An attempt to indicate the extra-borderlands between the biological sciences and the humanities.

Jtc

GERARD, R.W. A biological basis for ethics. *Phil.Sci.*, 1942, 9: 92-120.

HOLMES, S.J. Life and morals. xi, 232 p. New York: Macmillan, 1948. [CB 73/180]

Jtd

HALDANE, J.S. Biology and religion. From a paper read at the Conference of Modern Churchmen, at Oxford, on August 28, 1924. *Nature*, 1924, 114: 468-71.

HUARD, Pierre; MING WONG. Le taoïsme et la science. *Act.VIIIe Congr.Int.Hist.Sci.* (Florence, 1956), (3), p. 1096-8. Paris: Hermann, 1958.
Deals mainly with the influence of taoism on the biological sciences.

McDOUGALL, William. Religion and the sciences of life: with other essays on allied topics. xiv, 263 p. London: Methuen, 1934.
Reviewed by F.S. Marvin, *Nature*, 1934, 134: 7-8.

ROSTAND, Jean. Biologie et humanisme. 301 p. Paris: Gallimard, 1964.

SINNOTT, Edmund W. The biology of the spirit. 180 p. New York: Viking Press, 1955. [CB 81/264]

THOMSON, J. Arthur. The system of animate nature. The Gifford lectures delivered in the University of St. Andrews in the years 1915 and 1916. 2 vol. xx, 687 p. London: Williams and Norgate, 1920.
Reviewed by George Sarton, *Isis*, 1921, 4: 82-3.

THORPE, W.H. Biology, psychology and belief. 60 p. London: Cambridge University Press, 1960.
Reviewed by Marjorie Grene, *Brit.J.Phil.Sci.*, 1962, 13: 255-6.

Jth

SCHIERBEEK, A. Grote schrijvers als biologen. Een onbekende zijde van bekende mannen. [Great writers as biologists. An unknown aspect of well-known men. (In Dutch)] 96 p. 's-Gravenhage: De Hofstad, 1938.

Jw in different countries

CAULLERY, M. La contribution que les divers pays ont donnée au développement de la biologie. *Scientia*, 1922, 31: 23-47. [CB 12/625]

Jwb North America

Jwb-cj

GEISER, Samuel W. Biological publications in the second Texas Academy of Science Proceedings, 1892-1912. *Field Lab.*, 1948, 16: 8-18.

Jwb-da

REED, Howard S. A trio of biologists from Erie County. *West. Penn.Hist.Mag.*, 1945, 28: 147-52.
Apropos of Ernest Ingersoll, Milton Jay Greenman and Jesse More Greenman.

Jwb-f

ROSENBERG, Charles E. On the study of American biology and medicine: some justifications. *Bull.Hist.Med.*, 1964, 38: 364-76.

Jwb-oq

BENEDICT, Ralph C. History of biology course at Brooklyn College. *Isis*, 1936, 25: 456-8.

DAVIS, Donald W. Biology at William and Mary. *Alumni Gaz. Coll.William Mary*, 1940, 7: 6-7, 27-32.

NEEDHAM, James G. How biology came to Knox College. *Sci. Mon.*, 1945, 60: 365-72.

PEARL, Raymond. Progress in the biological sciences. In: Michigan University. A university between two centuries ..., p. 233-59. Ann Arbor: University of Michigan Press, 1937.

WENRICH, D.H. Biology at the University of Pennsylvania. *Bios*, 1951, 22: 151-88. [CB 79/178]

Jwb-qg

LANGLOIS, Thomas H. The biological station of the Ohio State University. 64 p., ill. (Franz Theodore Stone Laboratory: Contribution, 11) Columbus, Ohio: Ohio State University, 1949.
A brief history of the Station opened in 1896.

MARK, Edward Laurens. The Bermuda Biological Station for Research. An address made at the official opening of the Bermuda Biological Station for Research, Incorporated. *Harvard Alumni Bull.*, 1932, 3 p.

Jwc Latin America

BELTRAN, Enrique. Panorama de la biología mexicana. *Rev.Soc. Mex.Hist.Natur.*, 1951, 12: 69-99, 11 fig.

BELTRAN, Enrique. Veinticinco años de ciencias biológicas en México. *Rev.Soc.Mex.Hist.Natur.*, 1949, 10: 17-26.

CHAGAS, Carlos. Aspects et figures de la biologie au Brésil. *Arch.Int.Hist.Sci.*, 1948, 1: 655-6.

Jwc-cj

BELTRAN, Enrique. *La Revista Mexicana de Biologia* (1920-1935). Nota bibliografica e indice de sus diez y siete tomos. *Rev.Soc.Mex.Hist.Natur.*, 1951, 12: 375-97, 2 fig.

Jwc-pe

IZQUIERDO, J. Joaquín. Nuevas rutas para la especialización científica en México. 39 p. (Escuela Nacional de Ciencias Biológicas, Instituto Politécnico Nacional) México, D.F.: Editorial Cultura, 1947.

Jwd Europe

BOHN, Georges. Le mouvement biologique en Europe. 144 p. Paris: A. Colin, 1921.
Reviewed by L. Guinet, *Isis*, 1922, 4: 359-60.

ROSS, D.M. Some national features of the history of biology in Europe. *Act.VIIIe Congr.Int.Hist.Sci.* (Florence, 1956), p. 657-67. Paris: Hermann, 1958.

Jwd-op

CONSOLAZIO, William V. Dilemma of academic biology in Europe. *Science*, 1961, 133: 1892-6.

Jwe

GUNTHER, Robert William Theodore. Early science in Oxford. 3. i. The biological sciences; ii. Biological collections. xii, 564 p., ill. Oxford: Printed for the subscribers, 1925.
Reviewed by G. Sarton, *Isis*, 1926, 8: 375-7.

Jwe-nh

ANDREWS, Edmund. A history of scientific English. The story of its evolution based on a study of biomedical terminology. ix, 342 p., 18 fig., front. New York: Smith, 1947. [CB 71/127]

Jwe-qd

HINDLE, Edward. Biology and the Royal Society. *New Sci.*, 1960, 8: 233-5. [CB 86/465]

Jwf

CAULLERY, Maurice. Histoire des sciences biologiques. In: Histoire de la Nation Française. Vol. XV. Histoire des sciences en France, (2), p. 1-296. Paris: Plon, 1925. [CB 18/602]

MATISSE, G. Le mouvement scientifique contemporain en France. 1. Les sciences naturelles. 160 p., 25 fig. Paris: Payot, 1921. [CB 12/626]

Jwf-da

LACROIX, Alfred. Notice historique sur les membres et correspondants zoologistes et biologistes de l'Académie des Sciences ayant travaillé sur les côtes des colonies françaises de l'Afrique du Nord et du Nord-est depuis de XVIIIe siècle. Lecture faite en la séance annuelle du 20 décembre 1943. 42 p. Paris: Gauthier-Villars, 1943.

Jwg

DRIESCH, Hans Adolf Eduard. Lebenserinnerungen, Aufzeichnungen eines Forschers und Denkers in entscheidender Zeit. 311 p., portr. Basel: Reinhardt, 1951.
Reviewed by Maurice Caullery, *Arch.Int.Hist.Sci.*, 1952, 5: 144-7.

FRISCH, Karl von. Erinnerungen eines Biologen. viii, 172 p., ill. Berlin/Göttingen/Heidelberg: Springer-Verlag, 1957.
Reviewed by Bertil Kullenberg, *Lychnos*, 1957-58, 452-4.

Jwi

MONTALENTI, Giuseppe. La pensée biologique en Italie depuis la renaissance jusqu'à Spallanzani. *Cah.Hist.Mond.*, 1963, 7: 523-46.

Jwk-bx

UNGER, W.S. Tentoonstelling betreffende de geschiedenis der genees- en natuurkunde in Zeeland. [Exhibition illustrating the history of medicine and the natural sciences in Zeeland. (In Dutch)] *Bijdr.Gesch.Geneesk.*, 1926, 6: 191-9.

Jwk-da

OYE, P. van. Hugo de Vries, Julius MacLeod en Edward Verschaffelt. Vriendschap en wederkerige invloed. [Friendship and mutual influence. (In Dutch)] 23 p., ill. Brussels: Palais der Academiën, 1961.

Jwk-oq

COLE, F.J. The University of Leyden. Contributions to biology and medicine. *Nature*, 1941, 147: 161-3.

Jwn

ISTORIIA ESTESTVOZNANIIA V ROSSII. 3. Geologo-geograficheskie i biologicheskie nauki. [History of natural science in Russia. 3. Geological-geographical and biological sciences. Ed. by S.R. Mikulinskii. (In Russian)] 603 p., ill. Moscow: Izdatel'stvo Akademii Nauk SSR, 1962.

Jwn-sk

RAZUMOV, S.A. [V.I. Lenin and biological sciences. (In Russian)] *Bot.Zh.*, 1960, 45: no. 4, 473-9, portr.

Jwp Middle East

BODENHEIMER, Frederick Simon. A biologist in Israel: a book of reminiscences. 492 p., ill., fig., bibliogr. Jerusalem: Biological Studies, Publishers, 1959.
Reviewed by Walter Pagel, *J.Hist.Med.*, 1960, 15: 105-7; by Jaacov Lorch, *Isis*, 1961, 52: 611-12.

Jwt Far East

GRESSITT, J. Linsley. The war and biological sciences in Japan. *Science*, 1946, 103: 755-8.

TANG, Pei-Sung. Green thraldom. Essays of a Chinese biologist. Introd. by Joseph Needham. 127 p. London: Allen & Unwin, 1949.

Jwt-qg

TANG, Pei-Sung. Biology in war-time China. *Nature*, 1944, 154: 43-6.
The movements of biological institutions during the war and the activities of biologists associated with those institutions.

Jxw museology

REGNIER, Robert. Le biologiste et le conservateur de musée. Discours de réception à l'Académie de Rouen. 16 p. Rouen: Imprimerie Cagniard, 1927.

JA EXPERIMENTAL BIOLOGY; MICROSCOPY

for microscopes *see* CJxkm

PHILIPSBORN, Hellmut von. Calciumoxalat. 275 Jahre mikroskopischer Forschung. *Sudhoffs Arch.*, 1954, 38: 336-66, 41 ill.

PINEY, A., ed. Recent advances in microscopy. Biological applications. Medicine, by A. Piney; The living eye, by Basil Graves; Zoology, by E.W. MacBride and R.R. Hewer, Botany, by E.C. Barton-Wright. viii, 260 p., 83 fig. Philadelphia: Blakiston, 1931.
Reviewed by Charles A. Kofoid, *Isis*, 1932, 17: 446-7.

ROOSEBOOM, Maria. Influences of the invention of the microscope on biological thought. *Act.VIIe Congr.Int.Hist.Sci.* (Jerusalem, 1953), p. 522-30. Paris: Hermann, [n.d.]

ROOSEBOOM, Maria. The introduction of mounting media in microscopy and their importance for biological science. *Act.VIIIe Congr.Int.Hist.Sci.* (Florence, 1956), p. 602-7. Paris: Hermann, 1958.

ROOSEBOOM, Maria. Microscopium. 59 p., 115 ill. (Communication no. 95 from the Rijksmuseum voor de Geschiedenis der Natuurwetenschappen [National Museum for the History of Science] Leyden, Netherlands.) English translation by Emile van Loo, Leyden. Leyden: 1956. [CB 84/315]
This English translation appeared at the same time as the original Dutch edition.
For reviews *see* CB 83/202 and CB 84/315.

SCHIERBEEK, A. Uit de eerste eeuwen der mikroskopie. [On the first centuries of microscopy. (In Dutch)] *Vragen Dag*, 1934, 49: 505-28.

WOODRUFF, Lorande Loss. Microscopy before the nineteenth century. *Amer.Natur.*, 1939, 73: 485-516.

WREDDEN, J.H. The microscope: its theory and applications. With an historical introduction by W.E. Watson-Baker. xxiv, 296 p. London: Churchill, 1947. [CB 73/174]

ZERNIKE, Frits. How I discovered phase contrast. *Science*, 1955, 121: 345-8. [CB 81/343]
The author's Nobel prize address in 1953.

JAc-bx

RIJKSMUSEUM VOOR DE GESCHIEDENIS DER NATUURWETENSCHAPPEN. Catalogus: van vergrootglas tot oog der wetenschap; 2½ eeuw microscopie, 25 Juni - 19 September 1954. [Catalogue: the magnifying glass as the eye of science. 2½ centuries of microscopy, 25 June - 19 September 1954. (In Dutch)] 53 p. (Mededeling, 93) Leiden: 1954.
Reviewed by Friedrich Klemm, *Sudhoffs Arch.*, 1955, 39: 190.

ROOSEBOOM, Maria. Microscopy exhibition at Leyden. *Isis*, 1954, 45: 293.

JAda

FREUND, Hugo; BERG, Alexander; ed. Geschichte der Mikroskopie. Leben und Werk grosser Forscher. 2 vol. 1. Biologie. 392 p.; 2. Medizin. 522 p. Frankfurt: Umschau Verlag, 1963, 1964.
Consists of biographies, each followed by a list of the subject's writings.

HULT, O.T. [Sur A. Van Leeuwenhoek et les pionniers de la microscopie, ainsi que quelques notes sur l'histoire des débuts du microscope en Suède. (In Swedish, with French summary)] *Lychnos*, 1937, 2: 313-40, 14 fig.

WOODRUFF, Lorande Loss. Some pioneers in microscopy, with special reference to protozoölogy. *Trans.N.Y.Acad.Sci.*, 1939, 1: no. 5, 74-7.

JAwe-th

NICOLSON, Marjorie. The microscope and English imagination. 92p. (Smith College Studies in Modern Languages, 16, no. 4) Northampton, Mass.: Smith College Department of Modern Languages, 1935.
Repercussions of microscopy on English literature.

JAxd

BAKER, John R. The discovery of the uses of colouring agents in biological microtechnique. 22 p. (Monograph of Quekett Microscopical Club) London: Williams and Norgate, 1945.
Revision of article originally published in *J.Quekett Microscop.Club, ser. 4*, 1943, 1: no. 6.
Reviewed by H.J. Conn, *J.Hist.Med.*, 1948, 3: 179-80.

CONN, Harold J. Development of histological staining. Chronology; the evolution of histological staining; the staining of fixed tissues; vital staining; bibliography. *Ciba Symp.*, 1946, 7: 270-300, ill.

CONN, Harold J., ed. The history of staining. with contributions from Lloyd Arnold, A.F. Blakeslee, R.S. Cunningham, S.I. Kornhauser, F.W. Mallory, and Eugen Unna. 141 p. Geneva, N.Y.: Biological Stain Commission, 1933. [CB 40/403]

JB THEORETICAL BIOLOGY

AGAR, W.E. A contribution to the theory of the living organism. 207 p. London: Oxford University Press, 1943.
Reviewed in *Nature,* 1944, 154: 289.

BERTALANFFY, Ludwig von. Modern theories of development. An introduction to theoretical biology. Transl. and adapted from the German by J.H. Woodger. x, 204 p. London: Oxford University Press, 1933. [CB 39/456]
Emended translation of the author's *Kritische Theorie der Formbildung* (1928) in more precise form with additions of new matter.

BLANDINO, G. Problemi e dottrine di biologia teorica. x, 274 p., bibliogr. Torino: Edizioni Minerva Medica, 1960.

CAHN, Théophile. Les phénomènes biologiques dans le cadre des sciences exactes. 20 p. Paris: Hermann, 1933.

HARTOG, Marcus. Samuel Butler and recent mnemic biological theories. *Scientia,* 1914, 15: 38-52.

MASON, S.F. From hierarchy to evolution in the theory of biology. *Democracy and the labour movement; essays in honour of Dona Torr,* p. 67-83. London: Lawrence and Wishart, 1954.

REDFIELD, Robert, ed. Levels of integration in biological and social systems. 240 p. Lancaster, Pa.: The Jaques Cattell Press, 1942. [CB 63/272]

RIGNANO, Eugenio. Das Leben in finaler Auffassung. German transl. by Paul Graf Thun-Hohenstein. iv, 35 p. (Abhandlungen zur theoretischen Biologie, 26) Berlin: Gebrüder Borntraeger, 1927.
Translation of: La vita nel suo aspetto finalistico, Bologna: 1922.

SOMMERHOFF, G. Analytical biology. viii, 207 p. London: Oxford University Press, 1950.

WOODGER, Joseph Henry. Biological principles. A critical study. xii, 498 p. (International Library of Psychology) London: Kegan Paul, 1929.

JBkd

WILKIE, J.S. Causation and explanation in theoretical biology. *Brit.J.Phil.Sci.,* 1951, 1: 273-90.

JBmzLU

BRUES, C.T. Contributions of entomology to theoretical biology. *Sci.Mon.,* 1947, 64: 123-34.

JBmzOM

GOLDSTEIN, Kurt. The organism. A holistic approach to biology derived from pathological data in man. xviii, 533 p. (American Psychology Series) New York: American Book Co., 1939.
Reviewed by M.F. Ashley Montagu, *Isis,* 1949, 32: 390-3.

JByB BIOMATHEMATICS

for application of mathematics
to biophysics *see* JCyB
to evolution *see* JGyB
to heredity *see* JHyB

GENEVOIS, L. Charles Henry et l'application des mathématiques à la biologie. *Rev.Sci.,* 26 fév. 1927, 97-100, portr.

JANISCH, Ernst. Über die mathematische Erfassung biologischer Prozesse. *Sudhoffs Arch.,* 1934, 27: 286-92.

JByBW

MAGNAN, A.; SAINTE-LAGUË, A. D'un emploi de la méthode statistique dans les sciences biologiques. *Rev.Gén.Sci.,* 1931, 42: 539-45, 4 fig.

MATHER, K. Biometry and the inductive method. *Endeavour,* 1953, 12: 140-3.

JC BIOPHYSICS

(including biophysics and biochemistry combined)

ACHALME, P.J. Electronique et biologie; études sur les actions catalytiques, les actions diastasiques et certains transformations vitales de l'energie; photobiogénèse; fonction chlorophyllienne. 728 p. Paris: Masson, 1913.

BAYLISS, W.M. Life and the laws of thermodynamics. 12 p. (Boyle Lecture, Oxford 1922) Oxford University Press, 1922.

BERNAL, John Desmond. The physical basis of life. 80 p. London: Routledge and Kegan Paul, 1951.
Reviewed by C.H. Waddington, *Nature,* 1952, 169: 297.

BLIAKHER, L. IA., *et al.* Fizicheskie i khimicheskie osnovy zhiznennykh iavlenii; istoricheskie ocherki. [The physical and chemical foundations of the phenomena of life. Historical essays. (In Russian)] 214 p. Moscow: Akademiia Nauk SSSR, 1963.

CRANEFIELD, Paul F. The organic physics of 1847 and the biophysics of today. *J.Hist.Med.,* 1957, 12: 407-23.

HARRIS, D. Fraser. The biological approach to physics and chemistry. *Med.Life,* 1926, 33: 249-55.

MADDOX, John. Revolution in biology. 187 p., ill. New York: Macmillan, 1964.

SCIENTIFIC AMERICAN. Physics and chemistry of life. 270 p. New York: Simon & Schuster, 1955.

WILSON, Edmund B. The physical basis of life. 51 p. New Haven: Yale University Press, 1923.

WHYTE, L.L. One-way processes in physics and biophysics. *Brit.J.Phil.Soc.,* 1955, 6: 107-21.

JCmc

RASHEVSKY, N. The biophysics of space and time. *Phil.Sci.,* 1935, 2: 73-85.

JCyB

RASHEVSKY, N. The devious roads of science. *Synthese,* 1963, 15: 107-14.
Account of the development of mathematical biophysics.

RASHEVSKY, N. Foundations of mathematical biophysics. *Phil. Sci.,* 1934, 1: 176-96.

JD BIOCHEMISTRY

see also DW NATURAL PRODUCTS AND BIOCHEMICAL SUBSTANCES
KD PLANT CHEMISTRY AND BIOCHEMISTRY

BALDWIN, Ernest. Dynamic aspects of biochemistry. xviii, 457 p., 34 fig. Cambridge University Press; New York: Macmillan, 1947. [CB 72/272]

BALDWIN, Ernest. An introduction to comparative biochemistry. xvi, 164 p. Cambridge: University Press; New York: Macmillan, 1948. [CB 51/277 and CB 74/388]
First published 1937.

DOREMUS, Charles A. A retrospect in biochemistry. *Biochem. Bull.,* 1912, 1: 245-55.

FARBER, Eduard. Stoff und Form als Problem der biochemischen Forschung. Eine geschichtliche Betrachtung. *Isis,* 1934, 21: 187-202.

GLASS, Justine. The story of biochemistry. 232 p., 2 fig. New York: Philosophical Library, 1964.

HAMBURGER, H.J. Zur Geschichte und Entwicklung der physikalisch-chemischen Forschung in der Biologie. *Int.Z.Phys.Chem. Biol.,* 1914, 1: 6-27. [CB 6/460]

HOPKINS, Frederick Gowland. Hopkins and biochemistry 1861-1947. Papers concerning Sir Frederick Gowland Hopkins, O.M., P.R.S., with a selection of his addresses and a bibliography of his publications. Ed. by Joseph Needham and Ernest Baldwin. ix, 361 p., pl., portr., bibliogr. Cambridge: Heffer, 1949.
A commemoration volume prepared on the occasion of the First International Congress of Biochemistry, Cambridge 1949.

HOPKINS, Frederick Gowland. The influence of chemical thought on biology. *Science,* 1936, 84: 255-60.

KAHANE, Ernest. Biochemistry - its development and its tasks. *Impact*, 1964, 14: 101-18.

KOSHTOIANTS, Kh. S. [About the history of the discovery of the transformation of the oxides of carbon into carbon dioxide in living organisms. (In Russian)] *Tr.Inst.Ist.Est.*, 1952, 4: 267-72.

LABBÉ, A. L'autorégulation organique et les applications biologiques du théorème de le Chatelier. *Rev.Gén.Sci.*, 1926, 37: 38-43.

LEGRAND, L. Les caractères biochimiques de l'espèce. *Rev. Gen.Sci.*, 1918, 29: 333-40.
Reviewed by L. Guinet, *Isis*, 1920, 3: 88-9.

MITTASCH, Alwin. Der Stickstoff als Lebensfrage. Ein Überblick. vi, 34 p., 8 fig. (*Abhandl.Ber.Deut.Mus.*, 13) Berlin: VDI-Verlag, 1941.
Reviewed by R. Zaunick, *Mitt.Gesch.Med.*, 1941-42, 40: 123.

PHILIPSBORN, Hellmut von. See JA

SCHIERBEEK, A. Autostasie. De organische aanpassingen en het theorema van van't Hoff-Le Chatelier. ['Autostasy': biological adaptations in the theorem of van't Hoff-Le Chatelier. (In Dutch)] *Biol.Jaarb.*, 1936, 70-94.

STILES, Walter. Trace elements in plants and animals. xi, 189 p., 12 fig. Cambridge University Press; New York: Macmillan, 1946. [CB 73/173]
Chapter 1 is a historical introduction.

SÜSS, Rudolf. Skizzen zur Geschichte der Biochemie. *Naturwiss. Rundsch.*, 1961, 14: 416-19.

TEICH, Mikuláš. Historické základy moderní biochemie. [The historical foundations of modern biochemistry. (In Czech with English summary)] *Sb.Dějiny Přírodn.Věd Tech.*, 1964, 9: 147-66.
Lecture delivered in the Department of Biochemistry, Cambridge University on 1 May 1961.

JDc-br

Annual Review of Biochemistry. Vol. 1- Palo Alto, Calif.: Stanford University Press, [1932]-
For list of contents of vol. 6 *see* CB 53/265, vol. 7 CB 55/182, vol. 9 CB 60/152 and vol. 12 CB 65/81.

JDc-bt

NEEDHAM, Joseph. A chart to illustrate the history of biochemistry and physiology. Cambridge University Press, 1929. [CB 27/562]

JDcj

HENKLE, Herman H. The periodical literature of biochemistry. *Bull.Med.Libr.Ass.*, 1938, 27: 139-47.

JDk

BOHN, Georges; DRZEWINA, Anna. La chimie et la vie. 275 p. (Bibliothèque de Philosophie Scientifique) Paris: Flammarion, 1920.
Reviewed by G. Matisse, *Rev.Gén.Sci.*, 1921, 32: 313-14.

JDkv

MITTASCH, Alwin. Katalyse und Determinismus: ein Beitrag zur Philosophie der Chemie. ix, 203 p., 10 fig. Berlin: Springer, 1938.
Essay review by Eduard Farber, *Isis*, 1938, 29: 398-402.

MITTASCH, Alwin. Über katalytische Verursachung im biologischen Geschehen. x, 126 p. Berlin: Springer, 1935.
Essay review by Eduard Farber, *Isis*, 1938, 29: 398-402.

JDwb-qg

McDONALD, Ellice. Research and its organization. [92]p. Newark, Del.: Biochemical Research Foundation, 1950. [CB 77/364]
Various pagings.
Includes index to the publications of the Biochemical Research Foundation.

JDwe-qd

PLIMMER, R.H.A. The history of the Biochemical Society, 1911-1949. 24 p., pl., portr. Cambridge University Press (for the Biochemical Society), 1949.

JDwg-oq

SAUER, Gunter; RAPOPORT, Samuel M.; ROST, Gunther. Zur Geschichte der Biochemie in Berlin. *NTM Z.Gesch.Naturwiss. Tech.Med.*, [1961], 1: no. 2, 119-47.

JE VITAMINS; HORMONES; ENZYMES

for vitamins in plants *see* KE
in nutrition *see* NM
hormones *see also* PH endocrinology

ABEL, John J. Chemistry in relation to biology and medicine with especial reference to insulin and other hormones. *Science*, 1927, 56: 307-19, 337-46.

BACQ, Zénon-M. Historique et développement de la notion d'hormone. *Cah.Nord*, 1948, 21: no. 1, 71-7.

BACQ, Zénon-M. Hormones et vitamines. Un aspect du problème des quantités infinitésimales en biologie. 30 p., ill. Paris: Hermann, 1934.

FARBER, Eduard. Vorgeschichte der Enzymologie. *Enzymologia*, 1937, 3: xiii-xiv.

FLEURY, P.F.; COURTOIS, J.E. The development of enzymology. *Endeavour*, 1950, 9: 144-8.

FUNK, Casimir. Who discovered vitamines? *Science*, 1926, 63: 455-6. [CB 20/177]

HARRIS, Leslie J. Vitamins in theory and practice. xix, 240 p. Cambridge University Press, 1935.
Reviewed by M.F. Ashley-Montagu, *Isis*, 1936, 26: 228-9.

KAHLSON, G. [Histamine - buried and resurrected. (In Swedish)] *Svenska Läkartidn.*, 1964, 61: 1914-30.

LEERSUM, E.C. van. The discovery of vitamines. *Science*, 1926, 64: 357.
The discovery was anticipated by C.A. Pekelharing, professor of physiological chemistry in Utrecht, in *Ned.Tijdschr. Geneesk.*, 1905, 2: 111.

MEDICAL RESEARCH COUNCIL (Gt.Brit.). Report on the present state of knowledge of accessory food factors (vitamins). Compiled by a committee appointed jointly by the Lister Institute and Medical Research Council. 2nd ed. rev. enl. iv, 171 p., 9 pl. London: H.M. Stationery Office, 1924.

PFEIFFER, John E. Enzymes. They are the catalysts of life. Long known for their ability to turn sugar into alcohol, they engineer a host of other biochemical reactions. *Sci.Amer.*, 1948, 179: 28-9, ill.

JEc-bv

WODLINGER, Mark H. Bibliographical survey of vitamins, 1650-1930, with a section on patents. Compiled by Ella M. Salmonsen. Chicago: The Author, 1932.
Reviewed by C.A. Kofoid, *Isis*, 1933, 20: 318.

JExf-JR

SANDFORD, Mary. Historical development of microbiological methods in vitamin research. *Nature*, 1943, 152: 374-6.

JF ORIGIN OF LIFE; SPONTANEOUS GENERATION

BASTIAN, H. Charlton. La génération spontanée: sa réalité et ce qu'elle implique. (Translated from English) *Rev.Sci.*, 1913, 51: 2. semestre, 385-94.
Reviewed by Gaston Bonnier, *Rev.Hébd.*, 1914, 23: 433-54.

BASTIAN, H. Charlton. The origin of life. 2nd ed., with an appendix. 100 p., 12 pl. London: Watts and Co., 1913.
First publ. 1872.

BASTIAN, H. Charlton. L'origine de la vie. Compte rendu d'expériences faites avec certaines solutions salines surchauffées dans des vases hermétiquement clos. Transl. from the manuscript of the 2nd English ed. by Léon Guinet. 112 p., 12 pl. Bruxelles: H. Lamertin, 1913. [CB 4/780]
Translation of: The origin of life.

BELIN-MILLERON, J. L'idée de génération devant le mythe et la biologie. *Arch.Int.Hist.Sci.*, 1950, 3: 591-7.

BONNIER, Gaston. Encore la génération spontanée. *Rev.Hébd.*, 1914, 23: 433-54.
Apropos of H. Charlton Bastian's article: La génération spontanée: sa réalité et ce qu'elle implique, *see* above.

BOURDIER, Franck. Trois siècles d'hypothèses sur l'origine et la transformation des êtres vivants (1550-1859). *Rev. Hist.Sci.*, 1960, 13: 1-44.

BREWSTER, Edwin Tenney. Creation. A history of non-evolutionary theories. 295 p., 30 pl. Indianapolis: Bobbs-Merrill, 1927.
Reviewed by George Sarton, *Isis*, 1927, 9: 462-5.

CAULLERY, Maurice. La phylogénie et les données actuelles de la biologie. *Rev.Mois*, 1913, 15: 385-409.

CLAVIN, Melvin. Chemical evolution and the origin of life. *Amer.Scient.*, 1956, 44: 248-63.

DAUVILLIER, A. L'origine photochimique de la vie. 214 p., ill. (Evolution des Sciences) Paris: Masson, 1958.

DUCROCQ, Albert. The origins of life. Translated by Alec Brown. xvi, 213 p., 4 pl. London: Elek Books, Ltd., 1957.
Reviewed by T.H. Hawkins, *Nature*, 1958, 181: 1364-5.

FRANZ, Victor. Ontogenie und Phylogenie. Das sogenannte biogenetische Grundgesetz und die biometabolischen Modi. 51 p. (Abhandlungen zur Theorie der organischen Entwicklung, 3) Berlin: J. Springer, 1927.
Reviewed by R. Zaunick, *Mitt.Gesch.Med.*, 1928, 27: 175.

GRASSET, H. Étude historique et critique sur les générations spontanées et l'hétérogénie. *France Méd.*, 1911, 58: 421, 441, 461; 59: 3, 23, 43, 64, 84, 109, 123, 164, 184, 208, 223, 243, 266, 285, 301, 324.

GULICK, Addison. Phosphorus as a factor in the origin of life. *Amer.Scient.*, 1955, 43: 479-89. [CB 81/269]

GUTTMACHER, Alan Frank. Life in the making. With the assistance of Ellery Rand. xii, 297 p., 8 fig. New York: Viking Press, 1933. [CB 42/590]

HAECKEL, Ernst. Fünfzig Jahre Stammesgeschichte. Historisch-kritische Studien über die Resultate der Phylogenie. 70 p. Jena: Fischer, 1916.

HASSID, I. [Problems in biogenesis. (In Hebrew)] *Koroth*, 1961, 2: 443-61.

LEDUC, Stéphane. Études de biophysique: la biologie synthétique. 217 p., 118 fig. Paris: A. Poinat, 1912.
Continuation of: Théorie physico-chimique de la vie et générations spontanées (1910).

LINDROTH, Sten. Uralstringen: ett kapitel ur biologiens äldre historia. [Spontaneous generation: a chapter in the early history of biology. (In Swedish, with summary in French)] *Lychnos*, 1939, 159-92.

LIPPMANN, Edmund O. von. Urzeugung und Lebenskraft. Zur Geschichte dieser Probleme von den ältesten Zeiten an bis zu den Anfängen des 20. Jahrhunderts. viii, 136 p. Berlin: Springer, 1933. [CB 39/458]

OPARIN, A.I. The origin of life. Translated with annotations by Sergius Morgulis. xii, 270 p., 8 fig. New York: Macmillan, 1938. [CB 54/533]

OSBORN, Henry Fairfield. The origin and evolution of life. On the theory of action, reaction and interaction of energy. xxxi, 322 p., 136 ill. New York: Scribner, 1917.

ROSTAND, Jean. La formation de l'être. Histoire des idées sur la génération. 222 p., ill. Paris: Hachette, 1930.

ROSTAND, Jean. La genèse de la vie. Histoire des idées sur la génération spontanée. 203 p. Paris: Hachette, 1943.

SCHIERBEEK, A. De pangenesistheorie van Hugo de Vries. [In Dutch] *Bijdr.Gesch.Geneesk.*, 1943, 23: 64-7.

SERGI, Giuseppe. L'origine e l'evoluzione della vita. xii, 554 p. Torino: Bocca, 1921. [CB 15/211]

STÖLZLE, Remigius. Der Ursprung des Lebens. Kritische Untersuchung der verschiedenen Hypothesen. 61 p., portr. (Bücher der neuen Biologie und Anthropologie, 2) Habelschwerdt: Franke, 1925.

TROLAND, Leonard Thompson. The chemical origin of life. *Monist*, 1914, 24: 92-133. [CB 5/292]

WHERRY, Edgar T. Reflections on the origin of life. *Proc. Pennsylvania Acad.Sci.*, 1936, 10: 12-15.

JFkn

HAAS, Otto; SIMPSON, George Gaylord. Analysis of some phylogenetic terms, with attempts at redefinition. *Proc.Amer. Phil.Soc.*, 1946, 90: 319-49.

JG EVOLUTION

for studies on evolution and heredity *see* JH
plant evolution *see also* KG
animal evolution *see also* LG
human evolution *see also* MC

JGc general history

JGc-bm *large scale works*

AKADEMIA NAUK SSSR [Institutes of Genetics and Philosophy]. Darvinizm zhivet i razvivaetsia; trudy iubileinoi konferentsii, posviashchennoi 100-letiiu opublikovanii "Proiskhozhdeniia vidor" Ch. Darvina i 150-letiiu opublikovaniia "Filosofii zoologii" Zh. Lamarka (19-21 noiabria 1959 g.). [Darwinism is living and developing; proceedings of the conference in celebration of the 100th anniversary of the publication of Ch. Darwin's "Origin of species", and of the 150th anniversary of the publication of J. Lamarck's "Philosophy of zoology" (19-21 November 1959).] 218 p. Moscow: Izdatel'stvo Akademii Nauk SSSR, 1960. [CB 88/628]

BAITSELL, George Alfred, ed. The evolution of earth and man. xv, 476 p., 32 pl. New Haven: Yale University Press, 1929. [CB 29/290]
Reviewed in *Nature*, 1930, 125: 382.

BARNETT, S.A., ed. A century of Darwin. xvi, 376 p., 55 fig., 5 pl. Cambridge, Mass.: Harvard University Press; London: Heinemann, 1958.
Reviewed by Conway Zirkle, *Isis*, 1959, 50: 282-5; for other reviews see CB 84/317, CB 85/395 and CB 86/467.

BERG, Lev Semenovich. Nomogenesis: or evolution determined by law. Translated from the Russian by J.N. Rostovtsew. xviii, 477 p. London: Constable, 1926.
Reviewed by Henry Fairfield Osborn, *Nature*, 1926, 118: 617-18.
Original Russian edition publ. 1922.

BRUNELLI, Gustavo. Le teorie sull'origine e l'evoluzione della vita, da Darwin ai nostri giorni. 198 p. Bologne: Cappelli, 1933.
Reviewed by J.B.M., *Rev.Gén.Sci.*, 1933, 44: 685.

CAMERON, Thomas W.M., ed. Evolution, its science and doctrine - symposium presented to the Royal Society of Canada in 1959. xi, 242 p. (Studia Varia, 4) Toronto: University of Toronto Press for the Royal Society of Canada, 1960.
Reviewed by P.G. Fothergill, *Nature*, 1961, 189: 340-1.

CANNON, H. Graham. The evolution of living things. x, 180 p. Manchester: Manchester University Press, 1958.
Reviewed by T.H. Hawkins, *Nature*, 1958, 181: 1364-5.

CARTER, G.S. A hundred years of evolution. x, 206 p., 4 fig. London: Sidgwick and Jackson, 1957.
Reviewed by L.A. Harvey, *Nature*, 1958, 181: 1296-7; by G. Montalenti, *Scientia*, 1959, 94: 48-9.

CLARK, Robert E.D. Darwin: before and after. The story of evolution. 192 p. (The Second Thoughts Library, 1) London: Paternoster Press, 1948. [CB 73/172]

CONKLIN, Edwin G. A generation's progress in the study of evolution. (Penrose Memorial Lecture) *Proc.Amer.Phil.Soc.*, 1934, 74: 137-58. [CB 42/589]

CUÉNOT, Lucien. L'adaptation. 420 p., 82 fig. Paris: G. Doin, 1925. [CB 18/619]

CUÉNOT, Lucien; TÉTRY, Andrée. L'évolution biologique: les faits, les incertitudes. 592 p. Paris: Masson, 1951.
Reviewed by Richard Goldschmidt, *Science*, 1951, 114: 309.

DE BEER, G.R. Evolution. viii, 351 p. New York: Oxford University Press, 1938. [CB 56/393]

DEWAR, Douglas. Difficulties of the evolution theory. viii, 192 p., 6 fig. London: Edward Arnold, 1931. [CB 33/401]

DOBZHANSKY, Theodosius, ed. Temperature and evolution. Isolating mechanisms. Genetic control of embryonic development. xii, 355 p. (Biological Symposia, 6) Lancaster, Pa.: Jaques Cattell Press, 1942.

DOWDESWELL, W.H. The mechanism of evolution. x, 115 p., fig., tables, bibliogr. (The Science Library) New York: Harper Torchbooks, 1960.

DÜRKEN, Bernhard. Allgemeine Abstammungslehre. Zugleich eine gemeinverständliche Kritik des Darwinismus und des Lamarckismus. 205 p., 38 fig. Berlin: Gebrüder Borntraeger, 1923.

FOTHERGILL, Philip G. Historical aspects of organic evolution. xvii, 427 p. New York: Philosophical Library, 1953.
Reviewed by Conway Zirkle, *Isis*, 1954, 45: 103-5.

GAUSE, G.F. The struggle for existence. ix, 163 p. Baltimore: Williams and Wilkins, 1934.
Reviewed by Thomas Park, *Quart.Rev.Biol.*, 1935, 10: 209-12.

GOODRICH, Edwin S. Living organisms; an account of their origin and evolution. 200 p., 60 fig. New York: Oxford University Press, 1924. [CB 17/579]

GREGORY, William King. Evolution emerging. 2 vol. xxvi, 736 p.; vii, 1013 p. New York: Macmillan, 1951. [CB 78/190]

GUYÉNOT, Emile. La variation et l'évolution. 2 vol. 1. La variation. xxviii, 457 p., 46 fig.; 2. L'évolution. 414 p., 5 fig. (Encyclopédie scientifique) Paris: Doin, 1930. [CB 30/471 and CB 32/584]
Reviewed by L. Cuénot, *Rev.Gén.Sci.*, 1930, 41: 587-8.

HAGEDOORN, Arend L.; HAGEDOORN-VORSTHEUVEL LA BRAND, A.-C. The relative value of the processes causing evolution. 294 p., 20 fig. The Hague: Martinus Nijhoff, 1921. [CB 11/439]

HALDANE, J.B.S. The causes of evolution. vii, 235 p. London: Longmans, Green, 1932.
Reviewed by G.P.W., *Nature*, 1933, 131: 709-10.

HEBERER, G.; SCHWANITZ, F.; ed. Hundert Jahre Evolutionsforschung. Das wissenschaftliche Vermächtnis Charles Darwins. 458 p., 83 pl. Stuttgart: Gustav Fischer Verlag, 1960.
Reviewed by Gottfried Kurth, *Naturwiss.Rundsch.*, 1961, 4: 163.

HOLMES, S.J. Studies in evolution and eugenics. 261 p. New York: Harcourt Brace, 1923. [CB 15/210]

HURST, Charles Chamberlain. The mechanism of creative evolution. xxi, 365 p., 199 fig. New York: Macmillan, 1932.
Reviewed by C.A. Kofoid, *Isis*, 1932, 22: 297.

HUXLEY, Julian. Evolution in action. viii, 141 p., 9 pl. (Signet Science Books) New York: New American Library, 1964.

HUXLEY, Julian. Evolution: the modern synthesis. 645 p. London: Allen and Unwin, 1942; New York: Harper, 1943.
Reviewed by Conway Zirkle, *Isis*, 1944, 35: 192-4; by W.B. Turrill, *Nature*, 1942, 150: 747-9.

HUXLEY, Julian. The story of evolution: the wonderful world of life. 72 p., ill., portr. London: Rathbone Books, 1958.
Reviewed by T.H. Hawkins, *Nature*, 1958, 182: 1763.

HYNDMAN, Olan R. The origin of life and the evolution of living things. An environmental theory. xxii, 684 p. New York: Philosophical Library, 1952.
Reviewed by Conway Zirkle, *Isis*, 1953, 44: 81.

IHMELS, Carl. Die Entstehung der organischen Natur nach Schelling, Darwin und Wundt. Eine Untersuchung über den Entwicklungsgedanken. vi, 104 p. Leipzig: Deichert, 1916.

KEITH, Arthur. Darwinism and its critics. viii, 56 p., portr (Forum Series, 20) London: Watts, 1935. [CB 45/286]

KERR, John Graham. Evolution. xii, 278 p., 2 pl. London: Macmillan, 1926.
Reviewed by E.B.P., *Nature*, 1926, 118: 329-30.

LLOYD, R.E. What is adaptation? xii, 110 p. London: Longmans, 1914.

MacFARLANE, John Muirhead. The causes and course of organic evolution. A study in bioenergetics. 875 p. New York: Macmillan, 1918.

MASON, Frances, ed. Creation by evolution. A consensus of presentday knowledge as set forth by leading authorities in non-technical language that all may understand. Introduction by Sir Charles Scott Sherrington. xx, 392 p., ill. New York: Macmillan, 1928.

MEYER, F. L'accélération évolutive (essai sur le rythme évolutif et son interprétation quantique). 67 p. Paris: Librairie des Sciences et des Arts, 1947.

MOORE, Ruth. Man, time, and fossils. The story of evolution. xvii, 424 p., ill. New York: Knopf, 1953.
Reviewed by Bentley Glass, *Sci.Mon.*, 1955, 80: 67.

MORE, Louis Trenchard. The dogma of evolution. Louis Clark Vanuxem Foundation lectures delivered at Princeton University, January 1925. vi, 387 p. Princeton: Princeton University Press, 1925.

MORGAN, Thomas Hunt. A critique of the theory of evolution. x, 197 p., 95 fig. Princeton: Princeton University Press, 1916.

MORTON, Harold Christopherson. The bankruptcy of evolution. 196 p. London: Marshall Bros., 1925. [CB 18/620]

MULLER, H.J. Isolating mechanisms, evolution and temperature. In: Dobzhanskv, Theodosius. ed. Temperature and evolution. Isolating mechanisms ..., p. 71-125. (Biological Symposia, 6) Lancaster, Pa.: Jaques Cattell Press, 1942.

NEWMAN, Horatio Hackett. Evolution yesterday and today. x, 171 p. (A Century of Progress) Baltimore: Williams and Wilkins, 1932.
A brief impartial but critical summary of past concepts and current tendencies in evolutionary thought and investigations.

NOVIKOFF, Alex. Climbing our family tree. 95 p., ill. New York: International Publishers, 1945. [CB 72/275]
The story of evolution for young people.

OSTOYA, Paul. Les théories de l'évolution. Origine et histoire du transformisme et des idées qui s'y rattachent. 319 p. (Bibliothèque Scientifique) Paris: Payot, 1951.
Reviewed by Y. François, *Rev.Hist.Sci.*, 1952, 5: 97; by F.S. Bodenheimer, *Arch.Int.Hist.Sci.*, 1952, 5: 415-16; by Nils von Hofsten, *Lychnos*, 1953, 419-20.

PARKER, George Howard. What evolution is. vii, 173 p., 5 ill. Cambridge, Mass.: Harvard University Press, 1925.

PETRONIEVICS, Branislav. L'évolution universelle. Exposé des preuves et des lois de l'évolution mondiale et des évolutions particulières (inorganique, intellectuelle et sociale). 1. L'évolution mondiale, inorganique et organique. 214 p., ill. Paris: Felix Alcan, 1921.
Reviewed by L. Guinet, *Isis*, 1922, 4: 564-5.

RENSCH, Bernhard. Evolution above the species level. xvii, 419 p., bibliogr., fig. New York: Columbia University Press, 1960. [CB 86/468]

RIDDLE, Oscar. The unleashing of evolutionary thought. xxi, 414 p. New York: Vantage, 1955.
Reviewed by Paul B. Sears, *Sci.Mon.*, 1956, 82: 317; by A.J. Carlson, *Science*, 1956, 123: 144.

ROBSON, G.C. The species problem: an introduction to the study of evolutionary divergence in natural populations. vii, 283 p. (Biological Monographs and Manuals, 8) Edinburgh: Oliver and Boyd, 1928.

ROMANO, John, ed. Adaptation. xiv, 113 p. Ithaca, N.Y.: Cornell University Press, 1949. [CB 76/407]

ROMER, Alfred Sherwood. Man and the vertebrates. 3rd ed. ix, 405 p. Chicago: University of Chicago Press, 1941. [CB 62/79]
First publ. 1933.

ROSA, Daniele. L'ologénèse: nouvelle théorie de l'évolution et de la distribution géographique des êtres vivants. Adapté de l'italien par l'auteur. xii, 368 p. (Bibliothèque de Philosophie Contemporaine) Paris: Alcan, 1931.
Revised and expanded translation of: Ologenisi: nuova teoria dell'evoluzione e della distribuzione geografica dei viventi (Firenze: 1918).
Reviewed by A.K. *Nature*, 1931, 128: 429-30.

ROSTAND, Jean. L'évolution. 102 p., ill. (Encyclopédie essentielle. Série science, 4) Paris: Robert Delpire, 1960.

ROSTAND, Jean. The Orion book of evolution. [Translated from "L'évolution" by Rebecca Abramson] 105 p., ill. New York: Orion Press, 1961.
The first section of the book deals with the history of evolutionary theories.
Reviewed by G.G. Simpson, *Science*, 1961, 133: 1700.

SCHIERBEEK, A. Opkomst en bloei der evolutieleer. [The rise and success of the theory of evolution. (In Dutch)] 218 p. Haarlem: Volksuniversiteitsbibliotheek, De Erven F. Bohn, N.V., 1961.
Reviewed by P. van Oye, *Scient.Hist.*, 1961, 3: 101; by J. Huble, *Natuurwetensch.Tijdschr.*, 1961, 43: 171.

SCHMALHAUSEN, I.I. Factors of evolution. Transl. by Isadore Dordick. Ed. by Theodosius Dobzhansky. xiv, 327 p. Philadelphia: Blakiston, 1949.
Reviewed by Conway Zirkle, *Isis*, 1950, 41: 320.

SCHNEIDER, Georg. Die Evolutionstheorie, das Grundproblem der modernen Biologie. Ein Abriss des Entwicklungsgedankenes von Kaspar Friedrich Wolff über Darwin bis Lysenko. 2nd ed. 141 p. Berlin: Deutscher Bauernverlag, 1951.

SIMPSON, George Gaylord. The major features of evolution. xx, 434 p., 52 fig., 28 tables. New York: Columbia University Press, 1953. [CB 80/131]
Based on the author's Tempo and mode in evolution, *see* below.

SIMPSON, George Gaylord. The meaning of evolution. xv, 364 p. New Haven: Yale University Press, 1949.
Reviewed by Ashley Montagu, *Isis*, 1950, 41: 321-2.

SIMPSON, George Gaylord. Tempo and mode in evolution. 237 p. New York: Columbia University Press, 1944.
Reviewed by Conway Zirkle, *Isis*, 1947, 37: 109-10; by P. de Saint-Seine, *Rev.Quest.Sci.*, *5th ser.*, 1950, 11: 321-44.

SIMPSON, George Gaylord. This view of life; the world of an evolutionist. 308 p. New York: Harcourt, Brace, 1964.

SMITH, J. Maynard. The theory of evolution. 320 p., bibliogr. Harmondsworth/Baltimore: Penguin Books, 1958.

TAX, Sol; CALLENDER, Charles; ed. Evolution after Darwin. 3 vol. 1. The evolution of life - its origin, history and future. viii, 629 p.; 2. The evolution of man - man, culture and society. viii, 473 p.; 3. Issues in evolution. viii, 310 p. Chicago: University of Chicago Press; London: Cambridge University Press, 1960.
For reviews see CB 86/468, CB 87/510 and CB 87/634.

THOMSON, J. Arthur. Concerning evolution. viii, 245 p. New Haven: Yale University Press, 1925.

THORPE, Malcom Rutherford, ed. Organic adaptation to environment. xviii, 312 p. New Haven: Yale University Press, 1924.

TSCHULOK, Sinai. Deszendenzlehre (Entwicklungslehre). Ein Lehrbuch auf historisch-kritischer Grundlage. xii, 324 p., 63 fig. Jena: Fischer, 1922.
Reviewed by A. Fischel, *Naturwissenschaften*, 1922, 10: 789.

WALLACE, Alfred Russel. The world of life; a manifestation of creative power, directive mind and ultimate purpose. xv, 408 p., ill. London: Chapman, Hall, 1910; American ed. xvi, 441 p., ill. New York: Moffat, Yard, 1911.

WASMANN, Erich. Modern biology and the theory of evolution. xxxii, 539 p., 8 pl. London: Routledge, 1910. Reprinted 1923.
Translation of 3rd German edition, 1906, of "Die moderne Biologie und die Entwicklungstheorie". First published in articles in *Stimmen aus Maria-Laach*, 1901-3.

WEISMANN, August. Vorträge über Descendenztheorie, gehalten an der Universität von Freiburg i. Br. 3rd rev. ed. xiv, 342, 354 p., 3 pl., 137 fig. Jena: Gustav Fischer, 1913.

WHITEHEAD, George. A modern outline of evolution. viii, 324 p. London: Bale, Sons and Danielsson, 1933. [CB 41/604]

WILLIS, John Christopher. Age and area. A study in geographical distribution and origin of species. With chapters by Hugo de Vries, H.B. Guppy, Mrs E.M. Reid, and James Small. x, 259 p. Cambridge University Press, 1922.

WILLIS, John Christopher. The course of evolution. viii, 207 p. Cambridge University Press, 1940. [CB 61/403]

ZIMMERMANN, Walter. Evolution. Die Geschichte ihrer Probleme und Erkenntnisse. x, 623 p., fig. (Orbis Academicus. Problemsgeschichten der Wissenschaft in Dokumenten und Darstellungen. Naturwissenschaftliche Abteilung) Freiburg-München: Verlag Karl Alber, 1953.
Reviewed by Ernst Mayr, *Sci.Mon.*, 1954, 79: 57-8; by F.E. Fritsch, *Nature*, 1954, 174: 149-50; by R. Hooykaas, *Arch. Int.Hist.Sci.*, 1957, 10: 370-8.

JGc-bn *essays; articles*

ALMQUIST, E. Umwelt und Organismus bei Bildung neuer Formen. *Sudhoffs Arch.*, 1934, 27: 293-8.

BAKER, H.G. Darwin, and after Darwin. *Evolution*, 1960, 14: (2), 272-4.

BLUM, Harold F. Perspectives in evolution. *Amer.Scient.*, 1955, 43: 595-610.

BOURDIER, Franck. Poprzednicy Darwina w Latach 1550-1859. [Predecessors of Darwin, 1550-1859. (In Polish, with Russian summary)] *Kwart.Hist.Nauk.Tech.*, 1961, 6: 431-56, 607-43.

BRUNET, Pierre. La notion d'évolution dans la science moderne avant Lamarck. *Archeion*, 1937, 19: 21-43. [CB 49/196]

COOMARASWAMY, Ananda K. Gradation and evolution. *Isis*, 1944, 35: 15-16; 1947, 38: 87-94.

COULTER, John M. The history of organic evolution. *Science*, 1926, 63: 487-91.

CROMBIE, A.C. The idea of organic evolution. *Discovery*, 1953, 14: 92-7, 2 fig.

DAVENPORT, Charles B. The mechanism of organic evolution. *J.Wash.Acad.Sci.*, 1930, 20: 317-31. Also *Annu.Rep.Smithsonian Inst.for 1930*, p. 417-29, 1 pl., 3 fig. Washington, D.C.: 1931.
Presented before the two hundred and thirty-third meeting of the Washington Academy of Sciences, as one of the series of papers on origin and evolution.

DELPHY, Jean. Les théories de l'évolution: l'orthobionte. *Rev.Gen.Sci.*, 1925, 36: 76-9.
Charles Janet's theory.

DOBZHANSKY, Theodosius. Variation and evolution. *Proc.Amer. Phil.Soc.*, 1959, 103: 252-63.

DOUVILLÉ, Robert. L'irréversibilité de l'évolution et les adaptations aux différents milieux [d'après Dollo]. *Rev.Sci.*, 1912, 50: 2e semestre, 462-4.

HALDANE, J.B.S. A dialectical account of evolution. *Sci.Soc.*, 1937, 1: 473-86.

HALDANE, J.B.S. The theory of natural selection to-day. *Nature*, 1959, 183: 710-13.

HASSID, J. [The stages of evolution. (In Hebrew)] *Koroth*, 1959, 2: 120-8.

HERIBERT-NILSSON, N. Der Entwicklungsgedanke und die moderne Biologie. vi, 22 p. (Bios, 13) Leipzig: Barth, 1941.
Reviewed by R. Zaunick, *Mitt.Gesch.Med.*, 1941-42, 40: 159-61.

HOLMES, S.J. The principle of stability as a cause of evolution: a review of some theories. *Quart.Rev.Biol.*, 1949, 23: 324-32.

HOLMES, S.J. What is natural selection? *Sci.Mon.*, 1948, 67: 324-30.

JUST, Theodor. The rates of evolutionary processes. Presidential Address. *Proc.Indiana Acad.Sci.*, 1944, 53: 14-27.

KROPOTKIN, Peter Alekseevich. The direct action of environment and evolution. *Nineteenth Century*, 1919, 85: 70-89; also in *Annu.Rep.Smithsonian Inst.for 1918*, p. 409-27 Washington, D.C.: 1920.

LERNER, I. Michael. The concept of natural selection: a centennial view. *Proc.Amer.Phil.Soc.*, 1959, 103: 173-82.

LODGE, Oliver. Evolution. (From the Huxley Lecture delivered at Charing Cross Hospital on Thursday, December 3, 1925) *Nature*, 1925, 116: 932-42.

MacBRIDE, E.W. The theory of evolution since Darwin. *Nature*, 1925, 115: 52-5, 89-92.

MACPHAIL, Andrew. Evolution and life. *Ann.Med.Hist.*, 1929, 1: 553-61.

MAYR, Ernst. Isolation as an evolutionary factor. *Proc.Amer.Phil.Soc.*, 1959, 103: 221-30.

MONTAGU, M.F. Ashley. On the concepts of gradation and evolution. *Isis*, 1943, 34: 364.

MORRISON, Paul G. On evolution. *Tulane Stud.Phil.*, 1959, 8: 15-26.

NORDENSKIÖLD, Nils Erik. [Un aperçu sur l'évolution historique de la notion d'espèce dans la biologie. (In Swedish with French summary)] *Lychnos*, 1940, 1-20.

OMODEO, P. Centocinquant'anni di evoluzionismo. *Società*, 1959, 15: 833-4.

OSBORN, Henry Fairfield. The problem of the origin of the species as it appeared to Darwin in 1859 and as it appears today. *Nature*, 1926, 118: 270-3.

PERRIER, Edmond. L'évolution des organismes. *Rev.Sci.*, 1913, 51: 1er semestre, 129-35, 161-9.

PERRIN, C.J. Darwinism today. *Advance.Sci.*, 1959, 15: 468-74.

POULTON, Edward B. The history of evolutionary thought as recorded in meetings of the British Association. *Rep.Brit.Ass.Advance.Sci.*, 1937, 107: 1-23; also in *Science*, 1937, 86: 203-14; *Nature*, 1937, 140: 395-407.

POULTON, Edward B. A hundred years of evolution. *Science*, 1931, 74: 345-60.

PROSSER, C.L. The "Origin" after a century: prospects for the future. *Amer.Scient.*, 1959, 47: 536-50.

PRZIBRAM, Hans. Théorie apogénétique de l'évolution des organismes. *Rev.Gén.Sci.*, 1929, 40: 293-9.

RITCHIE, James. Perspective in evolution. *Annu.Rep.Smithsonian Inst.for 1940*, p. 249-69. Washington, D.C.: 1941.

ROSA, Daniele. Qu'est-ce que l'hologenèse? *Scientia*, 1923, 33: 113-25. [CB 14/542]

ROUSSEAU, Michel. Jean Rostand devant le ténébreux problème de l'évolution. *Hist.Méd.*, 1962, no. 3, 3-13.

SAINT-SEINE, P. de. Les théories de l'évolution. *Rev.Quest.Sci., 5th ser.*, 1950, 11: 321-44.

SIMPSON, George Gaylord. Anatomy and morphology: classification and evolution: 1859 and 1959. *Proc.Amer.Phil.Soc.*, 1959, 103: 286-306.

STEBBINS, G. Ledyard. The role of hybridization in evolution. *Proc.Amer.Phil.Soc.*, 1959, 103: 231-51.

TOMKEIEFF, S.J. The mnemic theories of evolution. *Scientia*, 1923, 34: 159-73, French transl. suppl., 39-51. [CB 15/212]

WADDINGTON, C.H. The evolution of adaptation. *Endeavor*, 1953, 12: 134-9.
An application of pre-adaptation to the animal kingdom.

ZIRKLE, Conway. Natural selection before the "Origin of species". *Proc.Amer.Phil.Soc.*, 1941, 84: 71-123. [CB 61/403]

ZIRKLE, Conway. Species before Darwin. *Proc.Amer.Phil.Soc.*, 1959, 103: 636-44.

JGj psychological aspects

COURTÈS, F. Pour une psychanalyse de l'évolutionnisme. In: Hommage à Gaston Bachelard, p. 161-89. Paris: Presses Universitaires de France, 1957.

JGk philosophy and methodology

BERNY, Adalbert. Organische und anorganische Evolution. *Ann.Natur.Kulturphil.*, 1913, 12: 162-9.

DE LAGUNA, Grace A. The role of teleonomy in evolution. *Phil.Sci.*, 1962, 29: 117-31.

GOUDGE, T.A. The ascent of life: a philosophical study of the theory of evolution. 236 p. Toronto: University of Toronto Press, 1961.
Reviewed by Perry Robinson, *Dialogue*, 1962, 1: 93-5.

JOSEPH, H.W.B. The concept of evolution. The Herbert Spencer lecture delivered at Oxford, 27 November 1924. 32 p. Oxford: Clarendon Press; New York: Oxford University Press, 1924. [CB 17/603]

LALANDE, André. Les illusions évolutionnistes. xii, 466 p. (Bibliothèque de Philosophie Contemporaine) Paris: Alcan, 1930. [CB 35/310]

LE ROY, Edouard. L'exigence idéaliste et le fait de l'évolution. xviii, 272 p. Paris: Boivin, 1927. [CB 26/243]

LOVEJOY, A.O. Bergson and romantic evolutionism. *Univ.Calif.Chron.*, 1914, 15: no. 4, 61 p.

MANDELBAUM, Maurice. The scientific background of evolutionary theory in biology. *J.Hist.Ideas*, 1957, 18: 342-61. [CB 83/269]

MEYER-ABICH, Adolf. The historico-philosophical background of the modern evolution-biology. 170 p., fig., bibliogr. (Acta Biotheoretica Supplementum Secundum) Leiden: Brill, 1964.
Nine lectures delivered during October and November 1960 at the Department of Zoology of the University of Texas.

RENSCH, Bernhard. Die Evolutionsgesetze der Organismen in naturphilosophischer Sicht. *Phil.Natur.*, 1961, 6: 288-326.

ROUSSEAU, Michel. "L'arbre de la vie", vivante image de l'évolution chez le P. Teilhard de Chardin. *Rev.Syn.*, 1958, 79: 113-21.

SMUTS, Jan Christiaan. Holism and evolution. ix, 361 p. London: Macmillan, 1926.
Reviewed by J. Graham Kerr, *Nature*, 1927, 119: 307-9.

JGkd

SCRIVEN, Michael. Explanation and prediction in evolutionary theory. *Science*, 1959, 130: 477-82.

JGke

WILKIE, J.S. Galton's contribution to the theory of evolution with special reference to his use of models and metaphors. *Ann.Sci.*, 1955, 11: 194-205.

JGkk

ROBERTY, Guy. Des règles de la logique à celles de l'évolution. *Gesnerus*, 1947, 4: 146-50.

JGkv

FISCHER, R.A. Indeterminism and natural selection. *Phil.Sci.*, 1934, 1: 99-117.

JGky

BEGOUEN, Henri, *Comte*. Quelques souvenirs sur le mouvement des idées transformistes dans les milieux catholiques, suivi de la mentalité spiritualiste des premiers hommes. 83 p. Paris: Bloud & Gay, [1945].
Catholic imprimatur, Paris, April 30, 1945.

CUÉNOT, Lucien. Le transformisme n'est-il qu'une illusion ou une hypothèse téméraire? *Rev.Gén.Sci.*, 1930, 41: 17-21.

GRASSET, Joseph. Le dogme transformiste. 158 p. Paris: Renaissance du Livre, 1919.
Short note by L. Guinet, *Isis*, 1920, 3: 88.

LABBÉ, Alphonse. Le conflit transformiste. Préface de Etienne Rabaud. xii, 204 p. Paris: Alcan, 1929. [CB 30/472]

LAIGNEL-LAVASTINE, Maxime. Etudes morphologiques: transformisme. *Thalès*, 1935, 1: 9-28.

LANESSAN, J.L. de. Transformisme et créationisme. Contribution à l'histoire du transformisme dupuis l'antiquité jusqu'à nos jours. 352 p. Paris: Alcan, 1914.
Reviewed by L. Guinet, *Isis*, 1914, 2: 229-30.

TEILHARD DE CHARDIN, Pierre. Le paradoxe transformiste. *Rev. Quest.Sci., 4e sèr.*, 1925, 7: 53-80. [CB 18/621]

VIALLETON, Louis. Morphologie générale; membres et ceintures des vertébrés tétrapodes; critique morphologique du transformisme. viii, 710 p., 270 fig. Paris: Gaston Doin, 1923.
Reviewed by L. Guinet, *Isis*, 1924, 6: 435-7.

VIALLETON, Louis. L'origine des êtres vivants. L'illusion transformiste. vi, 395 p. Paris: Plon, 1929.
Reviewed by L. Cuénot, *Rev.Gén.Sci.*, 1930, 41: 28-9.

JGmd

BLUM, Harold F. Time's arrow and evolution. xi, 222 p., 20 fig. Princeton, N.J.: Princeton University Press, 1951. [CB 78/180 and 186]
Reprinted in the Harper Torchbook series, 1962.

JGmzHU

DUFRENOY, Jean; DUFRENOY, Marie-Louise. Les fossiles et la notion d'évolution. *Action Univ.*, 1948, 15: 4-26.

LULL, Richard Swann. Organic evolution. xviii, 729 p., 253 fig., 30 pl. New York: Macmillan, 1917.
Chiefly from a palaeontological point of view.

SIMPSON, George G. Evolutionary determinism and the fossil record. *Sci.Mon.*, 1950, 71: 262-7.

JGmzHV

SCOTT, Dukinfield Henry. Extinct plants and problems of evolution. xiv, 240 p. London: Macmillan, 1924.
Reviewed by A.C. Seward, *Nature*, 1924, 113: 596-7.

JGmzHW

OSBORN, Henry Fairfield. The origin of species as revealed by vertebrate palaeontology. *Nature*, 1925, 115: 925-2, 961-3.

JGmzN

SKOWRON, Stanisław. Biology and medicine. *Rev.Pol.Acad.Sci.*, 1962, 7: no. 3, 19-26.
Relation of evolution and medical research.

JGs/t social and humanistic relations

JGsb

SANDOW, Alexander. Social factors in the origin of Darwinism. *Quart.Rev.Biol.*, 1938, 13: 315-26. [CB 57/194]

ZIRKLE, Conway. Evolution, Marxian biology and the social scene. 527 p., bibliogr. Philadelphia: University of Pennsylvania Press, 1959.
Reviewed by David Joravsky, with comments from Conway Zirkle, *Isis*, 1960, 51: 348-53; by Theodosius Dobzhansky, *Science*, 1959, 129: 1479-80; by G. Canguilhem, *Arch.Int. Hist.Sci.*, 1960, 13: 159-60.

JGt

GREENE, John C. Darwin and the modern world view. (Rockwell Lectures, Rice University) viii, 141 p. Baton Rouge: Louisiana State University Press, 1961; 126 p. New York: New American Library, 1963.
For reviews see CB 88/552, CB 89/496 and CB 90/603.

GREENE, John C. The death of Adam: evolution and its impact on Western thought. 382 p., fig., pl. New York: New American Library, 1961.
Reprinted (Mentor Books) New York: New American Library of World Literature, 1961. First publ. Ames, Iowa: 1959.
Reviewed by R. Furon, *Arch.Int.Hist.Sci.*, 1960, 13: 138-9; by Richard S. Westfall, *Amer.Hist.Rev.*, 1961, 66: 696-7; by M.J. Dunbar, *Isis*, 1961, 52: 594-6.

GRUBER, Jacob W. Darwinism and its critics. *Hist.Sci.*, 1964, 3: 115-23.
An essay review of John C. Greene: "Darwin and the modern world view".

ZIRKLE, Conway. Darwin's impact upon modern thought. The cultural heritage of 20th century man. The integration of Western culture; Nationalism and the great community of learning; Modern man: his 19th century heritage. (Philomathean Lecture Series, 1955) *Penn.Lit.Rev.*, 1956, 63-71.

JGtc

DEWEY, John. Evolution and ethics. *Sci.Mon.*, 1954, 78: 57-66.
Reprinted from *The Monist*, 1897-1901, vol. 8.

WIENER, Philip P. Chauncey Wright's defense of Darwin and the neutrality of science. *J.Hist.Ideas*, 1945, 6: 19-45, 1 pl.

JGtd

BATESON, William. Evolutionary faith and modern doubts. *Science*, 1922, 55: 55-61.
Address delivered before the A.A.A.S., Toronto, 1921.

COULTER, John Merle; COULTER, Merle C. Where evolution and religion meet. v, 105 p. New York: Macmillan, 1924.

FOTHERGILL, Philip G. Evolution and Christians. xix, 395 p., fig., pl., bibliogr. London/New York: Longmans, Green & Co., 1961.
Reviewed by John C. Greene, *Isis*, 1963, 54: 148-50.

LACK, David. The conflict between evolutionary theory and Christian belief. *Nature*, 1960, 187: 98-100.

MILLIKAN, Robert Andrews. Evolution in science and religion. v, 95 p. New Haven: Yale University Press (on the Dwight Harrington Terry Foundation), 1927.
Reviewed in *Nature*, 1927, 120: 435-6.

MORGAN, Conwy Lloyd. Emergent evolution: the Gifford lectures ... 1922. xii, 313 p. London: William & Norgate, 1923.

MORGAN, Conwy Lloyd. Life, mind and spirit: being the second course of the Gifford lectures delivered in 1923 under the general title of "Emergent evolution". xix, 316 p. London: Williams and Norgate, 1926.
Reviewed by G.C. Field, *Nature*, 1926, 118: 582-3.

SHIPLEY, Maynard. The war on modern science: a short history of the fundamentalist attack on evolution and modernism. xiv, 415 p. London/New York: Knopf, 1927.

JGth

IRVINE, William. The influence of Darwin on literature. *Proc. Amer.Phil.Soc.*, 1959, 103: 616-28.

JGw in different countries

JGwb-t

AMERICAN STUDIES ASSOCIATION OF TEXAS. The impact of Darwinian thought on American life and culture. Papers read at the fourth annual meeting of the American Studies Association of Texas at Houston, Texas. iii, 92 p. Austin: University of Texas, 1959.

PERSON, Stow, ed. Evolutionary thought in America. x, 462 p., 28 ill. New Haven: Yale University Press, 1950.
Reviewed by Conway Zirkle, *Isis*, 1951, 42: 275.

HOFSTADTER, Richard. Social Darwinism in American thought, 1860-1915. viii, 191 p. Philadelphia: University of Pennsylvania Press, 1944.
Reviewed by Morton G. White, *J.Hist.Ideas*, 1945, 6: 119-22; by M.F. Ashley Montagu, *Isis*, 1946, 36: 146-7.

JGwb-td

EVOLUTION and intellectual freedom. Suppl. to *Nature*, July 11, 1925, 113: 69-84.
Supplement entirely devoted to the trial of J.T. Scopes, a Tennessee high school science teacher, for having taught the theory of evolution in defiance of the State Law.

GIDDINGS, Franklin Henry. The mighty medicine. Superstition and its antidote: a new liberal education. 147 p. London/New York: Macmillan, 1929.

GINGER, Ray. Six days or forever? Tennessee vs. John Thomas Scopes. 258 p. Boston: Beacon Press, 1958.
Reviewed by C.I. Reed, *Science*, 1958, 128: 768.

OSBORN, Henry Fairfield. Evolution and religion in education: polemics of the fundamentalist controversy of 1922 to 1926. xiv, 240 p. New York: Scribner's, 1926.
Reviewed by J.C.H., *Nature*, 1926, 118: 652.

JGwi

BRAY, Edmondo. Su due precursori italiani della dottrina evoluzionistica. *Riv.Stor.Sci.*, 1930, 21: 293-301.

JGwn-da

RAIKOV, B.E. Russkiĕ biologi-evoliutsionisty do Darvina. [Russian evolutionary biologists before Darwin. (In Russian)] 4 vol. Moskva: Akademiia Nauk SSSR, 1952, 1951, 1955, 1959.
Reviewed in *Arch.Int.Hist.Sci.*, 1962, 15: 203-5.

JGyB application of mathematics

GAUSE, G.F. Vérifications expérimentales de la théorie mathématique de la lutte pour la vie. 64 p., ill. Paris: Hermann, 1935.

JH GENETICS

for bacterial genetics *see* JRyJH
plant genetics *see also* KH
animal genetics *see also* LH
human genetics *see also* NS

JHc general history

JHc-bm *large scale works*

BARTHELMESS, Alfred. Vererbungswissenschaft. 428 p. (Orbis Academicus, II: 2) Freiburg: Alber, 1942.

BATESON, William. Problems of genetics. ix, 258 p. New Haven: Yale University Press, 1913.
Reviewed by G. Sarton, *Isis*, 1914, 2: 230-1.

CANNON, H. Graham. Lamarck and modern genetics. xii, 152 p. Springfield, Ill.: Chas. Thomas, 1960. [CB 87/569-70]

CONKLIN, Edwin Grant. L'hérédité et le milieu. Leur rôle dans le développement de l'homme. 295 p. (Bibliothèque de Philosophie Scientifique) Paris: Flammarion, 1920.
Reviewed by L. Cuénot, *Rev.Gén.Sci.*, 1921, 32: 409.

CORRENS, Carl Erich. Gesammelte Abhandlungen zur Vererbungswissenschaft aus periodischen Schriften 1899-1924. ix, 1299 p., 128 fig. Berlin: J. Springer, 1924.

DARLINGTON, C.D. Evolution of genetic systems. 2nd ed. x, 265 p. Edinburgh/London: Oliver and Boyd; New York: Basic Books, 1958. [CB 84/314]
First publ. 1939.
Reviewed by Curt Stern, *Nature*, 1959, 183: 1553-4.

DARLINGTON, C.D. The facts of life. 467 p., front., 9 pl., 19 fig., 7 tables. New York: Macmillan Company, 1955.
Reviewed by Conway Zirkle, *Isis*, 1957, 48: 71-3.

DOBZHANSKY, Theodosius. Genetics and the origin of species. 3rd rev. ed. x, 364 p., 23 fig. New York: Columbia University Press, 1951. [CB 78/187]
First publ. 1937 and reviewed by Charles A. Kofoid, *Isis*, 1939, 30: 549-51; by Conway Zirkle, *Isis*, 1939, 30: 128-31. 2nd ed. 1941 reviewed by Conway Zirkle, *Isis*, 1942, 34: 181.

DUNN, Leslie Clarence, ed. Genetics in the 20th century: essays in the progress of genetics during its first 50 years. xi, 634 p., portr. New York: Macmillan, 1951. [CB 79/178]
Reviewed by Conway Zirkle, *Arch.Int.Hist.Sci.*, 1952, 31: 150-1; by Bentley Glass, *Bull.Hist.Med.*, 1953, 27: 294-6.

GENETICS and twentieth century Darwinism. xv, 321 p. (Cold Spring Harbor Symposia on Quantitative Biology, 24) Cold Spring Harbor, N.Y.: Long Island Biological Association, 1959.
Reviewed by H. Kalmus, *Nature*, 1960, 187: 726.

GOLDSCHMIDT, Richard Benedict. Einführung in die Vererbungswissenschaft; Vorlesungen für Studierende, Aerzte, Züchter. 4th rev. ed. xii, 547 p., 176 fig. Leipzig: E. Engelmann, 1923.

GOLDSCHMIDT, Richard Benedict. The material basis of evolution. xi, 436 p., bibliogr. (The Silliman Lectures, 1939) New Haven: Yale University Press, 1940. [CB 84/157]
The genetic processes involved in micro- and macro-evolution.

GUYÉNOT, Emile. L'hérédité. x, 464 p. (Encyclopédie Scientifique) Paris: G. Doin, 1924. [CB 16/289]

HUXLEY, Julian. Heredity, East and West. x, 246 p., portr. New York: Schuman, 1949.
Reviewed by Karl Sax, *Isis*, 1950, 41: 239.

JEPSEN, Glenn L.; MAYR, Ernst; SIMPSON, George Gaylord; ed. Genetics, paleontology, and evolution. Edited for the Committee on common problems of genetics, paleontology, and systematics, of the National Research Council. xiv, 474 p., fig., pl. Princeton: Princeton University Press, 1949. [CB 75/92]

JOHANNSEN, W. Elemente der exakten Erblichkeitslehre mit Grundzüge der biologischen Variationsstatistik. xi, 724 p. Jena: Fischer, 1913.

LE DANTEC, Félix. Évolution individuelle et hérédité. 2nd rev. ed. 276 p. Paris: Alcan, 1913.

MORGAN, Thomas Hunt. The theory of the gene. xvi, 343 p. (Yale University, Mrs. Hepsa Ely Silliman Memorial Lectures) New Haven: Yale University Press, 1926.
Reviewed by R.C. Punnett, *Nature*, 1926, 118: 435-7.

RABAUD, Et. L'hérédité. 190 p., 34 fig. Paris: Armand Colin, 1921. [CB 12/626]

SHEPPARD, P.M. Natural selection and heredity. 212 p., fig., bibliogr. New York: Philosophical Library, 1959.

SINNOTT, Edmund W.; DUNN, L.C.; DOBZHANSKY, TH. Principles of genetics. 4th ed. xiv, 505 p., 202 fig. New York: McGraw-Hill, 1950. [CB 77/373 and CB 78/188]
Contains many historical notes.

STUBBE, Hans. Kurze Geschichte der Genetik bis zur Wiederentdeckung der Vererbungsregeln Gregor Mendels. x, 232 p., ill. (Genetik. Grundlagen, Ergebnisse und Probleme in Einzeldarstellungen, 1) Jena: Gustav Fischer Verlag, 1963.
Reviewed by M.D. Grmek, *Arch.Int.Hist.Sci.*, 1963, 16: 448-9; by Heinz Degen, *Naturwiss.Rundsch.*, 1963, 16: 376; by Curt Stern, *Isis*, 1964, 55: 377-9.

STURTEVANT, Alfred Henry. Genetics and evolution. Selected papers of A.H. Sturtevant. Ed. by E.B. Lewis. x, 334 p., ill., tables. San Francisco, Calif.: Freeman, 1961.
Reviewed by William K. Baker, *Science*, 1962, 135: 782.

WADDINGTON, C.H. The strategy of the genes. A discussion of some aspects of theoretical biology. With an appendix by H. Kaeser. ix, 262 p. New York: Macmillan Company, 1957. [CB 84/315]
Reviewed by Jean Mayer, *Science*, 1958, 127: 968.

JHc-bn *essays; articles*

BABCOCK, Ernest B. The development of fundamental concepts in the science of genetics. 50 p. Washington, D.C.: American Genetic Association, 1950.

BABCOCK, Ernest B. The development of fundamental concepts in the science of genetics. *Port.Acta Biologica, Ser. A*, 1949, 1-45.
A brief account of the late nineteenth century background of genetics and of its twentieth century development.

BALTZER, Fritz. Theodor Boveri und die Entwicklung der Chromosomentheorie der Vererbung. Zu Boveris 100. Geburtstag am 12. Oktober 1962. *Naturwissenschaften*, 1963, 50: 141-6. [CB 89/568]

CAULLERY, Maurice. Génétique et évolution. *Rev.Gén.Sci.*, 1930, 41: 567-73.

CUÉNOT, Lucien. L'hérédité des caractères acquis. *Rev.Gén. Sci.*, 1921, 32: 544-50.

DOBZHANSKY, Theodosius. Biological adaptation. *Sci.Mon.*, 1942, 55: 391-402.
An application of modern genetics to an ancient problem.

DODSON, Edward O. Mendel and the re-discovery of his work. *Sci.Mon.*, 1955, 81: (4), 187-95, 4 fig.

DU BOIS, Anne-Marie. The development of genetics. *Ciba Symp.*, 1939, 1: 234-62.

EAST, E.M. Two decades of genetic progress. *Annu.Rep.Smithsonian Inst.for 1922*, p. 285-95. Washington, D.C.: 1924.
Reprinted from *J.Hered.*, May, 1922.

EVANS, Herbert M.; SWEZY, Olive. The chromosomes in man. Sex and somatic. 64 p., 11 pl., 33 x 26 cm. (Memoirs of the University of California, 9: no. 1) Berkeley, Calif.: University of California Press, 1929. [CB 27/560]
Includes historical introduction.

FISHER, R.A. Has Mendel's work been rediscovered? *Ann.Sci.*, 1936, 1: 115-37. [CB 48/531]

GILLES, Andre. Génétique et Néo-darwinisme. *Ann.Soc.Zool. Belg.*, 1959-60, 90: 37-40.

GLASS, Bentley. In pursuit of a gene. *Science*, 1957, 126: 683-9, 8 fig.

GRANT, Verne. The development of a theory of heredity. *Amer. Scient.*, 1956, 44: 158-79.
Contribution to the history of genetics.

GRUENBERG, Benjamin C. Spillman and genetics. *J.Hered.*, 1948, 39: 359-60. [CB 74/375]

HOMMEL, Hildebrecht. Moderne und Hippokratische Vererbungstheorien. *Arch.Gesch.Med.*, 1927, 19: 105-22.

JOHNSON, L.P.V. Dr. W.J. Spillman's discoveries in genetics. *J.Hered.*, 1948, 39: 247-54. [CB 74/375]

KEUDEL, Karl. Zur Geschichte und Kritik der Grundbegriffe der Vererbungslehre. *Arch.Gesch.Med.*, 1936, 28: 381-416.

LEDERBERG, Joshua. Genetic transduction. *Amer.Scient.*, 1956, 44: 264-80.
History of recent advances in the genetics of bacteria and, incidentally, of recent advances in genetic theory.

LEGRAND, L. L'emboîtement des plasmas. Aperçu d'une théorie mécanique de l'hérédité. *Rev.Gen.Sci.*, 1917, 28: 368-76, 396-403.
Reviewed by L. Guinet, *Isis*, 1920, 3: 88-9.

MacBRIDE, E.W. Mendel, Morgan and genetics. *Nature*, 1937, 140: 348-50, 2 fig.

McKUSICK, Victor A. Walter S. Sutton and the physical basis of Mendelism. *Bull.Hist.Med.*, 1960, 34: 487-97.

MAYER, Claudius Francis. Genesis of genetics. The growing knowledge of heredity before and after Mendel. A brief historical synopsis written in honor of the Institutum Gregorio Mendel and the International Symposium on Medical Genetics held in Rome, 6-7 September 1953. *Acta Genet.Med.Gemellol.*, 1953, 2: 237-332, 65 fig.

METALNIKOV, S. Sur l'hérédité de l'immunité acquise. *Compt. Rend.Acad.Sci.*, 8 Sept. 1924, 179: 514-16. [CB 16/290]

MONTALENTI, Giuseppe. Storia delle teorie dell'eredità. *Rass. Stud.Sessuali*, 1928, 8: 112-25.

MORGAN, Thomas Hunt. The bearing of Mendelism on the origin of species. *Sci.Mon.*, 1923, 16: 237-47.

MOURANT, A.E. Evolution, genetics, and anthropology. (Huxley Memorial Lecture, 1961) *J.Royal Anthropol.Inst.*, 1961, 91: (2), 152-65; reprinted in *Annu.Rep.Smithsonian Inst.for 1961*, p. 501-20. Washington, D.C.: 1962.

PUNNETT, R.C. Early days of genetics. *Heredity*, 1950, 4: 1-10.
An account of the coming of Mendelism to Britain and of the controversy which ensued.

RUDY, Z. [The history of hereditary doctrine from Aristotle to Mendelism. (In Hebrew)] *Koroth*, 1961, 2: 435-42.

SINGLETON, W. Ralph. Some highlights on the first half century of genetics. *Sci.Mon.*, 1950, 71: 401-7.

SONNEBORN, Tracy M. Beyond the gene. *Amer.Scient.*, 1949, 37: 33-59.
An account of our present knowledge of plasmagenes and their relationship to the nuclear genes.

STEIN, Emmy. Dem Gedächtnis von Carl Erich Correns (1864-1933) nach einem halben Jahrhundert der Vererbungswissenschaft. *Naturwissenschaften*, 1950, 37: 457-63.

STERN, Curt. Variation and hereditary transmission. *Proc. Amer.Phil.Soc.*, 1959, 103: 183-9.

SWINBURNE, R.G. The presence-and-absence theory. *Ann.Sci.*, 1962, 18: 131-45.

TATUM, Edward L. A case history in biological research. Chance and the exchange of ideas played roles in the discovery that genes control biochemical events. *Science*, 1959, 129: 1711-15.

TSCHERMAK-SEYSENEGG, E. The rediscovery of Gregor Mendel's work. *J.Hered.*, 1951, 42: 163-71.
An account of the early days of genetics by one of the trio who discovered Mendel's work in 1900.

VORTRÄGE auf der Tagung der Gesellschaft Deutscher Naturforscher und Ärzte in Essen. *Naturwissenschaften*, 1953, 40: 65-103. [CB 80/134]
To celebrate the Golden Jubilee of the discovery of Mendel's paper.

WHITE, M.D. Early observations on chromosomes and genes. *Ann. Sci.*, 1937, 2: 237.

WILKIE, J.S. Some reasons for the rediscovery and appreciation of Mendel's work in the first years of the present century. *Brit.J.Hist.Sci.*, 1962, 1: 5-17.

ZIMMERMANN, K.F. 100 Jahre Vererbungsforschung. *Wiss.Z. Humboldt-Univ.Berlin Math.Naturwiss.Reihe*, 1959-60, 9: 629-41.

ZIRKLE, Conway. The early history of the idea of the inheritance of acquired characters and of pangenesis. *Trans. Amer.Phil.Soc.*, 1946, 35: 91-151. [CB 70/259]

ZIRKLE, Conway. The inheritance of acquired characters and the provisional hypothesis of pangenesis. *Amer.Natur.*, 1935, 69: 417-45. [CB 45/286]

ZIRKLE, Conway. Further notes on pangenesis and the inheritance of acquired characters. *Amer.Natur.*, 1936, 70: 529-46. [CB 49/181]

ZIRKLE, Conway. The knowledge of heredity before 1900. In: Dunn, Leslie Clarence. Genetics in the 20th century, p. 35-57. New York: Macmillan, 1951.

ZIRKLE, Conway. Some oddities in the delayed discovery of Mendelism. *J.Hered.*, 1964, 55: 65-72.

JHda

ROBERTS, Herbert F. The founders of the art of breeding. *J.Hered.*, 1919, 10: 99-106, 147-52, ill.

JHdaj

PETERS, James A., ed. Classic papers in genetics. vi, 282 p., tables, fig. New York: Prentice-Hall, 1959.
Reviewed by Conway Zirkle, *Isis*, 1962, 53: 240-1.

JHk philosophy and methodology

BOSE, D.M. Rational and positivistic approach to science: on a recent trend in genetics. *Sci.Cult.*, 1961, 27: 160-74.

GOLDSCHMIDT, Richard B. Different philosophies of genetics. *Science*, 1954, 119: 703-10.

MALEK, I. Co je mičurinské zaměřeni biologie? [What is the michurinist orientation of biology? (In Czech)] *Fil.Čas.*, 1960, 7: 877-98.

PATTEN, Charles Joseph. The memory factor in biology: a sketch of the unity of life. xiii, 175 p. London: Baillière, Tindall and Cox, 1926.
Reviewed by E.S.R., *Nature*, 1927, 119: 741.

JHke

HERSH, A.H. *Drosophila* and the course of research. *Ohio J. Sci.*, 1942, 42: 198-200. [CB 64/452]

RUSSELL, E.S. The interpretation of development and heredity: a study in biological method. vi, 312 p. Oxford: Clarendon Press, 1930.
Reviewed by J. Gray, *Nature*, 1931, 127: 920-1.

YASUGI, Ryuichi. Methodological problems in the history of genetics. *Jap.Stud.Hist.Sci.*, 1964, 3: 108-13.

JHky

PORTO, César. Transformisme et hérédité. Les organismes et le milieu terrestre. 328 p., ill. Lisbonne: Bertrand, 1935. [CB 51/268]

JHmzHUwn

DAVITASHVILI, L.Sh. [The notion of heredity of acquired traits by organisms in Russian paleontology up to 1917. (In Russian)] *Tr.Inst.Ist.Est.*, 1953, 5: 51-92.

JHs relations with society

QUINTANILHA, A. Social implications of Mendelism versus Michurinism. *Nature*, 1959, 183: 1222-4.

JHsk

BROZEK, Josef. Extension of political domination beyond Soviet genetics. *Science*, 1950, 111: 389-91.

for Soviet genetics *see* JHwn

JHw in different countries

JHwb

DAVENPORT, C.B. The early history of research with *drosophila*. *Science*, 1941, 93: 305-6.
Note recalling that C.W. Woodworth suggested the use of this fly for breeding experiments in the Harvard Zoological Laboratory.

JHwe

PUNNETT, R.C. The early days of genetics. *Heredity*, 1950, 4: 1-10.
An account of the coming of Mendelism to Britain and of the controversy which ensued.

JHwg-or

PLATE, L. Begrüssung und Vortrag über "Jenaer Professoren als Förderer der Abstammungslehre". *Verhandl.Deut.Zool. Ges.*, 1925, 30: 14-45.

JHwg-qg

FRIEDRICH-FREKSA, H. Genetik und biochemische Genetik in den Instituten der Kaiser-Wilhelm-Gesellschaft und der Max-Planck-Gesellschaft. *Naturwissenschaften*, 1961, 48: (1), 10-22.

JHwh

DRUCE, Gerald. Some Czechoslovak contributions to genetics (1866-1938). *Nature*, 1943, 151: 495-6.

JHwm

BRÜCHER, Heinz. Pehr Bolin, ein skandinavischer Vorläufer bei der Wiederentdeckung der Vererbungsgesetze. *Forsch.Fortschr.*, 1950, 26: 313-14.

JHwn

BEALE, G.H. Timiriazev, founder of Soviet genetics. *Nature*, 1947, 159: 51-3.

DARLINGTON, C.D. A revolution in Soviet science. *Discovery*, 1947, 8: 40-3; also in *J.Hered.*, 1947, 38: 143-8. [CB 71/101]
First publ. in *Discovery*, 1947, 8: no. 2. On the Lysenko controversy.

DOBZHANSKY, Th. N.I. Vavilov, a martyr of genetics. *J.Hered.*, 1947, 38: 227-32. [CB 72/258]

DUBININ, N.P. Work of Soviet biologists: theoretical genetics. *Science*, 1947, 105: 109-12. [CB 71/121]

DUNN, L.C. Science in the U.S.S.R. *Science*, 1944, 99: 65-7.
Regarding the Lysenko controversy.

HUDSON, P.S.; RICHENS, R.H. The new genetics in the Soviet Union. 88 p. (Imperial Bureau of Plant Breeding and Genetics. Technical communication, 12) Cambridge, England: School of Agriculture, 1946.
Reviewed by Conway Zirkle, *Isis*, 1947, 37: 106-8; by Eric Ashby, *Nature*, 1946, 158: 285-7.

HUXLEY, Julian. Soviet genetics: the real issue. *Nature*, 1949, 163: 935-42. [CB 75/92]

JORAVSKY, David. Soviet Marxism and biology before Lysenko. *J.Hist.Ideas*, 1959, 20: 85-104.

LAPTEV, I. "The truth" about genetics. *J.Hered.*, 1948, 39: 18-21. [CB 73/173]
A translation of an article in *Pravda* on Sept. 2, 1947.

MORTON, Alan G. Soviet genetics. 174 p. London: Lawrence R. Wishart, 1951.
Reviewed by Conway Zirkle, *Isis*, 1952, 43: 379-80.

POLIAKOV, I.A. [On national biologists in the struggle with Mendelism. (In Russian)] *Tr.Inst.Ist.Est.*, 1949, 3: 3-27.

RAPOPORT, Anatol. Death of communication with Russia? *ETC*, 1950, 7: 83-96.
Apropos of Conway Zirkle's book, *see* below.

SAX, Karl. Soviet biology. *Science*, 1944, 99: 298-9.
Comment on statements made by L.C. Dunn, *see* above.

SOROKIN, C. Inbreeding is again in favor in Russia. *J.Hered.*, 1951, 42: 135-6. [CB 78/157]

STEBBINS, G.L. New look in Soviet genetics. *Science*, 1956, 123: 721-2.
An account of the rehabilitation of N.I. Vavilov in the Soviet Union.

ZHEBRAK, Anton B. Soviet biology. *Science*, 1945, 102: 357-8. [CB 72/272]
Supports the statements of L.C. Dunn, which were attacked by Karl Sax, *see* above.

ZIRKLE, Conway. The death of a science in Russia. xiv, 319 p. Philadelphia: University of Pennsylvania Press, 1949.
Reviewed by Karl Sax, *Isis*, 1950, 41: 238-9; by Eric Ashby, *Nature*, 1950, 165: 906; by Th. Dobzhansky, *J.Hist.Med.*, 1950, 5: 339-42.

JHwn-bv

LEIKIND, Morris C. The genetics controversy in the USSR. A bibliographic survey. *J.Hered.*, 1949, 40: 203-8.

JHwt

KOMAI, Taku. Genetics of Japan, past and present. *Science*, 1956, 123: 823-6.

JHxx museums

KŘIŽENECKÝ, Jaroslav. Die Errichtung der "Genetischen Abteilung Gregor Mendel" im Mährischen Museum in Brünn. *Naturwiss.Rundsch.*, 1963, 16: 477-80.

JHy related subjects

JHyB

L'HÉRITIER, Ph. Génétique et évolution. Analyse de quelques études mathématiques sur la sélection naturelle. 44 p. Paris: Hermann, 1934.

JHyBW

DE BEER, Gavin. Mendel, Darwin, and Fisher (1865-1965). *Notes Roy.Soc.Lond.*, 1964, 19: 192-226.

JHyCU

BEADLE, George. H.J. Muller and the Geneva Conference. [Editorial] *Science*, 1955, 122: 813. [CB 82/199]
Muller's paper, "Genetic effect of radiation: human interpretation", was censored out of the Geneva Conference on Peaceful Uses of Atomic Energy.

COOK, Robert C. Straws in a Lysenko wind. *J.Hered.*, 1955, 46: 195-200.
Includes the censored paper (see note above).

RESIGNATION of Prof. Muller from the Academy of Sciences of the USSR. *Science*, 1948, 108: 436. [CB 74/375]

SLATIS, Herman M. Current status of information on the induction of mutations by irradiation. *Science*, 1955, 121: 817-21. [CB 81/342]

JHyJD

SENCHENKOVA, E.M. Kratkii ocherk istorii voprosa o geneticheskoi sviazi khlorofilla i gemoglobina. [A brief sketch of the history of the problem of the genetic connection of chlorophyll and hemoglobin. (In Russian)] *Tr.Inst.Ist.Est.Tekh.*, 1962, 40: 157-97.
From the late 19th century to the present.

JHyJE

CUNNINGHAM, J.T. Hormones and heredity: a discussion of the evolution of adaptations and the evolution of species. xx, 246 p., 3 pl. London: Constable, 1921.
Reviewed by W.M. Bayliss, *Nature*, 1922, 109: 35-7.

JI MORPHOLOGY

for plant morphology *see also* KI
animal morphology *see also* LI

BLIAKHER, L. IA. Sootnoshenie formy i funktsii. (Etiudy po istorii morfologii, 4). [The correlation of form and function. (Studies in the history of morphology, 4). (In Russian)] *Tr.Inst.Ist.Est.Tekh.*, 1962, 40: 118-56.

BLIAKHER, L. IA. Tak nazyvaemaia idealisticheskaia morfologiia i ee mesto v istorii morfologicheskikh nauk. [So-called idealistic morphology and its place in the history of the morphological sciences. (In Russian)] *Tr.Inst.Ist.Est.Tekh.*, 1961, 36: 3-52. [CB 87/567]

BONNER, J.T. Morphogenesis. 296 p. Princeton, N.J.: Princeton University Press, 1952.
An essay on the nature of development.

BRACHET, A. La vie créatice des formes. 200 p., 29 fig. (Nouvelle Collection Scientifique) Paris: F. Alcan, 1927.

CROW, William Bernard. Contributions to the principles of morphology. viii, 94 p. London: Kegan Paul, 1929. [CB 27/552]

DALCQ, A. La pensée moderne devant le problème de la forme. *Arch.Inst.Int.Sci.Théor.Sér.A Bull.Acad.Int.Phil.Sci.*, 6. Problèmes de philosophie des sciences, 6, L'unité formelle et physiologie du vivant, p. 7-32. Discussion p. 33-6. (Actualités Scientifiques et Industrielles, 1068) Paris: Hermann, 1949.

EGGERS, Friedrich. Das Gesetz der Ungleichartigkeit der Organismen. *Sudhoffs Arch.*, 1934, 27: 235-42.

FREY-WYSSLING, A. Frühgeschichte und Ergebnisse der submikroskopischen Morphologie. *Mikroskopie*, 1964, 19: 2-12, ill.

KROGMAN, Wilton Marion. Morphology in ancient times. Morphology during the Renaissance. Morphology in modern times. *Ciba Symp.* (Summit, N.J.), 1944, 6: 1878-1904, fig.

THOMPSON, D'Arcy Wentworth. Growth and form. 2nd ed. 1116 p. Cambridge University Press, 1942.
Reviewed by Dorothy Wrinch, *Isis*, 1943, 34: 232-4.
First publ. 1917 [CB 7/128]

THOMPSON, D'Arcy Wentworth. On growth and form. Abridged ed. by John Tyler Bonner. xiv, 346 p., ill. Cambridge University Press, 1961.

WHYTE, L.L., ed. Aspects of form, a symposium on form in nature and art. ix, 249 p., 32 pl. New York: Pellegrini & Cudahy; London: Lund Humphries, 1951. [CB 79/169]
Reviewed by F.I.G. Rawlins, *Nature*, 1951, 168: 574.

JIkk

MEYER, Adolf. Logik der Morphologie: im Rahmen einer Logik der gesamten Biologie. vii, 290 p. Berlin: Springer, 1926.

JImc

SCHLIEPER, Hans. Das Raumjahr. Die Ordnung des lebendigen Stoffes. 360 p. Jena: Diederichs, 1929.
Reviewed by Richard Pfennig, *Arch.Gesch.Math.Naturwiss.Tech.*, 1929, 11: 446-7.

JItq

COOK, Theodore Andrea. The curves of life, being an account of spiral formations and their application to growth in nature, to science and to art, with special reference to the Mss. of Leonardo da Vinci. xxx, 479 p., 2 pl., 415 ill. London: Constable, 1914.

JJ COMPARATIVE ANATOMY

see INDEX for general and special anatomy

AMLINSKII, I.E. Nachal'nyi etap razvitiia metoda gomologii i ego rol' v reforme sravnitel'noi anatomii i sistematiki pozvonochnykh zhivotnykh. [First stage of the development of the method of homologies and its role in the reform of the comparative anatomy and taxonomy of vertebrates. (In Russian)] *Tr.Inst.Ist.Est.Tekh.*, 1961, 36: 286-93.

ARIËNS, Kappers C.U.; HUBER, G. Carl; CROSBY, Elizabeth Caroline. The comparative anatomy of the nervous system of vertebrates. 2 vol. xvii, 864 p.; xi, 981 p., 710 fig. New York: Macmillan, 1936. [CB 48/581]
This book is an outgrowth of "Die vergleichende Anatomie des Nervensystems" by Ariëns Kappers (Haarlem: 1920-21).

CHAINE, J. Histoire de l'anatomie comparative. vi, 461 p. Bordeaux: E. Daguerre, 1925.
Reviewed by Raoul M. May, *Isis*, 1927, 9: 480-2.

COLE, F.J. A history of comparative anatomy. From Aristotle to the eighteenth century. viii, 524 p. London: Macmillan, 1944.
Reviewed by M.F. Ashley Montagu, *Isis*, 1947, 37: 112-14; notes by F.J. Cole, Herbert Friedmann, and M.F. Ashley Montagu, *ibid.*, 1948, 38: 264-6.

RITTER, William Emerson. The California Woodpecker and I. A study in comparative zoology. In which are set forth numerous facts and reflections by one of us about both of us. xvi, 340 p., front., portr., 28 fig. Berkeley: University of California Press, 1938. [CB 57/252]
Reviewed by Charles A. Kofoid, *Isis*, 1940, 31: 479-80.

SIMPSON, George Gaylord. Anatomy and morphology: classification and evolution: 1859 and 1959. *Proc.Amer.Phil.Soc.*, 1959, 103: 286-306.

STROHL, J. Missbildungen im Tier- und Pflanzenreich. Versuch einer vergleichenden Betrachtung. 62 p., 17 fig. Jena: Fischer, 1929.
Reviewed by R. Zaunick, *Mitt.Gesch.Med.*, 1930, 29: 156.

SWINTON, W.E. Early history of comparative anatomy. *Endeavour,* 1960, 19: 209-14.
Early history of the subject with special reference to the contributions of Lamarck and Cuvier.

JJce

COLE, F.J.; EALES, Nellie B. The history of comparative anatomy. I. A statistical analysis of the literature. *Sci. Progr.,* 1916-17, 11: 578-96.

JJcm

GUDGER, E.W. Some early and late illustrations of comparative osteology. *Ann.Med.Hist.,* 1929, 1: 334-55, 15 fig.

JJwf-oq

ANTHONY, R. La chaire d'anatomie comparée du Muséum: ses traditions et son programme. *Rev.Gén.Sci.,* 1923, 34: 399-407. [CB 15/250]

FRIANT, Madeleine. Raoul Anthony et la chaire d'anatomie comparée du Museum. *Rev.Sci.,* 1941, 79: 397-8.
Notice by M. Friant, *Rev.Gén.Sci.,* 1940-41, 51: 229-30.

JJwj

BARBOSA SUEIRO, M.B. La contribution des scientistes de Lisbonne à l'étude de l'anatomie comparée. *Arq.Anat.Antropol.,* 1932, 14: 437-51.

JJxx-wk

KLAAUW, C.J. van der. Een verzameling uit den eersten tijd van de vergelijkende ontleedkunde (De collectie Brugmans). [A collection from the beginnings of comparative anatomy. (The Brugmans Collection) (In Dutch)] *Natuur,* 1930, 50: 20 p., ill.
Description of the collection made by Sebald Justinus Brugmans, now preserved in the Museums of the University of Leiden.

JK COMPARATIVE PHYSIOLOGY

BODENHEIMER, F.S. Zur Geschichte der verbesserten Wärmesummenregel. *Arch.Gesch.Math.Naturwiss.Tech.,* 1930, 13: 103-4.

BOSE, Jagadish Chandra. Réactions de la matière vivante et non vivante. Traduit par Ed. Monod-Herzen. 188 p. Paris: Gauthier-Villars, 1926.
Translation of Response in the living and non-living (London: 1902).

CHOLODNY, N. Charles Darwin and the modern theory of tropisms. *Science,* 1937, 86: 468. [CB 53/236]

DE BEER, G.R. Growth. viii, 120 p., 8 pl. London: Arnold, 1924.
Reviewed by T.S.P.S., *Nature,* 1924, 114: 709-10.

DEVAUX, Emile. Un caractère différentiel fondamental entre l'espèce et la race. *Rev.Gén.Sci.,* 1924, 35: 109-15.

DEVAUX, Emile. Les facteurs de l'état adulte et le problème des allures de développement. *Rev.Gén.Sci.,* 1928, 39: 170-4.

KOSHTOIANTS, Kh. S. [About the history of the discovery of the transformation of the oxides of carbon into carbon dioxide in living organisms. (In Russian)] *Tr.Inst.Ist.Est.,* 1952, 4: 267-72.

LANE, Alfred C. Eutopotropism. *Scientia,* 1935, 57: 279-84; French transl. suppl., 103-8.
"Eutopotropism is a tropism toward the environment for which one is best fitted by preadapted variations".

LUDWIG, Wilhelm. Das Rechts-Links-Problem im Tierreich und beim Menschen: mit einem Anhang, Rechts-Links-Merkmale der Pflanzen. xi, 496 p. (Monographien aus dem Gesamtgebiet der Physiologie der Pflanzen und der Tiere, 27) Berlin: Springer, 1932

MAST, S.O. Factors involved in the process of orientation of lower organisms in light. *Biol.Rev.,* 1938, 13: 186-224.
Opens with historical notes from Ray in 1693 onwards.

MERKELBACH, Otto. Zur Entwicklung der Beobachtung der aktiven elektrischen Erscheinungen im tierischen und menschlichen Körper. *Festschrift für Jacques Brodbeck-Sandreuter,* p. 271-97, 10 fig. Basel: Schwabe, 1942.

NICHOLAS, John S. Development of contractility. *Proc.Amer. Phil.Soc.,* 1950, 94: 175-83, ill.

ROSE, Maurice. La question des tropismes. vii, 469 p., 90 fig. (Les Problèmes Biologiques, XIII) Paris: Presses Universitaires de France, 1929.
Reviewed by W.J. Crozier, *J.Gen.Psychol.,* 1931, 5: 131-4.

SCHEER, Bradley T. The development of the concept of tissue respiration. *Ann.Sci.,* 1939, 4: 295-305.

VELDE, A.J.J. van de. Het leven en de dood. [Life and death. (In Dutch)] *Rev.Belg.Doc.Méd.*, 1947, 15 p. [CB 73/174]

JKyCJ

HARVEY, E. Newton. A history of luminescence from the earliest times until 1900. xxiii, 692 p., 50 pl. (*Mem.Amer. Phil.Soc.,* 44) Philadelphia: American Philosophical Society, 1957.
Reviewed by Conway Zirkle, *Isis,* 1959, 50: 68-9; for other reviews *see* CB 83/185, CB 84/314 and CB 85/392.

JKzf FERTILIZATION; SEX

COLE, F.J. Early theories of sexual generation. x, 230 p., 12 pl., 9 fig. Oxford: Clarendon Press, 1930.
Reviewed by Charles A. Kofoid, *Isis,* 1931, 16: 463-5.

DELAGE, Yves; GOLDSMITH, Marie. La parthénogénèse naturelle et expérimentale. 342 p. (Bibliothèque de Philosophie Scientifique) Paris: E. Flammarion, 1913.

FOX, H. Munro. Selene: or sex and the moon. 84 p. (Psyche Miniatures, General Series, 15) London: Kegan Paul, 1928.
Reviewed in *Nature,* 1928, 121: 981.

HERTWIG, Oscar. Dokumente zur Geschichte der Zeugungslehre. Eine historische Studie. 168 p., 25 fig. Bonn: Cohen, 1918.

KAMMERER, Paul. Ursprung der Geschlechtsunterschiede. *Fortschr.Naturwiss.Forsch.,* 1912, 5: 1-240.

KELLER, R. Historical and cultural aspects of hermaphroditism. The problem of sexual differentiation and hermaphroditism. Hermaphroditism in the animal kingdom. Experimental sex determination. *Ciba Symp.,* 1940, 2: 466-90.

LILLIE, Frank R. The history of the fertilization problem. *Science,* 1916, 43: 39-53.

LOEB, Jacques. Artificial parthenogenesis and fertilization. viii, 306 p., 39 tables, 86 fig. Chicago: University Press, 1913.

SCHIERBEEK, A. Het probleem der bevruchting in de loop der tijden. [The problem of fertilization in the course of time. (In Dutch)] 30 p. (*Mededeel.Vlaam.Acad.Wetensch.Lett. Schoone Kunsten Belg.Kl.Wetensch.,* 1952, 14: no. 12) Brussels: 1952.
Reviewed by H. Engel, *Centaurus,* 1954, 3: 263-4.

THOMSON, J. Arthur. Sex-characters. *Scientia,* 1914, 15: 382-402.
Resumé of the subject taken from article by Paul Kammerer, Ursprung der Geschlectsunterschiede, *see* above.

ZIRKLE, Conway. The discovery of sex-influences, sex-limited and sex-linked heredity. *Studies and Essays offered to George Sarton,* p. 169-94. New York: Schuman, 1947. [CB 71/121]

JL EMBRYOLOGY

for plant embryology *see also* KL
animal embryology *see also* LL
human embryology *see also* PU

ALLODI, Federico. Il cuore embrionale. *Riv.Stor.Sci.*, 1956, 47: 171-99.

BRACHET, A. L'évolution d'une science: l'embryologie. *Rev. Gén.Sci.*, 1915, 26: 512-17.

CAULLERY, Maurice. Les progrès récents de l'embryologie expérimentale. 236 p., 395 fig. Paris: Flammarion, 1939.
Reviewed by Charles A. Kofoid, *Isis*, 1947, 32: 222.

DE BEER, G.R. Embryos and ancestors. 3rd ed. xii, 197 p. Oxford: Clarendon Press, 1958.
First published as: Embryology and evolution. Oxford: Clarendon Press, 1930; revised edition, Embryos and ancestors. Oxford: Clarendon Press; New York: Oxford University Press, 1940. [CB 60/155]

FRANKLIN, K.J. A survey of the growth of knowledge about certain parts of the foetal cardio-vascular apparatus, and about the foetal circulation, in man and some other mammals. Part I: Galen to Harvey. *Ann.Sci.*, 1941, 5: 57-89, 4 fig.

HENNEGUY, F. Évolution de l'embryogénie depuis son origine et ses tendances actuelles. *Rev.Sci.*, 1913, 51: ler semestre, 312-7.

MEYER, Arthur William. The rise of embryology. xvi, 367 p., 97 fig. Stanford, Calif.: Stanford University Press, 1939. [CB 59/478]
Reviewed by Charles A. Kofoid, *Isis*, 1949, 32: 396-8; by F.H.A. Marshall, *Nature*, 1940, 146: 348-9.

MONTAGU, M.F. Ashley. Embryology from antiquity to the end of the eighteenth century. *Ciba Symp.* (Summit, N.J.), 1949, 10: 1009-28, ill.

NEEDHAM, Joseph. A history of embryology. 2nd ed. revised with the aid of A. Hughes. 304 p., 18 pl., bibliogr. Cambridge University Press; New York: Abelard-Schuman, 1959.
Reviewed by Charles W. Bodemer, *Isis*, 1961, 52: 109-10; for other reviews *see* CB 85/394, CB 86/466 and CB 87/568. First publ. 1934 and reviewed by C.A. Kofoid, *Isis*, 1937, 27: 98-102.

STREETER, George L. Development of the egg as seen by the embryologist. *Sci.Mon.*, 1931, 32: 495-506, 7 fig.

WILLIER, Benjamin H.; OPPENHEIMER, Jane M.; ed. Foundations of experimental embryology. xi, 225 p., ill. Englewood Cliffs, N.J.: Prentice-Hall, 1964. [CB 90/526]
A collection of 11 articles by leading contributors to the early development of experimental embryology.

JLh

OPPENHEIMER, Jane M. Problems, concepts and their history (1). Methods and techniques (2). In: Willier, Benjamin H.; Weiss, Paul A.; Hamburger, V.; ed. Analysis of development, p. 1-38. Philadelphia: Saunders, 1955. [CB 81/273]

JLwf-oq

FAURÉ-FREMIET, E. La chaire d'embryogénie comparée du Collège de France et l'évolution des sciences du développement. *Rev. Gén.Sci.*, 1929, 40: 37-45.

JLwn

BLIAKHER, L.Ia. Istoriia embriologii v rossii XIX-XX vv.: bespozvonotschnie. [History of embryology in Russia, 19th and 20th centuries. Invertebrate. (In Russian)] 626 p., ill. Leningrad: Biblioteka Akademii Nauk, SSSR, 1959.
Reviewed by Charles W. Bodemer, *Isis*, 1962, 53: 535-7.

JLyJD

NEEDHAM, Joseph. Biochemistry and morphogenesis. xvi, 787 p. Cambridge University Press, 1942.
Reviewed by John T. Edsall, *Isis*, 1943, 34: 523-5.

NEEDHAM, Joseph. Chemical embryology. 3 vol. xxii, 613 p., 11 pl.; xvi, 615-1253 p., 3 pl.; xvi, 1255-2021 p., 1 pl. Cambridge University Press, 1931.
Contains a detailed account of the origins of chemical embryology.
Reviewed by J.S.H., *Nature*, 1932, 129: 183-5.

JLyJH

DOBZHANSKY, Theodosius, ed. Temperature and evolution. Isolating mechanisms. Genetic control of embryonic development. xii, 355 p. (Biological Symposia, 6) Lancaster, Pa.: Jaques Cattell Press, 1942.

JM CYTOLOGY

for plant cytology *see* KM

JMc general history

ASCHOFF, A.; KÜSTER, E.; SCHMIDT, W.J. Hundert Jahre Zellforschung. 285 p. (Protoplasma Monographien, 19) Berlin: Borntraeger, 1938.
Reviewed by Charles A. Kofoid, *Isis*, 1949, 32: 393-4.

BAKER, J.R. The cell theory: a restatement, history and critique. 5 pt. *Quart.J.Microscop.Sci.*, 1948, 89: 103-75; 1949, 90: 87-108, 331; 1952, 93: 157-90; 1953, 94: 407-40; 1955, 96: 449-81. [CB 80/130 and CB 82/258]

BERG, Alexander. Die Lehre von der Faser als Form- und Funktionselement des Organismus. Die Geschichte des biologisch-medizinischen Grundproblems vom kleinsten Bauelement des Körpers bis zur Begründung der Zellenlehre. *Virchows Arch.Pathol.Anat.Physiol.*, 1942, 309: 333-460.
Reviewed by Nils von Hofsten, *Lychnos*, 1943, 418.

BONNER, J.T. Cells and societies. 234 p., ill. Princeton: Princeton University Press, 1955. [CB 82/207]

CASPERSSON, Torbjoern O. Cell growth and cell function, a cytochemical study. 185 p., 95 fig. New York: Norton, 1950. [CB 77/372]
The author begins with a brief historical account of the work of the Institute for Cell Research.

COWDRY, Edmund Vincent, ed. General cytology; a textbook of cellular structure and function for students of biology and medicine. 754 p., 173 fig., 9 pl. Chicago: University of Chicago Press, 1924.
Reviewed by Raoul M. May, *Isis*, 1926, 8: 213-15.

DARLINGTON, C.D. Recent advances in cytology. With a foreword by J.B.S. Haldane. 2nd ed. xvi, 671 p., 16 pl., 160 fig. London: Churchill; Philadelphia: Blakiston, 1937.
Reviewed by Charles A. Kofoid, *Isis*, 1938, 29: 472-4.
First publ. 1932.

FLORIAN, J. The early history of the cell theory. *Nature*, 1932, 130: 634-5.

HUGHES, Arthur. A history of cytology. x, 158 p., pl., bibliogr. New York/London: Abelard-Schuman, 1959. [CB 85/393]
Reviewed by John R. Baker, *Endeavour*, 1959, 18: 223; by R.C. von Borstel, *Amer.Scient.*, 1959, 47: 392A-4A; by Jean Théodoridès, *Rev.Hist.Sci.*, 1960, 13: 276-7.

KLEIN, Marc. À la recherche de l'unité élémentaire des organismes vivants; histoire de la théorie cellulaire. 33 p., bibliogr. (Conférences du Palais de la Découverte, 1960) Paris: Université de Paris, 1960.

KLEIN, Marc. Histoire des origines de la théorie cellulaire. 72 p. (Actualités Scientifiques et Industrielles, 328. Exposés d'histoire et philosophie des sciences, 3) Paris: Hermann, 1936. [CB 51/267]

LEGRAND, L. Une conception biologique nouvelle de la cellule. *Rev.Gen.Sci.*, 1919, 30: 397-408.
Reviewed by L. Guinet, *Isis*, 1920, 3: 88-9.

LEGRAND, L. La sélection du plasma spécifique. Esquisse d'une théorie cytomécanique et cytochimique de la vie. 187 p. Paris: Maloine, 1916.
Reviewed by L. Guinet, *Isis*, 1920, 3: 88-9.

MELSON, Everett White. Schwann's cell-theory. The basis of one hundred years investigation of vital processes. *Curr. Sci.*, 1938, 7: 267-70.

MENDELSOHN, Everett. Cell theory, the development of general physiology. *Arch.Int.Hist.Sci.*, 1963, 16: 419-29.

SEIFRIZ, William. Protoplasm. x, 584 p., 179 fig. New York: McGraw-Hill, 1936.
Reviewed by Th. Just, *Amer.Midland Natur.*, 1936, 17: 576.

STUDNIČKA, F.K. Aus der Vorgeschichte der Zellentheorie. H. Milne Edwards, H. Dutrochet, F. Raspail, J.E. Purkinje. *Anat.Anz.*, 1932, 73: 390-416.

STUDNIČKA, F.K. Quelques notions fondamentales de la physiologie générale de Jan Evangelista Purkyne (Purkinje), de la théorie cellulaire de Theodor Schwann et de la plasmatologie actuelle. *Arch.Int.Hist.Sci.*, 1949, 2: 718-27.

WEBER, Friedl. Neue Wege der Protoplasma-Forschung. *Scientia*, 1926, 40: 367-78; French transl. suppl., 130-9.

WILSON, Edmund Beecher. The cell in development and heredity. 3rd ed. 1232 p., 529 fig. New York: Macmillan, 1925.
Reviewed by Raoul M. May, *Isis*, 1926, 8: 213-15.

WILSON, J. Walter. Cellular tissue and the dawn of the cell theory. *Isis*, 1944, 35: 168-73.

JMs

HUSKINS, C. Leonard. Science, cytology and society. *Amer. Scient.*, 1951, 39: 688-99. [CB 78/180 and 191]

JMw in different countries

JMwf

KLEIN, Marc. Sur les débuts de la théorie cellulaire en France. *Thalès*, 1949-50, 6: 25-36.

JMwn

COOK, R.C. More about Lepeshinskaya's home-brewed cells. *J. Hered.*, 1951, 42: 121-3. [CB 78/157]

SHUBNIKOVA, E.A. [Priority of Russian scholars in the discovery of the indirect cellular division. (In Russian)] *Tr. Inst.Ist.Est.*, 1952, 4: 373-80.

JN ECOLOGY

HEDGPETH, Joel W. Progress - the flower of the poppy. *Amer. Sci.*, 1947, 35: 395-400.

INTERNATIONAL SYMPOSIUM ON MAN'S ROLE IN CHANGING THE FACE OF THE EARTH, Princeton, 1955. Man's role in changing the face of the earth. Ed. by W.L. Thomas, [*et al.*] xxxviii, 1193 p., 180 ill., 33 tables. Chicago: University of Chicago Press (for the Wenner-Gren Foundation for Anthropological Research and the National Science Foundation); London: Cambridge University Press; Toronto: University of Toronto Press, 1956. [CB 82/210]

MACFADYEN, A.; NEWBOULD, P.J. Fifty years of ecology. *Nature*, 1963, 198: 1247-8.

MILNE, Lorus J.; MILNE, Margery J. The eelgrass catastrophe. *Sci.Amer.*, 1951, 184: no. 1, 52-5.

JNkb

BEWS, J.W. The ecological viewpoint. *Nature*, 1931, 128: 245-8.

DICE, Lee R. What is ecology? *Sci.Mon.*, 1955, 80: 346-51.

FRIEDERICHS, Karl. Vom Wesen der Ökologie. *Sudhoffs Arch.*, 1934, 27: 277-85.

JNks

LASSEN, H. Der Umgebungsbegriff als Planbegriff. Ein Beitrag zu den erkenntnistheoretischen Grundfragen der Umweltlehre. *Arch.Gesch.Med.*, 1935, 27: 480-93.

JNmzNC

ADAMS, C.C. The relation of general ecology to human ecology. *Ecology*, 1935, 16: 316-35.

JNs

MERRIAM, John C. Conservation and evolution in a changing social program. *Proc.Amer.Phil.Soc.*, 1934, 73: 351-70.

JNwb-qg

GRAVIER, Ch. Le laboratoire de biologie tropicale de Tortugas (Floride). *Rev.Gén.Sci.*, 1913, 24: 874-82.

JNwe-qd

THE BRITISH ECOLOGICAL SOCIETY and the *Journal of Ecology*. *Isis*, 1913, 1: 262-3.

JNzm MARINE AND CAVE BIOLOGY
see also GY OCEANOGRAPHY

ADVANCES in marine biology. Vol. 1-2. Ed. by S. Russell. New York: Academic Press, 1963-4.
Volume 1 reviewed by Joel W. Hedgpeth, *Science*, 1963, 141: 1027.

CARSON, Rachel L. Under the sea-wind. A naturalist's picture of ocean life. [New ed. with corrections] 314 p. New York: Oxford University Press, 1952. [CB 79/178]
First published New York: Simon & Schuster, 1941.

GUDGER, E.W. Pomacenrid fishes symbiotic with giant sea anemones in Indo-Pacific waters. *J.Roy.Asiatic Soc.Bengal Sci.*, 1946, 12: 53-76, 2 pl.

HARVEY, H.W. Recent advances in the chemistry and biology of sea water. vii, 164 p. Cambridge University Press; New York: Macmillan Co., 1946. [CB 81/259]

RUSSELL, F.S.; YONGE, C.M. The seas. Our knowledge of life in the sea and how it is gained. Rev. ed. xiii, 379 p., ill. London: Warne, 1936. [CB 51/269]
First edition appeared in 1928.

JNzm-bv

HEDGPETH, Joel W. A century at the seashore. *Sci.Mon.*, 1945, 61: 194-8, 2 ill.

HEDGPETH, Joel W. Fishers of the Murex. (Notes for a bibliography of marine natural history). *Isis*, 1947, 37: 26-32, 6 fig.

JNzm-sp

CASTERET, Norbert. Speleology and war. *Isis*, 1947, 37: 75.

JNzm-tp

STEPHENSON, T.A. Seashore life and pattern. 28 p., 16 pl., 9 fig. London: King Penguin Books, 1944. [CB 68/57]

JNzm-wb-qg

DEXTER, Ralph W. The Annisquam seaside laboratory of Alpheus Hyatt (1838-1902). *Sci.Mon.*, 1952, 74: 112-16. [CB 79/141]

LILLIE, Frank R. The Woods Hole Marine Biological Laboratory. 284 p., 26 ill. Chicago, Ill.: University of Chicago Press, 1944.
Reviewed by Conway Zirkle, *Isis*, 1946, 36: 270-1.

JNzm-wf-qg

CAULLERY, Maurice. Les stations françaises de biologie marine. *Notes Roy.Soc.Lond.*, 1950, 8: 95-115.

CORSON, P.-S.; OUDRY, J. La biospéologie. *Hist.Méd.*, 1962, 12: no. 4, 3-14.
Includes account of the Laboratoire Souterrain du CNRS à Moulis.

PETIT, Georges. L'histoire de la biologie marine en France et la création des laboratoires maritimes. 32 p., fig. (Conférences du Palais de la Découverte, D 80) Paris: Palais de la Découverte, 1961.

JNzm-wi

FORTI, Achille. Origine e svolgimento dei primi studi biologici sul mare in Italia. 89 p., 10 pl. (*Atti Ist.Veneto*, 81) Venezia: 1922. [CB 15/210]

JNzm-wi-qg

DOHRN, Reinhard. The zoological station at Naples. *Endeavour*, 1954, 13: 22-6.
An account of the great institute for the study of marine life.

DOHRN, Reinhard. Stazione Zoologica Napoli. *Notes Roy.Soc. Lond.*, 1951, 8: 277-82, 2 pl.

STENTA, Mario. Trieste negli studi di biologia marina. *Atti Soc.Ital.Progr.Sci.XI Riunione* (Trieste, 1921), p. 382-408, bibliogr. Citta di Castello: 1922.
Work of the Stazione Zoologica at Trieste since its foundation in 1875.

JO EFFECT OF RADIATIONS, CLIMATE AND EXTRA-TERRESTRIAL PHENOMENA

for the effect of climate on trees *see* KXyJO
genetic effect of radiations *see* JHyCU
radiation hazards to public health *see* NH

CUVIER, Georges. Effets biologiques de la pression barométrique, leurs conséquences en climatologie. 28 p. (Les Conférences du Palais de la Découverte, 29 avril 1950) Paris: Université de Paris, [n.d.]
A lecture on the history of this subject, to accompany the exhibition: L'oeuvre scientifique de Blaise Pascal ... et trois siècles après, 1950.

FOX, H. Munro. Selene: or sex and the moon. 84 p. (Psyche Miniatures, General Series, 15) London: Kegan Paul, 1928.
Reviewed in *Nature*, 1928, 121: 981.

FREE, E.E. Lunar influences on living things. *Isis*, 1949, 32: 344.
Addition to Sarton's article, *see* below.

GRAY, Ernest. *Stylonichia mytillus* and the lunar periods. *Nature*, 1951, 167: 38.

HELLPACH, Willy. Die geopsychischen Erscheinungen: Wetter und Klima, Boden und Landschaft in ihrem Einfluss auf das Seelenleben. 3rd rev. ed. xx, 531 p. Leipzig: Engelmann, 1923.

HOPKINS, A.D. Notes on the bioclimatic law. *Nature*, 1924, 114: 608-9.

KENEALY, Arabella. The human gyroscope: a consideration of the gyroscopic rotation of earth as mechanism of the evolution of terrestrial living forms: explaining the phenomenon of sex: its origin and development and its significance in the evolutionary process. v, 313 p., 16 pl. London: Bale and Danielsson, 1934.
Reviewed in *Nature*, 1935, 135: 1059.

McADIE, Alexander George. Man and weather. vi, 99 p., 18 pl. Cambridge, Mass.: Harvard University Press, 1926.

McDANIEL, W.B. The moon, werewolves, and medicine. *Trans. Coll.Physicians Phila.*, 1950, 18: 113-22.

MacKINNEY, Loren. Moon-happy apes, monkeys and baboons. *Isis*, 1963, 54: 120-2.

SARTON, George. Lunar influences on living things. *Isis*, 1939, 30: 495-507.

SCHMID, Alfred. Biologische Wirkungen der Luft-Elektrizität. Mit Berücksichtigung der künstlichen Ionisierung. Beobachtungen, Versuche und Hypothesen von der Mitte des 18. Jhdts. bis zur Gegenwart. 135 p., 5 pl. Bern: Haupt, 1936.

STAHL, William Harris. Moon madness. *Ann.Med.Hist., new ser.*, 1937, 9: 248-63, 1 fig.

UVAROV, Boris Petrovitch. Insects and climate. *Trans. Entomol.Soc.London*, 1931, 79: 1-247.
Reviewed by Richard Joel Russell, *Geogr.Rev.*, 1933, 23: 170-2.

ZINNER, Ernst. Das Verhalten der Tiere bei Sonnenfinsternissen. *Ber.Naturforsch.Ges.Bamberg*, 1946, 29: 6-14.

JOc-br

Acta Phaenologica. International Phenological Journal. Internationale Phaenologische Zeitschrift. Vol. 1-3. 's Gravenhage: 1931-35. [CB 38/595]

JOpw

CLARK, J. Edmund. International co-operation in phenological research. *Nature*, 1924, 114: 607-8; 1925, 115: 602.

JOqx

DANNE, J., *et al.* Conférences de Radiumbiologie faites à l'Université de Gand en 1913. 214 p., fig. Bruxelles: L. Severeyns, 1914.

JOwe

CLARK, J. Edmund. The history of British phenology. *Quart. J.Roy.Meteorol.Soc.*, 1936, 62: 19-23.

JP PARASITISM, IN GENERAL

for animal parasitology *see* LP
medical parasitology *see* QS

CAULLERY, Maurice. Parasitisme et symbiose. 400 p. (Encyclopédie Scientifique) Paris: Doin, 1921.
Reviewed by L. Cuénot, *Rev.Gen.Sci.*, 1922, 33: 26.

JQ COMPARATIVE PATHOLOGY

JQwb-qg

ROCKEFELLER INSTITUTE FOR MEDICAL RESEARCH. History, organization, present scope of scientific work, buildings and equipment, publications. 36 p., 2 pl. New York: Rockefeller Institute for Medical Research, 1931. [CB 33/403]
This is an account of the Rockefeller Institute with its Medical Institute in New York and that of Comparative Pathology of Animals and Plants at Princeton, N.J.

SHUFELDT, R.W. The laboratory of comparative pathology of the Zoological Society of Philadelphia. *Pop.Sci.Mon.*, May 1914, 84: 507-13, 5 fig.

JQwf-qd

DUFRENOY, J.L.; DUFRENOY, J. A propos du cinquantenaire de la Société de Pathologie Comparée. *Rev.Pathol.Comp.*, 1950, 50: 789-93.

JR MICROBIOLOGY

for medical baceteriology *see* QN
medical mycology *see* QR
fungi *see also* KU

JRc general history

ASCOLI, Alberto. Random thoughts with a hopeful purpose. *Essays in the History of Medicine presented to Prof. Arturo Castiglioni*, p. 32-42. Baltimore: Johns Hopkins Press, 1944.
Notes on the history of bacteriology.

BELLONI, Luigi. Le "Contagium Vivum" avant Pasteur. 35 p., fig. (Conférences du Palais de la Découverte, D 74) Paris: Université de Paris, 1961.

BIGGER, Joseph W. Man against microbe. 304 p., ill. New York: Macmillan, 1939.
Reviewed by Morris C. Leikind, *Isis*, 1949, 32: 409.

BROCK, Thomas Dale, ed. Milestones in microbiology. xii, 275 p. Englewood Cliffs, N.J.: Prentice-Hall, 1961.
Reviewed by J.R. Porter, *Isis*, 1963, 54: 147; by Leland W. Parr, *Science*, 1961, 134: 44-5.

BRYSON, Vernon, ed. Microbiology yesterday and today. A symposium held in honor of the seventieth birthday of Selman A. Waksman, Nobel Laureate and Professor Emeritus, Institute of Microbiology, Rutgers University, June 5, 1958. v, 122 p. New Brunswick, N.J.: Institute of Microbiology, Rutgers University, 1959.

BUCHANAN, Estelle D.; BUCHANAN, Robert Earle. Bacteriology for students in general and household science. 5th ed. x, 678 p. New York: Macmillan, 1951.
4th edition 1938 [CB 56/393]
Includes a historical outline.

BULLOCH, William. The history of bacteriology. xii, 422 p. (Heath Clark Lectures, 1936) London: Oxford University Press, 1938.
Reviewed by Morris C. Leikind, *Isis*, 1940, 31: 480-2.
Reissued 1960. Reviewed in *Proc.Roy.Soc.Med.*, 1961, 54: 78.

CHAPMAN, A. Chaston. The yeasts: a chapter in microscopical science. *J.Roy.Microscop.Soc.*, 1925, 45: 1-16.

GRAINGER, Thomas H. A guide to the history of bacteriology. xi, 210 p. (Chronica Botanica, 18) New York: Ronald Press, 1958. [CB 84/315]
Reviewed by David T. Smith, *Bull.Hist.Med.*, 1959, 33: 289; by P. Huard and J. Théodoridès, *Rev.Hist.Sci.*, 1959, 12: 281-3.

HUARD, Pierre. Les structures vivantes microscopiques. Evolution de la technique et des idées. *Education* (Saigon), 1948, no. 10, 35-48.

MONTREUIL, Jean. Evolution des idées sur la nature et la multiplication des virus-protéines. *Rev.Quest.Sci.*, 1956, 17: 59-89, 13 fig.

NEUBURGER, Max. Early phases of microbiology. *Med.Life*, 1932, 39: 710-16.

NICOT, Jacqueline. Les levures et nous. *Hist.Med.*, 1962, 12: no. 4, 15-23.

NOVIKOVA, V.N. [Discovery of the phenomenon of chemoautotrophy and the earliest studies of it. (In Russian)] *Vop.Ist.Est.Tekh.*, 1959, 7: 136-41.

PRATT, Robertson. Armageddon of the microbes: a consideration of certain relationships in a microbiological society. *Tex.Rep.Biol.Med.*, 1949, 7: 12-21.

RYZHKOV, V.L. Kratkii ocherk istorii izucheniia virusov. [Short sketch of the history of the study of viruses. (In Russian)] *Tr.Inst.Ist.Est.Tekh.*, 1961, 36: 315-25.

SMITH, Kenneth M. The virus. viii, 176 p. Cambridge University Press, 1940. [CB 60/154]
Brief historical introduction.

VELDE, A.J.J. van de. L'enfance de la microbiologie, période historique de Moïse et Homère à van Leeuwenhoek, - à 1674. *Biol.Jaarb.*, 1953, 20: 219-34.

WAKSMAN, Selman A. The changing concept of microbiology. *Sci.Mon.*, 1953, 76: 127-33.
Address delivered at Tokyo on the commemoration of the centenary of the birth of S. Kitasato.

WAKSMAN, Selman A. Soil microbiology. vii, 356 p. New York: Wiley, 1952.
The first 28 pages are devoted to a history of the subject.

JRda

DE KRUIF, Paul. Microbe hunters. 368 p. New York: Harcourt Brace, 1926.
English edition: 320 p. (Life and letters series) London: Cape, 1930. German translation Zürich: Orell Füssli, 1927.
Reviewed by Fielding H. Garrison, *Med.Life*, 1926, 33: 199-201; by Henry Barton Jacobs, *ibid.* 1926, 33: 201-4.

WILLIAMS, Greer. Virus hunters. 503 p. New York: Knopf, 1959.
Reviewed in *Sci.Amer.*, 1960, 202: no. 4, 209-10.

JRdaj

DOETSCH, Raymond N., ed. Microbiology. Historical contributions from 1776 to 1908 by Spallanzani, Schwann, Pasteur, Cohn, Tyndall, Koch, Lister, Schloesing, Burrill, Ehrlich, Winogradsky, Warington, Beijerinck, Smith, Orla-Jensen. xii, 233 p., pl., fig. New Brunswick, N.J.: Rutgers University Press, 1960.

JRm/t special aspects

JRmzRX

HOBBY, Gladys L. Microbiology in relation to antibiotics. *J.Hist.Med.*, 1951, 6: 369-87.

JRnh

BIZZARRINI, Giotto. La paternità del vocabolo "microbio". *Riv.Stor.Sci.*, 1946, 35-37: 24-6.

JRqg

CHAPMAN, A. Chaston. The fungi imperfecti, and a further plea for an institute of industrial micro-biology. *J.Roy.Microscop.Soc.*, 1926, 46: 1-16.

JRs

BIRKELAND, Jorgen. Microbiology and man. Being an account of the diverse properties and characteristics of micro-organisms, a description of the various tools and techniques for their handling, and an inquiry into their subtle relationships to everyday life. x, 478 p. Baltimore: Williams and Wilkins, 1942.
Reviewed by R. St. John-Brooks, *Nature*, 1943, 152: 674-5.

JRt

DUBOS, René Jules. Microbiology in fable and art. *Bacteriol. Rev.*, 1952, 16: 145-51.

JRw in different countries

JRwb-da

CLARK, Paul Franklin. Pioneer microbiologists of America. xiv, 369 p., ill. Madison: University of Wisconsin Press, 1961.
Reviewed by J.R. Porter, *Isis*, 1963, 54: 147-8; by Leland W. Parr, *Science*, 1961, 134: 939-40; by Charles Rosenberg *Bull.Hist.Med.*, 1962, 36: 381-2.

JRwb-qd

WILSON, Perry W. The early and somewhat diverting history of the division of physiology, Society of American Bacteriologists. *Newsletter Soc.Amer.Bacteriol.*, 1953, 19: 2-3.

JRxd techniques

HITCHENS, Arthur Parker; LEIKIND, Morris C. The introduction of agar-agar into bacteriology. *J.Bacteriol.*, 1939, 37: 485-93, portr. [CB 58/545]

JRyJH BACTERIAL GENETICS

LEDERBERG, Joshua. Genetic transduction. *Amer.Scient.*, 1956, 44: 264-80.
History of recent advances in the genetics of bacteria and, incidentally, of recent advances in genetic theory.

RAVIN, Arnold W. Infection by viruses and genes. *Amer.Scient.*, 1955, 43: 468-78.
A brief summary of present knowledge.

JRzf FERMENTATION

PASTEUR Fermentation Centennial 1857-1957. A scientific symposium. On the occasion of the one hundredth anniversary of the publication of Louis Pasteur's "Mémoire sur la fermentation appelée lastique." xiii, 207 p., ill. New York: Charles Pfizer, 1958.
Reviewed by Roy G. Neville, *Isis*, 1959, 50: 161-2.

PFIZER, (Charles) AND COMPANY, INC. Our smallest servants: the story of fermentation. Foreword by John E. McKeen. 32 p., ill. Brooklyn, N.Y.: 1955. [CB 82/205]

WALKER, T.K. Pasteur's work on fermentation and its significance for present-day studies in biochemistry. *Nature*, 1958, 181: 940-2.

K BOTANY

for medical botany *see* RP
plant cultivation *see* SC
economic botany *see* SE

Kc general history

ARBER, Agnes. From medieval herbalism to the birth of modern botany. *Science, medicine and history. Essays in honour of Charles Singer*, (1), p. 317-36, 3 fig. London: Oxford University Press, 1953.

BOWER, Frederick Orpen. A century of botany, 1835-1885-1935. *Nature*, 1935, 136: 938-41, 976-8.

BOWER, Frederick Orpen. Seven decades of botany. From the Presidential Address to Section K (Botany) of the British Association entitled "1860-1894-1926", delivered at Oxford on August 5. *Nature*, 1926, 118: 413-16.

CAILLEUX, André. Progression du nombre d'espèces de plantes décrites de 1500 à nos jours. *Rev.Hist.Sci.*, 1953, 6: 42-9, table, 2 fig.

COSTANTIN, Julien. Aperçu historique des progrès de la botanique depuis cent ans (1834-1934). 185 p., 17 pl. (Annales des Sciences Naturelles, Botaniques, 16) Paris: Masson, 1934.
Reviewed by J. Dufrénoy, *Rev.Gén.Sci.*, 1935, 46: 346-7.

DARRAH, William C. An introduction to the plant sciences. xii, 332 p., 156 fig. New York: Wiley, 1942. [CB 63/273]
Includes a chapter entitled "A brief history of the plant sciences".

DAVY DE VIRVILLE, Adrien. De l'influence des idées préconçues sur le progrès de la botanique du XVe au XVIIIe siècle. *Rev. Hist.Sci.*, 1957, 10: 110-19, 2 fig.

HAMSHAW THOMAS, H. Experimental plant biology in pre-Linnean times. Presidential address, 1955. *Bull.Brit.Soc.Hist.Sci.*, 1955, 2: 1-22.

HARVEY-GIBSON, Robert John. Outlines of the history of botany. x, 274 p. London: Black, 1919.
Reviewed by Charles Singer, *Isis*, 1920, 3: 297-9.

HARVEY-GIBSON, Robert John. A short history of botany. vii, 96 p., 2 pl. London: J.M. Dent; New York: Dutton, 1926.

JESSEN, Karl F.W. Botanik der Gegenwart und Vorzeit in culturhistorischer Entwickelung. xx, 495 p. Waltham, Mass.: *Chronica Botanica*, 1948.
Photographic reprint of the original edition (Leipzig: 1864).
Reviewed by Conway Zirkle, *Isis*, 1949, 40: 82.

JOST, Ludwig. Die Entstehung der grossen Entdeckungen in der Botanik. Rede zur Reichsgründungsfeier am 18. Januar, 1930. 29 p. Heidelberg: Winter, 1930.
Reviewed by R. Zaunick, *Mitt.Gesch.Med.*, 1931, 30: 102.

MÖBIUS, Martin. Geschichte der Botanik von den ersten Anfängen bis zur Gegenwart. vi, 458 p. Jena: Fischer, 1937.
Reviewed by Charles A. Kofoid, *Isis*, 1939, 30: 304-6.

MOLISCH, Hans. Erinnerungen und Welteindrücke eines Naturforschers. xii, 232 p. Wien: 1934.

REED, Howard S. A short history of the plant sciences. 320 p., 37 ill. (A new series of plant science books, 7) Waltham, Mass.: Chronica Botanica, 1942.
Reviewed by Conway Zirkle, *Isis*, 1942, 34: 36.

RICKETT, Harold William. The green earth. 353 p. Lancaster, Pa.: Jaques Cattell Press, 1943. [CB 65/82]

STEERE, William Campbell. Fifty years of botany. xiii, 638 p., fig., tables. New York: McGraw-Hill, 1958.
Reviewed by Elizabeth B. Gasking, *Isis*, 1960, 51: 98-9.

TRANSCAU, Edgar N. The golden age of botany. *Science*, 1942, 95: 53-8.
Address of the retiring president of the Botanical Society of America, delivered at Dallas, Texas, on December 29, 1941.

TURRILL, W.B., ed. Vistas in botany. A volume in honour of the bicentenary of the Royal Botanic Gardens, Kew. xv, 547 p. (International Series of Monographs on Pure and Applied Biology: Botany, 2) London/New York: Pergamon Press, 1959.
Reviewed by W.H. Pearsall, *Nature*, 1959, 183: 1484-5; by A. Robyns, *Rev.Quest.Sci.*, 1960, 21: 146-7.

Kc-be

GATIN, Charles Louis. Dictionnaire aide-mémoire de botanique. Revised after death of author by Mme Allorge-Gatin. 847 p., 700 fig. Paris: Lechevalier, 1924.

Kc-br

Chronica Botanica: international plant science news. Vol. 1-5. Leiden: 1935-39; vol. 6- Waltham, Mass.: 1940- Volume 1 reviewed by John Hendley Barnhart, *Science*, 1933, 82: 279. For volume 2 *see* CB 48/575.

Kc-bv/cv bibliographies; literature; sources

Kc-bv

ARBER, Agnes. Recent work on the history of botany in the Old World. *Chron.Bot.*, 1942, 7: 263-4.

WANGERIN, Walter. Geschichte der Botanik.
Wangerin's general survey of writings on the history of botany covering the years 1910/11-1931/32 appeared in *Justs Bot.Jahresber.*, 1911-32, vol. 39-60. The years 1933/34 and 1935 were covered by Kurt Krause, *Justs Bot.Jahresber.*, 1933-34, 61-62: (1), 24-72; 1935, 63: (1), 7-24.

Kcb

HUNT BOTANICAL LIBRARY. The Rachel McMasters Miller Hunt Botanical Library, Carnegie Institute of Technology, its collection, program, and staff. vii, 35 p. Pittsburgh: Carnegie Institute of Technology, 1961.
Reviewed by Claus Nissen, *Sudhoffs Arch.*, 1963, 47: 191-2.

LAWRENCE, G.H.M. The Hunt Botanical Library. *Plant Sci. Bull.*, 1962, 8: no. 2, 1-3.

Kcd-bv

PELSENEER, Jean. Catalogue sommaire des manuscrits du fonds Léo Errera de l'Université de Bruxelles. *Bull.Soc.Bot.Belg.*, 1960, 92: 269-70.

Kce

GERTZ, Otto. Botaniken på de gamla örteböckernastid. Herbarius et herbarium. [Botanists in the time of the old plant books. (In Swedish, with summary in French)] *Lychnos*, 1939, 193-221, 8 fig.

STEVENS, Neil E. Factors in botanical publication and other essays. *Chron.Bot.*, 1947, 11: 121-204, front. [CB 72/259]
The essays deal not only with bibliographical topics, but also with the cultural and social relations of botany and the teaching of the subject.

STEVENS, Neil E. The fad as a factor in botanical publication. *Science*, 1932, 75: 499-504.

Kce-bv

GUITARD, E.H. Les dictionnaires et les traités de botanique. *Bull.Soc.Hist.Pharm.*, December 1926, 333-44, 4 pl.
Short bibliographical guide.

HUNT BOTANICAL LIBRARY. Catalogue of botanical books in the collection of Rachel McMasters Miller Hunt. 2 vol. 1. Printed books, 1477-1700, with several manuscripts of the 12th, 15th, 16th, and 17th centuries. Compiled by Jane Quinby; 2. Printed books, 1701-1800. Compiled by Allan Stevenson. Pittsburgh, Pa.: Hunt Botanical Library, 1958; 1961.
Reviewed by Claus Nissen, *Sudhoffs Arch.*, 1963, 47: 191-2.

Huntia: a yearbook of botanical and horticultural bibliography. 1-. Pittsburgh: Hunt Botanical Library, Carnegie Institute of Technology, 1964-.

SETCHELL, William Albert. History of botany. (Course at the University of California. Botany 150) List of original sources from Dioscorides to John Ray. Berkeley, Cal.: [n.d.].
List of the fundamental botanical books available in the Library of the University of California with their shelf-numbers, for the convenience of students taking Botany 150.

Kce-bx

BLUNT, Wilfrid. Flower books and their illustrators: catalogue of an exhibition arranged for the National Book League, London. 60 p. London/New York: Cambridge University Press, 1950.
Reviewed by Sonia S. Wohl, *Isis*, 1952, 43: 295-6.

Kcj

VERDOORN, Frans. Farlow's interest in an international abstracting journal. *Farlowia*, 1945, 2: 71-82. [CB 69/200]

Kcm

BAZIN, Germain. A gallery of flowers. Transl. by Jonathan Griffin. 206 p., 45 pl. London: Thames & Hudson, 1960. [CB 90/524]

BIDDLE, Moncure. A Christmas letter: some flower books and their makers. 49 p., 16 pl. Philadelphia: Moncure Biddle, 1945.
Illustrating the evolution of botanical iconography.

BLUNT, Wilfrid. The art of botanical illustration. *Advanc.Sci.*, 1960, 16: 402-11.

BLUNT, Wilfrid. The art of botanical illustration. With the assistance of William T. Stearn. xxxi, 304 p. (New Naturalist Series, 14) London: Collins, 1950; New York: Scribner, 1951.
Reviewed by Sonia S. Wohl, *Isis*, 1952, 43: 295-6.

DARMSTAEDTER, Ernst. Der Naturselbstdruck. *Philobiblon*, 1930, 3: 373-9, 5 fig.

KÜSTER-GIESSEN, Ernst. Ueber die Zeichnungen der Blätter und Blüten. iv, 83 p., 62 ill. (*Fortschr.Naturwiss.Forsch.*, 12: p. 71-153) Berlin: Urban und Schwarzenberg, 1926. [CB 21/578]

LANDAU, Paul. Das Blumenbildnis bei alten und neuen Meistern. 16 p., 47 ill. Berlin: Verlag der Gartenschönheit, 1929.
Reviewed by R. Zaunick, *Mitt.Gesch.Med.*, 1930, 29: 220-1.

MÖBIUS, Martin. Handgemalte Pflanzenbilder der Senckenbergischen Bibliothek in Frankfurt a. M. *Sudhoffs Arch.*, 1941, 33: 187-205.

NISSEN, Claus. Die botanische Buchillustration; ihre Geschichte und Bibliographie. 2 vol. viii, 264 p.; viii, 324 p. Stuttgart: Hiersemann, 1951.
Reviewed by Sonia S. Wohl, *Isis*, 1952, 43: 295-6; by M. Rooseboom, *Arch.Int.Hist.Sci.*, 1952, 5: 408-12.

NISSEN, Claus. Über Botanikmalerei. *Atlantis*, 1963, 35: 349-68.
Discusses and illustrates published and unpublished botanical illustrations from the 15th to the early 19th centuries.

NOTES on the history of botanical illustration. By E.A. *Missouri Bot.Gard.Bull.*, 1937, 25: 83-7, 3 fig.

PFISTER, Arnold. Die Pflanze und das Buch. *Librarium*, 1963, 6: 147-84.
Botanical illustration in old manuscripts and prints.

TIBERGHIEN, Albert. Phytotypie et phytotypes. Notice sommaire, bibliographique et historique sur l'impression des plantes à l'aide des plantes elles-mêmes. *Bull.Soc.Bot.Belg.*, 1931, 64: 81-91.

TREVIRANUS, Ludolf Christian. Die Anwendung des Holzschnittes zur bildlichen Darstellung von Pflanzen, nach Entstehung, Blüthe, Verfall und Restauration. (Leipzig 1855) vi, 75 p. (Classics of Natural History Reprint, 1) Utrecht: W. de Haan; Amsterdam: A. Asher, 1949.
Deals chiefly with the sixteenth and seventeenth centuries, with some information on the eighteenth. Index of artists, botanists, and printers added to the original work.

WEGENER, Hans. Das Pflanzenbild und die Anfänge der wissenschaftlichen Botanik. *Abhandlungen zur Wissenschaftsgeschichte und Wissenschaftslehre*, (1), p. 43-56. (Veröffentlichungen der Gesellschaft für Internationale Wissenschaftsgeschichte, 1951, no. 1) Bremen: Carl Schünemann, [n.d.].

Kd biography

Kda

BARNHART, John Hendley. Some fictitious botanists. *J.N.Y. Bot.Gard.*, 1919, 20: 171-81.
Apropos of 14 biographies of botanists, included in Appleton's Cyclopedia of American biography (1887-89), which are entirely fictitious!
Reviewed by M.C. Schindler, *Amer.Hist.Rev.*, 1937, 42: 680-90.

BUSH-BROWN, Louise. Men with green pens; lives of the great writers on plants in early times. 161 p. Philadelphia: Dorrance, 1964.

GUNDERSEN, Alfred. Some early botanists. 4 p. (*Brooklyn Bot.Gard.Leafl., ser. 4,* 13) Brooklyn: 1916.

INTERNATIONAL address book of botanists: being a directory of individuals and scientific institutions, universities, societies, etc., in all parts of the world interested in the study of botany. Prepared in accordance with a resolution passed at the Fifth International Botanical Congress, Cambridge, 1930. xv, 605 p. London: Baillière, Tindall, and Cox (for the Bentham Trustees), 1931.
Reviewed in *Nature,* 1932, 129: 563.

VERDOORN, Frans. On the aims and methods of biological history and biography. With some notes for the collaborators of the "Index Botanicorum". *Chron.Bot.,* 1944, 8: 427-8, ill.

Kdaj

KNOBLOCH, Irving William, ed. Selected botanical papers. xiv, 311 p. Englewood Cliffs, N.J.: Prentice-Hall, 1963.
58 selected papers, mostly on modern discoveries, but some from earlier, historically important works.
Reviewed by Conway Zirkle, *Science,* 1963, 141: 1169.

Kf/h history of botany: study; teaching; special aspects

Kfd

FOR biographies and bibliographies of individual historians of botany *see* Baranov, Pavel Aleksandrovich, 1: 108; Hamshaw Thomas, Hugh, 1: 536.

Kgg

SETCHELL, William Albert. History of botany. Tentative outline to be critically examined, criticized and verified or amended. 34 p. (Course at the University of California, Botany 150) Berkeley, Calif.: 1930.
Mimeographed. Very interesting syllabus of this course with chronological summaries and bibliographies.

Khd

VERDOORN, Frans. Problems of botanical historiography. *Act. VIe Congr.Int.Hist.Sci.* (Amsterdam, 1950), p. 297-306. Paris: Hermann, 1951. Also in *Arch.Int.Hist.Sci.,* 1951, 4: 448-57.

Khj

HAGBERG, Knut. Carl Linnaeus. Den linneanska traditionen. [The Linnean tradition. (In Swedish)] 148 p., ill., portr., map. Stockholm: Natur och Kultur, 1951.
Reviewed by Nils von Hofsten, *Lychnos,* 1952, 413.

Kk philosophy and methodology

BELIN-MILLERON, J. L'histoire des hypothèses de la fleur et la philosophie des sciences. *Congr.Int.Phil.Sci.* (Paris, 1949), (8), p. 59-67. (Actualités Scientifiques et Industrielles, 1166) Paris: Hermann, 1952.

BORZI, Antonino. Problemi di filosofia botanica. 344 p. Roma: Bardi, 1920.
Deals chiefly with ecological problems.

TANSLEY, Arthur George. The unification of pure botany. *Nature,* 1924, 113: 85-8. [CB 16/292]

WARDLAW, C.W. Unification of botanical science. *Nature,* 1944, 153: 125-30.

Kkn

PLANTEFOL, Lucien; PRÉVOST, Anne-Marie. La notion d'étamine à travers ses diverses dénominations. *Rev.Phil.,* 1962, 152: 145-72. [CB 90/525]

Kkx

COMBES, Raoul. Biologie végétale et vitalisme. *Cah.Rationalistes,* 1933, 118-46.

KmzOF

DARWIN, Francis. The relation of botany to medicine. *Proc. 17th Int.Congr.Med.* (London, 1913), sect. 23, p. 345-8. London: Oxford University Press; Hodder & Stoughton, 1914.
On the light thrown by botanists on certain fundamental physiological problems.

Kn/o means of communication; teaching

Knb

KENK, Vida Carmen. The importance of plants in heraldry. *Econ. Bot.,* 1963, 17: 169-79.

Knh

BAILEY, L.H. How plants get their names. 181 p., ill. New York: Dover, 1963.

JUST, Theodor. The proper designation of the vascular plants. *Bot.Rev.,* 1945, 11: 299-309.

LANJOUW, J., ed. Botanical nomenclature and taxonomy. A symposium organized by the International Union of Biological Sciences with support of UNESCO at Utrecht, the Netherlands, June 14-19, 1948. With a supplement to the international rules of botanical nomenclature, embodying the alterations made at the Sixth International Botanical Congress, Amsterdam, 1935, compiled by T. A. Sprague. *Chron.Bot.,* 1950, 12: 1-88,

MERRILL, E.D. On the significance of certain oriental plant names in relation to introduced species. *Proc.Amer.Phil.Soc.,* 1937, 78: 111-46.

VOSS, Andreas. Richtige Betonung der botanischen Namen. 2nd ed. 12 p. Berlin: Vossianthus Verlag, 1913.
First publ. 1912.

Knh-be

AHMED ISSA, bey. Dictionnaire des noms des plantes en latin, français, anglais et arabe. xiv, 227, 64 p. (Publication du Ministère de l'Instruction Publique d'Egypte) Cairo: Imprimerie Nationale, 1930.

ARTSCHWAGER, Ernest Friedrich; SMILEY, Edwina M. Dictionary of botanical equivalents. German-English, Dutch-English, Italian-English, by Ernest Artschwager; French-English, by Edwina M. Smiley. 2nd ed. 124 p. Baltimore: William and Wilkins, 1925.

BEDEVIAN, Armenag K. Illustrated polyglottic dictionary of plant names in Latin, Arabic, Armenian, English, French, German, Italian and Turkish languages including economic, medicinal, poisonous and ornamental plants and common weeds. With preface by W. Lawrence Balls. xv, 643, 455 p., ill. Cairo: Argus & Papazian Presses, 1936.

ZANDER, Robert. Handwörterbuch der Pflanzennamen und ihre Erklärungen. 2nd ed. 468 p. Berlin: Gärtnerische Verlagsgesellschaft, 1932.
First edition, 1927-28.

Ko

GRAVIS, A.; GOFFART, A. Méthodologie de la botanique à l'usage des écoles normales de l'enseignement moyen et des écoles normales de l'enseignement primaire. 697 p. Gand: I. Vanderpoorten, 1912.

STEVENS, Neil E. *See* Kce

Kp/s organizational and professional aspects; relations with society

Kpf

BAILEY, I.W. Cooperation versus isolation in botanical research. *Chron.Bot.* (*Biologia,* 1950-51), 1948-49, 12: (126-33).

Kq-bd

INTERNATIONAL address book of botanists: being a directory of individuals and scientific institutions, universities, societies, etc., in all parts of the world interested in the study of botany. Prepared in accordance with a resolution passed at the Fifth International Botanical Congress, Cambridge, 1930. xv, 605 p. London: Baillière, Tindall, and Cox (for the Bentham Trustees), 1931.
Reviewed in *Nature,* 1932, 129: 563.

Kqx

VERDOORN, Frans. The International Plant Science Congresses: their history and their aims. *Proc.VIIth Int.Bot.Congr.* (Stockholm, 1950), p. 42-56, 8 pl. Stockholm: Almqvist & Wiksell; Waltham, Mass.: *Chronica Botanica,* 1954.

Krd

STOCKBERGER, W.W. The social obligations of the botanist. *Science*, 1914, 39: 733-43.

Ks

ANDERSON, Edgar. Plants, man and life. 245 p., 16 ill. Boston: Little, Brown, 1952.
Reviewed by Conway Zirkle, *Isis*, 1953, 44: 81-2.

STEVENS, Neil E. *See* Kce

Ksc

BELIN-MILLERON, J. L'histoire des plantes, la formation de l'esprit scientifique et l'étude des civilisations. *Rev. Hist.Sci.*, 1951, 4: 78-84.

Kt/u relations with humanities; popular aspects

Kth

BAILEY, Liberty Hyde. My great oak tree and other poems. A keepsake issued by the editors of Chronica Botanica, for the members of the American Institute of Biological Sciences, attending the Cornell University Meetings, 8-10 September 1952. [10 p. Waltham, Mass.: 1952]

Ku

EXELL, A.W. Barometz: the vegetable lamb of Scythia. *Natur. Hist.Mag.*, 1932, 3: 194-200. [CB 37/595]

ROUHIER, Alexandre. Les plantes divinatoires. 32 p., ill. Paris: Doin, 1927.

SAINTYVES, P. Le thème du bâton sec qui reverdit: essai de mythologie liturgique. *Rev.Hist.Litt.Relig.*, 1912, 3: 330-49, 421-54.

SKINNER, Charles Montgomery. Myths and legends of flowers, trees, fruits, and plants in all ages and in all climes. Fifth impression, with additional illustrations. 302 p. Philadelphia: Lippincott, 1925.
First publ. 1911.

TEIRLINCK, Is. Flora Diabolica. De plant in de demonologie. [Flora diabolica. The plant in demonology. (In Dutch)] 322 p. Antwerpen-Santpoort: De Sikkel, 1924.

Kw in different countries

BERNARD, Charles J. La botanique coloniale et l'oeuvre du Professeur Melchior Treub. *Rev.Gén.Sci.*, 1935, 46: 631-7, 664-8.

Kwb North America

RODGERS, Andrew Denny, III. Liberty Hyde Bailey: a story of American plant sciences. 506 p., ill. Princeton, N.J.: Princeton University Press, 1949.
Reviewed in *Science*, 1949, 109: 406; by Conway Zirkle, *Isis*, 1950, 41: 242.

USHER, Robert James. Some notes on the botanical history of Louisiana. *Home Gard.* (New Orleans), 1941, 1: March no., 12-13, 19-20; April no., 12-13, 19-20; May no., 12-13.

WIGGINS, Ira L. Botanical investigations in Baja California. *Plant Sci.Bull.*, 1963, 9: no. 1, 1-6.
An account of the botanical explorations from 1696 to the present.

Kwb-da

GEISER, S.W. Some books about botanical explorers of the western part of the United States. *Field Lab.*, 1950, 18: 83-4.

HUMPHREY, Harry Baker. Makers of North American botany. 265 p. (Chronica Botanica, 21) New York: Ronald Press, 1961.
Reviewed by S. Earle Smith, *Econ.Bot.*, 1962, 16: 320-1.

REIFSCHNEIDER, Olga. Biographies of Nevada botanists, 1844-1963. 165 p., ill. Reno: University of Nevada Press, 1964.

Kwb-nj

KELLY, Howard Atwood. Some American medical botanists, commemorated in our botanical nomenclature. 216 p., portr., pl. New York: Appleton, 1929.

Kwb-oq

GAGER, C. Stuart. Wellesley College and the development of botanical education in America. *Science*, 1928, 67: 171-8.

TRANSCAU, Edgar N. The golden age of botany. *Science*, 1942, 95: 53-8.
Address of the retiring president of the Botanical Society of America, delivered at Dallas, Texas, on December 29, 1941. Mainly on the study of botany in American universities.

Kwb-qb

PEASE, Arthur Stanley. The New England Botanical Club a half century ago and later. *Rhodora*, 1951, 53: 97-105.

Kwb-rf

GREULACH, Victor A. Academic origin of American botanists. *Plant Sci.Bull.*, 1956, 2: no. 1, 4-7.

Kwc Latin America

MIGLIORATO GARAVINI, Erminio. Apontamentos e materiaes para um repertorio historico e bio-bibliographico da Botanica no Brasil. 1st fasc. 26 p. Roma: Tip. del Senato, 1913. [CB 13/283]

VERDOORN, Frans, ed. Plants and plant science in Latin America. xl, 384 p., 83 pl., ill. (A new series of plant science books, 16) Waltham, Mass.: Chronica Botanica, 1945. [CB 69/230]
Reviewed by Conway Zirkle, *Isis*, 1947, 37: 110-11.

Kwc-qd

VERDOORN, Frans; VERDOORN, J.G. Plant science institutions and societies of Latin America. In: Verdoorn, Frans, ed. Plants and plant science in Latin America, p. 337-49. Waltham, Mass.: Chronica Botanica, 1945.

Kwd Europe

ARBER, Agnes. On the history of European botany. *Chron.Bot.*, 1941, 6: 178-9.

Kwe British Isles

BOWER, Frederick Orpen. Sixty years of botany in Great Britain (1875-1935). Impressions of an eye-witness. xii, 112 p., 14 pl. London/New York: Macmillan, 1938.
Reviewed by Charles A. Kofoid, *Isis*, 1939, 31: 114.

GREEN, Joseph Reynolds. A history of botany in the United Kingdom from the earliest times to the end of the 19th century. xii, 648 p. London: Dent, 1914. [CB 8/357]

RAMSBOTTOM, J. Early botany at Oxford. *Nature*, 1940, 145: 993-6.

Kwe-cj

TURRILL, W.B. *Curtis's Botanical Magazine. Proc.VIIth Int. Bot.Congr.* (Stockholm, 1950), p. 83-7. Stockholm: Almqvist & Wiksell; Waltham, Mass.: Chronica Botanica Co., 1953.

Kwe-da

BRITTEN, James; BOULGER, George S. A biographical index of deceased British and Irish botanists. 2nd ed., revised and completed by A.B. Rendle. xxii, 342 p. London: Taylor and Francis, 1931. [CB 36/443]
Reviewed in *Nature*, 1932, 129: 563.
1st ed. 1893, with three supplements, 1899-1908.

GILMOUR, John. British botanists. 48 p., 27 ill. (Britain in Pictures) London: Collins, 1944. [CB 69/260]

GUNTHER, Robert William Theodore. Early British botanists and their gardens, based on unpublished writings of Goodyer, Tradescant and others. viii, 417 p. Oxford: priv. print., 1922.
Reviewed in *Nature*, 1922, 109: 806.

HORWOOD, Arthur Reginald; GAINSBOROUGH, Charles William Francis Noel, *earl of*. *See* KRE

OLIVER, F.W. Makers of British botany. A collection of biographies by living botanists. viii, 332 p., front., fig., 26 pl. Cambridge University Press, 1913.
Reviewed by George Sarton, *Isis*, 1913, 1: 282-4.

Kwf France

BECQUEREL, Paul. Les récents progrès de la biologie végétale en France. *Rev.Sci.*, 1923, 61: 675-87. [CB 15/212]

CHOUARD, Pierre. L'oeuvre de Léo Errera vue à travers la tradition botanique française. *Commémoration Léo Errera*, p. 85-90. Bruxelles: Institut Botanique Léo Errera, 1960.

COMBES, Raoul. Histoire de la biologie végétale en France. 169 p. (Bibliothèque de Philosophie Contemporaine) Paris: Alcan, 1933.

COUPIN, Henri. Coup d'oeil sur l'histoire de la botanique française. *Rev.Sci.*, 1929, 67: 449-57.

DAVY DE VIRVILLE, Adrien, *et al.* Histoire de la botanique en France. Préface de Roger Heim. Publié par le Comité du VIIIe Congrès International de Botanique, Paris-Nice, 1954. 395 p., ill. Paris: Société d'Edition d'Enseignement Supérieur, 1954. [CB 81/274]
Reviewed by J. Théodoridès, *Rev.Hist.Sci.*, 1955, 8: 189; by Nils von Hofsten, *Lychnos*, 1956, 419-20; by A. Delorme, *Rev.Syn.*, 1956, 77: 121-2.

Kwf-da

LACROIX, Alfred. Notice historique sur quatre botanistes, membres ou correspondants de l'Académie des Sciences, ayant travaillé pour la France d'Outre-Mer de la fin du siècle dernier à nos jours. Lecture faite en la séance annuelle du 19 décembre, 1938. 54 p. Paris: Gauthier-Villars, 1938.
Notices relatives à Henri Lecomte, Henri Perrier de la Bâthie, Édouard Heckel et Henri Jumelle.

TRELEASE, William. Four generations of memorable botanists. *Sci.Mon.*, 1924, 19: 53-62, portr. [CB 21/579]
The Candolle family.

Kwg/wh Central Europe

Kwg-cj

VERDOORN, Frans. Farlow's interest in an international abstracting journal. *Farlowia*, 1945, 2: 71-82. [CB 69/200]
Botanisches Centralblatt.

VERDOORN, Frans. At the centenary of the *Botanische Zeitung*. *Chron.Bot.*, 1943, 7: 294-6, facs.
Botanische Zeitung, vol. 1-68. Berlin: Leipzig: 1843-1910.

Kwg-da

CASPARY, Robert. Lebensbeschreibungen ost- und westpreussischer Botaniker. Aus den hinterlassenen Aufzeichnungen ausgewählt v. Prof. Dr Carl Fritsch. *Festschrift zum 50 - jährigen Bestehen des Preussischen Botanischen Vereins*, p. 189-290. Berlin: Friedländer, 1912.

LEHMANN, Ernst. Schwäbische Apotheker und Apothekergeschlechter in ihrer Beziehung zur Botanik. 218 p., ill. Stuttgart: Hempe, 1951.
Reviewed by D.A. Wittop Koning, *Arch.Int.Hist.Sci.*, 1952, 5: 417-18.

Kwg-nh

EGLI, Martha. Benennungsmotive bei Pflanzen an schweizerdeutschen Pflanzennamen untersucht. (Diss., Zurich) iv, 156 p. Bülach: Steinemann-Scheuchzer, 1930.
Reviewed by H. Marzell, *Mitt.Gesch.Med.*, 1931, 30: 105.

LOEWE, Richard. Germanische Pflanzennamen. Etymologische Untersuchungen über Hirschbeere, Hindebeere, Rehbockbeere und ihre Verwandten. xiii, 182 p. Heidelberg: C. Winter, 1913.

MARZELL, Heinrich. Die Tiere in deutschen Pflanzennamen. Ein botanischer Beitrag zum deutschen Sprachschatze. xxvi, 235 p. Heidelberg: C. Winter, 1913.

Kwg-th

RELING, Hermann; BROHMER, P. Unsere Pflanzen in Sage, Geschichte und Dichtung. 5th ed. 3 vol. viii, 106 p.; iv, 128 p.; iv, 120 p. Dresden: Ehlermann, 1922.

Kwg-u

BECKER, Kuno. Märkische Pflanzen im Volksaberglauben. *Brandenburgia*, 1931, 40: 64-6.

MARZELL, Heinrich. Bayerische Volksbotanik. Volkstümliche Anschauungen über Pflanzen im rechtsrheinischen Bayern. xxiv, 252 p. Nürnberg: Lorenz Spindler, 1926.

MARZELL, Heinrich. Die heimische Pflanzenwelt im Volksbrauch und Volksglauben. 134 p. (Wissenschaft und Bildung, 177) Leipzig: Quelle und Meyer, 1922.

MARZELL, Heinrich. Die Pflanzen im deutschen Volksleben. 96 p., 17 ill. (Deutsche Volkheit, 11) Jena: Diederichs, 1925.

MARZELL, Heinrich. Volksbotanik. Die Pflanze im deutschen Brauchtum. 195 p., pl. Berlin: Verlag der Deutschen Arbeitsfront, 1935.

NIESSEN, Joseph. Rheinische Volksbotanik. Die Pflanzen in Sprache, Glaube und Brauch des rheinischen Volkes. 2 vol. 1. Die Pflanzen in der Sprache des Volkes. 276 p.; 2. Die Pflanzen im Volksglauben und Volksbrauch. 341 p., 1 pl., 52 fig. Berlin: Dümmler, 1936-37.

SÖHNS, Franz. Unsere Pflanzen. Ihre Namenerklärung und ihre Stellung in der Mythologie und im Volksglauben. 6th ed. iv, 128 p. Leipzig: Teubner, 1921.
First publ. 1897.

STARCK, Adolf Taylor. Der Alraun. Ein Beitrag zur Pflanzensagenkunde. vii, 85 p. (New York University, Ottendorfer Memorial Series of Germanic Monographs, 14) Baltimore: Furst, 1917.

Kwg-u-bv

MARZELL, Heinrich. Volksbotanik 1905-1908: Die Pflanzen im Aberglaube, in Sage, im Volksbrauch und in Volkssitte: volkstümliche Pflanzennamen. *Justs Bot.Jahresber.*, 1911, 39: section 1, 1054-72.
Critical analysis of 106 articles published on folk botany published 1905-8.

Kwh

DRUCE, Gerald. Some early Czech contributions to botany. *Nature*, 1943, 151: 98-100.

HRYNIEWIECKI, Boleslaw. Rozwój botaniki w Polsce. [The development of botany in Poland. (In Polish with summary in French)] 53 p. (Polska Akademia Umiejetności, Historia Nauki Polskiej w Monografiach, 8) Cracow: 1948.

Kwh-nh

WALLMÉN, O. Alte tschechische Pflanzennamen und Rezepte im Botanicon Dorstens. Eine kulturgeschichtliche und sprachliche Untersuchung. 176 p. (Etudes de Philologie Slave Publiées par l'Institut Russe de l'Université de Stockholm, 5) Uppsala: Almqvist och Wiksell, 1954.
Reviewed by H. Marzell, *Sudhoffs Arch.*, 1956, 40: 187-8.

Kwh-oq

SZAFER, Władysław. Zarys historii botaniki w Krakowie na tle sześciu wiekow Uniwersytetu Jagiellonskiego. [Concise history of botany in Cracow - Jagellonian University, 600th anniversary. (In Polish with English summary)] 169 p., ill. Cracow: Jagellonian University's Editions, 1964.

Kwi Italy

Kwi-bv

BÉGUINOT, Augusto. La botanica. 116 p. (Guide "ICS": profili bibliografici de "L'Italia che scrive", 3) Roma: Istituto per la propaganda della cultura italiana, 1920. [CB 10/192]

Kwi-nh

PEDROTTI, G.; BERTOLDI, V. Nomi dialettali delle piante indigene del Trentino e della Ladina Dolomitica. Presi in esame dal punto di vista della botanica, della linguistica e del folclore. xii, 588 p., ill. Trenta: Monauni, 1930.
Reviewed by H. Marzell, *Mitt.Gesch.Med.*, 1931, 30: 35-6.

Kwi-u

PENZIG, Otto. Flora popolare italiana. Raccolta dei nomi dialettali delle principali piante indigene e coltivate in Italia. 2 vol. xvi, 542 p.; 616 p. Genova: Tipolitografia del R. Istituto Sordomuti, 1924.

Kwk Low Countries

LEFORT, François Léon. Contribution à l'histoire botanique du Luxembourg. *Bull.Soc.Natur.Luxembourgeois*, 1949, 43: 31-160, 18 pl.
Elaborate, well documented and well illustrated history of botany in the Grand Duchy of Luxemburg.

WILDEMAN, Emile de. Notes pour l'histoire de la botanique et de l'horticulture en Belgique. 832 p. (*Mém.Acad.Roy.Belg. Cl.Sci.*, 25) Bruxelles: 1950. [CB 78/188]

Kwk-ce

BALIS, Jan. Hortus Belgicus. 87 p., 6 pl., 16 fig. Brussels: Bibliothèque Albert I, 1962. [CB 90/524]
A study of 75 botanical books, each in some way connected with Belgium and exhibited at the Bibliothèque Royale, Brussels, in August 1962.

Kwk-da

GEORLETTE, René. Quelques botanistes belges. 83 p., 1 portr. (Collection Nationale, 95) Bruxelles: Office de Publicité, 1949.

WILDEMAN, Emile de. A propos de Belges dans l'histoire de la botanique. *Bull.Acad.Roy.Belg.Cl.Sci.*, 1945, 31: 433-58.

Kwk-oq

OYE, P. van. De plantkunde aan de Universiteit te Gent vóór de benoeming van J. MacLeod tot Professor in de Botanie. [Botany at the University of Ghent before the naming of J. MacLeod as Professor of Botany. (In Dutch)] 6, 29 p., 27 pl. (*Mededeel.Vlaam.Acad.Wetensch.Lett.Schoone Kunsten Belg. Kl.Wetensch.*, jaarg. 22) Brussel: 1960.
Reviewed by L. Elaut, *Sci.Hist.*, 1961, 3: 46-7.

Kwk-qd

WILDEMAN, Émile de. Crépin. La Société royale de Botanique de Belgique et le Jardin Botanique de l'État. Commémoration du 100e anniversaire de la naissance de François Crépin. *Bull. Jard.Bot.État,* 1931, 9: 66-77.

Kwk-qg

DUVIGNEAUD, P. Le laboratoire de botanique systématique et de phytogéographie de l'Institut Botanique Léo Errera. *Commémoration Léo Errera,* p. 135-94. Bruxelles: Institut Botanique Léo Errera, 1960.

Kwm Scandinavia

CHRISTENSEN, Carl. Den danske Botaniks Historie med tilhörende Bibliografi. [History of Danish botany with bibliography. (In Danish)] 2 vol. 1. Den danske Botaniks Historie fra de äldste Tider til 1912. 884 p., ill.; 2. Bibliografi. 580 p. Köbenhavn: Hagerup, 1924-26.
Reviewed by Axel Garboe, *Archeion,* 1928, 9: 532.

FRIES, Rob. E. A short history of botany in Sweden. With contributions by K.V. Ossian Dahlgren, Arne Müntzing, Börje Åberg and Hugo Osvald. 162 p., ill., front., 2 maps. (Seventh International, Botanical Congress, Stockholm, 1950) Uppsala: Almqvist & Wiksells, 1950.
Reviewed by Sten Lindroth, *Lychnos,* 1952, 420-1.

Kwm-ce-bv

CHRISTENSEN, Carl. Den danske botaniske Litteratur. Bibliographia Botanica Danica 1912-1939. [Danish botanical literature. (In Danish)] 350 p. København: Munksgaard, 1940.
Reviewed by Otto Gertz, *Lychnos,* 1941, 397-8.

Kwm-oq

SVEDELIUS, Nils. Botaniska sektionen i Uppsala 75 år. En återblick på sektionens äldre historia. [75 years of the history of the Botanical Department at Uppsala. (In Swedish)] *Svensk Bot.Tidskr.*, 1940, 34: 173-233.
Reviewed by Nils Hylander, *Lychnos,* 1943, 383-5.

Kwn Russia

SHCHERBAKOVA, A.A. Razvitie botanicheskikh znanii v Rossii do XVIII veka. [Development of botanical knowledge in Russia before the eighteenth century. (In Russian)] *Tr.Inst.Ist. Est.Tekh.*, 1961, 36: 136-75.
A substantial survey of herbals and the like. Extensive bibliography of manuscripts as well as printed materials.

Kwn-bv

ASMOUS, Vladimir C. Fontes historiae botanicae rossicae. *Chron.Bot.*, 1947, 11: 87-118, 4 pl., ill. [CB 73/174]
Bibliography of publications dealing with the history of botany in Russia.

Kwn-oq

POTAPENKO, G.I. Materialy po istorii botaniki v Odesskom Universitete (iz vospominanii). [Materials on the history of botany at the University of Odessa; reminiscences. (In Russian)] *Tr.Inst.Ist.Est.Tekh.*, 1962, 41: 44-62. [CB 88/533]
From the late 19th century to 1940.

Kwq/wx non-European countries

Kwq

MAIRE, René. Les progrès des connaissances botaniques en Algérie depuis 1830. 227 p., 8 pl. (Collection du Centenaire de l'Algérie) Paris: Masson, 1931.

Kwx

ROBYNS, W. Les connaissances actuelles en botanique congolaise. *Rapp.Annu.Inst.Rech.Sci.Afr.Cent.*, 1948, 1: 153-94.

WILDEMAN, Emile de. La botanique congolaise depuis 1830. *Compt.Rend.Ier Congr.Nat.Sci.* (Bruxelles, 1930), p. 711-14. Bruxelles: Secrétaire Général, [?1931].

Kwx-nh-be

GREENWAY, P.J. A Swahili dictionary of plant names. xvi, 112 p. Dar es Salaam: Government Printer, 1937.
Reviewed in *Nature,* 1938, 142: 498.

Kxx herbariums

BRITISH MUSEUM (NATURAL HISTORY). Department of Botany. The Sloane herbarium. An annotated list of the horti sicci composing it; with biographical accounts of the principal contributors. Based on records compiled by the late James Britten. Rev. and ed. by J.E. Dandy. 246 p., pl. London: The Museum, 1958.
Reviewed by W.B. Turrill, *Nature,* 1958, 182: 752-3; by Conway Zirkle, *Isis,* 1959, 50: 492-3; by Gunnar Eriksson, *Lychnos,* 1960-61, 361-2.

BUXANT, Fernand. Les herbiers du Musée d'Histoire Naturelle de la ville de Mons. *Bull.Soc.Natur.Mons Borinage,* 1961, 44: (5-6), 53-65.

CENTENARY of the Herbarium and Library, Royal Botanical Gardens, Kew. *Nature,* 1953, 171: 1086-7.

MERRILL, E.D. Destruction of the Berlin Herbarium. *Science,* 1943, 98: 490-1.

RAMSBOTTOM, J. Exhibition of historical collections in the department of botany. *Natur.Hist.Mag.*, 1930, 2: 266-70.
Notes on the growth of the plant collections, [in the British Museum] from the purchase of the Sloane collections in 1753 until the formation of the botany branch of the natural history department in 1835.

SCHUSTER, Julius. Das Herbarium in der Vergangenheit, Gegenwart und Zukunft. *Herbarium,* 1919, no. 50, 504-10. [CB 12/627]

SHINNERS, Lloyd H. Early plant collections return to Texas. *Field Lab.*, 1949, 17: 66-8.
Chiefly apropos of the collections in the Herbarium, Southern Methodist University.

Kxy botanical gardens

for physic gardens *see* RPxy

see also Royal Botanic Gardens, Kew, 2: 746.

BORN, Wolfgang. The garden in history. Early botanical gardens. Modern botanical gardens in Europe and the tropics. Botanical gardens in America. *Ciba Symp.*, 1949, 11: 1094-119, ill.

BURKILL, H.M. The Botanic Gardens, Singapore, 1859-1959. *Nature,* 1959, 184: 1602-4.

CHATTERJEE, D. Early history of the Royal Botanic Garden, Calcutta. *Nature,* 1948, 161: 362-4.

COATS, Peter. Great gardens of the Western World. Introd. by Harold Nicholson. 288 p., ill., 40 pl. London: Weidenfeld & Nicolson; New York: Putnam, 1963. [CB 90/524]
A description of 38 gardens in which much historical material is included.

GAGER, C. Stuart. Botanic gardens of the world. Materials for a history. 2nd ed. *Brooklyn Bot.Gard.Rec.*, 1938, 27: 151-406.
First ed. *Brooklyn Bot.Gard.Rec.*, 1937, 26: 149-353.
Reviewed by Conway Zirkle, *Isis*, 1938, 29: 185-6.

GAGER, C. Stuart. Who established the Elgin Botanic Garden? *Science*, 1942, 96: 439-41.

HARANT, Hervé. The Montpellier botanical garden. *Endeavour*, 1954, 13: 97-100, 5 fig.
An important botanical center since the early sixteenth century.

HARANT, Hervé. Notice historique sur le Jardin Botanique de Montpellier. *Année Biol.*, 1953, 29: 267-73.
Reviewed by J. Théodoridès, *Rev.Hist.Sci.*, 1954, 7: 189.

HEINRICHER, E. Geschichte des Botanischen Gartens der Universität Innsbruck. 36 p., 5 pl. Jena: Fischer, 1934.

HUNKIN, J.W. The garden at Tresco. *Endeavour*, 1949, 8: 125-9.
An account of a remarkable botanic and flower garden which has been developed on one of the Scilly Islands during the past hundred years.

JACK, J.G. The Arnold Arboretum. Some personal notes. *Chron. Bot.* (*Biologia*, 1950-51), 1948-49, 12: (4-6), 185-200.

KARSTEN, Mia C. The Old Company's garden at the Cape and its superintendents. Foreword by R.H. Compton; also a paper, "On some drawings of South African Proteaceae ascribed to Jan Hartog in the Herbarium at Leyden", by S.J. van Ooststroom. xvi, 188 p., 33 pl. Cape Town: Maskew Miller, 1951.
Reviewed by Conway Zirkle, *Isis*, 1952, 43: 296-7.

LACROIX, Alfred. Une famille de bons serviteurs de l'Académie des sciences et du Jardin des plantes, les Lucas. *Bull.Mus. Nat.Hist.Natur.*, 1938, 10: 446-71. [CB 56/348]

MALLET, Robert. Jardins et paradis. 94 p., 166 pl. Paris: Gallimard, 1959. [CB 90/524]

NEKRASOVA, V.L. [The Gorenski Botanical Garden. (In Russian)] *Tr.Inst.Ist.Est.*, 1949, 3: 330-50.

OSBORN, T.G.B. The Oxford Botanic Garden. *Endeavor*, 1951, 10: 70-7.
The Garden was founded in 1621 by Henry, *Earl of Danby*.

OSTENFELD, C. Hansen. Botanisk have gennem 50 aar. 1874-1924. [The Botanical Gardens during 50 years, 1874-1924. (In Danish)] 101 p. Kobenhavn: G.E.C. Gads Forlag, 1924.
Reviewed in *Nature*, 1925, 115: 210.

PURSEGLOVE, John W. History and functions of botanic gardens with special reference to Singapore. *Trop.Agr.*, 1957, 34: 165-89. [CB 90/509]

REINDL, Joseph. Ehemalige zoologische und botanische Gärten in Bayern. *Arch.Gesch.Naturwiss.Tech.*, 1912, 4: 79-86.

RODRIGUEZ, Lorenzo. The botanical garden of Manila and Sebastian Vidal y Soler. *Unitas* (Manila), 1962, 35: 258-77.
A history of the garden, its organization and its directors.

SCHMID, Günther. Aus der Frühgeschichte des botanischen Gartens in München. *Arch.Gesch.Med.*, 1938, 31: 148-64.

SCHMID, Günther. Zur Inschrift des Portals am ehemaligen botanischen Garten in München. *Sudhoffs Arch.*, 1942, 35: 238-42, 1 ill.

SENCHENKOVA, E.M. Zhemchuzhina Tavridy (150 let so dnia sozdania Gosudarstvennogo Nikitskogo Botanicheskogo Sada). [Pearl of the Tavridy. 150 years since the founding of the State Nikitsky Botanical Garden. (In Russian)] *Priroda*, 1962, no. 12: 78-82. [CB 88/631]

SPRINGER, Leonard F. Hartekamp på Linnés tid och dess senare öden. [Hartekamp in the days of Linnaeus and its later fortunes. (In Swedish)] *Svenska Linné-Sällsk.Årsskr.*, 1936, 19: 59-66. [CB 48/520]
Apropos of Clifford's garden at Hartekamp where Linnaeus spent two years of his stay in Holland as superintendent.

THIERY, L. Michel. Bij de 150e verjaring van de Plantentuin der Universiteit te Gent (1797-1947) [The 150th anniversary of the Botanical Garden of the University of Ghent. (In Dutch)] 461 p., pl. Gent: Snoeck-Ducaju, 1947. [CB 72/273]

VEENDORP, Hesso; BAAS BECKING, L.G.M. 1587-1937 Hortus Academicus Lugduno Batavus. The development of the gardens of Leyden University. 218 p., ill. Haarlem: Typographia Enschedaiana, 1938.
Reviewed in *Nature*, 1938, 142: 1013-15.

VERDOORN, Frans. L'arboretum moderne. *Nat.Can.*, 1952, 79: 189-97.

VERDOORN, Frans. Botanical gardens and arboretums of the past and their reconstruction. *Année Biol.*, 1953, 57: 277-82.

WENT, Frits W. Notes from the Missouri Botanical Garden. *Plant Sci.Bull.*, 1962, 8: (2), 3-4.

WILDEMAN, E. de. J. Gillet, S.J., et le Jardin d'Essais de Kisantu (1866-1893-1943). *Mém.Inst.Colon.Belg.Sect.Sci. Natur.Méd.*, 1946, 15: fasc. 3, 119 p., 4 fig.

WYMAN, Donald. The arboretums and botanical gardens of North America. *Chron.Bot.*, 1947, 10: 395-482, 17 pl., fig., bibliogr.

KD/KN PLANT BIOLOGY

KD PLANT CHEMISTRY AND BIOCHEMISTRY

for plant growth substances *see* KKyKE

KREMERS, Edward, *et al.* Phytochemistry. 1. Introduction. *Bull.Univ.Wis.*, 1931, no. 1732, 3-18.

PETERS, Rudolph. Biochemical light upon an ancient poison: a lethal synthesis. *Endeavour*, 1954, 13: 147-54. [CB 81/275]
The toxic properties of the South African plant, *Dichopetalum cymosum*, is due to fluoracetic acid.

KDce

KREMERS, Edward. Phytochemical literature. *J.Amer.Pharm.Ass.*, 1932, 21: 360-5; 1934, 23: 803-10. [CB 42/586]

KDnh

KREMERS, Edward, *et al.* Phytochemical terminology. *J.Amer. Pharm.Ass.*, 1932, 21: 252-7; 1933, 22: 227-32. [CB 42/586]

KDwn

OPARIN, A.I.; SISAKIAN, N.M.; GEL'MAN, N.S. [Materials for the history of plant biochemistry in the USSR. (In Russian)] *Tr.Inst.Ist.Est.*, 1952, 4: 236-66.

SISAKIAN, N.M.; GEL'MAN, N.S. Les voies du développement de la biochimie des plantes en Russie. *Act.VIIIe Congr.Int. Hist.Sci.* (Florence, 1956), p. 856-9. Paris: Hermann, 1958.

KE

SCHOPFER, William Henri. Plants and vitamins. Authorized translation by Norbert L. Noecker. Foreword by W.J. Robbins. xiv, 300 p. (A new series of plant science books, 11) Waltham, Mass.: Chronica Botanica, 1943.

KG PLANT EVOLUTION

for evolution of fungi *see* KUyKG

BERNARD, Noel. L'evolution des plantes. xxxii, 314 p., ill. Paris: Alcan, 1916.

BERNARD, Noel. Principes de biologie végétale. xii, 212 p., 18 fig. Paris: Félix Alcan, 1921. [CB 12/627]

CAMPBELL, Douglas Houghton. The evolution of the land plants (Embryophyta). x, 731 p., 351 fig. Stanford, Calif.: Stanford University Press, 1940. [CB 60/153]

CLAUSEN, Jens Christian; KECK, David D.; HIESEY, William M. Experimental studies on the nature of species. Vol. 1-4. (*Publ.Carnegie Inst.Wash.*, 520, 564, 581, 615) Washington, D.C.: 1940, 1945, 1948, 1958. [CB 60/153]

MAGROU, J. La symbiose, facteur d'évolution dans le règne végétal. *Rev.Quest.Sci.*, 1948, 9: 340-71.

STEBBINS, G. Ledyard. Variation and evolution in plants. xx, 643 p., 55 fig. (Biological Series, 16) New York: Columbia University Press, 1950. [CB 77/375]
Reviewed by Conway Zirkle, *Isis*, 1951, 42: 83.

KH PLANT GENETICS; HYBRIDIZATION

for fungal genetics *see* KUyKH

BLARINGHEM, Louis. Les problèmes de l'hérédité expérimentale. 317 p. Paris: Flammarion, 1919.
Reviewed by L. Guinet, *Isis*, 1920, 3: 295-6.

CHOUARD, Pierre. Eléments de génétique et d'amélioration des plantes: 1. Les mécanismes de l'hérédité élémentaire ou factorielle. 137 p. (Les Cours du Conservatoire National des Arts et Métiers) Paris: Centre de Documentation Universitaire, 1951. [CB 79/179]

CLELAND, Ralph E. A botanical nonconformist. *Sci.Mon.*, 1949, 68: 35-41.
An account of the botanical history of Oenothera Lamarckiana, the plant in which De Vries discovered 'mutations'.

FOCKE, Wilhelm Obers. History of plant hybrids. *Monist*, 1913, 23: 396-417.

GOWEN, John W., ed. Heterosis. A record of researches directed toward explaining and utilizing the vigor of hybrids. ix, 552 p., fig. Ames, Iowa: Iowa State College Press, 1952. [CB 79/179]

HOMES, Jacques L.A. La greffe des plantes. 1. Aperçu historique. *Natur.Belg.*, 1961, 42: 409-20.

HUDSON, P.S. New plants for old. *Sci.Mon.*, 1949, 69: 404-7. [CB 76/400]
A description of the problem first faced by N.I. Vavilov.

INTERNATIONAL CONGRESS OF GENETICS, 4th, Paris, 1911. IVe Conférence internationale de génétique. Comptes rendus et rapports. Ed. by Philippe de Vilmorin. 571 p., 10 pl., fig. Paris: Masson, 1913.
On plant breeding and hybridisation.

MENDEL, Kurt. The development of our knowledge of transplantations in plants. *Act.VIIe Congr.Int.Hist.Sci.* (Jerusalem, 1953), p. 444-50. Paris: Hermann. [n.d.].

ROBERTS, Herbert Fuller. Plant hybridization before Mendel. xiv, 374 p., ill. Princeton: University Press, 1929.
Reviewed by Robert K. Nabours. *Science*. 1930. 72: 274-5.

STOMPS, Theodoor Jan. Fünfundzwanzig Jahre Mutationstheorie. Vortrag, gegen Jahresschluss 1929 gehalten für die Mitglieder der wissenschaftlichen Gesellschaft Diligentia im Haag. iii, 68 p., 2 fig. Jena: Fischer, 1931.
Translation of: Vijf en twintig jaren mutatietheorie. (In Dutch) 's Gravenhaage: Van Stockum, 1930.
Reviewed by R. Zaunick, *Mitt.Gesch.Med.*, 1932, 31: 128.

VRIES, Hugo Marie de. The principles of the theory of mutation. *Science*, 1914, 40: 77-84.
Address delivered at the University of Brussels, January 17, 1914.

VRIES, Hugo Marie de. The origin of the mutation theory. *Monist*, 1917, 27: 403-10.
The theory was formulated in 1900.

ZIRKLE, Conway. The beginnings of plant hybridization. xiii, 231 p., 8 pl. Philadelphia: University of Pennsylvania Press, 1935.
Reviewed by George Sarton, *Isis*, 1936, 25: 507-8.

KHce-bv

WARNER, Marjorie Fleming; SHERMAN, M.A.; COLVIN, E.M. A bibliography of plant genetics. 552 p. (United States Department of Agriculture Miscellaneous Publication 164) Washington: U.S. Govt. Print. Off., 1934.
A bibliography of 10,156 items. An adequate subject and author index makes the material easily available.

KHwm

ÅKERMAN, Åke, *et al.* Swedish contributions to the development of plant breeding. 111 p., 62 fig. (New Sweden tercentenary publications) Stockholm: Bonnier, 1938.
Reviewed by Charles A. Kofoid, *Isis*, 1939, 31: 113.

KI PLANT MORPHOLOGY

ARBER, Agnes. The interpretation of leaf and root in the angiosperms. *Biol.Rev.*, 1941, 16: 81-105.

BAILEY, Irving W. Contributions to plant anatomy. xxvi, 262 p., ill. (*Chron.Bot.*, 15) Waltham, Mass.: Chronica Botanica, 1954.

BECQUEREL, Paul. La découverte de la phyllorhize. Ses conséquences pour la morphologie et la biologie des plantes vasculaires. *Rev.Gén.Sci.*, 1922, 33: 101-10.
Apropos of the work of Gustave Chauveaud summarized in his book "La constitution des plantes vasculaires révélée dans leur ontogénie" (Paris: Payot, 1921).

FRANCÉ, Raoul-Heinrich. Die Pflanze als Erfinder. 76 p., ill. Stuttgart: Kosmos, Gesellschaft der Naturfreunde, 1920.

HAMSHAW THOMAS, H. A hundred years of plant morphology. *Nature*, 1951, 168: 312-14.

LEWIS, Frederic T. A geometric accounting for diverse shapes of 14-hedral cells: the transition from dodecahedra to tetrakeidecahedra. *Amer.J.Bot.*, 1943, 30: 74-81, 8 fig.

LEWIS, Frederic T. Haphazard as a factor in the production of tetrakaidecahedra. *Torreya*, 1943, 43: 4-5.

SCHOPFER, William Henri. Les débuts de l'anatomie végétale moderne. L'histoire du cambium. *Act.Ve Congr.Int.Hist.Sci.* (Lausanne, 1947), p. 159-68. Paris: Hermann, 1948. Also in *Arch.Int.Hist.Sci.*, 1948, 1: 270-9.

WARDLAW, C.W. The study of growth and form in plants. *Endeavour*, 1952, 11: 97-106, 11 fig. [CB 79/180]

KIk

ARBER, Agnes. The interpretation of the flower: a study of some aspects of morphological thought. *Biol.Rev.*, 1937, 12: 157-84.

ARBER, Agnes. The natural philosophy of plant form. xiv, 247 p., 46 fig. Cambridge University Press, 1950.
Reviewed by H.W. Rickett, *Isis*, 1950, 41: 322-3.

KInh

SCHOPFER, William Henri. Remarque bibliographique sur l'histoire du terme "Cambium". *Arch.Int.Hist.Sci.*, 1949, 2: 457-8.

KK PLANT PHYSIOLOGY

BENEDICT, Ralph C. The first experiment in plant physiology. *Science*, 1939, 89: 411-12. [CB 57/258]
Apropos of the experiment commonly ascribed to J.B. van Helmont, but anticipated by Cusanus and F. Bacon.

BOSE, Jagadish Chandra. Plant autographs and their revelations. xiv, 231 p. London: Longmans, Green, 1927.
Reviewed by C.J. Patten, *Nature*, 1927, 110: 919-20.

BRACKETT, F.S.; JOHNSTON, Earl S. New researches on the effect of light waves on the growth of plants. *Annu.Rep.Smithsonian Inst.for 1930*, p. 255-64, 3 pl., 1 fig. Washington, D.C.: 1931.

BUESS, Heinrich. Zur Frühgeschichte experimenteller Befruchtungsstudien, insbesondere der Mikropylenforschung. *Gesnerus*, 1945, 2: 173-91.

DANGEARD, Pierre-Augustin. Discours. Institut de France, Académie des sciences, séance publique annuelle du lundi 16 décembre 1935. *Compt.Rend.Acad.Sci.*, 1935, 201: 1233-46.
On the utilisation of light by vegetation.

GOEBEL, Karl. Die Entfaltungsbewegungen der Pflanzen und deren teleologische Deutung. Ergänzungsband zur Organographie der Pflanzen. 2nd ed. x, 565 p. Jena: Gustav Fischer, 1924.
First publ. 1920. Contains historical information.

GUILCHER, J.M. The hidden life of flowers. With photographs by R.H. Noailles. 93 p., pl. New York: Philosophical Library, 1954.
A collection of photographs depicting various phases of the reproductive process of a number of plants.

JOHNSON, Duncan S. The history of the discovery of sexuality in plants. *Science*, 1914, 39: 299-319; also in *Annu.Rep. Smithsonian Inst.for 1914*, p. 383-406. Washington, D.C.: 1915.

KONINGSBERGER, V.J. L'actualité des idées de Léo Errera dans le domaine de la croissance et de la morphogénèse des plantes. *Commémoration Léo Errera*, p. 91-7. Bruxelles: Institut Botanique Léo Errera, 1960.

KOSTYCHEV, S. Kostychev's chemical plant physiology. Authorized edition in English with editorial notes. Transl. and ed. by C.J. Lyon. xvi, 497 p., 45 fig., portr. Philadelphia: Blakiston, 1931. [CB 33/402]
Two sections of this work on photosynthesis and on fermentations contain historical reviews of their fields.

LEROY, Jean F. Histoire de la notion de sexe chez les plantes. 40 p., pl. (Conférences du Palais de la Découverte, 68) Paris: Université de Paris, 1959.

LORCH, Jacob. History of theories on the function of nectar. *Proc.10th Int.Congr.Hist.Sci.* (Ithaca, 1962), (2), p. 949-51. Paris: Hermann, 1964.

MILLER, Edwin C. Forty years of plant physiology. Some general impressions. *Science*, 1943, 97: 315-19.

REED, H.S.; DUFRÉNOY, J. La croissance, phénomène autocatalytique. *Rev.Gén.Sci.*, 1934, 45: 565-9.

SENCHENKOVA, E.M. Istoriia voprosa o roli vody kak istochnika kisloroda v protsesse fotosinteza. [A history of the question of the role of water as a source of oxygen in the process of photosynthesis. (In Russian)] *Vop.Ist.Est.Tekh.*, 1961, 11: 100-4.

SIRKS, M.J. Altes und Neues über die Bestäubung und Befruchtung der höheren Pflanzen. *Naturwiss.Wochenschr., new ser.*, 1915, 14: 729-40.

STILES, Walter. Modern views of the mechanism of carbon assimilation. *Scientia*, 1927, 41: 117-26; French transl. suppl., 62-70.

TRÖNDLE, Arthur. Geschichte des Atmungs- und Ernährungsproblems bei den Pflanzen. 107 p., ill. (*Veröffentl.Schweiz. Ges.Gesch.Med.Naturwiss.*, 4) Zürich: Orell Füssli, 1925. [CB 19/806]

UNGERER, E. Die Regulationen der Pflanzen. Ein System der ganzheitbezogenen Vorgänge bei den Pflanzen. 2nd enl. ed. xxiv, 363 p. (Monographien aus dem Gesamtgebeit der Physiologie der Pflanzen und der Tiere) Berlin: Springer, 1926. [CB 21/579]
First publ. 1919.

VERNALIZATION and photoperiodism. A symposium by A.E. Murneek [and others]. Foreword by Kenneth V. Thimann. xv, 196 p., 12 pl., ill. (Lotsya - A Biological Miscellany, 1) Waltham, Mass.: Chronica Botanica; New York: Stechert-Hafner, 1948. [CB 73/175]
The history of both fields.

WERTH, Emil. Wie alt ist die Erkenntnis der Sexualität der Pflanzen? (Zur Geographie und Geschichte der Kulturpflanzen und Haustiere, 1) *Ber.Deut.Bot.Ges.*, 1929, 47: 608-13, 1 fig.

KKwb-qg

WENT, Frits W. The experimental control of plant growth, with special reference to the Earhart Plant Research Laboratory at the California Institute of Technology. With contributions by W.C. Ashby [and others] xvii, 343 p., 25 pl., 71 fig., ill. (*Chron.Bot.*, vol. 17) Waltham, Mass.: *Chronica Botanica* Company, 1957.

KKwk-oq

HOMES, M.V. L'activité de l'école de physiologie végétale de l'Institut Botanique Léo Errera. *Commémoration Léo Errera*, p. 109-20. Bruxelles: Institut Botanique Léo Errera, 1960.

WEEVERS, Th. Fifty years of plant physiology. [1895-1945 at the University of Amsterdam] 308 p. Amsterdam: Scheltema & Holkema; Waltham, Mass.: Chronica Botanica, 1949.
Reviewed by Conway Zirkle, *Isis*, 1951, 42: 165; by D. Müller, *Centaurus*, 1950, 1: 93-4.

KKwn

BELOKON', I.P. Istoriia otkrytiia zakonomernosti Zalenskogo i noveishie issledovaniia po ee izucheniiu. [History of the discovery of Zalenskii's law and recent investigations concerning the study of it. (In Russian)] *Tr.Inst.Ist.Est.Tekh.*, 1961, 36: 305-9.
An aspect of the development of plant physiology in the U.S.S.R.

MAKSIMOV, N.A. [Outline of the history of plant physiology in Russia. (In Russian)] *Tr.Inst.Ist.Est.*, 1947, 1: 21-79.

KKyKE

AUDUS, L.J. Plant growth substances. xix, 465 p., 42 pl. London: Leonard Hill, 1953.
Reviewed by R.L. Wain, *Nature*, 1953, 172: 1117-18.

KL PLANT EMBRYOLOGY

LORCH, Jacob W. Gleanings on the naked seed controversy. *Centaurus*, 1959, 6: 122-8.

SOUÈGES, René. L'embryologie végétale. Résumé historique. 2 vol. 1. Iere époque: des origines à Hanstein (1870). 58 p.; 2. De Hanstein (1870) à nos jours. 57 p. (Actualités Scientifiques et Industrielles, 142, 175) Paris: Hermann, 1934.

WODEHOUSE, R.P. Pollen grains. Their structure, identification and significance in science and medicine. xv, 574 p., 123 fig., 14 pl., 6 tables. New York: McGraw-Hill, 1935.
Reviewed by Th. Just, *Amer.Midland Natur.*, 1936, 17: 574-5.

KLwn

BARANOV, P.A. Contribution of Russian botanists to the development of plant embryology. *Act.VIIIe Congr.Int.Hist. Sci.* (Florence, 1956), p. 839-42. Paris: Hermann, 1958.

KM PLANT CYTOLOGY

COMBES, Raoul. La vie de la cellule végétale. 2 vol. 216 p., 16 fig.; 220 p., 13 fig. Paris: Colin, 1927-29. [CB 22/274 and CB 27/553]

CONARD, A. Le phragmoplaste de Léo Errera. *Commémoration Léo Errera*, p. 121-34. Bruxelles: Institut Botanique Léo Errera, 1960.

ZIRKLE, Conway. The plant vacuole. *Bot.Rev.*, 1937, 3: 1-30. [CB 51/270]

KN PLANT ECOLOGY

BORZI, Antonino. *See* Kk

CLEMENTS, Frederic E.; LONG, Frances L. Experimental pollination: an outline of the ecology of flowers and insects. viii, 274 p., 17 pl. (*Publ.Carnegie Inst.Wash.*, 336) Washington, D.C.: 1923. [CB 16/288]
Includes a history of the subject.

FERNALD, M.L. Must all rare plants suffer the fate of Franklinia? *J.Franklin Inst.*, 1938, 226: 383-97.

GROSSMANN, H. Der Einfluss der alten Glashütten auf den schweizerischen Wald. *Ber.Geobot.Forschungsinst.Rübel Zürich*, 1933, 15-32. [CB 42/588]

KRAMER, Paul J. International symposium on the methods of plant eco-physiology. *Plant Sci.Bull.*, 1962, 8: no. 2, 4-5.

MAGROU, J. La symbiose chez les plantes. *Bull.Inst.Pasteur*, 1922, 20: 169-83, 217-32.
Apropos of Noël Bernard's theory and recent research.

PURSEGLOVE, J.W. Neotropical Botany Conference. *Plant Sci. Bull.*, 1962, 8: no. 3, 5-7.
Opening address to the Conference held in Trinidad, July 1-7, 1962.

RÜBEL, Eduard. Die Entwicklung der Pflanzensoziologie. *Vierteljahrsschr.Naturforsch.Ges.Zürich*, 1920, 65: 573-604. [CB 12/627]

RÜBEL, Eduard. Geographie der Pflanzen.(Soziologie) In: Handwörterbuch der Naturwissenschaften, 2nd ed., (4), p. 1044-71. Jena: Fischer, 1934.

RÜBEL, Eduard. Ueber die Entwicklung der Gesellschaftsmorphologie. *J.Ecol.*, 1920, 8: 18-40. [CB 12/627]

SMITH, William Wright. Plant invaders. *Year Book Roy.Soc. Edinb.*, 1946, 5-12.

KNwg-qg

Bericht über das Geobotanische Forschungsinstitut Rübel Zürich, 1918/1928, 1929-58. Zürich: 1929-59. Continued as: *Bericht des Geobotanischen Institutes der Eidgenössischen Technischen Hochschule, Stiftung Rübel*, 1959- Zürich: 1960-

KR PLANT GEOGRAPHY; FLORA

for tree geography *see* KXyKR

BLAKE, S.F.; ATWOOD, Alice C. Geographical guide to floras of the world. An annotated list with special reference to useful plants and common plant names. Part 1. Africa, Australia, North America, South America, and Islands of the Atlantic, Pacific, and Indian Oceans. 336 p. (United States Department of Agriculture. Miscellaneous publication 401) Washington: U.S. Govt. Print. Off., 1942.
No more published.

BOR, Eleanor. Adventures of a botanist's wife. 204 p., ill. London: Hurst and Blackett, 1952.

FAIRCHILD, David Grandison. The world was my garden. Travels of a plant explorer. Assisted by Elizabeth and Alfred Kay. xiv, 494 p., 130 pl. New York: Scribner, 1938. [CB 57/200]
Reviewed by Conway Zirkle, *Isis*, 1947, 32: 164-5.

HJORTH, Harriet. Blomstervandringar. 3 vol. 1. Värens och försommarens örter. 223 p. 2. Högsommarens örter. 230 p. 3. Eftersommarens örter. 257 p. [Floral excursions. 1. The plants of spring and early summer. 2. The plants of high summer. 3. The plants of autumn. (In Swedish)] Stockholm: Rabén & Sjögren, 1958-62.
Reviewed by Nils von Hofsten, *Lychnos*, 1959, 414; 1960-61, 375; 1962, 486-7.

JUEL, H.O., ed. Plantae Thunbergianae. Ein Verzeichnis der von Carl Peter Thunberg in Südafrika, Indien und Japan gesammelten und der in seinen Schriften beschriebenen oder erwähnten Pflanzen, sowie von den Exemplaren derselben, die im Herbarium Thunbergianum in Upsala aufbewahrt werden. 462 p., 1 portr., 1 map. Uppsala: Akademiska Boghandeln, 1918.

PETERS, Hermann. Aus der Geschichte der Pflanzenwelt in Wort und Bild. Hrsg. von der Gesellschaft für Geschichte der Pharmazie. 176 p. Mittenwald (Bayern): Nemayer, 1928. [CB 25/424]

TURRILL, William Bertram. Pioneer plant geography; the phytogeographical researches of Sir Joseph Dalton Hooker. x, 267 p., portr., map, 20 pl., facs., bibliogr. (Lotsya, a Biological Miscellany, 4; International Biohistorical Commission. Contributions, no. 1) The Hague: M. Nijhoff, 1953. [CB 80/196-7]

WILSON, Ernest Henry. Plant hunting. 2 vol., ill. Boston, Mass.: Stratford, 1927.

WULFF, Eugenii V. An introduction to historical plant geography. Authorized translation by Elizabeth Brissenden. Foreword by Elmer D. Merrill. xv, 223 p., 35 fig. (New Series of Plant Science Books, 10) Waltham, Mass.: Chronica Botanica, 1943.
Includes a history of plant geography (p. 10-24), beginning with C. Willdenow (1792).

KRu

ROLLAND, Eugène. Flore populaire; ou, Histoire naturelle des plantes dans leurs rapports avec la linguistique et le folklore. 11 vol. in 8. Paris: Rolland, 1896-1914.

KRB NORTH AMERICA

KINGSBURY, John M. Knowledge of poisonous plants in the United States - brief history and conclusions. *Econ.Bot.*, 1961, 15: 119-30.

SHREVE, Forrest. The plant life of the Sonoran desert. 19 p., ill. (Carnegie Institution of Washington, supplementary publications, 22) Washington, D.C.: 1936.
Lecture delivered at the Administration building of the Carnegie Institution of Washington, December 3, 1935. Reprinted from *Sci.Mon.*, 1936, 42: 195-213.

KRBwf-da

LES BOTANISTES Français en Amérique du Nord avant 1850. Colloque international du C.N.R.S., 63. Edited by J. Leroy. (Paris, 11-14 septembre 1956). 360 p., front., 32 pl. Paris: 1957. [CB 83/203]
Reviewed by Jean Théodoridès, *Arch.Int.Hist.Sci.*, 1958, 11: 296; by Gunnar Eriksson, *Lychnos*, 1960-61, 362.

LEROY, Jean. Les botanistes-explorateurs français en Amérique du Nord. *Isis*, 1957, 48: 64-5.

KRC LATIN AMERICA

GOODSPEED, T. Harper. Plant hunters in the Andes. 430 p. London: Hale, 1950.

REICHE, Karl. Geografía botánica de Chile. (Grundzüge der Pflanzenverbreitung in Chile. Leipzig 1907) Por el Dr. Karl Reiche traducido del alemán por Gualterio Looser con varias ampliaciones y notas del traductor. *Rev.Chilena Hist.Geogr.*, 1929, 62: no. 66, 127-605; 63: no. 67, 205-36.

KRD EUROPE

STEARN, William T. Bonnier and Douin's "Flore complète, illustrée ... de France, Suisse et Belgique". *J.Soc.Bibliogr. Natur.Hist.*, 1950, 2: 212-15.

KRDu

MARZELL, Heinrich. Die Alpenpflanzen im Volksglauben. Ein botanischer Beitrag zur Volkskunde der Alpenländer. *Jahrb. Ver.Schutze Alpenpflanzen*, 1931, 3: 24-35, 4 fig.

KRE

GILBERT-CARTER, H. Glossary of the British flora. xviii, 79 p. Cambridge University Press, 1950.
Reviewed by T.H. Savory, *Nature*, 1951, 167: 296.

HORWOOD, Arthur Reginald; GAINSBOROUGH, Charles William Francis Noel, *earl of*. The flora of Leicestershire and Rutland: a topographical, ecological, and historical account with biographies of former botanists (1620-1933). ccxcvii, 687 p., 36 pl. London: Oxford University Press, 1933.
Reviewed by E.N.M.T., *Nature*, 1934, 133: 158-9.

SALMON, Charles Edgar. Flora of Surrey: being an account of the flowering plants, ferns and characeae, with notes on the topography, climate and geology, and a history of the botanical investigation of the county. Edited by William Harrison Pearsall. 688 p. London: Bell, 1931.

KRF

THELLUNG, A. La flore adventice de Montpellier. *Mém.Soc. Sci.Natur.Cherbourg*, 1911-12, 38: 57-728.

KRM

DAHL, Svend. Den danske plante- og dyreverdens udforskning. [Exploration of the Danish flora and fauna. (In Danish)] 340 p., ill. København: Udvalget for Folkeoplysnings Fremme, 1941.
Reviewed by Nils von Hofsten, *Lychnos*, 1942, 396-7.

KRN

BARANOV, P.A. U istokov otechestvennoi botaniki. [On the sources of native botany. (In Russian)] 46 p. (Komarovskie chteniia, 7) Moscow: Akademiia Nauk SSSR, 1953.
Reviewed by B. Hryniewiecki (in Polish), *Kwart.Hist.Nauk. Tech.*, 1956, 1: 410-15.

KRO

BALDACCI, Antonio. Le fonti della flora albanese. *Boll.Soc. Adriat.Sc.Natur.Trieste*, 1926-27, 29: 27-48.

KRP ASIA MINOR

BLATTER, Ethelbert. Flora arabica, the botanical exploration of Arabia. *Rec.Bot.Surv.India*, 1933, 8: 451-501.

POST, George E. Flora of Syria, Palestine and Sinai: a handbook of the flowering plants and ferns, native and naturalized, from the Taurus to Ras Muhammad and from the Mediterranean Sea to the Syrian Desert. Second edition, extensively revised and enlarged by John Edward Dinsmore. 2 vol. (American University of Beirut: Publications of the Faculty of Arts and Sciences, Natural science series, 1) Beirut: American Press, 1932-3.
Volume 2 reviewed by W.B.T., *Nature*, 1934, 134: 440.

ZOHARI, Michael. Plant life in Palestine. 262 p. New York: Ronald, 1962.
Reviewed by M.F. Buell, *Plant Sci.Bull.*, 1963, 9: no. 2, 5-6.

KRQ NORTH AFRICA

EMBERGER, Louis; MAIRE, René. L'exploration botanique du Maroc du XVIIe au XIXe siècle. *Archeion*, 1934, 16: 168-80.

KRQwf-da

LACROIX, Alfred. Notice historique sur les membres et correspondants de l'Académie des Sciences ayant travaillé dans l'Afrique du Nord française depuis le XVIIIe siècle. Les botanistes. 58 p. (*Mém.Acad.Sci.*, 64) Paris: Gauthier-Villars, 1941.

KRR ASIA

KINGDON-WARD, Francis. Plant hunter in Manipur. 254 p. London: Cape, 1952.

KINGDON-WARD, Francis. A plant hunter in Tibet. 317 p. London: Cape, 1934.

KINGDON-WARD, Francis. Plant hunting and exploration in Tibet. *Nature*, 1936, 138: 516.

KINGDON-WARD, Francis. Plant hunting on the edge of the world. 383 p. London: Gollancz, 1930.

KRS

CHAKRABERTY, Chandra. A comparative Hindu materia medica. ii, 196, 11, 6 p. Calcutta: The author, 1923. [CB 16/266]
An introduction of 27 p. contains a summary of systematic botany and of the geographical botany of India.

EVANS, Geoffrey. Botany in India. *Nature*, 1943, 151: 580-1.

NARAYANASVAMI, V. Indian botany. Pt. 1. A-J. xlii, 370 p. (A Bibliography of Indology, 2) Calcutta: National Library, 1961.
Reviewed by K. Biswas, *Sci.Cult.*, 1962, 28: 369-70.

SANTAPAU, H. The botanical survey of India. *Sci.Cult.*, 1964, 30: 2-11, ill.

KRT

COX, E.H.M. Plant-hunting in China. A history of botanical exploration in China and the Tibetan Marches. 230 p., 24 ill., maps. London: Collins, 1945. [CB 70/237]

KINGDON-WARD, Francis. The romance of plant hunting. xi, 275 p., 7 pl. London: Arnold, 1924.
A record of experiences on plant hunting excursions in China.

WILSON, Ernest Henry. China, mother of gardens. x. 408 p., 40 pl., map. Boston, Mass.: Stratford, 1929.
Revised edition of the author's "A naturalist in western China", 1913.

KRTce-bv

GOODRICH, L. Carrington. Some bibliographical notes on Eastern Asiatic botany. *J.Amer.Orient.Soc.*, 1940, 60: 258-60.
Apropos of the bibliography by Elmer D. Merrill and Egbert H. Walker, *see* below.

MERRILL, Elmer D.; WALKER, Egbert H. A bibliography of Eastern Asiatic botany. xlii, 719 p. Jamaica Plain, Mass.: Arnold Arboretum, 1938. [CB 65/82]
Reviewed by Charles A. Kofoid, *Isis*, 1939, 31: 115-16; by John H. Barnhart, *Science*, 1939, 89: 297; by Paul H. Oehser, *Science*, 1939, 89: 342.

KRTwd

KOIDZUMI, Geniti. [The early history of European botanical observations on the flora of Japan. (In Japanese)] *Acta Phytotaxonom.Geobot.*, 1932, 1: 1-10.

KRV

FAIRCHILD, David. Garden islands of the great east. Collecting seeds from the Philippines and Netherlands India in the Junk, "Chêng Ho". xiv, 239 p., 125 ill. New York: Scribner, 1943.
Reviewed by Conway Zirkle, *Isis*, 1944, 35: 194-5.

LAM, H.J. Fragmenta Papuana [Observations of a naturalist in Netherlands New Guinea]. Translated from the Dutch by Lily M. Perry. iv, 196 p., 2 maps, 32 fig. (Sargentia 5) Jamaica Plain, Mass.: Arnold Arboretum of Harvard University, 1945. [CB 69/222]
Translation of seven articles originally published in *Natuurk.Tijdschr.Ned.Ind.*, 1927-29, vol. 87-89. The first comprehensive account of the flora of Western New Guinea.

SARTON, George. The botanical exploration of Malaysia. Second preface to volume 42. Science and peace II. *Isis*, 1951, 42: 173-6.
Apropos of Steenis-Kruseman, M.J. van. Flora Malesiana, *see* below.

SETCHELL, William A. American Samoa: 1. Vegetation of Tutuila Island. 2. Ethnobotany of the Samoans. 3. Vegetation of Rose Atoll. vi, 275 p., 37 pl., 57 textfig. (Papers from the Department of Marine Biology, 20) Washington, D.C.: Carnegie Institution, 1924. [CB 16/298]

STEENIS-KRUSEMAN, M.J. van. Flora Malesiana. Vol. 1. Malaysian plants: collectors and collections. Being a cyclopaedia of botanical exploration in Malaysia and a guide to the concerned literature up to the year 1950. clii, 639 p., ill. Djakarta/Groningen: Noordhoff-Kolff; Waltham, Mass.: Chronica Botanica, 1950.
Reviewed by G. Sarton, *Isis*, 1951, 42: 173-6.

KRX AFRICA

BEQUAERT, J. Esquisse de géobotanique congolaise. *Agron. Trop.*, 1913, 5: 17-32, 33-8.

SYNGE, Patrick M. Mountains of the Moon. xxiv, 221 p. New York: Dutton, 1938.
An account of an expedition to the equatorial mountains of Africa in search of plants, abundantly illustrated from photographs, sketches, and paintings. There is a discussion of some legends relating to the sources of the Nile.

KRY

HUTCHINSON, John. A botanist in Southern Africa. Foreword by Field Marshal Smuts. xii, 686 p., 49 pl. London: Gawthorn, 1946.
Reviewed by George Taylor, *Nature*, 1946, 157: 206-8.

KRYxy

KARSTEN, Mia C. The Old Company's garden at the Cape and its superintendent. Foreword by R.H. Compton: also a paper; On some drawings of South African proteaceae ascribed to Jan Hartog in the Herbarium at Leyden, by S.J. van Ooststroom. xvi, 188 p., 33 pl. Cape Town: Maskew Miller, 1951.
Reviewed by Conway Zirkle, *Isis*, 1952, 43: 296-7.

KS SYSTEMATIC BOTANY

BAEHNI, Charles. Beiträge zur Geschichte der botanischen Systematik. 2. Naissance et développement de la systématique moderne de Linné aux temps actuels. *Gesnerus*, 1947, 4: 127-45.

BAEHNI, Charles. Les grands systèmes botaniques depuis Linné. *Gesnerus*, 1957, 14: 83-93.

BARTLETT, Harley Harris; *et al.* The concept of the genus. *Bull.Torrey Bot.Club*, 1940, 67: 349-89. [CB 63/272]

CROIZAT, Leon. History and nomenclature of the higher units of classification. *Bull.Torrey Bot.Club*, 1945, 72: 52-75.
A short history of the attempt, between the time of the publication of Linnaeus' *Systema naturae* (1735) and the present, to arrange plants in a natural system.

GUNDERSEN, Alfred. A sketch of plant classification from Theophrastus to the present. *Torreya*, 1918, 18: 213-19, 231-9.

RYTZ, W. Beiträge zur Geschichte der botanischen Systematik. Wege zum Artbegriff. Von den Kräuterbüchern bis zu C. von Linné. *Gesnerus*, 1947, 4: 121-7.

SHARP, A.J. Responsibilities and opportunities of the taxonomist today. *Plant Sci.Bull.*, 1962, 8: no. 3, 7-9.

VERDOORN, Frans, ed. Plant genera, their nature and definition. A symposium by G.H.M. Lawrence, *et al.* With an introductory essay on generic synopses and modern taxonomy by Theodor Just. *Chron.Bot.*, 1953, 14: 89-160, front., ill.
The two introductory essays by the editor and Theodor Just contain much historical material.

KSsg

MERRILL, E.D. Some economic aspects of taxonomy. *Torreya*, 1943, 43: 50-64.

KT FLOWERLESS PLANTS

for fungi *see* KU

LENOIR, Jacques. L'equisétologie (studies on equisetum). *Rev. Trim.Can.*, 1950, 36: no. 143, 247-59. [CB 77/374]

SETCHELL, William Albert. Some early algal confusions. *Univ. Calif.Publ.Bot.*, 1931, 16: 351-66, 31 pl.
Includes valuable notes on the early algologists.

TILDEN, Josephine E. The algae and their life relations. Fundamentals of phycology. xii, 550 p., 1 pl., 257 fig. Minneapolis: University of Minnesota Press, 1935. [CB 52/594]
Contains an historical discussion of the hypothesis concerning the phylogeny of the algae.

VERDOORN, Frans. The future of exotic cryptogamic botany. *Bryologist*, 1950, 53: 1-9.

KTnh

SMITH, Gilbert M. The historical significance of names applied to reproductive structures of algae. *Farlowia*, 1947, 3: 217-24.

KTyKG

MANTON, I. Problems of cytology and evolution in the Pteridophyta. xii, 316 p., 279 fig. Cambridge University Press, 1950. [CB 77/374]
The opening chapter gives an account of the growth of knowledge in evolution and heredity since Darwin and Mendel.

KU MYCOLOGY

see also JR MICROBIOLOGY
QR MEDICAL MYCOLOGY
SD PLANT PATHOLOGY
SL GREEN VEGETABLES AND FUNGI

LÜTJEHARMS, Wilhelm Jan. Zur Geschichte der Mykologie. Das 18. Jahrhundert. xxi, 262 p., 2 pl. Gouda: Koch & Knuttel, 1936. [CB 62/78]
The subject is wider than the title suggests. It covers the history of mycology before the eighteenth century.

MACBRIDE, T.H.; MARTIN, G.W. The myxomycetes. A descriptive list of the known species with special reference to those of North America. xi, 339 p., 21 pl. New York: Macmillan, 1934. [CB 42/591]

RAMSBOTTOM, J. Historical survey of mycology. *Nature*, 1939, 143: 992-3.
Extract from the Presidential address delivered to the Linnean Society of London on May 24, 1939.

ROLFE, Robert Thatcher; ROLFE, F.W. The romance of the fungus world; an account of fungus life in its numerous guises, both real and legendary. Foreword by J. Ramsbottom. xx, 309 p., 31 pl. London: Chapman and Hall, 1925.

SHEAR, C.L. Mycology, scientific and otherwise. *Mycologia*, 1934, 26: 201-9, 1 portr. [CB 42/593]

KUce-bv

TAMIYA, H.; MORITA, S. Bibliographie von *Aspergillus* 1729-1928. *Bot.Mag.Tokyo*, 1929, 43: 60-71, 145-56, 179-89, 237-49, 281-91, 321-32, 371-81, 427-38, 501-15.

KUcm

ARNDT, W. Die ältesten bildlichen Darstellungen von Schwämmen. *Sitzungsber.Ges.Naturforsch.Freunde Berlin*, 1931, 125-54, 30 fig.
Reviewed by R. Zaunick, *Mitt.Gesch.Med.*, 1932, 31: 36.

KUnh

SHEAR, C.L. Uniformity and stability of mycological nomenclature. *Mycologia*, 1936, 28: 337-46.
Showing that historical investigations are essential for the stabilization of generic and specific names.

KUyKH

BEADLE, George W. Genes and chemical reaction in neurospora. The concepts of biochemical genetics began with Garrod's 'inborn errors' and have evolved gradually. *Science*, 1959, 129: 1715-19.

KV SEED AND FLOWERING PLANTS

for garden flowers *see* SN

BURDETT, Frederick David. The Odyssey of an orchid hunter. Edited and annotated by Percy J. King. 320 p., front., pl. London: Jenkins, 1931.

CROIZAT, Leon. The family Euphorbiaceae: when and by whom published. *Amer.Midland Natur.*, 1943, 30: 808-9.
Gives additional reference for Jaume-St. Hilaire's authorship of the genera. *See* Wheeler, Louis Cutter, below.

ERHARDT-SIEBOLD, Erika von. The heliotrope tradition. *Osiris*, 1937, 3: 22-46, 10 fig.

KRUMBIEGEL, Ingo. Die Akelei (Aquilegia). Eine Studie aus der Geschichte der deutschen Pflanzen. *Janus*, 1932, 36: 71-92, 129-45, 4 pl. [CB 39/459]

LAUFER, Berthold. Malabathron. *J.Asiatique, ser. 11*, 1918, 12: 1-49, 12 fig. [CB 8/357]

O'NEILL, Hugh. What is the true shamrock? *Nature*, 1946, 157: 704-6.

RENAUD, H.P.J. Introduction des cactus et autres cactacées en Europe. Answer to Query no. 33 (*Isis*, 1934, 20: 442) *Isis*, 1935, 24: 110-13.

SARTON, George. Introduction of cacti and other Cactaceae into Europe. Query no. 33. *Isis*, 1934, 20: 442.
For answer, *see* Renaud, H.P.J., above.

SCHIERBEEK, A. Vier hondred jaar Linaria onderzoek. [The study of Linaria during four centuries. (In Dutch)] 45 p., 8 fig. (Problemen der natuurwetenschap in hun historische ontwikkeling, 2) Utrecht: Uitgeberij het Spectrum, 1946.

SIRKS, M.J. Geschichtliches über Pelorienblüten. *Naturwiss. Wochenschr., new ser.,* 1915, 14: 228-31.

WHEELER, Louis Cutter. The genera of the living Euphorbieae. *Amer.Midland Natur.,* 1943, 30: 456-503.
For additional reference, *see* Croizat, Leon, above.

KVce-bv

INDEX Kewensis plantarum phanerogamarum. 4th supplement, 1906-10 - 12th supplement, 1951-55. Oxford: Clarendon Press, 1913-59.
In progress.
7th supplement reviewed in *Nature,* 1929, 124: 832.

KVu

MARZELL, Heinrich. Die Frühlingsblumen im antiken und neuzeitlichen Zauberglauben. *Mitt.Gesch.Med.,* 1933, 32: 299.

MARZELL, Heinrich. Die Orchideen in der sexuellen Volkskunde. *Geschlecht Ges.,* 1926, 14: 211-23.

KX TREES AND SHRUBS

for forestry *see* SO

BAKER, Richard St. Barbe. Green glory, the story of the forests of the world. With a foreword by Howard Spring. 239 p., pl. London: Lutterworth, 1948.

KXu

PORTEOUS, Alexander. Forest folklore, mythology, and romance. 319 p. London: Allen and Unwin, 1928. [CB 25/424]

KXyJO EFFECT OF CLIMATE

DOUGLASS, A.E. Climatic cycles and tree-growth. 3 vol. 1, 2. A study of the annual rings of trees in relation to climate and solar activity; 3. A study of cycles. (*Publ. Carnegie Inst.Wash.,* 289) Washington, D.C.: 1919-36. [CB 51/275]

DOUGLASS, A.E. Some aspects of the use of the annual rings of trees in climatic study. *Sci.Mon.,* 1922, 15: 1-22. Also in *Annu.Rep.Smithsonian Inst.for 1922,* p. 223-39. Washington, D.C.: 1924.

DOUGLASS, A.E. Tree rings and their relation to solar variations and chronology. *Annu.Rep.Smithsonian Inst.for 1931,* p. 304-13, 5 pl. Washington, D.C.: 1932.

FULLING, E.H. Plant life and the law of man. 1. Growth rings in the determination of age of trees. *J.N.Y.Bot. Gard.,* 1942, 43: 152-7.

GLOCK, Waldo S. Principles and methods of tree-ring analysis. With a foreword by A.E. Douglass and a contribution by G.A. Pearson. viii, 100 p., ill. Washington, D.C.: Carnegie Institution, 1937.

GLOCK, Waldo S. Tree growth: growth rings and climate. *Bot. Rev.,* 1955, 21: 73-188.
A detailed review of the problems involved in tracing past climatic variations by the study of the annual tree rings.

SARTON, George. When was tree-ring analysis discovered? *Isis,* 1954, 45: 383-4.

SCHOVE, D. Justin. Droughts of the Dark Ages and tree-rings (A.D. 714-835). *Weather,* 1955, 10: [1-4].

SCHULMAN, Edmund. Tree-rings and history in the western United States. *Econ.Bot.,* 1954, 8: 234-50.

STUDHALTER, R.A. Tree growth; some historical chapters. *Bot.Rev.,* 1955, 21: 1-72.
An account of the botanical factors in the growth of trees, together with the application of the annual growth rings to dating past climates and archeological remains.

KXyKR TREE GEOGRAPHY

KXyKRB

BAY, J. Christian. Bibliophili epistola quinta eller et bibliografisk besøg iblandt de Californiske kaempetraeer samt tvende exkurser. [Bibliophili epistola quinta, or, A bibliographical visit to the Californian giant trees, together with two digressions. (In Danish)] 21 p., 2 pl. Holstebro: Julen, 1939.
Apropos of the California Sequoias.

CHANEY, Ralph W. Redwoods around the Pacific Basin. *Pacific Discovery,* 1948, 1: 4-14, ill.

KXyKRD

RUBNER, K. Ergebnisse der neueren Baumrassenforschung in Mitteleuropa. *Scientia,* 1960, 95: 351-5.

KXyKRE

EDWARDS, Paul. Trees and the English landscape. 108 p., 18 pl., fig. London: G. Bell, 1962. [CB 90/585]

KXyKRG

FISCHER, Hermann. Zur ursprünglichen Verbreitung der Bäume in Bayern. *Mitt.Deut.Dendrol.Ges.,* 1928, 97-100.

KXyKRK

GOBLET D'ALVIELLA, Félix Albert Joseph, *comte.* Historie des bois et forêts en Belgique. Des origines à la fin du régime autrichien. 4 vol. xvi, 491 p.; xii, 351 p.; 140 p.; 448 p. Bruxelles: Lamertin; Paris: Lechevalier, 1927-30.
Reviewed in *Rev.Gén.Sci.,* 1927, 38: 483; by B.M.B., *ibid.,* 1931, 42: 282.

KXyKRKu

CHALON, Jean. Les arbres fétiches de la Belgique. 83 p., ill. Anvers: Buschmann, 1912.

KXyKRS

STEBBING, Edward Percy. The forests of India. 3 vol. 1. 1796 to 1864. xv, 548 p., 27 pl.; 2. The development of the Indian Forest Service, 1865 to 1900. xii, 633 p., 36 pl., map; 3. 1901 to 1920. London: John Lane, 1922-26.

KY SPECIFIC TREES AND SHRUBS

DETERING, Alfred. Die Bedeutung der Eiche seit der Vorzeit. viii, 198 p., 81 fig. Leipzig: Kabitzsch, 1939.
Reviewed by H. Marzell, *Mitt.Gesch.Med.,* 1939, 38: 330-1.

HOWARD, Alexander L. The ash tree. *Nature,* 1944, 154: 27-9.

HOWARD, Alexander L. The beech tree. *Nature,* 1944, 154: 492-4.

HOWARD, Alexander L. The cedar tree. *Nature,* 1944, 153: 595-8.

HOWARD, Alexander L. Deciduous cypress (*Taxodium distichum*). *Nature,* 1944, 154: 775-6.

HOWARD, Alexander L. The elm tree. *Nature,* 1943, 152: 636-8.

HOWARD, Alexander L. The oak tree. *Nature,* 1944, 153: 438-41.

HOWARD, Alexander L. The plane tree. *Nature,* 1943, 152: 421-2.

HOWARD, Alexander L. The Scots pine (*Pinus sylvestris*). *Nature,* 1944, 154: 679-80.

HOWARD, Alexander L. The sycamore tree. *Nature,* 1944, 153: 348-9.

HOWARD, Alexander L. The willow tree (*Salix* sp.). *Nature,* 1944, 154: 835-7.

HOWARD, Alexander L. The yew tree (*Taxus baccata*). *Nature,* 1944, 154: 215-16.

LECLERC, Henri. Le cyprès. *Janus,* 1921, 25: 87-100.

LECLERC, Henri. Histoire du buis. *Janus,* 1922, 26: 1-14.

LECLERC, Henri. Histoire du lierre. *Bull.Soc.Hist.Méd.,* 1921, 15: 17-37.

LEHMANN, Heinrich. Beiträge zur Geschichte von *Sambucus nigra, Juniperus communis* und *Juniperus sabina.* 171 p. (Inaugural Diss., Basel) Zofingen: 1935.

MOULE, A.C. The name *Ginkgo biloba* and other names of the tree. *T'oung Pao*, 1937, 33: 193-219, 3 pl.

TIDBURY, G.E. The clove tree. xii, 212 p., 24 pl. London: Lockwood, 1949.

TUBEUF, Karl. Monographie der Mistel. Unter Beteiligung von Gustav Neckel und Heinrich Marzell. xii, 832 p., 35 tables, 181 fig., 5 maps. München: Oldenbourg, 1923.

ULM, Amanda. Remember the chestnut! *Amer.Forests*, 1948, 54: 156-9, 190, 192. Also in *Annu.Rep.Smithsonian Inst.for 1948*, p. 377-82, 4 pl. Washington, D.C.: 1949.

KYce-bv

BOGUSCH, E.R. A bibliography on mesquite. *Tex.J.Sci.*, 1950, 2: 528-38. [CB 77/374]

KYnh

THOMMEN, Eduard. Neues zur Schreibung des Namens Ginkgo. *Verhandl.Naturforsch.Ges.Basel*, 1949, 60: 77-103, ill.
Reviewed by E. Gaspardone, *J.Asiatique*, 1950, 238: 457.

KYsc

HIGINBOTHAM, Betty Wilson. Sassafras shaped history. *Natur. Hist.*, 1947, 56: 159-64, ill.

L ZOOLOGY

for veterinary medicine *see* S
animal husbandry *see* SP

Lc general history

BERTIN, Léon. La vie des animaux. 2 vol. 496 p.; 500 p., ill., 17 pl. Paris: Larousse, 1949-50.
Reviewed by P. Humbert, *Arch.Int.Hist.Sci.*, 1949, 2: 1219; 1951, 4: 228.

BURCKHARDT, Rudolf. Geschichte der Zoologie. 2nd ed. by H. Erhard. 2 vol. 103 p.; 163 p. (Sammlung Göschen) Berlin: Göschen, 1921.
The first edition appeared in 1907.

FEDOROWICZ, Zygmunt. Zarys historii zoologii. [A short history of zoology. (In Polish)] 349 p., ill., portr., facs., bibliogr. Warsaw: Państwowe Wydawnictwo Naukowe, 1962.

GOLDSCHMIDT, Richard. Fifty years of zoology. *Sci.Mon.*, 1950, 71: 359-68.

HAGBERG, Knut. Från Aristoteles till Brehm. Några blad ur djurskildringens historia. [From Aristotle to Brehm: some pages from the history of animal description. (In Swedish)] 99 p., ill. Stockholm: Bonnier, 1941.
Reviewed by Nils von Hofsten, *Lychnos*, 1942, 397.

HEGNER, Robert William. College zoology. 5th ed. xvii, 817 p., 441 fig. New York: Macmillan, 1942. [CB 63/273]
A short final chapter tells the history of zoology.

JOUBIN, L.; ROBIN, Auguste. Histoire naturelle illustrée: les animaux, les invertébrés, par L. Joubin ... Les vertébrés par A. Robin. 340 p., ill. Paris: Larousse, 1922. [CB 15/250]

KELLER, Conrad. Lebenserinnerungen eines schweizerischen Naturforschers. viii, 162 p., ill. Zurich: Füssli, 1928.
Reviewed by Aldo Mieli, *Archeion*, 1933, 15: 145-9.

KOLLER, Gottfried. Daten zur Geschichte der Zoologie. 61 p. Bonn: Atheneum Verlag, 1949.
Reviewed by Maurice Caullery, *Arch.Int.Hist.Sci.*, 1951, 4: 239.

LOCY, William Albert. The main currents of zoology. viii, 216 p. New York: Holt, 1918.
A simply written work designed to give students an interest in their scientific forbears.

MITCHELL, Peter Chalmers. My fill of days. 440 p. London: Faber and Faber, 1937. [CB 54/508]
The author was Secretary of the Zoological Gardens in London from 1903 to 1935.

PARKER, George Howard. The world expands. Recollections of a zoologist. ix, 252 p., front. Cambridge, Mass.: Harvard University Press, 1946. [CB 71/101]

PETIT, Georges; THÉODORIDÈS, Jean. Histoire de la zoologie. Des origines à Linné. xii, 360 p., 24 ill., bibliogr. (Histoire de la Pensée, 8) Paris: Hermann, 1962.
Reviewed by William Coleman, *Isis*, 1963, 54: 293-5; for other reviews see CB 88/550, CB 89/506 and CB 90/524.

SCIENTIFIC AMERICAN. First book of animals. By the editors of Scientific American. xi, 240 p. New York: Simon and Schuster, 1955.

SHULL, A. Franklin. Principles of animal biology. 5th ed. xiv, 417 p., ill. New York: McGraw-Hill, 1941. [CB 61/406]
The first chapter opens with a discussion of the growth of knowledge of biology. 6th ed. 1946.

STORER, Tracy. General zoology. xii, 798 p. New York: McGraw-Hill, 1943. [CB 64/452]
Includes a good brief history of zoology. 3rd ed. (with R.L. Usinger), 1957.

WOODRUFF, Lorande Loss. Animal biology. 2nd rev. ed. xiv, 535 p., 312 fig. New York: Macmillan, 1938. [CB 54/534]
First publ. 1932. The final chapter is on the development of the subject.

Lcb

COLE LIBRARY of Zoology and Early Medicine, University of Reading. *Nature*, 1960, 188: 1143-51.

Lce

COLE, Francis Joseph. Obiter dicta bibliographica. *J.Hist. Med.*, 1958, 13: 2-9.

Lce-bv

ALLEN, F.P. A check list of periodical literature and publications of learned societies of interest to zoologists in the University of Michigan libraries. 83 p. (Museum of Zoology, University of Michigan, circular 2) Ann Arbor: University of Michigan Press, 1935.
Contains about 1300 items.

SAWYER, F.C. Books of reference in zoology, chiefly bibliographical. *J.Soc.Bibliogr.Natur.Hist.*, 1955, 2: 72-91.

Lce-bx

BODENHEIMER, F.S. Über die Ausstellung alter zoologischer illustrierter Werke während des XI. Zoologenkongresses in Padua (September 1930). Mit besonderer Berücksichtigung der Entomologie-Geschichte. *Arch.Gesch.Math.Naturwiss.Tech.*, 1931, 13: 473-5.

ICHTHYOLOGIA et herpetologia Americana. A guide to an exhibition in the William L. Clements Library, illustrating the development of knowledge of American fishes, amphibians, and reptiles. 22 p., ill. (Bulletin, 25) Ann Arbor, Mich.: University of Michigan Press, 1936.

INTERNATIONAL CONGRESS OF ZOOLOGY, 11th, Padua, 1930. Mostra della illustrazione zoologica in opere a stampa dal sec. XVI al XVIII. Catalogo. 46 p., 11 pl. Padova: Tipografia del Seminario, 1930.

PIERPONT MORGAN LIBRARY. The animal kingdom. Illustrated catalogue of an exhibition of manuscript illuminations, book illustrations, drawings, cylinder seals, and bindings. New York, Nov. 19, 1940-Feb. 28, 1941. 70 p., 11 pl. New York: The Library, 1940.

Lcm

HIRASE, S.; *et al.* [Figuraro de Japanaj bestoj. (Japanese text)] Tokyo: Hokuryukwan, 1927.
Illustrations of animals with Japanese text. Latin index of 94 p.

LAPAGE, Geoffrey. Draughtsmanship in zoological work. *Endeavour,* 1949, 8: 70-9, 11 fig.

Lct

WAY, W. Dennis; STANDEN, O.D. Zoology in postage stamps. vii, 133 p., 33 pl. London: Harvey and Blythe, 1951.

Lda

DE BEER, G.R. Glimpses of some historic figures of modern zoology. *Science, Medicine and History. Essays in honour of Charles Singer* (2), p. 233-42, 3 pl. London: Oxford University Press, 1953. [CB 80/205]

Ldaj

HALL, Thomas S. A source book in animal biology. xv, 716 p., 17 fig. (Source Books in the History of the Sciences) New York: McGraw-Hill, 1951. [CB 77/376]

Lf

ENGEL, Hendrik. Over de geschiedenis van de zoölogie. Openbare les gehouden bij de opening van zijn colleges als Privaat-Docent in de geschiedenis der zoölogie aan de Universiteit van Amsterdam op Woensdag 10 November 1948. [Concerning the history of zoology. Public inaugural lecture ... at the University of Amsterdam ... (In Dutch)] 15 p. Amsterdam: Centen, [1949].

LmzHQ

GERMAIN, Louis. Le problème de l'Atlantide et la zoologie. *Ann.Géogr.,* 1913, 22: 209-26.

Ln means of communication

Lnh

CONGRÈS de zoologie (IXe), Monaco, mars 1913. *Isis,* 1913, 1: 261-2.
Zoological nomenclature discussed by conference.

DOBELL, Clifford. On *Teranympha* and other monstrous Latin parasites. *Parasitology,* 1939, 31: 255-62.
On zoological nomenclature.

SARTON, George. Nomenclature zoologique. *Isis,* 1913, 1: 501-2.
On the proposed Nomenclator animalium generum et subgenerum. *See* below: Schulze, Franz Eilhard; Kükenthal, W.; ed.

SCHENK, Edward T.; McMASTERS, John H. Procedure in taxonomy, including a reprint in translation of the Règles Internationales de la Nomenclature Zoölogique. (International Code of Zoological Nomenclature) with titles and notes on the opinions rendered to the present date (1907 to 1956), completely indexed. 3rd ed., enlarged and in part rewritten by A. Myra Keen and Siemon William Muller. vii, 119 p. Stanford: Stanford University Press, 1956. [CB 82/208]
First published 1936. [CB 48/578]

SCHULZE, Franz Eilhard. Nomenclator animalium generum et subgenerum. *Zool.Ann.,* 1912, 5: 7-276.

SCHULZE, Franz Eilhard; KÜKENTHAL, W.; ed. Nomenclator animalium generum et subgenerum. Im Auftrage der Preussischen Akademie der Wissenschaften zu Berlin. 5 vol. Berlin: 1926-54.

STEJNEGER, Leonhard Hess. A chapter in the history of zoological nomenclature. 21 p. (Smithsonian Miscellaneous Collections, 77: no. 1) Washington, D.C.: 1924.

VERRILL, A.E. Priority overworked. *Science,* 1914, 39: 607-9.
Relating to zoological nomenclature.

WERNER, C.F. Wortelemente lateinisch-griechischer Fachausdrücke in der Biologie, Zoologie und vergleichenden Anatomie. 397 p. Leipzig: Akademische Verlagsgesellschaft Geest & Portig K.-G., 1956.
Reviewed by Erik Wiksen, *Lychnos,* 1957-58, 446.

ZIEGLER, H.E. Ueber die neue Nomenklatur. *Zool.Ann.,* 1913, 5: 255-65.

Lnh-be

HIRSCH-SCHWEIGGER, Erwin. Zoologisches Wörterbuch. viii, 628 p., 477 fig. (Veit's Sammlung Wissenschaftlicher Wörterbücher) Berlin: Walter de Gruyter, 1925.

POCHE, Franz. Supplement zu C.O. Waterhouses Index Zoologicus. *Zool.Ann.,* 1908, 2: 273-343; 1914, 6: 33-46.

WATERHOUSE, C.O., comp. Index zoologicus. An alphabetical list of names of genera and subgenera proposed for use in zoology as recorded in the "Zoological Record" (and the Zoology volumes of the International Catalogue of Scientific Literature") for 1880-1900, (1901-1910). Edited by David Sharp. 2 vol. London: 1902-12.
For supplements to both volumes *see* above: Poche, Franz.

ZIEGLER, H.E., ed. Zoologisches Wörterbuch: Erklärung der zoologischen Fachausdrücke; zum Gebrauch beim Studium zoologischer, anatomischer, entwicklungsgeschichtlicher und naturphilosophischer Werke. 3rd ed., rev. by H.E. Ziegler and E. Bresslau. viii, 786 p. Jena: Fischer, 1927.
First published 1909; 2nd ed. 1912.
Reviewed in *Nature,* 1927, 119: 632.

Ls/u social and humanistic relations; popular aspects

Lsc

DENDY, Arthur, ed. Animal life and human progress. ix, 227 p. London: Constable, 1919.
Lectures by various scientists at King's College, London, 1917-18.

LEWINSOHN, Richard. Animals, men and myths. A history of the influence of animals on civilization and culture. 374 p., 80 ill., 31 pl. London: Gollancz, 1954.
American ed. 422 p. New York: Harper, 1954. Translation of: Eine Geschichte der Tiere, ihr Einfluss auf Zivilisation und Kultur. Hamburg: Rowohlt, 1952. The German and English editions were published under the pseudonym "Morus".
Reviewed by George Sarton, *Isis,* 1955, 46: 61-4.

LOEVENBRUCK, Pierre. Les animaux sauvages dans l'histoire. Préface de Marcel Duvau. 208 p. (Bibliothèque Historique) Paris: Payot, 1955.
Reviewed by John Bernström, *Lychnos,* 1956, 421-3.

Lsy

LILLIE, Frank R. Zoological sciences in the future. *Science,* 1938, 88: 65-72.
Address before the American Association for the Advancement of Science in the conference on science and society, Ottawa, June 28, 1938.

Lth

KRUTCH, Joseph Wood, ed. The world of animals. A treasury of lore, legend, and literature by great writers and naturalists from the 5th century B.C. to the present. 508 p., ill. New York: Simon and Schuster, 1961.
Reviewed by Lorus J. Milne and Margery Milne, *Science,* 1962, 136: 504.

Ltq

BORN, W. Votive animals. *Ciba Symp.,* 1939, 1: 129-32, fig.

BOYNTON, Mary Fuertes. Abbott Thayer and natural history. *Osiris,* 1952, 10: 542-55.
On paintings of animals and colour in animals.

Lu

LEY, Willy. The lungfish, the dodo, and the unicorn: an excursion into romantic zoology. 2nd ed. rev. & enl. xi, 361 p., 38 ill. New York: Viking, 1948.
Reviewed by Conway Zirkle, *Isis*, 1949, 40: 290.
First edition: The lungfish and the unicorn: an excursion into romantic zoology. (New York: Modern Age, 1941) [CB 61/405]

Lw in different countries

Lwb-oq

MARK, Edward Laurens. Zoölogy 1847-1921. In: Morison, S.E., ed. The development of Harvard University since the inauguration of President Eliot 1869-1929, p. 378-93, 1 ill. (The tercentennial history of Harvard College and University, 1) Cambridge, Mass.: Harvard University Press, 1930.

TORREY, Theodore W. Zoology and its makers at Indiana University. *Bios*, 1949, 20: 67-99.

Lwc

BELTRAN, Enrique. Un cuarto de siglo de zoología mexicana, 1936-1961. *Rev.Soc.Mex.Hist.Natur.*, 1961, 22: 113-52.

Lwc-cj

BELTRAN, Enrique. La *Gaceta Médica de México* 1865-1941, y sus aportaciones al conocimiento de la zoología. *Gac.Méd. Méx.*, 1942, 72: 580-90.

Lwd

LECLERCQ, Jean. Perspectives de la zoologie européene. Histoire, problèmes contemporains. 162 p., 41 fig. Gembloux: Duculot; Paris: Librairie agricole de la Maison rustique, 1959.
Reviewed by J. Théodoridès, *Rev.Hist.Sci.*, 1960, 13: 365-6; by A. Glenn Richards, *Science*, 1960, 131: 1218.

Lwe-oq

GATENBY, J. Brontë. Centenary of zoological teaching in Trinity College, Dublin. *Nature*, 1944, 153: 723.

Lwe-qd

GILLESPIE, Thomas Haining. The story of the Edinburgh Zoo: the Royal Zoological Society of Scotland and the Scottish National Zoological Park. An account of their origin and progress. xii, 123 p., ill. Aberdeen: Michael Slains, 1964.

MATTHEWS, L. Harrison. The Zoological Society of London. *Endeavour*, 1953, 12: 18-24, 11 pl.

MITCHELL, Peter Chalmers. Centenary history of the Zoological Society of London. xi, 307 p., 33 pl., 9 plans. London: Zoological Society, 1929.
Reviewed by J.R., *Nature*, 1929, 123: 973-4.

ZUCKERMAN, Solly. The Zoological Society of London. *Nature*, 1959, 183: 1082-4.

Lwe-th

ROBIN, Percy Ansell. Animal lore in English literature. ix, 196 p., 8 pl. London: Murray, 1932.

Lwf-da

LACROIX, Alfred. Notice historique sur les membres et correspondants zoologistes et biologistes de l'Académie des Sciences ayant travaillé sur les côtes des colonies françaises de l'Afrique du Nord et du Nord-est depuis le XVIIIe siècle. Lecture faite en la séance annuelle du 20 décembre 1943. 42 p. Paris: Gauthier-Villars, 1943.

Lwg

GOLDSCHMIDT, Richard Benedict. Erlebnisse und Begegnungen. Aus der grossen Zeit der Zoologie in Deutschland. 165 p., ill. Hamburg/Berlin: Paul Parey, 1959.
Translated from: Portraits from memory. Recollections of a zoologist.
Reviewed by Adolf Meyer-Abich, *Sudhoffs Arch.*, 1960. 44: 376-7.

GOLDSCHMIDT, Richard Benedict. Portraits from memory. Recollections of a zoologist. ix, 181 p., 13 fig. Seattle: University of Washington Press, 1956. [CB 83/268]
For German translation, *see* above.
Reviewed by Kenneth Mather, *Nature*, 1956, 178: 821-2; by Maurice Caullery, *Arch.Int.Hist.Sci.*, 1957, 10: 56-7; by Nils von Hofsten, *Lychnos*, 1957-58, 451-2.

Lwg-bv

PAZ, F.; TISCHBIEREK, H. Bibliographie der Schlesischen Zoologie. xii, 520 p. (Schlesische Bibliographie, 5) Breslau: Priebatsch, 1930. [CB 32/587]

Lwg-nh

KRAUSE, Hermann. Die Geschichte der neueren zoologischen Nomenklatur in deutscher Sprache. 67 p. (Diss., Göttingen) Braunschweig: Appelhans, 1918.

Lwg-oq

TEMBROCK, Günter. Die Geschichte des Zoologischen Institutes. *Wiss.Z.Humboldt Univ.Berlin*, Beiheft zum Jubiläumsjahrgang, 1959-60, 9: 107-25.

Lwg-q

TEMBROCK, Günter. Zur Geschichte der Zoologie in Berlin. *Wiss. Z.Humboldt Univ.Berlin Math.Naturwiss.Reihe*, 1958-59, 8: 184-95.
At the Humboldt University and in the Gesellschaft Naturforschender Freunde zu Berlin.

USCHMANN, Georg. Geschichte der Zoologie und der zoologischen Anstalten in Jena 1779-1919. xiii, 249 p., ill. Jena: Gustav Fischer Verlag, 1959.
Reviewed by Ernst Mayr, *Isis*, 1962, 53: 241; for other reviews *see* CB 86/466, CB 87/568 and CB 90/610.

Lwh

BRZEK, Gabriel. Historia zoologii w Polsce do r. 1918. [History of zoology in Poland till 1918. (In Polish)] 3 parts. 1, 2. vii, 253 p.; 3. xii, 455 p. (Annales Universitatis M. Sklodowska-Curie, Sectio C, no. 2, 7) Lublin: 1947-55.
Reviewed by August Dehnel, *Arch.Int.Hist.Sci.*, 1957, 10: 166-7.

HOYER, Henryk. Zarys dziejów zoologii w Polsce. [Outline of the history of zoology in Poland. (In Polish with summary in French)] 27 p. (Polska Akademia Umiejetnośći, Historia Nauki Polskiej w Monografiach, 9) Krakow: 1948.

Lwh-oq

FEDOROWICZ, Zygmunt. Materialy do historii zoologii na Uniwersytecie Jagiellonskim (1777-1914). [Materials concerning the history of zoology at Jagellonian University, 1777-1914. (In Polish)] 121 p., ill. (Memorabilia Zoologica, 9) Wroclaw/Warsaw/Cracow: Polish Academy of Sciences, Zoological Institute, 1962.

Lwi-qg

DOHRN, Reinhard. The zoological station at Naples. *Endeavour*, 1954, 13: 22-6.
An account of the great institute for the study of marine life.

DOHRN, Reinhard. Stazione Zoologica Napoli. *Notes Roy.Soc. Lond.*, 1951, 8: 277-82, 2 pl.

STENTA, Mario. Trieste negli studi di biologia marina. *Atti Soc.Ital.Progr.Sci.XI Riunione* (Trieste, 1921), p. 382-408, bibliogr. Citta di Castello: 1922.
Work of the Stazione Zoologica at Trieste since its foundation in 1875.

Lwi-tq

HOWE, W. Norton. Animal life in Italian painting. xvi, 234 p., ill. London: G. Allen, 1912.

Lwm

BROCH, Hjalmar. Zoologiens historie i Norge til annen verdenskrig. [The history of zoology in Norway up to the second World War. (In Norwegian)] 158 p., 34 portr. Oslo: Akademisk forlag, 1954.
Reviewed by Nils von Hofsten, *Lychnos*, 1956, 427-9.

Lwm-oq

SPÄRCK, Ragnar. Undervisningen i zoologi ved Københavns universitet; et tilbageblik over 300 år. [Teaching of zoology at the University of Copenhagen. 300 years in retrospect. (In Danish)] 301 p., ill., portr., facs. Copenhagen: 1962.

Lwm-qg

THEEL, Hjalmar. Bidrag till Kristinebergs historia: Kristinebergs Zoologiska Station, 1877-1927. [History of the Christineberg Zoological Station. (In Swedish)] 48 p., 4 pl. (Skrifserie utgiven av. K. Svenska Vetenskapsakademien, 1) Stockholm: 1928.

Lwn-oq

LEVIN, V.L. Materialy po istorii zoologii v russkikh universitetakh; zoologiia v trudakh obshchestv estestvoispytatelei. [Materials on the history of zoology in Russian universities; zoology in the proceedings of the societies of naturalists. (In Russian)] *Tr.Inst.Ist.Est.*, 1962, 41: 391-413.
19th and early 20th centuries.

Lxw museology

ROWLEY, John. Taxidermy and museum exhibition. Preface by Frank M. Chapman. xvi, 331 p., 29 pl., 20 fig. New York: Appleton, 1925.

Lxx

BLANC, H. Le Musée Zoologique de Lausanne. Ses origines. Son installation au palais de Rumine. Ses collections. 59 p., 1 portr., 19 fig. Lausanne: Imprimeries Réunies, 1912.

ENGEL, Hendrik. Het belang van het Zoölogisch Museum voor wetenschap en maatschappij. [The importance of the Zoological Museum for science and society. (In Dutch)] 17 p. Amsterdam: D.B. Centen, 1950.
Inaugural address.

ENGEL, Hendrik. Dedication. *Amsterdam Natur.*, 1950, 1: 2-3, 4 pl.
Historical dedication of the new journal explaining the part which the Zoologisch Museum, Amsterdam has played in the development of zoological knowledge.

HOWES, Paul Griswold. Handbook for the curious. xx, 364 p., 329 fig. New York: Putnam, 1936. [CB 53/265]
The natural history of animals brought by curious inquirers to the Bruce Museum of Natural History, Greenwich, Connecticut.

LAMBA, B.S. Progress of zoological museums in India. *Sci. Cult.*, 1963, 29: 185-8.

LOWEGREN, Yngve. Naturaliekabinett i Sverige under 1700-talet. Ett Bidrag till Zoologiens historie. [Natural history collections in Sweden: contribution to the history of zoology. (In Swedish)] 407 p., ill. Uppsala/Stockholm: Almquist & Wicksell, 1952.
Reviewed by M. Caullery, *Arch.Int.Hist.Sci.*, 1952, 5: 413-14.

NOVIKOV, P.A. La "Kunstkamera" de Pétersbourg et son rôle dans l'histoire de la zoologie. *Act.VIIIe Congr.Int.Hist.Sci.* (Florence, 1956), (2), p. 784-7. Paris: Hermann, 1958.

NOVIKOV, P.A. [Zoological department in the Petersburg Kunstkamera and its historical development. (In Russian)] *Tr. Inst.Ist.Tekh.*, 1957, 14: 302-52.

SPÄRCK, Ragnar. Zoologisk Museum i København gennem tre aarhundredar. [The Zoological Museum of Copenhagen during three hundred years. (In Danish)] 110 p. Copenhagen: Munksgaard, 1945.
Reviewed in *Nature*, 1946, 158: 183.

TOPSENT, E. Histoire abrégée du Musée zoologique de l'Université de la Ville de Strasbourg. *Bull.Soc.Zool.France*, 1920, 45: 7-13.

Lxy zoological gardens

for London Zoo *see* Lwe-qd

GILLESPIE, Thomas Haining. The story of the Edinburgh Zoo: the Royal Zoological Society of Scotland and the Scottish National Zoological Park. An account of their origin and progress. xii, 123 p., ill. Aberdeen: Michael Slains, 1964.

LOISEL, G. Histoire des ménageries de l'antiquité à nos jours. 3 vol. 60 pl. Paris: H. Laurens, 1912.

REINDL, Joseph. Ehemalige zoologische und botanische Gärten in Bayern. *Arch.Gesch.Naturwiss.Tech.*, 1912, 4: 79-86.

Lxy-bd

ENGEL, Hendrik. Alphabetical list of Dutch zoological cabinets and menageries. *Bijdr.Dierk.*, 1939, 27: 247-346.

LG/LP ANIMAL BIOLOGY

for animal physiology *see also* OF
the biology of insects and vertebrates *see* INDEX

LG

CAIN, A.J. Animal species and their evolution. vii, 190 p., fig. New York: Harper, 1960.

CUÉNOT, Lucien. La genèse des espèces animales. 3rd rev. ed. viii, 822 p., 162 fig. Paris: Alcan, 1932. [CB 38/602]
For 2nd ed. 1921, *see* CB 12/646.

GAISSINOVITCH, A.E. Élie Metchnikov et le darwinisme. *Proc. 15th Int.Congr.Zool.*(London, 1958), p. 110-13. London: The Congress, 1959.

MAYR, Ernst. Animal species and evolution. xiv, 797 p., fig., bibliogr. Cambridge, Mass.: Belknap Press of Harvard University Press, 1963.
Reviewed by L.C. Dunn, *Isis*, 1964, 55: 225-7.

MILLER, Alden H. Speciation in the avian genus Junco. *Univ. Calif.Publ.Zool.*, 1941, 44: 173-345, 33 fig. [CB 62/79]
This is a fundamental study in the mechanism of evolution.

RUSSELL, E.S. The diversity of animals. An evolutionary study. viii, 151 p., fig. (Acta Biotheoretica, Supplementum Primum, additum Actorum Biotheoreticorum Volumini 13; Bibliotheca Biotheoretica, 9) Leiden: E.J. Brill, 1962.

WHITE, M.J.D. Animal cytology and evolution. viii, 375 p. Cambridge University Press; New York: The Macmillan Co., 1945. [CB 70/263]

LGmzGN

HOOYKAAS, R. The parallel between the history of the earth and the history of the animal world. *Arch.Int.Hist.Sci.*, 1957, 10: 3-18. [CB 83/269]

LHwb

CAULLERY, Maurice. Impressions de voyage aux États-Unis (1933). *Bull.Soc.Zool.France*, 1933, 58: 181-96, portr. [CB 40/367]

LHwn

DOBZHANSKY, Th. Animal breeding under Lysenko. *Amer.Natur.*, 1954, 88: 165-7.

NOVIKOV, P.A. [The struggle against Weismannism-Mendelism-Morganism in native (Russian) zoology. (In Russian)] *Tr. Inst.Ist.Est.*, 1953, 5: 93-144.

LI

RUSSELL, Edward Stuart. Form and function, a contribution to the history of animal morphology. ix, 383 p., ill. London: J. Murray, 1916.
Note by George Sarton on the preparation of this work, *Isis*, 1913, 1: 244.

LIkv

ANTHONY, Raoul. Le déterminisme et l'adaptation morphologique en biologie animale. 1. Déterminisme morphologique et morphogénie. 374 p., 129 fig. (*Arch.Morphol.Gén.Exp.*, 14) Paris: Doin, 1923.
Reviewed by L. Guinet, *Isis*, 1923, 5: 455-6.

LJvm-tc

LEVIN, S.I.; BOYDEN, Edward A. The Kosher Code of the orthodox Jew. Being a literal translation of that portion of the sixteenth-century codification of the Babylonian Talmud which describes such deficiences as render animals unfit for food (*Hilkrot Terefot, Shulhan Aruk*); to which is appended a discussion of Talmudic anatomy in the light of the science of its day and of the present time. xx, 243 p. Minneapolis: University of Minnesota Press, 1940.
Reviewed by Solomon Gandz, *Isis*, 1941, 33: 282-5; by Harry A.Wolfson and Frederic T. Lewis, *Science*, 1940, 92: 173-5.

LK

HOFF, Hebbel E. Galvani and the pre-Galvanian electrophysiologists. *Ann.Sci.*, 1936, 1: 157-72.

LOEB, Jacques. Natural death and the duration of life. *Sci. Mon.*, 1919, 9: 578-85. [CB 9/484]

LOEB, Jacques. Regeneration: from a physico-chemical viewpoint. x, 143 p. New York: McGraw-Hill, 1924.

MAY, Raoul M. La transplantation animale. 352 p., 170 fig. Paris: Gauthier-Villars, 1932. [CB 37/596]
Includes brief historical notes at the beginning of chapters.

MENDELSOHN, Everett. Heat and life. The development of the theory of animal heat. xi, 208 p. Cambridge, Mass.: Harvard University Press, 1964.
Reviewed by J. Schiller, *Arch.Int.Hist.Sci.*, 1964, 17: 339-40.

PARKER, G.H. Color changes of animals in relation to nervous activity. x, 74 p., 40 fig. Philadelphia: University of Pennsylvania Press, 1936.
Reviewed by Charles A. Kofoid, *Isis*, 1938, 28: 146-9.

SCHELAR, Virginia M. Thermochemistry and animal metabolism. *J.Chem.Educ.*, 1964, 41: 226-9.
A brief survey of the 100 years after Lavoisier.

SCHMIDT-NIELSEN, Knut. Animal physiology. 118 p., ill. (Foundations of modern biology) Englewood Cliffs, N.J.: Prentice-Hall, 1960.

THAYER, Gerald Handerson. Concealing-coloration in the animal Kingdom. An exposition of the laws of disguise through color and pattern: being a summary of Abbot H. Thayer's disclosures. With an introductory essay by A.H. Thayer. New ed. xix, 260 p., 16 pl., 140 fig. New York: Macmillan, 1918. [CB 10/219]
Originally published in 1909.

WALKER, W. Cameron. Animal electricity before Galvani. *Ann. Sci.*, 1937, 2: 84-113, 4 pl.

LKu

ZIRKLE, Conway. Animals impregnated by the wind. *Isis*, 1936, 25: 95-130. [CB 48/575]

LKwi

TESTI, Gino. Il contributo italiano allo studio del calore animale. *Volume di scritti in onore del Prof. P. Capparoni*, p. 160-6. Torino: Minerva Medica, 1941.

LL

DALCQ, A.M. Form and causality in early development. iii, 197 p. Cambridge University Press, 1939. [CB 57/255]
On the nature and causes of the early development of the egg in a variety of animal forms.

FRIED, Boris M. The origin of species and macrophages. *Victor Robinson Memorial Volume*, p. 61-70, 2 fig. New York: Froben, 1948.

JOUBIN, Louis. Les métamorphoses des animaux marins. 272 p., 71 fig. (Bibliothèque de Philosophie Scientifique) Paris: Flammarion, 1926.

MEYER, A.W. Some historical aspects of the recapitulation idea. *Quart.Rev.Biol.*, 1935, 10: 379-96.

LN ANIMAL ECOLOGY

for insects *see* LUyLN
birds *see* LYyLN
mammals *see* LZyLN

BODENHEIMER, F.S. Der Massenwechsel in der Tierwelt. Grundriss einer allgemeinen tierischen Bevölkerungslehre. *Arch. Zool.Ital.*, 1931, 16: 98-111, fig.

BORRADAILE, L.A. The animal and its environment. A textbook of the natural history of animals. vii, 399 p., 426 fig., 4 pl. New York: Oxford University Press, 1923. [CB 14/568]

ELTON, Charles. The ecology of animals. vii, 97 p. New York: Wiley, 1950.
An account of the relations of animals to their environments.

GARBINI, Adriano. Antroponimie ed Omonimie nel campo della zoologia popolare. Part 2. Omonimie. 1, 2. 1598 p. Verona: La Tipografica Veronese, for Accademia di Agricoltura Scienze e Lettere, 1925.
Reviewed by W. Meyer-Lübke, *Deut.Lit.Zeitung*, 1927, 502-3.

GERMAIN, Louis. La vie des animaux à la surface des continents. iv, 260 p. Paris: Alcan, 1925. [CB 18/623]

HESSE, Richard; ALLEE, W.C.; SCHMIDT, Karl P. Ecological animal geography. An authorized, rewritten edition based on "Tiergeographie auf oekologischer Grundlage" [Jena: Fischer, 1924] xiv, 597 p., 135 fig. New York: Wiley, 1937.
2nd ed. (xii, 715 p.) 1951.
Reviewed by Charles A. Kofoid, *Isis*, 1938, 29: 474.

JACKSON, Hartley H.T. Conserving endangered wildlife species. *Ann.Rep.Smithsonian Inst.for 1945*, p. 247-71, 13 pl., 4 fig. Washington, D.C.: 1946.
Including list of species extinct or endangered.

WILLIAMS, Jay. Fall of the sparrow. With an introductory chapter by Stanley Edgar Hyman. Illustrated by Richard Taylor. 158 p. New York: Oxford University Press, 1951. [CB 78/188]
The story of why certain species of animals have vanished and why others are threatened.

LNk

KLAAUW, C.J. van der. Zur Geschichte der Definitionen der Ökologie, besonders auf Grund der Systeme der zoologischen Disziplinen. *Arch.Gesch.Med.*, 1936, 29: 136-77.

LO ANIMAL PSYCHOLOGY AND BEHAVIOUR

for the behaviour of insects *see* LUyLO;
fishes LWyLO; birds LYyLO; mammals LZyLO

CRAWFURD, Raymond. Legends and lore of the genesis of the healing art. *Proc.Roy.Soc.Med.*, 1917, 10: Hist.Sect., 1-32.
Deals with medicine in the earliest and crudest states and discusses healing acts among animals.

FISCHEL, Werner. Abstammungslehre und Tierpsychologie. *Arch. Gesch.Med.*, 1935, 27: 511-15.

GUILLAUME, P. La psychologie animale. 210, ii p. Paris: Colin, 1940. [CB 60/161]
History of subject in chapter 1.

GUSSIN, Arnold E.S. Jacques Loeb: the man and his tropism theory of animal conduct. *J.Hist.Med.*, 1963, 18: 321-36.

HÄBERLEIN, Paul. Zur Frage des Instinkts. *Phil.Natur.*, 1957, 4: 337-43.

HORWITZ, Hugo Th. Über den Gebrauch von Werkzeugen im Tierreich. *Geschichtsbl.Tech.Ind.*, 1927, 11: 26-9.

JANSSENS, Edg. Scientisme et vérité historique. Réponse à "L'âme des bêtes" de L. Verlaine. 158 p. Liège: La Pensée Catholique, 1932. [CB 35/304]

KALMUS, H. Animals as mathematicians. *Nature*, 1964, 202: 1156-60.

LOESER, J.A. Animal behaviour. x, 178 p. New York: Macmillan, 1941. [CB 61/406]

PIÉRON, Henri. L'évolution de l'opinion scientifique actuelle sur la question du mimétisme. *Scientia,* 1913, 14: 453-62.

REINKE, Johannes. Wissen und Glauben in der Naturwissenschaft mit besonderer Berücksichtigung der Tierpsychologie. v, 112 p., map. Leipzig: Barth, 1929.

RUSSELL, E.S. The behaviour of animals, an introduction to its study. viii, 184 p. London: Arnold, 1934.
Reviewed by M.F. Ashley-Montagu, *Isis,* 1937, 27: 348-9.

SCHIERBEEK, A. Instinkt of verstand? Een inleiding tot de dierpsychologie. [Instinct or intelligence? An introduction to animal psychology. (In Dutch)] 212 p., 90 fig. (Handboekjes Elck 't beste) Amsterdam: Maatschappij voor Goede en Goedkoope lectuur, 1927. [CB 24/546]

Tierseele. Zeitschrift für vergleichende Seelenkunde. Vol. 1, pt. 1-4. 468 p. Bonn: Emil Eisele, 1913-14. [CB 5/300]
No more published.

VERLAINE, L. L'âme des bêtes; quelques pages d'histoire. 202 p.. Paris: Alcan, 1931. [CB 35/304]

ZIEGLER, Heinrich Ernst. Der Begriff des Instinktes einst und jetzt. Eine Studie über die Geschichte und die Grundlagen der Tierpsychologie. Mit einem Anhang: Die Gehirne der Bienen und Ameisen. 3rd ed. 211 p., ill. Jena: Fischer, 1920.
First publ. 1904. Includes historical notices.

ZIEGLER, Heinrich Ernst. Tierpsychologie. 115 p., 17 fig. (Sammlung Göschen) Berlin: Vereinigung wissenschaftlicher Verleger, 1921. [CB 11/639]

ZINNER, Ernst. Das Verhalten der Tiere bei Sonnenfinsternissen. *Ber.Naturforsch.Ges.Bamberg,* 1946, 29: 6-14.

LOwk

BIERENS DE HAAN, J.A. La psychologie animale en Hollande de 1928 à 1930. *Rech.Phil.,* 1932, 1: 334-44.

VERLAINE, L. La psychologie animale en Belgique. *Rech.Phil.,* 1932, 1: 322-33.

LP ANIMAL PARASITOLOGY

for parasitic invertebrates *see also* LTyLP
medical parasitology *see* QS

HARANT, Hervé. Histoire de la parasitologie. 26 p. (Conférences du Palais de la Découverte, D, 35) Paris: Université de Paris, 1955.

THÉODORIDÈS, Jean. Contribution à l'étude des parasites et phorétiques des Coléoptères terrestres. 310 p., fig. Paris: Hermann, 1955.
Reviewed by P. Delaunay, *Arch.Int.Hist.Sci.,* 1956, 9: 275.

THÉODORIDÈS, Jean. Réflexions sur l'histoire de la parasitology. *Méd.France,* 1954, no. 58, 3-7, 2 fig.

LR ZOOGEOGRAPHY; FAUNA

for insects *see* LUyLR
fishes *see* LWvLR
birds *see* LYyLR
mammals *see* LZyLR

JANSSENS, Emile. Esquisse d'une histoire critique des théories zoogéographiques. *Bull.Soc.Belge Geogr.,* 1952, 76: 33-50.

TROUESSART, E.L. La distribution géographique des animaux. 332 p., 11 maps. Paris: G. Doin, 1922. [CB 13/313]

LRwn

ZENKEVICH, L.A. [Russian investigations of the fauna of the seas. (In Russian)] *Tr.Inst.Ist.Est.,* 1948, 2: 170-96.

LRB

GRINNELL, Joseph; STORER, Tracy Irwin. Animal life in the Yosemite: an account of the mammals, birds, reptiles, and amphibians in a cross-section of the Sierra Nevada. xviii, 752 p., 62 pl. Berkeley, Cal.: University of California Press, 1924.

LRC

BEEBE, William. High jungle. xii, 379 p., 49 ill. New York: Duell, Sloan and Pearce, 1949. [CB 75/92]
A study of animal life in the Venezuelan Andes.

LRM

DAHL, Svend. Den danske plante- og dyreverdens udforskning. [Exploration of the Danish flora and fauna. (In Danish)] 340 p., ill. København: Udvalget for Folkeoplysnings Fremme, 1941.
Reviewed by Nils von Hofsten, *Lychnos,* 1942, 396-7.

LROce-bv

KANELLIS, A.; HATZISSARANTOS, Ch. Bibliographia faunae graecae (1800-1950). *Vouno,* 1949-50, 78 p. [CB 81/292]
Reviewed by J. T., *Rev.Hist.Sci.,* 1955, 8: 90.

LRQ

SEURAT, L.G. Exploration zoologique de l'Algérie de 1830 à 1930. 708 p., 16 pl. (Collection du centenaire de l'Algérie, 1830-1930) Paris: Masson, 1930.

LRS

DEVELOPMENT of the Zoological Survey of India. *Sci.Cult.,* 1963, 29: 465-6.

SEWELL, R.B. Seymour. The Zoological Survey of India. *Nature,* 1932, 129: 530-2.

LRT

SOWERBY, Arthur de Cable. The natural history of China. *Annu.Rep.Smithsonian Inst. for 1923,* p. 351-68, 4 pl. Washington, D.C.: 1925.
Reprinted from *J.N.China Br.Roy.Asiatic Soc.,* 1922, vol. 53.
A survey of the zoology of China.

LS SYSTEMATIC ZOOLOGY

for invertebrates *see* LTyLS
insects *see* LUyLS
birds *see* LYyLS
mammals *see* LZyLS

BELTRAN, Enrique. El problema de las clasificaciones zoológicas y la enseñanza de la zoología. *Rev.Soc.Mex.Hist. Natur.,* 1944, 5: 83-97.

CALMAN, W.T. The classification of animals. vii, 54 p. New York: Wiley, 1950.
An introduction to zoological taxonomy. Descriptive, rather than analytic.

CALMAN, W.T. The taxonomic outlook in zoology. *Nature,* 1930, 126: 440-4; also in *Science,* 1930, 72: 279-84.
From the presidential address to Section D (Zoology) of the British Association, delivered at Bristol on Sept. 4, 1930.

COLE, Leon J. Each after his kind. *Science,* 1941, 93: 289-93, 316-19.

DALCQ, Albert. L'évolution des idées dans l'interprétation des espèces animales. *Rev.Gén.Sci.,* 1948, 55: 32-43.

MAYR, Ernst. Systematics and the origin of species from the viewpoint of a zoologist. xiv, 334 p., ill., maps. New York: Columbia University Press, 1943.
Reviewed by Conway Zirkle, *Isis,* 1944, 35: 44-5.

SCHENK, Edward T.; McMASTERS, John H. Procedure in taxonomy, including a reprint in translation of the Règles Internationales de la Nomenclature Zoölogique. (International Code of Zoological Nomenclature) with titles and notes on the opinions rendered to the present date (1907 to 1956), completely indexed. 3rd ed., enlarged and in part rewritten by A. Myra Keen and Siemon William Muller. vii, 119 p. Stanford: Stanford University Press, 1956. [CB 82/208]
First published 1936. [CB 48/578]

LT INVERTEBRATE ZOOLOGY

BARTSCH, Paul. Pirates of the deep. Stories of the squid and the octopus. *Annu.Rep.Smithsonian Inst.for 1916*, p. 347-75, 9 pl. Washington, D.C.: 1917.
Includes many historical notes concerning the octopus and the "sea serpent".

CALKINS, Gary N.; SUMMERS, Francis M.; ed. Protozoa in biological research. xlii, 1150 p. New York: Columbia University Press, 1941. [CB 61/405]

COLE, F.J. The history of protozoology. Two lectures delivered before the University of London at King's College in May 1925. 64 p., 2 pl. London: University of London Press, 1926. [CB 20/198]

GALLOWAY, J.J. A manual of foraminifera. xiv, 483 p., 42 pl. (James Furman Kemp memorial series, 1) Bloomington, Ind.: Principia Press, 1933.
Reviewed by Charles A. Kofoid, *Isis*, 1934, 20: 498-9.

GUDGER, E.W. Coelenterates as enemies of fishes. 1. Hydras and sessile colonial hydroids as fish-eaters. *Ann.Mag.Natur. Hist.*, 1934, 13: 192-212, 2 pl., 7 fig.; 2. Jelly fishes as fish-eaters. *Bull.N.Y.Zool.Soc.*, 1934, 37: 47-58, 16 fig.

GUDGER, E.W. Horseshoe crabs with forked tails. *Bull.N.Y. Zool.Soc.*, 1935, 38: 170-3.

GUDGER, E.W. Snow worms. Enchytraeid worms found in the snow and on the glaciers of high mountains. *Natur.Hist.*, 1923, 23: 450-6, 1 ill.

JANET, Charles. Le volvox. 3 vol. 151; 64; 180 p., 15 fig., 21 pl. Mâcon: Protat, 1912-23. [CB 18/620]

MOLL, Friedrich. Die Bohrmuschel (*Teredo navalis*) in der älteren Literatur. *Arch.Gesch.Math.Naturwiss.Tech.*, 1928, 11: 123-49, 7 ill.

NEVIANI, Antonio. Appunti per una storia intorno ai foraminiferi dall'antichità al secolo XVIII. Con appendice sugli antichi microscopi dell'Istituto di Bologna venduti all'esterno nel 1886. *Mem.Pontif.Accad.Sci.Nuovi Lincei*, 1935, *ser. 3*, 2: 131-210. [CB 48/577]

OUDEMANS, A.C. Kritisch-historisch overzicht der acarologie. [Critico-historical survey of acarology. (In Dutch)] 1. 850 v. Chr. tot 1758. viii, 500 p., 70 fig.; 2. 1759-1804. xvii, 1097 p., 269 fig. (*Tijdschr.Entomol.*, 1926, 69: suppl.; 1929, 72: suppl.) Den Haag: Nijhoff, 1926-29; 3. 1805-1850. 6 vol. xx, 3379 p. Leiden: Brill, 1936-37.
Parts 1 and 2 reviewed by G. Sarton, *Isis*, 1931, 15: 381-6.

SAVORY, Theodore H. Spiders, men and scorpions. vi, 191 p., 15 pl. London: University of London Press, 1963.
Reviewed by J. Théodoridès, *Arch.Int.Hist.Sci.*, 1964, 17: 187-8.

THORP, Raymond W.; WOODSON, Weldon D. Black widow. America's most poisonous spider. With a foreword by Emil Bogen. xi, 222 p., ill. Chapel Hill: University of North Carolina Press, 1945.
Includes brief chapters on spider lore and tarantism.

TILQUIN, André. La toile géométrique des araignées. 536 p., 8 pl. Paris: Presses Universitaires de France, 1942.
Reviewed by T.H. Savory, *Nature*, 1945, 155: 94.

LTce-bv

BONNET, Pierre. Bibliographia arancorum. Analyse méthodique de toute la littérature aranéologique jusqu'en 1939. 3 vol. in 7 parts. Toulouse: Frères Douladoure, 1945-61.
Vol. 1 reviewed by T.H. Savory, *Nature*, 1946, 157: 245-46; by Relis B. Brown, *Science*, 1946, 104: 19.

VOSMAER, G.C.J. Bibliography of sponges, 1551-1913. Edited by G.P. Bidder, and C.S. Vosmaer-Röell. xii, 234 p. Cambridge University Press, 1928. [CB 25/426]

LTdaj

NÄGLER, Kurt. Am Urquell des Lebens. Die Entdeckung der einzelligen Lebewesen von Leeuwenhoek bis Ehrenberg. 116 p., 38 fig. (Voigtländers Quellenbücher, 92) Leipzig: Voigtländer, 1918.

LTu

EITREM, S. Der Skorpion in Mythologie und Religionsgeschichte. *Symbolae Osloenses*, 1928, 7: 53-82, 6 fig.

GARDINER, J. Stanley. Black coral as a charm against rheumatism. *Nature*, 1921, 108: 505.
In Malay archipelago.

HERON-ALLEN, Edward. Barnacles in nature and in myth. xv, 180 p., 53 fig. London: Oxford University Press, 1928.
Reviewed by George Sarton, *Isis*, 1929, 12: 340.

HICKSON, Sydney J. Black coral. *Nature*, 1922, 110: 217-18.
On popular superstitions relative to black coral.

LTwb

DRAKE, Robert J. The history of non-marine malacology in British Columbia. 16 p., 1 fig. (National Museum of Canada, Bulletin 185. Contributions to Zoology) Ottawa: 1962.

LTwg-u

RIEGLER, Richard. Spinnenmythus und Spinnenaberglaube in der neueren Erzählungsliteratur. *Schweiz.Arch.Volksk.*, 1925, 26: 55-88.

WEIDNER, Herbert. Volkskundliches von Insekten, Spinnen, Tausendfüssern und Krebsen aus dem bayerischen Vogtland und dem östlichen Frankenwald. *Sudhoffs Arch.*, 1941, 33: 205-33, 2 fig.

LTxf-JA

WOODRUFF, Lorande Loss. Some pioneers in microscopy, with special reference to protozoölogy. *Trans.N.Y.Acad.Sci.*, 1939, 1: no. 5, 74-7.

LTyJO

GRAY, Ernest. *Stylonichia mytillus* and the lunar periods. *Nature*, 1951, 167: 38.

LTyLL

BLIAKHER, L.Ia. Istoriia embriologii v rossii XIX-XX vv.: bespozvonotschnie. [History of embryology in Russia, 19th and 20th centuries. Invertebrate. (In Russian)] 626 p., ill. Leningrad: Biblioteka Akademii Nauk, SSSR, 1959.
Reviewed by Charles W. Bodemer, *Isis*, 1962, 53: 535-7.

LTyLO

GUDGER, E.W. On spider webs and spider web fish nets. *Zool. Soc.Bull.N.Y.*, 1918, 21: 1687-9.

GUDGER, E.W. Spiders as fishermen. *Natur.Hist.*, 1922, 22: 565-8, 1 fig.

GUDGER, E.W. Spiders as fishermen and hunters. *Natur.Hist.*, 1925, 25: 261-75, ill.

LTyLP

REINHARD, Edward G. Landmarks of parasitology. 1. The discovery of the life cycle of the liver fluke. 2. Demonstrations of the life cycle and pathogenicity of the spiral threadworm. *Exp.Parasitol.*, 1957, 6: 208-32; 1958, 7: 108-23.

STEWART, Ileen E. Helminths in history. *Sci.Mon.*, 1951, 72: 345-52.
An account of parasitic worms from about 1600 B.C. to the present.

LTyLS

LAMEERE, Aug. Histoire de la classification des mollusques. *Mélanges Paul Pelseneer*, p. 1-12. (Mémoires du Musée Royal d'Histoire Naturelle de Belgique, *2e sér.*, fasc. 3) Bruxelles: 1936.

LU ENTOMOLOGY

see also SQ BEES
SR SILK WORM CULTURE

LUc general history

BODENHEIMER, F.S. Materialien zur Geschichte der Entomologie bis Linné. 2 vol. x, 498 p., 155 fig., 24 pl.; vi, 496 p., 100 fig. Berlin: Junk, 1928-29.
Reviewed by George Sarton, *Isis*, 1930, 13: 388-92; 14: 454-6.

CALVERT, Philip P. Entomology, scientific and human aspects. *Proc.Amer.Phil.Soc.*, 1942, 86: 123-9.

ELTRINGHAM, Harry. Butterfly lore. 180 p. Oxford: Clarendon Press; London: Oxford University Press, 1923.

ESSIG, E.O. A history of entomology. x, 1029 p., 263 fig. New York: Macmillan, 1931.
Reviewed by Charles A. Kofoid, *Isis*, 1932, 17: 447-50.

ESSIG, E.O. A sketch history of entomology. *Osiris*, 1936, 2: 80-123. [CB 48/577]

HORN, Walther; KAHLE, Ilse; KORSCHEFSKY, R. Über entomologische Sammlungen, Entomologen und Entomo-Museologie: Ein Beitrag zur Geschichte der Entomologie. 3 pt. vi, 536 p., 38 pl. (Entomologische Beihefte, 2-4) Berlin: Friedländer, 1935-37.
Reviewed by N.A. Kemmer, *Lychnos*, 1940, 455-7.

HOWARD, Leland Ossian. A history of applied entomology (somewhat anecdotal). viii, 564 p., 51 pl. (Smithsonian Miscellaneous Collections, 84) Washington, D.C.: Smithsonian Institution, 1930.

IMMS, A.D. Recent advances in entomology. viii, 374 p., 84 fig. Philadelphia: Blakiston, 1931. [CB 34/506]

MYERS, J.G. Insect singers. A natural history of the cicadas. xix, 304 p., 7 pl., 116 fig. London: Routledge, 1929. [CB 57/251]

OSBORN, Herbert. A brief history of entomology, including time of Demosthenes and Aristotle to modern times with over five hundred portraits. 303 p., 58 pl. Columbus, Ohio: Spahr and Glenn, 1952.

OSBORN, Herbert. Fragments of entomological history, including some personal recollections of men and events. vii, 394 p., portr., 47 pl. Columbus, Ohio: priv. print., 1937.
Reviewed by Charles A. Kofoid, *Isis*, 1938, 29: 183.

PERFIL'EV, P.P. K istorii izucheniia moskitov. [On the history of the study of mosquitoes. (In Russian)] *Tr.Inst. Ist.Est.Tekh.*, 1962, 41: 168-82.
Mainly 20th century.

RABAUD, Étienne. La biologie des insectes, avant, pendant, après J.H. Fabre. *J.Psychol.*, 1924, 14: 705-29.

SCHRÖDER, Christoph, ed. Handbuch der Entomologie. 3. Geschichte, Literatur, Technik, Paläontologie, Phylogenie, Systematik. Bearbeiter: Anton Handlirsch. viii, 1202 p. Jena: Fischer, 1925.

THÉODORIDÈS, Jean. Contribution .. *See* LP

LUc-br

Annual Review of Entomology. 1- Palo Alto, Calif.: Annual Reviews, Inc. in cooperation with the Entomological Society of America, 1956-
Reviewed by Harold Oldroyd, *Nature*, 1961, 190: 945-6.

LUc-bu/d bibliography; literature; biography

LUce-bu

ZAUNICK, Rudolph. Gründung einer Hagen-Gesellschaft für die Bibliographie der entomologischen Literatur. *Mitt.Gesch. Med.*, 1918, 17: 177. [CB 8/371]
An appeal to found a society to complete and keep up-to-date Hermann August Hagen's "Bibliotheca Entomologiae" (Leipzig: 1862).

LUce-bv

JUNK, W., firm, publishers. Bibliographia coleopterologica. [Priced catalogue] xiv, 146 p. Berlin: Junk, 1912.

JUNK, W., firm, publishers. Bibliographia coleopterologica. [Priced catalogue] xv, 149-323 p., portr. Den Haag: W. Junk, 1935.
Paged continuously with the catalogue with the same title published in 1912.

ROONWAL, M.L. Bibliographia Acrididiorum. A bibliography of the orthopterous insects of the family Acrididae (comprising the shorthorned grasshoppers and locusts) from the earliest times to the end of 1954 (with some additions for 1955-57). (*Rec.Indian Mus.*, 1958, 56: pts. 1-4) ix, 611 p., pl. Delhi: 1961.
Reviewed by B.C.B., *Sci.Cult.*, 1962, 28: 175-6.

LUcf

JUNK, Wilhelm. Das Werden einer grossen Encyclopaedie. Eine Jubilaeums-Schrift. 21 p., portr. 's Gravenhage: Junk, 1935. [CB 45/241]
To celebrate the 25th anniversary of the beginning of the *Coleopterorum catalogus*.

JUNK, Wilhelm. Das Werden einer grossen Encyclopaedie. Part 2. Die Wahrheit um den C.C. 72 p. 's-Gravenhage: Junk, 1938.
In defense of the great Coleopterorum catalogues.

SCHENKLING, Sigmund, ed. Coleopterorum catalogus. 31 vol. (170 parts). Berlin; 's Gravenhage: Junk, 1910-40.

LUcm

CURLE, Richard. Arcana entomologica; or illustrations of new, rare and interesting insects. By J.O. Westwood. (London: William Smith, 2 vol., 1845) *J.Soc.Bibliogr. Natur.Hist.*, 1949, 2: 167-8.

LUd-bv

CARPENTER, Mathilde M. Bibliography of biographies of entomologists. *Amer.Midland Natur.*, 1945, 33: 1-116. [CB 69/231]

WADE, J.S. A bibliography of biographies of entomologists, with special reference to North American workers. *Ann. Entomol.Soc.Amer.*, 1928, 21: 429-520.

LUda

JUNK, Wilhelm. Dipterologi. 24 p. Den Haag: Junk, 1935.
List of dipterologists all over the world, together with their addresses and special fields of study.

LUm/u special aspects

LUmzJB

BRUES, C.T. Contributions of entomology to theoretical biology. *Sci.Mon.*, 1947, 64: 123-34.

LUtp

ARROW, Gilbert John. Horned beetles. A study of the fantastic in nature. Edited by W.D. Hincks. vii, 154 p., 15 pl. The Hague: Junk, 1951.

LUu

WEIDNER, Herbert. Faunistik und Volkskunde. Volkszoologisches von der Heuschrecke. *Arch.Gesch.Med.*, 1939, 32: 155-66, 5 fig.

LUw in different countries

LUwb

HATCH, Melville H. A century of entomology in the Pacific Northwest. v, 43 p., 9 ill. Seattle: University of Washington Press, 1949. [CB 75/93]

MONTGOMERY, B. Elwood. A century of odonatology in Indiana. *Proc.Indiana Acad.Sci.*, 1945, 54: 161-8.
Describing research on dragonflies during the last hundred years.

LUwb-cj

WEISS, Harry B. *The Journal of the New York Entomological Society* 1893-1942. *J.N.Y.Entomol.Soc.*, 1943, 51: 285-94.

LUwb-oq

NEEDHAM, James G. The lengthening shadow of a man and his wife. *Sci.Mon.*, 1946, 62: 140-50, 219-29.
An account of the first university department of entomology (Cornell University).

LUwe-qd

GRIFFIN, Francis J. The first entomological societies. An early chapter in entomological history in England. *Proc. Roy.Entomol.Soc.London, Ser. A*, 1940, 15: 49-68.

NEAVE, S.A.; GRIFFIN, Francis J. The history of the Entomological Society of London, 1833-1933. xlvi, 244 p. London: Royal Entomological Society, 1933.
Reviewed in *Natur.Hist.Mag.*, 1933, 4: 147-8.

LUwf-nh

GILLIÉRON, Jules. Généalogie des mots qui désignent l'abeille, d'après l'Atlas linguistique de la France. 360 p. Paris: Champion, 1918.

LUwq

EFFLATOUN, Hassan C. The development of entomological science in Egypt. *Trans.4th Int.Congr.Entomol.* (Ithaca, 1928), (2), p. 737-42. Naumburg a/Saale: G. Pätz, 1929.

LUxe

KALMUS, H. Simple experiments with insects. viii, 132 p., 39 fig. London: Heinemann, 1948.
Reviewed by F. Carpentier, *Rev.Quest.Sci.*, 1949, 10: 299.

LUxw museology

HORN, Walther. Über den Verbleib der entomologischen Sammlungen der Welt: Ein Beitrag zur Geschichte der Entomo-Museologie. 133 p. (Supplementa Entomologica, 12) Berlin-Dahlem: Deutsches Entomologisches Institut, 1926.

HORN, Walther; KAHLE, Ilse; KORSCHEFSKY, R. Über entomologische Sammlungen, Entomologen und Entomo-Museologie: Ein Beitrag zur Geschichte der Entomologie. 3 pt. vi, 536 p., 38 pl. (Entomologische Beihefte, 2-4) Berlin: Friedländer, 1935-37.
Reviewed by N.A. Kemmer, *Lychnos*, 1940, 455-7.

LUyLK INSECT PHYSIOLOGY

GEROULD, John H. History of the discovery of periodic reversal of heart-beat in insects. *Biol.Bull.*, 1929, 56: 215-25.
History from Malpighi's Dissertatio epistolica de bombyce (London, 1669) down to Gerould (1924).

GEROULD, John H. History of the discovery of periodic reversal of heart-beat in insects. Supplementary note. *Science*, 1930, 71: 264-5. [CB 29/302]

GEROULD, John H. Periodic reversal of heart-beat in *Bombyx* and other moths. *Trans.4th Int.Congr.Entomol.* (Ithaca, 1928), (2), p. 516-22. Naumburg a. Saale: G. Pätz, 1929. [CB 29/303]

HOULBERT, C. Les insectes: anatomie et physiologie générales. 2nd rev. ed. 374 p., 207 fig. (Encyclopédie Scientifique) Paris: Doin, 1920.
There is a historical introduction with many portraits. 1st ed. 1910.

PUMPHREY, R.J. Hearing in insects. *Biol.Rev.*, 1940, 15: 107-32.
A review of the literature from Johannes Müller in 1826 onwards.

LUyLN

UVAROV, Boris Petrovitch. Insects and climate. *Trans. Entomol.Soc.London*, 1931, 79: 1-247.
Reviewed by Richard Joel Russell, *Geogr.Rev.*, 1933, 23: 170-2.

LUyLO INSECT BEHAVIOUR

FOREL, Auguste. Le monde social des fourmis du globe comparé à celui de l'homme. 5 vol. Genève: Kundig, 1921-23.
Reviewed by R.M. May, *Isis*, 1924, 6: 578-9.

HASKINS, Caryl P. Of ants and men. vii, 244 p., 15 pl. London: Allen and Unwin, 1946.
Reviewed by A.D. Imms, *Nature*, 1946, 157: 855-6.

HOWARD, Leland Ossian. Man and insects. *Annu.Rep.Smithsonian Inst.for 1930*, p. 395-9. Washington, D.C.: 1931.
Reprinted from *J.Maryland Acad.Sci.*, 1930, vol. 1.

IMMS, A.D. Social behaviour in insects. x, 117 p., 20 fig. (Dial Press Monographs on Biological Subjects) New York: MacVeagh, 1931. [CB 32/584]

MÜLLER-GRAUPA, Edwin. Der Hochzeitsflug der Bienenkönigin. Die Geschichte eines biologischen Problems von Aristoteles bis Maeterlinck. *Arch.Gesch.Med.*, 1938, 31: 350-64.

PIERCE, George W. The songs of insects. With related material on the production, propagation, detection, and measurement of sonic and supersonic vibrations. vii, 329 p., 242 fig. Cambridge: Harvard University Press, 1948. [CB 73/176]

WHEELER, William Morton. Social life among the insects. 375 p., 116 fig. New York: Harcourt, Brace, 1923.
Reviewed by R.M. May, *Isis*, 1924, 6: 578-9.

WHEELER, William Morton. Les sociétés d'insectes. Leur origine, leur évolution. xii, 468 p., 61 fig. Paris: Doin, 1926. [CB 22/279]

WILLEM, Victor. L'architecture des abeilles. *Bull.Acad.Roy. Belg.Cl.Sci.*, 1929, 14: 672-705, 5 pl., 9 fig. [CB 27/555]

LUyLR INSECT GEOGRAPHY

LUyLRB

MACY, Ralph W.; SHEPARD, Harold H. Butterflies. A handbook of the butterflies of the United States, complete for the region north of the Potomac and Ohio Rivers and east of the Dakotas. vii, 247 p., 4 pl. Minneapolis: University of Minnesota Press, 1941. [CB 62/79]

LUyLRH

PAX, F. Über das Aussterben der Gattung Parnassius in den Sudeten. *Zool.Ann.*, 1915, 7: 81-93.

LUyLRP

SCOTT, Hugh. In the High Yemen. xix, 260 p., ill., bibliogr. London: Murray, 1942. [CB 64/447]
Account of a journey the main purpose of which was entomological.

LUyLRTcm

ESAKI, Teiso, *et al.* Nippon Konchu Zukan. Iconographia insectorum Japonicorum. (In Japanese) [*ca.* 2500] p. Tokyo: Hokuryukwan, 1932.
Latin index of 97 p.

LUyLS SYSTEMATIC ENTOMOLOGY

STAIG, Robert A. The Fabrician types of insects in the Hunterian Collection at Glasgow University. Coleoptera: part I. xvi, 110 p., 28 pl. Cambridge University Press, 1931. [CB 32/576]

WILSON, H.F.; DONER, M.H. The historical development of insect classification. 133 p. Madison, Wis.: priv. print., 1937. [CB 54/536]

LUza APPLIED ENTOMOLOGY; INSECT CONTROL

for plant pests *see* SD

DÉCAMPS, Maurice. Mon voyage à Sainte-Hélène et destruction des termites dans la maison de l'empereur. 87 p., 11 fig., 1 map. Bordeaux: Delmas, 1937.

DETHIER, Vincent G. Chemical insect attractants and repellents. xv, 289 p., 69 fig. Philadelphia: Blakiston, 1947. [CB 73/170]
Chapter 1 is a historical introduction tracing the subject back to ethnological beginnings.

GRUVEL, Jean. Les coléoptères vésicants. 63 p., 1 pl. Paris: Foulon, 1957.
Reviewed by Jean Théodoridès, *Arch.Int.Hist.Sci.*, 1957, 10: 158-9.

HOWARD, Leland Ossian. Fighting the insects. The story of an entomologist. Telling of the life and experiences of the writer. xvii, 333 p. New York: Macmillan, 1933. [CB 38/603]

KOFOID, Charles A., ed. Termites and termite control. A report to the Termite investigations committee. xxv, 734 p., front., 181 fig. Berkeley, Calif.: University of California Press, 1934.

NICOL, Hugh. Biological control of insects. 173 p., 8 pl. Harmondsworth: Penguin Books, 1943.
Historical notes throughout.
Reviewed in *Nature*, 1943, 152: 399.

TOTHILL, John Douglas. The coconut moth in Fiji. A history of its control by means of parasites. By J.D. Tothill, assisted by T.H.C. Taylor and R.W. Paine. vii, 269 p., 34 pl. London: Imperial Bureau of Entomology, 1930.

LUza-bv

CLAPP, W.F.; KENK, R. Marine borers. An annotated bibliography. xii, 1136 p. Washington: Office of Naval Research, Department of the Navy, 1963.
Comprehensive bibliography covering the period from the earliest days of printing to 1954.

LUza-bx

REGNIER, Robert. Matériaux pour l'organisation d'une exposition de zoologie agricole et d'entomologie appliquée. L'Exposition Zoologique et Florale du Jardin des Plantes de Rouen (19-23 juin, 1924). (Avec la collaboration de R. Pussard et E. Le Graverend.) *Bull.Soc.Amis Sci.Natur.Rouen*, 1924-25, 60-61: 223-60.

LUza-wb

HOWARD, Leland Ossian. The rise of applied entomology in the United States. *Annu.Rep.Smithsonian Inst.for 1930*, p. 387-93. Washington, D.C.: 1931.
Paper read at the twelfth annual meeting of the Agricultural History Society, Washington, D.C., Apr. 29, 1929. Reprinted from *Agr.Hist.*, 1929, 3: 131-9.

LUza-wn

CHESNOVA, L.V. [The contribution of I.I. Mechnikov to the development of applied entomology in Russia. (In Russian)] *Vop.Ist.Est.Tekh.*, 1959, no. 7, 162-6.

LV VERTEBRATE ZOOLOGY

LVce

WOOD, Casey Albert. An introduction to the literature of vertebrate zoology: based chiefly on the titles in the Blacker Library of Zoology, the Emma Shearer Wood Library of Ornithology, the Bibliotheca Osleriana, and other Libraries of McGill University, Montreal. xix, 643 p. London: Oxford University Press, 1931.
Contains partially annotated catalogue of the titles on vertebrate zoology in the libraries of McGill University. Reviewed by C.A. Kofoid, *Isis*, 1932, 18: 207-8; by F.J. Cole, *Nature*, 1932, 130: 111-12.

LVwa

KRUMBIEGEL, Ingo. Die Amphibienkenntnisse im ältesten Amerika, nebst einigen ornithologischen Bemerkungen. *Zool. Anz.*, 1928, 79: 250-6, 4 fig.

LVyLG

LIPPMAN, Harold E. Stress, the adaptation mechanism, and the metamorphic evolution of the vertebrates. *J.Nat.Med.Ass.*, 1961, 53: 582-92.

LVyLI

VIALLETON, Louis. Morphologie générale; membres et ceintures des vertébrés tétrapodes; critique morphologique du transformisme. viii, 710 p., 270 fig. Paris: Gaston Doin, 1923.
Reviewed by L. Guinet, *Isis*, 1924, 6: 435-7.

LVyLL

HUETTNER, Alfred F. Fundamentals of comparative embryology of the vertebrates. 2nd ed. xviii, 309 p., 197 fig. New York: Macmillan, 1949. [CB 75/93]
First edition 1941. The first chapter is historical: History and theories of development.

LVyLS

AMLINSKII, I.E. Nachal'nyi etap razvitiia metoda gomologii i ego rol' v reforme sravnitel'noi anatomii i sistematiki pozvonochnykh zhivotnykh. [First stage of the development of the method of homologies and its role in the reform of the comparative anatomy and taxonomy of vertebrates. (In Russian)] *Tr.Inst.Ist.Est.Tekh.*, 1961, 36: 286-93.

BALSS, Heinrich. Zur Geschichte der Systematik der Wirbeltiere. *Archeion*, 1933, 15: 16-26.

LW ICHTHYOLOGY

see also SS FISHERY; FISHING

LWc general history

COLES, Robert R. Hippocampus the elusive. Ancient and present-day knowledge concerning the sea horse. *Natur.Hist.*, 1932, 32: 181-7, 9 fig.

EASTMAN, Charles R. Olden time knowledge of Hippocampus. *Annu.Rep.Smithsonian Inst.for 1915*, p. 349-57, 4 pl. Washington, D.C.: 1916.

GUDGER, E.W. Dolphins and fishes in harness. *Salmon Trout Mag.*, 1938, no. 91, 123-7, 4 fig.

GUDGER, E.W. The fish in the iron mask and other fishes with iron rings around their necks. *Sci.Mon.*, 1938, 46: 281-5.

GUDGER, E.W. Fishes and rings. Notes and illustrations of various fishes wearing rubber bands. *Sci.Mon.*, 1937, 45: 503-12.

GUDGER, E.W. Foreign bodies found embedded in the tissues of fishes. *Natur.Hist.*, 1922, 22: 452-7, 6 fig.

GUDGER, E.W. History of the spotted eagle ray, *Aëtobatus narinari* together with a study of its external structures. *Pap.Tortugas Lab.Carnegie Inst.*, 1914, 6: 243-323, 10 pl.
The earliest reference to the spotted eagle ray is by Claude d'Abbeville, Paris 1614.

GUDGER, E.W. The miraculous draught of fishes - an explanation. *Nature*, 1922, 110: 572-3.

GUDGER, E.W. The natural history and geographical distribution of the pointed-tailed ocean sunfish (*Masturus lanceolatus*), with notes on the shape of the tail. *Proc.Zool. Soc.London, ser. A*, 1937, 107: 353-96, 5 pl.

GUDGER, E.W. The quest for the smallest fish. *Natur.Hist. Mag.*, 1941, 48: 216-23, fig.

GUDGER, E.W. Rubber bands on mackerel and other fishes. *Ann. Mag.Natur.Hist.*, 1929, 4: 405-11, 1 pl.

GUDGER, E.W. Strange stories of fish. *Sci.Mon.*, 1942, 55: 532-5, 1 fig.

GUDGER, E.W. A three-eyed haddock, with notes on other three-eyed fishes. *Amer.Natur.*, 1928, 62: 559-70, 6 fig.

GUDGER, E.W. An unusually large (53 mm.) two-headed brook trout, *Salmo fontinalis*. 10 p., 3 fig. (*Amer.Mus. Novitates*, 369) New York: 1929.

GUDGER, E.W.; MACDONALD, Samuel M. The rarest of the ocean sunfishes. *Sci.Mon.*, 1935, 41: 396-408.

JAGOW, Kurt. Kulturgeschichte des Herings. v, 158 p. Langensalza: Wendt, 1920.

MACFARLANE, John Muirhead. The evolution and distribution of fishes. ix, 564 p. New York: Macmillan, 1923.

ROULE, Louis. Les poissons migrateurs. Leçon d'ouverture du cours d'ichthyologie professé au Muséum national d'histoire naturelle. 27 p. Paris: A. Davy, 1914.

SMITH, Bertram G. The heterodontid sharks: their natural history, and the external development of *Heterodontus japonicus* based on notes and drawings by Bashford Dean. In: The Bashford Dean Memorial Volume: archaic fishes, p. 649-770, 7 pl. New York: American Museum of Natural History, 1942.

LWc-bv

GUDGER, Eugene Willis. Bibliography of Dr E.W. Gudger's contributions to the history of ichthyology (1905-1951). *Isis*, 1951, 42: 237-42.

LWce-bu

GUDGER, E.W. A bibliographer turns detective. How a bibliographer of fish literature "ran down" an obscure citation to its ultimate source. *Sci.Mon.*, 1939, 48: 345-9.

LWce-bv

DEAN, Bashford. Bibliography of fishes. Enl. and ed. by C.R. Eastman. 3 vol. 1, 2. Author list. xii, 718 p.; 10,702 p.; 3. Subject index, list of general bibliographies, voyages, periodicals, etc. xvi, 707 p. Extended and enl. by E.W. Gudger, with the collaboration of A.W. Henn. New York: American Museum of Natural History, 1916-23.
Reviewed by George Sarton, *Isis*, 1924, 6: 456-9.
See also below: Gudger, E.W. The classified continuation card catalogue of the Bibliography of fishes.

GUDGER, E.W. The classified continuation card catalogue of the Bibliography of fishes [by Bashford Dean]. *Science*, 1925, 61: 516-17.

GUDGER, E.W. Dean's "Bibliography of fishes". A historical sketch. *Natur.Hist.*, 1924, 24: no. 3, 7 p.

LWcm

NISSEN, Claus. Die ichthyologische Illustration. *Folium*, 1951, 1: 105-10.

NISSEN, Claus. Schöne Fischbücher. Kurze Geschichte der ichthyologischen Illustration. Bibliographie fischkundlicher Abbildungswerke. 108 p. Stuttgart: Hempe, 1951. [CB 79/180]
Reviewed by A. Schierbeek, *Arch.Int.Hist.Sci.*, 1952, 5: 413.

LWyLG/LL FISHES: BIOLOGY

LWyLG

SMITH, J.L.B. Old fourlegs. The story of the coelacanth. 260 p., 7 fig., 7 pl. London: Longmans, Green, 1956.
Reviewed by D.R. Rome, *Rev.Quest.Sci.*, 1956, 17: 624-5.

LWyLJ

DANIEL, J. Frank. The Elasmobranch fishes. xii, 334 p., 260 fig. Berkeley, Calif.: University of California Press, 1922. [CB 14/568]
Elaborate anatomical description of *Heptanchus maculatus*.

GUDGER, E.W. Abnormal dentition in sharks, Selachii. *Bull. Amer.Mus.Natur.Hist.*, 1937, 73: 249-80, 21 fig.

GUDGER, E.W. Abnormalities in flatfishes (Heterosomata). 1. Reversal of sides. A comparative study of the known data. *J.Morphol.*, 1935, 58: 1-39, 5 fig.

GUDGER, E.W. Oral breathing valves in fishes. *J.Morphol.*, 1946, 79: 263-85, 11 fig.

LWyLK

ATZ, James W. The balanced aquarium myth. *Aquarist*, 1949, 14: 159-60, 179-82.

GUDGER, E.W. How difficult parturition in certain viviparous sharks and rays is overcome. *J.Elisha Mitchell Sci.Soc.*, 1951, 67: 56-86, 18 fig.

GUDGER, E.W. Is the sting ray's sting poisonous? A historical résumé showing the development of our knowledge that it is poisonous. *Bull.Hist.Med.*, 1943, 14: 467-504, 12 fig.

LWyLL

OPPENHEIMER, Jane M. Historical introduction to the study of teleostean development. *Osiris*, 1936, 2: pt. 5, 124-48. [CB 52/596]

SOUTHWELL, T.; PRASHAD, B. Embryological and developmental studies of Indian fishes. *Rec.Indian Mus.*, 1919, 16: 215-40. [CB 8/371]

LWyLO FISHES: BEHAVIOUR

EVANS, Bergen. Concerning rains of fishes. *Science*, 1946, 103: 713.
Sceptical answer to Gudger, *see* below.

GUDGER, E.W. The alleged pugnacity of the swordfish and the spearfishes as shown by their attacks on vessels. *Mem. Asiatic Soc.Bengal*, 1940, 12: 215-315, 9 pl., 22 fig. [CB 61/455]
A study of their behavior and the structures which make possible these attacks.

GUDGER, E.W. The angler-fishes, *Lophius piscatorius* et *americanus*, use the lure in fishing. *Amer.Natur.*, 1945, 79: 542-8, 1 fig.

GUDGER, E.W. The candiru, the only vertebrate parasite of man. Foreword by A.C. Warthin. xviii, 120 p., 18 ill. New York: Hoeber, 1930. [CB 32/586]

GUDGER, E.W. Does the sting ray strike and poison fishes? *Sci.Mon.*, 1946, 63: 110-16, 4 fig.

GUDGER, E.W. Fishes that play "leapfrog". *Amer.Natur.*, 1944, 78: 451-63, 1 fig.

GUDGER, E.W. Fishes that swim heads to tails in single file. *Copeia*, 1944, 152-4.

GUDGER, E.W. Is the giant catfish, *Silurus glanis*, a predator on man? *Sci.Mon.*, 1945, 61: 451-4, 1 fig.

GUDGER, E.W. Live fishes impacted in the pharynx of man. *Arch.Pathol.Lab.Med.*, Sept. 1926, 2: 355-75; Sept. 1927, 4: 346-55.

GUDGER, E.W. More live fishes impacted in the throats of men. *Amer.J.Surg.*, 1933, 22: 573-5.

GUDGER, E.W. More rains of fishes. *Ann.Mag.Natur.Hist.*, 1929, 3: 1-26, 2 fig., 1 pl. [CB 28/552]

GUDGER, E.W. The myth of the shipholder: studies in Echeneis or Remora. *Ann.Mag.Natur.Hist.*, 1918, 2: 271-307. Postscript, *ibid.*, 1919, 4: 17-21.

GUDGER, E.W. On the alleged penetration of the human urethra by an Amazonian catfish called candiru. With a review of the allied habits of other members of the family Pygidiidae. *Amer.J.Surg.*, 1930, 8: 170-88, 443-57.

GUDGER, E.W. Physalia, the fish-eater. The Portuguese Man-of-War sails the Tropic Seas and discharges its stinging batteries when small fishes touch its tentacles. *Anim.Kingdom*, 1942, 45: 62-6, 2 fig.

GUDGER, E.W. Rains of fishes. *Natur.Hist.*, 1921, 21: 607-19. [CB 12/646]

GUDGER, E.W. Rains of fishes - myth or fact? *Science*, 1946, 103: 693-4.

GUDGER, E.W. Sargasso weed fish "nests" made by flying fishes not by sargasso fishes (antennariids): a historical survey. *Amer.Natur.*, 1937, 71: 363-81, 8 fig.

GUDGER, E.W. Some instances of supposed sympathy among fishes. *Sci.Mon.*, 1929, 28: 266-71.

GUDGER, E.W. Some old time figures of the shipholder, Echeneis or Remora holding the ship. *Isis*, 1930, 13: 340-52, 9 fig.

GUDGER, E.W. Voracity in fishes. How fishes, in their search for food, occasionally choke on finny prey too large to be engulfed. *Natur.Hist.*, 1929, 29: 651-5, 5 ill.

GUDGER, E.W. The whale shark unafraid. The greatest of the sharks, *Rhineodon typus*, fears not shark, man nor ship. *Amer.Natur.*, 1941, 75: 550-68, 1 fig.

GUDGER, E.W. Wide-gab, the angler fish. How the all-mouth (*Lophius piscatorius*) sometimes attempts more than it can accomplish. Instances in which it has tried to swallow geese and sea gulls. With three drawings by Lynn Bogue Hunt. *Natur.Hist.*, 1929, 29: 155-9.

JOUBIN, Louis. Le docteur Schmidt et la vie des anguilles. *Rev.Deux Mondes*, 15 juillet, 1934, 401-23.

ROULE, Louis. Les poissons migrateurs, leur vie et leur pêche. Un important problème d'histoire naturelle océanographique et économique. 175 p. (Bibliothèque de Culture Générale) Paris: Flammarion, 1922.

ROULE, Louis. Les migrations et la ponte de l'anguille. *Rev. Sci.*, avril 1923, 28: 225-34. [CB 15/185]

LWyLR FISHES: GEOGRAPHY

GUDGER, E.W. The distribution of Ruvettus, the oil-fish, throughout the South Seas, as shown by the distribution of the peculiar wooden hook used in its capture. *Amer.Natur.*, 1928, 62: 467-77, 3 fig.

GUDGER, E.W. The geographical distribution of the whale-shark (*Rhineodon typus*). *Proc.Zool.Soc.London*, 1934, 863-93, 1 pl., 2 fig.

LWyLRB

GUDGER, E.W. Another capture on the New Jersey coast of the basking shark, *Cetorhinus maximus*. *Science*, 1930, 72: 341-3.

GUDGER, E.W. Giant fishes of North America. Titans such as the average angler envisions only in the most golden of his dreams come to light when we examine the records of the Oregon sturgeon and alligator gar. *Natur.Hist.Mag.*, 1942, 49: 115-21, 7 fig.

LWyLRC

GUDGER, E.W. The giant fresh-water fishes of South America. *Sci.Mon.*, 1943, 57: 500-13, 12 fig.

LWyLRD

GUDGER, E.W. Giant freshwater fish of Europe. *Field*, 1945, 186: 110-11, 3 fig.

LWyLRR

GUDGER, E.W. The giant freshwater fishes of Asia. *J.Bombay Natur.Hist.Soc.*, 1945, 45: 374-90, 5 pl., 4 fig.

LWyLRW

GUDGER, E.W. Bathytoshia, the giant stingaree of Australia. The largest of the sting-ray tribe in the Seven seas. *Australian Mus.Mag.*, 1937, 6: 205-10, 4 fig.

LWyLRWu

WHITLEY, Gilbert P. *Ompax spatuloides* Castelnau, a mythical Australian fish. *Amer.Natur.*, 1933, 67: 563-7.

LWyLRX

GUDGER, E.W. The giant fresh-water perch of Africa. *Sci. Mon.*, 1944, 58: 269-72, 5 fig.

LX HERPETOLOGY

BELLAIRS, Angus d'A. Reptiles: life history, evolution, and structure. 192 p., fig., tables. New York: Harper, 1960.

GOULD, Rupert Thomas. The case for the sea serpent. xii, 291 p. London: Allan, 1930.

LEY, Willy. Salamanders and other wonders. Still more adventures of a romantic naturalist. x, 293 p., 43 ill. by Olga Ley. New York: Viking Press, 1955.
Reviewed by Conway Zirkle, *Isis*, 1956, 47: 433-4.

LUCAS, Frederic A. Historic tortoises and other aged animals. *Natur.Hist.*, 1922, 22: 301-5.

PERRIER, Edmond. Les serpents de mer. *Aesculape*, 1913, 3: 25-9, 16 fig.

LXnb

HOWEY, M. Oldfield. The encircled serpent: serpent symbolism in all countries and ages. 423 p. London: Rider, 1926.

POTTER, Edwin S. Serpents in symbolism, art and medicine. xv, 85 p. Santa Barbara, Calif.: priv. print., 1937. [CB 52/596]

LXu

GUDGER, E.W. Jenny Hanivers, dragons and basilisks in the old natural history books and in modern times. *Sci.Mon.*, 1934, 38: 511-23.

INGERSOLL, Ernest. Dragons and dragon lore. Introduction by Henry Fairfield Osborn. 203 p. New York: Payson, 1928.

JACOBY, Adolf. Von verschluckten Schlangen und Eidechsen. *Oberdeut.Z.Volksk.*, 1932, 6: 13-27.

MOORE, Clifford B. America's mythical snakes. *Sci.Mon.*, 1949, 68: 52-8.

MOORE, Clifford B. The grinning crocodilian and his folklore. *Sci.Mon.*, 1954, 78: 225-31.
A history of the popular notions concerning crocodiles and alligators from Herodotus to the present.

SMITH, Grafton Elliot. The evolution of the dragon. xx, 234 p. Manchester: University Press, 1919.

LXwb

SCHMIDT, Karl P.; DAVIS, D. Dwight. Field book of snakes of the United States and Canada. With four colored plates and 103 drawings by Albert A. Enzenbacher and 82 photographs from life. xiii, 365 p. New York: Putnam, 1941.
The introduction includes a chapter on the history of herpetology in the United States (p. 11-16), with portraits.

LXyLJ

CUNNINGHAM, Bert. Axial bifurcation in serpents. vii, 117 p. Durham, N.C.: Duke University Press, 1937. [CB 54/535]

FRANCIS, Eric Thomas Brazil. The anatomy of the salamander. With an historical introduction by F.J. Cole. xxi, 381 p., 26 pl. Oxford: Clarendon Press, 1934.
Reviewed in *Nature*, 1935, 136: 87.

LY ORNITHOLOGY

LYc general history

BOUBIER, Maurice. L'évolution de l'ornithologie. ii, 308 p. (Nouvelle Collection Scientifique) Paris: Alcan, 1925.
New impression, 1932 [CB 38/602]
Reviewed by L. Guinet, *Isis*, 1926, 8: 515-17.

BOUBIER, Maurice. Les oiseaux. L'ornithologie et ses bases scientifiques. 308 p., 10 pl. Paris: Doin, 1926. [CB 20/198]

FISHER, James. A history of birds. x, 205 p., ill. Boston: Houghton Mifflin, 1954.
Reviewed by Frank A. Pitelka, *Sci.Mon.*, 1955, 81: 46-7.

HEILMANN, Gerhard. The origin of birds. vii, 208 p., ill., pl. London: Witherby, 1926.

HERRICK, Francis Hobart. The American eagle, a study in natural and civil history. xxii, 267 p., 32 pl., 24 fig. New York: Appleton-Century, 1934.
Reviewed by C.A. Kofoid, *Isis*, 1935, 24: 183-4.

KRUTCH, Joseph Wood; ERIKSSON, Paul S.; ed. A treasury of birdlore. xviii, 390 p. Garden City: Doubleday, 1962. [CB 88/550]

LAUFER, Berthold. Ostrich egg-shell cups of Mesopotamia and the ostrich in ancient and modern times. 51 p., 9 pl., 10 fig. (Anthropology Leaflet, 23) Chicago: Field Museum of Natural History, 1926. [CB 22/278]

McCLYMONT, James R. Essays on early ornithology and kindred subjects. 35 p., 3 pl. London: Quaritch, 1920. [CB 11/453]

MILLER, Loye Holmes. Lifelong boyhood. Recollections of a naturalist afield. 226 p. Berkeley: University of California Press, 1950. [CB 77/343]

ORNITHOLOGIE als biologische Wissenschaft. 28 Beiträge als Festschrift zum 60. Geburtstag von Erwin Stresemann (22. November 1949). Hrsg. von Ernst Mayr und Ernst Schüz. xii, 283 p., portr., fig. Heidelberg: Winter, 1949. [CB 79/147]

PRATT, Ambrose. The lore of the lyrebird. With a foreword by Colin Mackenzie. 71 p. Sydney: Endeavour Press, 1933.

SCOTT, Peter. Wild chorus. Written and illustrated by Peter Scott. x, 120 p., 68 pl. London: Country Life, 1939.
On wild geese and ducks.
Reviewed by James Ritchie, *Nature*, 1940, 145: 135.

STRESEMANN, Erwin. Beiträge zur Vogelkunde. Herrn Erwin Stresemann aus Anlass der Vollendung des 60. Lebensjahres gewidmet. Hrsg. v. Gerh. Creutz. 280 p., ill. Leipzig: Akademische Verlagsgesellschaft, 1949.

STRESEMANN, Erwin. Die Entwicklung der Ornithologie von Aristoteles biz zur Gegenwart. xv, 431 p., 15 pl., 3 fig. Berlin: F.W. Peters, 1951.
Reviewed by G.W. Cottrell, *Isis*, 1952, 43: 299-300.

STRESEMANN, Erwin. Stand und Aufgaben der Ornithologie 1850 und 1925. *J.Ornithol.*, 1926, 74: 225-32.

LYce

GURNEY, J.H. Early annals of ornithology. iv, 240 p., ill. London: Witherby, 1921. [CB 12/646]

LYce-bv

FIELD MUSEUM OF NATURAL HISTORY. Catalogue of the Edward E. Ayer Ornithological Library. By John Todd Zimmer. 2 vol. x, 706 p., 12 pl. Chicago, Ill.: The Museum, 1926.
Reviewed by George Sarton, *Isis*, 1928, 10: 94.

LOW, George Carmichael. The literature of the Charadriiformes from 1894-1928. 2nd ed. revised ... and brought up to date to the end of 1928. xiii, 637 p. London: Witherby, 1931.
First publ. 1924.

STRONG, Reuben Myron. A bibliography of birds: with special reference to anatomy, behavior, biochemistry, embryology, pathology, physiology, genetics, ecology, aviculture, economic ornithology, poultry culture, evolution and related subjects. 3 vol. 1, 2. Author catalogue. 464 p.; 469 p. 1939; 3. Subject catalogue. 522 p. 1946. (Zoological series, 25) Chicago: Field Museum of Natural History, 1939-46.
Reviewed by E.W. Gudger, *Science*, 1947, 106: 71.

LYcm

ALEXANDER, W.B. Ornithological illustration. *Endeavour*, 1953, 12: 144-53, 19 fig.

ANKER, Jean. Bird books and bird art. An outline of the literary history and iconography of descriptive ornithology. Based principally on the collection of books containing plates with figures of birds and their eggs now in the University Library at Copenhagen and including a catalogue of these works. Issued by the University Library Copenhagen to commemorate the inauguration of the new building of the library. xix, 251 p., 12 pl. Copenhagen: Levin & Munksgaard, 1938. [CB 60/155]

NISSEN, Claus. Die illustrierten Vogelbücher, ihre Geschichte und Bibliographie. 223 p., 16 pl., 8 fig. Stuttgart: Hiersemann, 1953.
Reviewed by G.W. Cottrell, *Isis*, 1955, 46: 370-2.

LYcv

ALLEN, Arthur A. Stalking birds with color camera. Edited by Gilbert Grosvenor. viii, 328 p., ill. Washington, D.C.: National Geographic Society, 1951. [CB 78/189]

LYdae

PALMER, T.S. The Deane collection of portraits of ornithologists - the development of an idea. *Science*, 1944, 100: 288-90.

LYdaj

PEATTIE, Donald Culross. A gathering of birds. An anthology of the best ornithological prose. Edited, with biographical sketches. Illustrated by Edward Shenton. xii, 379 p. New York: Dodd, Mean, 1939. [CB 57/252]

LYu

HARRISON, Thomas P. Bird of paradise: Phoenix Redivivus. *Isis*, 1960, 51: 173-80.

INGERSOLL, Ernest. Birds in legend, fable and folklore. v, 292 p. London: Longmans, Green, 1923.

LYw in different countries

LYwb

ALLEN, Elsa G. The history of American ornithology before Audubon. 207 p., 55 fig. (*Trans.Amer.Phil.Soc., new ser.*, 41: no. 3) Philadelphia: 1951.
Reviewed by G.W. Cottrell, *Isis*, 1952, 43: 298.

AMERICAN ORNITHOLOGISTS' UNION. Fifty years' progress of American ornithology, 1883-1933. Published by the American Ornithologists' Union on the occasion of its semi-centennial anniversary. 249 p., front. Lancaster, Pa.: 1933.
Reviewed by C.A. Kofoid, *Isis*, 1934, 22: 301-3.

LYwb-da

HUME, Edgar Erskine. Ornithologists of the United States Army Medical Corps. Thirty-six biographies. With foreword by Alexander Wetmore. xxv, 583 p., 110 ill. Baltimore: Johns Hopkins Press, 1942.
Reviewed by George Sarton, *Isis*, 1942, 34: 36-8.

LYwb-qb

BATCHELDER, Charles Foster. An account of the Nuttall Ornithological Club 1873-1919. 109 p., 1 pl., 36 portr. (Memoir, 8) Cambridge, Mass.: The Club, 1937. [CB 54/535]

LYwd-da

GEBHARDT, Ludwig. Die Ornithologen Mittel-Europas. 404 p. Giessen: Brühlscher Verlag, 1964.

LYwd-tq

FRIEDMANN, Herbert. The symbolic goldfinch. Its history and significance in European devotional art. xxxii, 254 p., 157 ill. (The Bollingen Series, 7) New York: Pantheon Books, 1946. [CB 70/262]

LYwe-bv

MULLENS, William Herbert; SWANN, H. Kirke. A bibliography of British ornithology from the earliest times to the end of 1912, including biographical accounts of the principal writers and bibliographies of their published works. 6 parts. xx, 673 p. 673-91 l. numbered on one side only. London: Macmillan, 1916-17. Supplement. A chronological list of British birds by H. Kirke Swann. xvii, 42 p. London: Wheldon & Wesley, 1923.

LYxx museums

STRESEMANN, Erwin. Die Anfänge ornithologischer Sammlungen. *J.Ornithol.*, 1923, 71: 112-27.

LYyLK/LN BIRDS: BIOLOGY

LYyLK

DANCHAKOVA, Vera. Histoire d'un coq. Sa cinétique sexuelle. Avec la collaboration de A. Vashkevitschuite, Jankovsky, Massiavitchus et Kinderis. 41 p., 12 fig. (Actualités Scientifiques et Industrielles, 370) Paris: Hermann, 1936.

LYyLL

ROMANOFF, Alexis L.; ROMANOFF, Anastasia J. The avian egg. xiii, 908 p., 424 ill. New York: Wiley, 1949.
Reviewed by Conway Zirkle, *Isis*, 1950, 41: 134.

LYyLN

BOUBIER, Maurice. L'oiseau et son milieu. 287 p. (Bibliothèque de Philosophie Scientifique) Paris: Flammarion, 1922.

PEARSON, Thomas Gilbert. Adventures in bird protection. An autobiography. xiv, 459 p. New York: Appleton-Century, 1937.

LYyLO BIRDS: BEHAVIOUR

ARMSTRONG, Edward A. Bird display. An introduction to the study of bird psychology. xvi, 381 p., 22 pl. Cambridge University Press, 1942.
Reviewed by B.W. Tucker, *Nature*, 1943, 151: 542-3.

DEWAR, John M. The bird as a diver: a contribution to the natural history of diving birds. xii, 173 p. London: Witherby, 1924.
Reviewed by J.S. Huxley, *Nature*, 1924, 114: 494.

GUDGER, E.W. How the laughing gull, the feathered buccaneer of Florida waters, gets its dinner. *Sci.Mon.*, 1929, 29: 435-9, 3 fig.

MORTENSEN, Hans Christian Cornelius. Studies in bird migration. Being the collected papers of H. Chr. C. Mortensen, 1856-1921. Edited by Poul Jespersen and A. Vedel Tåning. 272 p., ill., bibliogr. Copenhagen: Munksgaard (for the Dansk Ornithologisk Forening), 1950.
Reviewed by A. Landsborough Thomson, *Nature*, 1951, 168: 216.

NICE, Margaret M. The earliest mention of territory. *Condor*, 1953, 55: 316-17. [CB 83/202]

RITTER, Wm. E.; BENSON, Seth B. "Is the poor bird demented?" Another case of "shadow boxing". *Auk*, 1934, 51: 169-79.
Another authenticated report of birds' fighting their own images reflected from mirrors.

ROWAN, William. The riddle of migration. xiv, 151 p. Baltimore: Williams and Wilkins, 1931.
Reviewed by E.W. MacBride, *Nature*, 1932, 129: 561-2.

RYDZEWSKI, W. A historical review of bird marking. *Dansk Ornith.Foren.Tidsskr.*, 1951, 45: 61-95.

LYyLR BIRDS: GEOGRAPHY

LYyLRA

CHAPMAN, Frank Michler. Autobiography of a bird-lover. xiii, 420 p., 4 pl. by Louis Agassiz Fuertes, 81 ill. New York: Appleton, 1933. [CB 40/367 and CB 69/205]
Contains accounts of the author's ornithological investigations in the United States, South America, West Indies and Mexico.

LYyLRBce-bv

GRINNELL, Joseph. A bibliography of California ornithology. A contribution from the Museum of Vertebrate Zoology of the University of California. 106 p. (Pacific Coast Avifauna, 5) Santa Clara, Calif.: Cooper Ornithological Club, 1909. Second installment to end of 1923. 191 p. (Pacific Coast Avifauna, 16) Santa Clara, Calif.: 1924. Third installment to end of 1938. (Edited by A.H. Miller and H.W. Grinnell) 235 p. (Pacific Coast Avifauna, 26) Santa Clara, Calif.: 1939.

LYyLRD

YEATES, G.K. Bird life in two deltas. Being the diaries of a bird photographer in the estuaries of the Guadalquiver and the Rhone and their neighbourhoods. 159 p., 68 pl. London: Faber and Faber, 1946.
Reviewed by Frances Pitt, *Nature*, 1947, 159: 725.

LYyLRE

TICEHURST, Claud Buchanan. A history of the birds of Suffolk. xi, 502 p., 18 pl. London: Gurney and Jackson, 1932.
Reviewed in *Nature*, 1933, 131: 568.

LYyLRG

BRETSCHER, K. Geschichtliches über die Vogelwelt des Zürichgebietes. *Vierteljahrsschr.Naturforsch.Ges.Zürich*, 1912, 56: 479-506.

LYyLRKnh

RUITER, L. Coomans de; VAN HEURN, W.C.; KRAAK, W.K. Beteekenis en etymologie van de wetenschappelijke namen der Nederlandsche vogels. [Significance and etymology of the scientific names of Dutch birds. (In Dutch)] 160 p. Kampen: Club Nederlandsche Vogelkundigen, 1949. [CB 80/131]
Reviewed by H. Engel, *Centaurus*, 1951, 1: 277.

LYyLRM

LEWIS, Ernest, pseud. for Ernest Blakeman Vesey. In search of the gyr-falcon: an account of a trip to North-West Iceland. With a memoir of the author. xxiii, 235 p., 24 pl. London: Constable, 1938.
Reviewed by Seton Gordon, *Nature*, 1938, 142: 1141.

LYyLRP

ALLOUSE, Bashir E. A handlist of the birds of Iraq. With short notes on their status in the country. 66 p. (Iraq Natural History Museum's Publication, 2) Baghdad: Government Press, 1950.

LYyLRW

BUICK, T. Lindsay. The mystery of the Moa. New Zealand's avian giant. xvi, 357 p., front. New Plymouth, N.Z.: Avery, 1931.

DUFF, Roger. Pyramid Valley, Waikari, North Canterbury. 48 p., 31 ill. Christchurch, New Zealand: Association of Friends of the Canterbury Museum, 1949. [CB 77/342]
A swamp containing the richest find to date of moa remains.

LYyLRX

BANNERMAN, D.A. The birds of tropical West Africa, with special reference to those of the Gambia, Sierra Leone, the Gold Coast and Nigeria. 8 vol. London: Crown Agents for the Colonies, 1930-56.
The chapter on 'Ornithological history' gives an account of the most important field work done in the West African Colonies from 1690 to 1929.
Vol. 1 reviewed in *Natur.Hist.Mag.*, 1931, 3: 77-8.

HUTCHINSON, G. Evelyn. Marginalia. *Amer.Scient.*, 1954, 42: 300-8.
A history of (a) the dodo and solitaire, and (b) the Piltdown man.

LYyLRXnh

MOREAU, R.E. Bird-nomenclature in an East African area. *Bull.Sch.Orient.Afr.Stud.*, 1942, 10: 998-1006.

LYyLS BIRDS: SYSTEMATICS

STRESEMANN, Erwin. Die Entwicklung der Begriffe Art, Varietät, Unterart in der Ornithologie. *Mitt.Ver.Sächsischer Ornithol.*, 1927, 2: 1-8.
Reviewed by R. Zaunick, *Mitt.Gesch.Med.*, 1927, 26: 302.

LZ MAMMALOGY

ALLEN, Glover Morrill. Bats. 368 p. Cambridge: Harvard University Press, 1939. [CB 57/250]

BURRELL, Harry James. The platypus: its discovery, zoological position, form and characteristics, habits, life history, etc. ix, 227 p., 35 pl. Sydney: Angus and Robertson, 1927.
Reviewed by J.T.W., *Nature*, 1927, 120: 797-8.

CARRINGTON, Richard. Elephants. A short account of their natural history, evolution, and influence on mankind. 272 p., ill., pl. New York: Basic Books, 1959.
Reviewed by Edwin H. Colbert, *Science*, 1959, 129: 1733-4.

CARRUTHERS, Douglas. Arabian adventure. To the great Nafud in quest of the oryx. xii, 208 p., 33 pl., 2 maps. London: Witherby, 1935.

DERANIYAGALA, P.E.P. Some aspects of the Asiatic elephant in zoology and ethnography. *J.Ceylon Br.Roy.Asiatic Soc.*, 1938, 34: 126-62, 1 pl., 8 fig.; 1940, 35: 7-28, 5 fig.

THE DOLPHIN in history. Papers delivered at a symposium at the Clark Library, Oct. 13, 1962. 55 p., ill. Los Angeles: William Andrews Clark Memorial Library, University of California, 1963.

HOOIJER, Dirk Albert. Fact and fiction in hippopotamology. (Sampling the history of scientific error). *Osiris*, 1952, 10: 109-16.

KUNZ, George F. Ivory and the elephant in art, archaeology and in science. xxvi, 527 p., ill. Garden City, N.Y.: Doubleday, 1916.

LAUFER, Berthold. The giraffe in history and art. 100 p., 9 pl., 24 ill. (Anthropology Leaflet, 27) Chicago: Field Museum of Natural History, 1928. [CB 24/536]

O'MALLEY, C.D.; MAGOUN, H.W. Early concepts of the anthropomorpha. *Physis*, 1962, 4: 39-64.

OSBORN, Henry Fairfield. Proboscidea. A monograph on the discovery, evolution, migration and extinction of the mastodonts and elephants of the world. Edited by Mabel Rice Percy. 2 vol. 1. Moeitherioidea, Deinotherioidea, Mastodontoidea; 2. Stegodontoidea, Elephantoidea. New York: American Museum Press, 1936-42.
Volume 2 reviewed by D.M.S. Watson, *Nature*, 1944, 153: 5-7.

SUNAMOTO, Etsujiro. [The elephant. A general work on the elephant in all its aspects. (In Japanese with 16 p. summary in English)] 2 vol. 1-1151 p.; 1152-2169 p., ill. Osaka: Sanyusha, 1931-32.
Reviewed by Shio Sakanishi, *Isis*, 1936, 26: 191.

THOMSON, Alexander P.D. A history of the ferret. *J.Hist. Med.*, 1951, 6: 471-80, 2 fig.

ZIRKLE, Conway. The jumar or cross between the horse and the cow. *Isis*, 1941, 33: 486-506, 1 fig.

LZce-bv

RUCH, Theodore C. Bibliographia primatologica. xxvii, 241 p. Springfield: Thomas, 1941. [CB 62/79]
Classified bibliography of primates other than man.

LZcm

EASTMAN, Charles R. Early portrayals of the opossum. *Amer. Natur.*, 1915, 49: 585-94.

LZnh

SPITZER, Leo. Origin of the word jumar. *Isis*, 1942, 34: 163.

LZu

BÖHRINGER, Peter Hans. Das Wiesel, seine italienischen und rätischen Namen und seine Bedeutung im Volksglauben. 91 p. Zurich: Leeman, 1935.

BOULLET, Jean. La merveilleuse histoire de la Licorne. *Aesculape*, December 1959, 42: 3-62.
A profusely illustrated account of the history of the unicorn from antiquity to the present.

ELZE, Curt. Vom "ungeleckten Bären". *Arch.Gesch.Naturwiss. Tech.*, 1913, 5: 36-48.

HOWEY, M. Oldfield. The horse in magic and myth. xii, 238 p., ill. London: Rider, 1923.

LAUFER, Berthold. The story of the Pinna and the Syrian lamb. *J.Amer.Folklore*, 1915, 28: 103-28.

RIDDELL, W.H. Concerning unicorns. *Antiquity*, 1945, 19: 194-202, 2 pl., 1 fig.

SHEPARD, Odell. The lore of the unicorn. 312 p., 24 pl., front. London: Allen and Unwin, 1930.

LZwg-nh

SZALAY, B. Der grimme Schelch. Über "Glossentiere" und einige Tiernamen, wie Elch, Schelch, Tragelaphus, Bockhirsch, Onager, Waldesel, Brandhirsch, Equicervus. *Zool. Ann.*, 1916, 7: 127-92.

SZALAY, B. Der Meerochs. Ein Beitrag zur Geschichte des Zebu, des Büffels, des Elches, der mit "Meer" zusammengesetzten alten Tiernamen usw. *Zool.Ann.*, 1914, 6: 75-111.

LZxx

ZOOLOGICAL SOCIETY OF LONDON. List of the vertebrated animals exhibited in the gardens of the Zoological Society of London, 1828-1927. Centenary ed. 3 vol. London: Zoological Society of London, 1929.

LZyLJ/LN MAMMALS: BIOLOGY

LZyLJ

GREGORY, William King, ed. The anatomy of the gorilla: the studies of Henry Cushier Raven, and contributions by W.B. Atkinson [*et al.*]. The Henry Cushier Raven Memorial Volume. A collaborative work of the American Museum of Natural History and Columbia University. viii, 259 p., ill. New York: Columbia University Press, 1950.
Reviewed by George Erikson, *Isis*, 1952, 43: 81-3.

MIDLO, Charles; CUMMINS, Harold. Palmar and plantar dermatoglyphics in primates. iii, 198 p. (American Anatomical Memoirs, 20) Philadelphia: Wistar Institute of Anatomy and Biology, 1942. [CB 63/274]

MONTAGU, M.F. Ashley. The medio-frontal suture and the problem of metopism in the primates. *J.Roy.Anthropol.Inst.*, 1937, 67: 157-201.

MONTAGU, M.F. Ashley. The premaxilla in the primates. *Quart. Rev.Biol.*, 1935, 10: 32-59, 3 fig.; 181-208, 11 fig.

WALLS, Gordon Lynn. The vertebrate eye. xiv, 785 p. (Bulletin no. 19) Bloomfield Hills, Mich.: Cranbrook Institute of Science, 1942. [CB 64/452]

LZyLK

COURRIER, Robert. Le cycle sexuel chez la femelle des mammifères. Etude de la phase folliculaire. *Arch.Biol.*, 1924, 34: 369-477, 5 pl.
Reviewed by Henri V. Vallois, *Rev.Gén.Sci.*, 1925, 36: 218.

MUNRO, H.N. Historical introduction: the origin and growth of our present concepts of protein metabolism. In: Mammalian protein metabolism. Ed. by H.N. Munro and J.B. Allison, p. 1-29. New York: Academic Press, 1964.

LZyLL

PINCUS, Gregory. The eggs of mammals. 160 p., 33 fig. New York: Macmillan, 1936. [CB 51/271]
Comprehensive historical introduction to the subject.

LZyLN

ACADÉMIE DES SCIENCES. SECTION D'ANATOMIE ET DE ZOOLOGIE. Cétacés et phoques. [Resolution adopted by the Section on the preservation of cetaceans and seals.] *Compt.Rend.Acad. Sci.*, 1913, 157: 165. [CB 4/782]

ELTON, Charles. Voles, mice and lemmings. Problems in population dynamics. 496 p., 22 fig. Oxford: Clarendon Press, 1942. [CB 65/82]

LZyLO MAMMALS: BEHAVIOUR

GUDGER, E.W. Animal carts. How marmots, badgers and beavers serve as sleds or wagons. *Sci.Mon.*, 1935, 40: 153-7.

GUDGER, E.W. Cats as fishermen. *Natur.Hist.*, 1925, 25: 143-55, ill.

GUDGER, E.W. Does the jaguar use his tail as a lure in fishing? *J.Mammalogy,* 1946, 27: 37-49, 2 fig.

GUDGER, E.W. Feline fishermen. Some accounts of fishing by domestic cats. *Sci.Mon.,* 1945, 60: 89-96, 6 fig.

GUDGER, E.W. Fish-eating bats of India and Burma. *J.Bombay Natur.Hist.Soc.,* 1943, 43: 635-40, 1 pl., 4 fig.

GUDGER, E.W. The fish-eating bats of the Gulf of California. *Calif.Fish Game,* 1943, 29: 79-81, 2 fig.

GUDGER, E.W. Fisherman bats of the Caribbean region. *J. Mammalogy,* 1945, 26: 1-15, 5 fig.

GUDGER, E.W. How rats transport eggs. The rat-egg-wagon story traced back to 1291 A.D. *Sci.Mon.,* 1935, 40: 415-24.

GUDGER, E.W. Two fishing cats that made history. *Natur. Hist.,* 1944, 53: 371-4, ill.

MacKINNEY, Loren. Moon-happy apes, monkeys and baboons. *Isis,* 1963, 54: 120-2.

VERLAINE, Louis. Histoire naturelle de la connaissance chez le singe inférieur. 1. Le concret. 50 p.; 2. Le syncrétique. 58 p., 8 fig.; 3. L'abstrait. 54 p., 8 fig. (Actualités Scientifiques et Industrielles, 215, 320, 360) Paris: Hermann, 1935-36; 4. La notion du nombre. *Mem.Soc. Sci.Liège, sér. 4,* 1941, 4: 145-223.

YERKES, Robert M. Chimpanzees. A laboratory colony. xv, 321 p., 63 pl. New Haven: Yale University Press, 1943.
Reviewed by S. Zuckerman, *Nature,* 1944, 153: 65-6.

ZUCKERMAN, Solly. Laboratory monkeys and apes from Galen onwards. In: *Proceedings of a Conference on Research with Primates,* ed. by D.E. Pickering, p. 1-11. Beaverton, Or.: Tektronix Foundation, 1962.

LZyLR MAMMALS: GEOGRAPHY

LZyLRB

BERRY, S. Stillman. Observations of a Montana beaver canal. *J.Mammal.,* 1923, 4: 92-103, ill. Also in *Annu.Rep.Smithsonian Inst.* for 1922, p. 207-308, ill. Washington, D.C.: 1924.

HARPER, Francis. History and nomenclature of the pocket gophers (geomys) in Georgia. *Proc.Biol.Soc.Wash.,* 1952, 65: 35-8, bibliogr.

JOHNSON, David H. Systematic review of the chipmunks (genus eutamias) of California. *Univ.Calif.Publ.Zoöl.,* 1943, 48: 63-146, 1 pl., 12 fig.

ROE, Frank Gilbert. The North American buffalo: a critical study of the species in its wild state. viii, 957 p. Toronto: University of Toronto Press, 1951.
Reviewed by Edward Everett Dale, *Amer.Hist.Rev.,* 1952, 57: 557.

LZyLRR

ROOSEVELT, Kermit. The search for the giant Panda. The story of the first expedition ever to collect the strange raccoon bear near the border of Tibet. How the Field Museum Expedition obtained the first specimen of the rare Beishung, an animal never before seen by white men. With photographs by Suydam Cutting and Kermit Roosevelt. *Natur. Hist.,* 1930, 30: 3-16, ill.

LZyLS MAMMALS: SYSTEMATICS

KRUMBIEGEL, Ingo. Artkenntnis und -erkenntnis in der Säugetierkunde, ein Beitrag zur Geschichte der zoologischen Systematik. *Sitzungsber.Ges.Naturforsch.Freunde Berlin,* 1933, 110-25, 12 fig.

M SCIENCES OF MAN

for human biology *see* O

Mc

KIRKPATRICK, Edwin A. The sciences of man in the making. An orientation book. xvi, 396 p. (International Library of Psychology, Philosophy and Scientific Method) London: Kegan Paul; New York: Harcourt, Brace, 1932. [CB 38/608]

Mc-bv

BIBLIOGRAPHY of the history of the behavioral sciences. (History of the Behavioral Sciences Newsletter, 6) New York: Cornell University Medical College, Department of Psychiatry, 1963.
  This contains an addenda to the 1960 bibliography, together with the bibliography for 1961.

Mk

GUSDORF, Georges. The ambiguity of the sciences of man. *Diogenes,* 1959, no. 26, 48-70.

MA ANTHROPOLOGY, in general

for physical anthropology *see* ME
social and cultural anthropology *see* MQ

MAc general history

ANTHROPOLOGICAL SOCIETY OF WASHINGTON. Evolution and anthropology: a centennial appraisal. viii, 172 p. Washington, D.C.: The Society, 1959.
  Reviewed by H.H. Plough, *Amer.Scient.,* 1960, 48: 91-3.

BARNES, Harry Elmer. The natural state of man. *Monist,* 1923, 33: 33-80. [CB 15/218]
  Summary of the theories entertained since primitive times.

BOAS, Franz, ed. General anthropology. xi, 718 p. Boston: Heath, 1938. [CB 57/257]

BRITISH ASSOCIATION FOR THE ADVANCEMENT OF SCIENCE. Notes and queries on anthropology. 5th ed. Edited for the British Association for the Advancement of Science by a committee of section H. xvi, 404 p. London: Royal Anthropological Institute, 1929.
  First edition 1874.
  Reviewed by J.L.M., *Nature,* 1930, 126: 123-4.

CASSON, Stanley. The discovery of man. 339 p. London: Hamilton, 1939; New York: Harper, 1940.
  Reviewed by M.F. Ashley Montagu, *Isis,* 1941, 33: 302-3.

CHAPPLE, Eliot Dinsmore; COON, Carleton S. Principles of anthropology. xi, 718 p. New York: Henry Holt, 1942. [CB 63/275]

CLARK, Wilfrid Le Gros. The humanity of man. *Nature,* 1961, 191: 977-82.

DANIEL, Glyn E. The idea of man's antiquity. *Sci.Amer.,* 1959, 201: no. 5, 167-76.

ECKARDT, A. Roy. The contribution of Nomothesis in the science of man. *Amer.Scient.,* 1961, 49: 76-87.

EISELEY, Loren. The firmament of time. vii, 183 p., bibliogr. New York: Atheneum, 1960. [CB 87/567]
  Reviewed in *Amer.Scient.,* 1960, 48: 350A; by W.R. Matthews, *Nature,* 1961, 190: 943-4.

EISELEY, Loren. The immense journey. 210 p. New York: Random House, 1957.

ESSAYS in historical anthropology in honor of John R. Swanton. vi, 600 p. Washington, D.C.: Smithsonian Institution, 1940. [CB 60/159]

FROBENIUS, Leo. Des Menschen Schicksal auf dieser Erde. *Erdball,* 1931, 5: 145-58, 180-97.

GILLIN, John. The ways of men. xv, 469 p. New York: Appleton-Century-Crofts, 1948. [CB 73/177]
  An introduction to general anthropology.

GUYER, Michael F. Speaking of man. 321 p. New York: Harper, 1942. [CB 64/451]

HADDON, Alfred C. History of anthropology. 2nd ed. xiv, 144 p., ill. (The Thinker's Library, 42) London: Watts, 1934. [CB 45/291]
  First edition 1910.

KROEBER, Alfred L. Anthropology. xii, 895 p. New York: Harcourt Brace, 1948. [CB 73/177]

KROGMAN, Wilton Marion. Ancient man. The human family tree. Aboriginal physical types in the Western hemisphere. The antiquity of man and his culture in the Americas. *Ciba Symp.,* 1941, 790-824, ill.

LINTON, Ralph, ed. The science of man in the world crisis. 532 p. New York: Columbia University Press, 1945.
  Reviewed by Erwin H. Ackerknecht, *Bull.Hist.Med.,* 1945, 17: 325.

LOWIE, Robert H., ed. Essays in anthropology presented to Alfred Louis Kroeber. xxiii, 433 p. Berkeley: University of California Press, 1936.
  Reviewed by M.F. Ashley-Montagu, *Isis,* 1937, 27: 102-3.

MÜHLMANN, Wilhelm E. Geschichte der Anthropologie. 274 p. Bonn: Universitäts-Verlag, 1948. [CB 76/403]

PALMER, L.S. Man's journey through time. A first step in physical and cultural anthropochronology. xv, 184 p., ill. New York: Philosophical Library, 1959. [CB 85/396]
Reviewed by William L. Straus, *Science*, 1960, 131: 220-1.

PENNIMAN, T.K. A hundred years of anthropology. 400 p. New York: Macmillan, 1936.
Reviewed by M.F. Ashley-Montagu, *Isis*, 1936, 26: 229-32.

PHILADELPHIA ANTHROPOLOGICAL SOCIETY. Twenty-fifth anniversary studies, ed. by D.S. Davidson. vi, 235 p. (Publications of the Philadelphia Anthropological Society, 1) Philadelphia: University of Philadelphia Press, 1937. [CB 51/284]

SUCHODOLSKI, Bogdan. Remarques sur l'histoire de la philosophie de l'homme, du XVIe au XVIIIe siècle. *Rev.Syn.*, 1960, 81: 39-60.

WHITE, Lynn, ed. Frontiers of knowledge in the study of man. xiii, 330 p. New York: Harper, 1956.

MAc-br

Biennial Review of Anthropology. Vol. 1, 1959- Stanford: Stanford University Press, 1959-
Volume 1 reviewed by Melford E. Spiro, *Isis*, 1961, 52: 425-6.

MAcb

GASKIN, L.J.P. Anthropological and ethnological libraries. *Libr.Ass.Rec., 4th ser.*, 1934, 1: 193-9.

MAda

KARDINER, Abram; PREBLE, Edward. They studied man. 287 p., ill., bibliogr. Cleveland: World Publishing Company, 1961; London: Secker & Warburg, 1962. Reprinted. 255 p., ill., bibliogr. (Mentor Book) New York: New American Library, 1963. [CB 88/553]

MAdaj

COON, Carleton S. A reader in general anthropology. x, 624 p. New York: Holt, 1948. [CB 73/177]

HOEBEL, E. Adamson; JENNINGS, Jesse D.; SMITH, Elmer R.; ed. Readings in anthropology. xiv, 417 p., ill. New York/London: McGraw-Hill, 1955.
Reviewed by Alfred G. Smith, *Sci.Mon.*, 1955, 81: 200.

MAk philosophy and methodology

BRUNSCHVICG, Léon. De la connaissance de soi. 196 p. Paris: Alcan, 1931.
Reviewed by Pierre Brunet, *Isis*, 1933, 19: 212-14.

CONKLIN, Edwin Grant. What is man? A course of three public lectures delivered on the Sharp Foundation of the Rice Institute, May 7, 8, and 9, 1941. *Rice Institute Pamphlet*, 28, p. 153-281. Houston: 1941. [CB 62/78]
Revised edition: Man, real and ideal. xvi, 247 p. New York: Scribner, 1943.

MARVIN, F.S. The new vision of man. 171 p. London: Allen & Unwin, 1938.
Reviewed by M.F. Ashley-Montagu, *Isis*, 1939, 30: 312-13.

MEDAWAR, P.B. The uniqueness of the individual. 191 p. London: Methuen, 1957.
Reviewed by D.A. Parry, *Nature*, 1958, 181: 969.

DER MENSCH. Ed. by Olga Fröbe-Kapteyn. 436 p.; 489 p. (*Eranos-Jahrbuch*, 1947, 1948, vol. 15, 16) Zürich: Rhein-Verlag, 1948-49. [CB 75/97]
First part reviewed by Walter Pagel, *Isis*, 1950, 41: 138.

MONTAGU, M.F. Ashley. How to find happiness and keep it. 298 p. New York: Doubleday, Doran, 1942.
Reviewed by Mark Graubard, *Isis*, 1942, 34: 38.

MONTAGU, M.F. Ashley. On being human. 125 p. New York: Schuman, 1950.
Reviewed by Mark Graubard, *Isis*, 1951, 42: 90.

MORLEY, Felix, ed. Essays on individuality. 270 p. Philadelphia: University of Pennsylvania Press, 1958. [CB 84/318]

POLANYI, Michael. The study of man. 102 p. (Lindsay Memorial Lectures, 1958) London: Routledge; Chicago: University of Chicago Press, 1959.
Reviewed by William Earle, *Science*, 1959, 130: 912-13; in *Amer.Scient.*, 1959, 47: 356A-358A.

PORTMANN, Adolphe. Preface to a science of man. *Diogenes*, 1962, 40: 1-26.

RUNES, Dagobert. On the nature of man. An essay in primitive philosophy. 105 p. New York: Philosophical Library, 1956.

TEILHARD DE CHARDIN, Pierre. The phenomenon of man. With an introduction by Sir Julian Huxley. 318 p., fig. New York: Harper, 1959.
Reviewed by A. Irving Hallowell, *Isis*, 1961, 52: 439-41; for other reviews *see* CB 85/396 and CB 86/468.

WELLS, Herbert George. The fate of homo sapiens. An unemotional statement of the things that are happening to him now, and of the immediate possibilities confronting him. vi, 330 p. London: Secker and Warburg, 1939.

WHYTE, L.L. The next development in man. 275 p. London: Cresset Press, 1944.
Reviewed by Dorothea Waley Singer, *Isis*, 1946, 36: 271-3.

MAke

HODGEN, Margaret Trabue. Anthropology, history, and science. *Scientia*, 1952, 87: 282-7; French transl. suppl., 151-6.

HODGEN, Margaret Trabue. The doctrine of survivals. A chapter in the history of scientific method in the study of man. 191 p. London: Allenson, 1936.

HODGEN, Margaret Trabue. Similarities and dated distributions. *Amer.Anthropol.*, 1950, 52: 445-7.

MAq/s other special aspects

MAqx

CARTAILHAC, Émile. XIVe Congrès International d'Anthropologie et d'Archéologie Préhistoriques. Compte-rendu. *Anthropologie*, 1912, 23: 587-622.

MAs

KLUCKHOHN, Clyde. Mirror for man: the relation of anthropology to modern life. xi, 313 p. New York: Whittlesey House, 1949. [CB 74/391]

MAw in different countries

MAwb

LOWIE, Robert H. American contributions to anthropology. *Science*, 1944, 100: 321-7.

MEAD, Margaret; BUNZEL, Ruth L.; ed. The golden age of American anthropology. x, 630 p. New York: Braziller, 1960.
Reviewed by J. Alden Mason, *Science*, 1961, 133: 1699-700.

PAÑCHĀNANA MITRA. A history of American anthropology. x, 239 p. Calcutta: University of Calcutta, 1933. [CB 68/58] 1493/

MAwb-oq

VOEGELIN, Erminie W. Anthropology in American universities. *Amer.Anthropol.*, 1950, 52: 350-91.

MAwe

MARETT, Robert Ranulph. A Jerseyman at Oxford. xi, 346 p. New York: Oxford University Press, 1941. [CB 62/63]
Autobiography of one of the founders of anthropology at Oxford.

MYRES, John. A hundred years of anthropology in Britain. *Nature*, 1943, 152: 493-5.

MAwg-oq

SCHOTT, Lothar. Zur Geschichte der Anthropologie an der Berliner Universität. *Wiss.Z.Humboldt Univ.Berlin Math. Naturwiss.Reihe*, 1961, 10: 57-65.

MAwh

CZEKANOWSKI, Jan. [Histoire de l'anthropologie en Pologne. (In Polish with French summary)] 40 p. (Polska Akademia Umiejetności, Historia Nauki Polskiej w Monografiach, 12) Krakow: 1948.

MAwk

BORK, A.J. van. Anthropological research in the Netherlands. Historical survey. 166 p. (*Verhandel.Ned.Akad.Wetensch.Afd. Natuur.*, 2. Sectie, 37: no. 3) Amsterdam: 1938.

MAwn

VICHNEVSKII, Boris. Court aperçu de l'histoire de l'anthropologie en Russie. *Rev.Anthropol.*, 1929, 39: 109-16.

MAwn-qd

LEV, I.D. [The Anthropological Society in the Petersburg Military Medical Academy. (In Russian)] *Arkh.Anat.Gistol. Embriol.*, 1964, 46: 115-24.

MB HUMAN PALAEONTOLOGY

BONÉ, Eduard. La dynamique de l'espèce en paléontologie et en anthropologie préhistorique. *Rev.Quest.Sci.*, 1961, 22: 305-23.

BONÉ, Edouard. Oreopithecus bambolii. A propos du jalonnement tertiaire de l'homme. *Rev.Quest.Sci.*, 1959, 20: 215-46.

BOULE, M. Fossil men. [By M. Boule and H.V. Vallois. Transl. from 4th French ed. of Les hommes fossiles.] xxv, 535 p. London: Thames & Hudson; New York: Dryden Press, 1957.
For reviews *see* French original below.

BOULE, M. L'homme fossile de la Chapelle-aux-Saints. *Ann. Paléontol.*, 1911, 6: 109-72; 1912, 7: 21-56, 85-192; 1913, 8: 1-71.

BOULE, M. Les hommes fossiles. Eléments de paléontologie humaine. 3rd ed. by Henri V. Vallois. xii, 587 p. Paris: Masson, 1946.
Reviewed by W.E. Le Gros Clark, *Nature*, 1947, 159: 553.
First published 1921; reviewed by L. Joleaud, *Rev.Gén. Sci.*, 1921, 32: 69-74.
4th edition, x, 583 p. Paris: 1952.

BROOM, Robert; ROBINSON, J.T.; SCHEPERS, G.W.H. Sterkfontein ape-man Plesianthropus. 117 p. Pretoria: Transvaal Museum, 1950. [CB 77/378]

BROOM, Robert; ROBINSON, J.T. Swartkrans ape-man: Paranthropus crassidens. xi, 123 p. Pretoria, South Africa: Transvaal Museum, March 1952. [CB 79/183]

CRESSMAN, L.G.; HANSEN, H.P.; ALLISON, Ira S. Early man in Oregon. Stratigraphic evidence, by L.G. Cressman. Pollen analysis and post-glacial climate and chronology, by H.P. Hansen. Pluvial lakes and pumice, by Ira S. Allison. *Sci. Mon.*, 1946, 62: 43-65. [CB 70/244]

HRDLIČKA, Aleš. The Neanderthal phase of man. (The Huxley Memorial Lecture for 1927) *J.Roy.Anthropol.Inst.*, 1927, 57: 249-74, pl.; reprinted with minor alterations by the author in *Annu.Rep.Smithsonian Inst.for 1928*, p. 593-621, 4 pl. Washington, D.C.: 1929.

HRDLIČKA, Aleš. The skeletal remains of early man. x, 377 p., ill. (*Smithsonian Misc.Collect.*, 83) Washington: 1930. [CB 30/476]

JENKS, Albert Ernest. Pleistocene man in Minnesota. xiii, 197 p. Minneapolis: University of Minnesota Press, 1936. [CB 51/277]

KEITH, Arthur. The antiquity of man. New and enlarged ed. 2 vol. xxxii, 376 p.; xiv, 376 p. London: Williams and Norgate, 1925.

KEITH, Arthur. New discoveries relating to the antiquity of man. 512 p. London: Williams and Norgate, 1931.
Reviewed by G. Elliot Smith, *Nature*, 1931, 127: 963-7.

KEITH, Arthur. Recent discoveries of fossil man. *Nature*, 1930, 125: 935-42.
Abridged from six lectures given in the Royal College of Surgeons of England on May 5, 7, 9, 12, 14, 16, 1930.

KUO MO-JO, *et al.* Chung-kuo jĕn lei hua shih ti fa hsien yü yen chiu. [Exploration and discovery of fossil men in China. (In Chinese)] 104 p. Peking: Les Presses Scientifiques, 1955.
Reviewed by M. Wong, *Arch.Int.Hist.Sci.*, 1962, 15: 446.

McCOWN, Theodore D.; KEITH, Arthur. The fossil human remains from the Levalloiso-Mousterian. xxiv, 390 p., ill. (The stone age of Mount Carmel, 2) Oxford: Clarendon Press, 1939.
Reviewed by C.F.C. Hawkes, *Antiquity*, 1942, 16: 281-4.

MARSTON, Alvan T. The Swanscombe skull. *J.Roy.Anthropol. Inst.*, 1937, 67: 339-406. [CB 56/398]

MARTIN, Henri. L'homme fossile de La Quina. 260 p., ill. (*Arch.Morphol.Gen.Exp.*, 15) Paris: G. Doin, 1923. [CB 15/239]

MERRIAM, John C. The beginnings of human history read from the geological record: the emergence of man. *Sci.Mon.*, 1920, 10: 321-442, 425-37, ill.
Pt. two. Geological history of man. Delivered before the National Academy of Sciences in April 1910, as the sixth series of lectures on the William Ellery Hale Foundation.

MILLER, Gerrit S. The controversy over human "missing links". *Annu.Rep.Smithsonian Inst.for 1928*, p. 413-65, 5 pl. Washington D.C.: 1929.

OBERMAIER, Hugo. Fossil man in Spain. With introd. by Henry Fairfield Osborn. [Transl. by C.D. Matthew from El hombre fósil, Madrid 1916, with additions and alterations by the author]. xxviii, 495 p., ill. New Haven: Yale University Press for the Hispanic Society of America, 1924.
Reviewed by Christine D. Matthew, *Natur.Hist.*, 1924, 24: 697-703.

OBERMAIER, Hugo. Der Mensch der Vorzeit. xii, 592 p., ill. (Der Mensch aller Zeiten, 1) Berlin: Allgemeine Verlags-Gesellschaft, [1912].
Reviewed by George Sarton, *Isis*, 1914, 2: 234-7.

OSBORN, Henry Fairfield. The discovery of tertiary man. *Science*, 1930, 71: 1-7.
Address of the retiring president of the American Association for the Advancement of Science, Des Moines, Iowa, December 27, 1929.

PITHECANTHROPUS erectus - "the ape-man of Java". *News Serv. Bull.Carnegie Inst.Wash.*, 1938, 4: 227-32, fig.

PLACE, Robin. Finding fossil man. 126 p., ill. New York: Philosophical Library, 1957. [CB 83/214]

SENET, André. Man in search of his ancestors. The romance of paleontology. Transl. by Malcolm Barnes. x,274 p. London: Allen & Unwin, 1955; New York: McGraw-Hill, 1956. [CB 83/214]
Translation of: L'Homme à la recherche de ses ancêtres. Paris: Plon, 1954.

SMITH, G. Elliot. The cradle of mankind. *Scientia*, 1930, 47: 401-8; French transl. suppl. 161-8. [CB 30/476]

SMITH, G. Elliot. The search for man's ancestors. viii, 56 p. (Forum series) London: Watts, 1931.

SMITH, G. Elliot. The significance of the Peking man. 20 p., 6 pl. (The Henderson Trust Lectures, 11, delivered at the University of Edinburgh, 30th January, 1931) London: Oliver and Boyd, 1931.

STEWART, T. Dale. A reexamination of the fossil human skeletal remains from Melbourne, Florida. With further data on the *Vero* skull. 28 p., 8 pl. (*Smithsonian Misc.Collect.*, 106) Washington, D.C.: 1946.

TEILHARD DE CHARDIN, Pierre. L'Afrique et les origines humaines. *Rev.Quest.Sci.*, 1955, 16: 5-16.

TEILHARD DE CHARDIN, Pierre. Le "Sinanthropus" de Pékin. Etat actuel de nos connaissances sur le fossile et son gisement. *Anthropologie* (Paris), 1931, 41: 1-12.

USCHMANN, Georg. Der rezente Pithecanthropus. *Sudhoffs Arch.*, 1963, 47: 405-10.
Apropos of the ideas of Herman Marie Bernelot Moens in his correspondence with Ernst Haeckel on the origin of the human species.

VÉLEZ LÓPEZ, Lizardo. El interesante cráneo de las chullpas de Sinsicap. *An.Soc.Peruana Hist.Med.*, 1944, 6: 91-5, 2 pl.

MBnh

EVANS, F. Gaynor. The names of fossil men. *Science*, 1945, 102: 16-17.

MBwf

BOULE, Marcellin. The anthropological work of Prince Albert I of Monaco, and the recent progress of human paleontology in France (The Huxley Memorial Lecture for 1922). Translated, by permission, from the *J.Roy.Anthropol.Inst.Great Brit.*, 1922, vol. 52. *Annu.Rep.Smithsonian Inst.for 1923*, p. 495-507. Washington: U.S. Government Printing Office, 1924.

MBzp PILTDOWN MAN

CLARK, Wilfred Le Gros. The exposure of the Piltdown forgery. *Nature*, 1955, 175: 973-4.

HUTCHINSON, G. Evelyn. Marginalia. *Amer.Scient.*, 1954, 42: 300-8.
A history of (a) the dodo and solitaire, and (b) the Piltdown man.

MILLER, Gerrit S. The jaw of the Piltdown man. 31 p., 5 pl., bibliogr. (*Smithsonian Misc.Collect.*, 65: no. 12) Washington, D.C.: 1915. [CB 10/206]

OAKLEY, Kenneth P.; WEINER, J.S. Piltdown man. *Amer.Scient.*, 1955, 43: 533-82.
A detailed account of the hoax.

PILTDOWN bones and "implements". *Nature*, 1954, 174: 61-2, 65.
Account of exhibits and discussion at meeting of the Geological Society, 30 June 1954.

THE PILTDOWN man discovery. Unveiling of a monolith memorial. *Nature*, 1938, 142: 196-7, 1 fig.

STRAUS, William L. The great Piltdown hoax. *Science*, 1954, 119: 265-9.

WEINER, J.S. The Piltdown forgery. xii, 214 p., ill. London/New York: Oxford University Press, 1955.
Reviewed by William L. Straus, *Sci.Mon.*, 1956, 83: 209-10.

ZEITLIN, Solomon. The antiquity of the Hebrew scrolls and the Piltdown hoax: a parallel. *Jew.Quart.Rev.*, 1954, 45: 1-29.

MC HUMAN EVOLUTION

ANTHROPOLOGICAL SOCIETY OF WASHINGTON. Evolution and anthropology: a centennial appraisal. viii, 172 p. Washington, D.C.: The Society, 1959.
Reviewed by H.H. Plough, *Amer.Scient.*, 1960, 48: 91-3.

BAITSELL, George Alfred, ed. The evolution of man; a series of lectures delivered before the Yale Chapter of the Sigma Xi during the academic year 1921-1922. x, 202 p. New Haven: Yale University Press, 1922.

BREASTED, James H. The rise of man. *Science*, 1931, 74: 639-44.

CARRINGTON, Richard. A million years of man. The story of human development as a part of nature. 304 p., ill. New York: New American Library, 1964.

CLARK, Wilfrid E. Le Gros. The crucial evidence for human evolution. (Penrose Memorial Lecture) *Proc.Amer.Phil.Soc.*, 1959, 103: 159-72.
Also published in *Amer.Scient.*, 1959, 47: 299-313.

CONKLIN, Edwin G. The direction of human evolution. xiii, 247 p. New York: Scribner's, 1921.

COON, Carleton S. The history of man. 480 p., 86 ill. London: Cape, 1955.
Reviewed by O.G.S. Crawford, *Antiquity*, 1958, 32: 5-7.

EMERSON, Alfred E. Dynamic homeostasis: a unifying principle in organic, social and ethical evolution. *Sci.Mon.*, 1954, 78: 67-85.

EMILIANI, Cesare. Note on absolute chronology of human evolution. *Science*, 1956, 123: 924-6.

GIUFFRIDA-RUGGERI, V. La phylogénie humaine. *Scientia*, 1922, 31: 361-71. [CB 13/280]
Criticism of a theory on human ancestry put forward by Karl Pearson.

GREGORY, William King. Our face from fish to man. A portrait gallery of our ancient ancestors and kinsfolk, together with a concise history of our best features. With a foreword by William Beebe. xl, 295 p. New York/London: Putnam, 1929.

HASSID, I. [The treasures of anthropogenesis. (In Hebrew)] *Koroth*, 1962, 2: 545-61.

HEARD, Gerald. Pain, sex and time: a new outlook on evolution and the future of man. xxii, 301 p. New York: Harper, 1939.
Reviewed by M.F. Ashley Montagu, *Isis*, 1949, 32: 394-6.

HOOTON, Earnest Albert. Apes, men and morons. viii, 307 p New York: Putnam, 1937.

HOOTON, Earnest Albert. Twilight of man. xii, 308 p., ill. New York: Putnam, 1939.
Reviewed by M.F. Ashley Montagu, *Amer.Anthropol.*, 1940, 42: 341-4.

HOOTON, Earnest Albert. Up from the apes. xxii, 788 p. Rev. ed. New York: Macmillan, 1946. [CB 71/125]
First published 1931.

HOOTON, Earnest Albert. Why men behave like apes and vice versa. xxv, 234 p. Princeton: Princeton University Press, 1940. [CB 61/408]

HOWELLS, William. Back of history. The story of our own origins. Rev. ed. xiv, 384 p., fig. (The Natural History Library) Garden City, N.Y.: Doubleday, 1963.
First published 1954. For English edition, *see* below: Man in the beginning.

HOWELLS, William. Man in the beginning: the story of our own origins. 384 p. London: Bell, 1956.
American edition has title: Back of history: the story of our own origins. New York: Doubleday, 1954.
Reviewed in *Sch.Sci.Rev.*, 1956, 37: 457.

HOWELLS, William. Mankind in the making. The story of human evolution. 382 p., ill. Garden City, N.Y.: Doubleday, 1959; London: Secker & Warburg, 1960.
Reviewed by Carleton S. Coon, *Science*, 1959, 130: 1399-400.

HOWELLS, William, ed. Ideas on human evolution. Selected essays, 1949-1961. xiii, 555 p., ill. Cambridge, Mass.: Harvard University Press, 1962.
Reviewed by Loren Eiseley, *Science*, 1962, 138: 587.

HUXLEY, Julian. The uniqueness of Man. xiii, 300 p. London: Chatto and Windus, 1941.
Reviewed by H.G. Wells, *Nature*, 1941, 147: 247-8.

KEANE, Augustus Henry. Man past and present. Rev. and largely rewritten by A. Hingston Quiggin and A.C. Haddon. xi, 582 p., 16 pl. Cambridge University Press, 1920.
First edition 1899.

KEITH, Arthur. Darwin's theory of man's descent as it stands today. Supplement to *Nature*, 3 Sept. 1927, 120: 14-21; also in *Science*, 1927, 201-8.
Presidential address before the British Association for the Advancement of Science, Leeds 1927.

KEITH, Arthur. A new theory of human evolution. x, 451 p. New York: Philosophical Library, 1949.
Reviewed by M.F. Ashley Montagu, *Isis*, 1950, 41: 135-6.

KLAATSCH, Hermann. The evolution and progress of mankind. Edited and enlarged by Adolph Heilbron. Transl. by Joseph McCabe. 316 p. London: T. Fisher Unwin, 1923.
Translation of: Der Werdegang der Menschheit und die Entstehung der Kultur. xl, 392 p. Berlin: Bong, 1920.

LECHE, Wilhelm. Der Mensch, sein Ursprung und seine Entwicklung in gemeinverständlicher Darstellung. 2nd German ed. viii, 390 p., ill. Jena: Fischer, 1922.
Translated from the second Swedish edition, 1911. 1st edition of German translation 1911.

LODGE, Oliver. Making of man: a study in evolution. ix, 185 p. London: Hodder and Stoughton, 1924.

MACHIN, Alfred. The ascent of man by means of natural selection. xx, 325 p. London: Longmans Green, 1925.
Reviewed by B. Malinowski, *Nature*, 1926, 118: 506-9.

MATHER, Kirtley F. The future of man as an inhabitant of the earth. *Annu.Rep.Smithsonian Inst.for 1940*, p. 215-29. Washington, D.C.: 1941.

MEDAWAR, Peter B. The future of man. 128 p. New York: Basic Books, Inc., 1960.
Reviewed by Edward C. Moore, *Phil.Sci.*, 1962, 29: 217-18.

MENDES-CORRÉA, A.A. L'origine de l'homme. L'état actuel du problème. *Scientia*, 1924, 35: 339-50.

MONTANDON, Georges. L'ologenèse humaine (ologénisme). xii, 478 p., 21 fig., 14 graph., 23 maps, 14 pl. Paris: Alcan, 1928.
Reviewed by L. Joleaud, *Rev.Gén.Sci.*, 1929, 40: 483; by S. R. Steinmetz, *Deut.Lit.Zeitung*, 1929, 6: 2115-19.

PANNEKOEK, A. Anthropogenesis: a study of the origin of man. 120 p. Amsterdam: North-Holland Publishing Company, 1953.

PIVETEAU, Jean. L'origine de l'homme. L'homme et son passé. 201 p., ill. Paris: Hachette, 1962.
Reviewed by G. Kurth, *Naturwiss.Rundsch.*, 1963, 16: 288.

READ, Carveth. The origin of man and of his superstitions. xii, 350 p. Cambridge University Press, 1920.

ROSA, Daniele. Ologenesi: nuova teoria dell'evoluzione e della distribuzione geografica dei viventi. xi, 305 p. Milano: Bemporad, 1918.
French translation: L'ologenèse. Nouvelle théorie de l'évolution et de la distribution géographique des êtres vivants. Adapté de l'italien par l'auteur. xii, 368 p. Paris: Alcan, 1931.

ROSTAND, Jean. Can man be modified? Transl. from the French by Jonathan Griffin. 105 p. New York: Basic Books, 1959.
Translation of: Peut-on modifier l'homme? (Paris: Gallimard, 1956).
Reviewed by D.R. Newth, *Discovery*, 1959, 20: 313; by Garrett Hardin, *Science*, 1959, 129: 1606.

SERGI, Giuseppe. I mammiferi. xii, 360 p. Torino: Bocca, 1923. [CB 15/211]
An essay on the problem of the origin and evolution of man.

SMITH, Grafton Elliot. The evolution of man. Essays. viii, 159 p. New York: Oxford University Press, 1924.
Reviewed by George Sarton, *Isis*, 1925, 7: 149-52.

SMITH, Grafton Elliot. Human history. xviii, 472 p., ill. London: Cape, 1929.

TAX, Sol; CALLENDER, Charles; ed. Evolution after Darwin. 3 vol. 1. The evolution of life - its origin, history and future. viii, 629 p.; 2. The evolution of man - man, culture and society. viii, 473 p.; 3. Issues in evolution. viii, 310 p. Chicago: University of Chicago Press; London: Cambridge University Press, 1960.
For reviews see CB 86/468, CB 87/510 and CB 87/634.

VANDEL, Albert. L'homme et l'évolution. 201 p. (L'Avenir de la Science, 28) Paris: Gallimard, 1949.

WEIDENREICH, Franz. Apes, giants and man. v, 122 p. Chicago: University of Chicago Press, 1946. [CB 70/265]
An account of the origin and evolution of man.

WHITE, Anne Terry. Men before Adam. xii, 305 p. New York: Random House, 1942. [CB 64/453]

MCmzAJ

NORDAU, Max Simon. Morals and the evolution of man. Transl. by Marie A. Lewenz. 278 p. London: Cassell; New York: Funk and Wagnalls, 1922.
German original, Biologie der Ethik, first published Leipzig: 1921; French translation Paris: Alcan, 1930.

MCmzMG

KANTOR, J.R. Evolution and the science of psychology. *Psychol. Rec.*, 1959, 9: 131-42.

MAGOUN, H.W. Darwin and concepts of brain function. In: Council for International Organizations of Medical Sciences. Brain Mechanisms and Learning, p. 1-20. London: Blackwell Scientific Publications, 1961. [CB 87/623]
Also discusses the influence of Spencerian evolution on the growth of ideas in neurophysiology and psychology and examines the opinions of Darwin and Spencer about each other.

MCmzMI

DOBZHANSKY, Th.; MONTAGU, M.F. Ashley. Natural selection and the mental capacities of mankind. *Science*, 1947, 105: 587-90.

LE ROY, Edouard. Les origines humaines et l'évolution de l'intelligence. 388 p. Paris: Boivin, 1928. [CB 26/243]

MCmzMO

HARDY, A.C. Telepathy and evolutionary theory. *J.Soc.Psychical Res.*, 1950, 35: 225-38. [CB 77/376]

MCmzNS

HOLMES, S.J. Studies in evolution and eugenics. 261 p. New York: Harcourt Brace, 1923. [CB 15/210]

MCmzQ

HARPER, R.M.J. Evolution and illness, a short essay on the clinical significance of evolutionary vestiges. viii, 108 p., bibliogr. Edinburgh: E. & S. Livingstone, 1962.

MCsc

DOBZHANSKY, Th. The biological basis of human freedom. vi, 139 p. (The Page-Barbour Lectures for 1954 at the University of Virginia) New York: Columbia University Press, 1956.
On the relation of biological and cultural evolution.
Reviewed by Conway Zirkle, *Isis*, 1957, 48: 475-6.

GLASS, Bentley. A biological view of human history. *Sci.Mon.*, 1951, 73: 363-8.
Comments on Seidenberg, Roderick. Posthistoric man, *see* below.

GREENE, John C. Evolution and progress. *Johns Hopkins Mag.*, 1962, 14: 8-12, 32.

HENRY, Jules. Homeostasis, society and evolution. *Sci.Mon.*, 1955, 81: 300-9.
The author reaches toward a concept of the role of stability and instability in human evolution.

HUNTINGTON, Ellsworth. World power and evolution. 287 p., 30 fig. New Haven: Yale University Press, 1919.
Reprinted in part from the *Journal of Race Development* and the *Quarterly Journal of Economics*.

SEIDENBERG, Roderick. Posthistoric man. x, 246 p. Chapel Hill: University of North Carolina Press, 1950.
Reviewed by Bentley Glass, *Sci.Mon.*, 1951, 73: 363-8.

WHEELER, William Morton. Emergent evolution and the social. *Science*, 1926, 64: 433-40.
Address given at the Sixth International Congress of Philosophy. Cambridge, Mass., September 14, 1926.

MCt

MONTAGUE, M.F. Ashley, ed. Culture and the evolution of man. xiii, 376 p. (Galaxy Book) New York: Oxford University Press, 1962.

MCyOK

TILNEY, Frederick. The brain from ape to man, a contribution to the study of the evolution and development of the human brain. With chapters on the reconstruction of the gray matter in the primate brain stem, by Henry Alsop Riley. Foreword by Henry Fairfield Osborn. 2 vol. New York: Hoeber, 1928.
Reviewed by Francis R. Packard, *Ann.Med.Hist.*, 1928, 10: 506-8.

MD HUMAN GENETICS

see also NS EUGENICS; APPLIED GENETICS

APERT, Eugène. L'hérédité morbide. 306 p. (Bibliothèque de Philosophie Scientifique) Paris: Flammarion, 1919.
Reviewed by L. Guinet, *Isis*, 1920, 3: 295.

CONKLIN, Edwin Grant. Heredity and environment in the development of men. 6th ed. 387 p. Princeton: Princeton University Press, 1930.
First published 1915.

GATES, Reginald Ruggles. Human genetics. 2 vol. xviii, 1518 p., 326 fig. New York: Macmillan Co., 1946. [CB 70/265]
First publ. London: 1929 under the title "Heredity in man".

MONTAGU, M.F. Ashley. Human heredity. xiii, 364 p., fig., pl., tables, bibliogr. New York: New American Library of World Literature, 1960.

MOURANT, A.E. Evolution, genetics, and anthropology. (Huxley Memorial Lecture, 1961) *J.Royal Anthropol.Inst.*, 1961, 91: (2), 152-65; reprinted in *Annu.Rep.Smithsonian Inst.for 1961*, p. 501-20. Washington, D.C.: 1962.

MULLER, H.J. Progress and prospects in human genetics. *Amer. J.Hum.Genet.*, 1949, 1: 1-18.
Contains a brief history of human genetics and outlines a program for future research.

PASTORE, Nicholas. The nature-nurture controversy. xiv, 213 p. New York: King's Crown Press, 1949.
Reviewed by Conway Zirkle, *Isis*, 1950, 41: 240-2.

RICHET, Charles. La sélection humaine. 262 p. (Bibliothèque Scientifique Internationale) Paris: Alcan, 1919.

ROSENBERG, Charles E. Charles Benedict Davenport and the beginning of human genetics. *Bull.Hist.Med.*, 1961, 35: 266-76.

SCHULTE-VAERTING, Hermann. Die soziologische Abstammungslehre. 136 p. Leipzig: Thieme, 1923.
Reviewed by J. Arthur Thomson, *Nature*, 1924, 113: 74-5.

SNYDER, Laurence H. Modern heredity and its applications. *Amer.Scient.*, 1955, 43: 391-419.
A brief description of population genetics and its application to human beings.

WAARDENBURG, P.J. Zur Geschichte der Zwillingsmethode. *Sudhoffs Arch.*, 1955, 39: 123-33.
Mostly on Francis Galton and his predecessors.

ZIRKLE, Conway. Our biological inheritance. In: Gruber, Frederick C., ed. The emergence of the modern mind, p. 19-49. Philadelphia: University of Pennsylvania Press, 1958.

MDmzMF

MONTAGU, M.F. Ashley. The genetical theory of race, and anthropological method. *Amer.Anthropol.*, 1942, 44: 369-75.

MDmzMMzc

BROWNING, William. Medical heredity; distinguished children of physicians (United States, to 1910). 250 p. Baltimore: The Norman Remington Co., 1925.
Reviewed by F.R. Packard, *Ann.Med.Hist.*, 1926, 8: 210.

KURELLA, H. Die Intellektuellen und die Gesellschaft. Ein Beitrag zur Naturgeschichte begabter Familien. vii, 124 p. (Grenzfragen des Nerven- und Seelenlebens, 88) Wiesbaden: Bergmann, 1913.

OSTWALD, Wilhelm. Genie und Vererbung. *Isis*, 1913, 1: 208-14.

MDmzYB

LEMARCHAL, Robert. Hérédité et généalogie. *Act.IIIe Congr. Bénélux Hist.Sci.* (Luxembourg, 1960). *Janus*, 1960, 49: 175-81.

MDwb

STOCKING, George W., Jr. Lamarckianism in American social science: 1890-1915. *J.Hist.Ideas*, 1962, 23: 239-56.

ME PHYSICAL ANTHROPOLOGY

for anthropology, in general *see* MA

CAMERON, John. The skeleton of British neolithic man, including a comparison with that of other prehistoric periods and more modern times. 272 p., ill. London: Williams and Norgate, 1934.
Reviewed by M.I.A.R., *Antiquity*, 1934, 8: 491-2.

DULIÈRE, W.L. Spy et la leçon de sa grotte. *Flambeau*, 1952, no. 6, 637-50; 1953, no. 1, 25-37, ill.

FIELD, Henry. Contributions to the anthropology of Iran. 2 vol. 706 p., 144 pl. (Field Museum of Natural History. Anthropological Series, 1 and 2) Chicago: 1939.
An exhaustive report of the results of field work in physical anthropology.

HARDIN, Garrett. Nature and man's fate. xi, 375 p., fig., bibliogr. New York: Rinehart, 1959.
Reviewed by C. Zirkle, *Isis*, 1960, 51: 97-8; for other reviews *see* CB 85/395 and CB 86/467.

HOYME, Lucile E. Physical anthropology and its instruments: an historical study. *Southwest.J.Anthropol.*, 1953, 9: 408-30, 6 fig. [CB 80/135]

LEAKEY, Louis Seymour Bazett. The Stone age races of Kenya. With appendices by T.W.P. Lawrence, Sir Grafton Elliot-Smith, Sir F. Colyer, L.S.B. Leakey. xii, 150 p., 82 pl. London: Oxford University Press, 1935.
Reviewed by Arthur Keith, *Nature*, 1935, 135: 163-4.

MONTAGU, M.F. Ashley. An introduction to physical anthropology. 3rd ed. 771 p., ill. Springfield, Ill.: Charles C. Thomas, 1960.
2nd edition 1951. [CB 79/183] First published 1945. [CB 69/232]

REGNAULT, Félix. Les races humaines préhistoriques n'étaient point stéatopyges. *Rev.Sci.*, 1932, 70: 145-9.

SUDHOFF, K. Anthropologie, Anthropopathologie und historisch archäologische Forschung. *Verhandl.Ges.Deut.Naturforsch. Aerzte 84. Versamml.* (Münster i. W., 1912), part 2, (2), p. 92-3. Leipzig: F.C.W. Vogel, 1913.

WEINERT, Hans. Menschen der Vorzeit. Ein Überblick über die altsteinzeitlichen Menschenreste. 140 p., 61 fig. Stuttgart: Enke, 1930.

MEce-bv

KROGMAN, Wilton Marion. A bibliography of human morphology, 1914-1939. xxxi, 385 p. Chicago: University of Chicago Press, 1941. [CB 61/409]

MEmzN

MONTAGU, M.F. Ashley. Anthropology in medicine. *Interne*, March 1947, 114-16.

MEsc

CLAUDE, Georges. La taille de l'homme et la civilisation, [including correspondence with Albert Turpain]. *La Nature*, 1913, 41: 2e semestre, 133-4, 183. [CB 3/571]

MExd

HOYME, Lucile E. The earliest use of indices for sexing pelves. *Amer.J.Phys.Anthropol.*, 1957, 15: 537-46.

MExm

HAMBLY, Wilfrid D. Craniometry of New Guinea. *Publ.Field Mus.Natur.Hist.Anthropol.Ser.*, 1940, 25: 83-290.

HRDLIČKA, Aleš. Hrdlicka's practical anthropometry. 3rd ed. by T.D. Stewart. x, 230 p. Philadelphia: Wistar Institute, 1947.
First edition 1920.

STEWART, T. Dale; STRONG, William Duncan. Anthropometric observations on the Eskimos and Indians of Labrador. *Publ. Field Mus.Natur.Hist.Anthropol.Ser.*, 1939, 31: 1-163. [CB 60/138]

MExm-pw

RIVET, P. Entente internationale pour l'unification des mesures anthropométriques sur le vivant. *Anthropologie*, 1912, 23: 623-7.

MEyOD

HRDLIČKA, Aleš. The hypotrochanteric fossa of the femur. 49 p., 14 pl. (Smithsonian Miscellaneous Collections, 92) Washington, D.C.: Smithsonian Institution, 1934. [CB 42/596]

KLAATSCH, Hermann. Die Entstehung und Erwerbung der Menschenmerkmale. 2. Der Menschenfuss und der aufrechte Gang. *Fortschr.Naturw.Forsch.*, 1913, 7: 210-68.

KROGMAN, Wilton Marion. The anthropology of the hand. *Ciba Symp.* (Summit, N.J.), 1942, 4: 1294-306, fig.

MARCUS, H. Die durch Zahndruck bedingten Verstärkungen im künstlich deformierten Khollaschädel. *Verhandl.Anat.Ges. Jena*, 1964, 59: 358-67.

MONTAGU, M.F. Ashley. Medio-palatine bones. *Amer.J.Phys.Anthropol.*, 1940, 27: 139-50, 6 fig.

MEyOQ

KROGMAN, Wilton Marion. The anthropology of the eye. *Ciba Symp.* (Summit, N.J.), 1943, 5: 1607-16, fig.

MEyQC

MICHAËLIS, Lorenz. Vergleichende mikroskopische Untersuchungen an rezenten, historischen und fossilen menschlichen Knochen. Zugleich ein Beitrag zur Geschichte der Syphilis. viii, 92 p., 63 pl. (Veröffentlichungen aus der Kriegs- und Konstitutionspathologie, 24) Jena: Fischer, 1930. [CB 30/412] 15080
Reviewed by G. Sticker, *Mitt.Gesch.Med.*, 1930, 29: 182-4.

MEyRE

GREGORY, William K. The origin and evolution of the human dentition. xviii, 548 p., 15 pl. Baltimore: Williams and Wilkins, 1922.
Reviewed by A. Keith, *Nature*, 1922, 110: 834-6.

MF ETHNOLOGY; ETHNOGRAPHY

GENNEP, Arnold van. Les lacunes de l'ethnographie actuelle. *Scientia*, 1913, 14: 404-11.

GEORGE, Katherine. The civilized West looks at primitive Africa: 1400-1800. A study in ethnocentrism. *Isis*, 1958, 49: 62-72.

GREENE, John C. Some early speculations on the origin of human races. *Amer.Anthropol.*, 1954, 56: 31-41.

HERSKOVITS, Melville J. Past developments and present currents in ethnology. *Amer.Anthropol.*, 1959, 61: 391-8.

LOWIE, Robert H. The history of ethnological theory. xiii, 296 p. New York: Farrar & Rinehart, 1937.
Reviewed by M.F. Ashley Montagu, *Isis*, 1938, 29: 475-7.

MARETT, J.R. De La H. Race, sex and environment. 342 p. New York: Chemical Publishing Co., 1940. [CB 61/403]

SCHMIDT, W. Phases principales de l'histoire de l'ethnologie. *Rev.Sci.Phil.Théol.*, 1913, 7: 26-45.

UNITED NATIONS EDUCATIONAL, SCIENTIFIC AND CULTURAL ORGANIZATION. The race question in modern science. [Articles by various authors.] 373 p. Paris: Unesco; London: Sidgwick & Jackson, 1956; New York: Whiteside, and W. Morrow, 1957.
Reviewed by T.S. Simey, *Nature*, 1958, 181: 1232-3.

UNITED NATIONS EDUCATIONAL, SCIENTIFIC AND CULTURAL ORGANIZATION. The race question in modern science: race and science. 506 p. New York: Columbia University Press, 1961.
Contains all the brochures which have appeared separately in the Unesco series: The race question in modern science.

WASHBURN, S.L. Thinking about race. *Annu.Rep.Smithsonian Inst.for 1945*, p. 363-78. Washington, D.C.: 1946.

WOLFF, K.F. Der heutige Stand der Rassenforschung. *Mannus*, 1928, 20: 328-64.

MFc-br

L'Ethnographie. *Isis*, 1914, 2: 198-9.
Extracts from the introduction of the new series of the quarterly bearing this title, published by the Société d'Ethnographie de Paris.

Ethnohistory, a new quarterly journal [published by Indiana University under the auspices of the American Indian Ethnohistorical Conference]. *Isis*, 1956, 47: 57.

MFce-bu

OVERBERGH, Cyr. van. La documentation internationale et l'ethnographie. Contribution à l'élaboration de la documentation par les associations internationales scientifiques. *Vie Int.*, 1912, 1: 317-42.

MFce-bv

Ethnologischer Anzeiger: Jahresbibliographie und Bericht über die völkerkundliche Literatur. Vol. 1-4. Stuttgart: Schweizerbart, 1926-44.
Reviewed in *Nature*, 1931, 127: 700.

STEINMETZ, S.R. Essai d'une bibliographie systématique de l'ethnologie, jusqu'à l'année 1911. iv, 196 p. (Monographies Bibliographiques publiées par l'Intermédiaire Sociologique, Institut de Sociologie Solvay, 1) Bruxelles: Misch et Thron, 1911.
Reviewed by G. Sarton, *Isis*, 1913, 1: 133-5.

MFkb

FARMER, Henry George. The importance of ethnological studies. *Trans.Glasgow Univ.Orient.Soc.*, 1942-44, 11: 27-30.

MFke

FAUBLÉE, Jacques. L'expérience dans les sciences humaines: ethnologie. *Rev.Syn.*, 1963, 34: 215-20.

MARIN, Louis. Questionnaire d'ethnographie (Table d'analyse en ethnographie). 131 p. Paris: Maisonneuve, 1925.
Originally published in the *Bulletin de la Société d'Ethnographie de Paris*.

MONTAGU, M.F. Ashley. Karl Pearson and the historical method in ethnology. *Isis*, 1943, 34: 211-4.

SCHMIDT, Wilhelm. The culture historical method of ethnology: the scientific approach to the racial question. Transl. by S.A. Sieber. xxx, 382 p. New York: Fortuny, 1939. [CB 58/582]
Translation of: Handbuch der Methode der kulturhistorischen Ethnologie. Münster: Aschendorff, 1937.

MFmzJ

DUNN, Leslie Clarence. Race and biology. 48 p. (The Race Question in Modern Science) Paris: Unesco, 1951.

MFmzMD

MONTAGU, M.F. Ashley. The genetical theory of race, and anthropological method. *Amer.Anthropol.*, 1942, 44: 369-75.

MFmzMG

RIVERS, William Halse Rivers. Psychology and ethnology. xxviii, 324 p. (International Library of Psychology, Philosophy and Scientific Method) London: Kegan Paul; New York: Harcourt, Brace, 1926.

MFmzMMzc

MONTAGU, M.F. Ashley. The creative power of ethnic mixture. *Psychiatry*, 1942, 5: 523-36.

MFmzOG

WILSON, Elsie A. Basal metabolism from the standpoint of racial anthropology. *Amer.J.Phys.Anthropol.*, 1945, 3: 1-19. [CB 69/233]

MFmzSP

LECLAINCHE, Emmanuel. Discours prononcé à l'Académie des Sciences, séance publique annuelle du lundi 20 décembre 1937. *Compt.Rend.Acad.Sci.*, 1937, 205: 1269-82.
Includes comparison of the concepts of human races and of domestic animal breeds.

MFqx

CONGRÈS international d'ethnologie et d'ethnographie. *Isis*, 1914, 1: 712-13.
From report of organising committee on the conference to be held in Neuchâtel, June 1914.

MFsc

DANZEL, Theodor-Wilhelm. Gefüge und Fundamente der Kultur vom Standpunkte der Ethnologie (Prolegomena). 48 p. Hamburg: Friederichsen, de Gruyter, 1930.
Reviewed by Andreas Walther, *Deut.Lit.Zeitung*, 1932, 3: 851-3.

HANKINS, Frank Hamilton. The racial basis of civilization: a critique of the Nordic doctrine. Rev. ed. 389 p. New York: Knopf, 1931.
First published 1926.
French translation (Paris: Payot, 1935) reviewed by Pierre Brunet, *Archeion*, 1935, 17: 107-8.

LOWIE, Robert H. Culture and ethnology. 190 p., bibliogr. New York: McMurtrie, 1917. [CB 9/486]

PITTARD, Eugène. Race and history: an ethnological introduction to history. xx, 619 p., ill. London: Kegan Paul; New York: Knopf, 1926.
Translation of: Les races et l'histoire. Paris: La Renaissance du Livre, 1924; reviewed by Ales Hrdlicka, *Amer.Hist.Rev.*, 1924, 30: 109-10.

SNELL, George D. Hybrids and history: the role of race and ethnic crossing in individual and national achievement. *Quart.Rev.Biol.*, 1951, 26: 331-47. [CB 79/183]

MFsk

BENEDICT, Ruth. Race: science and politics. ix, 274 p. New York: Modern Age, 1940.
Reviewed by M.F.A. Montagu, *Isis*, 1941, 33: 303-4.
Spanish translation (México: Fondo de Cultura, 1941) reviewed by Angela Romera, *Archeion*, 1942, 24: 140-1.

MONTAGU, M.F. Ashley. Man's most dangerous myth: the fallacy of race. 4th ed. 499 p., bibliogr. Cleveland: World Publishing Company, 1964.
1st edition. With a foreword by Aldous Huxley. xi, 216 p. New York: Columbia University Press, 1942.
Reviewed by Clyde Kluckhohn, *Isis*, 1943, 34: 419-20.
2nd edition. xvi, 304 p. New York: Columbia University Press, 1945. [CB 69/233]

MFt

SCHEMANN, Ludwig. Die Rasse in den Geisteswissenschaften. Studien zur Geschichte des Rassegedankens. xvi, 480 p. München: Lehmann, 1928.

MFtq

STERN, Curt; BELAR, Gertrud. Race crossing in Paradise? *J.Hered.*, 1953, 44: 154-5. [CB 80/184]
Concerning a painting of Adam and Eve at Calw, S. Germany.

MFwb

ERASMUS, Charles I. Las dimensiones de la cultura. Historia de la etnología en los Estados Unidos entre 1900 y 1950. viii, 198 p., ill., bibliogr. Bogotá: Editorial Iqueima, 1953.

ODUM, Howard W. Race and rumors of race. Challenge to American crisis. x, 245 p. Chapel Hill, N.C.: University of North Carolina Press, 1943.
Reviewed by H.J. Fleure, *Nature*, 1944, 153: 667.

MFwb-qk

BENNETT, Wendell Clark. The Ethnogeographic Board. viii, 135 p. (Smithsonian Miscellaneous Collections, 107) Washington, D.C.: Smithsonian Institution, 1947. [CB 71/126]
The Board was established in Washington in June 1942, and was disbanded on Dec. 31,1945.

MFwf

METRAUX, Alfred. Les précurseurs de l'ethnologie en France du XVIe au XVIIIe siècle. *Cah.Hist.Mond.*, 1963, 7: 721-38.

MFwg-oq

SCHLENTHER, Ursula. Zur Geschichte der Völkerkunde an der Berliner Universität von 1810 bis 1945. *Wiss.Z.Humboldt Univ.Berlin Math.Naturwiss.Reihe*, 1960, 9: 67-79.

MFwh

KUTRZEBIANKA, Anna. Rozwój etnografii i etnologii w Polsce. [Esquisse de l'histoire de l'ethnographie et de l'ethnologie en Pologne. (In Polish with French summary)] 59 p. (Polska Akademia Umiejetności, Historia Nauki Polskiej w Monografiach, 14) Krakow: 1948.

MFwn

MARINUS, Albert. Ethnographie, folklore et archéologie en Russie soviétique. *Bull.Soc.Belge Anthrop.Préhist.*, 1934, 49: 173-86.

MFxf-YC

FLEURE, H.J. Racial evolution and archaeology. (Huxley memorial lecture, 1937) *J.Roy.Anthropol.Inst.*, 1937, 67: 205-29.

MFxx

BRAUNHOLTZ, H.J. History of ethnography in the [British] Museum after 1753-1938. *Brit.Mus.Quart.*, 1953, 18: 90-3, 109-20, pl.

BRITISH MUSEUM. Handbook to the ethnographical collections. 2nd ed. xvi, 319 p., 20 pl. London: British Museum, 1925.
First published 1910.

HOUGH, Walter. Racial groups and figures in the natural history building of the United States National Museum. *Annu.Rep. Smithsonian Inst.for 1920*, p. 611-56, 87 pl. Washington, D.C.: 1922.

JACOBI, Arnold. Fünfzig Jahre Museum für Völkerkunde zu Dresden (1875-1925). 79 p., 8 pl., 5 ill. Berlin/Dresden: Jul. Bard Verlag, 1925.

MFA RACES

BENEDICT, Ruth; WELTFISH, Gene. The races of mankind. 31 p., ill. New York: Public Affairs Committee, 1943.

BIRKNER, Ferdinand. Die Rassen und Völker der Menschheit. xii, 548 p., ill. (Der Mensch aller Zeiten, 2) Berlin: Allgemeine Verlagsgesellschaft, 1913.
Reviewed by George Sarton, *Isis*, 1914, 2: 237-8.

COON, Carleton S. The origin of races. 724 p. New York: Knopf, 1962.
Reviewed by George F. Carter, *Geogr.Rev.*, 1964, 54: 300-2.

DUFRENOY, Jean; DUFRENOY, Marie Louise. De la genèse à la bombe atomique. *Rev.Pathol.Comp.*, 1949, 49: 22-38, bibliogr. [CB 75/92]
On colour differences between the races.

HADDON, Alfred Court. The races of man and their distribution. 2nd ed. rev. and enl. viii, 184 p., 10 pl. Cambridge University Press, 1924. [CB 18/632]
First published 1909.

HRDLIČKA, Aleš. Remains in eastern Asia of the race that peopled America. 5 p., ill. (*Smithsonian Misc.Collect.*, 60: no. 16) Washington, D.C.: 1912.
Reprint of paper presented to the International Congress of Archaeology and Prehistoric Anthropology, Geneva, 1912.

SCHMIDT, Max. The primitive races of mankind, a study in ethnology. Transl. by Alexander K. Dallas. 360 p., 80 pl., maps. London: Harrap, 1926.
Translation of: Völkerkunde. Berlin: Ullstein, 1924.

SEIFFERT, Walter. Die Erbgeschichte des Menschen. Eine Vortragsfolge über die erbbiologische Stellung des Menschen als Gattung, Rasse und Persönlichkeit. 176 p., 108 fig. Stuttgart: Enke, 1935. [CB 47/286]

TAYLOR, Griffith. Environment and race: a study of the evolution, migration, settlement, and status of the races of man. xvi, 354 p., ill. London/New York: Oxford University Press, 1927.
Reviewed by R.B. Dixon, *Amer.Hist.Rev.*, 1928, 33: 621-2; by A.C. Haddon, *Nature*, 1928, 121: 532-3.

TAYLOR, Griffith. Environment, race and migration: fundamentals of human distribution ... 3rd ed. xviii, 493 p. Toronto: University of Toronto Press; New York: Oxford University Press, 1949.
3rd edition of: Environment and race. 1927. 2nd edition 1937, *see* above.

MFAdaj

COUNT, Earl W., ed. This is race. An anthology selected from the international literature on the races of man. Selected, edited, and with an introduction. xxviii, 747 p. New York: Schuman, 1950. [CB 76/403]

MFAmzMI

ZIRKLE, Conway. [Letter to the editor on the intelligence of the various races.] *Perspect.Biol.Med.*, 1962, 5: 384-90.

MFAs

GREGORY, J.W. The menace of colour: a study of the difficulties due to the association of white and coloured races, with an account of measures proposed for their solution, and special reference to white colonization in the Tropics. 264 p., 4 pl. London: Seeley, Service, 1925.

MFAvb

WARD, Robert De C. The acclimatization of the white race in the tropics. *Annu.Rep.Smithsonian Inst.for 1930*, p. 557-76. Washington, D.C.: 1931.
A lecture given at the Lowell Institute, Boston. Reprinted from the *New Engl.J.Med.*, 1929, 201: 617-27.

MFAvq

HUBERT, Henri. Les Celtes depuis l'époque de La Tène et la civilisation celtique. xvii, 369 p., 3 maps, pl. (Bibliothèque de Synthèse Historique; l'Évolution de l'Humanité, 21, bis) Paris: 1932.
Reviewed by Adrien Blanchet, *J.Savants*, 1933, 225-7.

MFAvr

SERBOIANU, Popp. Les Tsiganes. 400 p., pl. Paris: Payot, 1930.
Reviewed by V.A., *Rev.Gén.Sci.*, 1931, 42: 92.

VESEY-FITZGERALD, Brian. Gypsies of Britain. An introd. to their history. xvi, 204 p. London: Chapman and Hall, 1944.
Reviewed by Harry Roberts, *Nature*, 1945, 155: 65-6.

MFAvr-bv

BLACK, G.F. A Gypsy bibliography. vii, 226 p. (Gypsy Lore Society. Monographs, 1) Edinburgh: [1913].
First published 1909.

MFB

WOODS, Frederick Adams. The racial origin of successful Americans. *Pop.Sci.Mon.*, 1914, 84: 397-402. [CB 6/474]

MFD

GÜNTHER, Hans F.K. Racial elements of European history. Transl. from the 2nd German ed. by G.C. Wheeler. vii, 279 p., ill. London: Methuen, 1927.

GÜNTHER, Hans F.K. Rassenkunde Europas. 2nd ed. 225 p., ill. München: J.F. Lehmann, 1926.
First published under the title: Kleine Rassenkunde Europas. 1925.

HUXLEY, Julian S.; HADDON, Alfred Court. We Europeans: a survey of "racial" problems. viii, 246 p., maps, ill. New York: Harper, 1936.
Reviewed by H.J. Fleure, *Geogr.Rev.*, 1936, 26: 704; by E.G. R.T., *Antiquity*, 1936, 10: 112-13.

KRUSE, Walther. Die Deutschen und ihre Nachbarvölker. Neue Grundlegung der Anthropologie, Rassen-, Völker- Stammeskunde und Konstitutionslehre nebst Ausführungen zur deutschen Rassenhygiene. xv, 640 p., 17 fig., 5 pl. Leipzig: Thieme, 1929.

STODDARD, Theodore Lothrop. Racial realities in Europe. 252 p. New York: Scribner, 1924.

MFG

GERLACH, Kurt. Begabung und Stammesherkunft im deutschen Volke. Feststellungen über die Herkunft der deutschen Kulturschöpfer in Kartenbildern. 112 p., 23 maps, 1 pl. München: Lehmann, 1929.

MFN

HRDLIČKA, Aleš. The peoples of the Soviet Union. 29 p. (Smithsonian Institution, War Background Studies, 3) Washington, D.C.: 1942.

HRDLIČKA, Aleš. The races of Russia. 21 p. (*Smithsonian Misc.Collect.*, 69, no. 11) Washington: 1919. [CB 10/188]

MFV

KEESING, Felix M. The ethnohistory of northern Luzon. 362 p. Stanford: Stanford University Press, 1962.
Reviewed by Marion W. Ward, *Geogr.J.*, 1964, 130: 141.

MFZ

COLLINS, Henry B. The origin and antiquity of the Eskimo. *Annu.Rep.Smithsonian Inst.for 1950*, p. 423-67, 4 pl. Washington, D.C.: 1951.

MG PSYCHOLOGY

for psychological aspects of science *see* Aj
psychological aspects of the sciences *see* INDEX
social psychology *see* MW
medical psychology and psychiatry *see* OM
psychoanalysis *see* OMP

MGc general history

BOBROV, E.A. [Historical introduction to the study of psychology. (In Russian)] 170 p. St. Petersburg/Warsaw: Oros, 1913.

BORING, Edwin G. A history of experimental psychology. 2nd ed. vii, 777 p. New York: Appleton-Century-Crofts, 1950.
First published 1929.
Reviewed by Josef Brozek, *Isis*, 1951, 42: 87.

BORING, Edwin G. History, psychology, and science; selective papers. Ed. by Robert I. Watson and Donald T. Campbell. 372 p. New York: Wiley, 1963.

BORING, Edwin G. Psychologist at large. An autobiography and selected essays. 371 p., bibliogr. New York: Basic Books, 1961.
Reviewed by Josef Brožek, *Isis*, 1963, 54: 170-2; and in *Sci.Amer.*, 1962, 207: no. 5, 194.

BRETT, George Sidney. Brett's History of psychology. Ed. and abridged by R.S. Peters. 742 p. London: Allen & Unwin; New York: Macmillan, 1953.
Reviewed by J.O. Wisdom, *Brit.J.Phil.Sci.*, 1954-55, 5: 171-2.
First published: 3 vol. London: Allen & Unwin, 1911-21. Volume 2 reviewed by Walter Libby, *Isis*, 1922, 4: 376-8.

BRETT, George Sidney. Psychology ancient and modern. ix, 164 p., bibliogr. London: Harrap; New York: Longmans, Green & Co., 1928.

CUVILLIER, A. Manuel de philosophie à l'usage des classes de philosophie et de première supérieure. Vol. 1. Introduction générale. Psychologie. xxxix, 722 p., 90 fig. Paris: Colin, 1931. [CB 32/605]

ESPER, Erwin E. A history of psychology. xii, 368 p. Philadelphia: Saunders, 1964.
Reviewed by Leonard Carmichael, *Science*, 1964, 146: 908-9.

FARRELL, B.A., ed. Experimental psychology. A series of broadcast talks on recent research. xi, 66 p. Oxford: Blackwell; New York: Philosophical Library, 1955. [CB 81/276]

FLÜGEL, John C. A hundred years of psychology, 1833-1933. With an additional part: 1933-1963 by Donald J. West. 394 p., bibliogr. New York: Basic Books; London: Duckworth, 1964.
This is the 3rd edition of the first 4 parts, and the 2nd edition, with additions, to the 5th part. First published London/New York: 1933 [CB 42/597].

FOULQUIÉ, Paul; DELEDALLE, Gérard. La psychologie contemporaine. xv, 458 p. Paris: Presses Universitaires de France, 1951.
Reviewed by J.G. Beebe-Center, *Isis*, 1953, 44: 87.

GRUBER, Frederick C., ed. The emergence of the modern mind. 93 p. (The Martin G. Brumbaugh Lectures in Education) Philadelphia: University of Pennsylvania Press, 1958. [CB 84/296]
Reviewed by T.H.B. Hollins, *Nature*, 1959, 183: 953.

HOLLANDER, Bernard. In search of the soul and the mechanism of thought, emotion and conduct. 2 vol. 1. The history of philosophy and science from ancient times to the present day. 526 p.; 2. The origin and the mental capacities and dispositions of man and their normal, abnormal and super-natural manifestations. vii, 361 p. London: Kegan Paul, 1920.

JANET, Pierre. Auto-biographie psychologique. *Étud.Phil.*, 1946, no. 2, 81-7, portr.
Janet describes the evolution of his thought and work.

KANTOR, J.R. The scientific evolution of psychology. Vol. 1. xxii, 387 p., fig., ill. Chicago: Principia Press, 1963.
Reviewed by P. Huard, *Isis*, 1964, 55: 455-7.

MESSER, August. Die experimentelle Psychologie im Jahre 1911. *Jahrb.Phil.*, 1913, 1: 236-69, 375-7.

MITRA, S.C. Origin and development of psychology. *Sci.Cult.*, 1959, 25: 34-8.

MUELLER, F.L. Histoire de la psychologie de l'antiquité à nos jours. 444 p. Paris: Librairie Payot, 1960.
Reviewed by Josef Brožek, *Isis*, 1963, 54: 295-6.

MÜLLER-FREIENFELS, Richard. The evolution of modern psychology. Transl. from the German by W. Béran Wolfe. xvi, 513 p. New Haven: Yale University Press, 1935. [CB 48/583]

MURCHISON, Carl, ed. Psychologies of 1925. 3rd ed. xiii, 412 p. (The International University Series in Psychology) Worcester, Mass.: Clark University Press, 1928.

MURCHISON, Carl, ed. Psychologies of 1930. xix, 497 p. (The International University Series in Psychology) Worcester, Mass.: Clark University Press, 1930.

MURPHY, Gardner. An historical introduction to modern psychology. With a supplement by Heinrich Klüver. xvii, 470 p. (International Library of Psychology, Philosophy, and Scientific Method) London: Kegan Paul, 1929.

PILLSBURY, Walter Bowers. The history of psychology. x, 326 p. London: Allen and Unwin, 1929.

POSTMAN, Leo, ed. Psychology in the making. Histories of selected research problems. viii, 785, xxxiv p., fig. New York: Alfred A. Knopf, 1962. [CB 88/553]

ROBACK, A.A. Present-day psychology. An original study of departments, branches, methods and phases, including clinical and dynamic psychology. With the collaboration of forty experts in the various fields. 995 p. New York: Philosophical Library, 1955. [CB 81/343]

ROYCE, J.R. Psychology at mid-twentieth century. *Amer. Scient.*, 1957, 45: 57-73.

SCHACHTEL, Ernest G. Metamorphosis; on the development of affect, perception, attention and memory. viii, 344 p. New York: Basic Books, 1959.

SEGOND, J. Traité de psychologie. 502 p. Paris: Colin, 1930. [CB 32/595]

SETH, George. From Galton to Crowther. *Advance.Sci.*, 1961, 18: 273-83.

SKINNER, B.F. Cumulative record. x, 427 p., ill. (Century Psychology Series) New York: Appleton-Century-Crofts, 1959.
Reviewed by Robert B. MacLeod, *Science*, 1959, 130: 34-5.

SPEARMAN, Charles. Psychology down the ages. 2 vol. xi, 454 p.; vii, 355 p. New York: Macmillan, 1937. [CB 54/542]

WOODWORTH, Robert Sessions. Contemporary schools of psychology. viii, 247 p. London: Methuen, 1931.

WOODWORTH, Robert Sessions. Psychological issues: selected papers ... with a bibliography of his writings. x, 421 p., portr. New York: Columbia University Press, 1939.
This volume represents a collection of twenty-four papers, from the writings of Prof. Woodworth, and presented to him by his colleagues at Columbia University on the occasion of his seventieth birthday 17 October 1939.

MGc-be

ENCYCLOPEDIA of psychology. Ed. by Philip Lawrence Harriman. vii, 897 p., ill., bibliogr. New York: Philosophical Library, 1946. [CB 71/125]

MGc-br

L'Année psychologique. Fondée par Alfred Binet. Vol. 1- (1894)- Paris: 1895-

Annual Review of Psychology. Vol. 1- Stanford, California: *Annual Reviews*, 1950-
For note on 1950 volume *see* CB 79/185.

MGda

A HISTORY of psychology in autobiography. 4 vol. Vol. 1-3 ed. by Carl Murchison. Vol. 4 by Edwin G. Boring, *et al.* (International University Series in Psychology) Worcester, Mass.: Clark University Press, 1930, 1932, 1936, 1952. [CB 36/447 and CB 33/405]
Volume 1 reviewed by O. Lipmann, *Deut.Lit.Zeitung*, 1931, 2: 1482-4; volume 3 in *Nature*, 1937, 140: 830; volume 4 by Josef Brožek, *Isis*, 1953, 44: 86-7.

MURCHISON, Carl, ed. The psychological register. [A list of psychologists and their works.] Vol. 2. x, 580 p.; vol. 3. xii, 1269 p. (International University Series in Psychology) Worcester, Mass.: Clark University Press, 1929-32; London: Oxford University Press, 1930-32.
Volume 1 not published.
Volume 3 reviewed in *Nature*, 1933, 132: 121.

WATSON, Robert I. The great psychologists: from Aristotle to Freud. 572 p. Philadelphia: Lippincott, 1963.

MGdaj

BECK, Samuel J.; MOLISH, Herman B.; ed. Reflexes to intelligence. A reader in clinical psychology. xiv, 669 p., fig., tables. Chicago: Free Press of Glencoe, 1960.

DENIS, Wayne, ed. Readings in the history of psychology. xi, 587 p. (The Century Psychology Series) New York: Appleton-Century-Crofts, 1948.
Reviewed by Josef Brožek, *Isis*, 1951, 42: 276.

SHIPLEY, Thorne, ed. Classics in psychology. xx, 1342 p. New York: Philosophical Library, 1961.

MGhj

MURPHY, Gardner. The current impact of Freud upon psychology. *Amer.Psychol.*, 1956, 11: 663-72.
Impact evaluated in several subareas (e.g. personality, learning, physiological, etc.) using a 0-6 scale.

TOURNEY, Garfield. Empedocles and Freud, Heraclitus and Jung. *Bull.Hist.Med.*, 1956, 30: 109-23.

MGk philosophy and methodology

BERTRAND-BARRAUD, Daniel. Des bases critiques d'un empirisme psychologique radical . 132 p. Paris: J. Vrin, 1926. [CB 22/290]

BERTRAND-BARRAUD, Daniel. De la nature affective de la conscience. 156 p. Paris: J. Vrin, 1927. [CB 23/257]

BRUNSWIK, Egon. The conceptual focus of some psychological systems. *J.Unified Sci.*, 1939, 8: 36-49.

BRUNSWIK, Egon. The conceptual framework of psychology. iv, 102 p. (International Encyclopedia of Unified Science, Foundations of the Unity of Science, 1: no. 10) Chicago: University of Chicago Press, 1952.

COHEN, Jacques J. Philosophical essays. xiii, 176 p. London: Bale, Sons & Curnow, 1937. [CB 53/284]

COHN, Jonas. Grundfragen der Psychologie. *Jahrb.Phil.*, 1913, 1: 200-35, 374-5.

DRIESCH, Hans. The crisis in psychology. xvi, 275 p. Princeton, N.J.: Princeton University Press, 1925.

DRIESCH, Hans. Grundprobleme der Psychologie. Ihre Krisis in der Gegenwart. 2nd enl. ed. xii, 270 p. Leipzig. Reinicke, 1929.
Not completely identical with English version above.
Reviewed by H. Lipps, *Deut.Lit.Zeitung*, 1930, 1: 1493-5.

FEIGL, Herbert; SCRIVEN, Michael; ed. The foundations of science and the concepts of psychology and psychoanalysis. xiv, 346 p. (Minnesota Studies in the Philosophy of Science, 1) Minneapolis: University of Minnesota Press, 1956. [CB 82/197]

MISIAK, Henryk. The philosophical roots of scientific psychology. xii, 142 p. New York: Fordham University Press, 1961.

RUSSELL, Bertrand. The analysis of mind. 310 p. London: Allen; New York: Macmillan, 1921.
German translation (Leipzig: Felix Meiner, 1927) reviewed by Friedrich Kuntze, *Deut.Lit.Zeitung*, 1928, 49: 756-62.

TOLMAN, Edward Chace. Psychology versus immediate experience. *Phil.Sci.*, 1935, 2: 356-80.

WEIZSÄCKER, Viktor von. Le cycle de la structure (Der Gestaltkreis). Transl. by Michel Foucault and Daniel Rocher. Preface by H. Ey. 231 p. (Bibliothèque Neuro-psychiatrique de Langue Française) Paris/Bruges: Éditions Desclée de Brouwer, 1958. [CB 84/318]
German original: Der Gestaltkreis, first published Leipzig: 1940.

MGkb

ANTHONY, Raoul. Réflexions d'un biologiste sur l'objet, les méthodes et les limites de la psychologie: ses rapports logiques avec les autres branches de la science. 70 p. Paris: J. Vrin, 1926. [CB 20/203]

JAEGER, M. Sisyphus, or the limits of psychology. 94 p. London: Kegan Paul, 1929.

KATZ, David. Psychological atlas. x, 142 p., 395 ill. New York: Philosophical Library, 1948. [CB 72/276]

KIMBLE, Gregory A. Psychology as a science. *Sci.Mon.*, 1953, 77: 156-60.

McDOUGALL, William. The frontiers of psychology. xii, 235 p. (Contemporary Library of Psychology) New York: Appleton-Century, 1935.
Reviewed in *Nature*, 1935, 136: 239.

STEVENS, S.S. Psychology: the propaedeutic science. *Phil. Sci.*, 1936, 3: 90-103.

MGke

FRAISE, Paul. L'expérience dans les sciences humaines: psychologie. *Rev.Syn.*, 1963, 34: 207-14.

HARTSHORNE, Charles. The parallel development of method in physics and psychology. *Phil.Sci.*, 1934, 1: 446-59.

WALLON, Henri. Principes de psychologie appliquée. 224 p. Paris: Colin, 1930. [CB 32/595]
A discussion of the difference in methodology.

WOODGER, J.H. Physics, psychology and medicine: a methodological essay. 145 p. Cambridge University Press, 1956.

MGkk

FEIGL, Herbert; SCRIVEN, Michael; ed. The foundations of science and the concepts of psychology and psychoanalysis. xiv, 346 p. (Minnesota Studies in the Philosophy of Science, 1) Minneapolis: University of Minnesota Press, 1956. [CB 82/197]

PRATT, Carroll C. The logic of modern psychology. xvi, 185 p. New York: Macmillan, 1939. [CB 57/260]
Reviewed by Benjamin Ginzburg, *Isis*, 1947, 32: 223-5.

MGks

KERN, Berthold. Assoziationspsychologie und Erkenntnis. *Z.Positivistische Phil.*, 1913, 1: 65-91.

MGkt

BERGMANN, Gustav. The contribution of John B. Watson. *Psychol. Rev.*, 1956, 63: 265-76.
Analysis of the ideas of the founder of behaviorism.

BLONDEL, Ch. La psychologie selon Comte, Durkheim et Tarde. *J.Psychol.Norm.Pathol.*, 1927, 24: 381-99; 493-519; 591-610.

DRÜE, Herrmann. Edmund Husserls System der phänomenologischen Psychologie. xv, 326 p. Berlin: Walter de Gruyter, 1963.

GURWITSCH, Aron. Développement historique de la Gestaltpsychologie. *Thalès*, 1935, 2: 167-76.

HARDING, Mary Esther. Psychic energy: its source and goal. xii, 497 p. (Bollingen Series, 10) New York: Pantheon Books, 1948.
A representation of Jung's psychology.
2nd edition (1963) entitled "Psychic energy: its source and its transformation". German translation "Das Geheimnis der Seele" (Zürich: Rhein-Verlag, 1948) reviewed by Walter Pagel, *Isis*, 1950, 41: 137.

KRINGLEN, E. [The Eysenck school. A survey and criticism. (In Norwegian)] *Nord.Psykiat.Tidsskr.*, 1964, 18: 256-71.

LENOIR, Raymond. La psychologie de Ribot et la pensée contemporaine. *Rev.Métaphys.Morale*, 1919, 739-63. [CB 15/184]

RIGNANO, Eugenio. La teoria della forma della nuova scuola psicologica tedesca contrapporta all'associazione della scuola psicologica inglese. 1. La "Gestalt" in quanto ordine di elementi sensoriali; 2. La "Gestalt" in quanto unificazione di elementi sensoriali e in quanto significato d'un oggetto; 3. La "Gestalt" in quanto concetto. *Scientia*, 1927, 42: 145-58, 215-29, 281-90; French transl. suppl., 65-80, 99-114, 133-43.

ROBACK, A.A. Behaviorism and psychology. 284 p. Cambridge, Mass.: University Bookstore, 1923.
Reviewed by Raymond Lenoir, *Isis*, 1924, 6: 112-15.

ROBACK, A.A. Behaviorism at twenty-five. 256 p. Cambridge, Mass.: Sci-art, 1937. [CB 53/239]
Supplementary volume to: Behaviorism and psychology.

ROBACK, A.A. Fifty years of the dissociation school. *J.Abnorm. Soc.Psychol.*, 1936, 31: 131-7.

WANN, T.W., ed. Behaviorism and phenomenology: contrasting bases for modern psychology. xi, 190 p. Chicago: University of Chicago Press, 1964.

WARREN, Howard C. A history of the association psychology. x, 328 p. New York: Scribner, 1921.

MGkw

ADLER, Mortimer J. What man has made of man. A study of the consequences of Platonism and Positivism in psychology. xiii, 236 p. New York: Longmans Green, 1937. [CB 52/601]

MGkx

WARREN, Howard C. Mechanism versus vitalism, in the domain of psychology. *Phil.Rev.*, 1918, 27: 597-615.

MGmz relation with other scientific subject fields

MGmzA

BRUNSWIK, Egon. Historical and thematic relations of psychology to other sciences. *Sci.Mon.*, 1956, 83: 151-61, 3 tables.

RASHEVSKY, N. Physico-mathematical aspects of the Gestalt-Problem. *Phil.Sci.*, 1934, 1: 409-19, 4 fig.

MGmzMC

KANTOR, J.R. Evolution and the science of psychology. *Psychol. Rec.*, 1959, 9: 131-42.

MAGOUN, H.W. Darwin and concepts of brain function. In: Council for International Organizations of Medical Sciences. Brain Mechanisms and Learning, p. 1-20. London: Blackwell Scientific Publications, 1961. [CB 87/623]
Also discusses the influence of Spencerian evolution on the growth of ideas in neurophysiology and psychology and examines the opinions of Darwin and Spencer about each other.

MGmzMF

RIVERS, William Halse Rivers. Psychology and ethnology. xxviii, 324 p. (International Library of Psychology, Philosophy and Scientific Method) London: Kegan Paul; New York: Harcourt, Brace, 1926.

MGmzN

CULPIN, Millais. The history of psychology in medicine. *Proc.Roy.Soc.Med.*, 1936, 29: 1569-76, Hist. sect., 33-40.

JASTROW, Joseph. Relation of psychology to medicine. *Med. Life*, 1929, 36: 100-8.

PREMUDA, Loris. Storia della medicina e psicologia. [Summary.] *Act.VIIIe Congr.Int.Hist.Sci.* (Florence, 1956), p. 782. Paris: Hermann, 1958.

MGmzOK

FRANZ, V. Vergleichende Neurologie und Psychologie. *Fortschr., Naturwiss.Forsch.*, 1913, 7: 73-110.

MGn/u other special aspects

MGnh

RUCKMICH, C.A. The use of the term *function* in English text-books of psychology. *Amer.J.Psychol.*, 1913, 24: 99-123.

MGqg

CATTELL, J. McKeen. Early psychological laboratories. Address on the occasion of the inauguration of the Psychological Laboratory of Wittenberg College, Springfield, Ohio, Oct. 21, 1927. *Science*, 1928, 67: 543-8.

MGtc

THORNDIKE, Edward L. Science and values. *Science*, 1936, 83: 1-8.
Address of the retiring president of the A.A.A.S., St. Louis, December 30, 1935.

MGtd

ELIADE, Mircea. Psychologie et histoire des religions, à propos du symbolisme du "Centre". *Eranos-Jahrbuch*, 1950, 19: 247-82.

FRANKFORT, Henri. The archetype in analytical psychology and the history of religion. *J.Warburg Inst.*, 1958, 21: 166-78.

MISIAK, Henryk; STAUDT, Virginia M. Catholics in psychology. A historical survey. With a foreword by Edwin G. Boring. xv, 309 p., front. New York: McGraw-Hill, 1954.
Reviewed by Josef Brožek, *Isis*, 1956, 47: 438-9.

MGtq

KRIS, Ernst; GOMBRICH, Ernst. The principles of caricature. *Brit.J.Med.Psychol.*, 1938, 17: 319-42. [CB 60/166]

WÖLFFLIN, Heinrich. The sense of form in art. A comparative psychological study. 230 p., ill. in text. Transl. by Alice Muehsam and Norma A. Shatan. Published originally as Italien und das deutsche Formgefühl. New York: Chelsea Publishing Co., 1958. [CB 84/306]

MGu

MARETT, R.R. Psychology and folk-lore. ix, 275 p. London: Methuen, 1920.

WUNDT, Wilhelm. Elements of folk psychology. Outlines of a psychological history of the development of mankind. xxiii, 532 p. London: Allen & Unwin; New York: Macmillan, [1928].
First published 1916.

MGw in different countries

DREVER, J. The contributions of the various countries to the science of psychology. *Scientia*, 1922, 32: 83-93; French transl., suppl., 13-23. [CB 13/302]

HOLZNER, Burkart. Amerikanische und deutsche Psychologie: eine vergleichende Darstellung. 404 p., bibliogr. Wurzburg: Holzner Verlag, 1958. [CB 85/396]

MGwb

BRUNER, Jerome S.; ALLPORT, Gordon W. Fifty years of change in American psychology. *Psychol.Bull.*, 1940, 37: 757-6.

HOLZNER, Burkart. *See* MGw

LANGFELD, H.S. The development of American psychology. *Scientia*, 1951, 86: 264-9.

ROBACK, A.A. History of American psychology. xiv, 426 p., 28 pl. New York: Library Publishers; London: George Allen & Unwin, 1952.
Reviewed by Josef Brožek, *Isis*, 1954, 45: 303-4; by John Cohen, *Nature*, 1953, 172: 599-600.

MGwb-hj

SHAKOW, D.; RAPAPORT, D. The influence of Freud on American psychology. 243 p. (Psychological Issues Monograph, 13) New York: International Univ. Press, 1964.
Reviewed by Donald Kaplan, *Psychoanal.Rev.*, 1964, 51: 133-4.

MGwe

HEARNSHAW, L.S. A short history of British psychology, 1840-1940. xi, 331 p., bibliogr. London: Methuen, 1964.

MGwg

HOLZNER, Burkart. *See* MGw

MÜLLER-FREIENFELS, Richard. Les tendances principales de la psychologie allemande d'aujourd'hui. *Rech.Phil.*, 1932, 1: 312-21.

MGwn

LONDON, Ivan D. Contemporary psychology in the Soviet Union. *Science*, 1951, 114: 227-33.

RAZRAN, Gregory. Soviet psychology since 1950. *Science*, 1957, 126: 1100-7.

MGws

MITRA, S.C. Progress of psychology in India. *Indian J.Psychol.*, 1955, 30: 1-21, bibliogr.
Deals with the period since 1935.

MGx techniques

MGxd

OLDFIELD, R.C. Experiment in psychology - a centenary and an outlook. *Advanc.Sci.*, 1960, 17: 364-74.
Centenary of G.T. Fechner's Elements of psychophysics.

TASTEVIN, J.; COUCHOUD, P.-L. La méthode de l'interrogatoire. *Rev.Sci.Psychol.*, 1913, 1: 113-30.

MGxj

BASH, K.W. Testpsychologie in Grossbritannien und in den Vereinigten Staaten. *Ciba Z.*, 1951, 11: 4623-8, ill.

BRINKMANN, D. Aus der Geschichte der Testpsychologie. *Ciba Z.*, 1951, 11: 4606-13.

MGxm

BORING, Edwin G. The beginning and growth of measurement in psychology. *Isis*, 1961, 52: 238-57.

MGy related subjects

MGyB

LUCE, R. Duncan, ed. Developments in mathematical psychology. Information, learning, and tracking. 294 p. Glencoe, Ill.: Free Press, 1960.
Reviewed by Mymon Goldstein, *Science*, 1961, 133: 1350.

MILLER, George A. Mathematics and psychology. x, 295 p. (Perspectives in Psychology) New York: Wiley, 1964.

RASHEVSKY, N. Physico-mathematical aspects of the Gestalt-Problem. *Phil.Sci.*, 1934, 1: 409-19, 4 fig.

MGyMD

POYER, Georges. Les problèmes généraux de l'hérédité psychologique. 306 p. (Bibliothèque de Philosophie Contemporaine) Paris: Alcan, 1921.
Reviewed by L. Guinet, *Isis*, 1923, 5: 474-5.

MGyPW

ANTHONY, Sylvia. The child's discovery of death. xxi, 231 p. New York: Harcourt, Brace, 1940. [CB 61/410]

RICHTER, Friedrich. Die Entwicklung der psychologischen Kindersprachforschung bis zum Beginn des 20. Jahrhunderts. Ein Beitrag zur Geschichte der Kinderseelenkunde. v, 116 p. Münster i. W.: Münsterverlag, 1927.

MH PERSONALITY; TEMPERAMENT

for the personality of the scientist *see* Ajd

CABOT, P.S. de Q. The relationship between characteristics of personality and physique in adolescents. 120 p. (Genetic Psychology Monographs, 20: no. 1) Provincetown, Mass.: The Journal Press, 1938. [CB 56/397]

CRITCHLEY, Macdonald. The language of gesture. 128 p. London: Arnold; New York: Longmans, Green, 1939.
Published with the object of familiarizing medical men with the facts and theories relating to the dynamics of gesture.

EFRON, David. Gesture and environment. 195 p. New York: King's Crown Press, 1941.
A fundamental contribution demonstrating that gestural behaviour is determined by environmental factors and not by "race".

HALL, Calvin S.; LINDZEY, Gardner. Theories of personality. xi, 572 p. New York: Wiley; London: Chapman & Hall, 1957.
An historical and critical review of the theories of personality, beginning with Freud and Jung, and ending with the present.

JUNG, Carl Gustav. Psychological types, or the psychology of individuation. Transl. by Helton Goodwin Baynes. 654 p. London: Kegan Paul, 1923.

LAIGNEL-LAVASTINE, Maxime; VINCHON, Jean. Des tempéraments bilieux et mélancoliques. *Bull.Soc.Franç.Hist.Méd.*, 1926, 20: 165-71.

LUGARO, Ernesto. Les humeurs et le caractère. *Scientia*, 1923, 33: 253-63. [CB 14/562]

MENTRÉ, François. La noologie, science des types intellectuels. *Scientia*, 1924, 36: 89-98.

WOLFF, Charlotte. The hand in psychological diagnosis. xv, 218 p., pl. London: Methuen, 1951.

WOLFF, Charlotte. A psychology of gesture. 2nd ed. xvii, 255 p., ill., bibliogr. London: Methuen, 1948. [CB 74/393]
First edition 1945.

MHce-bv

ROBACK, A.A. A bibliography of character and personality. 340 p. Cambridge, Mass.: Sci-art, 1927. [CB 23/257]

MHke

BOLL, Marcel. La science des caractères dans ses relations avec la méthode scientifique. 40 p. (Actualités Scientifiques et Industrielles, 371) Paris: Hermann, 1936.

MHnh

WAGENINGEN, J. van. Die Namen der vier Temperamente. *Janus*, 1918, 23: 48-55. [CB 11/450]

MHyJO

HELLPACH, Willy. Geopsyche. Die Menschenseele unterm Einfluss von Wetter und Klima, Boden und Landschaft. 4th ed. xvi, 317 p. Leipzig: Engelmann, 1935. [CB 68/23]
First published 1911 under the title "Geopsychiche Erscheinungen".

McADIE, Alexander George. Man and weather. vi, 99 p., ill. Cambridge, Mass.: Harvard University Press, 1926.

MHzp PHRENOLOGY; PHYSIOGNOMY

FRANZ, Shepherd Ivory. New phrenology. *Science*, 1912, 35: 321-8.

MHzp-cm

KLEIN, Marc. Sur l'histoire des origines de l'iconographie physiognomonique. *Act.VIIIe Congr.Int.Hist.Sci.* (Florence, 1956), p. 597-601. Paris: Hermann, 1958.

MHzp-xx

ACKERKNECHT, Erwin H. P.M.A. Dumoutier et la collection phrénologique du Musée de l'Homme. *Bull.Soc.Anthropol.*, 1956, 7: 289-308. [CB 83/271]

MI ABILITY; INTELLIGENCE

CRESSON, André. Les réactions intellectuelles élémentaires. 152 p. (Bibliothèque de Philosophie Contemporaine) Paris: Alcan, 1922.
Reviewed by Hélène Metzger, *Isis*, 1923, 5: 473-4.

HALSTEAD, Ward C. Brain and intelligence. xiii, 206 p. Chicago: University of Chicago Press, 1947. [CB 72/275]

MARTIN, Robert. Les diversités mentales; enquête sur les écoliers. 216 p. Paris: Les Presses Universitaires, 1924. [CB 18/652]
Contains history of the question of mental types.

SPEARMAN, C. The abilities of man: their nature and measurement. viii, 415, xxxiii p. London/New York: Macmillan, 1927.

SPEARMAN, C.; JONES, Ll. Wynn. Human ability. A continuation of "The abilities of man". vii, 198 p. London: Macmillan, 1950. [CB 76/405]

THURSTONE, Louis Leon. The nature of intelligence. xvi, 167 p. (International Library of Psychology, Philosophy and Scientific Method) London: Kegan Paul, 1924.
Reviewed in *Nature*, 1924, 114: 819.

MImzMC

DOBZHANSKY, Th.; MONTAGU, M.F. Ashley. Natural selection and the mental capacities of mankind. *Science*, 1947, 105: 587-90.

LE ROY, Edouard. Les origines humaines et l'évolution de l'intelligence. 388 p. Paris: Boivin, 1928. [CB 26/243]

MImzMFA

ZIRKLE, Conway. [Letter to the editor on the intelligence of the various races.] *Perspect.Biol.Med.*, 1962, 5: 384-90.

MJ PHYSIOLOGICAL PSYCHOLOGY; PERCEPTION

see also OQzv VISION

ARMSTRONG, D.M. Perception and the physical world. xiii, 196 p. London: Routledge and Kegan Paul, 1961.
Reviewed by Walter B. Carter, *Dialogue*, 1962, 1: 338-40.

BORING, Edwin G. Sensation and perception in the history of experimental psychology. xv, 644 p. New York: Appleton-Century, 1942.
Reviewed by R.S. Woodworth, *Science*, 1942, 96: 64-5.

DEMBER, William. Visual perception. xii, 222 p., fig. (Perspectives in Psychology) New York: Wiley, 1964.

DEWEY, Richard; HUMBER, W.J. The development of human behavior. xv, 762 p. New York: Macmillan, 1951. [CB 78/194]

FEARING, Franklin. Reflex action. A study in the history of physiological psychology. xiii, 350 p. Baltimore: Williams & Wilkins, 1930.
Reviewed by B.F. Skinner and W.J. Crozier, *J.Gen.Psychol.*, 1931, 5: 125-9.

LACHMAN, Sheldon Joseph. History and methods of physiological psychology; a brief overview. 64 p., bibliogr. Detroit: Hamilton Press, 1963.

LANGFELD, Herbert S. The historical development of response psychology. *Science*, 1933, 77: 243-50.

LONDON, Ivan D. The scientific council on problems of the physiological theory of Academician I.P. Pavlov: a study in control. *Science*, 1952, 116: 23-7.

MASSEY, Irving. A note on the history of synaesthesia. *Mod. Lang.Notes*, 1956, 71: 203-6.

PAVLOV, Ivan Petrovich. L'inhibition des réflexes conditionnels. Transl. from Russian. *J.Psychol.*, 1913, 10: 1-15.

RAWDON-SMITH, A.F. Theories of sensation. xiii, 113 p. New York: Macmillan, 1938.
A review of the more important theories based on experimental investigations relating to the nature and mechanism of vision and audition.

SOLLEY, Charles M.; MURPHY, Gardner. Development of the perceptual world. 353 p., tables. New York: Basic Books, 1960. [CB 86/468]

WILLEMS, E. Une orientation nouvelle pour la psychologie des rapports de l'être avec son milieu. *Bull.Inst.Sociol.Solvay*, 1913, 28: 1049-67. [CB 4/785]
Article suggested by I.P. Pavlov: L'inhibition des réflexes conditionnels, see above.

MJk

BORING, Edwin G. The perception of objects. *Amer.J.Phys.*, 1946, 14: 99-107, 4 fig.

BORING, Edwin G. The relation of the attributes of sensation to the dimensions of the stimulus. *Phil.Sci.*, 1935, 2: 236-45.

BRAIN, Russell. The nature of experience. viii, 73 p. (The Riddell Memorial Lectures, Thirteenth Series delivered at King's College in the University of Durham, 12, 13 and 14 May 1958) London: Oxford University Press, 1959.
Reviewed by F.I.G. Rawlins, *Nature*, 1959, 184: 218; by H.H. Price, *Brit.J.Phil.Sci.*, 1960, 11: 71-6.

BROADBENT, D.E. Perception and communication. v, 338 p. London/New York: Pergamon Press, 1958.
Reviewed by J.A. Deutsch, *Nature*, 1958, 182: 1572.

GURWITSCH, Aron. Sur une racine perceptive de l'abstraction. *Act.XIe Congr.Int.Phil.* (Brussels, 1953), (2), p. 43-7. Amsterdam: North Holland Publishing Co., 1953.

HAMLYN, D.W. Sensation and perception. xii, 210 p. London: Routledge and Kegan Paul, 1961.
Reviewed by R.J. Hirst, *Brit.J.Phil.Sci.*, 1962, 13: 186.

MYERS, Charles M. Perceptual events, states, and processes. *Phil.Sci.*, 1962, 29: 285-91.

SELLARS, Wilfrid. Science, perception and reality. viii, 366 p. (International Library of Philosophy and Scientific Method) New York: Humanities Press, 1963.

MJme

BOURDON, B. Le rôle de la pesanteur dans nos perceptions spatiales. *Rev.Phil.*, 1913, 75: 441-51.

MJmf

KELLER, R. The asymmetry of the human body. Habitual asymmetrical attitudes and movements. Lefthandedness. The "inferiority" of inversion. The right-left problem in art. Two famous left-handers. *Ciba Symp.* (Summit, N.J.), 1942, 3: 1126-45, ill.

KOBLER, Richard. Der Weg des Menschen vom Links- zum Rechtshänder. Ein Beitrag zur Vor- und Kulturgeschichte des Menschen. ix, 142 p. Wien: Perles, 1932.
Reviewed by Berndt Götz, *Deut.Lit.Zeitung*, 1933, 1863-6; by W. Haberling, *Mitt.Gesch.Med.*, 1933, 32: 37.

SARASIN, Paul. Über Rechts-und Linkshändigkeit in der Prähistorie und die Rechtshändigkeit in der historischen Zeit. *Verhandl.Naturforsch.Ges.Basel*, 1918, 29: 122-96.

WOLFF, W. The right and the left face. *Ciba Symp.* (Summit, N.J.), 1942, 3: 1136-8, 3 fig.

MK MIND AND BODY

ANGEL, Ronald W. Jackson, Freud, Sherrington on the reaction of brain and mind. *Amer.J.Psychiat.*, 1961, 118: 193-7. [CB 87/624]

BREYSIG, Kurt. Die Geschichte der Seele im Werdegang der Menschheit. xxxvii, 526 p. Breslau: Marcus, 1931.

BROWN, Horace M. The anatomical habitat of the soul. *Ann. Med.Hist.*, 1923, 5: 1-22.

CORNER, George W. Anatomists in search of the soul. *Ann. Med.Hist.*, 1919, 2: 1-7.

DORAN, F.S.A. Mind, a social phenomenon, illustrated by the growth of medical knowledge. 182 p., bibliogr. London: Watts, 1952.

FANO, Giulio. Le cerveau et le coeur. Traduit de l'italien par G. Caputo. 211 p. (Nouvelle Collection Scientifique) Paris: Alcan, 1925.
Reviewed by L. Hédon, *Rev.Gén.Sci.*, 1926, 37: 377.

HOLLANDER, Bernard. *See* MGc

JORDAN, Hermann. Gehirn und Seele. *Sudhoffs Arch.*, 1934, 27: 250-66.

LEYACKER, Josef. Zur Entstehung der Lehre von den Hirnventrikeln als Sitz psychischer Vermögen. *Arch.Gesch.Med.*, 1927, 19: 253-86.

LHERMITTE, Jean. Le cerveau et la pensée. 206 p., 5 pl. Paris: Bloud et Gay, 1951.
Reviewed by P. Chauchard, *Rev.Hist.Sci.*, 1952, 5: 155-7.

PIRENNE, M.H. On physiology and consciousness. *Brit.J. Psychol.*, 1947, 37: 82-6.

RANK, Otto. Psychology and the soul. Transl. by William D. Turner. ix, 195 p. Philadelphia: University of Pennsylvania Press, 1950. [CB 78/192]

RICHET, Charles. L'intelligence et l'homme. Études de psychologie et de physiologie. x, 376 p. Paris: Alcan, 1927. [CB 22/300]

RÓVÉSZ, Béla. Geschichte des Seelenbegriffs und der Seelenlokalisation. 310 p. Stuttgart: Enke, 1917.

MKk

COHEN, Jacques J. Philosophical essays. xiii, 176 p. London: Bale, Sons & Curnow, 1937. [CB 53/284]

DRIESCH, Hans. Mind and body. A criticism of psychophysical parallelism. Transl. by Theodore Besterman with a bibliography of the author. xviii, 163 p. London: Methuen, 1927.
Translation of: Leib und Seele. Leipzig: E. Reinicke, 1923.

FEIGL, Herbert; SCRIVEN, Michael; MAXWELL, Grover; ed. Concepts, theories and the mind-body problem. xv, 553 p. (Minnesota Studies in the Philosophy of Science, 2) Minneapolis: University of Minnesota Press, 1958. [CB 84/301]
Reviewed by E.H. Hutten, *Bull.Brit.Soc.Hist.Sci.*, 1960, 10: 344-6; by Isaac Levi, *J.Phil.*, 1961, 58: 241-9.

MACH, Ernst. The analysis of sensations and the relation of the physical to the psychical. Translated from the 1st German ed. by C.M. Williams. Rev. and supplemented from the 5th German ed. by Sydney Waterlow. xvi, 380 p. Chicago/London: Open Court Publishing Company, 1914. [CB 8/369]

MOURGUE, Raoul. Le point de vue neuro-biologique dans l'oeuvre de M. Bergson et les données actuelles de la science. *Rev. Métaphys.Morale*, 1920, 27: 27-70. [CB 13/299]

MYERS, Charles S. The absurdity of any mind-body relation. 27 p. (L.T. Hobhouse Memorial Trust Lectures, 2) London: Oxford University Press, 1932. [CB 37/603]

NEW YORK UNIVERSITY INSTITUTE OF PHILOSOPHY, 3rd, 1959. Dimensions of mind, a symposium. Ed. by Sidney Hook. xiii, 281 p. New York: New York University Press, 1960.
Reviewed by Irving Sosensky, *Phil.Sci.*, 1962, 29: 218-20.

PIÉRON, Henri. Le cerveau et la pensée. 326 p. Paris: Alcan, 1923.
Reviewed by H. Laugier, *Rev.Gén.Sci.*, 1923, 34: 623.

PRATT, James Bissett. Personal realism. xi, 387 p. New York: Macmillan, 1937. [CB 53/284]

SAGUI, Cornelio L. La théorie de l'influx physique. *Sophia*, 1954, 22: 218-21.

THIERFELDER, A. Kritik des psychophysischen Parallelismus. Psychismus. *Ann.Natur.Kulturphil.*, 1913, 12: 264-88.

WENZL, Aloys. Das Leib- und Seeleproblem im Lichte der neueren Theorien der physischen und seelischen Wirklichkeit. iv, 104 p. Leipzig: Meiner, 1933.

MKtd

LAIGNEL-LAVASTINE, M.; ABADIE, Alfred. Notes sur trois stigmatisés (Véronique Guilliani, Lucie de Narni et le Père Pie de Pietrelcina) étudiés objectivement par des contemporains. *Bull.Soc.Franç.Hist.Méd.*, 1933, 27: 106-20.

SCHLEYER, Franz L. Die Stigmatisation mit den Blutmalen. 154 p. Hannover: Schmorl & von Seefeld, 1948.

STEYERTHAL, A. Stigmata diaboli. *Psychiatrisch-Neurol. Wochenschr.*, 1912, 13: 529-36.

MKwg

MOURGUE, R. Le mouvement psycho-biologique en Allemagne. 15 p., bibliogr. *Montpellier Méd.*, 1913, 36: 513, 537.

MKzf FIREWALKING

DARLING, Chas. R. Fire-walking. *Nature*, 1936, 137: 621.

FIREWALKING.[Review of Bulletin II of the University of London Council for Psychical Investigation]. *Nature*, 1936, 137: 649.

LEROY, Olivier. Les hommes salamandres. Recherches et réflexions sur l'incombustibilité du corps humain. 92 p. (Questions Disputées) Paris: De Brouwer, 1931. [CB 43/286]

THOMAS, Ernest S. Fire-walking. *Nature*, 1936, 137: 213-15.

ML FEELING AND EMOTION; MOTIVES

BAUMGARTEN, Franziska. Les forces régulatrices de l'âme et la structure psychique. *Rev.Syn.*, 1958, 79: 103-11.

BORING, Edwin G. A history of introspection. *Psychol.Bull.*, 1953, 50: 169-89.

COFER, C.N.; APPLEY, M.H. Motivation: theory and research. 958 p., bibliogr. New York: Wiley, 1964.
Includes a chapter on "Motivation in historical perspective" (p. 19-55).

ERNST, Fritz. Vom Heimweh. 127 p., ill. Zurich: Fretz & Wasmuth, 1949. [CB 78/192]
A history, followed by an anthology of relevant texts in many languages.
Reviewed by Henry E. Sigerist, *Bull.Hist.Med.*, 1951, 25: 196-8.

GARDINER, H.M.; METCALF, Ruth Clark; BEEBE-CENTER, John G. Feeling and emotion. A history of theories. xii, 445 p. New York: American Book Co., 1937.
Reviewed by C.A Kofoid, *Isis*, 1939, 31: 116-17.

HOWELLS, Thomas H. Hunger for wholiness. 307 p. Denver: World Press, 1940.
Reviewed by M.F. Ashley Montagu, *Isis*, 1941, 33: 288-9.

MONTAGU, M.F. Ashley. On the physiology and psychology of swearing. *Psychiatry*, 1942, 5: 189-201.

RIGNANO, Eugenio. Dell' origine e natura mnemonica delle tendenze affettive. *Atti IVo Congr.Int.Fil.* (Bologna, 1911), (3), p. 649-77. Genoa: Formiggini, 1914.

SALZA, Livia. Nostalgia. 99 p. Novara: Cattaneo, 1922.
A study of the feeling of nostalgia in life and art.

VORWAHL, Henner. Die Beseelung des Menschen. Ein Beitrag zur Geschichte der Psychologie. *Arch.Gesch.Med.*, 1921, 13: 126-7.

MLhj

LANKHOUT, J. Algemeene grondbegrippen der hedendaagsche affect-psychologie bij Spinoza. [General principles of present-day affect-psychology in the works of Spinoza. (In Dutch)] *Bijdr.Gesch.Geneesk.*, 1939, 19: 28-34.

MLth

VILHENA, Henrique. A expressão física da cólera na literatura. 2nd ed. 431 p. Lisboa: Instituto de Anatomia da Faculdade de Medicina de Lisboa, 1930. [CB 36/447]
First edition appeared in Lisbon, in 1909, under the title A expressão da cólera na litteratura.

MLvd

STRUNZ, Franz. Das Heimweh. Zur Psychologie und Geschichte des germanischen Naturgefühls. *Arch.Gesch.Med.*, 1939, 32: 137-54.

MM HIGHER MENTAL PROCESSES; LEARNING; MEMORY

BARNARD, Chester I. Mind in everyday affairs. An examination into logical and non-logical thought processes. An address delivered before Princeton University on March 10, 1936, in the Cyrus Fogg Brackett lectureship in applied engineering and technology. 40 p. Princeton: Guild of Brackett Lecturers, 1936.

HILGARD, Ernest R.; MARQUIS, Donald G. Conditioning and learning. xi, 429 p., bibliogr. New York: Appleton-Century, 1940. [CB 60/161]

JACCARD, Pierre. Le sens de la direction et l'orientation lointaine chez l'homme. Préface de J. Larguier des Bancels. Paris: Payot, 1932.

MANDLER, Jean Matter; MANDLER, George; ed. Thinking: from association to Gestalt. x, 300 p. (Perspectives in Psychology) New York: Wiley, 1964.

MOWRER, O. Hobart. Learning theory and personality dynamics. xviii, 776 p. New York: Ronald Press, 1950. [CB 77/381]

PILLSBURY, W.B. Recent naturalistic theories of reasoning. *Scientia*, 1924, 36: 23-32; French Transl. Suppl., 12-20. [CB 16/310]

RAPAPORT, David, ed. Organization and pathology of thought. xviii, 786 p. New York: Columbia University Press, 1951. [CB 78/192]

RIGNANO, Eugenio. Che cos' è il ragionamento? *Scientia*, 1913, 13: 45-69.

RIGNANO, Eugenio. Come funziona la nostra intelligenza. 47 p. (Attualità Scientifiche, 30) Bologna: 1922.
Summary of "Psicologia del ragionamento" (Bologna: 1920).
For review of French translation *see* below.

RIGNANO, Eugenio. L'evoluzione del ragionamento. *Scientia*, 1913, 14: 67-89, 213-39.

RIGNANO, Eugenio. Le fonctionnement de l'intelligence. *Scientia*, 1922, 31: 197-223. [CB 12/639]

RIGNANO, Eugenio. Psychologie du raisonnement. xii, 544 p. Paris: Alcan, 1920.
Translation of: Psicologia del ragionamento (Bologna: 1920).
Reviewed by George Sarton, *Isis*, 1921, 4: 90-3.
For English translation *see* below.

RIGNANO, Eugenio. The psychology of reasoning. Englished by Winifred A. Holl. viii, 395 p. London: Kegan Paul, 1923.
Translation of: Psicologia del ragionamento (Bologna: 1920).

ROSETT, Joshua. The mechanism of thought, imagery, and hallucination. xi, 289 p. New York: Columbia University Press, 1939. [CB 57/260]

SEGOND, J. L'imagination, étude critique. 300 p. (Bibliothèque de Philosophie Scientifique) Paris: Flammarion, 1922. [CB 13/303]

THOMSON, Robert. The psychology of thinking. 215 p. Harmondsworth: Penguin Books, 1959.
Reviewed by W.H.N. Hotopf, *Brit.J.Phil.Sci.*, 1962, 13: 342-3.

TROLAND, Leonard Thompson. The mystery of mind. xi, 253 p., ill. New York: Van Nostrand, 1926.

MMkq

MAYS, W. Probability models and thought and learning processes. *Synthese*, 1963, 15: 204-21.

MMzc CREATIVITY; GENIUS

for creativity in science *see* Ajg

BURKS, Barbara Stoddard; JENSEN, Dortha Williams; TERMAN, Lewis M. The promise of youth: follow-up studies of a thousand gifted children. Assisted by Alice M. Leahy, Helen Marshall, Melita H. Oden. xiv, 508 p. (Genetic Studies of Genius, 3) Stanford, Cal.: Stanford University Press, 1930.
Reviewed by Karl Pearson, *Nature*, 1931, 127: 772-4.

COX, Catharine Morris. The early mental traits of three hundred geniuses. xxiv, 842 p. (Genetic Studies of Genius, 2) Stanford, Cal.: Stanford University Press, 1926.

GRMEK, M.D. Histoire des recherches sur les relations entre le génie et la maladie. *Rev.Hist.Sci.*, 1962, 15: 51-68.

LANGE-EICHBAUM, Wilhelm. The problem of genius. Transl. by Eden and Cedar Paul. xix, 187 p. London: Kegan Paul, 1931.
Translation of: Das Genie-Problem (München: Reinhardt, 1931); reviewed by W. Enke, *Deut.Lit.Zeitung*, 1931, 2: 856-8.

OSTWALD, Wilhelm. Genie und Vererbung. *Isis*, 1913, 1: 208-14.

PRESSEY, Sickney L. Concerning the nature and nurture of genius. *Sci.Mon.*, 1955, 81: 123-9.
In part a study of precocity and of the conditions under which it developed.

SCHWARZ, Osias L. General types of superior men. A philosophico-psychological study of genius, talent and philistinism in their bearings upon human society and its struggle for a better social order. Prefaces by Jack London and Max Nordau. 435 p. Boston: Badger, 1916.

SEGOND, J. Le problème du génie. 283 p. (Bibliothèque de Philosophie Scientifique) Paris: Flammarion, 1930.
Reviewed by Marcel François, *Rev.Gén.Sci.*, 1931, 42: 287.

TERMAN, Lewis Madison. Mental and physical traits of a thousand gifted children. xv, 648 p. (Genetic Studies of Genius, 1) Stanford: Stanford University Press, 1925. 2nd ed. 1926.

TÜRCK, Hermann. The man of genius. Transl. by G.J. Tamson. 483 p. London: Black, 1914. [CB 6/480]

WEINSTEIN, Alexander. Genius. A review of the "promise of youth" - a progress report of a thousand gifted children. *J.Hered.*, 1933, 24: 417-24.

MMzc-mzMD for relations of genius with heredity *see* MDmzMMzc

MMzc-mzMF

MONTAGU, M.F. Ashley. The creative power of ethnic mixture. *Psychiatry*, 1942, 5: 523-36.

MMzc-mzON

LANGE-EICHBAUM, Wilhelm. Genie, Irrsinn und Ruhm. Eine Pathographie des Genies. 5th ed. completely rev. by Wolfram Kurth. 628 p. Munich/Basel: Reinhardt, 1961.
Reviewed by M.D. Grmek, *Rev.Syn.*, 1963, 84: 560-3.
First published 1928 and reviewed by Ernst Kretschmer, *Deut.Lit.Zeitung*, 1928, 740-4.

MMzc-mzQ

GRMEK, M.D. Histoire des recherches sur les relations entre le génie et la maladie. *Rev.Hist.Sci.*, 1962, 15: 51-68.

MN DEPTH PSYCHOLOGY

for psychoanalysis *see* OMP

BRAUCHLE, Alfred. Hypnose und Autosuggestion. 78 p. Leipzig: Reclam, 1929.

DURIG, A. Uber Automatie und die geschichtliche Entwicklung des Automatiebegriffes. *Festschrift zum 80. Geburtstag Max Neuburgers*, p. 119-26. Wien: Maudrich, 1948.

PETTAZZONI, Raffaele. La confessione dei peccati. 3 vol. (Storia della religione, 8, 11, 12) Bologna: Zanichelli, 1929-36.
Part 1 reviewed by Friedrich Heiler, *Deut.Lit.Zeitung*, 1930, 1: 2358-9.

QUERCY, Pierre. Les hallucinations. 180 p. (Nouvelle Encyclopédie Philosophique, 11) Paris: Alcan, 1936.

SANCTIS, Sante de. Religious conversion: a bio-psychological study. Transl. by Helen Augur. v, 324 p. (International Library of Psychology, Philosophy and Scientific Method) London: Kegan Paul, 1927.
Translation of: La conversione religiosa, studio bio-psicologico. Bologna: Zanichelli, 1923.

VIALLE, Louis. Le désir du néant. Contribution à la psychologie du divertissement. 748 p. (Bibliothèque de Philosophie Contemporaine) Paris: Alcan, 1933. [CB 38/605]

WHYTE, Lancelot Law. The unconscious before Freud. xiii, 219 p., bibliogr. New York: Basic Books, 1960; Anchor Books, Doubleday & Co., 1962. [CB 87/570]
Reviewed by Ilza Veith, *J.Hist.Med.*, 1961, 16: 323-4.

ZILBOORG, Gregory. Fear of death. *Psychoanal.Quart.*, 1943, 12: 465-75.

MNce-bv

BLACK, George F. A list of works relating to lycanthropy. *Bull.N.Y.Public Libr.*, 1919, 23: 811-15.

MNs

EISLER, Robert. Man into wolf, an anthropological interpretation of sadism, masochism, and lycanthropy. Introduction by Sir David K. Henderson. 286 p. New York: Philosophical Library, 1952. [CB 79/184]

ROSEN, George. Psychopathology in the social process. (The Fielding H. Garrison Lecture) *Bull.Hist.Med.*, 1962, 36: 13-44.
Study of "dance frenzies, demonic possession, revival movements and similar so-called psychic epidemics" from the Middle Ages to the American Indian.

MNzd DREAMS; SOMNAMBULISM

BINSWANGER, Ludwig. Wandlungen in der Auffassung und Deutung des Traumes von den Griechen bis zur Gegenwart. 112 p. Berlin: Springer, 1928.

BORN, Wolfgang. A history of dream interpretation. The dream and art. *Ciba Symp.* (Summit, N.J.), 1948, 10: 926-39, 940-51, ill.

FLOURNOY, Theodor. Spiritismus und Experimental-Psychologie. xxiii, 556 p. Leipzig: Felix Meiner, 1921.
Study of the case of the so-called Helène Smith, a case of somnambulism.
Reprint of: Die Seherin von Genf (1914) and translation of: Des Indes à la planète Mars. 4th ed. Paris: Fischbacher, 1910.

FREUD, Sigmund. The interpretation of dreams. Translated from the German and edited by James Strachey. 692 p. New York: Basic Books, 1955. [CB 81/336]
Reviewed by Jacques M. Quen, *J.Hist.Med.*, 1956, 11: 118-19.

LEROY, Eugène Bernard. Les visions du demi-sommeil (hallucinations hypnagogiques). xv, 132 p. (Bibliothèque de Philosophie Contemporaine) Paris: Alcan, 1926.
Reviewed in *Nature*, 1927, 120: 911.

ORBAN, Ludwig. Beitrag zur Geschichte der wissenschaftlichen Traumlehre. *Festschrift zum 80. Geburtstag Max Neuburgers*, p. 354-7. Wien: Maudrich, 1948.

WEISS, Harry B. Oneirocritica Americana. The story of American dream books. 37 p. New York: New York Public Library, 1944. [CB 68/58]
Reprinted from *Bull.N.Y.Public Libr.*, 1944, 48: 642-53.

MO SPECIAL PSYCHIC PHENOMENA; ESP

BAERWALD, Richard. Die intellektuellen Phänomene. ix, 382 p. (Der Okkultismus in Urkunden, 2) Berlin: Ullstein, 1925.
Reviewed by A.A. Roback, *Isis*, 1926, 8: 728-31.

BESTERMAN, Theodore. Crystal-gazing: a study in the history, distribution, theory, and practice of scrying. xiii, 184 p. London: Rider, 1924.

BOIRAC, E. Spiritisme et cryptopsychie. *Rev.Phil.*, 1913, 75: 29-50.

CAILLET, Emile. La prohibition de l'occulte. xii, 208 p. Paris: Alcan, 1930. [CB 32/601]

CARTER, Huntly, ed. Spiritualism. Its present day meaning. A symposium. 287 p., ill. London: Fisher Unwin, 1920.

CORNILLIER, Pierre Emile. La prédiction de l'avenir. Nouvelle théorie expérimentale. xii, 112 p. Paris: Alcan, 1926. [CB 22/293]

DESSOIR, Max. Vom Jenseits der Seele. Die Geheimwissenschaften in kritischer Beleuchtung. 6th ed. xiv, 562 p., 4 pl. Stuttgart: Enke, 1931.
First published 1917.
Reviewed by Carl von Klinckowstroem, *Isis*, 1932, 17: 453.

DINGWALL, E.J. Some human oddities. Studies in the queer, the uncanny and the fanatical. 198 p., 12 pl. London: Home & Van Thal, 1947.
Reviewed in *Nature*, 1947, 160: 39.
American reprint. New Hyde Park, N.Y.: University Books, 1962.
Reviewed by E. Gaskell, *Med.Hist.*, 1963, 7: 295.

DINGWALL, E.J. Very peculiar people. Portrait studies in the queer, the abnormal and the uncanny. 224 p., pl. London: Rider, 1950.
Reprinted. New Hyde Park, N.Y.: University Books, 1962.
Reviewed by E. Gaskell, *Med.Hist.*, 1963, 7: 295.

DOYLE, Arthur Conan. The history of spiritualism. 2 vol. xiii, 342 p., 8 pl.; vii, 342 p., 8 pl. London: Cassell, 1926.
Reviewed by R.J. Tillyard, *Nature*, 1926, 118: 147-9. *See also* resulting correspondence, *Nature*, 1926, 118: *passim.*

FOURNIER D'ALBE, Edmund Edward. Telekinesis and materialisation. *Nature*, 1927, 120: 446-8.

GARLAND, Hamlin. Forty years of psychic research. A plain narrative of fact. x, 394 p. New York: Macmillan, 1937. [CB 56/362]

GELEY, Gustave. Clairvoyance and materialisation; a record of experiments. Transl. by Stanley de Brath. xvi, 401 p., 51 pl. London: Fisher Unwin, 1927.
Translation of: L'ectoplasmie et la clairvoyance. Paris: Alcan, 1924.
Reviewed in *Nature*, 1927, 120: 111-12.

GUÉNON, René. L'erreur spirite. 408 p. Paris: Rivière, 1923. [CB 15/248]

GUILLAUME, Alfred. Prophecy and divination. A study of man's intercourse with the unseen world. xviii, 434 p. (Bampton Lectures for 1938) London: Hodder and Stoughton, 1938.
Reviewed by A.S. Tritton, *Bull.Sch.Orient.Stud.*, 1939, 10: 247.

GULAT-WELLENBURG, Walter von; KLINCKOWSTROEM, Carl von; ROSENBUSCH, Hans. Der physikalische Mediumismus. xiii, 494 p., ill. (Der Okkultismus in Urkunden, 1) Berlin: Ullstein, 1925.
Reviewed by A.A. Roback, *Isis*, 1926, 8: 728-31.

HEYWOOD, Rosalind. ESP: a personal memoir. Introd. by Sir Cyril Burt. 224 p. New York: Dutton, 1964.

HODSON, Geoffrey. The science of seership. A study of the faculty of clairvoyance, its development and use, together with examples of clairvoyant research. Diagrams by D. Kenrick. 224 p. London: Rider, 1929.

KLINCKOWSTROEM, Carl von. Zur Geschichte der Pseudotelepathie. *Z.Krit.Okkultismus*, October 1927, 3: 9-20.

LUDWIG, August Friedrich. Geschichte der okkultistischen-metapsychischen-Forschung von der Antike bis zur Gegenwart. vol. 1. Von der Antike bis zur Mitte des 19. Jahrhunderts. By A.F. Ludwig. 152 p.; 2. Von der Mitte des 19. Jahrhunderts bis zur Gegenwart. By Rudolf Tischner. 371 p. Pfullingen: Baum, 1922-24.

McCABE, Joseph. Spiritualism. A popular history from 1847. 243 p. London: Fisher Unwin, 1920.

MANN, Walter. The follies and frauds of spiritualism. viii, 191 p. London: Watts, 1919.

MAXWELL, Joseph. La divination, 84 p. (Bibliothèque de Philosophie Scientifique) Paris: Flammarion, 1927. [CB 25/432]

MOLL, Albert. Psychologie und Charakterologie der Okkultisten. 130 p. (Abhandlungen aus dem Gebiete der Psychotherapie und medizinischen Psychologie, 11) Stuttgart: Enke, 1929.
Reviewed by Karl Birnbaum, *Deut.Lit.Zeitung*, 1929, 6: 2273-4.

OESTERREICH, Traugott Konstantin. Occultism and modern science. Transl. from the 2nd German ed. 181 p. London: Methuen, 1923.
Translation of: Der Okkultismus im modernen Weltbild. 2nd ed. Dresden: Sibyllen Verlag, 1921.

OSTY, Eugène. Supernormal faculties in man. Transl. by Stanley de Brath. xi, 245 p. London: Methuen, 1923.
Translation of: La connaissance supra-normale. Paris: Alcan, 1923. [CB 15/240]

OSTY, Eugène; OSTY, Marcel. Les pouvoirs inconnus de l'esprit sur la matière, premières étapes d'une recherche. 153 p. Paris: Alcan, 1932.
Reviewed in *Nature*, 1932, 129: 921-2.

RAWCLIFFE, D.H. The psychology of the occult. iv, 551 p., 11 pl., bibliogr. London: Derricke Ridgway, 1952.
Reviewed by E.J. Dingwall, *Nature*, 1953, 170: 176-7.

RHINE, J.B. New frontiers of the mind. 275 p. New York: Farrar & Rinehart, 1937.
Reviewed by M.F. Ashley Montagu, *Isis*, 1938, 28: 531-4.

RICHET, Charles Robert. Thirty years of psychical research, being a treatise on metapsychics. Transl. by Stanley de Brath. xv, 646 p. New York: Macmillan, 1923.
Translation of: Traité de métapsychique. Paris: Alcan, 1922.

ROGOSIN, H. Telepathy, psychical research, and modern psychology. *Phil.Sci.*, 1938, 5: 472-83.

ROGOSIN, H. An evaluation of extra-sensory perception. *J. Gen.Psychol.*, 1939, 21: 203-17.

SCHRENK VON NOTZING, Albert Philibert Franz von. Phenomena of materialisation: a contribution to the investigation of mediumistic teleplastics. Transl. by E.E. Fournier d'Albe. xii, 340 p., ill. London: Kegan Paul; New York: Dutton, 1920.
Translation of: Materialisationsphänomene, and also of parts of: Der Kampf um die Materialisationsphänomene. München: Reinhardt, 1913, 1914.

TISCHNER, Rudolf. Telepathy and clairvoyance. Transl. by W. D. Hutchinson, with an introduction by E.J. Dingwall. xi, 226 p. London: Kegan Paul; New York: Harcourt, Brace, 1925.
Translation of: Über Telepathie und Hellsehen. 2nd ed. München: 1921.

WASILIEWSKI, Waldemar von. Ueber einen Fall von willkürlichen Hellsehen. *Ann.Natur.Kulturphil.*, 1913, 12: 236-63.

WOLFLE, Dael. Extrasensory perception. An editorial. *Science*, 1956, 123: 7. [CB 82/218]

MOc-be

FODOR, Nandor. Encyclopaedia of psychic science. With preface by Sir Oliver Lodge. lv, 416 p. London: Arthurs Press, 1933.

SPENCE, Lewis. An encyclopaedia of occultism. A compendium of information on the occult sciences, occult personalities, psychic science, magic, demonology, spiritism and mysticism. xiv, 451 p., ill. London: Routledge, 1920. [CB 10/216]

MOc-br

Metánoia. Revue internationale scientifique, spiritualiste, adogmatique et éclectique. Vol. 1. Lyon: 1925-26.

The Psychic Research Quarterly. Vol. 1, no. 1-4. London: Kegan Paul, Trench, Trubner, 1920-21. [CB 10/207]
Continued as *Psyche*.

Zeitschrift für kritischen Okkultismus und Grenzfragen des Seelenlebens. Vol. 1-3. Stuttgart: Enke, 1925-28. [CB 18/812]

MOce-bv

CAILLET, Albert L. Manuel bibliographique des sciences psychiques ou occultes. 3 vol. Paris: L. Dorbon, 1912.
Reviewed by G. Sarton, *Isis*, 1913, 1: 285-7.

PRICE, Harry. Short-title catalogue of works on psychical research, spiritualism, magic, psychology, legerdemain and other methods of deception, charlatanism, witchcraft, and technical works for the scientific investigation of alleged abnormal phenomena from circa 1450 A.D. to 1929 A.D. *Proc. Nat.Lab.Psychical Res.*, 1929, 1: (2), 67-422, 33 pl., 8 fig.
Reviewed by R. Zaunick, *Mitt.Gesch.Med.*, 1932, 31: 61.

MOda

HARTMANN, William C., ed. Who's who in occultism, new thought, psychism and spiritualism. 2nd ed. xviii, 350 p. Jamaica, N.Y.: Occult Press, 1927.
First published 1925.

MOke

CARRINGTON, Hereward. The problems of psychical research. 412 p. London: Rider, 1914.

GATTEFOSSÉ, Jean. La collaboration scientifique avec l'invisible. *Bull.Soc.Etud.Psychiques Lyon*, 1922, 8 p.

MEEHL, Paul E.; SCRIVEN, Michael. Compatibility of science and ESP. *Science*, 1956, 123: 14-15.

PRICE, George R. Science and the supernatural. *Science*, 1955, 122: 359-67.

PRICE, George R. Where is the definitive experiment? *Science*, 1956, 123: 17-18.

RHINE, J.B. Comments on "Science and the supernatural". *Science*, 1956, 123: 11-14.
Comments on article by George R. Price, *see* above.

RHINE, J.B. The experiment should fit the hypothesis. *Science*, 1956, 123: 19.

RUTOT, A.; SCHAERER, Maurice. Le mécanisme de la survie. Explication scientifique des phénomènes métapsychiques. 123 p. Bruxelles: La Vulgarisation Intellectuelle; Paris: Alcan, 1923. [CB 15/248]

SOAL, S.G. On "Science and the supernatural". *Science*, 1956, 123: 9-11.
Comments on article by George R. Price, *see* above.

MOkh

BRIDGMAN, P.W. Probability, logic, and ESP. *Science*, 1956, 123: 15-17.

CHOISNARD, P. Les probabilités en sciences d'observation. 168 p. Paris: Alcan, 1923. [CB 16/344]
The book deals with divination.

MOkv

WAELDER, Robert. Psychic determinism and the possibility of prediction. *Psychoanal.Quart.*, 1963, 32: 15-42.

MOmzAF

GATTERER, Alois. Der wissenschaftliche Okkultismus und sein Verhältnis zur Philosophie. viii, 175 p. (Philosophie und Grenzwissenschaften, 2: pt. 1) Innsbruck: F. Rauch, 1927.
Reviewed by K. Sudhoff, *Mitt.Gesch.Med.*, 1927, 26: 269.

MOmzMC

HARDY, A.C. Telepathy and evolutionary theory. *J.Soc.Psychical Res.*, 1950, 35: 225-38. [CB 77/376]

MOv

LAWRENCE, Edward. Occult phenomena among the lower races of man. *Occult Rev.*, January 1923, 14-24.
Completes: Spiritualism among civilised and savage races, *see* below.

LAWRENCE, Edward. Spiritualism among civilised and savage races: a study in anthropology. xiii, 112 p., ill. London: Black, 1921.
Reviewed by George Sarton, *Isis*, 1922, 4: 567-8.

MOwe-qd

BARRETT, W.F. Psychical research. 255 p. (Home University Library) London: Williams & Norgate, [1911].
Apropos of the Society for Psychical Research.

SALTER, W.H. The Society for Psychical Research. An outline of its history. 54 p. London: The Society, 1948.

MP SOCIAL SCIENCES

for anthropology in general *see* MA

MPc

BARNES, Harry Elmer, ed. The history and prospects of the social sciences. xxi, 534 p. New York: Knopf, 1925.
Reviewed by Raymond G. Gettell, *Amer.Hist.Rev.*, 1926, 31: 496-7.

CHAMPAULT, Ph. La science sociale d'après Le Play et de Tourville. *Rev.Syn.*, 1913, 26: 1-63, 241-81. [CB 5/278]

DESCAMPS, Paul. Résumé de l'histoire de la science sociale. *Petrus Nonius*, 1941, 4: 99-133.

HOSELITZ, Berthold F. The social sciences in the last two hundred years. *J.Gen.Educ.*, 1950, 4: 85-103.

MARSHALL, Leon Carroll. The story of human progress: an introduction to social studies. xvi, 548 p. New York: Macmillan, 1925.

RAY, Donald P., ed. Trends in social science. 169 p., index. New York: Philosophical Library, 1961.

WILLIAMS, R.R. Science and social problems. *Amer.Scient.*, 1948, 36: 116-26.
A discussion of the lag in the development of social sciences behind the natural sciences.

MPc-be

ENCYCLOPAEDIA of the social sciences. Editor-in-chief, Edwin R.A. Seligman. 15 vol. New York: Macmillan, 1930-35. [CB 53/282]
Reissued in 8 volumes 1937.

MPce-bv

FELLOWS, Erwin W. Current bibliographic services in the social sciences. *Amer.Doc.*, 1957, 8: 153-67.

HOSELITZ, Bert F., ed. A reader's guide to the social sciences. 256 p. Glencoe, Ill.: Free Press, 1959. [CB 85/406]

MAUNIER, René. Manuel bibliographique des sciences sociales et économiques. Préface de Charles Gide. 228 p. Paris: Sirey, 1920.

Social Science Abstracts. A comprehensive abstracting and indexing journal of the world's periodical literature in the social sciences. Vol. 1-vol. 5, no. 1. Menasha, Wisc.: 1929-33.

MPcj-bv

ZIMMERMAN, Irene. A guide to current Latin American periodicals. Humanities and social sciences. x, 357 p. Gainesville, Fla.: Kallman Publishing Company, 1961.
Reviewed by Hensley C. Woodbridge, *Pap.Bibliogr.Soc.Amer.*, 1962, 56: 274-5.

MPhd

OKA, Kunio. [The history of science and the social sciences. (In Japanese)]. *J.Hist.Sci.Japan*, 1952, no. 24, 1-5.

POSTAN, M.M. The historical method in social science. 38 p. Cambridge University Press; New York: Macmillan, 1939. [CB 59/482]
The inaugural lecture of the Professor of Economic History in the University of Cambridge.

SOCIAL SCIENCE RESEARCH COUNCIL. Social sciences in historical study. A report of the Committee on Historiography. x, 181 p. (Bulletin 64) New York: 1954.

VOISÉ, Waldemar. L'objet et la méthode de l'histoire des sciences sociales. *Kwart.Hist.Nauk.Tech.*, 1957-58, Special issue, 155-64.

MPhf

BOCK, Kennth E. The acceptance of histories: toward a perspective for social science. 132 p. Berkeley/Los Angeles: University of California Press, 1956.
Reviewed by Margaret T. Hodgen, *Isis*, 1957, 48: 473-5.

HOROWITZ, Irving Louis. Social science objectivity and value neutrality. Historical problems and projections. *Diogenes*, 1962, 39: 17-44.

MPk

HAYEK, F.A. The facts of the social sciences. *Ethics*, 1943, 54: 1-13.

OGBURN, William Fielding; GOLDENWEISER, Alexander; ed. The social sciences and their interrelations. viii, 506 p. Boston: Houghton and Mifflin, 1927.
Reviewed by Edwin E. Aubrey, *Amer.Hist.Rev.*, 1928, 33: 619-21.

POPPER, K.R. Prediction and prophecy and their significance for social theory. *Proc.10th Int.Congr.Phil.* (Amsterdam, 1948), p. 82-91. Amsterdam: North Holland Publishing Co., 1949.

PRESSLY, Thomas J. Common frontiers of the social sciences. *Kyklos* (Bern), 1958, 11: 547-50.

WINCH, Peter. The idea of a social science and its relation to philosophy. 143 p., bibliogr. (Studies in Philosophical Psychology) London: Routledge & Kegan Paul, 1958.
Reviewed by Robert K. Merton, *Isis*, 1961, 52: 596-9.

MPke

BAUMERT, Gerhart. Über quantitative und qualitative Verfahren in den Sozialwissenschaften. *Dialectica*, 1962, 16: 142-54.

HAYEK, F.A. The counter-revolution of science. Studies on the abuse of reason. 255 p. Glencoe, Ill.: Free Press, 1952.
Republished New York: Macmillan, 1964.
Reviewed by Donald Fleming, *Isis*, 1952, 43: 383-5.

KONIG, Rene. Grundlagen der Probleme der soziologischen Forschungsmethoden (Modelle, Theorien, Kategorien). *Dialectica*, 1962, 16: 115-42.

LAZARSFELD, Paul; ROSENBERG, Morris; ed. The language of social research. A reader in the methodology of social research. xiii, 590 p., ill. Glencoe, Ill.: Free Press, 1955.
An anthology compiled to present various points of view on methods of research and systems of explanation in the social sciences.

MAYER, Joseph. Scientific method and social science. *Phil. Sci.*, 1934, 1: 338-50.

MAYER, Joseph. Social science principles in the light of scientific method. xii, 573 p. Durham, N.C.: Duke University Press, 1941.
Reviewed by M.F.A. Montagu, *Isis*, 1942, 34: 181-2.

MAYER, Joseph. The techniques, basic concepts, and preconceptions of science and their relation to social study. *Phil.Sci.*, 1935, 2: 431-83.

MERTON, Robert K. Social theory and social structure. Toward the codification of theory and research. 423 p. Glencoe, Ill.: Free Press, 1949.
Reviewed by Charles H. Page, *Isis*, 1950, 41: 325-6.

STERN, Herold S. Implications of the methodology of the physical sciences for the social sciences. *Dialectica*, 1962, 16: 255-74.

VALDOUR, Jacques. Les méthodes en science sociale. Étude historique et critique. viii, 316 p. Paris: Rousseau, 1927.
Reviewed by J. Nippgen, *Ethnographie*, 1930, 133.

WEBER, Max. The methodology of the social sciences. Transl. by Edward A. Shils and Henry A. Finch. xvii, 188 p. Glencoe, Ill.: Free Press, 1949. [CB 78/195]
Three essays, two first published in *Archiv für Sozialwissenschaft* in 1904 and 1905 and the third in *Logos*, in 1917.

MPke-bv

CULVER, Dorothy C. Methodology of social science research: a bibliography. x, 159 p. Berkeley: University of California Press, 1936. [CB 51/287]

MPmzA

TOPITSCH, Ernst. Das Verhältnis zwischen Sozial- und Naturwissenschaften. Eine methodologisch-ideologiekritische Untersuchung. *Dialectica*, 1962, 16: 211-31.

MPmzH

BOWMAN, Isaiah. Geography in relation to the social sciences. Geography in the schools of Europe by Rose B. Clark. xxii, 382 p., 17 ill. (Report of the American Historical Association Commission on the Social Studies, part 5) New York: Scribner's, 1934. [CB 42/594]

MPmzMU

SOUSTELLE, Jacques. Les sciences sociales et la sociologie générale. *Thalès*, 1934, 1: 126-32.

MPmzNC

DARLING, F. Fraser. The ecological approach to the social sciences. *Amer.Scient.*, 1951, 39: 244-54.

MPmzYA

BARNES, Harry Elmer. The new history and the social studies. xvii, 605 p. New York: Century, 1925.
Reviewed by Gaston G. Dept, *Isis*, 1926, 8: 380-2.

SALVEMINI, Gaetano. Historian and scientist. An essay on the nature of history and the social sciences. ix, 203 p. Cambridge Mass.: Harvard University Press, 1940.
Reviewed by M.F. Ashley Montagu, *Isis*, 1941, 33: 82-3.

MPnh

IGGERS, Georg G. Further remarks about early uses of the term "social science". *J.Hist.Ideas*, 1959, 20: 433-6.

MPp

HALL, Harvey P. Annual survey of research in progress on the Middle East [in the social sciences, to be published by the Middle East Institute]. *Isis*, 1955, 46: 55.

LANTIS, Margaret. Where are the social sciences in Alaska? *Sci.Mon.*, 1953, 77: 24-30.
Need for social research on Alaska.

MPqx

LE PROGRÈS. Discours, mémoires et observations. 527 p. (*Ann.Inst.Int.Sociol.*, 14) Paris: Giard et Brière, 1913.
Contains the proceedings of the 8th International Congress held at Rome in 1912.
Reviewed by George Sarton, *Isis*, 1914, 2: 245.

MPs

LERNER, David, ed. The human meaning of the social sciences. 317 p. New York: Meridian Books, 1959.

MPst

CAIRNS, Huntington. Law as a social science. *Phil.Sci.*, 1935, 2: 484-98.

MPwb-p

OGG, Frederic Austin. Research in the humanistic and social sciences. Report of a survey conducted for the American Council of Learned Societies. viii, 454 p. New York: Century, 1928. [CB 24/553]

MPwb-qk

ALPERT, Harry. Geography, social science, and the National Science Foundation. *Prof.Geogr.*, 1957, 9: no. 6, 7-9.

ALPERT, Harry. The National Science Foundation and social science research. *Amer.Sociol.Rev.*, 1954, 19: 208-11.

ALPERT, Harry. The social sciences and the National Science Foundation, 1945-1955. *Amer.Sociol.Rev.*, 1955, 20: 653-61.

MPwb-sc

WATSON, Bruce William Tarr. The social sciences and American civilization. x, 584 p. New York: Wiley, 1964.

MPxm

DODD, Stuart C. A systematics for sociometry and for all science. *Sociometry*, 1948, 11: 7-30.

MPxx

GOLDSTEIN, Marcus S. A museum of the social sciences. *Science*, 1948, 107: 269.

MPyB

DAVIS, H.T. Mathematical adventures in social science. *Amer. Math.Mon.*, 1938, 45: 93-104.

MQ SOCIAL AND CULTURAL ANTHROPOLOGY

for anthropology, in general *see* MA
physical anthropology *see* ME

ALLIER, Raoul. Les non-civilisés et nous, différence irréductible ou identité foncière. 317 p. Paris: Payot, 1927.
Reviewed by Hélène Metzger, *Isis*, 1929, 12: 343-7.

BIDNEY, David. Theoretical anthropology. 506 p. New York: Columbia University Press, 1953.
Reviewed by Clyde Kluckhohn, *Isis*, 1954, 45: 107-9.

BOAS, Franz. Anthropology and modern life. 246 p. London: Allen and Unwin, 1928.

BRIFFAULT, Robert. The mothers: a study of the origins of sentiments and institutions. 3 vol. xix, 781 p.; xx, 789 p.; xv, 841 p. London: Allen and Unwin; New York: Macmillan, 1927.
Reviewed by B. Malinowski, *Nature*, 1928, 121: 126-8.

CHILDE, V. Gordon. Social evolution. viii, 184 p. (The Josiah Mason Lectures in Anthropology, 1947-48) London: Watts; New York: Schuman, 1951.
Reprinted 1963 (London: Collins; Cleveland: Meridian Books).

DUPREE, A. Hunter. Influence of the past: an interpretation of recent development in the context of 200 years of history. *Ann.Amer.Acad.Polit.Soc.Sci.*, 1960, 327: 19-26.

EVANS-PRITCHARD, E.E. Social anthropology. vii, 134 p. Glencoe, Ill.: Free Press, 1951.
Reviewed by M.F. Ashley Montagu, *Isis*, 1952, 43: 83.

FRAZER, James George. Anthologia anthropologica. Selection of passages for the study of social anthropology from the manuscript notebooks. Ed. by Robert Angus Downie. 4 vol. 1. The native races of Africa and Madagascar. xii, 578 p.; 2. The native races of Australasia. iv, 390 p.; 3. The native races of Asia and Europe. vi, 399 p.; 4. The native races of America. ix, 351 p. London: Lund, Humphries, 1938-39. [CB 59/479]
Volume 1 reviewed in *Nature*, 1939, 143: 5-6; volume 4, *ibid.*, 1940, 145: 242-3.

GOLDSCHMIDT, Walter, ed. The anthropology of Franz Boas. vii, 165 p. (Memoir of the American Anthropological Association, 89) Washington: American Anthropological Association, 1959.

HAYS, H.R. From ape to angel. An informal history of social anthropology. xii, 428 p., ill., bibliogr. New York: Knopf, 1958; London: Methuen, 1959.
Reviewed by Melville Jacobs, *Isis*, 1959, 50: 501-2; by T. H. Hawkins, *Nature*, 1960, 185: 721.

HERSKOVITS, Melville J. Franz Boas: the science of man in the making. 131 p. New York: Scribner's, 1953.
Reviewed by Robert H. Lowie, *Sci.Mon.*, 1954, 78: 47; by Ashley Montagu, *Isis*, 1954, 45: 106-7.

HEWETT, Edgar L. From cave dwelling to Mount Olympus. 143 p. (Man in the Pageant of the Ages) Albuquerque: University of New Mexico Press, 1943. [CB 66/269]

LEWIS, Aubrey. Agents of cultural advance. 29 p. (L.T. Hobhouse Memorial Trust Lecture, 30) London: Oxford University Press, 1961.

LOWIE, Robert H. Evolution in cultural anthropology; a reply to Leslie White. *Amer.Anthropol.*, 1946, 48: 223-33.
A commentary on articles by Leslie White in *Amer.Anthropol.*, 1943-46, *see* below.

MÜLLER-LYER, Franz. The history of social development. Transl. by Elizabeth Coote Lake and H.A. Lake. 362 p. (Studies in Economics and Political Science, 60) London: Allen & Unwin, 1920.
Reprinted 1935. Translation of: Phasen der Kultur und Richtungslinien des Fortschritts.

POCOCK, D.F. Social anthropology. vi, 118 p. (Newman History and Philosophy of Science Series, 7) London: Sheed and Ward, 1961.
Reviewed by I.C. Jarvie, *Brit.J.Phil.Sci.*, 1962, 13: 327-9; by Mary B. Hesse, *Hist.Sci.*, 1962, 1: 115-17.

SARTIAUX, Félix. Qu'est-ce qu'une civilisation? Ses principales étapes. *Cah.Rationalistes*, 1932, 2: 419-63.

SAYCE, A.H. The antiquity of civilized man. (The Huxley Memorial Lecture, 1930) *J.Roy.Anthropol.Inst.*, 1930, 60: 269-82; reprinted in *Annu.Rep.Smithsonian Inst.for 1931*, p. 515-29. Washington, D.C.: 1932.

SCHWALBE, G.; FISCHER E.; ed. Anthropologie. viii, 684 p., ill. (Die Kultur der Gegenwart, 3: 5) Leipzig: Teubner, 1923.
The historical introduction is contributed by E. Fischer. Reviewed by O. Hauser, *Naturwissenschaften*, 1923, 11: 288-90; in *Nature*, 1923, 112: 314.

SHAPIRO, Harry L., ed. Man, culture and society. vii, 380 p., ill. New York: Oxford University Press, 1960.

WARDEN, Carl J. The emergence of human culture. vi, 189 p., 10 pl. New York: Macmillan, 1936.
Reviewed by C.A. Kofoid, *Isis*, 1939, 30: 552-3.

WHITE, J.E. Manchip. Anthropology. 191 p., ill. London: English Universities Press; New York: Philosophical Library, 1955.

WHITE, Leslie A. Diffusion vs. evolution: an anti-evolutionist fallacy. *Amer.Anthropol.*, 1945, 47: 339-56.

WHITE, Leslie A. Energy and the evolution of culture. *Amer. Anthropol.*, 1943, 45: 335-56.

WHITE, Leslie A. Evolution in cultural anthropology: a rejoinder. *Amer.Anthropol.*, 1947, 49: 400-13.
An answer to Robert H. Lowie's article, *see* above.

WHITE, Leslie A. The science of culture: a study of man and civilization. xx, 444 p., bibliogr. New York: Farrar, Strauss, 1949. [CB 77/380]

MQk

KROEBER, Alfred L.; KLUCKHOHN, Clyde. Culture. A critical review of concepts and definitions. With the assistance of Wayne Untereiner; appendices by Alfred G. Meyer. 223 p. (Papers of the Peabody Museum of American Archaeology and Ethnology, Harvard University, 48: no. 1) Cambridge, Mass.: 1952. [CB 80/116]

MALINOWSKI, Bronislaw. The dynamics of culture change. xvii, 171 p. New Haven: Yale University Press, 1945. [CB 69/234]

MALINOWSKI, Bronislaw. A scientific theory of culture and other essays. ix, 228 p. Chapel Hill: University of North Carolina Press, 1944.
Reprinted 1960 (New York: Oxford University Press).

MQke

ANDERSON, Alan Ross; MOORE, Omar Khayyam. Toward a formal analysis of cultural objects. *Synthese*, 1962, 14: 144-70.

BOAS, Franz. The aims of anthropological research. *Science*, 1932, 76: 605-13.

SPENCER, Robert F., ed. Method and perspective in anthropology. Papers in honor of Wilson D. Wallis. xii, 323 p., portr. Minneapolis: University of Minnesota Press, 1954.
Special attention may be called to two articles: "On the comparative method in anthropology", by Erwin H. Ackerknecht, and "Research methodology in sociology: the first half-century", by Raymond V. Bowers.

WOLFF, Kurt H. A methodological note on the empirical establishment of culture patterns. Pt. 1-4. *Amer.Sociol. Rev.*, 1945, 10: 176-84. Pt. 5. Preliminary hypotheses regarding the culture of the Spanish people of an unnamed locality in New Mexico. 8 p. Richmond, Ind.: Earlham College, 1945. [CB 69/234]
Mimeographed.

MQmd

MONTAGU, M.F. Ashley. Time-binding and the concept of culture. *Sci.Mon.*, 1953, 77: 148-55.
Discussion of Alfred Korzybski's theory of man.

MQnb

MACKENZIE, Donald A. The migration of symbols: and their relations to beliefs and customs. xvi, 220 p., 16 pl., 53 text ill. (The History of Civilization Series) London: Kegan Paul, 1926.

MQs

SUMNER, William Graham. Folkways. A study of the sociological importance of usages, manners, customs, mores and morals. viii, 692 p., bibliogr. Boston: Ginn, 1907; reprinted New York: Dover Publications, 1959.

MQsc

BAGBY, Philip. Culture and history, prolegomena to the comparative study of civilization. ix, 244 p. Berkeley/Los Angeles: University of California Press, 1959.
Reviewed by Leon Goldstein, *Phil.Sci.*, 1962, 29: 93-4.

PEATE, Iorwerth C. The study of folklife: and its part in the defense of civilization. *Advance.Sci.*, 1958, 15: 86-94. [CB 84/318]

MQtc

KLUCKHOHN, Clyde. An anthropological approach to the study of values. *Bull.Amer.Acad.Arts Sci.*, 1951, 4: 2-3.

MQwf

VARAGNAC, André. Civilisation traditionelle et genres de vie. 402 p., 1 pl., 1 map. (Sciences d'Aujourd'hui) Paris: Michel, 1948.
Reviewed by Paul Schrecker, *Isis*, 1950, 41: 324-5.

MQz special topics

JEREMIAS, Alfred. Der Schleier von Sumer bis heute. 70 p., 23 fig. (Der Alte Orient, 31: no. 1-2) Leipzig: Heinrich, 1931.
Reviewed by W. Haberling, *Mitt.Gesch.Med.*, 1931, 30: 261.

MOSS, Leonard W.; CAPPAMAIR, Stephen C. The Black Madonna: an example of cultural borrowing. *Sci.Mon.*, 1953, 76: 319-24. [CB 80/135]

SAINTYVES, P. En marge de la légende dorée. Songes, miracles et survivances. Essai sur la formation de quelques thèmes hagiographiques. viii, 596 p. Paris: Emile Nourry, 1931. [CB 33/408]

MQzs SEXUAL BEHAVIOUR; MARRIAGE

for prostitution *see* NR

CAWADIAS, A.P. Male eunuchism considered in the light of the historical method. *Proc.Roy.Soc.Med.*, 1946, 39: Hist. Sect., 23-8.

CRAWLEY, Alfred Ernest. The mystic rose: a study of primitive marriage and of primitive thought in its bearing on marriage. A new edition, revised and greatly enlarged by Theodore Besterman. 2 vol. xx, 375 p.; vii, 340 p. London: Methuen, 1927.
First edition 1902.

GALLICHAN, Walter M. Women under polygamy. 340 p. London: Holden and Hardingham, 1914.

HIRSCHFELD, Magnus. Die Homosexualität des Mannes und des Weibes. xvii, 1067 p. (Handbuch der gesamten Sexualwissenschaft, 3) Berlin: L. Marcus, 1914.
Reviewed by G. Sarton, *Isis*, 1914, 2: 241-2.

MONTAGU, M.F. Ashley. Infibulation and defibulation in the Old and New Worlds. *Amer.Anthropol.*, 1945, 47: 464-7.

NEMECEK, Ottokar. Virginity, pre-nuptial rites and rituals. x, 129 p., 16 pl. New York: Philosophical Library, 1958.

NIEUWENHUIS, A.W. Die ursprünglichsten Ansichten über das Geschlechtsleben des Menschen. *Janus*, 1928, 32: 289-314.
Revised and completed version of lecture given at the Congress for the History of Medicine, Leiden, Amsterdam, July 1927.

POMERAI, Ralph de. Marriage, past, present and future: an outline of the history and development of human sexual relationships. xvii, 370 p. London: Constable, 1930.
Reviewed in *Nature*, 1930, 126: 163.

RUNEBERG, Arne. *See* MSc

SOMBART, Werner. Liebe, Luxus und Kapitalismus. *Scientia*, 1914, 15: 241-58. [CB 6/471]

SPENCER, Robert F. The cultural aspects of eunuchism. *Ciba Symp.* (Summit, N.J.), 1946-47, 8: 406-20, ill.

WALL, Otto Augustus. Sex and sex worship (phallic worship). A scientific treatise on sex, its nature and function and its influence on art, science, architecture and religion with special reference to sex worship and symbolism. xv, 607 p., ill. Saint-Louis: Mosby, 1919.

WESTERMARCK, Edvard. The future of marriage in western civilization. xiv, 281 p. New York: Macmillan, 1936. [CB 48/586]

WESTERMARCK, Edvard. The history of human marriage. 5th ed., rewritten. 3 vol. London: Macmillan, 1921; New York: Allerton Book Company, 1922. [CB 12/643]
First London edition 1891.

WESTERMARCK, Edvard. A short history of marriage. xiii, 327 p. London: Macmillan, 1926.
Reviewed by Arthur W. Calhoun, *Amer.Hist.Rev.*, 1927, 32: 558-9.

WINTHUIS, Josef. Die Wahrheit über das Zweigeschlechterwesen durch die Gegner bestätigt. vii, 100 p., 2 portr. (*Beil.Z.Völkerpsychol.Soziol.*, 1930, 6) Leipzig: Hirschfeld, 1930.
Reviewed by K. Th. Preuss, *Deut.Lit.Zeitung*, 1931, 2: 2141-5.

MQzs-ce-bv

GOODLAND, Roger. A bibliography of sex rites and customs: an annotated record of books, articles and illustrations in all languages. v, 752 p. London: Routledge, 1931.

MQzs-u

MARZELL, Heinrich. Die Orchideen in der sexuellen Volkskunde. *Geschlecht Ges.*, 1926, 14: 211-23.

MQzs-wf

GUIART, Jules. Le culte phallique en Bretagne. *Paris Méd.*, 1912, 477-81, 2 fig.

MQzt TOTEMS AND TABOOS

BESSON, Maurice. Le totémisme. 80 p., ill. Paris: Rieder, 1929.
Reviewed by J. Nippgen, *Ethnographie*, 1930, no. 21-22, 140-41.

DESCAMPS, Paul. Les origines du totémisme collectif. *Rev. Inst.Sociol.*, 1927, 7: 745-96.
Reviewed by J. Nippgen, *Ethnographie*, 1930, no. 21-22, 108-9.

FREUD, Sigmund. Totem and taboo. Some points of agreement between the mental lives of savages and neurotics. Authorized translation by James Strachey. x, 172 p. New York: W.W. Norton & Co., 1952. [CB 79/186]
Reviewed by Raymond Firth, *Nature*, 1951, 168: 888.
Translation of: Totem und Tabu, *see* below.

FREUD, Sigmund. Totem et tabou. Interprétation par la psychanalyse de la vie sociale des peuples primitifs. Traduit de l'allemand par le Dr. S. Jankelevitch. 225 p. Paris: Payot, 1924.
Reviewed by S. Zaborowski, *Rev.Gen.Sci.*, 1924, 35: 478-9.
Translation of: Totem und Tabu, *see* below.

FREUD, Sigmund. [Totem und Tabu]. Über einige Übereinstimmungen im Seelenleben der Wilden und der Neurotiker. *Imago*, 1912-13, 1: 17-33, 213-27, 301-33; 1913, 2: 1-21, 357-408.
Reprinted with title, Totem und Tabu. Leipzig/Vienna· 1913; 2nd ed. 1920; 3rd ed. 1922.

GENNEP, Arnold van. L'état actuel du problème totémique. 364 p. Paris: Leroux, 1920.

RADCLIFFE-BROWN, A.R. Taboo. 47 p. (The Frazer Lecture, 1939) Cambridge University Press; New York: Macmillan, 1939.

STEINER, Franz. Taboo. With a preface by E.E. Evans-Pritchard. Edited by Laura Bohannen. 154 p. New York: Philosophical Library, 1956. [CB 82/210]

WEBSTER, Hutton. Taboo. xii, 393 p. Stanford: Stanford University Press, 1942. [CB 64/454]

MR FOLKLORE; SUPERSTITIONS

for folklore and popular aspects of the sciences *see* INDEX
for natural magic and myths *see* AC

BUDGE, E.A. Wallis. Amulets and superstitions: the original texts with translations and descriptions of a long series of Egyptian, Sumerian, Assyrian, Hebrew, Christian, Gnostic and Muslim amulets and talismans and magical figures; with chapters on the evil eye, the origin of the amulet, the pentagon, the swāstika, the cross (pagan and Christian), the properties of stones, rings, divination, numbers, the ḳabbālāh, ancient astrology, etc. xxxix, 543 p., 22 pl. London/New York: Oxford University Press, 1930.

BURNE, Charlotte Sophia. The handbook of folklore. New ed., rev. and enl. x, 364 p. London: Sidgwick and Jackson, for the Folk Lore Society, 1914.
Retains only certain passages from the original edition (1890) by G.L. Gomme.

CLARENCE, E.W. Sympathie, Mumia, Amulette, okkulte Kräfte der Edelsteine und Metalle. 2 vol. 1. Sympathie und Mumia. xi, 322 p.; 2. Okkulte Kräfte der Edelstein und Metalle. iii, 224 p., ill. Berlin-Pankow: Linser-Verlag, 1927.

CORSO, Raffaele. Folklore. Storia, obbietto, metodo, bibliografia. xii, 150 p., 9 pl., 1 map. Roma: Leonardo da Vinci, 1923.

GORSLEBEN, Rudolf John. Hoch-Zeit der Menschheit. xxvii, 689 p., 200 fig. Leipzig: Koehler & Amelang, 1930.

GRAUBARD, Mark. Some contemporary observations on ancient superstitions. *J.Amer.Folklore*, 1946, 59: 124-33.

KNOWLSON, Thomas Sharper. The origins of popular superstitions and customs. x, 242 p. London: Laurie, 1930.

LAARSS, Richard Hans, *pseud.* of Richard Hummel. Das Geheimnis der Amulette und Talismane. 2nd ed. 214 p., ill. Leipzig: R. Hummel, 1926.
First published 1919; 3rd edition entitled: Das Buch der Amulette und Talismane (Leipzig: R. Hummel, 1932).

MARINUS, Albert. Culture et traditions. *Folklore Brabançon*, 1939, 18: 329-48.

MARINUS, Albert. Ethnographie, folklore et archéologie en Russie soviétique. *Bull.Soc.Belge Anthrop.Préhist.*, 1934, 49: 173-86.

MARINUS, Albert. Le néo-folklorisme. *Album. Verzamelde opstellen, opgedragen aan Isidoor Teirlinck*, p. 231-7. Leuven: Vlaamsche Drukkerij, 1931.

MARINUS, Albert. Thèses folkloriques. *Folklore Brabançon*, 1936, 15: 254-8.
Suggested topics for discussion by the Folklore Section of the next International Congress of Anthropology.

NEGELEIN, Julius von. Weltgeschichte des Aberglaubens. 2 vol. 1. Die Idee des Aberglaubens. Sein Wachsen und Werden. viii, 373 p.; 2. Haupttypen des Aberglaubens. xviii, 440 p. Berlin: de Gruyter, 1931-35.
Reviewed by H. Marzell, *Mitt.Gesch.Med.*, 1931, 30: 292.

OESTERLEY, W.O.E. The sacred dance: a study in comparative folklore. x, 234 p. Cambridge University Press, 1923.

READ, Carveth. The origin of man and his superstitions. xii, 350 p. Cambridge University Press, 1920.

SAINTYVES, P. Manuel de folklore. Lettre-préface de S. Charléty. vii, 218 p. Paris: Nourry, 1936. [CB 56/400]

SÉBILLOT, Paul. Le folklore: littérature orale et ethnographie traditionnelle. xxiii, 393 p. (Encyclopédie Scientifique. Bibliothèque d'Anthropologie, Pt. 1. Technologie des sciences anthropologiques, 18) Paris: Octave Doin, 1913.

SUMMERS, Montague. The werewolf. xiv, 307 p., 8 pl. London: Kegan Paul, 1933.
Reviewed in *Nature*, 1934, 133: 433.

THOMPSON, Charles John Samuel. The hand of destiny. The folklore and superstitions of everyday life. 303 p. London: Rider, 1932.

THURSTON, Herbert. Superstition. A backward glance over nineteen centuries. 127 p. London: Centenary Press, 1933.

VILLIERS, Elizabeth. Amulette und Talismane und andere geheime Dinge: eine volkstümliche Zusammenstellung von Glücksbringern, Sagen, Legenden und Aberglauben aus alter und neuer Zeit. Bearbeitet und erweitert von Anton Max Pachinger. 314 p., 26 pl. München: Drei Masken Verlag, 1927.

WEBSTER, Hutton. Magic, a sociological study. 524 p. Stanford: Stanford University Press, 1948.
Reviewed by Mark Graubard, *Isis*, 1950, 41: 138.

WESTERMARCK, Edvard. On the study of popular sayings. *Nature*, 1928, 122: 701-3.

MRc-be

FUNK & WAGNALL'S standard dictionary of folklore, mythology and legend. Maria Leach, ed. 2 vol. 1196 p. New York: Funk and Wagnalls, 1949-50.

RADFORD, Edwin; RADFORD, Mona A. Encyclopaedia of superstitions. ix, 269 p. London: Rider, [1948]. [CB 76/406]

MRc-bv

Volkskundliche Bibliographie für das Jahr 1917-1935/36. Published by the Verband deutscher Vereine für Volkskunde. Berlin: 1919-41.
Continued as: *Bibliographie Internationale des Arts et Traditions Populaires.*

WEINREICH, Otto. Kleine Anzeigen: zur Volkskunde. *Arch. Religionswiss.*, 1924, 22: 321-51.
A review of recent work in the field of folklore and fable; there is a special section on recent Greek contributions to folklore literature.

MRf

MARINUS, Albert. Un programme international d'étude des arts populaires. *Folklore Brabançon*, 1931, 10: 301-12.

MRgp

THOMPSON, Stith. Folklore in Indiana University. *Isis*, 1949, 40: 352.
Regarding the Center of Folkloric Studies at the University of Indiana.

MRj

STECKEL, W. Zur Psychogenese des Aberglaubens. *Zentralbl.Psychoanal.Psychotherap.*, 1913, 3: 531-2.

ZUCKER, Konrad. Psychologie de la superstition. Traduction de François Vaudou. 240 p. Paris: Payot, 1952.
Translation of: Psychologie des Aberglaubens. Heidelberg: Scherer Verlag, 1948.

MRk

DOBSON, Richard M. Theories of myth and the folklorist. *Daedalus Amer.Acad.Arts Sci.*, 1959, 88: 280-90.

MRke

MARINUS, Albert. Critique, méthode et conceptions dans le folklore. *Folklore Brabançon*, 1930, 9: 267-88.

MARINUS, Albert. L'observation directe dans le folklore. *Compt.Rend.Congr.Nat.Sci.* (Brussels, 1930), p. 1008-12. Liége: Thone, 1931.

MRs

MARINUS, Albert. Ethnographie, folklore et sociologie. *Folklore Brabançon*, 1931, 10: 507-29.

MARINUS, Albert. Le folklore dans le conformisme social. *Folklore Brabançon*, 1934, 14: 14-29.

MARINUS, Albert. Folklore historique et folklore sociologique. *Annu.Soc.Luxemb.Etud.Linguist.Dialectologiques*, 1930, 97-104.

MARINUS, Albert. L'importance sociologique du folklore. *Bull.Soc.Anthropol.Bruxelles*, 1927, 42: 136-54.

MRsp

DAUZAT, Albert. Légendes, prophéties et superstitions de la guerre. 283 p. Paris: Renaissance du Livre, [1919].

HELLWIG, Albert. Weltkrieg und Aberglaube. Erlebtes und Erlauschtes. viii, 159 p. Leipzig: Heims, 1916.

MRtd

HERTZ, Robert. Mélanges de sociologie religieuse et de folklore. Preface by Alice Robert Hertz. xvi, 252 p. Paris: Alcan, 1928.
Reviewed by P. A., *Rev.Hist.Relig.*, 1929, 99: 330.

MARINUS, Albert. Science des religions et folklore. *Bull. Soc.Belge Anthropol.*, 1936, 51: 186-98.

MRth

HUET, Gédéon. Les contes populaires. 192 p. (Bibliothèque de Culture Générale) Paris: Flammarion, 1923. [CB 17/599]

DIE MÄRCHEN der Weltliteratur. Ed. by F. von der Leyen and P. Zaunert. 42 vol. Jena: Diederichs, 1912-40. [CB 12/631]

THOMPSON, Stith. The folktale. x, 510 p., bibliogr. New York: Dryden Press, 1946. [CB 70/267]

THOMPSON, Stith. Motif-index of folk-literature. A classification of narrative elements in folk-tales, ballads, myths, fables, mediaeval romances, exempla, fabliaux, jest-books and local legends. 6 vol. (Indiana University Studies, 96/97, 100, 101, 105/106, 108/110, 111/112) Bloomington: 1932-36. [CB 38/607, CB 41/411 and CB 48/585]
Also issued as: FF Communications, no. 106-109, 116-117. Helsinki: 1932-36.

MRvm-ud

TRACHTENBERG, Joshua. Jewish magic and superstition. A study in folk religion. xii, 356 p., bibliogr. New York: Behrmans, 1939.
Reviewed by Jacob S. Minkin, *Isis*, 1947, 32: 182-3; by Joseph Sarachek, *Jew.Quart.Rev.*, 1940, 31: 92-4.

MRw

MARINUS, Albert. La cartographie du folklore. *Annu.Soc. Luxemb.Etud.Linguist.Dialectologiques*, 1931-32, 71-82.

MRwb

THOMAS, Daniel Lindsey; THOMAS, Lucy Blayney. Kentucky superstitions. viii, 334 p. Princeton: Princeton University Press, 1920.

MRwb-bv

HAYWOOD, Charles. Bibliography of North American folklore and folksong. xxxii, 1292 p. New York: Greenberg, 1951.

MRwb-th

COX, John Harrington, ed. Folk-songs of the South, collected under the auspices of the West Virginia Folklore Society. xxxi, 545 p. Cambridge, Mass.: Harvard University Press, 1925.

MRwe

HULL, Eleanor. Folklore of the British Isles. xii, 318 p. (Methuen's Anthropological Series) London: Methuen, 1928.

TAYLOR, Archer. English riddles from oral tradition. xxxi, 959 p. Berkeley: University of California Press, 1951. [CB 78/193]

MRwg-be

BÄCHTOLD-STÄUBLI, Hanns. Handwörterbuch des deutschen Aberglaubens. Herausgegeben unter besonderer Mitarbeit von E. Hoffmann-Krayer und Mitwirkung zahlreicher Fachgenossen. 10 vol. Berlin: de Gruyter, 1927-42.

MRwk

MARINUS, Albert. Caractéristiques du mouvement folklorique en Belgique. *Folklore Brabançon*, 1936, 15: 219-28.

MRwm

ODSTEDT, Ella. Varulven i svensk folktradition. [Werewolves in Swedish folklore. (In Swedish)] 243 p. (Skrifter utgivna genom Landsmåls- och Folkminnesarkivet i Uppsala Ser. B: 1) Uppsala: Lundequist, 1943.
Reviewed by Erland Ehnmark, *Lychnos*, 1943, 328-30.

MRwn

SOKOLOV, Yuri M. Russian folklore. Transl. by Catherine Ruth Smith. viii, 760 p. New York: Macmillan, 1950. [CB 76/406]
Originally published in Russia in 1938 as the first Soviet textbook on Russian folklore for institutions of higher learning.

ZELENIN, Dmitrij. Russische (ostslavische) Volkskunde. xxvi, 424 p., pl. (Grundriss der slavischen Philologie und Kulturgeschichte, 3) Berlin: de Gruyter, 1927.

MRwn-th

LÖWIS, August von. Finnische und estnische Volksmärchen. xv, 302 p. (Die Märchen der Weltliteratur, 20) Jena: Diederichs, 1922. [CB 12/631]

MRwo

SCHNEEWEIS, Edmund. Serbokroatische Volkskunde. 1. Volksglaube und Volksbrauch. xi, 218 p., ill. Berlin: Walter de Gruyter, 1961.
Reviewed by M.D. Grmek, *Arch.Int.Hist.Sci.*, 1963, 16: 456.
2nd edition of the author's Grundriss des Volksglaubens und Volksbrauchs der Serbocroaten.

MRwq

LEGEY, Françoise. Essai de folklore marocain. viii, 235 p., pl. Paris: Geuthner, 1926.
Reviewed by R. Hartmann, *Deut.Lit.Zeitung*, 1928, 445-6.

MRwz

JENNESS, Diamond. Eskimo folk-lore. Pt. A. Myths and traditions from Northern Alaska, the Mackenzie Delta and Coronation Gulf. Southern Party, 1913-16. iii, 90 p. (Report of the Canadian Arctic Expedition, 1913-18, vol. 13) Ottawa: F.A. Acland, 1924.

MRwz-nc

JENNESS, Diamond. Eskimo folk-lore. Pt. B. Eskimo string figures. Southern Party, 1913-16, 192 p. (Report of the Canadian Arctic Expedition, 1913-18, vol. 13) Ottawa: F.A. Acland, 1924.

MRxx

MARINUS, Albert. Pour un Musée National de Folklore [en Belgique]. *Folklore Brabançon*, 1934, 13: 442-65.
Includes accounts of some European museums of folklore.

MS WITCHCRAFT

MSc general history

DUMCKE, Julius. Zauberei und Hexenprozess. 323 p. Berlin: Scherl, 1912.

GRAF, Arturo. The story of the devil. Transl. from the Italian by Edward Noble Stone. With notes by the translator. xiv, 296 p. London: Macmillan, 1931.
Translation of Il diavolo. First published 1889.

GRAUBARD, Mark. The concept of the devil versus modern persecutions. *Relig.Educ.*, 1959, 54: 361-8.

GRILLOT DE GIVRY, Émile Angelo. Witchcraft, magic and alchemy. Translated by J. Courtenay Locke. 395 p., 10 pl. London: Harrap, 1931.
Reviewed in *Nature*, 1932, 130: 792-4.

KENYON, Theda. Witches still live. A study of the black art to-day. Illustrated by Siegel. 379 p. New York: Washburn, 1929.
Reviewed by M.A. van Andel, *Bijdr.Gesch.Geneesk.*, 1932, 12: 240.

LEA, Henry Charles. Materials toward a history of witchcraft. Arranged and edited by Arthur C. Howland, with an introduction by George Lincoln Burr. 3 vol. Philadelphia: University of Pennsylvania Press, 1939. [CB 58/588]
Reviewed by Roland H. Bainton, *Isis*, 1943, 34: 235-6.

LEA, Henry Charles. Minor historical writings and other essays. Edited by Arthur C. Howland. ix, 410 p. Philadelphia: University of Pennsylvania Press, 1942.
Reviewed by Roland H. Bainton, *Isis*, 1943, 34: 235-6.
Includes an essay on the persecution of witches.

OEFELE, Felix von. The roots of Voodooism. From Babylon to Atlantic City. *Med.Life*, 1925, 32: 308-12.

RUNEBERG, Arne. Witches, demons and fertility magic. Analysis of their significance and mutual relations in West-European folk religion. xii, 273 p. (Societas Scientiarum Fennica, Commentationes Humanarum Literarum 14: no. 4) Helsingfors: 1947.

SATAN. 506 p. London/New York: Sheed and Ward, 1951.
"Based upon a volume in the series Études carmélitaines, published in French under the editorship of Père Bruno de Jésus-Marie."

SERGEANT, Philip Walsingham. Witches and warlocks. Introduction by Arthur Machen. 290 p., 15 pl. London: Hutchinson, 1936.
Reviewed in *Nature*, 1937, 139: 268.

SOLDAN, Wilhelm Gottlieb. Geschichte der Hexenprozesse. Edited by Max Bauer. 2 vol. München: Müller, 1912.
First published 1843.

SUMMERS, Montague. The history of witchcraft and demonology. xv, 353 p., 8 pl. (The History of Civilisation Series) London: Kegan Paul, 1926.

SUMMERS, Montague. Witchcraft and black magic. 228 p., 16 pl. London: Rider, 1946.
Reviewed by John L. Myres, *Nature*, 1946, 158: 726.

THOMPSON, R. Lowe. The history of the devil: the horned God of the West. xiv, 172 p., 8 pl. London: Kegan Paul, 1929.

WICKWAR, J.W. Witchcraft and the black art: a book dealing with the psychology and folklore of the witches. 320 p. London: Herbert Jenkins, 1925.

WILLIAMS, Charles. Witchcraft. 316 p. London: Faber, 1941. Reprinted: New York: Meridian Books, 1959.

MSc-be

ROBBINS, Rossell Hope. The encyclopedia of witchcraft and demonology. 571 p., 250 ill. New York: Crown Publishers, 1959.
Reviewed by E.E. Ericson, *Renaiss.News*, 1960, 13: 178-80.

MSce-by

SCHNEIDER, Heinrich. Die Hexenliteratur-Sammlung der Cornell Universität in Ithaca, New York. *Hess.Bl.Volksk.*, 1950, 41: 196-208.
Apropos of the library of witchcraft assembled in Cornell by George Lincoln Burr.

MScp

JOHNSSON, John William Schibbye. En mystik genstand. [A mysterious object. (In Danish)] *Fra Ark.Mus.*, 1912-15, 5: 311-21, ill.
Apropos of a human bone fixed in the roof of a witch's house.

MSk

FERGUSON, Ian. The philosophy of witchcraft. 218 p. London: Harrap, 1924.

MSth

RUDWIN, Maximilian. The devil in legend and literature. xiv, 354 p. Chicago: Open Court, 1931.
Reviewed by Lynn Thorndike, *Isis*, 1932, 18: 208; by Berndt Götz, *Deut.Lit.Zeitung*, 1932, 3: 710-14.

MSw in different countries

SUMMERS, Montague. The geography of witchcraft. xi, 623 p. London: Kegan Paul; New York: Knopf, 1927.

MSwb

KITTREDGE, George Lyman. Witchcraft in Old and New England. 641 p. Cambridge: Harvard University Press, 1929.
Reviewed by Lynn Thorndike, *Isis*, 1929, 13: 138-41.

TALLANT, Robert. Voodoo in New Orleans. viii, 247 p. New York: Macmillan, 1946. [CB 70/245]

MSwb-bv

BLACK, George F. List of works in the New York Public Library relating to witchcraft in the United States. *Bull.N.Y.Public Libr.*, 1908, 12: 658-75.
Reviewed by George Sarton, *Isis*, 1940, 31: 486-7.

MSwd

MURRAY, Margaret Alice. The god of the witches. ix, 214 p. London: Low, Marston, 1934. [CB 44/523]
Reviewed by George L. Burr, *Amer.Hist.Rev.*, 1935, 40: 491-2.

MURRAY, Margaret Alice. The witch-cult in Western Europe. A study in anthropology. 303 p. Oxford: Clarendon Press, 1921. [CB 12/644]

SUMMERS, Montague. The vampire in Europe. xii, 330 p. London: Kegan Paul, 1929.

MSwd-bv

BLACK, George F. List of works relating to witchcraft in Europe. *Bull.N.Y.Public Libr.*, 1911, 15: 727-55.
Reviewed by G. Sarton, *Isis*, 1940, 31: 486-7.

MSwe

BLACK, George F. A calendar of cases of witchcraft in Scotland, 1510-1727. *Bull.N.Y.Public Libr.*, 1937, 41: 827-47, 917-36; 1938, 42: 34-74.
Reviewed by G. Sarton, *Isis*, 1940, 31: 486-7.

EWEN, C. L'Estrange. Witchcraft and demonianism: a concise account derived from sworn depositions and confessions obtained in the courts of England and Wales. 495 p., 8 pl. London: Cranton, 1933.
Reviewed in *Nature*, 1933, 132: 801-2.

EWEN, C. L'Estrange, ed. Witch hunting and witch trials: the indictments for witchcraft from the records of 1373 assizes held for the Home Circuit A.D. 1559-1736. Collected and edited by C. L'Estrange Ewen, with an introduction. xii, 345 p. London: Kegan Paul, 1929.
Reviewed by George L. Burr, *Amer.Hist.Rev.*, 1930, 35: 844-8; in *Nature*, 1930, 125: 371.

HOLE, Christina. Witchcraft in England. Illustrated by Mervyn Peake. 167 p., ill. London: Batsford, 1945.

KITTREDGE, George Lyman. *See* MSwb

MSwg

BYLOFF, Fritz. Hexenglaube und Hexenverfolgung in den österreichischen Alpenländern. xiv, 194 p. (Quellen zur deutschen Volkskunde, 6) Berlin: de Gruyter, 1934.
Reviewed by W. Haberling, *Mitt.Gesch.Med.*, 1934, 33: 310; by Robert Stumpfl, *Deut.Lit.Zeitung*, 1934, 5: 1857-60.

MSwi

ATZENI, Virgilio. Le streghe di Sardegna. *Pagine Stor.Med.*, 1958, 2: no. 3, 45-50.

MU SOCIOLOGY

for social relations of science *see* As;
social relations of the individual sciences *see* INDEX

MUc general history

ÅKESSON, Elof; WITTENBERG, Erich. Werner Sombart und Max Weber. Ein kritischer Beitrag zur modernen Wissenschaftsgeschichte. *Lychnos*, 1940, 86-131.

ARENDT, Hannah. The human condition. vi, 333 p. (Charles R. Walgreen Foundation Lectures) Chicago: University of Chicago Press, 1958.
Reprinted. ix, 385 p. Garden City, N.Y.: Doubleday, 1959.
Reviewed by Leonard Carmichael, *Technol.Cult.*, 1960, 2: 177-8.

BARNES, Harry Elmer. Historical sociology: its origin and development. Theories of social evolution from cave life to atomic bombing. x, 186 p. New York: Philosophical Library, 1948.

BARNES, Harry Elmer, ed. An introduction to the history of sociology. xvi, 960 p. Chicago: University of Chicago Press, 1948. [CB 73/178]

BARNES, Harry Elmer; BECKER, Howard. Social thought from lore to science. 2 vol. 1. A history and interpretation of man's ideas about life with his fellows. xiv, 790, lxxiv p.; 2. Sociological trends throughout the world. viii, p. 791-1178, lxxvii p. Boston: Heath, 1938.
Reviewed by M.F.Ashley Montagu, *Isis*, 1940, 31: 485.

HENDERSON, Lawrence J. Pareto's general sociology. A physiologist's interpretation. vii, 119 p. Cambridge, Mass.: Harvard University Press, 1935. [CB 44/523]

HOMANS, George C.; CURTIS, Charles P., Jr. An introduction to Pareto: his sociology. 299 p. New York: Knopf, 1934.
Reviewed by R.K. Merton, *Isis*, 1935, 23: 295-6.

HUXLEY, Julian. The science of society. *Virginia Quart.Rev.*, 1940, 16: 349-65.

LASBAX, Emile. La cité humaine. Esquisse d'une sociologie dialectique. 2 vol. 1. Histoire des systèmes sociologiques. xii, 316 p.; 2. Cinématique, statique et dynamique sociale. 370 p. Paris: Vrin, 1927. [CB 22/295]

LEVY, Marion Joseph. The structure of society. xvii, 584 p. Princeton: Princeton University Press, 1952. [CB 79/188]

MACIVER, R.M. Society, a textbook of sociology. xii, 596 p. New York: Farrar & Rinehart; London: Macmillan, 1937. [CB 53/566]
A rewriting, with substantial additions, of "Society: its structure and changes", 1931.

MACIVER, R.M.; PAGE, Charles C. Society; an introductory analysis. xvii, 697 p. New York: Rinehart; London: Macmillan, 1949.
Rewriting, with additions, of R.M. MacIver: Society, a textbook of sociology.

MANNHEIM, Karl. Systematic sociology. An introduction to the study of society. Edited by J.S. Erös and W.A.C. Stewart. xxx, 169 p. New York: Philosophical Library, 1958. [CB 84/305]

MAUS, Heinz. A short history of sociology. viii, 226 p. New York: Philosophical Library, 1962.
Reviewed by Roscoe C. Hinkle, *Technol.Cult.*, 1964, 5: 123-5.

MERRIAM, John C. Conservation and evolution in a changing social program. *Proc.Amer.Phil.Soc.*, 1934, 73: 351-70.

MERTON, Robert K.; BROOM, Leonard; COTTRELL, Leonard S.; ed. Sociology today: problems and prospects. xxxiv, 623 p., bibliogr. New York: Basic Books, 1959. [CB 84/318]

MILLS, C. Wright. The sociological imagination. 234 p. New York: Oxford University Press, 1959.
Reviewed by Paul Bohannan, *Science*, 1959, 130: 33-4.

MILLS, C. Wright, ed. Images of man: the classic tradition in sociological thinking. 534 p. New York: Braziller, 1960.

MUMFORD, Lewis. The culture of cities. xii, 586 p., 32 ill. New York: Harcourt, Brace, 1938. [CB 56/401]
Reviewed by M.F. Ashley Montagu, *Isis*, 1939, 30: 557-8.

PARETO, Vilfredo. The mind and society (Trattato di sociologia generale). Ed. by Arthur Livingston. Transl. by Andrew Bongiorno and Arthur Livingston. 4 vol. 2033 p. New York: Harcourt, Brace, 1935.
Reviewed by George C. Homans, *Isis*, 1936, 24: 456-67.
Italian original first published 1916. 2nd edition: Firenze: 1923.

REDFIELD, Robert. Papers. Ed. by Margaret Park Redfield. 2 vol. 1. Human nature and the study of society. xvi, 507 p.; 2. The social uses of social science. 287 p. Chicago: University of Chicago Press, 1962-63.

SCHELTING, Alexander von. Max Webers Wissenschaftslehre. viii, 420 p. Tübingen: J.C.B. Mohr, 1934.

SOROKIN, Pitirim A. Contemporary sociological theories through the first quarter of the twentieth century. xx, 783 p. New York: Harper and Row, 1964.

SOROKIN, Pitirim A. The crisis of our age. 338 p. New York: Dutton, 1942.
Reviewed by M.F. Ashley Montagu, *Isis*, 1944, 35: 46-7.

SOROKIN, Pitirim A. Society, culture, and personality: their structure and dynamics, a system of general sociology. xiv, 742 p. New York: Harper, 1947. [CB 73/179]

STUDIES in the science of society presented to Albert Galloway Keller ... edited by G.P. Murdock. xxii, 555 p. New Haven: Yale University Press, 1937. [CB 52/602]

THOMAS, Franklin. The environmental basis of society. A study in the history of sociological theory. vii, 336 p. (The Century Social Science Series) New York: Century Co., 1925.

TOZZER, Alfred Marston. Social origins and social continuities: a course of lectures delivered before the Lowell Institute, Boston, Massachusetts, February 1924. xix, 286 p. New York: Macmillan, 1925.

MUhg

SOROKIN, Pitirim A. A survey of the cyclical conceptions of social and historical process. *Soc.Forces*, 1927, 6: 28-40.

MUj

ROBINSON, James Harvey. The mind in the making. The relation of intelligence to social reform. With an introd. by Stuart Chase. xiii, 235 p. (Harper's Modern Classics) New York: Harper, 1950. [CB 13/308]
First published 1921.

WALTER, Emil J. Psychologische Grundlagen der geschichtlichen und sozialen Entwicklung. 172 p. (Internationale Bibliothek für Psychologie und Soziologie, 2) Zürich: Pan-Verlag, 1947.
Reviewed by Robert Ulich, *Isis*, 1948, 38: 266-7.

MUj-br

Psychoanalytic Study of Society. 1- New York: International Universities Press, 1960-
Supersedes *Psychoanalysis and the Social Order*, vol. 1-5. New York: International Universities Press, 1947-58. [CB 74/393]

MUk philosophy and methodology

FIRTH, Raymond. Elements of social organization. xi, 257 p., pl. (Josiah Mason Lectures, 1947) London: Watts; New York: Philosophical Library, 1951. [CB 78/194]

GIDDINGS, Franklin Henry. The scientific study of human society. vii, 247 p. Chapel Hill, N.C.: University of North Carolina Press, 1925.

GIDDINGS, Franklin Henry. Studies in the theory of human society. viii, 308 p. New York/London: Macmillan, 1922.

KELLER, Albert Galloway. Societal evolution: a study of the evolutionary basis of the science of society. Rev. ed. ix, 419 p. New York: Macmillan, 1931.
1st edition 1915.
Reviewed by W.G.L.C., *Nature*, 1932, 130: 979-81.

MENSCH und Frieden. (*Eranos-Jahrbuch*, 27) 502 p. Zürich: Rhein-Verlag, 1958. [CB 85/386]

MICHELS, Robert. Probleme der Sozialphilosophie. vi, 208 p. (Wissenschaft und Hypothese, 18) Leipzig: Teubner, 1914.

MILLER, Hugh. The community of man. 169 p. New York: Macmillan, 1949. [CB 76/407]

NEURATH, Otto. Empirische Soziologie. Der wissenschaftliche Gehalt der Geschichte und Nationalökonomie. 151 p. (Schriften zur wissenschaftlichen Weltauffassung, 5) Berlin: Springer, 1931.
Reviewed by Fr. Eulenburg, *Deut.Lit.Zeitung*, 1932, 3: 422-6.

ROSS, Edward Alsworth. The principles of sociology. xviii, 708 p. New York: Century, 1920; 3rd ed. xxxvi, 728 p. New York: Appleton-Century, 1938.

ROUX, Paul. Précis de science sociale. Méthode et enquêtes. 264 p. Paris: Giard et Brière, 1914. [CB 6/471]

SOROKIN, Pitirim A. Modern historical and social philosophies. xi, 345 p. New York: Dover, 1963. Also, Gloucester, Mass.: Peter Smith, 1964.
First published in 1950 under title of "Social philosophies of an age of crisis".

SOROKIN, Pitirim A. Social philosophies of an age of crisis. xi, 345 p. Boston: Beacon Press, 1950.
Reprinted under the title: Modern historical and social philosophies, *see* above.

SPANN, Othmar. Soziologie. *Jahrb.Phil.*, 1913, 1: 301-21, 378-9.

THOMAS, William Isaac. Social behavior and personality. Contributions of W.I. Thomas to theory and social research. Ed. by Edmund H. Volkart. ix, 338 p., bibliogr. New York: Social Science Research Council, 1951. [CB 78/195]

WIESE, Leopold von. Sociology. Ed. and annotated by Franz H. Mueller. xx, 136 p. New York: Piest, 1941.
A presentation of von Wiese's theory of social relations, by means of translations of several of his most characteristic articles.

MUke

BENTLEY, Arthur. Inquiry into inquiries. Essays in social theory. Edited and with an introduction by Sidney Ratner. xvi, 365 p. Boston: Beacon Press, 1954. [CB 80/120]

BRANFORD, Victor. Science and sanctity. A study in the scientific approach to unity. xvi, 253 p. London: Leplay House, 1923. [CB 16/341]

BRIDGMAN, P.W. The intelligent individual and society. vii, 305 p. New York: Macmillan, 1938.
Reviewed by M.F. Ashley-Montagu, *Isis*, 1939, 30: 310-12.

GREENWOOD, Ernest. Experimental sociology: a study in method. Foreword by Paul F. Lazarsfeld. xvi, 166 p. New York: King's Crown Press, 1945. [CB 69/235]

NOELLE-NEUMANN, Elisabeth. Über den methodischen Fortschritt in der Umfrageforschung. *Dialectica*, 1962, 16: 307-328.

SCHAAR, B.E. Scientific method and social relations. *Science*, 1932, 76: 551-7.

SOROKIN, Pitirim A. Sociology as a science. *Soc.Forces*, 1931-32, 10: 21-7, 326-7.

MUkh

LAZARSFELD, Paul F. Notes on the history of quantification in sociology - trends, sources and problems. *Isis*, 1961, 52: 277-333.

RASHEVSKY, Nicolas. Mathematical biology of social behavior. xii, 256 p. Chicago: University of Chicago Press, 1951. [CB 78/195]

RASHEVSKY, Nicolas. Outline of a mathematical theory of human relations. *Phil.Sci.*, 1935, 2: 413-30.

STEWART, John Q. Concerning "social physics". *Sci.Amer.*, 1948, 178: no. 5, 20-3, ill.

MUkk

BOODIN, John Elof. The social mind: foundations of social philosophy. xiii, 593 p. New York: Macmillan, 1939. [CB 61/412]

DUPRÉEL, E. Sur les rapports de la logique et de la sociologie ou théorie des idées confuses. *Atti IV Congr.Int.Fil.* (Bologna, 1911), (3), p. 406-11. Genoa: Formiggini, 1914.

LUNDBERG, George A. Foundations of sociology. 556 p. New York: Macmillan, 1939. [CB 59/481]

MUkq

WALTER, Emile J. Vers une classification scientifique de la sociologie. *Dialectica*, 1962, 16: 354-60.

MUkw

DENIS, H. La philosophie positive et le libre examen. *Rev. Univ.Bruxelles*, 1912-13, 18: 158-64.
Apropos of Comte's philosophy and its influence on sociology.

MUmz relation with other scientific subject fields

MUmzJ

FERRIÈRE, Adolphe. La loi du progrès en biologie et en sociologie et la question de l'organisme social. Etude précédée d'une introduction philosophique sur la méthode en sociologie. xii, 680 p. Paris: Giard et Brière, 1915.
Reviewed by L. Guinet, *Isis*, 1924, 6: 574-6.

GRAUBARD, Mark. Man the slave and master. x, 366 p. London: Dent, 1939.
Reviewed by K. Mather, *Nature*, 1939, 144: 310.

KELSEN, Hans. Society and nature. A sociological inquiry. viii, 391 p. Chicago: University of Chicago Press, 1943.
Reviewed by Aron Gurwitsch, *Isis*, 1946, 36: 142-6.

MONTAGU, M.F. Ashley. The origin and nature of social life and the biological basis of cooperation. *J.Soc.Psychol.*, 1949, 29: 267-83.

MONTAGU, M.F. Ashley. Social instincts. *Sci.Amer.*, 1950, 182: 54-6. [CB 76/399]

MUmzJP

STUNKARD, H.W. Freedom, bondage and the welfare state. *Science*, 1955, 121: 811-16. [CB 81/263]

MUmzLO

FOREL, Auguste. Le monde social des fourmis du globe comparé à celui de l'homme. 5 vol. Geneève: Kundig, 1921-23.
Reviewed by R.M. May, *Isis*, 1924, 6: 578-9.

HASKINS, Caryl P. Of societies and men. xiv, 282 p. New York: Norton, 1951.
Reviewed by George Sarton, *Isis*, 1952, 43: 84-5.
A comparative study of animal and human societies.

REDFIELD, Robert, ed. Levels of integration in biological and social systems. 240 p. Lancaster, Pa.: The Jaques Cattell Press, 1942. [CB 63/272]

MUmzMP

SOUSTELLE, Jacques. Les sciences sociales et la sociologie générale. *Thalès*, 1934, 1: 126-32.

MUmzOF

CANNON, Walter B. The body physiologic and the body politic. *Sci.Mon.*, 1954, 79: 20-6, 1 pl.

MUs/v other special aspects

MUsk

BOURGIN, Hubert. Les systèmes socialistes. 420 p. Paris: Gaston Doin, 1923.
Reviewed by L. Guinet, *Isis*, 1924, 6: 453-4.

HARVARD TERCENTENARY CONFERENCE OF ARTS AND SCIENCES, 1936. Authority and the individual. vii, 371 p. Cambridge: Harvard University Press, 1937.
Reviewed by Robert K. Merton, *Isis*, 1938, 28: 151-4.

MUsp

CLARKSON, Jesse D.; COCHRAN, Thomas C.; ed. War as a social institution. The historian's perspective. 333 p. New York: Columbia University Press, 1941.
Reviewed by Mark Graubard, *Isis*, 1943, 34: 422.

MUst

STAPLETON, Laurence. Justice and world society. 150 p. Chapel Hill: University of North Carolina Press, 1944.
Reviewed by M.F. Ashley Montagu, *Isis*, 1947, 37: 119-20.

MUsy

BLOCH, Ernst. Freiheit und Ordnung. Abriss der Sozial-Utopien. 190 p. New York: Aurora Verlag, 1946; Berlin: Aufbau Verlag, 1947. [CB 70/267]
Written as part of volume 2 of: Das Prinzip Hoffnung. Berlin: Aufbau Verlag, 1954-59.

BLOCH, Ernst. Das Prinzip Hoffnung. 3 vol. Berlin: Aufbau-Verlag, 1954-59.

KRUSE, Frederik Vinding. The community of the future. ix, 829 p. London: Oxford University Press; New York: Philosophical Library, 1952. [CB 79/187]
Translation of: Det kommende Samfund (Copenhagen: 1944).

MUtc

ALLEE, W.C. Where angels fear to tread: a contribution from general sociology to human ethics. *Science*, 1943, 97: 517-25. [CB 65/85]

MUtq

KALLEN, Horace M. Art and freedom. 2 vol. 1006 p. New York: Duell, Sloan and Pearce, 1943.
Reviewed by M.F. Ashley Montagu, *Isis*, 1948, 38: 268.

MUKERJEE, Radhakamal. The social function of art. 355 p., ill. (Lucknow University Studies) Bombay: Hind Kitabs, 1948.
Reviewed by Robert Ulich, *Isis*, 1950, 41: 247.

MUvd

PHILLPOTTS, Bertha Surtees. Kindred and clan in the Middle Ages and after. A study in the sociology of the teutonic races. xii, 302 p. (Cambridge Archaeological and Ethnological Series) Cambridge University Press, 1913.

MUw in different countries

SOROKIN, Pitirim A. Some contrasts of contemporary European and American sociology: I. *Soc.Forces*, 1929, 8: 57-62.

MUwb

GELLA, A. Spoteczny pragmatyzm jako tło rozwoju Amerykanskiej socjologii. [Social pragmatism as a background to the development of American sociology. (In Polish, with English summary)] *Kwart.Hist.Nauk.Tech.*, 1962, 7: 479-97.

MUwd

TÖNNIES, Ferdinand; MAEDGE, Carl. Die Soziologie und ihre Aussichten in Europa. *Akad.Rundsch.*, 1914, 2: 418-31.

MUwf

MERTON, Robert K. Recent French sociology. *Soc.Forces*, 1934, 12: 537-45.

MUz special topics

DESCAMPS, Paul. La signification sociale des gynécocraties. *Rev.Int.Sociol.*, 1928, 36: 249-58.
Reviewed by J. Nippgen, *Ethnographie*, 1930, no. 21-22, 109-10.

KLEIN, Franz. Das Organisationswesen der Gegenwart. Ein Grundriss. 298 p. Berlin: Vahlen, 1913.

MERTON, Robert K. Bureaucratic structure and personality. *Soc. Forces,* 1940, 18: 560-8, bibliogr.

MERTON, Robert K. Social structure and anomie. *Amer.Sociol. Rev.,* 1938, 3: 672-82.

MERTON, Robert K. The unanticipated consequences of purposive social action. *Amer.Sociol.Rev.,* 1936, 1: 894-904.

SOLVAY, Ernest. Solution générale formulée en un cycle de principes, au problème universel de l'organisation sociale. Pour servir éventuellement à éclairer les résolutions à prendre par la Conférence de la Paix. 4 p. Bruxelles: Institut de Sociologie Solvay, 1919.

WELLS, Herbert George. The work, wealth and happiness of mankind. 2 vol. xiii, 850 p., 32 pl. London: Heinemann, 1932.
Reviewed in *Nature,* 1932, 129: 558-60.

MV SOCIAL RELATIONS; SOCIAL GROUPS

ALIHAN, Milla Aïssa. Social ecology. xiii, 267 p. New York: Columbia University Press, 1938. [CB 57/263]

BIGELOW, Karl W., ed. Cultural groups and human relations. v, 214 p. New York: Bureau of Publications, Teachers College, Columbia University, 1951. [CB 79/187]

CONFERENCE ON SCIENCE, PHILOSOPHY AND RELIGION IN THEIR RELATIONS TO THE DEMOCRATIC WAY OF LIFE. Approaches to group understanding. Sixth symposium. xxv, 858 p. New York: Harpers, for the conference, 1947. [CB 71/126]

DAVIS, Allison; GARDNER, Burleigh B.; GARDNER, Mary R. Deep South. xv, 558 p. Chicago: University of Chicago Press, 1941.
A social anthropological study of caste and class in a Southern town.

HOCART, A.M. Caste. A comparative study. xv, 157 p., bibliogr. London: Methuen, 1950.

HUSZAR, George B. de., ed. The intellectuals. A controversial portrait. viii, 543 p. Glencoe, Ill.: Free Press, 1960.

KEITH, Arthur. The place of prejudice in modern civilization (Prejudice and politics): being the substance of a rectorial address to the students of Aberdeen University. 54 p. London: Williams and Norgate, 1931.
Reviewed by J.A.T., *Nature,* 1931, 128: 473-5.

KURELLA, H. Die Intellektuellen und die Gesellschaft. Ein Beitrag zur Naturgeschichte begabter Familien. vii, 124 p. (Grenzfragen des Nerven- und Seelenlebens, 88) Wiesbaden: Bergmann, 1913.

LEYBURN, James G. Frontier folkways. x, 291 p. New Haven: Yale University Press, 1935.
Reviewed by M.F. Ashley-Montagu, *Isis,* 1937, 27: 353.

LOWIE, Robert H. The family as a social unit. *Pap.Michigan Acad.Sci.Arts Lett.,* 1932, 18: 53-69.

PAIN, Jean. L'origine de l'inégalité sociale des sexes. *Merc. France,* 1926, 188: 343-70. [CB 21/589]

SÉE, Henri. Interprétation de quelques données historiques relatives à l'évolution des classes sociales. *Rev.Syn. Hist.,* 1924, 37: 141-50.

SINGER, Kurt. The idea of conflict. 181 p. New York: Cambridge University Press, 1950.
Reviewed by M.F. Ashley Montagu, *Isis,* 1951, 42: 92.

VAN LOON, Hendrik. Tolerance. 386 p. New York: Liveright, 1940.
Reviewed by M.F. Ashley Montagu, *Isis,* 1941, 33: 305-6.

WARNER, William Lloyd; LUNT, Paul S. The social life of a modern community. xx, 460 p. (Yankee City Series, vol. 1) New Haven: Yale University Press, 1942.
Reviewed by Bernard Barber, *Isis,* 1943, 34: 421.

WARNER, William Lloyd; LUNT, Paul S. The status system of a modern community. xx, 246 p. (Yankee City Series, vol. 2) New Haven: Yale University Press , 1942.
Reviewed by Bernard Barber, *Isis,* 1943, 34: 421.

MVo

MONTAGU, M.F. Ashley. The improvement of human relations through education. *Sch.Soc.,* 1947, 65: 465-9.

MVwb

DOLLARD, John. Caste and class in a southern town. iii, 502 p. New Haven: Yale University Press, 1937. [CB 51/287]

MVwb-v

WARNER, W. Lloyd; SROLE, Leo. The social systems of American ethnic groups. xii, 318 p. (Yankee City Series, 3) New Haven: Yale University Press, 1945.

MVwb-vm

BARON, Salo W. The Jewish community. Its history and structure to the American revolution. 3 vol. xxx, 1312 p. Philadelphia: Jewish Publication Society of America, 1942.
Reviewed by Solomon Gandz, *Isis,* 1944, 35: 41-2.

FRIEDMAN, Lee Max. Early American Jews. xiv, 238 p. Cambridge: Harvard University Press, 1934.

MW SOCIAL PSYCHOLOGY

ANASTASI, Anne; FOLEY, John P. Differential psychology. Individual and group differences in behavior. Rev. ed. xv, 894 p. New York: Macmillan, 1949. [CB 76/405]
First published 1937. [CB 51/279]

BLONDEL, Charles. Introduction à la psychologie collective. 211 p., bibliogr. Paris: Colin, 1928. [CB 25/430]

ETKIN, William. Social behavior and the evolution of man's mental faculties. *Amer.Natur.,* 1954, 88: 129-42.

HARVARD TERCENTENARY CONFERENCE OF ARTS AND SCIENCE, 1936. Factors determining human behaviour. vii, 168 p. Cambridge: Harvard University Press, 1937.
Reviewed by Robert K. Merton, *Isis,* 1938, 28: 151-4.

MÜLLER-FREIENFELS, Richard. Allgemeine Sozial- und Kulturpsychologie. xii, 292 p. Leipzig: Barth, 1930.
Reviewed by E. Meister, *Deut.Lit.Zeitung,* 1932, 3: 54-6.

THORNDIKE, E.L. Human nature and the social order. xx, 1019 p. New York: Macmillan, 1940. [CB 61/414]

TROTTER, W. Instincts of the herd in peace and war. 213 p. London: Unwin, 1916; New York: Macmillan, 1917; 3rd ed. 270 p. London: Benn; New York: Macmillan, 1947.
First two essays published in the *Sociological Review,* 1908-1909.

TROTTER, W. Instincts of the herd in peace and war, 1916-1919. [Edited by R.W. Chapman.] xvi, 219 p. London: Oxford University Press, 1953.

WUNDT, Wilhelm. Elements of folk psychology: outlines of a psychological history of the development of mankind. Authorized transl. by E.L. Schaub. xxiii, 532 p. London: Allen & Unwin; New York: Macmillan, 1916.
Translation of: Elemente der Völkerpsychologie (Leipzig: Kröner, 1912).

MX CRIMINOLOGY

BRANHAM, Vernon C.; KUTASH, Samuel B.; ed. Encyclopedia of criminology. xxxvii, 527 p. New York: Philosophical Library, 1949. [CB 78/95]

HOOTON, Earnest Albert. Crime and the man. xvi, 403 p. Cambridge: Harvard University Press, 1939.
Reviewed by Robert K. Merton, *Isis,* 1947, 32: 229-38.

MENDES-CORRÊA, António Augusto. La nouvelle anthropologie criminelle. *Scientia,* 1932, 51: 357-65.

PARENTI, F.; PAGANI, P.L. Nascita ed evoluzione della criminologia scientifica. *Castalia* (Milano), 1964, 20: 12-18.

RECKLESS, Walter C. Criminal behavior. xi, 532 p. New York: McGraw-Hill, 1940. [CB 60/163]
Includes an account of the historical development of the scientific study of crime.

SELLIN, Thorsten. Culture conflict and crime. A report of the sub-committee on delinquency of the Committee on Personality and Culture. ix, 116 p. (Bulletin, 41) New York: Social Science Research Council, 1938.

TAFT, Donald R. Criminology. A cultural interpretation. Rev. ed. xiv, 704 p., ill. New York: Macmillan, 1950. [CB 76/407]
First published 1942.

ZILBOORG, Gregory. Historical sidelights on the problem of delinquency. *Amer.J.Psychiat.*, 1944, 100: 757-61.

ZILBOORG, Gregory. Some primitive trends in civilized justice. *J.Crim.Psychopathol.*, 1943, 4: 599-604.

MXwb

HOOTON, Earnest Albert. The American criminal: an anthropological study. Vol. 1. The native white criminal of native parentage. 310 p., appendix of 480 p. of tables. Cambridge: Harvard University Press, 1939.
Reviewed by Robert K. Merton, *Isis*, 1947, 32: 229-38.

MXxd

CUMMINS, Harold; MIDLO, Charles. Finger prints, palms and soles: an introduction to dermatoglyphics. xi, 309 p. Philadelphia: Blakiston, 1943. [CB 65/83]

FAULDS, Henry. The hidden hand. Vestigia nulla retrorsum. 16 p. Hanley, Stoke-on-Trent: The author, [n.d.]. [CB 12/603]

HARRISON, Wilson R. Suspect documents; their scientific examination. viii, 583 p. London: Sweet and Maxwell, Ltd., 1958.
Reviewed by L.C. Nickolls, *Nature*, 1958, 182: 1399-400.

LAUFER, Berthold. Concerning the history of finger prints. *Science*, 1917, 45: 504-5.
Apropos of William J. Herschel's pamphlet, The origin of finger-printing. 1916 (London: Oxford University Press)

LAUFER, Berthold. History of the finger-print system. *Annu. Rep.Smithsonian Inst.for 1912*, p. 631-52. Washington, D.C.: 1913.

LOCARD, Edmond. Le crime et les criminels. 278 p., ill. Paris: La Renaissance du Livre, 1925. [CB 19/813]
Includes an account of laboratory method for criminal investigation.

MORLAND, Nigel. An outline of scientific criminology. 284 p. New York: Philosophical Library, 1950. [CB 78/195]
Includes brief histories of the various techniques for the detection of crime.

WILTON, George Wilton. Fingerprints: history, law and romance. With foreword by Robert Heindl. xix, 317 p., 10 pl. London: Hodge, 1938.

MY POPULATION; DEMOGRAPHY

BATES, Marston. The prevalence of people. 283 p. New York: Scribner's, 1955.
Reviewed by Conway Zirkle, *Isis*, 1956, 47: 434-8.

BONAR, James. Theories of population from Raleigh to Arthur Young. Lectures delivered in the Galtonian Laboratory, University of London, under the Newmarch Foundation, 1929, with two additional lectures and with references to authorities. 253 p. London: Allen and Unwin, 1931.

BOWMAN, Isaiah. The pioneering process. *Science*, 1932, 75: 521-8.

BOWMAN, Isaiah, ed. Limits of land settlement: a report on present day possibilities. 380 p. New York: Council on Foreign Relations, 1937. [CB 53/268]

BRUNHES, Jean. Human geography. An attempt at a positive classification. Principles and examples. Transl. by T.C. Le Compte. Ed. by Isaiah Bowman and Richard Elwood Dodge. xvi, 648 p. Chicago: Rand McNally; London: Harrap, 1922.
Translation of: La géographie humaine (first published Paris: Alcan, 1910).

DARWIN, Charles Galton. The problems of world population. 42 p. (Rede Lecture, 1958) Cambridge/New York: Cambridge University Press, 1958.

DENNERY, Etienne. Foules d'Asie: surpopulation japonaise, expansion chinoise, émigration indienne. 247 p., maps. Paris: Colin, 1930.
Reviewed by John E. Orchard, *Geogr.Rev.*, 1931, 21: 168-9.

DRYSDALE, C.V. The small family system. Is it injurious or immoral? 119 p., diagr. Prefatory note by Dr. Binnie Dunlop. London: A.C. Fifield, 1913; New York: B.W. Huebsch, 1914. [CB 6/469]

GINI, Corrado. Nascita, evoluzione e morte delle nazioni: la teoria ciclica della popolazione e i vari sistemi di politica demografica. 137 p. Rome: Littorio, 1930.
Reviewed by Lucien March, *J.Soc.Statist.Paris*, 1931, 72: 302-4.

GINI, Corrado, *et al.* Demografia, antropometria, statistica sanitaria, dinamica delle popolazioni. vii, 740 p. (Trattato italiano d'igiene, monografia, 18a) Torino: Unione tipografico-editrice torinese, 1930.
Reviewed by Lucien March, *J.Soc.Statist.Paris*, 1931, 72: 302-4.

HALBWACHS, Maurice. Morphologie sociale. 208 p. Paris: Colin, 1938. [CB 54/565]

HANSEN, Marcus Lee. The Atlantic migration. xvii, 390 p. Cambridge, Mass.: Harvard University Press, 1940. [CB 60/164]

HAUSER, Philip M.; DUNCAN, Otis Dudley; ed. The study or population; an inventory and appraisal. xvi, 864 p. Chicago: University of Chicago Press; London: Cambridge University Press, 1959.
Reviewed by B. Benjamin, *Nature*, 1959, 184: 1521-2.

KNIBBS, George Handley. The shadow of the world's future: or the earth's population possibilities and the consequences of the present rate of increase of the earth's inhabitants. 131 p. London: Benn, 1928.
Reviewed by R.A. Fisher, *Nature*, 1928, 123: 357-8.

KUCZYNSKI, Robert R. The balance of births and deaths. 2 vol. 1. Western and northern Europe. xii, 140 p.; 2. Eastern and southern Europe. 170 p. Washington: Brookings Institution, 1928-31.
Reviewed by R.A. Fisher, *Nature*, 1929, 123: 357-8.

LANDRY, Adolphe, *et al.* Traité de démographie. 651 p., 48 fig. Paris: Payot, 1945. [CB 70/268]

MARBUT, C.F. The rise, decline, and revival of Malthusianism in relation to geography and character of soils. *Ann.Ass. Amer.Geogr.*, 1925, 15: 1-29.

MEGAW, John. Over-population as a world problem. Foreword by A.V. Hill. 12 p. (Occasional Papers, 1) London: British Social Hygiene Council, [1948?].

MYRDAL, Gunnar. Population: a problem for democracy. xv, 237 p. (The Godkin Lectures, 1938) Cambridge: Harvard University Press, 1940.

PEARL, Raymond. The natural history of population. xii, 416 p. New York: Oxford University Press, 1939. [CB 57/265]

PEARL, Raymond. On biological principles affecting populations: human and other. *Amer.Natur.*, 1937, 71: 50-68.

PEARL, Raymond. Some aspects of the biology of human populations. In: Cowdry, E.V., ed. Human biology and racial welfare, p. 515-52, 11 fig. New York: Hoeber, 1930.

PEARL, Raymond; GOULD, Sophia A. World population growth. *Human Biol.*, 1936, 8: 399-419.

SAX, Karl. Standing room only. The challenge of over-population. 206 p. Boston: Beacon Press, 1955.
Reviewed by Conway Zirkle, *Isis*, 1956, 47: 434-8.

ZIRKLE, Conway. Population problems. *Isis*, 1947, 38: 28-33.

MYdaj

SPENGLER, Joseph J.; DUNCAN, Otis Dudley; ed. Population theory and policy. Selected readings. x, 522 p. Glencoe, Ill.: Free Press, 1956. [CB 82/210]

MYmzSA

BENNETT, M.K. Population and food supply: the current scare. *Sci.Mon.*, 1949, 68: 17-26.

CLARK, F. Le Gros; PIRIE, N.W.; ed. Four thousand million mouths. xii, 222 p. New York: Oxford University Press, 1952.

MYs

FISHER, R.A. The social selection of human fertility. 32 p. (The Herbert Spencer Lecture delivered at Oxford, June 8, 1932) Oxford: Clarendon Press, 1932. [CB 41/608]
Relation of birthrate to social organization.

MYsm

GREGORY, John Walter. Human migration and the future, a study of the causes, effects, and control of emigration. 218 p., pl., maps. London: Seeley, Service, 1928.

NUMELIN, Ragnar. The wandering spirit. A study of human migration. With a foreword by Edward Westermarck. xvi, 375 p. London: Macmillan, 1937.
Reviewed by Charles A. Kofoid, *Isis*, 1938, 29: 194-6.

MYwb-be

BOGUE, Donald J. The population of the United States. xix, 873 p., tables, graphs. Glencoe, Ill.: Free Press, 1959. [CB 87/554]

MYwb-qk

ALPERT, Harry. Demographic research and the National Science Foundation. *Soc.Forces*, 1957, 36: 17-21.

MYxd

AUSTRALIA. COMMONWEALTH BUREAU OF CENSUS AND STATISTICS. Census of the Commonwealth of Australia ... 1911. 3 vol. Melbourne: 1917, 1914.
Volume 1 contains a history of census-taking.

SHIRRAS, G. Findlay. The census of India, 1931. *Geogr.Rev.*, 1935, 25: 434-8.

MYyBW

FAIRCHILD, Henry Pratt. L'arithmétique ou étude scientifique de l'aspect quantitatif de la population. Une addition à la terminologie sociologique. *J.Soc.Statist.Paris*, 1931, 72: 268-70.

HOGBEN, Lancelot, ed. Political arithmetic: a symposium of population studies. 531 p. London: Allen & Unwin; New York: Macmillan, 1938.
Reviewed by Robert K. Merton, *Isis*, 1939, 30: 555-7.

KNIBBS, George Handley. The mathematical theory of population, of its character and fluctuations and of the factors which influence them; being an examination of the general scheme of statistical representation, with deductions of necessary formulae; the whole being applied to the data of the Australian census of 1911 and to the elucidation of Australian population statistics generally. xvi, 466 p. (Report of the Australian Census for 1911, Appendix A, vol. 1) Melbourne: McCarron, Bird, 1917.

N MEDICINE

Nc general history

Nc-be *encyclopaedias; systematic compendia*

ASCHOFF, L.; DIEPGEN, Paul. Kurze Übersichtstabelle zur Geschichte der Medizin. 7th ed. by P. Diepgen and H. Goerke. vi, 85 p. Berlin/Göttingen/Heidelberg: Springer, 1960.
First published 1909.
For reviews *see* CB 87/571 and 572, and CB 88/554.
For comments on 3rd edition (München: Bergmann, 1936) *see* CB 48/587.
4th edition (1940) reviewed by Ernst Nachmanson, *Lychnos*, 1942, 407-8.

GRIESBACH, Hermann. Medizinisches Wörter- und Nachschlagebuch. Ein Hilfsbuch für Studierende und Ärzte und alle mit der Medizin im Zusammenhang stehende Berufe. Mit Ableitung, Übersetzung und Erklärung der in der Medizin vorkommenden Fachausdrücke und mit biographischen und literarischen Angaben. 815, 313 p. Giessen: Alfred Töpelmann, 1927.

Nc-bm *large scale works*

ACKERKNECHT, Erwin H. Kurze Geschichte der Medizin. xii, 216 p. Stuttgart: Ferdinand Enke Verlag, 1959.
Reviewed by E. Bastholm, *Lychnos*, 1960-61, 375-6.

ACKERKNECHT, Erwin H. A short history of medicine. vii, 258 p., 28 fig., 1 pl. New York: Ronald Press, 1955.
Reviewed by J.B. de C.M. Saunders, *Isis*, 1957, 48: 73-6; for other reviews *see* CB 82/211 and CB 83/205.

AMERICAN FOUNDATION. Medical research: a midcentury survey. 2 vol. 1. American medical research: in principle and practice. xxxii, 765 p.; 2. Unsolved clinical problems: in biological perspective. xxxii, 740 p. Boston/Toronto: Little, Brown and Co., 1955.
Reviewed by Chauncey D. Leake, *Bull.Hist.Med.*, 1957, 31: 95-6.

BARBILLION, L. Etudes critiques d'histoire de la médecine. 239 p. Paris: Baillière, 1930.

BARDUZZI, Domenico. Manuale di storia della medicina. 2 vol. 286 p.; 302 p. Torino: Sten. editrice, 1923-27. [CB 24/559]

BARIÉTY, Maurice; COURY, Charles. Histoire de la médecine. 1217 p. (Les grandes études historiques) Paris: Fayard, 1963.
Contains table of synoptic chronology of general history and the history of medicine from the 5th millenary B.C. through 1963 and a biographic index.
Reviewed by L. Glesinger, *Arch.Int.Hist.Sci.*, 1964, 17: 345-50.

BEITRÄGE zur Geschichte der Medizin und der Naturwissenschaften. Festschrift für Professor Dr. Rudolph Zaunick zum 70. Geburtstag am 26.VIII.1963. 411 p., ill. (Acta Leopoldina no. 167, new ser., vol. 27) Leipzig: Johann Ambrosius Barth, 1963. [CB 89/483]

BENDER, George A. Great moments in medicine. (A collection of the first thirty stories and paintings in the continuing series. A history of medicine in pictures.) Paintings by Robert A. Thom. 265 p., pl. Detroit: Parke-Davis, 1961.
Reviewed by F.N.L.P., *Med.Hist.*, 1962, 6: 296; by Ernst W. Stieb, *Pharm.Hist.*, 1963, 8: 24.

BETTMANN, Otto L. A pictorial history of medicine. With a foreword by Philip S. Hench. xiii, 318 p. Springfield, Ill.: Charles C. Thomas, 1956. [CB 82/211]
Reviewed by Loren C. MacKinney, *Amer.Hist.Rev.*, 1957, 62: 599-600; by E. Bastholm, *Lychnos*, 1957-58, 457-8.

BORGHI, Bruno. La medicina. 2nd ed. 302 p. (Conoscere) Firenze: Salani, 1945.
Reviewed by A. Corsini, *Riv.Stor.Sci.*, 1946, 35-37: 27-8.

BUCK, Albert H. The growth of medicine from the earliest times to about 1800. xviii, 582 p., 28 fig. New Haven: Yale University, 1917.

BUSACCHI, Vincenzo. Storia della medicina. 329 p. Rocca San Casciano: Cappelli, 1951.
Reviewed by I. Cappellini, *Riv.Stor.Sci.*, 1951, 42: 280.

CABANÈS, Auguste. Les curiosités de la médecine. 4 vol. 1. 330 p.; 2. Les cinq sens. 312 p.; 3. Les fonctions de la vie. 368 p.; 4. Le sixième sens (sens génésique). 259 p. Paris: Le François, 1925-27.
Volume 1 reviewed by Francis R. Packard, *Ann.Med.Hist.*, 1926, 8: 210.

CALDER, Ritchie. From magic to medicine. 70 p. London: Rathbone Books, 1957.
The American edition of this illustrated book has the title: The wonderful world of medicine (Garden City, N.Y.: Garden City Books, 1957).
Reviewed in *School Sci.Rev.*, 1958, 39: 536.

CALDER, Ritchie. Medicine and man. The story of the art and science. 256 p. London: Allen & Unwin, 1958.
Reviewed by F.A. Sondervorst, *Rev.Quest.Sci.*, 1959, 20: 445, and *Scalpel*, 1960, 113: 708; by U.S. von Euler, *Lychnos*, 1959, 415-16.

CAMAC, Charles Nicoll Bancker. Imhotep to Harvey: backgrounds of medical history. Foreword by Henry Fairfield Osborn. xxv, 324 p., 4 ill. New York: Hoeber, 1931.

CASTIGLIONI, Arturo. Histoire de la médecine. French transl. by J. Bertrand. 781 p., 279 ill. Paris: Payot, 1931.
Reviewed by George Sarton, *Isis*, 1931, 16: 468-71.
French translation of: Storia della medicina, *see* below.

CASTIGLIONI, Arturo. A history of medicine. Translated from the Italian and edited by E.B. Krumbhaar. 2nd ed. rev. and enl. xxx, 1192, lvi p., 504 ill. New York: Knopf, 1947.
Reviewed by E. Ashworth Underwood, *Arch.Int.Hist.Sci.*, 1950, 3: 448-53.
First publ. 1941. English translation of Storia della medicina, *see* below.

CASTIGLIONI, Arturo. Storia della medicina. 1. Dalle origini alla fine del Seicento; 2. Dal 1700 ai giorni nostri. 3rd ed. 2 vol. xv, 1002 p., 516 fig., 10 pl. Verona: Mondadori, 1948.
First publ. in one volume 1927 [CB 26/251]; new rev. ed. 1936, reviewed by M.F. Ashley Montagu, *Isis*, 1937, 27: 536-8.
For English and French translations, *see* above.

CHAUMARTIN, Henry. Originaux et singuliers. Avec une préface d'Edmond Pilon. 101 p., facs. (Petite Histoire de la Médecine 6) Vienne: Ternet-Martin, 1947. [CB 71/129]
Seven essays.

CLARK, Paul F.; CLARK, Alice Schiedt. Memorable days in medicine: a calendar of biology and medicine. 305 p., ill. Madison, Wisc.: University of Wisconsin Press, 1942.
Reviewed by O. Temkin, *Bull.Hist.Med.*, 1943, 13: 246.

CLARK, Paul F.; CLARK, Alice Schiedt. Memorable days in medicine. A calendar. *Med.Life*, 1936, 43: 123-43, 223-66, 368-409, 473-86; 1937, 44: 65-126. [CB 51/292]
List of medical events which happened on particular days from April to March.

COHN, Alfred. Medicine, science and art. xiv, 212 p. Chicago: University of Chicago Press, 1931. [CB 32/505; CB 33/408]
Six essays, some previously published.

COPE, Zachary. Sidelights on the history of medicine. x, 246 p., ill. London: Butterworth, 1957.
Reviewed by Wolfram Kock, *Lychnos*, 1957-58, 458-60.

CREUTZ, Rudolf; STEUDEL, Johannes. Einführung in die Geschichte der Medizin in Einzeldarstellungen. 344 p. Iserlohn: Silva-Verlag, 1948.
Reviewed by Frans Jonckheere, *Arch.Int.Hist.Sci.*, 1952, 5: 152.

CUMSTON, Charles Greene. An introduction to the history of medicine: from the time of the Pharaohs to the end of the XVIIIth century. With an essay on the relation of history and philosophy to medicine, by F.G. Crookshank. xxxii, 390 p., 24 pl. (The History of Civilization Series) London: Kegan Paul, 1926. [CB 22/303]

CUSHING, Harvey. Concrecratio medici and other papers. 276 p. Boston: Little, Brown, 1928. [CB 26/252]
A group of sixteen essays.

DANA, Charles L. The peaks of medical history: an outline of the evolution of medicine for the use of medical students and practitioners. 105 p., 40 pl., 16 ill. New York: Paul B. Hoeber, 1926. [CB 23/266]

DAWSON, Bernard. The history of medicine: a short synopsis. xiv, 160 p., 31 ill. London: Lewis, 1931. [CB 33/409]

DELAUNAY, Paul. Mélanges médico-historiques. 90 p. Le Mans: Monnoyer, 1937.

DELAUNAY, Paul. La vie médicale aux XVIe, XVIIe et XVIIIe siècles. 556 p., 114 ill. (Collection Hippocrate) Paris: Le François, 1935. [CB 66/298]

DEL GUERRA, G. Introduzione allo studio della storia della medicina. 93 p. Pisa: Giardini, 1934.

DIEPGEN, Paul. Geschichte der Medizin. 5 vol. 1. Altertum. 116 p.; 2. Mittelalter. 118 p.; 3. Neuzeit: von Andreas Vesalius bis zur Begründung der Zellularpathologie durch Rudolf Virchow, 1858. 142 p.; 4, 5. Neueste Zeit: von der Begründung der Zellularpathologie bis zur Gegenwart. (i) Die Hilfswissenschaften und biologischen Disziplinen. 146 p.; (ii) Die Lehre von der Krankheit und die praktische Heilkunde. 129 p. Berlin: Goschen, [etc.], 1913-28.

DIEPGEN, Paul. Geschichte der Medizin. Die historische Entwicklung der Heilkunde und des ärztlichen Lebens. 2 vol. in 3. I. Von den Anfängen der Medizin bis zur Mitte des 18. Jahrhunderts. 355 p., 29 ill.; II.1. Hälfte. Von der Medizin der Aufklärung bis zur Begründung der Zellularpathologie (*ca.* 1740-*ca.* 1858). vii, 271 p., 22 ill.; II.2. Hälfte, Die Medizin vom Beginn der Zellularpathologie bis zu den Anfängen der modernen Konstitutionslehre (etwa 1858-1900), mit einem Ausblick auf die Entwicklung der Heilkunde in den letzten 50 Jahren. ix, 336 p., 33 fig. Berlin: de Gruyter, 1949-55.
Reviewed by George Urdang, *Isis*, 1951, 42: 166-7; 1952, 43: 385-6; 1957, 48: 93; for other reviews *see* CB 78/198, CB 80/137, CB 82/212 and CB 83/206.

DIEPGEN, Paul. Die Heilkunde und der ärztliche Beruf. Eine Einführung. 3rd rev. ed. 304 p. Berlin/München: Urban and Schwarzenburg, 1949.
First publ. Munich: Lehmann, 1938.
Reviewed by Edv. Gotfredsen, *Centaurus*, 1951, 1: 289; by José M. López Piñero, *Arch.Iberoamer.Hist.Med.*, 1959, 11: 88-9.

DOOLIN, William. Wayfarers in medicine. 284 p., ill. London: Heinemann, 1947.
27 essays on various people and aspects in the history of medicine.
Reviewed by Iago Galdston, *J.Hist.Med.*, 1951, 6: 435-6.

DUDLEY, Emilius Clark. The medicine man; being the memoirs of fifty years of medical progress. xii, 369 p., portr. New York: J.H. Sears, 1927.
Reviewed by William R. Nicholson, *Ann.Med.Hist.*, 1927, 9: 421.

DUMESNIL, René. Histoire illustrée de la médecine. 265 p., ill. Paris: Plon, 1935.

FAUVET, Jean. Les étapes de la médecine. 127 p. Préface de N. Fiessinger. (Collection "Que Sais-Je?", 31) Paris: Presses Universitaires de France, 1948.
Reviewed by Frans Jonckheere, *Arch.Int.Hist.Sci.*, 1953, 6: 516.

FICARRA, Bernard J. Essays on historical medicine. 220 p., ill. New York: Froben Press, 1948.

FIFTY years of medicine. A symposium from the *British Medical Journal*. Ed. by Hugh Clegg. viii, 330 p., ill. London: British Medical Association, 1950.
Reviewed by W. Pagel, *Arch.Int.Hist.Sci.*, 1951, 4: 1069; by Charlotte Ford, *J.Hist.Med.*, 1953, 8: 111-12.

FISHBEIN, Morris. Frontiers of medicine. x, 207 p. Baltimore: Williams & Wilkins, 1933.

GALDSTON, Iago. Progress in medicine. A critical review of the last hundred years. With a foreword by Henry E. Sigerist. ix, 347, xiv p. New York: Knopf, 1940.
Reviewed by Morris C. Leikind, *Isis*, 1941, 33: 551-3; in *Ann.Med.Hist.*, 1941, 3: 171-2.
Swedish translation (Stockholm: Bonnier, 1942) reviewed by Ernst Nachmanson, *Lychnos*, 1943, 418-20.

GARCÍA DEL REAL, Eduardo. Historia contemporanea de la medicina. 644 p. Madrid: Espasa-Calpe, 1934.

GARRISON, Fielding H. An introduction to the history of medicine. With medical chronology, suggestions for study and bibliographic data. Fourth ed., rev. and enl. 996 p., 286 portraits and other illustrations. Philadelphia: Saunders, 1929.
Reviewed by George Sarton, *Isis*, 1929, 13: 137-8.
First publ. 1914; 3rd ed. 1921, reviewed by George Sarton, *Isis*, 1922, 4: 554-6.

GASK, George. Essays in the history of medicine. 209 p., 1 portr., fig. London: Butterworth, 1950.

GIBSON, A.G. The physician's art. 240 p. Oxford: Clarendon Press, 1933. [CB 40/414]

GIBSON, William Carlton. Young endeavor: contributions to science by medical students of the past four centuries. 292 p. Springfield, Ill.: C.C. Thomas; Oxford: Blackwell Scientific Publications, 1958.
Reviewed by Edwin Clarke, *Med.Hist.*, 1959, 3: 338-9.

GIORDANO, Davide. Scritti e discorsi pertinenti alla storia della medicina e ad argomenti diversi. x, 630 p., ill. Milano: Rivista di Terapia Moderna e di Medicina Pratica, 1930.
Reviewed by Raymond Neveu, *Bull.Soc.Franç.Hist.Méd.*, 1930, 24: 353-4.

GLASSCHEIB, Herman Samuel. The march of medicine; the emergence and triumph of modern medicine: aberrations and triumphs of the healing art. Transl. from the German by Mervyn Savill. 360 p., ill., pl. London: MacDonald, 1963; New York: Putnam, 1964.
A popular history. Translation of Das Labyrinth der Medizin. (Reinbek bei Hamburg: Rowohlt, 1961).

GORDON, Benjamin Lee. The romance of medicine: the story of the evolution of medicine from primitive times and occult practices. xii, 624 p., 147 ill. Philadelphia: F.A. Davis Co., 1944. [CB 66/271]
Reviewed by E.H. Ackerknecht, *Bull.Hist.Med.*, 1944, 15: 549-50.

GOTFREDSEN, Edv. Medecinens historie. [History of medicine. (In Danish)] v, 514 p., ill. Copenhagen: Nyt Nordisk Forlag Arnold Busck, 1950.
For reviews *see* CB 79/192, CB 80/138 and CB 81/279.

GRUBER, Georg B. Einführung in Geschichte und Geist der Medizin, ein Lehrbuch in Vorlesungen. 4th ed. 343 p. Stuttgart: Georg Thieme, 1952.
First publ. 1934 as Einführung in Geist und Studium der Medizin.
Reviewed by Ernest Wickersheimer, *Arch.Int.Hist.Sci.*, 1952, 5: 420-1.

GUALINO, Lorenzo. Saggi di medicina storica. 399 p., 117 fig. Turin: Minerva Medica, 1930.

GUTHRIE, Douglas. A history of medicine. Rev. ed. with supplement. xvi, 464 p., ill. London: Thomas Nelson & Sons, Ltd.; Philadelphia: J.B. Lippincott, 1958.
For reviews *see* CB 85/399, CB 86/470 and CB 88/559.
First publ. 1945 and reviewed by George Rosen, *Bull.Hist. Med.*, 1946, 19: 346-9; by J. Marshall, *Nature*, 1946, 157: 280-1.

GUTHRIE, Douglas. Janus in the doorway. xi, 316 p., ill. London: Pitman; Springfield, Ill.: C.C. Thomas, 1963.
A collection of essays, many of which have been published previously, on a wide variety of topics in medical history.

HAAGENSEN, C.D.; LLOYD, Wyndham, E.B. A hundred years of medicine. xii, 444 p. New York: Sheridan House, 1943.
Reviewed by Helen Clapesattle, *Amer.Hist.Rev.*, 1944, 49: 455.

HAESER, Heinrich. Lehrbuch der Geschichte der Medicin und der epidemischen Krankheiten. 2nd rev. ed. 2 vol. xlvii, 923 p.; xvi, 832, 72 p. Jena: Mauke, 1853-65.
Vol. 1 reviewed by M. Landsberg, *Henschel's Janus*, 1852, 2: 612-37; reprinted, Leipzig: Alfred Lorentz, 1931.

HAESER, Heinrich. Lehrbuch der Geschichte der Medicin und der Volkskrankheiten. xxxiii, 922 p. Jena: F. Mauke, 1845.
Reviewed by F. Romeo-Seligmann, *Henschel's Janus*, 1846, 1: 856-8; reprinted, Leipzig: Alfred Lorentz, 1931.

HAGGARD, Howard W. Devils, drugs and doctors. The story of the science of healing from medicine-man to doctor. xxii, 405 p., 150 fig. New York: Harper, 1929; London: Heinemann, 1931.

HAGGARD, Howard W. Mystery, magic and medicine. The rise of medicine from superstition to science. 192 p., ill. Garden City, N.Y.: Doubleday, Doran, 1933.

HAHN, André; DUMAÎTRE, Paule; SAMION-CONTET, Janine; ed. Histoire de la médecine et du livre médical à la lumière des collections de la Bibliothèque de la Faculté de Médecine de Paris. 432 p., 8 pl., 25? fig. Paris: Olivier Perrin, 1962.
Reviewed by Ernest Wickersheimer, *Arch.Int.Hist.Sci.*, 1963, 16: 103-5; by F.N.L. Poynter, *Med.Hist.*, 1963, 7: 285-6; by Jean Théodoridès, *Rev.Hist.Sci.*, 1964, 17: 80-2.

HAWLEY, Paul R. New discoveries in medicine. Their effect on the public health. x, 134 p., 14 fig., front. New York: Columbia University Press, 1950. [CB 76/413]

HEMMETER, John C. Master minds in medicine, an analysis of human genius as the instrument in the evolution of great constructive ideas in the history of medicine, together with a system of historic methodology. Introduction by Karl Sudhoff. xxii, 771 p., ill. New York: Medical Life Press, 1927.
Reviewed by Francis R. Packard, *Ann.Med.Hist.*, 1927, 9: 419-21.

HISTORISCHE Studien und Skizzen zu Natur- und Heilwissenschaft. Festgabe George Sticker, ordentlichem Professor der Medizingeschichte zu Würzburg, zum siebzigsten Geburtstage dargeboten. vii, 152 p., portr., bibliogr. Berlin: Springer, 1930. [CB 29/316]

HOLLÄNDER, Eugen. Anekdoten aus der medizinischen Weltgeschichte. 224 p., 85 ill. Stuttgart: Ferdinand Enke, 1925.

HONIGMANN, Georg. Geschichtliche Entwicklung der Medizin in ihren Hauptperioden dargestellt. 132 p. München: J.F. Lehmann, 1925.

HONIGMANN, Georg. Das Wesen der Heilkunde. Historisch-genetische Einführung in die Medizin für Studierende und Aerzte. 319 p. Leipzig: Felix Meiner, 1924.

HORDER, Thomas Jeeves Horder, *baron*. Fifty years of medicine. 70 p. London: Duckworth, 1953; New York: Philosophical Library, 1954. [CB 80/205]
Reviewed by Morris C. Leikind, *Sci.Mon.*, 1955, 80: 69.

HÜBOTTER, Franz. 3000 Jahre Medizin. Ein geschichtlicher Grundriss, umfassend die Zeit von Homer bis zur Gegenwart unter besonderer Berücksichtigung der Zusammenhänge zwischen Medizin und Philosophie. 535 p., ill. Berlin: Oscar Rothacker, 1920.
Reviewed by George Sarton, *Isis*, 1922, 4: 369-70.

HÜHNERFELD, Paul. Kleine Geschichte der Medizin. 162 p., 13 fig. Frankfurt am Main: Heinrich Scheffler, 1956.
Reviewed by Robert Herrlinger, *Sudhoffs Arch.*, 1957, 41: 191-2.

ISENSEE, Emil. Die Geschichte der Medicin und ihrer Hülfswissenschaften. 2 pt. in 5 vol. 1. Aeltere und mittlere Geschichte. 2. Neuere und neueste Geschichte. Berlin: Liebmann, 1840-42; Nauck, 1843-45. [CB 33/410]
Reviewed by J.C.F. Harless, *Henschel's Janus*, 1847, 2: 199-209; reprinted, Leipzig: Alfred Lorentz, 1931.

KING, Lester S. The growth of medical thought. xi, 254 p. Chicago: University of Chicago Press, 1963.
Reviewed by Frederic L. Holmes, *Isis*, 1964, 55: 227-8; for other reviews *see* CB 89/511 and CB 90/532.

KOCK, Wolfram. Medicinhistoriens grunddrag. [Outline of the history of medicine. (In Swedish)] 293 p., 76 fig. Stockholm: Natur och Kultur, 1955.
Reviewed by E. Bastholm, *Lychnos*, 1956, 436-7; by Heinz Goerke, *Sudhoffs Arch.*, 1957, 41: 96.

LAIGNEL-LAVASTINE, Maxime, ed. Histoire générale de la médecine, de la pharmacie, de l'art dentaire et de l'art vétérinaire. 3 vol. 681 p., fig.; 670 p., 469 pl., fig.; 816 p., pl., fig. Paris: Michel, 1936, 1938, 1949. [CB 77/309 and CB 77/384]

LAIN ENTRALGO, Pedro. Historia de la medicina moderna y contemporánea. 773 p. Barcelona: Edit. Cientifico-Médica, 1963.
Reviewed by L.S. Granjel, *Cuad.Hist.Med.Españ.*, 1963, 2: 247-9.
First publ. 1954; reviewed by P. Huard and J. Brocas, *Arch.Int.Hist.Sci.*, 1957, 10: 279-80.

LAIN ENTRALGO, Pedro. Medicina y historia. xvi, 363 p. (Estudios de antropologia médica, 1) Madrid: Ediciones Escorial, 1941.
Reviewed by Werner Leibbrand, *Mitt.Gesch.Med.*, 1941-42, 40: 230-8.

LEIBBRAND, Werner. Heilkunde. Eine Problemgeschichte der Medizin. 437 p. (Orbis Academicus) Freiburg/München: Verlag Karl Alber, 1953.
Reviewed by José M. López Piñero, *Arch.Iberoamer.Hist. Med.*, 1959, 11: 87.

LEJEUNE, Fritz. Leitfaden zur Geschichte der Medizin. 216 p. Leipzig: Thieme, 1943.
Reviewed by O.T. Hult, *Lychnos*, 1943, 401-2.

LEONARDO, Richard A. History of medical thought. 92 p. New York: Froben Press, 1946. [CB 71/130]

LIBBY, Walter. The history of medicine in its salient features. xi, 427 p., 9 pl. Boston: Houghton, 1922.
Reviewed by George Sarton, *Isis*, 1923, 5: 478-9.

LÖBEL, Josef. Medicine: a voyage of discovery. Transl. from the German by L. Marie Sieveking and Jan F.D. Morrow. vii, 334 p. New York: Farrar and Rinehart, 1934.
Reviewed in *Ann.Med.Hist.*, 1934, 6: 379.
London edition has title: Whither medicine (London: Sidgwick & Jackson, 1934). Translation of Medizin oder dem Mann kann geholfen werden (Berlin: Rowohlt, 1933).

MacLAURIN, Charles. Mere mortals. Medico-historical essays. *2nd ser.* 291 p. London: Cape; New York: George H. Doran, 1925.
Reviewed by Herman T. Radin, *Med.Life*, 1926, 33: 208-12.

MacLAURIN, Charles. Post mortems: essays, historical and medical. 255 p. London: Cape; New York: Doran, 1923.
Reviewed by Herman T. Radin, *Med.Life*, 1924, 31: 490-2.

McMANUS, Joseph Forde Anthony. The fundamental ideas of medicine; a brief history of medicine. vii, 115 p. (Carl Vernon Weller Lecture Series) Springfield, Ill.: C.C. Thomas, 1963.
Reviewed by Lester S. King, *Bull.Hist.Med.*, 1964, 38: 387.

MAJOR, Ralph H. A history of medicine. 2 vol. xxv, 563 p.; xii, p. 565-1055, ill. Springfield, Ill.: Charles C. Thomas, 1954.
Reviewed by John F. Fulton, *Isis*, 1956, 47: 69-70; by Henry R. Viets, *J.Hist.Med.*, 1955, 10: 437-8.
Italian edition by Gustavo Barbensi, publ. Florence: 1959; reviewed by Pietro Franceschini, *Physis*, 1962, 4: 88-90.

MANFRÈ, Pasquale. Storia della medicina dalla suo origine fino a nostri tempi. Vol. 1, pt. 1. 418 p. Naples: 1844.
Reviewed by C.F. Heusinger, *Henschel's Janus*, 1847, 2: 609-17; reprinted Leipzig: Alfred Lorentz, 1931.

MARTÍ-IBÁÑEZ, Félix. Ariel. Essays on the arts and the history and philosophy of medicine. xiii, 294 p., ill. New York: MD Publications, 1962.
Reviewed by E. Bastholm, *Lychnos*, 1962, 499-500; by P. Huard, *Arch.Int.Hist.Sci.*, 1962, 15: 448-50.

MARTÍ-IBÁÑEZ, Félix. A prelude to medical history. xxiv, 253 p., chronology table. New York: MD Publications, Inc., 1961.
Reviewed by Acke Renander, *Lychnos*, 1962, 500-1.

MARTÍ-IBÁÑEZ, Félix, ed. The epic of medicine. xiv, 294 p., ill., bibliogr. New York: Clarkson N. Potter, 1962.

METTLER, Cecilia C. History of medicine: a correlative text arranged according to subjects. Edited by Fred A. Mettler. xxix, 1215 p., ill. Philadelphia: Blakiston, 1947.
Reviewed by J.B. de C.M. Saunders, *Isis*, 1949, 40: 88-90; by Chauncey D. Leake, *Science*, 1948, 107: 126; by Douglas Guthrie, *Bull.Hist.Med.*, 1948, 22: 337-9.

MEUNIER, Léon. Histoire de la médecine depuis ses origines jusqu'à nos jours. vi, 642 p. Paris: Le François, 1924. [CB 16/319]
Corrected reprint of first edition, Paris: Baillière, 1911. Russian transl. by J.A. Oksenov (with appendix on the development of medicine in Russia) Moscow: 1926; reviewed by H. Zeiss, *Mitt.Gesch.Med.*, 1926, 25: 250.

MEYER-STEINEG, Th.; SUDHOFF, Karl. Geschichte der Medizin im Überblick mit Abbildungen. 3rd rev. ed. x, 446 p., 217 fig. Jena: Gustav Fischer, 1928. [CB 24/561]
First publ. 1921, reviewed by George Sarton, *Isis*, 1922, 4: 368; 2nd ed. 1922, reviewed by George Sarton, *Isis*, 1923, 5: 188.

NEUBURGER, Max. Essays in the history of medicine. Transl. by various hands and ed. by Fielding H. Garrison. xviii, 210 p., portr. New York: Medical Life Press, 1930. [CB 32/610]

NEUBURGER, Max. History of medicine. Translated by Ernest Playfair. Vol. 1; vol. 2, pt. 1. (Oxford Medical Publications) London: Oxford University Press, 1910, 1925.
No more published.
Reviewed by Stephen d'Irsay, *Isis*, 1927, 9: 486-9.

NEW YORK ACADEMY OF MEDICINE. The march of medicine, 1939-50. 12 vol. (Lectures to the Laity, 4-15) New York: Columbia University Press, 1940-51. [CB 61/418, CB 62/86 and CB 74/375]
1941 volume reviewed by J.B. de C.M. Saunders, *Isis*, 1942, 34: 187.

NEW YORK ACADEMY OF MEDICINE. Milestones in medicine: laity lectures. ix, 276 p. New York: Appleton-Century, 1938. [CB 54/584]

OSLER, William. The evolution of modern medicine. 243 p. New Haven: Yale University Press, 1921.
Reviewed by Walter Libby, *Isis*, 1921-22, 4: 556-7.

PAGEL, Julius Leopold. Einführung in die Geschichte der Medizin in 25 akademischen Vorlesungen. 2nd ed. by Karl Sudhoff. xvi, 616 p. Berlin: Karger, 1915. [CB 10/202]
Pagel's Einführung first appeared in 1898. For 3rd ed. *see* below: Sudhoff, Karl. Kurzes Handbuch der Geschichte der Medizin.

PAPASPUROS, Nikos. Eisagoge sten historia kai philosophia tes iatrikes. [An introduction to the history and philosophy of medicine. (In Greek)] 3rd ed. 150 p. Athens: 1950.

PAZZINI, Adalberto. Il pensiero medico nei secoli. Dalle scuole italiche al secolo XIX. xvii, 334 p. Firenze: Sansoni, 1939.
Reviewed by D. Giordano, *Riv.Stor.Sci.*, 1939, 30: 105-6.

PAZZINI, Adalberto. Storia della medicina. 2 vol. 1. Dalle origini al XVI secolo. viii, 796 p., fig.; 2. Dal XVII secolo ai nostri giorni. vi, 708 p., fig., bibliogr. Milan: Società Editrice Libraria, 1947.

PODOLSKY, Edward. Doctors, drugs and steel. 384 p., ill. New York: Beechhurst Press, 1946.
Reviewed by Morris C. Leikind, *J.Hist.Med.*, 1948, 3: 450-2.

POWER, D'Arcy. The foundations of medical history. With an introductory note by William H. Welch. x, 182 p. (Johns Hopkins University, Institute of the History of Medicine) Baltimore: Williams and Wilkins, 1931. [CB 33/412]

POWER, D'Arcy. Selected writings, 1877-1930. x, 368 p., 16 pl., 1 map, 9 fig. Oxford University Press, 1931.
Reviewed by Charles A. Kofoid, *Isis*, 1931, 16: 471-2.

POWER, D'Arcy; THOMPSON, C.J.S. Chronologia Medica. A handlist of persons, periods and events in the history of medicine. iv, 278 p. London: John Bale Sons & Danielsson, 1923.

POYNTER, F.N.L.; KEELE, K.D. A short history of medicine. 160 p., fig. (Science in Society, 2) London: Mills & Boon, 1961.
For reviews *see* CB 88/561 and CB 89/513.

PREMUDA, Loris. Storia della medicina. 277 p. (Collana di Guida per esami universitari, 17) Padova: CEDAM, 1960.
Reviewed by Maria L. Bonelli, *Physis*, 1960, 2: 264-5; by Pierre Huard, *Rev.Hist.Sci.*, 1960, 13: 368-9.

RENOUARD, Pierre Victor. Histoire de la médecine depuis son origine jusqu'au XIXe siècle. 2 vol. in 1. 468 p.; 524 p. Paris: Baillière, 1846.
Reviewed by L. Choulant, *Henschel's Janus*, 1847, 2: 401-10; reprinted, Leipzig: Alfred Lorentz, 1931.

ROBINSON, Victor. The story of medicine. 564 p. (New Home Library) New York: Garden City Publishing Co., 1943.
Reviewed by George Rosen, *Bull.Hist.Med.*, 1944, 15: 227-8.

SAINT-JACQUES, Eugène. Histoire de la médecine. Coup d'oeil à vol d'oiseau. Les grandes époques. Les grandes figures. 223 p. Montréal: Beauchemin, 1935.

SAND, René. Histoire de la profession et des sciences médicales. Leçons professées à la Faculté de Médecine de l'Université libre de Bruxelles. 97 p. Liége: Desoer, 1945.

SANGIORGI, Giuseppe. Spunti, ricordi, ritratti. 158 p. Molfetta: Soc. Tipografica persordomuti dell'Istituto Prov. Apicella, 1950.
Reviewed by Loris Premuda, *Riv.Stor.Sci.*, 1952, 43: 142.

SCHWALBE, Ernst. Vorlesungen über Geschichte der Medizin. 3rd ed. x, 181 p. Jena: Gustav Fischer, 1920.
First ed. 1905.
Reviewed by George Sarton, *Isis*, 1922, 4: 557.

SCIENCE, medicine and history. Essays in honour of Charles Singer. Collected and edited by E. Ashworth Underwood. 2 vol. xxxii, 563 p., fig., 50 pl., front.; viii, 646 p., fig., 56 pl., front., bibliogr. London/New York/Toronto: Oxford University Press, 1953.
Reviewed by George Sarton, *Isis*, 1954, 45: 203-4; by E.N. da C. Andrade, *Nature*, 1954, 173: 651-2; by A.G. Drachmann, *Centaurus*, 1956, 5: 89-90.

SEELIG, Gabriel. Medicine: an historical outline. xviii, 207 p. Baltimore, Md.: Williams and Wilkins, 1925.

SEIDE, J. History of medicine. 205 p. Tel Aviv: M. Newman, 1954.
Reviewed by Joshua O. Leibowitz, *J.Hist.Med.*, 1955, 10: 446-7.

SHRYOCK, Richard H. The development of modern medicine: an interpretation of the social and scientific factors involved. 2nd ed. xi, 457 p., 10 ill. New York: Knopf, 1947. [CB 71/131]
First publ. Philadelphia: University of Pennsylvania Press; London: Oxford University Press, 1936.
German translation (Stuttgart: Enke, 1940) reviewed by L. Castaldi, *Riv.Stor.Sci.*, 1941, 32: 152; French translation of 1947 edition (New York: 1947) reviewed by P. Huard, *Arch.Int.Hist.Sci.*, 1957, 10: 281-3; by P. Astruc, *Rev.Hist.Sci.*, 1958, 11: 90-2.

SIGERIST, Henry E. Die Heilkunst im Dienste der Menschheit. 116 p. Stuttgart: Hippokrates-Verlag, 1954.
Reviewed by H. Fischer, *Gesnerus*, 1955, 12: 68-9.

SIGERIST, Henry E. Man and medicine. An introduction to medical knowledge. Translated by Margaret Galt Boise. Introduction by William H. Welch. x, 340 p. New York: Norton, 1932.
English translation of Einführung in die Medizin (Leipzig: Thieme, 1931). French translation (Paris: Payot, 1932) [CB 39/469] reviewed by Aldo Mieli, *Archeion*, 1933, 15: 127-32. Italian translation Firenze: Sansoni, 1938.

SIGERIST, Henry E. On the history of medicine. Edited by Félix Martí-Ibáñez. xi, 313 p. New York: MD Publications, 1960.
Reviewed by J.B. de C.M. Saunders, *Isis*, 1961, 52: 600-1; for other reviews *see* CB 87/575.

SINGER, Charles. New worlds and old: essays. 178 p. London: Heinemann, 1951.
Reviewed by Chauncey D. Leake, *Bull.Hist.Med.*, 1953, 27: 298.

SINGER, Charles; SIGERIST, Henry E.; ed. Essays on the history of medicine. Presented to Karl Sudhoff on the occasion of his seventieth birthday, November 26, 1923. vii, 418 p. London: Oxford University Press; Zurich: 1924.

SINGER, Charles; UNDERWOOD, E. Ashworth. A short history of medicine. 2nd rev. ed. xvi, 854 p., pl., fig. Oxford: Clarendon Press; New York: Oxford University Press, 1962.
First publ. 1928. [CB 26/254]
For reviews *see* CB 89/513.

SPECTOR, Benjamin. One hour of medical history. Vol. 1-5, ill. Boston: Tufts College Medical School, 1931-36. [CB 42/607]
Texts of a series of medical pageants, presented under the direction of Dr. Benjamin Spector by students of the Medical School of Tufts College.

SPRENGEL, Kurt. Versuch einer pragmatischen Geschichte der Arzneikunde. 4th ed. Mit Berichtigungen und Zusätzen versehen von Julius Rosenbaum. 1. Aelteste Geschichte der Medicin bis zur empirischen Schule. xviii, 644 p. Leipzig: Gebauer'sche Buchhandlung, 1846.
Complete work first published 1792-1803.
Reviewed by J.G. Thierfelder, *Henschel's Janus*, 1848, 3: 349-50; reprinted, Leipzig: Alfred Lorentz, 1931.

STANOJEVIĆ, Vladimir. Istorija medicine. [History of medicine. (In Serbo-Croatian)] 2nd ed. xvi, 522 p., ill. Beograd/Zagreb: Medicinska Knjiga, 1962.
Reviewed by Ferdinand Wagenseil, *Sudhoffs Arch.*, 1963, 47: 506.
First publ. 1953 and reviewed by J. Seide, *J.Hist.Med.*, 1956, 11: 365-6.

STAROBINSKI, Jean. A history of medicine. Transl. from French by Bernard C. Swift. 104 p., ill. (The New Illustrated Library of Science and Invention, 12) New York: Hawthorn, 1964.
English transl. of Histoire de la médecine. 104 p. (La science illustrée, 12) Lausanne: Rencontre, 1963.
Reviewed by John B. Blake, *Science*, 1964, 144: 725-6.

STUBBS, S.G. Blaxland; BLIGH, E.W. Sixty centuries of health and physic. The progress of ideas from primitive magic to modern medicine. Introduction by Sir Humphry Rolleston. xvi, 253 p., 64 pl. London: Sampson, Low, Marston, 1931.

SUDHOFF, Karl. Essays in the history of medicine. Translated by various hands and edited with foreword and biographical sketch by Fielding H. Garrison. xiii, 397 p. New York: Medical Life Press, 1926.
Translation of Skizzen (Leipzig: 1921) reviewed by E.C. Streeter, *Isis*, 1922, 4: 558-60.

SUDHOFF, Karl. Kurzes Handbuch der Geschichte der Medizin. 3rd and 4th ed. of J.L. Pagel's Einführung in die Geschichte der Medizin (1898). viii, 534 p. Berlin: S. Karger, 1922.
Reviewed by George Sarton, *Isis*, 1923, 5: 188.

SZUMOWSKI, Władysław. Historia medycyny. [History of medicine. (In Polish)] xvi, 395 p., pl. Warsaw: Panstwowyzaklad Wydawnictw Lekarskich, 1961.
Reviewed by L. Glesinger, *Arch.Int.Hist.Sci.*, 1964, 16: 102-4.

VEDRANI, Alberto. Le più belle pagine di storia della medicina di Alberto Vedrani. A cura di A. di Giovanni. 194 p. (Collana Scientia Veterum, 39) Genova: 1963.

VICTOR ROBINSON memorial volume. Essays on history of medicine. In honor of Victor Robinson on his sixtieth birthday, August 16, 1946. Solomon R. Kagan, ed. 447 p., ill., bibliogr. New York: Froben, 1948. [CB 73/183]

VIERORDT, Hermann. Medizin-geschichtliches Hilfsbuch mit besonderer Berücksichtigung der Entdeckungsgeschichte und der Biographie. vii, 469 p. Tübingen: Laupp, 1916. [CB 8/365]

VORWAHL, Henner. Geschichte der Medizin unter Berücksichtigung der Volksmedizin. 216 p. (Medizinisch-Biologische Schriftenreihe, 9) Berlin: Madaus, 1928.

WALKER, Kenneth. The story of medicine. 343 p., 51 ill. London: Hutchinson, 1954; New York: Oxford University Press, 1955.
Reviewed by J.B. deC. M. Saunders, *Isis*, 1957, 48: 73-6.
French translation (Verviers: Éditions Gerard, 1962) reviewed by Albert Delorme, *Rev.Syn.*, 1963, 84: 619-20.

WILBUR, Ray Lyman. The march of medicine; selected addresses and articles on medical topics, 1913-1937. x, 280 p. Stanford, Calif.: Stanford University Press, 1938.
Reviewed by David Riesman, *Ann.Med.Hist.*, 1939, 1: 314.

THE WILLIAM SNOW MILLER Festschrift. Contributions by the friends, associates and pupils of Dr. William Snow Miller, assembled on the occasion of his seventieth birthday, March 29, 1928. *Phi Beta Pi Quart.*, 1928, 25: 83-238. [CB 26/252]

WILSON, Robert McNair. A history of medicine. 80 p. (Benn's Sixpenny Library, 148) London: Benn, 1930.
Reviewed by F.M.G. de Feyfer, *Bijdr.Gesch.Geneesk.*, 1931, 11: 243.

WITHINGTON, Edward Theodore. Medical history from the earliest times. viii, 424 p. London: Holland Press, 1964.
Reprint of 1894 ed.

WOOD, W. Barry. From miasmas to molecules. 100 p., ill. New York/London: Columbia University Press, 1961.
Reviewed by John B. Blake, *Science*, 1962, 136: 770-1.

Nc-bn *essays; articles*

ALVAREZ, Walter C. The emergence of modern medicine from ancient folkways. *Annu.Rep.Smithsonian Inst. for 1937*, p. 409-30, 1 pl., 3 fig. Washington, D.C.: 1938.
Read at the open meeting of the Minnesota chapter, Jan. 24, 1936. Reprinted from *Sigma Xi Quart.*, September 1936, vol. 24.

BECHET, Paul E. A meditative excursion in the by-paths of the history of medicine. *Victor Robinson Memorial Volume*, p. 27-33, portr. New York: Froben, 1948.

BELLONI, Luigi. Da Asclepio ad Esculapio. A ricordo di Guido Baccelli promotore dei Congressi Nazionali di Medicina Interna, per il LX Congresso della Società Italiana di Medicina Interna. Roma, 19-21 Ottobre 1959. 31 p., ill. Milan: Stucchi, 1959.

BENEDICENTI, Alberico. Contributi sperimentali alla storia della medicina. *Festschrift zur Feier seines 60. Geburtstages ... Max Neuburger gewidmet*, p. 32-7. Wien: 1928. [CB 26/257]

BRAGMAN, Louis J. A rhymed outline of medical history. *Med. Life*, 1932, 39: 1-54, ill. [CB 36/455]

CASTIGLIONI, Arturo. Storia della medicina. In: Enciclopedia italiana di scienze, lettere ed arti, (22), p. 703-27. Rome: 1934.

CHAUMARTIN, Henry. Vieux os et vieilles querelles. 36 p. (Petite Histoire de la Médecine) Vienne: Ternet-Martin, 1957.
Reviewed by P. Delaunay, *Arch.Int.Hist.Sci.*, 1957, 36: 160-1.

COHEN OF BIRKENHEAD, Henry Cohen, *baron*. Peaks of medical history. *Mem.Manchester Lit.Phil.Soc.*, 1960-61, 103: 20-8.

COLE, Rufus. Progress of medicine during the past twenty-five years as exemplified by the Harvey Society lectures. *Science*, 1930, 71: 617-27.
Address given at the celebration of the 25th anniversary of the Society, May 15, 1930.

COPE, Zachary. How medicine became a science. *J.Franklin Inst.*, 1956, 261: 81-91.

DELASSUS, A. Les grandes découvertes de la médecine de 1876 à 1926. *Rev.Quest.Sci., 4e sér.*, 1926, 9: 398-411.

DELAUNAY, Paul. L'évolution médicale du XVIe au XXe siècle. *Bull.Soc.Franç.Hist.Méd.*, 1928, 22: 17-56.

DIEPGEN, Paul. Die Entwicklung der Medizin in den letzten 50 Jahren. *Naturwiss.Rundsch.*, 1951, 4: 331-5.

GALDSTON, Iago. Dark corners and obscure alcoves in medical history. *Bull.Hist.Med.*, 1955, 29: 317-28.

GALDSTON, Iago. The history of research, with particular regard to medical research. Wanted - A history of research; The beginnings of research; The dawn of experimental science; The rise of modern research; Research in the United States. *Ciba Symp.* (Summit, N.J.), 1946, 8: 338-72, ill.

GANDOLFO, Carlos Fonso. Reflexiones que sugieren veinticinco años de médico. *Rev.Argent.Hist.Med.*, 1942, 1: 11-32.

GARROD, Archibald E. The debt of science to medicine. The Harveian Oration delivered before the Royal College of Physicians of London on St. Luke's Day, 1924. 30 p. Oxford: Clarendon Press, 1924.

GIBSON, William Carlton. Significant scientific discoveries by medical students. *Sci.Mon.*, 1955, 81: 22-6.

HAGGARD, Howard W. Medicine through the ages. *Dent.Cosmos*, 1931, 73: 223-34.

HOUSSAY, Bernardo A. La medicina en el último medio siglo. *Cienc.Tecnol.*, 1952, 2: 49-66.

KOLMER, John A. The history of laboratory research in the past fifty years. *Med.Life*, 1927, 34: 3-14.

LESKY, Erna. Medizinische Pioniertaten, mitgeteilt in der Gesellschaft der Aerzte. *Wiener Klin. Wochenschr.*, 1963, 75: 534-6.
Mentions medical discoveries presented to the Vienna society from 1847 to 1933.

LOCKWOOD, Dean P. It is time to recognize a new "Modern Age". *J.Hist.Ideas*, 1943, 4: 63-5.
The author claims that modern medicine only began in the late 19th century.

McMENENEY, W.H. On medical history and literature. *Proc. Roy.Soc.Med.*, 1963, 56: 839-49.

MAYER, André. Cent ans de médecine expérimentale. *Rev. Cours Conf.*, 1930-31, 32: 193-213.
Lecture given at the Journées Médicales de Bruxelles, 28 June-2 July, 1930.

MAYER, Claudius F. Centennials in the medical hall of fame. An almanac of anniversaries for 1954 A.D. *Bull.Hist.Med.*, 1954, 28: 1-14, portr.

MAYER, Claudius F. Memorable events, lives and books: calendar of commemoration for 1953. *Mil.Surg.*, 1953, 112: 122-5; ... for 1954. *Ibid.*, 1954, 114: 45-51; ... for 1955. *Mil. Med.*, 1955, 116: 43-57; ... for 1956. *Ibid.*, 1956, 118: 37-52; ... for 1957. *Ibid.*, 1957, 120: 32-50; ... for 1958. *Ibid.*, 1958, 122: 36-52; ... for 1959. *Ibid.*, 1959, 124: 47-65; ... for 1960. *Ibid.*, 1960, 125: 36-51; ... for 1961. *Ibid.*, 1961, 126: 49-65; ... for 1962. *Ibid.*, 1962, 127: 54-67.
A series of ten articles, the first of which did not include the word events.

MELLANBY, Edward. Recent advances in medical science. 62 p. New York: Macmillan, 1939. [CB 59/490]

MOYNIHAN, Berkeley George Andrew Moynihan, *baron*. The advance of medicine. 64 p. Oxford: Clarendon Press, 1932.
The Romanes Lecture delivered 1 June 1932.

RAVEN, Charles E. Medicine - mother of the sciences. *Med. Hist.*, 1960, 4: 85-90.

RIESMAN, David. Three quarters of a century of medical progress. *Sci.Mon.*, 1936, 42: 129-36.

ROBINSON, Victor. Landmarks in modern medicine. A chronology with texts and eponyms. *Med.Life*, 1933, 40: 391-400.
Bichat to Rudolf Magnus (1800-1924).

SHRYOCK, Richard H. The rise of modern scientific medicine. In: Pennsylvania, University. Studies in the history of science (Bicentennial conference), p. 55-64. Philadelphia: University of Pennsylvania Press, 1941.

SIGERIST, Henry E. Die Geburt der abendländischen Medizin. *Essays on the history of medicine presented to Karl Sudhoff*, p. 185-205. London: Oxford University Press; Zurich: Verlag Sedwyla, 1924.

SUDHOFF, Karl. Aus der Entwicklung ärztlichen Wissens. *Leipziger Illus.Zeitung*, 1933, no. 4589, 224-8, 265.

UNDERWOOD, E. Ashworth. Medicine, surgery and their scientific development. In: Dingle, Herbert, ed. A century of science, p. 254-71. London/New York: Hutchinson's Scientific and Technical Publications, 1951.

WALSH, James J. Some historical questions in the light of our modern medical knowledge. *XVIIth Int.Congr.Med.* (London, 1913), sect. 23, p. 43-53. London: 1914.

Nc-bq *Symposia; Conference Proceedings*

CONVEGNO DELLA MARCA PER LA STORIA DELLA MEDICINA. Atti del I(-III) Convegno della Marca per la Storia della Medicina, Fermo. 1. 1955; 2. 1957; 3. 1959. Fermo: Tipografico Properzi e Spagnoli, 1955-60.
1st Conference Proceedings reviewed by M.G. Nardi, *Riv. Stor.Med.*, 1957, 1: 113; 2nd by M.G., *Pagine Stor.Med.*, 1958, 2: no. 3, 61.

INTERNATIONAL CONGRESS OF THE HISTORY OF MEDICINE. For details of conference proceedings, *see* Nfqx

Nc-br *periodicals*

Acta Medicae Historiae Patavina: vol. 1, anno accademico 1954/1955- Padova: La Garangola, 1955-
Volume 1 reviewed by S. Principe, *Riv.Stor.Sci.*, 1956, 47: 132.

Anales de la Sociedad Peruana de Historia de la Medicina. 1. Año 1939- Lima: Imp. "Lux" de E.L. Castro, [?1939]-

Annals of Medical History. Vol. 1-10; *new ser.* vol. 1-10; *3rd ser.*, vol. 1-4. New York: 1917-42.

Archivo Iberoamericano de Historia de la Medicina y Antropologia Medica. Vol. 1-15. Madrid: Consejo Superior de Investigaciones Cientificas, 1949-63.
Vol. 1-5 are entitled *Archivos Iberoamericanos de Historia de la Medicina.* From vol. 16 (1964) its title is *Asclepio.* Reviewed by José M.R. Delgando, *J.Hist.Med.*, 1952, 7: 208.

Basler Veröffentlichungen zur Geschichte der Medizin und der Biologie. Fasc. 1-. Basel: Benno Schwabe, 1953-.
Reviewed by George Rosen, *J.Hist.Med.*, 1955, 10: 448-9.

Bijdragen tot de Geschiedenis der Geneeskunde. Vol. 1-. Amsterdam: *Nederlandsch Tijdschrift voor Geneeskunde*, 1921-. [CB 18/648]

Bulletin of the Department of History of Medicine of Osmania Medical College. Vol. 1-. Hyderabad: 1963-.
Vol. 1, no. 1 reviewed by Ilza Veith, *Bull.Hist.Med.*, 1963, 37: 584.

Clio Medica: a series of primers on the history of medicine. Ed. by E.B. Krumbhaar. New York: Hoeber, 1930-39. [CB 40/489]

Indian Journal of the History of Medicine. Isis, 1956, 47: 423.
Journal founded by the Indian Association of the History of Medicine in 1956.

Janus. Archives internationales pour l'histoire de la médecine. Vol. 1 - Amsterdam: 1896 -
For comments *see* Nc-bu Rosen, George, and Vollgraff, J.A.

Janus. Central-Magazin für Geschichte und Literärgeschichte der Medicin, ärztliche Biographik, Epidemiographik, medicinische Geographie und Statistik. Ed. by H. Bretschneider, A.W.E. Th. Henschel, C. Fr. Heusinger, and J.G. Thierfelder. 2 vol. Gotha: 1851-52. Reprinted, Leipzig: Alfred Lorentz, 1931.
Reviewed by G. Sarton, *Isis*, 1932, 17: 283-4.

Janus. Zeitschrift für Geschichte und Literatur der Medicin im Verein mit L. Choulant, H. Haeser, J.F.C. Hecker, C.F. Heusinger, F. Jahn, J.C. Marx, J. Rosenbaum *et al.* Edited by A.W.E. Th. Henschel. 3 vol. Breslau: 1846-48. Reprinted, Leipzig: Alfred Lorentz, 1931.
Reviewed by G. Sarton, *Isis*, 1932, 17: 283-4.

Medical History: a quarterly journal devoted to the history and bibliography of medicine and the related sciences. Vol. 1, 1957-. London: Dawson, 1957-.
In progress. For notes on this journal *see Isis*, 1956, 47: 423; 1957, 48: 70.

Medical Progress: a review of medical advances. 1953-57. Editor: Morris Fishbein. 5 vol. New York: Blakiston, 1953-57.
1953 reviewed by Owsei Temkin, *Bull.Hist.Med.*, 1953, 27: 500.

Medicinhistorisk Årsbok. Yearbook of the Medical-Historical Museum, Stockholm. [In Swedish with short summaries in English] Stockholm: 1959-.
From 1953-58 entitled: *Årsskrift for Föreningen Medicinhistoriska Museets Vänner.*

Országos Orvostörteneti Könyvtar Közleményei. Communicationes ex Bibliotheca Historiae Medicae Hungarica, no. 1-. [In Hungarian; some resumés in Russian, German and English, etc.] Budapest: Library of Medical History, 1955-.
For lists of contents of no. 1-3 *see* CB 82/211; no. 12 CB 85/398; no. 13-26 CB 88/555-7; no. 27-29 CB 89/509-10; no. 31 CB 90/529.

Országos Orvostörteneti Könyvtar Közleményei. Communicationes ex Bibliotheca Historiae Medicae Hungarica. Suppl. no. 1-. [In Hungarian; some resumés in German, Russian, etc.] Budapest: Library of Medical History, 1962-.

Publicaciones del Instituto de Historia de la Medicina, Universidad de Buenos Aires. Vol. 12-. Buenos Aires: Imprenta de la Universidad, 1950-. Formerly *Publicaciones de la Catedra de Historia de la Medicina, Universidad de Buenos Aires.*

Revista Argentina de Historia de la Medicina. Publicación cuatrimestral. Organo oficial del Ateneo de Historia de la Medicina. Año 1-, 1942-. Buenos Aires: 1942-.

Revista de la Sociedad Venezolana de Historia de la Medicina. [Announcement of this new journal] *Isis*, 1954, 45: 293.

Sudhoffs Archiv für Geschichte der Medizin und der Naturwissenschaften. Vol. 1- Leipzig, Wiesbaden: 1907- [CB 79/193]
Volumes 1-20, 1907-28, entitled: Archiv für Geschichte der Medizin.
Not published 1944-52.

Trabajos de la Cátedra de Historia critica de la Medicina, Universidad de Madrid. Vol. 1-6. Madrid: Imprenta de los sobrinos de la sucesora de M. Muesa, 1932-35.

Nc-bu/cv bibliography; literature; sources

Nc-bu documentation

DOE, Janet; MARSHALL, Mary Louise, ed. Medical Library Association handbook of medical library practice, with a bibliography of the reference works in the history of medicine and the allied sciences. 2nd edition, revised and enlarged. xvi, 601 p. Chicago: American Library Association, 1956. [CB 82/212]
First publ. 1942 and reviewed by Claudius F. Mayer, *Isis*, 1944, 35: 48-51.

IRSAY, Stephen d'. An historical dictionary of medicine. *Kyklos*, 1928, 1: 157-9.

MANN, Gunter. Der systematische Katalog in Institutsbibliotheken am Beispiel der Medizinhistorik. 24 p. Frankfurt: 1962.
Reviewed by W. Kehr, *Sudhoffs Arch.*, 1963, 47: 94-5; by C.F.A. Marmoy, *Med.Hist.*, 1964, 8: 98-9.

ROSEN, George. *Janus*, 1846-1946. *J.Hist.Med.*, 1947, 2: 5-9.

STÜRZBECHER, Manfred. Medizingeschichte und Archivwesen. *Sudhoffs Arch.*, 1963, 47: 387-93.

VOLLGRAFF, J.A. *Janus* redivivus. *Janus*, 1957, 46: 1-2.

Nc-bv *bibliographies; literature surveys*

Annals of Medical History. Index (1917-1942). Compiled by Hilda C. Lipkin. With foreword by Francis R. Packard. viii, 84 p. New York: Schuman, 1946.

Bulletin of the History of Medicine. Index to volume 1-20, 1933-1946, prepared by Genevieve Miller. iv, 80 p. Baltimore: Johns Hopkins Press, 1950.

COHEN, I. Bernard. Current work in the history of medicine. *Isis*, 1955, 46: 278.
Concerning the lists issued by the Wellcome Historical Medical Library.

Current work in the history of medicine; an international bibliography. No. 1, January/March 1954- London: Wellcome Historical Medical Library, 1954- [CB 86/469]

DIEPGEN, Paul. Geschichte der Medizin (Literaturberichte. Eröffnungsbericht). *Arch.Kulturgesch.*, 1913, 10: 465-80.

DIEPGEN, Paul. Geschichte der Medizin, I & II. *Arch. Kulturgesch.*, 1931, 21: 240-56, 357-84.
Survey of recent publications on the history of medicine with bibliographical notes and discussion.

[DISSERTATIONS on history of medicine and history of public health presented from 1934 to 1958. (In Russian)] *Sovet. Zdravookhr.*, 1960, 19: 73-81.

GARRISON, Fielding Hudson; MORTON, Leslie T. Garrison and Morton's medical bibliography. *See* Nce-bv
This bibliography contains a short list of writings on the history of medicine.

KOCH, Michael S., ed. Gamble-Curran medical history. A classified bibliography. Preface by Jean A. Curran. Introduction by Paul F. Cranefield. 46 p. Brooklyn, N.Y.: State University of New York, Downstate Medical Center Library, 1957. [CB 83/207]

PEARL, Raymond. Historical papers in the journal *Human Biology. Isis,* 1936, 24: 415-18.

PILCHER, Lewis Stephen. *See* Nce-bv

POYNTER, F.N.L. The history of medicine in 1960-61. *Hist. Sci.,* 1962, 1: 44-56.

ROSEN, George. The new history of medicine. A review. *J. Hist.Med.,* 1951, 6: 516-22.

SCHLICHTING, Th. H. Some recent Dutch contributions to the history of medicine. *Centaurus,* 1951, 1: 284-6.

SIMON, I. *Revue Koroth* (Tel-Aviv - Juin 1960 - Xe année - Vol. II: 7-8) *Rev.Hist.Méd.Hébraique,* 1962, 15: no. 57, 117-30.
A review of these issues.

SUDHOFF, Karl, ed. Geschichte der Medizin und der Krankheiten. [A bibliography of current literature.] *Jahresber.Leist. Fortschr.Gesamten Med.,* 1912, 47(1): 262-337; 1913, 48(1): 318-402; 1914, 49(1): 281-336; 1915, 50(1): 348-64; 1916, 51(1): 286-352.

WONG, M. Quelques livres russes sur l'histoire de la médecine analysés. *Janus,* 1960, 49: 300-3.

Nc-bx exhibitions

BOLOGNA. UNIVERSITÀ. Catalogo della mostra tenutasi nella R. Biblioteca Univ. di Bologna in occasione del II Congresso della Società per la Storia della Scienze Mediche e Naturali. Settembre 1922. xviii, 101 p., ill. Roma: Libr. Bocca, 1924.

OPORTO. UNIVERSIDADE. FACULDADE DE MEDICINA. Catálogo da exposição retrospectiva de medicina. 101 p., 21 fig. (I Centenario da Régia Escola de Cirurgia do Pôrto, 1825-1925) Coordenado pelo Pedro Vitorino, Alberto Saavedra. Pôrto: Emp. Indust. Gráfica, 1925.

SOMOLINOS D'ARDOIS, Germán. La Exposicion Historica del Congreso del Centenario de la Academia Nacional de Medicina. *Gac.Méd.Méx.,* 1964, 94: 1235-44.

Ncb libraries and archives

BOSTON MEDICAL LIBRARY. Annual report of the Librarian by Henry R. Viets. *New Engl.J.Med.,* 1949, 240: 917-20; 1950, 242: 936-42. [CB 77/386]

BURKE, Margaret N. The Miller collection in the Library of the Richmond Academy of Medicine. *Bull.Hist.Med.,* 1946, 19: 200-25.

CELEBRATION of the centennial of the Library of the Medical and Chirurgical Faculty of the State of Maryland, 1830-1930. xii, 78 p., 34 pl. Baltimore: 1931.
Reviewed by Charles A. Kofoid, *Isis,* 1932, 17: 466-7.

CUSHING, Harvey. *See* Npe

DEDICATION ceremony of the Yale Medical Library. *Yale J.Biol. Med.,* 1941, 13: 863-89, 1 pl.

DUMAÎTRE, Paule. La biblioteca della Facoltà di medicina di Parigi e i tesori del passato. A proposito di un libro recente. [*See* Hahn, André, below.] *Minerva Med.,* 1964, 55: 867-73, ill.

FULTON, John F. Tenth annual report of the Historical Library, 1949-1950, Yale University School of Medicine. 40 p. New Haven: 1950. [CB 77/362]
This report dated 30 June 1950 includes a review of the first ten years.

FULTON, John F.; KILGOUR, Frederick G.; STANTON, Madeline E. Die Medizinische Bibliothek der Universität Yale. *Librarium,* 1959, 2: 87-102.

GNUDI, Martha Teach. The rare book and history of medicine section in a university medical library. *Bull.Med.Libr. Ass.,* 1964, 52: 524-44.

HAHN, André; DUMAÎTRE, Paule; SAMION-CONTET, Janine; ed. Histoire de la médecine et du livre médical à la lumière des collections de la Bibliothèque de la Faculté de Médecine de Paris. 432 p., 8 pl., 255 fig. Paris: Olivier Perrin, 1962.
Reviewed by Ernest Wickersheimer, *Arch.Int.Hist.Sci.,* 1963, 16: 103-5; by F.N.L. Poynter, *Med.Hist.,* 1963, 7: 285-6; by Jean Théodoridès, *Rev.Hist.Sci.,* 1964, 17: 80-2.

HOLMBERG, Arne. Karolinska Institutets Bibliotek i nya lokaler. [The library of the Caroline Institute in a new locale. (In Swedish)] *Nord.Tidskr.Bok Biblioteksväs.,* 1949, 36: 143-74, 9 fig.
Describing the reinstallation of the Library of the Caroline Medical Institute in Stockholm. The Institute was founded in 1810 and its Library is very rich.

HOLT, Anna C. The library of the Harvard Medical School 1847 and 1947. *Harvard Libr.Bull.,* 1948, 2: 32-43.

HÜNNCHER, -. Leipzig. Bibliothek des Institutes für Geschichte der Medizin. (Umschau aus und über Bibliotheken) *Zentralbl.Bibl.,* 1936, 53: 218-20.

HUME, Edgar Erskine. The Army Medical Library of Washington, the largest medical library that has ever existed. *Isis,* 1937, 26: 423-47, 2 portr.

HUME, Edgar Erskine. The centennial of the world's largest medical library: the Army Medical Library of Washington, founded 1836. *Mil.Surg.,* 1936, 78: 241-67. [CB 47/289]

KILGOUR, Frederick G. The library of the medical institution of Yale College and its catalogue of 1865. 74 p. New Haven, Conn.: Yale University Press (for the Yale Medical Library), 1960.
Reviewed by Genevieve Miller, *Isis,* 1962, 53: 540-1.

KRICKER, Gottfried. Medizinische Bibliotheken in Köln. 57 p., 8 pl. (*Abhandl.Gesch.Med.Naturwiss.,* 25) Berlin: Ebering, 1938.

LEAKE, Chauncey D. State Medical Library of California. A survey of the first year's work. *Calif.Western Med.,* 1933, 38: 421-2.

LEGRAND, N. Les bibliothèques médicales. *France Méd.,* 1913, 60: 84-90, 101-9, 127-9, 147-9.

McDANIEL, W.B. Expanding the use of the Library's historical collections. *Trans.Coll.Physicians Phila.,* 1956, 23: 135-9.

MEDICAL history collections in the United States and Canada. 1. The Dr. William Beaumont Collection of the University of Chicago. By Arno B. Luckhardt. 2. Collections in Cleveland, Ohio. By Howard Dittrick. 3. An unique collection of Osleriana [at the University of California]. By F.T. Gardner. 4. Historical collections of B.W. Weinberger in New York. By B.W. Weinberger. 5. The Paracelsus collection of the St. Louis Medical Society [Robert E. Schlueter Collection]. By Henry E. Sigerist. 6. Special collections in the Archibald Church Library, Northwestern University Medical School. By Henry E. Sigerist. 7. The William N. Bradley Collection in the Library of the College of Physicians of Philadelphia: an iconography of Philadelphia physicians as they are represented in works of art. By W.B. McDaniel. 8. Collections on the history of balneology in Saratoga Springs. By Walter S. McClellan. *Bull.Hist.Med.,* 1939, 7: 535-63; 1940, 8: 1214-15; 1941, 9: 332-4, 334-6, 545-79; 1942, 11: 87-9; 1942, 12: 616-18, ill.; 1946, 20: 571-82.

O'MALLEY, Charles D. The Barkan library of the history of medicine and natural science books; an account of its development. *Stanford Med.Bull.,* 1951, 9: 145-55.

POSTELL, William Dosite. A historical medical collection, and some of the problems it presents. *Bull.Med.Libr.Ass.,* 1964, 52: 320-7.
With special reference to Rudolph Matas Medical Library, Tulane University.

REDDY, D.V.S. The library of the Madras Medical College. *Bull.Hist.Med.*, 1949, 23: 90-4.

SALLANDER, Hans. The Bibliotheca Walleriana in the Uppsala University Library. 26 p. Uppsala: 1951. [CB 78/178]

SCHULLIAN, Dorothy M. Unfolded out of the folds. *Bull.Med. Libr.Ass.*, 1952, 40: 135-43.
Examining the early files of the American Federation of Medical Libraries.

SCHULLIAN, Dorothy M.; ROGERS, Frank B. The National Library of Medicine. *Libr.Quart.*, 1958, 28: 1-121.

SCHUMAN, Henry. A dream come true: The Lawrence Reynolds collection. *Bull.Med.Libr.Ass.*, 1959, 47: 235-52. [CB 85/401]
A discussion of some of the major items in the collection, now housed at the University of Alabama Medical Center.

SEVENTY-FIFTH anniversary of the presentation by Oliver Wendell Holmes of his personal medical library to the Boston Medical Library on 29th January 1889. 35 p., facs. Boston: Boston Medical Library, Harvard Medical Library, 1964. [CB 90/614]

SHRYOCK, Richard H. The value of the medical library to the social historian. *Trans.Coll.Physicians Phila.*, 1938, 6: 282-91.

SUDHOFF, Karl. Medizinische Bibliotheken. Eine historische Plauderei. 8 p. Leipzig: Gustav Fock, 1921. [CB 11/447]
Reprinted in *Sudhoffs Arch.*, 1929, 21: 296-310.

VIETS, Henry R. Letting substance into the texture. *Bull.Med. Libr.Ass.*, 1953, 41: 125-9.
Remarks made at the organization meeting of the Friends of the Armed Forces Medical Library, October 1952.

WADE, P. The history and development of the library of the Royal Society of Medicine. *Proc.Roy.Soc.Med.*, 1962, 55: 627-36.

THE WILLIAM H. WELCH MEDICAL LIBRARY of the Johns Hopkins University. An account of its origin and development together with a description of the building and an account of the exercises held on the occasion of the dedication of the Library and the inauguration of the Chair of the History of Medicine at the University, Baltimore, Maryland, Oct. 17-18, 1929. vii, 153 p., ill. (*Bull.Johns Hopkins Hosp.*, 46: 1) Baltimore, Md.: 1930. [CB 29/260]

Ncc historical sources

SHRYOCK, Richard H. Medical sources and the social historian. *Amer.Hist.Rev.*, 1936, 41: 458-73.

ÜNVER, A. Süheyl. Allgemeine Geschichte der Medizin: Einige Bilder und Dokumente. 66 p., fig. Istanbul: Institute of the History of Medicine, 1943. [CB 53/88]
Album of medico-historical documents taken from the Istanbul libraries, 65 figures with explanatory text in Turkish and German.

VELDE, Jean van de. A quelles sources puiser pour étudier l'histoire de la médecine. *Cah.Biloque*, 1959, 9: 1-8.

Ncd

CALLOMON, F. Aus der Autographenmappe eines Arztes. Unbekannte und unveröffentlichte Briefe und Dokumente berühmter Ärzte und Naturforscher. *Janus*, 1940, 44: 241-68, 5 facs.; 45: 1-39.

EBSTEIN, Erich. Ärztebriefe aus vier Jahrhunderten mit Bilden und Schriftproben. xii, 204 p. Berlin: Springer, 1920.

HAHN, André; DUMAITRE, Paule; SAMION, Janine. Les manuscrits à la Bibliothèque de la Faculté de Médecine de Paris. *Sem. Hôp.Paris*, 1954, 30: no. 79, 8 p., 6 fig.

STALKER, Hugh. Some medical letters of bygone days. *Ann. Med.Hist.*, 1942, 4: 199-206.

Ncd-bv

MEDICAL SOCIETY OF LONDON. Manuscripta medica. A descriptive catalogue of the manuscripts in the Library of the Medical Society of London. By Warren R. Dawson. 140 p. London: Bale, Sons & Danielsson, 1932.

Nce literature

for collections of classics *see* Ndaj

BLAKE, John B. Books, libraries, and medical history. *J. Amer.Med.Ass.*, 1964, 188: 263.

BRODMAN, Estelle. The development of medical bibliography. ix, 226 p., front., 2 pl., 7 fig., 2 charts, bibliogr. (Medical Library Association, Publication 1) Baltimore: Medical Library Association, 1954. [CB 80/136]
Reviewed by W.B. McDaniel, *J.Hist.Med.*, 1955, 10: 130-2; by E. Ashworth Underwood, *Nature*, 1955, 175: 182ff.

CHOULANT, Ludwig. Handbuch der Bücherkunde für die aeltere Medizin, zur Kenntnis der griechischen, lateinischen und arabischen Schriften im ärztlichen Fache und zur bibliographischen Unterscheidung ihrer verschiedenen Ausgaben, Uebersetzungen und Erläuterungen. [Reprint of 2nd ed. Leipzig: 1841] xxii, 434 p. München: Verlag der Münchener Drucke, 1926.

DAVISON, Wilburt C. Reflections on the medical book and journal situation. *Bull.Hist.Med.*, 1942, 11: 182-200, 1 diagr.

GARRISON, Fielding Hudson. Dangers besetting the literature of recent medicine. *Festschrift zum 80. Geburtstag Max Neuburgers*, p. 124-8. Wien: Maudrich, 1928.

GOSSEN, Hans. Medizin- und naturwissenschaftshistorische Lesefrüchte. *Med.Welt*, 1937, 11: 333-5.

JARCHO, Saul. Some hoaxes in the medical literature. *Bull. Hist.Med.*, 1959, 33: 342-7.

KEYS, Thomas E. The story of the medical printed book. *Proc. Staff Meetings Mayo Clin.*, 1939, 14: 577-81.

LEAKE, Chauncey D. A note on the medical books of famous printers. *Calif.Western Med.*, 1930, 32: 36-40, 106-10.

ÜNVER, A. Süheyl. Un ouvrage intéressant sur les anciens livres médicaux se trouvant dans nos bibliothèques. *Türk Tib Tarihi Arkivi*, 1937, 2: 61-2.

VIETS, Henry R. The bibliography of medicine. 15 p. Menasha, Wisc.: Banta, 1938. [CB 57/273]
Read at a symposium on medical literature at the fortieth annual meeting of the Medical Library Association, Boston, June 29, 1938.

Nce-bv literature: bibliographies

ASH, Lee, comp. *See* Ndaj-bv

CHOULANT, Ludovicus. Bibliotheca Medico-Historica sive Catalogus librorum historicum de re medica et scientia naturali systematicus. x, 270 p. Leipzig: 1842. Reprinted Hildesheim: Olms, 1960.

GARRISON, Fielding Hudson. Revised students' check-list of texts illustrating the history of medicine, with references for collateral reading. *Bull.Inst.Hist.Med.*, 1933, 1: 333-434. [CB 40/413]
New edition of the list originally published in the Index Catalogue of the Surgeon General's Library, 1912, 2: xvii, 89-178.

GARRISON, Fielding Hudson; MORTON, Leslie T. Garrison and Morton's medical bibliography. An annotated check-list of texts illustrating the history of medicine. By Leslie T. Morton. 2nd ed. xiv, 656 p. London Grafton, 1954. [CB 82/212]
Reviewed by José M. López Piñero, *Arch.Iberoamer.Hist. Med.*, 1959, 11: 90.
1943 edition reviewed by Julia E. Wilson, *Bull.Hist.Med.*, 1944, 16: 94-6.

GIOVANNI, Antonio di. La storia della medicina nella biblioteca di Pammatone (oggi Ospedale S. Martino di Genova) 58 p. (Scientia Veterum, 52) Pisa: Giardini, 1963. [CB 90/531]
A brief account of the vicissitudes of the Ospedale di Pammatone prefaces a catalogue of its early medical books.

GLASGOW UNIVERSITY. Hunterian Museum. The printed books in the library of the Hunterian Museum in the University of Glasgow. A catalogue prepared by Mungo Ferguson. With a topographical index by David Baird Smith. xxiii, 396 p. (Glasgow University Publications, 18) Glasgow: Jackson, Wylie, 1930.
Reviewed by H.D., *J.Savants*, 1931, 93.

Index Medicus. New ser., vol. 1- Washington, D.C.: National Library of Medicine, 1960-

KEYS, Thomas E. Medical works in facsimile, a bibliography. *Bull.Hist.Med.*, 1953, 27: 133-76.

MAYER, Claudius Francis. The Index Catalogue [of the National Library of Medicine]. *Isis*, 1949, 40: 119-20.

MAYER, Claudius Francis. The Index-Catalogue as a tool of research in medicine and history. *Science, Medicine and History, Essays in honour of Charles Singer*, (2), p. 482-93. London: Oxford University Press, 1953.

MAYER, Claudius Francis. Pages from the past of the "Index-Catalogue". 16 p. Washington, D.C.: The Author, 1950. [CB 77/385]
Typescript. Two 'pages' are presented to illustrate the life of the "Index-Catalogue" at two different stages of American culture - in 1949/50 and in 1915/16.

NEDERLANDSCHE MAATSCHAPPIJ TER BEVORDERING DER GENEESKUNST. Catalogus van de Bibliotheek der Nederlandsche Maatschappij tot Bevordering der Geneeskunst in bruikleen vereenigd met de Bibliotheek der Universiteit van Amsterdam. Edited by B.W. Th. Nuyens. With introduction in English. xvi, 659 p., ill. Amsterdam: International Antiquariaat, 1930.

O'MALLEY, Charles D. Catalogue of the medical history collection presented to U.C.L.A. by Dr. and Mrs. John A. Benjamin in honor of Bennett M. Allen and Boris Krichesky. 56 p. Los Angeles: University of California Press, 1964.

OSLER, William. Bibliotheca Osleriana: a catalogue of books illustrating the history of medicine and science, collected, arranged and annotated by Sir William Osler and bequeathed to McGill University. xxxvi, 786 p. Oxford: Clarendon Press 1929.

OXFORD UNIVERSITY. Catalogue of an exhibition of books on medicine, surgery and physiology. Bodleian Library, Oxford. Ed. by S. Gibson. 31 p., 2 pl. Oxford University Press, 1947. [CB 71/129]

PARIS. Université. Faculté de Médecine. Exposition de manuscrits et de livres illustrés. Inauguration de la Salle des Périodiques, Bibliothèque de la Faculté de Médecine de Paris, 25 novembre 1953. Catalogue. 24 p., ill. Paris: 1953.

PILCHER, Lewis Stephen. A list of books by some of the old masters of medicine and surgery together with books on the history of medicine and on medical biography in the possession of Lewis Stephen Pilcher, with biographical and bibliographical notes and reproductions of some title pages and captions. 201 p., ill. Brooklyn, N.Y.: 1918.

PIRES DE LIMA, Joaquin Alberto. Catalogo da bibliotheca da escola medico-cirurgica do Porto. xvii, 461 p. 1st suppl. x, 68 p. Porto: Encyclopedia Portugueza Illustrada, 1910-12.

PREISLER, Oscar Christian Strange. Bibliographischer Führer durch die medizinische Literatur. Ein Grundriss. 87 p. Köbenhavn: Det akademiske antikvariats haandböger, 1920.
Reviewed by George Sarton, *Isis*, 1921, 4: 109-10.

PUTTI, Vittorio. La raccolta Vittorio Putti. Antiche opere di medicina, manoscritte e stampate, lasciate all'Istituto Rizzoli di Bologna. viii, 107 p., front., portr. Milan: Bertieri, 1943.
Reviewed by Henry E. Sigerist, *Bull.Hist.Med.*, 1945, 17: 421-2.

SALLANDER, Hans. Bibliotheca Walleriana. The books illustrating the history of medicine and science collected by Dr. Erik Waller and bequeathed to the library of the Royal University of Uppsala. 2 vol. xii, 471 p., 48 pl.; 494 p., 7 pl. (Acta Bibliothecae R. Universitatis Upsaliensis, 8-9) Stockholm: Almqvist & Wiksells, 1955. [CB 82/268]
Reviewed by I. Bernard Cohen, *Isis*, 1957, 48: 353-5; for other reviews see CB 82/195, 85/401, and 87/554.

TITLEY, Joan. Printed catalogues of American medical libraries before 1850: a check list. *J.Hist.Med.*, 1964, 19: 61-5.

U.S. NATIONAL LIBRARY OF MEDICINE. Index-catalogue of the Library of the Surgeon General's office, United States Army (Army Medical Library), author and subjects. *Ser. 1*, A-Z. 1880-95; *ser. 2*, A-Z. 1896-1915; *ser. 3*, A-Z. 1918-32; *ser. 4*, A-Mn. 1936-55. 58 vol. Washington: Govt. Print. Off., 1880-1955.
A dictionary catalogue, including many references to periodical articles in addition to books and pamphlets.

WELLCOME HISTORICAL MEDICAL LIBRARY. A catalogue of printed books in the Wellcome Historical Medical Library. 2 vol. 1. Books printed before 1641. xvi, 408 p.; 2. Books printed from 1641-1850. xi, 540 p. London: Wellcome Historical Medical Library, 1962, 1966.
Vol. 1 reviewed by Walter Pagel, *Isis*, 1964, 55: 107-9; for other reviews see CB 89/456 and 88/555.

Nce-by

BISHOP, W.J. Some medical bibliophiles and their libraries. *J.Hist.Med.*, 1948, 3: 229-62, 2 pl.

Nce-da

FULTON, John F. The great medical bibliographers. A study in humanism. xv, 107 p. Philadelphia: University of Pennsylvania Press; London: Oxford University Press, 1951.
Reviewed by C.D. Leake, *Isis*, 1952, 43: 90; by Charles D. O'Malley, *J.Hist.Med.*, 1952, 7: 434-6; by H. Fischer, *Gesnerus*, 1954, 11: 47-9.

Ncf

ZISCHKA, Gert A. Ärzte in der Geschichte der enzyklopädischen Literatur. *Sudhoffs Arch.*, 1960, 44: 259-66.

Ncj-bv

ARTELT, Walter; HEISCHKEL, Edith; WEHMER, Carl. Periodica Medica, Titelabkürzungen medizinischer Zeitschriften. 4th ed. vii, 280 p. Stuttgart: Georg Thieme, 1952.
Reviewed by Frans Jonckheere, *Arch.Int.Hist.Sci.*, 1953, 6: 136-7.

JOHN CRERAR LIBRARY. A list of current medical periodicals and allied serials. 2nd ed. 32 p. Chicago, Ill.: 1913.

Ncm illustrations

FRANKEL, Walter K. Bookplates of famous physicians. *Merck Rep.*, Jan. 1950, 59: no. 1, 15-18, ill.

LEDOUX-LEBARD, R. La gravure en couleurs dans l'illustration des ouvrages médicaux, depuis les origines jusqu'à 1800. *Bull.Soc.Franç.Hist.Méd.*, 1911, 10: 218-25; 1912, 11: 171-93.

NETTER, Frank H. A medical illustrator at work. *Ciba Symp.* (Summit, N.J.), 1949, 10: 1087-92, ill.

OLIVIER, Eugène. Ce que nous apprennent les ex-libris de médecins et de pharmaciens d'autrefois: conférence ... 16 p., ill. Paris: Société Française des Collectionneurs d'Ex Libris, 1913.

PLASHKES, J. [Physicians' ex-libris. (In Hebrew)] *Koroth*, 1956, 1: 345-6.

ROLLINS, Carl Purington. Illustration in printed medical books. *Ciba Symp.*, 1949, 10: 1072-86, ill.

Nco

GOLDSCHMID, Edgar. Wachsplastik und ihre Museen. *Gesnerus*, 1951, 8: 91-7.

Ncp non-bibliographical sources

BALFOUR, Donald C.; KEYS, Thomas E. A stained glass window on the history of medicine. *Bull.Med.Libr.Ass.*, 1944, 32: 488-95, pl.
The window was dedicated in Sept. 1938 in the Mayo Foundation House.

CALIFORNIA'S medical story in fresco at the University of California Medical School, San Francisco. 24 p., ill. San Francisco: 1939.

CAPPARONI, Pietro. Un' antica tabacchiera a soggetto medico. *Riv.Stor.Crit.Sci.*, 1912, 3: 174-5, 1 pl.

DRAKE, T.G.H. Antique pewter articles of medical interest. *Bull.Hist.Med.*, 1941, 10: 272-87, 11 fig.

IZQUIERDO, José Joaquin. Los cuadros murales de la Facultad de medicina de San Francisco, California. 43 p., 16 fig. México: 1942.

STEVENSON, Lloyd G. History out of print; what the historian cannot learn from books. *Cincinnati J.Med.*, 1964, 45: 467-75.
Address on the reopening of the Howard Dittrick Museum of Historical Medicine.

Ncq

ALBERTI, Giuseppe. Memorie mediche epigrafiche nelle chiese di Rome (dal I al XIX secolo). 160 p. Roma: Edizioni Mediche e Scientifiche, 1942.
Reviewed by L. Castaldi, *Riv.Stor.Sci.*, 1943, 34: 54.

Ncs

GARRISON, Fielding Hudson. Medical numismatics. *Ann.Med. Hist.*, 1926, 8: 128-35.

HOLZMAIR, Eduard. Medicina in nummis. Katalog der Sammlung Dr. Josef Brettauer, hrsg. vom Kuratorium der Dr. Josef Brettauer-Stiftung. 384 p., 25 pl. Wien: 1937.

KISCH, Bruno. Suggestions for arranging a collection of *medicina in nummis*. *Bull.Med.Libr.Ass.*, 1945, 33: 80-9.

KRUMBHAAR, E.B. Some medical medals and tokens to be presented to the College of Physicians of Philadelphia. *Ann.Med.Hist.*, 1926, 8: 360-9.

STORER, Horatio Robinson. Medicina in nummis. A descriptive list of the coins, medals, jetons relating to medicine, surgery and the allied sciences. Edited by Malcolm Storer. 1146 p. Boston: Wright & Potter, 1931.
Reviewed in *Ann.Med.Hist.*, 1932, 4: 319-20.

WEBER, F. Parkes. Illustrations of information furnished by medals, small bronzes, etc. *Proc.17th Int.Congr.Med.* (London, 1913), Sect. 23, p. 425-31, 5 fig. London: Oxford University Press, Hodder & Stoughton, 1914.

Nct

BISHOP, W.J.; MATHESON, N.M. Medicine and science in postage stamps. 82 p., 33 pl. London: Harvey and Blythe, 1948.
Reviewed in *Nature*, 1949, 163: 270.

GALLAS, Tha. Medische philatelie. [Medical philately. (In Dutch)] *Bijdr.Gesch.Geneesk.*, 1939, 19: 203-5, 4 pl.
On medical postage stamps with 25 illustrations.

GARRISON, Fielding Hudson. A brief note on medical philately. *Ann.Med.Hist.*, 1929, 1: 451-2.

Ncv

KEYS, Thomas E.; JULIN, Leonard A. The development of the medical motion picture. *Surg.Gynecol.Obstet.*, 1950, 91: 625-36. [CB 77/384]

SUKHAREBSKII, L.M. [Motion picture documentation as a source of history of medicine. (In Russian)] *Sovet.Zdravookhr.*, 1964, 23: 57-61.

Nd biography

CASPARI-ROSEN, Beate; ROSEN, George. Autobiography in medicine, or the doctor in search of himself. *J.Hist.Med.*, 1946, 1: 290-9.

GARRISON, Fielding Hudson. Available sources and future prospects of medical biography. *Bull.N.Y.Acad.Med.*, 1928, 4: 586-607.

Nd-bv

HUARD, Pierre; MONTAGNÉ, M. Index biographique concernant les sciences biologiques et médicales. *Trav.Inst.Anat.Fac.Méd. Indochine*, 1944, 9: 39-104.

HUARD, Pierre; MONTAGNÉ, M. Index biographique succinct des anatomistes, morphologistes, anthropologistes et naturalistes. *Trav.Inst.Anat.Fac.Méd.Indochine*, 1944, 9: 1-37.

THORNTON, John L.; MONK, Audrey J.; BROOKE, Elaine S. A select bibliography of medical biography. 112 p., ill. (Library Association Bibliographies, 3) London: Library Association, 1961.
Reviewed by E. Gaskell, *Med.Hist.*, 1962, 6: 296-7; by Donald G. Bates, *Bull.Hist.Med.*, 1963, 37: 92-3; by P. Huard, *Arch.Int.Hist.Sci.*, 1963, 16: 100-1.

Nda collective biography

BAILEY, Hamilton; BISHOP, W.J. Notable names in medicine and surgery. 3rd ed. xiii, 216 p., 79 portr., 162 fig. London: H.K. Lewis, 1959.
Reviewed by Johannes Steudel, *Sudhoffs Arch.*, 1961, 45: 90.
2nd ed. 1946 reviewed by Walter Pagel, *Bull.Hist.Med.*, 1947, 21: 128-9.

CROWTHER, J.G. Six great doctors. Harvey, Pasteur, Lister, Pavlov, Ross, Fleming. 207 p., 6 fig. London: Hamish Hamilton, 1957.
Reviewed by G. Liljestrand, *Lychnos*, 1957-58, 460-1.

DIEPGEN, Paul. Unvollendete. Vom Leben und Wirken frühverstorbener Forscher und Ärzte aus anderthalb Jahrhunderten. 223 p., ill. Stuttgart: Georg Thieme Verlag, 1960.
For reviews *see* CB 87/572 and CB 88/557.

DUMESNIL, René; BONNET-ROY, Flavien; ed. Les médecins célèbres. Publié avec la collaboration de 73 auteurs. 371 p., pl. Genève: Mazenod, 1947.

GIBSON, William Carleton. Creative minds in medicine. xv, 238 p. Springfield, Ill.: Charles C. Thomas, 1963.

GOLDSCHMID, Edgar. Célébrités médicales. *Gesnerus*, 1952, 9: 30-42, 2 fig.

GROTE, L.R.R., ed. Die Medizin der Gegenwart in Selbstdarstellungen. 8 vol. Leipzig: Felix Meiner, 1923-1929. [CB 24/560]

HIRSCH, August, ed. Biographisches Lexikon der hervorragenden Ärzte aller Zeiten und Völker (vor 1880). 2nd ed. 5 vol. and suppl. Berlin: Urban & Schwarzenberg, 1929-35; reprinted Berlin: Urban & Schwarzenberg; New York: Stechert-Hafner, 1962. [CB 28/565, CB 29/314, CB 41/609]
First edition 1884-88.

INGLE, Dwight J., ed. A dozen doctors. Autobiographic sketches. vii, 287 p., ill. Chicago/London: University of Chicago Press, 1963. [CB 89/487]

JONAS, S. Cent portraits de médecins illustres. 350 p., portr. Gand: Academia; Paris: Masson, 1960.
Reviewed by P. Huard, *Arch.Int.Hist.Sci.*, 1962, 15: 215-16.

KAGAN, Solomon R. Five recent physicians. *Med.Life*, 1934, 41: 612-19.
Max Ballin, Frederick Forchheimer, Alfred Fabian Hess, Henry Illoway and Nathan Jacobson.

KAGAN, Solomon R. Leaders of medicine. Biographical sketches of outstanding American and European physicians. 176 p., 4 ill. Boston: Medico-Historical Press, 1941. [CB 62/86]

KISCH, Bruno. Forgotten leaders in modern medicine, Valentin, Gruby, Remak, Auerbach. *Trans.Amer.Phil.Soc.*, 1954, 44: part 2, 139-317, 68 fig.
Reviewed by Marcel Florkin, *Arch.Int.Hist.Sci.*, 1954, 7: 385-8; by J.B. de C.M. Saunders, *Isis*, 1955, 46: 383-5; by Ernest Wickersheimer, *Rev.Hist.Sci.*, 1956, 9: 279-80.

LAMBERT, Samuel W.; GOODWIN, George M. Medical leaders from Hippocrates to Osler. 330 p., ill. Indianapolis: Bobbs-Merrill, 1929.
Reviewed by Francis R. Packard, *Ann.Med.Hist.*, 1929, 1: 737.

LES MÉDECINS célèbres. 371 p., portr. (La Galérie des Hommes Célèbres, 3) Genève: Mazenod, 1947.

MOYNIHAN, Berkeley George Andrew Moynihan, *baron*. Truants: the story of some who deserted medicine yet triumphed. Based on the Linacre lecture delivered at Cambridge, May 6, 1936. 108 p. Cambridge University Press, 1936.

ROBINSON, Herbert Spencer. The Harveian orators. From Edmund Wilson to the orator of the plague year. *Med.Life,* 1927, 34: 316-54, 2 pl., 4 portr.

ROBINSON, Victor. Pathfinders in medicine. 2nd ed. xvii, 810 p., 150 pl. New York: Medical Life Press, 1929. [CB 29/315]
First ed. 1912.

ROWNTREE, Leonard G. Amid masters of twentieth century medicine. xviii, 684 p., ill. Springfield, Ill.: Charles C. Thomas; Oxford: Blackwell Scientific Publications, 1958.
Reviewed in *Proc.Roy.Soc.Med.*, 1959, 52: 222; by Edwin Clarke, *Med.Hist.*, 1959, 3: 337-8.

SIGERIST, Henry E. The great doctors, a biographical history of medicine. 436 p., ill. Translated by Eden and Cedar Paul. New York: Norton, 1933.
Reviewed in *Ann.Med.Hist.*, 1933, 5: 603.
For original *see* below.

SIGERIST, Henry E. Grosse Ärzte. Eine Geschichte der Heilkunde in Lebensbildern. 3rd rev. ed. 440 p., ill. München: J.F. Lehmanns Verlag, 1954.
First publ. 1932 [CB 36/457]. For English translation *see* above.

THIEL, Rudolf. Männer gegen Tod und Teufel. Aus dem Leben grosser Ärzte. 416 p., 17 fig. Berlin: Neff, 1931.

WILLIAMS, Harley. Doctors differ. Five studies in contrast. John Elliotson, Hugh Owen Thomas, James Mackenzie, William Macewen, R.W. Philip. xvii, 239 p., ill. Springfield, Ill. Charles C. Thomas, 1952.
Reviewed by Erwin H. Ackerknecht, *Bull.Hist.Med.*, 1953, 27: 192-3.

WOGLOM, William H. Discoverers of medicine. x, 229 p., 8 pl., 6 ill. New Haven: Yale University Press, 1949.
Reviewed by H. Buess, *Gesnerus*, 1957, 14: 71. [CB 74/397]

Nda-py

HERRLINGER, R. Die Nobelpreisträger der Medizin. 84 p., ill. (Forum Imaginum, 8) Munich: Heinz Moos Verlag, 1963.
Reviewed by H. Degen, *Naturwiss.Rundsch.*, 1964, 17: 452.

NOBELSTIFTELSEN, Stockholm. Physiology or medicine. (Vol. 3: 1942-1962) Nobel lectures, including presentation speeches and laureates' biographies. xiv, 837 p. Amsterdam/London/New York: Elsevier (for the Nobel Foundation), 1964.

STEVENSON, Lloyd G. Nobel prize winners in medicine and physiology, 1901-1950. 291 p. (Pathbreakers in 20th century science. Life of Science Library, 29) New York: Henry Schuman, 1953.
Reviewed by I. Bernard Cohen, *Isis*, 1954, 45: 407-8.

Ndae portraits

BORN, Wolfgang. The nature and history of medical caricature. *Ciba Symp.*, 1944, 6: 1910-24, ill.

BROCKMAN, William. Addendum to Bruno Kisch, Iconographies of medical portraits (*J.Hist.Med.*, 1957, 12: 366-87). *J. Hist.Med.*, 1957, 12: 524.

FRANCESCO, Grete de. The doctor's portrait from the fifteenth to the eighteenth century. *Ciba Symp.*, 1944, 6: 1750-65, ill.

KISCH, Bruno. Iconographies of medical portraits (with addendum by William Brockman). *J.Hist.Med.*, 1957, 12: 366-87, 524, 1 pl.

STRIKER, Cecil, ed. Medical portraits. xv, 279 p., ill. Cincinnati: Academy of Medicine of Cincinnati, 1963.

VETH, Cornelis, ed. Der Arzt in der Karikatur, mit einer Einleitung von Friedrich Krauss. 153 p., ill. Berlin: O. Stollberg, 1927.
Dutch edition (Amsterdam: Munster, 1927) reviewed by J.G. de Lint, *Bijdr.Gesch.Geneesk.*, 1927, 7: 410-11.

Ndae-by

BROWNE, George Buckston. Hunterian and other pictures in the Museum collection of the Royal College of Surgeons. 8 p. [London: Royal College of Surgeons, 1931.]

BUERRIERI, Lorenzo. Ritratti di medici nella Galleria degli Uffizi di Firenze. *Riv.Stor.Med.*, 1964, 8: 43-64.

DRIVER, A.H. Catalogue of engraved portraits in the Royal College of Physicians of London. 219 p. London: Royal College of Physicians, 1952. [CB 80/137]

GARDNER, L.I.; WELLS, L.G. The Wolff-Leavenworth Collection of engraved portraits at Syracuse University. *Bull.Hist.Med.*, 1961, 35: 175-7.
This collection contains more than 5900 engravings of physicians and naturalists, European and American.

JONES, Harold Wellington. A portrait gallery of physicians. The collection in the Army Medical Library. *Ann.Med.Hist.*, 1937, 9: 517-32, 25 fig.
Portraits of 25 physicians with brief biographies.

Ndae-ct

WERSCH, L. van; WOLFF, W.H. Artsen en postzegels. [Physicians on postage stamps. (In Dutch)] *Bijdr.Gesch.Geneesk.*, 1936, 16: 30-1, 21 fig.

Ndaj medical classics

AGGEBO, Anker. Fra Hippokrates till Carrel. Aforismer om Laeger og Laegekunst. [From Hippocrates to Carrel. Aphorisms on medical men and medicine. (In Danish)] 184 p. Kjøbenkavn: Nyt Nordisk Forlag, 1939.
Reviewed by H. Brinck, *Lychnos*, 1941, 422-3.

CAMAC, C.N.B. Classics of medicine and surgery. *Sci.Amer.*, 1961, 204: no. 5, 198.

CLENDENING, Logan. Source book of medical history. xiv, 685 p. New York: Dover Publications, Henry Schuman, 1960.
Reviewed by G. Liljestrand, *Lychnos*, 1962, 497; by P. Huard, *Rev.Syn.*, 1962, 83: 419-20.
First publ. New York: Hoeber, 1942 and reviewed by Morris C. Leikind, *Amer.Hist.Rev.*, 1942, 48: 61-2.

COOPE, Robert. The quiet art. A doctor's anthology. 284 p., ill. Edinburgh/London: E. & S. Livingstone; Baltimore: Williams & Wilkins, 1952.
Reviewed by Roland Hammond, *Bull.Hist.Med.*, 1953, 27: 294.

DIEPGEN, Paul; KAHLENBERG, Wilhelm. Lateinisches Lesebuch aus medizinischen Quellen zur Vorbereitung auf das kleine Latinum für Mediziner. viii, 68 p. Stuttgart: Enke, 1948.

GARRISON, Fielding Hudson. The historical collection of medical classics in the library of the Surgeon-General's Office. 23 p. Chicago, Ill.: American Medical Association, 1911.
Reprinted from *J.Amer.Med.Ass.*, 1911, vol. 56.

KELLY, Emerson Crosby. Encyclopedia of medical sources. 477 p. Baltimore: Williams and Wilkins, 1948. [CB 76/411]
References to medical eponyms and significant original articles, arranged alphabetically by author, with a subject index.

OPUSCULA selecta Neerlandicorum de arte medica quae curatores miscellaneorum quae vocantur *Nederlandsch Tijdschrift voor Geneeskunde* collegerunt et ediderunt. 18 vol. Amstelodami: Sumptibus Societatis, 1907-55.
For vol. 4 *see* CB 17/595; vol. 5 CB 22/304; vol. 6 CB 23/267; vol. 8 CB 31/567; vol. 11 CB 38/600; vol. 12 CB 42/606; vol. 13 CB 46/600; vol. 14 CB 51/294; vol. 15, 16 and 17 CB 71/130. Vol. 7, 9 and 10 are editions of single texts for which *see* under Scellinck, Leeuwenhoek and Jacobus Bontius.

ROLLESTON, Humphry. Medical aphorisms, chiefly in English. *Bull.Hist.Med.*, 1941, 10: 544-67.

SIGERIST, Henry E. Classics of medicine. *Bull.Hist.Med.*, 1944, 16: 1-12.

Ndaj-bv

ASH, Lee, comp. Serial publications containing medical classics. An index to citations in Garrison-Morton. With "The story of the Garrison-Morton bibliography of medical classics" by Leslie T. Morton. xxiv, 147 p. New Haven, Conn.: The Antiquarium, 1961.
Reviewed by F.N.L. Poynter, *Isis*, 1963, 54: 283; by F. Bloch, *Sudhoffs Arch.*, 1962, 46: 374-5; by Edwin Clarke, *J.Hist.Med.*, 1964, 19: 182-3.

GARRISON, Fielding Hudson. *See* Nce-bv

Nf history of medicine as a study

AGNEW, L.R.C. Concerning the history of medicine. *J.Med. Educ.*, 1958, 33: 731-5.

ARTELT, Walter. Einführung in die Medizinhistorik. Ihr Wesen, ihre Arbeitsweise und ihre Hilfsmittel. viii, 240 p. Stuttgart: Enke, 1949. [CB 77/384]
Reviewed by Edv. Gotfredsen, *Centaurus*, 1950, 1: 189-90.

BELTRAN, Juan Ramón. Introducción al estudio de la historia de la medicina. *Publ.Cátedra Hist.Med.Univ.Buenos Aires*, 1938, 1: 11-34.

BILLINGS, John Shaw. Two letters by John Shaw Billings on the history of medicine. With a foreword by Sanford V. Larkey. *Bull.Inst.Hist.Med.*, 1938, 6: 394-8.

BOLOGA, Valeriu L. Istoria medicinii şi a ştiinţelor, noul humanism, sinteză. [The history of medicine as a scientific as well as a humanist synthesis. (In Rumanian)] *Gândirea*, 1934, 14: 8 p.

BRUNN, Walter v. Was will die Geschichte der Medizin? *Jungarzt*, 1935, 11: 103-7.

CASTIGLIONI, Arturo. Aspetti ed indirizzi degli studi medico-storici. *Riv.Stor.Sci.*, 1947, 38: 1-9.

CONCEPTION actuelle de l'histoire de la médecine. *Progr. Méd.*, 1956, 84: no. 1, 18-21.

DIEPGEN, Paul. Wie stehen wir in der Medizingeschichte? *Deut.Med.Wochenschr.*, 1933, 59: 834-5.

ELAUT, L. Geschiedenis van de geneeskunde. Waarom en waarheen? [History of medicine. Why and whither? (In Dutch)] *Sci.Hist.*, 1962, 4: 1-11.

FLORKIN, Marcel. Ce qu'enseigne l'histoire de la médecine. 22 p. (Conférence au Palais de la Découverte, D 86) Paris: Université de Paris, 1962.

FLORKIN, Marcel. Pour une histoire vivante de la médecine scientifique. *Arch.Int.Hist.Sci.*, 1955, 8: 53-5.

GALDSTON, Iago, ed. On the utility of medical history. 73 p. (Monograph I, Institute on Social and Historical Medicine, The New York Academy of Medicine) New York: International Universities Press, 1957. [CB 84/320]
Reviewed by John B. Blake, *Science*, 1958, 127: 971.

GARRISON, Fielding Hudson. Transvaluations and deflations in the history of medicine and its teaching. *Bull.N.Y.Acad. Med.*, 1934, 10: 579-92.

GUTHRIE, Douglas. Whither medical history? *Med.Hist.*, 1957, 1: no. 4, 307-17.
Abstract in *Proc.Roy.Soc.Med.*, 1957, 50: 236.

HENSCHEL, August Wilhelm Eduard Theodor. Ein Blick auf das Ganze der Geschichte der Medicin. *Henschel's Janus*, 1848, 3: 1-28; reprinted Leipzig: Alfred Lorentz, 1931.

HENSCHEL, August Wilhelm Eduard Theodor. Ist die Geschichte der Medicin an der Zeit? Einleitende Worte. *Henschel's Janus*, 1851, 1: 1-23; reprinted Leipzig: Alfred Lorentz, 1931.

LETULLE, Maurice. [Introductory lecture to course in the history of medicine.] *France Méd.*, 1912, 30-2.

LICHTENTHAELER, Charles. Sur la vocation universitaire de l'histoire de la médicine (Leçon inaugurale). Le troisième épidémique d'Hippocrate vient-t-il vraiment après le premier? 74 p. Geneva: E. Droz; Paris: Minard, 1960.
Reviewed by R.E. Siegel, *Bull.Hist.Med.*, 1961, 35: 385-6; by E. Bastholm, *Lychnos*, 1962, 504-6.

MAYER, Claudius F. Research and medical history. *Bull. Hist.Med.*, 1946, 20: 173-83.

MILCH, Werner. Über die Stelle der Medicohistorie im System der Wissenschaften. *Janus*, 1938, 42: 142-64.

MULLETT, Charles F. Medical history: some problems and opportunities. *J.Hist.Med.*, 1946, 1: 189-207.

PAGEL, Walter. Julius Pagel and the significance of medical history for medicine. *Bull.Hist.Med.*, 1951, 25: 207-25, portr.

PAZZINI, Adalberto. Principi fondamentali di critica storico-medica. *Riv.Stor.Med.*, 1958, 2: 135-44.

POYNTER, F.N.L. Medicine and the historian. (The Fielding H. Garrison Lecture) *Bull.Hist.Med.*, 1956, 30: 420-35.

PREMUDA, Loris. L'avenir de l'histoire de la médecine. *Scientia*, 1960, 95: 203-4.

REY, Abel. La médecine dans l'histoire des sciences. *Act. IIIe Congr.Int.Hist.Sci.* (Portugal, 1934), p. 273-5. Lisbon: 1936.

SCHLUETER, Robert E. The necessity for studying medical history. *J.Missouri State Med.Ass.*, 1916, 13: 385-91.

SCHUMACHER, Joseph. Medizingeschichte - wozu? 36 p., 9 ill. Stuttgart: Wissenschaftliche Verlagsgesellschaft, 1958.
Reviewed by Ernest Wickersheimer, *Arch.Int.Hist.Sci.*, 1958, 11: 312-13; by Heinrich Schipperges, *Sudhoffs Arch.*, 1959, 43: 94.

SHRYOCK, Richard H. The historian looks at medicine. *Bull. Inst.Hist.Med.*, 1937, 5: 887-94.

SIGERIST, Henry E. Aufgaben und Ziele der Medizingeschichte. *Schweiz.Med.Wochenschr.*, 1922, 53: 318-22.

SIGERIST, Henry E. Die Geschichte der Medizin im Rahmen der Universitas litterarum. *Deut.Med.Wochenschr.*, 1927, 53: 777-9, 864, 949-50.

SIGERIST, Henry E. Die Geschichte der Medizin in ihrer Bedeutung für die Gegenwart. *Liječnički Vjesnik*, 1931, 53: 315-19.

SIGERIST, Henry E. Die historische Betrachtung der Medizin. *Arch.Gesch.Med.*, 1926, 18: 1-19.

SUDHOFF, Karl. Address delivered at the inauguration of the department of the History of Medicine at the Johns Hopkins University, Baltimore, October 18, 1929. Translated by Fielding H. Garrison. *Bull.Johns Hopkins Hosp.*, 1930, 46: (Welch Festschrift), 101-46, portr.

THOMSON, St. Clair. President's address: the present need for the study of the history of medicine. *Proc.Roy.Soc. Med.*, 1933-34, 27: 1-4.

Nf-a

BARBU, G. Le développement des recherches d'histoire de la médecine dans la République Populaire Roumaine. *Arch. Iberoamer.Hist.Med.*, 1957, 9: 61-4.

BUGIEL, V. L'état actuel des études d'histoire de la médecine en Pologne. *Compt.Rend.IIe Congr.Int.Hist.Méd.* (Paris, 1921), p. 522-5. Évreux: Imprimerie Ch. Hérissey, 1922.

FÖRDERUNG des medicinischen Geschichtsstudiums in Paris. *Henschel's Janus*, 1848, 3: 833-4; reprinted Leipzig: Alfred Lorentz, 1931.

GOTFREDSEN, Edv. The study of the history of medicine in Denmark. A short survey. *Bull.Hist.Med.*, 1951, 25: 388-94.

GUTHRIE, Douglas. Medical history in modern India. *Med. Hist.*, 1963, 7: 275-7.

KARCHER, Hans. Zur Entwicklung der medizin-historischen Forschung in der Schweiz. *Festschrift für Jacques Brodbeck-Sandreuter zu seinem 60. Geburtstag*, p. 13-19. Basel: Schwabe, 1942.

LEERSUM, E.C. van. De beoefening der geschiedenis der geneeskunde in Nederland. [The study of the history of medicine in the Netherlands. (In Dutch)] *Bijdr.Gesch. Geneesk.*, 1923, 3: 251-6.

NAKAGAWA, Yonezo. A survey of the interest for the history of medicine in Japan. *Jap.Stud.Hist.Sci.*, 1962, 1: 38-44.

NAVA, Pedro. Introducão ao estudo da historia da medicina no Brasil. *Brasil Med.Cir.*, 1947, 9: 115-30.

PAZ SOLDÁN, Carlos Enrique. La historia de la medicina y necesidad de su estudio en América. *Rev.Argent.Hist.Med.*, 1945, 4: 19-36.

ROSSIISKII, D.M. The study of the history of medicine in Russia. An historical outline. Translated by Henry E. Sigerist from an original manuscript. *Bull.Hist.Med.*, 1947, 21: 959-65.

SIGERIST, Henry E. Medical history in Central and South America. *Bull.Hist.Med.*, 1941, 9: 342-60.

Nf-mzAf

DEL GUERRA, G. La storia come scienza; la storia della scienza e la storia della medicina. *Sci.Veterum*, 1954, 2: no. 4, 1-5.

LAIGNEL-LAVASTINE, Maxime. Histoire de la médecine et histoire des sciences. *Act.Ve Congr.Int.Hist.Sci.* (Lausanne, 1947), p. 185-8. Paris: Hermann, 1948. Also in *Arch.Int.Hist.Sci.*, 1948, 1: 490-3.

MIELI, Aldo. Historiens de la médecine et historiens de la science. *Archeion*, 1935, 17: 405-9.
Apropos of Sarton's preface on "The history of science versus the history of medicine", *see* below.

SARTON, George. The history of science versus the history of medicine. Second preface to vol. XXIII. *Isis*, 1935, 23: 313-20.

SIGERIST, Henry E. The history of medicine and the history of science. An open letter to George Sarton, Editor of *Isis*. Preface to vol. IV. *Bull.Inst.Hist.Med.*, 1936, 4: 1-13. [CB 46/585]

Nfb

TEMKIN, Owsei. On the interrelationship of the history and the philosophy of medicine. *Bull.Hist.Med.*, 1956, 30: 241-51.

TESDORPT, Paul. Über die Notwendigkeit der Verbindung der Geschichte der Medizin mit der Philosophie der Medizin. *Bl.Angew.Ophthalmol.Physiol.Iriskopie*, 1924, 2: no. 1, 2, 3; additional note, *ibid.*, 1925, 3: 33-44.

Nfd

FOSSEYEUX, Marcel. Les historiens de la médecine en France. *Archeion*, 1927, 8: 305-12. [CB 24/485]

GUIART, J. Les historiens de la médecine à Lyon. *Bull.Soc. Franç.Hist.Med.*, 1933, 27: 351-68, 6 fig.

POYNTER, F.N.L.; BISHOP, W.J. British historians of medicine. *Med.Bookman Hist.*, 1947, 1: 19-24; 1948, 2: 103-10, 4 portr.

SAVITZ, Harry A. Jewish medical historians. *Victor Robinson Memorial Volume*, p. 359-67. New York: Froben, 1948.

FOR biographies and bibliographies of individual historians of medicine *see* volumes 1 and 2 under:-

Allbutt, Thomas Clifford; Aschoff, Ludwig; Barduzzi, Domenico; Brunn, Walter von; Capparoni, Pietro; Castiglioni, Arturo; Crainiceanu, Gheorghe; Cushing, Harvey Williams; Delaunay, Paul; Diepgen, Paul; Foucault, Michel Jean Pierre; Fulton, John Farquar; Garrison, Fielding Hudson; Godfredsen, Edvard; Grassi, Giovanni Battista; Haberling, Wilhelm Gustav Moritz; Harvey, Samuel Clark; Héger, Paul; Huard, Pierre; Irsay, Stephen d'; Johnsson, John William Schibbye; Kelly, Howard Atwood; Krumbhaar, Edward Bell; Lachtin, Mikhail Iurievich; Laignel-Lavastine, Maxime; Leite de Vasconcellos, José; Lewin, Louis; Magyary-Kossa, Gyula; Masie, A.; Meyerhof , Max; Miller, William Snow; Neuburger, Max; Osler, William (article by John F. Fulton dc(bn)); Pagel, Julius Leopold; Pazzini, Adalberto; Pieri, Gino; Power, D'Arcy; Putti, Vittorio; Ranvier, Louis Antoine; Robinson, Victor; Seide, Jacob; Sigerist, Henry Ernest; Singer, Charles Joseph; Sticker, Georg; Sudhoff, Karl; Thayer, William Sidney; Tricot-Royer, Jean Joseph Ghislain; Ünver, A. Suheyl; Walsh, James Joseph; Welch, William Henry.

Nfp/fq historical studies: organization

Nfpd

AGNEW, L.R.C. Medical history: profession or pastime? *Lancet*, 31 August, 1957, 273: 423-4.

GALDSTON, Iago. The amateur in medical history. *Yale J. Biol.Med.*, 1946, 18: 129-34.

McDANIEL, W.B. The place of the amateur in the writing of medical history. *Bull.Hist.Med.*, 1939, 7: 687-95.

MEYER-STEINEG, Th. Geschichte der Medizin und Dilettantismus. *Reichs.Med.Anz.*, 1912, 37: 1-3.

Nfpx

MOORMAN Award in medical history. *Isis*, 1956, 47: 54.

Nfqd

BUESS, Heinrich. Tagung der schweizerischen Gesellschaft für Geschichte der Medizin und der Naturwissenschaften in Basel. *Gesnerus*, 1956, 13: 219-21.

CASTALDI, Luigi; TERGOLINA, Umberto. Trant' anni di vita della Società Italiana di Storia delle Scienze Mediche e Naturali (Ottobre 1907-Ottobre 1937). Cenni illustrativi e Indice delle pubblicazioni sociali. A cura dell'Ufficio Stampa Medica Italiana diretto dal Prof. P. Piccinini. 121 p. Siena: S. Bernardino, 1938.

CHINESE MEDICAL HISTORY SOCIETY, Shanghai. [Notice of organization] *Isis*, 1942, 34: 28-9.

DEUTSCHE GESELLSCHAFT FÜR GESCHICHTE DER MEDIZIN, DER NATURWISSENSCHAFTEN UND DER TECHNIK. Verhandlungsbericht der Sektion für Geschichte der Medizin und der Naturwissenschaften auf der Versammlung Deutscher Naturforscher und Aerzte zu Nauheim, Sept. 1920. Zugleich wissenschaftliche Tagung der deutschen Gesellschaft für Geschichte der Medizin. *Janus*, 1921, 25: 101-22.
From 1921 to 1934 reports of the annual meetings of the Society were published in *Janus*.

KRUMBHAAR, E.B. Notes on the early days of the American Association of the History of Medicine. *Bull.Hist.Med.*, 1949, 23: 577-82.

LONG, Esmond R. Edward Bell Krumbhaar, physician, historian, founder of the American Association of the History of Medicine. *Bull.Hist.Med.*, 1957, 31: 493-504.

UNE NOUVELLE société d'histoire de la médecine (Londres, 1912). *Isis*, 1913, 1: 249-50.
Formation of the History of Medicine Section of the Royal Society of Medicine.

PALESTINE SOCIETY FOR MEDICAL HISTORY. [Announcement of first meeting] *Isis*, 1947, 37: 182.

PAZ SOLDÁN, Carlos E. Las labores de la Sociedad Peruana de Historia de la Medicina. Año 1945-1946. Memoria presentada por el Presidente de la Institución. *An.Soc.Peruana Hist.Med.*, 1946, 8: 1-7.

ROYAL SOCIETY OF MEDICINE. Section of the History of Medicine Jubilee Meeting 1912-1962, 21 November 1962. iii, 70 p., ill. (Supplement to *Proc.Roy.Soc.Med.*, vol. 56) London: 1963. [CB 89/586]
Includes appreciations of Sir William Osler, founder of the section and of other distinguished members, and chronological, subject, biographical, and author indices to the papers presented 1912-1962.

SAKANISHI, Shio. The (study of the) history of science in Japan. *Isis*, 1936, 25: 137.
A brief note on a Japanese Society for the History of Medicine.

SOCIETÀ DI STORIA CRITICA DELLE SCIENZE MEDICHE E NATURALI. [Notice of first national congress, 1912] *Isis*, 1913, 1: 110-11.

Nfqg

ARTELT, Walter. Das Institut für Geschichte der Medizin und der Naturwissenschaften in Berlin. *Mitt.Gesch.Med.*, 1937, 36: 281-4, fig.

BRUNN, Walter von. Das Institut für Medizingeschichte an der Universität Leipzig. *Mitt.Gesch.Med.*, 1937, 36: 1-4, 1 fig.

DIEPGEN, Paul. Die Aufgaben und Ziele des Institutes für Geschichte der Medizin und der Naturwissenschaften in Berlin. *Klin.Wochenschr.*, 1931, 10: 269-71.

DIEPGEN, Paul. Das Berliner Institut für Geschichte der Medizin und der Naturwissenschaften. *Lychnos*, 1936, 1: 230-4.

HABERLING, Wilhelm. Das Institut für Geschichte der Medizin an der Medizinischen Akademie in Düsseldorf. *Mitt.Gesch.Med.*, 1937, 36: 145-7.

UN ISTITUTO storico dell' arte sanitaria italiana. *Arch.Stor.Sci.*, 1921, 2: 291-3. [CB 11/446]
Apropos of the recent foundation of this Institute for the History of Medicine in Rome.

MORENO, Guido Ruiz. El Instituto de Historia de la Medicina de la Universidad Johns Hopkins. *Publ.Cátedra Hist.Med. Univ.Buenos Aires*, 1940, 4: 277-90, 1 fig.

NIȚULESCU-BOLOGA, Valeria. Institutul de Istoria Medicinei și Farmaciei și de Folklor Medical din Cluj. [The Institute of the History of Medicine, Pharmacy and Medical Folklore at Cluj. (In Rumanian)] *Viața Med.*, 1929, 5: no. 1, 10-14.

OLIARO, T. L'Istituto di Storia della Medicina in Vienna. *Minerva Med.*, 1933, 1: 18 p., ill.
Description of the Institute established in Vienna by Max Neuburger.

PAZZINI, Adalberto. The Institute of the History of Medicine, University of Rome, Italy. *Indian J.Hist.Med.*, 1956, 1: 58-61, 2 fig.

SHRYOCK, Richard Harrison. Report of the activities of the Institute of the History of Medicine of the Johns Hopkins University during the academic year, 1949/1950-[1956/1957]. *Bull.Hist.Med.*, 1950, 24: 586-9; 1951, 25: 585-9; 1952, 26: 477-82; 1953, 27: 568-72; 1954, 28: 555-65; 1955, 29: 569-73; 1956, 30: 569-72; 1957, 31: 571-4.

SIGERIST, Henry E. Bericht über die Tätigkeit des Instituts für Geschichte der Medizin an der Univ. Leipzig in den Jahren 1926-27; 1927-28; 1928-29; 1929-31. *Kyklos*, 1928, 1: 160-9; 1929, 2: 287-92; 1930, 3: 445-52; 1932, 4: 81-8.

SIGERIST, Henry E. Forschungsinstitute für Geschichte der Medizin und der Naturwissenschaften. 15 p. In: Brauer, Ludolph, ed. Forschungsinstitute; ihre Geschichte, Organisation und Ziele. Hamburg: P. Hartung, 1930.

SIGERIST, Henry E. Report of the activities of the Institute of the History of Medicine of the Johns Hopkins University during the academic year 1937/1938-[1946/1947]. *Bull.Hist.Med.*, 1938, 6: 858-88; 1939, 7: 847-73; 1940, 8: 1127-1134; 1941, 10: 364-416; 1942, 12: 445-63; 1943, 14: 250-70; 1944, 16: 193-213; 1945, 18: 228-38; 1946, 20: 379-85; 1947, 21: 556-72.

SIGERIST, Henry E. The need for an institute for the history of medicine in India. *Bull.Hist.Med.*, 1945, 17: 113-26.

STICKER, Georg. Das Institut für Geschichte der Medizin an der Universität Würzburg. *Mitt.Gesch.Med.*, 1937, 36: 5.

WELLCOME FOUNDATION. Spanish influence on the progress of medical science. With an account of the Wellcome Research Institution and the affiliated research laboratories and museums founded by Sir Henry Wellcome. Commemorating the tenth International Congress of the History of Medicine held at Madrid 1935. 121 p., ill. London: Wellcome Foundation, 1935.

ZEISS, Heinz. Der Arbeitsplan des neugegründeten Moskauer Forschungsinstituts für Geschichte und Methodologie der Medizin. *Arch.Gesch.Med.*, 1931, 24: 258-63.

Nfqv

SIGERIST, Henry E. Letter from Pura. *Bull.Hist.Med.*, 1950, 24: 77-83.
Report on the 5th National Congress of the History of Medicine, Milan, October 1949.

Nfqx

FOSSEYEUX, Marcel. La médecine au Congrès de Varsovie (21-28 août 1933). *Bull.Soc.Franç.Hist.Méd.*, 1933, 27: 325-40.

INTERNATIONAL CONGRESS OF THE HISTORY OF MEDICINE. [Publication dates of Proceedings and accounts of congresses.]

1st (Antwerp, 1920) Anvers: 1921.
Janus, 1921, 25: 32-32.
2nd (Paris, 1921) Evreux: 1922.
Bull.Soc.Franç.Hist.Méd., 1921, 15: 235-66.
3rd (London, 1922) Anvers: 1923.
Nature, 1922, 110: 296-7.
4th (Brussels, 1923) Anvers: 1927.
Arch.Stor.Sci., 1923, 4: 306-7.
5th (Geneva, 1925) Genève: 1926.
Med.Life, 1925, 32: 400-6.
6th (Leyden-Amsterdam, 1927) Anvers: 1929.
Bull.Soc.Franç.Hist.Méd., 1927, 21: 335-61; *Janus*, 1927, 31: 423-43.
7th (Oslo, 1928)
Bull.Soc.Franç.Hist.Méd., 1928, 22: 391-412.
8th (Rome, 1930) Pisa: 1931.
Aesculape, 1931, 21: 225-48, 31 fig.; *Bull.Soc.Franç.Hist.Méd.*, 1930, 24: 288-94.
9th (Bucharest, 1932) Bucharest: 1935.
Aesculape, 1932, 22: 121-44; *Archeion*, 1932, 14: 537-48; *Bull.Soc.Franç.Hist.Méd.*, 1932, 26: 442-61.
10th (Madrid, 1935) [Official handbook. Madrid: 1935]
Bull.Soc.Franç.Hist.Méd., 1935, 29: 249-73, 309-20; *Janus*, 1935, 39: 203-6.
11th (Zagreb, 1938)
Bull.Hist.Med., 1939, 7: 99-147, 26 fig..; *Bull.Soc.Franç.Hist.Méd.*, 1938, 32: 202-8.
12th (Amsterdam, 1950) In: *Act.VIe Congr.Hist.Sci.* Paris: 1951.
13th (Nice, 1952) Bruxelles: 1954.
Bull.Hist.Med., 1953, 27: 69-71.
14th (Rome, 1954) Roma: 1956.
Arch.Int.Hist.Sci., 1955, 8: 99-101.
15th (Madrid, 1956) In: *Arch.Iberoamer.Hist.Med.*, 1956-57, vol. 8-9.
Bull.Hist.Med., 1957, 31: 87-9.
16th (Montpellier, 1958) Bruxelles: 1959.
Bull.Hist.Med., 1959, 33: 78-9.
17th (Athens, 1960) Athènes: 1960.
Bull.Hist.Med., 1961, 35: 463-4.
18th (Warsaw, 1962) Warszawa: 1962.
19th (Basle, 1964) Basel, 1966.

PAN-AMERICAN CONGRESS OF THE HISTORY OF MEDICINE. *Isis*, 1957, 48: 69; 1958, 49: 75.

ROBINSON, Victor. A medico-historical pilgrimage to the Third International Congress of the History of Medicine at London, followed by visits to medical historians at Edinburgh, Strassburg, Vienna and Leipzig. *Med.Life,* 1923, 30: 551-98, ill.

SARTON, George. Le XVIIe Congrès international de Médecine (Londres, 1913). *Isis,* 1914, 2: 199-200; also 1913, 1: 112-15 [programme].
Quotes resolution setting up a provisional international commission to examine a proposal to hold international congresses of the history of medicine.

THOMPSON, C.J. [Account of the proceedings of the History of Medicine section at the 5th International Congress of Historical Sciences, Brussels, 1923.] *Janus,* 1923, 27: 149-53.

Ng teaching history of medicine

KLEBS, Arnold C. The history of medicine as a subject of teaching and research. *Bull.Johns Hopkins Hosp.,* 1914, 25: 1-10.

PINA, Luiz de. O ensino da história das ciências, em especial da medicina. *An.Fac.Ciênc.Porto,* 1934, 18: 42 p.

ROBINSON, Victor. The teaching of medical history in America. *VIe Congr.Int.Hist.Méd.* (Leyde-Amsterdam, 1927), p. 274-5. Anvers: de Vlijt, 1929.

SIMON, I. Avant-propos: l'enseignement de l'histoire de la médecine et de l'histoire de la biologie en Israël. *Rev. Hist.Méd.Hébraique,* 1957, 10: 3-18.

ZABLUDOVSKI, P. The teaching of medical history in the USSR. *Bull.Hist.Med.,* 1946, 20: 85-8.

ZEMBRZUSKI, L. L'enseignement de l'histoire de la médecine en Pologne. *Bull.Soc.Franç.Hist.Méd.,* 1931, 25: 471-86.

Ngd-cv

BERGHOFF, Ludwig. Der Film als medizinhistorischer Lehrbehelf (Bemerkungen zu meinem Filmdrama "Der Ball der Leprakranken".) *Festschrift zum 80. Geburtstag Max Neuburgers,* p. 40-6. Wien: Maudrich, 1948.

Ngg

ROBINSON, Victor. Medico-historical curriculum: specimen questions and answers. *Med.Life,* 1930, 37: 619-50.

ROBINSON, Victor. Questions and answers in medical history. *Med.Life,* 1931, 38: 659-97.

ROBINSON, Victor. Specimen questions and answers from the lectures of Victor Robinson, M.D., Professor of the History of Medicine, Temple University School of Medicine. 2nd ed. 32 p. Philadelphia: 1931. [CB 32/611]

ROBINSON, Victor. Syllabus of medical history. 110 p., 15 pl., 6 facs., front. New York: Froben Press, 1933. [CB 38/613]

ROGERS, Fred B. A syllabus of medical history. xiv, 112 p. Boston: Little, Brown, 1962.
Reviewed by Ernst W. Stieb, *Pharm.Hist.,* 1963, 8: 24.

Ngp

BARDUZZI, Domenico. Prelezione al corso libero di storia critica delle scienze mediche nella R. Università di Siena. *Riv.Stor.Crit.Sci.,* 1913, 4: 29-40.

BELTRÁN, Juan Ramón. La Cátedra de Historia de la Medicina juzgada en el extranjero. *Semana Méd.,* 31 Oct. 1940, 2: no. 44, 1014-16.

BETT, Walter, R. Johns Hopkins' graduate week in medical history. *Med.Life,* 1938, 45: 153-60.

FEDELI, Carlo. Le Scuole di Storia della Medicina nell' Università di Pisa. *Arch.Stor.Sci.,* 1920, 1: 141-50.

INAUGURATION of the Department of the History of Medicine of the Johns Hopkins University, and the opening of the William H. Welch Medical Library. *Ann.Med.Hist.,* 1930, 11: 122-7.

LASTRES, Juan B. Cátedra de la Historia de la Medicina de la Facultad de Medicina de la Universidad de Lima. Conferencia inaugural. *An.Soc.Peruana Hist.Med.,* 1947, 9: 39-51.

LÉVY-VALENSI, J. Chaire d'histoire de la médecine. Leçon inaugurale. *Sem.Hôp.Paris,* 1946, 22: 1709-19. [CB 71/130]

MENETRIER, P. L'enseignement de l'histoire de la médecine à l'Ecole de Santé et à la Faculté de Médecine de Paris. *Bull.Soc.Franç.Hist.Méd.,* 1930, 24: 362-86.

PREMUDA, Loris. Essenze ed obietti d'un insegnamento storico-medico nell'ateneo Ferrarese. Prolusione al corso libero di Storia della medicina presso la Facoltà di medicina e chirurgia dell'Università di Ferrara nell'anno accademico 1948-9. *Riv.Stor.Sci.,* 1949, 40: 104-14.

ST. LOUP B., Enrique. Palabras de inauguración del curso de la Historia de la Medicina en la Universidad Mayor de San Andrés de la Paz, Escuela de medicina y cirugia, año escolar de 1947. *An.Soc.Peruana Hist.Med.,* 1947, 9: 59-65.

SUDHOFF, Karl. Neuordnung des Studiums und medizingeschichtlicher Hochschulunterricht. Entwicklungsepochen der Heilkunde. *Jahreskurse Ärztl.Fortbild.,* 1920, 31-9.

VASCONCELLOS, Ivolino de. Dez anos da criacão dos "Cursos de história da medicina" e de luto em pról do estabelecimento da "Cátedra de História da medicina" no ensino médico nacional. *Rev.Brasil.Hist.Med.,* 1957, 8: 55-6.

Ngt in teaching medicine

ACKERKNECHT, Erwin H. History in medical education. *Scalpel,* (Alpha Epsilon Delta), 1953, [4 p.].

ACKERKNECHT, Erwin H. The role of medical history in medical education. *Bull.Hist.Med.,* 1947, 21: 135-45.

ASCHNER, Bernhard. Necessity and advantage of medical history in every-day practice. *Festschrift zum 80.Geburtstag Max Neuburgers,* p. 9-13. Wien: Maudrich, 1948.

ASCHNER, Bernard. The utilitaristic approach to the history of medicine. (What can the practising physician learn from historical methods of healing?) *Bull.Hist.Med.,* 1943, 13: 291-9.

ASCHNER, Bernhard. Der Wert medizingeschichtlichen Studiums für die Erziehung und das praktische Handeln des Arztes. *Festschrift zur Feier seines 60. Geburtstag Max Neuburger gewidmet,* p. 22-31. Wien: Verlag des Komitees, 1928.

BELTRAN, Juan Ramón. La historia de la medicina y el perfeccionamiento médico. *Essays in the History of Medicine presented to Prof. Arturo Castiglioni,* p. 43-7. Baltimore: Johns Hopkins Press, 1944.

BOLOGA, Valeriu L. Die historischen Grundlagen des Medizinunterrichtes im heutigen Rumänien. *Sudhoffs Arch.,* 1931, 24: 90-116.

CREUTZ, Rudolf. Das Wissen um die Geschichte der Medizin. Worte der Zielweisung an den studierenden ärztlichen Nachwuchs. *Sudhoffs Arch.,* 1941, 34: 52-60.

DIEPGEN, Paul. Ueber das Verhältnis der Geschichte der Medizin zur modernen Heilkunde und den Wert medizin-historischer Forschung für diese. *Naturwissenschaften,* 1913, 1: 1290-4.

FORMAN, Jonathan. The importance of local medical history to the medical student. *Festschrift zum 80. Geburtstag Max Neuburgers,* p. 140-3. Wien: Maudrich, 1948.

GARRISON, Fielding Hudson. The uses of medical bibliography and medical history in the medical curriculum. *J.Amer.Med. Ass.,* 1916, 66: 319-24.

KOCH, Richard. Die Geschichte der Medizin im Universitätsunterricht. *Arch.Gesch.Med.,* 1928, 20: 1-16.

LEAMAN, William G. Medical history in clinical teaching. *Bull.Hist.Med.,* 1939, 7: 794-8, 3 fig.

PINA GUIMARAES, Luiz José de. Humanisme et éducation médicale au Portugal. *Arch.Iberoamer.Hist.Med.,* 1956, 8: 59-86.

ROSEN, George. The place of history in medical education. *Bull.Hist.Med.*, 1948, 22: 594-629.

ROSEN, George. The writing of medical history. History in medical education. *Ciba Symp.*(Summit, N.J.), 1951, 11: 1350-66, ill.

SIGERIST, Henry E. History of medicine in academic teaching. Results of a questionnaire of the Institute. Translated from *Kyklos* [1928, 1: 147-56]. *Med.Life*, 1929, 36: 41-55.

SIGERIST, Henry E. Medical history in the medical schools of Canada. *Bull.Hist.Med.*, 1940, 8: 303-8.

SIGERIST, Henry E. Medical history in the medical schools of the United States. *Bull.Hist.Med.*, 1939, 7: 627-62.

SIGERIST, Henry E. La storia della medicina negli studi medici universitari. *Riv.Stor.Sci.*, 1952, 43: 182-92.

SZUMOWSKI, Wladislas. Sur la nécessité de rendre l'étude de l'histoire de la médecine obligatoire dans les universités. *Atti VIII° Congr.Int.Stor.Med.* (Roma, 1930), 13 p. Pisa: V. Lischi & Figli, 1931.

TEMKIN, Owsei. An essay on the usefulness of medical history for medicine. *Bull.Hist.Med.*, 1946, 19: 9-47.

VEITH, Ilza. The function and place of the history of medicine in medical education. *J.Med.Educ.*, 1956, 31: 303-9.

VIETS, Henry R. Medical history, humanism and the student of medicine. 32 p., 5 ill. Hanover: Dartmouth Publications, 1960.

WALSH, James J. The pleasant pathway to medical wisdom through medical history. *Med.Life*, 1930, 37: 345-60.

ZILBOORG, Gregory. Medical history as a force in medical functioning. *Victor Robinson Memorial Volume*, p. 415-20. New York: Froben, 1948.

Nh historiography and particular aspects of the history of medicine

Nhd historiography; historical research

DIEPGEN, Paul. Die Medizingeschichtsschreibung der letzten 80 Jahre. *Mitt.Gesch.Med.*, 1933, 32: 297.

DIEPGEN, Paul. Wahrheit und Dichtung in der Medizingeschichte. *Klin.Wochenschr.*, 1935, 14: 278-9.

GRININA, O.V. [On medico-geographic and sanitary-statistical correlation in investigating the past. (In Russian)] *Sovet Zdravookhr.*, 1964, 23: 43-7.

HEISCHKEL, Edith. Medizingeschichtschreibung und Volksmedizin. *Sudhoffs Arch.*, 1941, 34: 125-8.

HEMMETER, John C. *See* Nc-bm

KAWAKAMI, T. [Methodology of history in medicine. (In Japanese)] *J.Hist.Sci.Japan*, 1955, no. 33, 7-16.

PAPI, Giuseppe Ugo. Valore e significato dell'indagine storica. *Riv.Stor.Med.*, 1957, 1: 5-8, 1 fig.

ROSEN, George. Critical levels in historical process. A theoretical exploration dedicated to Henry Ernest Sigerist. *J.Hist.Med.*, 1958, 13: 179-85.

ROSEN, George. Levels of integration in medical historiography: a review. *J.Hist.Med.*, 1949, 4: 460-7.

ROSEN, George. A theory of medical historiography. *Bull. Hist.Med.*, 1940, 8: 655-65.

ROSEN, George. The writing of medical history. History in medical education. *Ciba Symp.* (Summit, N.J.), 1951, 11: 1350-66, ill.

SCHULLIAN, Dorothy M. A decade of medical historiography. *Bull.Med.Libr.Ass.*, 1957, 45: 285-90.

SIGERIST, Henry E. Probleme der medizinischen Historiographie. [Abstract]. *Atti VIII° Congr.Int.Stor.Med.* (Roma, 1930), p. 119-21. Pisa: V. Lischi & Figli, 1931.
[Full text] *Sudhoffs Arch.*, 1931, 24: 1-18.

TESDORPF, Paul. Betrachtungen über die Aufgaben der medizinischen Geschichtsschreibung. *Festschrift zur Feier seines 60. Geburtstag Max Neuburger gewidmet*, p. 296-9. Wien: Verlag des Fest-Komitees, 1928.

Nhf history of medicine: philosophical aspects

ACKERKNECHT, Erwin H. Recurrent themes in medical thought. *Sci.Mon.*, 1949, 69: 80-3.

BUTLER, C.S. Pride of opinion and its influence upon the history of medicine. *Med.Life*, 1935, 42: 635-9.

BOLOGA, Valeriu L. The crisis in medical thought and in historical synthesis. *Med.Life*, 1935, 42: 202-6.

BOLOGA, Valeriu L. Criza medicinii si sinteza istorica. [La crise de la médecine et la synthèse historique. (In Rumanian, with French and German summaries)] *Clujul Med.*, 1 Nov. 1933, no. 11, 8 p. [CB 42/604]

DIEPGEN, Paul. Alte und neue Romantik in der Medizin. *Klin. Wochenschr.*, 1932, 11: 28-34. [CB 35/311]

DIEPGEN, Paul. Irrationales und rationales Denken in der Geschichte der Medizin. *Landarzt* (Stuttgart), 1954, 30: no. 10, 11 p.

DIEPGEN, Paul. Das physikalische Denken in der Geschichte der Medizin. 39 p. Stuttgart: Enke, 1939. [CB 57/271]
Reviewed by Aldo Mieli, *Archeion*, 1941, 23: 295-6.

DIEPGEN, Paul. Weltanschaulich bedingte Wandlungen in der Medizin. *Med.Welt*, 1935, 9: 1861-5.

EDELSTEIN, Ludwig. Platonism or Aristotelianism? A contribution to the history of medicine and science. *Bull.Hist. Med.*, 1940, 8: 757-69.

HARTMANN, Fritz. Der aerztliche Auftrag. Die Entwicklung der Idee des abendlaendischen Arzttums aus ihren weltanschaulich-anthropologischen Voraussetzungen bis zum Beginn der Neuzeit. 240 p. Goettingen: Musterschmidt Verlag, 1956.
Reviewed by E.H. Ackerknecht, *Arch.Int.Hist.Sci.*, 1957, 10: 59.

HEMMETER, John C. Mutationen in geschichtlichen Begriffen und der Zusammenhang medizinischer Ideen und Lehren. *Festschrift zur Feier seines 60. Geburtstag Max Neuburger gewidmet*, p. 160-71. Wien: Verlag des Komitees, 1928.

HONIGMANN, Georg. Das Wesen der Heilkunde. Historisch-genetische Einführung in die Medizin für Studierende und Ärzte. xii, 319 p. Leipzig: Felix Meiner, 1924.

KOLLER, Fritz. Forschung, Entdeckung und Irrtum in der Medizin. *Naturwiss.Rundsch.*, 1963, 16: 388-94.

LAIGNEL-LAVASTINE, Maxime. L'historisme médical, introduction à son étude. *Mém.Soc.Franç.Hist.Méd.*, 1946, 2: 61-70.

NEUBURGER, Max. An historical survey of the concept of nature from a medical viewpoint. *Isis*, 1944, 35: 16-28.

PAGEL, Walter. Ein Gang durch die älteren medizinischen Lehrsysteme. *Med.Welt*, 1931, 5: 319-20, 463-5.

ROEMER, Milton I. Medicine and social criticism. A comment on George Rosen's article [Disease and social criticism, *see* below]. *Bull.Hist.Med.*, 1942, 11: 228-34.

ROSEN, George. Disease and social criticism, a contribution to a theory of medical history. *Bull.Hist.Med.*, 1941, 10: 1-4.

TEMKIN, Owsei. Studien zum "Sinn"-Begriff in der Medizin. *Kyklos*, 1929, 2: 21-105.

Nhg history of medicine: evolutionary aspects

CASTIGLIONI, Arturo. Medical thought in its historical evolution. *Med.Life*, 1930, 37: 283-94, ill.

CLARK-KENNEDY, A.E. The art of medicine in relation to the progress of thought. A lecture in the History of Science course in the University of Cambridge, February 10th, 1945. 48 p. Cambridge University Press, 1945.
Reviewed by G. Lapage, *Nature*, 1945, 156: 488.

FRAZIER, Chester North. Heterodoxy and medical progress. *Bull.Hist.Med.*, 1946, 20: 58-68.

ROSEN, George. Negative factors in medical history. A preliminary inquiry into their significance for the dynamics of medical progress. *Bull.Inst.Hist.Med.*, 1938, 6: 1015-19.

Nhg-mzAhg

DANNEMANN, Friedrich. Über den Parallelismus in der Entwicklung der Naturwissenschaften und der Heilkunde nebst einigen Vorbemerkungen über die Einführung der Geschichte der Naturwissenschaften und ihrer Anwendungen in den Hochschulunterricht. *Essays of the History of Medicine presented to Karl Sudhoff*, p. 349-68. London: Oxford University Press; Zurich: 1924.

Nhh

DAREMBERG, Charles Victor. Essai sur la détermination et les caractères des périodes de l'histoire de la médecine. 43 p. (*Gazette Médicale de Paris, 3rd ser.*, 1850, vol. 5) Paris: Baillière, 1850.
Reviewed by J.G. Thierfelder, *Henschel's Janus*, 1851, 1: 129-37; reprinted, Leipzig: Alfred Lorentz, 1931.

Nhj

BOLOGA, Valeriu L.; MATEESCU, V.G. Noul Hipocratism. [Neo-Hippocratism. (In Rumanian)] (Note pe marginea cărţii profesorului Arturo Castiglioni "L'orientamento neoippocratico del pensiero medico contemporaneo" (Torino: 1933).) *Clujul Med.*, 1934, no. 7, 12 p.

CASTIGLIONI, Arturo. Neo-Hippocratic tendency of contemporary medical thought. *Med.Life*, 1934, 41: 115-46, 9 ill. [CB 42/605]

CASTIGLIONI, Arturo. L'orientamento neoippocratico del pensiero medico contemporaneo. 51 p. Torino: Edizioni *Minerva Medica*, 1933. [CB 38/509]
Reprinted, with additions, from *Minerva Med.*, 1932, 23: 621-30.
For comment on this work, *see* BOLOGA, Valeriu L.; MATEESCU, V.G. above.

CAWADIAS, Alexander. The cult of Asklepios and its rôle in the history of medicine. *Proc. 3rd Int.Congr.Hist.Med.* (London, 1922), p. 42-4. Antwerp: 1923.

DELMAS, Paul; GUÉRIN-VALMALE, Ch. L'hippocratisme montpelliérain. *Aesculape*, 1923, 13: 2-7, 36-41, 53-7, 90-5, 110-13, 135-8, 163-5. [CB 15/232]

IZQUIERDO, J. Joaquín. Lugares de Asclepio y de Hipocrates en las modernas escuelas de medicina. *Gac.Méd.Méx.*, 1961, 91: 1025-40.

KAGAN, Solomon R. Priority credit in medicine. *Med.Way*, 1953, 15: 3-4.

MACRI, Ionel P. [Quelques principes hippocratiques dans la lumière de la science médicale moderne. (In Rumanian)] 20 p. (Universitatea "Regele Ferdinand I" din Cluj, Facultatea de Medicina, 1011) Cluj: Institutul de Arte Grafice Ardealul, 1936.

MEYER, Adolf. The tradition of ancient biology and medicine in the vitalistic periods of modern biology and medicine. *Bull. Inst.Hist.Med.*, 1937, 5: 800-21.

STERNBERG, Maximilian. Die Bedeutung der scholastischen Philosophie für das heutige medizinische Denken. Eine historische und methodologische Studie. 22 p. (Abhandlungen zur theoretischen Biologie, 24) Berlin: Bornträger, 1926.

Nhm

MARTÍ-IBÁÑEZ, Félix. Centaur. Essays on the history of medical ideas. vii, xviii, 716 p. New York: MD Publications, 1958.
Reviewed by James W. Haviland, *Isis*, 1961, 52: 426-7; for other reviews *see* CB 85/400, CB 86/470, CB 87/573 and CB 89/512.

Nht

FILLIOZAT, Jean. L'apport de l'Inde à la médecine universelle. *Méd.France*, 1951, no. 20, 8-10.

Nj psychological aspects

see also Nu popular aspects; folk medicine

Njd

DUSTIN, A. Le courage scientifique. *Rev.Univ.Bruxelles*, 1936-37, 42: 21-47.
With examples mainly from the history of medicine of the 19th and 20th centuries.

Njj

GIBSON, William Carlton. Significant scientific discoveries by medical students. *Sci.Mon.*, 1955, 81: 22-6.

GIBSON, William Carlton. Young endeavor: contributions to science by medical students of the past four centuries. 292 p. Springfield, Ill.: C.C. Thomas; Oxford: Blackwell Scientific Publications, 1958.
Reviewed by Edwin Clarke, *Med.Hist.*, 1959, 3: 338-9.

HEMMETER, John C. *See* Nc-bm

Nk philosophy and methodology

ACHELIS, J.D., *et al.* Philosophische Grenzfragen der Medizin. Fünf Vorträge, gehalten während der Leipziger Universitätswoche 1929. 114 p. Leipzig: Thieme, 1930.
Reviewed by F.M.G. de Feyfer, *Bijdr.Gesch.Geneesk.*, 1930, 10: 141-2.

BUCHANAN, Scott. The doctrine of signatures: a defence of theory in medicine. xiv, 205 p. New York: Harcourt, Brace, 1938. [CB 56/403]

BUTTERSACK, F. Ärztliche Betrachtungsweisen. *Arch.Gesch. Med.*, 1929, 22: 48-59.

GERBER, Otto Paul. Gibt es eine Philosophie der Medizin? *Festschrift zum 80. Geburtstag Max Neuburgers*, p. 181-5. Wien: Maudrich, 1948.

HALLÉ, Noël. Éléments de philosophie médicale. Histoire, métaphysique, psychologie, logique, morale. 433 p. Paris: Rivière, 1925.

INLOW, William DePrez. Medicine: its nature and definition. *Bull.Hist.Med.*, 1946, 19: 249-73.

INLOW, William DePrez. The philosophy of medicine. *Med. Life*, 1937, 44: 399-434.

KNEUCKER, A.W. Richtlinien einer Philosophie der Medizin. viii, 197 p. Wien: Maudrich, 1949.
Reviewed by W. Szumowski, *Arch.Int.Hist.Sci.*, 1951, 4: 1069-73.

MUCH, Hans. Steht die scholastische Medizin vor einem unvermeidlichen Bankerott? 36 p. (Moderne Biologie, moderne Medizin, 14) Leipzig: Kabitzsch, 1931.

PHILLIPS, Bernard. Philosophy and medicine. 17 p. Basavangudi, Bangalore: Indian Institute of Culture, 1951.

PREMUDA, Loris. Prospettive filosofiche della medicina antica e moderna. *Acta Med.Hist.Patavina*, 1959-60, 6: 107-46.
Reviewed by Silvestro Marcucci, *Physis*, 1962, 4: 90-2.

RIESE, Walther. Philosophical presuppositions of present-day medicine. *Bull.Hist.Med.*, 1956, 30: 163-74.

ROTHSCHUH, Karl. Theoretische Medizin? Begründung ihrer Notwendigkeit in der Gegenwart und eine Umreissung des Gebietes. *Klin.Wochenschr.*, 1935, 14: 1401-5.

SCHUMACHER, Joseph. Vom Wesen des Arzttums. 2nd ed. viii, 153 p. Stuttgart: Enke, 1957.
Reviewed by Edwin Rosner, *Sudhoffs Arch.*, 1958, 42: 391-3.
First publ. Augsburg: Naumann, 1946.

STRÜNCKMANN, Karl. Der Ganzheits-Gedanke in der Heilkunst. 23 p. Siegen: Forschepiepe, 1940.

SZUMOWSKI, Wladyslaw. Filozofia medycyny. Sprawozdania, rozwazania. [The philosophy of medicine. Analyses, reflections. (In Polish)] 135 p., ill. Krakow: Gebethner i Wolff, 1948.
Reviewed by Arpád Herczeg, *Arch.Int.Hist.Sci.*, 1950, 3: 219-22.

SZUMOWSKI, Wladyslaw. La philosophie de la médecine, son histoire, son essence, sa dénomination et sa définition. *Arch.Int.Hist.Sci.*, 1949, 2: 1097-139.

Nke

GOLDFARB, A.J. Medical and other sciences. An inquiry of what is science? when is it taught scientifically? *Science*, 1930, 71: 77-81.
Address of the retiring vice-president and chairman of Section N - Medical Sciences, American Association for the Advancement of Science, Des Moines, Iowa, December, 1929.

GREENWOOD, Major. Authority in medicine: old and new. (Linacre Lecture, 6 May 1943) 32 p. Cambridge University Press, 1943.
On the methodology of modern medical research, with backward glances at Galen and Thomas Linacre.

GUTTENTAG, Otto Ernst. The phrase, "art and science of medicine". *Calif.Western Med.*, 1939, 50: 5 p.

SIGERIST, Henry E. Enzyklopädie und Methodologie der Medizin. *Festschrift zur Feier seines 60. Geburtstag Max Neuburger gewidmet*, p. 273-7. Wien: Verlag des Fest-Komitees, 1928.

Nkh

MILT, Bernhard. Empirie und das statistisch fundierte biologisch-medizinische Denken in der Geschichte. *Gesnerus*, 1956, 13: 1-28.

SHRYOCK, Richard H. The history of quantification in medical science. *Isis*, 1961, 52: 215-37.

UNDERWOOD, E. Ashworth. The history of the quantitative approach in medicine. *Brit.Med.Bull.*, 1951, 7: no. 4, 265-74.

Nkk

GAY, Frederick P. Medical logic. *Bull.Hist.Med.*, 1939, 7: 6-27.

KOCH, Richard. Der Anteil der Geisteswissenschaften an den Grundlagen der Medizin. *Arch.Gesch.Med.*, 1926, 18: 273-301.

Nkn

WOODGER, J.H. Biology and language: an introduction to the methodology of the biological sciences including medicine. The Tarner lectures, 1949-50. 364 p. Cambridge University Press, 1952.

Nkt

ASCHNER, Bernard. Empiricism and rationalism in past and present medicine. *Bull.Hist.Med.*, 1945, 17: 269-86.

DAGOGNET, François. Surréalisme thérapeutique et formation des concepts médicaux. In: *Hommage à Gaston Bachelard*, p. 191-214. Paris: Presses Universitaires de France, 1957.

FEIJFER, F.M.G. de. Autostasie en geneeskunst. [Autostasy and medicine. (In Dutch)] *Bijdr.Gesch.Geneesk.*, 1926, 6: 1-16.

LESIEUR, Charles. La renaissance de l'humorisme. *Presse Méd.*, 1912, 20: 533-7.

VILAR, Albert. A propos de doctrines médicales. Conceptions d'hier, idées d'aujourd'hui. 200 p. Paris: Jouve, 1921.

Nkv

BARACH, Joseph H. Entelechy and scientific determinism in medicine. *Ann.Med.Hist.*, 1932, 4: 474-86.

RIESE, Walther. La pensée causale en médecine. 93 p. (Bibliothèque de Philosophie Contemporaine) Paris: Presses Universitaires de France, 1950.
Reviewed by Owsei Temkin, *Bull.Hist.Med.*, 1952, 26: 605-6.

Nkx

DIEPGEN, Paul. Vitalismus und Medizin im Wandel der Zeiten. *Klin.Wochenschr.*, 1931, 10: 1433-8.

DIEPGEN, Paul. Die Lehre von der Konstitution in der vitalistischen Medizin. *Klin.Wochenschr.*, 1933, 12: 30-2.

MEYER, Adolf. El problema del vitalismo en la biología y en la medicina actual. *Anal.Univ.Chile, ser.* 2, 1929, 7: 1243-89. [CB 30/472]

Nkz

LOEBEL, Josef. Whither medicine? xi, 296 p. London: Sidgwick and Jackson, 1934.

MACKENZIE, James. The future of medicine. 238 p. London: Oxford University Press, 1919.
French translation (Paris: Alcan, 1922) reviewed by L. Guinet, *Isis*, 1923, 5: 189-90.

Nmz relations with other scientific fields

NmzB

MUNTNER, Sussman. [Mathematical thought in the service of medicine. (In Hebrew, with English summary)] *Koroth*, 1959, 2: 97-115.

NmzC

MUNTNER, Sussman. [The influence of modern physics on medical thought. (In Hebrew, with English summary)] *Koroth*, 1957, 1: 357-77.

NORTHROP, F.S.C. The history of modern physics in its bearing upon biology and medicine. *Yale J.Biol.Med.*, 1938, 10: 209-32.

WOODGER, J.H. Physics, psychology and medicine: a methodological essay. 145 p. Cambridge University Press, 1956.

NmzD

ABEL, John J. Chemistry in relation to medicine. *J.Chem. Educ.*, 1929, 6: 1045-64.

POYNTER, F.N.L., ed. Chemistry in the service of medicine. 207 p. London: Pitman; Philadelphia: Lippincott, 1963. [CB 90/519]
Reviewed by J.D. Whittet, *Med.Hist.*, 1963, 7: 386-7.

STIEGLITZ, Julius, ed. Chemistry in medicine. A cooperative treatise intended to give examples of progress made in medicine with the aid of chemistry. xxi, 757 p., 23 ill. New York: Chemical Foundation, 1928. [CB 26/233]

NmzDO

HILLE, Hermann. A history of colloids in medicine. *Med.Life*, 1925, 32: 419-53; 1930, 37: 111-63, 24 ill.

NmzJG

SKOWRON, Stanisław. Biology and medicine. *Rev.Pol.Acad.Sci.*, 1962, 7: no. 3, 19-26.
Relation of evolution and medical research.

NmzME

MONTAGU, M.F. Ashley. Anthropology in medicine. *Interne*, March 1947, 114-16.

NmzRB

MORRISON, Hyman. The borderland of medicine and surgery as conceived by Reginald Heber Fitz. *Bull.Hist.Med.*, 1948, 22: 680-4.

TEMKIN, Owsei. The role of surgery in the rise of modern medical thought. *Bull.Hist.Med.*, 1951, 25: 248-59.

WATSON-JONES, Reginald. Surgery is destined to the practice of medicine. 81 p. Edinburgh: E. & S. Livingstone, 1961.
Reviewed by H. Jackson Burrows, *Med.Hist.*, 1962, 6: 96-7.

NmzRM

RUSSELL, James Clifford Hamilton. The interrelationship of pharmacy and medicine. *Amer.J.Pharm.Educ.*, 1946, 10: 286-312.

NmzS

KLAUDER, Joseph V. Historical remarks on the interrelation of human and veterinary medicine. *Trans.Coll.Physicians Phila.*, 1958, 26: 27-33.

Nn communication

Nnb symbolism

BERGMAN, Emanuel. Medicinska emblem och symboler. [Medical emblems and symbols. (In Swedish)] 104 p. Karlskrona: Sveriges läkarförbunds förlag, 1941.
Reviewed by Nils Ludvig Rasmusson, *Lychnos*, 1943, 399.

BRUNN, Walter v. Das Maiglöckchen als Symbol des Arztes. *Med.Welt*, 1936, 10: 505-6.

CASTIGLIONI, Arturo. The serpent as healing god in antiquity. Snake worship and symbolism in the Orient and in America. Remedies against snake bite. Snake venom in modern medicine. *Ciba Symp.* (Summit, N.J.), 1942, 4: 1158-86, fig.

CORIAT, Isador H. The symbolism of the gold-headed cane. *Ann.Med.Hist.*, 1924, 6: 126-30.

FRANKEL, Walter K. Medical symbols and saints. *Merck Rep.*, July 1949, 20-25, ill.

DEONNA, Waldemar. Emblèmes médicaux des temps modernes. Du bâton serpentaire d'Asklépios au caducée d'Hermès. *Rev.Int. Croix Rouge*, 1933, 15: 128-51, 218-43, 310-39, ill.

GOSSET, Pol. Les sceaux de santé au musée de Reims. *Union Méd.Nord-Est*, 1913, 131-4, 2 fig.

HABERLING, Wilhelm. Woran erkennt man auf Bildnissen den Arzt? *Therap.Ber.*, 1928, no. 2-10. [CB 25/435]

HALLIER-SCHLEIDEN, H. Der Heilkünstler Asklepios auf der Wanderschaft. *Ärztl.Rundsch.*, 1931, 41: 125.
Reviewed by Marzell, *Mitt.Gesch.Med.*, 1931, 30: 268.

MÜLLER, Reiner. Der Aeskulapstab. Eine neue sinnvolle Deutung des ärztlichen Zunftzeichens. *Umschau*, 1950, (13), 1 p., ill.
The author's thesis is that the "Urbild" of the snake gliding on Aesculapios' staff is the female of the Guinea worm (Dracunculus medinensis).

NETTLESHIP, Anderson. The problem of symbolism in medicine: primitive and Greek era symbols in relationship to modern scientific medicine. *Proc.10th Int.Congr.Hist.Sci.* (Ithaca, 1962), (1), p. 513-15. Paris: Hermann, 1964.

PESSOA, Alberto. Emblèmes et figurations de la médecine à l'Université de Coimbra. *Act.IIIe Congr.Int.Hist.Sci.* (Portugal, 1934), p. 249-53, 8 fig. Lisbon: 1936.

SCHOUTEN, J. De slangestaf van Asklepios als symbool van de geneeskunde. [The snake staff of A. as symbol of medicine. (In Dutch)] (Diss.) Leiden: 1963.
Reviewed by [T.A.] Vos, *Hermeneus*, 1963, 34: 288-9.

ZWICK, Karl G. The origin and significance of the medical emblem. *Bull.Soc.Med.Hist.Chicago*, April 1928, 4: 94.
The classic symbol is the serpent staff of Aesculapius and not the caduceus of Mercury, although the latter seems to have been adopted by the United States Army Medical Corps.

Nnh terminology

ANDREWS, Edmund. Medical terminology. *Ann.Med.Hist.*, 1928, 10: 180-98.
Discussing the origin of many medical terms.

BLONDEL, -. La revision internationale de la terminologie médicale. *Vie Int.*, 1913, 4: 379-94. [CB 5/297]

BONORA, Fausto. Considerazioni sulla evoluzione del pensiero medico e sua influenza sul contenuto semantico di alcuni vocaboli del greco antico. *Riv.Stor.Med.*, 1964, 8: 92-104.

CORNEY, B. Glanvill. Some oddities in nomenclature. *Proc. Roy.Soc.Med.*, 1913, 6: 48-53.

EBSTEIN, Erich. Allgemeine Bemerkungen zur medizinischen Terminologie. *Mitt.Gesch.Med.*, 1912, 11: 445-6.

GERARDE, Horace William. The etymological approach to medical terminology. *Phi Chi Quart.*, January 1949, 15 p.
A thesis submitted for the degree of Doctor of Medicine at the University of Wisconsin, 1948.

HUARD, Pierre. Les confusions de noms en médecine. *Extrême-Orient Méd.*, 1950, 3: 105-16.

PEPPER, O.H. Perry. Medical history in medical words. *Trans.Coll.Physicians Phila.*, 1950, 18: 29-37.

ROBERTS, Ffrangcon. Medical terms: their origin and construction. viii, 92 p. 3rd ed. London: William Heinemann Medical Books, 1959.
Reviewed by William Brockbank, *Med.Hist.*, 1960, 4: 83.
1st ed. 1954.

SKINNER, Henry Alan. The origin of medical terms. x, 438 p., ill. 2nd ed. Baltimore: Williams & Wilkins, 1961.
Reviewed by William Sharpe, *Bull.Hist.Med.*, 1962, 36: 376; by W.R. Le Fanu, *Med.Hist.*, 1963, 7: 94-5.
1st ed. Baltimore: 1949. Reviewed by E. Bastholm, *Lychnos*, 1953, 433-4.

WAIN, Harry. The story behind the word - some interesting origins of medical terms. viii, 342 p. Springfield, Ill.: C.C. Thomas; Oxford: Blackwell Sci. Pub., 1958.
Reviewed by W.J. Bishop, *Med.Hist.*, 1958, 2: 321-2; by José M. Lopéz Piñero, *Arch.Iberoamer.Hist.Med.*, 1959, 11: 341.

Nnj

JAYLE, F. Les erreurs de paternité dans les dénominations médicales. *VIe Congr.Int.Hist.Méd.* (Leyde-Amsterdam, 1927), p. 366-9. Anvers: De Vlijt, 1929.

KELLY, Emerson Crosby. *See* Ndaj

ROBINSON, Victor. Landmarks in modern medicine. A chronology with texts and eponyms. *Med.Life*, 1933, 40: 391-400.
Bichat to Rudolf Magnus (1800-1924).

ROLLESTON, Humphry. Medical eponyms. *Ann.Med.Hist.*, 1937, 9: 1-12, 7 fig.

Nns publishing

Nns-cj

GARRISON, Fielding Hudson. The high cost of current medical periodicals. *Bull.Amer.Libr.Ass.*, 1932, 26: 19-23.

ROBERT, Alfred L.; SCHALTENBRAND, Hans H. The comparative cost of medical journals. *Bull.Med.Libr.Ass.*, 1932, 20: 140-55.

No study and teaching

see also Ngt teaching medical history in teaching medicine

ACKERKNECHT, Erwin H. The history of medical education - a new series. *J.Med.Educ.*, 1956, 31: 81-2.

BEGHOFF, Emanuel. Die Ausbildung zum ärztlichen Beruf im Wandel der Zeiten. *Festschrift zum 80. Geburtstag Max Neuburgers*, p. 26-39. Wien: Maudrich, 1948.

CUNNINGHAM, Eileen R. Development of medical education and schools of medicine. *Ann.Med.Hist.*, 1935, 7: 228-41.

DIEPGEN, Paul. Einführung in das Studium der Medizin. *Med. Welt*, 1931, 5: 684-6.

FERRARIO, E.V. L'arte di fare il medico. *Castalia* (Milano), 1964, 20: 47-50.

GALDSTON, Iago. Reflections on historical epochs in medical education. *Bull.Hist.Med.*, 1961, 35: 50-60.

HALLÉ, Noël. De l'éducation médicale. Essai de morale professionnelle. iv, 259 p. Paris: Édition Spes, 1925.

MARTÍNEZ DURÁN, Carlos. Tiempo y substancia del estudiante eterno. xiv, 196 p., ill. Guatemala: Imprenta Universitaria, 1956.
Reviewed by C. Lilian Temkin, *Bull.Hist.Med.*, 1958, 32: 482.
Emancipation of education, particularly medical education, is the theme of the book.

RIECKE, -. Entwicklung und Ziele der ärztlichen Fortbildung. *Deut.Ärztebl.*, 1931, 60: 249-51.

SIGERIST, Henry E. The study of medicine in wartime. An address to the entering class of the Johns Hopkins University School of Medicine. *Bull.Hist.Med.*, 1944, 15: 1-13.

SIGERIST, Henry E. Trends in medical education. A program for a new medical school. *Bull.Hist.Med.*, 1941, 9: 177-98, 1 fig.

WARTMAN, William B. Medical teaching in western civilization. 307 p., ill. Chicago: Year Book Medical Publishers, 1961.
Reviewed by George E. Miller, *Science*, 1962, 136: 251-2.

Nod

KOCH, Richard. Auslegung des zweiten hippokratischen Aphorismus. Beitrag zur Technik des Unterrichtes in der Geschichte der Medizin. *Festschrift zur Feier seines 60. Geburtstages Max Neuburger gewidmet*, p. 209-18. Wien: Verlag des Fest-Komitees, 1928.

STENN, Frederick. Teaching through medical exhibits. *Bull. Hist.Med.*, 1953, 27: 482-3, 1 pl.
In University of Illinois Medical School.

Nod-cm

JONES, Tom. The graphic arts in medical education. *Bull. Med.Libr.Ass.*, 1944, 32: 385-90.

Nog

BLUH, Otto. Physics in premedical education. *Amer.J.Phys.*, 1949, 17: 156-63.
Sketches course in use at the University of British Columbia, Vancouver.

KLICKSTEIN, Herbert S. David Hosack on the qualifications of a professor of chemistry in the medical department. With a short history of the Professorship of Chemistry at Columbia College Medical Department (1776-1876), College of Physicians and Surgeons of New York (1807-1860), and Rutgers Medical College (1826-1830). *Bull.Hist.Med.*, 1954, 28: 212-36.

Nop

RIESMAN, David. The making of a clinician. *N.C.Med.J.*, 1940, 1: 65-9.

RIESMAN, David. The organization of the medical clinic. *Bull. Amer.Coll.Surg.*, April 1926, 10: no. 2, 24-6.

RIESMAN, David. The rise and early history of clinical teaching. *Ann.Med.Hist.*, 1919, 2: 136-47.

Noq

EWING, James. The university and the medical profession. *Science*, 1932, 75: 173-81.

LABHARDT, Alfred. Wesen und Aufgaben der medizinischen Fakultät. 44 p. (Schriften der Freunde der Universität Basel, 5) Basel: Helbing & Lichtenhahn, 1936.

Nor-da

ACKERKNECHT, Erwin H. Not famous men, but great teachers. *Bull.Hist.Med.*, 1947, 21: 861-70.
Apropos of Ernst Neisser, Louis Lewin and Alois Pick.

Np organizational aspects

COHN, Edwin J. Research in the medical sciences. *Amer.Sci.*, 1949, 37: 69-90.

GALDSTON, Iago. The history of research, with particular regard to medical research. Wanted - A history of research; The beginnings of research; The dawn of experimental science; The rise of modern research; Research in the United States. *Ciba Symp.* (Summit, N.J.), 1946, 8: 338-72, ill.

KOLMER, John A. The history of laboratory research in the past fifty years. *Med.Life*, 1927, 34: 3-14.

ROSS, Ronald. The management of medical research. *Nature*, 1923, 112: 541-5.

Npe

CRUMMER, Le Roy. The extra-academic origin of medical specialties. *Calif.Western Med.*, 1930, 33: 884-6; 1931, 34: 46-9.
Introductory lecture in new Department of Medical History and Bibliography, University of California Medical School.

CUSHING, Harvey. The binding influence of a library on a subdividing profession. *Bull.Johns Hopkins Hosp.*, 1930, 46: (Welch Festschrift) 29-42.

ROSEN, George. Changing attitudes of the medical profession to specialization. *Bull.Hist.Med.*, 1942, 12: 343-54.

ROSEN, George. Origins of medical specialization. Medical thought and the rise of specialism. Social factors in the development of medical specialization. The public relations of medical specialism. *Ciba Symp.* (Summit, N.J.), 1949, 11: 1126-56, ill.

WALDENSTROM, J. The Linnean tradition and the importance of pigeon holes in medicine. *Trans.Ass.Amer.Physicians*, 1964, 77: 44-51.

Npw international relations

BONNER, Thomas Neville. American doctors and German universities: a chapter in international intellectual relations, 1870-1914. x, 210 p. Lincoln: University of Nebraska Press, 1963.
Reviewed by Donald Fleming, *Miss.Val.Hist.Rev.*, 1963, 50: 521-2; by Winfred Overholser, *Amer.Hist.Rev.*, 1963, 68: 1099; by Richard H. Shryock, *J.Hist.Med.*, 1964, 19: 309-10.

ESSO, I. van. De geneeskundige betrekkingen tusschen Holland en Rusland in de 16e, 17e en 18e eeuw. [Medical relations between Holland and Russia in the 16th, 17th and 18th centuries. (In Dutch)] *Ned.Tijdschr.Geneesk.*, 1938, 82: 1102-12, 1582-90, 2831-3, 5399-409.

ESSO, I. van. Hollandsche artsen in Russischen hof- en staatsdienst in de 16e, 17e en 18e eeuw. [Dutch medical men in Russian court and state service in the 16th, 17th and 18th centuries. (In Dutch)] *Bijdr.Gesch.Geneesk.*, 1938, 18: 40-50.

ESSO, I. van. Vreemde artsen in russischen Staatsdienst, in Holland gestudeerd hebbende. [Foreign medical men, who studied in Holland, in Russian State service. (In Dutch)] *Bijdr.Gesch.Geneesk.*, 1938, 18: 281-91.

FISCHER, I. British medicine and the old Viennese School. *Bull.Hist.Med.*, 1942, 11: 174-81.

GUTHRIE, Douglas. The influence of the Leyden School upon Scottish medicine. *Med.Hist.*, 1959, 3: 108-22.

JORGE, Ricardo. Relations médicales et scientifiques entre l'Angleterre et le Portugal. *Proc.3rd Int.Congr.Hist.Med.* (London, 1922), p. 82-4. Antwerp: de Vlijt, 1923.

KHAIRALLAH, Amin A. *See* Nwb-ap

KONOPKA, Stanislas. Les relations culturelles entre la France et la Pologne dans le domaine de la médecine. 21 p., 10 portr., bibliogr. Warsaw: Société polonaise d'Histoire de la Médecine, 1958.
Reviewed by P. Huard, *Rev.Hist.Sci.*, 1959, 12: 284-5.

NEUBURGER, Max. British medicine and the Vienna School. Contacts and parallels. 134 p., 13 pl. London: Heinemann, 1943.
Reviewed by J.B. de C.M. Saunders, *Isis*, 1943, 34: 531-2.

NEUBURGER, Max. British medicine and the old Vienna Medical School. *Bull.Hist.Med.*, 1942, 12: 486-528.

PANEFF, Assen Kr.; IZRAEL, S.; POPOFF, Miroslav. Quelques éminents médicins bulgares, élèves de l'école française jusqu'à l'an 1878. *Scalpel*, 1961, 114: 923-5.

PICK, Friedel. Prag und Montpellier. *Arch.Gesch.Med.*, 1925, 17: 157-64.

SELMON, Bertha L. They do meet. Cross-trails of American physicians and Chinese people. xvii, 254 p., 18 pl. New York: Froben Press, 1942. [CB 69/217]

SERGESCU, Pierre. *See* Nwo-oq

Npx prizes and awards

FISCHER, I. Medizinische Preisfragen. *Janus*, 1938, 42: 25-43, 2 pl.
Prize competitions as sources for the history of medicine.

Nq societies and institutions

for colleges and universities in general *see* Noq
colleges and universities in the different countries *see* INDEX
libraries *see* Ncb
museums *see* Nxx

BLAKE, John B. Scientific institutions since the Renaissance: their role in medical research. *Proc.Amer.Phil.Soc.*, 1957, 101: 31-62, 5 fig. [CB 83/205]

ROLLESTON, Humphry. Medical friendships, clubs and societies. *Ann.Med.Hist.*, 1930, 11: 249-66.

SPARN, E. Cronología, diferenciación, matrícula y distribución geográfica de las sociedades de ciencias médicas. 153 p. Argentina: Imprenta de la Universidad Nacional de Córdoba, 1938.

Nqq-da

WONG, K. Chimin, comp. Lancet and cross: biographical sketches of fifty pioneer medical missionaries. xi, 160 p., ill. Shanghai: Council on Christian Medical Work, 1950.
Reviewed by A. Dunlap, *Arch.Int.Hist.Sci.*, 1951, 4: 1068.

Nqx

HAFERKAMP, Hans Joachim. Die Internationalen medizinischen Kongresse und der Weltkrieg. 59 p. (*Abhandl.Gesch.Med. Naturwiss.*, 22) Berlin: Ebering, 1937.

SIMON, I. Avant-propos. Le 4e Congrès Mondial de l'A.M.I. [Association Médicale Israélienne]. *Rev.Hist.Méd.Hébraique*, 1957, no. 38, 147.

Nqx-bv

BISHOP, W.J. Bibliography of international congresses of medical sciences. Prepared ... under the auspices of the Council for International Organizations of Medical Sciences with the ... assistance of Unesco. xxii, 238 p. Oxford: Blackwell, 1958.
Supplementary publications in the *CIOMS Newsletter*.

NATIONAL LIBRARY OF MEDICINE. Congresses. Tentative chronological and bibliographical reference list of national and international meetings of physicians, scientists, and experts. Second supplement, fourth series, Index-catalogue, United States Army (Army Medical Library). 288 p. Washington, D.C.: 1938.

STÜMKE, Hans. Bibliographie der internationalen Kongresse und Verbände. In der preuss. Staatsbibl. bearb. Bd. I: Medizin. ix, 281 p. Leipzig: Harrassowitz, 1939.
No more published.

Nr the profession

ARMAS, Julio de. Contestación al trabajo titulado "Consideraciones generales sobre el médico de ayer y de hoy". *Rev.Soc.Venezolana Hist.Med.*, 1956, 4: 129-36.
See companion article below by J. Quintero Quintero.

BARJON, Louis. Le médecin. Textes choisis et présentés. 375 p., fig., ill. Le Puy: X. Mappus, 1948.

BASHFORD, Henry Howarth, ed. Doctors in shirt sleeves. lx, 294 p. London: K. Paul, Trench, Trubner, 1939; New York: Piest, 1940.
Twenty-five essays by working physicians, surgeons and medical teachers, reprinted from the *Lancet*.

BINGER, Carl. The doctor's job. 243 p., front. New York: Norton, 1945. [CB 69/236]

CLENDENING, Logan. Behind the doctor. With illustrations from contemporary sources, portraits, photographs, and original drawings by James E. Bodrero and Ruth Harris Bohan. xxi, 458, xi p. New York: Knopf, 1933.
Reviewed in *Ann.Med.Hist.*, 1934, 6: 189.

CUSHING, Harvey. The medical career and other papers. 302 p. Boston: Little, Brown, 1940. [CB 59/444]

DAVENPORT, William H., ed. The good physician: a treasury of medicine. x, 564 p. New York: Macmillan, 1962.
Reviewed by Henry R. Viets, *Bull.Hist.Med.*, 1963, 37: 489-90.

DELAUNAY, Paul. La vie médicale aux XVIe, XVIIe et XVIIIe siècles. 556 p., 114 ill. (Collection Hippocrate) Paris: Le François, 1935. [CB 45/298]

DIEPGEN, Paul. Die Wandlung des Arztideals. *Universitas* (Stuttgart), 1950, 5: 1331-44, 1461-72.

FLEURY, Maurice de. Le médecin. 126 p. Paris: Hachette, 1927.

HUTCHISON, Robert; WAUCHOPE, G.M. For and against doctors: an anthology. 168 p. London: Arnold, 1935.
Reviewed in *Nature*, 1936, 137: 764.

IRSAY, Stephen d'. The evolution of the physician's attitude. *Ann.Med.Hist.*, 1928, 10: 376-86.

LIEK, Erwin. The doctor's mission: reflections, reminiscences and revelations of a medical man. Transl. and introd. by J. Ellis Barker. xxxix, 276 p. London: Murray, 1930.
Transl. of: Der Arzt und seine Sendung (München: Lehmann, 1925).

MARGALITH, D. [Doctors and drugs in the disorienting mirror. (In Hebrew, with English summary)] *Koroth*, 1962, 3: 31-9.
A collection of popular sayings about doctors.

QUINTERO QUINTERO, J. Consideraciones generales sobre el médico de ayer y el de hoy. *Rev.Soc.Venezolana Hist.Med.*, 1956, 4: 105-28.
See companion article above by Julio de Armas.

RIESMAN, David. The art of medicine. *Science*, 1931, 74: 373-80.

ROSEN, George. The doctor looks at himself. *Ciba Symp.* (Summit, N.J.), 1943, 5: 1490-519, ill.
Extracts from medical biographies.

ROSEN, George; CASPARI-ROSEN, Beate. 400 years of a doctor's life. Collected and arranged by George Rosen and Beate Caspari-Rosen. xvii, 429 p. New York: Schuman, 1947. [CB 71/130]
Collection of extracts from medical autobiographies arranged according to subjects.

SIGERIST, Henry E. The physician's profession through the ages. *Bull.N.Y.Acad.Med.*, 1933, 9: 661-76.

SIGERIST, Henry E. The place of the physician in modern society. *Proc.Amer.Phil.Soc.*, 1946, 90: 275-9.

SIGERIST, Henry E. Wandlungen des Arztideals. *Soz.Med.*, 1930, 665-70.

TURNER, E.S. Call the doctor. A social history of medical men. 320 p., ill. London: Michael Joseph, 1958.
Reviewed by William Brockbank, *Med.Hist.*, 1959, 3: 169-70.

VEITH, Ilza. The physician: priest, craftsman, or philosopher? 12 p. (Transaction, 15) Basavangudi, Bangalore: The Indian Institute of Culture, 1952.

VIERORDT, Hermann. Todesursachen im ärztlichen Stande. Ein Beitrag zur Ärzte-Biographie. 107 p. Stuttgart: Enke, 1926.

Nr-mzNW

SUDHOFF, Karl. Die geschichtliche Entwicklung der Beziehungen zwischen ärztlichen Beruf und dem Krankenhause. *Nosokomeion*, 1931, 2: 1-20.

Nrf

DITTRICK, Howard. Fees in medical history. *Ann.Med.Hist.*, 1928, 10: 90-101.

SIGERIST, Henry E. The history of medical licensure. *J. Amer.Med.Ass.*, 1935, 104: 1057-60.

VOGT, Paul L. The need for a salaried medical profession. *Pop.Sci.Mon.*, 1914, 84: 605-8. [CB 6/467]

Nrg

BISHOP, W.J. Notes on the history of medical costume. *Ann. Med.Hist.*, 1934, 6: 193-218, 6 fig.

CABANÈS, Augustin. Le costume du médecin. 95 p. Paris: Les Laboratoires P. Longuet, 1927.

Nrh

FISCHER, Alfons. The doctor's office from the 16th to the 19th centuries. *Ciba Symp.* (Summit, N.J.), 1939, 1: 275-87.

Nrj medical ethics

see also Nxe-tc

BACHMAN, Margot. Die Nachwirkungen des hippokratischen Eides. 56 p. Würzburg: K. Triltsch, 1952.
Reviewed by Frans Jonckheere, *Arch.Int.Hist.Sci.*, 1953, 6: 517.

CUSHING, Harvey. Consecratio Medici. *J.Amer.Med.Ass.*, 1926, 87: 539-42.

DEICHGRÄBER, Karl. Die ärztliche Standesethik des hippokratischen Eides. *Quellen Stud.Gesch.Naturwiss.Med.*, 1932, 3: (2), 29-49.

DVORJETSKI, M. Science médicale et conscience médicale. *Act.VIIe Congr.Int.Hist.Sci.* (Jerusalem, 1953), p. 283-94. Paris: Hermann, [n.d.]. [CB 80/202]

EDMUNDS, Vincent; SCORER, C. Gordon; ed. Ideals in medicine. A Christian approach to medical practice. 192 p. London: Tyndale Press, for the Christian Medical Fellowship; Chicago: Christian Medical Fellowship, 1958.
Reviewed by Otto E. Guttentag, *Bull.Hist.Med.*, 1958, 32: 579.

ELAUT, L. Het medisch beroepsgeheim en zijn historische ontwikkeling. [Professional secrecy in medicine and its historical evolution. (In Dutch)] 71 p. (Katholieke Vlaamse Hogeschooluitbreiding. Verhandeling 456) Antwerp: Standaard-Boekhandel, 1958.
Reviewed by G.A. Lindeboom, *Janus*, 1958, 47: 259-60.

FISCHER, Isidor. Aerztliche Standespflichten und Standesfragen. Eine historische Studie. vii, 190 p. Wien/ Leipzig: W. Braumüller, 1912.

FISCHER, Isidor. Zur Geschichte der ärztlichen Schweigepflicht. *Arch.Gesch.Naturwiss.Tech.*, 1913, 6: 97-101.

FRINGS, Hermann-Josef. Aus fremden Leiden eigene Sorgen. Zur Geschichte einer ärztlichen Ethik-Formel. *Sudhoffs Arch.*, 1959, 43: 1-12.

GALDSTON, Iago. On the psychology of medical ethics. *Victor Robinson Memorial Volume*, p. 93-8. New York: Froben, 1948.

LEIBBRAND, Werner. Der göttliche Stab des Äskulap. Vom geistigen Wesen des Arztes. 3rd enl. ed. 480 p. Salzburg: Otto Müller, 1953.
Reviewed by Leo Norpoth, *Sudhoffs Arch.*, 1955, 39: 95-6.

NITTIS, Savas. Hippocratic ethics and present day trends in medicine. *Bull.Hist.Med.*, 1942, 12: 336-42.

THE OATH of Hippocrates modernized. *Isis*, 1949, 40: 350.

PAZZINI, Adalberto. Il medico di fronte alla morale. 202 p. Brescia: Morcelliana, 1951.
Reviewed by A. Corsini, *Riv.Stor.Sci.*, 1952, 43: 140-1.

RIESE, Walther. La pensée morale en médecine. Premiers principes d'une éthique médicale. Préface du Pr. Henri Baruk. xi, 84 p. (Bibliothèque de Philosophie Contemporaine) Paris: Presses Universitaires de France, 1954.
Reviewed by Owsei Temkin, *Bull.Hist.Med.*, 1956, 30: 386-8.

ROYSTER, Hubert Ashley. Medical morals and manners. x, 333 p. Chapel Hill: University of North Carolina Press, 1937. [CB 51/295]

SPERRY, Willard L. The ethical basis of medical practice. 185 p. New York: Hoeber, 1950. [CB 76/412]

TEMKIN, Owsei. Medicine and the problem of moral responsibility. *Bull.Hist.Med.*, 1949, 23: 1-20. [CB 76/414]

THAYER, William Sidney. Medical ethics. A lecture to the fourth year class of the Johns Hopkins medical school. *Bull.Inst.Hist.Med.*, 1935, 3: 613-22.

VEITH, Ilza. Medical ethics throughout the ages. *Arch. Intern.Med.*, 1957, 100: 504-12.

Nrk activities of medical men outside medicine

SCHLUETER, Robert E. Doctors who served outside the limits of medical science. *Bull.Med.Libr.Ass.*, July 1929, 18: 46-53.
Presented before the St. Louis chapter, American Library Association, October 1928.

Nrk-A

BRASCH, Frederick E. Medical men in mathematics, astronomy, and physics. *Med.Life*, 1929, 36: 219-36, portr.

Nrk-C

PODOLSKY, Edward. Physician physicists. *Ann.Med.Hist.*, 1913, 3: 300-7.

Nrk-G

BROWNING, William. Medical men as early American geologists. *Med.Life*, 1929, 36: 137-44.

Nrk-HK

GALDSTON, Iago. Medical explorers of Arabia. *Bull.N.Y.Acad. Med.*, 1937, 13: 512-38.

KONJIAS, Helen T. Physicians as explorers in the new world. *Ciba Symp.*, 1940 , 2: 643-52.

ROBINSON, Victor. Medical explorers in Africa. *Ciba Symp.*, 1940, 2: 633-42, fig.

ROBINSON, Victor. The physician as explorer in Asia. *Ciba Symp.*, 1940, 2: 626-32.

SEIDE, J. Doctors and naturalists as pilgrims and travellers to the Holy Land. *Janus*, 1959, 48: 53-61.

Nrk-RMo

URDANG, George. The part of doctors of medicine in pharmaceutical education. *Amer.J.Pharm.Educ.*, 1950, 14: 546-55.

Nrk-T

SCHAEFER, G.; NAUMANN, W. Technical achievements of physicians. *Ciba Symp.*(Summit, N.J.), 1941, 3: 1026-52.

Nrn cultural activities

DANA, Charles Loomis. Poetry and the doctors. A catalogue of poetical works written by physicians, with biographical notes and an essay on the poetry of certain ancient practitioners of medicine. xxiii, 83 p., ill. Woodstock, V.: Elm Tree Press, 1916.

FRANKEL, Walter K. Physicians as musicians and composers. *Merck Rep.*, October 1948, 57: no. 4, 26-31, ill.

McDONOUGH, Mary Lou, ed. Poet physicians, an anthology of medical poetry written by physicians. 212 p. Springfield, Ill.: C.C. Thomas, 1945. [CB 69/237]
Reviewed by George Rosen, *J.Hist.Med.*, 1946, 1: 342-3.

MARMELSZADT, Willard. Musical sons of Aesculapius. 115 p., 16 pl. New York: Froben Press, 1946.
Reviewed by Sidney Licht, *Bull.Hist.Med.*, 1947, 21: 410.

MONRO, Thomas Kirkpatrick. The physician as man of letters, science and action. viii, 212 p. Glasgow: Jackson, Wylie, 1933.

NESBIT, Louis. Physician-authors of the past and present. *Med.Life*, 1935, 42: 643-70.

Nrw women in medicine

HURD-MEAD, Kate Campbell. A history of women in medicine from the earliest times to the beginning of the nineteenth century. xvi, 569 p., 38 pl., 23 fig. Haddam, Conn.: Haddam Press, 1938.
Reviewed by John B. de C.M. Saunders, *Isis*, 1938, 29: 477-9.

SCHÖNFELD, Walther. Frauen in der abendländischen Heilkunde vom klassischen Altertum bis zum Ausgang des 19. Jahrhunderts. viii, 176 p., 5 pl., fig. Stuttgart: Enke, 1947.
Reviewed by Ernest Wickersheimer, *Arch.Int.Hist.Sci.*, 1951, 4: 256-9.

Ns relations with society

BRUES, Austin. Medicine and society: implications in the atomic age. *J.Mt.Sinai Hosp.*, 1953, 19: 812-20.

DE KRUIF, Paul; DE KRUIF, Rhea. Why keep them alive? vii, 293 p. London: Cape, 1936.
Reviewed by Clifford Dobell, *Nature*, 1936, 138: 523-5.

LEONARDO, Richard A. A surgeon looks at life. 128 p. New York: Froben Press, 1945. [CB 69/206]

MÜLLER-HEGEMANN, Dietfried. Ueber das Menschenbild in der Medizin. *Forsch.Fortschr.*, 1964, 38: 232-5.

NAVA, Pedro. Medicina e humanismo. *Brasil Méd.Cirúrg.*, 1946, 8: 97-102.

PETERS, John P. The social implications of medical science. *Yale J.Biol.Med.*, 1942, 14: 281-90.

RIESMAN, David. Medicine in modern society. 226 p. Princeton: Princeton University Press, 1938.

SHRYOCK, Richard H. The interplay of social and internal factors in modern medicine. *Centaurus*, 1953, 3: 107-25.

SHRYOCK, Richard H. The interplay of social and internal factors in the history of modern medicine. *Sci.Mon.*, 1953, 76: 221-30.

SIGERIST, Henry E. Das Bild des Menschen in der modernen Medizin. *Neue Bl.Sozialismus*, 1930, 1: 97-106.

SIGERIST, Henry E. The medical student and the social problems confronting medicine today. *Bull.Inst.Hist.Med.*, 1936, 4: 411-22.

SIGERIST, Henry E. Soziologische Faktoren in der Medizin. *Festschrift Heinrich Zangger*, p. 749-58. Zurich: Rascher, 1935.

ZILBOORG, Gregory. Humanism in medicine and psychiatry. *Yale J.Biol.Med.*, 1944, 16: 217-30.

Nsb impact of society on medicine; sociology of medicine

READER, George G.; GORS, Mary E.W. The sociology of medicine. In: Sociology today: problems and prospects, p. 229-46. New York: Basic Books, 1959.

SAINTYVES, P. L'art de guérir est-il d'origine empirique? 2. La thérapeutique magique. 3. La thérapeutique sacerdotale. 4. Empirisme et raisonnement dans la médecine mystique. *Janus*, 1917, 22: 372-90; 1918, 23: 56-76; 1919, 24: 192-217, 316-35.

SAINTYVES, P. Les origines de la médecine. Empirisme ou magie? 100 p. (Collection science et magie, 3) Paris: Nourry, 1920. [CB 10/203]

SHRYOCK, Richard H. The development of modern medicine: an interpretation of the social scientific factors involved. xv, 442 p., front., 7 ill. Philadelphia: University of Pennsylvania Press, 1936.
Reviewed by C.D. Leake, *Isis*, 1937, 27: 538-9.
Rev. enl. ed. xv, 457, xv p. New York: Knopf, 1947; English ed. 384 p. London: Gollancz, 1948. [CB 71/131]
German translation Stuttgart: Enke, 1939.

SIGERIST, Henry E. On the sociology of medicine. Ed. by Milton E. Roemer. xiii, 399 p. New York: MD Publications, 1960.
Reviewed by J.B. de C.M. Saunders, *Isis*, 1961, 52: 600-1; for other reviews *see* CB 86/471 and CB 87/575.

SIGERIST, Henry E. The social history of medicine. *West.J.Surg.Obstet.Gynecol.*, 1940, 48: 715-22.

STERN, Bernhard Joseph. Social factors in medical progress. 137 p. (Studies in History, Economics, and Public Law, 287) New York: Columbia University Press, 1927.
Reviewed by F.H. Garrison, *Amer.Hist.Rev.*, 1927, 33: 90-1; by Francis R. Packard, *Ann.Med.Hist.*, 1928, 10: 105-6.

STERN, Bernhard Joseph. Society and medical progress. xvii, 264 p. Princeton: Princeton University Press, 1941. [CB 62/86]

Nsc relation with the history of civilization

CABANÈS, Auguste. L'histoire éclairée par la clinique. 320 p. Paris: Albin Michel, 1921. [CB 12/635]

CASTIGLIONI, Arturo. La historia de la medicina y la solidaridad humana de los pueblos. *Rev.Argent.Hist.Med.*, 1944, 3: no. 2, 13-17.

DIEPGEN, Paul. Medizin und Kultur. Gesammelte Aufsätze von Paul Diepgen. Zu seinem 60. Geburtstag am 24. November 1938, herausgegeben von W. Artelt, E. Heischkel, J. Schuster. vii, 309 p., portr., bibliogr. Stuttgart: Enke, 1938. [CB 57/201]

DREWS, Robert S. The rôle of the physician in the development of social thought. *Bull.Hist.Med.*, 1940, 8: 874-908.

FULTON, John F. Medicine, warfare, and history. *Annu.Rep. Smithsonian Inst.for 1954*, p. 427-41. Washington, D.C.: 1955.

HAGGARD, Howard Wilcox. The doctor in history. xiii, 408 p. New Haven: Yale University Press; London: Oxford University Press, 1934.

HAGGARD, Howard Wilcox. The lame, the halt, and the blind. The vital role of medicine in the history of civilization. xxiv, 420 p. London: Heinemann; New York: Harper, 1932.

HOBSON, William. World health and history. 252 p., 46 pl., maps. Baltimore: Williams & Wilkins, 1963.

HOLLÄNDER, Eugen. Äskulap und Venus. Eine Kultur- und Sittengeschichte im Spiegel des Arztes. vii, 488 p., 330 ill. Berlin: Propylaen-Verlag, 1928.
Reviewed by Karl Birnbaum, *Deut.Lit.Zeitung*, 1927, 2622-4; by K. Sudhoff, *Mitt.Gesch.Med.*, 1928, 27: 56-8.

LOEB, Leo. Some considerations on certain relations between the history of medicine and general history. *Med.Life*, 1927, 34: 168-76.

MARTÍ-IBÁÑEZ, Félix. El pensamiento médico en la historia. 64 p. (Universidad de San Carlos, Facultades de Ciencias Médicas y de Humanidades, 2) Guatemala: 1947.

SHRYOCK, Richard H. Medicine and society: an historical perspective. *J.Mt.Sinai Hosp.*, 1953, 19: 699-715.

SUDHOFF, Karl. Civilization and health. A historical colloquy. *Med.Life*, 1927, 34: 159-64.

Nse public opinion

BURGER, H. The appreciation of the medical profession and the divine origin of medicine. *Ann.Med.Hist.*, 1929, 1: 37-49.

COHN, Alfred E. Changes in public attitudes toward medicine: historical aspects. *Bull.Hist.Med.*, 1942, 11: 12-35.

NETT, Emily M. A preliminary investigation of the social psychology of attitudes toward medical doctors. *Ohio J. Sci.*, 1958, 58: 317-23. [CB 84/322]

PAZZINI, Adalberto. Medicina denigrata e medici denigratori. 266 p. Roma: O.E.T. Polilibraria, [?1945].
Reviewed by A.C., *Riv.Stor.Sci.*, 1943, 34: 151.

RIESMAN, David. Medicine at the bar of public opinion. *Amer. Med.Ass.Bull.*, 1924, 19: 227-30.

SHRYOCK, Richard H. Public relations of the medical profession in Great Britain and the United States: 1600-1870. A chapter in the social history of medicine. *Ann.Med.Hist.*, 1930, 2: 308-39.

SIGERIST, Henry E. Der Arzt und die Umwelt. *Deut.Med. Wochenschr.*, 1931, 57: 1049-51.

Nsg/st relation with economics, politics and the law

Nsg

DIEPGEN, Paul. Wirtschaftsgeschichte und Medizingeschichte. *Deut.Med.Wochenschr.*, 1937, 63: 1705.

Nsh

HEISCHKEL, E. Die Strasse in der Geschichte der Medizin. *Technikgeschichte*, 1934, 23: 36-44, 3 fig.

Nsk

ENGLERT, Ludwig. Die politische Erziehung des Arztes. *Deut. Ärztebl.*, 1933, 63: no. 2, 53 *et seq.*

SIGERIST, Henry E. Nationalism and internationalism in medicine. *Bull.Hist.Med.*, 1947, 21: 5-16.

Nsp

KRUMBHAAR, Edward B. Superstition and medical progress in relation to the war. *Trans.Coll.Physicians Phila.*, 1942, 10: 168-74.

ROEMER, Milton I. History of the effects of war on medicine. *Ann.Med.Hist.*, 1942, 4: 189-98.

TALIAFERRO, William H., ed. Medicine and the war. A series of ten lectures, sponsored by the Charles R. Walgreen Foundation for the Study of American Institutions. 191 p., ill. Chicago: University of Chicago Press, 1944.
Reviewed by Jean C. Sabine, *Bull.Hist.Med.*, 1944, 15: 546-8.

VEITH, Ilza. Humane warfare and inhuman war: Japan and its treatment of war prisoners. *Bull.Hist.Med.*, 1946, 19: 355-74, 1 fig.

Nsr

DUSTIN, Albert. La médecine et le libre examen. *Rev.Univ. Bruxelles*, 1934-35, 40: 190-213.

GUERMONPREZ, François Jules Octave. Recherches sur les vicissitudes de la liberté en médecine depuis Louis XV jusqu'à nos jours. 314 p. Paris: Legrand, 1928. [CB 27/582]

SHRYOCK, Richard H. Freedom and interference in medicine. *Ann.Amer.Acad.Polit.Soc.Sci.*, 1938, 200: 32-59.

Nst

SPECTOR, Benjamin. The growth of medicine and the letter of the law. *Bull.Hist.Med.*, 1952, 26: 499-525.
The Fielding H. Garrison Lecture.

THORNDIKE, Lynn. The debate for precedence between medicine and law: further examples from the fourteenth to the seventeenth century. *Romanic Rev.*, 1936, 27: 185-90.

Nsy medical utopias

DUBOS, René J. Medical utopias. *Daedalus*, 1959, 88: 410-24.

ROSEN, George. Medicine in Utopia, from the eighteenth century to the present. *Ciba Symp.* (Summit, N.J.), 1945, 7: 188-200, ill.

SILVETTE, Herbert. Medicine in Utopia. *Bull.Hist.Med.*, 1939, 7: 1013-36.

TALLMADGE, G. Kasten. The physician in the ancient Utopias. Medicine in the Utopias of the Renaissance and the seventeenth century. *Ciba Symp.* (Summit, N.J.), 1945, 7: 166-87, ill.

Nt relations with the humanities

ANNAN, Gertrude L. Medicine and the arts. Some aspects of the history of medicine and culture. *Ciba Symp.* (Summit, N.J.), 1951, 11: 1367-76, ill.

Ntd relation with religion

see also Nud religious folklore

BARNES, Harry Elmer. Medical science versus religion as a guide to life. *Med.Life*, 1929, 36: 307-42.

BON, Henri. Précis de médicine catholique. xii, 768 p. Paris: Alcan, 1935.

EDMUNDS, Vincent; SCORER, C. Gordon; ed. *See* Nrj

HUME, Edward H. Doctors courageous. xiv, 297 p., ill. New York: Harper, 1950.
Missionary doctors.
Reviewed by Ilza Veith, *Bull.Hist.Med.*, 1952, 26: 197-9.

MATOUSEK, Miloslav. Medicina a Náboženstvi. [Medicine and religion. (In Czech)] 48 p., ill. Gottwaldov: Krajske Nakladatelstvi, 1960.
Reviewed by Eva Rozsivalova, *NTM Z.Gesch.Naturwiss.Tech. Med.*, [1962], 1: no. 3, 151-2.

MERZBACH, A.C. [Problems of the spiritual influence of medicine. (In Hebrew)] *Koroth*, 1957, 1: 409-11.

RIVERS, W.H.R. Medicine, magic, and religion, being the Fitzpatrick Lectures delivered before the Royal College of Physicians of London in 1915 and 1916. Preface by G. Elliot Smith. viii, 147 p. (International Library of Psychology, Philosophy and Scientific Method) London: Kegan Paul, 1924.

Ntf

ALVÁREZ-SIERRA, José. Las ordenes religiosas en la historia de la medicina. *Arch.Iberoamer.Hist.Med.*, 1957, 9: 13-22.

DIEPGEN, Paul. Les influences religieuses sur le développement de la médecine. *Bull.Soc.Franç.Hist.Méd.*, 1936, 32: 136-44.

FEDELI, Carlo. Nuove ricerche sui rapporti dell'Ordine di Malta con le scienze mediche. *Riv.Stor.Sci.*, 1920, 11: 7-16.

WALSH, James J. Rôle of Catholic physicians and scientists in the advancement of civilization. *Med.Life*, 1929, 36: 169-88, pl.

Ntf-da

FITZGERALD, William A. Medical men: canonized saints. *Bull. Hist.Med.*, 1948, 22: 635-46.

HOFFMANN, Karl Franz. Christliche Ärzte. Lebensbilder vom 16. bis 19. Jahrhundert. 225 p. Regensburg: Josef Habbel, 1950.
Reviewed by Gernot Rath, *Centaurus*, 1954, 3: 278.

Nth relation with literature

see also Nrn cultural activities of medical men

BRAUN, Adolf. Medizinisches aus der Weltliteratur von der Antike bis zur Gegenwart. iv, 152 p. Stuttgart: Enke, 1937.
Reviewed by Aldo Mieli, *Archeion*, 1938, 21: 155-7.

CORNER, George W. Medicine in the modern drama. *Ann.Med. Hist.*, 1938, 10: 309-17, 2 fig.

FINDLEY, Palmer. The doctor in literature. *Med.Life*, 1934, 41: 566-84.

KAHN, Max; KAHN, Ray G. Quixotic medicine. *Med.Life*, 1926, 33: 170-94.

PESSOA, Alberto. O médico de ontem e o médico de hoje vistos pelos homens de letras. *Coimbra Méd.*, 1939, 6: 19 p.

SHRYOCK, Richard H. Before and after: a medical drama of 1849 and 1949. *Bull.Hist.Med.*, 1949, 23: 554-76.

WACHSMUTH, Bruno. Der Arzt in der Dichtung unserer Zeit. With a preface by P. Diepgen. 244 p. Stuttgart: Enke, 1939.
Reviewed by W. Pagel, *Isis*, 1947, 32: 239-40.

WEBB, Gerald B. The rôle of the physician in literature. *Med.Life*, 1929, 36: 192-218, portr.

Ntk

ROLLESTON, Humphry. Poetry and physic. *Ann.Med.Hist.*, 1926, 8: 1-15.

SEIDENSCHNUR, Otto. Beiträge zur Kenntniss medicinischer Gedichte. *Henschel's Janus*, 1847, 2: 772-806; reprinted Leipzig: Alfred Lorentz, 1931.

Ntq relation with art

see also Ncm illustrations
Ncp non-bibiliographical sources

ACKERKNECHT, Erwin H. Medical art as a psychological safety-valve. *Bull.Med.Libr.Ass.*, 1955, 43: 465-71, 4 ill.

ANDEL, M.A. van. De gevelsteen en de geneeskunst. [Stone-work on facades and medicine. (In Dutch)] *Bijdr.Gesch. Geneesk.*, 1934, 14: 155-9, 10 fig.; 196-201, 8 pl.

CABANÈS, Auguste. Esculape chez les artistes. 401 p., 196 fig. Paris: Le François, 1928.
Reviewed by Laignel-Lavastine, *Bull.Soc.Franç.Hist.Méd.*, 1929, 23: 67-8.

COHN, Alfred E. No retreat from reason and other essays. xi, 279 p. New York: Harcourt, Brace, 1948.
On artistic aspects of medicine.
Reviewed by Chauncey D. Leake, *Isis*, 1949, 40: 92.

CORSINI, Andrea. Figurative arts in connexion with the history of medicine. *Proc.17th Int.Congr.Med.* (London, 1913), Sect. 23, p. 63-7. London: Oxford University Press, Hodder and Stoughton, 1914.

CULLEN, Thomas S. Max Brödel, director of the first department of art as applied to medicine in the world. *Bull.Med. Libr.Ass.*, 1945, 33: 5-29.

DITTRICK, Howard. Ex votos of medical interest. *Bull.Med. Libr.Ass.*, 1944, 32: 345-55, 7 fig.

FRANCESCO, Grete de. Four centuries of medical votive offerings. *Ciba Symp.* (Summit, N.J.), 1939, 1: 126-8, fig.

FRANCIS, Henry Sayles. Traditional representation of medicine and healing in the Christian hierarchy. *Bull.Med.Libr.Ass.*, 1944, 32: 332-44, 5 fig.

GERLITT, John. Votive offerings. *Ciba Symp.* (Summit, N.J.), 1939, 1: 122-5, fig.

GILS, J.B.F. van. Emblemata met geneeskundige voorstelling. [Emblems with medical significance. (In Dutch)] *Bijdr. Gesch.Geneesk.*, 1921, 1: 75-84, 8 fig.

GUIART, Jules. Le macabre dans l'art. 1. L'art antique; le Triomphe de la Mort du Campo Santo; la Peste Noire au XIVe siècle ... Danse macabres. 2. XVIe siècle. 3. XVIIe et XVIIIe siècles. 4. XIXe siècle. *Aesculape*, 1912, 2: 265-70; 1913, 3: 16-20, 71-4, 105-8, ill.

HOLLÄNDER, Eugen. Die Karikatur und Satire in der Medizin. Mediko-kunsthistorische Studie. 2nd ed. xvi, 404 p., ill. Stuttgart: Enke, 1921.
First publ. 1905.
Reviewed by George Sarton, *Isis*, 1922, 4: 370-1.

HOLLÄNDER, Eugen. Die Medizin in der klassischen Malerei. 4th ed. 488 p., 307 fig. Stuttgart: Enke, 1950.
First publ. 1903; 2nd ed. 1913.
Reviewed by Frans Jonckheere, *Arch.Int.Hist.Sci.*, 1951, 4: 1074-9.

HOLLÄNDER, Eugen. Plastik und Medizin. viii, 576 p., ill. Stuttgart: Enke, 1912.

KELLNER, -. (Medizinalrat Dr.). Geschichte der Medizin, Arzt, Pharmazeutische Industrie. *Janus*, 1937, 41: 29-32.
On art in medicine with particular reference to periodical publications by pharmaceutical firms.

KNIPPING, Hugo Wilhelm; KENTER, H. Heilkunst und Kunstwerk. Probleme zwischen Kunst und Medizin aus ärztlicher Sicht. 152 p., ill. Stuttgart: Friedrich-Karl Schattauer, 1961.
Reviewed by R. Herrlinger, *Sudhoffs Arch.*, 1963, 47: 86.

MEDICINE and art. *Isis*, 1936, 25: 459.
Concerning a show of water color sketches and photographic montages portraying modern activities in medicine at the University of California Medical School.

NIXON, J.A. The debt of medicine to the Fine Arts. The presidential address delivered on October 11, 1922, at the opening of the fiftieth session of the British Medico-Chirurgical Society. 29 p. Bristol: Arrowsmith, 1923.

REGNAULT, Félix. Les ex-voto de Provence et du Piémont. Peintures représentant des scènes médicales. *Bull.Soc. Franç.Hist.Méd.*, 1913, 12: 277-85.

RIJNBERK, G. van. De geneesheer en de geneeskunst in nederlandsche prentverbeeldingen. [The doctor and medicine in Dutch pictorial representation. (In Dutch)] *Bijdr.Gesch. Geneesk.*, 1921, 1: 32-47, 14 fig., 165-75, 9 fig.; 1922, 2: 1-12, 169-73; 1923, 3: 1-8, 8 fig.; 1929, 9: 73-83, 10 fig.

SARTON, George. The history of medicine versus the history of art. (The Fielding H. Garrison Lecture) *Bull.Hist. Med.*, 1941, 10: 123-35, 1 portr. [CB 62/86]
Partially reprinted in *Alumni*, 1950, 19: 332-41.

SIGERIST, Henry E. The historical aspect of art and medicine. *Bull.Inst.Hist.Med.*, 1936, 4: 271-97, 27 fig.

VALLERY-RADOT, Pierre. Les médecins et la statuaire. *Presse Méd.*, 1953, 61: 398, 2 fig.

WARTHIN, Alfred Scott. The physician of the dance of death. A historical study of the evolution of the dance of death mythus in art. xvi, 142 p., front., 92 fig. New York: Hoeber, 1931.
Reprinting, with additions and corrections, of articles in *Ann.Med.Hist.*, 1930, 2: 351-71, 453-69, 697-710; 1931, 3: 75-109, 134-65, ill.
Reviewed by Charles A. Kofoid, *Isis*, 1932, 17: 282-3.

WEBER, Frederick Parkes. Aspects of death and correlated aspects of life in art, epigram and poetry. Contributions towards an anthology and an iconography of the subject. Illustrated especially by medals, engraved gems, jewels, ivories, antique pottery, etc. 3rd rev. enl. ed. xi, 784 p., 145 ill. London: Fisher Unwin, 1918. [CB 13/296]
First edition 1910 was corrected and enlarged reprint of articles published in the *Numismatic Chronicle*, 1909-1910. 4th ed. xliv, 851 p. London: 1922.

ZEKERT, Otto. Kunst in Medizin und Pharmazie. 96 p., 40 pl. (HMW-Jahrbuch 1956) Wien: Heilmittelwerke Wien, 1955.
Reviewed by Martin Lundqvist, *Lychnos*, 1956, 437-9.

Ntq-bw

AMSTERDAM. STEDELIJK MUSEUM. Catalogue d'une collection d'art médico-historique. Tableaux, portraits, dessins, manuscrits, livres rares et précieux, sculptures, médailles. Exposée, à l'occasion du VIe Congrès international d'histoire de la médecine au Musée Municipal d'Amsterdam. 21 Juillet-1 Août 1927. 123 p., ill. Amsterdam: 1927. [CB 23/267]

Ntt relation with music

see also Nm cultural activities of medical men
RKtt occupational and psychotherapy

BERENDES, Julius. Musik und Medizin. *Ciba-Z.*, 1961, 9: 3314-43.
This includes Magische Musik and Kathartische Musik.

LICHT, Sidney. Music in medicine. With a foreword by Alexandre Tansman. 132 p. Boston: New England Conservatory of Music, 1946.
Reviewed by Willard Lee Marmelzat, *Bull.Hist.Med.*, 1947, 21: 411-13.

SCHULLIAN, Dorothy M.; SCHOEN, Max; ed. Music and medicine. x, 499 p., 18 ill. New York: Schuman, 1948.
Reviewed by Charles D. O'Malley, *Isis*, 1949, 40: 299; by Sidney Licht, *Bull.Hist.Med.*, 1948, 22: 340-2.

UNDERWOOD, E. Ashworth. Apollo and Terpsichore: music and the healing art (with special reference to B.M. Berenclow, F.N. Marquet and F.K. Harford). *Bull.Hist.Med.*, 1947, 21: 639-73, 8 fig., portr.

Nu popular aspects; folk medicine

see also Ru popular therapeutics
RMu popular materia medica
for the folk medicine of different countries
see INDEX

ALONSO, Aurelia E. La magia en la historia de la medicina. *Rev.Argent.Hist.Med.*, 1943, 2: no. 2, 27-35.

ANDEL, M.A. van. De heks en de volksgeneeskunst. [The witch and popular medicine. (In Dutch)] *Bijdr.Gesch.Geneesk.*, 1934, 14: 123-44.

BOUTEILLER, Marcelle. Chamanisme et guérison magique. 377 p. (Bibliothèque de Philosophie Contemporaine. Psychologie et Sociologie) Paris: Presses Universitaires de France, 1950.
Reviewed by J. Filliozat, *J.Asiatique*, 1951, 239: 90.

BURGER, H. The doctor, the quack, and the appetite of the public for magic in medicine. *Proc.Roy.Soc.Med.*, 1933-34, 27: 5-10. [CB 43/288]

COHEN, M.H. Over enkele volksgeneeskundige gebruiken. [On some customs in popular medicine. (In Dutch)] *Bijdr.Gesch. Geneesk.*, 1921, 1: 427-37.

CORIAT, Isador H. Medical magic. *Ann.Med.Hist.*, 1922, 4: 291-301.

DEETJEN, Christian. Witchcraft and medicine. *Bull.Inst. Hist.Med.*, 1934, 2: 164-75, 1 ill.

DELAUNAY, Paul. La médecine populaire, ses origines magiques, religieuses, dogmatiques et empiriques. 79 p., ill. Tours: La Médecine Internationale Illustrée, 1930.
Reviewed by Marcel Fosseyeux, *Bull.Soc.Franç.Hist.Méd.*, 1931, 25: 617.

DIEPGEN, Paul. Volksheilkunde und wissenschaftliche Medizin. In: Die Volkskunde und ihre Beziehungen zu Recht-Medizin-Vorgeschichte, p. 26-40. Berlin: Herbert Stubenrauch, 1928.

DIEPGEN, Paul. Volksmedizin und wissenschaftliche Heilkunde. *Scientia*, 1958, 93: 129-35; French transl. suppl., 66-71.

DIEPGEN, Paul. Volksmedizin und wissenschaftliche Heilkunde. Ihre geschichtlichen Beziehungen. Vortrag gehalten am 7.2. 1936 in der Berliner Gesellschaft für Geschichte der Naturwissenschaft, Medizin und Technik. In: Adam, Curt, ed. Die natürliche Heilweise im Rahmen der Gesamtmedizin, p. 8-25. Jena: 1938.

DIEPGEN, Paul. Volksmedizin und wissenschaftliche Heilkunde in Vergangenheit und Zukunft. Öffentlicher Vortrag auf dem 49. Deutschen Ärztetag in Kolberg am 26. Juni 1930. *Deut. Ärztebl.*, 1930, 57: no. 25, 38-44.

FOSSEL, Victor. Schulmedizin und Volksmedizin. *Arch.Gesch. Naturwiss.Tech.*, 1913, 6: 102-12.

GARÇON, Maurice; VINCHON, Jean. The devil: an historical, critical and medical study. Transl. by Stephen Haden Guest from the 6th French ed. 288 p. London: Gollancz, 1929.
Translation of Le diable. Paris: Nouvelle Revue Française, 1926.

GORDON, Benjamin L. Demonology and the eye. *Hebrew Med.J.*, 1964, 2: 219-39.

HANSEMANN, David Paul von. Der Aberglaube in der Medizin und seine Gefahr für Gesundheit und Leben. 2nd ed. 116 p. (Aus Natur und Geisteswelt) Leipzig: Teubner, 1914.
First publ. 1905.

HANSEN, H.P. Primitiv Folkemedicin. [Primitive popular medicine. (In Danish)] 32 p. Copenhagen: Munksgaard, 1945.

HERMANT, Paul; BOOMANS, Denis. La médecine populaire. xv, 240 p., ill. (Bulletin du Service de Recherches Historiques et Folkloriques du Brabant, 43-45) Bruxelles: Éditions du Folklore Brabançon, 1928. [CB 27/566]
Reviewed by A. Van Gennep, *Merc.France*, 15 June 1933, 679; reply to this review by A. Marinus, *Folklore Brabançon*, 1934, 13: 431-7.

HÖFLER, M. Die Verhüllung. Ein volksmedizinischer Heilritus. *Janus*, 1913, 18: 104-8, 4 fig.

HOVORKA, Oskar von. Geist der Medizin. Analytische Studien über die Grundideen der Vormedizin, Urmedizin, Volksmedizin, Zaubermedizin, Berufsmedizin. viii, 364 p. Wien: Braumüller, 1915. [CB 10/202]

HUMPHREYS, Humphrey. Magic and medicine. *Antiquity*, 1953, 27: 144-8.

JOHNSSON, John William Schibbye. Folkemedicinske undersögelser. [Researches in folk medicine. (In Danish)] *Danske Stud.*, 1921, 1-20, 1 pl. [CB 11/446]

KANNER, Leo. Medical folklore. *Med.Life*, 1931, 38: 523-7.

KANNER, Leo. Mistletoe, magic and medicine. *Bull.Hist.Med.*, 1939, 7: 875-936, 6 fig.

LAIGNEL-LAVASTINE, Maxime. Introduction à l'étude du folklore médical. *Bull.Soc.Franç.Hist.Méd.*, 1935, 29: 350-9.

LÖHR, Hanns. Aberglauben und Medizin. iv, 106 p. Leipzig: Barth, 1940.
Reviewed by O.T. Hult, *Lychnos*, 1941, 407-8.

McDANIEL, W.B. The moon, werewolves, and medicine. *Trans. Coll.Physicians Phila.*, 1950, 18: 113-22.

McKENZIE, Dan. The infancy of medicine: an enquiry into the influence of folk-lore upon the evolution of scientific medicine. xiv, 421 p. London: Macmillan, 1927.

MARINUS, Albert. A propos de "La médecine populaire" [par Paul Hermant et Denis Boomans, 1928]. *Folklore Brabançon*, 1934, 13: 431-7.
Reply to review of the book by A. Van Gennep, *Merc.France*, 15 June 1933, 679.

MATTHÄUS, Kurt. Alte Volksheilkunst in neuem Lichte. Eine wissenschaftliche Darstellung des volkstümlichen Heilwissens unter Zurückführung auf die zugrunde liegenden Naturgesetze. With the collaboration of Erich Zöbisch. 191 p., 84 fig., 10 pl. Dresden: Eulex, 1931.

PENNING, C.P.J. Iets over vampyrs. [Something about vampires. (In Dutch)] *Bijdr.Gesch.Geneesk.*, 1932, 12: 149-53.

PICCA, P. Il carattere sacerdotale delle origini della medicina. *Riv.Osped.*, 1913, 78-81.

PRECOPE, John. Medicine, magic and mythology. vi, 284, 2 p. London: Heinemann, 1954.
Reviewed by Dorothy M. Schullian, *Sudhoffs Arch.*, 1955, 39: 284-5.

RAILLIET, G. Médecine populaire (Glanes d'un practicien rémois). *Bull.Soc.Franç.Hist.Méd.*, 1936, 31: 98-116, 161-76.

SCARPA, Antonio. Nozioni di etnoiatrica. Storia, attualità, interpretazione e trasformazioni della medicina tradizionale dei popoli. viii, 313 p., 100 pl. Milan: Aldo Martello, 1962.
Reviewed by P. Huard, *Arch.Int.Hist.Sci.*, 1964, 17: 196-8.

SCHEVENSTEEN, A.F.C. van. Geneeskunde en folklore. [Medicine and folklore. (In Dutch)] *Oostvlaam.Zanten*, 1938, 13: 25-32.

SCHLAUCH, Margaret. The art of healing in folk-lore. *Med. Life*, 1930, 37: 295-302.

STEMPLINGER, Eduard. Antike und moderne Volksmedizin. 120 p. (Das Erbe der Alten. *2nd ser.*, 10) Leipzig: Dieterich, 1925.

STEMPLINGER, Eduard. Die Transplantation in der antiken Medizin. Ein Beitrag zur vergleichenden Volksmedizin. *Arch. Gesch.Med.*, 1920, 12: 33-49.

THORNDIKE, Lynn. Magic and medicine. *Med.Life,* 1929, 36: 148-55.
Presidential address delivered before the History of Science Society, at the New York meeting, Dec. 28, 1928.

Nu-bv

HOEFLER, Max. Die volksmedizinische Literatur der Jahre 1909-1912. *Arch.Religionswiss.,* 1913, 16: no. 3-4, 598-620.

Nu-f/t special aspects

Nu-hd

HEISCHKEL, Edith. Medizingeschichtschreibung und Volksmedizin. *Sudhoffs Arch.,* 1941, 34: 125-8.

WEHRLI, G.A. Das Wesen der Volksmedizin und die Notwendigkeit einer geschichtlichen Betrachtungsweise derselben. *Essays on the History of Medicine presented to Karl Sudhoff,* p. 369-88. London/Zurich: Oxford University Press, 1924.

Nu-j

TREBITSCH, Rudolf. Versuch einer Psychologie der Volksmedizin und des Aberglaubens. Eine ethnologische Studie. *Mitt.Anthropol.Ges.Wien,* 1913, 53: 169-209.

Nu-mzDY

ALLENDY, R. L'alchimie et la médecine. Etude sur les théories hermétiques dans l'histoire de la médecine. 157 p. (Thesis) Paris: Charcornac, 1912.

BERNUS, Alexander von. Alchimie et médecine. [Introduction and short bibliography by Prof. H. Hunwald and an appendix by Dr. R.A.B. Oosterhuis.] 191 p. Paris: Editions Dangles, 1960.
Reviewed by H.J.S., *Ambix,* 1960, 8: 118.

Nu-mzFY

MERCIER, Charles Arthur. Astrology in medicine. The Fitzpatrick lectures delivered before the Royal College of Physicians ... 1913. With addendum on saints and signs. 100 p. London: Macmillan, 1914.

RICHTER, Erwin. Einwirkung medicoastrologischen Volksdenkens auf Entstehung und Formung des Bärmutterkrötenopfers der Männer im geistlichen Heilbrauch. *Sudhoffs Arch.,* 1958, 42: 326-49.

WICKERSHEIMER, Ernest. La médecine astrologique dans les almanachs populaires du XXe siècle. *Paris Méd.,* 1912, partie paramédicale, p. 371-7. Also in *Bull.Soc.Franç.Hist.Méd.,* 1911, 10: 26-39.

Nu-r

GLEICHEN-RUSSWURM, Alexander. Der Wunderdoktor. Von der Heilsehnsucht der Jahrhunderte. 362 p., pl., portr. Augsburg: Haas, 1937.
Reviewed by M.F. van Andel, *Bijdr.Gesch.Geneesk.,* 1939, 19: 54.

HUNNIUS, Curt. Dämonen, Ärzte, Alchemisten. 347 p., ill. Stuttgart: Wissenschaftliche Verlagsgesellschaft, 1962.
Reviewed by H. Schadewaldt, *Naturwiss.Rundsch.,* 1962, 15: 487; by R. Niederhuemer, *Bl.Technikgesch.,* 1964, 26: 150.

JONES, Louis C. Practitioners of folk medicine. *Bull.Hist. Med.,* 1949, 23: 480-93.

MADDOX, John Lee. The medicine man. A sociological study of the character and evolution of Shamanism. With a foreword by A.G. Keller. xvi, 330 p., 4 pl. New York: Macmillan, 1923. [CB 14/546]

Nu-th

ANDEL, M.A. van. Folkmedical themes in myths, legends and folktales. *VIe Congr.Int.Hist.Méd.* (Leyde-Amsterdam, 1927), p. 19-23. Anvers: De Vlijt, 1929.

ANDEL, M.A. van. Volksgeneeskundige motieven in sprookjes, sagen en legenden. [Folk medical themes in fairy tales, sagas and legends. (In Dutch)] *Bijdr.Gesch.Geneesk.,* 1929, 9: 113-24.

PROVERBIAL medicine. Prognosis in proverbs and folklore. Proverbs of diet. Proverbs regarding alcohol. *Brit.Med.J.,* 1913, (1), 178-80, 291-3, 398-400.

Nu-tq

ROSENTHAL, Oskar. Wunderheilungen und ärztliche Schutzpatrone in der bildenden Kunst. 42 p., 102 pl. Leipzig: Vogel, 1925.

Nud

ARTELT, Walter. Kosmas und Damian, die Schutzpatrone der Aerzte und Apotheker. Eine Bildfolge. 28 p., fig., pl. Darmstadt: E. Merck, 1952.
Reviewed by Frans Jonckheere, *Arch.Int.Hist.Sci.,* 1952, 5: (31), 428-9.

AVALON, Jean. Sainte Gertrude de Nivelles, invoquée contre les souris et contre la maladie. *Aesculape,* 1931, 21: 169-75, 7 fig.

BACKMAN, E. Louis. Religious dances in the Christian Church and in popular medicine. Translated by E. Classem. xii, 364 p., 133 fig. London: Allen & Unwin, 1952.
Reviewed by Ernest Wickersheimer, *Arch.Int.Hist.Sci.,* 1955, 8: 85-7.
Originally publ. as: Den religiösa dansen inom kristen kyrka och folk-medicin. Stockholm: Norstedt, 1945.

FRANCESCO, Grete de. Saints in medicine. *Ciba Symp.* (Summit, N.J.), 1939, 1: 103-17, fig.

LOOMIS, C. Grant. Hagiological healing. *Bull.Hist.Med.,* 1940, 8: 636-42.

SAYE, Hymen. Holy wafers in medicine. *Bull.Inst.Hist.Med.,* 1935, 3: 165-7.

SCHEVENSTEEN, A.F.C. van. Contribution à l'iconographie des "Egerlander amuletten". Étude de folklore religieux. *Ve Congr.Int.Hist.Méd.* (Genève, 1925), p. 136-47. Genève: Albert Kundig, 1926.

Nv ethnic groups

Nvm Jews

for Jews in different countries *see* INDEX

BARUK, Henri; SIMON, I. Aspects de la médecine hébraique. *Rev.Pensée Juive,* 1951, no. 7, 1-32.

FRIEDENWALD, Harry. Apologetic works of Jewish physicians. *Jew.Quart.Rev.,* 1942, 32: 407-26.
Reprinted in the author's The Jews and medicine, (2), p. 31-68. Baltimore: Johns Hopkins University Press, 1944.

FRIEDENWALD, Harry. Jewish luminaries in medical history and a Catalogue of works bearing on the subject of the Jews and medicine from the private library of Harry Friedenwald. viii, 199 p., pl. Baltimore, Md.: Johns Hopkins Press, 1946. [CB 70/239]

FRIEDENWALD, Harry. The Jews and medicine. Essays. 2 vol. xxiv, 817 p. Baltimore: Johns Hopkins University Press, 1944.
Reviewed by Solomon Gandz, *Isis,* 1944, 35: 346-7.

GORDON, Benjamin L. Curiosities of Jewish medicine. *Bull. Hist.Med.,* 1946, 20: 196-200.

KRAUSS, Samuel. Geschichte der jüdischen Ärzte vom frühesten Mittelalter bis zur Gleichberechtigung. Preisgekrönte Arbeit, durchgesehen von Isidor Fischer. xvi, 180 p. (Veröffentlichungen der A.S. Bettelheim-Stiftung in Wien, 4) Vienna: Perles, 1930. [CB 38/585]
Reviewed by F.M.G. de Feyfer, *Bijdr.Gesch.Geneesk.,* 1931, 11: 278.

MERZBACH, Arnold. Jewish physicians in Central Europe during the transitional period from the ghetto to the Emancipation. *Act.VIe Congr.Int.Hist.Sci.* (Amsterdam, 1950), p. 707-12. Paris: Hermann, 1951-53; also in *Arch.Int.Hist.Sci.,* 1954, 7: 168-73.

NEUBURGER, Max. Die Stellung der jüdischen Aerzte in der Geschichte der medizinischen Wissenschaften. *Mitt.Ver.Jüdischer Aerzte*, 1936, no. 28, 3-32.
English translation: Jewish physicians in history of medicine, *Med.Leaves*, 1943, 5: 56-75.

SAVITZ, Harry Austryn. The role of the Jewish physician in the progress of his people. *Ann.Med.Hist.*, 1938, 10: 107-16.

Nvm-br

Medical Leaves: a review of the Jewish medical world and medical history. Vol. 1-5. Chicago: 1937-43.
Vol. 4 reviewed in *Ann.Med.Hist.*, 1942, 4: 339.

Nvm-bv

Revue d'Histoire de la Médecine Hébraique. Index analytique des Revues no. 43 à 49 inclus [mars 1959-décembre 1960]. *Rev.Hist.Méd.Hébraique*, 1960, 13: no. 50, 169-77.

Revue d'Histoire de la Médecine Hébraique. Sommaires, des nos. 1 à 49 (juin 1948 à décembre 1960). *Rev.Hist.Méd.Hébraique*, 1960, no. 50, 179-96.

Nvm-cj

SIMON, I. Le 35e anniversaire de la parution de la revue *Harofe Haivri*, Hebrew Medical Journal de New York. *Rev.Hist.Med.Hébraique*, 1962, no. 57, 131-9.

Nvm-da

KAGAN, Solomon R. Jewish medicine. 575 p., ill. Boston: Medico-Historical Press, 1952.
A biographical dictionary of Jewish medical men from the middle ages to the present.
Reviewed by Walter Pagel, *Bull.Hist.Med.*, 1953, 27: 288-90.

MARGALITH, D. [Physicians among "Hovevei Zion" and Zionist movements (to the 80th anniversary of the movements.) (In Hebrew, with English summary)] *Koroth*, 1963, 2: 127-44.
Biographical sketches.

Nvm-nh

RABINOWITZ, Solomon. [Comments on Hebrew medical terminology. (In Hebrew)] *Hebrew Med.J.*, 1937, 2: 129-44.

Nvm-nq

MUNTNER, Sussman. [The history of the Hebrew tongue as the language of medical learning. (In Hebrew)] *Leshonenu*, 1939, 10: 300-17. [CB 60/134]

Nvm-or

SHATZKY, Jacob. On Jewish medical students of Padua. *J.Hist.Med.*, 1950, 5: 444-7.

Nvm-rj

FISCHER, Isidor. On the ethics of the Jewish physician. *Med.Life*, 1933, 40: 403-10.

Nvm-td

SILBERSTEIN, Werner. La médecine et la Halakha. *Rev.Hist.Méd.Hébraique*, 1963, 16: 73-80.

Nvm-u

AMITIN-SHAPIRO, Z.A. [The popular medicine of the native ("Bokharean") Jews in Turkestan. (In Russian, with English summary)] *Biul.Sredne-aziat.Gos.Univ.*, 1926, no. 13, 1-17.

GLESINGER, Lavoslav. Le chien dans la médecine et dans la superstition médicale juives. *Rev.Hist.Méd.Hébraique*, 1956, 9: 235-44.

ZIMMELS, H.J. Magicians, theologians and doctors. Studies in folk-medicine and folklore as reflected in the rabbinical responsa (12th-19th centuries). viii, 293 p. London: E. Goldston, 1952.
Reviewed by Walter Pagel, *Arch.Int.Hist.Sci.*, 1953, 32: 524-5; by Samuel Rosenblatt, *Bull.Hist.Med.*, 1954, 28: 579-80.

Nw in different countries

Nwa North and South America

GUERRA, Francisco. Medical colonization of the New World. *Med.Hist.*, 1963, 7: 147-54.

VASCONCELLOS, Ivolino de. Asclepio e o pan-americanismo. *Rev.Brasil.Hist.Med.*, 1957, 8: 203-15, 1 fig.

Nwb North America

ABBOTT, Maude E. History of medicine in the province of Quebec. 97 p., 41 ill. Montreal: McGill University, 1931.

ACKERKNECHT, Erwin H. Wisconsin medicine in retrospect. *J.Lancet*, 1950, 70: 46-8.

AMERICAN FOUNDATION. Medical research: a midcentury survey. 2 vol. 1. American medical research: in principle and practice. xxxii, 765 p.; 2. Unsolved clinical problems: in biological perspective. xxxii, 740 p. Boston/Toronto: Little, Brown and Co., 1955.
Reviewed by Chauncey D. Leake, *Bull.Hist.Med.*, 1957, 31: 95-6.

BIRKETT, Herbert S. A short account of the history of medicine in Lower Canada. *Ann.Med.Hist.*, 1939, 1: 315-24.

BONNER, Thomas N. German doctors in America - 1887-1914. Their views and impressions of American life and medicine. *J.Hist.Med.*, 1959, 14: 1-17.

BONNER, Thomas N. The Kansas doctor. A century of pioneering. 334 p., ill., bibliogr. Lawrence, Kan.: University of Kansas Press, 1959.
Reviewed by Edward H. Hashinger, *J.Hist.Med.*, 1960, 15: 103-5.

BURN, C.B. Medical history of Michigan. 2 vol. xx, 829 p., 40 ill.; xi, 940 p., 23 ill. Minneapolis: Bruce, 1930. [CB 33/408]
Reviewed by Francis R. Packard, *Ann.Med.Hist.*, 1930, 2: 714-15.

CHARLTON, M. Outlines of the history of medicine in Lower Canada. *Ann.Med.Hist.*, 1923, 5: 150-74, 263-78; 1924, 6: 222-35, 312-54.

COWEN, David L. Medicine and health in New Jersey: a history. xv, 227 p., 12 fig. (New Jersey Historical Series, 16) Princeton/New York/Toronto/London: Van Nostrand, 1964.

DILLER, Theodore. Pioneer medicine in Western Pennsylvania. xiv, 230 p., ill. New York: Paul B. Hoeber, 1927. [CB 23/266]
Appeared originally, *Ann.Med.Hist.*

DITTRICK, Howard. Important discoveries by Cleveland physicians. *Festschrift zum 80. Geburtstag Max Neuburgers*, p. 97-103. Wien: Maudrich, 1948.

DUFFY, John, ed. The Rudolph Matas history of medicine in Louisiana. 2 vol. xvi, 522 p.; xiv, 599 p., ill., bibliogr. Baton Rouge, La.: Louisiana State University Press (for the Rudolph Matas Trust Fund), 1958, 1962.
Reviewed by Richard H. Shryock, *Amer.Hist.Rev.*, 1960, 65: 986.
For reviews of vol. 1 see CB 85/398 and CB 86/469; of vol. 2, CB 88/633 and CB 89/572.

ECKMAN, James; BIGELOW, Charles E. History of medicine in Dodge County. *Minn.Med.*, 1943, 26: 194-5, 290-4, 373-9, 447-52, 548-55, 629-34, 718-23, 805-10, 900-5, 992-6, 1067-75; 1944, 27: 37-41, 130-8, 204-8, 291-9.
Elaborate study of medicine in Dodge County in SE Minnesota, with a number of biographical sketches and 395 references.

FISHBEIN, Morris. A century of American medicine. *Bull.Med.Libr.Ass.*, 1947, 35: 146-57.

FLEXNER, Simon. A half century of American medicine. *Science*, 1937, 85: 505-12.

FLEXNER, Simon; FLEXNER, James Thomas. William Henry Welch and the heroic age of American medicine. x, 539 p., 26 ill. New York: Viking Press, 1941.
Reviewed by J.B. de C.M. Saunders, *Isis*, 1943, 34: 381-2.

HARRIS, Henry. California's medical story. With an introduction by Charles Singer. xx, 421 p., 28 ill. San Francisco: Stacey, 1932.
Reviewed by C.D. Leake, *Isis*, 1934, 22: 312-15; in *Ann. Med.Hist.*, 1932, 4: 594.

HEAGERTY, John J. Four centuries of medical history in Canada, and a sketch of the medical history of Newfoundland. Preface by A.S. Doughty. 2 vol. Chicago: University of Chicago Press, 1928.
Reviewed by Francis R. Packard, *Ann.Med.Hist.*, 1929, 1: 486-8.

HEATON, Claude E. Three hundred years of medicine in New York City. (The Fielding H. Garrison Lecture.) *Bull. Hist.Med.*, 1958, 32: 517-30.

HOWELL, William Boyman. Medicine in Canada. xiv, 138 p., ill. (Clio Medica) New York: Hoeber, 1933. [CB 39/468]

ILLINOIS STATE MEDICAL SOCIETY. History of medical practice in Illinois. Issued in commemoration of [the Society's] diamond jubilee. 2 vol. 1. Preceding 1850, compiled and arranged by L.H. Zeuch; 2. 1850-1900, arranged and ed. by J. Davis. Chicago: Book Press, 1927.

LARSELL, O. The doctor in Oregon. A medical history. xvi, 671 p., ill. Portland, Or.: Binfords and Mort (for the Oregon Historical Society), 1947.

LARSELL, O. An outline of the history of medicine in the Pacific Northwest. *Northwest Med.*, 1932, 31: 390-6, 437-43, 483-9, 10 fig.

McNEIL, Donald R. Collecting Wisconsin's medical history. *Bull.Hist.Med.*, 1954, 28: 333-40.

MARTÍ-IBÁÑEZ, Félix, ed. History of American medicine. A symposium. viii, 181 p. (MD International Symposia, 5) New York: MD Publications, 1959.
Reviewed by H. Degen, *Naturwiss.Rundsch.*, 1960, 13: 285; by Ernest Wickersheimer, *Rev.Hist.Sci.*, 1960, 13: 169-70; by G. Liljestrand, *Lychnos*, 1960-61, 412-13.

MEARS, J. Ewing. The triumphs of American medicine in the construction of the Panama canal. 25 p. Philadelphia: Wm. J. Dornan, 1912.

MERRITT, Webster. A century of medicine in Jacksonville and Duval County. xii, 201 p., ill. Gainsville: University of Florida Press, 1949.

MOORMAN, Lewis Jefferson. Pioneer doctor. With a foreword by Henry A. Christian. xvii, 252 p., ill. Norman, Okla.: University of Oklahoma Press, 1951.
Reviewed by O. Larsell, *J.Hist.Med.*, 1952, 7: 314-15; by Howard Dittrick, *Bull.Hist.Med.*, 1953, 27: 195-6.

MOORMAN, Lewis Jefferson. Pioneer medicine in the Southwest. *Bull.Hist.Med.*, 1947, 21: 795-810.

NIXON, Patrick Ireland. The medical history of early Texas, 1528-1853. With a foreword by Chauncey D. Leake. xv, 507 p., 28 ill. Lancaster, Pa.: Mollie Bennett Lupe Memorial Fund, 1946.
Reviewed by J. B. deC. M. Saunders, *Isis*, 1948, 38: 270.

PACKARD, Francis Randolph. History of medicine in the United States. New edition. 2 vol. xxv, 1323 p., 103 ill. New York: Hoeber, 1931.
Reprinted New York: Hafner, 1963 (with new introduction by John B. Blake).
Reviewed by C.D. Leake, *Isis*, 1933, 19: 245-7; by F.H. Garrison, *Ann.Med.Hist.*, 1932, 4: 104-5.

RICHARDSON, Edward Henderson. A doctor remembers. 252 p. New York: Vantage Press, 1959.
Reviewed by C.E. Heaton, *Bull.Hist.Med.*, 1961, 35: 484-5.

ROEMER, Milton I. Historic development of the current crisis of rural medicine in the United States. *Victor Robinson Memorial Volume*, p. 333-42. New York: Froben, 1948.

SEABORN, Edwin. The march of medicine in Western Ontario. xviii, 386 p., 113 ill. Toronto: Ryerson Press, 1944. [CB 69/238]

SEWARD, Blanton P. Pioneer medicine in Virginia. *Ann.Med. Hist.*, 1938, 10: 61-70, 169-87, 2 fig.

SHRYOCK, Richard H. American medical research, past and present. xiv, 350 p. New York: Commonwealth Fund, 1947.
Reviewed by John B. deC. M. Saunders, *Isis*, 1948, 39: 201-2; by George W. Gray, *Amer.Hist.Rev.*, 1948, 53: 849.

SHRYOCK, Richard H. Changing outlooks in American medicine over three centuries. *Sudhoffs Arch.*, 1953, 37: 377-8.

SHUMAN, John W. Southern California medicine. *Ann.Med.Hist.*, 1938, 10: 215-36, 8 fig.; 336-55, 1 fig.

SIGERIST, Henry E. American medicine. Translated by Hildegard Wagel. ix, 316 p., 30 ill. New York: Norton, 1934.
Translation of Amerika und die Medizin (Leipzig: Thieme, 1933) [CB 40/415]
Reviewed by John B. de C.M. Saunders, *Isis*, 1938, 29: 200-3.

SIGERIST, Henry E. The development of medicine and its trends in the United States, 1636-1936. *New Engl.J.Med.*, 1938, 218: 325-8.

SIGERIST, Henry E. Richtungen und Strömungen in der Medizin der Vereinigten Staaten. *Schweiz.Med.Jahrb.*, 1935, xci-xcvii.

SPECTOR, Benjamin. One hour of medical history. Vol. 5. xiv, 155 p., 20 ill. Boston: Tufts College Medical School, 1936.
This volume is devoted entirely to American medicine.

STERN, Bernhard J. American medical practice in the perspectives of a century. xi, 156 p. (Studies of the New York Academy of Medicine, Committee on Medicine and the Changing Order) New York: Commonwealth Fund, 1945. [CB 74/398]
Reviewed by Helen Clapesattle, *Amer.Hist.Rev.*, 1945, 51: 163.

TROUT, Hugh H. The "Scotch-Irish" of the Valley of Virginia and their influence on the medical progress in America. *Ann.Med.Hist.*, 1938, 10: 71-82, 162-8, ill.

TYLER, Albert Franklin, ed. History of medicine in Nebraska. Ella F. Auerbach, compiler. 662 p. Omaha: Magic City Printing Co., 1928.
Reviewed in *Ann.Med.Hist.*, 1931, 3: 357.

UHL, F. Amerikanische Medizin von Europäern beurteilt. 59 p. Horn, Niederösterreich: Ferdinand Berger, 1959.
Reviewed by C.E. Rosenberg, *Bull.Hist.Med.*, 1961, 35: 187-8.

VIETS, Henry R. A brief history of medicine in Massachusetts. xiv, 194 p., 8 pl. Boston: Houghton Mifflin, 1930.
Reviewed by Charles A. Kofoid, *Isis*, 1931, 15: 388-91.

WALSH, James Joseph. History of medicine in New York. Three centuries of medical progress. 5 vol., ill. New York: National Americana Society, 1919.
Volumes 4 and 5 are biographical.

WARTHEN, Harry J. Medicine and Shockoe Hill. *Ann.Med.Hist.*, 1938, 10: 83-90, 5 fig.

Nwb-ap

KHAIRALLAH, Amin A. A century of American medicine in Syria. *Ann.Med.Hist.*, *3rd ser.*, 1939, 1: 460-70, 5 fig.

Nwb-bv

BIBLIOGRAPHY of the history of medicine of the United States and Canada, 1961, 62, 63, ed. by Genevieve Miller; 1964, ed. by J.B. Koudelka. *Bull.Hist.Med.*, 1962, 36: 535-70; 1963, 37: 532-67; 1964, 38: 538-77; 1965, 39: 542-79.
In progress. For cumulation of the earlier bibliographies *see* below: Miller, Genevieve, ed.

GILBERT, Judson B. A bibliography of articles on the history of American medicine compiled from "Writings on American History" 1902-1937. viii, 44 p. (History of Medicine Series) New York: New York Academy of Medicine, 1951.
Reviewed by George Rosen, *J.Hist.Med.*, 1952, 7: 436; by Whitfield J. Bell, *Bull.Hist.Med.*, 1953, 27: 401.

MILLER, Genevieve, ed. Bibliography of the history of medicine of the United States and Canada, 1939-1960. xv, 428 p., index. Baltimore: Johns Hopkins Press, 1964.
Cumulation of the bibliographies up to 1960 which have appeared in *Bull.Hist.Med.* from vol. 8, 1940. For continuation, *see* above: Bibliography of the history of medicine of the United States and Canada.

Nwb-ce

AUSTIN, Robert B. Early American medical imprints. A guide to works printed in the United States, 1668-1820. x, 240 p. Washington, D.C.: U.S. Department of Health, Education and Welfare, 1961.
Reviewed by Genevieve Miller, *Isis*, 1963, 54: 497; by Francisco Guerra, *Med.Hist.*, 1963, 7: 281; by David A. Kronick, *Bull.Hist.Med.*, 1963, 37: 290-2.

GEISER, Samuel W. Some early medical writings on Texas, of interest to historians. *Southwest.Hist.Quart.*, 1945, 49: 145-8.

Nwb-ce-bx

NEW YORK ACADEMY OF MEDICINE. Catalogue of an exhibition of early and later medical Americana. Held for one month ... Nov. 18, 1926. [64] p. incl. pl., facs. [New York City: Press of Charles C. Marchand Co., 1927]

Nwb-cj

ECKMAN, James. Alexander J. Stone, M.D., LL.D. Founder of Minnesota's first medical journal. *Ann.Med.Hist.*, 1941, 3: 306-25, 4 fig.

ECKMAN, James. Minnesota's oldest medical journal. *J.Lancet*, 1940, 60: 60-8.

KRUMBHAAR, Edward B. The early days of the *American Journal of the Medical Sciences*. *Med.Life*, 1929, 36: 240-56, 7 pl.

PIZER, Irwin H. Medical journals in St. Louis before 1900. *Bull.Missouri Hist.Soc.*, 1964, 221-56.

Nwb-da

ADAMS, V.K. The medical pioneers. *New Mexico*, 1950, 28: no. 5, 15, 35, 37.
Early physicians in New Mexico.

BRAGMAN, Louis J. Some medical pioneers of central New York. A note on the local aspects of medical history. *Med.Life*, 1935, 42: 639-42.

JIRKA, Frank J. American doctors of destiny. xix, 316 p., 20 pl. Chicago: Normandie House, 1940.
Reviewed by J.B. de C.M. Saunders, *Isis*, 1941, 33: 306-7.

KELLY, Howard A.; BURRAGE, Walter L. Dictionary of American medical biography. Lives of eminent physicians of the United States and Canada, from the earliest times. 1364 p. Boston: Appleton, 1928.
Published in 1912 as "Cyclopedia of American medical biography", and in 1920 as "American medical biographies".

PUSEY, William Allen. Giants of medicine in pioneer Kentucky, a study of influences for greatness. *Med.Life*, 1938, 45: 35-64.

Nwb-dae

McDANIEL, W.B. The William N. Bradley collection in the library of the College of Physicians of Philadelphia: an iconography of Philadelphia physicians as they are represented in works of art. *Bull.Hist.Med.*, 1942, 12: 616-18.

Nwb-f

BELL, Whitfield J. Suggestions for research in the local history of medicine in the United States. *Bull.Hist.Med.*, 1945, 17: 460-76.

MILLER, Genevieve. The study of American medical history. *Bull.Hist.Med.*, 1945, 17: 1-8.

ROSENBERG, Charles E. On the study of American biology and medicine: some justifications. *Bull.Hist.Med.*, 1964, 38: 364-76.

Nwb-hj

SIGERIST, Henry E. Boerhaave's influence upon American medicine. *Ned.Tijdschr.Geneesk.*, 1938, 82: 4822-8.

Nwb-ht

TREILLE, G.F. Le mouvement des idées médicales en Amérique. *Janus*, 1913, 18: 273-81.

Nwb-mzREwb

SCHWARTZ, L. Laszlo. The historical relations of American dentistry and medicine. *Bull.Hist.Med.*, 1954, 28: 542-9.

Nwb-o study and teaching

ECKMAN, James. Osler in Minnesota. His interest in medical education and licensure. *Minn.Med.*, 1948, 31: 776-87, 2 fig.

FOSSIER, A.E. History of medical education in New Orleans. From its birth to the Civil War. *Ann.Med.Hist.*, 1934, 6: 320-52, 8 fig.; 427-47, 3 fig.

GEISER, Samuel Wood. Medical education in Dallas: 1900-1910. 23 p. (Southern Methodist University Studies, 7) Dallas: Southern Methodist University Press, 1952. [CB 79/147]
Reviewed by Chauncey D. Leake, *J.Hist.Med.*, 1953, 8: 352-3.

LARSELL, O. The development of medical education in the Pacific northwest. 48 p., 7 pl. Eugene, Ore.: Koke-Chapman, 1924.
Read at the meeting of the University of Oregon Medical History Club February 21, 1924.

MOORMAN, Lewis J. The influence of Kentucky medical schools on medicine in the Southwest. *Bull.Hist.Med.*, 1950, 24: 176-86, 4 fig.

MORRISON, Hyman. Reginald Heber Fitz's contribution to the development of medical education and practice in America. *Bull.Hist.Med.*, 1951, 25: 60-5.

RIESMAN, David. Clinical teaching in America, with some remarks on early medical schools. *Trans.Coll.Physicians Phila.*, 1939, 7: 89-110.

RIESMAN, David. Medical education and the distribution of physicians in the United States. *Atlantic Med.J.*, Oct. 1927, 31: 5-9.

ROBINSON, G. Canby. Adventures in medical education. A personal narrative of the great advances in American medicine. xii, 338 p., pl. Cambridge, Mass.: Harvard University Press (for the Commonwealth Fund), 1957.
Reviewed by John R. Blake, *Science*, 1958, 128: 469.

WEISKOTTEN, Harman G., *et al.* Medical education in the United States, 1934-1939. xi, 259 p. Chicago: American Medical Association, 1940.

Nwb-op

AMERICAN MEDICAL ASSOCIATION. Graduate medical education in the United States. 1. Continuation study for practicing physicians, 1937 to 1940. 243 p. Chicago: The Association, 1940.

CUTTER, J.B. Intern service in the old days at Chambers Street Hospital, N.Y. *Ann.Med.Hist.*, 1931, 3: 39-49.

MIDDLETON, William Shaine. Clinical teaching in the Philadelphia Almshouse and Hospital. *Med.Life*, 1933, 40: 191-200, 207-25.

STENGEL, Alfred. The importance of the Philadelphia General Hospital in medical education. *Med.Life*, 1933, 40: 153-6.

Nwb-oq

ALSOP, Gulielma Fell. History of the Woman's Medical College, Philadelphia, Pennsylvania, 1850-1950. xii, 256 p., ill. Philadelphia, Pa.: J.B. Lippincott Company, 1950.
Reviewed by Jean A. Curran, *Bull.Hist.Med.*, 1953, 27: 92-3; by William Frederick Norwood, *J.Hist.Med.*, 1951, 6: 549-51.

CHESNEY, Alan M. The Johns Hopkins Hospital and the Johns Hopkins School of Medicine. A chronicle. 3 vol. 1. Early years, 1867-1893. xviii, 318 p., ill.; 2. 1893-1905. xiv, 504 p., ill.; 3. 1905-1914. xv, 350 p., ill. Baltimore, Md.: Johns Hopkins Press, 1943, 1958, 1963.
Vol. 1 reviewed by Genevieve Miller, *Bull.Hist.Med.*, 1944, 16: 90-2; vol. 2 by John R. Blake, *Isis*, 1959, 50: 512-14.

DOUGHTY, Roger G. History of the Medical Department of the University of Georgia. A short story of its early struggles. *Ann.Med.Hist.*, 1928, 10: 80-5.

JACOBI, Abraham. The New York medical college, 1782-1906. *Ann.Med.Hist.*, 1917, 1: 368-73.

METTLER, Cecilia C. History of the Georgia School of Medicine. *Phi Chi Quart.*, Jan. 1937, 17-24.

READ, J. Marion. A history of the California Academy of Medicine, 1870-1930. viii, 186 p., pl., facs. San Francisco, Calif.: Grabhorn Press, 1930. [CB 30/490]

SHRYOCK, Richard Harrison. The unique influence of the Johns Hopkins University on American medicine. 78 p. (Acta Historica Scientiarum et Naturalium et Medicinalium, 10) Copenhagen: Ejnar Munksgaard, 1953.
Reviewed by Henry E. Sigerist, *Isis*, 1954, 45: 208-9.

SPECTOR, Benjamin. A history of Tufts College Medical School. Prepared for its semi-centennial 1893-1943. 414 p., pl. Boston, Mass.: Tufts College Medical Alumni Association, 1943. [CB 65/71]

TURNER, Roy H. Graefenberg, the Shepard family's medical school. *Ann.Med.Hist.*, 1933, 5: 548-60, 5 fig. [CB 40/363]

VEITH, Ilza; McLEAN, Franklin C. The University of Chicago clinics and clinical departments, 1927-1952. A brief outline of the origins, the formative years, and the present state of medicine at the University of Chicago. 91 p., ill. Chicago, Ill.: University of Chicago Press, 1952.

WAITE, Frederick Clayton. Western Reserve University Centennial History of the School of Medicine. 588 p., ill. Cleveland: Western Reserve University Press, 1946.
Reviewed by Howard Dittrick, *J.Hist.Med.*, 1946, 1: 684-6.

Nwb-p organization

Nwb-ph

ROEMER, Milton I. Government's role in American medicine - a brief historical survey. *Bull.Hist.Med.*, 1945, 18: 146-68.

Nwb-pw

BONNER, Thomas Neville. American doctors and German universities: a chapter in international intellectual relations, 1870-1914. x, 210 p. Lincoln: University of Nebraska Press, 1963.
Reviewed by Donald Fleming, *Miss.Val.Hist.Rev.*, 1963, 50: 521-2; by Winfred Overholser, *Amer.Hist.Rev.*, 1963, 68: 1099; by Richard H. Shryock, *J.Hist.Med.*, 1964, 19: 309-10.

SELMON, Bertha L. They do meet. Cross-trails of American physicians and Chinese people. xvii, 254 p., 18 pl. New York: Froben Press, 1942. [CB 69/217]

Nwb-q societies and institutions

Nwb-qb

BEAUMONT MEDICAL CLUB. Members, officers, papers presented, Beaumont lectures. 15 p. New Haven, Conn.: Yale Historical Library, 1951.

RIESMAN, David, *ed.* History of the Interurban Clinical Club, 1905-1937. vii, 279 p., ill. Philadelphia: Winston, [1938?]
History of medical club founded by William Osler.

Nwb-qd

BEAUMONT, William. Centennial celebration, St. Louis Medical Society, Nov. 21, 1933. *Weekly Bull.St.Louis Med.Soc.*, Dec. 8 and 15, 1933, 28: 21 p.

BURROW, James G. AMA: voice of American medicine. xii, 430 p. Baltimore: Johns Hopkins Press, 1963.
Reviewed by Thomas N. Bonner, *Miss.Val.Hist.Rev.*, 1963, 50: 522-3.

FISHBEIN, Morris. A history of the American Medical Association, 1847-1947. xvi, 1226 p., ill. Philadelphia, Pa.: Saunders, 1947.
Reviewed by Chauncey D. Leake, *Science*, 1947, 106: 478.

FOSSIER, A.E. History of the Orleans Parish Medical Society, 1878-1928. Illustrated with views of meeting places and portraits of members. 238 p., ill. New Orleans: Privately Printed, 1930.
Reviewed by Francis Packard, *Ann.Med.Hist.*, 1931, 3: 361.

GALDSTON, Iago. The New York Academy of Medicine 1847-1947. *J.Hist.Med.*, 1947, 2: 147-62.

HAMER, Philip M., ed. The centennial history of the Tennessee State Medical Association, 1830-1930. 580 p. Nashville, Tenn.: Tennessee State Medical Association, 1930.

JACOBS, Maurice S. The centennial of the Northern Medical Association. 100 years of medicine in Philadelphia. *Victor Robinson Memorial Volume*, p. 137-43. New York: Froben, 1948.

LUSK, Graham. The Harvey Society. *Science*, 1930, 71: 627-9.
Address delivered at the 25th anniversary of the Harvey Society, May 15, 1930.

McDANIEL, W.B. William Harvey, Weir Mitchell, and the College of Physicians of Philadelphia. *J.Hist.Med.*, 1957, 12: 241-7, 1 facs.

MACDERMOTT, H.E. History of the Canadian Medical Association, 1867-1921. xi, 209 p. Toronto: Murray, 1935.
Reviewed in *Ann.Med.Hist.*, 1936, 8: 92.

MORGAN, William Gerry. The American College of Physicians, its first quarter century. 275 p., ill. Philadelphia, Pa.: 1940.
Reviewed in *Ann.Med.Hist.*, 1941, 3: 535-6.

NORWOOD, William Frederick. The early history of American medical societies. *Ciba Symp.* (Summit, N.J.), 1947, 9: 762-72, ill.

PACKARD, Francis R. Medicine and the American Philosophical Society. *Proc.Amer.Phil.Soc.*, 1942, 86: 91-102.

POSTELL, William Dosite. The American Medical Association. *Ciba Symp.*(Summit, N.J.), 1947, 9: 773-84, ill.

RIDGE, Alan D. The minute book of the Montreal Medical Institution. *J.Soc.Archiv.*, 1964, no. 2, 435-8.

RIESMAN, David. Dr. Richard Mead and the motto of the College of Physicians of Philadelphia. *Med.Life*, 1935, 42: 187-201.

ROSEN, George. Special medical societies in the United States after 1860. *Ciba Symp.* (Summit, N.J.), 1947, 9: 785-92, ill.

SIGERIST, Henry E. Why academies were founded. *Trans.Coll. Physicians Phila.*, 1937, 4: 83-8.
An address at the celebration of the 150th anniversary of the founding of the College of Physicians of Philadelphia, May 15, 1937.

VAN INGEN, Philip. The New York Academy of Medicine. Its first hundred years. xii, 586 p., ill. (History of Medicine Series, 8) New York: Columbia University Press, 1949.

WARING, Joseph I. A brief history of the South Carolina Medical Association. vi, 197 p., ill. Columbia, S.C.: Bryan, 1948.

WIRTSCHAFTER, Jonathan Dine. The genesis and impact of the medical lobby: 1898-1906. *J.Hist.Med.*, 1958, 13: 15-49.
Of the American Medical Association.

Nwb-qg

ROCKEFELLER INSTITUTE FOR MEDICAL RESEARCH. History, organization, present scope of scientific work, buildings and equipment, publications. 36 p., 2 pl. New York: Rockefeller Institute for Medical Research, 1931. [CB 33/403]
This is an account of the Rockefeller Institute with its Medical Institute in New York and that of Comparative Pathology of Animals and Plants at Princeton, N.J.

Nwb-r the profession

BROWNING, William. Medical heredity; distinguished children of physicians (United States, to 1910). 250 p. Baltimore: The Norman Remington Co., 1925.
Reviewed by F.R. Packard, *Ann.Med.Hist.*, 1926, 8: 210.

JACKSON, Russell Leigh. The physicians of Essex County. vii, 152 p., ill. Salem: Essex Institute, 1948.

SHRYOCK, Richard H. The American physician in 1846 and in 1946. A study in professional contrasts. *J.Amer.Med.Ass.*, 1947, 134: 417-24.

Nwb-rd

BONNER, Thomas N. Social and political attitudes of midwestern physicians 1840-1940. *J.Hist.Med.*, 1953, 8: 133-64.

Nwb-rf

DITTRICK, Howard. Medical fee bills from Ohio and Georgia. *Bull.Hist.Med.*, 1945, 18: 544-55, 8 fig.

SIGERIST, Henry E. A fee bill of the Georgia Medical Society, revised in 1863. *Bull.Inst.Hist.Med.*, 1936, 4: 333, 1 facs.

Nwb-rj

KONOLD, Donald E. A history of American medical ethics, 1847-1912. vii, 119 p. Madison: State Historical Society of Wisconsin for the Department of History, University of Wisconsin, 1962.
Reviewed by Richard H. Shryock, *Amer.Hist.Rev.*, 1963, 68: 1152-3; by Chauncey D. Leake, *Bull.Hist.Med.*, 1963, 37: 293-4.

Nwb-rn

PARERGON. From the Greek word meaning "work by the side of work". 2nd ed. 96 p. Evansville, Ind.: Mead Johnson, 1942.
A collection of pictures illustrating the artistic versatility and talent of the American medical profession.

WALLERSTEIN, Marion Grace. American doctors as men of letters. *Bull.Hist.Med.*, 1943, 13: 507-13.

Nwb-rw

HURD-MEAD, Kate Campbell. Medical women of America. A short history of the pioneer medical women of America and of a few of their colleagues in England. 95 p., ill. New York: Froben Press, 1933.

KING, John W.; KING, Caroline R. Early women physicians in Vermont. *Bull.Hist.Med.*, 1951, 25: 429-41.

Nwb-s/v relation with society; ethnic groups

Nwb-sc

HALL, Courtney R. Doctors and the rise of civilization on Long Island. *Med.Times* (N.Y.), 1939, 67: 523-8.
An address delivered at the annual dinner of the Associated Physicians of Long Island (including Brooklyn), June 1, 1939.

SHRYOCK, Richard H. Medicine and society in America: 1660-1860. viii, 182 p. New York: New York University Press, 1960.
Reviewed by Donald Fleming, *Isis*, 1961, 52: 599-600; for other reviews *see* CB 86/472, CB 87/575, CB 88/562 and CB 89/495.

SHRYOCK, Richard H. The significance of medicine in American history. *Amer.Hist.Rev.*, 1956, 62: 80-91.

Nwb-vm

KAGAN, Solomon R. Contributions of early Jews to American medicine. xv, 63 p., 18 ill. Boston: Medical Publishing Co., 1934.

KAGAN, Solomon R. Jewish contributions to medicine in America. From colonial times to the present. Foreword by James J. Walsh. 2nd rev. enl. ed. xxxii, 792 p. Boston: Medical Publishing Co., 1939.
Reviewed in *Jew.Quart.Rev.*, 1940, 31: 103. First ed. publ. 1934, reviewed by Maurice S. Jacobs, *ibid.*, 1937, 28: 155-6.

MORRISON, Hyman. The early Jewish physicians in America. With reference to some in the nineteenth century. *Med. Life*, 1933, 40: 411-33.

ROBBINS, M. [The Jewish physician in the U.S.A. (In Hebrew)] *Koroth*, 1962, 2: 527-34.

SIMON, Sydney M. History of the Jewish physicians in the United States up to about 1900. *Ann.Med.Hist.*, 1935, 7: 285-91.

Nwb-vx

BOUSFIELD, M.O. An account of physicians of color in the United States. *Bull.Hist.Med.*, 1945, 17: 61-84.

Nwc Latin America

ARCHILA, Ricardo. Historia médica de Venezuela: Guayana. 174 p., ill. Caracas: Imprenta Nacional, 1958.
Reviewed by Georgianna S. Gittinger, *Bull.Hist.Med.*, 1959, 33: 388.

ARCHILA, Ricardo. Historia de la medicina en Venezuela: época colonial. xxiii, 617 p., ill. Caracas: Tip. Vargas, 1961.
Reviewed by Edward L. Suarez-Murios, *Bull.Hist.Med.*, 1963, 37: 289-90; by Georgianna Gittinger, *Hispanic Amer. Hist.Rev.*, 1963, 43: 119-21.

BONILLA-NAAR, Alfonso. Historia de la medicina en Colombia. *Arch.Iberoamer.Hist.Med.*, 1960, 12: 197-9.

CARRILLO, Pedro Emilio. Crónica médica de Trujillo. *Rev. Soc.Venezolana Med.*, 1959, 7: 119-293, ill. [CB 85/398]

CHAVEZ, Ignacio. México en la cultura médica. 187 p., 63 ill. Mexico, D.F.: Edición de el Colegio Nacional, 1947.
Reviewed by Henry E. Sigerist, *Bull.Hist.Med.*, 1947, 21: 847-52; by B. Imbasciati, *Riv.Stor.Sci.*, 1948, 39: 207.

EGUIGUREN, Luis Antonio. Los médicos, la medicina, la cirugía y la asistencia social. *An.Soc.Peruana Hist.Med.*, 1948-49, 10: 9-25.

GUERRA, Francisco. Historiografía de la medicina colonial hispanoamericana. Prólogo de Fidel Carrancedo. vi, 322 p. México, D.F.: Abastecedora de Impresos, S.A., 1953.
Reviewed by A.R.M., *Arch.Iberoamer.Hist.Med.*, 1954, 6: 593.

GUERRA, Gustavo S. Apuntes para la historia de la medicina en Puno. *An.Soc.Peruana Hist.Med.*, 1939, 50-77.

HUME, Edgar Erskine. Spanish colonial medicine. *Bull.Inst. Hist.Med.*, 1934, 2: 215-30.

LASTRES, Juan B. La cultura peruana y la obra de los médicos en la emancipación. 498 p. Lima: Editorial San Marcos, 1954.

LASTRES, Juan B. Historia de la medicina Peruana. 3 vol. 1. La medicina Incaica. xxxv, 352 p., 20 pl; 2. La medicina en el Virreinato. 368 p., 23 pl.; 3. La medicina su la Republica. 387 p., 35 pl. (Historia de la Universidad Nacional Mayor de San Marcos, 5) Lima: University of San Marcos, 1951.
Reviewed by Erwin L. Ackerknecht, *Arch.Int.Hist.Sci.*, 1952, 31: 424-5; by Pietro Franceschini, *Riv.Stor.Sci. Med.Natur.*, 1952, 43: 281-2; by Georgianna S. Gittinger, *Bull.Hist.Med.*, 1953, 27: 188-90.

MADERO, Mauro. Medicina ecuatoriana y sus puntos de contacto con la medicina peruana a través de la historia. *An.Soc. Peruana Hist.Med.*, 1946, 8: 129-36.

MARTINEZ DURÁN, Carlos. Las ciencias médicas en Guatemala (origen y evolución). 2nd ed. 579 p. Guatemala: Tipografia Nacional, 1945.
Reviewed by Arturo Castiglioni, *J.Hist.Med.*, 1947, 2: 270-2; by B. Imbasciati, *Riv.Stor.Sci.*, 1948, 39: 108. First publ. 1941 and reviewed by C.E. Paz Soldán and Juan B. Lastres, *An.Soc.Peruana Hist.Med.*, 1940, 176-80; by Aldo Mieli, *Archeion*, 1942, 24: 121-2.

MOLL, Aristides A. Aesculapius in Latin America. xii, 639 p., ill. Philadelphia: Saunders, 1944.
Reviewed by Chauncey D. Leake, *Isis*, 1945, 36: 81-2; by Philip Ainsworth Means, *ibid.* 82-3.

NAVA, Pedro. Capitulos da historia da medicina no Brasil. 136 p. Rio de Janeiro: Brasil Médico Cirúrgico, 1949.
Reprinted from *Brasil Médico Cirúrgico*, 1949, vol. 10. Reviewed by Arturo Castiglioni, *Riv.Stor.Sci.*, 1950, 41: 98-9.

OCARANZA, Fernando. Historia de la medicina en Mexico. 213 p., 22 ill. Mexico: 1934. [CB 52/604]

PAREDES BORJA, Virgilio. Médicos y medicaciones en el Ecuador. *Arch.Iberoamer.Hist.Med.*, 1960, 12: 179-95.

PARSONS, Robert P. History of Haitian medicine. xxviii, 196 p., 21 ill., 1 map. New York: Hoeber, 1930. [CB 33/411]

PARSONS, Robert P. History of Haitian medicine. *Ann.Med. Hist., new ser.*, 1929, 1: 291-324, 8 fig.

PINO Y ROCA, J. Gabriel. Breves apuntes para la historia de la medicina y suo progresos en Guayaquil [1530-1822]. 75 p. Guayaquil: Imp. y Papelería Sucre, 1915. [CB 11/447]

PULIDO MÉNDEZ, Manuel Antonio. Precedentes en la historia de la medicina peruana. *An.Soc.Peruana Hist.Med.*, 1944, 6: 103-7.

SANTOS, Lycurgo de Castro. Historia de medicina no Brasil (do século XVI ao século XIX). 2 vol. 379 p.; 429 p. (Colleçao Grandes Estudios Brasilienses', 3, 3a) São Paulo: Editora Brasiliense, 1947.
Reviewed by F.N.L. Poynter, *Med.Illus.*, 1949, 3: 13.

SCHIAFFINO, Rafael. Historia de la medicina en el Uruguay. 3 vol. Montevideo: Imprenta Nacional, 1927, 1937, 1952.

SIGERIST, Henry E. La historia de la medicina en la República Argentina. *Rev.Argent.Hist.Med.*, 1942, 1: 37-53.

SOMOLINOS D'ARDOIS, Germán. Figuras y hechos de la historiografía médica mexicana. 160 p., ill. (Colección Cultura Mexicana, 18) Mexico City: Imprenta Universitaria, 1957.
Reviewed by Arthur R. Steele, *Hispanic Amer.Hist.Rev.*, 1958, 38: 450.

Nwc-br

Archivos de Historia Medica de Venezuela. Año 1-2. Caracas: Cooperativa de artes graficas, 1934-35. [CB 42/607]
No more published.
Devoted to the medical history of Venezuela.

Nwc-bv

ARCHILA, Ricardo. Bibliografía médica venezolana. 2nd ed. 1041 p. Caracas: Bellas Artes C.A., 1955.
Reviewed by H. García-Arocha, *J.Hist.Med.*, 1957, 12: 284-5.

Nwc-ce

VAN PATTEN, Nathan. The medical literature of Mexico and central America. *Pap.Bibliogr.Soc.Amer.*, 1930, 24: 150-99.

VARGAS, José María. Trabajos antiguos de historia médica venezolana: memoria acerca de la medicina en Caracas y bosquejo biográfico de sus médicos. *Rev.Soc.Venezolana Hist.Med.*, 1953, 1: 117-40.

Nwc-da

LAVAL, M. Enrique. Noticias sobre los médicos en Chile en los siglos XVI, XVII y XVIII. 137 p. Santiago: Universidad de Chile, Centro de Investigación de Historia de la Medicina, 1958.
Reviewed by Francisco Guerra, *J.Hist.Med.*, 1960, 15: 220-1.

Nwc-hj

IZQUIERDO, José Joaquín. La medicina Hipocrática y los Hipocratistas de México (1578-1957). *Gac.Méd.Méx.*, 1958, 88: 359-72.

Nwc-o study and teaching

GARCÍA CHUECOS, Héctor. Les estudios de medicina en Mérida. *Rev.Soc.Venezolana Hist.Med.*, 1953, 1: 756-62.

IZQUIERDO, José Joaquín. Origenes y culminación de nuestro primer movimiento renovador de la enseñanza médica. *Gac. Méd.Méx.*, 1958, 88: 521-32.

Nwc-oq

ABASCAL, Horacio. Los primeros estudios médicos en Cuba. Fundación de la Universidad. *Rev.Argent.Hist.Med.*, 1942, 1: no. 1, 7-24.

GRANIER-DOYEUX, Marcel. Documentos para la historia de la medicina en Venezuela. La Sociedad de Instrucción Médica de Caracas, 1850-1851. *Rev.Soc.Venezolana Hist.Med.*, 1953, 1: 577-82.

IZQUIERDO, José Joaquín. La antigua facultad de medicina, las primeras academias médicas y la primera escuela de medicina de Puebla. *Gac.Méd.Mex.*, 1950, 80: 78-86.

IZQUIERDO, José Joaquín. Ojeada sobre el pasado y vistas hacia el futuro de nuestra Escuela Nacional de Medicina. *Gac.Méd. Méx.*, 1957, 87: 143-61, 7 fig.

PAREDES BORJA, Virgilio. La Facultad de Medicina de Quito. *Arch.Iberoamer.Hist.Med.*, 1957, 9: 407-13.

PAZ SOLDÁN, Carlos Enrique. Cayetano Heredia y las bases docentes de la Escuela Medical de Lima. 289 p. Lima: Biblioteca de Cultura Sanitaria, 1951. [CB 78/151]
Reviewed by Pietro Franceschini, *Riv.Stor.Sci.*, 1953, 44: 142.

PAZ SOLDÁN, Carlos Enrique. La organización de la Enseñanza Clínica en Lima. Discurso de inauguración de la Sociedad Peruana de Historia de la Medicina. *An.Soc.Peruana Hist. Med.*, 1939, 16-26.

PEIXOTO, Afranio. As minhas faculdades (memorias excolares). *Rev.Argent.Hist.Med.*, 1943, 2: no. 1, 23-47.

TURENNE, Augusto. Los precursores, la fundación y los primeros tiempos de la Facultad de Medicina de Montevideo. *Rev.Argent.Hist.Med.*, 1942, 1: 37-57.

VALDIZAN, Hermilio. La Facultad de Medicina de Lima. 2 vol. iv, 193 p.; ii, 124 p. Lima: 1927.

Nwc-q/u organizational and social aspects

Nwc-qd

BELTRAN, Juan Ramon. Síntesis histórica de la Academia nacional de medicina de Buenos Aires. *Publ.Cátedra Hist.Med.Univ. Buenos Aires*, 1938, 1: 35-76.

IZQUIERDO, José Joaquin. Un cuadro del momento evolutivo de la Academia de Medicina de México hacia 1923. *Gac.Méd.Mex.*, 1955, 85: 11-30, 5 fig.

Nwc-rk

MOLL, A.A. Physicians in public life, especially in Latin America. *Bull.Inst.Hist.Med.*, 1934, 2: 231-48.

Nwc-sc

CHAGAS, C.; NAVA, Pedro. Aspetos das influências médicas na evolução social do Brasil. *Act.VIe Congr.Int.Hist.Sci.* (Amsterdam, 1950), p. 370-84. Paris: Hermann, 1951.

Nwc-u

GUDIÑO KRAMER, Luis. Médicos, magos y curanderos. 108 p., 6 pl., bibliogr. Buenos Aires: Emecé Editores, 1942.
Reviewed by Aldo Mieli, *Archeion*, 1943, 25: 262-5.
Medical folklore and healing practices of Rio de la Plata.

Nwe British Isles

BICKERTON, Thomas Herbert. A medical history of Liverpool from the earliest days to the year 1920. From the data collected by the late Thomas H. Bickerton. xx, 313 p. London: Murray, 1936.

BROCKBANK, William. Country practice in days gone by (as recorded in contemporary diaries). 3 pt. *Med.Hist.*, 1960, 4: 65-9; 1961, 5: 173-7; 1962, 6: 177-83.

CLEMENS, J.R. Notes on English medicine (Henry VIII-George IV). *Ann.Med.Hist.*, 1931, 3: 308-17.

COMRIE, John Dixon. History of Scottish medicine. 2nd ed. 2 vol. 852 p. London: Baillière, Tindall and Cox (for the Wellcome Historical Medical Museum), 1932.
First publ. 1927.
Reviewed in *Nature*, 1932, 129: 812-13.

CUMMINS, N. Marshall. Some chapters of Cork medical history. viii, 116 p. Cork: University Press, 1957.
Reviewed by John E. Donley, *J.Hist.Med.*, 1959, 14: 253-4.

DOOLIN, William. Dublin's contribution to medicine. *J.Hist. Med.*, 1947, 2: 321-36.

FLEETWOOD, John. History of medicine in Ireland. xvi, 420 p., ill. Dublin: Browne and Nolan, 1951.
Reissued at Mystic, Conn.: Lawrence Verry, 1964.
Reviewed by John Donley, *J.Hist.Med.*, 1953, 8: 93-5; by T.G. Wilson, *Bull.Hist.Med.*, 1954, 28: 83-6.

JARAMILLO-ARANGO, Jaime. The British contribution to medicine. xii, 220 p., 45 pl. Edinburgh/London: Livingstone, 1953.
Reviewed in *Nature*, 1954, 173: 744-5.

MOLONEY, Michael F. Irish ethno-botany and the evolution of medicine in Ireland. 96 p. Dublin: Gill, 1919. [CB 12/631]

MOORE, Norman. The history of medicine in England. *XVIIth Int.Congr.Med.* (London, 1913), sect. 23, p. 1-9. London: 1914.

MULLETT, Charles F. Overseas expansion and English medicine to 1800. *Bull.Hist.Med.*, 1948, 22: 664-73.

POWER, D'Arcy. Medicine in the British Isles. ix, 84 p., 1 pl. (Clio Medica, 2) New York: Hoeber, 1930. [CB 30/490]

POYNTER, F.N.L., ed. The evolution of medical practice in Britain. vi, 168 p. London: Pitman Medical Publishing Co., 1961.
Reviewed by John Rendel-Short, *Bull.Hist.Med.*, 1962, 36: 480; by A.H.T. Robb-Smith, *Hist.Sci.*, 1962, 1: 111-12; by Cohen of Birkenhead, *Med.Hist.*, 1962, 6: 92-4; by Ernst W. Stieb, *Pharm.Hist.*, 1962, 7: 55-6.

ROLLESTON, Humphry. History of medicine in the City of London. *Ann.Med.Hist.*, 1941, 3: 1-17, 3 fig.

WHITTET, Martin M. Historical aspects of Celtic medicine. *Proc.Roy.Soc.Med.*, 1964, 57: 429-36.

WIGMORE, James. Medicine and its practitioners during the earlier years of the history of Bath. *Bristol Med.Chir.J.*, 1913, 31: 193-212.

Nwe-cj

BETT, Walter R. *The Medical Press and Circular*, 1839-1939. *Bull.Hist.Med.*, 1939, 7: 1004-7.

HOWELL, W.B. Concerning some old medical journals. *Ann. Med.Hist.*, 1926, 8: 155-75.
Dealing mainly with the *Lancet*.

LEFANU, W.R. British periodicals of medicine. A chronological list. *Bull.Inst.Hist.Med.*, 1937, 5: 735-61, 827-46; 1938, 6: 614-48.

ROWLETTE, Robert J. *The Medical Press and Circular*, 1839-1939. A hundred years in the life of a medical journal. x, 126 p. London: Medical Press and Circular, 1939.
Reviewed in *Ann.Med.Hist.*, 1939, 1: 311-12.

Nwe-d-bv

BISHOP, W.J. The autobiographies of British medical men. *Proc.Roy.Soc.Med.*, 1933, 26: 16-22.
List of British medical autobiographies; includes diaries and reminiscences.

Nwe-da

BLOOM, James Harvey; JAMES, R. Rutson. Medical practioners in the Diocese of London licensed under the Act of 3 Henry VIII, c. 11. An annotated list, 1529-1725. viii, 98 p. Cambridge University Press, 1935.

POWER, D'Arcy, ed. British masters of medicine. xv, 242 p., ill. Baltimore: William Wood, 1936.

ROLLESTON, Humphry. Some worthies of the Cambridge Medical School. *Ann.Med.Hist.*, 1926, 8: 331-48. [CB 22/305]

ROYAL COLLEGE OF PHYSICIANS OF LONDON. The roll of the Royal College of Physicians of London ... By William Munk ... 2nd ed., rev. and enl. Vol. 4. Lives of the Fellows of the Royal College of Physicians ... 1826-1925. Compiled by G.H. Brown. x, 637 p. London: 1955. [CB 81/277]
Vol. 1-3 published 1878; 1st edition 1861.
Reviewed by Emil Bovin, *Lychnos*, 1957-58, 496-7; by E. Ashworth Underwood, *Ann.Sci.*, 1960, 16: 59-62.

Nwe-dae

WOLSTENHOLME, Gordon. Royal College of Physicians of London. Portraits described by David Piper. 468 p., ill., portr. London: J. and A. Churchill, 1964. [CB 90/536]
A catalogue of portraits of over 170 Fellows and/or benefactors.

Nwe-nh

ANDREWS, Edmund. A history of scientific English. The story of its evolution based on a study of biomedical terminology. ix, 342 p., 18 fig., front. New York: Smith, 1947. [CB 71/127]

Nwe-o study and teaching

Nwe-op

BROCKBANK, Edward Mansfield. The foundation of provincial medical education in England, and of the Manchester School in particular. 204 p. Manchester: University Press, 1936.

SINGER, Charles; HOLLOWAY, S.W.F. Early medical education in England in relation to the pre-history of London University. *Med.Hist.*, 1960, 4: 1-17.

Nwe-oq

BICENTENARY of the faculty of medicine, University of Edinburgh, 1726-1926. Records of the celebration. 124 p. Edinburgh: John Thin, 1926.

FRANKLIN, K.J. A short sketch of the history of the Oxford Medical School. *Ann.Sci.*, 1936, 1: 431-46, 4 pl.

GUY'S HOSPITAL GAZETTE. *See* NWwe

HISTORY of the Birmingham Medical School, 1825-1925. 96 p. Birmingham: Cornish, 1925.

HUNTER, W. Historical account of Charing Cross hospital and medical school. xx, 309 p. London: Murray, 1914.

KIRKPATRICK, T. Percy C. History of the medical teaching in Trinity College, Dublin and of the School of Physic in Ireland. xi, 364 p. Dublin: Hanna and Neale, 1912.

KÜRY, H.; HAIG, H. Medical education at Oxford and Cambridge. *Ciba Symp.* (Summit, N.J.), 1941, 3: 864-6, ill.

LANGDON-BROWN, Walter. Some chapters in Cambridge medical history. viii, 119 p. Cambridge University Press; New York: Macmillan, 1946.
Reviewed by W. Pagel, *Bull.Hist.Med.*, 1947, 21: 630-2; by Phyllis Allen, *J.Hist.Med.*, 1948, 3: 177-8.

LYLE, H. Willoughby. King's and some King's men: being a record of the medical department of King's College, London, from 1830 to 1909 and of King's College Hospital Medical School from 1909 to 1934. x, 613 p. London: Oxford University Press, 1935.

LYLE, H. Willoughby. An addendum to King's and some King's men (London). viii, 211 p., ill. London: Oxford University Press, 1950.
Reviewed by Lloyd G. Stevenson, *J.Hist.Med.*, 1952, 7: 98-9.

RIEPPEL, F.W. Die Medizinschule von Edinburgh. *Ciba Z.*, 1948, 10: 4162-96, ill.

ROLLESTON, Humphry. The Cambridge medical school. A biographical history. ix, 235 p., 21 pl. Cambridge University Press, 1932.

THOMSON, H. Campbell. The story of the Middlesex Hospital Medical School. Written at the request of the Council of the School on the occasion of the centenary. xiii, 182 p., 20 pl. London: Murray, 1935.
Reviewed in *Nature,* 1936, 138: 142-4.

Nwe-p/r organizational and professional aspects

Nwe-pg

UNDERWOOD, E. Ashworth. Medicine and the crown. *Brit.Med.J.*, 1953, (1), 1185-91, ill.

Nwe-pw for relations of the British Isles with other countries *see* Npw (Fisher, I.; Guthrie, Douglas; Jorge, Ricardo; Neuburger, Max)

Nwe-qd

BROCKBANK, Edward Mansfield. A centenary history of the Manchester Medical Society. 101 p. Manchester: Sherratt and Hughes, 1934. [CB 53/287]

CLARK, George Norman. A history of the Royal College of Physicians. 2 vol. xxiii, 800 p., pl. Oxford: Clarendon Press (for the Royal College of Physicians), 1964, 1966.

GRAY, James. History of the Royal Medical Society 1737-1937. Ed. by Douglas Guthrie. xi, 355 p. Edinburgh: University Press, 1952.
Reviewed by Jack Peter Green, *J.Hist.Med.*, 1953, 8: 342-3; by Emil Bovin, *Lychnos,* 1953, 437-8.

LITTLE, Ernest Muirhead, comp. History of the British Medical Association, 1832-1932. viii, 342 p., 29 pl., portr. London: The Association, 1932.
Reviewed in *Nature,* 1932, 130: 119-20.

VAUGHAN, Paul. Doctors' commons. A short history of the British Medical Association. 254 p., 8 ill. London: Heinemann, 1959.
Reviewed by H. Degen, *Sudhoffs Arch.*, 1960, 44:286-7; by U.S. von Euler, *Lychnos,* 1960-61, 415.

WIDDESS, J.D.H. A history of the Royal College of Physicians of Ireland, 1654-1963. xii, 255 p., ill. Edinburgh/London: E. & S. Livingstone, 1963.
Reviewed by Zachary Cope, *Proc.Roy.Soc.Med.*, 1963, 56: 1107-8.

Nwe-qe

COPE, Zachary. The Worshipful Society of Apothecaries of London and the evolution of the family doctor. 15 p. London: Faculty of the History of Medicine and Pharmacy, Apothecaries Hall, 1963.

LLOYD, O.M. The Royal College of Physicians of London and some city livery companies. *J.Hist.Med.*, 1956, 11: 412-21.

Nwe-qg

FELL, Honor B. Fiftieth anniversary of the Strangeways Research Laboratory, Cambridge. *Nature,* 1962, 196: 316-18.

RITCHIE, John. History of the laboratory of the Royal College of Physicians of Edinburgh. xi, 158 p., 8 ill. Edinburgh: Royal College of Physicians, 1953.
Reviewed by Douglas Guthrie, *J.Hist.Med.*, 1955, 10: 347-8.

Nwe-r

BISHOP, W.J. The evolution of the general practitioner in England. *Science, Medicine and History. Essays in honour of Charles Singer,* (2), p. 351-7. London: Oxford University Press, 1953.

COPE, Zachary. *See* Nwe-qe

COX, Alfred. Among the doctors. 224 p., front. London: Johnson, 1950.

Nwe-rh

BISHOP, W.J. Transport and the doctor in Great Britain. *Bull.Hist.Med.*, 1948, 22: 427-40, 6 fig.

Nwe-rw

WAUCHOPE, Gladys Mary. The story of a woman physician. 146 p. Bristol: John Wright, 1963.
An autobiography.
Reviewed by Norah Schuster, *Med.Hist.*, 1964, 8: 95-6.

Nwf France

ALAJOUANINE, Théophile, *et al.* Ce que la France a apporté à la médecine depuis le début du XXe siècle. Préface de G. Duhamel. 276 p. Paris: Flammarion, 1946.

DI GIOVANNI, Antonio. Note per la storia della medicina in Parigi dal XII al XVII secolo. 85 p. (Collana Scientia Veterum, 46) Pisa: Giardini, 1963.

DOBROVICI, A. *See* Nwo-hj

DRIVON, Jules. Miscellanées médicales et historiques. Notes pour servir à l'histoire de la médecine à Lyon. 5th ser. 62 p. Lyon: Association typographique, 1912.

GUIART, Jules. Histoire de la médecine française, son passé, son présent, son avenir. 284 p., 8 pl. Paris: Nagel, 1947.
Reviewed by Maurice Caullery, *Arch.Int.Hist.Sci.*, 1948, 2: 257-8.

HINSDALE, Guy. Our medical debt to France. *Ann.Med.Hist.*, 1942, 4: 154-66, 4 portr.

LAIGNEL-LAVASTINE, Maxime; MOLINERY, Raymond. French medicine. Translated by E.B. Krumbhaar. 188 p., 14 ill. (Clio Medica, 15) New York: Hoeber, 1934.

LUSK, Graham. Some influences of French science on medicine. Pasteur Lecture. *J.Amer.Med.*, 1921, 76: 1-8.
French translation in *Rev.Sci.*, 1922, 60: 177-89.

MAURIAC, Pierre. Libre histoire de la médecine française. 287 p. Paris: Stock, 1956.
Reviewed by Marcel Florkin, *Arch.Int.Hist.Sci.*, 1956, 9: 280.

MERCIER, Raoul. Histoire de la médecine en Touraine. 53 p., 8 fig. Tours: Imprimerie Arrault, 1936.
Reviewed by Marcel Fosseyeux, *Bull.Soc.Franç.Hist.Méd.*, 1936, 34: 315.

MONTARIOL, L. Sur l'étude et l'exercice de la médecine depuis le XIVe siècle jusqu'à la Révolution française (médecins, chirurgiens, barbiers). 112 p. (Thesis) Toulouse: G. Mollat, 1912.

ROLANTS, E. Notes sur l'histoire médicale de Lille et de sa région; la désinfection à Lille pendant l'épidémie de choléra de 1832; les bains à Lille; les blessés de Fontenoy soignés à Lille. 40 p. Lille: Imprimerie centrale, 1930.
Reviewed in *Bull.Soc.Franç.Hist.Méd.*, 1931, 25: 214-15.

ROSEN, George. The philosophy of ideology and the emergence of modern medicine in France. *Bull.Hist.Med.*, 1946, 20: 328-39.

Nwf-cd

DES CILLEUILS, Jean. Note au sujet des archives historiques du service de santé; la collection Bergougnioux. *Mém.Soc. Franç.Hist.Méd.*, 1947, 3: 151-2.

LANNOIS, M. L'armoire aux archives du collège des médecins de Lyon. *Bull.Soc.Franç.Hist.Méd.*, 1937, 31: 83-90, 1 fig.

Nwf-ce

GARRISON, Fielding Hudson. The medical literature of France. *Bull.N.Y.Acad.Med.*, 1933, 9: 267-93.

Nwf-ch

DELAGE, Anna. Histoire de la thèse de doctorat en médecine, d'après les thèses soutenues devant la Faculté de Médecine de Paris. 155 p. Paris: Ollier-Henry, 1913.

LEGRAND, N. La collection des thèses de l'ancienne Faculté de Médecine [de Paris] depuis 1539 et son catalogue inédit jusqu'en 1793. Quelques documents sur l'histoire de la Faculté pendant la Révolution. *France Méd.*, 1913-14, passim.

Nwf-da

BARBOT, Marcel. Médecins, chirurgiens et apothicaires mendois des origines au XXe siècle. 500 p. Marseille: 1952; Etiolles (S-et-O): Imprimerie du Monastère de la Croix, 1954.
Reviewed by R. Weitz, *Rev.Hist.Pharm.*, 1960, 48: 384-5.

MONDOR, Henri. Anatomistes et chirurgiens. 530 p., ill. Paris: Fragance, 1949.

RIST, Edouard. 25 portraits de médecins français, 1900-1950. 219 p. Paris: Masson, 1955.
Reviewed by Ernest Wickersheimer, *Rev.Hist.Sci.*, 1956, 9: 283-4; by P. Delaunay, *Arch.Int.Hist.Sci.*, 1956, 35: 81-2.

TRICOT-ROYER, J.J.G. Quelques tombes médicales oubliées et retirées de l'ombre. *Bull.Soc.Franç.Hist.Méd.*, 1927, 21: 45-60. [CB 22/305]

Nwf-hj

HARIZ, Joseph. La part de la médecine arabe dans l'évolution de la médecine française. 164 p. (Thesis) Paris: Geuthner, 1922.

MENETRIER, M.P. Le millénaire de Razès. La médecine arabe, son rôle dans l'histoire et son influence sur la médecine française. *Bull.Soc.Franç.Hist.Méd.*, 1931, 25: 191-202.

Nwf-o study and teaching

Nwf-oq

BENARD, René. Le centre universitaire médical de Reims 1550-1950. *Hist.Méd.*, 1951, no. 2: 40-3.

BINET, Leon; VALLERY-RADOT, Pierre. La Faculté de Médecine de Paris, cinq siècles d'art et d'histoire. vii, 123 p., 115 fig. Paris: Masson & Cie., 1952.
Reviewed by Ernest Wickersheimer, *Rev.Hist.Sci.*, 1953, 6: 84-6.

CHEVALIER, A. Die medizinische Fakultät von Paris (bis zur Französischen Revolution). *Ciba Z.*, 1947, 9: 3769-808, ill.

DELMAS, Paul. La faculté de médecine de Montpellier. Son évolution à travers les siècles. 36 p., 23 fig. Montpellier: 1929.

DULIEU, Louis. Trois chaires de la Faculté de Médecine d'Aix mises au concours à Montpellier. *Rev.Hist.Sci.*, 1951, 4: 84-90.

GLEY, E. La véritable figure de la Faculté de Médecine de Montpellier. *Rev.Sci.*, 1921, 59: 571-9. [CB 12/635]

JONES, Harold Wellington. The Faculty of Medicine of Paris. A historical study of its origin and its influence through six centuries to the outbreak of the French Revolution. *Ann.Med.Hist.*, 1939, 1: 1-29, 5 fig.

PANEFF, Assen Kr. *See* Npw

PICK, Friedel. *See* Npw

TURCHINI, Jean. La Faculté de Médecine de Montpellier. Aperçu historique. 12 p. Montpellier: Causse-Graille-Castelnau, 1958.
Reviewed by Louis Dulieu, *Rev.Hist.Sci.*, 1960, 13: 174.

VALLERY-RADOT, Pierre. La Faculté de Médecine de Paris. Ses origines, ses richesses artistiques. 85 p., 26 ill. Paris: Masson, 1944.
Reviewed by Erwin H. Ackerknecht, *Bull.Hist.Med.*, 1947, 21: 127.

VIRES, -. Sept siècles de médecine à la Faculté de Montpellier. *Rev.Int.Enseign.*, 1922, 7-21.

Nwf-oq-cd

CARTULAIRE de l'Université de Montpellier. 2 vol. 1. Histoire de l'Université par A. Germain. 2. Inventaires des archives anciennes de la Faculté de Médecine avec une introduction par J. Calmette. Montpellier: 1890, 1912.

Nwf-or

COLLOQUE sur les médecins et naturalistes de l'Ecole de Montpellier. *Compt.Rend.86e Congr.Soc.Savantes* (Montpellier, 1961), p. 151-239. Paris: Gauthier-Villars, 1962.
Reviewed by Ernest Wickersheimer, *Arch.Int.Hist.Sci.*, 1962, 15: 461-2.

Nwf-p/v organizational aspects; social and humanistic relations

Nwf-ph

HELLER, Louis. Des rapports entre l'Ordre des médecins et l'Etat. 183 p. (Thesis) Paris: Legrand, 1941.
Reviewed by M. Laignel-Lavastine, *Bull.Soc.Franç.Hist.Méd.*, 1941, 35: 90-1.

Nwf-pw

KONOPKA, Stanislas. Les relations culturelles entre la France et la Pologne dans le domaine de la médecine. 21 p., 10 portr., bibliogr. Warsaw: Société polonaise d'Histoire de la Médecine, 1958.
Reviewed by P. Huard, *Rev.Hist.Sci.*, 1959, 12: 284-5.

Nwf-qd

ACADÉMIE NATIONALE DE MÉDECINE. Centenaire de l'Académie de Médecine 1820-1920. Publié par les soins du Bureau de l'Académie. 279 p., pl. Paris: Masson, 1921. [CB 14/525]

DELAUNAY, Paul. Histoire de la Société de Médecine du Mans (fondée en 1802) et des sociétés médicales de la Sarthe. viii, 185 p., 3 portr., 1 fig. Le Mans: A. de Saint-Denis, 1913.

Nwf-qe

CAMELIN, J. La compagnie du Saint-Sacrement de Lyon et les médecins. *Bull.Soc.Franç.Hist.Méd.*, 1936, 31: 85-97.

IRISSOU, Louis. Montpellier, centre de formation des compagnons-apothicaires. *Vortr.Ges.Gesch.Pharm.* (Basel, 1934), p. 48-69. Mittenwald: 1934.

LARUELLE, E. Les apothicaires rouennais. Histoire de la Corporation du Moyen Age à la Révolution. viii, 96, li, 9 pl. Rouen: Henri Defontaine, 1920. [CB 12/636]

Nwf-r-nh

THORN, Anders Christopher. Les désignations françaises du médecin et de ses concurrents, aujourd'hui et autrefois. 104 p. Jena/Leipzig: W. Gronau, 1932.
Reviewed in *Bull.Soc.Franç.Hist.Méd.*, 1932, 26: 390-2.

Nwf-rj

BOUQUET, Henri. Thèse et serment. *Temps*, 20 nov. 1938.
Apropos of the re-establishment of the Hippocratic oath by the Faculty of Nancy, and of other French Faculties.

Nwf-th

BISSON, L.A. Proust and medicine. *Literature and Science, Proc.Congr.Int.Fed.Mod.Lang.Lit.* (Oxford, 1954), p. 292-8. Oxford: Blackwell, 1955.

BOUTAREL, Maurice. La médecine dans notre théâtre comique depuis ses origines jusqu'au XVIe siècle. "Mirés, fisiciens, navrés" 144 p. Caen: Le Boyteux, 1918.

Nwf-tq

REGNAULT, Félix. Les ex-voto de Provence et du Piémont. Peintures représentant des scènes médicales. *Bull.Soc.Franç.Hist.Méd.*, 1913, 12: 277-85.

Nwf-u

MOLINÉRY, -. Folklore médical en Gascogne. L'énigme du Tuco de Lahas. *Bull.Soc.Franç.Hist.Méd.*, 1934, 28: 47-52.

REGNAULT, Félix. Les superstitions médicales aux environs de Paris. *La Nature*, 1931, 59: ler semestre, 406-9.
Reviewed in *Bull.Soc.Franç.Hist.Méd.*, 1932, 26: 71-2.

VIDAL, Charles. De quelques superstitions populaires, concernant la médecine dans le Castrais. *Bull.Soc.Franç.Hist. Méd.*, 1913, 12: 191-6.

Nwf-ud

BITTARD, A.L. Les saints limousins qui guérissent ou protègent. *Aesculape*, 1913, 3: 213-16, 11 fig.

Nwf-vr

VAUX DE FOLETIER, François de. Guérisseurs, chirurgiens, herboristes et vétérinaires chez les Tsiganes dans l'ancienne France. *Hist.Méd.*, 1962, 12: no. 5, 27-31.

Nwg Germany; Austria; Switzerland

BOLOGA, Valeriu L. *See* Nwo-hj

BREITNER, Burghard. Bemerkungen zu einer Geschichte der Medizin in Österreich. *Festschrift zum 80. Geburtstag Max Neuburgers*, p. 72-4. Wien: Maudrich, 1948.

BREITNER, Burghard. Geschichte der Medizin in Österreich. In Kommission bei Rudolf M. Rohrer. 270 p. (*Sitzungsber. Oesterr.Akad.Wiss.Phil.Hist.Kl.*, 226) (Veröffentlichungen der Kommission für Geschichte der Erziehung und des Unterrichts, 2) Wien: 1951.
Reviewed by Kurt Wuecke, *Centaurus*, 1955, 4: 94-5.

FLÜELER, Benno. Aerzte, Apotheker, Chirurgen und Hebammen im alten Stande Solothurn 1481-1798; ein Beitrag zur Geschichte des Medizinalwesens in der Schweiz. 89 p. (Inaugural-Dissertation, Basel). Solothurn: Gassmann, 1951.

HABERLING, Wilhelm. Die Bedeutung der Rheinländer für die Entwicklung der medizinischen Wissenschaft. *Klin.Wochenschr.*, 1926, 5: no. 38, 1704-5, ill.

HABERLING, Wilhelm. German medicine. Transl. by Jules Freund. xiii, 160 p., 9 fig. (Clio Medica, 13) New York: Hoeber, 1934.

KALLMORGEN, Wilhelm. Siebenhundert Jahre Heilkunde in Frankfurt am Main. xvi, 485 p., ill., 17 pl. Frankfurt a. M.: Diesterweg, 1937.

KORNS, Horace Marshall. Notes on the medical history of Vienna. *Ann.Med.Hist.*, 1937, 9: 345-70, 464-81.

MUNCK, Alexander. Das Medizinalwesen der Freien Reichsstadt Überlingen am Bodensee. 96 p., 8 pl. Überlingen: Internationale Gesellschaft für Geschichte der Pharmazie, 1951.
Reviewed by Ernest Wickersheimer, *Arch.Int.Hist.Sci.*, 1951, 4: 1043-4.

NEUBURGER, Max. Die Entwicklung der Medizin in Österreich. 104 p. (Österreichische Bücherei, 2) Wien: Fromme, 1918. [CB 12/636]

NEUBURGER, Max. Development of medical science in Vienna. *Lancet*, 1921, 2: 536-8. Also *Med.Life*, 1922, 29: 427-41.

OLIVIER, Eugène. Médecine et santé dans le pays de Vaud, des origines à la fin du XVIIe siècle. 2 vol. 1,033 p., pl. Lausanne: Payot, 1961.
Reviewed by P. Huard and J. Théodoridès, *Arch.Int.Hist. Sci.*, 1962, 15: 454-6; by Charles Lichtenthaeler, *Bibl. Hum.Renaiss.*, 1963, 25: 456-7.

REUTTER DE ROSEMONT, L. Comment nos pères se soignaient, se parfumaient et conservaient leur corps. Remèdes parfums, embaumement, suivi d'un aperçu de l'histoire de la médecine et de la pharmacie dans l'ancien comté français de Neuchâtel (Suisse). 355 p., 38 ill. Genève: Georg, 1917. [CB 12/637]

RÖNNE, Ludwig von; SIMON, Heinrich. Das Medicinalwesen des Preussischen Staates dargestellt unter Benutzung des Archivs des Ministeriums der Geistlichen-, Unterrichts- und Medicinal- Angelegenheiten. 2 vol. vii, 786 p.; 628 p. Breslau: Aderholz, 1844-46.
Reviewed by J. Rosenbaum, *Henschel's Janus*, 1846, 1: 867-70; reprinted, Leipzig: Alfred Lorentz, 1931.

SCHÖNBAUER, Leopold. Das medizinische Wien. Geschichte - Werden - Würdigung. 2nd rev. ed. xx, 484 p., 214 ill. Wien: Urban & Schwarzenberg, 1947. [CB 73/183]
First edition published 1944 [CB 70/272].

SIGERIST, Henry E. The history of medicine in Switzerland. *Bull.Hist.Med.*, 1952, 26: 187-90.

SIGERIST, Henry E. Die Rolle der Schweiz in der Entwicklung der Medizin. *Schweiz.Med.Wochenschr.*, 1925, 55: 929-32.

SPENGLER, Ludwig. Beiträge zur Geschichte der Medicin in Mecklenburg. viii, 49 p. Wiesbaden: Kreidel, 1851.
Reviewed by J.G. Thierfelder, *Henschel's Janus*, 1852, 2: 649-50; reprinted, Leipzig: Alfred Lorentz, 1931.

SPENGLER, Ludwig. Bruchstücke aus der Geschichte der Medicin in Meklenburg. *Henschel's Janus*, 1848, 3: 687-743; reprinted, Leipzig: Alfred Lorentz, 1931.

STICKER, Georg. Die Entwicklung der ärztlichen Kunst in Deutschland. 52 p., 19 pl. (Münchener Beiträge zur Geschichte und Literatur der Naturwissenschaft und Medizin, 6) München: Münchner Drucke, 1927.

STRACKE, Johannes C. Fünf Jahrhunderte Arzt und Heilkunst in Ostfriesland. 200 p. Aurich: Verlag Ostfriesische Landschaft, 1960.
Reviewed by Gernot Rath, *Sudhoffs Arch.*, 1963, 47: 189-90.

STRICKER, Wilhelm. Die Geschichte der Heilkunde und der verwandten Wissenschaften in der Stadt Frankfurt am Main. Nach den Quellen bearbeitet. viii, 368 p. Frankfurt a. M.: 1847.
Reviewed in *Henschel's Janus*, 1848, 3: 351-6; reprinted, Leipzig: Alfred Lorentz, 1931.

WEHRLI, G.A. Die Bader, Barbiere und Wundärzte im alten Zürich. 100 p., 4 pl., 44 fig. (*Mitt.Antiq.Ges.Zürich*, 30: no. 3) Zurich: 1927.
Reviewed by K. Sudhoff, *Mitt.Gesch.Med.*, 1927, 26: 200-1.

Nwg-bx

BUESS, Heinrich. Recherches, découvertes et inventions de médecins suisses; introduction biographique et bibliographique. iv, 137 p. Bâle: Ciba, SA, 1946.
On the occasion of an exhibition of books and manuscripts at the Bibliothèque Nationale in Berne.

Nwg-ce

SIGERIST, Henry E. Deutsche medizinische Handschriften aus Schweizer Bibliotheken. *Arch.Gesch.Med.*, 1925, 17: 205-40.

STEIN, Robert. Alte französische Zeitschriften für deutsche medizinische und naturwissenschaftliche Literatur. *Arch. Gesch.Math.Naturwiss.Tech.*, 1928, 10: 473-5.

Nwg-ch-bv

HUSNER, Fritz. Verzeichnis der Basler medizinischen Universitätsschriften von 1575-1829. *Festschrift für Jacques Brodbeck-Sandreuter*, p. 137-269, ill. Basel: Schwabe, 1942. [CB 71/129]

Nwg-cj

BRUNN, Walter von. Das deutsche medizinische Zeitschriftenwesen seit der Mitte des 19. Jahrhunderts. iv, 50 p. (Riedel-Archiv Sonderheft) Berlin: Idra-Verlagsanstalt, 1925.

KISSKALT, Karl. Scherz- und Kneipzeitungen als Quellen der Geschichte der Medizin. *Mitt.Gesch.Med.Naturwiss.Tech.*, 1937, 36: 147-9.

NEUBURGER, Max. Das Wiener medizinische Zeitschriftenwesen vor Begründung der *Wiener Medizinischen Wochenschrift*. *Wiener Med.Wochenschr.*, 1930, 80: 29-31.

SUDHOFF, Karl. Das medizinische Zeitschriftenwesen in Deutschland bis zur Mitte des 18. Jahrhunderts. Eine bibliographisch-literarische Skizze (1903). *Sudhoffs Arch.*, 1929, 21: (Ausgewählte Abhandlungen von Karl Sudhoff zum 75. Geburtstage), 273-82.

Nwg-da

JAGIC, N. von. Erinnerungen an Wiener Kliniker. *Festschrift zum 80. Geburtstag Max Neuburgers*, p. 246-9. Wien: Maudrich, 1948.

Nwg-da-py

ZEKERT, Otto. Österreichische Nobelpreisträger für Medizin, Physiologie und Chemie. 86 p., ill. (HMW-Jahrbuch, 1961) Wien: Heilmittelwerke, 1961.
Reviewed by Nils von Hofsten, *Lychnos*, 1960-61, 417.

Nwg-dae

GOTTLIEB, Bernward J.; BERG, Alexander. Das Antlitz des germanischen Arztes in vier Jahrhunderten. 54 p., ill. Berlin: Rembrandt, 1942.
Reviewed by Lloyd G. Stevenson, *J.Hist.Med.*, 1964, 19: 169-70.

Nwg-f

DIEPGEN, Paul. Das Schicksal der deutschen Medizingeschichte im Zeitalter der Naturwissenschaften und ihre Aufgaben in der Gegenwart. *Deut.Med.Wochenschr.*, 1934, 60: 66-70.

Nwg-ht

DIEPGEN, Paul. Der Weg von Boerhaaves Medizin nach Deutschland. *Ned.Tijdschr.Geneesk.*, 1938, 82: 4852-60.

Nwg-o study and teaching

Nwg-oq

ARTELT, Walter. Die Berliner Medizinische Fakultät. 1. Die Gründung und die ersten Jahrzehnte der Berliner Medizinischen Fakultät; 2. Die Berliner Medizinische Fakultät in den Jahren 1833 bis 1858; 3. Die Berliner Medizinische Fakultät vom Tode Johannes Müllers bis zur Jahrhundertwende. Literatur zum Thema. *Ciba Z.*, 1956, 7: no. 78, 2570-607, ill.

BILLROTH, Theodor. The medical sciences in the German universities: a study in the history of civilization. Translated from the German, with an introduction by William H. Welch. xii, 292 p. New York: Macmillan, 1924.

BONNER, Thomas Neville. *See* Npw

BRUGSCH, Theodor. Die Klinik in Halle (historisch). *Arch. Gesch.Med.*, 1928, 20: 17-32.

CASTIGLIONI, Arturo. The medical school of Vienna. *Ciba Symp.*(Summit, N.J.), 1947, 9: 634-64, ill.

DIEPGEN, Paul. Die alte Mainzer medizinische Fakultät und die Wissenschaft ihrer Zeit. 31 p. (Mainzer Universitäts-Reden, 18) Mainz: Kupferberg, 1951.

DIEPGEN, Paul. Die Freiburger Medizinische Fakultät am Anfang unseres Jahrhunderts. *Deut.Med.Wochenschr.*, 1938, 39: 1-12.

DIEPGEN, Paul; ROSTOCK, P.; ed. Das Universitätsklinikum in Berlin. Seine Ärzte und wissenschaftliche Leistung 1810-1933. viii, 200 p., 13 pl., 17 fig. Berlin: Müller, 1939

DISSELHORST, Rudolf. Die medizinische Fakultät der Universität Wittenberg und ihre Vertreter von 1503-1816. *Leopoldina, new ser.*, 1929, 5: 79-101.

FISCHER, I. *See* Npw

FRAATZ, Paul. Das Matrikelbuch der Münsterschen "Medizinisch-Chirurgischen Lehranstalt." *Sudhoffs Arch.*, 1942, 35: 68-97.

FRANKE, H.; SCHRÖDER, J. Die Würzburger Medizinische Universitäts-Poliklinik. 1807-1957. x, 123 p., 31 fig. Stuttgart: Thieme, 1957.
Reviewed by Marc Klein, *Arch.Int.Hist.Sci.*, 1960, 13: 173-4.

HOCHE, Alfred E. Jahresringe. Innenansicht eines Menschenlebens. 298 p. München: Lehmann, 1934.
Teaching medicine at the University at Freiburg in the early part of the entury.
Reviewed by W. Enke, *Deut.Lit.Zeitung*, 1934, 5: 2342-6; by M.A. van Andel, *Bijdr.Gesch.Geneesk.*, 1935, 15: 18.

NAUCK, E. Th. Die Zahl der Medizinstudenten deutscher Hochschulen im 14.-18. Jahrhundert. *Sudhoffs Arch.*, 1954, 38: 175-86.

NEUBURGER, Max. *See* Npw

ORTNER, Norbert. Zur Geschichte der II. Wiener medizinischen Universitätsklinik. *Festschrift zur Feier seines 60. Geburtstages Max Neuburger gewidmet*, p. 265-8. Wien: 1928.

SCHMIZ, Karl. Die medizinische Fakultät der Universität Bonn, 1818-1918. Gedruckt mit Unterstützung der Fakultät. viii, 103 p. Bonn: Marcus und Weber, 1920. [CB 12/602]

SCHUMACHER, Joseph. Zur Geschichte der medizinischen Fakultät Freiburg/Br. Festschrift zur Fünfhundert-Jahr-Feier der Albert-Ludwig-Universität. 53 p., 16 tables. Stuttgart: Ferd. Enke, 1957.
Reviewed by Edwin Rosner, *Sudhoffs Arch.*, 1959, 43: 92-3.

STICKER, Georg. Entwicklungsgeschichte der Medizinischen Fakultät an der Alma Mater Julia. *Festschrift zum 350jähr. Bestehen der Universität Würzburg*, p. 385-799, front. Berlin: Springer, 1932.
Reviewed by Haberling, *Mitt.Gesch.Med.*, 1932, 31: 279.

STÜBLER, Eberh. Geschichte der medizinischen Fakultät der Universität Heidelberg 1386-1925. xviii, 339 p. Heidelberg: C. Winter, 1926.

WOLF-HEIDEGGER, Gerhard. The medical faculty of Basle University, 1460-1959. *Ciba Symp.*, 1959, 6: 243-61.

Nwg-or

ACHELIS, Thomas Otto. Studenten der Medizin aus dem Herzogtum Schleswig von 1517-1864. *Sudhoffs Arch.*, 1960, 44: 357-65.

CASTIGLIONI, Arturo. Italienische Lehrer und Ärzte an der Wiener medizinischen Schule. *Festschrift zur Feier seines 60. Geburtstags Max Neuburger gewidmet*, p. 66-78, ill. Wien: Verlag des Fest-Komitees, 1928.

LÖWENSTEIN, Jakob Samuel. Biographien und Schriften der ordentlichen Professoren der Medicin an der Hochschule zu Frankfurth a. O. in den Jahren 1506 bis 1811. *Henschel's Janus*, 1848, 3: 283-315, 419-43; reprinted, Leipzig: Alfred Lorentz, 1931.

NAUCK, E.Th. Studenten und Assistenten der Freiburger medizischen Fakultät. Ein geschichtlicher Rückblick. 115 p., map. (Beiträge zur Freiburger Wissenschafts-und Universitätsgeschichte, 5) Freiburg i. Br.: E. Albert, 1955.
Reviewed by Erna Lesky, *Sudhoffs Arch.*, 1956, 40: 377-8.

PREMUDA, Loris. *See* Nwi-or

Nwg-q/r organizational and professional aspects

Nwg-qd

ARTELT, Walter. Die medizinische Lesegesellschaften in Deutschland. *Sudhoffs Arch.*, 1953, 37: 195-200.

DIEPGEN, Paul. Der Deutsche Ärztevereinsbund und seine Zeit bei der Gründung und heute. Über die Aufgaben einer Geschichte des Bundes. *Deut.Ärztebl.*, 1931, no. 18, 11 p.

FISCHER, I. Geschichte der Gesellschaft der Aerzte in Wien, 1837-1937. Hrsg. von der Gesellschaft. 299 p., 14 fig. Vienna: Springer, 1938.
Reviewed by Otto E. Guttentag, *Isis*, 1939, 30: 561-2.

LESKY, Erna. Neues zur Geschichte der Gesellschaft der Aerzte in Wien. *Wiener Klin.Wochenschr.*, 1953, 65: 1-14.

MANN, Gunter. Die medizinischen Lesegesellschaften in Deutschland. 120 p., ill. (Arbeiten aus dem Bibliothekar-Lehrinstitut des Landes Nordrhein-Westfalen, 11) Köln: Greven Verlag, 1956.
Reviewed by S. Principe, *Riv.Stor.Sci.*, 1956, 47: 385-6; by C. Lilian Temkin, *Bull.Hist.Med.*, 1958, 32: 88-9.

SUDHOFF, Karl. Der deutschen Naturforscherversammlungen Werden und wachsende Bedeutung in ihrem ersten Jahrhundert. *Wiss.Ind.*, Sept. 1922, 1: 33-8.

SUDHOFF, Karl. Hundert Jahre Deutscher Naturforscherversammlungen. Gedächtnisschrift zur Jahrhundert Tagung der Gesellschaft Deutscher Naturforscher und Aerzte. 80 p., 8 pl. Leipzig: F.C.W. Vogel, 1922.

Nwg-qg

KOLL, W.; SCHOEDEL, W. Die Medizinische Forschungsanstalt der Max-Planck-Gesellschaft. Zum 80. Geburtstag von Karl Thomas. *Naturwissenschaften*, 1963, 50: 703-4.

Nwg-qq

WIDMER, Edgar. Zur Geschichte der schweizerischen ärztlichen Mission in Afrika unter besonderer Berücksichtigung des medizinischen Zentrums von Ifakara, Tanganyika. 64 p., maps, ill. (*Basler Veröffentl.Gesch.Med.Biol.*, 16) Basel/Stuttgart: Benno Schwabe, 1963.

Nwg-r

ALBERTI, Julius Gustav. Der Stand der Aertze in Preussen. Ein historisch-kritischer Versuch, mit Beziehung auf die bevorstehende Reform des preussischen Medicinal-Wesens. 143 p. Leipzig: Brockhaus, 1846.
Reviewed by J. Rosenbaum, *Henschel's Janus*, 1846, 1: 699-702; reprinted, Leipzig: Alfred Lorentz, 1931.

Nwg-rj

GERMANY (Territory under Allied Occupation, 1945- U.S. Zone). MILITARY TRIBUNALS. Trials of war criminals before the Nuernberg Military Tribunals ... Vol. 1. Case 1: United States vs. Karl Brandt et al. (the medical case). Vol. 2. Case 1. (contd.). Case 2. United States vs. Erhard Milch (the Milch case). Washington: U.S. Govt. Print. Off., 1949.
For shorter account *see* below Mitscherlich, A.; Mielke, F. Doctors of infamy.

MITSCHERLICH, Alexander; MIELKE, Fred. Doctors of infamy. The story of the Nazi medical crimes. Translated by Heinz Norden. With statements by three American authorities identified with the Nuremberg medical trial: Andrew C. Ivy, Telford Taylor, and Leo Alexander. And a note on medical ethics by Albert Deutsch. (Including the new Hippocratic oath of the World Medical Association). xxxix, 172 p., ill. New York: Schuman, 1949. [CB 74/375]
Reviewed by C.K. Drinker, *Isis*, 1949, 40: 301.

SCHÖNBERG, J. Un nouveau chapitre dans l'histoire de la médecine. *Act.VIIe Congr.Int.Hist.Sci.* (Jerusalem, 1953), p. 557-63. Paris: Hermann, [n.d.].
On medical ethics in connection with medical experimentation in the concentration camps.

SIGERIST, H.E. Vom Hippokratischen Eid zur deutschen ärztlichen Standesordnung. *Deut.Ärztebl.*, Jan.1931, 22-4.

Nwg-rn

ROSENBERG, J.C. Friendships between Viennese physicians and musicians. *Bull.Hist.Med.*, 1958, 32: 366-9.

Nwg-rw

SIEBEL, Johanna. Das Leben von Frau Dr. Marie Heim-Vögtlin, der ersten Schweizer Aerztin (1845-1916). 296 p., 8 facs. Leipzig: Rascher, 1925.

Nwg-s/v social and humanistic relations

Nwg-sc

DIEPGEN, Paul. Deutsche Medizin und deutsche Kultur. *Deut.Ärztebl.*, 1933, 60: 266-72.

Nwg-th

NESBIT, Louis. Arthur Schnitzler (1862-1931). *Med.Life*, 1935, 42: 511-64. [CB 45/242]

WITTMANN, Fritz. Der Arzt im Spiegelbild der deutschen schöngeistigen Literatur seit dem Beginn des Naturalismus. 133 p. (*Abhandl.Gesch.Med.Naturwiss.*, 18) Berlin: Ebering, 1936.

Nwg-u

BÜTTNER, Ludwig. Fränkische Volksmedizin. Ein Beitrag zur Volkskunde Ostfrankens. ix, 269 p. Erlangen: Palm & Enke, 1935.

DIEPGEN, Paul. Deutsche Volksmedizin, wissenschaftliche Heilkunde und Kultur. viii, 136 p., 7 fig., pl. Stuttgart: Enke, 1935. [CB 43/285]

HEMPLER, Franz. Psychologie des Volksglaubens, insbesondere der volkstümlichen Natur- und Heilkunde des Weichsellandes. 112 p. (Einzelschriften der historischen Kommission für Ost- und Westpreussische Landesforschung, 4) Königsberg: Graefe, 1930.

JUNGBAUER, Gustav. Deutsche Volksmedizin. Ein Grundriss. 216 p. Berlin: De Gruyter, 1934.
Reviewed by M.A. van Andel, *Bijdr.Gesch.Geneesk.*, 1935, 15: 136.

LEJEUNE, F. Beiträge zur Kenntnis der niederdeutschen Zaubermedizin. *Arch.Gesch.Med.*, 1926, 18: 111-12.

LEJEUNE, F. Volksmedizinisches aus Vorpommern. *Arch.Gesch. Med.*, 1925, 16: 223-5.

MARX, Otto. Die Zahlen in der Volksheilkunde des schlesischen Raumes. viii, 51 p. (Diss., Breslau) Breslau: 1934.

MARZELL, Heinrich. Heilsegen aus dem bayerischen Franken. *Georg Sticker Festgabe*, p. 27-38. Berlin: Springer, 1930.

Nwg-vm

FELSENTHAL, S. Jüdische Ärzte in Alt-Mannheim. *Arch.Gesch. Med.*, 1930, 23: 184-96.

MERZBACH, Arnold. Jewish physicians in Central Europe during the transitional period from the ghetto to the Emancipation. *Act.VIe Congr.Int.Hist.Sci.* (Amsterdam, 1950), p. 707-12. Paris: Hermann, 1951-53; also in *Arch.Int.Hist.Sci.*, 1954, 7: 168-73.

Nwh Czechoslovakia; Hungary; Poland

ANDRÁS, Deési Daday. L'évolution de la science médicale en Hongrie. (Seventh International Congress of Historical Sciences, Warsaw, 1933) *Bull.Int.Comm.Hist.Sci.*, 1933, 5: 353-70.

GYÖRY, Tiberius von. Der Anteil Ungarns an der Entwicklung der Medizin. *Pester Lloyd*, 27 May, 1928, 29 p.
Reviewed by W. Haberling, *Mitt.Gesch.Med.*, 1928, 27: 329.

KLEY, J.J. van der. De Polen en de geneeskunde. [Poland and medicine. (In Dutch)] *Bijdr.Gesch.Geneesk.*, 1936, 16: 55-6.

PALLA, Ákos, *et al.*; ed. Nymphis medicis. 144 p., ill. Budapest: Medimpex, 1962. [CB 90/534]
On medical history in Hungary.
Reviewed by Liselotte Buchheim, *Sudhoffs Arch.*, 1964, 48: 96.

SKARŻYŃSKI, Bolesław. L'histoire de la médecine en Pologne. Aperçu sur son évolution. 23 p., 9 pl., front. Warsaw: PZWL, Editions Médicales d'Etat, 1956.
Reviewed by S. Principe, *Riv.Stor.Sci.*, 1956, 47: 384-5.

SOKOL, Stanislaw. Sur l'histoire de la médecine de Gdansk. *Act.VIIIe Congr.Int.Hist.Sci.* (Florence, 1956), p. 889-92. Paris: Hermann, 1958.

SZUMOWSKI, Wladislaw. Coup d'oeil sur l'évolution de la médecine en Pologne. 15 p. (Histoire sommaire des sciences en Pologne publiée à l'occasion du VIIe Congrès international des Sciences historiques) Cracow: 1933.

SZUMOWSKI, Wladislaw. La médecine polonaise à travers les siècles. *Paris Méd.*, May 1922, 12: 1-6.

ZEMBRZUSKI, Louis. Participation des médecins et des naturalistes polonais au progrès de la science universelle. *Bull. Soc.Franç.Hist.Méd.*, 1939, 33: 241-54.

Nwh-cj

PALLA, A.; TRENCSÉNI, T.; ed. Az *Orvosi Hetilap* centennaris emlékkönyve. Denkschrift zu dem Centennarium des *Orvosi Hetilap*. 175 p., 60 ill. Budapest: Medicina-Verlag, 1959.
Reviewed by Gy. Regöly-Mérei, *Sudhoffs Arch.*, 1961, 45: 88-9.

Nwh-da

ZEMBRZUSKI, Louis. Participation des médecins et des naturalistes polonais au progrès de la science universelle. *Bull. Soc.Franç.Hist.Méd.*, 1939, 33: 241-54.

Nwh-fqv

BUGIEL, V. Compte rendu du IVe Congrès d'Histoire de la Médecine Polonaise (Cracovie, 5-8 Octobre 1928). *Bull.Soc.Franç. Hist.Méd.*. 1929, 23: 85-95.

Nwh-k

SZUMOWSKI, Wladislaw. L'école polonaise médico-philosophique. In: La Pologne au VIIe Congrès des sciences historiques, (1), p. 39-47. Varsovie: Société Polonaise d'Histoire, 1933.

Nwh-oq

EDINBURGH. UNIVERSITY. POLISH SCHOOL OF MEDICINE. Polish School of Medicine at the University of Edinburgh. Ed. by Józef Brodzké. [An official account of the formation and inauguration of the School...] vii, 63 p., 61 pl., 18 ill. Edinburgh: Oliver and Boyd, 1942.
Reviewed by E.H. Ackerknecht, *Bull.Hist.Med.*, 1944, 15: 331.

PICK, Friedel. *See* Npw

WACHHOLZ, L. Johann Nep. Philip Rust. Beitrag zur Geschichte der medizinischen Fakultät in Krakau. *Arch.Gesch.Med.*, 1938, 31: 40-51.

Nwh-or for Polish students at Italian universities *see* Nwi-or

Nwh-pw

KONOPKA, Stanislas. Les relations culturelles entre la France et la Pologne dans le domaine de la médecine. 21 p., 10 portr., bibliogr. Warsaw: Société polonaise d'Histoire de la Médecine, 1958.
Reviewed by P. Huard, *Rev.Hist.Sci.*, 1959, 12: 284-5.

Nwh-u

BUGIEL, V. La personnification de la maladie dans le folklore polonais. *VIe Congr.Int.Hist.Méd.* (Leyde-Amsterdam, 1927), p. 302-5. Anvers: De Vlijt, 1929.

OWSLANNY, Stanislaus. Aus der polnischen Volksmedizin. (Ein Beitrag zur Volkskunde Polens.) 43 p. (Diss., Leipzig) Posen: 1920. [CB 10/202]

Nwh-vm

MERZBACH, Arnold. Jewish physicians in Central Europe during the transitional period from the ghetto to the Emancipation. *Act.VIe Congr.Int.Hist.Sci.* (Amsterdam, 1950), p. 707-12. Paris: Hermann, 1951-53; also in *Arch.Int.Hist.Sci.*, 1954, 7: 168-73.

Nwh-vm-oq

KISCH, Guido. Die Prager Universität und die Juden, 1348-1848. Mit Beiträgen zur Geschichte des Medizinstudiums. x, 239 p. Mährisch-Ostrau: 1935. [CB 56/374]

Nwi Italy

BILANCIONI, Guglielmo. Veteris vestigia flammae. Pagine storiche della scienza nostra. xvi, 544 p., 66 fig. Roma: Leonardo da Vinci, 1922.
19 essays dealing with the history of anatomy, physiology and medicine in Italy.
Reviewed by George Sarton, *Isis*, 1923, 5: 475-7.

CASTIGLIONI, Arturo. Italian medicine. xi, 134 p., front., 10 ill. (Clio Medica, 6) New York: Hoeber, 1932. [CB 36/455]

CASTIGLIONI, Arturo. Pagine di storia del pensiero medico Mediterraneo. *Rass.Clin.Sci.Ist.Biochim.Ital.*, 1936, 14: 381-9.

DE RENZI, Salvatore. Storia della medicina Italiana. 5 vol. Napoli: Filiatre-Sebezio, 1845-48.
Vol. 1-3 reviewed by C.F. Heusinger, *Henschel's Janus*, 1847, 2: 609-17; reprinted, Leipzig: Alfred Lorentz, 1931.

GAROSI, Alcide. Siena nella storia della medicina. 562 p., ill. Florence: Olschki, 1958.
Reviewed by L.P., *Riv.Stor.Med.*, 1958, 2: 122-4.

MANCINI, Clodomiro. Note per la storia della medicina Genovese. 56 p., pl. (Collana Scientia Veterum, 51) Pisa: Giardini, 1963. [CB 90/533]

PAZZINI, Adalberto. La storia della medicina in Italia nell' ultimo cinquantennio. *Riv.Stor.Sci.*, 1937, 28: 251-9; 1938, 29: 79-84, 218-31, 274-83; 1939, 30: 26-38.

RANDALL, John Herman, Jr. The development of scientific method in the school of Padua. *J.Hist.Ideas*, 1940, 1: 177-206.

SEMBIANTI, Pietro. Appunti di storia medica trentina e dell' Alto Adige. *Atti IIIo Congr.Naz.Soc.Ital.Stor.Sci. Med.Natur.* (Venezia, 1925), p. 157-62. Siena: 1926.

Nwi-bv

BILANCIONI, Guglielmo. La storia della medicina. 100 p. (Guide ICS, Profili bibliografici de l' "Italia che scrive") Roma: Istituto per la propaganda della cultura italiana, 1920. [CB 10/201]

PAZZINI, Adalberto. Bibliografia di storia della medicina Italiana. 455 p., ill. (Enciclopedia biografica e bibliografica Italiana, ser. 31: La medicina, 1) Milan: Tosi, 1939.
Reviewed (in Swedish) by Tönnes Kleberg, *Lychnos*, 1940, 466-7.

Nwi-cd

BARBIELLINI AMIDEI, Ademaro, ed. Lettere inedite di medici e chirurghi piemontesi dei sec. XVI, XVII, XVIII. 44 p. (Archivio del Castello di Verzuolo, 4) Torino: Arduini, 1939.
Reviewed by R. Bèttica-Giovannini, *Riv.Stor.Sci.*, 1942, 33: 21-2.

Nwi-cj

CASTIGLIONI, Arturo. Gli arbori del giornalismo medico italiano. *Archeografo Triestino, ser. 3*, 1923, 10: 1-40, 6 pl. [CB 14/555]

Nwi-da

CALANDRA, E. La celebrazione dei grandi medici siciliani. 139 p. Palermo: Salpietra, 1940.
Reviewed by D. Giordano, *Riv.Stor.Sci.*, 1941, 32: 106-7.

CAPPARONI, Pietro. Profili bio-bibliografici di medici e naturalisti celebri italiani dal sec. XV° al sec. XVIII°. 2 vol. 132 p., 30 pl.; 138 p., 30 pl. Roma: Istituto nazionale medico farmacologico, 1925, 1928. [CB 20/196]

MARSICO, Vincenzo. Medici Lucani. Saggio bio-bibliografico. 2nd ed. 301 p. Matera: Fratelli Montemurro, 1962. [CB 90/505]

PITRÈ, Giuseppe. Medici, chirurgi, barbieri e speziali antichi in Sicilia. Secoli XIII-XVIII. Curiosità storiche e altri scritti. A cura di Giovanni Gentile. 405 p. (Edizione nazionale, 41) Firenze: Barbèra, 1942. [CB 72/279]
First publ. 1910.

SINDICATO PROVINCIALE DEI MEDICI CHIRURGHI, Bologna. In memoria dei medici e studenti in medicina caduti nella lotta di liberazione. 32 p., portr. Bologna: 1945. [CB 70/226]
Speeches by G. Battista Facchini, A. Cucchi and A. Businco on the martyrs of Italian liberation from Nazi bondage, among the physicians and medical students of Bologna.

SOMEDA DE MARCO, Pietro. Medici forjuliensi dal sec. XIII al sec. XVIII. 206 p., ill. Udine: Il Friuli Medico, 1963. [CB 90/535]

VIVIANI, Ugo. Medici, fisici e cerusici della provincia Aretina vissuti dal V al XVII secolo d.C. 217, viii p. (Collana di pubblicazioni storiche e letterarie aretine, 7) Arezzo: Viviani, 1923. [CB 20/211]
Reviewed by A. Mieli, *Arch.Stor.Sci.*, 1924, 4: 185-6.

Nwi-dae-ct

APERLO, G. Medaglie coniate in onore di anatomici, medici, chirurghi, specialisti italiani dei secoli XVIII, XIX, e XX. (Contributo alla storia icono-biografica della medicina). *Riv.Stor.Sci.*, 1932, 23: 84-6, 117-28, 174-6. [CB 37/608 and CB 38/610]

Nwi-o study and teaching

Nwi-oq

BUSACCHI, Vincenzo. I primordi dell'insegnamento medico a Bologna. *Riv.Stor.Sci.*, 1948, 39: 128-44.

CASTIGLIONI, Arturo. Medical School of Padua. *Ciba Symp.* (Summit, N.J.), 1948, 10: 958-92, ill.

CASTIGLIONI, Arturo. The medical school at Padua and the renaissance of medicine. *Ann.Med.Hist.*, 1935, 7: 214-27, 4 fig.

CASTIGLIONI, Arturo. The origin of the University of Bologna; The School of Medicine at Bologna; Bologna in the Renaissance; The anatomical theater and the anatomists of Bologna. *Ciba Symp.*(Summit, N.J.), 1945, 7: 70-6, ill., 77-83, ill., 84-90, ill., 91-100, ill.

CASTIGLIONI, Arturo; BELLONI, Luigi. Die Medizinschule von Padua. *Ciba Z.*, 1950, 11: 4439-66, ill.

CORTI, Alfredo. Note storiche e biografiche su Bologna e il suo studio. *Riv.Stor.Sci.*, 1949, 40: 19-51, 14 ill.
Apropos of D.M.G. Galeazzi and of the anatomical theatre of Bologna.

FILIPPI, Angiolo. La storia della Scuola Medico-chirurgica Fiorentina. *Riv.Stor.Sci.*, 1923, 14: 4-14, 86-90.

PAZZINI, Adalberto. Storia dell'insegnamento medico in Roma. Dalla scuola patriarcale a quella della "Sapienza". 389 p. Bologna: Cappelli, 1935.
Reviewed by Aldo Mieli, *Archeion*, 1935, 17: 324-27.

PAZZINI, Adalberto. La storia della facoltà medica di Roma. 2 vol., 704 p., tables. Rome: Editore l'Istituto di Storia della Medicina dell'Università di Roma, 1961.
Reviewed by Pietro Franceschini, *Physis*, 1962, 4: 85-6.

PELLEGRINI, Francesco. La clinica medica padovana attraverso i secoli. viii, 212 p. Verona: La Tipografica Veronese, 1939.
Reviewed by L. Castaldi, *Riv.Stor.Sci.*, 1940, 31: 168.

Nwi-or

BUSACCHI, Vincenzo. [Poles at the University of Bologna. (In Italian)] *Atti Mem.Accad.Stor.Arte Sanit.*, 1964, 30: 71-4.

CASTIGLIONI, Arturo. Les étudiants en médecine flamands à l'Université de Padoue. *VIe Congr.Int.Hist.Méd.*(Leyde-Amsterdam, 1927), p. 313-17. Anvers: De Vlijt, 1929.

CASTIGLIONI, Arturo. Italienische Lehrer und Aerzte an der Wiener medizinischen Schule. *Festschrift zur Feier seines 60. Geburtstags Max Neuburger gewidmet*, p. 66-78, ill. Wien: Verlag des Fest-Komitees, 1928.

CASTIGLIONI, Arturo. Gli studenti di medicina polacchi all' Università di Padova. *Atti.Soc.Ital.Stor.Sci.Med.Natur.IV. Congr.Naz.*(Roma, 1933), p. 62-81. In: *Riv.Stor.Sci.*, 1933, vol. 15.

GASBARRINI, Antonio. Figure e maestri della scuola medica Padovana. *Riv.Stor.Sci.*, 1949, 40: 52-64, 15 fig.

LACHS, Giovanni. Alcune notizie sugli allievi Polacchi presso la scuola di medicina di Padova. In: Polska Akademija Umiejetności. Omaggio dell'Accademia Polacca di scienze e lettere all'Università di Padova nel settimo centenario, p. 275-328. Cracow: 1922.

PREMUDA, Loris. Die Natio germanica an der Universität Padua. Zur Forschungslage. *Sudhoffs Arch.*, 1963, 47: 97-105.

SHATZKY, Jacob. On Jewish medical students of Padua. *J. Hist.Med.*, 1950, 5: 444-7.

Nwi-p/u organizational and social aspects

Nwi-qd

FABRIS, Pietro. La commemorazione del 550 anno di fondazione della Società di Scienze Mediche di Conegliano e Vittorio. *Boll.Ist.Stor.Ital.Arte Sanit.*, 1931, 11: 330-40.

SOCIETÀ MEDICA-CHIRURGICA. Primo centenario de la Società Medica Chirurgica di Bologna (1823-1923). 995 p., 8 pl. Bologna: 1923.

Nwi-r

BAGLIONI, Silvestro. I medici stranieri nella storia della medicina italiana. *Atti IIIe Congr.Naz.Soc.Ital.Stor.Sci. Med.Natur.* (Venezia, 1925), p. 116-19. Siena: 1926.

Nwi-u

NARDI, G.M. Ricerche storiche intorno alle pratiche di medicina magica con particolare riguardo a quelle del popolo toscano. *Riv.Stor.Sci.*, 1937, 28: 136-49.

PAZZINI, Adalberto. La medicina popolare in Italia. 358 p. Trieste: Zigiotti, 1948.
Reviewed by A. Corsini, *Riv.Stor.Sci.*, 1948, 39: 212-13.

PITRÈ, Giuseppe. Medicina popolare siciliana. xxviii, 458 p. (Edizione Nazionale, 19) Firenze: Barbèra, 1949. [CB 72/279]
First publ. 1896.

TANFANI, Gustavo. Le streghe ed il malocchio nella medicina popolare veneta. *Riv.Stor.Sci.*, 1939, 30: 125-38.

Nwj Spain; Portugal

Estudios de Historia de la Medicina Española. New ser. Vol. 1. Salamanca: Ediciones del Seminario de Historia de la Medicina Española, 1959-60.
Reviewed by Juan A. Paniagua, *Arch.Int.Hist.Sci.*, 1962, 15: 216-19.

GARCIA DEL REAL, Eduardo. Historia de la medicina en España. 1148 p. Madrid: Reuss, 1921.
Reviewed by L. Guinet, *Isis*, 1924, 6: 568-9; by A. Corsini, *Riv.Stor.Sci.*, 1923, 14: 50-1.

GARRISON, Fielding Hudson. An epitome of the history of Spanish medicine. *Bull.N.Y.Acad.Med.*, 1931, 7: 589-634. [CB 34/523]

GRANJEL, Luis S. Historia de la medicina española. 206 p., ill. Barcelona: Sayma Ediciones, 1962.
Reviewed by Werner Leibbrand, *Sudhoffs Arch.*, 1963, 47: 498.

GRANJEL, Luis S. Estudio histórico de la medicina. Lecciones de metodología aplicadas a la historia de la medicina española. 177 p. Salamanca: 1961.
Reviewed by Edwin Clarke, *Bull.Hist.Med.*, 1962, 36: 477-8.

NASIO, Juan. Influencia de la medicina española de los siglos XVI, XVII y XVIII sobre la medicina internacional. *Arch.Iberoamer.Hist.Med.*, 1957, 9: 351-6.

PEZZI, Giuseppe. Relations médicales entre le monde ibérique et la Sardaigne pendant la domination Aragonaise-Espagnole. *Arch.Iberoamer.Hist.Med.*, 1956, 8: 321-3.

PINA GUIMARÃES, Luiz José de. Histoire de la médecine portugaise, abrégé. 132 p., ill. Pôrto: Enciclopédia portuguesa, 1934 [correctly 1935]. [CB 46/600]

PINA GUIMARÃES, Luiz José de. Vimaranes, materias para a história da medicina Portuguesa; arqueologia, antropologia, historia. 336 p., 66 fig. Porto: Araújo & Sobrinho, 1929.

PINA GUIMARÃES, Luiz José de. La médecine et les médecins portugais dans le monde européen. *Arch.Iberoamer.Hist. Med.*, 1956, 8: 325-33.

RICO-AVELLO, Carlos. Aportación al estudio de los médicos y medicina extremeña. *Arch.Iberoamer.Hist.Med.*, 1957, 9: 449-54.
Doctors and medicine in Extremadura from the 16th to the 19th century.

WELLCOME FOUNDATION. Spanish influence on the progress of medical science. With an account of the Wellcome Research Institution and the affiliated research laboratories and museums founded by Sir Henry Wellcome. Commemorating the tenth International Congress of the History of Medicine held at Madrid 1935. 121 p., ill. London: Wellcome Foundation, 1935.

Nwj-ce-bv

ASSOCIACIÓ GENERAL DE METGES DE LLENGUA CATALANA. Bibliografia medical di Catalunya. xxxii, 478 p., 8 pl. Barcelona: Impr. Elzeviriana, 1918.
Contains 2620 items arranged alphabetically by authors.

GRANJEL, Luis S.; TERESA SANTANDER, M. Bibliografía española de historia de la medicina. 242 p. (Vol. I. Publicaciones del Seminario de Historia de la Medicina de la Universidad de Salamanca, Serie B. Repertorios biobibliográficos) Salamanca: 1957.
Reviewed by José M. López Piñero, *Arch.Iberoamer.Hist. Med.*, 1959, 11: 343-4; by F. Guerra, *J.Hist.Med.*, 1959, 14: 260.

HERNANDEZ MOREJON, Antonio. Historia bibliografica de la medicina española. 7 vol. Madrid: 1842-52.
Reviewed by C.F. Heusinger, *Henschel's Janus*, 1847, 2: 609-17; reprinted Leipzig: Alfred Lorentz, 1931

Nwj-oq

LEMOS, Maximiliano. História do Ensino Médico no Pôrto. (I Centenario da Faculdade de Medicina do Pôrto 1825-1925). Desenhos de Salazar. 245 p. Pôrto: Enciclopédia Portuguesa, 1925. [CB 21/602]
This publication is a memorial of the first centenary of the Faculty of Medicine of Oporto.

MONTEIRO, Hernani. História do Ensino Médico no Pôrto. Suplemento coordenado. (I Centenario da Faculdade de Medicina do Pôrto, 1835-1935). Desenhos de Salazar. 94 p., portr. Pôrto: Enciclopédia Portuguesa, 1925. [CB 21/602]

Nwj-pw

JORGE, Ricardo. Relations médicales et scientifiques entre l'Angleterre et le Portugal. *Proc.3rd Int.Congr.Hist.Med.* (London, 1922), p. 82-4. Antwerp: de Vlijt, 1923.

Nwj-tf

PINA GUIMARÃES, Luiz José de. A Igreja na história da medicina portuguesa. *Arq.Hist.Port.*, 1935, 2: 138-62.

ZÚNIGA CISNEROS, Miguel. España, la medicina religiosa y los hospitales. *Rev.Soc.Venezolana Hist.Med.*, 1956, 4: 161-74.

Nwj-u

CASTILLO DE LUCAS, Antonio. Analogías de los "Proverbi Siciliani" de aplicación médica, citados en las obras folklóricas del doctor Pitré, y los Refranes Castellanos. *Arch. Iberoamer.Hist.Med.*, 1957, 9: 95-8.

LEITE DE VASCONCELLOS, José. A Figa. Estudo de etnografia comparativa, precedido de algumas palavras a respeito do "sobrenatural" na medicina popular portuguesa. Conferencia lida na Faculdade de medicina do Pôrto em 26 Junho de 1925. 136 p., fig. (I Centenario da Régia escola de Cirurgia do Pôrto, 1825-1925) Pôrto: Araujo & Sobrinho, 1925. [CB 21/586]

Nwj-vm

FRIEDENWALD, Harry. Jewish physicians of Spain and Portugal. Historical notes and anecdotes. *Med.Life*, 1938, 45: 205-20.

HALÉVY, Meyer A. *see* Nwo-vm

Nwk Low Countries

BAUMANN, E.D. Uit drie eeuwen Nederlandse geneeskunde. [1600-1900. Three centuries of Dutch medicine. (In Dutch)] 320 p., 46 ill. Amsterdam: Meulenhoff, 1951.
Reviewed by Frans Jonckheere, *Arch.Int.Hist.Sci.*, 1952, 5: 174-6.

FÉDÉRATION MÉDICALE BELGE. Cent ans de médecine en Belgique, 1830-1930. 351 p., ill. (*Scalpel*, 1931, 84: special number) Bruxelles: J. Vromans, 1931

FLORKIN, Marcel. Médecine et médecins au Pays de Liége. 231 p., 72 ill. (Université de Liége, Travaux du Séminaire d'Histoire de la Médecine, vol. 1) Liége: H. Vaillant-Carmanne, 1954.
Reviewed by George Sarton, *J.Hist.Med.*, 1954, 9: 471-5; by Ernest Wickersheimer, *Rev.Hist.Sci.*, 1954, 7: 192-3; by Erwin H. Ackerknecht, *Arch.Int.Hist.Sci.*, 1954, 7: 385.

MAYER, Charles. La médecine à la "belle époque": Léon Stienon, 1850-1945. 67 p., ill. Brussels: Editions Pharmacobel-Codipha, 1961.
Reviewed by L. Elaut, *Sci.Hist.*, 1961, 3: 203-4.

RENAUX, Ernest; DALCQ, Albert; GOVAERTS, Jean. Aperçu de l'histoire de la médecine en Belgique. 85 p., pl. (Collection Nationale, 84) Bruxelles: Office de Publicité, 1947. [CB 73/183]

RIBBIUS, P. Medici en medische toestanden te Arnhem door alle tijden. [Medical men and medical conditions at Arnhem throughout the ages. (In Dutch)] *Bijdr.Gesch.Geneesk.*, 1927, 7: 532-57.

SIGERIST, Henry E. Hollands Bedeutung in der Entwicklung der Medizin. *Deut.Med.Wochenschr.*, 1928, 54: 1489-92, ill.

TEN DOESSCHATE, A. Overzicht van de geschiedenis der geneeskunde te Zwolle. [An outline of the history of medicine at Zwolle. (In Dutch)] *Bijdr.Gesch.Geneesk.*, 1928, 8: 81-96.

Nwk-bx

UNGER, W.S. Tentoonstelling betreffende de geschiedenis der genees- en natuurkunde in Zeeland. [Exhibition illustrating the history of medicine and the natural sciences in Zeeland. (In Dutch)] *Bijdr.Gesch.Geneesk.*, 1926, 6: 191-9.

Nwk-ce-bv

VELDE, Albert J.J. van de. Zuid- en Noord- Nederlandsche bibliographie over natuur- en geneeskunde tot 1800. 12 parts. *Verslagen Mededeel. Vlaam.Acad.Taal Lett.*, 1937, 255-301, 425-87, 659-700; 1938, 199-265, 439-505; 1939, 47-111, 173-261, 525-603, 827-87; 1940, 53-133, 365-443; 1941, 195-301. [CB 73/165]
Supplement *ibid.*, 1947, 47-64.

Nwk-ch

KROON, J.E. Enkele mededeelingen omtrent Leidsche geneeskunde proefschriften der 16de, 17de en begin 18de eeuw. [Some notes on Leiden medical theses of the 16th, 17th and beginning of the 18th century. (In Dutch)] *Bijdr.Gesch. Geneesk.*, 1923, 3: 145-56.

Nwk-cj

DELPRAT, C.C. De geschiedenis der Nederlandsche geneeskundige tijdschriften van 1680 tot 1857. [The history of Dutch medicals from 1680 to 1857. (In Dutch)] *Bijdr. Gesch.Geneesk.*, 1927, 7: 1-114, 201-314, 417-90.
Important memoir describing carefully all the Dutch medical journals, concluding with a chronological list of the 83 Dutch medical journals discussed.

Nwk-cp

TRICOT-ROYER, J.J.G. Tabatières hollandaises à gravures médicales. *Bull.Soc.Franç.Hist.Méd.*, 1925, 19: 125-8.

Nwk-da

SCHEVENSTEEN, A.F.C. van. Naamlijsten van Antwerpsche Geneesheeren, Chirurgijens, enz. opgemaakt uit de voornaamste fondsen van het Stadtarchief. *Antwerpsch Archievenbl., 2nd ser.*, 1932, 7: 122-60.

SPRUNCK, Alphonse. Quelques figures remarquables de médecins de l'ancien pays de Luxembourg. *Act.IIIe Congr.Bénélux Hist.Sci.* (Luxembourg, 1960), p. 158-65. Leiden: E.J. Brill; and in *Janus*, 1960, 49: 158-65.

Nwk-o study and teaching

Nwk-op

SCHOUTE, D. Uit het verleden van ons academisch onderwijs aan het ziekbed. [On the history of academic teaching at the bedside. (In Dutch)] *Bijdr.Gesch.Geneesk.*, 1941, 21: 33-9.
History of clinical teaching in Holland from 1636 on.

Nwk-oq

BASTENIE, P.A.; LAMBERT, P.P. L'évolution des cliniques universitaires (de l'U.L.B.). *Méd.France*, 1958, 15-16, ill.

BRANS, P.H. Les collèges médicaux dans les Pays-Bas méridionaux. *Janus*, 1957, 46: 25-40.

COLE, F.J. The University of Leyden. Contributions to biology and medicine. *Nature*, 1941, 147: 161-3.

DOESSCHATE, G. Ten. De Utrechtse Universiteit en de geneeskunde, 1636-1900. [Utrecht University and medical science, 1636-1900. (In Dutch, with English summary)] 180 p., ill., portr. Nieuwkoop: De Graff, 1963. [CB 90/508]
Reviewed in *Sci.Hist.*, 1964, 6: 90-1.

GUTHRIE, Douglas. *See* Npw

LA BARRE, Jean. La Faculté de Médecine de l'Université Libre de Bruxelles depuis sa fondation jusqu'à nos jours. *Méd. France*, 1958, 3-7, ill.

NAPJUS, J.W. De geneeskundige faculteit van de hoogeschool en rijksathenaeum te Franeker, 1585-1843. *Bijdr.Gesch.Geneesk.*, 1927, 7: 577-601.

TRICOT-ROYER, J.J.G. Coup d'oeil sur l'ancienne Faculté de Médecine de Louvain. *Rev.Quest.Sci.*, 1927, 12: 47-72.

TRICOT-ROYER, J.J.G. L'histoire de la médecine à Lovenjoul. Coup d'oeil sur l'ancienne Faculté de Médecine de Louvain. *Rev.Méd.Louvain*, 1927, 8 p.

Nwk-or

CASTIGLIONI, Arturo. *See* Nwi-or

NAPJUS, J.W. De hoogleeraren in de geneeskunde aan de hoogeschool en het Athenaeum te Franeker (1585-1843). [The professors of medicine at the University and the Athenaeum at Franeker. (In Dutch)] *Bijdr.Gesch.Geneesk.*, 1936, 16: 163-70.

Nwk-p/v organizational aspects; social and humanistic relations

Nwk-pv

LINDEBOOM, G.A. Medisch-wetenschappelijke betrekkingen tussen Noord- en Zuid-Nederland in vroeger dagen (15e-17e eeuw). [Medical-scientific relations between the Northern and Southern Netherlands in former days (15th to 17th century). (In Dutch)] *Bijdr.Gesch.Geneesk.*, 1958, 38: 17-19; *Scalpel*, 1958, 111: 498-504; *Ned.Tijdschr.Geneesk.*, 1958, 102: 1753-5.

Nwk-pw for relations between Holland and Russia *see* Npw ESSO, I. van

Nwk-qd

TRICOT-ROYER, J.J.G. Deux ancêtres de l'Association Médicale Franco-Belge de la Vallée de l'Escaut, Jean de Saint-Amand et Jacques Despars. 15 p. Lille: Imprimerie Centrale du Nord, 1925.

Nwk-rk-ME

NIJESSEN, D.J.H. De nederlandsche arts als anthropoloog. [The Dutch physician as anthropologist. (In Dutch)] *Bijdr. Gesch.Geneesk.*, 1927, 7: 602-13, portr.

Nwk-tq

LINT, J.G. de. Geneeskundige volksprenten in de Nederlanden. [Medical popular prints in the Netherlands. (In Dutch)] 122 p., 78 ill. Gorinchem: J. Noorduyn, 1918. [CB 9/491]

LINT, J.G. de. Volkstümliche Bilder auf dem Gebiete der Medizin in den Niederlanden. *Janus*, 1919, 24: 253-315.

RIJNBERK, G. van. De geneesheer en de geneeskunst in nederlandsche prentverbeeldingen. [The doctor and medicine in Dutch pictorial representation. (In Dutch)] *Bijdr.Gesch. Geneesk.*, 1921, 1: 32-47, 14 fig., 165-75, 9 fig.; 1922, 2: 1-12, 169-73; 1923, 3: 1-8, 8 fig.; 1929, 9: 73-83, 10 fig.

Nwk-u

BAKKER, C. Volksgeneeskundige aanteekeningen in en om Broek in Waterland verzameld. [Notes on medical folklore collected in and around Broek in Waterland. (In Dutch)] *Bijdr. Gesch.Geneesk.*, 1927, 7: 356-69; 1928, 8: 45-61.

KOOI, D. van der. Folkloristische en volksgeneeskundige sprokkellingen in de friesche wouden. [Gleanings of folklore and folk medicine in the Frisian forest. (In Dutch)] *Bijdr. Gesch.Geneesk.*, 1933, 13: 1-17.

MEYERE, Victor de. De tooverij in Vlaanderen. Tooveraars, tooverheksen, aflezers en stuiters. Hunne practijken en geheimen. [Witchcraft in Flanders: magicians, witchdoctors, faith-healers and quacks: their practices and mysteries. (In Dutch)] *Ned.Tijdschr.Volksk.*, 1929, 34: 87-128, ill.
Reviewed by M.A. van Andel, *Bijdr.Gesch.Geneesk.*, 1930, 10: 297.

TRICOT-ROYER, J.J.G. Le folklore médical belge. *Petrus Nonius*, 1937-38, 1: 219-45, 357-79.

WIT, J. de. Volksgeneeskunde in West-Friesland. [Folk medicine in West-Friesland. (In Dutch)] *Bijdr.Gesch.Geneesk.*, 1924, 4: 215-20.

Nwk-vm

COHEN, D.E. De vroegere Amsterdamsche joodsche doctoren. [Early Jewish doctors of Amsterdam. (In Dutch)] *Bijdr. Gesch.Geneesk.*, 1927, 7: 625-41.

PINES, Jacques. Essai sur l'histoire des médecins juifs en Belgique. *Rev.Hist.Méd.Hébraique*, 1959, 12: 183-9.

Nwm Scandinavia

CARÖE, Kristian. Studier til Dansk medicinalhistorie. [Study of the history of medicine in Denmark. (In Danish)] 264 p. Copenhagen: 1912.

Nwm-oq

KAROLINSKA INSTITUTET. The Royal Medical School in Stockholm. 102 p., ill. Stockholm: Almquist and Wiksell, 1960.
Reviewed in *Med.Hist.*, 1962, 6: 99.

Nwm-qd

BERGSTRAND, Hilding. Svenska Läkaresällskapet 150 Ar. Dess Tillkomst och Utveckling. En återblick. [The Swedish Medical Society. Its origin and development. A review. (In Swedish)] 562 p., ill. Stockholm: Svenska Läkaresällskapet, 1958.
Reviewed by Anne Tjomsland, *Bull.Hist.Med.*, 1960, 34: 85-8; by Emil Bovin, *Lychnos*, 1960, 456-8.

JOHNSSON, John William Schibbye. Københavnske medicinske selskaber. Festkrift i anledning af Medicinsk Selskabs jubilaeum, 1772-1922. [The medical societies of Copenhagen. A Festschrift on the occasion of the jubilee of Det Medicinske Selskab, 1772-1922. (In Danish, with French summary)] 283 p. København: Th. Linds efterfølger L. Schmiegelow, 1922. [CB 14/555]

Nwm-qg

JORPES, Johan Erik; RAMGREN, Olof. Kemiska institutionen vid Kungl. Karolinska Medico-kirurgiska Institutet i Stockholm intill 1953. [The chemical institute of the Royal Caroline Medical Institute in Stockholm until 1953. (In Swedish)] 207 p., ill. Stockholm: P.A. Norstedt, 1954.
Reviewed by Adolph B. Benson, *J.Hist.Med.*, 1955, 10: 140-1.

Nwm-r

JOHNSSON, John William Schibbye. Les origines de la profession médicale au Danemark. Chamans d'autrefois et d'aujourd'hui. *VIe Congr.Int.Hist.Méd.* (Leyde-Amsterdam, 1927), p. 318-23. Anvers: De Vlijt, 1929.

JOHNSSON, John William Schibbye. Personalgeschichte der dänischen Aerzte. *Mitt.Gesch.Med.*, 1916, 15: 183-4.

Nwm-rj

GOTFREDSEN, Edv. Om Laegelöftet. [The doctor's oath. (In Danish, with English summary)] *Berlingske Tid.*, 26. Jan. 1955, 4 p.
The Danish doctor's oath, modelled on the Hippocratic oath, was introduced in 1815.

Nwm-u

REICHBORN-KJENNERUD, Ingjald. Vår gamle Trolldomsmedisin. [Our ancient magic medicine. (In Norwegian)] 5 vol. (*Skr. Norske Vidensk.Akad.Hist.Fil.Kl.*, 1927, no. 6; 1933, no. 2; 1940, no. 1; 1943, no. 2; 1947, no. 1) Oslo: Dybvad, 1928-47. [CB 25/431]
Reviewed by Anne Tjomsland, *J.Hist.Med.*, 1949, 4: 342-4.

TILLHAGEN, Carl-Herman. Folklig läkekonst. [Popular medicine. (In Swedish)] 378 p., ill. Stockholm: Nordiska museet, 1958.
Reviewed by Wolfram Kock, *Centaurus*, 1960, 7: 143-4.
Folk medicine in Sweden.

Nwn Russia; Baltic States; Finland

American Review of Soviet Medicine. Vol. 1-5. New York: American-Soviet Medical Society, 1943-48. [CB 65/87]

GARRISON, Fielding Hudson. Russian medicine under the old regime. *Bull.N.Y.Acad.Med.*, 1931, 7: 693-734. [CB 34/523]

KURY, Hans; JOLLER, Hansjürg. Die Medizin in Russland bis zum Tode Peters des Grossen. *Ciba Z.*, 1948, 10: 4202-36, ill.

LACHTIN, Michael J. Die Geschichte der russischen Medizin von 1807-1927. *Sudhoffs Arch.*, 1929, 22: 356-60.

MACNALTY, Arthur. Medical history in the U.S.S.R. during the Second World War. *Nature*, 1952, 169: 574-5.

MEUNIER, Léon. Histoire de la médecine depuis ses origines jusqu'à nos jours. vi, 642 p. Paris: Le François, 1924. [CB 16/319]
Corrected reprint of first edition, Paris: Baillière, 1911. Russian transl. by J.A. Oksenov (with appendix on the development of medicine in Russia) Moscow: 1926; reviewed by H. Zeiss, *Mitt.Gesch.Med.*, 1926, 25: 250.

OHANESSIAN, L.A. Illustrations relatives à l'histoire de la médecine en Arménie de l'antiquité jusqu'à nos jours. (In Armenian, Russian and French) [93] p., ill. Erevan: Armenian Academy of Sciences, 1958. [CB 86/471]
Reviewed by Louis Dulieu, *Rev.Hist.Sci.*, 1960, 13: 175.

PETROV, B. La contribución de los científicos Rusos a los progresos de la medicina universal. *Rev.Méd.Cubana*, 1958, 69: 473-500.

PONDOEV, G.S. Notes of a Soviet doctor. Introd. to the English transl. by Iago Galdston. Translated by Basil Haigh. iii, 238 p. New York: Consultants Bureau, 1959.
Translation of Zametki vracha. 2nd ed. 206 p. Tbilisi: Gruzmedgiz, 1957.

RAVITCH, Michael L. The romance of Russian medicine. xiv, 352 p. New York: Liveright, 1937. [CB 52/605]

SIGERIST, Henry E. L'inquiétude actuelle dans le monde médical. *Schweiz.Med.Wochenschr.*, 1935, 65: 1007-10. [CB 46/601]
On Soviet medicine.

SPERANSKII, Alekseĭ Dmitrīevich. On the present state of medical science. In: More glimpses of Soviet science, p. 7-13. (Society for Freedom in Science. Occasional Pamphlet, 10) Oxford: 1950.

Nwn-cb

BOGOIAVLENSKII, N.A. [The M.E. Saltykov-Shchedrin State Public Library in Leningrad and its significance in the history of Soviet medicine. (In Russian)] *Sovet.Zdravookhr.*, 1964, 23: 74-7.

Nwn-ce

BASMADJAN, K.J. Les livres de médecine chez les Arméniens. *J. Asiat.*, *11th ser.*, 1915, 5: 383-6.

LACHTIN, J. Altertümliche Denkmäler der medizinischen Literatur. *Janus*, 1912, 17: 485-505.
Apropos of the history of medicine in Russia.

Nwn-da

BRENNSOHN, Isidorus. Die Aerzte Estlands vom Beginn der historischen Zeit bis zur Gegenwart. Ein biographisches Lexikon nebst einer historischen Einleitung über das Medizinalwesen Estlands. 552 p. Berlin: G. Neuner, 1922.

Nwn-pw for relations between Russia and Holland *see* Npw ESSO, I. van.

Nwn-rf

TORKOMIAN, Vahram H. Liste des médecins arméniens diplomés de la Faculté de Paris de 1843 à 1921. *Compt.Rend.IIe Congr.Int.Hist.Méd.* (Paris, 1921), p. 479-90. Évreux: Imprimerie Ch. Hérissey, 1922.

Nwn-rj

TUSHNET, Leonard. Murder by disease. *Ann.Med.Hist.*, *3rd ser.*, 1939, 1: 121-7.
Death by disease induced by Soviet doctors on orders from politicians.

Nwn-u

EUSTAFIEFF, Victor K. The Znachary of the Ukraine. Witch doctors of the Ukraine. *Med.Life*, 1928, 35: 547-53.

HAHN, C.V. Aberglaube in der Medizin in Armenien. *Mitt. Gesch.Med.*, 1914, 13: 307-8.

MANNINEN, Ilmarl. Die dämonistischen Krankheiten im finnischen Volksaberglauben. Vergleichende volksmedizinische Untersuchung. 254 p. (F.F. Communications,45) Helsinki: Suomalainen Tiedeaktemia, 1922.

STEPPUHN, O.A.; LEWTSCHUK, A. Die russische Volksmedizin. 1. Bräuche und Aberglauben der russischen Volksmedizin. 2. Versuch einer Charakteristik der schriftlichen Quellen russischer Volksmedizin. With an introduction by H. Zeiss. *Arch.Gesch.Med.*, 1926, 18: 261-6; 1929, 22: 189-98.

Nwo South Eastern Europe

BARBU, G.; BRATESCU, G.; MANOLIU, V. Aspects du passé de la médecine dans la République Populaire Roumaine: iconographie. xii, 210 p. of pl., 1 map. Bucarest: Ministère de la Santé et de la Prévoyance Sociale, Institut de la Santé Publique et d'Histoire de la Médecine, 1957. [CB 83/205]
Reviewed by Nicholas A. Halasz, *J.Hist.Med.*, 1958, 13: 284-5.

BOLOGA, Valeriu L. [Contributions to the history of medicine in Transylvania. (In Rumanian)] 102 p. (Universitatea din Cluj, Biblioteca medico-istorică, 2) Cluj: Ardealul, 1927. [CB 42/603]

BOLOGA, Valeriu L. Geschichte der Naturwissenschaften und der Medizin bei den Rumänen. (Seventh International Congress of Historical Sciences, Warsaw, 1933) *Bull.Int.Comm.Hist.Sci.* 1933, 5: 371-88.

BOLOGA, Valeriu L. Inceputurile medicinii ştiinţifice romanesti. [Beginnings of Rumanian scientific medicine. (In Rumanian)] 89 p., 14 fig. Cluj: 1930.

BOLOGA, Valeriu L. [Les médecins macédo-roumains dans la monarchie des Habsbourg. (In Rumanian)] *Inchinare lui N.Iorga cu prilejul împlinirii vârstei de 60 de ani,* 11 p. Cluj: 1931.

BOLOGA, Valeriu L., ed. Din istoria medicinii Romînisti şi universale. [From the history of Rumanian and world medicine. (In Rumanian)] 517 p. Bucureşti: Editura Academiei Republicii Populare Romîne, 1962.
Reviewed by R.S. Roberts, *Med.Hist.*, 1963, 7: 395.

GOMOIU, V. Contribution de quelques médecins roumains au progrès des sciences. *Act.Ve Congr.Int.Hist.Sci.* (Lausanne, 1947), p. 220-5. Paris: 1948. Also in *Arch.Int.Hist.Sci.*, 1948, 1: 291-6.

GRMEK, M.D.; DUJMUŠIĆ, S.; ed. Iz hrvatske medicinske prošlosti. [From the medical past of Croatia. (In Croatian)] 314 p., 42 fig., 19 pl. Zagreb: Spomen Knjiga Zbora Liječnika Hrvatske, 1954. [CB 81/279]

[HISTORY of medicine number 19. (In Serbo-Croatian)] *Liječnicki vijesnik,* 1931, 53: no. 4. [CB 34/524]
A collection of articles on the history of medicine in Yugoslavia.

IORGA, N. Medici si medicina in trecutul românese. [Physicians and medicine in old Rumania. (In Rumanian)] 44 p. Bucarest: 1919.
Reviewed by V. Bologa, *Mitt.Gesch.Med.*, 1928, 27: 131.

Nwo-ce-bv

GRMEK, M.D., ed. Hrvatska medicinska bibliografija. Opis tiskanih knjiga i članaka s područja humane i veterinarske medicine i farmacije, koji se odnose na Hrvatsku. [Bibliographia medica Croatica. Descriptio librorum articulorumque de humana, veterinaria medicine pharmaceuticeque spectantium ad Croatiam. (In Croatian)] 1. Libri. Fasc. I: 1470-1875. 230 p., 32 pl. Zagreb: Znanstvena Knjižara, Izdavačkog Zavoda Jugoslavenske Akademije, 1955.

Nwo-ch-bv

BOLOGA, Valeriu; DIMA, Lia M. Bibliografia tezelor dela facultatea de medicină şi farmacie din Cluj (No. 1-1000). 102 p. (Biblioteca Facultătii de Medicină din Cluj) Cluj: 1936.

Nwo-cj

BOLOGA, Valeriu L. Les périodiques médicaux en Roumanie après la guerre. *Cultura* (Cluj), 1924, 1: 184-7.

Nwo-da

PANEFF, Assen Kr.; IZRAEL, S.; POPOFF, Miroslav. Quelques éminents médicins bulgares, élèves de l'école française jusqu'à l'an 1878. *Scalpel,* 1961, 114: 923-5.

Nwo-dae

PANEFF, Assen Kr.; POPOFF, Miroslav. Renseignements sur l'iconographie médicale en Bulgarie du XIIe au XVIIe siècle. *Scalpel,* 1962, 115: 596-600.

Nwo-hj

BOLOGA, Valeriu L. Deutsche Einflüsse auf die Entwicklung der rumänischen Medizin. *Südostdeut.Forsch.*, 1936, 1: 116-47.

BOLOGA, Valeriu L. Les influences occidentales dans la formation de la médecine scientifique roumaine. *Rev.Méd. Roum.*, 1932, 5: 39-45.

DOBROVICI, A. Les origines de l'école roumaine de médecine et le rôle de la France. *Bull.Sci.Roumain,* 1952, 1: 99-103.

Nwo-oq

GUIART, Jules. Histoire de la Faculté de médecine et de pharmacie de Cluj (Kolozsvar). Supplement to *Progr.Méd.*, 1933, 10: 1-8, ill.

SERGESCU, Pierre. L'Université de Cluj et ses relations avec l'étranger. *Rev.Transylvanie,* 1945, 10: 33-51.

Nwo-qd

BOLOGA, Valeriu L. Le 90ième anniversaire de la Société des Médecins et Naturalistes de Jassy. *Cultura* (Cluj), 1924, 1: 392-3.

Nwo-tf

ORIENT, Julius. Die Entstehung der Mönchsorden und geistlichen Ärzte, Spitäler und Apotheken in Siebenbürgen. *Vortr.Ges.Gesch.* (Basel, 1934), p. 153-78. Mittenwald: 1934.

Nwo-u

BOLOGA, Valeriu L. Lamachtou-Karina-Samca. [In Roumanian, with French summary] 22 p., 5 fig. (Biblioteca Medico-istorică) Cluj: Institutul de Istoria Medicinii şi de Etnografie Medicală, 1935. [CB 49/186]
The origins of the legend, in Roumanian popular medicine, of Samca, the demon slayer of children.

BOLOGA, Valeriu L. Von der Babylonischen Labartu über Arab. Karina zum Krankheitsbegriff Samca in der Rumänischen Volksmedizin. *Janus,* 1931, 35: 1-16, 6 pl.

Nwo-vm

HALÉVY, Meyer A. Médecins juifs d'origine hispano-portugaise dans les pays roumains. *Rev.Hist.Méd.Hébraique,* 1957, 10: 21-30.

MAYERSOHN, Lazare. Les Juifs dans la médecine roumaine. *Festschrift zum 80. Geburtstag Max Neuburgers,* p. 331-9. Wien: Maudrich, 1948.

ŠIK, Lavoslav. Jüdische Ärzte in Jugoslavien. 52 p., 11 pl. Osijek: Sekler, 1931.

Nwp/wy Asia; Africa; Australia

Nwp Near or Middle East; Turkey

AKSEL, H. Avni. The history of medicine in Turkey. *Asiatic Rev.*, 1944, 40: 320-3. [CB 66/270]
Translation of a lecture given at the Londra Türk Halkevi on March 21, 1944.

CHEVKI, Osman. Turk tababet tarini. [History of the practice of medicine in Turkey. (In Turkish)] 236 p. Istanbul: Imprimerie Nationale, 1925.
Reviewed by A. Adnan, *Archeion,* 1932, 14: 335-7.

HARRISON, Paul W. Doctor in Arabia. 304 p., ill. New York: Day, 1940. [CB 61/392]
Account of the life of a missionary doctor in Muscat and Oman.

MARGALITH, D. [Medicine, physicians, and hospitals in Jerusalem in the past 100 years. (In Hebrew, with English summary)] *Koroth,* 1962, 2: 435-44.

SAYILI, Aydin M. Turkish medicine. *Isis,* 1937, 26: 403-14. [CB 51/295]

TÜRK Hekimleri Jübilesi. [A jubilee of Turkish doctors. (In Turkish)] [Istanbul?]: Kader Basim Evi, [1939]. [CB 60/119]
Published in honour of some living Turkish doctors who have practised their profession for 50 years.

ÜNVER, A. Süheyl. [Rapport sur la médecine en Turquie. (In Turkish with French translation)] *Dirim,* 1937, 12: 4-7.

Nwp-cd

ÜNVER, A. Süheyl. [Quelques miniatures et documents concernant la médecine turque. (In Turkish with French translation)] *Tedavi Klin.Laboratuvari,* 1936, 6: no. 24, 6-9.

ÜNVER, A. Süheyl. Türkische medizin-geschichtliche Dokumente im Staatsarchiv. *Türk Tib Tarihi Arkivi,* 1940, 4: 130-1.

Nwp-ce

FRIK, Feridun. Türkiye cumhuriyetinde tib ve hifzissihha hareketleri, 1923-1938. [Works in medicine and public health in the Republic of Turkey, 1923-1938. (In Turkish)] 32 p. Leverkusen: Bayer, 1938.

Nwp-f

MEDICAL history and deontology in Istanbul. *Isis,* 1936, 25: 456.

Nwp-nh

ÜNVER, A. Süheyl. Medizinsprache in den alten Medizinbüchern. *Mitt.Gesch.Med.,* 1936, 35: 266-7; résumé of Turkish article in *Tedavi Notlari,* 1934.

Nwp-or

HANER, Gengiz. Tibbiye Şehitleri. [In Turkish] 55 p., fig. Istanbul: Türkiye Basimevi, 1940.
Dedicated to the professors and students of the Faculty of Medicine at the University of Istanbul who died between 1933 and 1940.

Nwp-tk

ÜNVER, A. Süheyl. L'idée médicale dans la poésie turque. *Liječnički Vjesnik,* 1938, 60: 524-5.

Nwp-u

AYDINER, Hüsnü. La médecine populaire à Pireler Kondu. *Türk Tib Tarihi Arkivi,* 1937, 2: 30-1.

ÜNVER, A. Süheyl. Les bases du folklore médical mystique chez les Turcs. *Liječnički Vjesnik,* 1938, 60: 522-4.

ÜNVER, A. Süheyl. Le folklore médical de nos pays. *Compt.Rend. IVe Sem.Méd.Balkanique* (Istanbul, 1936), p. 166-8. [Istanbul?: 1938?]

ÜNVER, A. Süheyl. Quelques exemples intéressants du folklore d'Anatolie. *Türk Tib Tarihi Arkivi,* 1938, 3: 78-80, 2 pl.

Nwq Egypt; North Africa

COURTADE, A. La médecine au Sahara. *Bull.Soc.Franç.Hist. Méd.,* 1913, 12: 32-41.

RAYNAUD, Lucien; SOULIÉ, Henri; PICARD, Paul. Hygiène et pathologie Nord-Africaines, assistance médicale. 2 vol. 550 p., 44 pl., ill.; 613 p., 34 pl., map. (Collection du Centenaire de l'Algérie, 1830-1930) Paris: Masson, 1932.

Nwq-u

'ABD al-RAHMĀN ISMĀ'ĪL. Folk medicine in modern Egypt. Being the relevant parts of the "Tibb al-rukka" or "Old wives' medicine" of 'Abd al-Rahmān Ismā'īl, by John Walker. 128 p., 4 pl. London: Luzac, 1934. [CB 43/264]

MEYERHOF, Max. Ein Beitrag zum Volksheilglauben der heutigen Aegypter. 1. Ueberreste aus dem Altertum; 2. Einflüsse fremder Voelker; 3. Bedeutung der Zeiten und Zahlen. *Festschrift Eduard Hahn,* p. 320-1. Stuttgart: Strecker und Schröder, 1917.

Nws/wv Asia

for Asia Minor *see* Nwp

Nws

REDDY, D.V.S. The beginning of modern medicine in Madras. xvi, 251 p. Calcutta: Spink, 1947.

Nws-cj

NEELAMEGHAN, A. *see* Nws-qd

Nws-qd

NEELAMEGHAN, A. Development of medical societies and medical periodicals in India, 1780-1920. viii, 120 p. (Iaslic Special Publications, 3) Calcutta: G.B. Ghosh (for the Indian Association of Special Libraries and Information Centres), 1963.

Nws-qk

McDONALD, Donald. The Indian Medical Service. A short account of its achievements 1600-1947. *Proc.Roy.Soc.Med.,* 1957, 49: 13-17.

McDONALD, Donald, comp. 'Surgeons twoe and a Barber'. Being some account of the life and work of the Indian Medical Service (1600-1947), comp. and furnished with an introductory essay. xix, 295 p., portr., pl., tables. London: William Heinemann, Medical Books, 1950.

Nws-rw

BALFOUR, Margaret I.; YOUNG, Ruth. The work of medical women in India. Foreword by Dame Mary Scharlieb. xv, 201 p. London: Oxford University Press, 1929.

Nwt

BÄLZ, Erwin Otto Eduard von. Das Leben eines deutschen Arztes im erwachenden Japan. Tagebücher, Briefe, Berichte, hrsg. von Toku Bälz. 454 p., 28 ill. Stuttgart: Engelhorn, 1931.
Reviewed by P. Diepgen, *Deut.Lit.Zeitung,* 1931, 2: 1240-2.

GERVAIS, Albert. Aesculape en Chine. 253 p. Paris: Gallimard, 1933. [CB 41/593]

GERVAIS, Albert. Medicine man in China. Transl. by Vincent Sheean. 336 p. New York: Stokes, 1934.
English edition published under the title: A surgeon's China. 302 p., ill. London: Hamish Hamilton, 1934.
Translation of: Aesculape en chine.

HÜBOTTER, Franz. Die chinesische Medizin zu Beginn des XX. Jahrhunderts und ihr historischer Entwicklungsgang. 356 p. Leipzig: Asia major, 1929.
Reviewed by George Sarton, *Isis,* 1930, 14: 255-63, 2 fig.

HUME, Edward Hicks. Doctors East. Doctors West. An American physician's life in China. 278 p., 13 ill. New York: Norton, 1946. [CB 70/237]

HUME, Edward Hicks. Medicine in China, old and new. *Ann.Med. Hist.,* 1930, 11: 272-80.

PENFIELD, Wilder. Oriental renaissance in education and medicine. A Canadian physician sees a sudden renaissance of Western learning on the Chinese mainland. *Science,* 1963, 141: 1153-61.

Nwt-nh

SCHRAMM, Gottfried. Schriftzeichenanalysen medizinischer Termini technici in der chinesischen Sprache. xi, 107 p. (Beiträge zur Orientalistik, 1) Leipzig: Harassowitz, 1958. [CB 87/574]

Nwv

JÜPTNER, H. Als Arzt in Indonesien. *Lebendige Med.,* 1955, no. 11, 1-2.

MAY, Jacques M. Siam doctor. 255 p. Garden City, N.Y.: Doubleday, 1949. [CB 76/380]
Reminiscences of a French surgeon in Siam and Indo-China, 1932-1940.

SCHOUTE, D. De geneeskunde in den dienst der Oost-Indische compagnie in Nederlandsch-Indië. [Study of medicine in the service of the Dutch East-India Company in the Dutch East Indies. (In Dutch)] 347 p. Amsterdam: De Bussy, 1929. [CB 56/368]
Reviewed by M.A. van Andel, *Bijdr.Gesch.Geneesk.,* 1929, 9: 296-7.

SEAGRAVE, Gordon S. Burma surgeon. 295 p., ill. New York: Norton, 1943.
Reviewed by Jean C. Sabine, *Bull.Hist.Med.,* 1944, 15: 141.

SEAGRAVE, Gordon S. Burma surgeon returns. Maps by Phoa Lieng Sing and Lucas Manditch. 268 p., 5 maps, ill. New York: Norton, 1946.

Nwv-cj

WINCKEL, Ch.W.F. De geschiedenis van het *Geneeskundig Tijdschrift voor Nederlandsch-Indië*. [The history of The Medical Journal for the Netherlands Indies. (In Dutch)] *Bijdr. Gesch.Geneesk.*, 1936, 16: 1-10.

Nwv-o

LANGEN, C.D. de. Medical training in the Netherlands Indies. *Med.Life*, 1938, 45: 23-31.

Nww Australia; New Zealand

GANDEVIA, Bryan. The pattern of Australian medical history. *Proc.Roy.Soc.Med.*, 1957, 50: 591-8.

GUTHRIE, Douglas. A medical historian in New Zealand and Australia. *Proc.Roy.Soc.Med.*, 1954, 47: 1059-60.

Nww-bv

GANDEVIA, Bryan. An annotated bibliography of the history of medicine in Australia. With a foreword by Sir Gordon Gordon-Taylor. 140 p. (Monographs of the Federal Council of the British Medical Association in Australia, 1) Glebe, Sydney: Australian Medical Publishing Company, 1955.
Reviewed by William C. Gibson, *J.Hist.Med.*, 1958, 13: 119-21.

Nww-oq

JONES, Dudley William Carmalt. Annals of the University of Otago Medical School, 1875-1939. 286 p. Wellington, New Zealand: Reed, 1945.

Nwx/wy Central and South Africa

for North Africa *see* Nwq

Nwx

BARKHUUS, Arne. Medicine in Ethiopia. *Ciba Symp.*, 1947, 9: 698-728, fig. [CB 72/267]

DAVIES, J.N.P. The development of "scientific" medicine in the African kingdom of Bunyoro-Kitara. *Med.Hist.*, 1959, 3: 47-57.

DUBOIS, A. Le développement de la médecine expérimentale au Congo Belge. *Rapp.Annu.Inst.Rech.Sci.Afr.Cent.*, 1949, 2: 82-147, 12 pl.

IMPERATO, Pascal James. Doctor in the land of the lion. 180 p., ill. New York/Washington/Hollywood: Vantage Press, 1964.

SCHWETZ, Jacques. L'évolution de la médecine au Congo belge. 132 p. (Université Libre de Bruxelles. Institut de Sociologie Solvay. Actualités Sociales, nouvelle série) Bruxelles: Office de Publicité, 1946.
Reviewed by Henry E. Sigerist, *Bull.Hist.Med.*, 1948, 22: 358-60.

Nwx-qq

LAMBIE, Thomas A. A doctor carries on. Foreword by Lowell Thomas. 173 p., front., pl. New York: Revell, 1942. [CB 65/71]
On medical missionary efforts in the Sudan and Ethiopia. A continuation of the work below.

LAMBIE, Thomas A. A doctor without a country. 252 p. New York: Revell, 1939. [CB 65/71]

WIDMER, Edgar. Zur Geschichte der schweizerischen ärztlichen Mission in Afrika unter besonderer Berücksichtigung des medizinischen Zentrums von Ifakara, Tanganyika. 64 p., maps, ill. (*Basler Veröffentl.Gesch.Med.Biol.*, 16) Basel/Stuttgart: Benno Schwabe, 1963.

Nwy

BURROWS, Edmund H. A history of medicine in South Africa to the end of the nineteenth century. 389 p., 46 ill., bibliogr., maps. Cape Town: A.A. Balkema, 1958.

LAIDLER, P.W. History of medicine; Aesculapius and hygeia at the Cape. *S.Afr.Med.J.*, 1936, 10: 677-89.

SIGERIST, Henry E. A physician's impression of South Africa. *Bull.Hist.Med.*, 1940, 8: 22-7.

Nwy-q

LAIDLER, P.W. Medical establishments and institutions at the Cape. 1. Seventeenth and eighteenth centuries; 2. During the opening years of the nineteenth century; 3. Civil hospitals, prisons and reformers; 4. Somerset Hospital, the slave hospital and the first pauper establishment; 5. Ethics: the first S.A. Medical Society; 6. Dr. J. Atherstone and the introduction of anaesthetics; 7. Through epidemics to reform. *S.Afr.Med.J.*, 1937, 11: 202-8, 481-6, 635-41, 641-9; 1938, 12: 273-8, 453-6; 1939, 13: 223-9.

Nwz

WALLQUIST, Einar. Can the doctor come? Translated from the Swedish by Paula Wiking. Ill. by Bip Pares. 221 p. London: Hodder & Stoughton, 1936. [CB 57/202]
The life of a Swedish doctor in the Arctic regions.

Nwz-ce

JOHNSSON, John William Schibbye. Medizinisch-historische und epidemiologische Literatur über Grönland. *Mitt.Gesch.Med.*, 1915, 14: 42-3.

Nx techniques and instruments; experimentation

for diagnostic instruments *see* QDxk
for surgical instruments *see* RBxk

Nxb

FOOTE, Helen S. Silver in the service of medicine. *Bull. Med.Libr.Ass.*, 1944, 32: 369-75, 5 fig.

DRAKE, T.G.H. Antique pewter articles of medical interest. *Bull.Hist.Med.*, 1941, 10: 272-87, 11 fig.

Nxe

EBSTEIN, Erich. Medical men who experimented upon themselves. A contribution to the causes of death in physicians. *Med. Life*, 1931, 38: 216-18.

GLASER, Hugo. The drama of medicine: doctors risk their lives in research. 169 p. London: Lutterworth Press, 1962.
English translation of: Dramatische Medizin: Selbstversuche von Ärzten. 246 p. Zurich: Füssli, 1959.
Dutch translation: Dramatische experimenten in de geneeskunde (Amsterdam/Brussels: Elsevier, 1961) reviewed by L. Elaut, *Sci.Hist.*, 1961, 3: 205-6.

PODACH, E.F. Selbstversuche von Ärzten mit lebenden Krankheitserregern. *Ciba Z.*, 1960, 9: 3278-312.

Nxe-tc

IVY, A.C. The history and ethics of the use of human subjects in medical experiments. *Science*, 1948, 108: 1-5.

STEVENSON, Lloyd G. Science down the drain. On the hostility of certain sanitarians to animal experimentation, bacteriology and immunology. *Bull.Hist.Med.*, 1955, 29: 1-26, 1 pl.

Nxk

BROWN, Leland A. Early philosophical apparatus at Transylvania College (and relics of the Medical Department). 117 p., 115 fig. Lexington, Ky.: Transylvania College Press, 1959.

MEYERSON, Åke, *et al.* Studier i Serafimerlasarettets instrumentsamling. Utgivna med anledning av lasarettets 200-års-jubileum. [Studies in the instrument collection at the Seraphim Hospital. Published on the occasion of the 200th anniversary of the hospital. (In Swedish)] 135 p., ill. Stockholm: Karolinska Institutets Kirurgiska Klinik vid Serafimerlasarettet, 1952.
Reviewed by Bert G. Anderson, *J.Hist.Med.*, 1953, 8: 349-50.

SCHULZ, Ernst Hermann. Zur Frage der Entwicklung des Stahles für ärztliche Instrumente. *Sudhoffs Arch.*, 1955, 39: 30-4.

USHER, Abbott Payson. The development of the microscope and its application to medicine and public health. *Amer.J. Pharm.Educ.*, 1951, 15: 319-38.

Nxw museology

EDWARDS, J.J.; EDWARDS, M.J. Medical museum technology. x, 172 p., ill., pl. London/New York: Oxford University Press, 1959.
Reviewed by Frank B. Johnson, *Science*, 1959, 130: 786-7; by Cuthbert Dukes, *Med.Hist.*, 1960, 4: 82; by Rembert Watermann, *Sudhoffs Arch.*, 1960, 44: 283-4.

GOLDSCHMID, Edgar. Wachsplastik und ihre Museen. *Gesnerus*, 1951, 8: 91-7.

Nxx museums

ACKERKNECHT, Erwin H. The world of Asclepios: a history of medicine in objects. 92 p., ill. Bern: Huber, 1963.
Describes exhibits from the collection of History of Medicine in the Tower of the University of Zurich.
Reviewed by John B. Blake, *Science*, 1964, 144: 725-6.

CRUMMER Room for the History of Medicine at the University of California Medical School, San Francisco. By C.D.L. *Isis*, 1936, 25: 458.

FINOT, André. Le Musée d'Histoire de la Médecine à la Faculté de Paris. *Hist.Méd.*, 1951, no. 2, 45-8.

FOSSEYEUX, Marcel. Un musée médical historique parisien. *Aesculape*, 1914, 4: 36-41, 12 fig. [CB 5/305]

GODLEE, Rickmann John. The Hunterian oration on Hunter and Lister and on the Museum of the Royal College of Surgeons of England. *Brit.Med.J.*, 1913, 373-8.

KØBENHAVNS UNIVERSITETS Medicinsk-Historiske Museum. Arsberetning 1954-57. [Annual reports, 1954-57. (In Danish, with summaries in English)] 2 vol. København: 1954-57. [CB 83/186 and 81/280]

LABORATORIOS DEL NORTE DE ESPAÑA. Museo Retrospectivo de Farmacía y Medicina de los Laboratorios del Norte de España. 73 p., 159 fig. Masnou: 1952.
Reviewed by P.H. Brans, *Arch.Int.Hist.Sci.*, 1953, 6: 530-1.

LINT, J.G. de. Openingsrede voor de geneeskundige afdeeling van het natuurwetenschappelijk museum te Leiden op 28 April 1934. [Inaugural address before the Medical Section of the Natural Science Museum of Leyden on 28 April 1934. (In Dutch)] *Bijdr.Gesch.Geneesk.*, 1934, 14: 118-22, 1 pl.

McFARLAND, Joseph. Dr. Joseph Leidy's petrified lady. Rummaging in the Mütter Museum, of the College of Physicians of Philadelphia. *Ann.Med.Hist.*, 1942, 4: 268-75, 1 fig.

MOLLIÈRE, A. Le Musée Médico-Historique de l'Université de Lyon. *Aesculape*, 1912, 112-14, 7 fig.

MONTALENTI, Giuseppe. L'Accademia di Storia dell'Arte Sanitaria e il suo museo. *Archeion*, 1935, 17: 413-19, 5 fig.
Description of the medico-historical museum in Rome.

PAZZINI, Adalberto. Le musée de l'Académie d'histoire de l'art de guérir. *Rev.Hist.Pharm.*, 1959, 47: 122-34.

RICH, Ida. Einiges vom medizinhistorischen Museum der Universität Kopenhagen. *Arch.Gesch.Med.*, 1938, 31: 61-76.

ROOSEBOOM, Maria. De geneeskundige afdeeling van het Nederlandsch Historisch natuurwetenschappelijk museum te Leiden. [The medical section of the Netherlands museum for the history of natural sciences at Leyden. (In Dutch)] *Bijdr.Gesch.Geneesk.*, 1938, 18: 168-72, 3 fig.

SCHENCK, H.P. The Mütter Museum of the College of Physicians of Philadelphia. *Ann.Med.Hist.*, 1931, 3: 69-74, 4 fig.

SONDERVORST, F.A. Le Musée d'Histoire de la Médecine de l'Université de Louvain. *Hist.Méd.*, 1951, no. 8, 3-9, 2 ill.

TRICOT-ROYER, J.J.G. Commentaires médicaux sur les musées d'Anvers. 31 p. Anvers: De Vlijt, 1921.

WADE, Ella N. The history and growth of the Mütter Museum. *Trans.Coll.Physicians Phila.*, 1946, 14: 24-8. [CB 70/272]

WADE, Ella N. The Mütter Museum - then and now. *Trans.Coll. Physicians Phila.*, 1955, 23: 24-8.

WITTOP KONING, D.A. The Amsterdam Historical Medical-Pharmaceutical Museum. *Endeavour*, 1954, 13: 128-33, 11 fig.

ZUM Anlass der Ausbreitung des medisch-pharmazeutischen Museums in Amsterdam. *Janus*, 1912, 17: 62-3.

NA PUBLIC HEALTH AND SOCIAL MEDICINE

NAc general history

BELTRÁN, Juan Ramón. Historia de la medicina social. Bosquejo preliminar. *Semana Méd.*, 1941, 1: 94-101.

BERG, Fredrik. Hygienens omfattning i äldre tider. [The scope of hygiene in earlier times. (In Swedish, with English summary)] *Lychnos*, 1962, 91-127, ill.

BRUCE, David. Prevention of disease. Inaugural address delivered to the British Association at Toronto on August 6. *Nature*, 1924, 114: 213-27.

CEUSTER, P. de. Uit de geschiedenis van de hygiëne. [From the history of hygiene. (In Dutch)] *Ons Heem*, 1961-62, 16: 1-4.

DEUTSCH, Albert. Historical inter-relationships between medicine and social welfare. *Bull.Hist.Med.*, 1942, 11: 485-502.

DIEPGEN, Paul. Geschichte der sozialen Medizin. Ein Überblick. 29 p. (Staatsmedizinische Abhandlungen, 1) Leipzig: Barth, 1934.

DUBOS, René. Mirage of health. Utopias, progress, and biological change. xv, 236 p. (World Perspectives, 22) New York: Harper, 1959.
For reviews *see* CB 85/398 and CB 87/572.

FREEMAN, Allen W. Preventive medicine in evolution. *Bull. Inst.Hist.Med.*, 1936, 4: 65-74.

GALDSTON, Iago. Humanism and public health. *Ann.Med.Hist.*, *3rd ser.*, 1941, 3: 513-23.

GALDSTON, Iago. Humanism and public health. *Bull.Hist.Med.*, 1940, 8: 1032-40.

INSTITUTE ON SOCIAL MEDICINE, New York, 1947. Social medicine. Ed. by Iago Galdston. xvi, 294 p. New York: Commonwealth Fund, 1949. [CB 74/397]
Institute held in connection with the centennial celebration of the New York Academy of Medicine.

KERSHAW, John D. An approach to social medicine. viii, 329 p. Baltimore: Williams and Wilkins, 1946.

LEFF, S.; LEFF, Vera. From witchcraft to world health. 236 p., front., 28 ill. New York: Macmillan, 1957. [CB 83/207]

NEW YORK ACADEMY OF MEDICINE. The epidemiology of health. Iago Galdston, ed. ix, 197 p. New York: Health Education Council, 1953.
Based on the 11th Annual Eastern States Health Education Conference.
Reviewed by John B. Blake, *Isis*, 1954, 45: 110.

NEWMAN, George. The rise of preventive medicine. xii, 270 p. London: Oxford University Press, 1932.
Reviewed by Sanford V. Larkey, *Isis*, 1934, 22: 318-19.

NEWSHOLME, Arthur. Evolution of preventive medicine. xv, 226 p., 6 fig. London: Baillière; Baltimore: Williams & Wilkins, 1927.

NEWSHOLME, Arthur. The story of modern preventive medicine; being a continuation of the Evolution of preventive medicine, 1927. xii, 295 p., ill. Baltimore: Williams & Wilkins, 1929.

ROLLESTON, Humphry. The progress and pioneers of preventive medicine. *Ann.Med.Hist.*, 1934, 6: 95-109.

ROSEN, George. A history of public health. Foreword by Félix Martí-Ibáñez. 551 p. (MD Monographs on Medical History, 1) New York: MD Publications, 1958.
Reviewed by Karl F. Meyer, *Isis*, 1960, 51: 101-2; for other reviews *see* CB 85/401 and CB 87/574.

ROSEN, George. Osler and public health. *N.C.Med.J.*, 1949, 10: 277-9.

ROSEN, George. Society and medical care. An historical analysis. *McGill Med.J.*, 1948, 17: 410-25.

RYLE, John A. Changing disciplines. Lectures on the history, method and motives of social pathology. x, 122 p. London/New York: Oxford University Press, 1948.
Reviewed by Iago Galdston, *J.Hist.Med.*, 1952, 7: 305-8.

SAND, René. The advance to social medicine. xii, 655 p. London: Staples, 1952.
Translation of: Vers la médecine sociale (Paris: Baillière, 1948) reviewed by George Sarton, *Isis*, 1949, 40: 90.

SAND, René. Health and human progress: an essay in sociological medicine. Translated from the author's revised French text by C.F. Marshall. x, 278 p. London: Kegan Paul, 1935; New York: Macmillan, 1936.
Reviewed by J.B.O., *Nature*, 1936, 137: 339.
Translation of: L'économie humaine par la médecine sociale. Paris: Rieder, 1934. [CB 42/601]

SIGERIST, Henry E. Landmarks in the history of hygiene. viii, 78 p., 4 fig. London/New York: Oxford University Press, 1956. [CB 83/209]
For reviews *see* CB 83/209 and CB 84/323.

SIGERIST, Henry E. Medicine and human welfare. xiii, 148 p., 20 ill. New Haven: Yale University Press, 1941.
Reviewed by George Sarton, *Isis*, 1941, 33: 553.

SIMMONS, James Stevens, ed. Public health in the world today. xviii, 332 p. Cambridge: Harvard University Press, 1949.
Reviewed by George Rosen, *J.Hist.Med.*, 1951, 6: 143-4.

SIMPSON, W.J.R. Preventive aspects of endemics in modern times. *Proc.3rd Int.Congr.Hist.Med.* (London, 1922), p. 45-9. Antwerp: de Vlijt, 1923. Also *J.Trop.Med.Hyg.*, 1922, 25: 257-60.

VORWAHL, H. Die Wurzeln der Sozialhygiene. *Sudhoffs Arch.*, 1930, 23: 384-7.

WELCH, William Henry. Public health in theory and practice: an historical review. 51 p. (Sedgwick Memorial Lecture) New Haven: Yale University Press, 1925.

NAce-by

SHRYOCK, Richard H. Library collections in social medicine. *Bull.Amer.Libr.Ass.*, 1936, 351-62.

NAda

SUDHOFF, Karl. Grosse Ärzte in der Entwicklung der Hygiene. Eine Rückschau. In: Das Deutsche Hygiene-Museum, p. 55-60. Dresden: 1930.

WALKER, M.E.M. Pioneers of public health. The story of some benefactors of the human race. With a foreword by Humphry Rolleston. xvi, 270 p., 23 pl. New York: Macmillan, 1930.
Reviewed by Charles A. Kofoid, *Isis*, 1931, 16: 472-4.

NAf

SUDHOFF, Karl. Wege und Aufgaben der Geschichte der Hygiene (1911). *Sudhoffs Arch.*, 1929, 21: 156-63.

NAk/o philosophy and methodology; study and teaching

NAk

GALDSTON, Iago, The meaning of social medicine. viii, 137 p. (A Commonwealth Fund Book) Cambridge: Harvard University Press, 1954.

GALDSTON, Iago. Social medicine and the epidemic constitution. *Bull.Hist.Med.*, 1951, 25: 8-21.

ROSEN, George. What is social medicine? A genetic analysis of the concept. *Bull.Hist.Med.*, 1947, 21: 674-733.
Spanish version in *Rev.Méd.Cubana*, 1958, 69: 279-302, 325-47.

SIGERIST, Henry E. The philosophy of hygiene. *Bull.Inst. Hist.Med.*, 1933, 1: 323-31.

NAmzRB

LEARMONTH, James. The contribution of surgery to preventive medicine. 55 p. (Heath Clark Lectures, 1949, delivered at the London School of Hygiene and Tropical Medicine) London/New York: Oxford University Press, 1951.
Reviewed by Samuel C. Harvey, *J.Hist.Med.*, 1952, 7: 431-3.

NAo

SAND, René. The Bengué memorial award lecture, 1949. World trends in the teaching of social medicine and public health. *J.Roy.Inst.Public Health Hyg.*, 1949, 12: 359-67.

TEMKIN, Owsei. Health education through the ages. *Amer.J. Public Health*, 1940, 30: 1091-5.

NAo-bv

ROSEN, George. The health educator's bookshelf. *Amer.J. Public Health*, 1949, 39: 433-42.

NAov

KORACH, Alfred. Extra-mural teaching of preventive medicine and public health. 143 p. (Medical Bulletin, University of Cincinnati, 9) Cincinnati: Roessler, 1942.
Reviewed by E.H. Ackerknecht, *Bull.Hist.Med.*, 1943, 13: 694.

PATERSON, Robert G. Foundations of community health education. xix, 288 p., ill. New York: McGraw-Hill, 1950.
Reviewed by George Rosen, *J.Hist.Med.*, 1951, 6: 539-41.

NAp/s organizational and social aspects

NAp

CHARLES, John. Research and public health. 114 p. (University of London. Heath Clark Lectures) London: Oxford University Press, 1961.
Reviewed by Erna Lesky, *Sudhoffs Arch.*, 1963, 47: 500.

NAph

MUSTARD, Harry S. Government in public health. xvi, 219 p. New York: Commonwealth Fund, 1945.
Reviewed by Leona Baumgartner, *J.Hist.Med.*, 1946, 1: 348; by Milton I. Roemer, *Bull.Hist.Med.*, 1946, 19: 127-30.

NApw

BARKHUUS, Arne. The dawn of international cooperation in medicine. The sanitary conferences. Modern international control of disease. *Ciba Symp.* (Summit, N.J.), 1943, 5: 1554-84, ill.

NAqy

LYON, Robert A. The development of international health organizations. *Ann.Med.Hist.*, 1939, 1: 519-24.

RODRIGUEZ EXPOSITO, Cesar. La primera secretaria de sanidad del mundo se creó en Cuba. 151 p. (*Cuad.Hist.Salud Publ.*, 25) La Habana: 1964.

NAsc

SUDHOFF, Karl. The hygienic idea and its manifestations in world history. *Ann.Med.Hist.*, 1917, 1: 111-17.
Transl. of: Hygienische Gedanken und Manifestationen in der Weltgeschichte. *Deut.Rev.*, 1911, 4: 40-50.

NAsg

ROSEN, George. Economic and social policy in public health. *J.Hist.Med.*, 1953, 8: 406-30.

TELEKY, L. Industrielle Entwicklung und Gesundheit. *Med. Welt*, 1931, 5: 646-8.

ZEISS, H. Hygiene und Technik. *Technikgeschichte*, 1936, 25: 66-73.

NAw in different countries

International Health Yearbook (Annuaire Sanitaire International) Reports on the public health progress of ... countries, 1924-30, vol. 1-6. (Publication of the League of Nations) Genève: 1925-32.

SAND, René. Organisation industrielle, médecine sociale et éducation civique en Angleterre et aux Etats-Unis. 896 p. Bruxelles: Lamertin; Paris: Baillière, 1920.
Reviewed by George Sarton, *Isis*, 1921, 4: 122-3.

TELEKY, Ludwig. Die Entwicklung der Gesundheitsfürsorge; Deutschland, England, Berlin, U.S.A. 142 p. Berlin: Springer Verlag, 1950.
Reviewed by George Rosen, *J.Hist.Med.*, 1953, 8: 352.

NAwb North America

BLAKE, John B. Public health in the town of Boston, 1630-1822. x, 278 p. Cambridge: Harvard University Press, 1959.
For note on thesis on which the book is based, *see Isis*, 1954, 45: 200.
Reviewed by James H. Cassedy, *J.Hist.Med.*, 1960, 15: 98-9; by Richard M. Jellison, *William Mary Quart.*, 1960, 18: 148-50; by Cecil G. Sheps, *Bull.Hist.Med.*, 1961, 35: 91-3.

CASSEDY, James H. Charles V. Chapin and the public health movement. x, 310 p., front. Cambridge, Mass.: Harvard University Press; London: Oxford University Press, 1962.
Reviewed by R.R. Trail, *Med.Hist.*, 1963, 7: 286; by Charles E. Rosenberg, *Bull.Hist.Med.*, 1963, 37: 390-1; by A. Hunter Duprée, *J.Hist.Med.*, 1964, 19: 423-4.

FREEMAN, Allen W. Five million patients. xiii, 299 p. New York: Scribner's, 1946.
Autobiography of Dr. A.W. Freeman, the first professor of Public Health Administration.
Reviewed by Ernest L. Stebbins, *J.Hist.Med.*, 1947, 2: 398.

HOWARD, William Travis. Public health administration and the natural history of disease in Baltimore, Maryland, 1797-1920. vi, 565 p., 2 maps. (*Publ.Carnegie Inst.Wash.*, 351) Washington, D.C.: 1924.

KLEINSCHMIDT, Earl E. The development of a state health service in Michigan. *Bull.Hist.Med.*, 1943, 13: 462-80.

LERNER, Monroe; ANDERSON, Odin W. Health progress in the United States: 1900-1960. xvi, 354 p., charts, tables. Chicago/London: University of Chicago Press, 1963.

MOORE, Harry H. American medicine and the people's health: an outline with statistical data on the organization of medicine in the United States with special reference to the adjustment of medical service to social and economical change. 647 p. New York: Appleton, 1927.
A source book for information regarding current medical organization in the United States.

NEW YORK ACADEMY OF MEDICINE. Committee on Medicine and the Changing Order. Medicine in the changing order. 240 p. New York: Commonwealth Fund, 1947.
Reviewed by Leslie A. Falk, *Bull.Hist.Med.*, 1948, 22: 111-14.

ROEMER, Milton I.; FAULKNER, Barbara. The development of public health services in a rural county [Monongalia County, W. Virginia, U.S.A.], 1838-1949. *J.Hist.Med.*, 1951, 6: 22-43.

ROSEN, George. The idea of social medicine in America. *Can. Med.Ass.J.*, 1949, 61: 316-23.

SHRYOCK, Richard H. The health of the American people. An historical survey. *Proc.Amer.Phil.Soc.*, 1946, 90: 251-8.

SHRYOCK, Richard H. The origins and significance of the public health movement in the United States. *Ann.Med.Hist.*, 1929, 1: 645-65.

WINSLOW, Charles Edward Amory. The life of Hermann M. Biggs (1859-1923), M.D., D.Sc., LL.D. Physician and statesman of the public health. 432 p., 35 fig. Philadelphia: Lea and Febiger, 1929.
Reviewed by Haberling, *Mitt.Gesch.Med.*, 1930, 29: 201.

NAwb-o

MEANS, Richard K. A history of health education in the United States. 412 p., 32 fig., 5 tables. Philadelphia: Lea & Febiger, 1962.
Reviewed by Eunice R. Bonow, *Amer.J.Pharm.Educ.*, 1963, 27: 350-1.

NAwb-qk

CASSEDY, James H. Stimulation of health research: catalytic activities of Public Health Service study sections from 1946 to 1964. *Science*, 1964, 145: 897-902.

HUME, Edgar Erskine. Contributions of the Medical Corps of the Army to the public health laboratory. *Science*, 1943, 97: 293-300.

MACDONALD, Eleanor J. A history of the Massachusetts Department of Public Health. *Commonhealth*, 1936, 23: 44 p.

SWAIN, Donald C. The rise of a research empire: NIH, 1930 to 1950. *Science*, 1962, 138: 1233-7.
Apropos of the National Institutes of Health, research branch of the U.S. Public Health Service.

WILLIAMS, Ralph Chester. The United States Public Health Service, 1798-1950. 890 p. Washington, D.C.: Commissioned Officers Association of the United States Public Health Service, 1951.
Reviewed by Ira Hiscock, *J.Hist.Med.*, 1952, 7: 428-9.

NAwc Latin America

BELTRÁN, Juan Ramón. Historia del Protomedicato de Buenos Aires. xvi, 316 p. Buenos Aires: El Ateneo, 1937.
Reviewed by Lesley Byrd Simpson, *Isis*, 1939, 30: 560.

DESCOLA, Jean. L'hygiène et les maladies au Pérou au temps des Espagnols. *Hist.Med.*, 1962, 12: no. 3, 15-22.

LASTRES, Juan B. Terremotos, hospitales y epidemias de la Lima colonial. *Archeion*, 1940, 22: 141-53. Also in *An.Soc. Peruana Hist.Med.*, 1940, 30-41.

PAZ SOLDÁN, C.E. La OMS y la soberania sanitaria de las Americas. 264 p. Lima, Peru: Instituto de Medicina Social de la Universidad Mayor de San Marcos, 1949. [CB 76/414]
OMS (Organizacion Mundial de la Salud) is the translation of WHO (World Health Organization). Its origin (1946), development, and functioning, especially as regards the Americas, are described.

SANTOVENIA, Emeterio S. El Protomedicato de La Habana. 78 p. (Cuadernos de Historia Sanitaria) Havana: Ministerio de Salubridad y Asistencia Social, 1952. [CB 79/193]

NAwd Europe

NAwe

CHALMERS, A.K. The health of Glasgow, 1818-1925: an outline. xviii, 461 p. Glasgow: The Corporation, 1930.

DELMEGE, James Anthony. Towards national health; or, Health and hygiene in England from Roman to Victorian times. xiv, 234 p., ill. London: Heinemann, 1931.
Reviewed in *Nature*, 1932, 130: 525-6.

FERGUSON, Thomas. Scottish social welfare, 1864-1914. xii, 610 p., ill. Edinburgh/London: Livingstone; Baltimore: Williams & Wilkins, 1958.
Reviewed by David Roberts, *Isis*, 1959, 50: 286-7.

FIFTY years of health services in Britain. *Chem.Drug.*, 1962, 178: 41-4.

FRAZER, W.M. A history of English public health, 1834-1939. 498 p., ill. London: Baillière, 1950.

MORRIS, Malcolm. The story of English public health. xii, 166 p. London: Cassell, 1919.

UNDERWOOD, E. Ashworth. The centenary of British public health. *Brit.Med.J.*, 1948, 1: 1-9, 3 fig.

WILLIAMS, John Hargreaves Harley. A century of public health in Britain, 1832-1929. With a foreword by W.W. Jameson. xv, 314 p. London: Black, 1932.

NAwe-da

GREENWOOD, Major. Some British pioneers of social medicine. viii, 118 p. (Heath Clark Lectures 1946, delivered at the London School of Hygiene and Tropical Medicine) London/New York: Oxford University Press, 1948.

NAwf

PILLEMENT, P. L'organisation de la médecine municipale à Nancy du XVIe siècle à la Révolution. 55 p. Nancy: Thomas, 1938.
Reviewed in *Bull.Soc.Franç.Hist.Méd.*, 1940, 34: 95-6.

NAwg

BERTRAND, J.B. Notes sur la santé publique et la médecine en Valais jusqu'au milieu du XIXe siècle. iv, 60 p., 8 fig. (Reprinted from *Ann.Valaisannes*, December, 1939) St. Maurice: Annales Valaisannes, 1940.
Reviewed by F. Schwerz, *Mitt.Gesch.Med.*, 1940, 39: 299.

BOLDUAN, Charles F. Hermann M. Biggs (1859-1923), Bahnbrecher in der öffentlichen Gesundheitspflege. *Festschrift zum 80. Geburtstag Max Neuburgers*, p. 66-8. Wien: Maudrich, 1948.

DIEPGEN, Paul. Die historischen Wurzeln des deutschen Gesundheitswesens und ihre Lehren. Zu Alfons Fischers: Geschichte des deutschen Gesundheitswesens. *Deut.Med. Wochenschr.*, 1934, 60: 905-8.

FISCHER, Alfons. Geschichte des deutschen Gesundheitswesens. Hrsg. von der Arbeitsgemeinschaft sozialhygienischer Reichsfachverbände. 2 vol. 1. Vom Gesundheitswesen der alten Deutschen zur Zeit ihres Anschlusses an die Weltkultur bis zum Preuss. Medizinaledikt (die ersten 17 Jahrhunderte unserer Zeitrechnung). xix, 343 p., 72 fig.; 2. Von den Anfängen der hygienischen Ortsbeschreibungen bis zur Gründung des Reichsgesundheitsamtes (das 18. und 19. Jahrhundert). viii, 591 p., 106 fig. Berlin: Herbig, 1933.

MOGK, Werner. Esslinger Wohlfahrtspflege im 15.-18. Jahrhundert. 43 p. (Diss., Leipzig) Zeulenroda i.Th.: Oberreuter, 1920.
Based upon archival documents of Esslingen, the earliest dated 1496.

SCHELENZ, Hermann. Wohlfahrtsbestrebungen in Hessen vom 16. bis zum 18. Jahrhundert. *Deut.Geschichtsbl.*, 1913, 229-43.

SOZIALE Kultur und Volkswohlfahrt während der ersten 25 Regierungsjahre Kaiser Wilhelm II. Ein Gedenkwerk in ausgewählten Einzelabschnitten. Schriftleitung v. Behr-Pinnow, Dietrich, Kayserling. 869 p. Berlin: Georg Stilke, 1913.

STUDER, German. Das Medizinalwesen im Wallis von 1798-1930. 71 p., 4 fig. Basel: Waldstein, 1940.
Reviewed by F. Schwerz, *Mitt.Gesch.Med.*, 1940, 39: 299.

TUTZKE, Dietrich. Das Budissiner Landphysikat. *Sudhoffs Arch.*, 1963, 47: 394-404.

NAwh-vm

TUSHNET, Leonard. Health conditions in the ghetto of Lodz. *J.Hist.Med.*, 1963, 18: 64-73.
An account of the extermination of the Jews of Lodz, Poland, during World War II by the Nazis.

NAwi

BERTONE, Carlo. Per la storia dell'igiene in Piemonte: i protomedici generali dall' epoca di Emanuele Filiberto in poi. *Riv.Stor.Sci.*, 1933, 24: 19-20, 1 facs.

CELLI-FRAENTZEL, Anna. Comment la Gaule civilisée par Rome se dévoua à l'assainissement de Rome au Moyen-Age et dans les temps modernes. 48 p., 33 fig. Alger: La Typo-Litho, 1930.

FELTEN, Josef. Hygiene im faschistischen Italien. 102 p., 6 fig. (Arbeitsmedizin, Abhandlungen über Berufskrankheiten und deren Verhütung, 15) Leipzig: Barth, 1941.
Reviewed by H. Zeiss, *Mitt.Gesch.Med.*, 1940, 39: 300.

NAwj

CORREIA, Fernando da Silva. Portugal dans l'histoire de l'hygiène. *Act.IIIe Congr.Int.Hist.Sci.* (Portugal, 1934), p. 354-65. Lisbon: 1936.

ROLDAN Y GUERRERO, Rafaël. Précocité de l'organisation sanitaire dans la péninsule ibérique. *Rev.Hist.Pharm.*, 1962, 50: 326-7.
Reviewed by Pierre F. Smith, *Pharm.Hist.*, 1963, 8: 29.

NAwk

WEYDE, A.J. van der. Iets over het toezicht op de volksgezondheit te Utrecht in vroeger tijd. [Concerning the supervision of public health in Utrecht in earlier times. (In Dutch)] *Bijdr.Gesch.Geneesk.*, 1926, 6: 199-205.

NAwn

SIGERIST, Henry E. Twenty-five years of health work in the Soviet Union. *Amer.Rev.Soviet Med.*, 1943, 1: 66-78, 1 chart.

SZUMOWSKI, W. [Die Geschichte der sog. "ziemskaja medicina", der medizinischen Organisation im "Semstwo" system Russlands 1864-1914. (In Polish)] 95 p. Warsaw: Gebethner i Wolff, 1919.
Reviewed by Bilikiewicz, *Mitt.Gesch.Med.*, 1931, 30: 112.

WILLIG, Doris. Public health in Soviet Russia. *Med.Life*, 1937, 44: 197-225.

NAwp/wx Africa; Asia

NAwq

DES CILLEULS, Jean. La participation des médecins des groupes sanitaires mobiles à l'assistance médicale indigène et à la conquête pacifique du Maroc. *Hist.Méd.*, 1959, 9: no. 6, 5-39.

NAwt

HASHIMOTO, Michio. Development of social consciousness in the history of public health in Japan. *Jap.Stud.Hist.Sci.*, 1964, 3: 127-92.

NAwx

DUBOIS, A.; DUREN, A. Soixante ans d'organisation médicale au Congo Belge. *Ann.Soc.Belg.Med.Trop.* [Supplément à l'année 1947] *Liber jubilaris J. Rodhain*, p. 1-36. Bruxelles: Goemaere, 1947.

GELFAND, Michael. Lakeside pioneers: socio-medical study of Nyasaland (1875-1920). 330 p. Oxford: Basil Blackwell, 1964.
Reviewed by W.B. Morgan, *Geogr.J.*, 1964, 130: 552-3.

SQUIRES, H.C. The Sudan Medical Service. An experiment in social medicine. xii, 138 p. London: William Heinemann, 1958.
Reviewed by Kenneth D. Keele, *J.Hist.Med.*, 1959, 14: 124-6; by C.A. Bozman, *Med.Hist.*, 1959, 3: 171.

NAxw museology

GEBHARD, Bruno. Art and science in a health museum. *Bull. Med.Libr.Ass.*, 1945, 33: 39-49, 3 fig.

GEBHARD, Bruno. From medicine show to health museum. *Ciba Symp.* (Summit, N.J.), 1947, 8: 566-600, ill.

GEBHARD, Bruno. From medicine show to health museum. (Historical aspects of public health education in the United States of America) *Ohio State Med.J.*, 1955, 51: 145-7.

GEBHARD, Bruno. Health museums - growth of an idea. 3 p., 5 ill. [Philadelphia: 1959.]
Reprinted from *Amer.Ger.Rev.*, Dec. 1957 - January 1958.

NB MEDICAL STATISTICS

ANDERSON, Odin W. Age-specific mortality differentials historically and currently; observations and implications. *Bull.Hist.Med.*, 1953, 27: 521-9, 4 fig., 4 tables.

CIOCCO, Antonio; PERROTT, Dorothy. Statistics on sickness as a cause of poverty. An historical review of U.S. and English data. *J.Hist.Med.*, 1957, 12: 42-60, 5 tables.

D'ALFONSO, G.; BISCIONE, C. Linee storiche di statistica sanitaria. *Arch.Tisiol.* (Naples), 1964, 19: 140-60.

DROOGLEEVER FORTUYN, H.J.W. De sterftelijn in de laatste driekwart eeuw. [Mortality statistics in the last seventy five years. (In Dutch)] *Bijdr.Gesch.Geneesk.*, 1924, 4: 176-86.

GREENWOOD, Major. Medical statistics from Graunt to Farr. 73 p. (Fitzpatrick Lectures for the years 1941 and 1943, Royal College of Physicians of London) Cambridge University Press, 1948.

KISSKALT, Karl. Ueber historisch-medizinische Statistik. *Arch.Gesch.Med.*, 1925, 17: 165-70.

NEWSHOLME, Arthur. The elements of vital statistics, in their bearing on social and public health problems. New ed. entirely rewritten. 623 p. London: Allen and Unwin, 1923.
First ed. 1889.

PELLER, Sigismund. Studies on mortality since the Renaissance. *Bull.Hist.Med.*, 1943, 13: 427-61; 1944, 16: 362-81: 1947, 21: 51-101.

NBwb

BLAKE, John B. The early history of vital statistics in Massachusetts. *Bull.Hist.Med.*, 1955, 29: 46-68.

DUBLIN, Louis I.; LOTKA, Alfred J. Twenty-five years of health progress. A study of the mortality experience among the industrial policyholders of the Metropolitan Life Insurance Company, 1911 to 1935. xii, 611 p. New York: Metropolitan Life Insurance Co., 1937.
Reviewed by Charles A. Kofoid, *Isis*, 1940, 31: 453-4.

NBwd

ANDERSON, Odin W. Age-specific mortality in selected Western European countries with particular emphasis on the nineteenth century. Observations and implications. *Bull.Hist. Med.*, 1955, 29: 239-54, 9 tables, 9 fig.

NBwe

McCONAGHEY, R.M.S. Medical records of Dartmouth, 1425-1887. A contribution to the history of medical practice. *Med. Hist.*, 1960, 4: 91-111.

NC ENVIRONMENTAL HYGIENE; HUMAN ECOLOGY

BELTRÁN, Enrique. Problemas medicos en la conservación de los recursos naturales. *Gac.Méd.Méx.*, 1945, 75: 255-63.

CORWIN, E.H.L., ed. Ecology of health. xiii, 196 p. New York: Commonwealth Fund, 1949.
Discussion by seven authorities on human health in relation to environment.

GALDSTON, Iago. Prometheus and the gods - an essay on ecology. *Bull.N.Y.Acad.Med.*, 1964, 40: 560-75.

OSBORN, Fairfield. Our plundered planet. xiv, 217 p. Boston; Little, Brown, 1948.
Reviewed by Conway Zirkle, *Isis*, 1949, 40: 76.

UNITED STATES. ARMY MEDICAL DEPARTMENT. Environmental hygiene. vii, 404 p. (Preventive Medicine in World War II, 2) Washington, D.C.: Office of the Surgeon General, 1955.

VOGT, William. Road to survival. xvi, 335 p. New York: William Sloane, 1948; London: Gollancz, 1949.

NCmzH

SCHWIND, Martin. Das Verhältnis des Menschen zu seiner Umwelt als geographisches Problem. *Abhandlungen zur Wissenschaftsgeschichte und Wissenschaftslehre*, p. 25-41. (Veröffentlichungen der Gesellschaft für Internationale Wissenschaftsgeschichte, 1952, no. 2) Bremen: Carl Schünemann, [n.d.].

NCmzJN

ADAMS, C.C. The relation of general ecology to human ecology. *Ecology*, 1935, 16: 316-35.

NCmzMP

DARLING, F. Fraser. The ecological approach to the social sciences. *Amer.Scient.*, 1951, 39: 244-54.

NCwb

EKIRCH, Arthur A. Man and nature in America. ix, 231 p. New York/London: Columbia University Press, 1963.

NCwe-ph

BECK, Ann. Some aspects of the history of anti-pollution legislation in England, 1819-1954. *J.Hist.Med.*, 1959, 14: 475-89.

NCwz

DUNBAR, M.J. Greenland - an experiment in human ecology. *Com.J.*(Toronto), March 1947, 69-109.

ND SANITATION; WATER SUPPLY

BARTOW, Edward. Progress in sanitation. *Science*, 1936, 84: 317-22.
Address of the President of the American Chemical Society, Pittsburgh, September 9, 1936

GARRISON, Fielding Hudson. The history of drainage, irrigation, sewage-disposal and water-supply. *Bull.N.Y.Acad.Med.*, 1929, 5: 887-938.

NDwb

HUTCHISON, John D. Small-town fluoridation fight. *Sci.Mon.*, 1953, 77: 240-3. [CB 80/205]

McNEIL, Donald R. The fight for fluoridation. xii, 241 p. New York: Oxford University Press, 1957.
Reviewed by Nell Snow Talbot, *Bull.Hist.Med.*, 1958, 32: 93.

NDwc

GORGAS, William Crawford. Sanitation in Panama. 297 p., ill. New York: Appleton, 1915.

NDwi

SPADA, Nicolo. Leggi veneziane sulle industrie chimiche a tutela della salute pubblica del secolo XIII al XVIII. 33 p. Venezia: R. Deputazione di Storia Patria, 1930.
Reviewed by C.R. de Gino Testi, *Archeion*, 1931, 13: 278-9.

NDwk

BOONE, R. Overheidszorg voor drinkwater in Vlaanderen. [Public control of drinking water in Flanders. (In Dutch)] 293 p. Gent: 1958.
Reviewed by C. Devyt, *Ann.Soc.Emulation Bruges*, 1961, 98: 120.

NDwy

LAIDLER, P.W. Locations: health and sanitation. Being an extract from the "Annual Report of the Medical Officer of Health, East London", 1st July, 1934-30th June, 1935. 11 p. East London: Griffith-Standard, 1936.

NE AIR POLLUTION

PARKER, Albert. Cities without smoke. *J.Roy.Soc.Arts*, 1950, 99: 85-104, ill.
Contains historical material on the efforts which have been made to reduce the pollution of the atmosphere caused by smoke and grit.

VOGEL, Otto. Rauchbelästigung in alter Zeit. *Rauch Staub*, 1912, 2: 118-20.

NEwk

WOLTER, Friedrich. Die Nebelkatastrophe im Maastal südlich von Lüttich: eine vergleichend-epidemiologische Studie. *Klin. Wochenschr.*, 1931, 10: 785-8.

NF DISPOSAL OF THE DEAD; EMBALMING

BOUDET, Jacques. Médecins et embaumeurs. *Hist.Méd.*, 1951, 1: 35-41.

BRADFORD, Charles Angell. Heart burial. 256 p. London: Allen and Unwin, 1933.
Reviewed in *Nature*, 1933, 132: 44-5.

MENDELSOHN, Simon. Embalming fluids. ix, 166 p. New York: Chemical Publishing Co., 1940. [CB 61/408]

MENDELSOHN, Simon. Preservation of human remains through natural agencies; the evolution of artificial mummification; embalming from the medieval period to the present time. *Ciba Symp.* (Summit, N.J.), 1944, 6: 1782-94, 1805-12, ill.

NETOLITZKY, Fritz. Vom Asphalt über die Mumie zum Ichthyol. *Pharm.Zentralhalle*, 1927, 68: no. 4, 2-7.

POLSON, C.J.; BRITTAIN, R.P.; MARSHALL, T.K. The disposal of the dead. xii, 300 p. New York: Philosophical Library, 1953. [CB 80/135]

NFs

BENDANN, E. Death customs: an analytical study of burial rites. xiii, 304 p. (The History of Civilization Series) London: Kegan Paul, 1930.
Reviewed in *Nature*, 1931, 127: 8.

PUCKLE, Bertram S. Funeral customs: their origin and development. 283 p., ill. London: T.W. Laurie, 1926.

VULLIAMY, Colwyn Edward. Immortal man: a study of funeral customs and of beliefs in regard to the nature and fate of the soul. 215 p. London: Methuen, 1926.

NFtq

RYDH, Hanna. On symbolism in mortuary ceramics. *Bull.Mus. Far East.Antiquities*, 1929, 1: 71-120, 11 pl., 62 fig.
Reviewed by J. Nippgen, *Ethnographie*, 1930, 127-8.

NFu

DURVILLE, Gaston. Les mains qui momifient. *Aesculape*, 1913, 3: 87-9, ill.

NG PREVENTIVE MEASURES

EBSTEIN, Erich. Historical jottings in prophylaxis. *Med. Life*, 1930, 37: 710-12.

HOVELL, Thomas Mark. Rats and how to destroy them. With introduction by S.L. Bensusan. xlii, 465 p. London: Bale, Sons and Danielsson, 1924.

MEYER, K.F. Disinfected mail. 341 p., ill. Holton, Kans.: Gossip Printery, 1962.
Reviewed by Frank R. Smith, *Bull.Hist.Med.*, 1963, 37: 487-8; by Vihl Møller-Christensen, *Centaurus*, 1963, 9: 66; by Hans H. Lauer, *Sudhoffs Arch.*, 1963, 47: 501.

MEYER, K.F. Historical notes on disinfected mail. *J.Nerv. Ment.Dis.*, 1952, 116: 523-54, 16 ill.

NGph-ce

CATELAN, -. Une collection de patentes de santé. *Aesculape*, 1914, 4: 29-31, 6 fig. [CB 5/276]
Collection given by the author to the Académie de Médecine in 1899.

NGwb-sm

SOLIS-COHEN, Rosebud T. The exclusion of aliens from the United States for physical defects. *Bull.Hist.Med.*, 1947, 21: 33-50.

NGwk-ph

TRICOT-ROYER, J.J.G. Les ordonnances du Magistrat d'Anvers contre les maladies dites pestilentielles. 12 p. Anvers: De Vlijt, 1923.

NH PHYSICAL AND CHEMICAL HAZARDS

see also JO EFFECT OF RADIATIONS

KATHREN, Ronald L. William H. Rollins (1852-1929), x-ray protection pioneer. *J.Hist.Med.*, 1964, 19: 287-94.

NJ QUARANTINE

GERLITT, John. The development of quarantine. *Ciba Symp.* (Summit, N.J.), 1940, 2: 566-80, fig.

NJwb

LEIKIND, Morris C. Quarantine in the United States. *Ciba Symp.*(Summit, N.J.), 1940, 2: 581-2.
Apropos of the Public Health Service.

LEIKIND, Morris C. The quarantine station at Miami, Florida. *Ciba Symp.*(Summit, N.J.), 1940, 2: 583-92.
Under the direction of the U.S. Public Health Service.

NJwp

SEHSUVAROGLU, Bedi N. Aperçu sur l'histoire de la quarantaine en Turquie. *Act.VIe Congr.Int.Hist.Sci.* (Amsterdam, 1950), p. 505-6, 1 pl. Paris: Hermann, 1953. Also in *Arch.Int.Hist.Sci.*, 1952, 5: 66-9. [CB 79/138]

NK PERSONAL HYGIENE AND HEALTH

FELDHAUS, Franz Maria; SIEGFRIED, Karl. Das blaue Badewannenbuch. 93 p., 48 fig. Schwarzenberg i. Sa.: Krauss, 1932. [CB 38/598]

GRUMAN, Gerald J. The rise and fall of prolongevity hygiene 1558-1873. *Bull.Hist.Med.*, 1961, 35: 221-9.

MARTIN, Alfred. Auswahl und Bedeutung der Steine zum Erhitzen des Wasser- und des Dampfbades. *Proteus*, 1937, 2: 162-5.

MARTIN, Alfred. Neue Gesichtspunkte zur Geschichte des Badewesens und der Sittlichkeit in Deutschland. *Deut.Med. Wochenschr.*, 1913, 39: 172-3, 229-30, ill.

MARTIN, Alfred. On bathing. Oriental baths. The bath in Japan. *Ciba Symp.* (Summit, N.J.), 1939, 1: 134-62, fig.

MARTIN, Alfred. Die Wandlung des Sittlichkeitsbegriffes auf Grund der Geschichte des Badewesens. *Mitt.Gesch.Med.*, 1913, 12: 272.
Abstract of paper presented to the Gesellschaft für Geschichte der Naturwissenschaften, der Medizin und der Technik am Oberrhein (5th meeting), Düsseldorf, Nov. 1912.

NÉGRIER, Paul; CALMETTES, Pierre; MARÉCHALAR, -. Les bains à travers les âges. 350 p., 150 ill. Paris: La Construction Moderne, 1925. [CB 19/813]

REUTTER DE ROSEMONT, L. Comment nos pères se soignaient, se parfumaient et conservaient leur corps. Remèdes parfums, embaumement, suivi d'un aperçu de l'histoire de la médecine et de la pharmacie dans l'ancien comté français de Neuchâtel (Suisse). 355 p., 38 ill. Genève: Georg, 1917. [CB 12/637]

SCHMIDT, Frederick Rehm. Cosmetics and history. *Med.Life*, 1935, 42: 628-31.

VERRILL, A. Hyatt. Perfumes and spices. Including an account of soaps and cosmetics. The story of the history, source, preparation, and use of the spices, perfumes, soaps, and cosmetics which are in everyday use. xvi, 304 p. Boston: Page, 1940.

WRIGHT, Lawrence. Clean and decent. The fascinating history of the bathroom and the water closet and of sundry habits, fashions and accessories of the toilet principally in Great Britain, France, and America. xii, 282 p., ill., bibliogr. London: Routledge & Kegan Paul; New York: Viking Press, 1960.

NKj

CHAVIGNY, P. Psychologie de l'hygiène. 288 p. Paris: Flammarion, 1921. [CB 13/295]

NKtd

DAVID, René. L'hygiène religieuse dans les livres sacrés. 44 p. (*Thèse, Paris*) Paris: Vigne, 1926.

NL PHYSICAL TRAINING

BELLIN DU COTEAU, Marc; BERGERON, Marcel. L'histoire de l'éducation physique dans ses rapports avec la médecine. *Bull.Soc.Franç.Hist.Méd.*, 1930, 24: 215-28.

JOSEPH, Ludwig H. Physical education in the early Middle Ages. Gymnastics during the Renaissance as a part of the humanistic educational program. Medical gymnastics in the sixteenth and seventeenth centuries. Gymnastics in the pre-revolutionary eighteenth century. *Ciba Symp.*(Summit, N.J.), 1949, 10: 1030-60 ,ill.

LEONARD, Fred Eugene. A guide to the history of physical education. 361 p., 99 ill. Philadelphia: Lea and Febiger, 1923.

LUNN, Arnold. A history of ski-ing. xv, 492 p. London: Oxford University Press, 1927.

NLwg

NEUENDORFF, Edmund. Geschichte der neueren deutschen Leibesübung vom Beginn des 18. Jahrhunderts bis zur Gegenwart. 4 vol. 1. Vom Beginn des 18. Jahrhunderts bis zu Jahn. vii, 467 p.; 2. Jahn und seine Zeit. 1809-1820. 511 p.; 3. Die Zeit von 1820 bis 1860. 566 p.; 4. Die Zeit von 1860 bis 1932. 752 p. Dresden: Limpert, 1930-36.

NLwn

DAWSON, Percy Millard. Soviet samples: diary of an American physiologist. xiv, 568 p. Ann Arbor, Mich.: Edwards, 1938. [CB 56/359]
An American physiologist who spent eleven months in the Soviet Union and visited laboratories, schools, etc. His main interests were physical education and physiology of sport.

NM NUTRITION; DIETETICS

for children's nutrition *see* PWyNM
digestion *see* OY
vitamins *see also* JE

NMc general history

BERCZELLER, L. Zur Geschichte der Ernährungsforschung. *Festschrift zur Feier seines 60. Geburtstages Max Neuburger gewidmet*, p. 38-40. Wien: Verlag des Fest-Komitees, 1928.

CARLONI, Francesco. Concetti antichi e moderni per la prevalenza vegetariana nel regime alimentare. *Ann.Med.Nav. Colon.*, 1913, 19: 546-62, 562-77.

CHRISTIANSEN, Johanne. Gyldne Laegeraad saerlight om Diaet. [Golden maxims on diet. (In Danish)] Copenhagen: Nordisk-Forlag, 1933.
Reviewed by Kate C. Mead, *Isis*, 1936, 25: 520-1.

CURTIS-BENNETT, Noel. The food of the people. 320 p., 30 ill. London: Faber, 1949.

EBSTEIN, Erich. Historical notes on vegetarianism. *Med. Life*, 1924, 31: 469-72.

ELVEHJEM, C.A. Seven decades of nutrition research. *Science*, 1949, 109: 354-8.

GALDSTON, Iago, ed. Human nutrition; historic and scientific. xvii, 321 p., ill. (Institute of Social and Historical Medicine. Monographs, 3) New York: International Universities Press, 1960.

GRAUBARD, Mark. Man's food, its rhyme or reason. x, 213 p. New York: Macmillan, 1943.
Reviewed by Conway Zirkle, *Isis*, 1944, 35: 196-7.

HALLER, Albert von. The vitamin hunters. Transl. from the German by H.F. Bernays. 307 p. Philadelphia: Chilton Book Co., 1962.
Translation of: Die Küche unterm Mikroskop. Düsseldorf: 1959.
Popular account of the history of nutrition with special reference to advances in knowledge during the last eighty years.

HINTZE, Karl. Geographie und Geschichte der Ernährung. 330 p. Leipzig: Thieme, 1934.
Reviewed by Bertha Bessmertny, *Archeion*, 1934, 16: 242.

HOFF, J.J.; HOFF, C.G. De vitamines. Een overzicht ten dienste van allen die in onze voeding belangstellen. [The vitamins. A survey in the service of all who take an interest in nutrition. (In Dutch)] 5th ed. 106 p. Gorinchem: Noorduyn, 1939.
Reviewed by J.A.V., *Janus*, 1939, 43: 335.

JENSEN, L.B. Man's foods. 278 p. Champaign, Ill.: Garrard Press, 1953.
Reviewed by Mark Graubard, *Isis*, 1953, 44: 395-6.

KEYS, Ancel, *et al.* The biology of human starvation. With forewords by J.C. Drummond, Russell M. Wilder, Charles Glen King and Robert R. Williams. 2 vol. xxxii, 763 p.; 765-1385 p. Minneapolis: University of Minnesota Press, 1950. [CB 77/379]

LICHTENFELT, H. Die Geschichte der Ernährung. xvii, 365 p. Berlin: Georg Reimer, 1913.

LUSK, Graham. Contributions to the science of nutrition. A tribute to the life and work of Max Rubner. *Science*, 1932, 76: 129-35.

McCOLLUM, Elmer Verner. Fifty years progress in nutritional research. *Sci.Mon.*, 1950, 71: 376-9.

McCOLLUM, Elmer Verner. A history of nutrition. The sequence of ideas in nutrition investigations. x, 451 p. Boston: Houghton Mifflin, 1957. [CB 84/315]
Reviewed by Leslie J. Harris, *Nature*, 1959, 184: 484-5; by U.S. von Euler, *Lychnos*, 1960-61, 380-1.

MAURIZIO, Adam. Die Geschichte unserer Pflanzennahrung von den Urzeiten bis zur Gegenwart. 480 p., 90 fig., 1 pl. Berlin: Parey, 1927.
French translation: Histoire de l'alimentation végétale depuis la préhistoire jusqu'à nos jours. 672 p., 82 fig. Paris: Payot, 1931.

MAURIZIO, Adam. Die Getreidenahrung im Wandel der Zeiten. vii, 237 p., 53 ill. Zürich: Füssli, 1916.

MENDEL, Lafayette B. Nutrition: the chemistry of life. 150 p. New Haven: Yale University Press, 1923.
Reviewed by R.M. May, *Isis*, 1924, 6: 447-8.

PRICE, Weston A. Nutrition and physical degeneration, a comparison of primitive and modern diets and their effects. Foreword by E.A. Hooton. xviii, 431 p., ill. New York: Hoeber, 1939.
Reviewed in *Ann.Med.Hist.*, 1940, 2: 355-6.

RICHTER, Curt P. The self-selection of diets. *Essays in Biology in honor of Herbert M. Evans*, p. 499-506. Berkeley, Calif.: University of California Press, 1943.

SHERMAN, Henry C. Chemistry of food and nutrition. 6th ed. x, 611 p. New York: Macmillan, 1941. [CB 61/410]
First publ. 1911. 8th ed. 1963.

SHERMAN, Henry C. The science of nutrition. xi, 253 p. New York: Columbia University Press, 1943. [CB 65/84]

STEFANSSON, Vilhjalmur. Not by bread alone. With introductions by Eugene F. Du Bois and E.A. Hooton. xvi, 339 p. New York: Macmillan, 1946.
Reviewed by M.F. Ashley Montagu, *Isis*, 1948, 38: 271-2.

VELDE, A.J.J. van de. [Men and food. (In Dutch)] *Alumni*, 1949, 18: 280-91. [CB 76/399]

ZIEGLER, Mildred R. The history of the calorie in nutrition. *Sci.Mon.*, 1923, 15: 520-6.

NMs/u social and humanistic relations

NMsc

PRENTICE, Ezra Parmalee. Hunger and history: the influence of hunger on human history. 268 p. New York: Harper, 1939.
Reviewed by Conway Zirkle, *Isis*, 1947, 32: 227-9.

NMtd

ALBERTI, Giuseppe. Diaeta parca e salute. Lineamenti psicofisiologici nelle antiche regole religiose. xii, 218 p. Milano: Hoepli, 1941.
Reviewed by L. Castaldi, *Riv.Stor.Sci.*, 1942, 33: 75.

NMu

CLAIR, André. La géophagie et les mangeurs de terre. *Hist. Méd.*, 1951, no. 7, 46-8.

PROVERBIAL medicine. Prognosis in proverbs and folklore. Proverbs of diet. Proverbs regarding alcohol. *Brit.Med.J.*, 1913, (1), 178-80, 291-3, 398-400.

REGELSPERGER, Gustave. Notes sur la géophagie. *Rev.Gén.Sci.*, 1921, 32: 430-5.

NMw in different countries

NMwb

CARLSON, A.J. Food and fitness. *Sci.Mon.*, 1942, 55: 403-7.
A critical examination of the often repeated statement that "one third of the American people are ill fed".

CUMMINGS, Richard Osborn. The American and his food. A history of food habits in the United States. 267 p., 12 pl. Chicago: University of Chicago Press, 1940.
Reviewed by Conway Zirkle, *Isis*, 1941, 33: 350-1.

NMwe

DRUMMOND, Jack C. Historical studies of English diet and nutrition. Cantor lectures. Three lectures given before the Royal Society of Arts on Nov. 29th, December 6th and 13th, 1937. 39 p. London: Royal Society of Arts, 1938.

DRUMMOND, Jack C.; WILBRAHAM, Anne. The Englishman's food. A history of five centuries of English diet. Revised and with a new chapter by Dorothy Hollingsworth. 482 p., 8 pl. London: Cape, 1958.
Reviewed by Leslie J. Harris, *Nature*, 1959, 184: 484-5; by Jean Causeret, *Rev.Quest.Sci.*, 1959, 20: 315-16.
First publ. 1939 and reviewed by Conway Zirkle, *Isis*, 1941, 33: 300-1.

PRENTICE, Ezra Parmalee. Food in England. *Agr.Hist.*, 1950, 24: 65-9.
A brief description of over one thousand years of a defective diet.

NMwt

BOURNE, Geoffrey H. Nutrition in Japan. *Nature*, 1946, 157: 177-8.

NMzf FOODS: NUTRITIONAL VALUES

BECK, Bodog Felix; SMEDLEY, Dorée. Honey and your health. 231 p. London: Museum Press, 1947.

CHATFIELD, Charlotte. Food composition tables for international use. v, 56 p. (FAO Nutritional Studies, 3) Washington, D.C.: Food and Agriculture Organization of the United Nations, 1949. [CB 76/404]

DEWAILLY, Ph.; THÉODORIDÈS, J. Remarques sur l'usage passé et présent des insectes dans l'alimentation et la thérapeutique. (Contribution à l'histoire de la zoölogie médicale.) *Rev.Gén.Sci.*, 1953, 60: 165-72, bibliogr.

LECLERC, Henri. Les fruits de France, historique, diététique et thérapeutique. 274 p. Paris: Masson, 1925.

LECLERC, Henri. Les légumes de France. Leur histoire, leurs usages alimentaires, leurs vertus thérapeutiques. 217 p. Paris: Masson, 1928.
Reviewed by M. Laignel-Lavastine, *Bull.Soc.Franç.Hist.Méd.*, 1928, 22: 221-2.

PEDERSON, C.S.; ALBURY, M.N. Sauerkraut through the ages. *Farm Res.*, 1953, 19: 4-16. [CB 80/134]

VELDE, A.J.J. van de. Over de voedingswaarde van dierlijke zeevoortbrengselen. [On the food value of animal products of the sea. (In Dutch)] *Verhandel.Vlaam.Acad.Geneesk.Belg.*, 1949, 338-54.

NMzf-wp

KRAUSE, K. Über den giftigen Honig des pontischen Kleinasien. *Naturwissenschaften*, 1926, 14: 976-8. [CB 22/275]

ÜNVER, A. Süheyl. [Quelques mots sur l'ancienneté de l'histoire du "Yogourt" chez les Turcs. (In Turkish with French translation)] *Tedavi Klin.Laboratuvari*, 1936, 6: no. 22, 3-6.

NO NARCOTICS; ALCOHOL

see also RZyOK drugs acting on NERVOUS SYSTEM
for alcohol as medicine *see* under RU

DIEPGEN, Paul. Der Alkohol in der Medizingeschichte. *Jahrb. Ges.Gesch.Bibliogr.Brauw.*, 1937, 7-30.

GAVIT, John Palmer. Opium. xi, 308 p. London: Routledge, 1925.

GOLDSMITH, Margaret. The trail of opium, the eleventh plague. 286 p. London: Hale, 1939.

PEARL, Raymond. Alcool e biologia umana. *Scr.Biol.*, 1931, 6: 235-46.

ROBINSON, Victor. Hashish: a drug and a dream; concerning *Cannabis indica;* experiments with hashish. *Ciba Symp.* (Summit, N.J.), 1946, 8: 374-96, 404, ill.

STARLING, Ernest Henry. The action of alcohol on man. With essays on 1. Alcohol as a medicine, by Robert Hutchison. 2. Alcohol and its relations to problems in mental disorders by Frederick Mott. 3. Alcohol and mortality, by Raymond Pearl. vi, 291 p. London: Longmans, 1923.

VERNON, Horace Middleton. The alcohol problem. Preface by Viscount D'Abernon. xv, 252 p. London: Baillière, Tindal and Cox, 1928.

NOu

PROVERBIAL medicine. Prognosis in proverbs and folklore. Proverbs of diet. Proverbs regarding alcohol. *Brit.Med.J.*, 1913, (1), 178-80, 291-3, 398-400.

NOwb

JONES, Bartlett C. Prohibition and eugenics 1920-1933. *J. Hist.Med.*, 1963, 18: 158-72.

JONES, Bartlett C. A prohibition problem: liquor as medicine, 1920-1933. *J.Hist.Med.*, 1963, 18: 353-69.

WALTON, Robert Petrie. Marihuana, America's new drug problem. A sociologic question with its basic explanation dependent on biologic and medical principles. Foreword by E.M.K. Geiling and a chapter by Frank R. Gomila and M.C. Gomila Lambou. ix, 223 p., 12 pl. Philadelphia: Lippincott, 1938.
Reviewed by A.R. Todd, *Nature*, 1939, 144: 611-12.

NOwc

WOLFF, Pablo Osvaldo. Marihuana in Latin America, the threat it constitutes. 56 p. Washington, D.C.: Linacre Press, 1949.
Transl. of: La marihuana en la America latina; la amenaza que constituye. 55 p., bibliogr. Buenos Aires: Ateneo, 1948. [CB 76/415]

NP TOBACCO

ARENTS, George. Tobacco. Its history, illustrated by the books, manuscripts and engravings in the library of George Arents, [a catalogue of the library], together with an introductory essay, glossary and bibliographical notes by Jerome E. Brooks. 5 vol. ill. New York: Rosenbach, 1937-52.
Vol. 1 reviewed by George Sarton, *Isis*, 1938, 29: 186-8.

BROOKS, Jerome E. The mighty leaf: tobacco through the centuries. x, 361 p. Boston: Little, Brown, 1952.
Reviewed by Conway Zirkle, *Isis*, 1953, 44: 394-5.

BÜHLER-OPPENHEIM, K. Zur Geschichte des Tabaks. *Ciba Z.*, 1949, 10: 4278-84, ill.

CORTI, Egon Caesar. A history of smoking. Transl. from the German. 295 p., ill. London: Harrap, 1931.
Translation of Die trockene Trunkenheit. (Leipzig: Insel-Verlag, 1930).

HOLMES, George K. Some features of tobacco history. *Annu. Rep.Amer.Hist.Ass. for 1919*, (1), 387-407.

JAHN, Raymond, ed. Tobacco dictionary. 199 p., front., 1 fig. New York: Philosophical Library, 1954.

LARSON, P.S.; HAAG, H.B.; SILVETTE, H. Tobacco: experimental and clinical studies. A comprehensive study of the world's literature. xii, 932 p., ill. Baltimore: Williams and Wilkins, 1961.
Reviewed by Chauncey D. Leake, *Science*, 1961, 134: 184-5.

MAMLOCK, G. Der Tabak in der Heilkunde. *Ciba Z.*, 1949, 10: 4294-301, ill.

SEIG, Louis. The spread of tobacco. A study in cultural diffusion. *Prof.Geogr.*, 1963, 15: 17-21.

SETCHELL, William Albert. Aboriginal tobaccos. *Amer.Anthropol.*, 1921, 23: 397-414, map. [CB 38/600]

UGATA, Tamekichi. Igaku tabaco kô. [Notes on tobacco from the medical view point. (In Japanese)] 314 p., front., ill. Tokyo: Ryûshô-kaku. 1934. [CB 45/264]

NPcc-by

ARENTS, George, Jr. Books, manuscripts and drawings relating to tobacco from the collection of George Arents, Jr. On exhibition at the Library, 113 p. Washington, D.C.: Library of Congress, 1938. [CB 54/534]
Adapted from: "Tobacco. Its history illustrated by the books, manuscripts and engravings in the Library of George Arents, Jr.", by Jerome E. Brooks.

NPce

POTTER, Alfred C. Some early books on tobacco. A paper read before the Club of Odd Volumes in Boston, April 10, 1910, with some omissions and a few additions. *Harvard Libr.Notes*, 1936, 3: 101-18.

NPce-bv

ARENTS, George. Early literature of tobacco. [Bibliography] 13 p. Washington, D.C.: Library of Congress, 1938.

NPth

BAIN, John. Tobacco in song and story. 144 p. (Arents Tobacco Collection. Publication, 4) New York: New York Public Library, 1953.
First published 1896.

NPwa-nh

WIENER, Leo. The philological history of "Tobacco" in America. *Compt.Rend.XXIe Congr.Int.Amér.* (Göteborg, 1924), p. 305-14, 3 maps. Göteborg: Museum, 1925. [CB 18/622]

NPwe

MULLETT, Charles F. Tobacco as a drug in earlier English medicine. *Ann.Med.Hist.*, 1940, 2: 110-23.

NPwh

ČAPEK, A. Tabák v Čechách. [Tobacco in Bohemia. (In Czech)] 420 p. Prague: Librairie technique, 1947.
History of the cultivation, handling and trade of tobacco in Bohemia since the 16th century.

NPwx

LAUFER, Berthold; HAMBLY, Wilfrid D.; LINTON, Ralph. Tobacco and its use in Africa. 45 p., 6 pl. (Anthropology Leaflet, 29) Chicago: Field Museum of Natural History, 1930.

NPxx

CUDELL, Robert. Die Sammlung Neuerburg. Ein Büchlein vom Rauchen und Rauchgerät. 59 p., 70 pl. Köln: Neuerburg, 1930.

NQ SEXUAL HYGIENE

for sexual behaviour *see* MQzs

NR PROSTITUTION

BLOCH, Iwan. Die Prostitution. Vol. 1. xxxvi, 870 p. Vol. 2, pt. 1. (with Georg Loewenstein) 728 p. (Handbuch der gesamten Sexualwissenschaft in Einzeldarstellungen) Berlin: Louis Marcus, 1912-25.
No more published.
Vol. 1 reviewed by George Sarton, *Isis*, 1913, 1: 284-5; Vol. 2 by Stephen d'Irsay, *ibid.*, 1926, 8: 521-5.

BULLOUGH, Vern L.; BULLOUGH, Bonnie. The history of prostitution. x, 304 p. New Hyde Park, N.Y.: University Books, 1964.

DUFOUR, Pierre. Geschichte der Prostitution bei allen Völkern von der Urzeit bis zur Gegenwart. Ins Deutsche übertragen von Adolf Stille und Bruno Schweigger. Mit Geleit- und Schlusswort von Erich Wulffen, bis zum Ende des 19. Jahrhunderts erg. von Franz Helbing. Völlig neu bearb. und bis zur Gegenwart fortgeführt von Paul Langenscheidt. 7th rev. ed. 482 p., 16 pl. Berlin: Langenscheidt, 1925.
Pierre Dufour is the pseudonym of Paul Lacroix.

HABERLING, Wilhelm. Das Dirnenwesen in den Heeren der Vergangenheit und seine Bekämpfung. iv, 103 p., ill. (Z. *Bekämpfung Geschlechtskrankheiten*, 1914, vol. 15) Leipzig: Barth, 1914.

STROPPIANA, Luigi; GUIDO, Francesco. Problemi medico-sociali del meretricio e sua regolamentazione dagli inizi all' epoca moderna. *Atti Mem.Accad.Stor.Arte Sanit.*, 1964, 30: 141-53.

NRwd

FLEXNER, Abraham. Prostitution in Europe. Introduction by John D. Rockefeller. ix, 455 p. (Publications of the Bureau of Social Hygiene) New York: The Century Co., 1914.

NS EUGENICS; APPLIED GENETICS

for human genetics *see* MD

EUGÉNIQUE et sélection par E. Apert, L. Cuénot [*et al.*]. 248 p. (Bibliothèque Générale des Seiences Sociales) Paris: Alcan, 1922.

HOLMES, S.J. Studies in evolution and eugenics. 261 p. New York: Harcourt Brace, 1923. [CB 15/210]

INTERNATIONAL EUGENICS CONFERENCE, 3rd, New York, 1932. A decade of progress in eugenics. Scientific papers of the Third International Congress of Eugenics held at the American Museum of Natural History, New York, 1932. xii, 531 p., 4 portr., 28 pl. Baltimore: Williams & Wilkins, 1934. [CB 43/277]

KATSAINOS, George M. Marriage and syphilis. A treatise on eugenics. 164 p., ill. Boston: Four Seas Company, 1923. [CB 27/581]

POPENOE, Paul; JOHNSON, Roswell Hill. Applied eugenics. xii, 459 p. New York: Macmillan, 1918.

WEINSTEIN, Alexander. Palamedes. *Amer.Natur.*, 1933, 67: 222-53. [CB 40/404]
A discussion of the principles and applications of eugenics.

NSce-bv

HOLMES, Samuel J. A bibliography of eugenics. *Univ.Calif. Publ.Zool.*, 1924, 25: 1-514. [CB 16/342]

NSq

DARWIN, Leonard. The aims and methods of eugenical societies. *Science*, 1921, 54: 313-23.

NSs

DARWIN, Leonard. The need for eugenic reform. xviii, 529 p. London: John Murray, 1926.
Reviewed by E.W.M., *Nature*, 1926, 118: 39-42.

HUXLEY, Julian S. Eugenics and society. *Eugen.Rev.*, 1936, 28: 11-31.

NSsk

HALDANE, J.B.S. Heredity and politics. 202 p. New York: Norton, 1938. [CB 54/565]

SCHILLER, Ferdinand Canning Scott. Eugenics and politics. xi, 220 p. London: Constable, 1926.

NSwb

HALLER, Mark H. Eugenics. Hereditarian attitudes in American thought. vii, 264 p. New Brunswick, N.J.: Rutgers University Press, 1963.

JONES, Bartlett C. Prohibition and eugenics 1920-1933. *Hist.Med.*, 1963, 18: 158-72.

NSwb-cb

LAUGHLIN, Harry H. The Eugenics Record Office at the end of twenty-seven months work. 28 p. (Report, 1) Cold Spring Harbor, N.Y.: Eugenics Record Office, 1913.

NT HEALTH SERVICES; SOCIAL WELFARE

GALDSTON, Iago. The future of the voluntary health organization. In: Public Health Association of New York City. Tomorrow's horizon in public health; transactions of the 1950 conference, p. 9-17. New York: 1950.

LOMBARDI, Felice. L'evoluzione storica dell'assistenza sanitaria. 47 p. (Collana Scientia Veterum, 54) Pisa: Giardini, 1963.

SIGERIST, Henry E. Socialized medicine. *Yale Rev.*, 1938, 27: 463-81.

STERN, Bernhard J. Medical services by government - local, state, and federal. xvii, 208 p. (Studies of the New York Academy of Medicine, Committee on Medicine and the Changing Order) New York: Commonwealth Fund, 1946. [CB 74/398]

TERRIS, Milton. Hermann Biggs' contribution to the modern concept of the health center. *Bull.Hist.Med.*, 1946, 20: 387-412.

NTqm

GUNN, Selskar M.; PLATT, Philip S. Voluntary health agencies. An interpretive study. xviii, 364 p. New York: Ronald Press Co., 1945.
Reviewed by George Rosen, *J.Hist.Med.*, 1946, 1: 344-6.

NTqp

HUME, Edgar Erskine. Medical work of the Knights Hospitallers of Saint John of Jerusalem. xxii, 371 p., ill. (Institute of the History of Medicine of the Johns Hopkins University) Baltimore, Md.: Johns Hopkins Press, 1940.
Reprinted from *Bull.Inst.Hist.Med.*, 1938, vol. 6.
Reviewed in *Ann.Med.Hist.*, 1941, 3: 169-70; by Loren C. MacKinney, *Amer.Hist.Rev.*, 1941, 46: 857-8.

KINGSLEY, Rose G. The Order of St. John of Jerusalem (past and present). 160 p. London: Skeffington, 1918.

MAJOR, Ralph H. The Knights of St. John of Jerusalem. *J.Kans. Med.Soc.*, 1964, 65: 141-8.

RUSSOTTO, Gabrielle. Fatebenefratelli in Sardegna. Roma: 1956.
Reviewed by Francesco Carta, *Riv.Stor.Med.*, 1957, 1: 115-16.

NTqx

QUATRIÈME Conférence Internationale des Assurances Sociales. *Vie Int.*, 1914, 5: 559-62. [CB 6/468]
Programme de la conférence.

NTtd

MAZZEO, Mario. L'assistenzia sanitaria ispirata dal cristianesimo. 6 pt. 1, 2, 4. *Med.Morale*, 1954, fasc. 6; 1955, fasc. 1; 3. *Riv.Stor.Sci.*, 1955, 46: 7-38; 5. *Ann.Sanit. Pubblica*, 1956, 17: 1143-78; 6. *Ig.Sanit.Pubblica*, 1954, 10: 737-45.

NTwb

ANDERSON, Odin W. Health insurance in the United States, 1910-1920. *J.Hist.Med.*, 1950, 5: 363-96.

BACHMAN, George W.; MERIAM, Lewis. The issue of compulsory health insurance. ix, 271 p. Washington, D.C.: Brookings Institution, 1948. [CB 73/185]

CURTI, Merle. The history of American philanthropy as a field of research. *Amer.Hist.Rev.*, 1957, 62: 352-63.

NTwb-qm

DEUTSCH, Albert. Some wartime influences on health and welfare institutions in the United States. *J.Hist.Med.*, 1946, 1: 318-29.

NTwe

LINDSEY, Almont. Socialized medicine in England and Wales. The National Health Service, 1958-1961. xiii, 561 p. Chapel Hill: University of North Carolina Press, 1962.
Reviewed by George A. Wolf, *Science*, 1962, 138: 504.

STEWART, J. Anderson. Jubilee of the National Insurance Act. *Pharm.J.*, 1962, 135: 33-5.

WILLIAMS, Harley. The morphology of state medicine in Great Britain. *Proc.Roy.Soc.Med.*, 1932, 25: 1745-52.

NTwf

DU COUËDIC, -, *Mère*. Les Hospitalières de Besançon (histoire et souvenirs). 320 p., ill. [Besançon?]: 1935.
Reviewed by Marcel Fosseyeux, *Bull.Soc.Franç.Hist.Méd.*, 1937, 31: 56-8.

WEIL, Georges. Histoire du mouvement social en France (1852-1924). 3rd ed. viii, 512 p., bibliogr. Paris: F. Alcan, 1924. [CB 18/574]
1st edition 1902; 2nd edition 1910.

NTwk

HELLINGA, G. Geschiedenis der geneeskundige armenverzorging buiten de gasthuizen te Amsterdam. [The history of medical care for the poor outside the hospitals in Amsterdam. (In Dutch)] *Bijdr.Gesch.Geneesk.*, 1932, 12: 157-73; 1933, 13: 37-52.

NTwn

SIGERIST, Henry E. Medicine and health in the Soviet Union. With the cooperation of Julia Older. xix, 364 p. New York: Citadel Press, 1947.
First published as Socialized medicine in the Soviet Union, *see* below.
Reviewed by George Sarton, *Isis*, 1948, 39: 202-3.

SIGERIST, Henry E. Socialized medicine in the Soviet Union. 378 p. New York: Norton, 1937. English edition (with additional material). 397 p. London: Gollancz, 1937.
For 2nd edition entitled Medicine and health in the Soviet Union, *see* above.
Reviewed by John B. de C.M. Saunders, *Isis*, 1938, 29: 200-3.

NU MOTHERS AND CHILDREN

BLAKE, John B. Origins of maternal and child health programs. 42 p. New Haven: Yale University, School of Medicine, Department of Public Health, 1953.

HAUPT, M. Schulhygiene und schulärztlicher Dienst im Spiegel der *Zeitschrift für Schulgesundheitspflege* 1888-1938. *Öffentl. Gesundheitsdienst*, 1964, 26: 273-81.

UNDERWOOD, E. Ashworth. The quest for child health - the historical beginnings. *Rep.Annu.Conf.Nat.Ass.Matern.Child Welfare* (London, 1951), p. 3-10. London: 1951.

WACHTEL, Curt. Laienärzte und Schulmedizin, ihre hauptsächlichen und sozialen Beziehungen im Lichte der zeitgenössischen Medizin und Philosophie. 130 p. Leipzig: Curt Kabitzsch, 1923.

NUwc-qm

ALONSO, Aurelia E. La Sociedad de Beneficencia de Buenos Aires, en la asistencia a la infancia. *Rev.Argent.Hist.Med.*, 1942, 1: 69-74.

NUwd

SÄNGLINGSFÜRSORGE und Kinderschutz in den europäischen Staaten; ein Handbuch für Ärzte, Richter, Vormünder, Verwaltungsbeamte und Sozialpolitiker, für Behörden, Verwaltungen und Vereine. xi, 1548 p. Berlin: J. Springer, 1912.

NUwf

LANNOIS, M. Les enfants assistés de l'hôtel-dieu et de la Charité à Lyon et leurs sceaux d'immatriculation. *Bull.Soc. Franç.Hist.Méd.*, 1934, 28: 305-13, 7 fig.

NUwo

BOLOGA, Valeriu L. Die Anfange der rumänischen Schulmedizin. *Med.Z.*, 1935, 10: 293-6.

NV PRISONERS

NVwf

BIZARD, Léon. Souvenirs d'un médecin des prisons de Paris. 240 p., ill. Paris: Grasset, 1925.

SÉRIEUX, Paul; GOULARD, Roger. Le service médical au donjon de Vincennes (Prison d'État). *Bull.Soc.Franç.Hist.Méd.*, 1927, 21: 419-35.

NW HOSPITALS

for hospitals for special diseases *see* INDEX

NWc general history

CUMMING, Hugh S. The municipal general hospital of the future and its relation to public health. *Med.Life*, 1933, 40: 158-62.

FOOTE, John. Hospitals, their origin and evolution. *Pop. Sci.Mon.*, 1913, 82: 478-91.

FREIDSON, Eliot, ed. The hospital in modern society. xx, 346 p. New York: Free Press of Glencoe, 1963.
Reviewed by Lloyd G. Stevenson, *J.Hist.Med.*, 1964, 19: 87-8.

GASK, George E.; TODD, John. The origin of hospitals. *Science, Medicine and History. Essays in honour of Charles Singer*, (1), p. 122-30. London: Oxford University Press, 1953.

GOLDHAHN, Richard. Spital und Arzt von Einst bis Jetzt. 188 p., 40 ill. Stuttgart: Enke, 1940.
Reviewed (in Swedish) by O.T. Hult, *Lychnos*, 1940, 469.

GRAFFAR, Marcel. L'évolution hospitalière. *Rev.Univ.Bruxelles*, 1962, 14: 292-301.

HELLINGA, G. Gasthuistoestanden in den "Goeden ouden tijd". [Conditions in hospitals in the "good old days". (In Dutch)] *Bijdr.Gesch.Geneesk.*, 1927, 7: 501-12.

HELLINGA, G. Sprokkelingen uit het gasthuisarchief. [Gleanings from the hospital archives. (In Dutch)] *Bijdr.Gesch. Geneesk.*, 1934, 14: 91-6.

KILDUFFE, Robert A. Highlights in the history of hospitals. *Med.Life*, 1936, 43: 9-24.

NASALLI-ROCCA, Emilio. Il diritto ospedaliero nei suoi lineamenti storici. 244 p. (Biblioteca della Rivista di storia del diritto italiano, 20) Milan: Fondazione Sergio Mochi Onory, 1956.
Reviewed by Ernest Wickersheimer, *Arch.Int.Hist.Sci.*, 1958, 11: 83-4.

SIGERIST, Henry E. An outline of the development of the hospital. *Bull.Inst.Hist.Med.*, 1936, 4: 573-81.

SORGO, Josef. Zur Geschichte der Volksheilstättenbewegung. *Festschrift zum 80. Geburtstag Max Neuburgers*, p. 440-3. Wien: Maudrich, 1948.

WICKERSHEIMER, Ernest. Les édifices hospitaliers à travers les âges. 27 p., 6 fig. (Conférences du Palais de la Découverte, D, 20) Paris: Université de Paris, 1953. Also in *Arch.Iberoamer.Hist.Med.*, 1956, 8: 87-108.

NWmzNr

SUDHOFF, Karl. Die geschichtliche Entwicklung der Beziehungen zwischen ärztlichen Beruf und dem Krankenhause. *Nosokomeion*, 1931, 2: 1-20.

NWqp

GALLASSI, A. Note ed appunti sulla assistenza ospedaliera e gli ordini religiosi. *Riv.Stor.Sci.*, 1950, 41: 166-72.

NWw in different countries

NWwb North America

see also Philadelphia General Hospital, 2: 740

BERNHEIM, Bertram M. The story of the Johns Hopkins. xi. 235 p., ill. New York: McGraw-Hill, 1948.

CHESNEY, Alan M. The Johns Hopkins Hospital and the Johns Hopkins School of Medicine. A chronicle. 3 vol. 1. Early years, 1867-1893. xviii, 318 p., ill.; 2. 1893-1905. xiv, 504 p., ill.; 3. 1905-1914. xv, 350 p., ill. Baltimore, Md.: Johns Hopkins Press, 1943, 1958, 1963.
Vol. 1 reviewed by Genevieve Miller, *Bull.Hist.Med.*, 1944, 16: 90-2; vol. 2 by John R. Blake, *Isis*, 1959, 50: 512-14.

CLARK, Sydney P. Franklin's hospital, our hospital and the hospital of the future. *J.Franklin Inst.*, 1956, 261: 93-9.

CLARK, Sydney P. Pennsylvania Hospital since May 11, 1751. Two hundred years in Philadelphia. 44 p. New York: Newcomen Society of North America, 1951. [CB 79/194]

COOPER, Page. The Bellevue story. x, 277 p. New York: Crowell, 1948.

EDWARDS, Linden F. Centenary anniversary of the oldest medical college hospital in the United States. St. Francis Hospital, Columbus, Ohio. *Bull.Hist.Med.*, 1952, 26: 269-76, 1 fig.

HISTORY of the Reading Hospital. Published by the Board of Managers on occasion of the 75th anniversary of the Hospital, Dec. 9, 1942. 287 p., ill. Reading, Pa.: The Hospital, 1942.
Reviewed by Genevieve Miller, *Bull.Hist.Med.*, 1943, 14: 416.

HOWELL, William Boyman. L'Hôtel-Dieu de Quebec. *Ann.Med.Hist.*, 1934, 6: 396-409.

HUME, Edgar Erskine. The oldest hospital in America. The hospital of Jesus of Nazareth in the city of Mexico, established in 1524, it is still in use. *Med.Life*, 1937, 44: 317-30, ill.

MacQUIDY, Ernest L. Early American hospitals. *Hospitals*, 1938, 12: 76-9.

PACKARD, Francis R. Some account of the Pennsylvania Hospital from its first rise to the beginning of the year 1938. xii, 133 p. Philadelphia, Pa.: Engle Press, 1938.
Reviewed by David Riesman, *Ann.Med.Hist.*, 1938, 10: 360-1.

RANSOM, John E. The beginnings of hospitals in the United States. *Bull.Hist.Med.*, 1943, 13: 514-39.

RICHARDSON, J.T. The origin and development of group hospitalization in the United States, 1890-1940. 101 p. (*Univ. Missouri Stud.*, 20: no. 5) Columbia: University of Missouri, 1945.
Reviewed by Milton Terris, *Bull.Hist.Med.*, 1946, 20: 488-9.

ROONEY, William E. The founding of the New Orleans Marine Hospital. *Bull.Hist.Med.*, 1951, 25: 260-8.

SCHLUETER, Robert E. The story of St. Boniface Hospital at St. Louis. *Bull.Hist.Med.*, 1941, 9: 475-80.

SHADID, Michael A. A doctor for the people. The autobiography of the founder of America's first co-operative hospital - and how he successfully defended it against the attacks of the medical trust. 277 p. New York: Vanguard Press, 1939.
Reviewed by George Sarton, *Isis*, 1943, 34: 382.

WASHBURN, Frederick A. The Massachusetts General Hospital, its development, 1900-1935. Boston, Mass.: Houghton, Mifflin, 1939.
Reviewed in *Ann.Med.Hist.*, 1939, 1: 485-6.

NWwb-vm

SALTZSTEIN, Harry C. Sinai Hospital and the North End Clinic. Reminiscences of the history of the Jewish hospital movement in Detroit. 71 p., ill. Detroit: Wayne State University Press, 1963.

NWwc Latin America

ALVÁREZ-SIERRA, J. La Orden de San Juan de Dios llevó la medicina y la hospitalidad por el Continente americano. *Arch.Iberoamer.Hist.Med.*, 1957, 9: 23-32.

CORPAS, Juan N. El viejo Hospital de San Juan de Dios, de Bogotá. *Rev.Argent.Hist.Med.*, 1943, 2: no. 2, 11-19.

DÁVILA, Guillermo Fernández. Algunos apuntes para la historia del hospital "San Bartolomé". *An.Soc.Peruana Hist.Med.*, 1940, 2: 64-74.

GUIJARRO OLIVERAS, Jose. Aportación a la historia del Hospital Real de San Andrés de españoles, de la ciudad de Lima. *Arch. Iberoamer.Hist.Med.*, 1957, 9: 263-8.

MARROQUÍN, José. Historia de la Orden Hospitalaria de San Juan de Dios en Puno. *An.Soc.Peruana Hist.Med.*, 1943, 4: 89-92.

MARTINEZ DURÁN, Carlos. Los hospitales de América durante la época colonial. *Essays in the History of Medicine presented to Prof. Arturo Castiglioni*, p. 170-83, 4 fig. Baltimore: Johns Hopkins Press, 1944.

PALM, Erwin Walter. Hospitales antiguos de la Española. 1. El Hospital de San Nicolás de Bari. *Multa Paucis Méd.*, 1946, 3: 49-75, ill.

RENZO, Alberto. Carlos Seidl e o Hospital São Sebastião. *Rev.Brasil.Hist.Med.*, 1956, 7: 143-50.

VALENTIN F., Luis. Recordando el tricentenario de fundación del Hospital de San Bartolomé. *An.Soc.Peruana Hist.Med.*, 1946, 8: 45-9.

VILLACIS, Manuel Humberto. El hospital San Juan de Dios de la Ciudad de San Francisco de Quito. *Rev.Argent.Hist.Med.*, 1943, 2: no. 1, 49-59.

NWwe British Isles

ANNING, S.T. The General Infirmary at Leeds. xii, 107 p., ill. Edinburgh/London: Livingstone, 1963.
Reviewed by J.G. McCrie, *Med.Hist.*, 1964, 8: 92.

BROCKBANK, William. Portrait of a hospital, 1752-1948. To commemorate the bicentenary of the Royal Infirmary, Manchester. x, 217 p., ill. London: William Heinemann, 1952.
Reviewed by Samuel C. Harvey, *J.Hist.Med.*, 1953, 8: 338-40; by W. Pagel, *Bull.Hist.Med.*, 1954, 28: 98.

CLARK-KENNEDY, A.E. The London. A study in the voluntary hospital system. 2 vol. 1. The first hundred years, 1740-1840. xiii, 264 p., ill.; 2. The second hundred years, 1840-1948. 310 p., ill., pl., maps. London: Pitman Medical Publications, 1962, 1963.
Vol. 1 reviewed in *Proc.Roy.Soc.Med.*, 1963, 56: 140; by W.H. McMenemey, *Med.Hist.*, 1963, 7: 391-2.

DAINTON, Courtney. The story of England's hospitals. 184 p., 28 ill. London: Museum Press, 1961; Springfield, Ill.: Charles C. Thomas, 1962.
Reviewed by John H. Raach, *Bull.Hist.Med.*, 1963, 37: 391-2.

FISHER, Reginald. An early cottage hospital. The beginnings of the West Herts Hospital. *Med.Hist.*, 1963, 7: 268-70.

GIBSON, Alexander George. The Radcliffe Infirmary. ix, 316 p. London: Oxford University Press, 1926.

GUY'S HOSPITAL GAZETTE. Special number in commemoration of the bi-centenary of the hospital and the centenary of the Medical School, 1725-1925. Ed. by Leslie George Housden. Sub-editor, Gordon Gould Cameron. 216 p. London: Guy's Hospital, 1925.

HIGHAM, A.R.C. The history of St. Paul's Hospital, London *Proc.Roy.Soc.Lond.*, 1957, 50: 164-6.

HUNTER, W. Historical account of Charing Cross hospital and medical school. xx, 309 p. London: Murray, 1914.

JEWESBURY, Eric C.O. The Royal Northern Hospital, 1856-1956. The story of a hundred years' work in North London. xi, 157 p., ill. London: H.K. Lewis, 1956.
Reviewed by W.J. Bishop, *Med.Hist.*, 1957, 1: 83-4.

LYLE, H. Willoughby. King's and some King's men: being a record of the medical department of King's College, London, from 1830 to 1909 and of King's College Hospital Medical School from 1909 to 1934. x, 613 p. London: Oxford University Press, 1935.

McCRAE, Thomas. The octocentenary of St. Bartholomew's Hospital (1123). *Ann.Med.Hist.*, 1923, 5: 279-82, ill.

McINNES, E.M. St. Thomas's Hospital. 230 p., ill. London: G. Allen, 1963.
Reviewed by W.S.C. Copeman, *Med.Hist.*, 1964, 8: 94-5.

McMENEMEY, William Henry. A history of the Worcester Royal Infirmary. xvi, 356 p. London: Press Alliances, 1947.
Reviewed by Leona Baumgartner, *J.Hist.Med.*, 1948, 3: 175-7.

MOORE, Norman. The history of St. Bartholomew's Hospital. 2 vol. xxii, 614 p.; xiv, 992 p. London: Pearson, 1918.

POWER, D'Arcy. A short history of St. Bartholomew's Hospital, 1123-1923: past and present. xv, 201 p. London: St. Bartholomew's Hospital, 1923.

ST. BARTHOLOMEW'S HOSPITAL. The 800th anniversary of its foundation (1123). *Nature*, 1923, 111: 777.

TURNER, A. Logan. Story of a great hospital. The Royal Infirmary of Edinburgh, 1729-1929. London: Oliver and Boyd, 1938.

UNDERWOOD, E. Ashworth. Guy's hospital. *Nature*, 1955, 176: 893-4.

NWwe-cd

DARLINGTON, Ida. King Edward's hospital fund for London and its records. *J.Soc.Arch.*, 2: 423-30.

POWER, D'Arcy. The archives of St. Bartholomew's Hospital. *Festschrift zum 80. Geburtstag Max Neuburgers*, p. 378-80. Wien: Maudrich, 1948.

NWwe-mzNce-by

THORNTON, John L. St. Bartholomew's Hospital, London, and its connection with eminent book collectors. *J.Hist.Med.*, 1951, 6: 481-90.

NWwf France

CABANÈS, Auguste. La Salle de Garde. Histoire anecdotique des salles de garde des hôpitaux de Paris. 130 p., 9 pl., ill. Paris: Montagu, 1917.

COLLY, Marcel. Les lits multiplaces, d'anciennes conditions de couchage en usage dans les hôpitaux de Lyon. *Bull.Soc.Franç. Hist.Méd.*, 1938, 32: 26-43.

CROZE, A., et al. Histoire de l'Hôpital de l'Antiquaille de Lyon. 237 p., 16 ill. Lyon: Audin, 1937.

DULIEU, Louis. Essai historique sur l'Hôpital Saint-Eloi de Montpellier (1183-1950). x, 388 p. Montpellier: Imprimerie Charles Déhan, 1953.
Reviewed by J.B.deC.M. Saunders, *Isis*, 1958, 49: 353-4.

GONNET, P. L'histoire et la légende des hôpitaux de la Chanal et Sainte Catherine de Lyon. *Bull.Soc.Franç.Hist. Méd.*, 1935, 29: 92-114.

GUILLAIN, Georges; MATHIEU, Pierre. La Salpêtrière. 92 p. Paris: Masson, 1925.
Reviewed in *Bijdr.Gesch.Geneesk.*, 1925, 5: 288-90.

HASSENFORDER, Colonel. Note au sujet du tricentenaire de la fondation de l'Église du Val-de-Grâce. *Mém.Soc.Franç. Hist.Méd.*, 1947, 3: 25-32.

LACASSAGNE, Jean. Histoire du Grand Hôtel-Dieu de Lyon, des origines à l'année 1900, par le conseil général d'administration des Hospices civils de Lyon. 462 p. Lyon: 1924.

PRADELLE, V. Les maisons de Charité de Toulouse. *Mém.Acad. Sci.Inscriptions Belles Lett.Toulouse*, 1934, 12: 193-226.
Reviewed in *Bull.Soc.Franç.Hist.Méd.*, 1936, 30: 188.

QUYNN, Dorothy Mackay. A medical picture of the Hôtel-Dieu of Paris. *Bull.Hist.Med.*, 1942, 12: 118-28, 7 fig.

RAMADIER, J.; FLURIN, H.; GAUSSEN, Ivan. L'Hôpital de la Charité, son passé évoqué par quelques images. 87 p., 38 fig. Paris: Baillière, 1935.
Reviewed by Marcel Fosseyeux, *Bull.Soc.Franç.Hist.Méd.*, 1936, 31: 126.

RIBIER, L. de. L'Hôtel-Dieu de Clermont-Ferrand et ses bienfaiteurs. 35 p. (Bibliothèque Historique de la France Médicale, 44) Paris: H. Champion, 1912.

VALLÉRY-RADOT, Pierre. Un siècle d'histoire hospitalière, de Louis-Philippe jusqu'à nos jours (1837-1949): nos hôpitaux parisiens. 219 p., 110 ill. Paris: Dupont, 1948.

NWwf-bv

FOSSEYEUX, Marcel. Bibliothèque de l'Administration Générale de l'Assistance Publique à Paris. Catalogue des séries concernant l'histoire et la législation hospitalières. 214 p. Bicêtre: 1912.

NWwf-cm

WEST, Eva. The William Bebb collection of prints of Paris hospitals. *Calif.Western Med.*, 1930, 33: 809-12, 5 fig.

NWwg/wh Central Europe

NWwg

DENEKE, Th. Festschrift zum hundertjährigen Bestehen des allgemeinen Krankenhauses St. Georg in Hamburg. x, 184 p., 42 ill. Leipzig: Leopold Voss, 1925.

GRÜNEIS, P. Die Wiener Allgemeine Poliklinik, ihre Entstehung und ihr Werdegang. *Festschrift zum 80. Geburtstag Max Neuburgers*, p. 208-16, 1 fig. Wien: Maudrich, 1948.

HABERLING, Wilhelm. Die Geschichte der Düsseldorfer Ärzte und Krankenhäuser bis zum Jahre 1907. 141 p., 14 pl., 50 fig. Düsseldorf: Lintz, 1936.

HUMBOLDT UNIVERSITÄT ZU BERLIN. Die Humboldt-Universität gestern, heute, morgen. Zum einhundertfünfzigjährigen Bestehen der Humboldt-Universität zu Berlin und zum zweihundertfünfzigjährigen Bestehen der Charité, Berlin ... 250 p., ill. Berlin: Deutscher Verlag der Wissenschaften, 1960.

KERCHENSTEINER, H. Geschichte der Münchener Krankenanstalten, insbesondere des Krankenhauses links der Isaar. 298 p., 11 pl., 50 fig. (*Ann.Städt.Allg.Krankenhäuser München,* 15) München: 1913.

RENNEFAHRT, Hermann; HINTZSCHE, Erich. Sechshundert Jahre Inselspital, 1354-1954. 544 p., ill. Bern: Hans Huber, 1954.
Reviewed by Wolfram Kock, *Sudhoffs Arch.*, 1956, 40: 94-5.

SEYFARTH, Carly. Das Hospital zu St. Georg in Leipzig durch acht Jahrhunderte 1212-1940. Vol. 1. Das Hospital zu St. Georg vom Jahre 1212 bis zum Jahre 1631. 248 p., 9 fig. Leipzig: Thieme, 1939.
No other volumes traced.

WEHRLI, G.A. Die Krankenanstalten und die öffentlich angestellten Ärzte und Wundärzte im alten Zürich. 94 p., 10 fig. (*Mitt.Antiq.Ges.Zürich*, 31; no. 3) Zürich: 1934.

WILLE, Paul Friedrich Carl. Geschichte der Berliner Hospitäler und Krankenhäuser. Von der Gründung der Stadt bis zum Jahre 1800. 56 p. (Diss., Berlin) Berlin: Hoffmann, 1931.

NWwg-cm

WILLE, Paul Friedrich Carl. Die Ikonographie der Berliner Charité. *Sudhoffs Arch.*, 1955, 39: 113-22, 12 ill.

NWwh

BUGIEL, V. Les hôpitaux de Cracovie de 1220 à 1920. *Bull. Soc.Franç.Hist.Méd.*, 1924, 18: 211-24.

NEUGEBAUER, Karl. [A brief history of the Protestant Hospital at Warsaw. (In Polish)] *Medycyna*, 1931, no. 7-12.
Reviewed by Josef Fritz, *Mitt.Gesch.Med.*, 1931, 30: 287.

NWwi/wj Southern Europe

NWwi

CANEZZA, Alessandro. Gli arcispedali di Roma nella sita cittadina nella storia e nelle arte. Prefazione del G. Spano. 233 p., fig. Rome: 1933.
Reviewed by Marcel Fosseyeux, *Bull.Soc.Franç.Hist.Méd.*, 1937, 31: 128.

PAPPALARDO, I. L'Ospedale Apostolico di Santo Spirito in Saxia e i papi. *Atti Mem.Accad.Stor.Arte Sanit.*, 1964, 29: 45-7.

PAZZINI, A. Assistenza e ospedali nella storia dei Fatebenefratelli. 578 p. Roma: Ediz. Marietti, 1956.
Reviewed by L. Stroppiana, *Riv.Stor.Med.*, 1957, 1: 114-15.

NWwi-cd

BETTICA-GIOVANNINI, R. Regesti degli antichi documenti relativi agli ospedali torinesi esistenti nell'Archivio Communale di Torino. *Atti Mem.Accad.Stor.Arte Sanit.*, 1964, 29: 59-63.

NWwi-vm

CAPPARONI, Angelo. Storia dell'Ospedale Israelitico in Roma. *Arch.Iberoamer.Hist.Med.*, 1957, 9: 81-91.

NWwj

DITTRICK, Howard. Some old hospitals in Spain. *Victor Robinson Memorial Volume*, p. 35-48, 3 fig. New York: Froben, 1948.

JETTER, Dieter. Hospitalgebäude in Spanien. *Sudhoffs Arch.*, 1960, 44: 239-58.

PESSOA, Alberto. Hôpitals de Coimbra. 54 p., 12 pl. Coimbra: Imprensa de Universidade, 1931.
Elaborate study based on archival documents of the hospitals of Coimbra

STUCKERT, Guillermo V. Páginas de la historia hospitalaria de Córdoba. *Publ.Cátedra Hist.Med., Univ.Buenos Aires*, 1940, 4: 171-97, portr., 7 fig.

NWwk/wm Northern Europe

NWwk

BEURDEN, A.F. van. Het Sint Elisabeth's Gast- of Ziekenhuis te Amersfoort. [St. Elizabeth's Hospital in Amersfoort. (In Dutch)] Amersfoort: Drukkerij de Eembode, 1924.
Reviewed by D. Schoute, *Bijdr.Gesch.Geneesk.*, 1926, 6: 79-83.

BOURICIUS, L.G.N. Eenige grepen uit de geschiedenis van het St. Joris gasthuis te Delft. [A part of the history of St. George's Hospital in Delft. (In Dutch)] *Bijdr.Gesch.Geneesk.*, 1928, 8: 29-37, 2 fig.

HELLINGA, G. De Amsterdamsche gasthuizen beoordeeld door vreemdelingen. [The hospitals of Amsterdam judged by foreigners. (In Dutch)] *Bijdr.Gesch.Geneesk.*, 1932, 12: 105-19; 1933, 13: 85-99, 2 pl.

HELLINGA, G. "Amsterdamsche hulpziekenhuizen". [Emergency hospitals in Amsterdam. (In Dutch)] *Bijdr.Gesch.Geneesk.*, 1936, 16: 21-8.

HELLINGA, G. Een sombere bladzijde uit de geschiedenis van het voormalige Amsterdamsche Buitengasthuis. [A somber page from the history of the former Buitengasthuis in Amsterdam. (In Dutch)] *Bijdr.Gesch.Geneesk.*, 1940, 20: 28-38, 4 fig.

KERSBERGEN, L.C. Geschiedenis van het St. Elisabeth's of Groote Gasthuis te Haarlem. [History of St. Elisabeth's Hospital in Haarlem. (In Dutch)] 487 p., ill. Haarlem: Enschedé, 1931.
Reviewed by F.M.G. de Feyfer, *Bijdr.Gesch.Geneesk.*, 1931, 11: 257-8.

MADE, Raoul van der. Le Grand Hôpital de Huy. Organisation et fonctionnement (1263-1795). 241 p. (Anciens Pays et Assemblées d'États, 20) Louvain/Paris: 1960.
Reviewed by Luc F. Genicot, *Rev.Hist.Ecclésiastique*, 1962, 17: 259.

MARTINY, V.G. L'ancien hôpital à Asse. *Brabant*, 1960, 7-8: 28-32.

MOLL, W. Een eeuw ziekenhuis geschiedenis. Het Haagsche gemeenteziekenhuis (1823-1923). [One century of hospital history. The Hague Hospital (1823-1923). (In Dutch)] Gevolgd door een Overzicht van den tegenwoordigen toestand der gemeenteziekenhuizen door E.A. Koch. 's-Gravenhage: Mouton, 1925.
Reviewed by P. Muntendam, *Bijdr.Gesch.Geneesk.*, 1926, 6: 21-2.

PEKELHARING, C.A. Geschiedenis van het Algemeen Ziekenhuis. (Geschiedenis van de Vereenigde Gods- en Gasthuizen te Utrecht van 1817 tot 1917. Eerste gedeelte.) [History of the General Hospital. (History of the United Charity Hospitals and Almshouses at Utrecht from 1817 to 1917).(In Dutch)] Utrecht: Bartholomaeus-Gasthuis, 1921.
Reviewed by Van der Weyde, *Bijd.Gesch.Geneesk.*, 1921, 1: 332-5.

SCHOUTE, D. De stad Groningen en de geschiedenis onzer oude ziekenhuizen. [The city of Groningen and the history of our old hospitals. (In Dutch)] *Bijdr.Gesch.Geneesk.*, 1939, 19: 172-9.

TOVELL, Harold M. Notes on the medical history of Bruges and the Hospital of St. John. *Ann.Med.Hist.*, 1932, 4: 398-409, 3 fig.

TRICOT-ROYER, J.J.G. Anvers nosocomial de l'an mille à nos jours. *Compt.Rend.IIe Congr.Int.Hist.Méd.* (Paris, 1921), p. 592-6. Évreux: Imprimerie Ch. Hérissey, 1922.

see also Amsterdam. Binnengasthuis, 2: 664.

NWwm

GOTFREDSEN, E. Det Kongelige Frederiks Hospital i tohundredåret for dets oprettelse. [The Royal Frederiks Hospital in 200 years since its founding. (In Danish)] 48 p., ill. København: 1957.

NWwo South Eastern Europe

PRUTEANU, Paul. Contributie la Istoricul Spitalelor din Moldava. [Contribution to the history of hospitals in Moldavia. (In Rumanian)] 275 p. Bucarest: Editura Medical, 1957.
Reviewed by Louis Dulieu, *Rev.Hist.Sci.*, 1960, 13: 175.

NWwp/wy Africa; Asia; Australia

NWwp

SAYILI, Aydin M. [A hospital in Kütahya. (In Turkish with English summary)] *Belleten*, 1948, 12: 679-82. [CB 74/382]

ÜNVER, A. Süheyl. Sur l'histoire des hôpitaux en Turquie du moyen âge jusqu'au XVIIe siècle. *Compt.Rend.IXe Congr.Int. Hist.Méd.* (Bucarest, 1932), p. 263-78, ill. București: Furnica, 1935.

ÜNVER, A. Süheyl. [Haseki Hospital, on the occasion of its fourth centenary, 1539-1939. (In Turkish)] 16 p., 19 ill. Istanbul: Institute of the History of Medicine in Turkey, 1939. [CB 60/170]
This paper deals with the history of the Haseki Hospital, one of the early hospitals of Istanbul, up to the present time.

NWwv

MIANET, H. Un siècle d'évolution hospitalière en pays tropical. Histoire de l'Hôpital Grall de Saigon (1861-1961). (Thèse) 130 p., fig. Paris: Foulon, 1962.
Reviewed by P. Huard, *Rev.Hist.Sci.*, 1964, 17: 91.

NWww

CRAIG, Clifford. The first hundred years, 1863-1963, of the Launceston General Hospital, Tasmania. vi, 162 p. Tasmania: Board of Management, Launceston General Hospital, 1963.
Reviewed by Ffrangcon Roberts, *Med.Hist.*, 1964, 8: 96.

NWwy

LAIDLER, P.W. Medical establishments and institutions at the Cape. 4. Somerset Hospital, the slave hospital and the first pauper establishment. *S.Afr.Med.J.*, 1937, 11: 641-9.

NX AUXILIARY SERVICES

RANSOM, John E. The ambulance. *Ciba Symp.* (Summit, N.J.), 1947, 8: 534-64, ill.

NY DOCTORS AND PATIENTS

BAEHR, George. The role of medical group practice in the changing order. *Trans.Coll.Physicians Phila.*, 1950, 17: 129-38.

HENDERSON, L.J. Physician and patient as a social system. *New Engl.J.Med.*, 1935, 212: 819-23.

JACOBY, George W. Physician, pastor and patient. Problems in pastoral medicine. ix, 390 p. New York: Hoeber, 1936.
Reviewed in *Ann.Med.Hist.*, 1936, 8: 565-6.

SIGERIST, Henry E. Die Sonderstellung des Kranken. *Kyklos*, 1929, 2: 11-20.

NYwb

HASHINGER, Edward H. Arthur E. Hertzler: the Kansas horse-and-buggy doctor. Ninth series of the Logan Clendening Lectures on the History and Philosophy of Medicine. 37 p. Lawrence, Kansas: University of Kansas Press, 1961.

HERTZLER, Arthur E. The doctor and his patients. The American domestic scene as viewed by the family doctor. 316 p. New York: Harper, 1940.
Reviewed in *Ann.Med.Hist.*, *3rd ser.*, 1941, 3: 257-8.

VANDEGRIFT, George Wonson. Castor oil and quinine: once a doctor always a doctor. 252 p. New York: Dutton, 1942.
Biography of Dr. George Vandegrift, the author's father.
Reviewed by Miriam Drabkin, *Bull.Hist.Med.*, 1943, 13: 364.

WILLIAMS, Thomas Franklin. Cabot, Peabody, and the care of the patient. (The William Osler Medal Essay) *Bull.Hist. Med.*, 1950, 24: 462-81.

NYwe

WARD, Ernest. Medical adventure: some experiences of a general practitioner. xii, 291 p. London: Bale, 1929.

NZ NURSING

ABEL-SMITH, Brian. A history of the nursing profession. xiv, 290 p., ill. London: Heinemann, 1960.
Reviewed by Wolfram Kock, *Lychnos*, 1960-61, 382-3.

BAAS, Karl. Uranfänge und Frühgeschichte der Krankenpflege. *Arch.Gesch.Med.*, 1914, 8: 146-64.

BULLOUGH, Bonnie; BULLOUGH, Vern L. The emergence of modern nursing. vi, 243 p. New York: Macmillan, 1964.

DIETZ, Lena Dixon. History of modern nursing. 365 p., ill. Philadelphia: F.A. Davis; London: Blackwell Scientific Publications, 1963.
Reviewed by Lucy Seymer, *Med.Hist.*, 1964, 8: no. 1, 96-7.

DOCK, Lavinia L.; STEWART, Isabel Maintland. A short history of nursing from the earliest times to the present day. vi, 392 p. New York: Putnam, 1920.
An abridgment of the History of nursing by M. Adelaide Nutting and Lavinia L. Dock (4 vol. New York: Putnam, 1907-12).
4th ed. 1938.

GOODNOW, Minnie. Outlines of nursing history. 370 p. Philadelphia: Saunders, 1916.
Reviewed by Victor Robinson, *Med.Life*, 1938, 45: 91-2.

JENSEN, Deborah Maclurg. History and trends of professional nursing. 4th ed. 630 p., ill., bibliogr. St. Louis: Mosby, 1959.
Reviewed by Ernestine Wiedenbach, *J.Hist.Med.*, 1961, 16: 97-8.
First publ. 1943 as A history of nursing and reviewed by Victor Robinson, *Bull.Hist.Med.*, 1944, 16: 92.

KAJITA, Akira. [History of nursing. (In Japanese)] *J.Hist. Sci.Japan*, 1951, no. 20, 21-5.

PAVEY, Agnes E. The story of the growth of nursing as an art, a vocation, and a profession. 3rd ed. xv, 498 p. London: Faber and Faber, 1951. First publ. 1938.
Reviewed by Ernest Wickersheimer, *Arch.Int.Hist.Sci.*, 1952, 5: 159-61.

SEYMER, Lucy Ridgely. A general history of nursing. 2nd ed. 332 p., ill. London: Faber & Faber, 1949.
First publ. 1932.
Reviewed by Edv. Gotfredsen, *Centaurus*, 1951, 1: 286-7.

SHRYOCK, Richard H. The history of nursing. An interpretation of the social and medical factors involved. x, 330 p. Philadelphia/London: Saunders, 1959.
Reviewed by Ann L. Austin, *Bull.Hist.Med.*, 1960, 34: 387-8.

STEWART, Isabel M; AUSTIN, Anne L. A history of nursing, from ancient to modern times. A world view. 5th ed. x, 516 p., ill. New York: Putnam, 1962.
Reviewed by Vern L. Bullough, *J.Hist.Med.*, 1964, 19: 181-2; by Lucy Seymer, *Med.Hist.*, 1964, 8: 97.

NZo

STEWART, Isabel M. The education of nurses. 399 p. New York: Macmillan, 1943.
Reviewed by Victor Robinson, *Bull.Hist.Med.*, 1944, 16: 93.

NZtd

DONINCK, A. van. Ste-Dimphna-cultus en gezinsverpleging. [The St. Dymphna cult and home nursing. (In Dutch)] *Bijdr. Gesch.Geneesk.*, 1930, 10: 307-14, 1 pl.

NZwb

McFARLAND, Joseph. The history of nursing at the Blockley Hospital. *Med.Life,* 1932, 39: 631-44; 1933, 40: 177-91.

WRITERS' PROGRAM, Kansas. Lamps on the prairie. A history of nursing in Kansas. Compiled by the Writers' Program of the Work Projects Administration in the State of Kansas. 292 p., ill. Emporia: Emporia Gazette Press, 1942.
Reviewed by Genevieve Miller, *Bull.Hist.Med.,* 1943, 13: 688-9.

NZwb-o

LEE, Eleanor. History of the School of Nursing of the Presbyterian Hospital, New York, 1892-1942. xiv, 286 p., 57 ill. New York: Putnam, 1942. [CB 63/259]

PECK, Elisabeth S. Nurses in time: developments in nursing education, 1898-1963. 65 p. Berea, Ky.: Berea College, 1964.

NZwk

DONINCK, A. van. Gezinsverpleging te Gheel. Het vraagstuk der infirmerie. [Family nursing at Gheel. The problem of the infirmary. (In Dutch)] *Bijdr.Gesch.Geneesk.,* 1933, 13: 53-60.

DONINCK, A. van. Gezinsverpleging in vroegere tijden te Gheel, de duivelbanning. [Family nursing in old times at Gheel; exorcising the devil. (In Dutch)] *Bijdr.Gesch.Geneesk.,* 1932, 12: 85-90, 4 fig.

O ANATOMY AND PHYSIOLOGY

for the anatomy and physiology of special systems of the body *see* INDEX under the system concerned

Oc general history

CIOCCO, Antonio. The historical background of the modern study of constitution. *Bull.Inst.Hist.Med.,* 1936, 4: 23-38.

GRASSET, Joseph. La biologie humaine. 344 p. (Bibliothèque de Philosophie Scientifique) Paris: Flammarion, 1917.
Reviewed by L. Guinet, *Isis,* 1920, 3: 88.

JENNINGS, Herbert Spencer. The biological basis of human nature. xviii, 384 p. London: Faber and Faber, 1930.
Reviewed in *Nature,* 1931, 127: 263-4.

JENNINGS, Herbert Spencer. Prometheus; or, biology and the advancement of man. vii, 86 p. (Today and Tomorrow series) London: Kegan Paul, 1925.

KROGMAN, Wilton Marion. The historical aspect of the study of human constitutional types. *Ciba Symp.* (Summit, N.J.), 1941, 3: 1058-65, fig.

LESSA, William A. Somatomancy - precursor of the science of human constitution. *Sci.Mon.,* 1952, 75: 355-65, 13 fig.

NEUBURGER, Max. The doctrine of the natural constitution. *Med.Life,* 1932, 39: 698-706.

NEUBURGER, Max. Zur Geschichte der Konstitutionslehre. *Z. Angewandte Anat.Konst.,* 1913, 1: no. 1, 4-10.

PEARL, Raymond. Studies in human biology. 653 p., ill. Baltimore: Williams and Wilkins, 1924.

SIGERIST, Henry E. Wandlungen des Konstitutionsbegriffs. *Karlsbad.Ärztl.Vortr.,* 1929, 10: 97-108.

SINGER, Charles. A short history of anatomy and physiology from the Greeks to Harvey. xii, 209 p., ill. (New edition of The evolution of anatomy) New York: Dover, 1957.
First publ. London and New York: 1925 and reviewed by Chauncey D. Leake, *Isis,* 1928, 10: 521-4. For reviews of the new edition *see* CB 84/317 and 323 and CB 85/394.

Ohj

SCHÄR, Rita. Albrecht von Hallers neue anatomisch-physiologische Befunde und ihre heutige Gültigkeit. 56 p. (*Berner Beitr.Gesch.Med.Naturwiss.,* 16) Bern: Paul Haupt Verlag, 1958.
Reviewed by Hans Schadewaldt, *Sudhoffs Arch.,* 1959, 43: 379; by E. Bastholm, *Lychnos,* 1959, 433-4.

Om/o special aspects

Omf

KELLER, R. The asymmetry of the human body. Habitual asymmetrical attitudes and movements. Lefthandedness. The "inferiority" of inversion. The right-left problem in art. Two famous left-handers. *Ciba Symp.* (Summit, N.J.), 1942, 3: 1126-45, ill.

Onj

HERRLINGER, Robert. Eigennamen in Anatomie und Physiologie, Histologie, Embryologie und Physiologische Chemie. 32 p. Jena: Fischer, 1941.
Reviewed by L. Castaldi, *Riv.Stor.Sci.,* 1942, 33: 27.

Oo

PEARL, Raymond. Human biology in schools and colleges. *Sch. Soc.,* 27 July 1935, 42: 111-18.

OB ANATOMY

OBc general history

CORNER, George W. Anatomy. xvii, 82 p., ill., bibliogr. (Clio Medica, 3) New York: Hafner, 1964. [CB 30/475]
Reprint of 1930 edition.

DIEPGEN, Paul. Das Erwachen des anatomischen Blicks bei den Ärzten. *Mitt.Gesch.Med.,* 1941-42, 40: 304.

HUNTER, Richard H. A short history of anatomy. 2nd ed. 87 p. London: Bale, 1931. [CB 33/405]
First publ. 1925.

LINT, J.G. de. Atlas of the history of medicine. I. Anatomy. With a foreword by Charles Singer. 96 p. London: H.K. Lewis; New York: Paul B. Hoeber, 1926. [CB 23/255]
Dutch original: Atlas van de geschiedenis der geneeskunde. 1. De ontleedkunde. Amsterdam: 1925. Reviewed in *Bijdr.Gesch.Geneesk.,* 1926, 6: 42-4.

PHAM-VAN-GHÉ. Contribution à l'histoire de l'anatomie. 43 p. (Thesis) Hanoi: Impr. Sainte Thérèse, 1947.

STANKOV, A.G. Anatomiya tchélovéka. [Human anatomy. (In Russian)] 456 p., ill. Moskva: Gosudarstvennoe Izdatel'stvo Meditsinkoi Literatury, 1959.
Reviewed by P. Huard and M. Wong, *Arch.Int.Hist.Sci.,* 1962, 15: 444-6.

VELDE, Jean van de. Grepen uit de geschiedenis der anatomie. [Gleanings from the history of anatomy. (In Dutch)] 38 p., 25 pl. (*Mededeel.Vlaam.Acad.Wetensch.Lett.Schoone Kunsten Belg.Kl.Wetensch.*, 21: no. 6) Brussel: 1959.
Reviewed by E. Elaut, *Sci.Hist.*, 1960, 2: 34-5.

OBc-br

Arquivo de Anatomia e Anthropologia. Vol. 1, 1912- Lisboa: Imprensa Libanio da Silva (for Instituto de Anatomia, Faculdade de Medicina da Universidade de Lisboa), 1913 - [CB 18/631]

OBc-bx

SIGERIST, Henry E., *et al.* An exhibit illustrating the history of anatomy. *Bull.Inst.Hist.Med.*, 1933, 1: 193-234, 10 pl.

OBce-bv

NAPLES. UNIVERSITÀ. BIBLIOTECA. Opere di anatomia; esposte dalla Biblioteca universitaria di Napoli in occasione del XIV Congresso Nazionale di Anatomia, Napoli, 1952. Ed. by G. Castellano-Lanzara. 46 p., ill. Napoli: Libreria Scientifica, 1956.

OBcm illustrations

see also OBtq relation with art

CHOULANT, Johann Ludwig. History and bibliography of anatomic illustrations. Transl. and annot. by Mortimer Frank. Rev. ed. Further essays by Fielding H. Garrison, Mortimer Frank, Edward C. Streeter. With a new historical essay by Charles Singer and a bibliography of Mortimer Frank. xxvii, 435 p. New York: Schumann, 1945.
Translation of: Geschichte und Bibliographie der anatomischen Abbildung (Leipzig: Weigel, 1852). Reprinted New York: Hafner, 1962.
Reviewed by K.D. Keele, *Med.Hist.*, 1963, 7: 290; in *Proc. Roy.Soc.Med.*, 1963, 56: 138; for review of the original edition *see* CB 33/404; for review (by George Sarton) of the 1920 edition of the translation *see Isis*, 1922, 4: 357-9.

PREMUDA, Loris. Storia dell'iconografia anatomica. Con un'appendice di Gaetano Ottaviani. xiii, 235 p., 138 pl. Milano: Aldo Martelli, 1957.
Reviewed by Dorothy M. Schullian, *J.Hist.Med.*, 1959, 14: 128-9.

WEGNER, Richard N. Das Anatomenbildnis. Seine Entwicklung im Zusammenhang mit der anatomischen Abbildung. 199 p., 105 fig. Basel: Schwabe, 1939.

OBco

GOLDSCHMID, Edgar. Histoire des cires anatomiques. *Act. VIIe Congr.Int.Hist.Sci.* (Jerusalem, 1953), p. 320-3. Paris: Hermann, [n.d.].

HIRSCHLER, Pierre. Anthropoid and human endocranial casts. vii, 150 p. Amsterdam: Noord-Hollandsche Uitgeversmaatschappij, 1942.
A study of casts of the interior of the brain-box in anthropoids and man.

MÜLLER, Reinhold F.G. Über Skelett-Darstellungen in Asia major. *Asia Major*, 1925, 2: fasc. 3-4, 531-63, 24 fig.

OBda collective biography

MONDOR, Henri. Anatomistes et chirurgiens. 530 p., ill. Paris: Fragance, 1949.

OBh history; particular aspects

OBhf

HERRLINGER, Robert. Die Rolle von Idee und Technik in der Geschichte der Anatomie. *Sudhoffs Arch.*, 1962, 46: 1-16.

OBht

HUARD, Pierre. La diffusion de l'anatomie européenne dans quelques secteurs de l'Asie. *Arch.Int.Hist.Sci.*, 1953, 32: 266-78.
Persia, India, China, Japan, Manila, Indonesia.

OBk philosophy and methodology

DETWEILER, S.R. Anatomy as a science. *Science*, 1929, 70: 563-6.
Address delivered at the opening exercises of the College of Physicians and Surgeons, Columbia University, New York, September 25, 1929.

GUERREIRO, Luís. Sobre o sentido e a significacão do "Quadro geral da anatomia" (1920) do Prof H. de Vilhena. *Arq.Anat. Anthropol.*, 1924, 8: 473-86. [CB 18/632]

GUERREIRO, Luís. Sobre a doutrina e a escola anatómica do Prof. H. de Vilhena. [With French translation] *Arq.Anat. Anthropol.*, 1921, 7: 1-38, 39-73. [CB 18/632]

ROUVIÈRE, H. Anatomie philosophique. La finalité dans l'évolution. 124 p., fig. Paris: Masson, 1941.
Reviewed by René Porak, *Rev.Gén.Sci.*, 1942, 52: 91.

VILHENA, Henrique de. Quadro geral da anatomia. *Arq.Anat. Anthropol.*, 1920, 6: 1-36, 1 pl. [CB 18/632]

OBn means of communication

OBnh

FIELD, E.J.; HARRISON, R.J. Anatomical terms, their origin and derivation. vi, 165 p. Cambridge: Heffer, 1947. [CB 72/275]

HERNANDO, Teofilo. Los nombres de las costillas (étimología y semántica). *Arch.Iberoamer.Hist.Med.*, 1957, 9: 273-80.

KOPSCH, Fredrich. Nomina anatomica. Vergleichende Übersicht der Basler, Jenaer und Pariser Nomenklatur. 5th ed. by K.-H. Knese. xi, 155 p., ill. Stuttgart: Georg Thieme, 1957.
1st ed. 1910.
Reviewed by Johannes Steudel, *Sudhoffs Arch.*, 1960, 44: 379.

MORTON, William Cuthbert; BRIDGES, Robert. The language of anatomy. 28 p. Tract no. IX of the Society for Pure English. Oxford: Clarendon Press, 1922.

SAUSER, Gustav. Von der medicohistorischen Potenz anatomischer Namen. *Festschrift zum 80. Geburtstag Max Neuburgers*, p. 410-13. Wien: Maudrich, 1948.

SINGER, Charles. The strange histories of some anatomical terms. *Med.Hist.*, 1959, 3: 1-7.

STEUDEL, Johannes. Der anatomische Terminus "Netz". *Sudhoffs Arch.*, 1963, 47: 383-6.
Anatomical nomenclature from Hippocrates to Bartholinus.

TRIEPEL, Hermann. Die anatomischen Namen. Ihre Ableitung und Aussprache. 25th ed. by Robert Herrlinger. 82 p. München: J.F. Bergmann, 1957.
1st ed. 1906.
For reviews *see* CB 83/203 and CB 84/317 and 323.

OBnj

DOBSON, Jessie. Anatomical eponyms. Being a biographical dictionary of those anatomists whose names have become incorporated into anatomical nomenclature, with definitions of the structures to which their names have been attached and references to the works in which they are described. 2nd ed. 235 p., front. Edinburgh/London: E. & S. Livingstone, 1962.
First publ. 1946 [CB 71/125]
Reviewed by L.T. Morton, *Med.Hist.*, 1963, 7: 294.

RODRÍGUEZ RIVERO, Plácido Daniel. Eponimias Anatómicas. *Rev. Soc.Venezolana Hist.Med.*, 1953, 1: 215-31.

SERRANO, José Antonio. Relação alphabetica dos anatomicos, physiologistas, histologistas, embriologistas, medicos e cirurgiões cujos nomes figuram na nomenclatura anatomica actual. *Arq.Anat.Anthropol.*, 1912-14, 1: 102-219. [CB 18/632]
First published at Lisbon in 1891-92. Brief biographical dictionary of the men whose names occur in the present anatomical nomenclature.

OBo study and teaching

GUTIÉRREZ, Avelino. La anatomía, como modelo práctico para la enseñanza de las demás ciencias médicas. *Publ.Cátedra Hist.Med.Univ.Buenos Aires*, 1940, 3: 341-62.

HERRLINGER, Robert. Wandlungen im anatomischen Unterricht seit Hermann Braus [gest. 1924]. *Sudhoffs Arch.*, 1953, 37: 266-77.

OBorw

LANDER, Kathleen F. The study of anatomy by women before the nineteenth century. *Proc.3rd Int.Congr.Hist.Med.* (London, 1922), p. 125-34. Antwerp: De Vlijt, 1923.

OBr/t professional aspects; social and humanistic relations

OBrj

MENETRIER, P. L'anatomiste charitable. *Proc.3rd Int.Congr. Hist.Med.* (London, 1922), p. 114-16. Antwerp: De Vlijt, 1923.
On medical ethics.

OBsb

KOCH, Tankred. Über die Abhängigkeit der anatomischen Wissenschaft von den jeweiligen gesellschaftlichen Kräften. *Wiss. Z.Humboldt-Univ.Berlin Math.Naturwiss.Reihe*, 1962, 11: 371-6.

OBtq relation with art

see also OBcm illustrations

AMEISENOWA, Zofia. Problem modeli anatomicznych écorches i trzy statuetki w Bibliotece Jagiellońskiej. [The problem of the écorché and the three anatomical models in the Jagellonian Library. (In Polish)] 82 p., 48 pl. (Polska Akademia Nauk. Zaktad Historii Nauki i Techniki. Monografie z dziejów nauki i techniki) Wroclaw: Zakład Narodowy im. Ossolińskich, 1962.
Reviewed by P. Huard, *Arch.Int.Hist.Sci.*, 1964, 17: 194-6. Includes a history of the relation of anatomy and art.

ANILE, A. L'anatomia dell'uomo nella storia dell'arte. Napoli: Gianini, 1912.

CAPPARONI, Pietro. La persistenza delle forme degli antichi "donaria" anatomici negli "ex voto" moderni. *Boll.Ist.Stor. Ital.Arte Sanit.*, 1927, 7: 39-57, 38 fig.

GOLDSCHMID, Edgar. Les scènes anatomiques vues par les artistes au cours des siècles. *Riv.Stor.Sci.*, 1952, 43: 193-208, ill.

HUARD, Pierre; WONG, M. Le problème de la représentation du corps humain. Son évolution en Eurasie. *Scientia*, 1962, 97: 83-90.

LINDEBOOM, G.A. L'anatomie dans l'art des Pays-Bas septentrionaux. *Act.IIIe Congr.Bénélux Hist.Sci.* (Luxembourg, 1960), p. 182-6. Leiden: E.J. Brill, 1960. Also in *Janus*, 1961, 49: 182-6.

PEUGNIEZ, Paul. Le squelette dans l'art. *Aesculape*, 1912, 2: 234-40, 20 fig.

REGNAULT, Félix. Les ex-voto anatomiques modernes. *Aesculape*, 1913, 3: 102-4, 15 fig.

STRATZ, C.H. Die Darstellung des menschlichen Körpers in der Kunst. x, 322 p., ill. Berlin: Springer, 1914.

TRICOT-ROYER, J.J.G. La figuration de l'âme dans l'art chrétien. *Aesculape*, 1927, 17: 11-16, ill.

VELDE, A.J.J. van de. De les van anatomie. [The anatomy lesson. (In Dutch)] *Verhandel.Vlaam.Acad.Geneesk.Belg.*, 1952, 14: 297-311, 8 pl.
On the many paintings depicting the anatomy lesson.

OBw in different countries

OBwb North America

OBwb-oq

COBB, W. Montague. The laboratory of anatomy and physical anthropology of Howard University. x, 107 p., 13 pl. Washington, D.C.: 1936.
Reviewed by Raymond Pearl, *J.Negro Hist.*, October 1936, 447-9.

OBwb-qd

MICHELS, Nicholas A. The American Association of Anatomists. A sketch of its origin, aims and meetings. *Anat.Rec.*, 1955, 122: 685-714.

OBwe/wh British Isles; Central Europe

OBwe-ce-bv

RUSSELL, Kenneth F. A bibliography of anatomical books published in English before 1800. *Bull.Hist.Med.*, 1949, 23: 268-306.

RUSSELL, Kenneth F. British anatomy, 1525-1800. A bibliography. xvii, 254 p., ill. Melbourne: Melbourne University Press, 1963; New York: Cambridge University Press, 1964.
Reviewed by Thomas R. Forbes, *J.Hist.Med.*, 1964, 19: 428-9.

OBwe-o

ROLLESTON, Humphry. The early history of the teaching of: 1. Human anatomy in London; 2. Morbid anatomy and pathology in Great Britain. *Ann.Med.Hist.*, 1939, 1: 203-38, 16 fig.

OBwe-oq

SINCLAIR, H.M.; ROBB-SMITH, A.H.T. A short history of anatomical teaching in Oxford. 81 p., 21 pl., front. London: Oxford University Press, 1950. [CB 77/378]
Reviewed by Eyv. Bastholm, *Lychnos*, 1952, 435-6.

OBwg-oq

HINTZCHE, E. Die geschichtliche Entwicklung anatomischer Arbeit in Bern bis zur Gründung der Hochschule. iv, 84 p., ill. Bern: Haupt, 1942.
Reprinted from *Berner Zeitschrift für Geschichte und Heimatkunde*, 1942.

KOLB, Werner. Geschichte des anatomischen Unterrichtes an der Universität zu Basel 1460-1900. 214 p., ill. Basel: Benno Schwabe & Co., 1951.
Reviewed by Ernest Wickersheimer, *Arch.Int.Hist.Sci.*, 1952, 5: 172-4; by Emil Bovin, *Lychnos*, 1953, 435-7.

KOPSCH, Fr. Zweihundert Jahre Berliner Anatomie. *Deut.Med. Wochenschr.*, 1912, 39: 948-9, 1003-9, 7 pl.

NEULAND, Werner. Geschichte des Anatomischen Instituts and des anatomischen Unterrichts an der Universität Freiburg i. Br. xv, 288 p. (Geschichte der Medizin in Freiburg i. Br., I) Freiburg i. Br.: Schulz, 1941.

PRIBILLA, Walter. Die Geschichte der Anatomie an der Universität Köln von 1478-1798. 50 p., ill. (Arbeiten der Deutsch-Nordischen Gesellschaft für Geschichte der Medizin, 26) Greifswald, Bamberg: 1940.

WEGNER, Richard Nikolaus. Frankfurts Anteil an der Verbreitung anatomischer Kenntnisse im XVI. bis XVIII. Jahrhundert. Ein Beitrag zur Urgeschichte der Frankfurter Hochschule. 39 p., 10 fig. Frankfurt a. M.: Englert und Schlosser, 1925.

OBwh-da

LOTH, E. Gdanska skola anatomiczna (1584-1812). [The Danzig anatomical school. (In Polish)] *Folia Morphol.*, 1929, 1: 98-9. [CB 33/418]
Biographical notes on several Danzig anatomists.

OBwi/wj Southern Europe

OBwi

PIERRO, F. Il secolo dell'anatomia in Italia. *Castalia*, 1964, 20: 25-31.

OBwi-oq

COSTA, A. La Scuola anatomo-patologica fiorentina da Antonio Benivieni a Guido Banti. *Riv.Stor.Sci.*, 1952, 43: 297-334, 31 fig.

FRANCO, Enrico Emilio. La tradizione anatomica veneziana e l'insegnamento dell' anatomica chirurgica nella scuola Minich. *Riv.Stor.Sci.*, 1925, 16: 49-63.
Inaugural lecture of the course in surgical anatomy given at the Ospedale Civile, Venice, January 23, 1925.

GABELLI, Vincenzo. The restoration of the anatomical theatre at Bologna. *J.Hist.Med.*, 1956, 11: 440-3, 6 fig.

MASSON, Louis. Le vieil amphithéâtre d'anatomie de Bologne. *Aesculape*, 1931, 28: 275-80.

UNDERWOOD, E. Ashworth. The early teaching of anatomy at Padua, with special reference to a model of the Padua anatomical theatre. *Ann.Sci.*, 1963, 19: 1-26.

OBwj

GUISANDE, Gumersindo Sanchez. Datos para la históría de la anatomia en España. *Arq.Anat.Antropol.*, 1948, 25: 671-705.

OBwj-da

LEJEUNE, Fritz. Die wichtigsten spanischen Anatomen nach Vesal. *VIe Congr.Int.Hist.Méd.* (Leyde/Amsterdam, 1927), p. 178-85. Anvers: De Vlijt, 1929.

OBwj-oq

COSTA, A. Celestino da. L'histologie et l'embryologie à la Faculté de médecine de Lisbonne. *Arq.Anat.Antropol.*, 1932-33, 15: 537-46, ill.

INSTITUTO DE ANATOMIA. Sumula dos trabalhos de investigação (1911-1925). (I Centenario da Faculdade de Medicina do Pôrto, 1825-1925). Pôrto: Enciclopédia Portuguesa, 1925. [CB 21/543]
Summary of the anatomical work done from 1911 to 1925 followed by a bibliography.

SUEIRO, M.B. Barbosa; FONTES, Victor. Aperçu historique de l'enseignement de l'anatomie humaine à Lisbonne. *Arq.Anat. Antropol.*, 1932-33, 15: 489-520, ill.

VILHENA, H. de. Aperçu de l'oeuvre de l'Institut d'anatomie de Lisbonne. *Arq.Anat.Antropol.*, 1932-33, 15: 521-36.

OBwk/wn Northern Europe; Russia

OBwk-ce

VELDE, A.J.J. van de. Het aandeel der Nederlandse wetenschappelijke literatuur tot de leer der anatomie tot 1800. [The contribution of Dutch scientific literature to the theory of anatomy until 1800. (In Dutch) *Verhandel.Vlaam. Acad.Geneesk.Belg.*, 1948, 117-228.

OBwk-da

ANTEUNIS, Annie. Quelques anatomistes d'autrefois. Gand XVIIe-XIXe siècle. *Biol.Jaarb.*, 1958, 26: 145-67.

OBwk-o

HELLINGA, G. De beteekenis van het Amsterdamsche St. Pietersgasthuis voor het ontleedkundige onderwijs in ons land, in vroeger tijden. [The significance of St. Peter's Hospital of Amsterdam in the teaching of anatomy. (In Dutch)] *Bijdr. Gesch.Geneesk.*, 1933, 13: 157-69.

NUYENS, B.W.Th. Het ontleedkundig onderwijs en de geschilderde anatomische lessen van het Chirurgijns Gilde te Amsterdam in de jaren 1550 tot 1789. [Anatomical teaching and the painted anatomy lessons of the Amsterdam Surgeons' Guild in the years 1550 to 1798. (In Dutch)] 50 p., 25 pl. Amsterdam: P.N. van Kampen, 1928.
Reviewed by F.M.G. de Feyfer, *Bijdr.Gesch.Geneesk.*, 1928, 8: 344-5.

OBwk-oq

BARGE, J.A.J. De Leidsche anatomie herdacht. Toespraak op bij de opening van het Anatomisch Laboratorum der Rijksuniversiteit te Leiden op 2 October 1923 gehouden. [Anatomy at Leyden remembered. An address at the opening of the Anatomy Laboratory at Leyden University held on 2 October 1923. (In Dutch)] Leiden: S.C. Van Doesburgh, 1923.
Reviewed by P. Muntendam, *Bijdr.Gesch.Geneesk.*, 1924, 4: 108.

OBwn

KAJAVA, Yrjö. Die Geschichte der Anatomie in Finland. 1640-1901. Eine Übersicht. 137 p., 26 fig. (Acta Societatis Medicorum Fennicae Duodecim, 10: fasc. 3) Helsingfors: 1928.

OBwn-or

LÖNNQUIST, Bernt. Einige bemerkenswerte Aerzte an der Akademie zu Åbo (Finland) 1640-1837. *Janus*, 1927, 31: 368-74.

OBwx Africa

OBwx-nh

HOMBURGER, Lilias. Noms des parties du corps dans les languages Négro-Africains. v, 118 p. (Collection linguistique, 25) Paris: Champion, 1929.
Reviewed by E. Zyhlarz, *Orient.Lit.Zeitung*, 1932, 35: 504.

OBxw museology

OBxx-wk

GEYSKES, D.C.; KLAAUW, C.J. van der. Der heutige Zustand der anatomischen Kabinette früherer Jahrhunderte in Leiden. *Janus*, 1934, 38: 179-92, 6 fig.

OC DISSECTION

BLANCHET, A. Contribution à l'histoire de l'anatomie (dissection; vivisection). *Compt.Rend.IIe Congr.Int.Hist.Méd.* (Paris, 1921), p. 233-6. Évreux: Imprimerie Ch. Hérissey, 1922.

LASSEK, A.M. Human dissection; its drama and struggle. x, 310 p., 15 fig. Oxford: Blackwell Scientific Publications; Springfield, Ill.: Charles C. Thomas, 1958. [CB 85/394]
Reviewed by Charles Donald O'Malley, *J.Hist.Med.*, 1960, 15: 221-3.

NICAISE, Victor. Sur les origines de la dissection. *Act.Ve Congr.Int.Hist.Méd.* (Genève, 1925), p. 268-70. Genève: Albert Kundig, 1926.

SUEIRO, M.B. Barbosa. Notas históricas sôbre a vivissecção humana. *Arq.Anat.Anthropol.*, 1929-30, 13: 273-85.

OCcm

GOLDSCHMID, Edgar. Autopsie und Sektion im Bild. *Schweiz. Z.Pathol.Bacteriol.*, 1948, 11: 256-71, 8 pl.

OCtf

MASSON, Louis. Les papes et la dissection. *Aesculape*, 1927, 17: 121-4. [CB 23/256]

TRICOT-ROYER, J.J.G. L'église et la mutilation du cadavre humain, décarnisation - dissection pour enseignement, embaument - autopsie. 16 p. *Rev.Med.Louvain*, 1935, no. 23; 1936, no. 3, 4, 6.

OCwb

WAITE, Frederick C. Grave robbing in New England. *Bull.Med. Libr.Ass.*, 1945, 33: 272-94.

OCwb-ph

BLAKE, John B. The development of American anatomy acts. *J. Med.Educ.*, 1955, 30: 431-9.

OCwe-ph

EVANS, C.A. Lovatt. Physiological research and the vivisection act. *Fight Dis.*, 1949, 37: 2-13.
Events of 1874-1912 in Britain.

OCxb

RICHTER, Gottfried. Das anatomische Theater. 156 p. (Abhandlungen zur Geschichte der Medizin und der Naturwissenschaften, 16) Berlin: Ebering, 1936.

OCxd

COLE, F.-J. The history of anatomical injections. In: Singer, Charles. Studies in the History and Method of Science, (2), p. 285-343, ill. Oxford: Clarendon Press, 1921. [CB 11/435]

OD REGIONAL ANATOMY

ARTELT, Walter. "Ossa mandibulae inferioris duo". *Sudhoffs Arch.*, 1955, 39: 193-215, 17 pl.

KROGMAN, Wilton Marion. The anthropology of the hand. *Ciba Symp.* (Summit, N.J.), 1942, 4: 1294-306, fig.

MOISÃO, R. Evolução histórica das teorias sobre a arquitectura do crãnio. *J.Soc.Sci.Méd.Lisboa,* 1964, 128: 27-53.

MONTAGU, M.F. Ashley. The location of the nasion in the living. *Amer.J.Phys.Anthropol.,* 1935, 20: 81-93, 1 fig.

MONTAGU, M.F. Ashley. The premaxilla in man. *J.Amer.Dent. Ass.,* 1936, 23: 2043-57, 9 fig. [CB 51/276]

MONTGOMERY, Douglass W. The knee. *Ann.Med.Hist.,* 1939, 1: 388-95, 2 fig.

ODtq

REININGER, W. The hand in art. *Ciba Symp.* (Summit, N.J.), 1942, 4: 1323-6, fig.

VOIGT, Rolf; PFISTER, Kurt. Hände. Eine Sammlung von Handabbildungen grosser Toter und Lebender. Mit einer Einführung in die Handkunde von Rolf Voigt und einem kunsthistorischen Geleitwort von Kurt Pfister. 31, 28 p., 96 pl. Hamburg: Enoch, 1929.

OE HISTOLOGY

HURD-MEAD, Kate Campbell. Nathalie Zylberlast-Zand: Warsaw histologist. A review of her investigations, 1912-1936. *Med. Life,* 1937, 44: 252-4.

PEARSE, Antony Guy Everson. The history of histochemistry. In: Pearse, Antony Guy Everson. Histochemistry, theoretical and applied, p. 1-10. Boston: Little Brown; London: Churchill, 1953.

ZANOBIO, Bruno. L'immagine filamentoso reticolare nell'anatomia microscopica dal XVII al XIX secolo. *Physis,* 1960, 2: 299-317.

OEk

FRANCESCHINI, Pietro. Epistemologia del concetto di epitelio. *Physis,* 1961, 3: 49-81.

RIÓ HORTEGA, Pío del. Art and artifice in histologic science. Transl. by E.W. Wolfe and G.M. Butler. *Tex.Rep.Biol.Med.,* 1949, 7: 363-90. [CB 77/378]
This statement of the ideals of biological science was originally printed in *Residencia,* a student journal at the University of Madrid (1933, 4: 191-206).

OF PHYSIOLOGY

OFc general history

BAYLISS, William Maddock. Principles of general physiology. 4th ed. xxxiii, 882 p., 261 ill. London: Longmans, Green, 1924. [CB 17/598]
First publ. 1915. Includes many historical references.

BROOKS, Chandler McC. The development of physiology in the last fifty years. *Bull.Hist.Med.,* 1959, 33: 249-62.

BROOKS, Chandler McC.; CRANEFIELD, Paul F.; ed. The historical development of physiological thought. A symposium held at the State University of New York, Downstate Medical Center. xiii, 401 p., fig. New York: Hafner, 1959.
Reviewed by Charles Bodemer, *Isis,* 1960, 51: 353-4; by K.E. Rothschuh, *Bull.Hist.Med.,* 1960, 34: 576-8.
A brief note on this symposium appeared in *Isis,* 1957, 48: 69.

CANNON, Walter B. The wisdom of the body. Rev. and enl. ed. xviii, 333 p. New York: Norton, 1939. [CB 57/258]
First published 1932.

COWGILL, George R. Some historical aspects of experimental physiology. *Sci.Mon.,* 1924, 18: 401-7.

DALE, Henry Hallett. Adventures in physiology. With excursions into autopharmacology. A selection from the scientific publications of Sir Henry Hallett Dale, with an introduction and recent comments by the author. xvi, 652 p. London: Pergamon Press, 1953.
Reviewed by J.H. Gaddum, *Nature,* 1953, 172: 825.

DEMOOR, J. Les sciences physiologiques au cours des cinquante dernières années. *Rev.Univ.Bruxelles,* 1930-31, 36: 111-36, 22 fig.

FOSTER, Michael. Lectures on the history of physiology during the sixteenth, seventeenth and eighteenth centuries. vii, 306 p. Cambridge University Press, 1924.
First publ. 1901.

FRANKLIN, Kenneth J. Fifty years of physiology. *Proc.Roy. Soc.Med.,* 1950, 43: 789-96, 1 fig.

FRANKLIN, Kenneth J. A short history of physiology. 2nd ed. 147 p., ill. London/New York: Staples Press, 1949.
First publ. London: 1933.[CB 53/283]
Reviewed by Edv. Gotfredsen, *Centaurus,* 1951, 1: 280-1; by Owsei Temkin, *Bull.Hist.Med.,* 1956, 30: 480-2.

FULTON, John F. Physiology. xvi, 141 p., front., 7 ill. (Clio Medica, 5) New York: Hoeber, 1931.
Reviewed by C.D. Leake, *Isis,* 1931, 16: 174-6.

GIGON, Alfred. Vorträge zur Geschichte der Respiration und der Ernährung. In: Sammlung medizinischer Vorträge, *new ser.,* no. 658, p. 355-69. Leipzig: J.A. Barth, 1912.

GOODFIELD, G.J. The growth of scientific physiology: physiological method and the mechanist - vitalist controvery, illustrated by the problems of respiration and animal heat. 174 p., bibliogr. London: Hutchinson, 1960.
Reviewed by Leonard G. Wilson, *Isis,* 1962, 53: 541-2; by R.F.J. Withers, *Brit.J.Phil.Sci.,* 1962, 12: 346-7.

HALDANE, John Scott. The new physiology and other addresses. vii, 156 p. London: Griffin, 1919.

HILL, A.V. Living machinery: six lectures delivered before a "Juvenile auditory" at the Royal Institution, Christmas, 1926. xiv, 256 p., 24 pl. London: G. Bell, 1927.

KEITH, Arthur. The engines of the human body: being the substance of Christmas Lectures given at the Royal Institution of Great Britain, Christmas, 1916-1917. 2nd rev. ed. xvi, 343 p., 2 pl. London: Williams and Norgate, 1925; Philadelphia: Lippincott, 1927.
First publ. 1919.[CB 26/243]

LUCKHARDT, Arno B. The beginnings of physiology. *Amer.J. Pharm.Educ.,* 1945, 9: 299-312.
Surveys 17th to 19th century physiology with emphasis on the work of Harvey.

MAYER, André. Cinquante ans de physiologie. *Rev.Phil.,* 1953, 143: 509-52.

NEEDHAM, Joseph. A chart to illustrate the history of biochemistry and physiology. Cambridge University Press, 1929. [CB 27/562]

NOVIKOFF, Alex. From head to foot. 96 p. New York: International Publishers, 1946. [CB 72/275]
The story of human physiology for young people.

O'MALLEY, Charles Donald. The evolution of physiology. *J. Int.Coll.Surg.,* 1958, 30: 115-27.

RANZI, Silvio. Esistono i gradienti fisiologici di Child? *Scientia,* 1932, 51: 348-56.

ROTHSCHUH, K.E. Dynamische Momente in der Entfaltung der Wissenschaft, gezeigt an der Geschichte der Physiologie. *Naturwiss.Rundsch.,* 1961, 14: 379-84.

ROTHSCHUH, K.E. Entwicklungsgeschichte physiologischer Probleme in Tabellenform. viii, 122 p. München-Berlin: Urban & Schwarzenberg, 1952.
Reviewed by Walter Pagel, *Isis,* 1954, 45: 105-6; for other reviews *see* CB 81/276 and CB 82/209.

ROTHSCHUH, K.E. Geschichte der Physiologie. xi, 249 p., 123 text ill. Berlin: Springer, 1953.
Reviewed by Walter Pagel, *Isis*, 1954, 45: 105-6; for other reviews *see* CB 81/276, CB 82/209 and CB 88/551.

STARLING, Ernest H. A century of physiology: being the first of a series of centenary addresses, delivered on Monday, February 28, 1927. 33 p. (University College Centenary Celebrations, 1) London: University of London Press, 1927.

VEITH, Ilza, ed. Perspectives in physiology. An international symposium, 1953. xi, 171 p. Washington: American Physiological Society, 1954. [CB 80/133]

OFc-be

RICHET, Charles. Dictionnaire de physiologie. 10 vol. Paris: Alcan, 1895-1928.

OFc-br

Annual Review of Physiology. Vol. 1-. Stanford University Press, 1939.
For vol. 1 *see* CB 57/258; vol. 2 reviewed by C.A. Kofoid, *Isis*, 1941, 33: 301-2; vol. 3 CB 62/81; vol. 4 CB 63/275; vol. 5 CB 65/84; vol. 6 CB 69/233.

OFc-bx

SIGERIST, Henry E. With students. A student's exhibit illustrating the history of physiology. *Bull.Inst.Hist. Med.*, 1935, 3: 641-96, ill.

OFce-bv

Journal of Physiology. Author index to vol. 1-60. Issued by the Physiological Society and published as a Supplement to The *Journal of Physiology*, June 1928. ii, 235 p. London: Cambridge University Press, 1928.
Further indexes published for vol. 61-100, 101-115, 116-134, 135-154, 154-175 (1964).

OFcj

ROTHSCHUH, K.E.; SCHAEFER, A. Quantitative Untersuchungen ueber die Entwicklung des physiologischen Fachschrifttums (periodica) in den letzten 150 Jahren. *Centaurus*, 1955, 4: 63-6, 1 pl.

OFdaj

FULTON, John F. Selected readings in the history of physiology. xx, 317 p., front., 60 fig. Springfield, Ill.: Charles C. Thomas, 1930.
Reviewed by S.V. Larkey, *Isis*, 1931, 15: 386-8.

OFf

HENDERSON, Yandell. On the history of physiology and some of its lessons. *Sci.Mon.*, 1923, 16: 414-31.

FRANKLIN, Kenneth J. History and the physiologist. *Science, Medicine and History. Essays in honour of Charles Singer*, (2), p. 494-500, pl. London: Oxford University Press, 1953.

RICHARDS, Oscar W. Graphic scientific history. As illustrated by the history of physiology. *Ann.Med.Hist.*, 1927, 9: 74-5.

OFhf

ROTHSCHUH, K.E. Der Begriff der "Physiologie" und sein Bedeutungswandel in der Geschichte der Wissenschaft. *Arch. Int.Hist.Sci.*, 1957, 10: 217-25.

ROTHSCHUH, K.E. Idee und Methode in ihrer Bedeutung für die geschichtliche Entwicklung der Physiologie. *Sudhoffs Arch.*, 1962, 46: 97-119.

ROTHSCHUH, K.E. Wissenschaftstheoretische Bemerkungen zur Physiologie und zur Geschichte der Physiologie. *Sudhoffs Arch.*, 1953, 37: 361-9.

OFk/m philosophy and methodology

OFk

IRSAY, Stephen d'. A physiological synthesis. *Kyklos*, 1929, 2: 117-30.

LEATHES, J.B. Function and design. Address by the president of Section I - physiology - of the British Association for the Advancement of Science, Oxford, August, 1926. *Science*, 1926, 64: 387-94; also *Nature*, 1926, 118: 519-22.

LILLIE, Ralph S. Suggestions for physical investigations bearing upon fundamental problems of physiology and medicine. *Science*, 1920, 51: 525-8. [CB 9/492]

OLMSTED, J.M.D. Physiology as an independent science. In: Science in the University, p. 293-303. Berkeley/Los Angeles: University of California Press, 1944.

OFke

LUCKHARDT, Arno B. Academic or unsuccessful research. *Amer. J.Pharm.Educ.*, 1939, 3: 165-77.
Defense of pure research. Examples drawn from author's own research in physiology.

OFkx

GOODFIELD, G.J. *See* OFc

HARRIS, Fraser. Physiology and "vital force". *Nature*, 1925, 115: 608-10.

OFmc

CYON, Elie de. La solution physiologique du problème de l'espace et du temps et ses conséquences pour la psychologie. *Atti IV°Congr.Int.Fil.* (Bologna, 1911), (3), p. 570-81. Genoa: Formiggini, 1914.

OFmd

LECOMTE DU NOUY, Pierre. Biological time. x, 180 p., 31 fig. London: Methuen, 1936; New York: Macmillan, 1937. [CB 54/532]
Translation of: Le temps et la vie. Paris: 1936.

LECOMTE DU NOUY, Pierre. Physiological time. *Proc.Amer.Phil. Soc.*, 1944, 87: 435-7.

OFmzB

IZQUIERDO, José Joaquín. Las matemáticas y la fisiología. *Gac.Méd.Méx.*, 1943, 73: 280-99.

OFmzK

DARWIN, Francis. The relation of botany to medicine. *Proc. 17th Int.Congr.Med.* (London, 1913), sect. 23, p. 345-8. London: Oxford University Press; Hodder & Stoughton, 1914.
On the light thrown by botanists on certain fundamental physiological problems.

OFmzMU

CANNON, Walter B. The body physiologic and the body politic. *Sci.Mon.*, 1954, 79: 20-6, 1 pl.

OFmzQ

BEECHER, Henry K., ed. Disease and the advancement of basic science. 416 p., ill. (The Lowell Institute Lectures, 1958) Cambridge: Harvard University Press, 1960.
Reviewed in *Sci.Amer.*, 1961, 204: no. 2, 183.
Certain advances in the knowledge of physiology have arisen out of the study of disease.

McMICHAEL, J. The contributions of clinical medicine to physiology. *Advance.Sci.*, 1963, 20: 254-8.

OFp/t organizational aspects; humanistic relations

OFp

CANNON, Walter Bradford. The way of an investigator. A scientist's experiences in medical research. 229 p. New York: Norton, 1945.
Reviewed by George Sarton, *Isis*, 1946, 36: 259-60, portr.

LUCKHARDT, Arno B. Academic or unsuccessful research. *Amer. J.Pharm.Educ.*, 1939, 3: 165-77.
Defense of pure research. Examples drawn from author's own research in physiology.

OFqx

FRANKLIN, K.J. A short history of the international congresses of physiologists. *Ann.Sci.*, 1938, 3: 241-335, 16 pl.

OFw in different countries

HERLITZKA, A. La contribution des divers pays au développement de la physiologie. *Scientia,* 1922, 32: 167-72, 237-49. [CB 14/561]

OFwb-qd

FENN, Wallace Osgood. History of the American Physiological Society. The third quarter century, 1937-1962. viii, 182 p., ill., portr. Washington, D.C.: 1963.

HOFF, Hebbel E.; FULTON, John F. The centenary of the first American physiological society founded at Boston by William A. Alcott and Sylvester Graham. *Bull.Inst.Hist.Med.,* 1937, 5: 687-734, 6 fig.

OFwc

IZQUIERDO, José Joaquin. Balance cuatricentenario de la fisiologia en Mexico. vi, 358 p. Mexico: Ediciones Ciencia, 1934. [CB 51/278]

IZQUIERDO, José Joaquin. Panorama evolutivo de la fisiologia en Mexico. *Rev.Soc.Mex.Hist.Natur.,* 1951, 12: 31-68. [CB 78/192]

OFwc-op

IZQUIERDO, José Joaquin. En que ha contribuido la escuela médico militar al desarrollo de la fisiología experimental en México. Reflexiones a propósito de la inauguración de su nuevo laboratorio. 51 p., 31 fig. México: 1937.

OFwc-oq

IZQUIERDO, José Joaquín. Ideas fundamentales para la estructuracion material y funcional del nuevo departamento de fisiologia de la Facultad de Medicina, basadas en los antecedentes del actual departamento. 45 p. México, D.F.: Universidad Nacional Autonoma de México, 1950.

OFwe-op

THORNTON, John L. The history of physiology at St. Bartholomew's Hospital, London. *Ann. Sci.,* 1951, 7: 238-47.

OFwe-ph

EVANS, C.A. Lovatt. Physiological research and the vivisection act. *Fight Dis.,* 1949, 37: 2-13.
Events of 1874-1912 in Britain.

OFwe-qd

SHARPEY-SCHAFER, Edward. History of the Physiological Society during its first fifty years, 1876-1926. iv, 198 p. Cambridge University Press, 1927.
Reviewed in *Nature,* 1928, 121: 491-2.

OFwf

MATISSE, Georges. Le mouvement scientifique contemporain en France. 2. Les sciences physiologiques. 154 p., 30 fig. Paris: Payot, 1924. [CB 16/328]

OFwf-op

MAYER, André. L'histoire naturelle et la physiologie au Collège de France. Collège de France. Livre jubilaire composé à l'occasion de son quatrième centenaire, p. 169-90, 5 pl. Paris: Presses Universitaires de France, 1932.

OFwg-da-py

ZEKERT, Otto. Österreichische Nobelpreisträger für Medizin, Physiologie und Chemie. 86 p., ill. (HMW-Jahrbuch, 1961) Wien: Heilmittelwerke, 1961.
Reviewed by Nils von Hofsten, *Lychnos,* 1960-61, 417.

OFwi-ce-bv

BAGLIONI, Silvestro. La fisiologia. Guide bibliografiche. 54 p. Roma: Fondazione Leonardo, 1923.
Bibliography of Italian works relative to physiology.

OFwk

FLORKIN, Marcel. Léon Frédericq et les débuts de la physiologie en Belgique. 104 p., ill. Bruxelles: Office de Publicité, 1943. [CB 69/199]
Reviewed by Gustaf Göthlin, *Lychnos,* 1943, 423-4.

ROOSEBOOM, M.; VRIEND-VERMEER, W.; ed. Some Dutch contributions to the development of physiology. 60 p., pl., bibliogr. (Mededeling, 118) Leiden: Rijksmuseum voor de Geschiedenis der Natuurwetenschappen, 1962. [CB 88/551]

OFwk-o

FRÉDÉRICQ, Léon. L'enseignement de la physiologie en Belgique depuis un siècle. In: Fédération Médicale Belge. Cent ans de médecine en Belgique, 1830-1930, p. 21-7, ill. (*Scalpel,* 1931, vol. 84, special number) Bruxelles: J. Vromans, 1931.

OFwk-py

SÉANCE extraordinaire du 27 janvier 1940. Réception solennelle de M. C. Heymans, Membre titulaire, Prix Nobel 1938 de Physiologie et de Médecine. *Bull.Acad.Méd.Belg., 6th ser.,* 1940, 5: (1), 1-38, portr.

OFwn

ARSHAVSKII, I.A. Fiziolog-materialist - N.E. Vvedenskii i ego nauchnoe nasledie. [A materialist-physiologist - N.E. Vvedenskii and his scientific legacy. (In Russian)] *Priroda,* 1964, no. 12, 83-6.

KOSHTOIANTS, Kh.S. Essays on the history of physiology in Russia. Ed. by Donald B. Lindsley. English transl. by David Boder, Kristan Hanes, and Natalie O'Brien. xiv, 321 p., facs., portr. Washington: American Institute of Biological Sciences, 1964.
Translation of: Ocherki po istorii fizidogii v Rossii. Moscow: Izdatelstvo Akademii Nauk SSSR, 1946.

MERKULOV, V.L. Vliianie issledovanii russkikh fiziologov na nauchnoe tvorchestvo Svante Arreniusa. [Influence of Russian physiologists' investigations on the scientific work of Svante Arrhenius. (In Russian)] *Tr.Inst.Ist.Est.Tekh.,* 1961, 36: 217-43.
Several letters from Arrhenius to the Russian physiologist, E.S. London, 1908-1911.

OFwn-qd

FEDOROVA-GROT, A.K. Materialy k istorii fiziologicheskikh uchrezhdenii Akademii Nauk (1864-1917). [Materials on the history of the physiological institutions of the Academy of Sciences, 1864-1917. (In Russian)] *Tr.Inst.Ist.Est.Tekh.,* 1962, 41: 257-93.

OFx techniques and instruments

OFxd

LEERSUM, E.C. van. Old physiological experiments. *Janus,* 1913, 18: 325-62. [CB 4/782]

OFxf-JA

CRANEFIELD, Paul F. Microscopic physiology since 1908. *Bull. Hist.Med.,* 1959, 33: 263-75.

OFxt

HOFF, Hebbel E.; GEDDES, L.A. Graphic recording before Carl Ludwig: an historical summary. *Arch.Int.Hist.Sci.,* 1959, 12: 3-25.

HOFF, Hebbel E.; GEDDES, L.A. Graphic registration before Ludwig; the antecedents of the kymograph. *Isis.* 1959, 50: 1-21.

OFzd DEVELOPMENT AND GROWTH; LIFE AND DEATH

BERKSON, Joseph. Evidence of a seasonal cycle in human growth. *Hum.Biol.,* 1930, 2: 523-38, 2 fig.

CAPPARELLI, Vincenzo. L'ordine dei tempi e delle forme in natura. Introduzione allo studio generale delle funzioni periodiche. 2 vol. 258 p.; 533 p. Bologna: Cappelli, 1928-29.
Reviewed by Giuseppe Montalenti, *Archeion,* 1928, 9: 533; 1929, 11: 265-6.

GARRISON, Fielding Hudson. Life as an occupational disease. *Bull.N.Y.Acad.Med.,* 1934, 10: 679-94.

GLASS, Bentley. Genes and the man. xii, 386 p. New York: Bureau of Publications, Teachers College, Columbia University, 1943.
On the nature of growth, development and aging.

HALLUIN, M. d'. La mort, cette inconnue. 429 p. Paris: Beauchesne, 1941.
Reviewed by M. Laignel-Lavastine, *Bull.Soc.Franç.Hist. Méd.*, 1941, 35: 89.

OFzd-j

ANTHONY, Sylvia. The child's discovery of death. xxi, 231 p. New York: Harcourt, Brace, 1940. [CB 61/410]

KOOPMAN, J. De vrees voor schijndood in het verleden. [The fear of apparent death in the past. (In Dutch)] *Bijdr. Gesch.Geneesk.*, 1929, 9: 309-14.

OFzd-sd

TOLL, Hugo. Dog Jesus pa Korset? [Did Jesus die on the cross? (In Swedish)] 190 p. Stockholm: Wahlstrom and Widstrand, 1928. [CB 26/145]

OFzd-wg-tq

DIEPGEN, Paul. Eine volkstümliche Darstellung des Todes vom Oberrhein. *Z.Volkskunde, new ser.*, 1930, 2: 189-92, 13 fig.

OFze ELECTROPHYSIOLOGY

see also OFxt

HOFF, Hebbel E. Galvani and the pre-Galvanian electrophysiologists. *Ann.Sci.*, 1936, 1: 157-72.

HOFF, Hebbel E.; GEDDES, L.A. The rheotome and its prehistory: a study in the historical interrelation of electrophysiology and electro-mechanics. *Bull.Hist.Med.*, 1957, 31: 212-34, 1 fig., 327-47.

MERKELBACH, Otto. Zur Entwicklung der Beobachtung der aktiven elektrischen Erscheinungen im tierischen und menschlichen Körper. *Festschrift für Jacques Brodbeck-Sandreuter*, p. 271-97, 10 fig. Basel: Schwabe, 1942.

PUPILLI, G.C.; FADIGA, E. The origins of electrophysiology. *Cah.Hist.Mond.*, 1963, 7: 547-89.

WALKER, W. Cameron. Animal electricity before Galvani. *Ann. Sci.*, 1937, 2: 84-113, 4 pl.

OFzh HEAT AND COLD

BODENHEIMER, F.S. Zur Geschichte der verbesserten Wärmesummenregel. *Arch.Gesch.Math.Naturwiss.Tech.*, 1930, 13: 103-4.

LUYET, R.J. Human encounters with cold, from early primitive reactions to modern experimental modes of approach. *Cryobiology*, 1964, 1: 4-10.

MENDELSOHN, Everett. Heat and life. The development of the theory of animal heat. xi, 208 p. Cambridge, Mass.: Harvard University Press, 1964.
Reviewed by J. Schiller, *Arch.Int.Hist.Sci.*, 1964, 17: 339-40.

OFzh-wi

TESTI, Gino. Il contributo italiano allo studio del calore animale. *Volume di scritti in onore del Prof. P. Capparoni*, p. 160-6. Torino: Minerva Medica, 1941.

OFzr REST AND SLEEP

LHERMITTE, Jean. Le sommeil. 212 p. Paris: Colin, 1931. [CB 54/540]

MORUZZI, Giuseppe. The historical development of the deafferentation hypothesis of sleep. *Proc.Amer.Phil.Soc.*, 1964, 108: 19-28.

PIÉRON, Henri. Le problème physiologique du sommeil. xvi, 520 p. Paris: Masson, 1913.

RIGNANO, Eugenio. Une nouvelle théorie du sommeil et des rêves. *Rev.Métaphys.Morale*, 1921, 28: 521-35. [CB 13/303]

SARTON, George. Sleeping along the meridian. *Isis*, 1935, 22: 525-9.

OG METABOLISM; PHYSIOLOGICAL CHEMISTRY

see also JD BIOCHEMISTRY

ACKERKNECHT, Erwin H. Metabolism and respiration, from Erasistratus to Lavoisier. Metabolism from Liebig to the present. The history of metabolic diseases. *Ciba Symp.* (Summit, N.J.), 1944, 6: 1815-44, ill.

ALBERTI, Giuseppe. Da Anassagora ad Abderhalden. Idee e nomi nella storia di un fondamentale capitolo della chimica fisiologica: i protidi. *Riv.Stor.Sci.*, 1941, 32: 91-9.

BROWN, W. Langdon. The history of the introduction of biochemistry into medicine. *Proc.Roy.Soc.Med.*, 1932, 25: 1046-54.

FEIJFER, F.M.G. de. Autostasie en geneeskunst. [Autostasy and medicine. (In Dutch)] *Bijdr.Gesch.Geneesk.*, 1926, 6: 1-16.

FLORKIN, Marcel. Histoire de la technique de mesure du métabolisme en circuit fermé (appareils de Schwann, oxygénographe, de Léon Fredericq, manuscrits). *Arch.Int.Physiol.*, 1951, 59: 254-6.

HOLMES, Frederic L. Elementary analysis and the origins of physiological chemistry. *Isis*, 1963, 54: 50-81.

IZQUIERDO, José Joaquín. Bases físico-químicas para que la fisiologia sea base effectiva en la formacion del médico. *Gac.Méd.Méx.*, 1961, 91: 499-508.

LIEBEN, Fritz. Geschichte der physiologischen Chemie. x, 742 p. Leipzig: Deuticke, 1935.
Reviewed by Eduard Farber, *Isis*, 1936, 25: 164-6.

MAGNUS-LEVY, A. Energy metabolism in health and disease. *Hist.Med.*, 1947, 53: 307-20.

SCHELAR, Virginia M. Thermochemistry and animal metabolism. *J.Chem.Educ.*, 1964, 41: 226-9.
A brief survey of the 100 years after Lavoisier.

OGmzMF

WILSON, Elsie A. Basal metabolism from the standpoint of racial anthropology. *Amer.J.Phys.Anthropol.*, 1945, 3: 1-19. [CB 69/233]

OGwb

CHITTENDEN, Russell H. The development of physiological chemistry in the United States. 427 p. (American Chemical Society Monograph Series, 54) New York: Chemical Catalog Co., 1930.

OH SYSTEMS OF THE BODY; SPECIALTIES OF MEDICINE

including their anatomy, physiology and pathology, but excluding special therapies

OI LOCOMOTOR SYSTEM

OIc *see also* QUyOI

BASTHOLM, E. The history of muscle physiology, from the natural philosophers to Albrecht von Haller. Translation by W.E. Calvert. 256 p. (Acta Historica Scientiarum Naturalium et Medicinalium, 7) Copenhagen: Munksgaard, 1950.
Reviewed by Samuel Gelfan, *Isis*, 1951, 42: 276; by Owsei Temkin, *Bull.Hist.Med.*, 1953, 27: 197.

BEARN, J.G. The history of the ideas on the function of the biceps brachii muscle as a supinator. *Med.Hist.*, 1963, 7: 32-42.

FERNÁNDEZ, Octavio C. Historia de la kinesiología. *Publ. Cátedra Hist.Med. Univ.Buenos Aires*, 1940, 3: 235-73.

FULTON, John F. Muscular contraction and the reflex control of movement. xv, 644 p., ill. Baltimore: Williams and Wilkins, 1926.
Elaborate historical introduction, p. 3-55, with chronological bibliography.
Reviewed in *Nature*, 1927, 120: 437-8.

GALLEGO, Antonio. Precisiones históricas sobre la inervación motriz de los husos musculares. *Arch.Iberoamer.Hist.Med.*, 1959, 11: 245-50.

HALDANE, J.S.; HENDERSON, Yandell. The rate of work done with an Egyptian shadouf. *Nature*, 1926, 118: 308-9.

HUARD, Pierre; MONTAGNE, M. Le squelette humain et l'attitude accroupie. *Bull.Soc.Etud.Indochinoises Saigon, new ser.*, 1950, 25: 401-26, ill.

MOURGUE, Raoul. L'activité statique du muscle. Origine historique de cette notion. *Encéphale*, 1921, 16: 297-304.

OIda

BERGERON, Marcel. Note historique sur les physiologistes du mouvement. Introduction à leur étude. *Bull.Soc.Franç. Hist.Méd.*, 1937, 31: 266-78.

OIyNT HEALTH SERVICES

KIRMSSE, Max. Zur Geschichte der frühesten Krüppelfürsorge. *Z.Krüppelfürsorge*, 1911, 4: 3-18.

OJ LOCOMOTOR SYSTEM: DISORDERS AND DISEASES

for bone tuberculosis *see* QPztu-yOJ
orthopaedics *see* RCC
physiotherapy *see* RJ
pharmacotherapy *see* RUyOJ

OJc

ARNOLD, Hermann. Zur Frühgeschichte der chronischen Wirbelsäulenversteifung. *Klin.Wochenschr.*, 1937, 16: 1286-8, 2 fig.

BAZZI, Franco; DONADI, G. Storia di un sintoma: il Lasègue. *Riv.Stor.Med.*, 1964, 8: 159-71.

BETT, Y.W.R. Some notes on osteitis deformans before and after Paget. *Festschrift zum 80. Geburtstag Max Neuburgers*, p. 47-9. Wien: Maudrich, 1948.

BLEYER, Adrien. The antiquity of achondroplasia. *Ann.Med. Hist.*, 1940, 2: 4

BORAK, J. Zur Geschichte des Krankheitsbegriffes der Ostitis fibrosa. *Festschrift zur Feier seines 60. Geburtstags Max Neuburger gewidmet*, p. 54-65. Wien: Verlag des Fest-Komitees, 1928.

BRIGHETTI, A. Evoluzione delle conoscenze sulla iperostosi frontale interna. *Arch.Patol.Clin.Med.*, 1964, 41: 196-216.

COPEMAN, W.S.C. *See* QL

KELLY, Michael. History of immobilization. *Rheumatism*, 1962, 18: 27-32.

KEYNES, Geoffrey. The history of myasthenia gravis. *Med. Hist.*, 1961, 5: 313-26.

MESSELOFF, Charles R. Historical aspects of rheumatism. *Med. Life*, 1930, 37: 3-56, 11 portr.

MITTELSTRASS, Hans. Die Geschichte des Rheumatismus. (Diss.) 33 p. Düsseldorf: 1936.

PICKETT, Justus C. A short historical sketch of osteomyelitis. *Ann.Med.Hist.*, 1935, 7: 183-91.

VALENTIN, Bruno. Die Geschichte der Osteopsathyrosis (osteogenesis imperfecta). *Centaurus*, 1955, 4: 132-47, 7 pl.

OJc-bv

RODNAN, G.P.; EAKIN, Laurabelle. A bibliography of the history of the rheumatic diseases, 1940-1962. *Arthritis Rheum.*, 1964, 7: 75-9.

OJwc

BARROS, B. Historia de la reumatologia urugaya. (In Spanish and English) *A.I.R.*, 1964, 7: 259-69, 280-8.

OK NEUROLOGY

see also MJ PHYSIOLOGICAL PSYCHOLOGY
for paediatric neurology *see* PWyOK

OKc general history

ANDREOLI, Armando. Zur geschichtlichen Entwicklung der Neuronentheorie. 88 p., ill. (*Basler Veröffentl.Gesch. Med.Biol.*, 10) Basel/Stuttgart: Schwabe, 1961.
Reviewed by Rolf Ortmann, *Sudhoffs Arch.*, 1963, 47: 88; by Paul F.A. Hoefer, *J.Hist.Med.*, 1964, 19: 315.

ARIËNS KAPPERS, C.U.; HUBER, G. Carl; CROSBY, Elizabeth Caroline. The comparative anatomy of the nervous system of vertebrates. 2 vol. xvii, 864 p.; xi, 981 p., 710 fig. New York: Macmillan, 1936. [CB 48/581]
This book is an outgrowth of "Die vergleichende Anatomie des Nervensystems" by Ariëns Kappers (Haarlem: 1920-21).

ASHBY, W. Ross. Design for a brain. 260 p. New York: Wiley, 1952. [CB 79/184]

BENDHEIM, Otto L. On the history of Hoffmann's sign. *Bull. Inst.Hist.Med.*, 1937, 5: no. 7, 684-6.

BENTON, Arthur L. Jacques Loeb and the method of double stimulation. *J.Hist.Med.*, 1956, 11: 47-53.

BORUTTAU, H. Ueber den jetzigen Stand unserer Kenntnisse von den Elementarfunktionen des Nervensystems. *Z.Positivistische Phil.*, 1913, 1: 91-110, bibliogr.

BRAIN, Russell. The contribution of medicine to our idea of the mind. 30 p. The Rede Lecture for 1952. Cambridge/New York: Cambridge University Press, 1952.
Reviewed by Owsei Temkin, *Bull.Hist.Med.*, 1953, 27: 299.

BRAZIER, Mary A.B. A history of the electrical activity of the brain: the first half century. vii, 119 p. New York: Macmillan, 1961.
Reviewed by Edwin Clarke, *Bull.Hist.Med.*, 1963, 37: 91-2.

BRAZIER, Mary A.B. The history of the electrical activity of the brain as a method for localizing sensory function. *Med.Hist.*, 1963, 7: 199-211.

CANNON, Walter B. The story of the development of our ideas of chemical mediation of nerve impulses. *Amer.J.Med.Sci.*, 1934, 188: 145-59. [CB 57/199]
Account of the circumstances of the discovery which earned Otto Loewi the Nobel prize.

CANNON, Walter B.; ROSENBLEUTH, A. Autonomic neuro-effector systems. xvi, 229 p., 42 fig. New York: Macmillan, 1937. [CB 56/399]

FULTON, John F. The historical contribution of physiology to neurology. *Science, Medicine and History. Essays in honour of Charles Singer*, (2), p. 537-44, 1 pl. London: Oxford University Press, 1953.
Refers to the contributions of Sherrington.

FULTON, John F. Physiology of the nervous system. 2nd ed. ix, 614 p. London: Oxford University Press, 1943. [CB 65/84]
First ed. publ. 1938. Each chapter after the first is introduced by a short historical note.

FULTON, John F. Reflections on the history of reflex action. *Arch.Iberoamer.Hist.Med.*, 1956, 8: 27-32.

FULTON, John F. Somatic functions of the central nervous system. *Annu.Rev.Physiol.*, 1953, 15: 305-28.

G. CARL HUBER. Memorial volume. *J.Comp.Neurol.*, 1936, 65: li, 711 p., 173 fig., portr.
Reviewed by Charles A. Kofoid. *Isis*, 1938, 29: 133.

GARRISON, Fielding Hudson. History of neurology. In: Dana, Charles L. Textbook of nervous disease. 10th ed., p. 15-56. New York: Wm. Wood, 1925.

HOFF, Hebbel E. The history of vagal inhibition. *Bull.Hist.Med.*, 1940, 8: 461-96.

HOFF, Hebbel E. John Fulton's contributions to neurophysiology. *J.Hist.Med.*, 1962, 17: 16-37.

HOFF, Hebbel E.; KELLAWAY, Peter. The early history of the reflex. *J.Hist.Med.*, 1952, 7: 211-49. [CB 80/133]

INTERNATIONAL CONFERENCE ON THE DEVELOPMENT, GROWTH AND REGENERATION OF THE NERVOUS SYSTEM, University of Chicago, 1949. Genetic neurology. Ed. Paul Weiss. xii, 239 p. Chicago: University of Chicago Press, 1950. [CB 78/191]

IZQUIERDO, José Joaquin. Simposio acerca de la organización funcional del sistema nervioso para la percepción sensoria. 1. Presentación del simposio. *Gac.Méd.Méx.*, 1963, 93: no. 6, 485-90.

JANDOLO, Michele. Il concetto di "impulso nervoso" dai primordi ai Nobel per la medicina 1963. *Riv.Stor.Med.*, 1964, 8: 151-8.

KOSHTOIANTS, Kh. S. The history of the problem of brain cortex excitability. *Act.VIIIe Congr.Int.Hist.Sci.* (Florence, 1956), p. 862-4. Paris: Hermann, 1958.

LAIGNEL-LAVASTINE, Maxime. Note sur l'histoire du grand sympathique. *Bull.Soc.Franç.Hist.Méd.*, 1923, 17: 401-6.

LAIGNEL-LAVASTINE, Maxime. Le sympathique et l'âme végétative. *Bull.Soc.Franç.Hist.Méd.*, 1926, 20: 381-8.
Shows how recent researches on the sympathetic nervous system elucidate the tripartite theories of Plato and Aristotle.

LAPICQUE, Louis. L'isochronisme neuro-musculaire comme fait empirique. *Thalès*, 1936, 3: 12-14.

LEVINSON, A. History of cerebrospinal fluid. *Festschrift zur Feier seines 60. Geburtstages Max Neuburger gewidmet*, p. 225-30. Wien: Verlag des Fest Komitees, 1928.

MAGOUN, H.W. Darwin and concepts of brain function. In: Council for International Organizations of Medical Sciences. Brain Mechanisms and Learning, p. 1-20. London: Blackwell Scientific Publications, 1961. [CB 87/623]
Also discusses the influence of Spencerian evolution on the growth of ideas in neurophysiology and psychology.

MONAKOW, C. von; MOURGUE, Raoul. Introduction biologique à l'étude de la neurologie et de la psychopathologie. Intégration et désintégration de la fonction. xi, 416 p., 33 fig., 2 pl. Paris: Alcan, 1928.
For reviews *see* CB 29/300.

PARKER, G.H. The origin and development of the nervous system. *Scientia*, 1923, 34: 23-33. French transl. suppl., 11-21. [CB 15/205]

PAZZINI, Adalberto. Il canale vidiano e il suo nervo (saggio di ricerca storico-medica). *Atti Soc.Ital.Stor.Sci.Med. Natur.IV Congr.Naz.* (Roma, 1933). In: *Riv.Stor.Sci.*, 1934, 25: suppl. 159-70.
History of our knowledge of the Vidian nerve and canal.

POYNTER, F.N.L., ed. The history and philosophy of knowledge of the brain and its functions. An Anglo-American Symposium, London, July 15-17, 1957. x, 272 p., ill. Oxford: Blackwell Scientific Publications; Springfield, Ill.: Charles C. Thomas, 1958.
Reviewed by John M. Brookhart, *Isis*, 1960, 51: 99-101; for other reviews *see* CB 85/400 and CB 86/471.
For note on the Symposium *see J.Hist.Med.*, 1957, 12: 520-1.

RAMÓN Y CAJAL, Santiago. Degeneration and regeneration of the nervous system. Transl. and edited by Raoul M. May. 2 vol., ill. London: Oxford University Press, 1928. [CB 25/428]
Translation of: Estudios sobre la degeneración y regeneración del sistema nervioso (Madrid: 1913-14). [CB 16/280]
The first chapter (vol. 1, p. 3-26) is devoted to the history of the subject from the time of Augustus Volney Waller (1850, 1852), down to Ramón's own time.

RASMUSSEN, A.T. Some trends in neuroanatomy. 93 p. Dubuque, Iowa: Brown, 1947.
A valuable short survey of the historical development of the science of neuroanatomy.

RIESE, Walter. A history of neurology. Foreword by Félix Martí-Ibáñez. 223 p., 4 fig., bibliogr. (MD Monographs on Medical History, 2) New York: MD Publications, 1959. [CB 85/401]
For reviews *see* CB 85/401, CB 86/467 and 471.

RIESE, Walter. The 150th anniversary of S.T. Soemmerring's "Organ of the Soul". The reaction of his contemporaries and its significance today. *Bull.Hist.Med.*, 1946, 20: 310-21, 1 fig.

RIESE, Walter; HOFF, Ebbe C. A history of the doctrine of cerebral localization. 1. Sources, anticipations, and basic reasoning. 2. Methods and main results. *J.Hist.Med.*, 1950, 5: 50-71; 1951, 6: 439-70.

ROTHSCHUH, K.E. Vom Spiritus animalis zum Nervenaktionsstrom. *Ciba Z.*, 1958, 8: 2950-80, ill. [CB 84/317]

SHERRINGTON, Charles. The integrative action of the nervous system. xxiv, 433 p., bibliogr. Cambridge University Press, 1947. [CB 72/275]
First published 1906.
Reviewed by E.D. Adrian, *Nature*, 1947, 160: 623-4.

TIZARD, Barbara. Theories of brain localization from Flourens to Lashley. *Med.Hist.*, 1959, 3: 132-45.

VALKENBURG, C.T. van. De outplooiing van de neurologie sinds 1900. [The development of neurology since 1900. (In Dutch)] *Bijdr.Gesch.Geneesk.*, 1958, 38: 7-10.

VIETS, Henry R. The history of neurology in the last one hundred years. *Bull.N.Y.Acad.Med.*, 1948, 24: 772-83.

WALTER, W. Grey. The living brain. xxii, 311 p., fig. New York: W. W. Norton, 1963.

OKcd

ROOFE, Paul G. The Herrick papers, an unusual scientific archive. *Isis*, 1964, 55: 85-7.
Papers of the neurologist, C. Judson Herrick, in the library of the University of Kansas.

OKda

KOLLE, Kurt, ed. Grosse Nervenärzte. 3 vol. 1. 21 Lebensbilder viii, 284 p., 21 pl.; 2. 22 Lebensbilder. viii, 251 p., 21 pl.; 3. 22 Lebensbilder. vii, 228 p. Stuttgart: Thieme, 1956-63.
Reviewed by G. Rosen, *J.Hist.Med.*, 1956, 11: 362; 1960, 15: 445-60; by E. Bastholm, *Lychnos*, 1957-58, 464; 1959, 443-4.

OKdaj

BURR, H.S. ed. Classics in neurology. Selected by Richard Sherman Lyman. vii, 176 p. Springfield, Ill.: Charles C. Thomas, 1963.

OKhm

RIESE, Walter. An outline of a history of ideas in neurology. *Bull.Hist.Med.*, 1949, 23: 111-36, 2 fig.

OKk/y special aspects

OKk

HEBB, D.O. The organization of behavior. xix, 335 p. New York: Wiley, 1949. [CB 77/380]
A neurophysiological theory.

PAPILLAULT, G. L'animisme dans les théories régnantes sur le neurone. *Arq.Anat.Anthropol.*, 1924, 8: 526-32.

VON NEUMANN, John. The computer and the brain. xiv, 82 p. New Haven: Yale University Press, 1958.
Reviewed by A.H. Taub, *Isis*, 1960, 51: 94-6.

YOUNG, J.Z. Doubt and certainty in science; a biologist's reflections on the brain. x, 168 p., fig. (B.B.C. Reith Lectures, 1950) London/New York: Oxford University Press, 1960.

OKmzMG

FRANZ, V. Vergleichende Neurologie und Psychologie. *Fortschr. Naturwiss.Forsch.*, 1913, 7: 73-110.

OKsp

FULTON, John F. Neurology and war. *Trans.Coll.Physicians Phila.*, 1940, 8: 157-65.

OKwb

TUCKER, Beverley R. Development of psychiatry and neurology in Virginia. *Ann.Med.Hist.*, 1938, 10: 91-7, 2 fig.

OKwg

HOFF, Hans; SEITELBERGER, Franz. The history of the Neurological School of Vienna. *J.Nerv.Ment.Dis.*, 1952, 116: 495-505.

KRÜCKE, W.; SPATZ; H., ed. Ludwig Edinger 1855-1918. Gedenkschrift zu seinem 100. Geburtstag und zum 50. jährigen Bestehen des Neurologischen Instituts (Edinger-Inst.) der Universität Frankfurt a.M. 97 p., front., 17 pl. (Schriften der wissenschaftlichen Gesellschaft an der Johann Wolfgang Goethe-Universität Frankfurt a.M., Naturwissenschaftliche Reihe) Wiesbaden: Steiner, 1959.
Reviewed by Gunter Mann, *Sudhoffs Arch.*, 1960, 44: 372-3.

OKwi

PENSA, A. Contributions apportées par l'Italie à la biologie du système nerveux depuis un siècle. *Cah.Hist.Mond.*, 1963, 7: 591-603.

OKyCDzb

HOFF, Hebbel E.; GEDDES, L.A. Ballistics and the instrumentation of physiology: the velocity of the projectile and of the nerve impulse. *J.Hist.Med.*, 1960, 15: 133-46.

HOFF, Hebbel E.; GEDDES, L.A. The technological background of physiological discovery: ballistics and the graphic method. *J.Hist.Med.*, 1960, 15: 345-63.

OKyNWwc

LASTRES, Juan B. Las enfermedades nerviosas en el coloniaje. xii, 173 p., ill. Lima: Editorial Rimac, 1938.
Discussed by G. Marañón, *Publ.Cátedra Hist.Med.Univ.Buenos Aires*, 1940, 3: 405-14.

MARAÑÓN, Gregorio. España fuera de España. Divagaciones sobre un libro de historia. [Las enfermedades nerviosas en el coloniaje. By Juan B. Lastres] *Publ.Cátedra Hist.Med.Univ. Buenos Aires*, 1940, 3: 405-14.

OKyNWwe

CRITCHLEY, Macdonald. The Black Hole and other essays. x, 288 p. London: Pitman, 1964.
Includes a detailed account of Samuel Johnson's aphasia and an account of the National Hospital for Nervous Diseases.
Reviewed by Edwin Clarke, *Med.Hist.*, 1964, 8: 391.

OL NERVOUS DISORDERS AND DISEASES

for aphasia *see* OLza
epilepsy *see* OLze
nervous diseases caused by microorganisms *see* QP; by parasites *see* QT
neurosurgery *see* RCD

ARIËNS KAPPERS, C.U. *See* OMc

CURTIUS, Friedrich; DRÜGER, Karl-Heinz; TÖWE, Anna-Luise. Zur Entwicklung der Lehre von der konstitutionellen Vasolabilität. *Sudhoffs Arch.*, 1953, 37: 170-86.

DE JONG, Russell N. George Huntington and his relationship to the earlier descriptions of chronic hereditary chorea. *Ann.Med.Hist.*, 1937, 9: 201-10, 2 fig.

DEJONG, Russell N. Migraine. Personal observations by physicians subject to the disorder. *Ann.Med.Hist.*, 1942, 4: 276-83, 3 fig.

DROGENDIJK, A.C. Over encephalitis postvaccinalis. [Concerning Encephalitis postvaccinalis. (In Dutch)] 111 p. Amsterdam: H.J. Paris, 1939.
Reviewed by J.A.V., *Janus*, 1939, 43: 335.

LEWY, F.H. The first authentic case of major trigeminal neuralgia, and some comments on the history of this disease. *Ann. Med.Hist.*, 1938, 10: 247-50, 1 fig.

MALTSBERGER, John Terry. Even unto the twelfth generation - Huntington's chorea. *J.Hist.Med.*, 1961, 16: 1-17.

MENDELSON, J.H.; SIGER, L.; KUBZANSKY, P.E. *See* OTmzOL

OLda

HAYMAKER, Webb. Guide to the exhibit on the history of neuropathology. Presented at the Annual Meetings of the American Psychiatric Assocation, Washington, D.C., May 17-20, 1948. xi, 121 p. Washington, D.C.: Army Institute of Pathology, 1948. [CB 73/182]
Succinct biobliographical accounts with portraits of fifty leading neuro-pathologists arranged by countries.

OLkq

RIESE, Walter. History and principles of classification of nervous diseases. A short history of the doctrines of nervous function under pathological conditions and a general scheme of classification of nervous diseases according to function. *Bull.Hist.Med.*, 1945, 18: 465-512, 5 fig.

OLmzOT

MENDELSON, J.H.; SIGER, L.; KUBZANSKY, P.E. The brain and disorders of communication. The language of signs and symbolic behavior of the deaf. *Res.Publ.Ass.Res.Nerv.Ment.Dis.*, 1964, 42: 151-70.

OLwc

LASTRES, Juan B. Cómo se trataban las enfermedades nerviosas durante la colonia. *Publ.Cátedra Hist.Med.Univ.Buenos Aires*, 1940, 3: 363-404.

LASTRES, Juan B. Le traitement des maladies nerveuses pendant l'époque coloniale au Pérou. *Bull.Soc.Franç.Hist.Méd.*, 1940, 34: 11-29.

OLwg

NEUBURGER, Max. Studien zur Geschichte der deutschen Gehirnpathologie. 1. Aus der Frühgeschichte der Encephalomalacie. 2. Aus den ersten vier Dezennien der Tumorenforschung. *Jahrb. Psychiat.Neurol.*, 1913, 34: no. 1, 1-73; no. 2, 229-86.

SCHOLZ, W., ed. 50 Jahre Neuropathologie in Deutschland, 1885-1935. 123 p., fig. Stuttgart: Thieme, 1961.
Reviewed by N. Antoni, *Lychnos*, 1962, 518; by Aubrey Lewis, *Med.Hist.*, 1962, 6: 399-400.

OLwg-ce

NEUBURGER, Max. Streifzüge durch die ältere deutsche Myelitisliteratur. *Jahrb.Psychiat.Neurol.*, 1912, 33: 225-91, ill.

OLza APHASIA

CRITCHLEY, Macdonald. The origins of asphasiology. *Scot.Med. J.*, 1964, 9: 231-42.

EBSTEIN, Erich. Zur Vorgeschichte der Aphasie. *Mitt.Gesch. Med.*, 1918, 17: 172-3.

ELIASBERG, W.G. A contribution to the prehistory of aphasia. *J.Hist.Med.*, 1950, 5: 96-101.

RIESE, Walter. The early history of aphasia. *Bull.Hist.Med.*, 1947, 21: 322-34.

SCHOENWALD, Richard L. A turning point in Freud's life: "Zur Auffassung der Aphasien". *Osiris*, 1954, 11: 119-26.
Includes text.

VERJAAL, A. Quelques remarques sur l'histoire de l'aphasie frontale. *Janus*, 1961, 49: 130-6.

OLza-sd

CRITCHLEY, Macdonald. The Black Hole and other essays. x, 288 p. London: Pitman, 1964.
Includes a detailed account of Samuel Johnson's aphasia and an account of the National Hospital for Nervous Diseases.
Reviewed by Edwin Clarke, *Med.Hist.*, 1964, 8: 391.

OLze EPILEPSY

for pharmacotherapy *see* RRyOLze

BISCHLER, W. Histoire de l'épilepsie. L'épilepsie chez les primitifs et les peuples sauvages. L'épilepsie chez les anciens. *Scientia*, 1955, 49: 295-301.

BOLTEN, G.C. Eenige historische bijzonderheden betreffende epilepsie. [Some historical details concerning epilepsy. (In Dutch)] *Bijdr.Gesch.Geneesk.*, 1922, 2: 123-36.

DONINCK, A. van. Geschiedenis der behandeling van de vallende ziekte. [History of the treatment of the falling sickness. (In Dutch)] *Bijdr.Gesch.Geneesk.*, 1929, 9: 207-24, 245-53.

FULTON, John F. Clifford Allbutt's description of psychomotor seizures. *J.Hist.Med.*, 1957, 12: 75-7.

KANNER, Leo. The folklore and cultural history of epilepsy. *Med.Life*, 1930, 37: 167-214. [CB 29/316]

PIRKNER, E.H. Epilepsy in the light of history. *Ann.Med.Hist.*, 1929, 1: 453-80.

STORCH, T.C. von. An essay on the history of epilepsy. *Ann. Med.Hist.*, 1930, 2: 514-50.

TEMKIN, Owsei. The falling sickness. A history of epilepsy from the Greeks to the beginning of modern neurology. xiv, 380 p. Baltimore: Johns Hopkins Press, 1945.
Reviewed by Walter Pagel, *Isis*, 1946, 36: 275-8.

OLze-ud

MURPHY, Edward L. The saints of epilepsy. *Med.Hist.*, 1959, 3: 303-11.

OM MEDICAL PSYCHOLOGY AND PSYCHIATRY

for paediatric psychiatry *see* PWyOM

OMc general history

ACKERKNECHT, Erwin H. A short history of psychiatry. Translated from the German by Sulammith Wolff. vi, 98 p., bibliogr., ill. New York: Hafner, 1959.
Reviewed by Walter O. Jahrreiss, *Bull.Hist.Med.*, 1960, 34: 88-9; by Richard A. Hunter, *J.Hist.Med.*, 1960, 15: 107.
Translation of: Kurze Geschichte der Psychiatrie (Stuttgart: Enke, 1957) reviewed by Iago Galdston, *Isis*, 1959, 50: 270-1; for other reviews *see* CB 84/318 and CB 85/397.

ADAM, H.A. Geisteskrankheit in alter und neuer Zeit. Ein Stück Kulturgeschichte in Wort und Bild. 160 p., 96 ill. Regensburg: Rath, 1928.

ALTSCHULE, Mark D.; RUSS, Evelyn. Roots of modern psychiatry. Essays in the history of psychiatry. viii, 184 p., ill. New York/London: Grune and Stratton, 1957.
Reviewed by Walter O. Jahrreiss, *Bull.Hist.Med.*, 1958, 32: 381-2; by Richard A. Hunter, *J.Hist.Med.*, 1958, 13: 277-9.

ARIËNS KAPPERS, C.U. L'histoire de la thérapie des maladies nerveuses et mentales et son état actuel. *VIe Congr.Int. Hist.Méd.* (Leyde-Amsterdam, 1927), p. 7-18. Anvers: De Vlijt, 1929.

ARIËNS KAPPERS, C.U. Overzicht van de geschiedenis der therapie van geestes- en zenuwziekten en haar tegenwoordigen stand. [Survey of the history of the treatment of psychiatric and neurological diseases and its present position. (In Dutch)] *Bijdr.Gesch.Geneesk.*, 1927, 7: 649-64.

BARUK, H. Traité de psychiatrie: séméiologie,psychopathologie, thérapeutique, étiologie. 2 vol. 1570 p. Paris: Masson, 1959.
Reviewed by Walter Riese, *Bull.Hist.Med.*, 1961, 35: 189-90.

BROMBERG, Walter. The mind of man: the story of man's conquest of mental illness. xiv, 323 p. New York: Harper, 1937.
Reviewed by Richard H. Shryock, *Amer.Hist.Rev.*, 1939, 44: 676.

CABANÈS, Auguste. Les étapes de la psycho-pathologie historique. Les précurseurs. *Compt.Rend.IIe Congr.Int.Hist.Méd.* (Paris, 1921), p. 538-43. Évreux: Imprimerie Ch. Hérissey, 1922.

CULPIN, Millais. The history of psychology in medicine. *Proc.Roy.Soc.Med.*, 1936, 29: 1569-76, Hist. sect., 33-40.

DEL GRECO, Francesco. Il largo giro di applicazioni della psicologia morbosa ed il vario giudizio degli uomini colti. *Pensiero Med.*, 1913, 3: 465-71.

GALDSTON, Iago. Psychiatry without Freud. *A.M.A.Arch.Neurol. Psychiat.*, 1951, 66: 69-81.

GOLDSTEIN, Kurt. Human nature in the light of psychopathology. x, 258 p. (William James Lectures, 1937-38) Cambridge: Harvard University Press, 1940. [CB 60/160]
The lectures present a re-discussion of the views set out in the author's The Organism (New York: 1939).

HARRISON, Forrest M. Psychiatry in historical retrospect. *Ann. Med.Hist.*, 1932, 4: 565-74; 1933, 5: 85-95.

HUNTER, Richard; MACALPINE, Ida. Three hundred years of psychiatry, 1535-1860. xxvi, 1107 p. London: Oxford University Press, 1963.
Reviewed by J.M. Hinton, *Proc.Roy.Soc.Med.*, 1963, 56: 859; by Macdonald C. Critchley, *Med.Hist.*, 1963, 7: 387-8; by W.G. Niederland, *Psychoanal.Quart.*, 1964, 33: 586-7; by E. Ashworth Underwood, *J.Soc.Arch.*, 1964, 2: 447-8.

JASPERS, Karl. General psychopathology. Transl. from the German by J. Hoenig and Marian W. Hamilton. xxxii, 922 p., fig. Manchester: Manchester University Press, 1962; Chicago: University of Chicago Press, 1963.
Translation of: Allgemeine Psychopathologie. 7th edition. Berlin: Springer, 1959.

JASTROW, Joseph. Relation of psychology to medicine. *Med. Life*, 1929, 36: 100-8.

KANNABICH, I.V. Istoria psychiatrii. [History of psychiatry. (In Russian)] 520 p. Moskva: 1929.
Reviewed by H. Zeiss, *Mitt.Gesch.Med.*, 1930, 29: 189-90.

KIRCHHOFF, Th. Geschichte der Psychiatrie. 48 p. In: Handbuch der Psychiatrie, Allgemeiner Teil. IV. Abt. Wien: F. Deuticke, 1912.

KRAEPELIN, Emil. One hundred years of psychiatry. Transl. by W. Baskin, epilogue by H.P. Laqueur. 163 p., ill. London: Peter Owen; New York: Philosophical Library, 1962
Reviewed by Richard Hunter, *Med.Hist.*, 1964, 8: 93-4.
Translation of: Hundert Jahre Psychiatrie. Berlin: Springer, 1918.

LAIGNEL-LAVASTINE, Maxime; VINCHON, Jean. Les maladies de l'esprit et leurs médecins du XVIe au XIXe siècle. 577 p., 42 ill. Paris: Maloine, 1931.
Reviewed by Marcel Fosseyeux, *Bull.Soc.Franç.Hist.Méd.*, 1931, 25: 220.

LEIBRAND, Werner; WETTLEY, Annemarie. Der Wahnsinn. Geschichte der abendländischen Psychopathologie. xii, 698 p. (Orbis Academicus) Freiburg/Munich: Alber, 1961.
Reviewed by E. Bastholm, *Lychnos*, 1962, 503-4.

LEUBUSCHER, Rudolf. Der Wahnsinn in den vier letzten Jahrhunderten. Nach dem Französischen des Calmeil bearbeitet. viii, 296 p. Halle: Schwetschke, 1848.
Reviewed by A.W.E. Th. Henschel, *Henschel's Janus*, 1848, 3: 819-20; reprinted Liepzig: Alfred Lorentz, 1931.

LEWIS, Nolan D. A short history of psychiatric achievement. 275 p. New York: Norton, 1941. [CB 61/418]

MARGETTS, Edward L. The concept of the unconscious in the history of medical psychology. *Psychiat.Quart.*, 1953, 27: 115-38.

MENNINGER, William C. Psychiatry in a troubled world: yesterday's war and today's challenge. xiv, 636 p. New York: Macmillan, 1948.
Reviewed by C.D. Leake, *Isis*, 1949, 40: 91-2.

ORGEL, S.Z. Psychiatry today and tomorrow. 514 p. New York: International Universities Press, 1946. [CB 72/278]

PREMUDA, Loris. Storia della medicina e psicologia. [Summary.] *Act.VIIIe Congr.Int.Hist.Sci.* (Florence, 1956), p. 782. Paris: Hermann, 1958.

SCHNECK, Jerome M. A history of psychiatry. ix, 196 p., ill. Springfield, Ill.: Charles C. Thomas; Oxford: Blackwell Scientific Publications, 1960.
For reviews *see* CB 87/574 and CB 89/513.

VEITH, Ilza. On the causes of insanity: some pre-Freudian views. *J.Amer.Med.Ass.*, 1961, 175: 156-7. [CB 88/562]

VEITH, Ilza. Psychiatric nosology: from Hippocrates to Kraepelin. *Amer.J.Psychiat.*, 1957, 114: 385-91.

WHITWELL, J.R. Analecta psychiatrica. xvi, 160 p. London: Lewis, 1946. [CB 71/125]

ZILBOORG, Gregory. A history of medical psychology. 606 p. New York: Norton, 1941.
Reviewed by M.F. Ashley Montagu, *Isis*, 1942, 34: 189-90.

OMc-bx

PARIS. EXPOSITION INTERNATIONALE DE L'HISTOIRE ET DE PROGRÈS DE LA PSYCHIATRIE. Exposition internationale de l'histoire et de progrès de la psychiatrie au Palais de la Découverte, 20 septembre-20 décembre, 1950. 43 p., ill., portr. (Congrès International de Psychiatrie, Paris, 1950) Paris: Palais de la Découverte, 1950.

OMda

RAY, Marie Beynon. Doctors of the mind. xii, 335 p. Boston: Little, Brown, 1942. [CB 63/279]

OMf

HARMS, Ernest. Historical considerations in the science of psychiatry. *Dis.Nerv.Syst.*, 1957, 18: 397-400, bibliogr.

HARMS, Ernest. A new approach to a history of psychiatry. *Proc.10th Int.Congr.Hist.Sci.* (Ithaca, 1962), (2), p. 1049-51. Paris: Hermann, 1964.

OMfd

HARMS, Ernest. The early historians of psychiatry. *Amer.J. Psychiat.*, 1957, 113: 749-52.

LAIGNEL-LAVASTINE, Maxime; VINCHON, Jean. Trois historiens français de la psychiatrie: Calmeil, Morel, Ulysse Trélat. *Compt.Rend.IVe Congr.Int.Hist.Med.* (Brussels, 1923), p. 92-5. Anvers: 1927.

OMgt

KANNER, Leo. The status of historical perspective in psychiatric instruction. *Bull.Hist.Med.*, 1955, 29: 329-36.

OMhd

MORA, George. Historiographic and cultural trends in psychiatry: a survey. *Bull.Hist.Med.*, 1961, 35: 26-36.

OMhf

LEIBBRAND, Werner. Die Stellung der Stoischen Affektenlehre innerhalb einer Geschichte der allgemeinen Psychopathologie. *Arch.Iberoamer.Hist.Med.*, 1956, 8: 33-40.

OMhj

GALDSTON, Iago. Descartes and modern psychiatric thought. *Isis*, 1944, 35: 118-28.

OMhm

LEIGH, Denis. Recurrent themes in the history of psychiatry. *Med.Hist.*, 1957, 1: 237-48, fig.

OMk philosophy and methodology

CAMPBELL, Charles MacFie. A present-day conception of mental disorders. 54 p. (Harvard Health Talks) Cambridge: Harvard University Press, 1924.

MAY, Rollo; ANGEL, Ernest; ELLENBERGER, Henri F.; ed. Existence, a new dimension in psychiatry and psychology. 445 p. New York: Basic Books, 1958.
Reviewed by Fritz Schmidl, *Isis*, 1959, 50: 271-2.

MIGNARD, Maurice. L'unité psychique et les troubles mentaux. xiv, 320 p. (Bibliothèque de Philosophie Contemporaine) Paris: Alcan, 1928. [CB 27/563]

OMmz relation with other subject fields

OMmzJB

GOLDSTEIN, Kurt. The organism. A holistic approach to biology derived from pathological data in man. xviii, 533 p. (American Psychology Series) New York: American Book Co., 1939.
Reviewed by M.F. Ashley Montagu, *Isis*, 1949, 32: 390-3.

OMmzMMzc

LANGE-EICHBAUM, Wilhelm. Genie, Irrsinn und Ruhm. Eine Pathographie des Genies. 5th ed. completely rev. by Wolfram Kurth. 628 p. Munich/Basel: Reinhardt, 1961.
Reviewed by M.D. Grmek, *Rev.Syn.*, 1963, 84: 560-3.
First published 1928 and reviewed by Ernst Kretschmer, *Deut.Lit.Zeitung*, 1928, 740-4.

OMmzQPztu

GRIGG, E.R.N. Historical and bibliographical review of tuberculosis in the mentally ill. *J.Hist.Med.*, 1955, 10: 58-108, 6 fig.

OMs relation with society

ZILBOORG, Gregory. Humanism in medicine and psychiatry. *Yale J.Biol.Med.*, 1944, 16: 217-30.

ZILBOORG, Gregory. Psychiatry as a social science. *Amer.J. Psychiat.*, 1943, 99: 585-8.

OMsc

BROMBERG, Walter. Some social aspects of the history of psychiatry. *Bull.Hist.Med.*, 1942, 11: 117-32.

NÄCKE, P. Die Psychiatrie als Hilfswissenschaft, auch in der Historik. Die Pathographien, insbesondere die von Jesus-Christus. *Neurol.Zentralbl.*, 1913, 32: 1074-80.

NORMAN, Hubert J. The relation of mental disorder to events in history. *Bull.Med.Libr.Ass.*, 1945, 33: 60-79.

OPLER, Marvin K., ed. Culture and mental health. vii, 533 p. New York: Macmillan, 1959.
Reviewed by Ilza Veith, *J.Hist.Med.*, 1961, 16: 194-5.

STIER, Ewald. Die Bedeutung der Psychiatrie für den Kulturfortschritt: Akademische Antrittsvorlesung. 40 p. Jena: Fischer, 1911.

VINAR, Joseph. La signification des épidémies psychiques dans l'histoire. *Festschrift zum 80. Geburtstag Max Neuburgers*, p. 470-2. Wien: Maudrich, 1948.

OMsd

CABANÈS, Auguste. Fous couronnés. 439 p., 56 ill. Paris: Albin Michel, [1914].
Medical biographies of Joanna, the mad, Philip II of Spain, Peter the Great, Peter III, Paul I of Russia, Christian VII of Denmark, Otto and Lewis II of Bavaria.

MERSEY, Paul R. L'amour de la mort chez les Habsbourg. Contribution à la pathologie historique. (Thèse) 86 p. Paris: Ollier-Henry, 1912.

OMst

POLLACK, S. Franz Alexander's observations on psychiatry and law. *Amer.J.Psychiat.*, 1964, 121: 458-64.

OMt relation with the humanities

DEL GRECO, Francesco. Il problema dei contributi della psichiatra alle scienze dello spirito. *Atti IV Congr.Int.Fil.* (Bologna, 1911), (3), p. 625-31. Genoa: Formiggini, 1914.

SIGERIST, Henry E. Psychopathologie und Kulturwissenschaft. *Abhandl.Neurol.Psychiat.Psychol.*, 1931, no. 61, 140-6.

OMtd

CHALUS, Paul. Psychiatrie et religion. *Rev.Syn.*, 1960, 81: 142-3.

GALDSTON, Iago. Psychiatry and religion. *J.Nerv.Ment.Dis.*, 1950, 112: 46-57.

OMth

HOLLANDER, Fernand d'. La folie d'Ajax. Essai médico-épique. *Bull.Acad.Méd.Belg.*, 1941, 6: 278-87.

MARTÍ IBÁÑEZ, Félix. Psicopatologia de los mitos y leyendas, y de los cuentos infantiles. *Rev.Clín.São Paulo*, 1947, 22: 41-59.

OMtq

BORN, Wolfgang. The art of the insane. *Ciba Symp.* (Summit, N.J.), 1946, 7: 202-36, ill., bibliogr.

TRAPP, Carl E.; TRAPP, Mary C. Psychiatry in art. *Ann.Med.Hist.*, 1936, 8: 511-17, 13 fig.

OMw in different countries

OMwb

AMERICAN PSYCHIATRIC ASSOCIATION. One hundred years of American psychiatry. xxvi, 649 p., 32 pl. New York: Columbia University Press, 1944.
Reviewed by J.B. de C.M. Saunders, *Isis*, 1947, 37: 114-18.

ARIETI, Silvano, ed. American handbook of psychiatry. 2 vol. xix, 999 p.; ix, 1003-2098 p., fig., bibliogr. New York: Basic Books, 1959. [CB 85/397]
Includes an essay by Nolan D.C. Lewis on "American psychiatry from its beginnings to World War II".
Reviewed by John F. Fulton, *J.Hist.Med.*, 1960, 15: 215-16.

DEUTSCH, Albert. The mentally ill in America. A history of their care and treatment from colonial times. With an introduction by William A. White. xvii, 530 p., 8 ill. New York: Doubleday, Doran, 1937.
Reviewed by C. Macfie Campbell, *Isis*, 1938, 29: 197-200.
Reprinted New York: Columbia University Press, 1946 and reviewed by G.W.T.H. Fleming, *Nature*, 1947, 160: 279.

LEMKAU, P.V. Notes on the development of mental hygiene in the Johns Hopkins School of Hygiene and Public Health. *Bull.Hist.Med.*, 1961, 35: 169-74.

OVERHOLSER, Winfred. Jacksonville 1847; psychiatry then and now. *J.Hist.Med.*, 1948, 3: 381-94.
Memorial address at Centennial of Jacksonville State Hospital, Illinois, July 26, 1947.

TUCKER, Beverley R. Development of psychiatry and neurology in Virginia. *Ann.Med.Hist.*, 1938, 10: 91-7, 2 fig.

WHITE, William Alanson. The autobiography of a purpose. With an introduction by Ray Lyman Wilbur. xix, 293 p. New York: Doubleday, Doran, 1938. [CB 56/362]

WHITE, William Alanson. Thoughts of a psychiatrist on the war and after. x, 28 p. Washington, D.C.: William Alanson White Psychiatric Foundation, 1942.
Reprint of a volume originally published in 1919.

OMwc-oq

SICCO, Antonio. Historia de la cátedra de clínica psiquiátrica de la Facultad de Medicina de Montevideo. *Rev.Argent.Hist.Med.*, 1944, 3: (2), 53-65.

OMwd-sk

HARMS, Ernest. Carl Gustav Jung - defender of Freud and the Jews. A chapter of European psychiatric history under the Nazi yoke. *Psychiat.Quart.*, Apr. 1946, 20: 199-230.

OMwe

BOLL, Theophilus E.M. May Sinclair and the medico-psychological clinic of London. *Proc.Amer.Phil.Soc.*, 1962, 106: 310-26.

HENDERSON, David Kennedy. The evolution of psychiatry in Scotland. viii, 300 p. Edinburgh/London: Livingstone, 1964. [CB 90/527]

OMwf

BARUK, H. [The important trends in the history of French psychiatry. (In Hebrew)] *Koroth*, 1963, 2: 122-6.

COURBON, Paul. La psychiatrie en Alsace à travers les âges. *Compt.Rend.IIe Congr.Int.Hist.Méd.* (Paris, 1921), p. 497-510. Évreux: Imprimerie Ch. Hérissey, 1922.

LAIGNEL-LAVASTINE, Maxime. L'histoire et les progrès de la psychiatrie au Palais de la Découverte. *Hist.Méd.*, 1951, no. 1, 43-8.

MOURGUE, Raoul. Note sur l'histoire de l'hygiène mentale en France. *Inform.Aliénistes Neurol.*, 1922, 17: 16-21.

OMwf-cj

SAUSSURE, Raymond de. Centennial of the *Annales Médico-psychologiques*. *Bull.Hist.Med.*, 1943, 14: 517-20.

OMwf-da

SEMELAIGNE, René. Les pionniers de la psychiatrie française, avant et après Pinel. 2 vol. 352 p.; 285 p. Paris: Baillière, 1930-32.
Reviewed by Pierre Brunet, *Archeion*, 1933, 15: 292-4.

OMwf-qd

RITTI, Ant. Histoire des travaux de la Société Médico-Psychologique et éloges de ses membres. 2 vol. 450, 510 p. Paris: Masson, 1914.

OMwg

GRUBER, Georg B. Zur Geschichte der Psychiatrie in Göttingen. *Sudhoffs Arch.*, 1956, 40: 345-71.

OMwg-da

KIRCHHOFF, Theodor. Deutsche Irrenärzte. Einzelbilder ihres Lebens und Wirkens. 2 vol. 282 p., ill.; 345 p., ill. Berlin: Springer, 1921-24.

OMwi

GIANNULI, Francesco. Il manicomio di S. Maria della Pietà e la scuola neuro-psichiatrica Romana. *Arch.Stor.Sci.*, 1924, 5: 272-83; 6: 214-21, 331-46.

OMwj

ULLERSPERGER, Johann Baptist. La historia de la psicología y de la psiquiatría en España desde los mas remotos tiempos hasta la actualidad. Prólogo, versión, notas y apendices por el Dr. V. Peset. xvi, 206 p. Madrid: Alhambra, 1954.
A translation into Spanish of work first published in German in Würzburg in 1871.
Reviewed by Jaime Pi-Sunyer, *J.Hist.Med.*, 1955, 10: 351-2; by George Mora, *ibid.*, 1958, 13: 279-81; by José M. López Piñero, *Arch.Iberoamer.Hist.Med.*, 1959, 11: 339-40.

OMwn

ZILBOORG, Gregory. Russian psychiatry - its historical and ideological background. *Bull.N.Y.Acad.Med.*, 1943, 19: 713-28.

ZILBOORG, Gregory. Some aspects of psychiatry in the U.S.S.R. *Amer.Rev.Sov.Med.*, 1944, 1: 564-75.

OMxx museums

FOÀ, Carlo. O museu de psiquiatria e de antropologia criminal organizado por Cesare Lombroso. *Essays in the History of Medicine presented to Prof. Arturo Castiglioni*, p. 62-4. Baltimore, Md.: Johns Hopkins Press, 1944.

RICH, Ida. *See* OMyNT

OMyNT HEALTH SERVICES

BREUKINK, H. Overzicht van opvatting en behandeling van geesteszieken in oude tijden. [Survey of opinions on the treatment of the mentally ill in olden times. (In Dutch)] *Bijdr.Gesch.Geneesk.*, 1921, 1: 243-61, 438-46; 1922, 2: 207-22; 1926, 6: 319-26, ill.

BRUNN, Walter von. Von Irrenpflege in alter Zeit. *Med.Mitt. Schering-Kahlbaum*, 1935, 7: 14-16, 2 fig.

DONINCK, A. van. Het gebruik der boeien bij de behandeling der krankzinnigen in vroeger tijd. [The use of shackles in the treatment of lunatics in former times. (In Dutch)] *Bijdr. Gesch.Geneesk.*, 1929, 9: 105-10.

HAISCH, Erich. Irrenpflege in alter Zeit. *Ciba Z.*, 1959, 8: 3142-72.
An illustrated account of the treatment of the mentally sick from prehistoric times to the end of the nineteenth century.

NORMAN, Hubert J. Some factors in the reform in the treatment of the insane. *Proc.Roy.Soc.Med.*, 1931, 24: 1068-74. [CB 34/526]

RICH, Ida. Fragmenter af sindssygevaesenets historie. [Fragments of the history of mental health services. (In Danish, with English summary)] *Tidsskr.for Sygeplejersker*, 1955, no. 6-7, 1-16. [CB 83/208]
A detailed account of the psychiatric department of the Medical-Historical Museum, University of Copenhagen.

WALSH, James J. Some chapters in the history of care for the insane. *Med.Life*, 1932, 39: 208-20.

OMyNTwe

KIRKPATRICK, T. Percy C. A note on the history of the care of the insane in Ireland. 43 p., 3 pl. Dublin: Ponsonby & Gibbs, 1931.

OMyNTwk

WEYDE, A.J. van der. De behandeling der krankzinnigen in vroeger tijd te Utrecht. [The treatment of the insane in earlier times in Utrecht. (In Dutch)] *Bijdr.Gesch.Geneesk.*, 1931, 11: 265-77, 3 fig.

OMyNW MENTAL HOSPITALS

PADOVANI, Emilio. Appunti di storia dell'assistenza ospedaliera degli infermi di mente con particolare riguardo a quella italiana. *Arch.Iberoamer.Hist.Med.*, 1957, 9: 383-94.

PAOLO, Amaldi. Vicende di nomi e di studi manicomiali. *Riv. Stor.Sci.*, 1926, 17: 49-70.

STANTON, A.H.; SCHWARTZ, M.S. The mental hospital. 492 p. New York: Basic Books, 1954.
Reviewed by Stephen Fleck, *J.Hist.Med.*, 1955, 10: 449-51.

OMyNWtq

FILASSIER, A; VINCHON, J. Les anciennes maisons de fous. Trois documents iconographiques. *Aesculape*, 1913, 3: 12-14, 3 fig.
Goya, Hogarth, Aubry.

OMyNWwb

RUSSELL, William L. The New York Hospital. A history of the psychiatric service, 1771-1936. xvii, 556 p., 35 ill. New York: Columbia University Press, 1945.
Reviewed by Erwin H. Ackerknecht, *Bull.Hist.Med.*, 1945, 18: 463-4; by William Brown, *Nature*, 1946, 157: 317-18.

STOUFFER, J.F. History of psychopathic department ("Old Blockley"). *Med.Life*, 1933, 40: 270-4.

OMyNWwe

BROCKBANK, Edward Mansfield. A short history of Cheadle Royal from its foundation in 1766 for the humane treatment of mental disease. ix, 76 p. Manchester: Sherratt & Hughes, 1934.

OMyNWwh

ISTVÁN, Zsako. [The origin of the first national lunatic asylum. (In Hungarian with summaries in Russian and German)] *Országos Orv. Könyvtar Közleményei*, 1956, no. 4, 84-107, 2 fig. [CB 83/207]

OMyNWwi

GIANNULI, Francesco. Il manicomio di S. Maria della Pietà e la scuola neuro-psichiatrica Romana. *Arch.Stor.Sci.*, 1924, 5: 272-83; 1925, 6: 214-21, 331-46.

OMyNWwj

NAVLET, J. Las enfermedades mentales en la prensa popular madrileña. *Arch.Iberoamer.Hist.Med.*, 1957, 9: 357-62.

OMyNWwk

BOURICIUS, L.G.N. Geschiedenis van het geneeskundig gesticht voor krankzinnigen. Het St. Joris Gasthuis en het daarmede verbonden geweest zijnde "Tuchthuis binnen Delft". Uitgegeven ter gelegenheid van het 250-jarig zelfstandig bestaan 1677-1927. [History of the medical institution for lunatics. The St. Joris Hospital and the "House of Correction in Delft" which was connected with it. Published on the occasion of the 250th year of independent existence, 1677-1927. (In Dutch)] Delft: 1927.
Reviewed in *Bijdr.Gesch.Geneesk.*, 1927, 7: 670.

DONINCK, A. van. Verblijf der krankzinnigen in het gemeentelijk gasthuis te Gheel, 1680-1860. [The quarters of the insane in the City Hospital of Gheel. (In Dutch)] *Bijdr. Gesch.Geneesk.*, 1929, 9: 157-67.

DONINCK, A. van. Verplegingsoord van geesteszieken te Gheel: de Ziekenkamer. [Nursing home for the mentally sick in Gheel: the sickroom. (In Dutch)] *Bijdr.Gesch.Geneesk.*, 1931. 11: 293-301, 5 fig.

HELLINGA, G. Het Amsterdamsche dol- of krankzinnigenhuis. [The mad house or asylum of Amsterdam. (In Dutch)] *Bijdr. Gesch.Geneesk.*, 1932, 12: 61-78, 7 fig.

LEEN, J. van. Geschiedenis van het pest- en dolhuis der gemeente Rotterdam. [History of the plague hospital and lunatic asylum of Rotterdam. (In Dutch)] 48 p., ill. Rotterdam: H.A. Kramers, 1934.
Reviewed by M.A. van Andel, *Bijdr.Gesch.Geneesk.*, 1935, 15: 17.

SCHADE, H. De geschiedenis van het krankzinnigengesticht Reynier van Arkel ('s-Hertogenbosch, 1442). [History of the Reynier van Arkel lunatic asylum. (In Dutch)] *Bijdr. Gesch.Geneesk.*, 1922, 2: 101-8.

OMP PSYCHOANALYSIS

OMPc general history

ALEXANDER, Franz. The scope of psychoanalysis, 1921-1961: selected papers. 594 p., bibliogr. New York: Basic Books, 1961.
Reviewed by E. Glover, *Psychoanal.Quart.*, 1964, 33: 97-109.

ALEXANDER, Franz; ROSS, Helen; ed. Dynamic psychiatry. xii, 578 p. Chicago: University of Chicago Press, 1952. [CB 79/184]

ALEXANDER, Franz; ROSS, Helen; ed. Twenty years of psychoanalysis. A symposium in celebration of the twentieth anniversary of the Chicago Institute for Psychoanalysis. 309 p. New York: W.W. Norton & Co., 1953.
Reviewed by Iago Galdston, *Isis*, 1955, 46: 78-80.

ANDERSSON, Ola. Studies in the prehistory of psychoanalysis. The etiology of psychoneuroses and some related themes in Sigmund Freud's scientific writings and letters, 1886-1896. viii, 237 p. (Studia Scientiae Paedagogicae Upsaliensia, 3) Uppsala: Norstedts, 1962.
Reviewed by Fritz Schmidl, *Isis*, 1964, 55: 467.

BLONDEL, Ch. La psychanalyse. xiv, 252 p. Paris: Felix Alcan, 1924. [CB 16/331]

CHALUS, Paul. Psychanalyse du lien interhumain. *Rev.Syn.*, 1960, 81: 154-5.

DORER, Maria. Historische Grundlagen der Psychoanalyse. 184 p. Leipzig: Meiner, 1932.

FENICHEL, Otto. The psychoanalytic theory of neurosis. x, 703 p. New York: Norton, 1945. [CB 74/392]
An exposition of the theory of Freudian psychoanalysis.

FREUD, Sigmund. Collected papers. 5 vol. 1. Early papers. On the history of the psycho-analytic movement. 359 p.; 2. Clinical papers. Papers on technique. 404 p.; 3. Case histories. 607 p.; 4. Papers on metapsychology. Papers on applied psycho-analysis. 508 p.; 5. Miscellaneous papers, 1888-1938. Ed. by James Strachey. 396 p. Reference bibliography in each volume. New York: Basic Books, 1959.

FREUD, Sigmund. The origins of psychoanalysis, letters to Wilhelm Fliess, drafts and notes: 1887-1902. Edited by Marie Bonaparte, Anna Freud, Ernst Kris. Authorized translation by Eric Mosbacher and James Strachey. Introduction by Ernst Kris. xi, 486 p. New York: Basic Books, 1954. [CB 80/197]

FREUD, Sigmund. An outline of psychoanalysis. 127 p. New York: Norton, 1949. [CB 74/392]

FREUD, Sigmund. The psychopathology of every-day life. Translation and introduction by A.A. Brill. vi, 342 p. London: 1914.

GALDSTON, Iago. The place of psychoanalysis in modern medicine. (Sigmund Freud Memorial Address) *Can.Psychiat.Ass.J.*, 1956, 1: 45-56.

HARDING, Mary Esther. Psychic energy: its source and goal. xii, 497 p. (Bollingen Series, 10) New York: Pantheon Books, 1948.
A representation of Jung's psychology.
2nd edition (1963) entitled "Psychic energy: its source and its transformation".
German translation "Das Geheimnis der Seele" (Zürich: Rhein-Verlag, 1948) reviewed by Walter Pagel, *Isis*, 1950, 41: 137.

HILGARD, Ernest R.; KUBIE, Lawrence S.; PUMPIAN-MINDLIN, E. Psychoanalysis as a science. x, 174 p., ill. (The Hixon Lectures on the Scientific Status of Psychoanalysis) New York: Basic Books, 1956. [CB 82/213]
The last of the three essays begins with a historical introduction.

JONES, Alfred Ernest. Free associations: memoirs of a psychoanalyst. 263 p., ill. New York: Basic Books, 1959.
Reviewed by W.G. Niederland, *J.Amer.Psychoanal.Ass.*, 1964, 12: 223-41.

McCLELLAND, David C. Freud and Hull: pioneers in scientific psychology. *Amer.Scient.*, 1957, 45: 101-13.

SALZMAN, Leon. Developments in psychoanalysis. 302 p. New York: Grune and Stratton, 1962.
Reviewed by R. Munroe, *Psychoanal.Quart.*, 1964, 33: 277-8.

SALZMAN, Leon. Psychoanalysis in evolution. *Compr.Psychiat.*, 1964, 5: 364-73.

THOMPSON, Clara; MULLAHY, Patrick. Psychoanalysis: evolution and development. xii, 252 p. London: Allen & Unwin, 1952.
French translation (Paris: Gallimard, 1956) reviewed by S. Colnort, *Rev.Hist.Sci.*, 1957, 10: 284-5.

WAELDER, Robert. Basic theory of psychoanalysis. 273 p., bibliogr. New York: International Universities Press, 1960.
Part 1: Historical development of psychoanalytic thought.

ZILBOORG, Gregory. Present trends in psychoanalytic theory and practice. *Bull.Menninger Clin.*, 1944, 8: 3-8.

OMPk philosophy and methodology

FEIGL, Herbert; SCRIVEN, Michael; ed. The foundations of science and the concepts of psychology and psychoanalysis. xiv, 346 p. (Minnesota Studies in the Philosophy of Science, 1) Minneapolis: University of Minnesota Press, 1956. [CB 82/197]

MONEY-KYRLE, R.E. Man's picture of his world. 190 p. London: Duckworth, 1961.
An essay in psycho-analysis for philosophers.
Reviewed by Brigid Brophy, *Brit.J.Phil.Sci.*, 1962, 13: 253-4.

OMPkd

FENICHEL, Otto. The psychoanalytic theory of neurosis. x, 703 p. New York: Norton, 1945. [CB 74/392]
An exposition of the theory of Freudian psychoanalysis.

MALMQUIST, Carl P. Problem of the nosology and theory construction. *Psychoanal.Rev.*, 1963, 50, 3-23.

WALLERSTEIN, R.S. The role of prediction in the theory building in psychoanalysis. *J.Amer.Psychoanal.Ass.*, 1964, 12: 675-91.

OMPke

BROWN, J.F. Freud and the scientific method. *Phil.Sci.*, 1934, 1: 323-37.

HORNEY, Karen. New ways in psychoanalysis. 313 p. New York: Norton, 1939. [CB 57/259]

MARIE, A. La psychanalyse et les nouvelles méthodes d'investigation de l'inconscient. Étude des problèmes de l'inconscient au point de vue du déterminisme psychologique et de la psychanalyse. 274 p. (Bibliothèque de Philosophie Contemporaine) Paris: Flammarion, 1928. [CB 26/244]

NEW YORK UNIVERSITY INSTITUTE OF PHILOSOPHY, 2nd, 1958. Psychoanalysis, scientific method and philosophy. A symposium ed. by Sidney Hook. xiii, 370 p. New York: New York University Press, 1959.
Reviewed by Max Teichmann, *Brit.J.Phil.Sci.*, 1962, 13: 56-65.

RAMZY, Ishak. Research aspects of psychoanalysis. *Psychoanal. Quart.*, 1963, 32: 58-76.

SCHMIDL, Fritz. Psychoanalysis as science. *J.Amer.Psychoanal. Ass.*, 1959, 7: 127-45. [CB 85/396]

WOLMAN, B. Evidence in psychoanalytic research. *J.Amer.Psychoanal.Ass.*, 1964, 12: 717-33.

OMPkt

TIEBOUT, Harry M., Jr. Tillich, existentialism, and psychoanalysis. *J.Phil.*, 1959, 56: 605-12.

OMPkv

WAELDER, Robert. Psychic determinism and the possibility of prediction. *Psychoanal. Quart.*, 1963, 32: 15-42.

OMPm/t special aspects

OMPmzPJ

BERG, Charles. The unconscious significance of hair. vi, 106 p. London: Allen and Unwin, 1951.
Reviewed by Clifford Allen, *Nature*, 1952, 169: 301.

OMPnh-be

FODOR, Nandor; GAYNOR, Frank; ed. Freud: dictionary of psychoanalysis. xii, 208 p. New York: Philosophical Library, 1950. [CB 77/380]
Definitions of Freud's psychoanalytic concepts, given in Freud's own words.

OMPs

GITELSON, Maxwell. On the present scientific and social position of psychoanalysis. *Int.J.Psychoanal.*, 1963, 44: 521-7.
Presidential address to the 23rd International Psychoanalytic Congress.

OMPs-br

Psychoanalytic Study of Society. 1- New York: International Universities Press, 1960-
Supersedes *Psychoanalysis and the Social Order*, vol. 1-5. New York: International Universities Press, 1947-58. [CB 74/393]

OMPsb

SCHICK, A. The cultural background of Adler's and Freud's work. *Amer.J.Psychotherap.*, 1964, 18: 7-24.

OMPsc

HORNEY, Karen. The neurotic personality of our time. 299 p. New York: Norton, 1937. [CB 51/287]

SCHMIDL, Fritz. Psychoanalysis and history. *Psychoanal.Quart.*, 1962, 31: 532-48.

OMPsd

BYCHOWSKI, Gustav. Dictators and disciples from Caesar to Stalin. 264 p. New York: International Universities Press, 1948. [CB 74/394]
A Freudian analysis of Julius Caesar, Oliver Cromwell, Robespierre, Hitler, and Stalin.

OMPse

FREUD, Sigmund. Das Interesse an der Psychoanalyse. 1. Das psychologische Interesse; 2. Ihr Interesse für die nicht psychologischen Wissenschaften. *Scientia*, 1913, 14: 240-50, 369-84.

OMPtc

FEUER, Lewis Samuel. Psychoanalysis and ethics. vi, 134 p. (American Lectures in Philosophy) Springfield, Ill.: Charles C. Thomas, 1955.
Reviewed by Chauncey D. Leake, *Isis*, 1956, 47: 192-4.

OMPth

GALDSTON, Iago. Sophocles contra Freud: a reassessment of the Oedipus complex. *Bull.N.Y.Acad.Med.*, 1954, 30: 803-17.

OMPw in different countries

OMPwb

OBERNDORF, C.P. A history of psychoanalysis in America. 280 p. New York: Grune and Stratton, 1953.
Reviewed by Iago Galdston, *Isis*, 1955, 46: 78-80.

WANGH, Martin, ed. Fruition of an idea. Fifty years of psychoanalysis in New York. In honor of the fiftieth anniversary of the New York Psychoanalytic Society, 1911-1961, and the thirtieth anniversary of the New York Psychoanalytic Institute, 1931-1961. 124 p., ill. New York: International Universities Press, 1962.
Reviewed by W.H. Gillespie, *Int.J.Psychoanal.*, 1963, 44: 118.

OMPwd-sk

HARMS, Ernest. Carl Gustav Jung - defender of Freud and the Jews. A chapter of European psychiatric history under the Nazi yoke. *Psychiat.Quart.*, Apr. 1946, 20: 199-230.

OMPws

RAMANA, C.V. On the early history and development of psychoanalysis in India. *J.Amer.Psychoanal.Ass.*, 1964, 12: 110-34.

OMPy applications

OMPyBY

MARTÍ IBÁÑEZ, Félix. Notas e informaciones psicoanalíticas. Psicoanálisis del ajedrez. *Rev.Psicoanál.*, 1944, 2: 187-97.
Psychoanalytic study of the game of chess.

OMPyJG

COURTÈS, F. Pour une psychanalyse de l'évolutionnisme. In: Hommage à Gaston Bachelard, p. 161-89. Paris: Presses Universitaires de France, 1957.

OMPyQZ

ZILBOORG, Gregory. The contribution of psychoanalysis to forensic medicine. *Int.J.Psychoanal.*, 1956, 37: 318-24.

OMPyYR

PFISTER, O. Psychoanalysis in the service of education, being an introduction to psychoanalysis. Authorized translation. xii, 176 p. London: H. Kimpton, 1922.
Translation of: Was bietet die Psychoanalyse dem Erzieher (Leipzig: Klinkhardt, 1917; 2nd ed. 1923). For French translation (Berne: 1921) *see* CB 13/303.

ON SPECIFIC MENTAL DISEASES

BAUMANN, E.D. De goddelijke waanzin. Vier studies over de ekstase. [The divine madness. Four studies of ecstasy. (In Dutch)] 113 p. Assen: Van Gorcum, 1932.
Reviewed by M.A. van Andel, *Bijdr.Gesch.Geneesk.*, 1933, 13: 170.

BESSIÈRE, Aug. Ch. René. Paranoia et psychose périodique. Essai historique, clinique, nosographique, médico-légal. 163 p. Paris: A. Leclerc, 1913.

BLÜHER, Hans. Traktat über die Heilkunde, insbesondere die Neurosenlehre. 123 p. Jena: Diederichs, 1926.
Reviewed by J.D. Achelis, *Mitt.Gesch.Med.*, 1926, 25: 248-9.

BREUER, Joseph; FREUD, Sigmund. Studies on hysteria. Transl. from the German and ed. by James Strachey, in collaboration with Anna Freud, assisted by A. Strachey and Alan Tyson. xxxi, 335 p., front., 1 pl. New York: Basic Books, 1957. [CB 83/204]
The importance of Freud's collaboration with Breuer is evaluated in the introduction.

COUCHOUD, P.L. Histoire de la manie jusqu'a Kraepelin. *Rev. Sci.Psychol.*, 1913, 1: 149-73. [CB 5/299]

EY, H. Introduction à l'étude actuelle de l'hystérie: historique et analyse du concept. *Rev.Prat.*, 1964, 14: 1417-31.

FENICHEL, Otto. The psychoanalytic theory of neurosis. x, 703 p. New York: Norton, 1945. [CB 74/392]
An exposition of the theory of Freudian psychoanalysis.

GALDSTON, Iago. Psychopathia intellectualis. *Pacific Spectator*, 1956, 10: 100-7.

GEDO, J.E.; *et al.* "Studies on hysteria": a methodological evaluation. *J.Amer.Psychoanal.Ass.*, 1964, 12: 734-51.
Apropos of Breuer and Freud's "Studies on hysteria", *see* above.

HARTOGS, Renatus. Application of Hartmann's ego psychology to the Schreber case. *Psychoanal.Rev.*, 1964, 51: no. 4, 22-8. [CB 90/611]

KAECH, René. Die somatische Auffassung der Hysterie; Die Hysterie seit Charcot. *Ciba Z.*, 1950, 10: 4406-25, ill.

LE SAVOUREUX, H. Quelques mots d'historique sur la démence précoce. *Rev.Psychiât.*, 1913, 17: 72-7.

LÓPEZ PIÑERO, José. Orígenes históricos del concepto de neurosis. 206 p. (Cuadernos Valencianos de Historia de la Medicina, 1) Valencia: Cátedra e Instituto de Historia de la Medicina, 1963.
Reviewed by L.S. Granjel, *Cuad.Hist.Med.Españ.*, 1963, 2: 246-7.

MARTINO, Ernesto de. La terra del rimorso. 439 p., ill. Milan: Il Saggiatore, 1961. [CB 89/512]
A study of the disease choreomania or tarantism.
Reviewed by H. Ellenberger, *Bull.Hist.Med.*, 1963, 37: 286-7.

MORA, George. An historical and sociopsychiatric appraisal of tarantism and its importance in the tradition of psychotherapy of mental disorders. *Bull.Hist.Med.*, 1963, 37: 417-39.

MOURGUE, Raoul. Etude critique sur l'évolution des idées relatives à la nature des hallucinations vraies. 67 p. (Thèse) Paris: Jouve, 1919. [CB 12/639]

OESTERREICH, Traugott Konstantin. Possession, demoniacal and other, among primitive races, in antiquity, the Middle Ages, and modern times. Authorized translation by D. Ibberson. xi, 400 p. London: Kegan Paul, 1930.
Translation of: Die Besessenheit (Langensalza: Wendt u. Klauwell, 1921) reviewed in *Deut.Lit.Zeitung*, 1922, 43: 967. For French translation (Paris: Payot, 1927) *see* CB 24/550.

ROMANO, John. Early contributions to the study of delirium tremens. *Ann.Med.Hist.*, 1941, 3: 128-39, 5 fig.

ROSEN, George. Psychopathology in the social process. (The Fielding H. Garrison Lecture) *Bull.Hist.Med.*, 1962, 36: 13-44.
Study of "dance frenzies, demonic possession, revival movements and similar so-called psychic epidemics" from the Middle Ages to the American Indian.

SCHREBER, Daniel G. Paul. Memoirs of my nervous illness. Translated, edited, with introduction, notes and discussion by Ida MacAlpine and Richard A. Hunter. 416 p., front., 5 pl. (Psychiatric Monograph Series, 1) London: Wm. Dawson & Sons, Ltd., 1955. [CB 83/275]
Reviewed by Henry R. Viets, *J.Hist.Med.*, 1956, 11: 117-18.

SEGUIN, Alberto. Historia de las psicosis paranoides. *Rev. Argent.Hist.Med.*, 1944, 3: no. 1, 73-8.

STAHL, William Harris. Moon madness. *Ann.Med.Hist., new ser.*, 1937, 9: 248-63, 1 fig.

STEYERTHAL, A. Altes und Neues über Hysterie. *Fortschr.Med.*, 1912, 30: 481-6, 524-9.

SUTTER, Paul. Lucifer, or the true story of the famous diabolic possession in Alsace. Compiled from original documents. Translated into English by Theophilus Borer. 94 p. London: Bouch, 1922.

TELLENBACH, Hubert. Melancholie. Zur Problemgeschichte, Typologie, Pathogenese, und Klinik. 184 p. Heidelberg: Springer, 1961.
Reviewed by H. Schipperges, *Sudhoffs Arch.*, 1962, 46: 282.

THOMÄ, Helmut. Anorexia nervosa. 352 p. Bern/Stuttgart: Huber & Klett, 1961.
Reviewed by H.W. Loewald, *Int.J.Psychoanal.*, 1963, 44: 110-12.

VAILLANT, George E. An historical review of the remitting schizophrenias. *J.Nerv.Ment.Dis.*, 1964, 138: 48-56.

VINCHON, Jean; GARÇON, Maurice. La genèse des idées modernes sur les démoniaques. *Aesculape*, 1926, 16: 211-15. [CB 22/294]

WYRSCH, Jakob. Zur Geschichte und Deutung der endogenen Psychosen. 98 p. Stuttgart: Thieme, 1956.

ZELMANOWITS, Joseph. A historical note on the simple dementing form of schizophrenia. *Proc.Roy.Soc.Med.*, 1953, 46: 931-3.

ONce-bv

GOLDFARB, William; DORSEN, Marilyn M. Annotated bibliography of childhood schizophrenia and related disorders as reported in the English language through 1954. vi, 170 p. New York: Basic Books, 1956.
An alphabetical list of 584 entries.

ONnh

PAPATHOMOPOULOS, Evangelos; KNOFF, William F. A historical footnote to the term catatonia. *Amer.J.Psychiat.*, 1964, 120: 817-19.

ONsc

CULLEREE, A. Les psychoses dans l'histoire. *Arch.Int.Neurol., 10th ser.*, 1912, 1: 229-49, 299-311, 359-70; 2: 23-36, 89-110, 162-77, 211-24.

ONsp

MILLER, Emanuel, ed. The neuroses in war. xii, 250 p. New York: Macmillan, 1940. [CB 61/380]

ONth

LIDZ, T. August Strindberg: A study of the relationship between his creativity and schizophrenia. *Int.J.Psychoanal.*, 1964, 45: 399-410.

ONu

DEICHERT, H. Die Geschichte des Hexenwahns. *Med.Klin.*, 1912, 8: 1765-6.

ONwg

STRANSKY, Erwin. Die Schizophrenie und die Wiener Psychiatrische Schule. *Festschrift zum 80. Geburtstag Max Neuburgers*, p. 444-6. Wien: Maudrich, 1948.

OO MENTAL DEFICIENCY

CRANEFIELD, Paul F. The discovery of cretinism. *Bull.Hist. Med.*, 1962, 36: 489-511.

KANNER, Leo. A history of the care and study of the mentally retarded. x, 150 p., ill. Springfield, Ill.: Charles C. Thomas, 1964.

NOWREY, Joseph E. A brief synopsis of mental deficiency. *Amer. J.Ment.Defic.*, 1945, 49: 319-57.

OQ OPHTHALMOLOGY

OQc general history

AMSLER, M.; ARRUGA, A.; BERG, F. Beiträge zur Geschichte der Ophthalmologie. 119 p. (Supplement to *Ophthalmologica*, vol. 134) Basel/New York: S. Karger, 1957.
Reviewed by Erich Weigelin, *Sudhoffs Arch.*, 1959, 43: 91-2.

ARRINGTON, George E. A history of ophthalmology. Foreword by Félix Martí-Ibáñez. xvii, 174 p., bibliogr. (MD Monographs on Medical History, 3) New York: MD Publications, Inc., 1959. [CB 85/397]
For reviews *see* CB 85/397 and CB 86/469.

CHANCE, Burton. Ophthalmology. xvii, 240 p., ill. (Clio Medica Series) New York: Hafner, 1962.
Paperback reprint of 1939 edition [CB 59/488]
Reviewed in *Proc.Roy.Soc.Med.*, 1963, 56: 60; by Arnold Sorsby, *Med.Hist.*, 1963, 7: 294.

FRIEDENWALD, Harry. The paths of progress of ophthalmology. (De Schweinitz lecture, Section on Ophthalmology of the College of Physicians of Philadelphia, November 19, 1941) *Arch.Ophthalmol.*, 1942, 27: 1047-96, 15 fig.

HOEVEN, J. van der. De ontwikkeling der oogheelkunde gedurende het tijdperk 1849-1924. [The development of ophthalmology during the period 1849-1924. (In Dutch)] *Bijdr. Gesch.Geneesk.*, 1924, 4: 156-65.

MASSON, -. Le globe oculaire. Histoire de son nom, de son anatomie et de sa physiologie en général. *Courr.Méd.*, 1912, 62: 407-8, 427.

MASSON, -. Problèmes et légendes en ophthalmologie. *France Méd.*, 1912, 1-3, 21-3.

ROSEN, George. The specialization of medicine with particular reference to ophthalmology. 94 p. New York: Froben Press, 1944.
Reviewed by Genevieve Miller, *Bull.Hist.Med.*, 1946, 19: 125-7.

WALLS, Gordon L. The history of the human eye. *Ciba Symp.*, 1943, 5: 1586-606. fig.

OQc-bv

SNYDER, Charles. A bibliography of the history of ophthalmology. 1952 through 1954. *Arch.Ophthalmol.*, 1956, 55: 397-407; 1955 and 1956. *Ibid.*, 1958, 59: 885-94; 1957 and 1958. *Ibid.*, 1960, 63: 330-46; 1959 and 1960. *Ibid.*, 1961, 66: 739-59; 1961 and 1962. *Ibid.*, 1964, 71: 267-83.

OQcm

KRONFELD, Peter C.; McHUGH, Gladys; POLYAK, Stephen L. The human eye in anatomical transparencies. Explanatory text. Anatomical transparencies. Historical appendix. xi, 99 p., ill. Rochester, N.Y.: Bausch & Lomb, 1943. [CB 70/265]

SUDHOFF, Karl. Augendurchschnittsbilder aus Abendland und Morgenland. *Arch.Gesch.Med.*, 1914, 8: 1-21, 2 pl.

OQnh

REVILLET, L. A propos du globe oculaire et de l'histoire de son nom. *France Méd.*, 1912, 371.

OQpw

FUCHS, A. Über die Beziehungen der Augenheilkunde zwischen Frankreich und Österreich. *Festschrift zum 80. Geburtstag Max Neuburgers*, p. 170-80. Wien: Maudrich, 1948.

OQu

ROLLESTON, J.D. Ophthalmic folk-lore. *Brit.J.Ophthalmol.*, 1942, 26: 481-502.

OQw in different countries

OQwb-qg

BURIAN, Hermann M. The history of the Dartmouth Eye Institute. *Arch.Ophthalmol.*, 1948, 40: 163-75.

OQwc

ESPINO, José Manuel. Historia de la oftalmología en Venezuela hasta 1955. *Rev.Soc.Venezolana Hist.Med.*, 1954, 2: 237-468, portr., ill., bibliogr. [CB 81/278]

OQwe

JAMES, R. Rutson. Studies in the history of ophthalmology in England prior to the year 1800. x, 255 p., 9 pl. Cambridge University Press, 1933.

OQwf

ONFRAY, René. L'ophtalmologie française au XXe siècle. Les progrès de l'enseignement de la clinique et de la thérapeutique. viii, 237 p. Paris: Masson, 1959.
Reviewed by P. Huard, *Rev.Hist.Sci.*, 1960, 13: 278-9; by L. Glesinger, *Arch.Int.Hist.Sci.*, 1960, 13: 176-7.

OQwg-nh

PERGENS, Ed. Ueber ältere niederdeutsche Benennungen zur Anatomie, Physiologie und Pathologie der Augen. *Janus*, 1913, 18: 423-38.

OQwg-oq

HELFREICH, Friedrich. Geschichte der Augenheilkunde an der Universität Würzburg. *Verhandl.Phys.Med.Ges.Würzb.*, 1912, 41: 171-90.

OQwh

BARTÓK, Imre. Geschichte der ungarischen Augenheilkunde. *Festschrift zum 80. Geburtstag Max Neuburgers*, p. 14-20. Wien: Maudrich, 1948.

BARTÓK, Imre. A magyar szemészet története. [A history of Hungarian ophthalmology. (In Hungarian)] 212 p., 59 fig. Budapest: Akadémiai Kiadó, 1954.
Reviewed by C.K., *Arch.Int.Hist.Sci.*, 1959, 12: 202-3.

BEDNARSKI, Adam. Historya okulistyki w Polsce w wieku XIII-XVIII. [History of ophthalmology in Poland from the 13th to the 18th century. (In Polish)] 116 p. (*Arch.Tow.Nauk. Lwow*, sect. 3, 4: part 11) Lwow: 1928.
Reviewed by Josef Fritz, *Mitt.Gesch.Med.*, 1929, 28: 110.

OQwh-oq

GRÓSZ, Emil von. Geschichte der Augenklinik Nr. 1 der königl. ungar. Universität in Budapest. Festschrift *zur Feier seines 60. Geburtstages Max Neuburger gewidmet*, p. 141-3. Wien: Verlag des Fest-Komitees, 1928.

OQwi

OVIO, Giuseppe. L'oftalmologia in Italia. 104 p., ill. (*Acta Med.Ital.*, anno 6, fasc. 2) Milano: 1940.
Reviewed by L. Castaldi, *Riv.Stor.Sci.*, 1941, 32: 107.

SCALINCI, Noè. Priorità e rivendicazioni italiane nel campo della oftalmologia. 24 p. Roma: Soc. per il Progresso delle Scienze, 1940.
Reviewed by L. Castaldi, *Riv.Stor.Sci.*, 1941, 32: 108.

OQwi-o

ALBERTOTTI, G. Note intorno all' insegnamento dell' oculistica in Italia (1785-1912). *Clin.Oculist.*, 1912, 12: 953-60.

OQwk-qd

APPELMANS, M. La Société Belge d'Ophthalmologie. *Mouvement Sci.Belg.*, 1961, 5: 330-2.

OQwm

BERG, Fredrik. Bidrag till oftalmologiens äldre historia i Sverige. [Contribution to the early history of ophthalmology in Sweden. (In Swedish)] 300 p., ill. (Lychnos-bibliotek, 16) Uppsala: Almquist & Wiksell, 1958.
Reviewed by K.G. Ploman, *Lychnos*, 1957-58, 504-6.

OQwp

ÜNVER, A. Süheyl; AYBERK, Nuri Fehmi. Türk göz hekimliği tarihine ait notlar. [Notes on the history of ophthalmology in Turkey. (In Turkish)] 90 p. Istanbul: Kadir Basimevi, 1946.
Reviewed by A. Mazaheri, *Arch.Int.Hist.Sci.*, 1950, 3: 466-7.

OQwq

OSBORNE, Alfred. Ophthalmic development in Egypt during the last 25 years. *Bull.Ophthalmol.Soc.Egypt*, 1927, 20: 53-61.

OQwt

PI, H.T. Western ophthalmology in China. *Nat.Med.J.China*, 1931, 17: 120-30, 4 fig.

OQyNT HEALTH SERVICES

VILLEY, Pierre. L'aveugle dans le monde des voyants. Essai de sociologie. 336 p. (Bibliothèque de Philosophie Scientifique) Paris: Flammarion, 1927. [CB 22/295]

WAGG, Henry John; THOMAS, Mary G. A chronological survey of work for the blind (with an appendix on the prevention of blindness, and a bibliography). From the earliest records up to the year 1920. xii, 235 p. London: Pitman, 1932.

OQyNW HOSPITALS

OQyNWwb

POSEY, William Campbell; BROWN, Samuel Horton. The Wills Hospital of Philadelphia. The influence of European and British ophthalmology upon it and the part it played in the last 100 years in developing ophthalmology in America. x, 340 p., ill., pl., portr. Philadelphia, Pa.: Lippincott, 1931.
Reviewed in *Ann.Med.Hist.*, 1932, 4: 105-7.

OQyNWwe

SORSBY, Arnold. The Royal Eye Hospital, 1857-1957. 24 p., ill. London: The Hospital, 1957.
Reviewed by M. Klein, *Med.Hist.*, 1958, 2: 234-5.

OQyNWwh

ARLT, C.F. Die Anstalten für Blinde und Augenkranke in Prag. Historische Skizze. 30 p., portr. Prag: 1846.
Reviewed by L. Spengler, *Henschel's Janus*, 1846, 1: 702-4; reprinted Leipzig: Alfred Lorentz, 1931.

OQzv VISION

BOUMA, P.J. Physical aspects of colour, an introduction to the scientific study of colour stimuli and colour sensations. 312 p., 113 fig. Eindhoven: N.V. Philips Gloeilampenfabrieken; New York: Elsevier, 1948. [CB 79/184]
Transl. of: Kleuren en kleurindrukken. 1946.

HECHT, Selig; SHLAER, Simon; PIRENNE, Maurice Henri. Energy, quanta, and vision. *J.Gen.Physiol.*, 1942, 25: 819-40, 7 fig.

LAUBER, H. Zur Geschichte der Untersuchung des Gesichtsfeldes. *Festschrift zur Feier seines 60. Geburtstags Max Neuburger gewidmet*, p. 219-24. Wien: Verlag des Fest Komitees, 1928.

MÜLLER, Georg Elias. Ueber die Farbenempfindungen. ix, 214 p. (Psychologische Untersuchungen, 2) Leipzig: Barth, 1930.

PIÉRON, Henri. La connaissance sensorielle et les problèmes de la vision. 91 p. (Actualités Scientifiques et Industrielles, 377) Paris: Hermann, 1936.

PIRENNE, M.H. Vision and the eye. xx, 187 p., 4 pl., 99 fig. (Frontiers of Science Series) London: Pilot Press, 1948. [CB 73/177]
The author's interest in the historical aspect of his subject appears many times in the text and illustrations.

POLYAK, Stephen L. The retina. x, 607 p., 100 pl. Chicago: University of Chicago Press, 1941.
Reviewed by Charles A. Kofoid, *Isis*, 1943, 34: 234-5.

RAYLEIGH, Robert John Strutt, *4th baron*. Vision in nature and vision aided by science; science and warfare. *Science*, 1938, 88: 175-81, 204-8.

ROMAINS, Jules. Eyeless sight: a study of extraretinal vision and the paroptic sense. Translated by C.K. Ogden. x, 228 p. London/New York: Putnam, 1924.
Translation of: La vision extra-rétinienne et le sens paroptique. Paris: 1921.

RUNGE, I. Grundlagen des Farbensehens. *Licht Lampe*, 1927, no. 11, 361-3.

SIEGEL, Rudolph E. Theories of vision and color perception of Empedocles and Democritus; some similarities to the modern approach. *Bull.Hist.Med.*, 1959, 33: 145-59.

STILES, W.S. Colour vision: a retrospect. *Endeavour*, 1952, 11: 33-40, 17 fig.

STUDNITZ, G. von. Grundvorgänge des Sehens; 100 Jahre Sehstoffe. *Nova Acta Leopoldina*, 1940, 9: 51-73.
Reviewed by R. Zaunick, *Mitt.Gesch.Med.*, 1941-42, 40: 87.

TROLAND, Leonard Thompson. The present status of visual science. 120 p. (*Bull.Nat.Res.Counc.*, 5; pt. 2, no. 27) Washington, D.C.: 1922.
Reviewed by H. Hartridge, *Nature*, 1923, 112: 532-3.

OR EYE DISORDERS AND DISEASES

for eye surgery *see* RCF
for special remedies *see* RIyOR, RPyOR, RQyOR, RRyOR

BILANCIONI, Guglielmo. Alcuni spunti sulla storia del nistagmo. *Atti Clin.Oto-rino-laringoiatrica Univ.Roma*, 1930, 28: 239-63, ill. Also in *Boll.Ist.Stor.Ital.Arte Sanit.*, 1931, 11: 1-14.

CUMSTON, Charles Greene. A brief historical summary of the treatment of trachoma with special reference to the Arabian school and the writing of Ali ibn-el-Aïssa (Jesu Hali). *Ann.Med.Hist.*, 1921, 3: 244-51.

DUNPHY, E.B. The story of retinoblastoma. *Trans.Amer.Acad. Ophthalmol.Oto-laryngol.*, 1964, 68: 249-64.

FARRELL, Gabriel. The story of blindness. viii, 270 p. Cambridge, Mass.: Harvard University Press; London: Oxford University Press, 1956.
Reviewed by Arnold Sorsby, *Med.Hist.*, 1957, 1: 81-2.

LAUGHLIN, Robert Clark. Glaucoma, a historical essay. *Bull. Inst.Hist.Med.*, 1934, 2: 141-63.

MEYERHOF, Max. Neues zur Geschichte des Begriffes Pannus. *Arch.Gesch.Med.*, 1927, 19: 240-52. [CB 23/269]

MEYERHOF, Max. Remarks on trachoma healing without visible scar formation. *Bull.Ophthalmol.Soc.Egypt*, 1937, 30: 145-50.

PRITIKIN, Roland I. History of the introduction to the management of mass eye casualties resulting from radiation trauma. (Synopsis) *Act.VIIIe Congr.Int.Hist.Sci.* (Florence, 1956), p. 824-9. Paris: Hermann, 1958.

PRITIKIN, Roland I. History of treatment of hereditary and congenital eye condition. *Act.VIIIe Congr.Int.Hist.Sci.* (Florence, 1956), p. 830-8. Paris: Hermann, 1958.

TERSON, A. Les premières mentions de l'hypertonie de l'oeil dans le glaucome. *Bull.Soc.Franç.Hist.Méd.*, 1925, 19: 53-62.

ORnh

BEHRE, Jan; ÖBERG, Lars. Glaucoma. The development of a medical term from Homer to Graefe. *Lychnos*, 1962, 164-83.

EBSTEIN, Erich. Zur Etymologie der Nyktalopie und Hemeralopie. *Mitt.Gesch.Med.*, 1912, 11: 443-5.

ORwk-nh

PERGENS, Ed. Over het "stael", eene oude Nederduitsche benaming der Cataracte. [On the word "stael", an old Dutch name of cataract. (In Dutch)] *Handel.16e Vlaam.Natuur. Geneesk.Congr.* (Leuven, 1912), (1), p. 318-19. Gent: Ad. Hoste, 1912.

ORyQD DIAGNOSIS

ORyQDxj

PERGENS, E. Optotypen in oostersche talen. [Sight-testing types in oriental languages. (In Dutch)] *Handel.16e Vlaam. Natuur- Geneesk.Congr.* (Leuven, 1912), p. 303-17, ill. Gent: Ad. Hoste, 1912.

ORyQDxk

KEYS, Thomas Edward. Contributions leading to the invention of the ophthalmoscope. *Proc.Staff Meetings Mayo Clin.*, 1951, 26: 209-16, 2 fig.

RUCKER, Charles Wilbur. The development of the ophthalmoscope and of knowledge of the interior of the eye. *Proc.Staff Meetings Mayo Clin.*, 1951, 26: 217-21, 3 fig.

RUCKER, Charles Wilbur; KEYS, Thomas Edward. The atlases of ophthalmoscopy, 1850-1950. 33 p., front. [n.p.]: 1950.
Exhibit in commemoration of the centennial of Helmholtz's invention of the ophthalmoscope prepared for the section on ophthalmology, A.M.A., San Francisco, June 1950.

ORzs SPECTACLES

AMES, A.; GLIDDON, Gordon H.; OGLE, Kenneth N. Lenses for changing the size and shape of dioptric images. *Ann.Distinguished Serv.Found.Optom.*, 1932, 1: 61-70.

DOESSCHATE, G. ten. Some historical notes on spectacles and on beryllus. *Brit.J.Ophthalmol.*, November 1946, 660-4.

DRAKE, Stillman. Note on the invention of eyeglasses. *Isis*, 1961, 52: 95-6.

GORDON, Benjamin L. A short history of spectacles. *J.Med. Soc.N.J.*, 1951, 48: 3-8.

GREEFF, Richard. Die Erfindung der Augengläser; kulturgeschichtliche Darstellungen nach urkundlichen Quellen. 120 p., 10 pl. (Optische Bücherei, 1) Berlin: Ehrlich, 1921.

JOLY, Jean-Paul. Petite histoire des lunettes. *Rev.Deux Mondes*, 1954, 7: 474-86.

KONOPKA, S. The history of an invention. A treatise on spectacles. *Arch.Hist.Med.* (Warszawa), 1959, 22: 413-21.

ROHR, Moritz von. Aus der Geschichte der Brille, mit besonderer Berücksichtigung der auf der Greeffschen beruhenden Jenaischen Sammlung. *Beitr.Gesch.Tech.Ind.*, 1927, 17: 30-50, 20 fig.; 1928, 18: 95-117, 34 fig. [CB 27/546]

ROHR, Moritz von. Die Brille als optisches Instrument. 3rd ed. xiv, 254 p., 112 fig. (Handbücher der gesamten Augenheilkunde) Berlin: Springer, 1921.
First published 1911. The last part is historical and the text is full of historical references.

ROHR, Moritz von; STEGMANN, K. Zur Entwicklung des Gestells von Brille und Augenglas. *Opt.Rundsch.*, 1933, 24: 551-5, 576-9, 602-4, 625-30, 31 fig.

RONCHI, Vasco. Sull'invenzione degli occhiali. *Atti Fond. Ronchi*, 1956, 11: 474-80.

ROSEN, Edward. The invention of eyeglasses. *J.Hist.Med.*, 1956, 11: 13-46, 183-218.
Reviewed by Vasco Ronchi, *Arch.Int.Hist.Sci.*, 1956, 9: 252-3.

RUCKER, C.W. The invention of eyeglasses. *Proc.Mayo Clin.*, 1960, 35: 209-16.

SCHNELL, Ivar. Glasögonens historia. [History of spectacles. (In Swedish)] 147 p., 47 ill. Karlshamn: Sveriges Läkarförbunds Förlag, 1943.
Reviewed by Frederik Berg, *Lychnos*, 1943, 424-5.

WADE, Ella N. Our old spectacles. *Trans.Coll.Physicians Phila.*, 1952, 19: 130-4.
Apropos of the spectacles kept in the Mütter Museum, College of Physicians, Philadelphia.

ORzs-c-bv

ROHR, Moritz von. Die Entwicklung der Brille. [1] - 10. *Naturwissenschaften*, 1913, 1: 676-7; 1914, 2: 616-17; 1915, 3: 294, 663-4; 1917, 5: 202-4; 1919, 7: 209-11; 1920, 8: 533-4; 1921, 9: 98-9; 1922, 10: 284-6; 1923, 11: 249-52.
A survey of the literature.

ORzs-cm-bx

KATALOG einer Bilderausstellung zur Geschichte der Brille. Im Auftrage des Vorstandes des 13. Internationalen Ophthalmologischen Kongresses zu Amsterdam zusammengestellt von R. Greeff, *et al.* 266 p., fig. Amsterdam: d'Oliveira, 1929.

ORzs-tq

WEVE, H. Over brillenafbeeldingen in de plastische kunst. [Representations of spectacles in sculpture. (In Dutch)] *Bijdr.Gesch.Geneesk.*, 1927, 7: 558-70, 6 fig.

ORzs-wk

WEVE, H. Zur Geschichte der Brille in den Niederlanden. *VIe Congr.Int.Hist.Méd.* (Leyde-Amsterdam, 1927), p. 127-32 6 fig. Anvers: De Vlijt, 1929.

OS OTOLOGY

see also OU OTO-RHINO-LARYNGOLOGY

BÉKÉSY, Georg von; ROSENBLITH, Walter A. The early history of hearing - observations and theories. *J.Acoust.Soc.Amer.*, 1948, 20: 727-48, 19 fig.

O'MALLEY, Charles Donald; CLARKE, E. The discovery of the auditory ossicles. *Bull.Hist.Med.*, 1961, 35: 419-41.

POLITZER, Adam. Geschichte der Ohrenheilkunde. 2 vol. 1. Von den ersten Anfängen bis zur Mitte des neunzehnten Jahrhunderts. xiii, 467 p.; 2. 1850-1911, unter Mitwirkung bewährter Fachkräfte. xvi, 484 p., ill. Stuttgart: F. Enke, 1907-13.

POLITZER, Adam. Rückblick auf den Fortschritt der Otologie im letzten Halbjahrhundert. *Wiener Med.Wochenschr.*, 1913, 63: 2522-7.

ROBINSON, Victor. Chronology of otology. *Bull.Hist.Med.*, 1941, 10: 199-208.

WILKINSON, George; GRAY, Albert A. The mechanism of the cochlea: a restatement of the resonance theory of hearing. xx, 253 p., 4 pl. London: Macmillan, 1924.

WODAK, Ernst. Kurze Geschichte der Vestibularisforschung. 162 p., 8 ill. Stuttgart: Thieme, 1956.

OStt

LE POUTOUNEL, Nestor. L'audition et la musique. *La Nature*, 1914, 42: 1er sem., 445-8, 5 fig. [CB 6/476]

OSu

ROLLESTON, J.D. Otology and folk-lore. *J.Laryngol.*, 1942, 57: 311-18.

OSwf

CHAUVEAU, Claude. Contribution à l'étude de l'otologie française au cours de ces cinquante dernières années. Vol. 1. cviii, 455 p. Paris: J.-B. Baillière, 1913.

OSwj

PINA GUIMARÃES, Luis José de. Observações sobre a morfologia da orelha nos Portugueses. *Arq.Anat.Antropol.*, 1931, 14: 91-105, 2 fig., 8 tables.

OT EAR DISORDERS AND DISEASES

for ear surgery *see* RCH

BARAJAS-GARCÍA-ANSORENA, José Maria. El tratamiento de la sordera a través de la historia de la medicina. *Arch.Iberoamer.Hist.Med.*, 1957, 9: 53-9.

BÁRÁNY, Robert. Der Schwindel und seine Beziehungen zum Bogengangapparat des inneren Ohrs. Bogengangapparat und Kleinhirn. (Historische Darstellung. Eigene Untersuchungen) *Naturwissenschaften*, 1913, 1: 396-401, 425-8.

HEIMANN, T. [A short history of the treatment of ear diseases. (In Polish)] xvi, 208 p. Warsaw: 1912.

SALINGRE, Eric. Drag ur öronläkekonstens historia - från Vesalius till Hans Wilhelm Meyer. [Excerpts from the history of the treatment of ear diseases from Vesalius to Meyer.] *Medicinhistorisk Årsbok*, 1959, 7 p. (separate pagination).

WERNER, Hans. Die Taubstummheit. Das medizinische Problem der Taubheit. Neuere medizinische Forschungen über die Taubstummheit. Das pädagogische Problem der Stummheit. Moderne Taubstummenpädagogik. Notizen zum Thema. *Ciba Z.*, 1956, 7: 2678-712, ill.

OTmzOL relation with NERVOUS DISEASES

MENDELSON, J.H.; SIGER, L.; KUBZANSKY, P.E. The brain and disorders of communication. The language of signs and symbolic behavior of the deaf. *Res.Publ.Ass.Res.Nerv.Ment.Dis.*, 1964, 42: 151-70.

OTyQD DIAGNOSIS

FELDMANN, Harold. Die geschichtliche Entwicklung der Hoerpruefungsmethoden. 92 p., 40 ill. (Zwanglose Abhandlungen aus dem Gebiet der Hals-Nasen-Ohren Heilkunde, 5) Stuttgart: Thieme, 1960.

ROBINSON, Victor. Examination in the history of otology. *Laryngoscope*, 1941, 51: 315-29.

OU OTO-RHINO-LARYNGOLOGY

see also OS OTOLOGY

BILANCIONI, Guglielmo. Sulla storia dei nervi della voce. *Arch.Stor.Sci.*, 1925, 6: 18-27.

BRESGEN, Maximilian. Die Nasenheilkunde in den letzten fünfzig Jahren. *Arch.Gesch.Naturwiss.Tech.*, 1913, 6: 12-19.

BURGER, H. De keel-neus-oorheelkunde in de laatste vijf-enzeventig jaren. [Otorhinolaryngology in the last seventy five years. (In Dutch)] *Bijdr.Gesch.Geneesk.*, 1924, 4: 166-70.

CATTANEO, L. Le basi morfologiche dell'olfatto nelle conoscenze antiche e nelle attuali. *Rass.Med.Sarda*, 1964, 67: 151-70.

HENNING, Hans. Der Geruch. Ein Handbuch für die Gebiete der Psychologie, Physiologie, Zoologie, Botanik, Chemie, Physik, Neurologie, Ethnologie, Sprachwissenschaft, Literatur, Ästhetik und Kulturgeschichte. 2nd rev. ed. 434 p., 14 fig. Leipzig: Barth, 1924. [CB 26/242]

JAMES, J.A. The rise of otorhinolaryngology. *Bristol Med. Chir.J.*, 1964, 79: 26-34.

KASSEL, Karl. Geschichte der Nasenheilkunde von ihren Anfängen bis zum 18. Jahrhundert. Vol. 1. 476 p. Würzburg: Kabitzsch, 1914.

STEVENSON, R. Scott; GUTHRIE, Douglas. A history of otolaryngology. vii, 155 p. Baltimore: Williams & Wilkins, 1949.

THOMSON, St. Clair. The historical evolution of otolaryngology. *Proc.Roy.Soc.Med.*, 1931, 24: 1074-80. [CB 34/527]

WALSH, James J. Two chapters in the history of laryngology and rhinology. *Ann.Med.Hist.*, 1919, 2: 23-33. [CB 8/365]

WESSELY, E.A. Zur Geschichte der Entstehung der Laryngologie. *Festschrift zum 80. Geburtstag Max Neuburgers*, p. 473-7. Wien: Maudrich, 1948.

OUwb

BRYAN, Joseph Hammond. The history of laryngology and rhinology and the influence of America in the development of this specialty. *Ann.Med.Hist.*, 1933, 5: 151-70, 13 fig.

KAGAN, Solomon R. Jacob da Silva Solis-Cohen (1838-1927). *Med.Life*, 1937, 44: 291-313, portr., bibliogr.
Biography of the founder of laryngology in the U.S.A.

OUwf

AUBRY, Maurice. Histoire de l'oto-rhinolaryngologie parisienne. *Hist.Méd.*, 1960, 10: 3-7.

OUwg

KINDLER, W.; KREBS, B.; HOMM, G. Die Geschichte der Otorhino-laryngologie in Berlin. viii, 98 p., ill. Stuttgart: Thieme, 1956.
Reviewed by G. Aschan, *Lychnos*, 1957-58, 497; by Douglas Guthrie, *J.Hist.Med.*, 1959, 14: 126-7.

OUwo

BIRMAN-BERA, -. L'histoire de l'otorhinolaryngologie de Roumanie. *Festschrift zum 80. Geburtstag Max Neuburgers*. p. 50-3. Wien: Maudrich, 1948

OV NOSE AND THROAT: DISORDERS AND DISEASES

see also QPzdi diphtheria

for nose and throat surgery *see* RCJ

LECLERC, Henri. Les sternutatoires à travers les âges. *Janus*, 1916, 21: 254-62.

OVu

KANNER, Leo. Contemporary folk-treatment of sternutation. *Bull.Hist.Med.*, 1942, 11: 273-91.

KANNER, Leo. Superstitions connected with sneezing. *Med. Life*, 1931, 38: 549-75. [CB 33/406]

SAINTYVES, P. L'éternuement et le bâillement dans la magie, l'ethnographie et le folklore médical. 146 p. Paris: Nourry, 1921.

OW RESPIRATORY SYSTEM

ARNETT, John H. The vital capacity of the lungs. Early observations and instruments. *Med.Life*, 1936, 43: 3-6, 4 fig.

DEMEOCQ, André. Physiologie de la plongée. 20 p. (Les Conférences du Palais de la Découverte, 1 juin 1950) Paris: Université de Paris, 1951.
Historical lecture to accompany the exhibition: L'oeuvre scientifique de Blaise Pascal et trois siècles après.

HALDANE, John Scott. Respiration. xviii, 427 p. (Silliman Memorial Lectures) New Haven: Yale University Press, 1922.

KRAMMER, Ludwig. Streit und Widerstreit um die Beweiskraft der Lungenschwimmprobe in geschichtlicher Darstellung. *Sudhoffs Arch.*, 1933, 26: 253-76.

KROGH, August. The comparative physiology of respiratory mechanisms. vii, 172 p. Philadelphia: University of Pennsylvania Press, 1941. [CB 61/410]

MILLER, William Snow. The lung. xiv, 209 p., 152 ill. Springfield, Ill.: Charles C. Thomas, 1937. [CB 50/398]
A special chapter is devoted to the historical development of our knowledge of lung structure.

OLMSTED, J.M.D. Historical note on the *noeud vital* or respiratory center. *Bull.Hist.Med.*, 1944, 16: 343-50.

SEWALL, Henry. Visualizing medical history. The physiology of respiration. *Ann.Med.Hist.*, 1927, 9: 76-90.

OWdaj

TAYLOR, Clara M. The discovery of the nature of the air and of its changes during breathing. 84 p., 8 ill. (Classics of Scientific Method) London: Bell, 1923. [CB 17/599]

OWxk

OESPER, Peter. The history of the Warburg apparatus. *J.Chem. Educ.*, 1964, 41: 294-6.

OWyJM

FINLAYSON, R. The vicissitudes of sputum cytology. *Med.Hist.*, 1958, 2: 24-35.

OX RESPIRATORY DISORDERS AND DISEASES

see also QM allergic diseases
QPztu tuberculosis
QUyOX industrial diseases

for lung surgery *see* RCG
artificial respiration *see* RJyOX

BAFFONI, Aroldo. Storia delle pleuriti da Ippocrate a Laennec. 177 p., 5 ill. Rome: 1947.
Reviewed by Walter Pagel, *Med.Illus.*, 1949, 3: 15.

HIRSH, Joseph. Pneumonia. Early history of diagnosis and treatment. *Ann.Med.Hist.*, 1940, 2: 144-50.

KEENEY, E.L. The history of asthma from Hippocrates to Meltzer. *J.Allergy*, 1964, 35: 215-226.

LANGLEY, L.L. An historical introduction to the physiology of anoxia. *Bull.Hist.Med.*, 1943, 14: 321-40, 2 fig.

MAJOR, Ralph H. A note on the history of asthma. *Science, Medicine and History. Essays in honour of Charles Singer*, (2), p. 518-29. London: Oxford University Press, 1953.

STICKER, Georg. Die Geschichte des Alpensticks. *Proc.17th Int.Congr.Med.* (London, 1913), Sect. 23, p. 183-5. London: Oxford University Press; Hodder & Stoughton, 1914.
A lung infection which occurs in mountainous areas.

STOLKIND, E. History of bronchial asthma. *Janus*, 1933, 37: 300-19.

STOLKIND, E. The history of bronchial asthma and allergy. *Proc.Roy.Soc.Med.*, 1933, 26: 36-42. [CB 40/416]

OY GASTROENTEROLOGY

see also NM NUTRITION

ASGIS, Alfred J. History of stomatology. *Med.Life*, 1926, 33: 294-340, ill.

CAWADIAS, A.P. Gastro-enterology and metabolism: a historical survey. *Proc.Roy.Soc.Med.*, 1933, 26: 43-50.

DARMSTAEDTER, Ernst. Leber- und Galle-Forschung im Laufe der Jahrhunderte. *Riedel-Arch.*, 1934, 23: 51-4.

ELIAS, Hans. The liver-cord concept after one hundred years. *Science*, 1949, 110: 470-2.
Brief history of the prevailing idea of the finer histological structure of the liver.

GARRISON, Fielding Hudson. History of gastro-enterology. *Bull.N.Y.Acad.Med.*, 1934, 10: 629-42.

HERRLINGER, R. Die Milz. *Ciba Z.*, 1958, 8: 2982-3012, ill. [CB 84/316]

KANNER, Leo. Historical notes on rumination in man. *Med. Life*, 1936, 43: 27-60, 12 ill. [CB 47/286]

LOEPER, Maurice. Histoire de la sécrétion gastrique. 120 p., 25 fig. Paris: Masson, 1924. [CB 17/598]

LUCKHARDT, Arno B. Digestion. *Amer.J.Pharm.Educ.*, 1945, 9: 312-29.

LUSK, Graham. Nutrition. xii, 142 p., 13 ill. (Clio Medica, 10) New York: Hoeber, 1933.
History of the physiology of nutrition.
Reprinted New York: Hafner, 1964.

NASIO, Juan. Historia de la gastroenterologia. *Act.VIII Congr.Int.Hist.Sci.* (Florence, 1956), p. 778-9. Paris: Hermann, 1958.

PANEBAKER, George. Historical notes on digestion. *Med.Life*, 1925, 32: 170-80.

RIESMAN, David. Address on the history of gastroenterology, 1897-1927. *Med.Life*, 1927, 34: 630-8.

SATTERLEE, G. Reese. History of our knowledge of gastric digestion. *Med.Life*, 1927, 34: 645-53.

THOMSON, Stewart C. Musings on the biliary tract. *Amer.J. Surg.*, 1940, 47: 687-90.

YOUNG, John R. An experimental inquiry into the principles of nutrition and the digestive process. With an introductory essay by William C. Rose. xxvi, 48 p. Urbana: University of Illinois Press, 1959.
Reviewed by Owen H. Wangensteen, *J.Hist.Med.*, 1960, 15: 116-18.

OYwb

BASSLER, Anthony. A chapter of American gastroenterology. My experience with the gastroenterology section of the American Medical Association, and a forecast into the future of the specialty. *Med.Life*, 1927, 34: 654-62.

GRAY, Irving. Zur Geschichte der Gastro-Enterologie in den Vereinigten Staaten. *Festschrift zur Feier seines 60. Geburtstags Max Neuburger gewidmet*, p. 136-40. Wien: Verlag des Fest-Komitees, 1928.

OYwb-cj

GOLDSTEIN, Hyman I. *The American Journal of Gastroenterology. Rev.Gastroenterol.*, 1941, 8: 341-2.

OYwg-u

BARGHEER, Ernst. Eingeweide. Lebens- und Seelenkräfte des Leibesinnern im deutschen Glauben und Brauch. xv, 443 p., 8 fig., 8 pl. Berlin: De Gruyter, 1931.

OYwh-r

LORINCZY-LANDGRAF, E. Die Entstehung des Stomatologenstandes in Ungarn. *Festschrift zum 80. Geburtstag Max Neuburgers*, p. 308-9. Wien: Maudrich, 1948.

OZ DIGESTIVE DISORDERS AND DISEASES

for enteric fevers in general *see* QNyOZ; cholera QPzc; dysentery QPzdy; tuberculosis QPztu-yOZ; abdominal surgery RCK; specific remedies RJyOZ, RUyOZ

CARSON, Herbert W. The iliac passion. *Ann.Med.Hist.*, 1931, 3: 638-49.
Relating the slow groping toward the idea of acute intestinal obstruction.

CUMSTON, Charles Greene. L'histoire de la physiologie pathologique des ictères. *Arch.Gesch.Med.*, 1915, 8: 225-35.

DÖRFLER, Hans. Geschichte des Icterus catarrhalis. (Diss., Würzburg) 41 p. Bamberg: J.M. Reindi, 1913.

GOLDSTEIN, Hyman I. Historical notes on ulcer of the stomach and duodenum. *J.Int.Coll.Surg.*, 1939, 2: 379-408.

GOLDSTEIN, Hyman I. The history of regional enteritis (Saunders-Abercrombie-Crohn's ileitis). *Victor Robinson Memorial Volume*, p. 99-104. New York: Froben, 1948.

HEUSINGER, Johann Christian Karl Friedrich von. Ein Beitrag zu den Antiquitäten der Noma. *Henschel's Janus*, 1851, 1: 127-8; reprinted Leipzig: Alfred Lorentz, 1931.

KAHN, Max. History of acidosis. *Med.Life*, 1925, 32: 189-206.

LEVINSON, A. The history of acidosis. *Med.Life*, 1923, 30: 343-8; 1925, 32: 207-17.

MACK, Harold C. A history of the hypertrophic pyloric stenosis and its treatment. *Bull.Hist.Med.*, 1942, 12: 465-85, 1 fig.; 595-615, 8 fig.; 666-89, 6 fig.

MORRISON, Hyman. The chapter on appendicitis in a biography of Reginald Heber Fitz. *Bull.Hist.Med.*, 1946, 20: 259-69, 1 pl.

MORRISON, Hyman. Reginald Heber Fitz's contribution to the understanding of acute pancreatitis. *Bull.Hist.Med.*, 1948, 22: 263-72.

PAGEL, W. Geschichte des runden Magengeschwürs. (Beiträge zur historischen Pathologie und zur Geschichte der Diagnose, 1) *Sudhoffs Arch.*, 1932, 25: 330-48.

PATTERSON, S.W. The history of diverticulitis of the intestine. *Proc.Roy.Soc.Med.*, 1950, 43: 785-9.

RAAF, John E. Hernia healers. *Ann.Med.Hist.*, 1932, 4: 377-89.

RAVITCH, Mark M. Jonathan Hutchinson and intussusception. *Bull.Hist.Med.*, 1951, 25: 342-53, 1 fig.

SCHMITZ-CLEVIER, Egon. Zur Geschichte der Dysphagia Lusoria. *Sudhoffs Arch.*, 1960, 44: 229-38.

THOREK, Max; THOREK, Philip. Historical notes on perforation, ulcer of the stomach, and gastric fistula. *Victor Robinson Memorial Volume*, p. 385-95, 2 fig. New York: Froben, 1948.

WEISS, Samuel. History of gall-tract and biliary disease. *Med.Life*, 1927, 34: 663-76.

OZce-bv

SCHMIDT, Benno. Bibliotheca herniologica. 24 p. Amsterdam: International Antiquariaat, 1926. [CB 20/212]
Catalogue of the collection of books on hernia made by Professor Dr. Benno Schmidt, of Heidelberg, formerly of Leipzig (1826-96).

OZcp-by

SCHMIDT, Werner. Die Gallensteinsammlung Bernhard Naunyns. *Sudhoffs Arch.*, 1954, 38: 378-81.

OZnh

COLIN, Georges S. "Passion iliaque", "Kyrie eleison!" et "colique de miséréré". *Hespéris*, 1945, 32: 77-80.
Apropos of obsolete terms for colic and ileus.

KATNER, Wilhelm. Zur Wortgeschichte von "Splanchnomegalie". *Sudhoffs Arch.*, 1956, 40: 106-15.

OZu

BAKKER, C. Volksgeneeskundige aanteekeningen omtrent den hik. [Ideas in popular medicine concerning hiccough. (In Dutch)] *Bijdr.Gesch.Geneesk.*, 1926, 6: 55-8.

OZyQF

GOLDSTEIN, Hyman I. Cancer of the stomach in children and young adults; review of literature. *J.Int.Coll.Surg.*, 1941, 4: 361-75.

PA CARDIOVASCULAR SYSTEM; CARDIOLOGY

ALLODI, Federico. Il cuore embrionale. *Riv.Stor.Sci.*, 1956, 47: 171-99.

BISHOP, Louis Faugères; NEILSON, John. History of cardiology. *Med.Life*, 1926, 33: 392-440, ill.

BISHOP, Louis Faugères; NEILSON, John. History of cardiology. Introduction by Victor Robinson. 71 p. New York: Medical Life Press, 1927.

BOYD, Linn J. Some landmarks in the medico-history of the pericardium. *Festschrift zum 80. Geburtstag Max Neuburgers*, p. 69-71. Wien: Maudrich, 1948.

BRIM, Charles J. The story of blood pressure. *Med.Life*, 1930, 37: 60-108, 42 ill.

BUESS, H. Notizen zur Geschichte der Sphygmographie. 1. [No sub-title]; 2. Die Anfänge der physikalischen Pulsforschung im 17. und 18. Jahrhundert; 3. Der Übergang von der blutigen zur unblutigen Pulsschreibung. *Experientia*, 1947, 3: 165-7, 1 fig; 250-3, 3 fig.; 334-8, 5 fig.

FAHRAEUS, Robin. L'air dans les artères. *Arch.Iberoamer.Hist.Med.*, 1957, 9: 151-3.

FRANCESCHINI, Pietro. L'automatismo del cuore nelle osservazioni di Giulio Chiarugi e di Giulio Fano. *Physis*, 1960, 2: 163-82.

GOTFREDSEN, Edvard. Oldtidens laere om hjerte, kar og puls. En medicinsk-historisk studie. [Early views on heart, blood-vessels and pulse. (In Danish, with German summary)] x, 332 p., bibliogr. (Acta Historica Scientiarum Naturalium et Medicinalium. Edidit Bibliotheca Universitatis Hauniensis, 1) København: Munksgaard, 1942.
Reviewed by Ernst Nachmanson, *Lychnos*, 1942, 409-14.

GUILLAUME, A. Les étapes d'une grande découverte physiologique et médicale. Historique du développement de la connaissance en matière de pression artérielle. *Biol.Méd.*, 1952, 41: 231-63.
Reviewed by P. Delaunay. *Arch.Int.Hist.Sci.*, 1952, 5: 436-7.

GUTHRIE, Douglas. The evolution of cardiology. *Science, Medicine and History. Essays in honour of Charles Singer*, (2), p. 508-17, pl. London: Oxford University Press, 1953.

HAMBURGER, Walter W. Contrasting concepts of the heart and circulation in ancient and modern times. *Bull.Hist.Med.*, 1943, 14: 148-58, 2 fig.

HERRICK, James B. A short history of cardiology. xvi, 258 p., 48 pl. Springfield, Ill.: Charles C. Thomas, 1942.
Reviewed by J.B. de C.M. Saunders, *Isis*, 1943, 34: 530-1; by O. Temkin, *Bull.Hist.Med.*, 1943, 13: 113-15.

IRSAY, Stephen d'. Modern cardiology. *Sci.Mon.*, 1926, 22: 445-52.

KROGH, August. The anatomy and physiology of capillaries. xvii, 276 p. (The Silliman Lectures for 1922) New Haven: Yale University Press, 1922.
Reviewed by Yandell Henderson, *Science*, 1923, 57: 614.
2nd enl. ed. 1929.
German translation Berlin: Springer, 1924.

LATRONICO, N., *et al.* Il cuore nella storia della medicina. 144 p., ill. (Monografie cardiologiche, 4) Milano: Amilcare Pizzi, 1955.

LEIKIND, Morris C. The history of cardiology - an outline sketch. *Mil.Med.*, 1957, 120: 250-6, 5 portr.

LUISADA, Aldo A. A short chronology of important events in cardiology. *Essays in the History of Medicine presented to Prof. Arturo Castiglioni*, p. 152-60. Baltimore: Johns Hopkins Press, 1944.

MOUQUIN, M. Le passé, le present et l'avenir de la cardiologie. *Hist.Méd.*, 1962, 12: no. 6, 3-13, ill.

PICK, Joseph. The discovery of the carotid body. *J.Hist. Med.*, 1959, 14: 61-73, 9 fig., bibliogr.

WIBERG, Jul. The anatomy of the heart in the 16th, 17th, and 18th century (Andreas Vesalius, Richard Lower, and Raimond Vieussens). *Janus*, 1927, 31: 279-85.

WILLIUS, Frederick A.; DRY, Thomas J. A history of the heart and the circulation. xvii, 456 p., ill. Philadelphia: Saunders, 1948. [CB 74/392]

PAcm

NEBEL, Werner. Zur Geschichte der Herzdarstellung. *Sudhoffs Arch.*, 1935, 28: 279-95, 30 fig.

SCHOTT, A. Historical notes on the iconography of the heart. *Cardiologia*, 1956, 28: 229-68, 20 fig. [CB 83/214]

PAdaj

WILLIUS, Frederick A.; KEYES, Thomas E. Cardiac classics. A collection of classic works on the heart and circulation with comprehensive biographic accounts of the authors. Fifty-two contributions by fifty-one authors. xix, 858 p. St. Louis: Mosby, 1941.
Reviewed in *Ann.Med.Hist.*, 1942, 4: 85.

PAht

GRMEK, Mirko Drazen. Les reflets de la sphygmologie chinoise dans la médecine occidentale. 120 p., ill. (Biologie Médicale, 51: numéro hors série) Paris: Specia, 1962.
Reviewed by E. Hintzsche, *Arch.Int.Hist.Sci.*, 1963, 16: 450-4.

PAnh

HEYMANS, C. Oorsprong van de naam: "carotis" of "halsslagader". [Origin of the name "carotis" or neck artery. (In Dutch)] *Sci.Hist.*, 1960, 2: 21.

PAu

HORINE, Emmet Field. An epitome of ancient pulse lore. *Bull. Hist.Med.*, 1941, 10: 209-49, 7 fig.

ROLLESTON, J.D. Cardiac folk-lore. *Proc.Roy.Soc.Med.*, 1946, 39: 119-22; Hist.Sect., 19-22.

PAwi

CASTIGLIONI, Arturo. Il contributo degli italiani alla fisiologia ed alla patologia del cuore. *Nuova Antologia*, 1930, 352: 364-77.

PAxg

GRIFFENHAGEN, George B.; HUGHES, Calvin H. The history of the mechanical heart. *Annu.Rep.Smithsonian Inst.for 1955*, p. 339-56. Washington, D.C.: 1956.
Reviewed by John H. Fulton, *J.Hist.Med.*, 1957, 12: 96-7.

PB CIRCULATION OF THE BLOOD

ASCHOFF, Ludwig. Über die Entdeckung des Blutkreislaufs. Eine Stellungnahme zum Streit um William Harvey und ein Ausblick auf die spätere Entwicklung der Geschichte der Medizin. 47 p. (Freiburger Forschungen zur Medizingeschichte, 1) Freiburg i.B.: Speyer, 1938.

BAYON, H.P. The lifework of William Harvey and modern medical progress. *Proc.Roy.Soc.Med.*, 1951, 44: Hist.Sect., 213-18.

BOENHEIM, Felix. From Huang-Ti to Harvey. *J.Hist.Med.*, 1957, 12: 181-8.

DIEPGEN, Paul. Aus der Geschichte des Blutkreislaufs. *Fortschr.Med.*, 19 Feb. 1932, 50: 130-3.

FISHMAN, Alfred P.; RICHARDS, Dickinson W. Circulation of the blood. Men and ideas. xiv, 859 p., ill. New York: Oxford University Press, 1964.

FRANKLIN, Kenneth J. Ductus Venosus [Arantii] and Ductus Arteriosus [Botalli]. *Bull.Hist.Med.*, 1941, 9: 580-4.

FRANKLIN, Kenneth J. The history of circulatory research, leading to a wider view of the circulation. *Trans.Coll. Physicians Phila.*, 1952, 20: 23-33, 1 fig.

FRANKLIN, Kenneth J. The history of research upon the renal circulation. *Proc.Roy.Soc.Med.*, 1949, 42: Hist.Sect. 721-30.

GARRISON, Fielding Hudson. An outline of the history of the circulatory system. *Bull.N.Y.Acad.Med.*, 1931, 7: 781-806.

HEYMANN, Robert Christian. Die Geschichte der Entdeckung des Kreislaufs und der Einfluss dieser Entdeckung auf die medizinische Wissenschaft und Praxis der folgenden Zeit. 51 p. Leipzig: Institut für Geschichte der Medizin an der Universität, 1934.

KROGH, August. Reminiscences of work on capillary circulation. A lecture to the students in the Harvard Medical School, 1946. *Isis*, 1950, 41: 14-20, 1 portr., 6 fig.

LINDBORG, J. [The "Ductus arteriosus" (Galeni) and observations on blood circulation before Harvey. (In Swedish)] *Svenska Läkartidn.*, 1964, 61: 4025-30.

McDONALD, D.A. Harvey's influence on modern trends in circulatory research. *St. Bartholomew's Hosp.J.*, 1957, 61: 164-7.

ROY, Philip S. Historical development of our knowledge of the circulation and its disorders. *Ann.Med.Hist.*, 1917, 1: 141-58.

SCHACHT, Joseph. Ibn al-Nafīs, Servetus and Colombo. *Al-Andalus*, 1957, 22: 317-31. [CB 84/353]

SIEGEL, Rudolph E. The influence of Galen's doctrine of pulmonary bloodflow on the development of modern concepts of circulation. *Sudhoffs Arch.*, 1962, 46: 311-32.

STIRLING, William. Servetus, Harvey, Hunter and C. Richet. *Mélanges biologiques*, p. 385-98. Paris: L'Imprimerie de la Cour d'Appel, 1912.

ZÜRBACH, Karl. Early ideas and theories on the motion of the blood. *Ciba Symp.* (Summit, N.J.), 1939, 1: 71-7, fig.

PBda

DOBY, Tibor. Discoverers of blood circulation. From Aristotle to the times of da Vinci and Harvey. xiii, 285 p., 57 ill., bibliogr. London/New York/Toronto: Abelard-Schuman, 1963.
Reviewed by Gert H. Brieger, *Isis*, 1964, 55: 379.

PBdaj

GRAUBARD, Mark. Circulation and respiration. The evolution of an idea. ix, 278 p., ill., index. New York: Harcourt, Brace & World, 1964. [CB 90/525]
An account told through extracts from the original sources.

PBwj

IZQUIERDO, J.J. On Spanish neglect of Harvey's "De motu cordis" for three centuries, and how it was finally made known to Spain and Spanish-speaking countries. *J.Hist. Med.*, 1948, 3: 105-24, 8 fig.

PC CARDIAC AND CIRCULATORY DISORDERS AND DISEASES

for haemostasis *see* RBzh
heart and cardiovascular surgery *see* RCL
bloodletting *see* RFzb
drugs acting on the system *see* RZyPC

ANNING, S.T. The historical aspects of venous thrombosis. *Med.Hist.*, 1957, 1: 28-37.

BUESS, Heinrich. Marksteine in der Entwicklung der Lehre von der Thrombose und Embolie. *Gesnerus*, 1955, 12: 157-89, 5 fig.

EAST, Terrence. The story of heart disease. 148 p., ill. (The Fitzpatrick Lectures for 1956 and 1957 given before The Royal College of Physicians of London) London: Dawson, 1957.
Reviewed by Nathan Flaxman, *Bull.Hist.Med.*, 1958, 32: 478-9; by A. Schott, *Med.Hist.*, 1958, 2: 231-2; by Edgar F. Mauer, *J.Hist.Med.*, 1959, 14: 111-12.

FLAXMAN, Nathan. A cardiology anomaly: Albert Abrams (1863-1924). *Bull.Hist.Med.*, 1953, 27: 252-68.

FLAXMAN, Nathan. Historical aspects of mitral stenosis. *Med. Life*, 1938, 45: 3-19.

FLAXMAN, Nathan. History of aortic insufficiency. *Bull.Hist. Med.*, 1939, 7: 192-209.

FLAXMAN, Nathan. The history of heart-block. *Bull.Inst.Hist. Med.*, 1937, 5: 115-30.

GIERLICH, Hugo. Zur Frühgeschichte der Paracentesis pericardii. *Sudhoffs Arch.*, 1956, 40: 119-55.

HABERLING, Wilhelm. Der Herzpolyp. (Ausgewählte Kapitel aus der Geschichte der Krankheiten, 1) *Med.Welt,* 16 April 1927, 1: no. 11, 405-7.

LIAN, Camille; MILON, Robert. Remarques sur l'histoire de l'insuffisance aortique. *Mém.Soc.Franç.Hist.Méd.*, 1947, 3: 33-7.

LONG, Esmond R. Concepts of cardiac pathology before Morgagni. *Ann.Med.Hist.*, 1936, 8: 442-7, 3 fig.

MAJOR, Ralph H. Notes on the history of endocarditis. *Bull. Hist.Med.*, 1945, 17: 351-9.

NAVA, Pedro. Notas para a história da patogenia do Icto Apoplético (Morgagni, Hoffman, De Malon, Pomme e o brasileiro João Vicente Torres Homem - precursores da idéia do espasmo vascular como determinante patogênica do Icto Apoplético). *Med.Cir.Farm.*, Feb.-Mar. 1948, no. 142-143, 67-71, fig., bibliogr.

NEUBURGER, Max. Die Entwicklung der Lehre von den Herzkrankheiten. *Wiener Med.Wochenschr.*, 1928, 78: 79-81, 122-6.

RIESMAN, David. High blood pressure and longevity, and other essays selected from the published writings. xii, 726 p., front., portr., bibliogr. Philadelphia: Winston, 1937.
Volume published to celebrate the author's seventieth birthday on March 27, 1937.

ROLLESTON, Humphry. Cardio-vascular diseases since Harvey's discovery. The Harveian Oration, 1928. 149 p. Cambridge University Press, 1928.

ROLLESTON, Humphry. History of aortic regurgitation. *Ann. Med.Hist.*, 1940, 2: 271-9, 3 fig.

ROMBERG, Ernst von. Die Herzkrankheiten und ihre Behandlung in den letzten 50 Jahren (Leyden-Vorlesung zum 50-jährigen Bestehen des Berliner Vereins für innere Medizin.) *Deut. Med.Wochenschr.*, 1931, 57: 611-14, 667-70, 708-10.

STEHBENS, W.E. History of aneurysms. *Med.Hist.*, 1958, 2: 274-80.

TÖNNES, Heinrich. Die Geschichte der Aneurysmen. (Diss.) 40 p. Düsseldorf: Nolte, 1940.
Reviewed by W. Haberling, *Mitt.Gesch.Med.*, 1941-42, 40: 88.

PCdaj

RUSKIN, Arthur, ed. Classics in arterial hypertension. xxiii, 358 p., bibliogr. (American Lecture Series. Classics in Science and Medicine, 290) Springfield, Ill.: Charles C. Thomas; Oxford: Blackwell Scientific Publications, 1956. [CB 83/208]
Reviewed by Ralph H. Major, *J.Hist.Med.*, 1957, 12: 274-5.

PCwg-oq

KEYS, T.E.; WILLIUS, F.A. Cardiac clinics. 95. The achievements of Karel Frederik Wenckebach (1864-1940). *Proc.Staff Meetings Mayo Clin.*, 1942, 17: 332-6.

PCwi

CASTIGLIONI, Arturo. Il contributo degli italiani alla cardiopatologia. *Minerva Med.*, 1931, 22: 789-92.

PCyOZ

EBSTEIN, Erich. A contribution to the history of hemorrhoids and their treatment from the time of Hippocrates to the modern bacteriological era. *Med.Life,* 1928, 35: 5-18, 2 portr., bibliogr.

PCyQD DIAGNOSIS

for auscultation *see also* QD

FINOT, André. L'auscultation cardio-vasculaire avant Laënnec. *Hist.Méd.*, 1951, 1: no. 9, 14-18.

HEERSWYNGHELS, J. La phonocardiographie. Aperçu historique des méthodes utilisées. *Acta Cardiol.*, 1964, 19: 321-6.

HOFF, Hebbel E.; GUILLEMIN, Roger; GEDDES, L.A. The early history of cardiac catheterization. *Arch.Int.Hist.Sci.*, 1963, 16: 377-404.

JOSEPH, G. Geschichte der Physiologie der Herztöne vor und nach Laënnec bis 1852. *Janus,* 1852, 2: 1-39, 345-74, 505-27; reprinted, Leipzig: Alfred Lorentz, 1931.

LIAN, Camille. Quelques omissions et erreurs traditionnelles dans l'histoire des signes stéthoscopiques du rétrécissement mitral. *Mém.Soc.Franç.Hist.Méd.*, 1946, 2: 92-6.

McKUSICK, Victor A. The history of methods for the diagnosis of heart disease. *Bull.Hist.Med.*, 1960, 34: 16-18.

McKUSICK, Victor A.; SHARPE, William D.; WARNER, Allen O. An exhibition on the history of cardiovascular sound including the evolution of the stethoscope. *Bull.Hist.Med.*, 1957, 31: 463-87, 9 fig.

PALADINI, Pantaleo. Breve storia del sondaggio cardiovasale *Riv.Stor.Med.*, 1957, 1: 98-103.

SHAPIRO, Edward; STRAUSS, L. Oskar Minkowski's registration of left atrial pressure curves in mitral valve disease. *Amer.J.Cardiol.*, 1964, 14: 107-11.

PCyQDxk

LEIKIND, Morris C. The stethoscope. Some notes on its history. *J.Nat.Med.Ass.*, 1955, 47: 177-80, 2 fig.

PCyQDxq

ARINCHIN, N.I.; ZENKEVICH, E.S. Half a century of the application and further development of Korotkov's auditory method of determining blood pressure. *Sechenov Physiol.J.USSR*, 1957, 43: 81-6. [CB 83/267]

MAJOR, Ralph H. The history of taking the blood pressure. *Ann.Med.Hist.*, 1930, 11: 47-55, 14 fig.

SARTON, George. History of the practical measurement of blood pressure. When was such measurement introduced in medical practice? (Query no. 101) *Isis,* 1941, 33: 243-4; 3rd answer, *ibid.*, 1956, 47: 60.
For other answers, *see* below: Singer, Dorothea W. and Viets, Henry R.

SINGER, Dorothea W. Determination of blood pressure in medical practice. (2nd answer to Query 101). *Isis,* 1942, 34: 25.

VIETS, Henry R. History of the practical measurement of blood pressure. Answer to Query no. 101. *Isis,* 1941, 33: 244-5.
For Query *see* Sarton, George, above.

PCyQDze

EINTHOVEN, W.; FAHR, G.; WAART, A. de. On the direction and manifest size of the variations of potential in the human heart and on the influence of the position of the heart on the form of the electrocardiogram. Transl. by Hebbel E. Hoff and Paul Sekelj. *Amer.Heart J.*, 1950, 40: 163-211, 30 fig.

LEAMAN, William G. The history of electrocardiography. *Ann. Med.Hist.*, 1936, 8: 113-17.

WILLEM EINTHOVEN. Grondlegger van de elektrocardiografie. [In Dutch] *Geneesk.Gids,* 1960, 38: 223.

PCyQDze-wb

COHN, Alfred E. Recollections concerning early electrocardiography in the United States. With a letter of Horatio B. Williams. *Bull.Hist.Med.*, 1955, 29: 469-74.

PD HAEMOPOIETIC SYSTEM; HAEMATOLOGY

for bloodletting *see* RFzb
blood transfusion *see* RVzb

ABEL, John J. Experimental and chemical studies of the blood with an appeal for more extended chemical training for the biological and medical investigator. 45 p., 5 fig. (Mellon Lecture) Pittsburgh: University of Pittsburgh, 1915.
The historical introduction deals with bloodletting, the use of leeches, etc.

ANDRIEU, Raymond. Origines et destinées d'une banque de sang. *Hist.Méd.*, 1951, 1: 21-4, ill.

BARCROFT, Joseph. The respiratory function of the blood. x, 320 p. Cambridge University Press, 1914.
2nd ed. 2 vol. 1. Lessons from high altitudes; 2. Haemoglobin. Cambridge University Press, 1925-28.

COHN, Edwin J. Blood and blood derivatives. *Annu.Rep.Smithsonian Inst.for 1945*, p. 413-39, 1 pl., 2 fig. Washington, D.C.: 1946.

DI PIETRO, Pericle. Breve storia dell'ematologia. 156 p., 15 fig. Padova: Istituto di Storia de la Medicina, Università di Padova, 1958.
Reviewed by J. Théodoridès, *Rev.Hist.Sci.*, 1960, 13: 277.

DREYFUS, Camille. Some milestones in the history of hematology. vii, 87 p., ill. New York/London: Grune and Stratton, 1957.
Reviewed by Robert J. Faulconer, *Bull.Hist.Med.*, 1958, 32: 93-4; by Erwin H. Ackerknecht, *Arch.Int.Hist.Sci.*, 1958, 11: 316.

FARBER, Eduard. The color of venous blood. *Isis*, 1954, 45: 3-9, 1 fig.

HENDERSON, Lawrence Joseph. Blood: a study in general physiology. xix, 397 p. (Yale University: Mrs. Hepsa Ely Silliman Memorial Lectures) New Haven: Yale University Press, 1928.
French transl. Paris: 1931.

RADFIELD, Alfred C. Quelques aspects du problème de l'évolution de la fonction respiratoire du sang. *Rev.Quest. Sci.*, 1931, 20: 38-54.

ROBB-SMITH, A.H.T. Unravelling the functions of the blood. *Med.Hist.*, 1962, 6: 1-21.

ROLLESTON, Humphry. The history of haematology. *Proc.Roy. Soc.Med.*, 1933-34, 27: 31-48, bibliogr. [CB 43/290]

SABINE, Jean Captain. A history of the classification of human blood corpuscles. *Bull.Hist.Med.*, 1940, 8: 696-720, 785-805.

SCUDDER, John. Shock: blood studies as a guide to therapy. xvii, 315 p., 55 ill. Philadelphia: 1940. [CB 61/420]

TÉCHOUEYRES, E. Le sang. Réflexions sur sa constitution humorale. *Rev.Sci.*, 1912, 50: 2e semestre, 107-14.

WALKER, Kenneth. The story of blood. 213p., ill. London: Herbert Jenkins, 1958; New York: Philosophical Library, 1963.
Reviewed by Robin Fahraeus, *Lychnos*, 1960, 379-80.

WIENER, Alexander S. History of the rhesus blood types. *J. Hist.Med.*, 1952, 7: 369-83.
An account of Karl Landsteiner's work on bloodgroups and the discovery of the Rhesus blood factor.

PDcb

IZQUIERDO, José Joaquín. La Hemerobiblioteca del Departamento de Fisiología de la Facultad de Medicina. *Gac.Méd. Méx.*, 1958, 88: 749-66.

PDce-bv

CATALOGO de la Hemerobiblioteca del Departamento de Fisiología. Facultad de Medicina de la Universidad Nacional Autónoma de México. Preface by J.J. Izquierdo. 206 p., ill. México: Universidad Nacional Autónoma de México, 1958.

PDce-bx

HARVARD UNIVERSITY LIBRARY. The development of knowledge of blood. Represented by manuscripts, and by selected books published from 1490 to the 19th century. An exhibition sponsored by the University Library [and others]. 54 p., 2 pl. Cambridge: Harvard University, 1951. [CB 78/192]
Catalogue with a foreword by Edwin J. Cohn, and introduction by I. Bernard Cohen.

PDwf

VERSO, M.L. Some notes on a contemporary review of French hematology. *Med.Hist.*, 1961, 5: 239-52.

PE BLOOD DISORDERS AND DISEASES

for bio- and organotherapy *see* RVyPE

BRAMMER, Carl. Die Geschichte der Chlorose. 29 p. (Diss., Inst.Gesch.Med., Düsseldorf) Düsseldorf: 1937.

DARMSTAEDTER, Ernst. Ein Beitrag zur Erforschungsgeschichte der Hämoglobinämie und Hämoglobinurie. *Sudhoffs Arch.*, 1935, 28: 338-46.

FOWLER, W.M. Chlorosis - an obituary. *Ann.Med.Hist.*, 1936, 8: 168-77, 4 fig.

GOLDSTEIN, Hyman I. Early references to anemia [and its treatment with iron preparations]. *Med.Life*, 1932. 39: 646-7.
Expression *anaima* originally used by Aristotle.

HANSEN, Axel. Om Chlorosens, den aegte Blegsots, Optraeden i Europa gennem Tiderne: en medico-historisk undersøgelse. [Concerning chlorosis, the real green sickness; its appearance in Europe through the ages: a medical historical investigation. (In Danish)] xxviii, 202 p., xviii, 29 fig. Kolding: Schäffer, 1928. [CB 25/437]

ILLIS, L. On porphyria and the aetiology of werwolves. *Proc. Roy.Soc.Med.*, 1964, 57: 23-6.

JONES, Harold W.; TOCANTINS, Leandro M. The history of Purpura hemorrhagica. *Ann.Med.Hist.*, 1933, 5: 349-59, 1 fig.

SCHACHTER, M. L'histoire de l'hémophilie: quelques précisions. *Bull.Soc.Franç.Hist.Méd.*, 1933, 27: 101-5.

SOMMERLAD, Georg. Geschichte der Hämophilie. (Diss.) 55 p. Leipzig: 1927.

PEyQD DIAGNOSIS

PEyQDxj

VERSO, M.L. The evolution of blood-counting techniques. *Med. Hist.*, 1964, 8: 149-58.

PEyQDxq

MINNIGERODE, Wilhelm. Die Methoden der Bestimmung des Volumens und des Gewichts der körperlichen Elemente im Blut, historisch und kritich dargestellt. 59 p. (Diss.) Greifswald: 1914.

PF LYMPHATIC AND RETICULOENDOTHELIAL SYSTEM

PG LYMPHATIC DISORDERS AND DISEASES

for scrofula *see* QPztu-yPG

JONES, George W. An historical review of Hodgkin's disease with special reference to its histology and characteristic cells. *Ann.Med.Hist.*, 1940, 2: 471-81.

WEISS, Arthur. Hodgkin's disease. *Med.Life*, 1930, 37: 701-7 (27-33).

PH ENDOCRINOLOGY

for hormones in general *see* JE
hormones in gynaecology *see* PQyPH

ABDERHALDEN, R. Die innere Sekretion. *Ciba Z.*, 1951, 11: 4535-91, ill.

ABEL, John J. Some recent advances in our knowledge of the ductless glands. *Bull.Johns Hopkins Hosp.*, 1926, 38: 1-32.

ABEL, John J. Physiological, chemical and clinical studies on pituitary principles. *Harvey Lect.*, 1923-24, 19: 154-211.

AZNAR-GARCÍA, Joaquin. Evolución de la endrocrinología. *Clin. Lab.*, 1964, 77: 161-74.

BUSACCHI, Vincenzo. Le reazioni di difesa e di adattamento vitale e l'opera di Hans Selye. *Riv.Stor.Sci.*, 1950, 41: 3-6.

COLLIN, R. Les régulations hormonales et la physiologie du vivant. *Arch.Inst.Int.Sci.Théor.Sér.A.Bull.Acad.Int.Phil. Sci.*, 6. Problèmes de philosophie des sciences. 6. L'unité formelle et physiologie du vivant, p. 37-59. Discussion, p. 60-76. (Actualités Scientifiques et Industrielles, 1068) Paris: Hermann, 1949.

GLEY, E. Comment s'est formée et comment a évolué la notion de sécrétion interne. *Rev.Gén.Sci.*, 1915, 26: 368-74.

GLEY, E. Les étapes de l'endocrinologie et son état actuel. *Rev.Gén.Sci.*, 1922, 33: 638-45.

GLEY, E. La notion de sécrétion interne: ses origines et son développement. *Rev.Sci.*, 1913, 51: 2e semestre, 645-54.

HIRSCH, Max. Alte und neue Heilkunde im Lichte der Lehre von der inneren Sekretion. In: Handbuch der inneren Sekretion, ed. by Max Hirsch, (1), p. 1-24. Berlin: 1926.
Reviewed by P. Diepgen, *Mitt.Gesch.Med.*, 1927, 26: 66.

KOCH, Richard. Geschichtliche Einleitung. In: Bayer, Gustav; Velden, Reinhard von den; ed. Klinisches Lehrbuch der Inkretologie und Inkretotherapie, p. 1-12. Leipzig: Thieme, 1927.
Reviewed by K. Sudhoff, *Mitt.Gesch.Med.*, 1927, 26: 67.

KOOPMAN, J. Bijdrage tot de geschiedenis der ontwikkeling van de endocrinologie. [Contributions to the history of the development of endocrinology. (In Dutch)] *Bijdr.Gesch. Geneesk.*, 1926, 6: 117-23; 1928, 8: 96-100, 333-41; 1931, 11: 169-73.

LENARD, A. The history of research on the adrenals 1563-1900. *J.Hist.Med.*, 1951, 6: 496-505.

LUCKHARDT, Arno B. Outlines for lectures on historical endocrinology. *Amer.J.Pharm.Educ.*, 1944, 8: 163-76.

NIEUWENHUIS, G. Einige Anschauungen über die Funktion der Hypophyse. *Janus*, 1931, 35: 345-59.

PARISOT, Jacques; GABRIEL, Richard. Les glandes endocrines et leur valeur fonctionnelle. 248 p. Paris: Gaston Doin, 1924. [CB 17/599]

RODT, Walther E. von. Beitrag zur Geschichte der Schilddrüse. *Deut.Z.Chir.*, 1912, 116: 628-42.

ROLLESTON, Humphry. The endocrine organs in health and disease with an historical review. xi, 521 p., 45 ill. London: Oxford University Press, 1936. [CB 49/184]

SCHUMACKER, Harris B. The early history of the adrenal glands. With particular reference to theories of function. *Bull.Inst.Hist.Med.*, 1936, 4: 39-56.

SELYE, Hans. Textbook of endocrinology. xxxii, 914 p. Montreal: Acta Endocrinologica, 1947. [CB 73/178]
Historic introductions to every chapter for each endocrine gland considered.

SHARPEY-SCHAFER, Edward Albert. The physiology of internal secretion. *Nature*, 1931, 128: 441-52.
From the John Mallet Purser lecture delivered in Trinity College, Dublin, on June 26, 1931.

VORWAHL, Henner. Zur Geschichte des Synchronismus. *Arch. Gesch.Med.*, 1925, 17: 203-4.
Apropos of correlation between internal secretions.

WEIL, Arthur. The history of internal secretions. *Med.Life*, 1925, 32: 73-97.

PHwh

SKARZYNSKI, B. The part of Polish science in the discovery of the adrenal hormone. *Act.VIIIe Congr.Int.Hist.Sci.* (Florence, 1956), p. 712-15. Paris: Hermann, 1958.

PHwo

PARHON, C.I. Une page d'histoire sur la contribution de l'Ecole roumaine à l'étude des rapports entre la constitution somatopsychique et le fonctionnement des glandes à secretion interne. *Festschrift zum 80.Geburtstag Max Neuburgers*, p. 366-7. Wien: Maudrich, 1948.

PI ENDOCRINE DISORDERS AND DISEASES

for diabetes *see* PIzd
goiter *see* PIzg
surgery of the endocrine glands *see* RCN

CRANEFIELD, Paul F. The discovery of cretinism. *Bull.Hist. Med.*, 1962, 36: 489-511.

POMERANTZ, Jacob. Melasma suprarenale. *Med.Life*, 1930, 37: [689-700], suppl. 15-26, 3 pl.

WEINBERG, S.J. Gigantism and acromegaly (hyperpituitarism). *Ann.Med.Hist.*, 1931, 3: 650-73, bibliogr.
Historical survey.

PIzd DIABETES

for diet therapy *see* RLyPIzd
bio- and organotherapy *see* RVyPIzd

BARACH, Joseph H. Historical facts in diabetes. *Ann.Med. Hist.*, 1928, 10: 387-401.

FEASBY, W.R. The discovery of insulin. *J.Hist.Med.*, 1958, 13: 68-84.
This paper emphasises the work of Banting, Best, Collip and others.

HOUSSAY, B.A. History of hypophysial diabetes. *Essays in Biology in honor of Herbert M. Evans*, p. 245-56. Berkeley, Calif.: University of California Press, 1943.

KING, Lester S. Empiricism, rationalism, and diabetes. *J. Amer.Med.Ass.*, 1964, 187: 521-6.

KOOPMAN, J. Iets uit de geschiedenis van den diabetes. [Some notes on the history of diabetes. (In Dutch)] *Bijdr.Gesch. Geneesk.*, 1934, 14: 81-91.

LIPPMANN, Edmund O. von. Zur Geschichte des diabetischen Zuckers. *Chem.Zeitung*, 1920, 44: 1. Also in: Lippmann, Edmund O. von. Beiträge zur Geschichte der Naturwissenschaften und der Technik, (1), p. 211-13. Berlin: Springer, 1923. [CB 14/556]

McCRADIE, Andrew Ross. The discoveries in the field of diabetes mellitus and their investigators. *Med.Life*, 1924, 31: 214-50, ill. [CB 16/319]

MEINDL, Rudolf. Zur Geschichte der Zuckerharnruhr. (Anhang mit Erstdaten zur Geschichte der Harnruhr, Originaltexten und einem philologischen Exkurs zu Diabetes mellitus. Literaturverzeichnis sowie einem Schlusswort) 65, 24, 9 p. Berlin: Selbstverlag, 1950.
Reviewed by B. Milt, *Gesnerus*, 1951, 8: 255-6; by E. Bastholm, *Centaurus*, 1954, 3: 271-2.

MINKOWSKI, Oscar. Die Lehre vom Pankreasdiabetes in ihrer geschichtlichen Entwicklung. *Münch.Med.Wochenschr.*, 1929, 76: 311-15.

MURLIN, John R.; KRAMER, Benjamin. A quest for the anti-diabetic hormone, 1913-1916. *J.Hist.Med.*, 1956, 11: 288-98, 5 tables.

NOTHMAN, Martin M. The history of the discovery of pancreatic diabetes. *Bull.Hist.Med.*, 1954, 28: 272-4.
Deals mainly with Minkowski and Mering.

PAPASPYROS, N.S. The history of diabetes mellitus. Foreword by Dr. R.D. Lawrence. xvi, 100 p. London: Robert Stockwell, 1952.
Reviewed by Edward Tolstoi, *Isis*, 1954, 45: 110-11; by Owsei Temkin, *Bull.Hist.Med.*, 1954, 28: 97-8; by John F. Fulton, *J.Hist.Med.*, 1955, 9: 132-3.
2nd ed. rev. and suppl. xv, 104 p., ill. Stuttgart: Thieme, 1964.

PRATT, Joseph H. A reappraisal of researches leading to the discovery of insulin. *J.Hist.Med.*, 1954, 9: 281-9.
This paper emphasises the teamwork of Banting, Best, Collip and others, with particular reference to Banting and Best.

PRATT, Joseph H. Zur Geschichte der Entdeckung des Insulins. *Sudhoffs Arch.*, 1954, 38: 48-57.

PIzd-da

STRIKER, Cecil, ed. Famous faces in diabetes. xi, 256 p. Boston: G.K. Hall, 1961.
Reviewed by Robert Smith, *Med.Hist.*, 1962, 6: 96; by Lloyd G. Stevenson, *J.Hist.Med.*, 1964, 19: 91-2.

PIzg GOITER

GOITER number. *Med.Life*, 1925, 32: 33-70. [CB 17/596]
Israel Bram: Historical data on exophthalmic goiter. O.P. Kimball: The progress of goiter prevention. J.F. Gudernatsch: History of iodine therapy. Otto Raubenheimer: The discovery of iodine. Victor Robinson: Goiter chronology.

GREENWALD, Isidor. A note on Chatin and the hypothesis that endemic goiter is due to lack of iodine. *Science*, 1950, 111: 501-2. [CB 76/364]

IFF, Wilhelm. Die Entwicklung der Kropfbehandlung. Zum 70. Geburtstag von Professor Dr. F. De Quervain, Bern, 4. Mai, 1938. *Janus*, 1938, 42: 69-88.

LEERSUM, E.C. van. Bijdrage tot de geschiedenis der goedaardige schildklierzwelling. [Contribution to the history of the non-malignant enlargement of the thyroid gland. (In Dutch)] *Bijdr. Gesch.Geneesk.*, 1925, 5: 184-96, 10 ill.

LEERSUM, E.C. van. Contribution to the history of the simple enlargement of the thyroid gland. *Janus*, 1925, 29: 282-9. [CB 20/210]

PANEBAKER, George. The history of goiter. *Med.Life*, 1925, 32: 97-105.

SARTON, George. When was the cause of endemic goiter recognized? (Query no. 113) [Answer by] Claudius F. Mayer. *Isis*, 1947, 37: 71-3, bibliogr.
Includes bibliography of the history of goiter.

PIzg-we-th

PITFIELD, Robert Lucas. The Shropshire lass and her goitre. Some account of Mary Meredith Webb and her works. *Ann.Med. Hist.*, 1942, 4: 284-93.

PIzg-wg-da

ROCH, Maurice. Le goître et le rôle des médecins genevois dans les découvertes le concernant. *Alma Mater* (Geneva), 1946, 3: 407-17, 5 ill.

PIzg-yQA

CZYŻEWSKI, Kazimierz; ŠILINK, Karel; ed. Endemic goitre in the hill regions between the Elbe and the Oder rivers. 259 p. Warsaw: Polish State Medical Publishers, 1962.

GREENWALD, Isidor. The early history of goiter in the Americas, in New Zealand, and in England. A contribution to the etiology of the disease. *Bull.Hist.Med.*, 1945, 17: 229-69.

GREENWALD, Isidor. Goiter in Peru. *Bull.Hist.Med.*, 1953, 27: 483.

GREENWALD, Isidor. The history of goiter in Africa. *Bull.Hist. Med.*, 1949, 23: 155-85.

GREENWALD, Isidor. The history of goiter in the Netherlands. *Janus*, 1960, 49: 285-99.

GREENWALD, Isidor. The history of goiter in the Philippine Islands. *Bull.Hist.Med.*, 1952, 26: 263-8.

GREENWALD, Isidor. Notes on the history of goiter in Spain and among Jews. *Bull.Hist.Med.*, 1958, 32: 121-36.

GREENWALD, Isidor. Notes on the history of goitre in Sweden (Remarks on its significance for the aetiology of the disorder.) *Med.Hist.*, 1960, 4: 196-209.

GREENWALD, Isidor. Observations on the history of goiter in Ohio and in West Virginia. *J.Hist.Med.*, 1955, 10: 277-89.

LASTRES, Juan B. Goiter in Peru. *Bull.Hist.Med.*, 1953, 27: 483-4.

PJ DERMATOLOGY

CUMMINS, Harold; MIDLO, Charles. Finger prints, palms and soles: an introduction to dermatoglyphics. xi, 309 p. Philadelphia: Blakiston, 1943. [CB 65/83]

ÉTUDES sur la chimie physiologique de la peau par MM. Dejust, Verne, Combes, Parat, Urbain, Dujarric de la Rivière, de Saint-Rat. 381 p. (Publication du Laboratoire de Chimie de la Clinique des Maladies Cutanées de la Faculté de Médecine à l'hôpital Saint Louis) Paris: Amédée Legrand, 1928.
Reviewed by R.M. May, *Isis*, 1929, 13: 134-5.

GARRISON, Fielding Hudson. The skin as a functional organ of the body. *Bull.N.Y.Acad.Med.*, 1933, 9: 417-32.

GÜNTHER, Hans. Historische Notizen über die Reactio pilomotorica (Gänsehaut). *Arch.Gesch.Med.*, 1918, 11: 101-7.

HEIMANN, Walter James. The evolution of dermatology. *Ann.Med. Hist.*, 1917, 1: 427-8.

PUSEY, William Allen. The history of dermatology. xvii, 233 p., 32 ill. Springfield, Ill.: C.C. Thomas, 1933.
Reviewed by C.D. Leake, *Isis*, 1934, 20: 504-5; by Léon Brodier, *Bull.Soc.Franç.Hist.Méd.*, 1933, 27: 317-18.

RAVOGLI, Augustus. History of dermatology. *Med.Life*, 1926, 33: 492-538. [CB 22/307]

RICHTER, Paul. Geschichte der Dermatologie. iv, 278 p. (Handbuch der Haut- und Geschlechtskrankheiten, 14: 2) Berlin: Springer, 1928.
Reviewed by W. Haberling, *Mitt.Gesch.Med.*, 1929, 28: 94.

SCHÖNFELD, W. Kurze Geschichte der Dermatologie und Venerologie und ihre kulturgeschichtliche Spiegelung. 150 p. (Heilkunde und Geisteswelt, 6) Hannover-Kirchrode: Oppermann, 1954.
Reviewed by Wolfram Kock, *Lychnos*, 1956, 439-40.

SIGERIST, Henry E. Die ärztliche Kosmetik im Wandel der Jahrhunderte. *Med.Welt*, 1931, nos. 47-49, 1696-7, 1732-3, 1765-6.

PJmzMFAvb

EBSTEIN, Erich. Zur Ethnologie und Synonymik des Albinos. *Mitt.Gesch.Med.*, 1915, 14: 284, 295.

FROGGATT, P. The legend of a white native race. (A contribution to the history of albinism.) *Med.Hist.*, 1960, 4: 228-35.

PJmzOMP

BERG, Charles. The unconscious significance of hair. vi, 106 p. London: Allen and Unwin, 1951.
Reviewed by Clifford Allen, *Nature*, 1952, 169: 301.

PJmzQD

SCHÖNFELD, W. Die Haut als Ausgang der Behandlung, Verhütung und Erkennung fernörtlicher Leiden. Eine geschichtliche Studie. *Sudhoffs Arch.*, 1943, 36: 43-89, 3 fig.

PJtq

BOLTE, O. Über die malerische Darstellung menschlicher Haut und menschlicher Kopfbehaarung als Ausdruck stilistischer und kunstgeschichtlicher Wandlung. *Hautarzt*, 1964, 15: 442-8.

PJwb

BECHET, Paul E. L'hôpital Saint-Louis. *See* PJyNWwf

BECHET, Paul E. An outline of the achievements of American dermatology arranged in chronological order. *Bull.Hist.Med.*, 1946, 19: 291-318, 25 portr.

FOX, George Henry. Reminiscences. 248 p., front., portr. New York: Medical Life Press, 1926.
Recollections of an American dermatologist.

PJwb-qd

BECHET, Paul E. A history of the American Dermatological Association in commemoration of its seventy-fifth anniversary, 1876-1951. 392 p., ill. New York: Froben Press, 1952.
Reviewed by L.M. Ketron, *Bull.Hist.Med.*, 1953, 27: 499-500.

PJwc

RODRIGUES, Obdulla; SAUL, Amado. La dermatologia en México. 1. Sus origines; 2. La enseñanza; 3. Los primeros dermatólogos. [With French and English summaries] *Dermatología*, 1961, 5: 123-8, 251-6; 1962, 6: 3-17.

PJwg

LESKY, E. Die Entwicklung der wissenschaftlichen Kosmetik in Österreich. *Aesthet.Med.*, 1960, 9: 199-210.

PJwp-u

ÜNVER, A. Süheyl. Le folklore dermatologique en Turquie. *Deliberationes Congr.Dermatol.Int.IX-I* (Budapest, 1935), (2), p. 800-6, ill. Budapestini: Institutum Typographicum "Patria", 1936; also (in Turkish and French) *Deri Hastalikları Frengi Klin.Arşivi*, 1935, 2: no. 11/12.

PJyNW HOSPITALS

PJyNWwe

RUSSELL, Brian, ed. St. John's Hospital for Diseases of the Skin, 1863-1963. viii, 71 p., ill. Edinburgh/London: E. & S. Livingstone, 1963.
Reviewed by David I. Williams, *Proc.Roy.Soc.Med.*, 1963, 56: 955.

PJyNWwf

BECHET, Paul E. L'hôpital Saint-Louis. A brief biographical sketch of its early teachers, and their influence upon American dermatology. *Ann.Med.Hist.*, 1938, 10: 405-12, 5 fig.

PK SKIN DISORDERS AND DISEASES

for St. Anthony's fire *see* PKzs
infectious diseases affecting the skin *see* QP
scabies *see* QTzs

CUMSTON, Charles Greene. The history of herpes from the earliest times to the nineteenth century. With remarks on dermatological lesions in general. *Ann.Med.Hist.*, 1926, 8: 284-91.

GRANT, R.N.R. The history of acne. *Proc.Roy.Soc.Med.*, 1951, 44: Hist. Sect., 647-52.

MACHT, David I. Job's disease. An historical and experimental study. *Victor Robinson Memorial Volume*, p. 241-50. New York: Froben, 1948.

MONTGOMERY, Douglass W. The historical position of coccidioides immitis among the pathogenic fungi of the skin. *Ann. Med.Hist.*, 1932, 4: 199-202.

NEUBURGER, Max. Die Lehre von den Hautkrankheiten vor Hebra. *Wiener Med.Wochenschr.*, 1928, 78: 343-5, 382-7.

POMERANTZ, Jacob. Melasma suprarenale. *Med.Life*, 1930, 37: [689-700], suppl. 15-26, 3 pl.

PUSEY, William Allen. Disease, gadfly of the mind, especially the stimulus of skin-diseases in the development of the mind. *Brit.J.Dermatol.*, 1934, 46: 341-60.

RENBOURN, E.T. The history of sweat and sweat rash from earliest times to the end of the 18th century. *J.Hist.Med.*, 1959, 14: 202-27.

RONCHESE, F. Les dartres. *Centaurus*, 1954, 3: 236-43, 7 pl.

SAINTYVES, P. La guérison des verrues. De la magie médicale à la psychothérapie. 85 p. Paris: E. Nourry, 1913.
Reviewed by George Sarton, *Isis*, 1914, 2: 242-3.

PKnh

BESWICK, T.S.L. The origin and the use of the word Herpes. *Med.Hist.*, 1962, 6: 214-32.

MONTGOMERY, Douglass W. The naming of Alopecia areata. *Ann. Med.Hist.*, 1931, 3: 540-6.

PKnj

CIPRIANI, Mariano. I nomi di persona nella terminologia dermo-e venereopatica (sintomi, sindromi, malattie). Dizionario. 408 p. Ascoli Piceno: Società Tipo-Litografica, 1942.
Reviewed by L. Castaldi, *Riv.Stor.Sci.*, 1943, 34: 54.

GOODMAN, Herman. Master dermatologists, based on diseases named after them. *Ann.Med.Hist.*, 1925, 7: 47-59.

PKwp

ÜNVER, A. Süheyl. Aperçu sur les dermatoses chez les Ouigours. (In Turkish and French) *Deri Hastaliklari Frengi Klin.Arşivi*, 1935, 2: no. 11/12, 4 pl.

PKyNH

GLASSER, Otto. First observations on physiological effects of Roentgen rays on human skin. *Amer.J.Roentgenol.*, 1932, 28: 75-80.

PKzs SAINT ANTHONY'S FIRE

CAIRES, Alvaro de. Le feu Saint Antoine et l'ordre des Antonins au Portugal. *Bull.Soc.Franç.Hist.Méd.*, 1938, 32: 101-12.

CHAUMARTIN, Henry. L'abbaye de Saint Antoine de Viennois et le feu Saint-Antoine. (Thèse, Lyon) 200 p., 8 pl. Vienne: Henri Martin, 1926. [CB 21/600]

CHAUMARTIN, Henry. Le mal des ardents et le feu Saint-Antoine: étude historique, médicale, hagiographique et légendaire. 203, xli p., ill. Vienne-la-Romaine: Ternet-Martin, 1946. [CB 71/131]
Based on articles in *La Médecine Internationale Illustrée*, 1935-37.

CHAUMARTIN, Henry. Quelques documents et pièces d'archives pour servir à l'histoire du feu Saint-Antoine. *Bull.Soc. Franç.Hist.Méd.*, 1928, 22: 375-81.

CHAVANT, Dr. Extraits choisis sur le feu de Saint-Antoine. *Proc.17th Int.Congr.Med.* (London, 1912), *Sect.* 23, p. 87-96. London: Oxford University Press; Hodder & Stoughton, 1914.

PKzs-wg

MARTIN, Alfred. Beiträge zür Geschichte des Aussatzes, der Syphilis, des Antoniusfeuers, der Pest und der an diesen Erkrankten in Deutschland. *Arch.Gesch.Med.*, 1919, 11: 189-99.

PL UROLOGY

for urine analysis *see* QDzu

DESNOS, E. Histoire de l'urologie. 294 p., ill. Paris: Doin, 1914. [CB 6/466]
Also published as part of: Encyclopédie française d'urologie. 6 vol. Paris: Doin, 1914-23.

GRONDONA, Felice. Strutturística renale da Galeno al Highmore. *Physis*, 1963, 5: 173-95.

LEWIS, Bransford, ed. History of urology. Prepared under the auspices of the American Urological Association. 2 vol. xii, 386 p.; vii, 362 p., ill. Baltimore: Williams and Wilkins, 1933.

RICHTER, Paul. Historische Beiträge zur Urologie. *Z.Urol.*, 1913, 7: 735-8, ill.

PLtq

MEIGE, Henri. Les urologues dans l'art. *Aesculape*, 1928, 18: 54-67, 14 ill.

PLvm-cc

MARGALITH, D. [Sexology and urology in Jewish sources. (In Hebrew with English summary.)] *Koroth*, 1962, 2: 426-34.

PLwj

CARVALHO, Silva, Historia da urologia em Portugal até ao meiado do seculo XIX. 84 p. Lisboa: Sociedade nacional de tipografia, 1925.

PLwq

BITSCHAI, J.; BRODNY, Leopold. A history of urology in Egypt. 122 p., 14 fig. Cambridge, Mass.: Riverside Press, 1956.
Reviewed by P. Huard and J. Brocas, *Rev.Hist.Sci.*, 1957, 10: 279-81.

PLyNW HOSPITALS

PLyNWwe

DUKES, Cuthbert E. The History of St. Peter's Hospital for Stone, London. *Proc.Roy.Soc.Med.*, 1957, 50: 161-4.

MORSON, Clifford, ed. St. Peter's Hospital for Stone, 1860-1960. viii, 64 p., ill. Edinburgh/London: E. & S. Livingstone; Baltimore, Md., 1960.
Reviewed by W.J. Bishop, *Med.Hist.*, 1961, 5: 99-100; by J. Steudel, *Sudhoffs Arch.*, 1961, 45: 183-4; in *Proc.Roy.Soc. Med.*, 1961, 54: 163.

PM URINARY DISORDERS AND DISEASES

for urological surgery *see* RCQ

ANDEL, M.A. van. Geneesmiddelen tegen den steen der nieren en der blase. [Remedies for kidney and bladder stone. (In Dutch)] *Bijdr.Gesch.Geneesk.*, 1935, 15: 152-7.

CHRISTIAN, Henry A. Kidney disease as described by Richard Bright in the light of the knowledge of a century later. *Ann.Med.Hist.*, 1927, 9: 337-46, 8 fig.

KAHN, Max. History of the chemistry of renal and cystic calculi (with Jacob Rosenbloom). *Med.Life*, 1926, 33: 356-62.

MAJOR, Ralph H. Notes on the history of nephritis. *Bull.Hist. Med.*, 1949, 23: 453-60.

OSATHANONDH, Vitoon; POTTER, Edith L. Pathogenesis of polycystic kidneys. Historical survey. *Arch.Path.*, 1964, 77: 459-65.

POUSSON, A. L'affection calculeuse à travers les âges. *J. Urol.*, 1912, 1: 1-26, ill.

PMcp

RANDALL, Alexander. Curiosities from the collection of calculi in the Museum of the Royal College of Surgeons. *Ann.Med.Hist.* 1925, 7: 181-9.

PMwk-u

BAKKER, C. Enuresis nocturna in de volksgeneeskunst in en om Broek in Waterland. [Enuresis nocturna in popular medicine in and around Broek in Waterland. (In Dutch)] *Bijdr.Gesch. Geneesk.*, 1925, 5: 210-18.

PMxd

CHEVASSU, Maurice. Les débuts du cathétérisme urétéral. *Hist. Méd.*, 1951, 1: no. 3, 29-33.

PMyQD DIAGNOSIS

CAU, Giovanni, Urologhi, uromanti, uroscopi e la matula. *Riv. Stor.Sci.*, 1927, 18: 244-59.

CHRISTOFFEL, Hans. Grundzüge der Uroskopie. *Gesnerus*, 1953, 10: 89-122, 5 fig.

PMyQDcm

ROSENBLOOM, Jacob. The ancient practice of uroscopy. *Med.Life*, 1923, 30: 385-400.
Apropos of the author's collection of 140 reproductions of paintings and art objects dealing with uroscopy, with a bibliography.

PMyQDxk-wg

HRYNTSCHAK, Th. Wiens Anteil an der Erfindung des Kystoskopes. *Festschrift zum 80. Geburtstag Max Neuburgers*, p. 239-45, 3 fig., facs. Wien: Maudrich, 1948.

PMyQDxp

EBSTEIN, Erich. Die klinische Geschichte der Urometers. *Festschrift zur Feier seines 60. Geburtstags Max Neuburger gewidmet*, p. 83-9, 3 ill. Wien: Verlag des Fest-Komitees, 1928.

PN SEXOLOGY

for sexual behaviour *see* MQzs
sexual hygiene *see* NQ
circumcision *see* RCS

BAUMANN, E.D. Historische Betrachtungen über das Koitus-Konzeptions-Problem. 99 p. Arnhem: Misset, 1940.
Reviewed by M.A. Van Andel, *Bijdr.Gesch.Geneesk.*, 1940, 20: 177-8; by J.A.V., *Janus*, 1940, 44: 317-18.

HIRSCHFELD, Magnus. Die Homosexualität des Mannes und des Weibes. xvii, 1067 p. (Handbuch der gesamten Sexualwissenschaft, 3) Berlin: L. Marcus, 1914.
Reviewed by G. Sarton, *Isis*, 1914, 2: 241-2.

JOEL, Charles A. Studien am menschlichen Sperma. 154 p., 10 pl. Basel: Schwabe, 1942.
Part 1 is devoted to a historical outline.
Reviewed by Arthur Walton, *Nature*, 1946, 158: 729.

JOYET-LAVERGNE, Ph. Les théories métaboliques et la théorie physico-chimique de la sexualité. *Scientia*, 1931, 49: 197-206.

KATSAINOS, George M. The physiology of love. 326 p. Boston, Mass.: priv. print., 1929. [CB 27/401]

MARCUSE, Max. Handwörterbuch der Sexualwissenschaft; Enzyklopädie der natur- und kulturwissenschaftlichen Sexualkunde des Menschen. iv, 481 p. Bonn: Marcus und Weber, 1923.

NIEUWENHUIS, A.W. Die ursprünglichsten Ansichten über das Geschlechtsleben des Menschen. *Janus*, 1928, 32: 289-314.
Revised and completed version of lecture given at the Congress for the History of Medicine, Leiden, Amsterdam, July 1927.

PADOA, Emanuele. Storia naturale del sesso. 560 p., ill. Turin: Einaudi, 1948.

PNu

BYLOFF, Fritz. Nestelknüpfen und- lösen. *Arch.Gesch.Med.*, 1927, 19: 203-8. [CB 22/293]

PO FAMILY PLANNING; CONTRACEPTION; ARTIFICIAL INSEMINATION

AMERICAN NEUROLOGICAL ASSOCIATION. Committee for the Investigation of Eugenical Sterilization. Eugenical sterilization. A reorientation of the problem. viii, 211 p. New York: Macmillan, 1936. [CB 53/532]

CHURCH OF ENGLAND. Artificial human insemination. The report of a commission appointed by the Archbishop of Canterbury. 70 p. London: S.P.C.K., 1948. [CB 74/392]

DINGWALL, Eric John. The girdle of chastity: a medico-historical study. x, 171 p., 10 pl. London: Routledge, 1931.

DINGWALL, Eric John. Male infibulation. vii, 145 p. London: Bale and Danielsson, 1925.

FINCH, B.E.; GREEN, Hugh. Contraception through the ages. 174 p. Springfield, Ill.: Charles C. Thomas, 1964.

GOSNEY, Ezra Seymour; POPENOE, Paul. Sterilization for human betterment. A summary of results of 6000 operations in California, 1909-1929. xviii, 202 p. (Publication of the Human Betterment Foundation) New York/London: Macmillan, 1929.

HIMES, Norman E. Forerunners of the modern condom. *Janus*, 1938, 42: 1-6, 10 fig.

HIMES, Norman E. The medical history of contraception. With a medical foreword by R.L. Dickinson. xxxi, 521 p., 29 tables, 30 fig. (Medical Aspects of Human Fertility issued by the National Committee on Maternal Health) Baltimore: Williams and Wilkins, 1936. [CB 48/574]

HIMES, Norman E. Medical history of contraception. *New Engl. J.Med.*, 1934, 210: 576-81.

LANDMAN, Jacob Henry. Human sterilization: the history of the sexual sterilization movement. xviii, 341 p. New York: Macmillan, 1932. [CB 40/404]

MONTAGU, M.F. Ashley. Infibulation and defibulation in the Old and New Worlds. *Amer.Anthropol.*, 1945, 47: 464-7.

STOPES, Marie Carmichael. Contraception (birth control), its theory, history and practice: a manual for the medical and legal professions. xxiii, 418 p., 4 pl. London: J. Bale, Sons and Danielsson, 1923.

STREICH, Artur. Zur Geschichte des Condoms. *Arch.Gesch.Med.*, 1929, 22: 208-13.

POtc

NATIONAL COUNCIL OF PUBLIC MORALS. The ethics of birth-control. Report of the Special Committee of the National Council. xvi, 179 p. London: Macmillan, 1925.
Reviewed by J.S. Huxley, *Nature*, 1925, 116: 455-7.

PP DISEASES AFFECTING THE GENITAL SYSTEM; VENEREAL DISEASES

for women's diseases *see* PT
gonorrhea *see* QPzg
syphilis *see* QPzsy

BERNARDIS, Giovanni de. Compendio storico della veneorologia. 127 p. Roma: Studio Editoriale degli Istituti Universitari, 1937.
Reviewed by G. Verità, *Riv.Stor.Sci.*, 1938, 29: 285.

KEIL, Harry. A note on the antiquity of the adreno-genital syndroma. *Bull.Hist.Med.*, 1949, 23: 201-2.

LE PETIT, Jacques. Historique du chancre mou. (Thèse) 123 p. Paris: Ollier-Henry, 1913.

PADILLA, Mariano. Ensayo historico sobre el origen de la enfermedad venera o de las bubas. 2nd ed. 64 p. Guatemala: Universidad de San Carlos: 1948. [CB 73/147]

PENFOLD, John B. The early history of elephantiasis of the scrotum. *Ann.Med.Hist.*, 1937, 9: 125-32.

ROLLESTON, J.D. Penis captivus: a historical note. *Janus*, 1935, 39: 196-202. [CB 47/285]

SIGERIST, Henry E. Die Bekämpfung der Geschlechtskrankheiten in früheren Zeiten. *Schweiz.Z.Gesundheitspflege*, 1922, 2: 184-98.

STICKER, Georg. Entwurf einer Geschichte der ansteckenden Geschlechtskrankheiten. In: Handbuch der Haut- und Geschlechtskrankheiten, vol. 23, p. 263-603, 37 fig. Berlin: Springer, 1931.
Reviewed by W. Haberling, *Mitt.Gesch.Med.*, 1931, 30: 195-7.

PPu

ROLLESTON, J.D. The folk-lore of venereal disease. *Brit.J. Vener.Dis.*, 1942, 18: 1-13.

PPwf

GOLDSCHMIDT, D. De l'introduction et de la propagation des maladies vénériennes en Alsace et en particulier à Strasbourg. *Bull.Soc.Franç.Hist.Méd.*, 1913, 12: 395.

PPxe

LACASSAGNE, Jean; PIGEAUD, -. Les inoculations expérimentales de maladies vénériennes à des médecins (dévouements trop ignorés). *Ann.Mal.Vénér.*, 1924, 19: 865-80.

PPyNG

BAUDE, E.L.A. Prophylaxie antivénérienne individuelle à travers les âges. Essai historique. (Thèse) 48 p. Paris: Le Francois, 1927. [CB 24/559]

PQ GYNAECOLOGY AND OBSTETRICS

for health services for mothers and children *see* NU
obstetrics *see also* PS
surgery in gynaecology and obstetrics *see* RCT

PQc

ARNOLD, Clement H. Historical gynecology. *Calif.Western Med.*, 1936, 44: 40-3.
Brief summary.

CIANFRANI, Theodore. A short history of obstetrics and gynecology. xvi, 449 p., ill. Springfield, Ill.: Charles C. Thomas; Oxford: Blackwell Scientific Publications, Ltd., 1960.
Reviewed in *Proc.Roy.Soc.Med.*, 1961, 54: 252; by John MacLean Morris, *J.Hist.Med.*, 1961, 16: 92-3; by Emil Bovin, *Lychnos*, 1962, 502-3.

FISCHER, Isidor. Geschichte der Gynäkologie. 202 p., ill. Berlin/Wien: Urban u. Schwarzenberg, 1923. [CB 16/318]

GRAHAM, Harvey, *pseud.* of I. Harvey Flack. Eternal Eve. The history of gynecology and obstetrics. xx, 699 p., ill. London: Heinemann; Garden City, N.Y.: Doubleday & Co., 1951.
Reviewed by M. Pierce Rucker, *Bull.Hist.Med.*, 1953, 27: 82-4; by Claude Heaton, *J.Hist.Med.*, 1953, 8: 112-13.

JAMESON, Edwin Milton. Gynecology and obstetrics. xv, 170 p., ill. (Clio Medica Series, 17) New York: Hafner Publishing Co., 1962.
Paperback reprint of 1936 edition (reviewed by William R. Nicholson, *Ann.Med.Hist.*, 1937, 9: 95-6.)
Reviewed in *Proc.Roy.Soc.Med.*, 1963, 56: 134; by H.J. Malkin, *Med.Hist.*, 1963, 7: 295.

LEONARDO, Richard A. History of gynecology. xx, 434 p., 25 pl. New York: Froben Press, 1944.
Reviewed by J.B. de C.M. Saunders, *Isis*, 1947, 37: 123-4.

PLOSS, Hermann Heinrich; BARTELS, Max; BARTELS, Paul. Woman. An historical gynaecological compendium. Edited by Eric John Dingwall. 3 vol. xiii, 655 p.; 820 p.; 543 p., 1002 ill., 7 pl. London: Heinemann, 1935.
Reviewed by M.F. Ashley-Montagu, *Isis*, 1936, 25: 167-9.

RICCI, James V. The genealogy of gynaecology: history of the development of gynaecology throughout the ages: 2000 B.C.-1800 A.D. 2nd ed. xvi, 494 p. Philadelphia: Blakiston, 1950. [CB 77/387]
Reviewed by O. Temkin, *Bull.Hist.Med.*, 1944, 16: 422-4.

SIGERIST, Henry E. Developments and trends in gynecology. *Amer.J.Obstet.Gynecol.*, 1941, 42: 714-22.

PQda

SPEERT, Harold. Obstetric and gynecologic milestones. Essays in eponymy. ix, 700 p. New York: Macmillan, 1958.
Reviewed by Herbert Thoms, *J.Hist.Med.*, 1959, 14: 539-40; by Alistair Gunn, *Med.Hist.*, 1959, 3: 256.

PQdaj

THOMS, Herbert. Classical contributions to obstetrics and gynecology. With a foreword by Howard A. Kelley. xxiii, 265 p., ill. Springfield, Ill.: Thomas, 1935.
Reviewed by M.F. Ashley-Montagu, *Isis*, 1936, 25: 174-5.

PQnj

SPEERT, Harold. *See* PQda

PQqx

BÉCLÈRE, Claude. Congrès international jubilaire de la Société Française de Gynécologie. *Hist.Méd.*, 1951, 1: no. 5, 3-6.

PQwb

SCHEFFEY, Lewis C. The earlier history and the transition period of obstetrics and gynecology in Philadelphia. *Ann. Med.Hist.*, 1940, 2: 215-24.

SELLERS, Thomas Benton. Louisiana's contributions to obstetrics and gynecology. *Bull.Hist.Med.*, 1948, 22: 196-207.

PQwc

NORIEGA TRIGO, Manuel. Labores gíneco-obstetricas en la "Casa de Beneficencia" de Maracaibo, entre 1896 y 1916. *Rev.Soc. Venezolana Hist.Med.*, 1957, 5: 129-47.

PQwc-oq

PASTORINI, Raul. Apuntes para la historia de la cátedra de ginecologia de la Facultad de ciencias médicas de Buenos Aires. *Publ.Cátedra Hist.Med.Univ.Buenos Aires*, 1938, 1: 279-94.

PQwe

KERR, J.M. Munro; JOHNSTONE, R.W.; PHILLIPS, Miles H. Historical review of British obstetrics and gynaecology 1800-1950. viii, 420 p. Edinburgh/London: Livingstone, 1954.
Reviewed by P.F.C. Wille, *Sudhoffs Arch.*, 1955, 39: 192.

PQwg

MARTIN, August Eduard. Werden und Wirken eines deutschen Frauenarztes. 370 p. Berlin: S. Karger, 1924.
Autobiography.

PQwg-oq

LESKY, Erna. Die Wiener geburtshilflich-gynäkologische Schule. Geist und Leistung. *Deut.Med.Wochenschr.*, 1962, 41: 1-13.

PHILIPP, E.; HÖRMANN, G. Die Kieler Universitäts-Frauenklinik und Hebammen-Lehranstalt, 1805-1955. x, 149 p., 13 fig. Stuttgart: Georg Thieme Verlag, 1955.
Reviewed by Emil Bovin, *Lychnos*, 1957-58, 494-6.

PQwi

VIANA, Odorico; VOZZA, Francesco. L'ostetricia e la ginecologia in Italia. 1191 p. Milan: Cordi, 1933.
Reviewed by D.G., *Riv.Stor.Sci.*, 1933, 24: 156.

PQwi-da

PEDOTE, V. Saggio iconografico e profili bio-bibliografici degli ostetrici e ginecologi dell' Università de Bologna dalla creazione della clinica (1757) al periodo attuale. *Riv. Stor.Med.*, 1964, 8: 3-35.

PQwo

ANDRIANAKOS, Tryphon. Exelixis kai proodoi tēs maieutikēs kai gynaikologias en tē neōtera Helladi. [Evolution and progress of obstetrics and gynaecology in modern Greece. (In Greek)] xiv, 190 p. Thessalonica: 1937. [CB 51/292]
Reprinted from *Hellēnikē Iatrikē*, 1937, vol. 11.

PQwp

KESKIN, Refik Münür; SAGLIK, Saim. A sketch of the history of gynecology and obstetrics in Turkey. *Bull.Inst.Hist.Med.*, 1938, 6: 899-906, 4 fig.

PQxb

DRAKE, T.G.H. Antiques of medical interest: nipple shields. *J.Hist.Med.*, 1946, 1: 316-17, 4 fig.

LENGHEL, Alexandre. Anciens pessaires trouvés en Hongrie et en Transylvanie. *Bull.Soc.Franç.Hist.Méd.*, 1928, 22: 185-8.

PQxx museums

NAJĪB MAḤFŪẒ, *Pasha*. Atlas of Mahfouz's obstetric and gynaecological museum. 3 vol. xviii, 417 p., 436 fig.; xiv, p. 419-860, 467 fig.; xiv, p. 861-1276, 492 fig. Altrincham, England: Sherratt, 1949. [CB 77/386]
Magnificent atlas representing the museum which Najīb Maḥfūz presented to the Faculty of Medicine of Cairo in 1932.

PQyNW HOSPITALS FOR WOMEN

for maternity hospitals *see* PSyNW

PQyNWwc

MORENO, Anibal Ruiz. Organización colonial del hospital de mujeres. *Publ.Cátedra Hist.Med.Univ.Buenos Aires*, 1938, 1: 237-51.

PQyNWwe

WINTERTON, W.R. The story of the London gynaecological hospitals. *Proc.Roy.Soc.Med.*, 1961, 54: 191-8.

PQyNWwg

LABHARDT, Alfred. Das Frauenspital Basel-Stadt. 71 p., 69 fig. Basel: Kunstanstalt Frobenius, 1929.

PR WOMEN: ANATOMY AND PHYSIOLOGY

CORNER, George W. The hormone of the Corpus luteum. *Edinb. Med.J.*, 1937, 44: *suppl. Trans.Edinb.Obstet.Soc.*, 61-80.

CORNER, George W. The hormones in human reproduction. xix, 265 p., 24 pl. Princeton: Princeton University Press, 1942. [CB 63/275]
Many historical data are scattered through book.

CORNER, George W. Our knowledge of the menstrual cycle, 1910-1950. (4th Annual Addison Lecture) *Lancet*, 1951, 260: 919-23.

FISCHER, Isidor. Menstruation und Ovulation. Ein Beitrag zur Vorgeschichte der inneren Sekretion der Ovarien. *Wiener Med.Wochenschr.*, 1923, 73: 1851-4.

KURZROK, Raphael. The endocrines in obstetrics and gynecology. xvi, 488 p. Baltimore: Williams & Wilkins, 1937. [CB 53/280]

LA TORRE, Felice. L'utero attraverso i secoli. Da Erofilo ai giorni nostri. xx, 831 p., 560 fig., 22 pl. Città di Castello: Unione Arti Grafiche, 1917. [CB 13/279]

MÜLLER-HESS, Hans Georg. Die Lehre von der Menstruation vom Beginn der Neuzeit bis zur Begründung der Zellenlehre. 102 p. (*Abhandl.Gesch.Med.Naturwiss.*, 27) Berlin: Ebering, 1938.

PRu

CRAWFURD, Raymond. Of superstitions concerning menstruation. *Proc.Roy.Soc.Med.*, 1916, 9: Hist. Sect., 49.
Traces these beliefs from primitive to modern times in connection with magic, milk supply, crops, etc.

PS OBSTETRICS

for puerpural fever *see* QPzpu
Caesarian section *see* RCU
anaesthesia *see* RDyPS
drug administration *see* ROyPR

PSc general history

BESSIM, Omer. Dogum tarihi. [History of obstetrics. (In Turkish)] 56 p., ill. Istanbul: Ihsan, 1932.
Reviewed by A. Adnan, *Archeion*, 1932, 14: 335-7.

BUCCARELLI, G.; NICCOLAI, G.C. Cenni storici sulla rianimazione neonatale. *Riv.Ostet.Ginec.Prat.*, 1964, 46: 1064-9.

BUESS, H. Die Anfänge der Geburtshilfe. *Ciba Z.*, 1950, 11: 4470-500, ill.

BYERS, John. The evolution of obstetric medicine; with illustrations from some old midwifery books. *Brit.Med.J.*, 1912, (1), 1345-50.

DEVRAIGNE, L. L'obstétrique à travers les âges. 139 p., ill. Paris: Doin, 1939.

FINDLEY, Palmer. On the history of childbirth. *Med.Life.*, 1935, 42: 632-4.

FINDLEY, Palmer. The story of childbirth. xx, 376 p. Garden City, N.Y.: Doubleday, Doran, 1933.
Reviewed in *Ann.Med.Hist.*, 1934, 6: 190.

FLACK, I. Harvey. The pre-history of midwifery. *Proc.Roy. Soc.Med.*, 1947, 40: Hist. Sect., 713-22.

JARCHO, Julius. Postures and practices during labor among primitive peoples, adaptations to modern obstetrics, with chapters on taboos and superstitions, and post-partum gymnastics. xvi, 175 p., 130 ill. New York: Hoeber, 1934.
Reviewed in *Ann.Med.Hist.*, 1934, 6: 560.

KANNER, Leo. Born with a caul. *Med.Life*, 1931, 528-48.

MALCOVATI, Piero. Introduzione storica al trattato di ostetricia. In: Cova, Ercole, ed. Trattato di ostetricia minore. 3 vol. Milano: Montuoro, 1947.
Reviewed by A.C., *Riv.Stor.Sci.*, 1947, 38: 70.

MARR, James Pratt. Historical background of the treatment of placenta praevia. *Bull.Hist.Med.*, 1941, 9: 258-93.

MARTIN, Alfred. Gebärlage der Frau. Bad der Neugeborenen und Wochenbett in Mitteleuropa auf Grund bildlicher und textlicher Darstellung. *Arch.Gesch.Med.*, 1917, 10: 209-50, 2 ill.

OSIANDER, Johann Friedrich. Einige geschichtliche Beiträge zur Medicin und Geburtshülfe. *Henschel's Janus*, 1846, 1: 753-63; reprinted Leipzig: Alfred Lorentz, 1931. [CB 33/411]
Historical notes on obstetrics including a short note on Alphonse Leroy.

SALOMONSON, Joh. G. Barenspijn en haar bestrijding in den loop der tijden. [Birth pain and the fight against it in the course of time. (In Dutch)] *Bijdr.Gesch.Geneesk.*, 1926, 6: 125-40.

SNOECK, Jean. L'évolution et l'avenir de l'obstétrique. *Rev. Univ.Bruxelles*, 1937-38, 43: 266-80.

SURINGAR, J. Valckenier. "Het verzien" (Versehen; maternal impression; influence de l'imagination maternelle). [In Dutch] *Bijdr.Gesch.Geneesk.*, 1927, 7: 176-87.

VOGELER, Hans. Die Therapie der Nachgeburtsblutungen in der Geschichte der Medizin. 53 p. (Diss.) Freiburg i. Br.: Speyer und Kaerner, 1912.

PSce

FINDLEY, Palmer. The midwives' books. *Med.Life*, 1935, 42: 167-86. [CB 44/524]

RUCKER, M. Pierce. Leaves from a bibliotheca obstetrica. *Bull.Hist.Med.*, 1946, 19: 177-99, 13 fig.

PSce-by

HELLMAN, C. Doris. Additions to the Alfred M. Hellman collection of early obstetrical books. *Acad.Bookman*, 1958, 11: 2-11, ill.

PSda

FINDLEY, Palmer. Priests of Lucina. xiv, 421 p. Boston: Little, Brown, 1939. [CB 59/489]

PSo/u special aspects

PSof

HOEVEN, J. van der. Een en ander over de examens bij de chirurgijns-gilden en over het "vroedkundig examen". [Some notes on the examinations by the surgeon-guilds and on the "midwifery examinations". (In Dutch)] *Bijdr.Gesch.Geneesk.*, 1937, 17: 121-6, 1 facs.

PSr

MENGERT, William F. The origin of the male midwife. *Ann. Med.Hist.*, 1932, 4: 453-65, 9 fig.

PACHINGER, -. (*Hofrat*, Linz a. D.). Die Hebamme. *Arch.Gesch. Med.*, 1920, 12: 73-8.

PSr-cp

ANDEL, M.A. van. Vroedvrouwendordjes. [Midwives' plates. (In Dutch)] *Bijdr.Gesch.Geneesk.*, 1928, 8: 149-53, 3 fig.

PStq

BOUCHACOURT, L. Présentation du moulage de la statuette en ivoire du musée de Cluny, inscrite au catalogue sous le no. 1210, et portant comme titre: Le mystère de la génération. *Compt.Rend.IIe Congr.Int.Hist.Méd.* (Paris, 1921), p. 555-8. Évruex: Imprimerie Ch. Hérissey, 1922.
Anatomical model of a pregnant woman.

STRATZ, C.H. Schwangerschaft in der Kunst. *Z.Geburtsh.Gynäkol.*, 1913, 74: 899-913, ill.

PSu

DRAKE, T.G.H. The eagle stone, an antique obstetrical amulet. *Bull.Hist.Med.*, 1940, 8: 128-32.

HÖFLER, M. Ein alter Heilritus. *Arch.Gesch.Med.*, 1914, 7: 390-5. [CB 19/809]

KRUEGER, Felix. Magical factors in the first development of human labor. *Amer.J.Psychol.*, 1913, 24: 256-61.

PSw in different countries

PSwb

RUCKER, M. Pierce. Sir William Osler's obstetrical interests. *Bull.Hist.Med.*, 1952, 26: 153-61.

THOMS, Herbert. Chapters in American obstetrics. 2nd ed. xiii, 158 p., ill. Springfield, Ill.: Charles C. Thomas, 1961.
First published 1933 and reviewed by C.D. Leake, *Isis*, 1934, 20: 503.
Reviewed in *Proc.Roy.Soc.Med.*, 1963, 56: 135.

PSwb-r

FERGUSON, James H. Mississippi midwives. *J.Hist.Med.*, 1950, 5: 85-95.

PSwc

FISHBEIN, Morris; DE LEE, Sol Theron. Joseph Bolivar De Lee, crusading obstetrician. 313 p., portr. New York: Dutton, 1949.

PSwg-r

BURCKHARD, Georg. Die deutschen Hebammenordnungen von ihren ersten Anfängen bis auf die Neuzeit. 1.Teil. xviii, 258 p. (Studien zur Geschichte des Hebammenwesens, I: 1) Leipzig: W. Engelmann, 1912.

HABERLING, Elseluise. Beiträge zur Geschichte des Hebammenstandes. 1. Der Hebammenstand in Deutschland von seinen Anfängen bis zum Dreissigjährigen Krieg. v, 119 p., 14 fig. Berlin: Staude, 1940.
Reviewed by P. Diepgen, *Mitt.Gesch.Med.*, 1940, 39: 295-7.

MUHEIM, Edwin. Zur Geschichte des Hebammenwesens und der staatlichen Gebäranstalt St. Gallen. 74 p. (*Zürcher Medizingesch. Abhandl.*, 17) Zürich: Leemann, 1941.
Reviewed by Zaunick, *Mitt.Gesch.Med.*, 1941-42, 40: 91.

PSwi-oq

BELLONI, Luigi. La Scuola Ostetrica Milanese dai Moscati al Porro. 87 p., pl., fig. Milano: Per il VI Congresso della Societa di Ostetricia e Ginecologia del Mediterraneo Latino, 1960.

PSwj-ce-bv

DA COSTA SACADURA, S.C. Bibliografia portuguesa da obstetrícia. Subsidios. 2 vol. 1. Séculos XVI e XVII. 27 p., ill.; 2. Séculos XVII e SVIII. 47 p., ill. Lisboa: Imprensa Médica, Calçada do Moinho de Vento, 1933, 1934.
Reviewed by Arlindo Camilo Monteiro, *Petrus Nonius*, 1939, 2: 158-65.

PSwk

DROGENDIJK, A.C. De verloskundige voorziening in Dordrecht van ongeveer 1500 tot heden. [Obstetrical care at Dordrecht from about 1500 to the present. (In Dutch)] 341 p. (Thesis) Paris/Amsterdam: 1935.
Reviewed by M.A. van Andel, *Bijdr.Gesch.Geneesk.*, 1935, 15: 157-8.

NIJHOFF, G.C. Het onderwijs in de verloskunde en de uitoefening der verloskunst in Nederland gedurende de laatste 75 jaaren. [The teaching of obstetrics and the practice of the art of obstetrics in the Netherlands during the last 75 years. (In Dutch)] *Bijdr.Gesch.Geneesk.*, 1924, 4: 148-55.

STARMANS, J.H. Verloskunde en kindersterfte in Limburg. Folklore, geschiedenis, heden. [Obstetrics and infant mortality in Limburg. Folklore, history, the present. (In Dutch)] 451 p. (Thesis) Maastricht: van Aalst, 1930.
Reviewed by M.A. van Andel, *Bijdr.Gesch.Geneesk.*, 1930, 10: 229-30.

PSwk-op

NIJHOFF, G.C. *See* PSwk

PSwk-oq

THIERY, M. De obstetrie aan de Gentse Universiteit; verleden en toekomst. [Obstetrics at Ghent University; past and future. (In Dutch)] *Sci.Hist.*, 1964, 6: 2-15. [CB 90/616]
Inaugural lecture as professor in obstetrics at Ghent University, 10 Dec. 1963.

PSwk-u

FOLMER, H.R. Volksgebruiken in Zeeland bij geboorte en kraambed. [Popular customs in Zeeland at birth and childbed. (In Dutch)] *Bijdr.Gesch.Geneesk.*, 1927, 7: 377-83.

PSwn-u

TORKOMIAN, Vahram H. Folklore obstétrical arménien. *Bull. Soc.Franç.Hist.Méd.*, 1939, 33: 193-5.

PSwt

VEITH, Ilza. The beginnings of modern Japanese obstetrics. *Bull.Hist.Med.*, 1951, 25: 45-59, 9 fig.

PSwx

PERTIS, Teresa de. Manuale di ostetricia adattato dallo svedese di Groth e Lindblom in lingua tigrigna. 280 p., 215 ill., 1 pl. Asmara: Missione Evangelica, 1928.
First obstetrical treatise printed in the Tigrigna language. Abbreviated translation of the Swedish treatise by Groth and Lindblom (4th ed., Stockholm, 1920).
Reviewed by Oscar Löfgren, *Monde Orient.*, 1933, 26: 345-9.

PSxb

DILLING, Walter J. Girdles, their use in obstetric practice. *Proc.17th Int.Congr.Med.*(London, 1913), Sect. 23, p. 69-72. London: Oxford University Press; Hodder & Stoughton, 1914.

PSyNW MATERNITY HOSPITALS

PSyNWwb

HARRAR, James A. The story of the Lying-in Hospital of the City of New York. 83 p., ill. New York: Lying-in Hospital, 1938.
Reviewed in *Ann.Med.Hist.*, 1938, 10: 563.

PSyNWwk

HELLINGA, G. Eenige mededeelingen uit de geschiedenis der voormalige Amsterdamsche Kraamzaal. [Some contributions on the history of the former Maternity Ward in Amsterdam. (In Dutch)] *Bijdr.Gesch.Geneesk.*, 1927, 7: 665-70.

PSza ABORTION

BRONDEGAARD, V.J. Der Sadebaum als Abortivum. *Sudhoffs Arch.*, 1964, 48: 331-51.

LAIGNEL-LAVASTINE, Maxime. Histoire de l'avortement provoqué des origines à 1810. *Mém.Soc.Franç.Hist.Méd.*, 1945, 1: 1-16.

ZANCAROL, Jacques D. L'évolution des idées sur l'avortement provoqué; étude morale et juridique. 166 p. Paris: Lipschutz, 1934.
Reviewed by Marcel Fosseyeux, *Bull.Soc.Franç.Hist.Méd.*, 1936, 31: 126.

PT WOMEN'S DISORDERS AND DISEASES

for gynaecological surgery *see* RCT

BERG, Alexander. Der Krankheitskomplex der Kolik- u. Gebärmutterleiden in Volksmedizin und Medizingeschichte unter besonderer Berücksichtigung der Volksmedizin in Ostpreussen. Ein Beitrag zur Erforschung volkstümlicher Krankheitsvorstellungen. 195 p. (*Abhandl.Gesch.Med.Naturwiss.*, 9) Berlin: Ebering, 1935.

BONINO, Alberto. Il "Roc della vita" in Oropa e la sterilità femminile. *Riv.Stor.Med.*, 1957, 1: 104-8.

GOODALL, Archibald L. The history of fibroadenosis of the breast. *Bull.Hist.Med.*, 1951, 25: 226-35.

OBER, William B.; FASS, Richard O. The early history of choriocarcinoma. *J.Hist.Med.*, 1961, 16: 49-73.

PAGEL, Walter. Historical notes on haemoptysis due to vicarious menstruation. *Victor Robinson Memorial Volume*, p. 299-312. New York: Froben, 1948.

VIALA, Frank. Traitement de la stérilité involontaire. *Hist. Méd.*, 1951, no. 3, 16-21.

PTce

GESCHICKTER, Charles F. The early literature on chronic cystic mastitis. *Bull.Inst.Hist.Med.*, 1934, 2: 249-57, 2 fig.

PU HUMAN EMBRYOLOGY

for general embryology *see* JL

BARCLAY, Alfred E.; FRANKLIN, Kenneth J.; PRICHARD, Marjorie M.L. The foetal circulation and cardiovascular system, and the changes that they undergo at birth. 275 p. Oxford: Blackwell Scientific Publications, 1944.
Includes a history of the subject, p. 1-33.
Reviewed by H. Fischer, *Gesnerus*, 1946, 3: 213.

BONNET, A. Les problèmes de la détermination du sexe. 348 p., ill. Lyon: A. Rey, 1914.

FORBES, Thomas R. The prediction of sex: folklore and science. *Proc.Amer.Phil.Soc.*, 1959, 103: 537-44.
A review of methods of predicting the sex of an unborn child from ancient Egypt to the present.

MACKINNEY, Loren. Sex determination. A scientific superstition. *Med.Illus.*, 1949, 3: 8-10.

MEYER, A.W. The elusive human allantois in older literature. *Science, Medicine and History, Essays in honour of Charles Singer*, (1), p. 510-20, 3 pl. London: Oxford University Press, 1953.

ROSTAND, Jean. Sur l'histoire des idées relatives à la parthénogenèse dans l'espèce humaine. *Rev.Hist.Sci.*, 1956, 9: 221-5.

SIGERIST, Henry E. Zur Geschichte der Geschlechtsprognostik. *Fortschr.Med.*, 1921, 39: 965-6.

WINDLE, William Frederick. Physiology of the fetus. xii, 249 p. Philadelphia: Saunders, 1940. [CB 60/160]

PUqg

MALL, Franklin P. A plea for an Institute of Human Embryology. *J.Amer.Med.Ass.*, 1913, 60: 1599-601.

PUzm MULTIPLE BIRTHS

BONUZZI, Silvio. I parti umani poligemellari a traverso i secoli. *Riv.Stor.Sci.*, 1931, 22: 94-7.

GEDDA, Luigi. Studio dei gemelli. xvi, 1381 p., ill. Roma: Edizioni Orizzonte Medico, 1951. [CB 78/191]
Reviewed by Claudius F. Mayer, *Amer.J.Hum.Genet.*, 1951, 3: 285-91.

LINT, J.G. de. Meervoudige geboorten. [Multiple births. (In Dutch)] *Bijdr.Gesch.Geneesk.*, 1935, 15: 201-7, 2 fig.

LINT, J.G. de. Vijflingen. [Quintuplets. (In Dutch)] *Bijdr. Gesch.Geneesk.*, 1935, 15: 185-96, 1 pl.

MAYER, Claudius F. Sextuplets and higher multiparous births. *Acta Genet.Med.Gemellol.*, 1952, 1: 1-53, 8 pl.

POLL, Heinrich. Zwillinge in Dichtung und Wirklichkeit. 52 p. Berlin: Springer, 1930.
Reviewed by Friedrich Pfister, *Deut.Lit.Zeitung*, 1931, 2: 2249-50.
Originally published in *Z.Gesamte Neurol.Psychiat.*, 1930, 128: 423-74.

STEVENSON, Isobel. Twins as magicians and healing gods: twin myths; twins among primitive peoples; research on twins; twins, the psychological aspects of the problem. *Ciba Symp.*, 1941, 2: 694-701, 702-5, 706-11, 712-16.

PV TERATOLOGY

BEINS, Jan F.A. Misvorming en verbeelding. [Malformation and imagination. (In Dutch)] 231 p., ill. (Thesis. Groningen) Amsterdam: Van Oorschot, 1948. [CB 73/177]

FUTCHER, Palmer Howard. Giants and dwarfs. A study of the anterior lobe of the hypophysis. 80 p. Cambridge, Mass.: Harvard University Press, 1932.

GLENISTER, T.W. Fantasies, facts and foetuses. The interplay of fancy and reason in teratology. *Med.Hist.*, 1964, 8: 15-30.

GRUBER, Georg B. Historisches und Aktuelles über das Sirenen-Problem in der Medizin. 38 p., 10 fig., 10 pl. (*Nova Acta Leopoldina, new ser.*, 17: no. 117) Leipzig: J.A. Barth, 1955.
Reviewed by Walter Pagel, *Sudhoffs Arch.*, 1956, 40: 187.

GRUBER, Georg B. Studien zur Historik der Teratologie. *Zentralbl.Allg.Path.*, 1964, 105: 219-37, 293-316; 106: 512-62.

HOLLÄNDER, Eugen. Wunder, Wundergeburt und Wundergestalt in Einblattdrucken des fünfzehnten bis achzehnten Jahrhunderts. Kulturhistorische Studie. xvi, 373 p., 202 ill. Stuttgart: Enke, 1921.
Reviewed by George Sarton, *Isis*, 1922, 4: 566-7.

HRDLIČKA, Aleš. Ear exostoses. 100 p., 5 pl. (*Smithsonian Misc.Collect.*, 93: no. 6) Washington: Smithsonian Institution, 1935.
Includes a history of the subject from the time of J.H. F. Autenrieth (1809) on.

KEITH, Arthur. The nature of man's structural imperfections. The Lloyd Roberts Lecture delivered to the Royal Society of Medicine on November 16, 1925. *Nature*, 1925, 116: 821-3, 867-9.

THOMPSON, Charles John Samuel. The mystery and lore of monsters. With accounts of some giants, dwarfs and prodigies. With a foreword by D'Arcy Power. 256 p. London: Williams and Norgate, 1930.

WOLFF, Étienne. La science des monstres. 265 p., ill. Paris: Gallimard, 1948.

PW PAEDIATRICS

for health services for children *see* NU

ABT, Isaac A. Baby doctor. 310 p. New York: Whittlesey House, 1944.
Reviewed by J.B. Bilderback, *Bull.Med.Libr.Ass.*, 1944, 32: 523-5.

ALLARIA, Giuvanni Battista. Dentitio difficilis. Nota di storia della pediatria. 55 p. Torino: Bona, 1941.
Reviewed by R. Bèttica-Giovannini, *Riv.Stor.Sci.*, 1941, 32: 154-5.

BARRAUD, G. La puériculture éternelle. 160 p., 19 ill. Paris: Vigot, 1941.
Reviewed by E. Olivier, *Bull.Soc.Franç.Hist.Méd.*, 1941, 35: 91-3.

BEL GEDDES, Joan. Small world. A history of baby care from the Stone Age to the Spock age. 287 p. New York: Macmillan, 1964. [CB 90/528]

BÓKAY, Janos. Die Geschichte der Kinderheilkunde. 122 p., 99 ill. Berlin: Springer, 1922.

DERUISSEAU, L.G. Infant hygiene in the older medical literature. The care of the new-born infant. Infant feeding. *Ciba Symp.*, 1940, 2: 530-6, 536-47, 548-55, ill.

KAGAN, Solomon R., ed. Abraham Levinson anniversary volume. Studies in pediatrics and medical history in honor of Dr. Abraham Levinson on his sixtieth birthday. xviii, 365 p., ill. New York: Froben Press, 1949.

PEIPER, Albrecht. Chronik der Kinderheilkunde. 3rd ed. xvi, 527 p., ill. Leipzig: Georg Thieme, 1958.
Reviewed by John Rendle-Short and John Lorber, *Med.Hist.*, 1959, 3: 257. 2nd ed. 1955 reviewed by José M. López Piñero, *Arch.Iberoamer.Hist.Med.*, 1959, 11: 87-8.

RENDLE-SHORT, John. The history of teething in infancy. *Proc. Roy.Soc.Med.*, 1955, 48: 132-8.

SEIBERT, Henri. The progress of ideas regarding the causation and control of infant mortality. *Bull.Hist.Med.*, 1940, 8: 546-98.

STILL, George Frederic. The history of paediatrics. The progress of the study of diseases of children up to the end of the eighteenth century. xviii, 526 p. Oxford University Press, 1931.

WATSON, E.H.; LOWREY, G.H. Growth and development of children. 260 p., ill. Chicago: Year Book Publishers, 1951. [CB 78/195]

PWce-bv

RUHRÄH, John. A bibliography of pediatrics. *Bull.Med.Libr. Ass.*, Jan. 1921, 10: 21-4.

PWda

LEVINSON, Abraham. Pioneers of pediatrics. *Med.Life*, 1929, 36: 345-89, portr.; 1935, 42: 329-82, 385-420, 441, portr.

LEVINSON, Abraham. The three Meigs and their contribution to pediatrics. *Ann.Med.Hist.*, 1928, 10: 138-48, 4 fig.

ROSHEM, S. Trois précurseurs des puériculteurs modernes: Laurent Joubert, Scévole de Sainte-Marthe, Philippe Hecquet. *France Méd.*, 1913, 182-4, 204-7.

PWdaj

RUHRÄH, John. Pediatrics of the past. An anthology. With a foreword by Fielding H. Garrison. xxvi, 592 p., 54 text ill., 18 pl. New York: Paul B. Hoeber, 1925.
Reviewed by George Sarton, *Isis*, 1926, 8: 386-8.

PWmzFY

PEIPER, Albrecht. Das Neugeborene in der Sterndeutung (Astrologie). *Kinderärztl.Prax.*, 1964, 32: 329-33.

PWtk

FOOTE, John. Ancient poems on infant hygiene. *Ann.Med.Hist.*, 1919, 2: 213-27.

PWu

GESELL, Arnold. The biography of a wolf-child. *Harper's Mag.*, Jan. 1941, 183-93. [CB 61/408]

HUTTON, J.H. Wolf-children. (Presidential address, The Folk-Lore Society, 21st February, 1940) *Folk-lore*, 1940, 51: 9-31. [CB 60/162]

MAYERHOFER, E. Paediatrie und Volksmedizin (mit besonderer Berücksichtigung der Südslawen). *Festschrift zum 80. Geburtstag Max Neuburgers*, p. 310-30. Wien: Maudrich, 1948.

PWwb

ACKERKNECHT, Erwin H. "White Indians". Psychological and physiological peculiarities of white children abducted and reared by North American Indians. *Bull.Hist.Med.*, 1944, 15: 15-36, 4 fig.

PWwg-qg

HOCHSINGER, Carl. Zur Geschichte des ersten oeffentlichen Kinder-Kranken-Institutes in Wien. *Festschrift zur Feier seines 60. Geburtstages Max Neuburger gewidmet*, p. 172-82. Wien: Verlag des Fest-Komitees, 1928.

PWwh

GÓRNICKI, Boleslaw. Medicina pediátrica polaca en los siglos XIV, XV, XVI y XVII. *Arch.Iberoamer.Hist.Med.*, 1957, 9: 235-40.

PWwn-cc

KONIUS, E.M. Istoki russkoĭ pediatrii. [Sources of Russian pediatrics. (In Russian)] 414 p., ill. Moscow: Narkomzdrav SSSR Gosudarstvennoe Izdatelstvo Meditskinskoi Literaturi "Medgiz", 1946.

PWxb

RICH, Ida. Narresutten i historisk perspectiv. [Infants' comforters in historical perspective. (In Danish)] *Med. Forum*, 1957, 3: 90-6, ill.

PWxb-by

MEAD JOHNSON & COMPANY. The Mead Johnson collection of pediatric antiques. 48 p., 47 ill. Evansville, Ind.: Mead Johnson, 1942.

PWxb-wb

WEISS, Harry B. American baby rattles from Colonial times to the present. With ninety-seven illustrations of silver, terra cotta, tin, wood, celluloid and plastic rattles. 28 p., 16 pl. Trenton, N.J.: Privately printed, 1941.

PWyNM NUTRITION

DRAKE, T.G.H. Pap and panada. *Ann.Med.Hist.*, 1931, 3: 289-95, 4 fig.
History of infant nutrition.

PWyNMxb

KLEBE, Dieter; SCHADEWALDT, Hans. Gefässe zur Kinderernährung im Wandel der Zeit. 53 p., ill. Frankfurt am Main: Schirmer & Mahlau Verlag, 1955. [CB 83/207]

PRIBILLA, Walther. Zur Geschichte der Säuglingstrinkgefässe. *Deut.Med.Wochenschr.*, 1956, 81: 1824-5, bibliogr.

PWyNMxb-wb

DITTRICK, Howard. The nursing can, an early American infant feeding device. *Bull.Hist.Med.*, 1939, 7: 696-704, 5 fig.

PWyNW CHILDREN'S HOSPITALS

LATRONICO, N. Nascita e primi sviluppi degli ospedali per bambini. *Riv.Stor.Med.*, 1957, 1: 157-65.

PWyNWwe

GUTHRIE, Douglas. The Royal Edinburgh Hospital for Sick Children, 1860-1960. 75 p., ill. Edinburgh: E. & S. Livingstone; Baltimore, Md.: Williams & Wilkins, 1960. [CB 87/572]
Reviewed by A. Peiper, *Sudhoffs Arch.*, 1961, 45: 90; by John Rendle-Short, *Med.Hist.*, 1960, 4: 262-3.

PWyNWwi

MESSEDAGLIA, Luigi. Per la verità e per la giustizia: Dante Cervesato e la clinica pediatrica di Padova. *Riv.Stor.Sci.*, 1942, 33: 15-16.

PWyO PAEDIATRIC SPECIALTIES

PWyOK

LEVINSON, Abraham. Notes on the history of pediatric neurology. *Victor Robinson Memorial Volume*, p. 225-40, 5 fig. New York: Froben, 1948.

PWyOM

KANNER, Leo. Outline of the history of child psychiatry. *Victor Robinson Memorial Volume*, p. 163-76, 1 fig. New York: Froben, 1948.

PX CHILDREN'S DISORDERS AND DISEASES

for children's diseases of an infectious nature *see under* QP and QSyPX

PXyOR

BERG, Fredrik. Ophthalmia neonatorum i Sverige, en historisk återblick. [Ophthalmia neonatorum in Sweden. (In Swedish)] *Lychnos*, 1957-58, 151-80.

PY GERONTOLOGY

BENARD, René. A propos de la communication de M. Grmek (Yougoslavie). *Arch.Iberoamer.Hist.Med.*, 1957, 9: 253-4.
Comment on Grmek's Les aspects historiques des problèmes fondamentaux de la gérontologie, *ibid.*, 245-51, *see* below.

COMFORT, Alex. The biology of senescence. xiii, 257 p. London: Routledge & Kegan Paul; New York: Rinehart, 1956.
Reviewed by Gerald Gruman, *Isis*, 1957, 48: 481-2.
2nd ed. entitled Ageing: the biology of senescence. xvi, 365 p. London: Routledge & Kegan Paul; New York: Holt, Rinehart and Winston, 1964.

COMFORT, Alex. The process of ageing. 144 p., pl. (Signet Science Library) New York: New American Library, 1964.
English ed. 151 p. London: Weidenfeld & Nicolson, 1965.

GRMEK, Mirko D. Les aspects historiques des problèmes fondamentaux de la gérontologie. *Arch.Iberoamer.Hist.Med.*, 1957, 9: 245-51.
Comment by René Benard, *see* above.

GRMEK, Mirko D. On ageing and old age. Basic problems and historic aspects of gerontology and geriatrics. 106 p., ill. (Monographiae Biologicae, 1958, 5: no. 2) Den Haag: Junk, 1958. [CB 85/399]
Reviewed by Edwin Clarke, *Med.Hist.*, 1959, 3: 336; by G. Montalenti, *Scientia*, 1960, 95: 68-9; by Gerald J. Gruman, *Bull.Hist.Med.*, 1960, 34: 283-5.

KOTSOVSKY, Dimu. Alte und neue Wege in der Erforschung des Alterns. *Sudhoffs Arch.*, 1954, 38: 58-70.

KOTSOVSKY, Dimu. Das Alter in der Geschichte der Wissenschaft. *Isis*, 1933, 20: 220-45. [CB 40/408]

MALISOFF, William Marias. The span of life. 339 p. Philadelphia/New York: Lippincott, 1937. [CB 53/281]

PEARL, Raymond; PEARL, Ruth DeWitt. The ancestry of the long-lived. xiii, 168 p., front. Baltimore: Johns Hopkins Press, 1934. [CB 42/596]

ROLLESTON, Humphry. Concerning old age. (Discourse delivered at the Royal Institution, May 13, 1927) *Nature*, 1927, 120: Suppl. 2-12.

ROLLESTON, Humphry. Medical aspects of old age. Being a revised and enlarged edition of the Linacre lecture, 1922. London: Macmillan, 1932.

RUDY, Z. [Conceptions about old age in history. (In Hebrew)] *Koroth*, 1964, 3: 317-25.

VARIGNY, Henry de. La mort et la biologie: la mort devant la biologie, les organismes immortels, l'antiquité de la maladie, vieillesse et rajeunissement. 312 p. Paris: Alcan, 1926. [CB 23/249]

PYc-bv

GRUMAN, Gerald. An introduction to literature on the history of gerontology. *Bull.Hist.Med.*, 1957, 31: 78-83.

PYce-bv

SHOCK, Nathan W. A classified bibliography of gerontology and geriatrics. xxvii, 599 p. Supplement 1, 1949-55. xxviii, 525 p. Stanford: Stanford University Press, 1951, 1957.
Supplement reviewed by Gerald Gruman, *Bull.Hist.Med.*, 1958, 32: 188.

PYwb-k

GRUMAN, Gerald. Death and progress: the idea of prolongevity in American science and philosophy. (Diss.) *Isis*, 1957, 48: 351.

PYwf

HUET, J.A. La médecine française ne peut méconnaitre l'intérêt de la gérontologie. *Hist.Méd.*, 1951, 4: 29-33.

PYyOM

GENIL-PERRIN, G. Histoire des origines et de l'évolution de l'idée de dégénérescence en médecine mentale. 280 p. Paris: Alfred Leclerc, 1913.

PZ GERIATRICS

BIZZARINI, Giotto. Gl'innesti animali e la loro distinzione secondo Giard. Alcune osservazioni su quanto scrive Voronoff. Innesti eteroplastici praticati da Paolo Mantegazza. Anche Diacinto Cestoni esperimentò innesti animali. *Riv.Stor.Sci.*, 1938, 29: 148-52.

CODELLAS, Pan. S. Rejuvenations and satyricons of yesterday. *Ann.Med.Hist.*, 1934, 6: 510-20, 2 fig.

DARTIGUES, Louis. Le rajeunissement humain par les greffes animales. *Aesculape*, 1924, 129-34.
A study of testicular grafts practised in France by Voronoff and Dartigues.

DUFRENOY, Marie-Louise; DUFRENOY, Jean. Senescence en pathologie comparée; historique, courbes de croissance. *VI Congr. Int.Patol.Comp.* (Madrid, 1952), 1: (3), p. 33-8. [Madrid: 1952?]

FREEMAN, Joseph T. The history of geriatrics. *Ann.Med. Hist.*, 1938, 10: 324-35, 3 fig.

KOTSOVSKY, D. Zur Geschichte der Lehre über Altersautointoxikation. *Arch.Iberoamer.Hist.Med.*, 1957, 9: 289-92.

MARSHALL, Francis Hugh Adam. Rejuvenescence and the testicular graft. *Nature*, 1923, 112: 904-5.
Includes account of work by S. Voronoff.

STEUDEL, Johannes. Zur Geschichte der Lehre von den Greisenkrankheiten. *Sudhoffs Arch.*, 1942, 35: 1-27.

Q PATHOLOGY AND CLINICAL MEDICINE

for diseases affecting special parts of the body
see INDEX

Qc general history

ACKERKNECHT, Erwin H. Geschichte und Geographie der Krankheiten. *Berliner Gesundheitsbl.*, 1954, 5: 321-3.

ACKERKNECHT, Erwin H. Geschichte und Geographie der wichtigsten Krankheiten. 191 p., ill. Stuttgart: Enke, 1963.
Reviewed by H. Degen, *Naturwiss.Rundsch.*, 1964, 17: 161.

BARUK, Henri. Médecine de prognostique ou thérapeutique dans l'antiquité et de nos jours. *Rev.Hist.Méd.Hébraique*, 1963, 16: 119-36.

BETT, Walter R. The history and conquest of common diseases. ix, 355 p. Norman: University of Oklahoma Press, 1954.
Reviewed by Morris C. Leikind, *Isis*, 1956, 47: 195-6.

BETT, Walter R., ed. A short history of some common diseases. By divers authors. vii, 211 p. (Oxford Medical Publications) London: Oxford University Press, 1934.

CAWADIAS, A.P. Clinical science in the light of history. *Proc. Roy.Soc.Med.*, 1947, 40: 453-62, Hist. Sect., 17-26.

DAUWE, Octave. Cinquante ans d'études cliniques, gynécologiques, obstétricales, médico-sociales et historiques. 612 p., ill. Averbode: Altiora, 1961.
Reviewed by E.C., *Scalpel*, 1961, 114: 1013-14.

DI GIOVANNI, Antonio. Malati e malattie di altri tempi. 69 p. (Colland Scientia Veterum, 58) Pisa: Giardini, 1964.

FABER, Knud. Nosography. The evolution of clinical medicine in modern times. 2nd rev. ed. xvii, 222 p. New York: Hoeber, 1930.
Reviewed by Thomas McCrae, *Ann.Med.Hist.*, 1931, 3: 247.
First publ. 1923 under the title Nosography in modern internal medicine and reviewed by G. Sarton, *Isis*, 1924, 6: 98-9.

FINOT, André. Notes sur l'histoire de la clinique médicale et de son enseignement. D'Imhotep à Trousseau. 92 p., ill. Paris: Amédée Legrand, 1958.
Reviewed by Louis Dulieu, *Rev.Hist.Sci.*, 1960, 13: 175-6 and *Arch.Int.Hist.Sci.*, 1960, 13: 174-5.

FORBUS, Wiley D. Reaction to injury: pathology for students of disease based on the functional and morphological responses of tissues to injurious agents. xix, 797 p., ill. Baltimore: Williams and Wilkins, 1943.
Begins with a twenty-eight page philosophical introduction and survey of the history of pathology.

FOSTER, W.D. A short history of clinical pathology. xii, 154 p., ill. Edinburgh/London: E. & S. Livingstone, 1961.
Reviewed by Roy Cameron, *Med.Hist.*, 1962, 6: 94-5; by Cuthbert E. Dukes, *Hist.Sci.*, 1963, 2: 172.

FOUCAULT, Michel. Naissance de la clinique. Une archéologie du regard médical. xv, 213 p. ("Galien", Histoire et philosophie de la biologie et de la médecine) Paris: Presses Universitaires de France, 1963.

GARCÍA-LUQUERO, C. Historia de las luchas sanitarias (no infecciosas). *Arch.Iberoamer.Hist.Med.*, 1957, 9: 189-226.

HORDER, Thomas Jeeves Horder, *baron*. Old diseases and new. *Nature*, 1937, 139: 571-4.
From a Friday evening discourse delivered at the Royal Institution on February 26.

KAUSCH, Friedrich. Mit Krankheit und Tod durch drei Jahrhunderte. 96 p. Burg b. Magdeburg: Selbstverlag, 1931.

KEELE, Kenneth David. The evolution of clinical methods in medicine; being the Fitzpatrick lectures, delivered at the Royal College of Physicians in 1960-61. 115 p., ill. London/New York: Pitman; Springfield, Ill.: Charles C. Thomas, 1964.

KRUMBHAAR, Edward Bell. Pathology. xvii, 206 p., ill., bibliogr. (Clio Medica, 19) New York/London: Hafner, 1962.
Reviewed by Cuthbert E. Dukes, *Med.Hist.*, 1963, 7: 291.
First published 1937 and reviewed in *Ann.Med.Hist.*, 1937, 9: 512.

LAIN ENTRALGO, Pedro. La historia clínica. Historia y teoría del relato patográfico. 2nd ed. xvi, 668 p. Barcelona: Salvat, 1961.
Reviewed by Francisco Guerra, *Med.Hist.*, 1963, 7: 97-8.
First publ. Madrid: Consejo Superior de Investigaciones Cientificas, 1950 and reviewed by Th. H. Schlichting, *Arch.Int.Hist.Sci.*, 1952, 5: 425-6.

LAPAGE, Geoffrey. Man against disease. 189 p., ill. New York/London: Abelard-Schuman, 1964.

LECTURES on the history of pathology and experimental medicine. (Given by Dr. Morris C. Leikind) *Isis*, 1956, 47: 187.

LONG, Esmond R. A history of pathology. xxiv, 291 p., 49 pl. Baltimore: Williams and Wilkins, 1928. [CB 25/436]

MASTER, David. The conquest of disease. With an introduction by James Cantlie. xiv, 353 p. New York: Dodd, Mead, 1925.

NAVA, Pedro. Esboço dos fundamentos históricos das especializações no terreno da medicina interna. *Brasil Méd.Cir.*, 1946, 8: 273-85.

RIESMAN, David. Deceased diseases. *Ann.Med.Hist.*, 1936, 8: 160-7.

ROLLESTON, Humphry. Internal medicine. ix, 92 p. (Clio Medica, 4) New York: Hoeber, 1930. [CB 31/569]
An account of discoveries in the fundamental medical sciences as related to internal medicine.

ROUECHÉ, Berton. Eleven blue men, and other narratives of medical detection. 215 p. Boston: Little, Brown, 1953.
An account of particular diseases in historical perspective.

ROUECHÉ, Berton. The incurable wound, and further narratives of medical detection. 177 p. Boston/Toronto: Little, Brown, 1958.
Sequel to: Eleven blue men, *see* above.
Reviewed by Victor A. McKusick, *Bull.Hist.Med.*, 1958, 32: 481.

SCHULTZ, Adolph H. Notes on diseases and healed fractures of wild apes and their bearing on the antiquity of pathological conditions in man. *Bull.Hist.Med.*, 1939, 7: 571-82, 3 pl.

SOLIS-COHEN, Myer. Recognition through the centuries of the relationship between local and general diseases. *Bull.Hist. Med.*, 1952, 26: 526-37.

TOBEY, James Alner. Riders of the plagues: the story of the conquest of disease. xv, 348 p., 8 pl. New York: Scribner, 1930.

WIGHTMAN, W.P.D. Idols in the history of pathology. *Scientia*, 1964, 99: 166-71.
Includes French translation.

Qc-bx

BROOKE, Helen C. An exhibit illustrating the history of pathology. *Bull.Inst.Hist.Med.*, 1934, 2: 447-76, 9 pl.

Qce-bv

BLOOMFIELD, Arthur L. A bibliography of internal medicine, selected diseases. viii, 312 p. Chicago: University of Chicago Press, 1960.
Reviewed by William J. Cathey, *Bull.Hist.Med.*, 1960, 34: 580-1.

Qcm

GOLDSCHMID, Edgar. Entwicklung und Bibliographie der pathologisch-anatomischen Abbildung. 301 p., ill. Leipzig: Hiersemann, 1925.

GOLDSCHMID, Edgar. The influence of the social environment on the style of pathological illustration. *J.Hist.Med.*, 1952, 7: 258-70, 7 pl.

HABERLING, Wilhelm. Die Darstellung von Krankheiten im Laufe der Jahrtausende. *Arch.Gesch.Med.*, 1923, 15: 1-13. [CB 16/318]

Qdaj

LONG, Esmond R., ed. Selected readings in pathology. 2nd ed. ix, 306 p., ill. Springfield, Ill.: Charles C. Thomas, 1961.
This second edition has been updated and includes papers of the late 19th and early 20th centuries.
Reviewed by L.R.C. Agnew, *Bull.Hist.Med.*, 1963, 37: 90-1.
First publ. 1929 [CB 30/490] and reviewed by B.C., *Nature*, 1930, 125: 488.

MAJOR, Ralph H. Classic descriptions of disease. With biographical sketches of the authors. 3rd ed. xxxii, 679 p. Springfield, Ill.: Charles C. Thomas, 1945. [CB 69/237]
1st ed. 1932.
Reviewed by H.R. Viets, *Isis*, 1933, 19: 518-20.

Qf

WELCH, William H. Address on the history of pathology. *Bull. Inst.Hist.Med.*, 1935, 3: 1-18. [CB 43/289]

Qh

RIESE, W. The structure of the clinical history. *Bull.Hist. Med.*, 1944, 16: 437-49.

Qhj

ANDREEV, S.V. Hippocrates' ideas and modern pathology. *Arch.Int.Hist.Sci.*, 1962, 15: 59-61.

ASCHNER, Bernard. Neo-Hippocratism in everyday practice. *Bull.Hist.Med.*, 1941, 10: 260-71.

VILAR, Albert. Pour la défense de l'Ancienne Médecine. 40 p. Montpellier: L'Abeille, 1923. [CB 16/320]

Qk philosophy and methodology;

MAYER, Claudius F. Metaphysical trends in modern pathology. *Bull.Hist.Med.*, 1952, 26: 71-81. [CB 79/192]

PASTORI, Carlo. Il problema gnoseologico e i problemi limite della conoscenza. 27 p. Massa: Medici, 1932.

RIESMAN, David. The clinical approach. *J.S.C.Med.Ass.*, 1936, 32: 34-9.

SUNDERMAN, F. William; BOERNER, Frederick. Normal values in clinical medicine. xxx, 845 p. Philadelphia: Saunders, 1949. [CB 77/385]

Qm/t other special aspects

QmzMC

HARPER, R.M.J. Evolution and illness, a short essay on the clinical significance of evolutionary vestiges. viii, 108 p., bibliogr. Edinburgh: E. & S. Livingstone, 1962.

QmzMMzc

GRMEK, M.D. Histoire des recherches sur les relations entre le génie et la maladie. *Rev.Hist.Sci.*, 1962, 15: 51-68.

QmzOF

BEECHER, Henry K., ed. Disease and the advancement of basic science. 416 p. Cambridge: Harvard University Press, 1960.
Reviewed in *Sci.Amer.*, 1961, 204: no. 2, 183.

McMICHAEL, J. The contributions of clinical medicine to physiology. *Advance.Sci.*, 1963, 20: 254-8.

QmzSD

HEUSINGER, Johann Christian Karl Friedrich von. Die Pflanzenwelt, ihr Wechsel und ihr Erkranken, in Beziehung auf die Geschichte und die Verbreitung der Krankheiten der Menschheit. *Henschel's Janus*, 1851, 1: 24-47; reprinted Leipzig: Alfred Lorentz, 1931.

Qnh

GÜNTHER, Hans. Geschichtliche Erläuterung der Ausdrücke "akute" und "chronische" Krankheit. *Sudhoffs Arch.*, 1941, 34: 105-24.

Qsc

EULNER, Hans-Heinz. Krankheit und Geschichte. *Sudhoffs Arch.*, 1963, 47: 209-14.

MAJOR, Ralph H. Disease and destiny; Logan Clendening. (Logan Clendening Lectures on the History and Philosophy of Medicine, 8th series) iv, 49 p., front., 6 ill. Lawrence, Kansas: University of Kansas Press, 1958. [CB 84/321-2]

RIBBERT, Hugo. Die Bedeutung der Krankheiten für die Entwicklung der Menschheit. 194 p. Bonn: Fr. Cohen, 1912.

SIGERIST, Henry E. Civilization and disease. xi, 255 p., ill. Ithaca, N.Y.: Cornell University Press, 1943.
Reviewed by Iago Galdston, *Isis*, 1944, 35: 220.

SIGERIST, Henry E. Kultur und Krankheit. *Kyklos*, 1928, 1: 60-3.

STEWART, David A. Disease and history. *Ann.Med.Hist.*, 1935, 7: 351-71.

WICKERSHEIMER, Ernest. Civilisation et maladie, d'après un article récent. *Bull.Soc.Franc.Hist.Med.*, 1929, 23: 31-4.
Critical comments on Sigerist's article Kultur und Krankheit, *see* above.

Qsd

BRAUN, Adolf. Krankheit und Tod im Schicksal bedeutender Menschen. iv, 104 p. Stuttgart: Enke, 1934.
Reviewed by Aldo Mieli, *Archeion*, 1938, 21: 155-7.

RICO-AVELLO, C. Breve evocación sobre mortalidad egregia. *Arch.Iberoamer.Hist.Med.*, 1957, 9: 465-71.
A brief discussion of the final illnesses and deaths of Spanish monarchs of the sixteenth to eighteenth centuries.

Qsd-bv

GILBERT, Judson Bennett. Disease and destiny, a bibliography of medical references to the famous. With additions and an introduction by Gordon E. Mestler and a preface by Emerson Crosby Kelly. 535 p. London: Dawson, 1962.
For reviews *see* CB 88/558 and CB 89/510.

STEVENSON, R. Scott. Famous illnesses in history. 239 p. London: Eyre and Spottiswoode, 1962.
Reviewed in *Proc.Roy.Soc.Med.*, 1963, 56: 248.

Qsf

CIOCCO, Antonio; PERROTT, Dorothy. Statistics on sickness as a cause of poverty. An historical review of U.S. and English data. *J.Hist.Med.*, 1957, 12: 42-60, 5 tables.

Qsq

COPELMAN, Louis. Nouvelles recherches sur la pathologie des déportés. *Rev.Hist.Méd.Hébraique*, 1959, 46: 205-8.

Qtc

SIEBENTHAL, Wolf von. Krankheit als Folge der Sünde. 99 p. Hannover: Schmorl & von Seefeld, 1950.

Qth

POLITZER, Heinz. The 'break-through' - Thomas Mann and the deeper meaning of disease. *Ciba Symp.*, 1961, 9: 36-42.

Qtq

BÖKELMANN, F. Ueber Krankheitsdarstellung im Gemälde. *Virchows Arch.Pathol.Anat.Physiol.*, 1912, 209: 1-12.

RICO-AVELLO, C. La pintura española en relación con la patología. *Arch.Iberoamer.Hist.Med.*, 1956, 8: 447-56.

RICO-AVELLO, C. Influencia de la patología en la iconografia. *Arch.Iberoamer.Hist.Med.*, 1956, 8: 441-5.

Qud

BOLOGA, Valeriu L.; DIMA, L. A propos de quelques patrons de maladies et de certains saints guérisseurs de la religion gréco-orientale. *Knoll's Mitt.Ärzte*, March 1934, 9 p., 7 fig.

Qud-nh

FLETCHER, Robert. Diseases bearing the names of saints. *Bristol Med.Chir.J.*, 1912, 30: 295-315, pl.

Qw in different countries

Qwb

LONG, Esmond R. A history of American pathology. xv, 460 p., fig. Springfield, Ill.: Charles C. Thomas, 1962.
Reviewed by Erwin H. Ackerknecht, *Isis*, 1964, 55: 457-8; by Franklin C. McLean, *Science*, 1962, 138: 1390; by Paul Kemperer, *Bull.Hist.Med.*, 1963, 37: 393-4.

RIESMAN, David. American contributions to nosography. *New Engl.J.Med.*, 1938, 219: 591-611.

U.S. ARMY MEDICAL SERVICE. Internal medicine in World War II. Vol. 1. Activities of medical consultants. 880 p., ill.; Washington, D.C.: Office of the Surgeon General, Department of the Army, 1961.
Reviewed by Arthur S. Macnalty, *Med.Hist.*, 1963, 7: 95-6.

Qwb-qd

RIESMAN, David. Men and events in the history of the Philadelphia Pathological Society. *Ann.Med.Hist.*, 1934, 6: 359-75.

Qwe

FOSTER, W.D. The early history of clinical pathology in Great Britain. *Med.Hist.*, 1959, 3: 173-87.

Qwg

RISCHER, Walther; GRUBER, Georg B. Fünfzig Jahre Pathologie in Deutschland. 334 p., 2 pl. Stuttgart: Thieme, 1949.

Qwg-qd

HIS, W. Zum 50-jährigen Bestehen des Vereins für innere Medizin in Berlin. *Deut.Med.Wochenschr.*, 1931, 57: 641-3.

KLEMPERER, Georg. 50 Jahre Kongress für innere Medizin, 1882-1932. 164 p. München: Bergmann, 1932.
Reviewed by David Riesman, *Ann.Med.Hist.*, 1933, 5: 102.

Qwi

MARIOTTI, Maurizio. Breve storia della clinica medica Italiana. 61 p. (Collana Scientia Veterum, 50) Pisa: Giardini, 1963.

Qwk

WEYDE, A.J. van der. De inwendige geneeskunde in ons vaderland gedurende de afgeloopen 75 jaren. [Internal medicine in our country during the last 75 years. (In Dutch)] *Bijdr. Gesch.Geneesk.*, 1924, 4: 129-43.

Qwo-u

LETTENBAUER, Wilhelm. Über Krankheitsdämonen im Volksglauben der Balkanslaven. *Serta Monacensia, Franz Babinger als Festgruss durgebracht*, p. 120-35. Leiden: Brill, 1952.

Qxx museums

Qxx-wb

OLCOTT, Charles T. The pathological cabinet of the New York Hospital. *Ann.Med.Hist.*, 1936, 8: 54-64, 9 fig.

QA MEDICAL GEOGRAPHY; AETIOLOGY

for aetiological aspects of specific diseases *see* INDEX

ACKERKNECHT, Erwin H. Geschichte und Geographie der wichtigsten Krankheiten. 191 p., ill. Stuttgart: Enke, 1963.
Reviewed by H. Degen, *Naturwiss.Rundsch.*, 1964, 17: 161.

BARKHUUS, Arne. Medical surveys from Hippocrates to the world travellers. Medical geographies. Geomedicine and geopolitics. *Ciba Symp.* (Summit, N.J.), 1945, 6: 1986-2020, ill.

EFFERTZ, Otto. Zur Pathologie der Rassen. Vortrag. *Janus*, 1913, 18: 536-42.
"Virulentia celerior immunitas hereditaria"

GARRISON, Fielding Hudson. Geomedicine: a science in gestation. *Bull.Inst.Hist.Med.*, 1933, 1: 2-9.

GARRISON, Fielding Hudson. Medical geography and geographic medicine. *Bull.N.Y.Acad.Med.*, 1932, 8: 593-612.

HÉRICOURT, J. Le terrain dans les maladies. Préface de Ch. Richet. 250 p. (Bibliothèque de Philosophie Scientifique) Paris: Flammarion, 1927. [CB 24/562]

LIGHT, Richard Upjohn; WRIGHT, J.K. The progress of medical geography, by R.U. Light. A proposed atlas of diseases with a note on the terminology of certain map symbols, by J.K. Wright. *Geogr.Rev.*, 1944, 34: 636-54.
Reviewed by George Rosen, *J.Hist.Med.*, 1947, 2: 595-6.

OBERHUMMER, Eugen. Medizinische Geographie. *Petermanns Mitt.*, 1935, 81: 329-41.
General summary of the subject with abundant references.

SEIDEL, Ernst. Europäische Krankheiten als literarische Gäste im vorderen Orient. *Arch.Gesch.Naturwiss.Tech.*, 1913, 6: 372-86.

SIGERIST, Henry E. Problems of historical-geographical pathology. *Bull.Inst.Hist.Med.*, 1933, 1: 10-18. [CB 38/614]

SUDHOFF, Karl. Anthropogeographia, világtörtenelem és a gyógyitás tudományának fejlödése. [Anthropogeography, world history and the evolution of medicine. (In Hungarian)] *Orvosi Hetilap*, 1925, 69: 827-9.

SUDHOFF, Karl. Anthropogeography and medical history. *Med. Life*, 1925, 32: 391-7.

QAsc

GRMEK, M.D. Géographie médicale et histoire des civilisations. *Ann.Écon.Soc.Civilizations*, 1963, 18: 1071-97.

QAwi-ce

MUZIO, Carlo. Geografia medica: primo saggio nella litteratura medica italiana. xix, 1212 p. (Manuali Hoepli) Milano: U. Hoepli, 1922.

QAA/QAR by regions

QAA

ASHBURN, P.M. The ranks of death: a medical history of the conquest of America. Edited by Frank D. Ashburn. xix, 298 p. New York: Coward-McCann, 1947.
Reviewed by Gaylord W. Anderson, *Amer.Hist.Rev.*, 1949, 54: 650.

QAG

FUCHS, C.F. Das Verhältniss der Krankheiten in senkrechter Richtung von der Küste der Nordsee bis zum Rücken des Thüringerwaldes. *Second Janus*, 1851, 1: 66-87; 1852, 2: 40-89, 294-320, 527-611, pl.; reprinted Leipzig: Alfred Lorentz, 1931.

QAM

SCHLEISNER, P.A. Forsög til en nosographie of Island. [An attempt at a nosography of Iceland. (In Danish)] 101 p. Kjøbenhavn: 1849.
Reviewed by A.W.E.Th. Henschel, *Second Janus*, 1851, 1: 298-318; reprinted Leipzig: Alfred Lorentz, 1931.

SCHLEISNER, P.A. Island undersögt fra et laegevidenskabeligt Synspunkt. [Iceland examined from a medico-scientific point of view. (In Danish)] 198 p. Kjøbenhavn: 1849.
Reviewed by A.W.E.Th. Henschel, *Second Janus*, 1851, 1: 318-19; reprinted Leipzig: Alfred Lorentz, 1931.

QAR

KUCZYNSKI, Max Hans. Steppe und Mensch, kirgisische Reiseeindrücke und Betrachtungen über Leben, Kultur und Krankheit in ihren Zusammenhängen. 188 p. Leipzig: Hirzel, 1925.
Reviewed by K. Sudhoff, *Mitt.Gesch.Med.*, 1927, 26: 65.

QB DISEASES: THEORETICAL ASPECTS

BERGHOFF, Emanuel. Entwicklungsgeschichte des Krankheitsbegriffes. 2nd ed. 201 p. Wien: Maudrich, 1947.

BUESS, Heinrich. Zur Entwicklung der Irritabilitätslehre. *Festschrift für Jacques Brodbeck-Sandreuter zu seinem 60. Geburtstag*, p. 299-333. Basel: Schwabe, 1942.

DEBOVE, G.M. Les causes des maladies. *Rev.Sci.*, 1912, 50: 2e semestre, 801-5.

DIEPGEN, Paul. Die Lehre von der Entzündung, von der Begründung der Zellularpathologie bis zum Aufkommen der Bakteriologie. *Abhandl.Akad.Wiss.Lit.Mainz Math.Naturwiss.Kl.*, 1953, no. 3, 67-85.

DIEPGEN, Paul. Die Stellung der nosologischen Systeme in der Geschichte der Medizin. *Sudhoffs Arch.*, 1941, 34: 61-7.

FIENNES, Richard. Man, nature and disease. 287 p., ill., bibliogr. London: Weidenfeld and Nicolson; New York: New American Library, 1964. [CB 90/530]

GALDSTON, Iago. The concept of the specific in medicine. *Trans.Coll.Physicians Phila.*, 1941, 9: 25-34.

GALDSTON, Iago. Homines ad deos: or the clinical bull in the ecological china shop. *Bull.Hist.Med.*, 1954, 28: 515-24.

GOLDSCHMID, Edgar. Natürliche Nosologie. *Verhandl.Schweiz. Naturforsch.Ges.*, 1945, 230-1.

GOLDSCHMID, Edgar. Nosologia naturalis. *Science, Medicine and History, Essays in honour of Charles Singer*, (2), p. 103-22, 6 pl. London: Oxford University Press, 1953.
Illustrated from the history of dermatology in the 18th and 19th centuries.

JANDOLO, Michele. L'evoluzione del pensiero etiopatogenetico dall'antichità ad oggi. *Ann.Med.Nav.*, 1964, 69: 417-29.

LERI, André. Le développement historique de la doctrine des diathèses. *Prog.Méd., 3rd ser.*, 1912, 28: 133-6.

LINDEBOOM, G.A. A glance at the history of the idea of specificity in medicine. *Act.VIIIe Congr.Int.Hist.Sci.* (Florence, 1956), p. 656. Paris: Hermann, 1958.

LINDEBOOM, G.A. Uit de geschiedenis van het begrip specificiteit. [From the history of the concept of specificity. (In Dutch)] *Bijdr.Gesch.Geneesk.*, 1957, 37: 1-6.

LINDEBOOM, G.A. From the history of the concept of specificity. *Janus*, 1957, 46: 12-24.

MEERLOO, A.M. Het ziektebegrip in verleden en heden: een kort historisch overzicht. [The concept of disease in the past and today: a short historical survey. (In Dutch)] *Bijdr.Gesch.Geneesk.*, 1933, 13: 136-50.

RENBOURN, R.T. The natural history of insensible perspiration: a forgotten doctrine of health and disease. *Med.Hist.*, 1960, 4: 135-52.

RICHMOND, Phyllis Allen. Some variant theories in opposition to the germ theory of disease. *J.Hist.Med.*, 1954, 9: 290-303, 1 fig.

RIESE, Walther. The conception of disease, its history, its versions and its nature. 120 p. New York: Philosophical Library, 1953.
Reviewed by Owsei Temkin, *Bull.Hist.Med.*, 1956, 30: 386-8.

ROBERTS, Morley. Warfare in the human body. Essays on method, malignity, repair, and allied subjects. With an introduction by Arthur Keith. xiii, 286 p. London: Eveleigh Nash, 1920.
Reviewed by W.M. Bayliss, *Nature*, 1921, 106: 622-4.

ROLLESTON, Humphry. Aspects of age, life and disease. 304 p. (The Anglo-French Library of Medical and Biological Science) London: Paul Trench, Trubner, 1928.

SIGERIST, Henry E. Die historische Entwicklung des Entzündungsbegriffes. Leyden-Vorlesung im Berliner Verein für Innere Medizin und Kinderheilkunde, gehalten am 7. VI. 1926. *Deut.Med.Wochenschr.*, 1927, 53: 349-52.

SINGER, Charles; SINGER, Dorothea. The development of the doctrine of *Contagium vivum*, 1500-1750. *Proc.17th Int. Congr.Med.* (London, 1913), Sect. 23, p. 187-206. London: Oxford University Press and Hodder & Stoughton, 1914.

STICKER, Georg. Entwicklungsgeschichte der spezifischen Therapie. *Janus*, 1929, 33: 131-90, 213-34, 245-70.

SUDHOFF, Karl. Zur Geschichte der Lehre von den kritischen Tagen im Krankheitsverlaufe (1901). *Sudhoffs Arch.*, 1929, 21: 1-22.
Reprinted from *Wiener Med.Wochenschr.*, 1902.

THIESSEN, Norman W. An outline of the development of concepts of humoral medicine. *Med.Life*, 1934, 41: 3-19.

TRILLAT, A. La théorie miasmatique et les idées du jour. *Rev.Sci.*, 1912, 50, 2e semestre, 646-55.

QBwj

PINA GUIMARÃES, Luiz José de. História das doutrinas humorais e constitucionais em Portugal. (Resumo) *Act.IIe Congr.Int. Hist.Sci.*(Portugal, 1934), p. 262-3. Lisbon: 1936.

QC MORBID ANATOMY; EXPERIMENTAL PATHOLOGY

GOODHART, James. The Harveian oration on the passing of morbid anatomy. *Lancet*, 1912, 1129-33.

MICHAELIS, Lorenz. Vergleichende mikroskopische Untersuchungen an rezenten, historischen und fossilen menschlichen Knochen. Zugleich ein Beitrag zur Geschichte der Syphilis. viii, 92 p. Jena: Fischer, 1930.

MIERZECKI, H. Symbolism and pathognomy of the hand. *Ciba Symp.* (Summit, N.J.), 1942, 4: 1319-22, fig.

QCsd

FICARRA, Bernard J. Eleven famous autopsies in history. *Ann. Med.Hist.*, 1942, 4: 504-20.
Autopsies of St. Ignatius, M. Malpighi, Pepys, George II of England, Admiral John Paul Jones, Napoleon, Pedro I of Brazil, Lincoln, James A. Garfield, Frederick III of Prussia, Wm. McKinley.

QCwi

BARAHONA, Roberto. Italia, cuna de la anatomía patológica. *An.Chilenos Hist.Med.*, 1962, 1: 39-52.

QCwi-oq

COSTA, A. La scuola anatomo-patologica fiorentina da Ant Benivieni a Guido Banti. *Riv.Stor.Sci.*, 1952, 43: 297-334, fig.

QCyNWr

RIESMAN, David. Relations and functions of the clinical pathologist in the hospital staff. *Amer.J.Clin.Pathol.*, 1932, 2: 1-6.

QCyNWwb

CLARK, Jefferson H. The development of a pathological laboratory at Blockley. *Med.Life,* 1933, 40: 237-52, ill.

KRUMBHAAR, E.B. The history of pathology at the Philadelphia General Hospital. *Med.Life,* 1933, 40: 162-77.

QCyNWwe

FOSTER, W.D.; PINNIGER, L. History of pathology at St. Thomas's Hospital, London. *Med.Hist.*, 1963, 7: 330-47.

QD DIAGNOSIS; SYMPTOMS

for examination of special systems *see* INDEX

DOLL, -. Die Entwicklungsgeschichte der Auskultation. Zu ihrem hundertjährigen Gedächtnis. *Arch.Gesch.Med.*, 1921, 13: 43-63.

GALDSTON, Iago. Diagnosis in historical perspective. *Bull. Hist.Med.*, 1941, 9: 367-84.

GILBERT, A.; GUTMANN, R.A.; TZANCK, A. Les étapes historiques de la percussion. *Paris Méd.*, 27 fév. 1926, 193-202. [CB 20/210]

KEELE, K.D. Anatomies of pain. x, 206 p., ill. Oxford: Blackwell Scientific Publication, 1957.
Reviewed by Ragnar Granit, *Lychnos,* 1957-58, 462-3.

KEELE, K.D. James Mackenzie and pain. *J.Hist.Med.*, 1962, 17: 116-28.

KOCH, Richard. Die ärztliche Diagnose. Beitrag zur Kenntnis des ärztlichen Denkens. 2nd rev. ed. xv, 206 p. Wiesbaden: Bergmann, 1920.
First publ. 1917.

KORNS, Horace Marshall. A brief history of physical diagnosis. *Ann.Med.Hist.*, 1939, 1: 50-67.

MOLINÉRY, R. Notes sur le traitement de "l'étisie" à travers les âges de "Susçruta à Reichenbach". *Bull.Soc.Franç.Hist. Méd.*, 1935, 29: 40-8.

NEUBURGER, Max. Zur Geschichte der Auskultation. *Mitt. Gesch.Med.*, 1919, 18: 159-61. [CB 8/346]
Skoda developed the auscultation method.

NEWMAN, Charles. Diagnostic investigation before Laënnec. *Med.Hist.*, 1960, 4: 322-9.

RIESMAN, David. Differential diagnosis of diseases of the chest and abdomen. *Proc.Int.Assembly Inter-State Post Grad. Med.Ass.N.Amer.* (Philadelphia, 1938), p. 365-8. [Freeport, Ill.: 1939]

ROBERTSON, William Egbert. Physical diagnosis from the time of Röntgen. *Ann.Med.Hist.*, 1934, 6: 255-63.

SCHÖNFELD, W. Die Haut als Ausgang der Behandlung, Verhütung und Erkennung fernörtlicher Leiden. Eine geschichtliche Studie. *Sudhoffs Arch.*, 1943, 36: 43-89, 3 fig.

UNDERWOOD, E. Ashworth. How not to make a diagnosis. A historical fantasy. *West Lond.Med.J.*, 1952, 57: 58-67.

QDc-bx

ROBERTSON, William Egbert; ROBERTSON, Harold Frederick. An exhibit of books and memorabilia illustrative of the history of physical diagnosis throughout the ages. *Med.Life,* 1935, 42: 129-41.

QDda

MIDDLETON, William Shainline. A biographic history of physical diagnosis. *Ann.Med.Hist.*, 1924, 6: 426-52, 14 fig.

QDwb

JARCHO, Saul. The introduction of percussion in the United States. *J.Hist.Med.*, 1958, 13: 259-60.

QDxk

EBSTEIN, Erich. Die Gestalt und klinische Bedeutung des Perkussionshammers. *Z.Ärztl.Fortbild.*, 1912, 9: no. 9, 12 p.

EBSTEIN, Erich. Der Perkussionshammer. Ein Beitrag zur Geschichte der mittelbaren Perkussion. *Arch.Gesch.Med.*, 1912, 6: 245-70, 13 pl.

LEIKIND, Morris C. The stethoscope. Some notes on its history. *J.Nat.Med.Ass.*, 1955, 47: 177-80, 2 fig.

QDxp

BUSACCHI, Vincenzo. La scoperta del termometro e l'evoluzione della termometria clinica. *Riv.Stor.Sci.*, 1935, 26: 233-42.

EBSTEIN, Erich. Die Entwicklung der klinischen Thermometrie. *Ergeb.Inn.Med.Kinderheilk.*, 1928, 33: 407-503.

GERSHON-COHEN, J. A short history of medical thermometry. *Ann.N.Y.Acad.Sci.*, 1964, 121: 4-11.

McGUIGAN, Hugh A. Medical thermometry. *Ann.Med.Hist.*, 1937, 9: 148-54.

RATH, Gernot. Hundert Jahre klinische Thermometrie. *Deut. Med.Wochenschr.*, 1952, 77: 784-7.
Describes Wunderlich's introduction of temperature charts for his patients in October 1851.
Reviewed by Frans Jonckheere, *Arch.Int.Hist.Sci.*, 1952, 5: 437-8.

THOMPSON, C.J.S. The clinical thermometer. Its history and development. *Med.Life,* 1927, 34: 510-13.

QDxp-wk

EBSTEIN, Erich. Die Verdienste der holländischen Schule um die Entwicklung der klinischen Thermometrie. *VIe Congr.Int. Hist.Méd.* (Leyde-Amsterdam, 1927), p. 190. Anvers: De Vlijt, 1929.

QDxx

REICHERT, Philip. The Reichert collection, illustrative of the evolution and development of diagnostic instruments and techniques in medicine. Loan exhibit [at the] Wellcome Exhibition Galleries, 1942. 71 p., ill., pl. New York: Burroughs Wellcome, 1942.
Reviewed by E.H. Ackerknecht, *Bull.Hist.Med.*, 1943, 13: 505.

QDyNWwe

NEWMAN, Charles. Physical signs in the London hospitals. A chapter in the history of the introduction of physical examination. *Med.Hist.*, 1958, 2: 195-201.

QDze ELECTRODIAGNOSIS

for electrocardiography *see* PCyQDze

COLWELL, Hector A. An essay on the history of electrotherapy and diagnosis. xv, 180 p. London: Heinemann, 1922.

LICHT, Sidney. The history of electrodiagnosis. *Bull.Hist. Med.*, 1944, 16: 450-67.

QDzu URINE ANALYSIS

EBSTEIN, Erich. Zur Entwicklung der klinischen Harndiagnostik. *Wiener Klin.Wochenschr.*, 1913, 26: 1900-2.

EBSTEIN, Erich. Zur Geschichte der Kochprobe auf Eiweiss im Harn. *Mitt.Gesch.Med.*, 1912, 11: 328-33.

GUYOTJEANNIN, Charles. Contribution à l'histoire de l'analyse des urines. 104 p., 7 pl., 1 fig. (Thèse, Strasbourg) Créteil: R. Marest, 1951.
Reviewed by Ernest Wickersheimer, *Rev.Hist.Sci.*, 1953, 6: 89-90.

HELD, Wilhelm. Die Urinschau des Mittelalters und die Harnuntersuchung der Gegenwart. 150 p., 13 fig. Leipzig: Krüger, 1931.

MARTIN, Alfred; CLEMM, -. Aus der ärztlichen Praxis vom 15. bis zum 18. Jahrhundert. (Ein Beitrag zur Harndiagnostik). *Münch.Med.Wochenschr.*, 1931, 78: 594-5, 1 fig.

QDzu-wg-cs

DIEPGEN, Paul. Ueber die alten Siegel der medizinischen Fakultät der Albert-Ludwig-Universität in Freiburg i.Br. Ein Beitrag zur Geschichte der Harnschau. *Arch.Gesch.Med.*, 1914, 8: 165-74.

QE RADIOLOGY; RADIOGRAPHY

see also NH PHYSICAL AND CHEMICAL HAZARDS
RI RADIOTHERAPY

BRUWER, André J., ed. Classic descriptions in diagnostic roentgenology. 2 vol. xxi, 2059 p. Springfield, Ill.: Charles C. Thomas, 1964.

CIPRIANI, Mariano. Raggi invisibili dello spettro fotoelettrico (infrarossi, ultravioleti e Roentgen) utilizzati per esplorare il corpo umano. Breve rassegna storica. *Riv. Stor.Med.*, 1964, 8: 65-91.

CORNACCHIA, Vio. Storia della radiologia medica. *Riv.Stor. Med.*, 1961, 5: 261-73; 1962, 6: 114-32; 1963, 7: 73-93; 1964, 8: 105-22; 1965, 9: 106-24.

CURIE, Marie Sklodowska. La radiologie et la guerre. 144 p., 16 pl. Paris: Alcan, 1921.

DEWING, Stephen B. Modern radiology in historical perspective. 200 p. Springfield, Ill.: Charles C. Thomas, 1962.

FUCHS, Franz. Elektrische Strahlen und ihre Anwendung (Röntgentechnik). 35 p., 19 fig. (Werdegang der Entdeckungen, 3) München: Oldenbourg, 1922.

UNDERWOOD, E. Ashworth. Wilhelm Conrad Roentgen (1845-1923) and the early development of radiology. *Proc.Roy.Soc.Med.*, 1944-45, 38: Hist. Sect., 27-36.

QEwh

BUGYI, Balázs. Zur Geschichte der Röntgenologie in Ungarn (1896-1916). *NTM Z.Gesch.Naturwiss.Tech.Med.*, [1962], 1: no. 3, 87-114.

QEwh-oq

RATKÓCZY, Nándor. Die Entwicklung der Budapester Universitäts-Röntgenklinik und des Röntgenunterrichtes in Ungarn. *Festschrift zum 80. Geburtstag Max Neuburgers*, p. 386-91. Wien: Maudrich, 1948.

QF TUMOURS; CANCER

for cancer affecting special systems of the body, for cancer surgery and specific remedies *see* INDEX

FISCHER, I. The doctrine of metastasis in the lapse of times. *Janus*, 1940, 44: 173-84.

HADDOW, Alexander. Historical notes on cancer from the Mss. of Louis Westenra Sambon. *Proc.Roy.Soc.Med.*, 1935-36, 29: (2), 1015-28, Hist.Sect., 19-32. [CB 57/274]

KAHN, Max. Historical aspects of cancer research (written 1921). *Med.Life*, 1926, 33: 345-55.

KELLY, Michael. Sir James Mackenzie and cellular pathology. *Med.Hist.*, 1960, 4: 170-85.

KÖRBLER, Juraj. Zur Geschichte der Krebskrankheit. *Festschrift zum 80. Geburtstag Max Neuburgers*, p. 264-8. Wien: Maudrich, 1948.

KRUMBHAAR, Edward Bell. Experimental cancer, an historical retrospect. (From the laboratories of the Philadelphia General Hospital.) *Ann.Med.Hist.*, 1925, 7: 132-40.

LACASSAGNE, Antoine. Kennaway and the carcinogens. *Nature*, 1961, 191: 743-7.

LE DANTEC, F. Considérations biologiques sur le cancer. 52 p. Paris: A. Poinat, 1914.

LEHMANN, F.M. Denkrichtungen in der Krebsforschung. Eine ideengeschichtliche Untersuchung. *Med.Klin.*, 1964, 59: 668-71, 707-11.

MEYER, Willy. Cancer, its origin, its development and its self-perpetuation. The therapy of operable and inoperable cancer in the light of a systemic conception of malignancy. xxxiii, 427 p., portr. New York: Hoeber, 1931. [CB 31/571]

ONUIGBO, Wilson I.B. The age-old dictum on the spread of tumours. *Centaurus*, 1963, 8: 263-8.

ONUIGBO, Wilson I.B. A history of the cell theory of cancer metastasis. *Gesnerus*, 1963, 20: 90-5.

ROFFO, Angel H. Evolución histórica del cáncer. *Publ.Cátedra Hist.Med.Univ.Buenos Aires*, 1940, 3: 451-61.

SIGERIST, Henry E. The historical development of the pathology and therapy of cancer. *Bull.N.Y.Acad.Med.*, 1932, 8: 642-53.

WOLFF, Jacob. Die Lehre von der Krebskrankheit von den ältesten Zeiten bis zur Gegenwart. 2nd ed. 753 p., 52 fig. Jena: Fischer, 1929.

QFnh

KEIL, Harry. The historical relationship between the concept of tumor and the ending -oma. *Bull.Hist.Med.*, 1950, 24: 352-77.

QFwb-qg

ROSENGARTEN, A.G. A romance in research. A story on cancer research as it is being developed and conducted at the Lankenau Hospital Research Institute. *Gen.Mag.Hist.Chron.*, Oct. 1937, 12 p., 2 ill.

QFwp

ÜNVER, A. Süheyl. Meinungen über den Krebs und seine Behandlung in der türkischen Medizin-Geschichte. *Mitt.Gesch. Med.*, 1936, 35: 288: résumé of Turkish article in *Tib Dünyasi*, May 1935.

QFyQAvm

WOLFF, Georg. Cancer and race with special reference to the Jews. *Amer.J.Hyg.*, 1939, 29: 121-37.

QH PSYCHOSOMATIC MEDICINE

BLEULER, Eugen. Physisch und Psychisch in der Pathologie. Nach einem Vortrag gehalten in der Gesellschaft der Ärzte in Zürich in der Sitzung vom 30. Januar 1915. 52 p. Berlin: Springer, 1916.
Reprinted from *Z.Gesamte Neurol.Psychiat.*, 1916, 30: pt. 5.

DUNBAR, H. Flanders. Emotions and bodily changes. 2nd ed. xli, 601 p. New York: Columbia University Press, 1938. [CB 58/580]
1st ed. 1935. Many historical references.

MARGETTS, Edward L. Historical notes on psychosomatic medicine. In: Wittkower, E.D.; Cleghorn, R.A.; ed. Recent developments in psychosomatic medicine, p. 41-68. London: Pitman, 1954.

SELYE, Hans. The physiology and pathology of exposure to stress. xx, 822, 203 p. Montreal: Acta, 1950. [CB 77/385]
Contains an historical account of the development of the concepts of general-adaptation-syndrome and the disease of adaptation.

TASTEVIN, J. Les émotions afflictives. 1. Historiques des faits [serrement épigastrique]. *Rev.Sci.Psychol.*, 1913, 1: 282-94.

VEITH, Ilza. On hysterical and hypochondriacal afflictions. *Bull.Hist.Med.*, 1956, 30: 233-40.

WACHTEL, Curt S. The idea of psychosomatic medicine. Scientific foundation, spirit and scope. xiv, 239 p. New York: Froben, 1951. [CB 78/199]

QJ DISEASES DUE TO PHYSICAL FACTORS

BARCROFT, Joseph. Mountain sickness. *Nature,* 1924, 114: 90-2.

BLUM, Harold Francis. Photodynamic action and diseases caused by light. xii, 309 p. (American Chemical Society. Monograph series, 85) New York: Reinhold, 1941. [CB 61/402]

DOESSCHATE, G. Ten. De geschiedenis van de bergziekte. [The history of mountain sickness. (In Dutch)] *Bijdr.Gesch.Geneesk.,* 1957, 37: 32-3.

GÜNTHER, Siegmund. Die ältesten Beobachtungen über die Bergkrankheit der Kordilleren. *Arch.Gesch.Naturwiss.Tech.,* 1913, 6: 122-31.

JELLINEK, Stefan. Entstehung und Entwicklung der Elektropathologie. ***Festschrift zur Feier seines 60. Geburtstags Max Neuburger gewidmet,*** **p. 198-202. Wien: Verlag des Fest-Komitees, 1928.**

MULLENER, E.R. Ein Hinweis auf die Bergkrankheit in Europa aus dem 14. Jahrhundert [in ***Dittamondo*** **by Fazio degli Uberti].** ***Gesnerus,*** **1964, 21: 66-71.**

QK TOXICOLOGY

see also NO NARCOTICS; ALCOHOL

LELEUX, Charles. Le poison à travers les âges. 320 p., ill. Paris: A. Lemerre, 1923. [CB 15/234]

LENOBLE, Robert. Le thème du poison. *Arch.Int.Hist.Sci.,* 1955, 8: 41-52.

MAJOR, Ralph H. Some landmarks in the history of lead poisoning. *Ann.Med.Hist.,* 1931, 3: 218-27, 5 fig., front.

MALLOCH, Archibald. Lead poisoning. *Ann.Med.Hist.,* 1931, 3: 455-8.

PERROT, Em.; VOGT, Em. Poisons de flèches et poisons d'épreuves. xii, 367 p. Paris: Vigot, 1913.

STENN, Frederick. The pioneer history of milk sickness. *Ann.Med.Hist.,* 1937, 9: 23-9, 2 fig.

STEVENSON, Lloyd G. The meaning of poison. 53 p. (Logan Clendening Lectures on the History of and Philosophy of Medicine, 7th series) Lawrence: University of Kansas Press, 1959.
Reviewed by Glenn Sonnedecker, *Isis,* 1960, 51: 578-9; by Chauncey D. Leake, *J.Hist.Med.,* 1960, 15: 101-2.

QKsc

LEWIN, Louis. Die Gifte in der Weltgeschichte. Toxikologische, algemeinverständliche Untersuchungen der historischen Quellen. xvi, 596 p. Berlin: Springer, 1920.
Reviewed by George Sarton, *Isis,* 1922, 4: 371-3.

LEWIN, Louis. Die Pfeilgifte nach eigenen toxikologischen und ethnologischen Untersuchungen. xi, 517 p. Leipzig: Barth, 1923.
This completes the author's study of the malicious use of poisons throughout the ages: Die Gifte in der Weltgeschichte, *see* above.

THOMPSON, Charles John Samuel. Poison mysteries in history, romance and crime. 412 p. London: Scientific Press, 1923.

QKyK PLANT POISONS

BARGER, George. Ergot and ergotism: a monograph based on the Dohme lectures delivered in Johns Hopkins University, Baltimore. xvi, 279 p., 6 pl. London: Gurney and Jackson, 1931.
Reviewed in *Nature,* 1932, 129: 335-6.

BARNES, Byron A.; FOX, Lauretta E. Poisoning with *Dieffenbachia. J.Hist.Med.,* 1955, 10: 173-81.

COUCH, James Fitton. The toxic constituent of richweed or white snakeroot *(Eupatorium urticaefolium). J.Agr. Res.,* 1927, 35: 545-76, 1 fig. [CB 31/573]

DESOILLE, Henri. L'empoisonnement par les cigües. *Presse Méd.,* 1936, 63: 1267. [CB 50/402]

FOURNIER, P. Le livre des plantes médicinales et vénéneuses de France. 3 vol. (Encyclopédie Biologique, 25, 31, 32) Paris: Lechevalier, 1947-48.
Vol. 1 reviewed by W.O. James, ***Nature,*** **1949, 163: 383-4.**

HEUSINGER, Johann Christian Karl Friedrich von. Die von den Englischen Aerzten in Ostindien unter dem Namen "Burning of the feet" beschriebene Krankheit. Ein Beitrag zur Geschichte der Kriebelkrankheit. ***Henschel's Janus,*** **1846, 1: 257-95; reprinted Leipzig: Alfred Lorentz, 1931.**
Study of ergotism.

KINGSBURY, John M. Knowledge of poisonous plants in the United States - brief history and conclusions. ***Econ.Bot.,*** **1961, 15: 119-30.**

PETERS, Rudolph. Biochemical light upon an ancient poison: a lethal synthesis. ***Endeavour,*** **1954, 13: 147-54. [CB 81/275]**
The toxic properties of the South African plant, ***Dichopetalum cymosum,*** **is due to fluoracetic acid.**

STEINER, Irma. Die geschichtliche Entwicklung der chemischen und pharmakologischen Mutterkornforschung bis zum Jahre 1918. 44 p. (Inaugural-Diss.) Basel: Berchten, 1951.

STOCKMAN, Ralph. Historical notes on poisoning by leguminous foods. *Janus,* 1932, 36: 180-9.

TURNER, Terence D. The cruel poison. [Strychnine. With subsequent letter from M.P. Earles.] *Pharm.J.,* 1962, 189: 151-3, 186.

QKyL ANIMAL POISONS

ABEL, John J.; MACHT, David I. The poisons of the tropical toad, *Bufo agua.* A preliminary communication. *J.Amer.Med. Ass.,* 1911, 56: 1531-6.

ARTHUS, Nicolas Maurice. Les venins. *Rev.Gén.Sci.,* 1914, 25: 99-105.

BETHENCOURT FERREIRA, J. Sur un nouveau chapitre de la médecine thérapeutique, la sérologie des venins de cobra. *Festschrift zum 80. Geburtstag Max Neuburgers,* p. 137-9. Wien: Maudrich, 1948.

CASTIGLIONI, Arturo. The serpent as healing god in antiquity. Snake worship and symbolism in the Orient and in America. Remedies against snake bite. Snake venom in modern medicine. *Ciba Symp.* (Summit, N.J.), 1942, 4: 1158-86, fig.

GUDGER, E.W. Is the sting ray's sting poisonous? A historical résumé showing the development of our knowledge that it is poisonous. ***Bull.Hist.Med.,*** **1943, 14: 467-504, 12 fig.**

GUDGER, E.W. Poisonous fishes and fish poisonings, with special reference to Ciguatera in the West Indies. ***Amer. J.Trop.Med.,*** **1930, 10: 43-53.**

GUDGER, E.W.; BREDER, C.M. The Barracuda (Sphyraena) dangerous to man. ***J.Amer.Med.Ass.,*** **1928, 90: 1938-43, 5 fig.**

MOUSSON-LANAUZE, -.; HARIZ, -. A propos du venin du cobra. *Bull.Soc.Franç.Hist.Méd.,* 1934, 28: 103-6.

PAVLOVSKII, E.N. Gifttiere und ihre Giftigheit. xvi, 516 p., ill. Jena: Gustav Fischer, 1927.

PHISALIX, Marie. Animaux venimeux et venins. 2 vol. Paris: Masson, 1922.

PHISALIX, Marie. Les serpents venimeux. *Rev.Sci.,* 1922, 60: 684-93. [CB 14/569]

THORP, Raymond W.; WOODSON, Weldon D. Black widow. America's most poisonous spider. With a foreword by Emil Bogen. xi, 222 p., ill. Chapel Hill: University of North Carolina Press, 1945.
Includes brief chapters on spider lore and tarantism.

QL METABOLIC AND DEFICIENCY DISEASES

ABASCAL, Horacio. Reseña histórica y sinonimia de la frambuesa y de la pelagra. 35 p., 10 ill. (Cuadernos de Historia Sanitaria, 9) Havana: Ministerio de Salubridad y Asistencia Social, 1955. [CB 83/205]

ACKERKNECHT, Erwin H. The history of metabolic diseases. *Ciba Symp.*(Summit, N.J.), 1944, 6: 1834-44.

BRÜCK, Dietrich. Zur Geschichte und Klinik des Skorbuts. (Diss.) 105 p. Leipzig: 1935.

BRUNN, Walther von. Beiträge zur Geschichte der Mangelkrankheiten. *Münch.Med.Wochenschr.*, 1937, 84: 223-7.

COPEMAN, W.S.C. A short history of the gout and rheumatic diseases. ix, 236 p., ill. Berkeley/Los Angeles: University of California Press, 1964.
Reviewed by A.S. Macnalty, *Med.Hist.*, 1964, 8: 394-5.

FRAZIER, Chester N.; MARMELSZADT, Willard L. Vitamin A deficiency and the skin in retrospect. An historical search into nosological antecedents. *Bull.Hist.Med.*, 1948, 22: 766-95, 6 fig.

HARRIS, Leslie J. Vitamins and vitamin deficiencies. Vol. 1. Introductory and historical; vitamin B1 and beri-beri. xiv, 204 p. London: Churchill, 1938.
Reviewed by A.L. Bacharach, *Sci.Progr.*, 1939, 34: 421-2.

HEUSINGER, Johann Christian Karl Friedrich von. Der Cak in Sennaar. Eine epidemische, wahrscheinlich dem Maispellagra u. s. w. zu vergleichende Krankheit. *Henschel's Janus*, 1846, 1: 296-9; reprinted Leipzig: Alfred Lorentz, 1931.

KLIBANOFF, Meyer. Zur Lehre der Gicht in geschichtlicher Beziehung von Hippokrates zu Paracelsus. (Diss.) 22 p. Berlin: H. Blanke, 1912.

LLOYD, C.C. The conquest of scurvy. *Brit.J.Hist.Sci.*, 1963, 1: 357-63.

ROLLIS, Richard H. Cellular pathology and the development of the deficiency disease concept. *Bull.Hist.Med.*, 1960, 34: 291-317.

SCHNITKER, Maurice A. A history of the treatment of gout. *Bull.Inst.Hist.Med.*, 1936, 4: 89-120.

WILLIAMS, Robert R. Toward the conquest of beriberi. 338 p. Cambridge: Harvard University Press, 1961.
Reviewed by P. Huard, *Arch.Int.Hist.Sci.*, 1962, 15: 222-4; by C.A. Bozman, *Med.Hist.*, 1962. 6: 198-9.

QLhj

SIEGEL, Rudolph E. Hippocratic description of metabolic diseases in relation to modern concepts. *Bull.Hist.Med.*, 1960, 34: 355-64.

QLnh

KLUYVER, A. Aanteekening over het woord scheurbuik (scorbutus). [A note on the word scurvy. (In Dutch)] *Bijdr. Gesch.Geneesk.*, 1923, 3: 235-8.

REICHBORN-KJENNERUD, I. Zur Etymologie des Wortes Skorbutus. *Festschrift zum 80. Geburtstag Max Neuburgers*, p. 392-5. Wien: Maudrich, 1948.
The word is of Scandinavian origin.

QLt

VIVIANI, Ugo. Panciuti, grassi ed obesi nell'arte, nella storia, nella letteratura. 167 p. (Collana di Pubblicazioni Storiche, Letterarie ed Artistiche Aretine, 17) Arezzo: 1926. [CB 20/211]

QLwc

GUERRA, Francisco. Hispanic-American contribution to the history of scurvy. *Centaurus*, 1950, 1: 12-23, 8 facs. [CB 80/138]

QLyQA

DVORJETSKI, Marc. Sur la pathologie de la famine dans les ghettos. *Rev.Hist.Méd.Hébraique*, 1954, 7: 259-68.

QLyQAF

CLAUDIAN, J. Aperçu sur l'histoire du scorbut en France. *Bull.Sci.Roumain*, 1956-57, 4-5: 66-95.

QLyQAK

ANDEL, M.A. van. De scheurbuik als nederlandsche volksziekte. [Scurvy as a disease common in the Netherlands. (In Dutch)] *Bijdr.Gesch.Geneesk.*, 1927, 7: 519-31.

ANDEL, M.A. van. Der Skorbut als niederländische Volkskrankheit. *Arch.Gesch.Med.*, 1927, 19: 82-91.

QM ALLERGIC DISEASES

for asthma *see also* OX

ARTHUS, Nicolas Maurice. *See* QO

BELLAGARDA, G. Le più antiche descrizioni occidentali della pollinosi. *Minerva Med.*, 1964, 55: 2241-3.

BLITTERSDORF, Friedrich. Zur Geschichte der Serumkrankheit. *Sudhoffs Arch.*, 1952, 36: 149-58.

BRAY, George W. Recent advances in allergy (asthma, hay-fever, eczema, migraine, etc.). Foreword by A.F. Hurst. xii, 432 p., 4 pl., 98 fig. London: Churchill; Philadelphia: Blakiston, 1931. [CB 34/504]
Practically a complete history of the field.

COCA, Arthur F. The development of theories of familial allergies. *Ciba Symp.* (Summit, N.J.), 1951, 11: 1390-7, 1412, ill.

FARMER, Laurence. History of the clinical recognition of allergic states. *Ciba Symp.* (Summit, N.J.), 1951, 11: 1382-9, ill.

FEINBERG, Samuel M. Experimental and clinical evolution of therapy in allergy. *Ciba Symp.* (Summit, N.J.), 1951, 11: 1398-412, ill.

LUMIÈRE, Auguste. Le problème de l'anaphylaxie. 242 p., 24 pl. Paris: Doin, 1924. [CB 16/327]

PIRQUET, Clemens von; SCHICK, Bela. Serum sickness. xi, 130 p. Baltimore: Williams & Wilkins, 1951.
Translation of "Die Serumkrankheit" (1905), the first treatise on allergy.
Reviewed by Arthur F. Coca, *J.Hist.Med.*, 1951, 6: 536-7.

SARTON, George. Earliest writings on coryza, hay fever, pollen allergy? (Query, 141) *Isis*, 1954, 45: 199.
Mentions lost work of al-Rāzī "Dissertation on the course of the coryza which occurs in the spring when roses give forth their scent".

SCHADEWALDT, Hans. Zur Frühgeschichte allergischer Erkrankungen. *Sudhoffs Arch.*, 1958, 42: 363-76.

STOLKIND, E. The history of bronchial asthma and allergy. *Proc.Roy.Soc.Med.*, 1933, 26: 36-42. [CB 40/416]

WODEHOUSE, Roger P. Hayfever plants. Their appearance, distribution, time of flowering, and their role in hayfever, with special reference to North America. xix, 245 p., 73 fig. Waltham, Mass.: Chronica Botanica, 1945. [CB 69/230]

QMyQD

SCHADEWALDT, Hans. La historia de las pruebas diagnósticas en la alergia. *Folia Clin.Int.*, 1964, 14: 545-9.

QN INFECTIOUS AND COMMUNICABLE DISEASES; MEDICAL BACTERIOLOGY

for specific infectious diseases *see* QP
infectious diseases in the army *see* QVyQN

see also JR MICROBIOLOGY

QNc general history

BERG, Alexander. Miasma und Kontagium, die Lehre von der Ansteckung im Wandel der Zeiten. Zur 80-jährigen Wiederkehr der Entdeckung des Tbc-Bazillus (1882). *Naturwissenschaften*, 1963, 50: 389-96.
History of theories of contagion from the 14th century through Koch's discovery of the tubercle bacillus in 1882.

BURNET, Macfarlane. Natural history of infectious disease. 3rd ed. x, 377 p., 14 fig., 2 tables. Cambridge/New York: Cambridge University Press, 1962. [CB 89/585]
Reviewed by Elbert Voss, *Amer.J.Pharm.Educ.*, 1963, 27: 186.
First published 1940 under title: Biological aspects of infectious disease.

COCKBURN, Aidan. The evolution and eradication of infectious diseases. 255 p. Baltimore: Johns Hopkins Press, 1963.
Reviewed by John R. Paul, *J.Hist.Med.*, 1964, 19: 173-4.

DIOSI, Peter. Long-term changes in the natural history of infectious diseases. *Centaurus*, 1964, 9: 288-92.

EBERSON, Frederick. The microbe's challenge. viii, 354 p. Lancaster, Pa.: Jacques Cattell Press, 1941. [CB 62/85]
This book is full of historical references to all of the major diseases of man of bacterial, protozoan, and virus origin.

EBERSON, Frederick. Microbes militant: a challenge to man: the story of modern preventive medicine and control of infectious diseases. x, 401 p., 25 ill. New York: Ronald Press, 1948.

EFFERTZ, O. Vergleichende Pathologie der Infektions-Krankheiten, mit allgemeiner physiologischer und pathologischer Einleitung und mit besonderer Berücksichtigung der Indianer. 176 p. Bonn: Muttmacher, 1920.
Reviewed by Z., *Janus*, 1921, 25: 338-9.
The first part of this treatise was published in *Janus*, 1919, 24: 1-56.

FLEXNER, Simon. Epidemiology and recent epidemics. *Science*, 1919, 50: 313-19.

FLEXNER, Simon. Twenty-five years of bacteriology: a fragment of medical research. *Science*, 1920, 52: 615-32. [CB 10/158]

GALDSTON, Iago. The epidemic constitution in historic perspective. *Bull.N.Y.Acad.Med.*, 1942, 18: 606-19.

GAMAS, Azevedo. La notion d'infection focale et ses vicissitudes. *Hist.Med.*, 1960, 10: 43-5.

GARRISON, Fielding Hudson. The newer epidemiology. *Essays on the History of Medicine presented to Karl Sudhoff*, p. 255-68. London: Oxford University Press; Zurich: K. Hönn, 1924.

GILL, Clifford Allchin. The genesis of epidemics and the natural history of disease: an introduction to the science of epidemiology based upon the study of epidemics of malaria, influenza, and plague. xxvi, 550 p. London: Baillière, Tindall and Cox, 1928.
Reviewed by R.T.H., *Nature*, 1929, 124: 221-2.

GREENWOOD, Major. Epidemiology historical and experimental. x, 80 p., 5 fig. (The Herter Lectures for 1931) Baltimore: Johns Hopkins Press, 1932. [CB 37/609]

HAESER, Heinrich. Lehrbuch der Geschichte der Medicin und der epidemischen Krankheiten. 2nd rev. ed. 2 vol. xlvii, 923 p.; xvi, 832, 72 p. Jena: Mauke, 1853-65.
Vol. 1 reviewed by M. Landsberg, *Henschel's Janus*, 1852, 2: 612-37; reprinted, Leipzig: Alfred Lorentz, 1931.

HAMER, William. Epidemiology old and new. x, 180 p. (Anglo-French Library of Medical and Biological Science) London: Kegan Paul, 1929.
Reviewed by A.S.M., *Nature*, 1929, 124: 435.
For French version (Paris: Doin, 1931) *see* CB 33/415.

HAMER, William. The history of epidemiological research during the last seventy years. *17th Int.Congr.Med.* (London, 1913), Sect. 23, p. 305-11. London: 1914.

HANSSEN, Peter. Geschichte der Epidemien bei Menschen und Tieren im Norden. 228 p. Glückstadt: Augustin, 1925.

HARE, Ronald. Pomp and pestilence, infectious disease, its origins and conquest. 224 p. New York: Philosophical Library, 1955.
Reviewed by Morris C. Leikind, *Isis*, 1956, 47: 195-6.

HILL, Justina. Germs and the man. xvi, 461 p., ill. New York: Putnam, 1940.
Reviewed by Morris C. Leikind, *Isis*, 1942, 33: 641-2.

JAHN, Ferdinand. Beiträge zur Geschichte der Carbunkel-Krankheiten mit Ausschluss der Pest. *Henschel's Janus*, 1846, 1: 367-414, 485-550; reprinted Leipzig: Alfred Lorentz, 1931.

KLEBS, Arnold C. The history of infection. *Ann.Med.Hist.*, 1917, 1: 159-73.

LEIKIND, Morris C. The discovery of pathogenic germs. Ancient ideas of infection. The invention of the microscope and the discovery of bacteria. Spontaneous generation and fermentation. The final victory. *Ciba Symp.* (Summit, N.J.), 1941, 2: 726-54.

MARTÍNEZ FORTÚN Y FOYO, José A. Epidemiología (Síntesis cronológica). Prólogo del Dr. Enrique Saladrigas y Zayas. 51 p. (Cuadernos de historia sanitaria, 5) Habana: Ministerio de Salubridad y Asistencia Social, 1952.

MURRAY, D. Stark. Science fights death. x, 149 p., 18 fig. London: Watts, 1936. [CB 54/584]
A popular survey of the present status of medical warfare against communicable diseases.

OLIVER, Wade W. Stalkers of pestilence. The story of men's ideas of infection. Introduction by Theobald Smith. xxi, 251 p., 23 fig. New York: Hoeber, 1930. [CB 32/614]
Reviewed by Thomas McCrae, *Ann.Med.Hist.*, 1931, 3: 121-2.

ROLLESTON, J.D. The history of the acute exanthemata: the Fitz-Patrick lectures for 1935 and 1936, delivered before the Royal College of Physicians of London. ix, 114 p., 10 pl. London: Heinemann, 1937.
Reviewed by S.H.D., *Nature*, 1937, 139: 1037.

SEIFFERT, Gustav. Virus diseases in man, animal and plant. ix, 332 p. New York: Philosophical Library, 1944. [CB 66/265]

SUDHOFF, Karl. Grundfragen der historischen Epidemiologie. *Verhandl.Ges.Deut.Naturforsch.Aerzte 84.Versamml.* (Münster i. W., 1912), part 2, (2), p. 103-5. Leipzig: F.C.W. Vogel, 1913.

SUDHOFF, Karl. Infektion und Infektionsverhütung im Wandel der Zeiten und Anschauungen. (Ausgewählte Abhandlungen von Karl Sudhoff zum 75. Geburtstage) *Sudhoffs Arch.*, 1929, 21: 207-18.
Originally published in *Jahreskurse Arztl.Fortbild.*, 1914, 5: no. 9, 42-50.

TEMKIN, Owsei. An historical analysis of the concept of infection. In: Johns Hopkins University. History of Ideas Club. Studies in intellectual history, p. 123-47. Baltimore: Johns Hopkins Press, 1953.

UNITED STATES. ARMY MEDICAL DEPARTMENT. Communicable diseases transmitted chiefly through respiratory and alimentary tracts. xxi, 544 p. (Preventive Medicine in World War II, 4) Washington, D.C.: Office of the Surgeon General, 1958.

UNITED STATES. ARMY MEDICAL DEPARTMENT. Communicable diseases transmitted through contact or by unknown means. xxiii, 530 p. (Preventive Medicine in World War II, 5) Washington, D.C.: Office of the Surgeon General, 1961.

UNITED STATES. ARMY MEDICAL DEPARTMENT. Internal medicine in World War II. Ed. by John Boyd Coates, Jr. and W. Paul Havens, Jr. Vol. II. Infectious diseases. xxvii, 649 p., ill. Washington, D.C.: Office of the Surgeon General, 1963.
Reviewed by Arthur S. Macnalty, *Med.Hist.*, 1964, 8: no. 1, 93.

WINSLOW, Charles-Edward Amory. The conquest of epidemic diseases: a chapter in the history of ideas. xii, 411 p. Princeton, N.J.: Princeton University Press, 1943.
Reviewed by J.B. de C.M. Saunders, *Isis*, 1944, 35: 347; by Gaylord W. Anderson, *Amer.Hist.Rev.*, 1944, 49: 272-3.

WINSLOW, Charles-Edward Amory. Man and epidemics. ix, 246 p., ill. Princeton, N.J.: Princeton University Press, 1952. [CB 79/194]
Reviewed by John B. Blake, *J.Hist.Med.*, 1953, 8: 228-30.

QNc-br

Matériaux pour l'Etude des Calamités. (Société de Géographie de Genève) No. 1-40. Genève: 1924-37. [CB 21/589]

QNce-bx

STREETER, Edward C. Exhibit of medical texts illustrating practice in fevers, plague, etc. 44 p. Boston: Boston Public Library, 1921. [CB 11/448]
Catalogue of an exhibition organized by Dr. Streeter for the annual session of the American Medical Association.

QNhj

SIEGEL, Rudolph E. Epidemic and infectious diseases at the time of Hippocrates. Their relation to modern accounts. *Gesnerus*, 1960, 17: 77-98.

QNk/n philosophy and methodology; communication

QNk

BURNET, F.M. Biological aspects of infectious disease. xi, 310 p. New York: Macmillan, 1940. [CB 61/417]

FROST, Wade Hampton. Papers of Wade Hampton Frost, M.D. A contribution to epidemiological method. Edited by Kenneth F. Maxcy. viii, 628 p., 54 fig., portr., bibliogr. New York: The Commonwealth Fund; London: Oxford University Press, 1941. [CB 62/63]

MURRAY, E.G.D. A plea for constructive speculation. *Bull. Hist.Med.*, 1955, 29: 69-74.
In the author's own field of medical bacteriology.

QNnh

BIRAUD, Yves. Polyglot glossary of communicable diseases: contribution to the International Nomenclature of diseases. *Bull.Health Organ.League Nat.*, 1944, 10: 201-556.
Reviewed by J.A. Wilcken, *Endeavour*, 1945, 4: 39.

QNs/u social and humanistic relations

QNs

LONG, Esmond R. The decline of chronic infectious disease and its social implications. (The Fielding H. Garrison Lecture) *Bull.Hist.Med.*, 1954, 28: 368-84.

QNsc

GERHARDT, Oswald. Mikroben im Weltgeschehen. Sieg über die Seuchen. 182 p., 6 pl. (List-Bücher, 30) München: Paul List, 1954.
Reviewed by Robert Herrlinger, *Sudhoffs Arch.*, 1955, 39: 96.

SIEGFRIED, André. Itinéraires de contagions; epidémies et idéologies. 165 p., maps. Paris: Colin, 1960.

QNsp

GLASER, Erhard. Seuchen und Krieg in vergangenen Zeiten. *Festschrift zur Feier seines 60. Geburtstags Max Neuburger gewidmet*, p. 129-35. Wien: Verlag des Fest-Komitees, 1928.

PRINZING, Friedrich. Epidemics resulting from wars. Ed. by Harold Westergaard. xii, 340 p. (Carnegie Endowment for International Peace. Division of economics and history. Publications.) Oxford: Clarendon Press, 1916. [CB 13/297]

SUDHOFF, Karl. Kriege und Seuchen in früheren Zeiten. (Ausgewählte Abhandlungen von Karl Sudhoff zum 75. Geburtstage) *Sudhoffs Arch.*, 1929, 21: 248-60.
Originally published in *Jahreskurse Ärztl.Fortbild.*, Sept. 1915, 6: 32-40.

QNtd

OLIVIER, E. En Beaufortain, un oratoire et une chapelle contre la peste et le choléra. *Mem.Soc.Franç.Hist.Méd.*, 1947, 3: 135-6.

QNu

ROLLESTON, J.D. The folk-lore of the acute exanthemata. *Proc. Roy.Soc.Med.*, 1942, 35: 535-8.

WRIGHT, Jonathan. Demonology and bacteriology in medicine. *Sci.Mon.*, 1917, 4: 494-508.

QNw in different countries

QNwb

LONG, Esmond R. Frederick G. Novy and some origins of American bacteriology. *Trans.Coll.Physicians Phila.*, 1958, 26: 34-9. [CB 84/383]

STITT, E.R. Our disease inheritance from slavery. *U.S.Nav. Med.Bull.*, 1928, 26: 801-17. [CB 33/417]

TOP, Franklin H. The history of American epidemiology. 190 p. St. Louis: Mosby, 1952. [CB 79/194]

WINSLOW, Charles-Edward Amory; SMILLIE, W.G.; DOULL, J.A.; GORDON, J.E. The history of American epidemiology. 190 p. St. Louis: Mosby, 1952.
Reviewed by Erwin H. Ackerknecht, *Arch.Int.Hist.Sci.*, 1953, 6: 527-8; by B. Imbasciata, *Riv.Stor.Sci.*, 1953, 44: 214-15.

QNwc

BELTRAN, Juan Ramon. Síntesis histórica de la epidemiología en la Argentina. *Rev.Argent.Hist.Med.*, 1943, 2: no. 3, 13-26.

BESIO MORENO, Nicolás. Historia de las epidemias de Buenos Aires. Estudio demográfico estadistico. *Publ.Cátedra Hist. Med.Univ.Buenos Aires*, 1940, 3: 81-178, maps.

DOBYNS, Henry F. An outline of Andean epidemic history to 1720. *Bull.Hist.Med.*, 1963, 37: 493-515.

KRAUS, Richard. Zehn Jahre Südamerika. Vorträge über Epidemiologie und Infektionskrankheiten der Menschen und Tiere. 182 p., 108 ill. Jena: Fischer, 1927.

LUTZ, Adolpho. A contribution to the history of medicine in Brazil. The early work and reports of Dr. Adolpho Lutz. Foreword - cholera - dysentery. *Mem.Inst.Oswaldo Cruz*, 1943, 39: 191-200, 219-27, 243-52, ill.

QNwc-qg

BEAUREPAIRE ARAGÃO, Henrique de. Noticia histórica sôbre a fundação do Instituto Oswaldo Cruz (Instituto de Manguinhos). 50 p., ill. (*Mem.Inst.Oswaldo Cruz*, 48) Rio de Janeiro: 1950. [CB 78/158]

QNwe

SCOTT, H. Harold. Some notable epidemics. xx, 272 p. London: Arnold, 1934. [CB 43/290]
The histories of twenty-three epidemics in Great Britain between 1854 and 1933.

QNwe-qg

CHICK, Harriette. The Lister Institute of Preventive Medicine. *Endeavour*, 1949, 8: 106-11, ill.
An illustrated brief history of the Institute founded in London in 1891.

QNwf

BON, H. Essai historique sur les épidémies en Bourgogne. 186 p. Dijon: Berthier, 1912.

CLEU, Hubert. Les maladies épidémiques et contagieuses en Lorraine du IXe au XIXe siècle. *Bull.Soc.Franç.Hist.Méd.*, 1914, 13: 236-49.

QNwg

SCHMITZ-CLIEVER, Egon. Ergebnisse seuchengeschichtlicher Untersuchungen für die Reichsstadt Aachen bis zum Ausgang des 18. Jahrhunderts. *Sudhoffs Arch.*, 1954, 38: 289-302.

QNwh-ce

TKACZ, B. Ważniejsze traktaty o chorobach zakaźnych z Krakowskiej szkoly od XV do XVII wieku. [The most important works of infectious diseases in the Krakow school from 15th to 17th century.(In Polish)] *Przegl.Epidemiol.*, 1964, 18: 249-54.

QNwv

SCHOUTE, D. Enkele volksplagen in het verleden van nederlandsch Indië. [Some epidemic diseases of the Netherlands Indies in the past. (In Dutch)] *Bijdr.Gesch.Geneesk.*, 1935, 15: 1-16, 21-37, 52-68, 74-91, 101-18.

QNwx

MATHIS, C. L'oeuvre des pastoriens en Afrique noire, Afrique Occidentale Française. Préface de Maurice Caullery. xi, 580 p., 32 pl., 1 map. (Colonies et Empires, *1st ser.*, Études Coloniales, 2) Paris: Presses Universitaires de France, 1946.

QNy related subjects

QNyNT

MEFFERT, Franz. Caritas und Volksepidemien. xvi, 267 p. Freiburg i. Br.: Caritasverlag, 1925.

QNyOZ

PATRICK, Adam. The enteric fevers 1800-1920. 46 p. Edinburgh: Royal College of Physicians of Edinburgh, 1955.
Reviewed by Joseph L. Melnick, *J.Hist.Med.*, 1956, 11: 116-17.

QO IMMUNOLOGY

for sera and vaccines used for specific diseases *see* INDEX
see also QKyL ANIMAL POISONS

APERT, E. Vaccins et sérums. 283 p. Paris: Flammarion, 1922.
Reviewed by L. Guinet, *Isis*, 1923, 5: 190-1.

ARTHUS, Nicolas Maurice. De l'anaphylaxie à l'immunité. xxxv, 361 p. Paris: Masson, 1921.

ARTHUS, Nicolas Maurice. Maurice Arthus' philosophy of scientific investigation. Preface to "De l'Anaphylaxie à l'Immunité", Paris: 1921. Transl. from the French, with an introd. by Henry E. Sigerist. 26 p. (Reprinted from *Bull. Hist.Med.*, 1943, 14: 366-90) Baltimore, Md.: John Hopkins Press, 1943. [CB 66/241]

BOYDEN, A. Fifty years of systematic serology. *Syst.Zool.*, 1953, 2: 19-30.

BURROUGHS, WELLCOME AND CO. The history of inoculation and vaccination for the prevention and treatment of disease. 310, xvi p., ill. London: 1913.

DAGOGNET, François. L'immunité, histoire et méthode. 23 p. (Conférences du Palais de la Découverte, D94) Paris: Université de Paris, 1964.

EYQUEM, A. The development of immunology. *Impact*, 1963, 13: 25-47.

NEUBURGER, Max. Forerunners of serum therapy. *Med.Life*, 1932, 39: 707-10.

PAILLOT, A. Une science nouvelle: l'immunologie comparée. *Rev.Gén.Sci.*, 1924, 35: 422-9.

PINEL, E. Le mécanisme de la vaccinothérapie. *Thalès*, 1935, 1: 94-125. [CB 45/299]

RICHET, Charles. Les origines de la sérothérapie; son passé, son présent, son avenir. *Bull.Acad.Méd.*, 1932, 108: 1164-9. [CB 39/406]

QOwm-qg

MADSEN, Thorvald. Seruminstitutets tilblivelse. [The origin of the Serum Institute. (In Danish, with English summary)] *Med.Forum*, 1956, 9: 161-77, 9 fig. [CB 83/280]

QOyJH

METALNIKOV, S. Sur l'hérédité de l'immunité acquise. *Compt. Rend.Acad.Sci.*, 8 Sept. 1924, 179: 514-16. [CB 16/290]

QP SPECIFIC DISEASES CAUSED BY MICROORGANISMS

REGNAULT, Félix. Rôle de la clinique et du laboratoire dans les découvertes de pathologie: fièvre puerpérale et typhus exanthématique. *Bull.Soc.Franç.Hist.Méd.*, 1929, 23: 359-63.

RENBOURN, R.T. Roter Hund and Roodvonk (Red Dog and Red Spark). A chapter in the history of prickly heat, German measles and scarlet fever. *Sudhoffs Arch.*, 1960, 44: 341-57.

QPs

ACKERKNECHT, Erwin H. Maladies et sociétés: la peste noire; la fièvre jaune; le paludisme. *Arch.Int.Hist.Sci.*, 1952, 5: 309-19.

QPwe

GOODALL, Archibald L. Glasgow's place in the distinction between typhoid and typhus fevers. *Bull.Hist.Med.*, 1954, 28: 140-53, 1 pl.

QPwg

MARTIN, Alfred. Beiträge zür Geschichte des Aussatzes, der Syphilis, des Antoniusfeuers, der Pest und der an diesen Erkrankten in Deutschland. *Arch.Gesch.Med.*, 1919, 11: 189-99.

QPza ANTHRAX

RICHTER, Paul. Die Bedeutung des Milzbrandes für die Geschichte der Epidemien. *Arch.Gesch.Med.*, 1912, 6: 281-98.

SEIDEL, Günter. Historische Betrachtungen über den Milzbrand. *NTM Z.Gesch.Naturwiss.Tech.Med.*, 1960, 1: 72-93.

QPzc CHOLERA

NÉLIS, Paul. Essai sur le choléra asiatique. *Rev.Quest.Sci.*, 1948, 9: 372-402.

STICKER, Georg. Die Cholera. iv, 592 p. (Abhandlungen aus der Seuchengeschichte und Seuchenlehre, 2) Giessen: A. Töpelmann, 1912.

STICKER, Georg. Zur Geschichte der Cholera-Abwehr. *Verhandl. Ges.Deut.Naturforsch.Aerzte 84.Versamml.* (Münster i. W., 1912), part 2, (2), p. 96. Leipzig: Vogel, 1913.

TORKOMIAN, Vahram H. Pages inédites de l'histoire de l'ostéoplastie et du choléra. *Compt.Rend.IIe Congr.Int.Hist.Méd.* (Paris, 1921), p. 491-6. Évreux: Imprimerie Ch. Herissey, 1922.

QPzc-wb

CHAMBERS, John Sharpe. The conquest of cholera, America's greatest scourge. xiv, 366 p. London: Macmillan, 1938.

QPzc-we

UNDERWOOD, E. Ashworth. The history of cholera in Great Britain. *Proc.Roy.Soc.Med.*, 1948, 41: 165-73, 1 fig.

QPzc-yQO

BESREDKA, Alexandre. De la vaccination contre le choléra. *Bull.Inst.Pasteur*, 1922, 20: 1-9, 41-52.
History of vaccination against cholera.

QPzdi DIPHTHERIA

DARMSTAEDTER, Ernst. Anfänge und Entwicklung der modernen Diphtherie-Forschung. (Die Entdeckung und Erforschung des Diphtherie-Erregers vor 50 Jahren) *Münch.Med.Wochenschr.*, 1934, 81: 1473-4.

ENGLERT, Ludwig. Aus der Geschichte der Diphtherie: Bretonneau, Löffler und Behring. *Med.Welt*, 1934, 8: 1676-9.

NÉLIS, Paul. Une expérience qui a duré 55 ans. *Scalpel*, 1941, 94: 923-9.
The decline in the incidence of diphtheria.

RICO-AVELLO, Carlos. Los classicos del "garrotillo" [diphtheria]. (With French resumé) 7 p. [Madrid: 1956].
Presented to 15th International Conference of Medicine, Madrid, 1956 but not published in the *Actas* (*Arch.Iberoamer.Hist.Med.*, vol. 8 and 9).

WOOD, W. Barry. From miasmas to molecules. xii, 100 p. (Bampton Lectures in America, 13) New York: Columbia University Press, 1961.
The history of diphtheria.
Reviewed by Richard H. Shryock, *Technol.Cult.*, 1963, 4: 368-9.

QPzdi-yQO

ABT, G. Le titre antitoxique et la valeur thérapeutique des sérums anti-diphtériques. *Bull.Inst.Pasteur*, 1922, 20: 305-17, 353-62, bibliogr.
A historical note.

QPzdy DYSENTERY

DESCHIENS, R.; COSTE, Christine. L'histoire médicale des dysenteries sensibles à l'ipéca avant la découverte de l'amibe dysentérique. *Mem.Soc.Franç.Hist.Méd.*, 1946, 2: 97-105.

GLEITSMANN, Hans. Ueber Ruhrentstehung. Ein epidemiologischer Beitrag zum Ruhrproblem. 32 p. München: Lehmann, 1925.

MAYER, Claudius F. Bacillary dysentery as a military problem, and the Pavlovian doctrine. *Mil.Surg.*, 1952, 111: 268-76.

QPze ENCEPHALITIS LETHARGICA

RIETTI, Fernando. Contributo alla storia dell'encefalite epidemica (encephalitis letargica di Economo). *Archeion*, 1929, 11: 198-205.

QPzga GAS GANGRENE

KELLETT, C.E. The early history of gas gangrene. *Ann.Med.Hist.*, 1939, 1: 452-9.

QPzgo GONORRHEA

DARMSTAEDTER, Ernst. Fünfzig Jahre Blennorrhoe-Prophylaxe. Carl Sigmund Franz Credé zum Gedächtnis. *Riedel-Archiv*, 1934, 23: 33-7.

HIRSCH, Edwin W. An historical survey of gonorrhea. *Ann.Med. Hist.*, 1930, 2: 414-23, 4 fig.

NELSON, Nels A.; CRAIN, Gladys L. Syphilis, gonorrhea, and the public health. xvii, 359 p. New York: Macmillan, 1938. [CB 54/586]

SCHÖNFELD, Walther. Von der örtlichen Behandlung des Trippers beim Manne mit Einspritzungen bis zur Entdeckung des Gonokokkus und den dabei verwendeten Spritzenformen. *Sudhoffs Arch.*, 1942, 35: 43-67, 3 fig.

WEHRBEIN, H.L. Therapy in gonorrhea, an historical review. *Ann.Med.Hist.*, 1935, 7: 492-7.

QPzgo-daj

GONORRHEA number 1 and 2. Readings in the history of gonorrhea. *Med.Life*, 1932, 39: 475-524; 527-88.[CB 37/609]

QPzgo-nh

SCHÖNFELD, Walther. Medizinische Fachausdrücke für den Tripper der Harnröhre des Mannes in geschichtlicher Beleuchtung. *Sudhoffs Arch.*, 1941, 34: 169-78.
Terminology of gonorrhea.

QPzi INFLUENZA

BURCKHARD, Georg. Zur Geschichte der Influenza. *Arch.Gesch. Med.*, 1929, 22: 201-5.

BURNET, F.M.; CLARK, Ellen. Influenza. A survey of the last 50 years in the light of modern work on the virus of epidemic influenza. viii, 118 p. (Monographs from the Walter and Eliza Hall Institute of Research in Pathology and Medicine, 4) Melbourne: Macmillan, 1942.
Reviewed by C.H. Andrewes, *Nature*, 1943, 151: 263-4.

CAMPBELL, Eugene P. The epidemiology of influenza. Illustrated by historical accounts. *Bull.Hist.Med.*, 1943, 13: 389-403, 6 charts.

CORSINI, Andrea. L'influenza oggi e nel passato. *Arch.Stor. Sci.*, 1919, 1: 48-75. [CB 7/143]

GALLACHER, Stuart A. "Stuff a cold and starve a fever." *Bull. Hist.Med.*, 1942, 11: 576-81.

HELFFT, -, *Doktor*. Zur Geschichte der Influenza. *Henschel's Janus*, 1848, 3: 828-32; reprinted Leipzig: Alfred Lorentz, 1931.

PRYOR, H.B. Influenza: that extraordinary malady. Notes on its history and epidemiology. *Clin.Ped.Phila.*, 1964, 3: 19-24.

TOWNSEND, John F. History of influenza epidemics. *Ann.Med. Hist.*, 1933, 5: 533-47.

QPzl LEPROSY

QPzl-c general history

BISWAS, H.G. History of leprosy and its treatment. *Sci.Cult.*, 1962, 28: 513-15.

COCHRANE, R.G.; DAVEY, T.F.; ed. Leprosy in theory and practice. 2nd ed. xviii, 659 p. Bristol: Wright; Baltimore: Williams and Wilkins, 1964.
First publ. 1959.

D'AMATO, Vincenzo. La lebbra nella storia, nella geografia e nell' arte. 64 p., 29 fig. Roma: 1923.

FROHN, Wilhelm. Lepra und Syphilis. Zum Vergleich der Ursprungsgeschichte beider Seuchen. *Proteus* (Bonn), 1937, 2: 138-43.

HEUSINGER, Johann Christian Karl Friedrich von. Die maculösen Leproiden, nach ihrer Verbreitung und nach ihren Ursachen, so wie in ihrem Verhältniss zur Geschichte des Aussatzes. *Henschel's Janus*, 1848, 3: 495-524, 794-812: reprinted Leipzig: Alfred Lorentz, 1931.

JEANSELME, E. La lèpre. 680 p., 259 fig., 15 pl. Paris: Doin, 1933.

JEANSELME, E. Questionnaire relatif à l'histoire de la lèpre. *Bull.Soc.Franç.Hist.Méd.*, 1929, 23: 344.

LONG, E.R. Leprosy in historical perspective. *Int.J.Leprosy*, 1964, 32: 424-7.

MØLLER-CHRISTENSEN, Vilhelm. Bone changes in leprosy. 51 p. Copenhagen: Munksgaard, 1961.
From the excavation of the Naestved leper graveyard.
Reviewed by Peter Richards, *Centaurus*, 1963, 9: 134-5.

MØLLER-CHRISTENSEN, Vilhelm. Location and excavation of the first Danish leper graveyard from the Middle Ages - St. Jørgen's Farm, Naestved. *Bull.Hist.Med.*, 1953, 27: 112-23, 9 fig.

MØLLER-CHRISTENSEN, Vilhelm; JOPLING, W.H. An examination of the skulls in the catacombs of Paris. *Med.Hist.*, 1964, 8: 187-8.

MONTESTRUC, E. Lépreux d'hier et d'aujourd'hui. *J.Méd.Bordeaux*, 1961, 138: 737-48.
Reviewed by G. Duwe, *Scalpel*, 1961, 114: 1065.

ROGERS, Leonard; MUIR, Ernest. Leprosy. xii, 301 p. Bristol: Wright, 1926.

UNNA, P.G. Ein typischer Fall von "Papierwissenschaft". 27 p. München: E. Reinhardt, [1913].
Reprinted from *Monist.Jahrhundert*, 1912.
The leprosy of the Bible.
Reviewed by H. Lautsch-Graudenz, *Dermatol.Wochenschr.*, 1913, 56: 551-2.

UNNA, P.G. Ein typischer Fall von "Papierwissenschaft". (Zaraath, der Aussatz der Bibel). *Lepra*, 1912-13, 13: 218-36.

ZAPPA, Paolo. Unclean! unclean! Translated from the Italian by Edward Storer. With an introduction by Sir Leonard Rogers. 191 p. London: Dickson, 1933.
About leprosy. Translation of Fra i lebbrosi.

QPzl-ce-bv

KEFFER, Luiza, comp. Indice bibliográfico de lepra, 1500-1943. 3 vol. Sao Paulo: Biblioteca, Departamento de Profilaxia da Lepra, 1944-48.

QPzl-n/u special aspects

QPzl-nh

LENDRUM, F.C. The name "Leprosy". *Amer.J.Trop.Med.Hyg.*, 1952, 1: 999-1008.

QPzl-s

KATSAINOS, George M. The relation of leprosy to the community. *Boston Med.Surg.J.*, 1915, 173: 53-7.

QPzl-t

KLINGMÜLLER, V.; GRÖN, K. Die Lepra. Lepra in Literatur und Kunst. xviii, 907 p., 219 fig. Berlin: Springer, 1930.

QPzl-th

ZAMBACO, Démétrius Alexandre. La lèpre à travers les siècles et les contrées. Anthologie. xii, 845 p., portr. Paris: Masson, 1914.

QPzl-tq

ANDEL, M.A. van. Contribution à l'iconographie de la lèpre. *Janus,* 1926, 30: 192-4. [CB 22/306]

ANDEL, M.A. van. De leproos in de plastische kunst. [The leper in the plastic arts. (In Dutch)] *Bijdr.Gesch.Geneesk.,* 1937, 17: 145-51, 6 fig.

QPzl-ud

TRICOT-ROYER, J.J.G. Les saints protecteurs des lépreux. *Bull. Soc.Franç.Hist.Méd.,* 1932, 26: 245-8.

QPzl-w in different countries

QPzl-wb

WASHBURN, Walter L. Leprosy among Scandinavian settlers in the Upper Mississippi Valley, 1864-1932. *Bull.Hist.Med.,* 1950, 24: 123-48.

QPzl-wc

MAURANO, Flavio. História da lepra em S. Paulo. 2 vol. xvi, 271 p.; viii, 283 p., 132 ill. (Monografia dos Arquivos do Sanatorio Padre Bento, 3) S. Paulo: Emprêsa Grafica da "Revista dos Tribunais", 1939.
Reviewed by Aldo Mieli, *Archeion,* 1941, 23: 296-7.

QPzl-wf

MAZEYRIE, J. Contribution à l'étude de la lèpre en France. La lèpre en Bas-Limousin. 112 p., 11 pl. (Thèse, Lyon) Tulle: Juglard, 1924. [CB 21/601]

QPzl-wg

FROHN, Wilhelm. Arzt und Lepra im Rheinlande. 32 p. (Diss.) Bonn: 1929.

FROHN, Wilhelm. Der Aussatz im Rheinland, sein Vorkommen und seine Bekämpfung. 300 p., ill. (Arbeiten zur Kenntniss der Geschichte der Medizin im Rheinland und in Westfalen, 11) Jena: Fischer, 1933.

KEUSSEN, Hermann. Beiträge zur Geschichte der Kölner Lepra-Untersuchungen. *Lepra,* 1913, 14: 80-112.

SUDHOFF, Karl. Vier Schemata für Lepraschau-Atteste der Wiener medizinischen Fakultät. *Arch.Gesch.Med.,* 1913, 6: 392-3.

QPzl-wg-tq

FROHN, Wilhelm. Lepradarstellungen in der Kunst des Rheinlandes. 104 p., 49 fig. (Neue Deutsche Forschungen: Geschichte der Medizin und Naturwissenschaften) Berlin: Junker u. Dünnhaupt, 1936.

QPzl-wj

SILVA, Carvalho Augusto da. Historia da lepra em Portugal. 223 p., 28 fig. (Epidemiologia Portuguesa, 1) Porto: Oficinas Gráficas da Sociedade de Papelaria, 1932.
Reviewed by Arlindo Camillo Monteiro, *Archeion,* 1933, 15: 133-6.

QPzl-wk

KETTING, Gerard Nicolaas Adriaan. Bijdrage tot de geschiedenis van de lepra in Nederland. [Contribution to the history of leprosy in the Netherlands. (In Dutch)] 298 p. (Thesis, Amsterdam) 's Gravenhage: Mouton, 1922.

SCHEVENSTEEN, A.F.C. van. La lèpre dans le marquisat d'Anvers aux temps passés. *Mém.Acad.Méd.Belg.,* 1930, 24: no. 3, 1-125, 4 pl.
Reviewed by George Sarton, *Isis,* 1934, 22: 315-17; by P. Delaunay, *Bull.Soc.Franç.Hist.Méd.,* 1931, 25: 215-17.

TRICOT-ROYER, J.J.G. Les lépreux de Tongerloo. 4 p. Geneva: Kundig, 1926.

TRICOT-ROYER, J.J.G. Le nombre des lépreux dans l'ancien duché de Brabant. *Bull.Acad.Méd.Belg., ser. 8,* 1928, 5: 342-9.

TRICOT-ROYER, J.J.G. Un point d'histoire: quelles étaient les affections qualifiées de lépreuses dans l'ancien duché de Brabant? *Mém.Acad.Méd.Belg., new ser.,* 1927, 23: 10-19.

TRICOT-ROYER, J.J.G. Les signes distinctifs des lépreux en Belgique. *Aesculape,* 1929, 19: 215-26. Also in *Yperman,* 1929, 2: 5-20, 2 fig.

QPzl-wk-tq

ANDEL, M.A. van. Quelques figures de lépreux dans l'art classique des Pays Bas. *Janus,* 1919, 24: 135-45, 6 ill.

QPzl-wm

HULT, O.T. Ur leprans tidigare historia i Sverige: en översikt. [From the early history of leprosy in Sweden. A survey. (In Swedish, with English summary)] *Lychnos,* 1950-51, 1-25.

RICHARDS, Peter. Leprosy in Scandinavia. *Centaurus,* 1960, 7: 101-33.

QPzl-wr

LIBERT, Lucien. Chez les lépreux d'Orient. *Aesculape,* 1913, 3: 97-101, 8 fig.

QPzl-yNTwf

MORISSET, -. L'assistance aux lépreux dans le Maine. *Compt. Rend.IIe Congr.Int.Hist.Méd.* (Paris, 1921), p. 431-5. Évreux: Imprimerie Ch. Hérissey, 1922.

QPzl-yNW LEPER HOSPITALS

LINT, J.G. de. Leproserieën. [Leproseries. (In Dutch)] *Bijdr. Gesch.Geneesk.,* 1921, 1: 3-12, 4 fig.

QPzl-yNWwf

BOISMOREAU, E. Notes sur les maladreries de Vendée. *Bull. Soc.Franç.Hist.Méd.,* 1921, 15: 319-27.

GREMILLET, *Abbé.* La léproserie de la Madeleine à Epinal. 40 p. Epinal: Imprimerie Lorraine, 1913.

LAIGNEL-LAVASTINE, Maxime. Note sur quelques leproseries du Blésois. *Mém.Soc.Franç.Hist.Méd.,* 1945, 1: 31-40.

LEBLOND, Victor, ed. Le cartulaire de la maladrerie de Saint-Lazare de Beauvais, comprenant 406 chartes conservées aux archives hospitalières de cette ville. cxv, 663 p. Paris: Champion et Picard, 1922.

QPzl-yNWwg

STICKER, Georg. Aussatzhäuser in Westfalen. *Verhandl.Ges.Deut. Naturforsch.Aerzte 84.Versamml.* (Münster i. W., 1912), part 2, (2), p. 102. Leipzig: F.C.W. Vogel, 1913.

QPzl-yNWwi

PAZZINI, Adalberto. Historia ecclesiae et Hospitalis S.Lazari Leprosorum de Monte Malo. (Contributo allo Studio della Storia della Lebbra in Roma.) *Atti VIIIe Congr.Int.Stor.Med.* (Roma, 1930), 54 p., 4 fig. Pisa: V. Lischi & Figli, 1931.

QPzl-yNWwk

LINT, J.G. de. Les léproseries d'Amsterdam. *Bull.Soc.Franç. Hist.Méd.,* 1921, 15: 107-14.

TRICOT-ROYER, J.J.G. Les haitiés dans les léproseries belges. *Atti VIIIo Congr.Int.Stor.Med.* (Roma, 1930), p. 59-86. Pisa: Lischi, 1931.

TRICOT-ROYER, J.J.G. La léproserie d'Hérenthals (Sint-Jan-ter-Lazarijen). 16 p. Anvers: De Vlijt, 1923.

VIAENE, A. Leprozen en leprozerijen in het oude graafschap Vlaanderen. Algemens inleiding. Bibliografisch overzicht. [Lepers and leper hospitals in the old county of Flanders. General introduction. Bibliographical survey. (In Dutch)] 47 p. Brugge: Gidsenbond, 1962.

QPzl-yNWwp

ÜNVER, A. Süheyl. About the history of the leproseries in Turkey. *Festschrift zum 80. Geburtstag Max Neuburgers*, p. 447-50, 7 fig. Wien: Maudrich, 1948.

QPzl-yNWwx

SCHWEITZER, Albert. Mitteilungen aus Lambarene. 2 vol. 1/2. Frühjahr 1924 bis Herbst 1925 [2nd ed.]. 164 p. 3. Herbst 1925 bis Sommer 1927. 74 p. München: Beck, 1928.
Reviewed by W. Haberling, *Mitt.Gesch.Med.*, 1929, 28: 234.

QPzm MEASLES

RADBILL, Samuel X.; HAMILTON, Gloria R. Measles in fact and fancy. *Bull.Hist.Med.*, 1960, 34: 430-42.

QPzpl PLAGUE

QPzpl-c general history

GUERRINI, Guido. Notizie storiche e statistiche sulla peste. *Riv.Stor.Sci.*, 1925, 16: 293-316.
Summary of statistical data on the plague from antiquity to the present.

HIRST, L. Fabian. The conquest of plague. A study of the evolution of epidemiology. With a foreword by Lt.-Gen. Sir William Macarthur. xvi, 478 p., 16 fig. in text, 6 pl., 3 maps. New York/Oxford: Clarendon Press, 1953.
Reviewed by René J. Dubos, *Isis*, 1954, 45: 207-8; by Gaylord W. Anderson, *Amer.Hist.Rev.*, 1954, 60: 62; by E. Ashworth Underwood, *Bull.Brit.Soc.Hist.Sci.*, 1955, 2: 23-4.

JEANSELME, Édouard. Inondations, famines et tremblements de terre sont les avant-coureurs de la peste. *Proc.3rd Int. Congr.Hist.Med.* (London, 1922), p. 37-41. Antwerp: De Vlijt, 1923.

JOURDAN, Victor J.C. Bubonic plague: its history and prevention. *Mon.Cyclopedia Med.Bull.*, 1913, 27: 270-4.

SCHRÖDER, Hermann. Ist Zentral-Afrika der primäre Pestherd? *Arch.Gesch.Naturwiss.Tech.*, 1913, 6: 359-66.

SMITH, Geddes. Plague on us. vi, 365 p., 10 pl., 11 fig. New York: Commonwealth Fund, 1941. [CB 62/87]
A summary of modern scientific knowledge of the nature, behavior, and defeat of this ancient enemy of mankind.

QPzpl-n/u special aspects

QPzpl-nh

IRSAY, Stephen d'. Notes to the origin of the expression: "Atra mors". *Isis*, 1926, 8: 328-32. [CB 21/597]

QPzpl-sc

ACKERKNECHT, Erwin H. *See* QPs

GRANGER, John Parlane. The plague as a factor in history. *Glasgow Med.J.*, 1912, 77: 178-86, 260-73.

THORNDIKE, Lynn. The blight of pestilence on early modern civilization. *Amer.Hist.Rev.*, 1927, 32: 455-74.

QPzpl-sk

VEITH, Ilza. Plague and politics. *Bull.Hist.Med.*, 1954, 28: 408-15.

QPzpl-t

CRAWFURD, Raymond Henry Payne. Plague and pestilence in literature and art. viii, 222 p., ill. Oxford: Clarendon Press, 1914.

QPzpl-tq

NEUSTATTER, Otto. Mice in plague pictures. *J.Walters Art Gallery*, 1941, 4: 105-13, 7 fig.

QPzpl-u

BÜHLER, Alfred. Schutzzettel gegen die Pest. *Festschrift für Jacques Brodbeck-Sandreuter zu seinem 60. Geburtstag*, p. 365-70, 4 fig. Basel: Schwabe, 1942.

QPzpl-ud

CHMELA, Th. Pestheilige. *Sudetendeut.Z.Volksk.*, 1930, 3: 277.

QPzpl-w in different countries

QPzpl-wb

EVANS, George H. Plague epidemics in San Francisco: historical notes. *Calif.Western Med.*, 1938, 49: 383-8, 458-60; 1939, 50: 24-5. [CB 57/274]

QPzpl-we

MULLETT, Charles F. The bubonic plague and England: an essay in the history of preventive medicine. vii, 401 p. Lexington: University of Kentucky Press, 1956.
Reviewed by L.R.C. Agnew, *Isis*, 1959, 50: 162-3; for further reviews *see* CB 82/213, CB 83/207 and CB 84/322.

MULLETT, Charles F. The bubonic plague in England: a problem in public health. *Bull.Hist.Med.*, 1946, 20: 299-309.

WILLIAMSON, Raymond. The plague in Cambridge. *Med.Hist.*, 1957, 1: 51-64.

QPzpl-wf

GUIART, Jules. Histoire de la peste à Bourg-en-Bresse. 59 p., 3 pl. (*Annales de l'Université de Lyon*, 1) Lyon: Rey, 1933.
Reviewed by M. Laignel-Lavastine, *Bull.Soc.Franç.Hist.Méd.*, 1934, 28: 375-6.

QPzpl-wg

LESKY, Erna. Die österreichische Pestfront an der k.k. Militärgrenze. *Saeculum*, 1957, 8: 82-106.

SCHÖPPLER, Hermann. Die Geschichte der Pest zu Regensburg. 192 p., ill. München: Otto Gmelin, 1914.

QPzpl-wh

CHAREWICZOWA, L. Klęski zaraz w dawnym Lwowie. [The plague in old Lvov. (In Polish)] 89 p., ill. (Bibljoteka Lwowska, 28) Lwów: Nakładem Towarzystwa miłośników przeszłości Lwowa, 1930.

QPzpl-wk

BERTRAND, Léon. Contribution à l'étude de la peste dans les Flandres du XIVe au XVIIe siècle. *Compt.Rend.IIe Congr.Int. Hist.Méd.* (Paris, 1921), p. 42-53. Évreux: Imprimerie Ch. Hérissey, 1922.

KATE, W. ten. De pestkeuren in Kampen. [Plague inspection in Kampen. (In Dutch)] *Bijdr.Gesch.Geneesk.*, 1923, 2: 241-5; 3: 9.

SCHEVENSTEEN, A.F.C. van. Documents pour servir à l'étude des maladies pestilentielles dans le marquisat d'Anvers jusqu'à la chute de l'ancien régime. 2 vol. 927 p. Brussels: Lamertin, 1931-32.

SCHEVENSTEEN, A.F.C. van. Over Pestepidemien te Antwerpen in vroeger tijden. [On plague epidemics in Antwerp in former times. (In Dutch)] *Verslagen Mededeel.Vlaam.Acad.Taal.Letterk.*, November 1932, 1055-92.

WEYDE, A.J. van der. Bijdrage tot de geschiedenis der pest te Utrecht. [Contribution to the history of the plague at Utrecht. (In Dutch)] *Bijdr.Gesch.Geneesk.*, 1927, 7: 384-404.

QPzpl-wk-ce

DONINCK, A. van. Tractaeten van de peste vóór de 18de eeuw in Vlaanderen. [Tracts on the plague in Flanders before the 18th century. (In Dutch)] *Bijdr.Gesch.Geneesk.*, 1930, 10: 185-95.

SCHEVENSTEEN, A.F.C. van. Les traités de pestilence publiés à Anvers. 102 p., 33 fig. Antwerp: de Coker, 1931.

QPzpl-wp

ÜNVER, A. Süheyl. Sur l'histoire de la peste en Turquie. *Compt.Rend.IXe Congr.Int.Hist.Méd.* (Bucarest, 1932), 7 p. Bucharest: Turnica, 1935.

ÜNVER, A. Süheyl. Sur l'histoire de la peste en Turquie. [In Turkish and French] *Tedavi Klin.Laboratuvari*, 1935, 5: 19 p.

EVIL

QPzpl-wq

DAREMBERG, C. Notices sur l'antiquité et l'endémicité de la peste en Orient et particulièrement en Egypte. 11 p. No. 1 des "Pièces et documents à l'appui du rapport sur la peste et les quarantaines" par René Clovis Prus. Paris: Baillière, 1846.
Reviewed by A.W.E.Th. Henschel, *Henschel's Janus*, 1848, 3: 815-18; reprinted Leipzig: Alfred Lorentz, 1931.

WAKIL, A.W. The third pandemic of plague in Egypt. Historical and statistical epidemiological remarks on the first thirty-two years of its prevalence. 169 p., 26 charts. (Publication 3, Faculty of Medicine, Egyptian University) Cairo: 1932.
Reviewed by C.A. Kofoid, *Isis*, 1935, 23: 297-8.

QPzpl-wt

WU LIEN-TEH. Plague fighter. Autobiography of a modern Chinese physician. x, 667 p. Cambridge: Heffer and Sons, 1959.
Reviewed by G.H. Wang, *J.Hist.Med.*, 1959, 14: 542-3.

QPzpl-wv

LOGHEM, J.J. van. The first plague epidemic in the Dutch-Indies. *Janus*, 1912, 17: 153-90.

QPzpl-yNF/NW plague burial; prevention; hospitals

QPzpl-yNFwg

SIEVEKING, G. Herman. Der "Pesthügel" an der Tiergartenstrasse im Gelände des früheren Zoologischen Gartens in Hamburg, nebst Nachweisen über die zu Pestzeiten üblichen Arten der Leichenbestattung. *Sudhoffs Arch.*, 1935, 28: 1-13, 2 fig.

QPzpl-yNG

CRAWFORD, Raymond. Plague banners. *Proc.Roy.Soc.Med.*, 1913, 6: 37-48, 4 fig.

QPzpl-yNGwf

GUIART, Jules. La peste et les Bureaux de Santé. *Clujul Med.*, 1929, no. 5, 2 p., fig.

QPzpl-yNGwg

ANNECKE, Kurt. Die Pestordnungen des 16. bis 18. Jahrhunderts und ihr geschichtlicher Einfluss. *Vortr.Ges.Gesch.Pharm.* (München, 1938), p. 1-78. Wien: 1939.

QPzpl-yNGwk

ANDEL, M.A. van. Plague regulations in the Netherlands. *Janus*, 1916, 21: 410-44, 4 ill.

QPzpl-yNGwt

LIEN-TEH, W. Manchurian plague prevention service. Memorial volume, 1912-1932. 469 p., 14 pl. Shanghai: National Quarantine Service, 1934.
Reviewed by Charles A. Kofoid, *Isis*, 1935, 23: 485-7.

QPzpl-yNW

JETTER, Dieter. Zur Typologie des Pesthauses. *Sudhoffs Arch.*, 1963, 47: 291-300.

QPzpl-yNWwk

EMCK, W.F. De voormalige pesthuizen te Gorinchem. [The former pest houses at Gorinchem. (In Dutch)] *Bijdr.Gesch. Geneesk.*, 1929, 9: 183-6.

HELLINGA, G. De amsterdamsche Pesthuizen. [Amsterdam plague hospitals. (In Dutch)] *Bijdr.Gesch.Geneesk.*, 1928, 8: 357-83, ill.

LEEN, J. van. Geschiedenis van het pest- en dolhuis der gemeente Rotterdam. [History of the plague hospital and lunatic asylum of Rotterdam. (In Dutch)] 48 p., ill. Rotterdam: H.A. Kramers, 1934.
Reviewed by M.A. van Andel, *Bijdr.Gesch.Geneesk.*, 1935, 15: 17.

PENNING, C.P.J. Het vroegere pesthuis te Harderwijk. [In Dutch] *Bijdr.Gesch.Geneesk.*, 1929, 9: 181-3.

QPzpo POLIOMYELITIS

RIVERS, Thomas M. The story of research on poliomyelitis. *Proc.Amer.Phil.Soc.*, 1954, 98: 250-4.

QPzpo-ce-bv

FISHBEIN, Morris, ed. A bibliography of infantile paralysis, 1789-1944. With selected abstracts and annotations. Prepared under direction of the National Foundation for Infantile Paralysis. Compiled by Ludvig Hektoen and Ella M. Salmonsen. 672 p. Philadelphia: Lippincott, 1946.
Reviewed by Henry E. Sigerist, *Bull.Hist.Med.*, 1947, 21: 855-7.

QPzpo-yQO

FERGUSON, J.K. The story of poliomyelitis vaccines. *Can.J. Public Health*, 1964, 55: 183-90.

QPzpu PUERPERAL FEVER

BÖTTGER, Herbert. Förderer der Semmelweisschen Lehre. *Sudhoffs Arch.*, 1955, 39: 341-62.

LÜTZHÖFT, Fr. Ein Abschnitt aus der Geschichte des Kindbettfiebers. *Janus*, 1917, 22: 357-71.

PECKHAM, C.H. A brief history of puerperal infection. *Bull. Inst.Hist.Med.*, 1935, 3: 187-212.

REGNAULT, Félix. *See* QP

QPzra RABIES

PHIRAEUS, D.I. De hydrophobiae historia antiquissima, aetiologia et therapia. (Diss.) Würzburg: 1849.
Reviewed by A.W.E.Th. Henschel, *Henschel's Janus*, 1852, 2: 495; reprinted Leipzig: Alfred Lorentz, 1931.
Another edition: De maniae hydrophobicae historia antiquissima, aetiologia et therapia. 31 p. Würzburg: F.E. Thein, 1859.

ROSHEM, Jules. Curieux traitements contre la rage. *Paris Méd.*, 2 déc. 1922, 1-4. [CB 14/557]

ROSHEM, Jules. Le traitement de la rage de Démocrite à Pasteur. *France Méd.*, 1912, 59: 381-5, 405-9, 425-9, 442-6.

QPzra-u

FROEHNER, Reinhard. Der Tollwurm. *Proteus*, 1937, 2: 152-62.
Popular view of rabies.

QPzra-we

MULLETT, Charles F. Hydrophobia: its history in England to 1800. *Bull.Hist.Med.*, 1945, 18: 44-65.

QPzra-wp-u

ÜNVER, A. Süheyl. [Folklore concerning the treatment of rabies in Turkey. (In Turkish, with French translation)] *Prat. Doktor*, 1936, no. 9, 3-5.

QPzrat RAT-BITE FEVER

COHEN, Herbert G. Rat bite fever. Contributions to its history and war significance. *Bull.Hist.Med.*, 1944, 16: 108-15.

QPzrh RHEUMATIC FEVER

MURPHY, George Edward. The evolution of our knowledge of rheumatic fever. An historical survey with particular emphasis on rheumatic heart disease. (The William Osler Medal Essay) *Bull.Hist.Med.*, 1943, 14: 123-47.

MUSSA, B. L'evoluzione storica dei concetto di malattia reumatica. *Minerva Pediat.*, 1964, 16: 1366-7.

WILSON, May G. Rheumatic fever. xvi, 595 p. New York: Commonwealth Fund, 1940. [CB 61/380]

QPzrh-sc

GLOVER, J. Alison. Acute rheumatism in military history. *Proc.Roy.Soc.Med.*, 1946, 39: Hist. Sect., 13-18.

QPzsm SMALLPOX

KLEIJ, J.J. van der. Pokkenbestrijding en pokkenbehandeling in vroeger tijd. [The fight against small pox and its treatment in former times. (In Dutch)] *Bijdr.Gesch.Geneesk.*, 1929, 9: 233-7.

McVAIL, John C. Half a century of small pox and vaccination; being the Milroy Lectures delivered before the Royal College of Physicians of London in March 1919. viii, 87 p. Edinburgh: Livingstone, 1919. [CB 12/601]

MACVAIL, John C. The history of small-pox. *Proc.17th Int. Congr.Med.* (London, 1913), sect. 23, p. 297-303. London: Oxford University Press; Hodder & Stoughton, 1914.

NANNINI, Marco Cesare. La storia del vaiolo. 105 p. Modena: Toschi, 1963.

RICHTER, Paul. Ueber Variola. *Arch.Gesch.Med.*, 1913, 7: 46-7.

ROGINA, Julius. Historija Variole. [History of smallpox. (In Serbo-Croatian)] 66 p. Belgrade: [Hygienic Institute], 1930.

SEIFFERT, G.; DU DSCHENG-HSING. Zur Geschichte der Pocken und Pockenimpfung. *Sudhoffs Arch.*, 1937, 30: 26-34, 5 fig.

QPzsm-th

FRASER-HARRIS, D.F. Smallpox in non-medical literature. *Med. Life*, 1930, 37: 552-67.

QPzsm-wb-vv

STEARN, E. Wagner; STEARN, Allen E. The effect of smallpox on the destiny of the Amerindian. 153 p. Boston: Humphries, 1945.
Reviewed by Mark Graubard, *Isis*, 1947, 37: 124.

QPzsm-wp

HEUSINGER, C.F. Hitzig über das Alter der Pocken in Arabien. Eine Bemerkung. *Henschel's Janus*, 1846, 1: 775-8; 1847, 2: 422-3; reprinted, Leipzig: Alfred Lorentz, 1931.

QPzsm-yNG

QPzsm-yNGwc

LASTRES, Juan B. La salud pública y la prevención de la viruela en el Perú. 244 p. Lima: Imprenta del Ministerio de Hacienda y Comercio, 1957.
Reviewed by F. Guerra, *J.Hist.Med.*, 1959, 14: 261-2.

QPzsm-yQO

KLEBS, Arnold C. The historic evolution of variolation. *Bull. Johns Hopkins Hosp.*, 1913, 24: 69-83.
Reprinted with bibliography, 27 p.

LEIKIND, Morris C. Variolation in Europe and America; vaccination in Europe; the introduction of vaccination into the United States. *Ciba Symp.*, 1942, 3: 1090-101, 1124; 1102-13; 1114-24, fig.

QPzsm-yQOwb-vv

STEARN, E. Wagner; STEARN, Allen E. Smallpox immunization of the Amerindian. *Bull.Hist.Med.*, 1943, 13: 601-13.

QPzsm-yQOwc

QURQUEJO, A. Gonzalès. Historia de la vacuna en Cuba. *Crónica Méd.Quir.*, 1912, 38: passim.

QPzsm-yQOwe

BECK, Ann. Issues in the anti-vaccination movement in England. *Med.Hist.*, 1960, 4: 310-21.

QPzsm-yQOwk-cs

WEYDE, A.J. van der. Nederlandsche penningen, uitgereikt in verband met het inenten tegen pokken. [Dutch medals issued in conjunction with vaccination against smallpox. (In Dutch)] *Bijdr.Gesch.Geneesk.*, 1929, 9: 289-95, 4 fig.

QPzsm-yQOwn

TORKOMIAN, Vahram H. Une page arménienne de l'histoire de l'inoculation variolique. *Proc.3rd Int.Congr.Hist.Med.* (London, 1922), p. 106-8. Antwerp: De Vlijt, 1923.

QPzsm-yQOwp

ÜNVER, A. Süheyl. [An outlook on the history of smallpox vaccination during the last century in Turkey and in the whole world. (In Turkish with English summary)] iv, 298 p., 33 pl. (Tib Tarihi Enstitüsü, 38) Istanbul: 1948. [CB 73/185]

QPzsw SWEATING SICKNESS

FILIPPI, Eduardo. Una malattia epidemica scomparsa: la migliare. *Riv.Stor.Sci.*, 1929, 20: 217-45.

SEIDENSCHNUR, Otto. Ein Beitrag zur Geschichte des Englischen Schweisses. *Henschel's Janus*, 1846, 1: 161-82; reprinted Leipzig: Alfred Lorentz, 1931.

SHAW, Manley Bradford. A short history of the sweating sickness. *Ann.Med.Hist.*, 1933, 5: 246-74, 10 fig.

QPzsw-yQA

SENF, Herbert. Ein kartographischer Beitrag zur Geschichte des Englischen Schweisses. *Kyklos*, 1930, 3: 273-9.

QPzsy SYPHILIS

for specific remedies *see* INDEX

ASCHOFF, Ludwig. War die Syphilis von Alters her eine europäische Krankheit? 12 p. Freiburg i. Breisgau: H. Speyer, 1939.
Reviewed by J.A.V., *Janus*, 1939, 43: 335.

BOLOGA, Valeriu L. Din istoria sifilisului. [The history of syphilis. (In Rumanian)] 70 p. Cluj: Tipografia nationala, 1931.

BURKART, F.; VORBERG, G.; SECKENDORF, E. Der Streit um den Ursprung der Syphilis. *Med.Welt*, 1931, 5: 905-7.
Reviewed by W. Haberling, *Mitt.Gesch.Med.*, 1931, 30: 277.

BUTLER, Charles S. Syphilis sive Morbus humanus, a rationalization of Yaws so-called. For scientists and laymen interested in the damage to man from venereal disease. 137 p., 18 pl. Brooklyn, N.Y.: U.S. Navy, 1936.
Reviewed in *Ann.Med.Hist.*, 1936, 8: 568.

DENNIE, Charles Clayton. A history of syphilis. x, 137 p., ill. Springfield, Ill.: Charles C. Thomas, 1962.
Reviewed by Richard D. Hahn, *Bull.Hist.Med.*, 1963, 37: 297-8; by L.S. Granjel, *Cuad.Hist.Med.Españ.*, 1963, 2: 526; by Jean Théodoridès, *Arch.Int.Hist.Sci.*, 1964, 16: 101-2.

DOHI, Keizo. Beiträge zur Geschichte der Syphilis inbesondere über ihren Ursprung und ihre Pathologie in Ostasien. 145 p., ill., bibliogr. Tokyo: Verlag von Nankodo, 1923.
Based on the author's work in Japanese: Sekai baidokushi. Tokyo: Asakaya, 1921. [CB 54/585]
Reviewed in *Bijdr.Gesch.Geneesk.*, 1925, 5: 286-7.

DOWNING, Andree F. Syphilis: the story of its treatment, old and new. *Boston Med.Surg.J.*, 1912, 167: 715-20.

DUJARDIN, B. Propos sur la syphilis et son histoire. 14 p., pl. [Bruxelles]: Union Chimique Belge, 1949.

ESSED, W.F.R. Over den oorsprong der syphilis, een kritisch-historisch-epidemiologische studie, tevens ontwerp eener nieuwe theorie. [On the origin of syphilis, a critical historical epidemiological study, including a sketch of a new theory. (In Dutch)] Amsterdam: H.J. Paris, 1933. [CB 78/199]
Reviewed by J.J. van Loghem, *Arch.Int.Hist.Sci.*, 1951, 4: 465-7.

ESSED, W.F.R. Syphilis en framboesia. [Syphilis and yaws. (In Dutch)] *Bijdr.Gesch.Geneesk.*, 1933, 13: 274-6; 1934, 14: 100.

FROHN, Wilhelm. Lepra und Syphilis. Zum Vergleich der Ursprungsgeschichte beider Seuchen. *Proteus* (Bonn), 1937, 2: 138-43.

GILS, J.B.F. van. Een legende over het ontstaan van de syphilis. [A legend on the origin of syphilis. (In Dutch)] *Bijdr.Gesch. Geneesk.*, 1939, 19: 205-9, 1 pl.

HOFFMANN, Erich. Vorträge und Urkunden zur 25-jährigen Wiederkehr der Entdeckung des Syphiliserregers *(Spirochaeta pallida)*. 124 p., fig. Berlin: Karger, 1930.

HOLCOMB, Richmond C. The antiquity of congenital syphilis. *Bull.Hist.Med.*, 1941, 10: 148-77, 4 fig.

HOLCOMB, Richmond C. The antiquity of syphilis. *Med.Life*, 1935, 42: 275-325. [CB 45/301]

HOLCOMB, Richmond Cranston. Who gave the world syphilis? The Haitian myth. With an introduction by C.S. Butler. 189 p. New York: Froben Press, 1937.
Reviewed by M.F. Ashley-Montagu, *Isis*, 1938, 28: 101-2; in *Ann.Med.Hist.*, 1937, 9: 514-15.

JEANSELME, Edouard. Histoire de la syphilis: son origine, son expansion. 432 p., 58 fig. (Traité de la Syphilis, vol. 1) Paris: Doin, 1931.
Reviewed by C.D. Leake, *Isis*, 1933, 19: 249-52; by P. Delaunay, *Rev.Hist.Pharm.*, 1931, 19: 127-8.

JEANSELME, Edouard. Sur l'origine de la syphilis. *Rass.Stud. Sessuali*, 1928, 8: 57-64.

LINT, J.G. de. Syphilis en framboesia. [Syphilis and yaws. (In Dutch)] *Bijdr.Gesch.Geneesk.*, 1933, 13: 214-16; 1934, 14: 31-2.

LOGHEM, J.J. van. Essed's theory on the great pox epidemic in Europe. *Act.VIe Congr.Int.Hist.Sci.*(Amsterdam, 1950), (1), p. 361-3. Paris: Hermann, 1953. [CB 79/117]

MARTÍ IBAÑEZ, Félix. Prelude to the history of syphilis. From the days of Columbus to the times of Ehrlich. *Int.Rec.Med.*, 1952, 165: no. 7, 415-26.

MARTÍ IBAÑEZ, Félix. Preludio a la historia de la sífilis. *Rev.Argent.Hist.Med.*, 1944, 3: no. 3, 37-72.

MARTIN, Alfred. Die ersten Nachrichten über die Syphilis in der Schweiz und ihre Bedeutung für die allgemeine Geschichte der Syphilis. *Schweiz.Med.Wochenschr.*, 1924, 54: 178-80.

MARTÍNEZ DURÁN, Carlos. El primer trabajo americano sobre el origen no americano de la sifilis. *Arch.Iberoamer.Hist. Med.*, 1957, 9: 339-43.
Dr. Mariano Padilla in 1856 presented a pamphlet (published in Guatemala in 1861) that argued for the world-wide, rather than the exclusively American, origin of syphilis.

MEYER-STEINEG, Th. Zur Frage nach dem Ursprunge der Syphilis. *Reichs Med.Anz.*, 1912, 27: 35-9.

MICHAELIS, Lorenz. Vergleichende mikroskopische Untersuchungen an rezenten, historischen und fossilen menschlichen Knochen. Zugleich ein Beitrag zur Geschichte der Syphilis. viii, 92 p., 63 pl. (Veröffentlichungen aus der Kriegs- und Konstitutionspathologie, 24) Jena: Fischer, 1930. [CB 30/412]
Reviewed by G. Sticker, *Mitt.Gesch.Med.*, 1930, 29: 182-4.

MILLER, Joseph L. History of syphilis. *Ann.Med.Hist.*, 1930, 2: 394-405. [CB 30/412]

MONTEROS-VALDIVIESO, M.Y. La sifilis: origen e historia (algunos apuntes compilados). *Rev.Méd.Cubana*, 1958, 69: 521-59.

MORRIS, Henry. Observations on the history of syphilis, on the Wassermann reaction and parasyphilis and on treatment. *Lancet*, Aug.1912, 497-504.

NEBENFÜHRER, László. [Historical research in syphilis. (In Hungarian, with Russian and German summaries)] *Commun.Bibl. Hist.Med.Hung.*, 1956, 4: 108-32, 11 fig.

PACKARD, Francis R. The earlier methods employed in the treatment of syphilis. *Ann.Med.Hist.*, 1923, 5: 225-8. [CB 16/321]

PORTUGAL, Hildebrando. A história definitiva nos nosodidades de Lutz-Jeanselme. With transl.: The full history of the discovery of juxta articular nodes. *Mem.Inst.Oswaldo Cruz*, 1944, 41: 525-33, ill., bibliogr.
Contains brief biography of Adolpho Lutz, 1855-1940.

PUSEY, William Allen. The history and epidemiology of syphilis. xxii, 113 p., ill. (Gehrmann lectures, University of Illinois, 1933) Springfield, Ill.: Thomas, 1933.
Reviewed in *Ann.Med.Hist.*, 1933, 5: 510.

SARTON, George. The beginning of European syphilis. Query no. 77. *Isis*, 1938, 29: 406-7.
Discusses Ashley-Montagu's review of Holcomb's book, *see* above.

SASPORTAS, L. A propos du réveil d'une controverse ancienne: le mal vénérien à Tahiti est-il français ou anglais? *Mém. Soc.Franç.Hist.Méd.*, 1946, 2: 56-60.

SIGERIST, Henry E. Kritische Betrachtungen über die Frühgeschichte der Syphilis. *Deut.Med.Wochenschr.*, 18 June 1926, 52: no. 25, 1050-2. [CB 23/179]

SIGERIST, Henry E. L'origine della sifilide. *Arch.Stor.Sci.*, 1923, 4: 163-9; also in *Rass.Stud.Sessuali*, 1923, 3: 161-8.
Against the American theory, with a bibliography of Sudhoff's writings on the subject, 1911-1923.

SIGERIST, Henry E. L'origine della sifilide. *Arch.Stor.Sci.*, 1926, 7: 243-55. [CB 22/141]

SIGERIST, Henry E. Zur Frühgeschichte der Syphilis. *Münch. Med.Wochenschr.*, 1921, 68: no. 39, 1257-8.

SUDHOFF, Karl. Der Ursprung der Syphilis. *Proc.17th Int.Congr. Med.* (London, 1913), sect. 23, p. 25-35. London: Oxford University Press; Hodder & Stoughton, 1914.

SULLA storia della sifilide. [By A.B.] *Riv.Stor.Crit.Sci.*, 1912, 3: 68-9.

TEMKIN, Owsei. Therapeutic trends and the treatment of syphilis before 1900. (In memory of Max Neuburger) *Bull.Hist.Med.*, 1955, 29: 309-16.

TOLMAN, Mayo. The origin of syphilis. *J.Soc.Hyg.*, 1923, 9: 546-51.

VENZMER, Gerhard. Eine sterbende Krankheit. Vom Aufstieg und Niedergang der Syphilis. 3rd ed. 100 p., 54 fig. Leipzig: Konegen, 1929.

VORBERG, Gaston. Ueber den Ursprung der Syphilis. Quellengeschichtliche Untersuchungen. vi, 112 p., 11 pl. Stuttgart: Püttmann, 1924. [CB 16/201]
Reviewed by A. Mieli, *Rass.Stud.Sessuali*, 1924, 4: 114-16.

WIEDMANN, A. Über den Ursprung der Syphilis. *Festschrift zum 80. Geburtstag Max Neuburgers*, p. 482-91. Wien: Maudrich, 1948.
The author believes that syphilis existed in Europe before the discovery of America.

ZIMMERMANN, Ernest L. The pathology of syphilis as revealed by autopsies performed between 1563 and 1761. *Bull.Inst. Hist.Med.*, 1935, 3: 355-99.

QPzsy-c-bv

SUDHOFF, Karl. [For a bibliography of his writings on the origin of syphilis, 1911-1923, *see* Sigerist, Henry E. L'origine della sifilide, QPzsy-c.]

QPzsy-ce-bv

NOURRY, Emile. Médecine ancienne, chirurgie-anatomie, sciences anciennes. 152 p. Paris: E. Nourry, 1927.
Bookseller's catalogue which includes a collection of more than 200 items relating to syphilis from the 15th to the 18th century.

QPzsy-ce-bx

KRUMBHAAR, E.B.; GARNER, V.C. Luesiana in the library of the College of Physicians of Philadelphia exhibited to celebrate the 25th anniversary of the discovery of the spirocheta pallida. *Ann.Med.Hist.*, 1933, 5: 96-100.

QPzsy-mzNS

KATSAINOS, George M. Marriage and syphilis. A treatise on eugenics. 164 p., ill. Boston: Four Seas Company, 1923. [CB 27/581]

QPzsy-nh

CIPRIANI, Mariano. Contributo allo studio etimologico del vocabolo "sifilide". *Riv.Stor.Sci.*, 1948, 39: 21-37.

KEIL, Harry. The evolution of the term chancre and its relation to the history of syphilis. *J.Hist.Med.*, 1949, 4: 407-16.

SIGERIST, Henry E. The disease called syphilis. *Med.Life*, 1931, 38: 381-2.
Translation of the paper, Der Krankheitsname Syphilis, *Münch.Med.Wochenschr.*, 1930, 1418.

SPITZER, Leo. The etymology of the term "syphilis". *Bull. Hist.Med.*, 1955, 29: 269-73.

QPzsy-s

KATSAINOS, George M. Syphilis and its accomplices in mischief: society, the state and the physician. 676 p. Athens, Greece: Privately printed, 1939.
Includes a long preface and introduction (150 p.) discussing the sociological aspects of the subject.

QPzsy-wf-nh

LEVY, Raphael. A note on French slang. *Jew.Forum,* March 1935. [CB 43/482]
Apropos of the word *nazi* used in French slang for syphilis.

QPzsy-wm

EHLERS, Edv. Le syphiloïde du Jutland. 88 p., 1 map. Paris: Masson, 1923. [CB 16/320]

QPzsy-yNA

NELSON, Nels A.; CRAIN, Gladys L. Syphilis, gonorrhea, and the public health. xvii, 359 p. New York: Macmillan, 1938. [CB 54/586]

QPzsy-yNGph

SCHOUTE, D. Syphilisbestrijding van overheidwege in Nederland en in Nederlandsch Indie. [The fight against syphilis by government regulations in Holland and the Dutch Indies. (In Dutch)] *Bijdr.Gesch.Geneesk.,* 1943, 23: 60-3, 78-81.

QPzsy-yON

HESSELMANN, Erika. Geschichte der progressiven Paralyse. 34 p. (Diss., Int.Gesch.Med., Düsseldorf) Düsseldorf: 1939.

QPzsy-yPK

CHURCH, Franklin H. Syphilis of the center of the face. *Bull. Hist.Med.,* 1939, 7: 705-18, 7 fig.

ZIMMERMANN, Ernest L. The early history of Alopecia syphilitica. *Janus,* 1935, 39: 105-26.

QPzsy-yQO

KAHN, Reuben L. Historical notes on the serology of syphilis. *Victor Robinson Memorial Volume,* p. 157-61. New York: Froben, 1948.

THIBIERGE, G.; LACASSAGNE, J. Les inoculations expérimentales de la syphilis à l'homme. *Ann.Dermatol.Syphilogr., 6th ser.,* 1923, 4: 497-525, 584-604.
Reviewed by L. Brodier, *Bull.Soc.Franç.Hist.Méd.,* 1923, 17: 432-4.

QPzte TETANUS

CHALIAN, William. An essay on the history of lockjaw. *Bull. Hist.Med.,* 1940, 8: 171-201.

DARMSTAEDTER, Ernst. Die Erforschung der Tetanus-Aetiologie. *Münch.Med.Wochenschr.,* 12 Oct. 1934, 81: 1585-6.

QPztu TUBERCULOSIS

for the surgical treatment of pulmonary tuberculosis *see* RCG

BOCHALLI, Richard. Die Geschichte der Schwindsucht. 73 p. (Practische Tuberkulose-Bücherei, 24) Leipzig: Thieme, 1940.
Reviewed by Gustaf Neander, *Lychnos,* 1941, 414-15.

BROWN, Lawrason. The story of clinical pulmonary tuberculosis. ix, 411 p., portr. Baltimore: Williams and Wilkins, 1941.
Reviewed in *Ann.Med.Hist.,* 1941, 3: 459-60.

BURKE, Richard M. An historical chronology of tuberculosis. 2nd ed. xiii, 125 p., 6 ill. Springfield, Ill.: Charles C. Thomas, 1955.
Reviewed by John F. Fulton, *J.Hist.Med.,* 1956, 11: 123.
First published 1938. [CB 56/406]

CASTIGLIONI, Arturo. History of tuberculosis. Transl. from the Italian by Emilie Recht. *Med.Life,* 1933, 40: 5-58, ill., facs.; 63-96, portr. [CB 38/613]

CASTIGLIONI, Arturo. Storia della tubercolosi. 74 p., 17 fig. (From Trattato della tubercolosi diretto da Luigi Devoto, vol. 1) Milan: Francesco Vallardi, 1931.

DELASSUS, A. Progrès des connaissances médicales sur la tuberculose pulmonaire. *Rev.Quest.Sci.,* 1932, 21: 329-60.

FLICK, Lawrence. Development of our knowledge of tuberculosis. xiii, 783 p. Philadelphia: 1925.
Reviewed by Francis R. Packard, *Ann.Med.Hist.,* 1926, 8: 208.

LAVALLE, Carlos Robertson. Rumbo biológico en el tratamiento de la tuberculosis. *Publ.Cátedra Hist.Med.Univ.Buenos Aires,* 1940, 3: 415-50.

LONG, Esmond R. The decline of tuberculosis, with special reference to its generalized form. *Bull.Hist.Med.,* 1940, 8: 819-43.

MEACHEN, George Norman. A short history of tuberculosis. iv, 105 p. London: Bale, Sons & Danielsson, 1936.

MYERS, J. Arthur. Man's greatest victory over tuberculosis. ix, 419 p., ill., bibliogr. Springfield, Ill.: Thomas, 1940.
Reviewed in *Ann.Med.Hist., 3rd ser.,* 1941, 3: 259-60.

NICOLSON, Dorothy C. White. Twenty years of medical research. 97 p. New York: National Tuberculosis Association, 1943.
Reviewed by Henry E. Sigerist, *Bull.Hist.Med.,* 1943, 14: 410-12.

PAGEL, Walter. Humoral pathology. A lingering anachronism in the history of tuberculosis. (To the memory of Max Neuburger) *Bull.Hist.Med.,* 1955, 29: 299-308, 1 facs.

PIÉRY, M.; ROSHEM, J. Histoire de la tuberculose. xvi, 479 p., 77 fig. Paris: Doin, 1931. [CB 36/457]

POTTENGER, Francis Marion. The fight against tuberculosis: an autobiography. xii, 276 p., ill. New York: Henry Schuman, 1952.
Reviewed by G. Canby Robinson, *Bull.Hist.Med.,* 1953, 27: 587-8.

ROBINSON, Victor. Trudeau and tuberculosis. *Festschrift zur Feier seines 60. Geburtstages Max Neuburger gewidmet,* p. 269-72. Wien: Verlag des Fest-Komitees, 1928.

WAKSMAN, Selman Abraham. The conquest of tuberculosis. xiv, 241 p., ill., bibliogr. Berkeley/Los Angeles: University of California Press, 1964.

WALLACE, A.T. Sir Robert Philip: a pioneer in the campaign against tuberculosis. *Med.Hist.,* 1961, 5: 56-64.

WEBB, Gerald Bertram. Tuberculosis. xv, 205 p., 17 ill., bibliogr. (Clio Medica) New York: Hoeber, 1936.
Reviewed in *Ann.Med.Hist.,* 1936, 8: 274.

QPztu-mzON

GRIGG, E.R.N. Historical and bibliographical review of tuberculosis in the mentally ill. *J.Hist.Med.,* 1955, 10: 58-108, 6 fig.

QPztu-s

BEZANÇON, Fernand. Les bases actuelles du problème de la tuberculose. vi, 197 p. (Science et Civilisation, 2) Paris: Gauthier-Villars, 1922. [CB 13/297]

DUBOS, Rene J.; DUBOS, Jean. The white plague. Tuberculosis, man and society. vii, 277 p. Boston: Little, Brown and Co., 1952.
Reviewed by Morris C. Leikind, *Isis,* 1954, 45: 221-3.

LONG, Esmond R. Tuberculosis in modern society. *Bull.Hist. Med.,* 1953, 27: 301-19, 3 fig.

QPztu-sc

CHALKE, H.D. The impact of tuberculosis on history, literature and art. *Med.Hist.,* 1962, 6: 301-18.

CUMMINS, S. Lyle. Tuberculosis in history. From the 17th century to our own times. With an introduction by Sir Arthur Salusbury Macnalty. xiv, 205 p., 12 pl. London: Baillière, Tindall and Cox, 1949.
Reviewed by Allan Beskow, *Lychnos,* 1952, 434-5.

WOLFF, Georg. Tuberculosis and civilization. Part 1. Basic facts and figures in the epidemiology of tuberculosis. Part 2. Interpretation of the etiological factors in the epidemiology of tuberculosis. *Hum.Biol.*, 1938, 10: 106-23, 251-84.

QPztu-sd

EBSTEIN, Erich. Tuberkulose als Schicksal. Eine Sammlung pathographischer Skizzen von Calvin bis Klabund, 1509-1928. Mit einer Einführung von Georg W. Gruber. vii, 184 p., 8 pl. Stuttgart: Enke, 1932.

LONG, Esmond R. A history of the therapy of tuberculosis and the case of Frédéric Chopin. (Logan Clendening Lectures on the History and Philosophy of Medicine, 6th series) v, 71 p. Lawrence, Kansas: University of Kansas Press, 1956. [CB 82/213]
Reviewed by Ernest Wickersheimer, *Rev.Hist.Sci.*, 1956, 9: 373-5.

MOORMAN, Lewis. Tuberculosis and genius. xxxv, 271 p., portr. Chicago: University of Chicago Press, 1940.
Reviewed in *Ann.Med.Hist.*, 1941, 3: 263-4.

NADEAU, Gabriel. A T.B.'s progress. The story of Norman Bethune. *Bull.Hist.Med.*, 1940, 8: 1135-71, portr.

QPztu-t

CHALKE, H.D. The impact of tuberculosis on history, literature and art. *Med.Hist.*, 1962, 6: 301-18.

QPztu-u

GALDSTON, Iago. Tuberculosis in folk medicine. *Med.Life*, 1924, 31: 393-6.

QPztu-wb

POSTELL, William Dosite. Some stages in the development of tuberculosis therapy in the Lower Mississippi Valley. *J. Hist.Med.*, 1948, 3: 400-16, 2 fig.

QPztu-wb-da

PRICE, Esther Gaskins. Pennsylvania pioneers against tuberculosis. Preface by Richard H. Shryock. 294 p., ill. New York: National Tuberculosis Association, 1952.
Reviewed by Esmond R. Long, *Bull.Hist.Med.*, 1954, 28: 93-4.

QPztu-yN public health aspects

QPztu-yNG

ITALY. Direzione Generale della Sanità pubblica. La tubercolosi. Scienza e legge nella lotta contro la tubercolosi traverso i tempi e nei diversi paesi. 4 vol. Roma: Provveditorato generale dello Stato, 1928.
Published for the 6th International Conference against Tuberculosis, Rome 1928.

SCHUCHARDT, H.E. Das rote Doppelkreuz, das Wahrzeichen der Tuberkulose-Bekämpfung. *Janus*, 1940, 44: 45-8.

QPztu-yNGwb

KNOPF, S. Adolphus. The American anti-tuberculosis crusade, as an inspiration to modern health activities. *Med.Life*, 1926, 33: 558-88, ill.

QPztu-yNGwf

WEIL, V. Jacques. Problèmes actuels de la lutte antituberculeuse en France. 26 p. (Palais de la Découverte, A 294) Paris: Université de Paris, 1963.

QPztu-yNTwb

PATERSON, Robert G. Antecedents of the National Tuberculosis Association. 25 p. (Historical Series, 2). New York: National Tuberculosis Association, 1945.
Reviewed by Jean C. Sabine, *Bull.Hist.Med.*, 1945, 18: 358.

SHRYOCK, Richard Harrison. National Tuberculosis Association, 1904-1954. A study of the voluntary health movement in the United States. 342 p., ill. New York: National Tuberculosis Association, 1957.
Reviewed by George Rosen, *Bull.Hist.Med.*, 1961, 35: 286-7.

QPztu-yNWwm

ANKER, Jean. Vejlefjord Sanatorium Gennem 50 år. [50 years of the Vejle Fjord (Denmark) Sanatorium. (In Danish)] Festskrift udgivet i anledning af Vejlefjord Sanatoriums 50 års jubilaeum. 132 p., front., map. Copenhagen: 1950. [CB 76/369]

QPztu-yO/Q related fields

QPztu-yOJ

LITTLE, E. Muirhead. History of the recognition of tuberculosis as a factor in bone and joint surgery. *Proc.Roy.Soc. Med.*, 1932, 25: 627-38.

PALTRINIERI, M. La storia della tubercolosi osteoarticolare. *Chir.Organi Movimento*, 1964, 53: 4-17.

QPztu-yOZ

EBSTEIN, Erich. Einige Beiträge zur Geschichte der sekundären Darmtuberkulose. *Arch.Gesch.Med.*, 1926, 18: 202-8.

QPztu-yPG

GARRISON, Fielding Hudson. Medizinisch-historische Denkmäler des Königsübels in der medizinischen Bibliothek des Kriegsministeriums zu Washington. *Arch.Gesch.Naturwiss.Tech.*, 1913, 6: 113-17, 1 ill.

POWER, D'Arcy. Touchpieces and the cure of the King's evil. *Ann.Med.Hist.*, 1931, 3: 127-33, 5 ill.

SLUYS, Felix. Les curiosités de l'histoire de la médecine révélées par les oeuvres d'art: le mal du roy. *Beaux-Arts*, 1960, 24: 5, 10.

QPztu-yPK

KOCKEL, Heinz. Lupus in fabula. *Arch.Gesch.Med.*, 1927, 19: 349-50.

RUSSELL, Brian. The history of lupus vulgaris: its recognition, nature, treatment and prevention. *Proc.Roy.Soc.Med.*, 1955, 48: 127-32.

QPztu-yPKwk

MENDES DA COSTA, S. Lupus en zijn bestrijding in Nederland. [The fight against tuberculosis of the skin in the Netherlands. (In Dutch)] *Bijdr.Gesch.Geneesk.*, 1924, 4: 171-5.

QPztu-yQO

KERVAN, Roger. Albert Calmette et le B.C.G. 222 p. Paris: Hachette, 1962.
Reviewed by P. Huard, *Arch.Int.Hist.Sci.*, 1962, 15: 450-2.

QPzty TYPHUS

CRAWFURD, Raymond. Contributions from the history of medicine to the problem of the transmission of typhus. *Proc.Roy. Soc.Med.*, 1912-13, 6: Hist. Sect., 6-17.

DARMSTAEDTER, Ernst. Die Erforschung der Typhus-Aetiologie. Ein Ueberblick. *Münch.Med.Wochenschr.*, 15 Nov. 1934, 81: no. 46, 1772-4.

REGNAULT, Félix. *See* QP

ZINSSER, Hans. Rats, lice and history, being a study in biography, which, after twelve preliminary chapters indispensable for the preparation of the lay reader, deals with the life history of typhus fever. xii, 301 p. Boston: Little, Brown, 1935.

QPzty-wf-ce

SEITZ, Franz. Bemerkungen über die ältere französische Literatur des Pestilenzialtyphus. *Henschel's Janus*, 1848, 3: 444-55; reprinted Leipzig: Alfred Lorentz, 1931.

QPzty-wo

HUME, Edgar Erskine. Fighting typhus fever in Serbia. *Med. Life*, 1938, 45: 99-124.

QPzw WHOOPING COUGH

for treatment with minerals *see* RSyQPzw

RADBILL, Samuel X. Whooping cough in fact and fancy. *Bull. Hist.Med.*, 1943, 13: 33-53.

STÉVENIN, Henri. La coqueluche. 214 p. Paris: Flammarion, 1926. [CB 21/602]

QPzya YAWS

ABASCAL, Horacio. Reseña histórica y sinonimia de la frambuesa y de la pelagra. 35 p., 10 ill. (Cuadernos de Historia Sanitaria, 9) Havana: Ministerio de Salubridad y Asistencia Social, 1955. [CB 83/205]

DUARTE, Eustaquio. Subsidios para a historia da framboesia trópica. *Rev.Argent.Hist.Med.*, 1945, 4: 37-46.

ESSED, W.F.R. *See* QPzsy

HERMANS, E.H. Enkele beschouwingen over de geschiedenis van de framboesia tropica. [Some thoughts on the history of tropical yaws. (In Dutch)] *Bijdr.Gesch.Geneesk.*, 1927, 7: 188-95.

LINT, J.G. de. Syphilis en framboesia. [Syphilis and yaws. (In Dutch)] *Bijdr.Gesch.Geneesk.*, 1933, 13: 214-16; 1934, 14: 31-2.

QPzye YELLOW FEVER

ABASCAL, Horacio; RODRÍGUEZ EXPÓSITO, César. Permanencia de la doctrina de Finlay. *Arch.Iberoamer.Hist.Med.*, 1957, 9: 3-8.

ABASCAL, Horacio; RODRÍGUEZ EXPÓSITO, César. Permanencia de la doctrina de Finlay ante el XV Congreso Internacional de Historia de la Medicina. 75 p., portr., ill. (Cuadernos de Historia Sanitaria, 11) La Habana: Ministerio de Salubridad y Asistencia Social, 1957.

ACKERKNECHT, Erwin H. *See* QPs

AGRAMONTE, Aristides. A review of research in yellow fever. *Ann.Intern.Med.*, Aug. 1928, 2: 1-38. [CB 26/255]

CARTER, Henry Rose. Yellow fever. An epidemiological and historical study of its place of origin. Edited by Laura Armistead Carter and Wade Hampton Frost. xii, 308 p., 5 fig. Baltimore: Williams & Wilkins, 1931.
Reviewed by C.A. Kofoid, *Isis*, 1932, 17: 464-6.

DR. CARLOS J. FINLAY and the 'Hall of Fame' of New York. 140 p., portr., facs., bibliogr. (Booklet on Sanitation History, 15) Havana: Ministry of Health and Hospital's Assistance, 1959.
Contains facsimiles of documents supporting the priority of Dr. Finlay's discovery of the transmitting agent of yellow fever.

NAVA, Pedro. O quarteirão de febre amarela. *Med.Cir.Farm.*, Sept. 1948, no. 149, 487-96.

QPzye-ce-bv

BLOOMFIELD, Arthur L. A bibliography of internal medicine: yellow fever. *Bull.Hist.Med.*, 1956, 30: 213-32.

QPzye-wb

HEATON, Claude Edwin. Yellow fever in New York City. *Bull. Med.Libr.Ass.*, 1946, 34: 67-78.

QPzye-wc

DUARTE, Eustaquio. Orígenes de la fiebre amarilla en el Brasil. *Rev.Argent.Hist.Med.*, 1943, 2: no. 3, 27-34.

PAZ SOLDÁN, Carlos Enrique. Medidas de seguridad contra la fiebre amarilla durante el virreynato del Perú. *Essays in the History of Medicine presented to Prof. Arturo Castiglioni*, p. 260-6. Baltimore: Johns Hopkins Press, 1944.

QPzye-xd

NOGUEIRA, Pedro. Some points on Lazear Camp. 16 p., ill. At head of title: 51st Annual Meeting, Southern Medical Association, Section on Public Health, Miami Beach, Florida, 12 November 1957. [Marianao, Cuba: Imprenta "El Sol", 1957]
On the restoration of the site of the famous yellow fever experiment of 1900.

QR MEDICAL MYCOLOGY

AINSWORTH, G.C. A century of medical and veterinary mycology in Britain. *Trans.Brit.Mycol.Soc.*, 1951, 34: 1-16, portr.

MONTGOMERY, Douglass W. *See* PK

ZAKON, S.J.; BENEDEK, T. David Gruby and the centenary of medical mycology, 1841-1941. *Bull.Hist.Med.*, 1944, 16: 155-68, portr.

QS MEDICAL ENTOMOLOGY AND PARASITOLOGY

see also LP ANIMAL PARASITOLOGY
LUza APPLIED ENTOMOLOGY

BELTRAN, Enrique. Notas de historia protozoológica. 1. El descubrimento de los sarcodarios y los trabajos de F. Dujardin. 2. Cien años de estudio de las amibas parasitas del hombre, 1848-1949. *Rev.Soc.Mex.Hist.Natur.*, 1948, 9: 341-5; 1949, 10: 285-307, 10 fig.

DOBELL, Clifford. The common flagellate of the human mouth, *Trichomonas tenax* (O.F.M.): its discovery and its nomenclature. *Parasitology*, 1939, 31: 138-46, 1 fig.

DOBELL, Clifford. Michal Siedlecki (1873-1940), a founder of modern knowledge of the Sporozoa. *Parasitology*, 1941, 33: no. 1, 1-7, portr.

FUTCHER, Palmer Howard. Notes on insect contagion. *Bull.Inst. Hist.Med.*, 1936, 4: 536-58.

GUDGER, E.W. The candiru, the only vertebrate parasite of man. Foreword by A.C. Warthin. xviii, 120 p., 18 ill. New York: Hoeber, 1930. [CB 32/586]

GUDGER, E.W. On the alleged penetration of the human urethra by an Amazonian catfish called candiru. With a review of the allied habits of other members of the family Pygidiidae. *Amer.J.Surg.*, 1930, 8: 170-88, 443-57.

HOEPPLI, R. The knowledge of parasites and parasitic infections from ancient times to the 17th century. *Exp.Parasitol.*, 1956, 5: 398-419.

HOEPPLI, R. Parasites and parasitic infections in early medicine and science. xiv, 526 p., 23 pl. Singapore: University of Malaya Press, 1959.
Reviewed by Ilza Veith, *Isis*, 1961, 52: 427-8; for other reviews *see* CB 86/470 and CB 87/573.

HOEPPLI, R. The role of parasites in medicine before the development of modern parasitology. *Proc.Alumni Ass.King Edward VII Coll.Med.Singapore*, 1952, 5: 297-320, bibliogr.
Reviewed by P. Huard, *Arch.Int.Hist.Sci.*, 1957, 10: 65-6.

HOWARD, L.O. A fifty year sketch history of medical entomology. *Annu.Rep.Smithsonian Inst.for 1921*, p. 565-86. Washington, D.C.: 1922. [CB 15/182]

PARASITOLOGY number, Professor Fülleborn memorial. *Chin.Med. J.*, 1933, 47: 1075-476.
Consists of twenty-nine original articles on parasitology. Reviewed in *Ann.Med.Hist.*, 1934, 6: 379.

REGNAULT, Félix. Le rôle du pou dans l'histoire. *VIe Congr. Int.Hist.Méd.* (Leyde-Amsterdam, 1927), p. 370-1. Anvers: De Vlijt, 1929.

UNITED STATES. ARMY MEDICAL DEPARTMENT. Arthropodborne diseases other than malaria. xxiv, 397 p. (Preventive Medicine in World War II, 7) Washington, D.C.: Office of the Surgeon General, 1964.

QSda

HUARD, P.; THÉODORIDÈS, J. Cinq parasitologistes méconnus. *Biol.Méd.*, Apr. 1959, 48: numéro hors série, xci p., fig., pl.
Reviewed by M.D. Grmek, *Sudhoffs Arch.*, 1960, 44: 93.

QSyPX

RENDLE-SHORT, John. Worms in history with special reference to children. *Proc.Roy.Soc.Med.*, 1957, 50: 1013-18, 2 fig.

QT SPECIFIC DISEASES CAUSED BY PARASITES AND INSECTS

BAZZOCCHI, Giuseppe. Cenni storici e clinici su la leishmaniosi americana. *Riv.Stor.Sci.*, 1946, 35-37: 46-54, 5 fig.

BEN-AMRAM, H. L'histoire de la draconculose et de la bilharziose et leur incidence économique et sociale. (Thesis) ix, 98 p. Rennes: 1960.
Reviewed by M.D. Grmek, *Arch.Int.Hist.Sci.*, 1959, 12: 320-1.

HECKMANN, Bernhard. Geschichte und Wesen des Peitschenwurms (*Trichuris, Trichocephalus dispar*) und dessen klinische Bedeutung. 25 p. (Diss. Göttingen) Quakenbrück: Kleinert, 1940.
Reviewed by R. Zaunick, *Mitt.Gesch.Med.*, 1941-42, 40: 90.

MEDRANO, José Miguel, ed. Oncocercosis (Enfermedad de Robles) 257 p., 64 fig. Guatemala, C.A.: Universidad de San Carlos 1947. [CB 73/185]
Collected reprints of articles describing the filarial disease, also called Robles disease. Robles' original memoir is included.
Reviewed by Aldo Mieli, *Arch.Int.Hist.Sci.*, 1949, 2: 1237-8.

QTzm MALARIA

see also RQzci CINCHONA

for malaria in the treatment of syphilis *see* RVyQPzsy

ACKERKNECHT, Erwin H. The development of our knowledge of malaria; the history of malaria; the treatment and prevention of malaria; malaria in the United States. *Ciba Symp.*, 1945, 7: 38-50, 51-6, 57-62, 63-8, ill.

BALFOUR, Andrew. Historical aspects of malaria. *Nature*, 1925, 115: 17-20.

BARBER, Marshall A. A malariologist in many lands. v, 158 p. Lawrence, Kansas: University of Kansas Press, 1946.
Reviewed by Erwin H. Ackerknecht, *Bull.Hist.Med.*, 1947, 21: 634; by Saul Jarcho, *J.Hist.Med.*, 1947, 2: 268-70.

BELTRAN, Enrique; PEQUENO, Eduardo Aguirre. Lecciones de paludologia. 112 p., 5 fig. Monterrey, N.L., Mexico: Ediciones del Instituto de Investigaciones cientificas de la Universidad de Nuevo Leon, 1948.
The first chapter is a brief historical outline and there are other historical notes in the rest of the book.

JARAMILLO-ARANGO, Jaime. The conquest of malaria. xiv, 125 p. London: Heinemann, 1950.
Reviewed by George Rosen, *J.Hist.Med.*, 1952, 7: 205; by U.S. von Euler, *Lychnos*, 1952, 433.

JARCHO, Saul. Contemporary tendencies in the history of malariology. *Bull.Hist.Med.*, 1944, 16: 389-98.

LEBLANC, L. La malaria et la lutte antimalarique. *Rev.Quest. Sci.*, 1931, 50: 79-105.

MANSON-BAHR, Philip. The malaria story. *Proc.Roy.Soc.Med.*, 1961, 54: 91-100.

PERFIL'EV, P.P. K istorii izucheniia moskitov. [On the history of the study of mosquitoes. (In Russian)] *Tr.Inst. Ist.Est.Tekh.*, 1962, 41: 168-82.
Mainly 20th century.

RUSSELL, Paul F. Man's mastery of malaria. xvi, 308 p., 21 ill. (University of London, Heath Clark Lectures 1953, delivered at the London School of Hygiene and Tropical Medicine) London/New York/Toronto: Oxford University Press, 1955.
Reviewed by Morris C. Leikind, *Isis*, 1957, 48: 483-4; by Erwin H. Ackerknecht, *J.Hist.Med.*, 1956, 11: 116; by Ernest Carroll, *Bull.Hist.Med.*, 1956, 30: 388-9.

SEHRWALD, E. Zur Geschichte der Malariaübertragung. *Münch.Med. Wochenschr.*, 1913, 60: 1040.

UNITED STATES. ARMY MEDICAL DEPARTMENT. Communicable disease: malaria. xxv, 642 p., ill. (Preventive Medicine in World War II, 6) Washington, D.C.: Office of the Surgeon General, 1963.

VARGAS, Luis. Algunos de los hechos más salientes en la historia del paludismo. *Rev.Soc.Mex.Hist.Natur.*, 1944, 5: 1-23, 1 pl.

WARSHAW, Leon J. Malaria, the biography of a killer. 348 p. New York: Rinehard, 1949.
Reviewed by Morris C. Leikind, *Isis*, 1950, 41: 327.

QTzm-nh

SIGERIST, Henry E. The term "plasmodium falciparum". A note in defense of Dr. Welch. *Bull.Hist.Med.*, 1942, 11: 587-8.

QTzm-s

ACKERKNECHT, Erwin H. Maladies et sociétés: la peste noire; la fièvre jaune; le paludisme. *Arch.Int.Hist.Sci.*, 1952, 5: 309-19.

QTzm-tk

CELLI, Anna. I riferimenti alla "febbre palustre" nella poesia. *Atti Soc.Ital.Stor.Sci.Med.Nat.IVo Congr.Naz.* (Roma, 1933) In: *Riv.Stor.Sci.*, 1933, 24: suppl. 5-12.

QTzm-wb

FAUST, Ernest Carroll. Malaria in the United States. *Amer. Scient.*, 1951, 39: 121-30.

QTzm-wf

HARANT, H.; RIOUX, J. Le paludisme authochtone en Languedoc-Roussillon (Historique-Régression). *Rev.Pathol.Gén.Comp.*, 1953, no. 652, 1240-51.
Reviewed by J. Théodoridès, *Rev.Hist.Sci.*, 1954, 7: 292.

QTzm-wg

KORTENHAUS, Friedrich. Das Wechselfieber in der Rheinprovinz und sein Verschwinden. *Arch.Gesch.Med.*, 1928, 20: 120-36, 2 pl.

QTzm-wi

BIANCHI, Vincenzo. L'antimalarico che ha appassionato gli Italiani per mezzo secolo. *Riv.Stor.Sci.*, 1950, 42: 73-81, 2 fig.

CELLI, Angelo. The history of malaria in the Roman Campagna from ancient times. Ed. and enl. by Anna Celli-Fraentzel. viii, 226 p., 1 map. London: Bale, Sons & Danielsson, 1933.
Reviewed by C.A. Kofoid, *Isis*, 1934, 22: 319-21.
Translation of Storia della malaria nell'agro romano. *Atti Accad.Naz.Lincei Rendic.Cl.Sci.Fis.Mat.Natur.*, *6th ser.*, 1925, 1: 73-468. [CB 20/211]
Shortened German version Leipzig: Thieme, 1929.

CELLI FRAENTZEL, Anna. Quellen zur Geschichte der Malaria in Italien und ihrer Bedeutung für die deutschen Kaiserzüge des Mittelalters. *Quellen Stud.Gesch.Naturwiss.Med.*, 1935, 4: 1-85. [CB 45/300]

CHARLES, Thomas Edmonston. Letters from Rome on certain discoveries connected with malaria by T. Edmonston Charles; and addenda, consisting of an article by S. Calandruccio, letters from Robert Koch and A. Laveran, and a statement by Lord Lister. Preface and remarks by Sir Ronald Ross. 78 p. London: Harrison & Sons, 1929.

MISSIROLI, A. Varieties of *Anopheles maculipennis* and the malaria problem in Italy. *7th Int.Congr.Entomol.* (Berlin, 1938), p. 1619-40, ill. Berlin: Friedrich-Wilhelms Universität, [1938]. [CB 70/272]
Italian version in *Rendic.Ist.Super.Sanit.*, 1939, 2: 151-74.

RUSSEL, Paul F. Italy in the history of malaria. *Riv.Parassit.*, 1952, 13: 93-104. [CB 80/140]

QTzm-wk

HONIG, P.J.J.; SWELLENGREBEL, N.H.H. Bijdrage tot de geschiedenis der malaria in Nederland. [Contribution to the history of malaria in the Netherlands. (In Dutch)] *Bijdr. Gesch.Geneesk.*, 1925, 5: 109-26; 1926, 6: 233-49, 289-300; 1928, 8: 1-10.

QTzm-wo

ÜNVER, A. Süheyl; BELGER, Metiné. Sur l'histoire du paludisme dans les provinces ottomanes de Yougoslavie. *Liječnički Vjesnik,* 1938, 60: 525-7, ill.

QTzm-yOZ

LANDSBERG, M. Wechselfieber und Milzanschwellung. *Henschel's Janus,* 1848, 3: 358-60; reprinted Leipzig: Alfred Lorentz, 1931.

QTzm-yQA

HACKETT, Lewis Wendell. Malaria in Europe. An ecological study. xvi, 336 p. Oxford University Press, 1937.

NIEUWENHUIS, A.W. Körperliche und kulturelle Volksentartung in Gebieten endemischer Malaria. Mittel Sumatra. *Janus,* 1934, 38: 121-36, 163-78, 193-211, map; 1935, 39: 37-48, 94-104, 127-34, 212-18.

ÜNVER, A. Süheyl. Quelques mots sur l'ancienneté de la malaria en orient. *Turk.Tib Tarihi Arkivi,* 1938, 2: no. 6, 3-4.

WATSON, Malcolm. The geographical aspects of malaria. *Annu. Rep.Smithsonian Inst. for 1942,* p. 339-50, 2 fig. Washington, D.C.: 1943; also in *Geogr.J.,* 1942, 99: 161-72.

QTzsc SCABIES

BERTELLI, Siro. Verità ed errori in tema di storia della scabbia, vista da un omeopatico. *Riv.Stor.Sci.,* 1938, 29: 121-47.

CHRISTOPHE, Marie. Histoire de la gale. 122 p. (Thèse de la Faculté de Médecine de Rennes, 65) Rennes: Faculté de Médecine, 1959.
Reviewed by P. Huard, *Rev.Hist.Sci.,* 1960, 13: 280.

DUJARDIN, B. L'histoire de la gale et le roman de l'acare. 158 p., fig. Bruxelles: Imprimerie médicale et scientifique, 1947. [CB 73/184]
First published in *Arch.Belg.Dermatol.Syphiligr.,* 1946, 2: 13-75; 3: 1-49, fig.; 1947, 3: 129-75, fig.

FAUCCI, Ugo. Un centenario (1834-1934): la 'resurrezione' parigina dell'acaro della scabbia, per opera di Simon Francesco Renucci. *Riv.Stor.Sci.,* 1934, 25: 192-202.

FAUCCI, Ugo. Contributo alla storia della scabbia. *Riv.Stor. Sci.,* 1931, 22: 153-69, 198-215, 257-371, 441-75.

FRIEDMAN, Reuben. Biology of *Acarus scabiei.* xiii, 183 p., 112 ill. New York: Froben Press, 1942.

FRIEDMAN, Reuben. The paleontology of the *Acarus scabiei. Med. Life,* 1938, 45: 188-90.

FRIEDMAN, Reuben. Scabies - civil and military. Its prevalence, prevention and treatment. xviii, 288 p. New York: Froben Press, 1941.
Reviewed in *Ann.Med.Hist.,* 1941, 3: 535.

FRIEDMAN, Reuben. The story of scabies. 2 vol. xxxi, 468 p., ill. New York: Froben Press, 1947.
Volume 1. The prevalence (civil and military), prevention and treatment of scabies, and the biology of *Acarus scabiei,* from the earliest times to the beginning of World War II.

FRIEDMAN, Reuben. The story of scabies. Written for the centenary of Renucci's re-discovery of the *Acarus scabiei. Med.Life,* 1934, 41: 381-424, 426-76; 1935, 42: 218-68, 551-64.

LINT, J.G. de. De ontdekking van den parasitairen oorsprong der scabies. [The discovery of the parasitological origin of scabies. (In Dutch)] *Bijdr.Gesch.Geneesk.,* 1933, 13: 27-8.

MONTGOMERY, Douglass W. The strange history of the vesicle in scabies. *Ann.Med.Hist.,* 1937, 9: 219-29.

OUDEMANS, A.C. Iets over de geschiedenis omtrent scabies en de *Acarus siro.* [Some notes on the history of scabies and *Acarus siro.* (In Dutch)] *Bijdr.Gesch.Geneesk.,* 1927, 7: 369-75.

QTzsc-wb-sm

FRIEDMAN, Reuben. The influence of immigration on the incidence of scabies in the United States. *Ann.Med.Hist.,* 1940, 2: 393-400, 1 facs.

QTzsl SLEEPING SICKNESS

QTzsl-wx

BLOSS, J.F.E. The history of sleeping sickness in the Sudan. *Proc.Roy.Soc.Med.,* 1960, 53: 421-6.

FRAGA DE AZEVEDO, João; PINTO, Manuel R. O desenvolvimento da luta contra a doença do sôno nos territórios portugueses de África. *Arch.Iberoamer.Hist.Med.,* 1957, 9: 183-8.

QU/QY ENVIRONMENTAL MEDICINE

QU INDUSTRIAL MEDICINE

GARRISON, Fielding Hudson. Life as an occupational disease. *Bull.N.Y.Acad.Med.,* 1934, 10: 679-94.

GOLDWATER, Leonard J. From Hippocrates to Ramazzini. Early history of industrial medicine. *Ann.Med.Hist.,* 1936, 8: 27-35.

KEMBLE, James. Occupational diseases: a historical note. *Proc.Roy.Soc.Med.,* 1933, 26: 33-6.

HAMILTON, Alice. Exploring the dangerous trades. x, 433 p., 8 pl. Boston: Little, Brown, 1943.
Reviewed by J.B. de C.M. Saunders, *Isis,* 1944, 35: 188.

HAMILTON, Alice. Nineteen years in the poisonous trades. *Harper's Mag.,* 1929, 159: 580-91.

McCORD, Carey P. A blind hog's acorn; vignettes of the maladies of workers. 311 p. Chicago: Cloud, 1945.
Reviewed by George Rosen, *J.Hist.Med.,* 1947, 2: 275.

NEUBURGER, Max. Die historische Grundlage der Lehre von den Berufskrankheiten. *Volksgesundheit,* 1927, 1: no. 12, 10 p. [CB 24/563]

ROSEN, George. The history of miners' diseases. A medical and social interpretation. With an introduction by Henry E. Sigerist. 490 p., ill. New York: Schuman, 1943.
For reviews *see* CB 68/62 and CB 69/239.

SIGERIST, Henry E. Historical background of industrial and occupational diseases. *Bull.N.Y.Acad.Med.,* 1936, 12: 597-609.

STERN, Bernhard J. Medicine in industry. xv, 209 p. (Studies of the New York Academy of Medicine, Committee on Medicine and the Changing Order) New York: Commonwealth Fund, 1946. [CB 74/397]
Reviewed by Alfred Whittaker, *J.Hist.Med.,* 1947, 2: 273-5.

TELEKY, Ludwig. History of factory and mine hygiene. xvi, 341 p. New York: Columbia University Press, 1948.

QUce-bv

BELLINGTON, Ellen F.; BLOOMFIELD, J.J.; DREESEN, W.C. Bibliography of industrial hygiene, 1900-1943. A selected list. 95 p. Washington: U.S. Public Health Service, 1945.

QUf

ROSEN, George. On the historical investigation of occupational diseases. An aperçu. *Bull.Inst.Hist.Med.,* 1937, 5: 941-6.

QUwg

AUER, Erich. Entwicklung und Stand der sozial-medizinischen Reform in der schweizerischen Industrie. Ein Beitrag zur Geschichte der Arbeitshygiene. 76 p., ill. (*Basler Veröffentl.Gesch.Med.Biol.,* 5) Basel: Benno Schwabe, 1955. [CB 81/277]
Reviewed by Bruno Schuler, *Sudhoffs Arch.,* 1955, 39: 287; by George Rosen, *J.Hist.Med.,* 1956, 11: 119-20.

QUyNTqe

CORSINI, Andrea. L'assistenza ospitaliera e le antiche corporazioni di arti e mestieri. *V° Congr.Naz.Med.Lav.* (Firenze, 1922), 14 p. Prato: 1922.

QUyNTwg

MARTIN, Alfred. Die Knappschafts- und die Armenkasse des Nauheimer (Bad-Nauheimer) Salzwerks. *Arch.Gesch.Med.,* 1938, 30: 220-46.

QUyOI

ROSEN, George. The miner's elbow. *Bull.Hist.Med.*, 1940, 8: 1249-51.

ROSEN, George. The worker's hand. *Ciba Symp.* (Summit. N.J.), 1942, 4: 1307-18, fig.

QUyOX

BASTENIER, H. Introduction historique à l'étude de l'asbestose pulmonaire. *Acta Tuberc.Belg.*, 1964, 55: 73-82.

ROSEN, George. Osler on miner's phthisis. *J.Hist.Med.*, 1949, 4: 259-66.

QUyOXwt

MIURA, Toyohiko. [A short history of silicosis in Japan. (In Japanese)] *Rodo Kagaku*, 1961, 37: 178-87.
English abstract in *Jap.Stud.Hist.Sci.*, 1962, 1: 137

QV ARMY MEDICINE AND MILITARY MEDICINE IN GENERAL

for military surgery *see* RByQV

CASARINI, Arturo. La medicina militare nella legenda e nella storia. Saggio storico sui servizi negli eserciti. 688 p., 155 fig. Roma: *Giornale di Medicina Militare*, 1929.

CASPARI-ROSEN, Beate. The doctor at war. Early military medicine; Disease and war; Battle surgery; War experiences; Reflections on war. *Ciba Symp.* (Summit, N.J.), 1945, 6: 2022-52, ill.

CHAMBERLAIN, Weston P. History of military medicine and its contributions to science. *Boston Med.Surg.J.*, 1917, 176: 479-86. Reprinted in *Annu.Rep.Smithsonian Inst.for 1918*, p. 235-49. Washington, D.C.: 1920.

DELAUNAY, Paul. Médecine militaire d'autrefois ... 149 p. Lille: Imprimerie centrale du Nord, 1913.

GARRISON, Fielding Hudson. Notes on the history of military medicine, expanded from two lectures at the Medical Field Service School, Carlisle Barracks, Pa., June 21-22, 1921. vi, 206 p. Washington: Association of Military Surgeons, 1922.
Reprinted from *Mil.Surg.*, 1921-22.

MOORMAN, Lewis J. Medicine in the dugout. *Bull.Hist.Med.*, 1946, 19: 274-81.

SIGERIST, Henry E. War and medicine. *J.Lab.Clin.Med.*, 1943, 28: 531-8.

QVcb

ARMY Medical Library number. Centenary celebration. *Med.Life*, 1936, 43: 533-604, 1 facs., 1 portr. [CB 50/401]

QVrj

MAYER, Claudius F. The Hippocratic oath, the pledge of Geneva, and ABC warfare. *Mil.Surg.*, 1952, 111: 369-70.

QVwb

ARNOLD, Harry L., Jr. Fielding H. Garrison, the caduceus, and the United States Army Medical Department. *Bull.Hist.Med.*, 1943, 13: 627-30.

BAXTER, James Phinney. Scientists against time. Foreword by Vannevar Bush. 473 p. Boston: Little, Brown, 1946.
Brief official history of the U.S. Office of Scientific Research and Development in World War II.

DAVIDSON, Wilson Thompson. Years of an army doctor: an autobiography. 189 p., pl., portr. San Antonio, Tex.: Naylor, 1944.
Reviewed by Jean C. Sabine, *Bull.Hist.Med.*, 1945, 17: 216.

FISHBEIN, Morris, ed. Doctors at war. 418 p. New York: Dutton, 1945.
Account of the work done by American physicians during the war, written by sixteen specialists.

HUME, Edgar Erskine. Scientific accomplishments of the United States Army Médical Corps. Part I. *Trans.Coll.Physicians Phila.*, 1942, 10: 23-47, 1 pl.

HUME, Edgar Erskine. Victories of army medicine: scientific accomplishments of the Medical Department of the United States Army. xiv, 250 p., ill. Philadelphia: Lippincott, 1943.
Reviewed by Genevieve Miller, *Bull.Hist.Med.*, 1943, 14: 536-8.

MACPHAIL, Andrew. Official history of the Canadian forces in the great war, 1914-1919. The medical services. viii, 428 p. Ottawa: F.A. Acland, printer, 1925.

STEVENSON, Isobel. Beginnings of American military medicine. The Medical Department of the U.S. Army in the World War. *Ciba Symp.* (Summit, N.J.), 1940, 1: 344-59, 360-3, ill.

U.S. OFFICE OF SCIENTIFIC RESEARCH AND DEVELOPMENT. COMMITTEE ON MEDICAL RESEARCH. Advances in military medicine made by American investigators; ed. by E.C. Andrus [*et al.*]. 2 vol. liv, 472 p.; xvii, 428 p., ill. (Science in World War II: Office of Scientific Research and Development) Boston: Little, Brown, 1948.
Reviewed by Morris Leikind, *Science*, 1948, 108: 342.

QVwb-cs

HUME, Edgar Erskine. The medals of the United States Army Medical Department and medals honoring Army medical officers. 146 p., 23 pl. (Numismatic notes and monographs, 98) New York: American Numismatic Society, 1942.
Reviewed by Genevieve Miller, *Bull.Hist.Med.*, 1943, 13: 246.

QVwb-f

McNINCH, J.H. Plans for the preparation of the Army Medical Department history, World War II. *Bull.Hist.Med.*, 1946, 20: 167-72.

QVwb-qk

SIMON, S. William. The medical history of the Veterans Administration Center, Dayton, Ohio, 1868-1900. *Bull.Hist. Med.*, 1951, 25: 539-53, 3 fig.

SIMON, S. William. The medical history of the Veterans Administration Center at Dayton, Ohio (1900-1930). *Bull.Hist. Med.*, 1954, 28: 73-9.

QVwb-qm

GOODE, Paul R. The United States Soldiers' Home. A history of its first hundred years. xiv, 289 p. Richmond, Va.: William Byrd Press, 1957.
Reviewed by Robert J.T. Joy, *J.Hist.Med.*, 1959, 14: 129-30.

QVwc

IZQUIERDO, J.J. Un veterano del ejército permanente. 525 p., ill. Mexico, D.F.: Ediciones Ciencia, 1951.
Reviewed by José M.R. Delgado, *J.Hist.Med.*, 1953, 8: 348-9.

MARTÍNEZ PÁEZ, Julio. Médicos en la Sierra Maestra (apuntes históricos). 72 p. (Cuadernos de Historia Sanitaria, 14) La Habana: 1959.
The organization of medical services in Fidel Castro's guerrilla army.

QVwe

CREW, F.A.E. The Army medical services. Campaigns. Vol. 4. North-West Europe. xlv, 687 p., ill. London: Her Majesty's Stationery Office, 1962.
Reviewed by B.H. Rutledge, *Bull.Hist.Med.*, 1963, 37: 583-4.

MACPHERSON, William Grant. Medical services: general history. 4 vol. 1. Medical services in the United Kingdom, in British garrisons overseas and during operations against Tsingtan, in Togoland, the Cameroons and South West Africa; 2. The medical services on the western front and during operations in France and Belgium in 1914 and 1915; 3. Medical services during the operations on the western front in 1916, 1917 and 1918; in Italy; and in Egypt and Palestine; 4. Medical services during the operations on the Gallipoli Peninsula; in Macedonia; in Mesopotamia and North West Persia; in East Africa; in the Aden Protectorate and in North Russia; Ambulance transport during the war. xvi, 711 p. (History of the Great War, based on official documents) London: H.M. Stationery Off., 1921-24.

QVwf

SIEUR, Pierre Marie Marcel. Histoire des tribulations du Corps de Santé Militaire depuis sa création jusqu'à nos jours. *Bull.Soc.Franç.Hist.Méd.*, 1928, 22: 92-163.

QVwf-da

BLAESSINGER, Edmond. Les grandes figures du Service de Santé Militaire. 1. Quelques grandes figures de la chirurgie et de la médecine militaire. 423 p., 30 fig.; 2. Quelques grandes figures de la pharmacie militaire. 388 p., 26 fig.; 3. Quelques grandes figures de la chirurgie, de la médecine et de la pharmacie militaire. 418 p. Paris: Baillière, 1947-52.
Reviewed by André Hahn, *Arch.Int.Hist.Sci.*, 1949, 2: 789-93.

QVwg-da

KIRCHENBERGER, S. Lebensbilder hervorragender österreichisch-ungarischer Militär- und Marineärzte. 241 p., ill. (Militärärztliche Publikationen, 150) Wien: J. Safár, 1913.

QVwh

GIEDROYC, Franciszek. Służba zdrowia w dawnym Wojsku Polskim. [The medical service in the old Polish army. (In Polish)] 550 p. Warszawa: 1927.
Reviewed by Josef Fritz, *Mitt.Gesch.Med.*, 1928, 27: 110; by V. Bugiel, *Bull.Soc.Franç.Hist.Méd.*, 1928, 22: 84-5.

QVwn

MAYER, Claudius F. Medical history of the Russo-German war, 1941-1945. A brief study, with review of the first-born official medical history of the Second World War. *Mil. Surg.*, 1951, 109: 207-21, 1 ill. [CB 78/158]
Review of the first six volumes of the Russian report: Opȳt sovetskoĭ meditŝiny v velikoĭ Otechestvennoi Voĭne, 1941-1945 gg., *see below.*

OPȲT sovetskoĭ meditŝiny v Velikoĭ Otechestvennoi Voĭne, 1941-1945 gg. [The experience of Soviet medicine in the Great War for the Fatherland, 1941-1945. (In Russian)] 35 vol. Moskva: Gos. Izd-vo Med. Lit-rȳ, 1949-.
Vol. 1 publ. 1951.

QVyNAwb

HUME, Edgar Erskine. Contributions of the Medical Corps of the Army to the public health laboratory. *Science*, 1943, 97: 293-300.

HUME, Edgar Erskine. The United States Army Medical Department and its relation to public health. *Science*, 1931, 74: 465-76.

QVyNAwi

TESTI, Francesco. Storia retrospettiva della igiene nell' esercito italiano: monografia. viii, 112 p. (Collana medico-militare, 1) Roma: 1912.

QVyNB

LOVE, Albert G.; HAMILTON, Eugene L.; HELLMAN, Ida L. Tabulating equipment and army medical statistics. x, 202 p. Washington, D.C.: Govt. Print. Off., 1958.
A history of the development of Army Medical Corps Statistics and of the IBM punchcard machines.
Reviewed by Robert J.T. Joy, *J.Hist.Med.*, 1960, 15: 225-6.

QVyND

HEIZMANN, Charles L. Military sanitation in the sixteenth, seventeenth and eighteenth centuries. *Ann.Med.Hist.*, 1917, 1: 281-300.

QVyNT

GUERRA-COPPIOLI, Luigi. Qualche ricordo storico sull' assistenza al feriti e ai malati in guerra. *Riv.Stor.Sci.*, 1952, 43: 130-5.

SUDHOFF, Karl. Aus der Vergangenheit der Verwundetenfürsorge. (1915). *Sudhoffs Arch.*, 1929, 21: 261-72.

QVyNTqy

FLORIAN, A. [Jean Henri Dunant - founder of the International Red Cross - Zionist visionary. (In Hebrew)] *Koroth*, 1962, 2: 584-91.

GUMPERT, Martin. Aid to the wounded: the pre-history of the Red Cross; Jean Henri Dunant, the founder of the Red Cross; origin and development of the American Red Cross in war and peace. *Ciba Symp.*(Summit, N.J.), 1942, 4: 1362-92, fig.

GUMPERT, Martin. Dunant: the story of the Red Cross. 323 p. New York: Oxford University Press, 1938.
Reviewed in *Ann.Med.Hist.*, 1938, 10: 563-4; by Theodore Collier, *Amer.Hist.Rev.*, 1940, 45: 645-6.

JUNOD, Marcel. Warriors without weapons. xvi, 283 p. New York: Macmillan, 1951. [CB 78/159]

QVyNWwb

VIETS, Henry R. The "first" U.S. military hospital. *J.Hist. Med.*, 1957, 12: 394-5.
At Roxbury, Massachusetts.

QVyNWwf

LECLAIR, Henri. Les hôpitaux militaires de Lille avant la Révolution. Essai historique. 172 p., 8 pl. Lille: Morel, 1925.

QVyNX

MONÉRY, André. Le transport des blessés de la Révolution à nos jours. *Aesculape*, 1925, 15: 7-10. [CB 18/572]

POTTLE, Frederick Albert. Stretchers, the story of a hospital unit on the western front. xvi, 366 p. New Haven: Yale University Press, 1929.
Reviewed by Francis R. Packard, *Ann.Med.Hist.*, 1930, 2: 129-30.

QVyQwb-qg

HENRY, Robert S. The Armed Forces Institute of Pathology. Its first hundred years, 1862-1962. 422 p. Washington, D.C.: Office of the Surgeon General, Department of the Army, 1964.
Reviewed by Dwight F. Miller, *J.Hist.Med.*, 1964, 19: 307-8.

QVyQwe

SACHS, A. The centenary of British military pathology. *J. Roy.Army Med.Corps*, 1955, 101: 100-21. [CB 81/282]

QVyQNwn

TARARIN, R.A. [Essay on the history of Soviet military epidemiology during World War II. (In Russian)] *Pathol.Biol.*, 1964, 12: 149-52.

QVyQPzdy

MAYER, Claudius F. Bacillary dysentery as a military problem, and the Pavlovian doctrine. *Mil.Surg.*, 1952, 111: 268-76.

QW NAVAL AND MARITIME MEDICINE

for naval surgery *see* RByQW

PEZZI, Giuseppe. Sui progressi dell'igiene e della medicina navale nei secoli 19 e 20. *Riv.Stor.Sci.*, 1953, 44: 194-206.

RICHELOT, -. Die Entwicklung der Schiffshygiene. *Z.Balneol. Klim.*, 1913, 6: 260-3.

RODDIS, Louis H. A short history of nautical medicine. *Ann. Med.Hist.*, 1941, 3: 203-47, 2 fig., 326-52, 8 fig., 418-47, 3 fig.; 1942, 4: 338-9.

SCHADEWALDT, Hans. L'importance historique de la médecine navale dans le cadre de l'art médical. *Hist.Méd.*, 1963, 12: 3-24.

SCHADEWALDT, Hans. Der Schiffsarzt: Die Entwicklung der Seefahrt und des Schiffsarztes im Laufe der Jahrhunderte; Die Geschichte der wichtigsten Schiffskrankheiten; Allgemeine Schiffshygiene; Lazarettschiffe und Marinelazarette; Notizen zum Thema. *Ciba Z.*, 1955, 7: 2502-36, ill., bibliogr.
An extensive bibliography available from CIBA A.G. Wehr/ Baden.

QWwb

DIDDLE, Albert W. Medical events in the history of Key West. *Bull.Hist.Med.*, 1944, 15: 445-67, 1 fig.

STRAUS, Robert. Medical care for seamen. The origin of public medical service in the United States. xvi, 165 p. (Merchant Seamen Studies, 1) New Haven: Yale University Press, 1950.

QWwe

ALLISON, Richard Sydney. Sea diseases. The story of a great natural experiment in preventive medicine in the Royal Navy. ix, 218 p., 12 ill. London: Bale, 1943.
Reviewed by E.H. Ackerknecht, *Bull.Hist.Med.*, 1944, 15: 330-1.

KEEVIL, John J. Medicine and the Navy, 1200-1900. 4 vol. 1. 1200-1649. 255 p.; 2. 1649-1714. xii, 332 p.; 3. 1714-1815. By C. Lloyd and J.L.S. Coulter. xi, 402 p.; 4. 1815-1900. By C. Lloyd and J.L.S. Coulter. xi, 300 p. Edinburgh/London: Livingstone, 1957-63.
Volumes 1 and 2 reviewed by F.N.L. Poynter, *Isis*, 1958, 49: 354-5; for other reviews *see* CB 84/321 and CB 85/399. For reviews of volume 3 *see* CB 88/560 and CB 89/557; of volume 4 *see* CB 89/572 and CB 90/615.

QWwg

BAUER, Werner. Geschichte des Marinesanitätswesens bis 1945. 138 p. (*Marine-Rundschau*, Beiheft 4) Berlin/Frankfurt: Mittler, 1958.
Reviewed by Hans Schadewaldt, *Sudhoffs Arch.*, 1961, 45: 94.

QWwi

CANEVA, Giuseppe. Les Corsaires genois et leur organisation sanitaire. *Rev.Hist.Pharm.*, 1960, 48: 357-61.

QWwk

POP, G.F. De geneeskunde bij het Nederlandsche zeewezen. Geschiedkundige nasporingen. [Medicine in Dutch maritime affairs. Historical studies. (In Dutch)] Reprint of the series published in *Geneeskundig Tijdschrift voor de Zeemacht*, 1866-68. Ed. by L.S.A.M. von Römer. 406 p. Batavia: G. Kolff, 1922.
Reviewed by M.A. van Andel, *Bijdr.Gesch.Geneesk.*, 1925, 5: 315-16.

QWyNWwb

HOLCOMB, Richmond Cranston. A century with the Norfolk Naval Hospital, 1830-1930. A story of the oldest naval hospital, the medical department of the Navy and the progress of medicine through the past one hundred years. 543 p., ill. Portsmouth, V.: Printcraft Publishing Company, 1930.
Reviewed by Robert P. Parsons, *Ann.Med.Hist.*, 1931: 3: 123-4.

WARING, Joseph Ioor. The Marine Hospitals of Charleston. *Bull.Hist.Med.*, 1941, 10: 651-65, 1 pl.

QX AVIATION MEDICINE

CARDOSO DE MORAES, Clovis. Ligeiro esboço historico da medicina de aviação. *Rev.Argent.Hist.Med.*, 1944, 3: no. 1, 43-55.

FULTON, John F. Aviation medicine in its preventive aspects. 174 p., 43 ill. London: Oxford University Press, 1948.
Reviewed by C.K. Drinker, *Isis*, 1949, 40: 302.

POYNTON, F. John. Doctors and the dawn of aerostation. *Proc. 3rd Int.Congr.Hist.Med.* (London, 1922), p. 101-5. Antwerp: de Vlijt, 1923.

ROBINSON, Victor. Origin of aviation medicine. Aviation medicine in the A.E.F. Aviation medicine in America. Airmarks 1903-1943. *Ciba Symp.* (Summit, N.J.), 1943, 5: 1624-51, ill.

QXce-bv

HOFF, Ebbe Curtis; FULTON, John Farquhar. A bibliography of aviation medicine. 237 p. Springfield, Ill.: Charles C. Thomas, 1942.
Reviewed by Eugene F. Du Bois, *Science*, 1942, 96: 361.

QXda

GIBSON, William C. Medical pioneers in aviation. *J.Hist. Med.*, 1962, 17: 83-93.

QXwb

LINK, Mae Mills; COLEMAN, Hubert A. Medical support of the Army Air Forces in World War II. 1027 p., front., 97 tables, 19 charts, 52 ill. Washington: Office of the Surgeon-General, Department of the Air Force, 1955. [CB 82/266]

QXwg

U.S. AIR FORCE. German aviation medicine, World War II. Prepared under the auspices of the Surgeon General, U.S. Air Force. 2 vol., 1302 p. Washington, D.C.: Department of the Air Force, 1950.

QY TROPICAL MEDICINE

for specific infectious tropical diseases *see under* QP and QT

BERRY, L.H. Black men and malignant fevers. *J.Nat.Med.Ass.*, 1964, 56: 43-7.

EXPOSITION UNIVERSELLE ET INTERNATIONALE DE GAND. Ghent Exhibition, 1913. Handbook to the tropical diseases illustrated in the British section. 150 p. London: H.M. Stationery Off., 1913.
Includes historical notes on each disease.

LAMBERT, Sylvester Maxwell. A Yankee doctor in paradise. x, 393 p., front. Boston: Little, Brown, 1941. [CB 61/380]

ROGERS, Leonard. Happy toil. Fifty-five years of tropical medicine. xvi, 271 p., 8 pl. London: Muller, 1950.

SCOTT, H. Harold. A history of tropical medicine, based on the Fitzpatrick Lectures delivered before the Royal College of Physicians of London, 1937-38. 2 vol. xx, 648 p.; iv, p. 649-1165, 13 pl., 12 fig. London: Arnold; Baltimore: Williams & Wilkins, 1939. [CB 59/490]

SINGER, Charles. Notes on some early references to tropical diseases. *Ann.Trop.Med.Parasitol.*, 1912, 6: 379-402, 1 pl., fig.

TAYLOR, Stephen; GADSDEN, Phyllis. Shadows in the sun. 187 p. London: Harrap, 1949.
History of contemporary tropical medicine.
Reviewed by George Rosen, *J.Hist.Med.*, 1951, 6: 273.

QYda

BARRETO DE ARAGÃO, Egas Moniz. Os fundadores da medicina tropical. *Brotéria Ser.Vulg.Sci.*, 1913, 11: 163-9.

OLPP, Gottlieb. Charakterköpfe der Tropenmedizin. 96 p., fig. Berlin: Die Brücke zur Heimat, 1936.

OLPP, Gottlieb. Hervorragende Tropenärzte in Wort und Bild. 446 p., 71 p., 280 ill. München: Gmelin, 1932.

QYwb

HOLCOMB, R.C. Rear Admiral Charles St. John Butler, Medical Corps, United States Navy. An American pioneer in tropical medicine. *Bull.Hist.Med.*, 1945, 18: 185-94, portr.

MEARS, J. Ewing. The triumphs of American medicine in the construction of the Panama canal. 25 p. Philadelphia: Wm. J. Dornan, 1912.

WILSON, Charles Morrow. Ambassadors in white; the story of American tropical medicine. x, 372 p., ill. New York: Henry Holt, 1942. [CB 69/238]

QZ FORENSIC MEDICINE

for surgery in forensic medicine *see* RByQZ

ACKERKNECHT, Erwin H. History of legal medicine. *Ciba Symp.* (Summit, N.J.), 1951, 11: 1286-316, ill.

DAVISON, M.H. Armstrong. Medicine, murder and man. *Med.Leg. J.*, 1964, 32: part 1, 28-39.

PARRY, Leonard Arthur. Some famous medical trials. x, 326 p. London: Churchill, 1928.

VORKASTNER, W. Über Werden und Wesen der gerichtlichen Medizin. *Klin.Wochenschr.*, 1931, 10: 738-53.

WHITLOCK, F.A. Medical evidence and criminal responsibility: an historical review of a medico-legal problem. *Med.Leg.J.*, 1964, 32: 176-85.

ZILBOORG, Gregory. Murder and justice. *J.Crim.Psychopathol.*, 1943, 5: 1-25.

QZce-bv

BRITTAIN, Robert P. Bibliography of medico-legal works in English. 252 p. London: Sweet and Maxwell, 1962.
Reviewed by Keith Simpson, *Med.Hist.*, 1963, 7: 95.

QZkb

REUTER, Fritz. Lässt sich der Standpunkt, den Eduard von Hofmann bezüglich des Umfanges der gerichtlichen Medizin eingenommen hat, auch im sozialen Staat der Zukunft noch aufrecht erhalten? *Festschrift zum 80. Geburtstag Max Neuburgers*, p. 396-400. Wien: Maudrich, 1948.

QZwg

GUGGENBÜHL, Dietegen. Gerichtliche Medizin in Basel von den Anfängen bis zur Helvetik. 111 p., ill. (*Basler Veröffentl. Gesch.Med.Biol.*, fasc. 15) Basel/Stuttgart: Benno Schwabe, 1963.

REUTER, Fritz. Eduard von Hofmanns Erbe. Ein Beitrag zur Geschichte der gerichtlichen Medizin in Alt-Österreich (1898-1938). *Nova Acta Leopoldina*, 1940, 9: 561-632.
Reviewed by Zaunick, *Mitt.Gesch.Med.*, 1941-42, 40: 61.

QZwg-sc

KELLER, Albrecht. Der Scharfrichter in der deutschen Kulturgeschichte. viii, 324 p. Bonn: Schroeder, 1921.

QZwk

THOMAS, F. Milestones in forensic medicine: the Belgian contribution. *Med.Sci.Law*, 1964, 4: 155-70.

QZyOMP

ZILBOORG, Gregory. The contribution of psychoanalysis to forensic medicine. *Int.J.Psychoanal.*, 1956, 37: 318-24.

QZyON

BRETEILLE, René Ch. Etude historique et médico-légale du masochisme. 64 p. (Thèse.) Paris: Ollier-Henry, 1913.

QZyQC

HULST, J.P.L. De geschiedenis van de longproef en van hare beteekenis voor de gerechtelijke geneeskunde, en de rechtspraak. [The history of the lung test and its significance in forensic medicine and the administration of justice. (In Dutch)] *Bijdr.Gesch.Geneesk.*, 1922, 2: 151-68, 251-73.

QZzs SUICIDE

DARMSTAEDTER, Ernst. Kritisch-historische Bemerkungen über "Selbstverbrennung des menschlichen Körpers". *Deut.Z.Gesamte Gerichtl.Med.*, 1932, 18: 437-45.

QZzs-wk

SPEYER, N. Overzicht van de geschiedenis van den zelfmoord in Nederland (met bibliographie van nederlandsche schrijvers over het zelfmoordvraagstuk). [Survey of the history of suicide in the Netherlands with a bibliography of Dutch writers on the problem of suicide. (In Dutch)] *Bijdr.Gesch. Geneesk.*, 1938, 18: 70-9, 2 fig.

QZzs-yON

ACHILLE-DELMAS, F. Psychologie pathologique du suicide. xii, 238 p. (Bibliothèque de Philosophie Contemporaine) Paris: Alcan, 1932. [CB 38/605]

R THERAPEUTICS

Rc general history

ACKERKNECHT, Erwin H. Aspects of the history of therapeutics. (Hideyo Noguchi Lectures) *Bull.Hist.Med.*, 1962, 36: 389-419. [CB 88/554]

ASCHNER, Bernhard. The art of the healer. Translated from the German by Ruth and Heinz Norden. 306 p. New York: Dial Press, 1942.
Transl. of: Der Arzt als Schicksal, 1939.
Reviewed by Henry E. Sigerist, *Bull.Hist.Med.*, 1943, 13: 360-2.

BENEDICENTI, Alberico. Medici, malati, farmacisti: storia dei rimedi traverso i secoli e delle teorie che ne spiegano l'azione sull'organismo. 2nd ed. 2 vol. 1456 p., 522 fig. Milano: Hoepli, 1949-51.
Reviewed by Arturo Castiglioni, *Riv.Stor.Sci.*, 1952, 43: 279.
First published 1924-25 [CB 18/650 and CB 42/257] and reviewed by A. Mieli, *Arch.Stor.Sci.*, 1924, 5: 301-2.

DAWSON, George Gordon. Healing, pagan and Christian. ix, 322 p. London: S.P.C.K., 1935.

DIEPGEN, Paul. Die volkstümlichen und die wissenschaftlichen Grundlagen der Therapie in der Geschichte der Medizin. *Fortschr.Therap.*, 1936, 12: 14-23.

FÅHRAEUS, Robin. Terapiens tre huvudepoker. [Les trois époques principales de la thérapeutique. (In Swedish, with summary in French)] *Lychnos*, 1943, 33-42.

HOLLIDAY, Carl. How our ancestors were cured. *Sci.Mon.*, 1915, 1: 278-82.

LESKY, Erna. Von den Ursprüngen des therapeutischen Nihilismus. *Sudhoffs Arch.*, 1960, 44: 1-20.

MARTÍ-IBÁÑEZ, Félix. Los milagros curativos en la historia de la medicina. In: Martí-Ibáñez, Felix. Milagros curativos, p. 5-26. (Claris, 20) Barcelona: Nueva Era, 1937.

MUNTNER, Suessmann. The origins of a scientific therapy. *Koroth*, 1964, 3: 197-201 (in Hebrew); i-vi (in English).

NEUBURGER, Max. Resumption of discredited methods of treatment. *Med.Life*, 1932, 39: 694-8.

STEINER, Rudolf; WEGMANN, Ita. Fundamentals of therapy: an extension of the art of healing through spiritual knowledge. Authorized transl. by G. Kaufmann. 165 p. New York: Anthroposophic Press; London: Anthroposophical Publishing Co., 1938.
Transl. of: Grundlegendes für eine Erweiterung der Heilkunst nach geisteswissenschaftlichen Erkenntnissen (Dornach: Goetheanum, 1925) reviewed by Richard Koch, *Mitt. Gesch.Med.*, 1926, 25: 243-8.

Ru popular aspects

ANDEL, M.A. van. The ceraunia or thunder-axe. Its use in folk medecine. *Ann.Med.Hist.*, 1924, 6: 452-6, 2 fig.

CRAWFURD, Raymond. Legends and lore of the genesis of the healing art. *Proc.Roy.Soc.Med.*, 1917, 10: Hist. Sect., 1-32.
Deals with medicine in the earliest and crudest states and discusses healing acts among animals.

JOHNSSON, John William Schibbye. Die Muskatnuss, ein kosmetisch-erotisches Amulett. Volksmedizinische Untersuchungen. *Proc.3rd Int.Congr.Hist.Med.* (London, 1922), p. 225-32. Antwerp: De Vlijt, 1923.

KLEIWEG DE ZWAAN, J.-P. Kleidung und Krankheiten. Ethnologische und historische Betrachtungen. *Janus*, 1916, 21: 63-110.

MACKENZIE, D. Folk cures by constriction and rings. *Proc. Roy.Soc.Med.*, 1916, 9: Hist. Sect., 143-54.
Describes the process by which the spirit of disease is squeezed or pushed out of the affected parts.

POSNER, Carl. Volkstümliche Mittel in der modernen Medizin. *Z.Ver.Volksk.*, 1913, 23: 372.

RAILLIET, G. Médecine populaire (Glanes d'un praticien Rémois). 2. Thérapeutique et matière médicale. *Bull.Soc. Franç.Hist.Méd.*, 1936, 33: 193-212.

SELIGMANN, S. Die magischen Heil- und Schutzmittel aus der unbelebten Natur. Mit besonderer Berücksichtigung der 4
Mittel gegen den bösen Blick. Eine Geschichte des Amulettwesens. Mit zahlreichen Abbildungen. xi, 310 p. Stuttgart: Strecker und Schröder, 1927.
Reviewed by Ernst Darmstaedter, *Mitt.Gesch.Med.*, 1928, 27: 125.

Ru-pg

BLOCH, Marc. Les rois thaumaturges. Etude sur le caractère surnaturel attribué à la puissance royale, particulièrement en France et en Angleterre. vii, 542 p., 4 pl. (Publications de la Faculté des lettres de l'Université de Strasbourg, fasc. 19) Strasbourg: Istra, 1924.
Reviewed by George Sarton, *Isis*, 1925, 7: 520-1.

MARTIN, Alfred. Sympathische Heilungen durch bestimmte Personen und Heilung durch Arznei aus Fürstenhand. *Med.Klin.*, 1915, 11: 304, bibliogr.

MARTINOTTI, Giovanni. Le toucher royal des écrouelles. *Aesculape*, 1926, 16: 112-17. [CB 20/205]

Rw in different countries

Rwg-u

STAAK, Gerhard. Die magische Krankheitsbehandlung in der Gegenwart in Mecklenburg. 356 p. (Beiträge zur magischen Krankheitsbehandlung) Rostock: Grundgeyer, 1930.

Rwv

SCHOUTE, D. Occidental therapeutics in the Netherlands East Indies during three centuries of Netherlands settlement (1600-1900). vi, 214 p. (Publications of the Netherlands Indies public health service) Amsterdam: Kolff, 1937.
Reviewed by B.W. Th. Nuyens, *Bijdr.Gesch.Geneesk.*, 1937, 17: 177-9.

STEINMETZ, H.C. Medieval treatment in modern practice. *Med. Life*, 1932, 39: 629-30.
Apropos of the study of Filipino medicine by the late Dr. T.H. Pardo de Tavera posthumously translated c. 1930 by A.W. Prautch.

Rzh HOMOEOPATHY

BRUNN, Walter von. Homöopathie als medizingeschichtliches Problem. *Sudhoffs Arch.*, 1964, 48: 137-56.

DEJUST, L.H. Examen critique de l'homoeopathie (un chapitre d'histoire de la médecine). viii, 96 p. Paris: Vigot, 1922. [CB 14/523]
A history of homoeopathy since Hahnemann.

EBSTEIN, Erich. Arzt und Homöopathie. Mit zwei Briefen aus den Jahre 1836. *Arch.Gesch.Med.*, 1923, 15: 141-6.

FEYFER, F.M.G. de. De wijsgeerige achtergrond der homoeopathie (proeve eener historische synthese). [The philosophical background of homeopathy: attempt at an historical synthesis. (In Dutch)] *Bijdr.Gesch.Geneesk.*, 1926, 6: 69-79.

GUTTENTAG, Otto Ernst. Trends toward homeopathy, present and past. *Bull.Hist.Med.*, 1940, 8: 1172-93.

HELM, Otto. Die homöopathischen Prinzipien (historische Entwicklung, Wesen und Kritik). (Diss.) Marburg: 1923.

OOSTERHUIS, R.A.B., *et al.* Homoeopathie, natuurgeneeskunde, synthese. Een pleidooi voor universitaire leerstoelen in de natuurgeneeswijze. [Homeopathy, the healing power of nature, a synthesis. A plea for the establishment of chairs of "natural medicine" in the universities. (In Dutch)] 127 p. Amsterdam: Bom & Zoon, 1948. [CB 73/183]

PLANER, Reinhard. Der Kampf um die Homöopathie *pro et contra*. 354 p. Leipzig: Hügel, 1926.

PROKOP, Otto; PROKOP, Ludwig. Homöopathie und Wissenschaft. Eine Kritik des Systems. 223 p., 13 ill., 32 tables. Stuttgart: Enke, 1957.
Reviewed by Edwin Rosner, *Sudhoffs Arch.*, 1959, 43: 90-1.

SPERLING, Arthur. Die Brücke zur Homöopathie und der Weg zur Einheit der Arzneimittellehre; historische, biologische, therapeutische Studien für Ärzte, Studierende und alle Gebildeten. x, 256 p. Leipzig: Schwabe, 1927.

TISCHNER, Rudolf. Geschichte der Homöopathie. 4 vol. 1. Die Vorläufer der Homöopathie; 2. Hahnemann: Leben und Werke; 3. Ausbreitung der Homöopathie; 4. Die Homöopathie seit 1850. Leipzig: Schwabe, 1932-39.
Reviewed by O.T. Hult, *Lychnos*, 1940, 469-71. Volume 1 reviewed by W. Haberling, *Mitt.Gesch.Med.*, 1932, 31: 162.

TISCHNER, Rudolf. Hahnemann und die hippokratische Medizin (ein historisch-methodologischer Versuch). *Janus*, 1923, 27: 219-40.

WEIR, John. Samuel Hahnemann and his influence on medical thought. *Proc.Roy.Soc.Med.*, 1933, 26: 24-32, 76.

Rzh-xx

HAEHL, Erich; WOLF, Immanuel. Samuel Hahnemann. Das Hahnemann Museum in Stuttgart und sein Schöpfer Richard Haehl. 36 p., 6 fig. Stuttgart: Hippokrates-Verlag, 1932.

Rzm MESMERISM

ARTELT, Walter. Der Mesmerismus im deutschen Geistesleben. *Gesnerus*, 1951, 8: 4-14.

Rzn NATURE CURES

BAUMANN, E.D. Historische Betrachtungen über die vis medicatrix naturae. *Janus*, 1936, 40: 148-70, 197-217.

NEUBURGER, Max. The doctrine of the healing power of nature, throughout the course of time. Transl. by Linn J. Boyd. 184 p. New York: priv. print., 1932.
Translation of: Die Lehre von der Heilkraft der Natur im Wandel der Zeiten. Stuttgart: Ferdinand Enke, 1926. [CB 21/598]

NEUBURGER, Max. Vis medicatrix naturae. *Med.Life*, 1932, 39: 657-92.

NEUBURGER, Max. Zur Geschichte des Problems der Naturheilkraft. *Essays on the History of Medicine presented to Karl Sudhoff*, p. 325-48. London: Oxford University Press; Zurich: K. Hönn, 1924.

Rzy QUACKERY

AMERICAN MEDICAL ASSOCIATION. Nostrums and quackery: articles on the nostrum evil, quackery and allied matters affecting the public health reprinted ... from the *Journal of the American Medical Association*. 3 vol. Chicago: 1911-36.
2nd edition of volume 1 published January 1913; volumes 2 and 3 edited by A.J. Cramp, 1921-36.

BURGER, H. The doctor, the quack, and the appetite of the public for magic in medicine. *Proc.Roy.Soc.Med.*, 1933-34, 27: 5-10. [CB 43/288]
By way of illustration, Burger reviews the work of Valentin Zeileis of Gallspach.

CORSINI, Andrea. Medici ciarlatani e ciarlatani medici. 114 p. Bologna: Zanichelli, 1922.

DIEPGEN, Paul. Kurpfuscherei und wissenschaftliche Medizin im Wandel der Zeiten. *Gesundheitslehrer*, 1933, 36: 213-18.

GARRISON, Fielding Hudson. On quackery as a reversion to primitive medicine. *Bull.N.Y.Acad.Med.*, 1933, 9: 601-12.

GIBBES, J. Heyward. Quacks and quackeries. *Sci.Mon.*, 1925, 21: 533-50.

HOLBROOK, Stewart H. The golden age of quackery. viii, 302 p., bibliogr. New York: Macmillan, 1959.

JAMESON, Eric. The natural history of quackery. 224 p., ill. London: Michael Joseph, 1961.
Reviewed by R.M.S. McConaghey, *Med.Hist.*, 1962, 6: 299-300; by Heinz Degen, *Sudhoffs Arch.*, 1963, 47: 188-9.

NEUSTÄTTER, Otto. Kurierzwang und Kurpfuschereifreiheit. *Arch.Gesch.Naturwiss.Tech.*, 1913, 6: 272-82.

STEINER, Walter R. The conflict of medicine with quackery. *Ann.Med.Hist.*, 1924, 6: 60-70, ill.

Rzy-rj

MINTY, Leonard Le Marchant. The legal and ethical aspects of medical quackery. xviii, 212 p. London: Heinemann, 1932.

Rzy-wb

SHRYOCK, Richard H. Quackery and sectarianism in American medicine. *Scalpel* (Alpha Epsilon Delta), 1949, 19: 91-6.

YOUNG, James H. American medical quackery in the age of the common man. *Miss.Val.Hist.Rev.*, 1961, 47: 579-93.

Rzy-we

THOMPSON, Charles John Samuel. The quacks of old London. xvi, 356 p., ill. London/New York: Brentano's, 1928.

Rzy-wg-cj

BUCHNER, Eberhard. Aerzte und Kurpfuscher. Kulturhistorisch interessante Dokumente aus alten deutschen Zeitungen. 329 p. München: Albert Langen, 1922.

RA FIRST AID; ACCIDENTS

for activities of Red Cross *see* QVyNTqy

DAVIS, Robert H. Deep diving and under-water rescue. 62 p., ill. London: Royal Society of Arts, 1934.
Historical summary.

EYSSELSTEIJN, G. van. Die Methoden der künstlichen Atmung und ihre Anwendung in historisch-kritischer Beleuchtung mit besonderer Berücksichtigung der Wiederbelebungsmethoden von Ertrunkenen und Erstickten. vi, 166 p. Berlin: J. Springer, 1912.

GORTER, R.A. Het einde van de tabaksrook-klisteer als middel tot het opwekken der levensgeesten van schijndoden. [The end of the tobacco smoke clyster as a means of resuscitating the apparently dead. (In Dutch)] *Reddingwezen*, 1950, 39: 1-10.

GORTER, R.A. De oudste middelen tot het opwekken der levensgeesten. [The oldest means for resuscitation. (In Dutch)] *Reddingwezen*, 1948, 37: 192-204, 229-68, 15 fig. [CB 74/392]

GORTER, R.A. De tabaksrook-klister voornamelijk als reanimator. [The tobacco-smoke clyster as a resuscitator. (In Dutch, with English summary at the end of each part)] 163 p., 66 fig., bibliogr. Amsterdam: Maatschappij tot Redding van Drenkelingen, 1953.

GORTER, R.A. Therapie en reanimatie door staatische electriciteit. [Therapeutics and reanimation, e.g., of drowned people, by means of static electricity. (In Dutch)] *Reddingwezen*, 1951, 40: 27-32, 41-51, ill. [CB 80/186]

RAu

MAYER, Moritz. Volksheilmittel und Unfallheilkunde. *Med. Klin.*, 1913, 9: 413 et seq., 469 et seq.

RAwk-qm

SNUIF, M.G. Uit de kinderjaren van de Maatschappij tot Redding van Drenkelingen. [From the early years of the Life Saving Association. (In Dutch)] *Bijdr.Gesch.Geneesk.*, 1934, 14: 70-7.

RAyHJ

BURROUGHS WELLCOME & CO. The romance of exploration and emergency first-aid from Stanley to Byrd. 160 p., 59 ill. New York/London: Burroughs Wellcome, 1934. [CB 46/595]
An illustrated handbook of an exhibit at the Century of Progress Fair at Chicago.

RB SURGERY

RBc general history

ALLAINES, Claude d'. Histoire de la chirurgie. 128 p. (Que sais-je?, 935) Paris: Presses Universitaires, 1961.
Reviewed by F. Moreau, *Rev.Syn.*, 1962, 83: 420-4.

BANKOFF, George Alexis. The story of surgery. 248 p., ill. London: Barker, 1947.

BERNHEIM, Bertram M. A surgeon's domain. 253 p. New York: Norton, 1947.
Reviewed by Henry E. Sigerist, *Bull.Hist.Med.*, 1947, 21: 858-60.

BISHOP, W.J. The early history of surgery. 192 p., ill. London: Robert Hale Ltd., 1960.
Reviewed by A. Renander, *Lychnos*, 1960-61, 381-2; in *Proc. Roy.Soc.Med.*, 1961, 54: 80; by L.M. Zimmerman, *Bull.Hist. Med.*, 1961, 35: 481.

BRUNN, Walter von. Geschichtliche Einführung in die Chirurgie. In: Kirschner, Martin; Nordmann, Otto; ed. Die Chirurgie. 2nd ed. Vol. 1, p. 1-32. Berlin: Urban u. Schwarzenberg, 1939.
Reviewed by L. Castaldi, *Riv.Stor.Sci.*, 1940, 31: 127.

BRUNN, Walter von. Kurze Geschichte der Chirurgie. iv, 339 p. Berlin: Jul. Springer, 1927.
Reviewed by Ernst Hirschfeld, *Deut.Lit.Zeitung*, 1928, 1128-30.

EDGAR, Irving I. Modern surgery and Lord Lister. *J.Hist.Med.* 1961, 16: 145-60.

GOTFREDSEN, E. De laudibus chirurgiae. [In Danish] *Nord. Med.*, 1959, 61: 579-89.

GRAHAM, Evarts A. Two centuries of surgery. In: Pennsylvania University. Studies in the history of science (Bicentennial Conference), p. 65-87. Philadelphia: University of Pennsylvania Press, 1941.

GRAHAM, Harvey, pseud. [FLACK, Isaac Harvey] Surgeons all. Foreword by Oliver St. John Gogarty. 426 p., front., 23 pl. London: Rich and Cowan, 1939.
American edition entitled The story of surgery (New York: Doubleday, Doran, 1939). [CB 59/489]

HURWITZ, Alfred; DEGENSHEIM, George A. Milestones in modern surgery. xvii, 520 p., ill. London: Cassell & Co., Ltd., 1958.
Reviewed by W.R. Bett, *Med.Hist.*, 1959, 3: 336-7; in *Proc. Roy.Soc.Med.*, 1959, 52: 220.

LECÈNE, Paul. L'évolution de la chirurgie. 354 p., 40 fig. Paris: Flammarion, 1923. [CB 14/556]

LEONARDO, Richard A. History of surgery. xvii, 504 p., ill. New York: Froben Press, 1943.
Reviewed by O. Temkin, *Bull.Hist.Med.*, 1944, 15: 430-2.

LERICHE, René. La chirurgie à l'ordre de la vie. Introduction par le Dr. Joachim Beer. 249 p., 1 fig. Paris/Aix les Bains: La Presse française et étrangère, 1944.
Reviewed by Erwin H. Ackerknecht, *Bull.Hist.Med.*, 1946, 20: 487.

RB

MANNINGER, Wilhelm. Kampf und Sieg der Chirurgie. 292 p., ill. Zürich: Rascher Verlag, 1942.
Reviewed by Wolfram Kock, *Lychnos*, 1944-45, 444-6; by O. Temkin, *Bull.Hist.Med.*, 1947, 21: 269-70.

POWER, D'Arcy. A short history of surgery. 91 p. London: Bale, Sons and Danielsson, 1933.

SCHLEGEL, J. Jakob. Experiment und Chirurgie. *Naturwiss. Rundsch.*, 1960, 13: 256-60.

THORWALD, Jürgen. The century of the surgeon. 416 p., 66 fig., bibliogr. London: Thames and Hudson; New York: Pantheon Books, 1957.
Reviewed by P. Huard, *Arch.Int.Hist.Sci.*, 1958, 11: 316-18. Translation of Das Jahrhundert der Chirurgen (Stuttgart: 1956). The 1961 (Frankfurt/Berlin) edition of this was reviewed by P. Boeynaems, *Periodiek*, 1962, 17: 25.

THORWALD, Jürgen. The triumph of surgery. Transl. by Richard and Clara Winston. ix, 454 p., ill. New York: Pantheon Books, Inc., 1959.
Reviewed by Mark M. Ravitch, *Bull.Hist.Med.*, 1960, 34: 480-1.
Translation of Das Weltreich des Chirurgen (2nd ed. Stuttgart: 1957) - sequel to The century of the surgeon (*see above*).

ZIMMERMAN, Leo M.; VEITH, Ilza. Great ideas in the history of surgery. xii, 587 p., ill., bibliogr. London: Baillière, Tindall, and Cox; Baltimore: Williams & Wilkins Company, 1961.
Reviewed by Zachary Cope, *Med.Hist.*, 1962, 6: 298-9; by Luigi Belloni, *Bull.Hist.Med.*, 1963, 37: 578-9.

RBcv

FAURE, J.L. Les films chirurgicaux. *Bull.Soc.Franç.Hist.Méd.*, 1937, 31: 245-8.

RBda

MONDOR, Henri. Anatomistes et chirurgiens. 530 p., ill. Paris: Fragance, 1949.

PAZZINI, Adalberto. Bio-bibliografía di storia della chirurgia. 525 p. Rome: Edizioni Cosmopolita, 1948.
Reviewed by Davide Giordano, *Riv.Stor.Sci.*, 1948, 39: 115-16; by José M. López Piñero, *Arch.Iberoamer.Hist.Med.*, 1959, 11: 341-2.

RBdaj

BROWN, Alfred. Old masterpieces in surgery, being a collection of thoughts and observations engendered by a perusal of some of the works of our forebears in surgery. xviii, 263 p. Omaha, Neb.: Privately printed, 1928.
Reviewed by Francis R. Packard, *Ann.Med.Hist.*, 1929, 1: 488.

POWER, D'Arcy. A mirror for surgeons; selected readings in surgery. xii, 230 p. Boston: Little, Brown, 1939
Reviewed in *Ann.Med.Hist.*, 1940, 2: 357.

RBm/u special aspects

RBmzN

MORRISON, Hyman. The borderland of medicine and surgery as conceived by Reginald Heber Fitz. *Bull.Hist.Med.*, 1948, 22: 680-4.

TEMKIN, Owsei. The role of surgery in the rise of modern medical thought. *Bull.Hist.Med.*, 1951, 25: 248-59.

WATSON-JONES, Reginald. Surgery is destined to the practice of medicine. 81 p. Edinburgh: E. & S. Livingstone, 1961.
Reviewed by H. Jackson Burrows, *Med.Hist.*, 1962, 6: 96-7.

RBmzNA

LEARMONTH, James. The contribution of surgery to preventive medicine. 55 p. (Heath Clark Lectures, 1949, delivered at the London School of Hygiene and Tropical Medicine) London/New York: Oxford University Press, 1951.
Reviewed by Samuel C. Harvey, *J.Hist.Med.*, 1952, 7: 431-3.

RBr

DA COSTA, John Chalmers. The trials and triumphs of the surgeon and other literary gems. Ed. by Frederick E. Keller. 401 p., front. Philadelphia: Dorrance, 1944.

ODY, François. Testament d'un chirurgien. 285 p. Genève: Editions du Cheval Ailé, 1948. [CB 77/344]

SMITH, Ernest V. The making of a surgeon. 350 p., ill. Fond du Lac, Wis.: Berndt, 1942.
Reviewed by O. Temkin, *Bull.Hist.Med.*, 1943, 13: 247-8.

THOREK, Max. A surgeon's world. An autobiography. 410 p. Philadelphia: Lippincott, 1943; 333 p. London: Robert Hale, 1949.
Reviewed by Erwin H. Ackerknecht, *Bull.Hist.Med.*, 1943, 15: 140-1.

RBrh

WEHRLI, G.A. The barber-surgeon's shop. *Ciba Symp.*(Summit, N.J.), 1939, 1: 270-4.

RBud

LEGRAND, N. Les saints chirurgiens. *France Méd.*, 1913, 2-5, 28-31.

RBw in different countries

RBwb North America

BEHREND, Moses. Surgery at Blockley, then and now. *Med.Life*, 1933, 40: 276-8.

CROWE, Samuel James. Halsted of Johns Hopkins - the man and his men. 247 p., ill. Columbia, Mo.: E.W. Stephens, 1957. [CB 83/272]
Reviewed by Zachary Cope, *Med.Hist.*, 1957, 1: 369-71.

IVY, R.H. A link with the past. ix, 148 p., bibliogr. Baltimore: Williams & Wilkins, 1962.
American surgery.

WHIPPLE, Allen O. The evolution of surgery in the United States. xii, 180 p., ill. Springfield, Ill.: Charles C. Thomas, Publisher, 1963.

RBwb-oq

DAMON, William A. A brief history of the John Rhea Barton chair of surgery [University of Pennsylvania]. *Trans.Coll. Physicians Phila.*, 1955, 23: 94-104, 1 fig.

RBwb-qd

DAVIS, Loyal. Fellowship of surgeons. A history of the American College of Surgeons. vi, 523 p. Springfield, Ill.: Charles C. Thomas; Oxford: Blackwell Scientific Publications, 1960.
Reviewed in *Proc.Roy.Soc.Med.*, 1960, 53: 893.

RBwc Latin America

DURAN, Carlos Martinez. Evolución de la cirugía en Guatemala. *Publ.Inst.Hist.Med.Univ.Buenos Aires*, 1940, 4: 101-41, portr.

RBwd Europe

LEONARDO, Richard A. American surgeon abroad. xv, 235 p., 20 pl. New York: Froben Press, 1943. [CB 62/61]
An account of the author's studies in Europe.

RBwe British Isles

ABRAHAM, J. Johnston. Surgeon's journey. The autobiography of J. Johnston Abraham. 441 p. London: William Heinemann, 1957.
Reviewed by Gustaf F. Lindskog, *J.Hist.Med.*, 1958, 13: 271-3.

PARKER, G. The early history of surgery in Great Britain. Its organization and development. x, 204 p., 8 pl. (Comrie's Medical History Manuals) London: Black, 1920. [CB 11/446]

RBwe-da

ROYAL COLLEGE OF SURGEONS OF ENGLAND. Plarr's Lives of the Fellows of the Royal College of Surgeons of England. Revised by Sir D'Arcy Power, with the assistance of W.G. Spencer and G.E. Gask. 2 vol. xxvi, 752 p.; 596 p. (Thelwall Thomas Memorial) Bristol: Wright, 1930. [CB 33/411]
Reviewed by W.R.L., *Nature*, 1930, 126: 513-14; by Francis R. Packard, *Ann.Med.Hist.*, 1931, 3: 120-1.

RBwe-dae

ROYAL COLLEGE OF SURGEONS OF ENGLAND. A catalogue of the portraits and other paintings, drawings and sculpture in the Royal College of Surgeons of England by William Lefanu. xii, 119 p., ill. Edinburgh/London: E. & S. Livingstone; Baltimore: Williams & Wilkins, 1960.
Reviewed by Donald O'Malley, *J.Hist.Med.*, 1960, 15: 437; by W.J. Bishop, *Med.Hist.*, 1960, 4: 365-6; by Edwin Clarke, *Bull.Hist.Med.*, 1960, 34: 578-9.

RBwe-oq

WIDDESS, J.D.H. An account of the schools of surgery, Royal College of Surgeons, Dublin, 1789-1948. 108 p., 16 ill. Edinburgh: Livingston, 1949.

RBwe-qd

COPE, Zachary. The Royal College of Surgeons of England: A history. xii, 360 p., ill. London: Anthony Blond, 1959.
Reviewed by F.N.L. Poynter, *Isis*, 1962, 53: 241-2: for other reviews see CB 86/469 and 87/557.

CRESWELL, Clarendon Hyde. The Royal College of Surgeons of Edinburgh. Historical notes from 1505 to 1905. xv, 315 p., pl. Edinburgh: Oliver and Boyd (for the College), 1926.
Reviewed by Francis R. Packard, *Ann.Med.Hist.*, 1926, 8: 448.

LEFANU, W.R. The Royal College of Surgeons of England and medical history. *Bull.Hist.Med.*, 1964, 38: 184-6.

ROYAL COLLEGE OF SURGEONS OF ENGLAND. A record of the years from 1901 to 1950. 80 p. London: The College, 1951.
Reviewed by Samuel C. Harvey, *J.Hist.Med.*, 1952, 7: 427-8.

RBwe-qe

PYBUS, F.C. The Company of Barber Surgeons and Tallow Chandlers of Newcastle-on-Tyne. *Proc.Roy.Soc.Med.*, 1929, 22: Hist.Sect., 297-300. [CB 28/489]

RBwe-r

PARKER, G. The history and powers of the barber surgeons in Great Britain. *Proc.17th Int.Congr.Med.* (London, 1913), sect. 23, p. 285-95. London: Oxford University Press; Hodder & Stoughton, 1914.
With Annals of Barber surgeons, from the XIIth century to now (p. 293-5).

POWER, D'Arcy. The evolution of the surgeon in London. Address delivered at the Abernethian Society. *St.Bartholomews Hosp.J.*, 1912, 19: 83-93.

TELEKY, Ludwig. Certifying surgeons - examining surgeons, a century of activity (Great Britain 1844-1944). *Bull.Hist. Med.*, 1944, 16: 382-8.

RBwe-rf

STEVENSON, Lloyd G. A note on the relation of military service to licensing in the history of British surgery. *Bull.Hist. Med.*, 1953, 27: 420-7.

RBwe-rw

MARTINDALE, Louisa. A woman surgeon. 253 p. London: Gollancz, 1951.
Autobiography of an English surgeon.

RBwf France

FORGUE, E. Sept siècles de chirurgie à Montpellier. *Rev. Int.Enseign.*, janvier 1922, 21-42.

FOURMESTRAUX, I. de. Histoire de la chirurgie française (1790-1920). Préface de J.L. Faure. 232 p. Paris: Masson, 1934.

FRUCHAUD, H. La tradition chirurgicale angevine. *Arch.Méd. Angers*, 1930, 34: 181-9; 1931, 35: 52-9.
Reviewed in *Bull.Soc.Franç.Hist.Méd.*, 1931, 25: 211.

HUARD, Pierre. La France et les progrès de la chirurgie. Conférence faite à l'Exposition médicale de Hanoi, décembre 1941. 16 p. [Hanoi: 194-]

RBwf-o

RAMBAUD, Pierre. L'enseignement de la chirurgie à Poitiers avant le XIXe siècle. *Janus*, 1916, 21: 182-95, 2 ill.

RBwf-qe

DAUPHIN, V. Les anciennes corporations d'Angers, les chirurgiens. *Mem.Soc.Agr.Sci.Arts Angers*, 1930, 5: 5-49.
Reviewed in *Bull.Soc.Franç.Hist.Med.*, 1932, 26: 72-3.

HUE, François. La communauté des chirurgiens de Rouen: chirurgiens, barbiers chirurgiens, collège de chirurgie, 1407-1791. 564 p., 7 pl., 1 fig. Rouen: Lestringant, 1913.

RBwf-qh

DARTIGUES, -. La mission sanitaire chirurgicale française du Caucase (1er juillet 1917-13 juillet 1918). *Bull.Soc. Franç.Hist.Méd.*, 1940, 34: 66-70.

RBwf-r

DORVEAUX, Paul. Les chirurgiens de Metz. *Compt.Rend.IIe Congr.Int.Hist.Méd.* (Paris, 1921), p. 436-51. Évreux: Imprimerie Ch. Hérissey, 1922.

RBwg/wh Central Europe

RBwg

KILLIAN, H.; KRÄMER, G. Meister der Chirurgie und die Chirurgenschulen im deutschen Raum: Deutschland, Oesterreich, Schweiz. viii, 232 p., ill. Stuttgart: Georg Thieme Verlag, 1951.
Reviewed by Ernest Wickersheimer, *Arch.Int.Hist.Sci.*, 1952, 5: 164-6; by Wolfram Kock, *Lychnos*, 1953, 435; by Th.H. Schlichting, *Centaurus*, 1955, 4: 93-4.

MAKOWSKY, Ludwig. Fünf Jahrhunderte Chirurgie in Tübingen. xii, 403 p., 21 pl. Stuttgart: Enke, 1949.

SCHELL, O. Zur Geschichte der Chirurgie am Niederrhein. *Arch.Gesch.Med.*, 1915, 8: 429-38.

RBwg-cj

BRÜNING, F. 100 Bände *Archiv für Klinische Chirurgie*. *Arch. Klin.Chirurg.*, 1913, 100: suppl., 1-124.

RBwg-oq

REDWITZ, Erich Freiherr von. Der Lehrstuhl für Chirurgie an der Rheinischen Friedrich-Wilhelms-Universität Bonn 1818-1953. Mit einer Ergänzung von Alfred Gütgemann. 115 p., 18 portr., fig. Bonn:[Nicht im Buchhandel] 1957.
Reviewed by E. Th. Nauck, *Sudhoffs Arch.*, 1957, 41: 381-2.

RBwg-qe

BRUNN, Walter von. Von den Gilden der Barbieren und Chirurgen in den Hansastädten. iv, 80 p. Leipzig: Barth, 1921.

WEHRLI, G.A. Die Wundärzte und Bader Zürichs als zünftige Organisation. Geschichte der Gesellschaft Zum Schwarzen Garten. 132 p., 105 fig. (Mitteilungen der Antiquarischen Gesellschaft in Zürich, 30: no. 8) Zürich: 1931.

RBwh

ZEMBRZUSKI, L. Abriss der Geschichte der Chirurgie in Polen. *Pol.Przegl.Chir.*, 1929, 8: 259-301.

RBwh-qe

SOKÓL, Stanislaw. Historia Gdańskiego cechu chirurgów, 1454-1820. [History of the corporation of surgeons of Danzig. (In Polish)] 270 p., 18 fig. Wrocław: Zakład Narodowy in Ossolińskich, Wydawn. Polskiej Akademie Nauk, 1957.
Summary in French and German.
Reviewed by S. Szpilczynski, *Arch.Int.Hist.Sci.*, 1959, 12: 200-1.

RBwi/wj Southern Europe

RBwi-oq

FORNI, G.C. La chirurgia nello studio di Bologna, delle origini a tutto il secolo XIX. 192 p., 65 ill. Bologna: Cappelli, 1948.
Reviewed by Arturo Castiglioni, *Riv.Stor.Sci.*, 1949, 40: 149.

RBwi-r

GAROFALO, Fausto. I barbieri-chirurghi a Roma. 31 p. (Rome. Università. Istituto di Storia della Medicina. Studi e Ricerche Storico-Mediche) Rome: 1949.

RBwj

MONTEIRO, Hernâni. Origens da cirurgia portuense. (I Centenario da Régia Escola de Cirurgia do Pôrto, 1825-1925). 371 p., 33 fig. Porto: Araújo & Sobrinho, 1926. [CB 21/598]
Elaborate history of Portuguese surgery.

RBwj-oq

CARDONER PLANAS, Antoine. Fondation et histoire du Collège Royal de Chirurgie de Barcelone. *Act.IIIe Congr.Int.Hist. Sci.*(Portugal, 1934), p. 227-43. Lisbon: 1936.

CARVALHO, Augusto da Silva. A régia escola de cirurgia de Lisboa. 288 p., portr. Lisboa: Anuario Comercial, 1926. [CB 24/564]

RBwk Low Countries

HUSTIN, A. Pratique, travaux et doctrines des chirurgiens belges depuis 1830. In: Fédération Médicale Belge. Cent ans de médecine en Belgique, 1830-1930, p. 1-83. (*Scalpel*, 1931, 84: special number) Bruxelles: J. Vromans, 1931.

SCHEVENSTEEN, A. van. Les chirurgiens de l'hôpital Sainte-Elisabeth à Anvers, jusqu'à la fin de l'Ancien Régime. 46 p. (*Mém.Acad.Méd.Belg.*, 23) Bruxelles: Imprimerie l'Avenir, 1927.

RBwk-of

HOEVEN, J. van der. Een en ander over de examens bij de chirurgijns-gilden en over het "vroedkundig examen". [Some notes on the examinations by surgeon-guilds and on the "midwifery examination". (In Dutch)] *Bijdr.Gesch.Geneesk.*, 1937, 17: 121-6, 1 facs.

RBwk-qe

BIJL, W.F. Th. van der. Uit de geschiedenis der chirurgijnsgilden in Zeeland. [From the history of surgeons' guilds in Zeeland. (In Dutch)] *Bijdr.Gesch.Geneesk.*, 1933, 13: 110-28.

HOEVEN, J. van der. Het chirurgijns-gilde te Deventer. [The surgeons guild in Deventer. (In Dutch)] *Bijdr.Gesch.Geneesk.*, 1934, 14: 57-69.

LOON, L. van. Het Rotterdamsche chirurgijnsgilde "S. Cosmos et Damianus" van 1467-1798. *Bijdr.Gesch.Geneesk.*, 1939, 19: 61-8, 193-201, 7 fig.

METS, A. de. La caisse de prévoyance de l'ancienne corporation des chirurgiens-barbiers d'Anvers. *Ve Congr.Int. Hist.Méd.* (Genève, 1925), p. 122-7. Genève: Albert Kundig, 1926.

METS, A. de. Les catalogues de la corporation des chirurgiens-barbiers d'Anvers. *Ve Congr.Int.Hist.Méd.* (Genève, 1925), p. 175-9, 2 pl. Genève: Albert Kundig, 1926.

RBwk-vm

COHEN, D.E. De amsterdamsche joodsche chirurgijns. [The Jewish surgeons of Amsterdam. (In Dutch)] *Bijdr.Gesch. Geneesk.*, 1930, 10: 113-35, 4 ill.

RBwn Russia

OPPEL, V.A. [History of Russian surgery. (In Russian)] 409 p. Vologda: Government Press, 1923.

RBx surgical techniques and instruments

RBxb

PROSKAUER, Curt. Development and use of the rubber glove in surgery and gynecology. *J.Hist.Med.*, 1958, 13: 373-81.

RANDERS-PEHRSON, Justine. The surgeon's glove. 95 p., 12 ill., bibliogr. Springfield, Ill.: Charles C. Thomas, [1960].
Reviewed by Zachary Cope, *Med.Hist.*, 1961, 5: 301-2.

RBxd

BUISSERET, J.; HANQUET, M.; HONORÉ, D., *et al.* Hypothermie et chirurgie. Histoire du froid en médecine *Acta Chir. Belg.Suppl.*, 1964, 1: 119-25.

CATHELIN, F. La chirurgie simplifiée. *Rev.Mois*, 1913, 15: 662-76.

ELLIOTT, Isabelle M.; ELLIOTT, James Rawlings. A short history of surgical dressing. x, 118 p., 22 fig. London: Pharmaceutical Press, 1964.
Reviewed by Pierre Huard, *Arch.Int.Hist.Sci.*, 1964, 17: 365-6.

FEIJFER, F.M.G. de. De omhulling in de volksgeneeskunst. [Bandaging in popular medicine. (In Dutch)] *Bijdr.Gesch. Geneesk.*, 1922, 2: 13-23.

FRANCESCHINI, Pietro. Appunti per una storia della legatura delle arterie. *Riv.Stor.Sci.*, 1956, 47: 201-36.

GIORDANO, D. Prosopurgia. *Festschrift zum 80. Geburtstag Max Neuburgers*, p. 186-9. Wien: Maudrich, 1948.

HOLMES, William. The repair of nerves by suture. *J.Hist. Med.*, 1951, 6: 44-63.

KUNSTLER, Walter E. Aesthetic considerations in surgical operations from antiquity to recent times. *Bull.Hist.Med.*, 1942, 12: 27-69, 12 fig.

LEMELAND, Pierre. Ancienneté de l'utilisation de la corde à boyau comme fil de ligature. *Bull.Soc.Franç.Hist.Méd.*, 1922, 16: 373-80.

ROFFO, A.E. D'Arsonvalcirugía. Evolución histórica de la electrocirugía. *Rev.Argent.Hist.Med.*, 1942, 1: no. 3, 57-69.

RUCKER, M. Pierce. Silver sutures. *Bull.Hist.Med.*, 1950, 24: 190-2, 1 fig.

RBxe

REGNAULT, Jules. A propos de ceux qui s'opèrent eux mêmes (autotomie, mutilations spontanées et auto-chirurgie). *Bull.Acad.Var.*, 1912, 16 p.

RBxk surgical instruments

for instruments used in gastro-intestinal surgery *see* RCKxk; in urological surgery RCQxk; in gynaecology and obstetrics RCTxk; in dental surgery REXk

CATALANO, Fernando E. Evolución histórica de la sierra como instrumento de cirugía. *Rev.Argent.Hist.Med.*, 1943, 2: no. 2, 37-49, 19 fig.

GIRINDRANATH, Mukhopadhyaya. The surgical instruments of the Hindus with a comparative study of the surgical instruments of the Greek, Roman, Arab and modern European surgeons. 2 vol. xxxii, 444 p.; 11 p., 82 pl. Calcutta: Calcutta University, 1913-14. [CB 9/473]

KLAAUW, C.J. van der. Het eertijds verplichte instrumentarium van den heelmeester. [The instruments required by the surgeon in former days. (In Dutch)] (Mededeeling no. 48 uit het Nederlandsch Historisch Natuurwetenschappelijk Museum te Leiden) *Bijdr.Gesch.Geneesk.*, 1939, 19: 179-89.

ROYAL COLLEGE OF SURGEONS OF ENGLAND. Guide to the surgical instruments and objects in the historical series, with their history and development. By C.J.S. Thompson. With a foreword by the conservator, Sir Arthur Keith. iv, 92 p. (Museum, Royal College of Surgeons of England) London: Taylor and Francis, 1930.

TABANELLI, Mario. Lo strumentario chirurgico e la sua storia dalle epoche greca e romana al secolo decimosesto. 187 p., 127 tables. Forlì: Romagna Medica, 1958.
Reviewed by Pietro Franceschini, *Physis*, 1962, 4: 86-8.

THOMPSON, C.J.S. The history and evolution of surgical instruments. With a foreword by Chauncey D. Leake. 113 p., 115 fig. New York: Schuman's, 1942.

RBxk-tq

HOLLÄNDER, Eugen. Die Säge. Kunsthistorische medizinische Studie. *Proc.17th Int.Congr.Med.* (London, 1913), sect. 23, p. 137-42. London: Oxford University Press; Hodder & Stoughton, 1914.

RByN/Q surgical clinics; special fields

RByNWwg

REICHEN, Gwer. Die chirurgische Abteilung des Bürgerspitals Basel zur Zeit der Antiseptik. Ein Beitrag zur Geschichte der Basler chirurgischen Klinik. 107 p., bibliogr. (*Veröffentl.Schweiz.Ges.Gesch.Med.Naturwiss.*, 18) Aarau: Sauerländer, 1949. [CB 76/365]

RByNWwk

HELLINGA, G. Van "Verbanthuys" tot dubbele chirurgische cliniek. [From "Bandaging house" to the dual surgical clinic. (In Dutch)] *Bijdr.Gesch.Geneesk.*, 1939, 19: 221-8, 5 fig.

RByQF

ONUIGBO, Wilson I.B. Historical trends in cancer surgery. *Med.Hist.*, 1962, 6: 154-61.

RByQV

BRUNN, Walter von. Der Krieg als Lehrmeister der Chirurgie. *Münch.Med.Wochenschr.*, 1935, 5: no. 7, 243-6.

CABANÈS, Auguste. Chirurgiens et blessés à travers l'histoire. Des origines à la Croix-Rouge. 624 p., ill. Paris: Albin Michel, 1918.

SAUNDERS, R.L. de C.H. The gunner with the silver mask. *Ann. Med.Hist.*, 1941, 3: 283-7, 4 fig.

TALLOT, L. The early army surgeon. *Ciba Symp.* (Summit, N.J.), 1940, 1: 334-9, ill.

RByQVxb

WEHRLI, G.A. Equipment of the first army surgeons. *Ciba Symp.* (Summit, N.J.), 1940, 1: 340-3, ill.

RByQW

ACKERKNECHT, Erwin H. Naval surgery from 1500 to 1800. Naval surgery since 1800. The case of the sick and wounded sailor in the United States. The naval surgeon. *Ciba Symp.* (Summit, N.J.), 1943, 4: 1394-424, ill.

RByQZ

ANDEL, M.A. van. De chirurgijn in dienst der justitie. [Surgeons in the service of justice. (In Dutch)] *Bijdr.Gesch. Geneesk.*, 1932, 12: 90-4.

CARØE, Kristian. Bøddel og Kirurg. [Executioner and surgeon. (In Danish)] 61 p. (Medicinsk-historiske Smaaskrifter, 2) Kobenhavn: V. Tryde, 1912.

RBzh HAEMOSTASIS; WOUND HEALING

see also RY ANTISEPSIS

for haemostatics *see* RZyPA

BORDEN, W.C. A history of surgical hemostasis. *N.Y.Med.J.*, 1912, 96: 373-7, 430-4.

BOSCH ARANA, Guillermo. Historia de la hemostasia. *Publ. Cátedra Hist.Med.Univ.Buenos Aires*, 1940, 3: 181-93.

CHURCHILL, Edward D. Healing by first intention and with suppuration: studies in the history of wound healing. *J. Hist.Med.*, 1964, 19: 193-214.

COPE, Zachary. The treatment of wounds through the ages. *Med.Hist.*, 1958, 2: 163-74.

HARVEY, Samuel C. The history of hemostasis. *Ann.Med.Hist.*, 1929, 1: 127-54, 16 fig.

SAINTIN, Henri. Contribution à l'histoire de l'hémostase chirurgicale. Les origines de la tension des artères. 46 p. Paris: Legrand, 1922.
Reviewed by J. Avalon, *Bull.Soc.Franç.Hist.Méd.*, 1922, 16: 397.

WHIPPLE, Allen O. The story of wound healing and wound repair. xii, 135 p., ill. Springfield, Ill.: Charles C. Thomas, 1963.
Reviewed by Zachary Cope, *Proc.Roy.Soc.Med.*, 1963, 56: 861.

RBzp PLASTIC SURGERY

ALBEE, Fred H. A surgeon's fight to rebuild men. 349 p. New York: Dutton, 1943.
Reviewed by O. Temkin, *Bull.Hist.Med.*, 1943, 14: 121-2.

MALTZ, Maxwell. Evolution of plastic surgery. 368 p., 108 ill. New York: Froben Press, 1946.
Reviewed by Josiah Charles Trent, *Bull.Hist.Med.*, 1946, 20: 93-4.

ZOLTAN, J. [The development of plastic surgery since the time of Balassa to the present time. (In Hungarian)] *Orv.Hétil.*, 1964, 105: 385-90.

RBzp-wi

GRASSI, Giuseppe. Il contributo del pensiero italiano alla chirurgia riparatrice. *Riv.Stor.Sci.*, 1936, 27: 215-32.

RC REGIONAL SURGERY

COOPER, William A. The history of the radical mastectomy. *Ann.Med.Hist.*, 1941, 3: 36-54, 10 fig.

RCC SURGERY OF THE LOCOMOTOR SYSTEM; ORTHOPAEDIC SURGERY

ELIASON, E.L. A saga of fracture therapy. *Trans.Coll.Physicians Phila.*, 1943, 11: 65-76, 11 fig.

LOON, L. van. Historisch overzicht van de fractuurbehandeling der lange pijpbeenderen. [Historical survey of the treatment of fractures of the long bones. (In Dutch)] (Thesis) Wageningen: Zomer en Keuning, 1935.
Reviewed by D. Schoute, *Bijdr.Gesch.Geneesk.*, 1936, 16: 42.

MENCKE, Stephan. Zur Geschichte der Orthopädie. 160 p. München: Beckstein, 1930.

NEUSTAETTER, Otto. Bilderatlas zur Geschichte des Krüppelwesens und der Orthopädie. Mit einer Einleitung. 160 pl. München: Münchner Drucke, 1926.

ORR, H. Winnet. On the contributions of Hugh Owen Thomas of Liverpool, Sir Robert Jones of Liverpool and London, John Ridlon, M.D., of New York and Chicago, to modern orthopedic surgery. xiv, 253 p., 26 fig. Springfield, Ill.: Thomas, 1949.
Reviewed by John G. de C.M. Saunders, *Isis*, 1950, 41: 145-6.

STUCK, Walter G. Historic backgrounds of orthopedic surgery. *Ann.Med.Hist.*, 1935, 7: 36-48, 5 fig.

TORKOMIAN, Vahram H. Pages inédites de l'histoire de l'ostéoplastie et du choléra. *Compt.Rend.IIe Congr.Int.Hist.Méd.* (Paris, 1921), p. 491-6. Évreux: Imprimerie Ch. Herissey, 1922.

VALENTIN, Bruno. Geschichte der Orthopädie. xiv, 288 p., ill. Stuttgart: Thieme, 1961.
Reviewed by M. Michler, *Sudhoffs Arch.*, 1961, 45: 282-3; by Carl Hirsch, *Lychnos*, 1962, 501-2; by H. Buess, *Bull. Hist.Med.*, 1963, 37: 88-9.

RCCtq

EPSTEIN, Sigmund. Art, history and the crutch. *Ann.Med. Hist.*, 1937, 9: 304-13, 11 fig.

RCCwg

ERLACHER, Ph. Beiträge zur Geschichte der Orthopädie in Österreich. *Festschrift zum 80. Geburtstag Max Neuburgers*, p. 127-31. Wien: Maudrich, 1948.

RCCwg-qd

BADE, Peter. Die Geschichte der deutschen orthopädischen Gesellschaft. 344 p., ill. (Abhandlungen zur Geschichte der Medizin und der Naturwissenschaften, 30) Berlin: Ebering, 1939.

RCCxd

GUITARD, E.H. L'emplâtre. *Rev.Hist.Pharm.*, 1960, 48: 409-15.

VALENTIN, Bruno. Die Geschichte des Gipsverbandes. 50 p., 7 fig. (Beilageheft zur Zeitschrift für Orthopädie, vol. 87) Stuttgart: Enke, 1956.
Reviewed by Johannes Steudel, *Sudhoffs Arch.*, 1957, 41: 96.

RCCyQPztu

LITTLE, E. Muirhead. History of the recognition of tuberculosis as a factor in bone and joint surgery. *Proc.Roy.Soc. Med.*, 1932, 25: 627-38.

RCD NEUROSURGERY

BALLANCE, Charles A. A glimpse into the history of the surgery of the brain. iv, 110 p. (Thomas Vicary Lecture, Royal College of Surgeons, 1921) London: Macmillan, 1922.

FULTON, John F. Frontal lobotomy and affective behavior. 159 p. New York: Morton, 1951.
Reviewed by M.F.A. Montagu, *Isis*, 1952, 43: 89.

FULTON, John F. Functional localization in relation to frontal lobotomy. xii, 140 p., ill. New York: Oxford University Press, 1949.

GERLITT, John. The trepan. *Ciba Symp.*, 1939, 1: 194-6.

HORRAX, Gilbert. Neurosurgery: an historical sketch. xi, 135 p., ill. (American Lecture Series, Publication 117) Springfield, Ill.: Charles C. Thomas, 1952.
Reviewed by A. Earl Walker, *Bull.Hist.Med.*, 1953, 27: 84-5; by Ernest Sachs, *J.Hist.Med.*, 1953, 8: 103-4.

MONIZ, Egas. Zur Geschichte der präfrontalen Leukotomie. *Ciba Symp.*, 1955, 3: 98-101, 1 portr.

ROBINSON, Victor. Trepanation after Lister. *Ciba-Symp.* (Summit, N.J.), 1939, 1: 187-93.

ROGERS, Lambert. The history of craniotomy: an account of the methods which have been practiced and the instruments used for opening the human skull during life. *Ann.Med.Hist.*, 1930, 2: 495-514, 18 fig.

SACHS, Ernest. Fifty years of neuro-surgery, a personal story. 186 p., ill. New York: Vantage Press, 1958.
Reviewed by John F. Fulton, *J.Hist.Med.*, 1959, 14: 108-10.

SACHS, Ernest. The history and development of neurological surgery. 158 p., ill. New York: Paul B. Hoeber, 1952.
Reviewed by Samuel C. Harvey, *J.Hist.Med.*, 1953, 8: 230-1; by Henry R. Viets, *Bull.Hist.Med.*, 1954, 28: 83.

WAKEFIELD, E.G.; DELLINGER, Samuel C. Possible reasons for trephining the skull in the past. *Ciba Symp.*(Summit, N.J.), 1939, 1: 166-9.

WALKER, A. Earl, ed. A history of neurological surgery. xii, 583 p., 152 ill. Baltimore: Williams and Wilkins Co., 1951.
Reviewed by John F. Fulton, *J.Hist.Med.*, 1952, 7: 430-1.

WEHRLI, G.A. Trepanation in former centuries. *Ciba Symp.* (Summit, N.J.), 1939, 1: 178-86, fig.

RCDcp

LENGHEL, Alexandro. Zwei trepanierte Schädel aus dem siebenbürgischen Landesmuseum in Cluj-Klausenburg. *Arch.Gesch. Med.*, 1930, 23: 98-9, 2 fig.

RCDwb

SPURLING, R. Glen; WOODHALL, Barnes; ed. Surgery in World War II: neurosurgery. Vol. 2. xxvi, 705 p., ill. (Medical Department, United States Army) Washington, D.C.: Office of the Surgeon General Dept. of the Army, 1959.
Reviewed by Neal I. Aronson, *Bull.Hist.Med.*, 1961, 35: 285-6; by John R. Green, *J.Hist.Med.*, 1964, 19: 305-7.

STOOKEY, Bryon. Early neurosurgery in New York: its origin in neurology and general surgery. *Bull.Hist.Med.*, 1952, 26: 330-59.

RCF EYE SURGERY

CUMSTON, Charles Greene. The history of the treatment of the surgical affections of the lacrymal apparatus. *Ann. Med.Hist.*, 1921, 3: 368-73.

FEIGENBAUM, Aryeh. Cataract operation - its origin in antiquity and its spread from East to West. *Act.VIIe Congr. Int.Hist.Sci.* (Jerusalem, 1953), p. 298-301. Paris: Hermann, [n.d.].

FEIGENBAUM, Aryeh. Early history of cataract and the ancient operation for cataract. *Amer.J.Ophthalmol., ser. 3*, 1960, 49: 305-26.

HALBERTSMA, K.T.A. Honderd jaren scheelzienoperatie (1839-1939). [Hundred years of surgery to correct squinting. (In Dutch)] *Bijdr.Gesch.Geneesk.*, 1939, 19: 235-42, 1 pl.

HALBERTSMA, K.T.A. Uit de ontwikkelingsgeschiedenis van de staaroperatie. [From the history of the development of the cataract operation. (In Dutch)] *Bijdr.Gesch.Geneesk.*, 1937, 17: 25-35, 1 portr.

SACHS, Moriz. Zur Geschichte der Cataractoperation: von der Reklination zur Entfernung der Linse im geschlossenen Kapselsack. *Festschrift zum 80. Geburtstag Max Neuburgers*, p. 404-6. Wien: Maudrich, 1948.

RCFwb

UNITED STATES. ARMY MEDICAL DEPARTMENT. Surgery in World War II: ophthalmology and otolaryngology. Ed. by M. Elliott Randolph and Morton Canfield. xxiii, 605 p., ill. Washington: Office of the Surgeon-General, Department of the Army, 1957.
Reviewed by Roland I. Pritikin, *Bull.Hist.Med.*, 1958, 32: 384-5.

RCFwr

GAUDEBERT, Gabriel Louis. Notes sur l'histoire de l'opération de la cataracte en Orient. 79 p. (Thesis) Metz: Impr. L. Hellenbrand, 1937.
Reviewed by A. Terson, *Bull.Soc.Franç.Hist.Méd.*, 1935, 29: 171-3.

RCG LUNG SURGERY; CHEST SURGERY IN GENERAL

BOTTERO, A. Carlo Forlanini inventore del pneumotorace artificiale. 130 p. Milano: Hoepli, 1947.
Reviewed by A. Corsini, *Riv.Stor.Sci.*, 1948, 39: 106.

BOTTERO, Aldo. La chirurgia del polmone attraverso i tempi. 197 p., 43 fig. (Studi di Storia della Medicina, 1) Milano: Hoepli, 1945. [CB 71/129]

EBSTEIN, Erich. Die Idee des künstlichen Pneumothorax und der Lungenchirurgie. Historische Bemerkungen. *Arch.Gesch. Med.*, 1926, 18: 93-9.

EBSTEIN, Erich. Ueber die chirurgische Behandlung der Lungenkavernen. *Arch.Gesch.Med.*, 1928, 20: 180.

HERBSMAN, Horace. Early history of pulmonary surgery. *J.Hist. Med.*, 1958, 13: 329-48.

HOCHBERG, L.A. Thoracic surgery before the 20th century. 858 p. New York/Washington/Hollywood: Vantage Press, 1960.
Reviewed by L.M. Zimmerman, *Bull.Hist.Med.*, 1961, 35: 389-90.

LAVALLE, Carlos Robertson. Historia del tratamiento quirúrgico de la tuberculosis pulmonar. *Publ.Inst.Hist.Med.Univ. Buenos Aires*, 1940, 4: 143-70, portr.

MEADE, Richard H. A history of thoracic surgery. 933 p., ill. Oxford: Blackwell Publications; Springfield, Ill.: Charles C. Thomas, 1961.
Reviewed by Clement Price Thomas, *Med.Hist.*, 1962, 6: 196-7; by D. de Moulin, *Bull.Hist.Med.*, 1963, 37: 288-9.

NISSEN, Rudolph; WILSON, Roger H.L. Pages in the history of chest surgery. vii, 166 p. Springfield, Ill.: Charles C. Thomas, 1960.
Reviewed by Gustaf E. Lindskog, *J.Hist.Med.*, 1961, 16: 196-7; by Russell Brock, *Med.Hist.*, 1961, 5: 201-2; by L.M. Zimmerman, *Bull.Med.Hist.*, 1961, 35: 583-4.

UNITED STATES. ARMY MEDICAL DEPARTMENT. Surgery in World War II. Ed. by John Boyd Coates, Jr. and F.B. Berry. Vol. 1. Thoracic surgery. xxiv, 394 p., ill. Washington, D.C.: Office of the Surgeon General, 1963.
Reviewed by Thomas Holmes Sellors, *Med.Hist.*, 1964, 8: no. 1, 98; by Carl J. May, *J.Hist.Med.*, 1964, 19: 304-5.

RCGwc

AGUILAR, Hernan D. Historia del tratamiento quirúrgico de la tuberculosis pulmonar, en la República Argentina. *Publ. Inst.Hist.Med.Univ.Buenos Aires*, 1940, 4: 201-13.

RCJ SURGERY IN OTO-RHINO-LARYNGOLOGY

BORMAN, J.B.; DAVIDSON, J.T. [The attitude to tracheotomy along the past centuries. (In Hebrew, with English summary)] *Koroth*, 1963, 2: 162-8.

CLERF, Louis H. Historical aspects of foreign bodies in the air and food passages. *Trans.Coll.Physicians Phila.*, 1952, 20: 9-16.

CLERF, Louis H. Historical notes on foreign bodies in the air passages. *Ann.Med.Hist.*, 1936, 8: 547-52.

COLLET, F.J. Les premières trachéotomies. *Ann.Otolaryngol.*, 1945, 12: 365-70.
Since antiquity.

GUDGER, E.W. Live fishes impacted in the pharynx of man. *Arch.Pathol.Lab.Med.*, Sept. 1926, 2: 355-75; Sept. 1927, 4: 346-55.

GUDGER, E.W. More live fishes impacted in the throats of men. *Amer.J.Surg.*, 1933, 22: 573-5.

GUTHRIE, Douglas. Early records of tracheotomy. *Bull.Hist. Med.*, 1944, 15: 59-64.
Includes George Martine's account of "bronchotomy" performed in 1730.

KASSEL, Karl. Die Anfänge der Nasenchirurgie. *Arch.Laryngol. Rhinol.*, 1911, 25: 141-3.

LEGRAND, Michel. Contribution à l'histoire de la trachéotomie. (Thèse) Rennes: 1962.
Reviewed by P. Huard, *Rev.Hist.Sci.*, 1964, 17: 86-7.

SONNENSCHEIN, Robert. A brief consideration of the history of the development of mastoidectomy. *Ann.Med.Hist.*, 1936, 8: 500-10.

RCJwb

UNITED STATES. ARMY MEDICAL DEPARTMENT. Surgery in World War II: ophthalmology and otolaryngology. Ed. by M. Elliott Randolph and Morton Canfield. xxiii, 605 p., ill. Washington, D.C.: Office of the Surgeon-General, Department of the Army, 1957.
Reviewed by Roland I. Pritikin, *Bull.Hist.Med.*, 1958, 32: 384-5.

RCK GASTRO-INTESTINAL SURGERY

ANDREWS, Edmund. A history of the development of the technique of herniotomy. *Ann.Med.Hist.*, 1935, 7: 451-66.

CASTIGLIONI, Arturo. Storia della chirurgia dell'ernia. 28 p. *Scritti di chirurgia erniaria, per commemorare il cinquantenario della operazione di Bassini.* Padova: R. Università di Padova, [n.d.].

CLERF, Louis H. *See* RCJ

GUDGER, E.W. *See* RCJ

KRUMBHAAR, E.B. The history of extirpation of the spleen. *N.Y.Med.J.*, Feb. 6, 1915, 101: 232-4.

LEONARDO, Richard A. A short history of gastric resection. *Festschrift zum 80. Geburtstag Max Neuburgers*, p. 297-301. Wien: Maudrich, 1948.

RCKce-bv

ALVAREZ, Walter C. Sixty years of vagotomy; a review of some 200 articles. *Gastroenterology*, 1948, 10: 413-41.

RCKda

COPE, V. Zachary. Pioneers in acute abdominal surgery. 148 p. Oxford University Press, 1939.
Fifteenth to nineteenth century.
Reviewed in *Ann.Med.Hist.*, 1940, 2: 541.

RCKxk

FRIEDENWALD, Julius. Note on the discovery and early use of the stomach tube. *Med.Life*, 1927, 34: 639-44.

FRIEDENWALD, Julius; MORRISON, Samuel. The history of the development of the stomach tube with some notes on the duodenal tube. *Bull.Inst.Hist.Med.*, 1936, 4: 425-54, 5 fig.

GARRISON, Fielding Hudson. A brief history of gastric intubation. *Boston Med.Surg.J.*, 1916, 174: 267-70. [CB 9/463]

MAJOR, Ralph H. History of the stomach tube. *Ann.Med.Hist.*, 1934, 6: 500-9, 8 fig.

RCKyQF

BRUNN, Walther von. Wem verdankt die Welt die Erfindung und Einführung der Operation des Magenkrebses? *Zentralbl.Chir.*, 1938, 65: 2130-4.

RCL HEART AND CARDIOVASCULAR SURGERY

BECK, Claude S. The operative story of the heart. *Ann.Med. Hist.*, 1926, 8: 224-33.

CASINI ROPA, E. La chirurgia nella cura della ipertensione arteriosa. (Notize storiche) *Policlinico Sez.Prat.*, 1964, 71: 766-75.

CLOWES, George H.A. The historical development of the surgical treatment of heart disease. *Bull.Hist.Med.*, 1960, 34: 29-51.

DEL GAUDIO, A.; BERARDI, P. Profilo storico della chirurgia conservatrice delle arterie. *Gazz.Int.Med.Chir.*, 1964, 69: 834-50, 1487-528, bibliogr.

LAVENNE, F.; TREMOUROUX, J. La chirurgie cardiaque. *Rev. Quest.Sci.*, 1961, 22: 391-414.

RCN SURGERY OF ENDOCRINE GLANDS

KLOSE, H. Chirurgie der Thymusdrüse. *Neue Deut.Chir.*, 1912, 3: 1-6.

RCQ UROLOGICAL SURGERY

CUMSTON, Charles Greene. A short account of the early history of suprapubic cystotomy. *Boston Med.Surg.J.*, 1912, 166: 516-25.

FAURE, Jean Louis. Guyon et la chirurgie urinaire. *Aesculape*, mars 1928, 18: 68-71.
Portraits of J. Civiale, J.C.F. Guyon and J. Albarran.

GILS, J.B.F. van. Het snijden van den kei. [Cutting for the stone. (In Dutch)] *Bijdr.Gesch.Geneesk.*, 1940, 20: 57-65, 4 pl.

GUDGER, E.W. On the alleged penetration of the urethra ... *See* QS

KAHN, Max. History of the lithotomy operation. *Med.Rec.*, 1912, 82: 652-8.

NEVERMANN, J.F. Der Steinschnitt, eine der ältesten Operationen der Chirurgie. *Henschel's Janus*, 1846, 1: 791-8; reprinted Leipzig: Alfred Lorentz, 1931.

NICAISE, Victor. Esquisse d'une histoire de la lithotritie. *Paris Méd.*, 1912, 6: 687-91.

SHELLEY, Harry S. Cutting for the stone. *J.Hist.Med.*, 1958, 13: 50-67.

SHELLEY, Harry S. Intravesical destruction of bladder stones. *J.Hist.Med.*, 1964, 19: 46-60.

STAVEREN, C. van. Aanteekeningen omtrent operatiën van den steen. [Notes on lithotomies. (In Dutch)] 127 p., ill. (Thesis) (Medische Bibliothek, 23) Assen: van Gorcum, 1934.
Reviewed by F.M.G. de Feyfer, *Bijdr.Gesch.Geneesk.*, 1934, 14: 237.

WEIJDE, A.J. van der. Iets over steensnijden en steensnijders. [Notes on lithotomies and those performing them. (In Dutch)] *Bijdr.Gesch.Geneesk.*, 1924, 4: 191-202.

YOUNG, Hugh Hampton. A surgeon's autobiography. xiii, 554 p. New York: Harcourt Brace, 1940. [CB 60/122]

RCQxk

ZEMAN, Emil. Vývoj nástrojů pro drcení kamenů močového měchýře. [The development of instruments for crushing calculi in the urinary bladder. (In Czech)] *Sb.Dějiny Přír. Věd Tech.*, 1963, 8: 201-38, ill., bibliogr. [CB 90/536]

RCQxk-wf

PASTEAU, Octave. Les instruments de chirurgie urinaire en France d'après les documents originaux du XVIe au XXe siècle. 28 p., 30 pl. Paris: Ch. Boulangé, 1914.

RCR SURGERY OF MALE SEX ORGANS

RCS CIRCUMCISION

ALMKVIST, Johan. Zur Geschichte der Circumcision. *Janus,* 1926, 30: 86-104, 152-71.

BRYK, Felix. Die Beschneidung bei Mann und Weib: ihre Geschichte, Psychologie und Ethnologie. x, 319 p. (Monographien zur Ethno-Psychologie, 1) Neubrandenburg: Feller, 1931.

MARCONI, Enzo. Origini e motivi della circoncisione rituale. *Riv.Stor.Sci.,* 1931, 22: 215-34.

SCHAPIRO, David. La péritomie. *Janus,* 1923, 27: 161-91, 241-54, 259-85; 1924, 28: 120-42, 192-8; 1925, 29: 71-97, 113-39; 1927, 31: 183-212, 227-63; 1928, 32: 155-67, 187-206, 231-42, 278-88, 315-20, 338-52, 378-82; 1930, 34: 241-52, 279-303, 326-34, 351-68; 1931, 35: 169-83, 207-16, 221-48.

RCSwq

LOIR, A. La circoncision en Tunisie. *Paris Méd.,* 8 March 1913, 625-33, 3 fig.

RCT SURGERY IN GYNAECOLOGY AND OBSTETRICS

for abortion *see* PSza

FARIA, Tasso Viera de. Nótula histórico-cronológica sôbre as histerectomias e miomectomias abdominais de 1800 a 1900. (Anais do I Congresso Brasileiro de História da Medicina ... 1st Part. Generalidades) *Rev.Brasil.Hist.Med.*. 1954, 5: 239-53.

RICCI, James V. The development of gynaecological surgery and instruments. ix, 594 p., ill. Philadelphia/Toronto· Blakiston Co., 1949.
Reviewed by Alan F. Guttmacher. *Bull.Hist.Med.,* 1953, 27: 588-9.

SPENCER, Herbert R. The history of ovariotomy. *Proc.Roy.Soc. Med.,* 1933-34, 27: 49-56. [CB 43/291]

RCTwk

FEYFER, F.M.G. de. Zur Geschichte des Schamfugenschnittes in Holland (bis 1840). *Janus,* 1914, 19: 312-27, 341-79.

RCTxd

BELLONI, Luigi. Historical notes on the inclined inverted or so-called Trendelenburg position. *J.Hist.Med.,* 1949, 4: 372-81, 10 fig.

IFF, Wilhelm. Beitrag zur Geschichte der Beckenhochlagerung. *Janus,* 1937, 41: 153-66, 9 fig.

RCTxk

BOERMA, N.J.A.F. Iets uit de oudste geschiedenis van de verloskundige tang. [Some notes on the earliest history of gynaecological forceps. (In Dutch)] *Bijdr.Gesch.Geneesk.,* 1937, 17: 12-20, 4 fig.

BRADTMÖLLER, Hans. Die Geschichte der geburtshilflichen Zangen und Hebel, dargestellt an Hand der Instrumentensammlung der Göttinger Universitäts-Frauenklinik. 50 p., 20 pl., fig. (Vorabeiten zur Geschichte der Göttinger Universität und Bibliothek, 20) Göttingen: Vandenhoeck & Ruprecht, 1935.

NIJHOFF, G.C. Tang, hefboom of speculum matricis? [Tongs, lever or mirror of the womb? (In Dutch)] *Bijdr.Gesch. Geneesk.,* 1929, 9: 137-49, 1 fig.

RCU CAESAREAN SECTION

ANDRIANAKOS, Tryphon K. Kaiserschnitt und Pyelotomie. Reform der Geburtshilfe. xii, 311 p. Leipzig: Barth, 1939. [CB 58/590]

HOFSCHLAEGER, Reinhard. Der Ursprung des Kaiserschnittes. *Sudhoffs Arch.,* 1952, 36: 284-99; 1953, 37: 77-92.

HULT, O.T. [Sur l'histoire des débuts de la Césarienne. (In Swedish, with French summary)] *Lychnos,* 1939, 243-61, 8 fig.

KULSDOM, M.E. Uit de geschiedenis van de keizersnede. [From the history of the Caesarean section. (In Dutch)] *Bijdr. Gesch.Geneesk.,* 1962, 42: 21-8.

PONZI, E. Una documentazione trascurata nella storia del taglio cesareo. *Riv.Stor.Sci.,* 1936, 27: 103-10, 3 fig.

QUECKE, K. Über die Anfänge des Kaiserschnittes. Der Kaiserschnitt an der Toten. Der Kaiserschnitt an der Lebenden. *Ciba Z.,* 1952, 11: 4706-25, fig.

RENDINA, G.M. Considerazione storiche sull'operazione cesarea. *Riv.Ostet.Ginec.Prat.,* 1964, 46: 497-523.

WEINDLER, F. Der Kaiserschnitt nach den ältesten Überlieferungen unter zugrundelegen von 18 Geburtsdarstellungen. *Janus,* 1915, 20: 1-40, 9 pl.

YOUNG, J.H. Caesarean section. The history and development of the operation from earliest times. 254, viii p. London: Lewis, 1944.
Reviewed by O. Temkin, *Bull.Hist.Med.,* 1945, 17: 528-9; by Emil Bovin, *Lychnos,* 1946-47, 473-9.

RCUce

RUCKER, M. Pierce; RUCKER, Edwin M. A librarian looks at Caesarean section. *Bull.Hist.Med.,* 1951, 25: 132-48, 1 fig.

RD ANAESTHESIA

for dental anaesthesia *see* REyRD

RDc general history

ANESTHESIA centennial number. *J.Hist.Med.,* 1946, 1: no. 4, 505-676. [CB 70/215]

ARONSON, Samuel. Geschichte der Lachgasnarkose. *Kyklos,* 1930, 3: 183-257.

BAUR, Marguerite Louise. Recherches sur l'histoire de l'anesthésie avant 1846. (Diss.) *Janus,* 1927, 31: 24-39, 63-90, 124-37, 170-82, 213-25, 264-70. [CB 24/559]

BUESS, H. Einführung und Verbreitung der Allgemeinnarkose. *Experientia,* 1946, 2: 504-6.

BUESS, H. Narkoseversuche zur Zeit des Aufschwungs der Chemie. *Experientia,* 1946, 2: 465-7.

BUESS, H. Zur Vorgeschichte der Narkose. *Experientia,* 1946, 2: 418-20.

DARMSTAEDTER, Ernst. Begründung und Ausbau der Cocain-Lokalanästhesie. *Schmerz Narkose Anaesth.,* 1938, 10: 196-204.

DARMSTAEDTER, Ernst. Spongia somnifera, ein Beitrag zur Geschichte der Anaesthesie. *Atti VIIIe Congr.Int.Stor.Med.* (Roma, 1930), 7 p. Pisa: V. Lischi & Figli, 1931.

DARMSTAEDTER, Ernst. Ein Ueberblick über Begründung und Ausbau der Cocain-Lokalanästhesie. *Schmerz Narkose Anaesthesie,* Dec. 1936, 9: 155-69.

DARMSTAEDTER, Ernst. Zur Geschichte der Narkose und Anästhesie. *Schmerz Narkose Anaesthesie,* June-July 1931, 4: 117-29.

ELLIS, E.S. Ancient anodynes; primitive anaesthesia and allied conditions. With foreword by T.K. Penniman. 187 p. London: Heinemann, 1946.
Reviewed by Thomas E. Keys, *Bull.Hist.Med.,* 1946, 20: 721.

GOTTLIEB, B.J. Das Originelle an der Infiltrationsanästhesie Carl Ludwig Schleichs. *Sudhoffs Arch.,* 1956, 40: 340-4.

HEIRONIMUS, T.W. History of nitrous oxide. *Clin.Anesth.,* 1964, 1: 1-19.

KEYS, Thomas Edward. The history of surgical anesthesia. Introd. by Chauncey D. Leake; concluding chapter on the future of anesthesia by Noel A. Gillespie; app. by John F. Fulton. New rev. and enl. ed. xxx, 193 p., ill. New York: Dover, 1963.
First published in 1945 and reviewed by J.B. de C.M. Saunders, with note by George Sarton, *Isis,* 1947, 37: 122-3.

LEAKE, Chauncey D. Discovery of the anesthetic properties of cocaine (1884). *Isis*, 1935, 23: 253-6.
Discovered by Dr. Carl Koller.

LEAKE, Chauncey D. The historical development of surgical anesthesia. *Sci.Mon.*, 1925, 20: 304-28, ill.
A summary followed by a chronology.

LEAKE, Chauncey D. Historical notes on the pharmacology of anesthesia. *J.Hist.Med.*, 1946, 1: 573-82.

LEAKE, Chauncey D. Letheon. The cadenced story of anesthesia. 128 p. Austin, Texas: University of Texas Press, 1947. [CB 72/278]

MIRANDA, Juan Miguel Márquez. Historia de la anestesia. *Publ.Cátedra Hist.Med.Univ.Buenos Aires*, 1938, 1: 181-98.

NEUBURGER, Max. Zur Zentenarfeier der Narkose. *Wiener Klin. Wochenschr.*, 1947, 59: 177 *et seq.*, 203 *et seq.* (20 p.) [CB 72/96]

PACKARD, Francis R. The conquest of surgical pain. 48 p., portr. (Jayne Memorial Lecture, 1940) [Lancaster, Pa.: American Philosophical Society, 1940].

RAPER, Howard Riley. Man against pain: the epic of anesthesia. x, 337 p., ill. New York: Prentice-Hall, 1945.
Reviewed by Gwynneth A. Gminder, *Bull.Hist.Med.*, 1945, 18: 564-5; by Morris C. Leikind, *J.Hist.Med.*, 1946, 1: 683-4.

ROBINSON, Victor. Victory over pain. A history of anesthesia. xiv, 338 p., 17 ill., 30 pl. New York: Henry Schuman 1946. [CB 70/272]

SANDRA, H. Van narcose in vroegere eeuwen. [On anaesthesia in earlier centuries. (In Dutch)] *Bijdr.Gesch.Geneesk.*, 1941, 20: 169-76.

SYKES, W. Stanley. Essays on the first hundred years of anaesthesia. 2 vol. 171 p., ill.; viii, 187 p., ill. Edinburgh: E. & S. Livingstone, 1960-61.
Reviewed by K. Bryn Thomas, *Med.Hist.*, 1960, 4: 364-5; 1962, 6: 98-9; vol. 1 reviewed by G. Liljestrand, *Lychnos*, 1960-61, 410-11; vol. 2 by Donald F. Proctor, *Bull.Hist. Med.*, 1963, 37: 94.

UNDERWOOD, E. Ashworth. Before and after Morton. A historical survey of anaesthesia et seq. for the Centenary Exhibition at the Wellcome Historical Medical Museum. p., 11 fig. London: British Medical Association, [1946].
Reprinted from the *Brit.Med.J.*, 1946, 2: 525

RDc-bv

FULTON, John F.; STANTON, Madeline E. The centennial of surgical anesthesia. An annotated catalogue. 102 p. New York: Schuman, 1946.
Reviewed by John C. Krantz, *Bull.Hist.Med.*, 1946, 20: 721.

KEYS, Thomas E. Selected references for the history of surgical anesthesia. *Anesthesia Analg.*, 1945, 24: 66-77, 100-12.

RDc-by

HISTORY of anesthesia. *Isis*, 1937, 26: 453.
A note on the collection given by Chauncey D. Leake to the Crummer Medical History Room of the University of California Medical School.

RDce

CLENDENING, Logan. Literature and material on anaesthesia in the Library of Medical History of the University of Kansas Medical Department, Kansas City, Kansas. *Bull.Med.Libr.Ass.*, 1945, 33: 124-38.

RDw in different countries

RDwc

CÓRDOBA, Salvador. Historia de la anestesia en Venezuela. *Rev.Soc.Venezolana Hist.Med.*, 1953, 1: 729-55.

RDwi

GAROFALO, Fausto. Contributi italiani diretti e indiretti nella storia della narcosi per inalazione. 24 p. Roma: 1946.
Reviewed by G. Verità, *Riv.Stor.Sci.*, 1947, 38: 72.

RDyPS in OBSTETRICS

DUFFY, John. Anglo-American reaction to obstetrical anesthesia. *Bull.Hist.Med.*, 1964, 38: 32-44.

RE DENTISTRY; DENTAL SURGERY

REc general history

ANDRÉ-BONNET, J.-Léonard. Histoire générale de la chirurgie dentaire. 252 p., ill. Lyon: Editions du Fleuve, 1955.
Reviewed by Ernest Wickersheimer, *Arch.Int.Hist.Sci.*, 1957, 10: 271-3.

ARTELT, Walter. Die Geschichte der Zahnheilkunde, ihre gegenwärtige Lage und ihre Aufgaben. *Deut.Zahn-Mund-Kieferheilk.*, 1937, 4: 72-7.

BISSELING, G.H. Uit de geschiedenis der tandheelkunde. [From the history of dentistry. (In Dutch)] *Bijdr.Gesch.Geneesk.*, 1921, 1: 341-61.

BREMNER, M.D.K. The story of dentistry, from the dawn of civilization to the present. 2nd ed. xiii, 332 p., ill. Brooklyn, N.Y.: Dental Items of Interest Publishing Co., 1946.
First published 1939.
Reviewed by Curt Proskauer, *J.Hist.Med.*, 1951, 6: 430-3.

LINDSAY, Lilian. A short history of dentistry. 88 p. London: Bale and Danielsson, 1933.

LUFKIN, Arthur Ward. A history of dentistry. 2nd ed., enl. rev. 367 p., 104 ill. Philadelphia: Lea & Febiger, 1948.
First published 1938.

MARYLAND STATE DENTAL ASSOCIATION. Proceedings. Dental centenary celebration. Baltimore-Maryland, March ... 1940. Ed. by G.M. Anderson. vii, 1061 p., ill. Baltimore: Waverly Press, 1940.
Section X devoted to dental history, p. 973-1048.

MURATORI, G. Evoluzione storica degli implanti alloplastici in stomatologia. *Arcisped.S.Anna Ferrara*, 1964, 17: 1335-49.

PICCA, P. Denti, dentisti e ciarlatani. *Riv.Osped.*, 1913, 3: 287-90, 4 fig.

PIPERNO, Arrigo. Descrizione storica del trattamento delle frature delle ossa mascellari. *Riv.Stor.Crit.Sci.*, 1912, 3: 93-8.

PRINZ, Hermann. Dental chronology. A record of the more important historic events in the evolution of dentistry. 189 p., 97 ill. Philadelphia: Lea & Febiger, 1945.
Reviewed by Curt Proskauer, *Bull.Hist.Med.*, 1947, 21: 635-6.

PROELL, Friedrich Wilhelm. Von den Uranfängen der Zahnbehandlung. *Proteus*, 1937, 2: 134-8.

PROSKAUER, Curt; WITT, Fritz H. Pictorial history of dentistry. 220 p., ill. Cologne: M. DuMont Schaurberg, 1962.
Reviewed by George B. Denton, *Bull.Hist.Med.*, 1963, 37: 488-9.

SMITH, Maurice. A short history of dentistry. 120 p. London: Allan Wingate, 1958.
Reviewed by F.E.R. de Maar, *Janus*, 1959, 48: 139-40; by H.L. Strömgren, *Lychnos*, 1959, 419-20.

SOGNNAES, Reidar F. Dentistry at its centennial crossroads. *Science*, 1959, 130: 1681-8.

SUDHOFF, Karl. Geschichte der Zahnkeilkunde. 2nd rev. enl. ed. vii, 222 p., 134 ill. Leipzig: J.A. Barth, 1926. [CB 21/599]
First published 1921.

WALLIS, C. Edward. Ancient and modern dentistry. *Sci.Progr.*, 1915, 9: 500-9, pl. Also in *Brit.Dent.J.*, 1915, 36: 274-85.

WEINBERGER, Bernhard Wolf. Ancient dentistry in the old and new world. *Ann.Med.Hist.*, 1934, 6: 264-79, 5 fig.

WEINBERGER, Bernhard Wolf. Did dentistry evolve from the barbers, blacksmiths or from medicine? *Bull.Hist.Med.*, 1940, 8: 965-1011, 9 fig.

WEINBERGER, Bernhard Wolf. Orthodontics, an historical review of its origin and evolution including an extensive bibliography of orthodontic literature up to the time of specialization. 2 vol. ill. St. Louis: Mosby, 1926.

REc-bu/cv bibliography; literature; sources

REc-bv

WEINBERGER, Bernhard Wolf. A survey of our dental bibliographies and dental histories. *Ber.9.Int.Zahnärztekongr. F.D.I.* (Vienna, 1936), p. 297-320. Wien/Berlin: Urban & Schwarzenberg, 1936-37.

REcb

DENTON, George B. The beginnings and growth of dental libraries. In: Maryland State Dental Association. Proceedings Dental Centenary Celebrations, p. 941-51, 9 fig. Baltimore: Waverly Press, 1940.

MARSHALL, Madelene. A history of dental libraries in the United States. With sketches of important dental libraries in Canada and foreign countries. *Bull.Med.Libr.Ass.*, 1937, 26: 86-99.

WEINBERGER, Bernhard Wolf. The dental library - its past and its present. *J.Amer.Dent.Ass.*, 1927, 14: 1183-9.

WEINBERGER, Bernhard Wolf. Historical collections of B.W. Weinberger in New York. (Medical History Collections in the United States and Canada, 4) *Bull.Hist.Med.*, 1941, 9: 334-6.

WEINBERGER, Bernhard Wolf. Orthodontic bibliotheca. *Dent. Cosmos*, 1921, 63: 1126-40.

WEINBERGER, Bernhard Wolf. The superb library of Bernhard W. Weinberger, D.D.S. on the history and folklore of dentistry. With a preface by Curt Proskauer. 50 p. (Catalogue, 112) New York: Old Hickory Bookshop, 1951-52.
691 items.

REce

GREVE, H. Christian. Aphorismen zur Kulturgeschichte der Zahnheilkunde und des zahnärztlichen Standes. 91 p., 22 fig. Leipzig: Thieme, 1930.

MARSHALL, Madelene. Some influential books in the history of dentistry. *Bull.Med.Libr.Ass.*, 1946, 34: 207-14.

WEINBERGER, Bernhard Wolf. Dental literature: its origin and development. *J.Dent.Res.*, 1924-26, 6: 305-88, 33 fig. [CB 27/580]

WEINBERGER, Bernhard Wolf. Dental literature; its relation to development of better dentistry. *Dent.Surv.*, September 1930, 6: no. 9, 66-70.

WEINBERGER, Bernhard Wolf. Early dental literature. *Bull. Med.Libr.Ass.*, 1938, 26: 222-47, bibliogr. [CB 56/406]

WEINBERGER, Bernhard Wolf. The preservation of dental literature in libraries. A function of the American dental library and museum association, appended to which is a bibliography of dental bibliographies and histories. *J.Amer.Dent. Ass.*, 1923, 10: 952-71.

REce-bv

BLACK, Arthur Davenport. Index of the periodical dental literature published in the English language, 1839-1936/8. 15 vol. Buffalo: Dental Index Bureau; Chicago: American Dental Association, 1921-39.
Volumes unnumbered and not issued in regular chronological sequence. Continued by: Index to dental literature.

CAMPBELL, J. Menzies. A dental bibliography, British and American, 1682-1880. With an index of authors. 63 p. London: Low, 1949.
Reviewed by Curt Proskauer, *J.Hist.Med.*, 1951, 6: 541.

Index to Dental Literature (in the English Language). 1939, vol. 1- Chicago: American Dental Association, 1943-
Continuation of: Black, Arthur Davenport. Index of the periodical dental literature.

NEW YORK ACADEMY OF MEDICINE. LIBRARY. Dental bibliography ... literature of dental science and art as found in the libraries of the New York Academy of Medicine and Bernhard Wolf Weinberger, compiled by B.W. Weinberger. 2nd ed. 2 pt. 1. A reference index. 183 p.; 2. A subject index. p. 189-262. New York: First District Dental Society, State of New York, 1929-32.
Historical preface.

STRÖMGREN, Hedvig Lidforss. Index of dental and adjacent topics in medical and surgical works before 1800. 255 p. (Library Research Monographs, 4, University Library, Copenhagen, Scientific and Medical Department) Copenhagen: Munksgaard, 1955. [CB 82/214]

REcm

BRUCK, Walther. Zahnärztliche Darstellungen aus alter Zeit. 71 p., 32 ill. Berlin: Berlinische Verlagsanstalt, 1921. [CB 12/635]

PROSKAUER, Curt. Iconographia Odontologica. 250 p., 186 ill. (Kulturgeschichte der Zahnheilkunde in Einzeldarstellungen) Berlin: Meusser, 1926. [CB 22/305]

REf/h historical studies

REf

CAMPBELL, J. Menzies. A hobby for a dentist. [History of dentistry] *Dent.Mag.*, Dec. 1962, 79: 201-8.

CAMPBELL, J. Menzies. What about dental history? *Edinb.Dent. Hosp.Gaz.*, April 1963, 4: 11-15.

DENTON, George B. A reading public for the history of dentistry. *J.Amer.Coll.Dent.*, 1953, 20: 170-9.

PROSKAUER, Curt. Zur Einführung. Kulturgeschichtliche Beiträge aus dem Forschungs-Institut für Geschichte der Zahnheilkunde des Reichsvervandes der Zahnärzte Deutschlands (E.V. Leiter Curt Proskauer). *Zahnärztl.Mitt.*, 1931, 22: 393-8.
Reviewed by W. Artelt, *Mitt.Gesch.Med.*, 1931, 30: 283.

WEINBERGER, Bernhard Wolf. The history of dentistry and dental bibliography as a subject of teaching and research, with a plea for the establishment of an index dentalis. *Dent.Cosmos*, 1917, 49: 315-20.

REhd

WEINBERGER, Bernhard Wolf. The cause of errors in dental history. A reply to articles by J. Ben Robinson and L. Parmly Brown relating to Horace H. Hayden and John Harris. [*Dent.Cosmos*, 1932, 74: 783-7 and *J.Amer.Dent.Ass.*, 1932, 19: 1409-19.] *Dent.Cosmos*, April 1933, 75: 334-47.

REhf

ARTELT, Walter. "Zahnheilkunde". Versuch einer historischen Analyse ihres Wesens. Aus dem Institut für Geschichte der Medizin und der Naturwissenschaften der Universität Berlin. *Zahnärztl.Mitt.*, 1933, 24: 205-12.

REo/r teaching; professional aspects

REoq

WEINBERGER, Bernhard Wolf. The educational evolution of the dental surgeon. Development and progress toward the formation of the first dental college. *Dent.Cosmos*, 1929, 71: 516-26, 565-75.

RErf

ROBINSON, J. Ben. The foundations of professional dentistry. In: Maryland State Dental Association. *Proceedings, Dental Centenary Celebration* (Baltimore, March 1940), p. 975-1048. Baltimore: 1940.

ROBINSON, J. Ben. Weinberger and his review of "The foundations of professional dentistry" [by J.B. Robinson]. *Bull. Hist.Med.*, 1942, 11: 356-67.

WEINBERGER, Bernhard Wolf. The origin of organized dentistry. With particular reference to the part played by the dental profession in New York. *Bull.Dent.Soc.State N.Y.*, 1937, 5: 51-90.

WEINBERGER, Bernhard Wolf. Robinson's "The foundations of professional dentistry". *Bull.Hist.Med.*, 1942, 11: 340-55. Review of Robinson's book. For reply to review by Weinberger see *ibid.*, 1942, 11: 356-7.

REt/v other special aspects

REtq

PROSKAUER, Curt. The dentist in caricature. *Ciba Symp.* (Summit, N.J.), 1944, 6: 1933-47, ill.

SCHULLIAN, Dorothy M. Piperno, Trilussa and dental caricature. *J.Hist.Med.*, 1954, 9: 273-80, 19 pl.

REu

BALDINGER, Max. Aberglaube und Volksmedizin in der Zahnheilkunde. vii, 70 p. Basel: Helbing u. Lichtenhahn, 1936.

BLÜTHNER, Gertrud. Beiträge und kritische Betrachtungen zur Volksmedizin in der Zahnheilkunde. 31 p. (Diss.) Leipzig: Edelmann, 1936.

KANNER, Leo. Folklore of the teeth. xii, 316 p., front., fig. New York: Macmillan, 1928.

KANNER, Leo. The teeth of gods, saints, and kings. Mythologic and historical contributions to dental folklore. *Med.Life*, 1931, 38: 506-18.

LINDSAY, Lilian. The sun, the toothdrawer and the saint. (The C.E. Wallis Memorial Lecture) *Proc.Roy.Soc.Med.*, 1933, 26: 33-44. [CB 40/414]

TOWNEND, B.R. The story of the tooth-worm. *Bull.Hist.Med.*, 1944, 15: 37-58, map.

REvm

SALAMON, Henrik. Dentistry in the ghetto. *Bull.Hist.Med.*, 1945, 18: 66-101.

REw in different countries

REwb North America

AMERICAN COUNCIL ON EDUCATION. COMMISSION ON THE SURVEY OF DENTISTRY IN THE UNITED STATES. The survey of dentistry: the final report. Byron S. Hollinshead, director. xxiv, 605 p. Washington, D.C.: 1961.

ANTHONY, L. Pierce. The influence of the South in the development of dentistry in America. *Dent.Cosmos*, 1931, 73: 359-69, 468-81.

CLARK, J. Stanley. Open wider, please. The story of dentistry in Oklahoma. xi, 391 p., 21 pl. Norman: University of Oklahoma Press, 1955.

JACKSON, Julian; JACKSON, Eleanor. Justifying the title, 'Dentists to the world'. Illinois's influence on the growth of the profession. *Bull.Hist.Dent.*, 1964, 12: 55-66.

WEINBERGER, Bernhard Wolf. An introduction to the history of dentistry in America. Washington's need for medical and dental care. Houdon's life mask versus his portraitures. 408 p., ill. St. Louis, Mo.: Mosby, 1948.
A considerable part of the book is devoted to a detailed description of George Washington's dental troubles.
Reviewed by George Urdang, *Isis*, 1949, 40: 299-301.

REwb-mzNwb

SCHWARTZ, L. Laszlo. The historical relations of American dentistry and medicine. *Bull.Hist.Med.*, 1954, 28: 542-9.

REwb-op

GURLEY, John E. The evolution of dental education, including a chronological history of the Dental Educational Council of America, the Dental Faculties Association of American Universities, reorganized Dental Educational Council of America; report of the historian. 276 p., ill. St. Louis: American College of Dentists, 1960.

REwb-oq

EDWARDS, Ralph W. A history of the Wisconsin Dental College. *Bull.Hist.Med.*, 1954, 28: 154-63, 1 pl.

WEINBERGER, Bernhard Wolf. The contributions of the Eastern Association of Graduates of the Angle School of Orthodontia to Orthodontics. A review and index of its Proceedings, 1909-1927. 48 p. New York: Eastern Association of Graduates of the Angle School of Orthodontia, 1927.

REwb-qd

McCLUGGAGE, Robert W. A history of the American Dental Association. A century of health service. 520 p., ill., bibliogr Chicago, Ill.: American Dental Association, 1959.
Reviewed by J. Menzies Campbell, *Bull.Hist.Med.*, 1960, 34: 287-8; by David D. van Tassel, *Amer.Hist.Rev.*, 1960, 66: 234.

WEINBERGER, Bernhard Wolf. Eighteen years of the American Society of Orthodontists. A review, with an index of its Transactions. 40 p. [Orange, N.J.] American Society of Orthodontists, 1921.

REwc Latin America

FIORINI, José María. Algunos aportes para la historia de la odontología en la Argentina. Fundación de la Escuela de Odontología de Buenos Aires. Biografía del Dr. Nicasio Etchepareborda. *Publ.Cátedra Hist.Med.Univ.Buenos Aires*, 1938, 1: 219-36.

REwc-rf

CARREA, Juan U. Los primeros odontólogos diplomados en la Argentina. *Publ.Cátedra Hist.Med.Univ.Buenos Aires*, 1938, 1: 155-80, 19 fig.

REwd Europe

REwe

LINDSAY, Lilian. Notes on the history of dentistry in England up to the beginning of the nineteenth century. *Ve Congr. Int.Hist.Méd.* (Genève, 1925), p. 153-9. Genève: Albert Kundig, 1926.

REwe-oq

DOUBLEDAY, F.N. The contributions of King's College, London, to the science of dentistry. *Proc.Roy.Soc.Med.*, 1949, 42: 783-90.

REwe-rf

COPE, V. Zachary. The making of the dental profession in Britain. *Proc.Roy.Soc.Med.*, 1964, 57: 919-26.

REwm-qd

STRÖMGREN, Hedvig Lidforss. Skandinavisk Tandlaegeforenings Historie 1866-1941. [History of the Society of Scandinavian Dentists 1866-1941. (In Danish)] 152 p., ill. København: Munksgaard, 1941.
Reviewed by Ernst Nachmanson, *Lychnos*, 1942, 431-3.

REwn-op

CROSS, W.G. Dental education in Russia before the revolution. *Brit.Dent.J.*, 1961, 110: 297-9.
Adapted from an article in Russian by D.A. Bassalik, *Stomatologija*, 1961, 40: 82-8.

REwt Far East

JIN, Pack Myeong. Dentistry in Korea (1893-1955). *J.Korean Acad.Hist.Dent.*, 1961.

REx techniques and instruments

REXd

CAMPBELL, J. Menzies. Transplanting teeth. *Dent.Practit.*, 1963, 13: 520-5.

COHEN, R.A. Methods and materials used for artificial teeth (C.E. Wallis Memorial Lecture) (Abridged) *Proc.Roy.Soc. Med.*, 1959, 52: 775-86.

HOLLENBACK, George M. A brief history of the cast restoration. *J.Southern Calif.State Dent.Ass.*, 1962, 30: 8-18.
Development of methods of casting gold from Cellini to modern dentistry.

REXk

CAMPBELL, J. Menzies. Forceps, pelicans and elevators. *Dent. Mag.*, March 1963, 1-7, ill.

CAMPBELL, J. Menzies. Keys, tokens and medals. *Dent.Mag.*, June 1963, 80: no. 2, 80-7.

COLYER, Frank. A note on the dental key. *Proc.Roy.Soc.Med.*, 1951, 44: Hist. Sect., 652-5, 3 fig.

DRIAK, Fritz. Historische Zahnzangen und ihre Verwendung. *Festschrift zum 80. Geburtstag Max Neuburgers*, p. 104-18, 23 fig. Wien: Maudrich, 1948.

HINTZE, Rudolf. Beiträge zur Geschichte der Zahnbürste und anderer Mittel zur Mund- und Zahnpflege. 61 p. (Diss.) Berlin: Meissner & Wermke, 1930.

SACHS, Hans. Der Zahnstocher und seine Geschichte. Eine kulturgeschichtliche kunstgewerbliche Studie. 52 p., ill. (Kulturgeschichte der Zahnheilkunde in Einzeldarsstellungen) Berlin: Meusser, 1913.

REXX museums

DE MARR, F.E.R. The Kalman Klein Collection. *Janus*, 1963, 50: (1), 66-70.
In 1960 the collection was officially accepted by Utrecht University; it comprises rare dental books, dental prints and engravings and old dental instruments.

REy related subjects

REyNWwb

FAGGART, Harold L. Dr. James E. Garretson and the first hospital of oral surgery. *Bull.Hist.Med.*, 1945, 17: 360-76, 11 fig.
Concerns the Philadelphia Dental College.

REyNWwe

COHEN, R.A. The History of the Birmingham Dental Hospital and Dental School, 1858-1958. 40 p., ill. Birmingham: Board of Governors of the United Birmingham Hospitals. 1958.
Reviewed in *Med.Hist.*, 1959, 3: 171-2.

REyOD

BRASHEAR, Alton D. The controversy concerning the innervation of the teeth. *J.Dent.Res.*, February 1937, 16: 5-17.

LINDSAY, Lilian. Dental anatomy from Aristotle to Leeuwenhoek. *Science, Medicine and History. Essays in honour of Charles Singer*, (2), p. 123-8. London: Oxford University Press, 1953.

REyOE

PINDBORG, Jens J. Studies in the history of dental histology. *J.Hist.Med.*, 1962, 17: 388-92.

REyPW

ALLARIA, Giuvanni Battista. Dentitio difficilis. Nota di storia della pediatria. 55 p. Torino: Bona, 1941.
Reviewed by R. Bèttica-Giovannini, *Riv.Stor.Sci.*, 1941, 32: 154-5.

REyQ

KAHN, Max. Ancient conceptions of dental caries. *Med.Life*, 1924, 31: 85-96.

REyQS

DOBELL, Clifford. The common flagellate of the human mouth, *Trichomonas tenax* (O.F.M.): its discovery and its nomenclature. *Parasitology*, 1939, 31: 138-46, 1 fig.

REyRD

LERICHE, E. Evolution historique de l'anesthésie en odontostomatologie. *Extrême Orient Méd.*, 1951, 1: 61-102.

WOLFRAM, S. Der Kampf gegen den Schmerz bei operativen Eingriffen vom Altertum bis zur Gegenwart mit besonderer Beziehung auf die Zahnheilkunde. 66 p. Leipzig: Barth, 1912.

RF THERAPEUTIC ARTS AND PRACTICE

BROCKBANK, William. Ancient therapeutic arts. 162 p., ill. (The Fitzpatrick Lectures delivered in 1950 and 1951 at the Royal College of Physicians) London: William Heinemann, 1954; Springfield, Ill.: Charles C. Thomas, 1955.
Reviewed by Johannes Steudel, *Sudhoffs Arch.*, 1956, 40: 188; by Genevieve Miller, *J.Hist.Med.*, 1959, 14: 255.

FRIEDENWALD, Julius; MORRISON, Samuel. The history of the enema with some notes on related procedures. *Bull.Hist.Med.*, 1940, 8: 68-114, 14 fig; 239-76, 7 fig.

GLOWACKI, Witold Wlodzimierz. L'introduction de l'ouate dans la thérapeutique. *Rev.Hist.Pharm.*, 1959, 47: 57-62.

LIEBERMAN, William. History of the enema. Notes and literary references to the clyster. *Ciba Symp.* (Summit, N.J.), 1944, 5: 1694-711, ill.

PEPPER, O.H. Perry. A note on the placebo. *Trans.Coll.Physicians Phila.*, 1945, 13: 81-2.

SHAPIRO, Arthur K. A historic and heuristic definition of the placebo. *Psychiatry*, 1964, 27: 52-8.

RFzb BLOODLETTING

ABEL, John J. Experimental and chemical studies of the blood with an appeal for more extended chemical training for the biological and medical investigator. 45 p., 5 fig. (Mellon Lecture) Pittsburgh: University of Pittsburgh, 1915.
The historical introduction deals with bloodletting, the use of leeches, etc.

ANDEL, M.A. van. De aderlating in theorie en practijk. [Bloodletting in theory and practice. (In Dutch)] *Bijdr. Gesch.Geneesk.*, 1932, 12: 181-201, 224-39, 4 fig.; 1933, 13: 61-7, 3 pl.

BOTTENBERG, Heinz. Die Blutegelbehandlung. Ein vielseitiges Verfahren der biologischen Medizin. 128 p., 6 fig. Stuttgart: Hippokrates-Verlag, 1935.

BRUNN, Walter von. Vom Aderlass. *Med.Welt*, 1935, 9: no. 33, 1201-3.

GARRISON, Fielding Hudson. The history of bloodletting. *N.Y. Med.J.*, 1913, 97: 432-7, 498-501.

ISTVAN, Ludwig; EIBEN, Otto. Ueber die heutige Form des Schröpfens und seine alte volkstümliche Anwendung. *NTM Z. Gesch.Naturwiss.Tech.Med.*, 1963, 1: no. 4, 91-103.

LANDSBERG, M. Ueber das Alterthum des Aderlasses. Ein Beitrag zur Geschichte der Medicin. *Henschel's Janus*, 1851, 1: 161-92; 1852, 2: 89-141; reprinted Leipzig: Alfred Lorentz, 1931.

PICCA, P. Il salasso periodico nei conventi. *Riv.Osped.*, 1913, 540-3.

ROCHÉ, Henri. La ventouse. *Paris Méd.*, 1912, 8: (2), partie paramédicale, 713-17.

ULUDAĞ, O. Sevki. La sangsue dans l'histoire de notre médecine. *Türk Tib Tarihi Arkivi*, 1939, 4: 61-3.

RFzb-ce

HOEPPLI, R.; TANG, C.C. Leeches in old Chinese and European medical literature. *Chin.Med.J.*, 1941, 59: 359-78.
Reviewed by P. Huard, *Arch.Int.Hist.Sci.*, 1957, 10: 62.

RFzb-nh

MERINGER, Rudolf. Schröpfkopf. Lateinisch: cucurbita ventosa; italienisch: ventoa; französisch: ventouse. *Wörter Sachen*, 1912, 4: 177-97.

RG AERO- AND HYDROTHERAPY

RGc general history

DAGOGNET, F. La cure d'air: essai sur l'histoire d'une idée en thérapeutique médicale. *Thalès*, 1959, 10: 75-96.

DEVRIENT, Wilhelm. Uberwärmungsbäder. Weg zur Wärmekultur. 4th ed. 215 p., front., ill. Berlin: Marcus & Weber, 1950. [CB 77/386]

GUITARD, E.-H. Le prestigieux passé des eaux minérales. Histoire du thermalisme et de l'hydrologie des origines à 1950. 324, xvi p., 70 fig. Paris: Société d'Histoire de la Pharmacie, 1951. [CB 81/283]
Reviewed by George Urdang, *Isis*, 1952, 43: 386.

MARTIN, Alfred. Historical sketch of balneology. *Med.Life*, 1927, 34: 256-300, ill., bibliogr.

SCHINDLER, W. Zur Geschichte der Hydro- und Balneotherapie. *Arch.Phys.Therap.*, 1964, 16: 327-35.

SIGERIST, Henry E. Health resorts. European spas through the centuries. Rise and fall of the American spa. Towards a renaissance of the American spa. *Ciba Symp.* (Summit, N.J.), 1946, 8: 302-36, ill.

STEWART, Charles E. History of hydrotherapy. *Med.Life*, 1926. 33: 101-10.

RGce-by

McCLELLAN, Walter S. Collections on the history of balneology in Saratoga Springs, N.Y. (Medical history collections in the United States and Canada, 8) *Bull.Hist.Med.*, 1946, 20: 571-82.

RGw in different countries

RGwb

HINSDALE, Guy. Doctors at the White Sulphur Springs. *Bull. Hist.Med.*, 1943, 13: 585-600, 4 fig.

OEFELE, Felix von. Geschichte der amerikanischen Balneologie bei den weissen Ansiedlern. *Mitt.Gesch.Med.*, 1914, 13: 460-5.

SIGERIST, Henry E. American spas in historical perspective. *Bull.Hist.Med.*, 1942, 11: 133-47.

VAN ARSDALL, C.A. A medical history of the Harrodsburg Springs. (The William Osler Medal Essay) *Bull.Hist.Med.*, 1949, 23: 387-418, 2 fig., bibliogr.

RGwc

SALES DE COGORNO, Natalia M. Historia de la terapéutica hidromineral en la República Argentina. *Publ.Cátedra Hist.Med. Univ.Buenos Aires*, 1940, 4: 215-44, ill.

RGwf

BAUDOUIN, Marcel. La fontaine thérapeutique du Boussegnoux, à Largeasse (D.S.). Origine traditionaliste de ses vertus médicales. *Bull.Soc.Franç.Hist.Méd.*, 1913, 12: 355-70.

BITTARD, A.L. Les "bonnes fontaines" en Limousin. *Aesculape*, 1913, 3: 144-7, 11 fig.

MOLINÉRY, Pierre M.J. Luchon: évolution de ses doctrines thermales à travers les âges. (Thesis) 262 p. Méracq, Basses Pyrénées: Impr. Couderq, 1938.
Reviewed by Marcel Fosseyeux, *Bull.Soc.Franç.Hist.Méd.* 1939, 57, 33.

MOLINÉRY, Raymond; MOLINÉRY, Pierre M.J. Luchon dans l'histoire de l'hydrologie. Réflexions et hypothèses sur l'action des eaux minérales suivies d'une étude sur le radiovaporarium sulfuré de Luchon, technique, clinique et résultats. 130 p., ill. Paris: Lépine, 1936.
Reviewed by Marcel Fosseyeux, *Bull.Soc.Franç.Hist.Méd.*, 1937, 31: 55.

RGwf-ph

MALLAT, A. L'Inspectorat des Eaux Minérales existe-t-il en France? *Compt.Rend.IIe Congr.Int.Hist.Méd.* (Paris, 1921), p. 517-21. Évreux: Imprimerie Ch. Hérissey, 1922.

RGwg

BENEKE, Rudolf. Vom Einfluss Hallischer Kliniker auf die Entwicklung der deutschen Balneologie. *Leopoldina*, 1929, 5: 110-23.

BUSER, Ernst Rolf. Zur Entwicklung des Badewesens im Unterengadin. Ein Beitrag zur Geschichte der Balneologie der Schweiz. 51 p. (*Basler Veröffentl.Gesch.Med.Biol.*, fasc. 4) Basel: Benno Schwabe, 1954.
Reviewed by George Rosen, *J.Hist.Med.*, 1955, 10: 448-9.

DÖRBECK, Franz. Die Anfänge der Hydrotherapie und Balneotherapie in Deutschland. *Arch.Gesch.Naturwiss.Tech.*, 1913, 6: 59-67.

RGwh

GÖRGÉNYI, Géza; PÉCZELI, Piroska; SÁGI, Karolyi. [Data on the history of Hévizfürdö. (In Hungarian with summaries in German and French)] *Országos Orv.Könyvtar Közleményei*, 1957, no. 5, 202-36, 2 fig. [CB 83/273]
Heviz is the largest thermal spa in Europe.

SIGERIST, Henry E. Wandlungen des Konstitutionsbegriffs. *Karlsbad.Ärztl.Vortr.*, 1929, 10: 97-108.
With special reference to balneology and balneotherapy at Karlsbad.

RGwi

NEL XXX anno di Direzione Sanitaria del Prof. D. Barduzzi delle R.R. Terme di S. Giuliano 1915. Siena: S. Bernardino, 1916.

PICCININI, P. Idrologia e crenoterapia (Le acque minerali d'Italia). viii, 608 p., 72 ill. Milano: Hoepli, 1924. [CB 18/629]

TRICOT-ROYER, J.J.G. Chianciano. Une station thermale étrusque de l'antiquité à nos jours. *Aesculape*, 1935, 25: 169-92.

RGwi-bv

RAVAGLIA, Giuseppe. Bibliografia idrologica Italiana. 553 p. Roma: Ente Nazionale Industrie Turistiche, 1928.

RGwj

CALDAS DA RAINHA. Eaux sulfureuses: centre de tourisme, d'art et d'histoire. 23 p., ill. Caldas da Rainha: Tipografia Caldense, 1934.

RGwk

HERMANIDES, C.H. Het begin der Thalassotherapie in Nederland. [The beginning of thalassotherapy in the Netherlands. (In Dutch)] *Bijdr.Gesch.Geneesk.*, 1935, 15: 161-7.

RGwm

NÄSSTRÖM, Gustaf. Det gamle Medevi. [Old Medevi. (In Swedish)] 286 p., 76 fig. Stockholm: Nils Bruzelius, 1928. [CB 24/436]

RGwp

ÜNVER, A. Süheyl; CEVAT, Ismail. Mineralbäder von Sivas. *Mitt. Gesch.Med.*, 1936, 35: 296-7; résumé of Turkish article in *Tib Dünyasi*, 1933, no. 7.

RGyNWwj

FERRARI, António de Melo; FERRARI, Manuel de Melo; CORREIA, Fernando da Silva. O hospital termal das Caldas da Rainha. A sua história as suas águas as suas curas. xv, 358 p., pl. Caldas da Rainha: 1930.

PAULO, Jorge de S. Historia da Rainha D. Leonor e da Fundação do hospital das Caldas. Escrito em 1656, editado em 1928. 209 p., ill. Lisbon: Tip. da Emprêsa Nacional de Publicidade, [n.d.]

RGyQ special applications

RGyQPzra

ROSHEM, Jules. Les enragés au bain. *Paris Méd.*, January 1913, 201-7.

RGyQPzsy

BOLOGA, Valeriu L. Schiţe balneo-istorice. 1. Balneoterapia sifilisului. [Historical sketches of balneology. 1. Baths in the treatment of syphilis. (In Rumanian)] *Clujul Med.*, 1928, 9: no. 4, 291-3.

SCHMITZ-CLEVIER, Egon. Die Balneotherapie der Syphilis im Aachener Thermenschrifttum (1546-1903). *Sudhoffs Arch.*, 1957, 41: 97-104.

RGyQPztu

CHALMERS, Stephen. The beloved physician, Edward Livingston Trudeau. xxiii, 74 p., ill. Boston: Houghton Mifflin, 1916. [CB 16/240]
Trudeau pioneered aerotherapy in the treatment of consumption.

RH LIGHT- AND HEAT THERAPY

BERNHARD, Oskar. Die historische Entwicklung der Lichttherapie. In: Handbuch der Lichttherapie, ed. by W. Hausmann and R. Volk, p. 3-12. Wien: Springer, 1927.

GLESY, J.U. Historical consideration of ultra-violet light *Med.Life,* 1926, 33: 132-7.

RIVIER, Gustave. La cure de soleil à travers les âges. *Presse Méd.,* 1913, 21: suppl., 177-80, 1 fig.

STURMER, J.W. The modern sun cult. *Annu.Rep.Smithsonian Inst. for 1930,* p. 191-206, 1 fig. Washington, D.C.: 1931.
One of a series of popular science lectures given at the Philadelphia College of Pharmacy and Science, 1929 season. Reprinted from the *Amer.J.Pharm.,* February 1930, vol. 102.

RHda

FREUND, Leopold. Vergessene Pioniere der Lichttherapie. *Festschrift zur Feier seines 60. Geburtstags Max Neuburger gewidmet,* p. 97-104. Wien: Verlag des Fest-Komitees, 1928.

RHwh

OSZAST, Z. [Development of Finsen therapy in Poland. (In Polish)] *Przegl.Dermatol.,* 1964, 51: 515-20.

RI ELECTRO- AND RADIOTHERAPY

for radiography *see* QE

BERG, Alexander. Zur Geschichte der Strahlentherapie. *Sudhoffs Arch.,* 1953, 37: 210-13.

BLEICH, Alan Ralph, ed. The story of X-rays from Roentgen to isotopes. 186 p., ill. New York: Dover Publications, 1961.
Reviewed by P. de Plaen, *Rev.Quest.Sci.,* 1962, 23: 275; by F.A. Tubbs, *Med.Hist.,* 1963, 7: 291.

COLWELL, Hector A. An essay on the history of electrotherapy and diagnosis. xv, 180 p. London: Heinemann, 1922.

FREUND, Leopold. Ein Beitrag zur Geschichte der Entstehung der Röntgentherapie. *Festschrift zum 80. Geburtstag Max Neuburgers,* p. 144-51. Wien: Maudrich, 1948.

GOODMAN, Herman. Story of electricity and a chronology of electricity and electrotherapeutics. With an introduction by Victor Robinson. 62 p., ill. New York: Medical Life Press, 1928.
First published in *Med.Life,* 1927, 34: 576-626, ill.

GRMEK, Mirko Drazen. La contribution de Tesla à la médecine. *Arch.Int.Hist.Sci.,* 1963, 16: 43-51.

HARMS, Ernest. The origin and early history of electrotherapy and electroshock. *Amer.J.Psychiat.,* 1955, 111: 933-4.

HOLZKNECHT, G. Abriss der historischen Entwicklung der wissenschaftlichen Anwendung der Röntgenstrahlen. *Festschrift zur Feier seines 60. Geburtstages Max Neuburger gewidmet,* p. 183-7. Wien: Verlag des Fest-Komitees, 1928.

JELLINEK, Stephan. Die Entdeckung der biologischen Fernwirkung der Elektrizität. Anlässlich d'Arsonvals 80. Geburtstage am 8. Juni 1931. *Wiener Klin.Wochenschr.,* 1931, 44: 1343-4.

JONES, H. Lewis. The history of medical electricity. *Proc. 17th Int.Congr.Med.* (London, 1913), Hist. Sect., 347-50. London: Oxford University Press and Hodder & Stoughton, 1914.

KELLAWAY, Peter. The part played by electric fish in the early history of bioelectricity and electrotherapy. *Bull. Hist.Med.,* 1946, 20: 112-37, 5 pl.

LAURENTIUS, Paul. Geschichte der Krankenbehandlung mittels Elektrizität. (Diss.) 95 p. Krefeld: Greven, 1936.

LICHT, Sidney. Therapeutic electricity and ultraviolet radiation. 373 p., fig., bibliogr. New Haven, Conn.: Licht, 1959.
Reviewed by Jean Torlais, *Rev.Hist.Sci.,* 1960, 13: 179-80.

LOZ, Albert de. Histoire de l'électricité médicale. *Scalpel,* 1962, 115: 542-56, 570-9.

MABILEAU, Jean F. Contribution à l'histoire de la réglementation des substances radioactives. *Rev.Hist.Pharm.,* 1959, 47: 1-7.

PIZON, Pierre. Les origines de la roentgenthérapie en France (1896-1904). *Presse Méd.,* 1953, 61: 282-4, 5 fig.

SCHMID, Alfred. Zur Geschichte der Elektrotherapie vom Altertum bis zum Beginn des 19. Jahrhunderts. *Festschrift für Jacques Brodbeck-Sandreuter zu seinem 60. Geburtstag,* p. 73-121, 24 fig. Basel: Schwabe, 1942.

RIwe

IREDELL, C.E. The early history of radium in London. *Proc. Roy.Soc.Med.,* 1951, 44: Hist. Sect., 207-9.

RIwf

PIZON, Pierre. Les origines de la roentgenthérapie en France (1896-1904). *Presse Méd.,* 1953, 61: 282-4, 5 fig.

RIyOR

MEYERHOF, Max. Radiological treatment of tumours of the sellar region. *Bull.Ophthalmol.Soc.Egypt,* 1938, 31: 56-73.

RJ PHYSIOTHERAPY; MECHANOTHERAPY; PROSTHETICS

COULTER, John S. Physical therapy. xvii, 142 p., 15 ill. (Clio Medica, 7) New York: Hoeber, 1932. [CB 38/610]

CABANÈS, Auguste. L'histoire de la vibrothérapie. *Bull.Gén. Thérap.,* 1912, 164: 241-54.

CYRIAX, Edgar F. On some points as regards priority in mechano-therapeutics. *Janus,* 1921, 25: 230-7; 1925, 29: 1-6; 1933, 37: 271-4.

CYRIAX, Richard J. A short history of mechano-therapeutics in Europe until the time of Ling. *Janus,* 1914, 19: 178-240. [CB 11/445]

EBSTEIN, Erich. Ueber das Schaukeln als Heilfaktor. *Klin. Therap.Wochenschr.,* 1912, no. 39, 7 p.

NORSTRÖM, Gustave. Aperçu historique sur le massage. 16 p. Paris: Baillière, 1912.

PANEBAKER, George. Historical notes on physiotherapy. *Med. Life,* 1926, 33: 111-19.

PUTTI, Vittorio. Historic artificial limbs. xii, 64 p.. 11 ill. New York: Hoeber, 1930. [CB 33/400]

ROBINSON, Victor. Historical aspects of physiotherapy. *Med. Life,* 1930, 37: 533-51, 11 ill.

RJwg

KLARE, V. Die Entwicklung der physikalischen Medizin im Rahmen der Wiener medizinischen Schule. *Festschrift zum 80. Geburtstag Max Neuburgers,* p. 254-7. Wien: Maudrich, 1948.

RJwi-oq

CENTENARIO dell' Accademia Medico-Fisica Fiorentina (1824-1924). *Sperimentale,* 1924, 78: 179-406.

RJyON

GOTFREDSEN, Edv. Homo centrifugus. [In Danish, with English summary.] *Med.Forum,* 1956, 9: 22-5. [CB 83/206]

RJyOX

PRICE, J.L. The evolution of breathing machines. *Med.Hist.,* 1962, 6: 67-72.

RJyOZ

RAINAL, Jules; RAINAL, Léon. Bandages herniaires et prothèse du XVIIe à la fin du XIXe siècle. Collection classée et cataloguée sous la direction des prof. Berger et Hartmann. 15 p., ill. Paris: A. Maréchal, 1912.

RJzo OSTEOPATHY

COLE, Wilbur V. Osteopathic research. *J.Amer.Osteopath.Ass.,* 1964, 63: 821-2.

see also STILL, Andrew Taylor, 2: 509

RK OCCUPATIONAL AND PSYCHOTHERAPIES

BRAUCHLE, Alfred. Hypnose und Autosuggestion. 78 p. Leipzig: Reclam, 1929.

CABANÈS, Auguste. La thérapeutique des couleurs. *Bull.Gén. Thérap.*, 1912, 164: 334-49.

COHEN, Jacques J. Psychotherapy. viii, 149 p. London: Bale and Danielsson, 1936.
A criticism of current theories of psychotherapy, especially of Couéism, and an advocacy of psychophonism, a negation of the instinct of self-preservation.

JANET, Pierre. Principles of psychotherapy. viii, 322 p. New York: Macmillan, 1924; London: Allen & Unwin, 1925.
Translation of: La médecine psychologique. Paris: Flammarion, 1923.

JANET, Pierre. Psychological healing: a historical and clinical study. Transl. from the French by Eden and Cedar Paul. 2 vol. 698 p.; 566 p. London: Allen and Unwin, 1925.
Translation of: Les médicamentations psychologiques (Paris: Alcan, 1919) [CB 11/446]

KOGERER, H. Zur Geschichte der Suggestionstherapie. *Festschrift zum 80. Geburtstag Max Neuburgers*, p. 258-63. Wien: Maudrich, 1948.

KRANEFELDT, Wolfgang Müller. Therapeutische Psychologie, Freud-Adler-Jung. Mit einer Einführung von C.G. Jung. 2nd ed. 152 p. (Sammlung Göschen, 1034) Berlin: de Gruyter, 1950. [CB 77/380]

MEIER, Joseph I. Origin and development of group psychotherapy. A historical survey, 1930-1945. 44 p. (Psychodrama Monographs, 17) New York: Beacon House, 1946.
Reviewed by Raymond de Saussure, *J.Hist.Med.*, 1948, 3: 452.

PHILIPON, Emmanuel. La médication mentale dans la doctrine "Christian Science". (Thèse) 51 p. Paris: Ollier Henry, 1913.

RIESE, Walter. An outline of a history of ideas in psychotherapy. *Bull.Hist.Med.*, 1951, 25: 442-56.

RIVERS, William Halse Rivers. Mind and medicine. 2nd ed. 23 p. Manchester: University Press, 1920.
First publ. in *Bull.John Rylands Libr.*, 1919, vol. 5.

STEMPLINGER, Eduard. Sympathieglaube und Sympathiekuren in Altertum und Neuzeit. 91 p. München: Otto Gmelin, 1919.

STOCKER, A. Le traitement moral des nerveux. 221 p. (Bibliothèque des Archives de Philosophie, 2e section, Logique et Psychologie, 1) Paris: Beauchesne, 1948. [CB 75/95]

THORN, Josephine van Slyck. An unfinished manuscript. Notes for a book on the Vittoz method. 140 p. Lancaster, Pa.: Lancaster Press (privately printed), 1937. [CB 56/361]

WALKER, Nigel, A short history of psychotherapy in theory and practice. xii, 185 p., ill. London: Routledge and Kegan Paul, 1957.
Reviewed by Nils Antoni, *Lychnos*, 1957-58, 464-5.

RKtt

POLTER, Karl-Heinz. Musik als Heilmittel. (Thesis) iv, 59 p. Düsseldorf: Nolte, 1934.

RKyNWwf

SCHNECK, Jerome M. The school of the Hospital de la Charité in the history of hypnosis. *J.Hist.Med.*, 1952, 7: 271-9, 3 pl. [CB 80/197]

RL DIET THERAPY

RLyPIzd

MAGNUS-LEVY, Adolf. Diabetikerdiäten der Vorinsulinära. *Essays in the History of Medicine presented to Prof. Arturo Castiglioni*, p. 161-9. Baltimore: Johns Hopkins Press, 1944.

RLyRE

RUTTER, Richard Remmel. Diet analysis applied to periodontal therapy - an historical resumé. *Acad.Rev.Calif.Acad.Periodontol.*, 1959, 23-6.

RM PHARMACY; MATERIA MEDICA; PHARMACOTHERAPY

see also QX TOXICOLOGY
QO IMMUNOLOGY

RMc general history

ACKERKNECHT, Erwin H. Wendepunkte in der Geschichte der Pharmakotherapie. *Schweiz.Apoth.Zeitung*, 1957, 95: 751-7, portr.

ANDEL, M.A. van. Klassieke wondermiddelen. [Classical wonder drugs. (In Dutch)] 262 p., 40 fig. Gorinchem: Noorduyn, 1928.
First published in *Bijdr.Gesch.Geneesk.*, 1921, 1: 405-19; 1922, 2: 90-4, 231-6; 1923, 3: 105-15, 141; 1924, 4: 97-103, 202-9; 1925, 5: 137-48; 1926, 6: 105-12; 1927, 7: 161-76, 315-22; 1928, 8: 197-206, 207-15; 1928, 8: 285-94.

BENDER, George A. Great moments in pharmacy: the stories and paintings in the series. A history of pharmacy in pictures, by Parke, Davis & Company. Stories by George A. Bender, paintings by Robert A. Thom. 238 p., ill., bibliogr. Detroit: Northwood Press, 1966.
The first six plates appeared in 1951 [CB 78/200].

BOUSSEL, Patrice. Histoire illustrée de la pharmacie. 193 p., ill. Paris: Guy le Prat, 1949.
Reviewed by F. Guerra, *Centaurus*, 1950, 1: 188; by George Urdang, *J.Hist.Med.*, 1951, 6: 274-7.

CABANÈS, Auguste. Comment se soignaient nos pères. Remèdes d'autrefois. viii, 514 p. Deuxième série, 393 p. Paris: A. Maloine, 1910, 1912.

CONCI, G. Pagine di storia della farmacia. 351 p. Milan: Vittoria, 1934.
Reviewed by A. Castiglioni, *Riv.Stor.Sci.*, 1935, 17: 43.

EMMANOUIL, Em. J. [History of pharmacy. (In Greek)] 784 p. Athens: Pyrsos, 1948.
Reviewed by Chr. Papanastassiou, *Arch.Int.Hist.Sci.*, 1949, 2: 536-8.

FINK-FINOWICKI, Czeslaw. Zarys historii i propedeutyki farmacji. [An outline of the history and the basic principles of pharmacy. (In Polish)] 150 p., ill. Warsaw: Państwowe Zaklady Wydawnictw Lekarskich, 1959.
Reviewed by C.D., *Kwart.Hist.Nauk.Tech.*, 1961, 6: 154.

FOLCH Y ANDREU, Rafael. Elementos de historia de la farmacía. 2nd ed. 622 p. Madrid: Izquierdo, 1927.
Reviewed by Aldo Mieli, *Archeion*, 1933, 15: 120.
First publ. 1923.

FULLER, Henry Corbin. The story of drugs. A popular exposition of their origin, preparation, and commercial importance. 358 p., ill. New York: Century Co., 1922.

GADDUM, J.H. Medicines ancient and modern. *Mem.Manchester Lit.Phil.Soc.*, 1957-58, 99: 60-75.

GILG, Ernst; SCHÜRHOFF, P.N. Aus dem Reiche der Drogen. Geschichtliche, kulturgeschichtliche und botanische Betrachtungen über wichtigere Drogen. 272 p., ill. Dresden: Schwarzeck, 1926.

HAAS, Hans. Spiegel der Arznei, Ursprung, Geschichte und Idee der Heilmittelkunde. ii, 256 p. Berlin: Springer, 1956.
Reviewed by Ernest Wickersheimer, *Arch.Int.Hist.Sci.*, 1957, 10: 60-1.

HEFTER, A. Die Auffindung von Arzneimitteln. Festrede gehalten am Stiftungstage der Kaiser-Wilhelms-Akademie, 2 Dezember 1913. 35 p. Berlin: 1914.

IHDE, Aaron John. History of pharmacy. 1. Paracelsus - genius or charlatan? 2. Serendipity (quinine to 606). Lecture. 3. Molds, sulfa, and science. In: The Sixth Annual Lecture Series in the Pharmaceutical Sciences 1962-1963, 36 p. Austin: University of Texas College of Pharmacy, [1963?].

KREMERS, Edward; URDANG, George. History of pharmacy. 3rd ed. rev. by Glenn Sonnedecker. xii, 464 p., ill. Philadelphia: Lippincott, 1963.
First publ. 1940.
Reviewed by Morris C. Leikind, *Isis*, 1941, 33: 307-8.
For other reviews *see* CB 62/88, CB 80/141 and CB 90/537.

LANGDON-BROWN, Walter. From witchcraft to chemotherapy. 60 p. Cambridge University Press, 1941. [CB 62/88]

LAWALL, Charles H. Four thousand years of pharmacy. 665 p., ill. Philadelphia/London: Lippincott, 1927. [CB 22/309]

LECLERC, Henri. En marge du Codex. Notes d'histoire thérapeutique. xii, 188 p. Paris: Masson, 1924. [CB 16/322]

MALACRIDA, Gaetano. Cenni di storia dell' arte di curare e della farmacia. *Pensiero Med.*, 1912, 2: ?p.

MATHISON, Richard. The eternal search. The story of man and his drugs. 381 p., bibliogr. New York: Putnam's; Toronto: Longmans, Green and Co., 1958.
Reviewed by Glenn Sonnedecker, *Isis*, 1960, 51: 226-7.

REUTTER DE ROSEMONT, Louis. Histoire de la pharmacie à travers les âges. 2 vol. 1. De l'antiquité au XVIe siècle. 606 p., ill.; 2. Du XVIIe siècle à nos jours. 670 p., ill. Paris: Peyronnet, 1931. [CB 35/313 and CB 38/615]
Reviewed by A. Castiglioni, *Riv.Stor.Sci.*, 1933, 24: 175.

SCHELENZ, Hermann. Geschichte der Pharmacie. x, 935 p., pl. Hildesheim: Georg Olms, 1962.
Reprint of the 1904 German edition.
Reviewed by W.P., *Ambix*, 1963, 11: 159.

SEEMAN, Bernard. Man against pain: 3,000 years of effort to understand and relieve physical suffering. 210 p. Philadelphia: Chilton Books, 1962.
Reviewed by George E. Osborne, *Amer.J.Pharm.Educ.*, 1963, 27: 340-1.

SILVERMAN, Milton. Magic in a bottle. xii, 332 p. New York: Macmillan, 1941. [CB 74/398]
Reviewed by Charles A. Kofoid, *Isis*, 1941, 33: 553-5.
This book traces the development of modern pharmacotherapy.

STERNON, F. Quelques aspects de l'art pharmaceutique et du médicament à travers les âges. 226 p. Paris: Masson, 1933.

TEMKIN, Owsei. Historical aspects of drug therapy. In: Johns Hopkins University Conference on Drugs in our Society, 1963. Drugs in our Society, p. 3-16. Baltimore: Johns Hopkins Press, 1964.

THOMPSON, Charles John Samuel. The mystery and art of the apothecary. ix, 287 p. London: Lane, 1929.

URDANG, George, ed. The history of the application of science in the health field. 10th anniversary conference of the American Institute of the History of Pharmacy, in cooperation with the University of Wisconsin School of Pharmacy, May 10, 1951. *Amer.J.Pharm.Educ.*, 1951, 15: 285-366.

URDANG, George. Pharmacy's part in society. 93 p., 47 ill. Madison, Wis.: American Institute of the History of Pharmacy, 1946. [CB 70/274]
An introduction to the history of pharmacy, especially in the United States.

VALERDI, Agustin Muruay. Compendio de historia de la quimica y de la farmacia. 201 p. Madrid: E. Raso, 1912.

ZÖRNIG, H. Erläuterungen zur Geschichte der Arzneidrogen. *Vortr.Ges.Gesch.Pharm.* (Basel, 1934), p. 203-11. Mittenwald: 1934.

RMc-bq

Die Vorträge der Hauptversammlung der Internationalen Gesellschaft für Geschichte der Pharmazie. Vol. 1- Stuttgart: 1953-
Volume 13 reviewed by E.H.G., *Rev.Hist.Pharm.*, 1959, 47: 45-6.

RMc-br

Illustrierter Apotheker-Kalender. Vol. 1- 1925- Hrsg. vom Deutschen Apotheker-Verein. Stuttgart: Deutscher Apotheker-Verlag, 1924-
The places of publication and publishers have changed through the years and there have been some years when it was not published. For vol. 1 *see* CB 17/596, vol. 3. CB 22/104, vol. 4 CB 24/565, vol. 12 CB 58/278.
1962 volume reviewed by P.H. Brans, *Arch.Int.Hist.Sci.*, 1962, 15: 463.

RMc-bu/cv bibliography; literature; sources

RMc-bv

KREMERS, Edward. A bibliographic guide for students of the history of pharmacy. 55 p. Madison, Wis.: University of Wisconsin, 1916.

SCHNEIDER, Wolfgang. A bibliographical review of the history of pharmaceutical chemistry (with particular reference to German literature). *Amer.J.Pharm.Educ.*, 1959, 23: 161-72.

SONNEDECKER, Glenn. Some bibliographic aids for historical writers in pharmacy. In collaboration with Alex Berman. 15 p. Madison, Wis.: American Institute of the History of Pharmacy, 1958.
Mimeographed.

URDANG, George. History, ethics, and literature of pharmacy. A select bibliography. *Amer.J.Pharm.Educ.*, 1944, 8: 491-503. [CB 69/240]

RMc-bx

URDANG, George. The scope of pharmacy. An exhibit. 61 p., ill. Madison, Wis.: American Institute of the History of Pharmacy, 1946.

WELLCOME HISTORICAL MEDICAL MUSEUM. Catalogue of an exhibition illustrating the history of pharmacy. 59 p. London: Oxford University Press, 1951.
Reviewed by George Urdang, *J.Hist.Med.*, 1952, 7: 315-16.

RMc-by

GRIFFENHAGEN, George; SONNEDECKER, C. American pharmacy's historical collections. A guide. [i, 5] p. Madison, Wis.: American Institute of the History of Pharmacy, [1965].

HÄFLIGER, Josef Anton. Pharmazeutische Altertumskunde und die Schweizer Sammlung für historisches Apothekenwesen an der Universität Basel. 203 p., 32 pl. Basel: Wepf, 1931.

RMcb

SIMON, Corinne. History of Lloyd Library. *Lloydia*, 1964, 27: 141-7.

RMcd

RUBIOLA, C.; RUSSO, A. Fonti archivistiche per la storia della farmacia. *Minerva Farm.*, 1964, 13: 44-5.

RMce-bv

BAER, Karl A. Bibliographical tools for selection of published materials in pharmacy. *Amer.J.Pharm.Educ.*, 1954, 18: 373-81.

BERLIN. PHARMAZIEHISTORISCHE BIBLIOTHEK. Katalog der pharmaziehistorischen Bibliothek in Berlin. Hrsg. von der Gesellschaft für Geschichte der Pharmazie. 110 p., 1 ill. Mittenwald: Nemayer, 1936.

BIANCHI, V.; MASINO, C.; VITOLO, A.E. Bibliografia italiana di storia della farmacia. *Minerva Farm.*, 1960, 9: 55-7, 90-2, 125-6, 222, 255; 1961, 10: 25-7, 95-6, 124-5, 159-60, 189-90, 220-2, 254-6; 1962, 11: 57-60, 88-92, 159-60, 191-20.

MASINO, Christoforo; VITOLO, A.E. Bibliografia italiana di storia della farmacia. *2 serie. Minerva Farm.*, 1964. 13: 27-9.

SONNEDECKER, Glenn. Some guidelines into the historical literature on pharmacy. *Amer.J.Pharm.Educ.*. 1959, 23: 143-53.

RMce-bx

HÄFLIGER, J.A. Einführung zu der Sonderausstellung von pharm.-med. Handschriften und Drucken. *Vortr.Ges.Gesch. Pharm.* (Basel, 1934), p. 189-95. Mittenwald: 1934.

WISCONSIN. University. Library. Rare Book Department. Pharmacy through four centuries. Guide to an exhibit commemorating the 75th anniversary of the School of Pharmacy, University of Wisconsin, prepared by Glenn Sonnedecker and Samuel A. Ives... Oct.-Dec. 1957. 28 p., ill., facs. [Madison, Wisc.: 1957]

RMce-by

SONNEDECKER, Glenn. The pharmacist as a book collector. *Amer.J.Hosp.Pharm.*, 1961, 18: 24-30, ill.

RMcg

AMERICAN INSTITUTE OF THE HISTORY OF PHARMACY. Three essays on formularies. Early Russian military and naval formularies, 1765-1840, by Alex Berman. A Confederate recipe book, by Norman Franke. The Canadian formulary, by G.R. Paterson. 24 p., ill. Madison: 1961.

HAMARNEH, Sami. At the Smithsonian ... exhibits in pharmaceutical dosage forms. *J.Amer.Pharm.Ass., new ser.*, 1962, 2: 478-9.

TALLMADGE, G. Kasten. The prescription. *Ciba Symp.* (Summit, N.J.), 1947, 9: 730-60, ill. [CB 72/279]

URDANG, George. The development of pharmacopoeias. 25 p. New York: 1950.

URDANG, George. Pharmacopoeias as witnesses of world history. *J.Hist.Med.*, 1946, 1: 46-70, 18 fig.

URDANG, George; SONNEDECKER, Glenn. Authoritative English-language drug compendia supplementing pharmacopoeias. *Food Drug Cosmet.Law J.*, 1953, 8: 485-94.

ZEKERT, O. Das Ärztliche Rezept. 50 p., ill. Ingelheim am Rhein: Boehringer, 1960.

RMcm

ZIMMERMANN, Walther. Apotheker-Exlibris mit pharmaziegeschichtlichen Inhalt. *Vortr.Ges.Gesch.Pharm.* (München, 1938), p. 137-40, fig. Wien: 1939.

RMda collective biography

CALDER, Ritchie. The life savers. 192 p., ill. London: Hutchinson, 1962.
A popular account of contributions of research chemists to the development of life-saving drugs.

FERCHL, Fritz, ed. Chemisch-Pharmazeutisches Bio- und Bibliographikon. Im Auftrage der Gesellschaft für Geschichte der Pharmazie. 2 vol. 603 p. Mittenwald: Nemayer, 1937-38.
Reviewed by Max Speter, *Isis*, 1939, 30: 125-7.

RMdaj

DOYLE, Paul A., ed. Readings in pharmacy. xiv, 429 p. New York/London: Interscience (Wiley), 1962.
Reviewed by Glenn Sonnedecker, *Science*, 1962, 137: 1044-5; by Leslie G. Matthews, *Med.Hist.*, 1963, 7: 392-3.

HOLMSTEDT, B.; LILJESTRAND, G. Readings in pharmacology. x, 395 p., ill. New York: Pergamon Press of the Macmillan Co., 1963.
An assembly of texts from ancient Egyptian to contemporary sources.

SHUSTER, Louis, ed. Readings in pharmacology. xii, 294 p., 49 fig., 37 tables. Boston: Little, Brown, 1962.
Reviewed by David E. Mann, *Amer.J.Pharm.Educ.*, 1963, 27: 502.

RMf history of pharmacy as a study

COLLE, Henry. The study of the history of pharmacy. *Australasian J.Pharm.*, 1944, 25: 682-4; 1947, 28: 13-15.

COLLE, Henry. The United States as the new center for the study of the history of pharmacy. *Amer.J.Pharm.*, 1945, 117: 35-9.

COWEN, David L. The history of the science of pharmacy *Pharm.Hist.*, 1962, 7: 17-20.

GUITARD, E.H. Histoire de la pharmacie. *Thalès*, 1935, 177-9.

KREMERS, Edward. Introductory lecture to a course in history of pharmacy. *J.Amer.Pharm.Ass.*, Dec. 1933, 22: 1270-9.

URDANG, George. The idea and the tasks of the history of pharmacy. *J.Amer.Pharm.Ass.*, 1938, 27: 909-13.

URDANG, George. The pharmaceutico-historical movement. *Amer. J.Pharm.Educ.*, 1952, 16: 206-15.

URDANG, George. Wesen und Bedeutung der Geschichte der Pharmazie. Drei Vorträge. 42 p. Berlin: Springer, 1927.

RMfpx

SEVENTH Urdang medal awarded. *Isis*, 1961, 52: 587-8.
The George Urdang medal is conferred by the American Institute of the History of Pharmacy. The first one was struck in 1952.

RMfqd

CERCLE BENELUX D'HISTOIRE DE LA PHARMACIE. [Reports of meetings] *Isis*, 1956, 47: 185-6, 421; 1957, 48: 457; 1958, 49: 74.

GESELLSCHAFT FÜR GESCHICHTE DER PHARMAZIE. [Notice of the first annual meeting.] *Isis*, 1928, 10: 56-7.

KREMERS, Edward. History of pharmacy. *Isis*. 1930, 13: 359-61.
Regarding meetings of societies.

PROCÈS-VERBAL de la séance de fondation de la Société d'Histoire de la Pharmacie, le 1er février 1913. *Bull.Soc.Hist.Pharm.*, 1913, 1: 2-11.

SOCIÉTÉ D'HISTOIRE DE LA PHARMACIE (fondée à Paris en 1913). *Isis*, 1913, 1: 250.

UHL, Arthur H. The American Institute of the History of Pharmacy and the A.Ph.A. Section on Historical Pharmacy. *Amer. J.Pharm.Educ.*, 1947, 11: 149-53.

URDANG, George. The American Pharmaceutical Association's section on historical pharmacy. *Amer.J.Pharm.Educ.*, 1953, 17: 389-400.

RMfqg

UHL, Arthur H. The American Institute of the History of Pharmacy and the A.Ph.A. Section on Historical Pharmacy. *Amer.J.Pharm.Educ.*, 1947, 11: 149-53.

URDANG, George. The American Institute of the History of Pharmacy, Inc. *Amer.J.Pharm.Educ.*, 1947, 673-82.

URDANG, George. The facilities for the establishment of a center of pharmaceutical historical work and information at Madison, Wisconsin. *Amer.J.Pharm.Educ.*, 1941, 5: 300-13.

URDANG, George. The first five years of the American Institue of the History of Pharmacy. Foreword by Arthur H. Uhl. 15 p. Madison, Wisc.: 1947.

RMfqx

HÜGEL, Herbert. Internationaler pharmaziegeschichtlicher Kongress in Heidelberg, 7.-9. Oktober 1957. *Deut.Apoth. Zeitung*, 1957, 97: 948-74.

for *Conference Proceedings* see RMc-bq

RMfqy

BRANS, P.H. Les organisations mondiales d'histoire de la pharmacie. *Arch.Int.Hist.Sci.*, 1954, 7: 49-52.

FOUNDING of an international academy of the history of pharmacy (Académie Internationale d'Histoire de la Pharmacie). *Bull.Hist.Med.*, 1952, 26: 385-6.

RMg teaching history of pharmacy

RMgp

BUNNELL, Kevin P. Liberal education and American pharmacy. 43 p., bibliogr. New York: Columbia University, [1958?]. Mimeographed by the author.

JERMSTAD, Axel. Die Geschichte der Pharmazie als Hochschulfach. *Vortr.Ges.Gesch.Pharm.* (Basel, 1934), p. 136-7. Mittenwald: 1934.

KREMERS, Edward. Teaching of the history of pharmacy. *Isis*, 1934, 21: 304.

NEWCOMER, James; BUNNELL, Kevin P.; McGRATH, Earl J. Liberal education and pharmacy. x, 125 p. New York: Bureau of Publication, Teachers College, Columbia University, 1960
Reviewed by Louis D. King, *Pharm.Hist.*, 1962, 7: 44-6.

SONNEDECKER, Glenn. The character of research at the doctoral level in the history of pharmacy. *Amer.J.Pharm.Educ.*, 1954, 18: 239-49.

SONNEDECKER, Glenn. Ueber die Promotion in Pharmaziegeschichte. *Pharm.Zeitung*, 1953, 89: no. 26, 651-5.

URDANG, George. History of pharmacy as an academic discipline. *J.Hist.Med.*, 1948, 3: 5-10. [CB 73/186]

URDANG, George; SONNEDECKER, Glenn. Teaching history of pharmacy. 33 p. Madison, Wis.: American Institute of the History of Pharmacy, 1950.

RMgt

COLLE, Henry. On teaching history of pharmacy in the colleges of pharmacy in the United States. *Amer.J.Pharm.Educ.*, 1947, 11: 277-9.

PETERS, -. Die Geschichte der Pharmazie als Erziehungsfach des Standes. *Vortr.Ges.Gesch.Pharm.* (Basel, 1934), p. 41-7. Mittenwald: 1934.

SONNEDECKER, Glenn; URDANG, George. A survey of the status of history of pharmacy in American pharmaceutical education. *Amer.J.Pharm.Educ.*, 1952, 16: 11-21.

RMh historiography and particular aspects of the history of pharmacy

RMhd

URDANG, George. Historical research in pharmacy. *Amer.J.Pharm.Educ.*, 1946, 10: 271-85.

RMhd-d

URDANG, George. Las biografías como material y tema de historia de la farmacía. *Rev.Argent.Hist.Med.*, 1945, 4: 41-63.

RMht

PARDAL, Ramon. El balance positivo de la medicina aborigena americana. Historia de los remedios del indio americano adoptados por la medicina europea. *Actualidad Méd.Mundial*, 1937, 7: 28-38.
Reviewed by L. Castaldi, *Riv.Stor.Sci.*, 1938, 29: 40.

RMmz relations with other subject fields

RMmzDY

MAHDIHASSAN, S. Alchemy and its connection with astrology, pharmacy, magic and metallurgy. *Janus*, 1957, 46: 81-103.

RMmzN

RUSSELL, James Clifford Hamilton. The interrelationship of pharmacy and medicine. *Amer.J.Pharm.Educ.*, 1946, 10: 286-312.

RMn/o communication; teaching

RMnb

STIEB, Ernst. Symbols of pharmacy. *J.Amer.Pharm.Ass., new ser.*, 1962, 2: 206-9.

RMnb-be

SCHNEIDER, Wolfgang. Lexikon alchemistisch-pharmazeutischer Symbole. 140 p., pl. Weinheim: Verlag Chemie, 1962.
For reviews *see* CB 88/564.

RMnh

SCHOEFFLER, Herbert. Antioche. *Mitt.Gesch.Med.*, 1918, 17: 83.
The use of the name of the city of Antioch in naming drugs.

URDANG, George. The place of Latin in the official standards of pharmacy. *Bull.Nat.Formulary Comm.*, 1944, 12: 201-20. [CB 68/63]

RMo

DIECKMANN, Hans. Geschichte und Probleme der Apothekerausbildung in erster Linie in Frankreich und Deutschland. 263 p., 8 fig. Frankfurt a. M.: Govi-Verlag, 1954.
Reviewed by Günther Kerstein, *Sudhoffs Arch.*. 1956, 40: 95.

SONNEDECKER, Glenn; URDANG, George. Pharmaceutical education. *Higher Educ.*, 1953, 9: 133-41.

URDANG, George. Pharmaceutical education from the historical point of view. *Amer.J.Pharm.Educ.*, 1942, 6: 53-60.

RMo-ce

URDANG, George. The development of the pharmaceutical textbook. A synopsis. *Amer.J.Pharm.Educ.*, 1944, 8: 328-33.

RMor

URDANG, George. The part of doctors of medicine in pharmaceutical education. *Amer.J.Pharm.Educ.*, 1950, 14: 546-55.

RMorg

DILLEMANN, G. Les costumes des professeurs des facultés de pharmacie. *Produits Pharm.*, 1964, 19: 314-20.

RMp/r organizational and professional aspects

RMpe

SONNEDECKER, Glenn. Professionalization as a social process. *Leban.Pharm.J.*, 1956, 4: 1-11.

RMph

COOK, E. Fullerton. National and international standards for medicines. *Annu.Rep.Smithsonian Inst.for 1937*, p. 431-50. Washington, D.C.: 1938.

STIEB, Ernst W. Drug adulteration: the development of scientific and social controls in Anglo-Saxon countries. (Diss.) *Isis*, 1957, 48: 351.

RMpw

WITTOP KONING, D.A. Les relations pharmacologiques entre la France et les Pays-Bas. 22 p., bibliogr., ill. (Les Conférences du Palais de la Découverte, 64) Paris: Université de Paris, 1959.
From Roman times to the nineteenth century.

RMqy

HOFMAN, J.J. La Fédération Pharmaceutique Internationale. Son but. Ses aspirations. *Vie Internationale*, 1914, 5: 312-18.

RMr

SCHMIDT, Alfredus. De origine apothecarum. *VIe Congr.Int.Hist.Méd.* (Leyde-Amsterdam, 1927), p. 108-11. Anvers: De Vlijt, 1929.

SCHNEIDER, Wolfgang. Das pharmazeutische Personal in der Vergangenheit. *Pharm.Zeitung*, 1964, 109: 1210-15.

WHITTET, Thomas D. From apothecary to pharmacist. A study of changes of title. 1. Derivation of the titles. 2. Titles used in Greece and Italy. 3. Titles used in Germany. 4. Titles used in Denmark. 5. Titles used in Sweden. 6. Titles used in Iceland. 7. Titles used in Austria. 8. Titles used in England and Wales. i. The apothecaries gain a charter. ii. Apothecaries take up medicine. iii. Army and Navy apothecaries. iv. Present position of the apothecaries. v. The chemists and druggists organize. vi. Emergence of the pharmacist. *Chem.Drug.*, 1962, 177: 734-6; 178: 385-6; 1963, 179: 100, 172; 180: 317, 451, 630; 1964, 182: 63-4, 86, 111, 130, 153-4, 175-6.

WITTOP KONING, A. Verschuivingen in het apothekersvak in de loop der eeuwen. [Changes in the pharmaceutical profession in the course of centuries. (In Dutch)] 16 p. Amsterdam: Centen, 1949.
Inaugural lecture of the course on the history of pharmacy at the University of Amsterdam, 23 March 1949.

RMrk-TX

URDANG, George. Pharmacy and aviation. *Bull.Hist.Med.*, 1944, 15: 324-6.
Notes on pharmacists who were connected with balloon aviation.

RMs/t social and humanistic relations

RMsb

RATH, Gernot. Zeiteinflüsse in der Pharmakologie des 16. bis 19. Jahrhunderts. *Sudhoffs Arch.*, 1963, 47: 1-18.

RMsc

COWEN, David L. Pharmacy and civilization. *Amer.J.Pharm. Educ.*, 1958, 22: 70-6.

GRIFFENHAGEN, George B. Pharmacy in history. (Editorial) *J.Int.Coll.Surg.*, 1958, 29: 789-803.

SCHÄR, Eduard. Die kommerzielle und kulturgeschichtliche Bedeutung der Arznei- und Genussmittel. 28 p. (Rede.) Strassburg: 1913.

RMse

KOFLER, L. Das Vertrauen zur Arznei im Wandel der Zeiten. *Vortr.Ges.Gesch.Pharm.* (Basel, 1934), p. 138-52. Mittenwald: 1934.

RMsg

VERSHOFEN, Wilhelm. Die Anfänge der chemisch-pharmazeutischen Industrie. Eine wirtschaftshistorische Studie. 2 vol. 151 p; 120 p. Berlin: Deutscher Betriebswirte-Verlag, 1949; Aulendorf in Württemberg: Editio Cantor K.G., 1952.
Reviewed by George Urdang, *Arch.Int.Hist.Sci.*, 1952, 5: 400-2; 1954, 7: 208.

YOUNG, James Harvey. Patent medicines, an early example of competitive marketing. *J.Econ.Hist.*, 1960, 20: 648-56.

RMth

SPRIGGE, S. Squire. Physic and fiction. xi, 307 p. London/New York: Hodder and Stoughton, 1921.
Reviewed by F.R. Packard, *Ann.Med.Hist.*, 1922, 4: 319.

URDANG, George. Der Apotheker als Objekt und Subjekt der Literatur. *Pharm.Zeitung*, 1925, 70: 1767-70. [CB 19/822]

URDANG, George. Der Apotheker als Subjekt und Objekt der Literatur. 181 p., 16 pl. Berlin: Springer, 1926. [CB 19/822]

URDANG, George. Der Apotheker im Spiegel der Literatur. 157 p. Berlin: Springer, 1921.

RMtq

HÄFLIGER, J.A. Apotheker und Glasgemälde. *Vortr.Ges.Gesch. Pharm.* (München, 1938), p. 109-28, 11 fig. Wien: 1939.

KELLNER, -. (Medizinalrat Dr.). Geschichte der Medizin, Arzt, Pharmazeutische Industrie. *Janus*, 1937, 41: 29-32.
On art in medicine with particular reference to periodical publications by pharmaceutical firms.

WITTOP KONING, D.A. Art and pharmacy. A collection of 42 reproductions, published in the Dutch pharmaceutical calendars, with an introduction. 12 p., ill. Deventer: De Ijsel Press, 1950.
Reviewed by George Urdang, *Arch.Int.Hist.Sci.*, 1951, 4: 1079-80.

ZEKERT, Otto. Kunst in Medizin und Pharmazie. 96 p., 40 pl. (HMW-Jahrbuch 1956) Wien: Heilmittelwerke Wien, 1955.
Reviewed by Martin Lundqvist, *Lychnos*, 1956, 437-9.

see also RNxb

RMu popular aspects

DÖRR, Walter. Quacksalbenverkäufer. *Vortr.Ges.Gesch.Pharm.* (Basel, 1934), p. 29-40. Mittenwald: 1934.

HEURCK, Emile H. van. L'onguent armaire et la poudre de sympathie dans la science et le folklore. 73 p., 1 pl. Anvers: Buschmann, 1915.
Reviewed by P. Dorveaux, *Bull.Soc.Franç.Hist.Méd.*, 1921, 15: 299.

LECLERC, Henri. La médecine des signatures magiques. *Janus*, 1918, 23: 5-28.
This article was wrongly attributed to Leclerc; it is the work of Saintyves (*see Janus*, 1919, 24: 192).

PEETERS, K.C. De apotheker en de artsenijbereidkunde in het volksleven. [The pharmacist and pharmacy in popular tradition. (In Dutch)] In: Koninklijke Apothekersvereniging van Antwerpen. 125-jarig jubileum, p. 39-66. Antwerp: 1960.

RMv ethnic groups

RMvm

RUHMER, Otto E.; ZUPKO, Arthur G. Some contributions by Jews to pharmacy, a historical survey. 25 p. Madison, Wis.: Jewish Pharmaceutical Society of American in cooperation with the American Institute of the History of Pharmacy, 1960.

RMw in different countries

RMwb North America

COOK, Roy Bird. The annals of pharmacy in West Virginia. 84 p., ill. Charleston, W.Va.: West Virginia Pharmaceutical Association, 1946.
Reviewed by George Urdang, *Bull.Hist.Med.*, 1947, 21: 271.

COWEN, David L. A store mixt, various, universal. *J.Rutgers Univ.Libr.*, 1961, 25: 1-9.
An advertisement in New York, 1784, of "a general collection of the materia medica, botanical, chymical, and Galenical" for sale.

FROHLICH, L.W. The physician and the pharmaceutical industry in the United States. *Proc.Amer.Phil.Soc.*, 1960, 53: 579-86.

GRIFFENHAGEN, George B. The story of California pharmacy. 58 p. Madison, Wis.: American Institute of the History of Pharmacy, 1950. [CB 77/387]

GRIFFENHAGEN, George B.; FELTER, William C. The Oregon trail of pharmacy. 54 p. Madison, Wis.: American Institute of the History of Pharmacy, 1952.

GRIFFENHAGEN, George B.; YOUNG, James Harvey. Old English patent medicines in America. (*Contrib.Mus.Hist.Technol.*, 10) *Bull.U.S.Nat.Mus.*, 1959, 218: 155-83, ill.

HOCH, J. Hampton. The history of pharmacy in South Carolina. 87 p. Charleston, S.C.: 1951.
Issued to commemorate the diamond jubilee of the South Carolina Pharmaceutical Association, 1876-1951.

HUND, Reid. Promotion of medicine and pharmacy. *Science*, 1931, 72: 49-58.
Presidential address at the 1930 U.S. Pharmacopoeial Convention, May 1930. Deals mainlv with American pharmacy.

KREMERS, Edward. The history of American pharmacy. *Amer. Drug.*, 1920, 68: March, 9-13; April, 9-14; May, 13-18, ill. [CB 10/203]

LASCOFF, J. Leon. Later history of pharmacy in America. *Med.Life*, 1926, 33: 75-94.

RAUBENHEIMER, Otto. Early history of pharmacy in America. *Med.Life*, 1926, 33: 53-74, ill.

SONNEDECKER, Glenn. Structure and stress of American pharmacy. *Pharm.J.*, April 1956, 14: 3-8.

URDANG, George. The early days of American pharmacy. *Amer.J. Pharm.Educ.*, 1941, 5: 337-40.

RMwb-cc

ZACHERT, Martha Jane K. American local history journals of interest to the historian of pharmacy: a bibliography. 16 p. (Bibliographic Contribution, 3) Atlanta, Ga.: Southern College of Pharmacy, Mercer University, 1961.
Reviewed in *Pharm.Hist.*, 1962, 7: 10.

RMwb-cg

COWEN, David L. America's pre-pharmacopoeial literature. 40 p. Madison, Wis.: American Institute of the History of Pharmacy, 1961.

THE DISPENSATORY of the United States of America. Centennial (22nd) ed. By H.C. Wood, C.H. LaWall [*et al.*] (Supplement) 76 p. Philadelphia: Lippincott, 1937-40. [CB 61/420]

LANGENHAN, H.A. Titles, synonyms and abbreviations. A century of the United States pharmacopoeia,1820-1920. 153 p. (*Bull. Univ.Wis.*, serial no. 1123. General series 907) Madison, Wis.: 1923.

PATERSON, G.R. The Canadian formulary. In: American Institud

URDANG, George. One hundred and twenty-five years of the United States Pharmacopoeia. *Victor Robinson Memorial Volume*, p. 397-402. New York: Froben, 1948.

RMwb-cj

MEYER, Minnie, The pharmaceutical journals of the United States: a preliminary report, with prefatory remarks and an appeal for cooperation by E. Kremers. *J.Amer.Pharm.Ass.*, 1933, 22: 424-9. [CB 42/611]

RMwb-o

KREMERS, Edward. Die Geschichte des pharmazeutischen Unterrichtes in USA. *Vortr.Ges.Gesch.Pharm.* (Basel, 1934), p. 1-7, fig. Mittenwald: 1934.

KREMERS, Edward. The old Northwest Territory and pharmaceutical education. 16 p. Lafayette, Ind.: Purdue University, 1934. [CB 42/610]
A convocation address delivered at the fiftieth anniversary of the Purdue School of Pharmacy, March 20, 1934.

URDANG, George. Edward Kremers (1865-1941), reformer of American pharmaceutical education. *Amer.J.Pharm.Educ.*, 1947, 11: 631-58.

URDANG, George. Edward Kremers (1865-1941), reformer of American pharmaceutical education. *Trans.Wis.Acad.Sci.Arts Lett.*, 1945, 37: 111-35.

RMwb-oq

NOBLE, Alice. The School of Pharmacy of the University of North Carolina. A history. 237 p. Chapel Hill, N.C.: University of North Carolina Press, 1961.
Reviewed by G.S., *Pharm.Hist.*, 1963, 8: 25-6.

RMwb-ph

JONES, Bartlett C. A prohibition problem: liquor as medicine 1920-1933. *J.Hist.Med.*, 1963, 18: 353-69.

SONNEDECKER, Glenn; URDANG, George. Legalization of drug standards under state laws in the United States of America. *Food Drug Cosmet.Law J.*, 1953, 8: 741-60.

RMwb-pw

HEYMANNS, Walter William. Die amerikanischen Drogen im Deutschen Arzneibuch VI. Ein Beitrag zu ihrer Geschichte im deutschen Arzneischatz. 147 p. (Abhandlungen zur Geschichte der Medizin und der Naturwissenschaft, 26) Berlin: Ebering, 1938.

RMwb-qd

BOWERS, Roy A.; COWEN, David L. Rho Chi Society. Development of the honor society of American pharmacy. 2nd ed. 55 p. Indianapolis, Ind.: 1961. First publ. 1955.
Reviewed in *Pharm.Hist.*, 1962, 7: 52-3.

SOLLMANN, Torald. The early days of the Pharmacological Society. *Amer.J.Pharm.Educ.*, 1949, 13: 606-14.

RMwb-rw-qb

BONOW, Eunice R. The history of professional pharmaceutical fraternities for women. *Amer.J.Pharm.Educ.*, 1954, 18: 410-13.

RMwb-sg

FRASER-HARRIS, D. The former importance of our sea-borne trade in drugs. *Med.Life*, 1929, 36: 548-50.

YOUNG, James Harvey. The toadstool millionaires. A social history of patent medicines in America before federal regulation. xii, 282 p., ill. Princeton: Princeton University Press, 1961.
Reviewed by Louis Lasagna, *Bull.Hist.Med.*, 1962, 36: 482; by T.D. Whittet, *Med.Hist.*, 1962, 6: 194-5; by David L. Cowen, *Amer.J.Pharm.Educ.*, 1962, 26: 147-9.

RMwc Latin America

DOMINGUEZ, Juan A. Contribuciones a la materia médica Argentina. (Primera contribucion) xxiii, 433 p. (Trabajos del Instituto de Botánica y Farmacologia, 44) Buenos Aires: Peuser, 1928. [CB 35/313]

FOLCH JOU, G.; HERRERO HINOGO, Pilar. Contribución de los Españoles al conocimiento y divulgación de la materia médica Americana. *Arch.Iberoamer.Hist.Med.*, 1957, 9: 173-81.

MUÑOZ, José E. Apuntes para la historia de la farmacía en el Ecuador. 214 p. Quito: Ed. "Rumiñahui", 1952.
Reviewed by P. Sergescu, *Arch.Int.Hist.Sci.*, 1953, 6: 354-5.

TORRES-DIAZ, Luis. A concise history of pharmacy in Puerto Rico. x, 52 p., ill. Madison, Wis.: American Institute of the History of Pharmacy, 1951. [CB 79/195]

RMwc-bv

GITTINGER, Georgiana Simmons. A selected bibliography of pharmacy in Latin America. *Amer.J.Pharm.Educ.*, 1959, 23: 424-9.
An annotated bibliography of materials relating to the history of pharmacy in the Latin American countries.

RMwe British Isles

GILMOUR, J.P. Pharmacy in Great Britain and Ireland. *Proc. 3rd Int.Congr.Hist.Med.* (London, 1922), p. 213-20. Antwerp De Vlijt, 1923.

MATTHEWS, Leslie G. History of pharmacy in Britain. Foreword by Sir Henry Dale. xiv, 427 p., 27 pl. Edinburgh/London: Livingstone; Baltimore: Williams & Wilkins Co., 1962.
Reviewed by David L. Cowen, *Isis*, 1964, 55: 109-10; for other reviews *see* CB 88/564, CB 89/515 and CB 90/537.

RMwe-cg

COWEN, David L. The Edinburgh Pharmacopoeia. 1. Historical development and significance. 2. Bibliography. *Med.Hist.*, 1957, 1: 123-39, 340-51.

RMwe-qd

URDANG, George. The first century of the Pharmaceutical Society of Great Britain. *J.Amer.Pharm.Ass.*, 1942, 3: 420-6, fig.

RMwe-qe

UNDERWOOD, E. Ashworth, ed. A history of the Worshipful Society of Apothecaries of London. Vol. I. 1617-1815. Abstracted and arranged from the MSS notes of Cecil Wall by H. Charles Cameron. xiv, 450 p., 27 ill. London: Oxford University Press for Wellcome Historical Medical Museum, 1963.
Reviewed by L. Pearce Williams, *Amer.Hist.Rev.*, 1964, 69: 1042-3; by Patricia Petruschke MacLachlan, *J.Hist.Med.*, 1964, 19: 315-6; by R.S. Roberts, *Med.Hist.*, 1963, 7: 388-9.

WHITTET, T.D. The Liverpool Apothecaries' Company. *Chem Drug.*, 1962, 178: 278-80.

RMwf France

BOUVET, Maurice. Histoire de la pharmacie en France des origines à nos jours. 445 p. Paris: Occitania, 1937.

FRAYSSE, Camille. Histoire de la pharmacie en Anjou depuis son origine jusqu'à la Révolution. 90 p. Paris: Occitania, 1929.

MICHON, Yvonne. La pharmacie en Bas-Poitou sous l'ancien régime. La récolte du salpètre en Vendée sous la Révolution. 192 p. (Thesis, Toulouse) Paris: Occitania, 1925. [CB 19/822]

WITTOP KONING, D.A. *See* RMpw

RMwf-ce-by

TORAUDE, L.G. Les "pharmaciens bibliophiles" de Paris. *Vortr.Ges.Gesch.Pharm.* (Basel, 1934), p. 89-94, ill. Mittenwald: 1934.

RMwf-hd

BOUVET, Maurice. Les travaux d'histoire locale de la pharmacie en France des origines à ce jour. 43 p. Paris: Société de la Pharmacie, 1957.
Reviewed by Owsei Temkin, *Bull.Hist.Med.*, 1958, 32: 579.

RMwf-ns

GUITARD, Eugène. Deux siècles de presse au service de la pharmacie et cinquante ans de l'Union Pharmaceutique. 2e éd. v, 316 p., 22 pl. Paris: Pharmacie Centrale de France, 1913.
Reviewed by George Sarton, *Isis*, 1913, 1: 529-30.

RMwf-o

DIECKMANN, Hans. *See* RMo

GAUTIER, L. Histoire et évolution de l'enseignement de la pharmacie en France. *J.Pharmacie Alsace Lorraine*, 1922, 49: 1-40. [CB 18/651]

GUITARD, E.H. L'élève en pharmacie sous l'ancien régime. *Bull.Soc.Hist.Pharm.*, 1925, 4: no. 47, 89-100; no. 48, 146-60. [CB 22/308]

RMwf-ph

BOUVET, Maurice. Sur l'histoire de la législation des toxiques. *J.Pharm.Chim., 7e sér.*, 1922, 25: 464-8. [CB 18/650]

RMwf-qe

BOUVET, Maurice. Le Bureau des Apothicaires-Epiciers et des épiciers de Paris, rue des Lombards. *Rev.Hist.Pharm.*, 1960, 48: 267-71.

BOUVET, Maurice. Les compagnons apothicaires étrangers en France des origines à 1803. *Rev.Hist.Pharm.*, 1959, 14: no. 160, 10-15.

IRISSOU, Louis. Montpellier, centre de formation des compagnons-apothicaires. *Vortr.Ges.Gesch.Pharm.* (Basel, 1934), p. 48-69. Mittenwald: 1934.

LARUELLE, E. Les apothicaires rouennais. Histoire de la Corporation du Moyen Age à la Révolution. viii, 96, li, 9 pl. Rouen: Henri Defontaine, 1920. [CB 12/636]

RMwf-qg

LES LABORATOIRES DAUSSE (1834-1934). Cent ans d'expérience pharmacologique. 24 p., fig. Étampes: Imprimerie Dausse, 1935.

RMwf-qs

GUITARD, E.-H. Deux siècles de presse au service de la pharmacie et cinquante ans de l'Union Pharmaceutique. 2e éd. v, 316 p., 22 pl. Paris: Pharmacie Centrale de France, 1913.
Reviewed by George Sarton, *Isis*, 1913, 1: 529-30.

RMwf-r

DIZERBO, A. Apothicaires et pharmaciens de Basse-Bretagne. 158 p. (Thesis, Strasbourg) Rennes: Riou-Reuzé, 1951.
Reviewed by D.A. Wittop Koning, *Arch.Int.Hist.Sci.*, 1953, 6: 530.

GUITARD, E.-H. Les apothicaires privilégiés dans l'ancienne France. *Proc.17th Int.Congr.Med.* (London, 1913), Sect. 23, p. 411-17. London: Oxford University Press, Hodder & Stoughton, 1914.

JUPPÉ, Fernand. L'apothicairerie en Béarn. Recherches sur les apothicaires béarnais depuis leur origine jusqu'à la Révolution. 160 p. Tarbes: Lesbordes, 1922. [CB 18/651]

LIOT, André. Les apothicaires dieppois du XVIe au XIXe siècle. 89 p. Rouen: 1912.

POUSSIER, A. Note sur les apothicaires dieppois; poursuites exercées par les apothicaires de Rouen contre les marchands de produits falsifiés. 12 p. Rouen: 1912.

WICKERSHEIMER, Ernest. Documents pour servir à l'histoire de la profession d'apothicaire à Strasbourg. 1. La taxe des médicaments de 1625; 2. L'apothicaire, créancier privilégié; 3. Falsification du Quinquina, 1735; 4. Encore un mot sur la thériaque céleste, dite "de Strasbourg". *Vortr.Ges.Gesch.Pharm.* (Basel, 1934), p. 70-81. Mittenwald: 1934.

RMwg Germany; Austria; Switzerland

ADLUNG, A.; URDANG, George. Grundriss der Geschichte der deutschen Pharmazie. Herausgegeben auf Veranlassung der Gesellschaft für Geschichte der Pharmazie mit Unterstützung durch die Deutsche Apothekerschaft. viii, 647 p. Berlin: Springer, 1935. [CB 45/303]

HÄFLIGER, J.A. Das Apothekenwesen Basels. 146 p., 4 pl., 7 fig. Berlin: Gesellschaft für Geschichte der Pharmazie, 1938.

SCHNIDERSCHITSCH, Norbert. Die Geschichte der Pharmazie in Steiermark bis zum Jahre 1850. Allgemeiner Teil. 140 p. (*Veröffentl.Int.Ges.Gesch.Pharm.*, 6) Mittenwald: Nemayer, 1929. [CB 27/584]

ZEKERT, Otto; GANZINGER, Kurt; ed. Beiträge zur Geschichte der Pharmazie in Oesterreich. 125 p., ill. (*Veröffentl. Int.Ges.Gesch.Pharm.*, 18) Wien: Oesterreichische Gesellschaft für Geschichte der Pharmazie, 1961.
Reviewed by R. Niederhuemer, *Bl.Technikgesch.*, 1964, 26: 152-3.

RMwg-cb

DÜSSELER, E. Vester's Archiv: Institut für Geschichte der Pharmazie. Düsseldorf-Neuss. *Archivar*, 1959, 12: no. 1, 17-22.
Vester's Archiv für Geschichte des deutschen Apothekerwesens.

RMwg-cg

HEYMANNS, Walter William. Die amerikanischen Drogen im Deutschen Arzneibuch VI. Ein Beitrag zu ihrer Geschichte im deutschen Arzneischatz. 147 p. (Abhandlungen zur Geschichte der Medizin und der Naturwissenschaft, 26) Berlin: Ebering, 1938.

RMwg-da

ZEKERT, Otto. Berühmte Apotheker. 2 vol., ill. Stuttgart: Deutscher Apotheker-Verlag, 1955-62.
Published also under title: Deutsche Apotheker.
Reviewed by Heinz Degen, *Naturwiss.Rundsch.*, 1962, 15: 449; in *Pharm.Hist.*, 1963, 8: 28.

RMwg-fqd

SCHWEIZERISCHER APOTHEKER-VEREIN. [La création d'une Commission d'histoire de la pharmacie helvétique] *Bull.Soc.Hist.Pharm.*, 1913, no. 1, 74. [CB 4/784]

RMwg-nh

HOLFERT, Johann. Volkstümliche Namen der Arzneimittel, Drogen und Chemikalien. 2nd rev. ed. by Georg Arends. iv, 283 p. Berlin: Springer, 1922.

RMwg-o

DIECKMANN, Hans. Geschichte und Probleme der Apothekerausbildung in erster Linie in Frankreich und Deutschland. 263 p., 8 fig. Frankfurt a. M.: Govi-Verlag, 1954.
Reviewed by Günther Kerstein, *Sudhoffs Arch.*, 1956, 40: 95.

SONNEDECKER, Glenn. Studying pharmacy in West Germany. *Amer. J.Pharm.Educ.*, 1958, 22: 169-78.

RMwg-oq

KALLINICH, Günter. Das Vermächtnis Georg Ludwig Claudius Rousseaus an die Pharmazie. Zweihundert Jahre Pharmazie an der Universität Ingolstadt-Landshut-München, 1760-1960. Festgabe zum zweihundertjährigen Bestehen des Münchener Instituts. 513 p., ill. Frankfurt am Main: Govi-Verlag, 1960.
Reviewed by Mark Jupiter, *Pharm.Hist.*, 1962, 7: 50-2.

RMwg-ph

NOGGLER, Josef. Die Wiener Apothekerordnungen, 1564-1770. *Vortr.Ges.Gesch.Pharm.* (Stuttgart, 1936), p. 27-46. Mittenwald: 1936.

RMwg-qe

KREMERS, Edward. History of pharmacy. *Isis*, 1934, 20: 447.
Concerning German guilds.

RMwg-rf

FERCHL, Fritz. Apotheker- Lehr- und Gehilfenbriefe aus drei Jahrhunderten. 48 p., ill. (*Veröffentl.Ges.Gesch.Pharm.*, 1) Stuttgart: Wissenschaftliche Verlagsgesellschaft, 1928. [CB 24/565]

RMwh-r

BARADLAY, Joh. Alteingewanderte deutsche Apotheker im Königreich Ungarn. *Vortr.Ges.Gesch.Pharm.* (Basel, 1934), p. 224-31. Mittenwald: 1934.

RMwi Italy

COLAPINTO, L. Quattro secoli di storia della farmacia nello stato pontificio attraverso i documenti conservati presso l'Archivio di Stato di Roma. *Ann.Med.Nav.Colon.*, 1964, 69: 563-72.

MASINO, Christoforo. Le "spezierie" nei pedaggi italiani. *Minerva Farm.*, 1963, 12: 106-10; 13: 11-19.

PEDRAZZINI, Carlo. La farmacia storica ed artistica italiana. 592 p., 743 ill. Milan: Vittoria, 1934.
Reviewed by A. Castiglioni, *Riv.Stor.Sci.*, 1935, 26: 96.

RMwi-da

MASINO, Christoforo. Notizie sparse sugli speziali piemontesi nei secoli XVI-XIX. *Minerva Farm.*, 1964, 13: 67-71.

RMwi-o

CORONEDI, Giusto. Studio critico-storico sopra Ranieri Bellini. Contributo alla storia della farmacologia in Italia e singolarmiente nella scuola medica fiorentina, dal 1847 al 1877. *Riv.Stor.Sci.*, 1928, 19: 1-36,

RMwi-ph

VITOLO, Antonio E. I fondamenti degli statuti degli speziali italiani. *Act.VIIIe Congr.Int.Hist.Sci.* (Florence, 1956), p. 587. Paris: Hermann, 1958.

RMwi-tq

CORNACCHIA, Vio. Il bambino nella farmacia artistica italiana. *Arch.Iberoamer.Hist.Med.*, 1956, 8: 423-7.

RMwj Spain and Portugal

RMwj-cg

FOLCH Y ANDREU, Rafael. Las farmacopeas nacionales españoles. *Arch.Iberoamer.Hist.Med.*, 1956, 8: 247-67

FOLCH Y ANDREU, Rafael. Die prähispanischen offizinellen Pharmakopöen und die Mitarbeit der Pharmazeuten. *Vorträge Ges. Gesch.Pharm.* (Basel, 1934), p. 212-23. Mittenwald: Nemayer, 1934.

RMwj-cj

MAS Y GUINDAL, Joachim. L'évolution des revues pharmaceutiques espagnoles. *Rev.Hist.Pharm.*, Dec. 1934, 4: 403-8.

RMwj-nh

MEYERHOF, Max. Sur les noms Ibéro-Portugais des drogues dans les manuscrits médicaux arabes. *Petrus Nonius*, 1939, 2: 85-96.

MEYERHOF, Max. Essai sur les noms portugais de drogues dérivés de l'arabe. *Petrus Nonius*, 1938, 2: 1-8.

RMwj-o

FOLCH Y ANDREU, Raphael. L'enseignement pharmaceutique en Espagne du Moyen-Age à nos jours. *Bull.Soc.Hist.Pharm.*, 1926, 4: no. 51, 253-7.

RMwk Low Countries

GRENDEL, E. De ontwikkeling van de artsenijbereidkunde in Gouda tot 1865. [The development of pharmacy in Gouda up to 1865. (In Dutch)] 590 p. (Thesis, Amsterdam) Gouda: Koch en Knuttel, 1958.
Reviewed by E. Elaut, *Sci.Hist.*, 1960, 2: 28-30.

SMET, Marc de. Oudenaarde en de farmacie. [Oudenaarde and pharmacy. (In Dutch)] 77 p., 19 pl. Bevere-Oudenaarde: 1960.
Reviewed by L.J. van de Wiele, *Sci.Hist.*, 1960, 2: 195-6.

URDANG, George. History of pharmacy in Holland. *J.Hist. Med.*, 1949, 4: 334-5.

WIELE, L.J. van de. Enkele losse bladzijden uit de geschiedenis van de farmacie to Antwerpen. [Some loose pages from the history of pharmacy at Antwerp. (In Dutch)] In: Koninklijke Apothekersvereniging van Antwerpen, 125-jarig jubileum, p. 19-37. Antwerp: 1960.

WITTOP KONING, D.A. Brielle en de pharmacie. [Pharmacy in Brill, South Holland. (In Dutch)] *Pharm.Weekbl.*, 1951, 86: 75-81.

WITTOP KONING, D.A. Les relations pharmacologiques entre la France et les Pays-Bas. 22 p., bibliogr., ill. (Les Conférences du Palais de la Découverte, 64) Paris: Université de Paris, 1959.
From Roman times to the nineteenth century.

RMwk-bv

GUISLAIN, A. Bibliografie van de geschiedenis der farmacie in België. [Bibliography of the history of pharmacy in Belgium. (In Dutch)] *Pharm.Tijdschr.Belg.*, 1960, 37: no. 1, 7-16.

RMwk-cg

DAEMS, W.F.; WIELE, L.J. van de. Noord- en Zuidnederlandse stedelijke pharmacopeeën. [North- and South Netherlands municipal pharmacopoeias. (In Dutch)] 199 p., ill. Mortsel-bij-Antwerp: Itico, 1955.
Reviewed by D.A. Wittop Koning, *Janus*, 1957, 46: 163-4.

GUISLAIN, A. A propos de la pharmacopée liégeoise. *Bull. Cercle Benelux Hist.Pharm.*, Oct. 1961, no. 27, 6 p.

WITTOP KONING, D.A. Éditions néerlandaises des pharmacopées étrangères. *Act.VIIIe Congr.Int.Hist.Sci.* (Florence, 1956), p. 555-60. Paris: Hermann, 1958.

RMwk-cm

COHEN, H. Les titres-planches de quelques anciens herbiers et pharmacopées édités en Hollande. *VIe Congr.Int.Hist. Méd.* (Leyde-Amsterdam, 1927), p. 112-13, 1 pl. Anvers: De Vlijt, 1929.

RMwk-da

REHM, G.J. De Bredase apothekers van de 15e tot het begin van de 19e eeuw. [Breda pharmacists from the 15th to the beginning of the 19th century. (In Dutch)] *Bull.Cercle Benelux Hist.Pharm.*, 1960, no. 22, 1-24.

RMwk-qd

WITTOP KONING, D.A. De nederlandsche maatschappij ter bevordering der pharmacie, 1842-1942. 251 p. Amsterdam: Centen, 1948.
Dutch Society for the promotion of pharmacy.

RMwn Russia

RMwn-cg

ALLEN, Edgard Yan. Russian pharmacopoeias and a method for their classification. *Amer.J.Pharm.*, 1944, 116: 162-3.

RMwo South Eastern Europe

ORIENT, Julius. Aus pharmazeutischer Vergangenheit Siebenbuergens und des Banates. Transl. by Edgar Mueller. 58 p., 18 ill. (*Veröffentl.Int.Ges.Gesch.Pharm.*) Mittenwald: Nemayer, 1930. [CB 29/317]

VRGOČ, A. Historisches aus der kroatischen Pharmazie. *Vortr. Ges.Gesch.Pharm.* (München, 1938), p. 129-36. Wien: 1939.

RMwp/wv Africa; Asia

RMwq

BEAUGÉ, Charles. Les médicaments usuels du Fellah égyptien. *Arch.Medicochir.Provence,* 1923, 13: 388-92.

RMws

CHOPRA, Ram Nath. Indigenous drugs of India, their medical and economic aspects. xxii, 655 p. Calcutta: Art Press, 1933.

RMwt

NOZOC, T. La pharmacie au Japon. *J.Pharm.Chim.*, 1926, *8th ser.*, 3: 41-6, 90-4. [CB 22/242]

RMwt-cg

JAPANESE PHARMACOPEIAL ASSOCIATION. Seventy-five years of the Japanese pharmacopoeia. 54 p. Tokyo: 1961.
Reviewed in *Pharm.Hist.*, 1962, 7: 9.

SIMIZU, Tootaroo. History of the Japanese pharmacopeia. *J. Pract.Pharm.*, 1961, 12: 697-700, 909-18.

RMwv-cg

UNE VIEILLE pharmacopée Siamoise inédite. Par G. *Rev.Hist. Pharm.*, 1932, 3: 96-7.
A note on the partial French translation of a Siamese formulary by Auguste Escaich and Professor Lorgeau.

RMxx museums

CABANIS, C.J. Le Musée George Sand fondé par Jean Depruneaux. *Rev.Hist.Pharm.*, 1959, 47: 137-9.

DAS DEUTSCHE APOTHEKENMUSEUM. Ein Geleitwort zu seiner Gründung. *Deut.Apoth.Zeitung.Gesch.Beil*, 1937, no. 6-7, 17-20.

FIEK, Wolfgang. Die pharmaziegeschichtliche Sammlung im Thüringer Museum zu Eisenach. *Vortr.Ges.Gesch.Pharm.* (Basel, 1934) 49 p., 34 fig. Mittenwald: 1934.

GRIFFENHAGEN, George. Pharmacy museums. 51 p., 7 ill. Madison, Wis.: American Institute of the History of Pharmacy. 1956.

IZSAK, S. La Collection - Musée d'Histoire de la Pharmacie de Cluj. *Arch.Iberoamer.Hist.Med.*, 1957, 9: 281-8.

MORITZ-VILLARME, Mme. Le musée cantonal fondé par Henri Piffault. *Rev.Hist.Pharm.*, 1959, 47: 135-6.
Many pharmaceutical objects were given to the Museum by its founder.

SCHOOR, Oscar van. Die Pharmazie der alten Abtei Orval und das neue Medico-Pharmazeutische Museum Orval's. *Vortr. Ges.Gesch.Pharm.* (Basel, 1934), p. 8-14, ill. Mittenwald: 1934.

URDANG, George. Die Pharmazie im Wellcome-Museum in London. *Pharm.Z.*, 1934, 214-17.

RMyNW HOSPITAL PHARMACY

RMyNWwe

ANNING, S.T. The apothecaries of the General Infirmary at Leeds. *Med.Hist.*, 1961, 5: 221-38.

RMyNWwf

BERMAN, Alex. The scientific tradition in French hospital pharmacy. *Amer.J.Hosp.Pharm.*, 1961, 18: 110-19.

RMyQV MILITARY PHARMACY

RMyQVfqd

MURAINE, R. The Museum of Val-de-Grace and the commission of the history of military pharmacy. *Rev.Hist.Pharm.*, 1962, 50: 329-31.

RMyQVwb

BIENFANG, Ralph. Thumbnail history of pharmacy in the U.S. Army. *Amer.J.Pharm.Educ.*, 1945, 9: 223-8.

BIENFANG, Ralph. The history of military pharmacy in the United States: a progress report. *Amer.J.Pharm.Educ.*, 1947, 11: 154-6.

RMyQVwf

BALLAND, A. La pharmacie militaire française des origines à nos jours. *J.Pharm.Chim.*, 1912, 6: 351-9, 400-7, 449-97, 500-9.

BALLAND, A. Les pharmaciens militaires. 418 p. Paris: L. Fournier, 1913.

BASTIAN, Emil. Grades et uniformes des pharmaciens militaires français. *Rev.Hist.Pharm.*, 1962, 50: 339-59, ill

NAUROY, -. Les pharmaciens militaires français au Maroc. *Rev.Hist.Pharm.*, 1962, 50: 315-25.

PHARMACIENS des armées. *Rev.Hist.Pharm.*, 1962, 50: 313-64.
A collection of articles in memory of some military pharmacists.
Reviewed by Pierre F. Smith, *Pharm.Hist.*, 1963, 8: 29.

RMyQVwj

ROLDAN Y GUERRERO, Rafael. Historia del cuerpo de farmacia militar del ejército Español. *Arch.Iberoamer.Hist.Med.*, 1953, 5: 3-72, 379-431; 1954, 6: 31-108, 283-344; 1955, 7: 43-93, 355-419, 485-535; 1958, 10: 161-80, 275-93; 1959, 11: 11-60, 262-73: 1960, 12: 95-119.

RMyQVwn-cg

BERMAN, Alex. Early Russian military and naval formularies. In: American Institute of the History of Pharmacy. Three essays on formularies, p. 7-10. Madison, Wis.: 1961.

BERMAN, Alex. Early Russian military and naval formularies 1765-1840. *Amer.J.Hosp.Pharm.*, 1960, 17: 210-18.

RMyQX AVIATION PHARMACY

URDANG, George. Pharmacy and aviation. *Amer.J.Pharm.Educ.*, 1945, 9: 207-9.

RN PRACTICAL PHARMACY

BRUNN, Walter von. Von alter Apothekerkunst. *Knoll's Mitt. Ärzte*, Sept. 1935, 10-14, 7 ill.

COLLARD, E. Il y a pommade et pommade. *Rev.Hist.Pharm.*, 1962, 15: fasc. 172, 243-6.

DIEPGEN, Paul. Das Elixir, die köstlichste der Arzneien. 45 p., ill. Ingelheim am Rhein: Boehringer, 1951.
Reviewed by Sten Lindroth, *Lychnos*, 1953, 441.

FOOTE, P.A. Tablets. 1. The evolution of the tablet machine. 2. A bibliography on tablets. 164 p., ill. (Bulletin of the University of Wisconsin, 1566) Madison: 1928.

URDANG, George. Pills for everything. *What's New*, 1943. 5-6, 13-14.

URDANG, George. Quintessence. The story of extracts. *What's New*, 1944, 6-9, 18-19, ill.

RNqt

BUCHET, Charles. Essai sur l'histoire de la droguerie. *Compt.Rend.IIe Congr.Int.Hist.Méd.* (Paris, 1921), p. 300-13. Évreux: Imprimerie Ch. Hérissey, 1922.

URDANG, George. Retail pharmacy as the nucleus of the pharmaceutical industry. *Essays in the History of Medicine presented to Prof. Arturo Castiglioni*, p. 325-46, 4 fig. Baltimore: Johns Hopkins Press, 1944.

RNwb-qs

URDANG, George. The precedents of the National Retail Druggists' Association and its founding fifty years ago. *Amer. J.Pharm.Educ.*, April 1949, 358-75.

RNwb-qt

GRIFFENHAGEN, George. Early American pharmacies. A pictorial catalog of apothecary shop restorations which are on exhibition in the United States. 23 p., ill. Washington: American Pharmaceutical Association, 1955.

URDANG, George; NITARDY, F.W. The Squibb ancient pharmacy. A catalogue of the collection. 190 p., ill. New York: Squibb, 1940. [CB 59/493]
Description of the ancient pharmacy established by the firm E.R. Squibb & Sons in New York and catalogue of the objects exhibited.

RNwe-qt

CHAPMAN-HUSTON, Desmond; CRIPPS, Ernest C. Through a city archway. The story of Allen & Hanburys, 1715-1954. xv, 326 p., front., 48 pl. London: John Murray, 1954. [CB 81/283]

CRIPPS, Ernest C. Plough Court, the story of a notable pharmacy, 1715-1927. xviii, 227 p., 43 ill. London: Allen and Hanburys, 1927. [CB 25/438]

RNwf-qp

COTINAT, Louis. L'Abbaye du Val-Saint-Pierre et les reliques de son apothicairerie. *Rev.Hist.Pharm.*, 1958, 46: 409-15.

RNwf-qt

APOTHICAIRERIES de France. *Libre Pharm.*, 1961, no. 167, ill.
Special number.

RNwg-qt

AUS der Geschichte der Engelapotheke zu Augsburg. *Deut.Apoth. Zeitung.Gesch.Beil*, 1936-37, no. 2, 5-8.

BORKOWSKY, Ernst. Die Löwenapotheke in Naumburg an der Saale. Eine Geschichte des städt. Medizinalwesens nach den Akten des Ratsarchivs. 64 p., ill. Mittenwald (Bayern): Nemayer, 1935.

BRUNN, Walter von. Der schöne Renaissance-Erker der Ratsapotheke zu Lemgo in Lippe. *Med.Welt*, 1939, 13: 199-200, 7 pl

FERCHL, Fritz. Münchens älteste Apotheke. Geschichte der Schützen-Apotheke von den Anfängen bis zur Jetztzeit. 62 p., ill. Stuttgart: Wissensch. Verlagsgesellschaft, 1927.

FESTSCHRIFT zum 350 jähr. Jubiläum der Stadt-Apotheke zum Löwen zu Pirna 1928. Bearb. von Herm. Kunz-Krause, nebst Beiträgen von H. Munkelt. Hrsg. von Julius Friedr. Leo. 154, xii p., portr., fig. Pirna: Selbstverlag, 1928.
Reviewed by Zaunick, *Mitt.Gesch.Med.*, 1930, 29: 48.

JENDREYCZYK, Ernst; POOTH, Peter. Aus der Geschichte der Stralsunder Apotheken. 2 vol., ill. Mittenwald, Bayern: Nemayer (im Auftrag der Gesellschaft für Geschichte der Pharmazie), [1939].

KLEBS, Arnold C. Die Lemgoer Ratsapotheke. Historische Reiseskizze [1612?]. *Arch.Gesch.Naturwiss.Tech.*, 1913, 5: 102-7, 2 pl.

KUNZ-KRAUSE, H. Die Mohren-Apotheke zu Dresden im Wandel der Zeiten. *Pharm.Zeitung*, 1930, 75: 740-1, ill.

NEUSS, Erich. Geschichte der Apotheke "Zum blauen Hirsch" in Halle a.d. Saale. 1535-1935. 61 p., ill. Mittenwald (Bayern): Nemayer, 1935.

SCHMIDT, Alfred. Die Kölner Apotheken. Von der ältesten Zeit bis zum Ende der Reichsstädtischen Verfassung. Vornehmlich auf Grund des von Friedrich Bellingrodt gesammelten Materials verf. und hrsg. 2nd ed. x, 164 p., 27 pl. Mittenwald: Nemeyer, 1930.
First publ. Bonn: Hanstein, 1918.

STELLJES, W. 350 Jahre Hofapotheke am Markt (zur Geschichte der Rats- und Hofapotheke zu Eisenach). Bildschmuck von Felix Schuchard. 40 p., ill. Berlin: Gesellschaft für Geschichte der Pharmazie, 1935.

TAUB, Ludwig. Die Entwicklung des Arzneimittelbestandes in den deutschen Apotheken. Vortrag. *Z.Angew.Chem.*, 1912, 25: 591.
Report of this lecture to the Wupperthaler Ortsgruppe des Rheinischen Bezirksvereins.

URDANG, George. A visit to a German pharmacy in 1950. An impressionistic report. *Amer.J.Pharm.Educ.*, 1950, 14: 571-7.

VESTER, Helmut. Topographische Literatursammlung zur Geschichte der deutschen Apotheken. 1. Deutsche Städte und Ortschaften; 2. Deutsche Länder, Provinzen, etc.; 3. Deutsches Reichsgebiet. 4 parts continuously paged. xii, 474 p. (Veröffentlichungen der Internationalen Gesellschaft für Geschichte der Pharmazie, *new ser.*, 9, 14, 17, 19) Eutin: 1956; Stuttgart: 1959, 1960, 1961.
Reviewed by David L. Cowen, *Pharm.Hist.*, 1963, 8: 26-7.

RNwh-qt

HALMAI, János. [The "Golden Horn" pharmacy in Debreczen. (In Hungarian with summaries in Russian and German)] *Országos Orv.Könyvtar Közleményei*, 1957, no. 5, 175-97, 3 fig. [CB 83/258]

RNwj-qp

DOMINGO JIMENO, P.; GOMEZ, P.I. La farmacia en los monasterios españoles de la Orden de los Cartujos. *An.Acad.Farm.Madrid*, 1964, 30: 77-104.

FOLCH JOU, Guillermo; HERRERO HINOJO, Pilar. Datos sobre la farmacia del Monasterio de Santo Toribio de Liébana. *Arch. Iberoamer.Hist.Med.*, 1960, 12: 169-77.

RNwk-qp

MULS, G. L'Abbaye d'Orval et sa pharmacie. *Ann.E.Merck*, 1935, 1ere partie. [CB 50/402]

SCHOOR, Oscar van. Die Pharmazie der alten Abtei Orval und das neue Medico-Pharmazeutische Museum Orval's. *Vortr.Ges. Gesch.Pharm.*(Basel, 1934), p. 8-14, ill. Mittenwald: 1934.

RNwk-qt

SEGERS, E.G.; WITTOP KONING, D.A. Apothicaireries anciennes en Benelux. 50 p., fig. Deventer: Davo, 1958.
Reviewed by G., *Rev.Hist.Pharm.*, 1959, 47: 45.

TRICOT-ROYER, J.J.G. La pharmacie du Taciturne à Anvers. *Compt.Rend.IIe Congr.Int.Hist.Méd.*(Paris, 1921), p. 590-1, 1 pl. Evreux: 1922.

RNwm-qt

DELPHIN, T. Akademie Apoteket Kronan i Uppsala 1628-1928. [The Academy Pharmacy Kronan in Uppsala. (In Swedish)] 262 p. Uppsala: Almqvist & Wiksells, 1942.
Reviewed by Martin Lundqvist, *Lychnos*, 1943, 425-6.

RNwn-qt

LIHBERT, Rudolf. Zur 500 Jahrfeier der Ratsapotheke in Reval 1422-1922. *Pharmacia*, 1922, 2: 157-64.

SEUBERLICH, Erich. Liv-und Estlands aelteste Apotheken. 271 p. Riga: W.F. Haecker, 1912. [CB 14/558]

RNwt-qt

CHEN, K.K. Chinese drug stores. *Ann.Med.Hist.*, 1925, 7: 103-9, ill.
Account of present day conditions.

RNx techniques and instruments; equipment

RNxb

CASTIGLIONI, Arturo. Apothecary jars in antiquity; Apothecary jars in the Renaissance; The pharmacy in the American colonies. *Ciba Symp.*, 1945, 6: 2054-60, 2061-81, 2082-4, ill.

CAZALA, Mme. Roger. Les mortiers d'apothicaires. 108 p., ill. Grenoble: Allier, 1953.
Reviewed by D.A. Wittop Koning, *Arch.Int.Hist.Sci.*, 1953, 6: 529.

DÖRR, Walter. Schrezheim, die schwäbische Apothekengefäss-Manufaktur. *Vortr.Ges.Gesch.Pharm.* (Stuttgart, 1936), p. 7-11, 1 fig. Mittenwald: 1936.

DORVEAUX, Paul. Les pots de pharmacie. Leur historique, suivi d'un dictionnaire de leurs inscriptions. 2nd ed. 89 p., 8 pl. Toulouse: Marqueste, 1923.

DRAKE, T.G.H. Antique pewter of medical interest. *Bull. Hist.Med.*, 1941, 10: 272-87; 1955, 29: 420-8, 7 fig.

FERCHL, Fritz. Deutsche Apotheken-Altertümer. 16 p., 24 ill. Nürnberg: Germanisches Nationalmuseum, 1936.

GOUNOT, Roger. Les mortiers du Puy-en-Velay. *Rev.Hist. Pharm.*, 1962, 175: 391-5.

HAEFLIGER, Josef Anton. Heilgefässe. *Festschrift für Jacques Brodbeck-Sandreuter, zu seinem 60.Geburtstag*, p. 23-26, 16 fig. Basel: Schwabe, 1942.

HAYTON, J.J. Seven ages of the container. *Chem.Drug.*, 1961, 176: 682-3.

MILLIKEN, William M. Majolica drug jars. *Bull.Med.Libr.Ass.*, 1944, 32: 293-303, 7 fig.

PESCE, Giovanni. Maioliche liguri da farmacia. li, 110 p., ill. Milan: Alfieri, 1960.
Reviewed by Ernst W. Stieb, *Pharm.Hist.*, 1962, 7: 13-14.

SPIERS, C.H. Glass, metal, pottery, wood, or what you will: pharmaceutical objects in one material copied in others. *Chem.Drug.*, 1962, 177: 715-22.

TERGOLINA-GISLANZONI-BRASCO, U. I vasi di farmacia di Cerreto Sannita. *Atti Mem.Accad.Stor.Arte Sanit.*, 1964, 29: 48-58.

THUILE, Jean. Les pots de pharmacie à l'exposition de l'ancienne faïence de Montpellier du Musée Fabre. 2. Après 1600. *Rev.Hist.Pharm.*, 1963, no. 179, 204-7.

ÜNVER, A. Süheyl. Les armoires à médicaments dans nos anciennes maisons. *Türk Tib Tarihi Arkivi*, 1938, 2: 94-5.

VANDEWIELE, L.J. Apothekerspotten in het Diocesaans Museum te Mechelen. [Chemists' pots in the Diocesan Museum of Mechelen. (In Dutch)] *Pharm.Tijdschr.Belg.*, 1958, 35: 98.

ZAYAS-BAZÁN Y PERDOMO, Héctor. El arte cerámico farmacéutico. *Rev.Argent.Hist.Med.*, 1944, 3: no. 2, 67-83.

RNxd

BRANDEL, I.W.; KREMERS, Edward. Percolation. 54 p., 43 fig. (Pharmaceutical Science Series, 22) Milwaukee: Pharmaceutical Review Publishing Co., 1928.
Historical introduction covering 5 p.

FLOSDORF, Earl W.; HULL, Lewis W.; MUDD, Stuart. Drying by sublimation. *J.Immunol.*, 1945, 501: 21-54. [CB 73/182]

RNxm

MERCK Y BANON, Augustin Maria. Antigua metrología farmacéutica. 176 p., ill. Valencia: Librería Prometeo, 1960.
Reviewed by G.E. Osborne, *Pharm.Hist.*, 1962, 7: 12-13.

RO MODE OF ADMINISTRATION OF DRUGS

DIEPGEN, Paul. Das Analzäpfchen in der Geschichte der Therapie. 44 p., 3 fig. Stuttgart: Thieme, 1953. [CB 80/137]

EBSTEIN, Erich. On the development of intravenous therapy. *Med.Life*, 1923, 30: 601-11.

HOWARD-JONES, Norman. A critical study of the origins and early development of hypodermic medication. *J.Hist.Med.*, 1947, 2: 201-49, 15 fig.

KREMERS, Edward. Modes of administration. *Proc.Wisc.Pharm. Ass.*, 1931, 51: 32-6. [CB 34/528]

SIMILI, Alessandro. Quando sorsero le iniezioni saline endovenose e ipodermiche? *Riv.Stor.Sci.*, 1934, 25: 123-43.

VILLARET, Maurice; MOUTIER, François. Les origines de l'injection thérapeutique intra-veineuse. *Compt.Rend.IIe Congr. Int.Hist.Méd.* (Paris, 1921), p. 201-10. Évreux: Imprimerie Ch. Hérissey, 1922.

VILLARET, Maurice; MOUTIER, François. La singulière histoire de l'injection intra-veineuse. *Hippocrate*, 1933, 1: no. 4. 785-812.
Reviewed in *Bull.Soc.Franç.Hist.Méd.*, 1934, 28: 254.

ROxk

GRUBER, Georg B. Die Sattenhäusener Spritze. (Zur Frage antiker Spritzen-Instrumente.) *Sudhoffs Arch.*, 1953, 37: 246-9.

RP PHARMACO-BOTANY; PHARMACOGNOSY

RPc general history

ANDEL, M.A. van. Giftplanten als genees- en toovermiddelen. Voordracht gehouden in de algemeene vergadering der Vereeniging van geschiedenis der genees-, natuur-, en wiskunde, op Zondag 17 October 1920 to Gorinchem. [Poisonous plants as materia medica and charms. (In Dutch)] *Bijdr.Gesch.Geneesk.*, 1921, 1: 18-32.

BERGMARK, Matts. Lust och lidande. Läkeörter, giftdroger och kärleksdrycker. [Pleasure and suffering. Medical herbs, poisonous drugs and love potions. (In Swedish)] 3rd enl. and rev. ed. 267 p., ill. Stockholm: Natur och Kultur, 1963.
Reviewed by Nils von Hofsten, *Lychnos*, 1962, 520-1.

BÖHNER, Konrad. Geschichte der Cecidologie. Ein Beitrag zur Entwicklungsgeschichte naturwissenschaftlicher Forschung und ein Führer durch die Cecidologie der Alten. Mit einer Vorgeschichte zur Cecidologie der klassischen Schriftsteller von Felix von Öfele. 2 vol. 1. Allgemeiner Teil. xxvii, 466 p., 27 fig.; 2. Besonderer Teil. 712 p., 138 fig. (Veröffentlichungen der Gesellschaft für Geschichte der Pharmazie) Mittenwald: Nemayer, 1933-35.
Reviewed by George Sarton, *Isis*, 1935, 24: 180-3, 2 fig.

DELATTE, Armand. Herbarius, recherches sur le cérémonial usité chez les anciens pour la cueillette des simples et des plantes magiques. 2nd ed. 177 p., ill. (Bibliothèque de la faculté de philosophie et lettres de l'Université de Liége, fasc. 81) Liége: 1938.
First publ. in *Bull.Acad.Roy.Belg.Cl.Lett.*. 1936, 22: 227-348 and reviewed by Conway Zirkle, *Isis*, 1937, 27: 531-2.

KREIG, Margaret B. Green medicine. The search for plants that heal. 462 p., ill. New York/Chicago: Rand McNally, 1964. [CB 90/536]

LEHNER, Ernst; LEHNER, Johanna. Folklore and odysseys of food and medicinal plants. 128 p. New York: Tudor Publishing Co., 1960.
Reviewed by Richard Evans Schultes, *Econ.Bot.*, 1963, 17: 154.

MacPHILLAMY, H.B. Drugs from plants. *Plant Sci.Bull.*, 1963, 9: no. 2, 1-5.

MARZELL, Heinrich. Der Zauber der Heilkräuter in der Antike und Neuzeit. *Arch.Gesch.Med.*, 1936, 29: 3-26.

MONTEIRO, Arlindo Camilo. Da fitologia sacra. Contribução histórica para o estudo da botânica, da terapêutica e da etnografia. 140 p., pl. [Lisboa]: Edição do autor, 1934.
Reviewed by Paul M. O'Sullivan, *Isis*, 1936, 26: 223-4.

NETOLITZKY, Fritz. Zur Geschichte der ersten Auffindung der Heil- und Gewürzpflanzen. *Heil Gewürzpflanzen*, 1930, 12: 152-60.

PROOIJEN, A.M. van. Farmacohistorische studiën. [Studies in the history of pharmacy. (In Dutch with summaries in French)] No. 1-. *Pharm.Tijdschr.Belg.*, 1937, 15: 2-.
A continuing series of articles on individual medicinal plants; no. 100. Zingiber [Ginger]. *ibid.*, 1962, 39: 99-107; no. 111.[the last covered by this Bibliography] Maydis amylum [Maize]. *ibid.*, 1964, 41: 259-69.

RAYMOND, Paul. Nos confrères les arbres guérisseurs. *Compt. Rend.IIe Congr.Int.Hist.Méd.* (Paris, 1921), p. 226-32. Évreux: Imprimerie Ch. Hérissey, 1922.

RODDIS, Louis H. Materials and outline for a short history of pharmacognosy. *Amer.J.Pharm.Educ.*, 1945, 9: 19-21.

SCHEER, Hermann. Fragmente zur Arzneigeschichte. 1. Warum treiben wir heute Geschichte der Heilmittel?; 2. Einleitung zur Geschichte einer Heilpflanze; 3. Mensch und Pflanze. *Speculum*, 1929, 131-44.

SCHWARZ, Hedwig. Pharmaziegeschichtliche Pflanzen-Studien. 76 p., ill. Mittenwald: Nemayer (for Gesellschaft für Geschichte der Pharmazie), 1931.

TREASE, George E. A textbook of pharmacognosy. 8th ed. London: Balliére, Tindall, & Cos, 1961.
Reviewed by J. Hampton Hoch, *Pharm.Hist.*, 1962, 7: 52.

URDANG, George. Materials and outline for a short history of pharmacognosy. *Amer.J.Pharm.Educ.*, 1945, 9: 199-206.

VERDOORN, Frans. From empiricism to applied science in pharmaco-botany, with some remarks on the need for institutions for certain branches of the history of science. 10th Anniversary Conference, American Institute of the History of Pharmacy, Madison, May, 1951. *Amer.J.Pharm.Educ.*, 1951, 15: 338-48.

RPc-bv

HOCH, J. Hampton. Bibliographic materials in English relating to the history of pharmacognosy. *Amer.J.Pharm.Educ.*, 1959, 23: 154-60.

RPcg

KROEBER, Ludwig. "Kräuterbücher" in alter und neuer Zeit. *Festschrift für A. Tschirsch zu seinem 70.Geburtstag,* p. 108-20. Leipzig: H. Tauchnitz, 1926.

MARCUS, Margaret Fairbanks. The herbal as art. *Bull.Med. Libr.Ass.*, 1944, 32: 376-84, 4 fig.

NISSEN, Claus. Kräuterbücher aus fünf Jahrhunderten. 50 Originalblätter aus deutschen, französischen, niederlandischen, englischen, italienischen und schweizerischen Kräuterbüchern. Mit medizinhistorischer Einleitung und Bibliographie. x, 84 p. 50 Originalblätter. In Leinenkassette, Aufl. von 200 numerierten Exemplaren (100 mit deutschem, 100 mit englishem Text). München/Zürich/Olten: 1956.
Reviewed by M. Rooseboom, *Arch.Int.Hist.Sci.*, 1956, 35: 270-1.
Also published with English text (Herbals of five centuries) and distributed by Dawson's. Reviewed by Glenn Sonnedecker, *Isis,* 1959, 50: 494-5.

SCHMID, Alfred. Ueber alte Kräuterbücher. 75 p., ill. Bern: Haupt, 1939.
Reviewed by Otto Gertz, *Lychnos,* 1940, 454.

RPcg-b

FISCH, Ruth B.; FISCH, Max H. The Marshall Collection of Herbals in the Cleveland Medical Library. *Bull.Hist.Med.* 1947, 21: 224-61.

RPda

PORTER, Charles Lyman. Contributions of early botanists to pharmaceutical knowledge. *Amer.J.Pharm.Educ.*, 1944, 8: 54-72.

RPr

BUDGE, E.A. Wallis. The divine origin of the craft of the herbalist. xii, 96 p., 13 ill. London: Society of Herbalists, 1928.

RPu-cc

REIS, Siri von. Herbaria: sources of medicinal folklore. *Econ.Bot.*, 1962, 16: 283-7.

RPw in different countries

RPwb

BALLARD, C.W.; CHENEY, R.H.; POCORNY, F.J. Medicinal uses of drug plants cultivated in the plant garden of the Brooklyn Botanic Garden. *Brooklyn Bot.Gard.Rec.*, 1943, 32: 187-209.
A short description of the medicinal history of ninety plants.

LLOYD, J.U.; LLOYD, C.G. Drugs and medicines of North America. A publication devoted to the historical and scientific discussion of the botany, pharmacy, chemistry and therapeutics of the medical plants of North America. Their constituents, products and sophistications. (1884-1887). 2 vol. viii, 304 p., pl., fig.; 162 p., pl., fig. (*Bull.Lloyd Libr.Bot. Pharm.Mater.Med.*, 29, 30, 31) Cincinnati: 1930-31.
A facsimile reprint.

RPwe-cg

ROHDE, Eleanour Sinclair. The old English herbals. xii, 243 p., ill. London: Longmans, Green, 1922. [CB 15/213]
Reviewed by G. Sarton, *Isis,* 1923, 5: 457-61.
Revised and enlarged edition, entitled A garden of herbs (London: 1926).

RPwe-u

DALL, Nan L.G. Scots herbal lore. *Proc.Scot.Anthropol.Soc.*, 1938, 3: 3-21.

MOLONEY, Michael F. Irish ethno-botany and the evolution of medicine in Ireland. 96 p. Dublin: Gill, 1919 [CB 12/631]

RPwf

FOURNIER, P. Le livre des plantes médicinales et véneneuses de France. 3 vol. (Encyclopédie Biologique, 25, 31, 32) Paris: Lechevalier, 1947-48.
Vol. 1 reviewed by W.O. James, *Nature,* 1949, 163: 383-4.

LECLERC, Henri. Les légumes de France. Leur histoire, leurs usages alimentaires, leurs vertus thérapeutiques. 217 p. Paris: Masson, 1928.
Reviewed by M. Laignel-Lavastine, *Bull.Soc.Franç.Hist.Méd.*, 1928, 22: 221-2.

LECLERC, Henri. Les fruits de France, historique, diététique et thérapeutique. 274 p. Paris: Masson, 1925.

RPwg

WEISS, Walter. Betrachtungen zur Förderung des Anbaues von Heilpflanzen im Erzgebirge. *Arch.Gesch.Med.*, 1936, 29: 313-20, 1 fig.

WEISS, Walter. Das schlesische Arzneipflanzenwesen im Spiegel der Gesetze und der Statistik. *Mitt.Gesch.Med.*, 1940, 39: 229-34.

RPwg-cg

KRAUSE, Ernst H.L. Anmerkungen zum elsass-lothringischen Kräuterbuche ("Florenklein"). *Bull.Ass.Philomath.Alsace Lorraine,* 1912, 4: 669-89.

RPwg-nh

SCHELENZ, Hermann. Daher der Name opodeldok. *Mitt.Gesch.Med.*, 1913, 12: 270.

RPwg-r

LEHMANN, Ernst. Schwäbische Apotheker und Apothekergeschlechter in ihrer Beziehung zur Botanik. 218 p., ill. Stuttgart: Hempe, 1951.
Reviewed by D.A. Wittop Koning, *Arch.Int.Hist.Sci.*, 1952, 5: 417-18.

RPwg-u

ARENDS, Georg. Volkstümliche Anwendung der einheimischen Arzneipflanzen. 2nd ed. 97 p. Berlin: Springer, 1925.

MARZELL, Heinrich. Heilkräuter in der deutschen und der südslawischen Volksmedizin. *Sudhoffs Arch.*, 1941, 34: 133-6.

MARZELL, Heinrich. Unsere Heilpflanzen, ihre Geschichte und ihre Stellung in der Volkskunde. Ethnobotanische Streifzüge. xxviii, 240 p., 38 ill. Freiburg im Breisgau: Theodor Fischer, 1922; München: Lehmann, 1930.
Reviewed by B. Laufer, *Isis,* 1923, 5: 456-7.

RPwk

COHEN, Hendrik. Bijdrage tot de geschiedenis der geneeskruidcultuur in Nederland. [A contribution to the history of the cultivation of medicinal plants in the Netherlands. (In Dutch)] xxiii, 251 p., 20 pl. (Thesis) Rotterdam: Brusse, 1927.
Reviewed by M.A. van Andel, *Bijdr.Gesch.Geneesk.*, 1927, 7: 375-6.

RPwm

ANKER, Jean. Flora Danica og Laegekunsten. [Flora Danica and the art of healing. (In Danish)] *Med.Forum*, 1951, 4: 1-15.

RPwo

BORZA, Al.; BUTURĂ, Valeriu. Bäuerliche Pflanzenheilmittel in der Moldau (Rumänien). *Arch.Gesch.Med.*, 1938, 31: 81-6.

MARZELL, Heinrich. Heilkräuter in der deutschen und der südslawischen Volksmedizin. *Sudhoffs Arch.*, 1941, 34: 133-6.

RPx techniques and instruments

RPxf-XF

TSCHIRCH, A. Die Erfindung der panchromatischen Platte und ihre Bedeutung für die Pharmakognosie. *Vortr.Ges.Gesch. Pharm.* (Basel, 1934), p. 196-202, ill. Mittenwald: 1934.

RPxy physic gardens

DREWITT, F. Dawtrey. The romance of the Apothecaries' Garden at Chelsea. 2nd ed. x, 136 p., ill. London: Chapman and Dodd, 1924. [CB 18/622]

POWER, D'Arcy. The Oxford Physic Garden. *Ann.Med.Hist.*, 1919, 2: 109-25, 7 ill. [CB 8/340]

VINES, S.H.; DRUCE, G.C. An account of the Morisonian "Herbarium" in the possession of the University of Oxford. Biographical and critical sketches of Morison and the two Bobarts, and their works and the early history of the physic garden (1619-1720). lxviii, 350 p. Oxford: Clarendon Press, 1914.

WHEELWRIGHT, Edith Grey. The physick garden. 288 p., 17 pl. Boston: Houghton Mifflin, 1935. [CB 46/593]

WILLIAMS, Trevor I. The Chelsea Physic Garden. *Endeavour*, 1960, 19: 179-80.

RPy0 specific uses

RPy0R

SCHEVENSTEEN, A.F.C. van. Les plantes dans les maladies des yeux; étude de folklore. *Compt.Rend.IIe Congr.Int.Hist. Méd.* (Paris, 1921), p. 341-67. Évreux: Imprimerie Ch. Hérissey, 1922.

RPy0X

TISCHER, Max. Ueber die Asthmabehandlung mit pflanzlichen Heilmitteln in der Volksheilkunde und in der Medizin seit dem 16. Jahrhundert. 86 p. (*Abhandl.Gesch.Med.Naturwiss.*, 32) Berlin: Ebering, 1939.

RQ NAMED MEDICINAL PLANTS

for cinchona, curare, digitalis and mandragora *see* RQz

ALSTON, A.H.G. What is lucerrage? Answer no. 2 to Query 104 [*see* Sarton, George, below] *Isis*, 1948, 39: 234.

BAKKER, C. De aanwending van het kruid *echium* in de oude geneeskunde. [The use of the herb *echium* in bygone medicine. (In Dutch)] *Bijdr.Gesch.Geneesk.*, 1929, 9: 149-51.

BERGMARK, Matts. Vallört och vitlök. Om folkmedicinens läkeörter. [Comfrey and garlic. About medicinal herbs of popular medicine. (In Swedish)] 268 p., ill. Stockholm: Natur och Kultur, 1961.
Reviewed by Nils von Hofsten, *Lychnos*, 1962, 519-20.

BÖTTCHER, Helmuth M. Wunderdrogen. Die abenteuerliche Geschichte der Heilpilze. 555 p. Cologne/Berlin: Kiepenheuer und Witsch, 1959.
Reviewed by Johannes Nabholz, *Pharm.Hist.*, 1963, 8: 24-5.

BRØNDEGAARD, V.J. Wegerich als Wundheilmittel in der Volks- und Schulmedizin. *Sudhoffs Arch.*, 1963, 47: 127-51.

BRUNN, Walter von. Das Maiglöckchen, eine alte, vielgerühmte Heilpflanze. Zum 50-jährigen Bestehen der Firma Degen & Kuth. 55 p., ill. Düren: 1937.
History of the lily-of-the-valley (*Convallaria maialis*) with a fine series of illustrations taken from the early herbals and many paintings.

BUESS, Heinrich. Zur Geschichte der *Atropa belladonna* als Arzneimittel. *Gesnerus*, 1953, 10: 37-52.

BURKILL, I.H.; MERRILL, E.D. What is lucerrage? Answer to Query 104 [*see* Sarton, George, below] *Isis*, 1944, 35: 176-7.
Probably *Gmelina villosa*.

CAMERON, G.R. The history of madder (*Rubia tinctorum*). *Ann. Med.Hist.*, 1932, 4: 466-73, 1 fig.

COPLEY, Alfred Lewin; BOSWELL, Helen. Aconite the love poison. *Bull.Hist.Med.*, 1944, 15: 420-6.

DARMSTAEDTER, Ernst. Die Ginseng-Wurzel. *Pharma-Med.*, 1935, 4: 75-80.

DARMSTAEDTER, Ernst. Moderne Knoblauch-Therapie. *Riedel-Arch.*, 1934, 23: 72-5.

DAU, Malve. Der Weissdorn (*Crataegus oxyacantha*). 103 p., 30 fig. (Monographien alter Heilpflanzen, 3) Hamburg: Hansischer Gildenverlag, 1941.
Reviewed by H. Marzell, *Mitt.Gesch.Med.*, 1941-42, 40: 167.

GNEKOW, Rolf. Die Goldrute. (*Solidago virga aurea* L.). 100 p., 44 fig. (Monographien alter Heilpflanzen, 1) Hamburg: Hansischer Gildenverlag, 1938.
Reviewed by H. Marzell, *Mitt.Gesch.Med.*, 1941-42, 40: 167.

GREVE, Paul. Der Sumpfpost (*Ledum palustre* L.). 120 p., 43 fig. (Monographien alter Heilpflanzen, 2) Hamburg: Hansischer Gildenverlag, 1938.
Reviewed by H. Marzell, *Mitt.Gesch.Med.*, 1941-42, 40: 167.

GÜNTZEL-LINGNER, H. Der Knoblauch. 76 p., 2 pl., fig. (Zinssers Kleine Heilpflanzen-Monographien, 1) Leipzig: Zinsser, 1941.
Reviewed by R. Zaunick, *Mitt.Gesch.Med.*, 1941-42, 40: 101.

GUTIERREZ-NORIEGA, Carlos; ORTIZ, Vicente Capata. Estudios sobre la coca y la cocaina en el Peru. 144 p. Lima: Ministerio de Educación Pública, 1947. [CB 73/186]

HABELT, Theodor. Zur Geschichte der medizinischen Verwendung der Kamille (*Matricaria chamomilla* L.). 31 p. Leipzig: Institut für Geschichte der Medizin, 1935.

HEYSER, Kurt. Die Alliumarten als Arzneimittel im Gebrauch der abendländischen Medizin. *Kyklos*, 1929, 1: 64-102.

HIRSCHFELD, Ernst. Studien zur Geschichte der Heilpflanzen. *Kyklos*, 1929, 2: 145-79, 5 fig.
1. Lilium convallium; 2. Scilla.

HODGE, W.H. The drug Aloes of commerce, with special reference to the Cape species. *Econ.Bot.*, 1953, 7: 99-129. [CB 80/138]

HOFSTEN, Nils von. Bedeguar och *Spina alba*: ett bidrag till "sömntornets" historia. [Bedeguar and *Spina alba*: a contribution to the history of the "sleep-thorn". (In Swedish)] *Lychnos*, 1953, 101-41.

KLEYN, H. Paddenstoelen en de geneeskunde. [Mushrooms in medicine. (In Dutch)] *Bijdr.Gesch.Geneesk.*, 1943, 23: 15-20.

LECLERC, Henri. Histoire de l'asphodèle. *Janus*, 1929, 33: 235-44.

LECLERC, Henri. Histoire de l'ail. *Janus*, 1918, 23: 167-91.

LECLERC, Henri. Histoire des ellébores et de l'elléborisme. *Janus*, 1917, 22: 223-38.

LECLERC, Henri. Histoire des sept plantes qui composent la tisane des quatre fleurs. *Janus*, 1923, 27: 74-97.

LECLERC, Henri. Histoire du pruneau. *Compt.Rend.IIe Congr. Int.Hist.Méd.*(Paris, 1921), p. 421-5. Évreux: Imprimerie Ch. Hérissey, 1922.

LECLERC, Henri. Histoire du romarin. *Janus,* 1930, 34: 196-204. [CB 32/616]

LECLERC, Henri. Histoire thérapeutique du cresson. *Janus,* 1931, 35: 313-34. [CB 36/459]

LECLERC, Henri. Les vieilles panacées: la livèche (*Ligusticum levisticum* L.). *Janus,* 1933, 37: 281-92.

LECLERC, Henri. Les vieilles panacées: la pimprenelle. *Janus,* 1933, 37: 19-30.

LIVET, Louis. Contribution à l'étude historique de la Jusquiame. *Bull.Soc.Franç.Hist.Méd.,* 1922, 16: 165-76.

MARZELL, Heinrich. Das Eisenkraut (*Verbena officinalis*) als Zauberpflanze. *Naturforscher,* 1926, 3: 419-25, ill.

MARZELL, Heinrich. Die Haselwurz (*Asarum europaeum* L.) in der alten Medizin. Eine Studie zur Geschichte einer deutschen Heilpfanze. *Sudhoffs Arch.,* 1958, 42: 319-25.

MARZELL, Heinrich. Zur Geschichte der Mariendistel (*Silybum marianum* Gärtn.) als Heilmittel. *Arch.Gesch.Med.,* 1939, 32: 94-103, 1 fig.

MARZELL, Heinrich. Zur Geschichte des Frauenblattes (*Chrysanthemum balsamita* L.). *Centaurus,* 1951, 1: 235-41, 1 fig.

MOÏSSIDÈS, M. Le fénugrec autrefois et aujourd'hui. *Janus,* 1939, 43: 123-30.

MÖLLER, Hans Jacob. *Lignum nephreticum.* 62 p., 2 pl. Copenhagen: 1912.

MONACHINO, Joseph. *Rauvolfia serpentina* - its history, botany and medical use. *Econ.Bot.,* 1954, 8: 349-65.
The source of a new drug for lowering high blood pressure.

MULLETT, Charles F. Tobacco as a drug in earlier English medicine. *Ann.Med.Hist.,* 1940, 2: 110-23.

NOACK, Barbara. Zur Geschichte des Thymians. 39 p. Leipzig: Institut für Geschichte der Medizin, 1936.

PARTINGTON, J.R. *Lignum nephriticum. Ann.Sci.,* 1955, 11: 1-26.

PICCININI, Prassitele. Il *Viscum album* nella storia delle scienze mediche e naturali. *Riv.Stor.Sci.,* 1923, 14: 78-86.

RATFISCH, Werner. Zur Geschichte der medizinischen Verwendung des Eibisch (*Althaea officinalis* L.). 34 p. (Diss., Institut für Geschichte der Medizin an der Universität Leipzig) Leipzig: Edelmann, 1936.

SAFFORD, William E. *Lignum nephreticum.* Its history and an account of the remarkable fluorescence of its infusion. *Annu.Rep.Smithsonian Inst. for 1915,* p. 271-98, 7 pl. Washington, D.C.: 1916. [CB 7/106]

SAFFORD, William E. Nature's magic. Rediscovery of a remarkable wood, first known in the sixteenth century (as lignum nephriticum), which produces with water a beautiful opalescence not yet explained by science. *Amer.Mus.J.,* 1918, 18: 48-54, ill.
Eysenhardtia polystachya of Mexico and *Pterocarpus indicus* of the Philippines.

SARTON, George. What is lucerrage? Query 104. *Isis,* 1943, 34: 512-13.
For answers, *see* above Alston, A.H.G. and Burkill, I.H., Merrill, E.D.

SCHADEWALDT, Hans. Das Johannisbrot, *Ceratonia siliqua* L. Eine kultur- und medizingeschichtliche Übersicht. *Ann. Nestle,* 1953, no. 2, 1-19, 9 fig.

SCHOFF, Wilfred H. Nard. *J.Amer.Orient.Soc.,* 1923, 43: 216, 228. [CB 16/291]

SHELLARD, E.J. An historical survey of some convolvulaceous drugs. *Chem.Drug.,* 1961, 176: 219-22.

SIGERIST, Henry E. *Herba momordica. Bull.Inst.Hist.Med.,* 1936, 4: 511-13. [CB 48/576]

SOULAIRE, Jacques. Cactus et médecine. Préface de M. Laignel-Lavastine. 190 p., 45 fig. Paris: Thiebaut, 1949.
Reviewed by B. Imbasciati, *Riv.Stor.Sci.,* 1951, 42: 110.

STANNARD, Jerry. The plant called moly. *Osiris,* 1962, 14: 254-307.

THOMPSON, C.J.S. The history of Hierapicra, one of the oldest known medicaments. *Proc.3rd Int.Congr.Hist.Med.* (London, 1922), p. 233-6. Antwerp: De Vlijt, 1923.

TORKOMIAN, Vahram H. A propos de l'histoire de la plante "kousso". *VIe Congr.Int.Hist.Méd.* (Leyde/Amsterdam, 1927), p. 104-7. Anvers: De Vlijt, 1929. Also *Rev.Etud.Arméniennes,* 1929, 8: 33-8. [CB 45/288]

TSCHOLAKOWA, Maria. Zur Geschichte der medizinischen Verwendung des Safran (*Crocus sativus*). *Kyklos,* 1929, 2: 179-90.

ZEKERT, Otto. Opiologia. Ein Beitrag zur Geschichte des Opiums und seiner Wirkstoffe. 172 p., ill. (HMW-Jahrbuch 1957) Wien: Heilmittelwerke Wien, 1956.
Reviewed by Martin Lundquist, *Lychnos,* 1957-58, 467-8.

RQwg

HORLBECK, Else. Die Salbei (*Salvia officinalis* L.). Ein Beitrag zu der Geschichte ihrer Verwendung in Deutschland vom Jahre 800 ab. 37 p. (Thesis, Leipzig) Eisfeld: C. Beck, 1937.

RQyOR

LECLERC, Henri. Deux plantes "casse-lunettes": le bleuet et l'euphraise. *Janus,* 1925, 29: 271-81. [CB 20/213]

MEYERHOF, Max. Histoire du chichm, remède ophtalmique des Égyptiens. *Janus,* 1914, 19: 261-88. [CB 11/448]
Refers chiefly to a powder made with the seeds of *Cassia absus L.*

ROUHIER, Alexandre. La plante qui fait les yeux émerveillés, le peyotl. (*Echinocactus Williamsi* Lem.) xii, 371 p., ill., map. Paris: Doin, 1927.

RQyQPzdy

DESCHIENS, R.; COSTE, Christine. L'histoire médicale des dysenteries sensibles à l'ipéca avant la découverte de l'amibe dysentérique. *Mem.Soc.Franç.Hist.Méd.,* 1946, 2: 97-105.

RQyQPzsy

KEIL, Harry. Comments on Munger's "Guaiacum, the holy wood from the New World". *J.Hist.Med.,* 1949, 4: 475-7
For Munger's article *see* below.

MUNGER, Robert S. Guaiacum, the Holy wood from the New World. *J.Hist.Med.,* 1949, 4: 196-229, 3 fig.
On the use of guaiacum in the treatment of syphilis.
For Harry Keil's comments on this article, *see* above.

RQyRE

MOLNAR, Eugene J. Cloves, oil of cloves, and eugenol. Their medico-dental history. *Dent.Items,* 1942, 64: 521-8, 663-7, 745-9, 876-80, 971-8.

RQzci CINCHONA

DURAN-REYNALS, M.L. The fever bark tree. The pageant of quinine. ix, 275 p. Garden City, N.Y.: Doubleday, 1946.
Reviewed by Erwin H. Ackerknecht, *Bull.Hist.Med.,* 1946, 20: 596; by Gaylord W. Anderson, *Amer.Hist.Rev.,* 1947, 52: 354.

HAGGIS, A.W. Fundamental errors in the early history of cinchona. *Bull.Hist.Med.,* 1941, 10: 417-59, fig., facs., 568-92.

JARAMILLO-ARANGO, Jaime. A critical review of the basic facts in the history of cinchona. *J.Linnean Soc.Bot..* 1949, 53: 272-309.

JARAMILLO-ARANGO, Jaime. Estudio critico acerca de los hechos basicos de la historia de la quina. *An.Soc.Peruana Hist. Med.,* 1948-49, 10: 31-88.

KREMERS, Edward. "Poudres des Jésuites" and ginseng. *Isis.* 1935, 23: 446.

LA WALL, Charles H. The history of quinine. *Med.Life*, 1931, 38: 195-216.

LULOFS, P.K. Drossaart. Een en ander uit de geschiedenis der kina. [A few points from the history of quinine. (In Dutch)] *Bijdr.Gesch.Geneesk.*, 1933, 13: 201-12.

RAMSBOTTOM, J. Jesuits' bark. *Natur.Hist.Mag.*, 1931, 3: 17-25.
The history of the use of cinchona from 1630 to the present day.

RICO-AVELLO, Carlos. Historia y leyenda en el descubrimiento de la quina. *Arch.Iberoamer.Hist.Med.*, 1957, 9: 445-8.

ROLLESTON, Humphrey. History of cinchona and its therapeutics. *Ann.Med.Hist.*, 1931, 3: 261-70.
Address at the Cinchona Tercentenary celebration at the Wellcome Historical Medical Museum, London, 10 December, 1930.

ST. LOUP BUSTILLO, Enrique. Acerca de la historia del descubrimiento de la quina. *Arch.Iberoamer.Hist.Med.*, 1957, 9: 491-6.

TAYLOR, Norman. Quinine: the story of cinchona. *Sci.Mon.*, 1943, 57: 17-32.

THE TERCENTENARY of cinchona in medicine. *Nature*, 1930, 126: 850-1, 975.

THOMPSON, C.J.S. The history and lore of cinchona. *Brit. Med.J.*, 1928, 2: 1188-90.

URDANG, George. The legend of cinchona. *Sci.Mon.*, 1945, 61: 17-20.
An inquiry as to the discovery of the value of quinine in curing malaria.

WELLCOME HISTORICAL MEDICAL MUSEUM, London. Souvenir. Cinchona tercentenary celebration and exhibition at the Museum. 114 p., ill., bibliogr. London: Wellcome Foundation, 1930.

WILSON, Charles Morrow. Quinine - reborn in our hemisphere. *Harper's Mag.*, 1943, 187: 275-80.

RQzci-wd

SERGI, Antonio. Introductione de cinchona in Europa. *Schola Vita*, 1931, 6: 173-6.

RQzci-wj

ROLDAM, R. Aportación de los espanoles al estudio de la quinología. *Arch.Iberoamer.Hist.Med.*, 1956, 8: 343-52.

RQzci-wv

TAYLOR, Norman. Cinchona in Java. Introduction by Pieter Honig. 87 p., 33 ill. New York: Greenberg, 1945. [CB 69/230]

RQzcu CURARE

BOVET, D.; BOVET-NITTI, F.; *et al.* El curaro. *Rendic.Ist. Super.Sanit.*, 1949, 12: 1-264. [CB 76/414]

McINTYRE, A.R. Curare: its history, nature and clinical use. 246 p., 22 fig. Chicago: University of Chicago Press, 1947. [CB 76/412]

NAUMANN, W. Historical aspects of curare. *Ciba Symp.*, 1941, 3: 995-1003.

THOMAS, K. Bryn. Curare: its history and usage. xi, 144 p., ill. Philadelphia/Montreal: Lippincott, 1963.

RQzd DIGITALIS

ALDAY REDONNET, T. Origen de la digital en España. *Arch. Iberoamer.Hist.Med.*, 1957, 9: 9-11.

CUSHNY, Arthur Robertson. The action and uses in medicine of Digitalis and its allies. xi, 303 p. London: Longmans, Green, 1925.

EBSTEIN, Erich. Zur Geschichte der Digitalisbehandlung. *Mitt. Gesch.Med.*, 1913, 12: 268-70.

FEIL, Harold. Story of the foxglove. *Bull.Cleveland Med. Libr.*, 1957, 4: 59-64, 1 fig.

JACOBS, Maurice S. The history of digitalis therapy. *Ann. Med.Hist.*, 1936, 8: 492-9.

LECLERC, Henri. Histoire de la digitale. *Aesculape*, 1926, 16: 86-9.

RQzm MANDRAGORA

BOULLET, Jean. Mandragore. *Aesculape*, 1960, 43: 3-37.

BURILLO MAZERES, Juan. La mandrágora. *Arch.Iberoamer.Hist. Med.*, 1960, 12: 255-9.

FRAZER, James George. Jacob and the mandrakes. *Proc.Brit. Acad.*, 1917-18, 8: 57-79.

LAUFER, Berthold. La Mandragore. *T'oung Pao*, 1917, 18: 1-30.

THE LEGEND of the Mandragora. *Ann.Med.Hist.*, 1917, 1: 102-5.

THOMPSON, C.J.S. The mystic mandrake. 253 p., front., 29 ill. London: Rider, 1934. [CB 43/278]

RQzm-wo

ELIADE, Mircea. Le culte de la mandragore en Roumanie. *Zalmoxis*, 1938, 1: 209-25.

RR PHARMACO-ZOOLOGY (including materia medica of human origin)

ANDEL, M.A. van. Adeps hominis. [In Dutch] (Klassieke wondermiddelen, 3) *Bijdr.Gesch.Geneesk.*, 1922, 2: 231-6

ANDEL, M.A. van. Het balneum animale. [In Dutch] (Klassieke wondermiddelen, 5) *Bijdr.Gesch.Geneesk.*, 1924, 4: 97-103.

ANDEL, M.A. van. Bezoar. [In Dutch] (Klassieke wondermiddelen, 7) *Bijdr.Gesch.Geneesk.*, 1925, 5: 137-48.

ANDEL, M.A. van. Bezoarsteenen. [Bezoar stones. (In Dutch)] (Klassieke wondermiddelen, 11) *Bijdr.Gesch.Geneesk.*, 1928, 8: 197-206.

ANDEL, M.A. van. Hippomanes. [In Dutch] (Klassieke wondermiddelen, 2) *Bijdr.Gesch.Geneesk.*, 1922, 2: 90-4.

ANDEL, M.A. van. Mumia. [In Dutch] (Klassieke wondermiddelen, 4) *Bijdr.Gesch.Geneesk.*, 1923, 3: 105-15, 141.

ANDEL, M.A. van. De slangentong of glossopetra. [Snake tongue or glossopetra. (In Dutch)] *Bijdr.Gesch.Geneesk.*, 1923, 3: 265-8.

ANDEL, M.A. van. Unicornu. [In Dutch] (Klassieke wondermiddelen, 1) *Bijdr.Gesch.Geneesk.*, 1921, 1: 405-19.

BARB, A.A. Birds and medical magic. 1. The eagle-stone; 2. The vulture epistle. *J.Warburg Courtauld Inst.*, 1950, 13: no. 3-4, 1-7.

BLANTON, Wyndham B. Madstones, with an account of several from Virginia. *Ann.Med.Hist.*, 1935, 7: 268-73, 2 fig.

BOUVET, M. La thérapeutique d'autrefois: l'aigle, le moineau, l'oie, les oeufs. *Paris Méd.*, 1926, 16: 129-33, 162-7. [CB 23/270]

BÜHLER-OPPENHEIM, K. Verbreitung und Nutzung der Milchtiere. Milch und Milchtiere im Kult. Die Tiermilch in der Volksheilkunde und im Heilaberglauben. *Ciba Z.*, 1948, 10: 4244-64, ill.

CASTIGLIONI, Arturo. The serpent as healing god in antiquity. Snake worship and symbolism in the Orient and in America. Remedies against snake bite. Snake venom in modern medicine. *Ciba Symp.* (Summit, N.J.), 1942, 4: 1158-86, fig.

CORNILLEAU, Robert. La bufothérapie, une médication nouvelle par le venin de crapaud. 61 p. Paris: Vigné, 1938.

DEWAILLY, Ph.; THÉODORIDÈS, J. Remarques sur l'usage passé et présent des insectes dans l'alimentation et la thérapeutique. (Contribution à l'histoire de la zoölogie médicale.) *Rev.Gén.Sci.*, 1953, 60: 165-72, bibliogr.

GARBOE, Axel. The angle-worm. A detail study in popular medicine. *Janus*, 1936, 40: 43-8.

GILLES, M. L'ornithothérapie. *Rev.Prat.Biol.Appl.Clin. Thérap.*, 1930, 23: 294-300.

GILS, J.B.F. van. Spaansche vlieg. [Spanish flies. (In Dutch)] *Bijdr.Gesch.Geneesk.*, 1946, 26: 4-7.
About cantharides.

GRUVEL, Jean. Les coléoptères vésicants. 63 p., 1 pl. Paris: Foulon, 1957.
Reviewed by Jean Théodoridès, *Arch.Int.Hist.Sci.*, 1957, 10: 158-9.

HAYWARD, Elizabeth. What about madstones? *Ciba Symp.* (Summit, N.J.), 1940, 1: 395-6.

LA CAVA, A. Francesco. Gli scorpioni in terapia. *Riv.Stor. Sci.*, 1947, 38: 24-39, 1 fig.

MacKINNEY, Loren C. Animal substances in materia medica. A study in the persistence of the primitive. *J.Hist.Med.*, 1946, 1: 149-70.

MacKINNEY, Loren C. The vulture in ancient medical lore. Vulture medicine in the medieval world. Vulture medicine in the modern world. *Ciba Symp.* (Summit, N.J.), 1942, 4: 1258-92, fig.

NIELSEN, Harald. Mumia Vera. (In Danish) *Nord.Med.*, 1959. 62: 1376-9.

REUTTER, Louis. De la momie ou d'un médicament démodé. *Bull. Soc.Franç.Hist.Méd.*, 1912, 11: 439-45.

ROBINSON, William. The healing properties of allantoin and urea discovered through the use of maggots in human wounds. *Annu.Rep.Smithsonian Inst.for 1937*, p. 451-61. Washington, D.C.: 1938.

RODRÍGUEZ-RIVERO, P.D. El ganado vacuno y su papel sanitario. La leche de vaca, panacea. *Arch.Hist.Méd.Venezuela*, 1934, 1: 126-30.

THORINGTON, J. Monroe. The ibex and chamois in ancient medicine. *Bull.Hist.Med.*, 1944, 15: 65-78, 6 fig.
From Pliny to the 17th century.

URDANG, George. The serpents in medicine. *Wis.Drug.*, Jan. 1947, 15: 8, 32.

WEISBACH, Walter W. Les vers de terre dans l'histoire des médicaments. *Act.VIIIe Congr.Int.Hist.Sci.* (Florence, 1956), p. 630-4. Paris: Hermann, 1958.

ZAUNICK, Rudolph. Beitrag zur Geschichte der Heilkraft der Kröte. *Mitt.Gesch.Med.*, 1916, 15: 78-9.

RRwk

WIELE, L.J. van de. Les animaux, leurs parties et leurs excréments, dans les pharmacopées communales des pays-bas méridionaux. *J.Pharm.Belg.*, 1964, 19: 351-70.

RRwo-u

BOLOGA, Valeriu L. Organ- und Körpersäfte in der rumänischen Volksmedizin. *Knoll's Mitt.Ärzte*, Oktober 1930, 115-19.

RRyOJ

GARDINER, J. Stanley. Black coral as a charm against rheumatism. *Nature*, 1921, 108: 505.
In Malay archipelago.

RRyOLze

ANDEL, A. van. L'hippomanes, un remède antiépileptique populaire. *Bull.Soc.Franç.Hist.Méd.*, 1921, 15: 369-72.

RRyOR

SCHEVENSTEEN, A.F.C. van. Les remèdes d'origine humaine dans les maladies des yeux. *Proc.3rd Int.Congr.Hist.Med.* (London, 1922), p. 194-206. Antwerp: De Vlijt, 1923.

RRyQF

DITMARS, Raymond Lee. Confessions of a scientist. xiv, 241 p., 23 pl. New York: MacMillan, 1934. [CB 43/278]
Includes a chapter of Sir Henry Gray's use of cobra venom on malignant growths.

RRyQK

CHEELY, Walter W. The madstone, a medical curio. *J.Ill.State Hist.Soc.*, 1960, 53: 409-13.
A stone to cure dog-bite and snake-bite.

RS PHARMACO-MINERALOGY

ANDEL, M.A. van. Amber. [In Dutch] (Klassieke wondermiddelen, 6) *Bijdr.Gesch.Geneesk.*, 1924, 4: 202-9.

ANDEL, M.A. van. Edelsteenen. [Precious stones. (In Dutch)] (Klassieke wondermiddelen, 9) *Bijdr.Gesch.Geneesk.*, 1927, 7: 161-76.

ANDEL, M.A. van. Terra sigillata. [In Dutch] (Klassieke wondermiddelen, 12) *Bijdr.Gesch.Geneesk.*, 1928, 8: 207-15.

BOUVET, Maurice. Les échantillons de terre sigillée du Musée du Louvre. *Compt.Rend.IIe Congr.Int.Hist.Méd.* (Paris, 1921), p. 588-9, 1 pl. Évreux: 1922.

BROMEHEAD, C.E.N. Aetites or the eaglestone. *Antiquity*, 1947, 21: 16-22, 2 pl. [CB 73/176]

JOHNSSON, John William Schibbye. Notice sur quelques objets de terre sigillée prétendus antitoxiques. *Compt.Rend.IIe Congr.Int.Hist.Méd.* (Paris, 1921), p. 282-9, 1 pl. Évreux: Imprimerie Ch. Hérissey, 1922.

LOOMIS, C. Grant. Lapidary medicine. *Bull.Hist.Med.*, 1944, 16: 319-24.

PAZZINI, Alberto. Le pietre preziose nella storia della medicina e nella leggenda. 355 p. Roma: Casa Editrice Mediterranea, 1939.

RIVIÈRE, Emile. Légendes et superstitions thérapeutiques. Les pierres grattées et leur poussière. *Bull.Soc.Franç. Hist.Méd.*, 1914, 13: 82-94, 160-71, 385-443.

ROBERTSON, W.G. Aitchison. The use of the unicorn's horn, coral and stones in medicine. *Ann.Med.Hist.*, 1926, 8: 240-8.

STRUNZ, Franz. Zaubersteine. *Sudhoffs Arch.*, 1941, 33: 233-48.

THOMPSON, C.J.S. Terra sigillata, a famous medicament of ancient times. *Proc.17th Int.Congr.Med.* (London, 1913), sect. 23, p. 438-44. London: Oxford University Press and Hodder & Stoughton, 1914.

VORWAHL, Heinrich. Das Salz in der Volksmedizin. *Münch.Med. Wochenschr.*, 1931, 78: 595-6.

RSyQPzw

BAUDOUIN, Marcel. Le traitement traditionaliste de la coqueluche par la poussière des pierres mégalithiques. *Bull. Soc.Franç.Hist.Méd.*, 1913, 12: 532-7.

RT CHEMICAL DRUGS

SIEDLER, Paul. Die chemischen Arzneimittel der letzten 113 Jahre, mit Rückblicken auf die Entwicklung der wissenschaftlichen Chemie und Pharmazie für Apotheker, Aerzte und Chemiker. viii, 179 p. Berlin: Borntraeger, 1914.

RTcg

OSBORNE, George E. Chemical compounds in the official compendia. *Amer.J.Pharm.Educ.*, 1962, 26: 19-23.

URDANG, George. How chemicals entered the official pharmacopoeias. *Arch.Int.Hist.Sci.*, 1954, 7: 303-14. Also in *Act. VIe Congr.Int.Hist.Sci.* (Amsterdam, 1950), p. 694-706. Paris: Hermann, 1953.

URDANG, George. How chemicals entered the official pharmacopoeias. *Pharm.Arch.*, 1944, 15: 17-37, 6 fig.

RTu

RÖMPP, Hermann. Chemische Zaubertränke. 286 p., 16 fig. Stuttgart: Franckh, 1939.
Reviewed by R. Zaunick, *Mitt.Gesch.Med.*, 1941-42, 40: 136.

RTwo

KARADJA, Constantin I. La thériaque vénitienne et son emploi dans les principautés roumaines. *Rev.Études Roum.*, 1953, 1: 116-29.

RU NAMED CHEMICAL DRUGS

ALVAREZ, Walter C. The impact of the introduction of iron on medical and religious thought. *Essays in Biology in honor of Herbert M. Evans*, p. 25-32. Berkeley/Los Angeles: University of California Press, 1943.

ANDEL, M.A. van. Antimoon. [Antimony. (In Dutch)] (Klassieke wondermiddelen, 13) *Bijdr.Gesch.Geneesk.*, 1928, 8: 285-94.

BIRCHER, E. Zur Geschichte der Milchzuckergewinnung, besonders in der Schweiz. *Gesnerus*, 1954, 11: 41-5.
Including its use in medicine.

BUESS, Heinrich. Historisches zur Schwefeltherapie. *Ciba Z.*, 1945, 9: 3516-25, ill.

DARMSTAEDTER, Ernst. Aus der Geschichte des Jods und der Jodtherapie. *Schweiz.Med.Wochenschr.*, 1932, 62: 98-100.

DARMSTAEDTER, Ernst. Per la storia dell' "Aurum potabile". *Arch.Stor.Sci.*, 1924, 5: 251-71.

GOLDWATER, Leonard J. A short history of iron therapy. *Ann. Med.Hist.*, 1935, 7: 261-7.

HABERLING, Wilhelm. Der Triumphwagen des Antimons. Der Kampf um die Einführung des Antimons in den Arzneischatz zu Beginn der Neuzeit. *Therap.Ber.*, 1927, 4: 471-8, 522-3, ill.

HARLESS, J.C.F. Über das Nitrum der Alten, seine Varietäten, und seine Gewinnungsweise. Ein Beitrag zur Geschichte der Materia medica im Alterthume. *Henschel's Janus*, 1846, 1: 455-84; reprinted Leipzig: Alfred Lorentz, 1931.
See also Thierfelder, J.G., below.

HEISCHKEL, Edith. Geschichte der medizinischen Verwendung des Silbers. In: Handbuch der experimentellen Pharmakologie, Part 3, 3, p. 1972-6. Berlin: Springer, 1934-.

JONES, Bartlett C. A prohibition problem: liquor as medicine, 1920-1933. *J.Hist.Med.*, 1963, 18: 353-69.

KAUFFEISEN, L. Le déclin d'une drogue. L'onguent napolitain. *Bull.Soc.Hist.Pharm.*, 1925, 4: no. 45, 72-80. [CB 18/652]

LATRONICO, Nicola. I vini medicinali nella storia e nella scienza. Prefazione di Giovanni Dalmasso. 217 p. (Collana di Studi di Storia della Medicina, 4) Milano: Hoepli, 1947. [CB 71/132]

LENOIR, Henri. Historique et législation du salpêtre. Les pharmaciens et les ateliers révolutionnaires du salpêtre (1793-1795). (Thèse) 236 p. Paris: *Vie Universitaire*, 1922. [CB 15/215]

MATIGNON, Camille. L'industrie de l'iode, son histoire, son état actuel. *Rev.Gén.Sci.*, 1914, 25: 511-16. [CB 24/457]

RICHTER, Paul. Über die Entstehung des Jod und ihre Vorgeschichte. *Arch.Gesch.Naturwiss.Tech.*, 1912, 4: 1-7, 168.

STARLING, Ernest Henry. The action of alcohol on man. With essays on 1. Alcohol as a medicine, by Robert Hutchison. 2. Alcohol and its relations to problems in mental disorders by Frederick Mott. 3. Alcohol and mortality, by Raymond Pearl. vi, 291 p. London: Longmans, 1923.

THIERFELDER, J.G. Über das Nitrum der Alten. Mit besonderer Berücksichtigung des gleichnamigen Aufsatzes von Dr. Harless. *Henschel's Janus*, 1848, 3: 29-53; reprinted Leipzig: Alfred Lorentz, 1931.
For the paper by J.C.F. Harless, *see* above.

URDANG, George. The early chemical and pharmaceutical history of calomel. *Chymia*, 1948, 1: 93-108, 2 facs.

VAN KLOOSTER, H.S. Three centuries of Rochelle Salt. *J.Chem. Educ.*, 1959, 36: 314-18.

RUnh

URDANG, George. The origin of the term calomel. *Festschrift zum 80. Geburtstag Max Neuburgers*, p. 464-9. Wien: Maudrich, 1948.

WICKERSHEIMER, Ernest. Paraffine ou parasine? *Rev.Hist. Pharm.*, 1952, 10: fasc. 134, 385-9.

RUwb-cg

DU MEZ, Andrew G. The galenical oleoresins. A century of the United States pharmacopoeia, 1820-1920. 288 p., fig. (*Bull. Univ.Wis.*, serial no. 980. General series, 764) *Trans.Wis. Acad.Sci.Arts Lett.*, 1917, vol. 12. Madison, Wis.: 1919.
Reprinted from *Trans.Wis.Acad.Sci.Arts Lett.*, 1919, 19: 907-1194.

LANGENHAN, H.A. Liquor potassii arsenitis. A century of the United States pharmacopoeia, 1820-1920. 57 p. (*Bull.Univ. Wis.*, serial no. 1153; General series, 936) Madison, Wis.: 1921.

NEUMANN, Arthur Henry. Pulvis effervescens compositus. A century of the United States pharmacopoeia, 1820-1920. 42 p. fig. (*Bull.Univ.Wis.*, serial no. 1304. General series, 1081) Madison, Wis.: 1925.

RUwq

MASSY, R. Le pharmacien général Moreau et la découverte des phosphates du Maroc. *Rev.Hist.Pharm.*, 1962, 50: 333-6.

RUyOJ

BERNABEO, Raffaele. Salicilato di sodio e reumatismo. *Policlinico Sez.Prat.*, 1964, 71: 1905-7.

RUyOZ

GOLDSTEIN, Hyman I. The use of magnesium trisilicate, colloidal kaolin and aluminum hydroxide in antacid gastric therapy. Historical notes on ulcer of the stomach and duodenum. *J. Int.Coll.Surg.*, 1939, 2: 379-408, fig.

RUyPE

GOLDSTEIN, Hyman I. Early references to anemia [and its treatment with iron preparations]. *Med.Life*, 1932, 39: 646-7.
Expression *anaima* originally used by Aristotle.

RUyQPzsy

BUSACCA, Attilio. Cenni storici sull' uso del mercurio nella sifilide. *Arch.Stor.Sci.*, 1923, 4: 245-55.

LESKY, Erna. Quecksilber. (Von Schmier- und Räucherkuren zur modernen Syphilistherapie. Die Arbeiter und das Quecksilber.) *Ciba Z.*, 1959, 8: 3174-91.

STEIN, John Bethune. The Rob. *Med.Rec.*, 1913, 83: 1021-5, 2 fig.
An antisyphilitic specific invented by Dr. Pierre Borveau-Laffecteur.

RV BIO- AND ORGANOTHERAPY

for sera and vaccines *see* QO
the discovery of insulin *see* QPzdi

NEUBURGER, Max. Something about organotherapy. *Med.Life*, 1932, 39: 693-4.

STROPPIANA, Luigi. L'organo-ormono terapia negli ultimi cento anni. *Atti Mem.Accad.Stor.Arte Sanit.*, 1964, 30: 183-91.

VALETTE, Guillaume. Inhibitions enzymatiques et actions médicamenteuses. 26 p. (Palais de la Découverte, A 295) Paris: Université de Paris, 1963.

VORWAHL, Henner. Zur Geschichte der Organotherapie. *Arch. Gesch.Med.*, 1925, 17: 201-3.

RVwb-ph

COHN, Edwin J. History of the development of a patent policy. Based on experiences in connection with liver extracts and blood derivatives, 1927-1951. 38 p. Boston: University Laboratory of Physical Chemistry related to Medicine and Public Health, Harvard University, 1951.

RVwg

SCHMIDT, Ferdinand. Erste Insulin-Herstellung in Deutschland vor 40 Jahren. *Deut.Apoth.Zeitung*, 1964, 104: 733-4.

RVyPE

GOLDSTEIN, Hyman I. The early use of liver in anemias by the French and Italians. With some historical notes on anemia. *Med.Life*, 1937, 44: 173-94.

GOLDSTEIN, Hyman I. Liver therapy in anemia. Earliest clinical and experimental use of liver in anemias (priority). *Med.Life*, 1935, 42: 207-16.

RVyQF

BELTRAN, Juan Ramon. Historia de un error contemporaneo. *Rev.Argent.Hist.Med.*, 1942, 1: 5-10.
Apropos of the therapeutic use of insulin in cancer.

RVyQPzsy

PILCZ, Alexander. Zur Geschichte der Malaria-Therapie der progressiven Paralyse nach Wagner-Jauregg. *Festschrift zum 80. Geburtstag Max Neuburgers*, p. 370. Wien: Maudrich, 1948.

RVzb BLOOD TRANSFUSION

ARTELT, Walter. Der Volksglaube als Wegbereiter der Bluttransfusion. *Sudhoffs Arch.*, 1941, 34: 29-34.

BUESS, Heinrich. Die Bluttransfusion. Zur Vorgeschichte der Bluttransfusion. Die Bluttransfusion im Anschluss an die Entdeckung des Blutkreislaufs. Die Lehre von der Bluttransfusion im 17. Jahrhundert. Die Bluttransfusion im Zeitalter der Naturphilosophie. Die Bluttransfusion als vorwiegend hämodynamisch wirkender Blutersatz. Die Bluttransfusion im Lichte der exakteren Physiologie und Hämatologie. Der Ausbau des Transfusionsverfahrens auf serologischer Grundlage. Notizen zum Thema. *Ciba Z.*, 1956, 7: 2610-44. [CB 82/212]

CE livre jubilaire fut offert au Dr. Albert Hustin par ses amis et ses anciens collaborateurs à l'occasion du quarantième anniversaire de la première transfusion citratée qu'il réalisa à l'Hôpital Saint-Jean de Bruxelles le 27 mars 1914. lix, 220 p., ill., portr. Bruxelles: Imprimerie des Sciences, 1954.

CLARKE, T. Wood. The birth of transfusion. *J.Hist.Med.*, 1949, 4: 337-8.

DE BAKEY, Michael E.; COOLEY, Denton A. Blood transfusion. The work of Crile and Hustin. *Procès-Verbaux XVIe Congr.Soc.Int.Chir.* (Copenhagen, 1955), p. 301-7. Bruxelles: [n.d.].

DENIS, Erich. Zur Geschichte der Bluttransfusion. 57 p. (Aus der chirurgischen Klinik des Krankenhauses Bergmannsheil i. Bochum) (Diss.) Düsseldorf: 1940.
Reviewed by W. Haberling, *Mitt.Gesch.Med.*, 1941-42, 40: 86.

FICARRA, Bernard J. The evolution of blood transfusion. *Ann. Med.Hist.*, 1942, 4: 302-23.

GRANGÉE, [F.M.?]. La transfusion du sang dans le passé. *Paris Méd.*, 1912, 8: (2), partie paramédicale, 181-5, ill.

HUSTIN, Albert. Court aperçu historique des débuts de la transfusion citratée. *Arch.Franc.Belg.Chir.*, 1923, 26: 7-12.

KOPACZEWSKI, W. Histoire de la transfusion sanguine. *Bull. Soc.Hist.Méd.*, 1923, 17: 254-68.

MALUF, N.S.R. History of blood transfusion. *J.Hist.Med.*, 1954, 9: 59-107, 24 fig.

SIMILI, Alessandro. Origine e vicende della trasfusione del sangue. Considerazioni storico critiche. 164 p., 8 pl. Bologna: Azzoguidi, 1933.
Reviewed by Aldo Mieli, *Archeion*, 1934, 16: 454; by L. Castaldi, *Riv.Stor.Sci.*, 1934, 25: 23.

SNYDER, Laurence Hasbrouck. Blood grouping in relation to clinical and legal medicine. xi, 153 p., 5 pl. London: Baillière, Tindall and Cox, 1929.
Includes a history of blood transfusion.
Reviewed by S.C. Dyke, *Nature*, 1930, 126: 716-17.

WEERDT, W.L. de. L'emploi du sang humain et de ses succédanés. *Rev.Quest.Sci.*, 1948, 9: 518-47.

ZIMMERMAN, Leo M.; HOWELL, Katharine, M. History of blood transfusion. *Ann.Med.Hist.*, 1932, 4: 415-33, 12 fig., front.

RW CHEMOTHERAPY

COWEN, David L.; HAMARNEH, Sami; OSBORNE, George. Some historical facets of chemotherapy. *Amer.J.Pharm.Educ.*, 1962, 26: 1-23.

EPSTEIN, Samuel; WILLIAMS, Beryl. Miracles from microbes; the road to streptomycin. With an introduction by Norman T. Kirk. xi, 155 p. New Brunswick, N.J.: Rutgers University Press, 1946.
Reviewed by Morris C. Leikind, *Isis*, 1948, 38: 270.

FLEMING, Alexander. Chemotherapy: yesterday, today, and tomorrow. 39 p., ill. Cambridge University Press, 1946.
An account of the main stages from Lister onwards.

GALDSTON, Iago. Behind the sulfa drugs. A short history of chemotherapy. With a preface by Perrin H. Long. xix, 174 p. New York: Appleton-Century, 1943.
Reviewed by Chauncey D. Leake, *Isis*, 1943, 34: 531.

GALDSTON, Iago. Some notes on the early history of chemotherapy. *Bull.Hist.Med.*, 1940, 8: 806-18.

GOLDSMITH, Margaret. The road to penicillin, a history of chemotherapy. 174 p., ill. London: Lindsay, Drummond, 1946.

JACOBS, Maurice S. Paul Ehrlich and his relation to modern chemotherapy. *Bull.Hist.Med.*, 1940, 8: 956-64.

McDONNELL, John N. The microbiotics. *Amer.J.Pharm.*, 1944, 116: 401-19. Also *Annu.Rep.Smithsonian Inst.for 1945*, p. 441-58. Washington, D.C.: 1946.

NICOLLE, Jacques. Une application de la symétrie à la lutte contre les microbes. 22 p., 5 fig. (Conférences du Palais de la Découverte, *ser. A*, 227) Paris: Université de Paris: 1957.

PAUL EHRLICH SYMPOSIUM. Some historical facets of chemotherapy - a fiftieth anniversary program honoring Paul Ehrlich. Washington: 1960. [CB 90/536]
Papers given at the Symposium were subsequently published in *Amer.J.Pharm.Educ.*, 1962, 26: 1-23.

SONNEDECKER, Glenn. The concept of chemotherapy. *Amer.J. Pharm.Educ.*, 1962, 26: no. 1, 1-3.

TAYLOR, Frank Sherwood. The conquest of bacteria. From salvarsan to sulphapyridine. Foreword by Henry E. Sigerist. 175 p. New York: Philosophical Library and Alliance Book Corporation, 1942. [CB 69/238]

WEINTRAUB, Robert L. Chemotherapeutic agents from microbes. *Annu.Rep.Smithsonian Inst.for 1943*, p. 545-68, 5 pl. Washington, D.C.: 1944.

RWyQPzsy

DIEPGEN, Paul; ZAUNICK, Rudolph. Zur Geschichte der Chemotherapie, insbesondere der Syphilis. *Deut.Med.Wochenschr.* 1955, 6: no. 1/2, 82-6.

NEISSER, Albert. On modern syphilotherapy, with particular reference to salvarsan. Translated by Isabelle von Sazenhofen Wartenberg. Biography and bibliography by Frances Tomlinson Gardner. 42 p., portr. Baltimore: Johns Hopkins Press, 1945.
The paper is one of the first based on the use of Ehrlich's 606.

RWyRBzh

FOX, Charles L. Sulfonamides in the treatment of war wounds and burns. *Annu.Rep.Smithsonian Inst. for 1943*, p. 569-74. Washington, D.C.: 1944.

RX ANTIBIOTICS

BRUNEL, Jules. Antibiosis from Pasteur to Fleming. *J.Hist. Med.*, 1951, 6: 287-301.

THE CHEMICAL study of penicillin: a brief history. By the Editorial Board of the Monograph on the Chemistry of Penicillin. *Science*, 1947, 105: 653-9.
Extract from the report by the National Academy of Sciences, *see* below.

DEL GUERRA, G. Chi ha scoperto la penicillina? *Riv.Stor.Sci.*, 1947, 38: 142-4.

FLOREY, Howard Walter. L'introduction de la pénicilline dans la médecine. 16 p. (Conférences du Palais de la Découverte, 10 jan. 1946) Alençon: Imprimerie Alençonnaise, 1949-50.

HOBBY, Gladys L. Microbiology in relation to antibiotics. *J.Hist.Med.*, 1951, 6: 369-87.

McDONNELL, John N. The microbiotics. *Amer.J.Pharm.*, 1944, 116: 401-19. Also *Annu.Rep.Smithsonian Inst.for 1945*, p. 441-58. Washington, D.C.: 1946.

MARTI-IBAÑEZ, Félix. Cinco apuntes para una historia de los antibióticos. *J.Int.Coll.Surg.*, 1949, 12: 6-15.

MARTÍ-IBÁÑEZ, Félix. Men, molds, and history. viii, 115 p., bibliogr. New York: MD Publications, 1958. [CB 84/322]
This book, which deals chiefly with antibiotics, includes an account of the work of Alexander Fleming.

MASTERS, David. Miracle drug. The inner history of penicillin. 191 p., 17 pl. London: Eyre and Spottiswoode, 1946.
Includes short life-histories and personal descriptions of Fleming and Florey.
Reviewed by L.P. Garrod, *Nature*, 1947, 160: 38.

NATIONAL ACADEMY OF SCIENCES. The chemistry of penicillin: report on a collaborative investigation by American and British chemists under the joint sponsorship of the office of Scientific Research and Development and the Medical Research Council. x, 1094 p. Princeton: Princeton University Press, 1949.

PAPP, Desiderio. Esquema de la prehistoria de los antibióticos. *Act.VIIe Congr.Int.Hist.Sci.* (Jerusalem, 1953), p. 461-4. Paris: Hermann, [1954].

PAPP, Desiderio. Histoire des antibiotiques. *Rev.Hist.Sci.*, 1954, 7: 124-38.

RATCLIFF, John Drury. Yellow magic, the story of penicillin. xv, 173 p., 9 ill. New York: Random House, 1945.

SOKOLOFF, Boris. The story of penicillin. ix, 167 p., bibliogr. Chicago/New York: Ziff-Davis, 1945.

URDANG, George. The antibiotics and pharmacy. *J.Hist.Med.*, 1951, 6: 388-405.

WAKSMAN, Selman A. Microbial antagonisms and antibiotic substances. 350 p. New York: Commonwealth Fund, 1945.
Reviewed by George Rosen, *J.Hist.Med.*, 1947, 2: 402.

WAKSMAN, Selman A. Streptomycin: isolation, properties, and utilization. *J.Hist.Med.*, 1951, 6: 318-47, 7 fig.

WELCH, Henry. Pharmacology of antibiotics. *J.Hist.Med.*, 1951, 6: 348-68.

WELSCH, Maurice. S.A. Waksman et la streptomycine. *Rev.Méd. Liège*, 1946, 1: 180-3.

RXnh

WELSCH, Maurice. De l'origine et de la signification du terme "antibiotique". *IIIe Congr.Nat.Sci.* (Bruxelles, 1950), (1), p. 59-62. Liège: 1951.

RXs

GALDSTON, Iago, ed. The impact of antibiotics on medicine and society. x, 222 p. New York: International Universities Press, 1958.
Reviewed by William Brockbank, *Med.Hist.*, 1958, 2: 235.

RXwb

RICHARDS, A.N. Production of penicillin in the United States (1941-1946). *Nature*, 1964, 201: 441-5.

RXwe

FLOREY, Howard Walter; ABRAHAM, E.P. The work on penicillin at Oxford. *J.Hist.Med.*, 1951, 6: 302-16, 5 fig.

RXwf

GUILHON, J. Précurseurs français de la pénicilline. *Nouv. Litt.*, 7 February 1946.

RY ANTISEPSIS

BRUNN-FAHRNI, Ruth von. Antiseptik und Aseptik. *Ciba Z.*, 1949, 10: 4374-402, ill.

MAGATH, Thomas B. The history of steam sterilization. *Ann. Med.Hist.*, 1937, 9: 338-44.

MULLER, Paul. Histoire du D.D.T. 22 p., 7 tables. (Les Conférences du Palais de la Découverte, 22 janvier 1947) Paris: Université de Paris, 1948.

FOSTER, Michaël. The pomander stock. *Proc.3rd Int.Congr. Hist.Med.* (London, 1922), p. 76-7. Antwerp: De Vlijt, 1923.

REDDISH, George F. Early history of antiseptics and disinfectants. *Amer.J.Pharm.Educ.*, 1959, 23: 197-201.

TERRILLON, Maurice. Note sur la découverte de l'asepsie. *Bull.Soc.Franç.Hist.Med.*, 1936, 34: 303-5.

THOMPSON, C.J.S. The pomander. A link in the history of preventive medicine. *Compt.Rend.IIe Congr.Int.Hist.Méd.* (Paris, 1921), p. 66-7. Évreux: Imprimerie Ch. Hérissey 1922.

RYyRB

GIORDANO, D. La jodio in chirurgia (nel centenario della scoperta di quel metalloide). *Riv.Stor.Crit.Sci.*, 1913, 4: 163-73.

RYyRBzh

VERAART, B.A.G. Over antisepsis als eisch voor aseptisch wondverloop. [On antisepsis as a requirement for aseptic wound healing. (In Dutch)] xvi, 191 p. (Thesis) Amsterdam: H.J. Koersen, 1925.
Reviewed in *Bijdr.Gesch.Geneesk.*, 1925, 5: 279-91.

RZ PHARMACOLOGY

for anaesthesia *see* RD

EARLES, M.P. Early theories of the mode of action of drugs and poisons. *Ann.Sci.*, 1961, 17: 97-110.

LECLERC, Henri. La thérapeutique par les simples. 1. Les diurétiques. *Courr.Méd.*, 1912, 62: 543-4, 567-9; 63: 3-6, 17-19, 39-40; 2. Les sudorifiques et les dépuratifs. *Ibid.*, 1913, 63: 111-13, 135-7, 159-60, 171-2.

PATON, William D.M. The growth of pharmacology with special reference to its dependence on the advance in chemical knowledge. *Proc.10th Int.Congr.Hist.Sci.* (Ithaca, 1962), (2), p. 895-7. Paris: Hermann, 1964.

ROBSON, J.M.; STACEY, R.S. Recent advances in pharmacology. 3rd ed. x, 406 p., 68 fig., 19 tables, 2 pl. Boston: Little, Brown & Co., 1962.
Reviewed by Marvin H. Malone, *Amer.J.Pharm.Educ.*, 1963, 27: 346.

RZk

LEAKE, Chauncey D. The classic problems of pharmacology. *Victor Robinson Memorial Volume*, p. 213-24. New York: Froben, 1948.

LEAKE, Chauncey D. The scientific status of pharmacology. *Science*, 1961, 134: 2069-79.

LEAKE, Chauncey D. The status of pharmacology as a science. *Amer.J.Pharm.Educ.*, 1959, 23: 173-96, bibliogr.

RZyOK drugs acting on the NERVOUS SYSTEM

see also NO NARCOTICS; ALCOHOL

HESSE, Erich. Narcotics and drug addiction. 219 p. New York: Philosophical Library, 1946. [CB 71/132]
Translation of Die Rausch- und Genussgifte (Stuttgart: Enke, 1938). 2nd ed. 1953.

KLÜVER, Heinrich. Mescal. The "divine" plant and its psychological effects. With an introduction by Macdonald Critchley. 111 p. London: Kegan Paul, 1928.

LEWIN, Louis. Phantastica: narcotic and stimulating drugs, their use and abuse. Translated from the 2nd German edition by P.H.A. Wirth. xi, 335 p. London: Kegan Paul, 1931.
Translation of: Phantastica: die betäubenden und erregenden Genussmittel. 2nd ed. Berlin: Stilke, 1927.
Reissued as: Drugs: their use and abuse. London: Routledge, 1938.

LEWIN, Louis; LOWENTHAL, John. Giftige Nachtschattengewächse bewusstseinstörender Eigenschaften im culturgeschichtlichen Zusammenhange. *Janus*, 1926, 30: 233-70. [CB 22/309]

SAFFORD, William E. Daturas of the old world and new. An account of their narcotic properties and their use in oracular and initiatory ceremonies. *Annu.Rep.Smithsonian Inst.for 1920*, p. 537-67, 13 pl. Washington, D.C.: 1922. [CB 13/284]

SONNEDECKER, Glenn. Emergence of the concept of opiate addiction. 25 p. Madison, Wis.: American Institute of the History of Pharmacy, 1963.
Reprinted from the *J.Mond.Pharm.*, 1962, no. 3, 275-90; 1963, no. 1, 27-34.

RZyOY drugs acting on the DIGESTIVE SYSTEM

RUBERTIS, Achille de. Per la storia della gialappa. *Riv. Stor.Sci.*, 1932, 23: 270-4.
History of the purgative root jalap. Name derived from that of its main source, the Mexican town of Jalapa.

THOMSON, St. Clair. Antimonyall Cupps: Pocula Emetica or Calices Vomitorii. *Proc.Roy.Soc.Med.*, 1926, 19: Hist. sect., 123-8. [CB 22/309]

RZyPA drugs acting on the CARDIOVASCULAR SYSTEM

MONACHINO, Joseph. *Rauvolfia serpentina* - its history, botany and medical use. *Econ.Bot.*, 1954, 8: 349-65.
The source of a new drug for lowering high blood pressure.

NETOLITZKY, Fritz. Volkstümliche Blutstillungsmittel und ihre Deutung. *Medizinisch-Pharmazeutische Technik*, Monatsbeiheft zu *Biol.Heilkunst*, Feb. 1927, 5 p.
Reviewed by H. Marzell, *Mitt.Gesch.Med.*, 1927, 26: 277.

RZyPD acting on the BLOOD

SINGER, I. [About E. Menzel's book concerning five hypoglycemic plants in Israel. (In Hebrew)] *Koroth*, 1964, 3: 238-245.

RZyPL drugs acting on the URINARY SYSTEM

BOUQUET, H. Les lithontriptiques. *France Méd.*, 1912, 59: 81-4, 105-9.

LE ROY, René; LANOS, Jean. Les diurétiques de nos ancêtres. *Paris Méd.*, 1912, (2), partie paramédicale, 719-24, 4 fig.

RZyPN drugs acting on SEX

ABELS, A. Arzneimittel zur Erregung des Geschlechtstriebes. 1. Kanthariden. *Arch.Kriminal-Anthropol.Kriminalistik*, 1912, 50: 201-30.

DENNINGER, Henri Stearns. A history of substances known as aphrodisiacs. *Ann.Med.Hist.*, 1930, 2: 383-93.

DOUGLAS, Norman. Paneros, some words on aphrodisiacs and the like. 103 p. London: Chatto and Windus, 1931.

VORWAHL, Henner. Knoblauch als Aphrodisiacum. *Arch.Gesch. Med.*, 1923, 14: 127-8.

RZyPQ drugs in GYNAECOLOGY AND OBSTETRICS

BARGER, George. Ergot and ergotism. *See* QKyK

BRONDEGAARD, V.J. Der Sadebaum als Abortivum. *Sudhoffs Arch.*, 1964, 48: 331-51.

HOFSTÄTTER, R. Einführung der Hypophysen-Medikation in die Geburtshilfe vor 40 Jahren. *Festschrift zum 80. Geburtstag Max Neuburgers*, p. 235-8. Wien: Maudrich, 1948.

S VETERINARY MEDICINE

Sc general history

BAILLET, L. Notice sur l'art vétérinaire. 1. Jusqu'au XVIIIe siècle inclusivement. 2. Au XIXe siècle. *Act.Acad.Sci. Belles Lettres Arts Bordeaux, 3rd ser.*, 1912, 74: 87-125.

LAIGNEL-LAVASTINE, Maxime, ed. *See* Nc-bm

LECLAINCHE, Emmanuel. Histoire de la médecine vétérinaire. xv, 812 p. Toulouse: Office du Livre, 1936.
Reviewed by George Sarton, *Isis*, 1937, 27: 360-3.

SENET, André. Histoire de la médecine vétérinaire. 117 p. ("Que sais-je?", 584) Paris: Presses Universitaires de France, 1953.
Reviewed by J. Théodoridès, *Rev.Hist.Med.*, 1954, 7: 195; by W. Hallgren, *Lychnos*, 1954-55, 494-5.

SMITHCORS, J.F. Evolution of the veterinary art. A narrative account to 1850. xvii, 408 p., ill. Kansas City: Veterinary Medicine Publishing Company, 1957.
Reviewed by Richard E. Shope, *Bull.Hist.Med.*, 1958, 32: 378-9.

Sc-bv

WINDISCH, Wilhelm. Titelbibliographie der deutschsprachigen Veterinarhistorik 1900-1957. 144 p. München: Institut für Staatsveterinärmedizin und Geschichte der Tiermedizin der Tierärztlichen Fakultät der Universität, 1958.
Reviewed by Johannes Steudel, *Sudhoffs Arch.*, 1959, 43: 96.

Sce

YASUDA, M. History of books on veterinary science, particularly on veterinary anatomy. *J.Jap.Vet.Med.Ass.*, 1964, 17: 35-9, 76-9.

SmzN

KLAUDER, Joseph V. Historical remarks on the interrelation of human and veterinary medicine. *Trans.Coll.Physicians Phila.*, 1958, 26: 27-33.

Sr

WEYDE, A.J. van der. Geneeskundigen als veeartsen. [Medical men as veterinary surgeons. (In Dutch)] *Bijdr.Gesch.Geneesk.*, 1930, 10: 136-8.

Su

NEWMAN, L.F. Folk-lore and history in veterinary medicine (summary). *Proc.Roy.Soc.Med.*, 1952, 45: 94-6.

Sw in different countries

Swb

SMITHCORS, J.F. Medical men and the beginnings of veterinary medicine in America. *Bull.Hist.Med.*, 1959, 33: 330-41.

Swe

SMITH, Frederick. The origin of the veterinary art in England. *Ve Congr.Int.Hist.Méd.* (Genève, 1925), p. 188-91. Genève: Albert Kundig, 1926.

Swe-ce

SMITH, Frederick. The early history of veterinary literature and its British development. 4 vol. 1. iv, 373 p.; 2. The eighteenth century. viii, 244 p.; 3. The nineteenth century, 1800-23. 184 p.; 4. The nineteenth century, 1823-60. London: Baillière, Tindall and Cox, 1919-33. [CB 40/415]
Vol. 1 reviewed by Charles Singer, *Isis*, 1920, 3: 307-8.

Swe-r

BULLOCK, Fred. Notes on the early history of the veterinary surgeon in England. *Proc.Roy.Soc.Med.*, 1929, 22: 627-33. [CB 28/564]

SMYTHE, Reginald Harrison. Healers on horseback; the reminiscences of an English veterinary surgeon. 135 p. Springfield, Ill.: Thomas, [1963].

Swe-u

DAVIDSON, T.D. A survey of some British veterinary folklore. *Bull.Hist.Med.*, 1960, 34: 199-232.

Swg-ce

RIECK, Wilhelm. 400 Jahre deutsche Veterinärdrucke. *Berliner Tierärztl.Wochenschr.*, 1931, 47: 254.

Swg-oq

GÜNTHER, Gustav. Die tierärztliche Hochschule in Wien. Ihre Geschichte, ihre Institute und Einrichtungen. 84 p., ill. Düsseldorf: Lindner, 1930.

NUSSHAG, Wilhelm. Zur Geschichte der Veterinärmedizinischen Fakultät und ihrer Institute. *Wiss. Z. Humboldt Univ. Berlin Math.Naturwiss.Reihe*, 1960, 9: 215-28.

Swm

HALLGREN, W. Svensk veterinärhistoria i ord och bilder. En minnesbok utgiven till firandet av Sveriges Veterinärförbunds 100-årsjubileum. [History of Swedish veterinary science in word and picture. A memorial volume published in commemoration of the centenary of the Swedish Veterinary Association. (In Swedish)] 197 p., ill. Malmo: Allhem, 1960.
Reviewed by Åke Olson, *Lychnos*, 1962, 521-2.

Swm-u

BOERS, Kristen. Dansk veterinaer Folkemedicin. Hest og Kvaeg. [Danish veterinary folk medicine. Horse and cattle. (In Danish)] 271 p. (*Dansk Veterinaerhist.Aarb.*, 1939, (1)) København: Dansk Veterinaerhistorisk Samfund, 1939.

BOERS, Kristen. Dansk veterinaer Folkemedicin. De mindre Husdyr. [Danish veterinary folk medicine. The smaller domestic animals. (In Danish)] 396 p. (*Dansk Veterinaerhist.Aarb.*, 1941, (2)) København: Dansk Veterinaerhistorisk Samfund, 1941.

Sx techniques and instruments

Sxk-wg

RIECK, Wilhelm. Das Veterinär-Instrumentarium im Wandel der Zeiten und seine Förderung durch die Instrumentenfabrik H. Hauptner. Nebst einem Anhang: Das Hauptner-Werk Solingen, von Konrad Hauptner. Das Geschäftshaus H. Hauptner Berlin, von Hans Hauptner. 116 p., fig. Berlin: H. Hauptner, 1932. [CB 51/294]
Offprint from the jubilee catalog of Firma H. Hauptner, Berlin.

SyN ANIMAL HEALTH

SyNFph

SEIDEL, Günter. Vom Wasenplatz zur Tierkörperverwertungs- und Beseitigungsanstalt. Die gesetzliche Entwicklung des Tierkörperbeseitigungswesens. *NTM Z.Gesch.Naturwiss.Tech. Med.*, [1962], 1: no. 3, 115-30.

SyNMwg-qg

MANGOLD, E. Chronik des Instituts für Tierernährungslehre der Humboldt Universität Berlin. *Beitr.Gesch.Landwirtschaftswiss.*, 1954, no. 1: 3-80.

SyNT

FAIRHOLME, Edward George; PAIN, Wellesley. A century of work for animals. The history of the R.S.P.C.A., 1824-1924. xx, 298 p. London: Murray, 1924.

SyO VETERINARY ANATOMY

for animal anatomy *see also* LJ
animal physiology *see* LK

SyOBwe

SMITH, Frederick. The position of veterinary anatomy in England during the 16th, 17th and 18th centuries. *Proc.3rd Int.Congr.Hist.Med.* (London, 1922), p. 288-94, 7 fig. Antwerp: De Vlijt, 1923.

SyOH SPECIALTIES OF VETERINARY MEDICINE

SyOJ

THOMAS, Fritz Carl. Geschichte der Therapie des Spates der Pferde. 71 p. Borna-Leipzig: R. Noske, 1912.

SyPO

IVANOW, Elie. L'insémination artificielle des mammifères en tant que méthode scientifique et zootechnique. *Rev.Gén. Sci.*, 1930, 41: 73-80.

SyPOwc

LEHMANN-NITSCHE, R. El retajo. (Folklore argentino, 2) *Bol. Acad.Nac.Cienc.Córdoba*, 1914, 20: 151-234.
Brief abstract in *Mitt.Gesch.Med.*, 1929, 28: 249.
German summary: Die Sterilisierung des Probierhengstes im lateinischen Amerika. *Arch.Wiss.Prakt.Tierheilk.*, 1916, 42: 223-42.

SyQ VETERINARY PATHOLOGY

SMITHCORS, J.F. Veterinary pathology: some lessons from the past. *Brit.Veterinary J.*, 1956, 112: 376-86.

SyQu

DAVIDSON, T.D. The cure of elf-disease in animals. *J.Hist. Med.*, 1960, 15: 282-91.

SyQN

HANSSEN, Peter. Geschichte der Epidemien bei Menschen und Tieren im Norden. 228 p. Glückstadt: Augustin, 1925.

KRUMBIEGEL, Ingo. Spirochäten in Säugetieren. *Z.Säugetierkunde*, 1928, 3: 49-54.

SEIFFERT, Gustav. Virus diseases in man, animal and plant. ix, 332 p. New York: Philosophical Library, 1944. [CB 66/265]

SyQNwc

KRAUS, Richard. Zehn Jahre Südamerika. Vorträge über Epidemiologie und Infektionskrankheiten der Menschen und Tiere. 182 p., 108 ill. Jena: Fischer, 1927.

SyQO

ROSENTHAL, Werner. Tierische Immunität. 329 p., 1 fig. Braunschweig: Vieweg, 1914.

SyQPztu

MYERS, J. Arthur. Man's greatest victory over tuberculosis. ix, 419 p., ill., bibliogr. Springfield, Ill.: Thomas, 1940.
With special reference to TB in domestic animals.
Reviewed in *Ann.Med.Hist.*, *3rd ser.*, 1941, 3: 259-60.

SyQR

AINSWORTH, G.C. A century of medical and veterinary mycology in Britain. *Trans.Brit.Mycol.Soc.*, 1951, 34: 1-16, portr.

SyQV

BLENKINSOP, Layton John; RAINEY, John Wakefield; ed. Veterinary services. ix, 782 p. (History of the Great War based on official documents) London: H.M. Stationery Off., 1925.

SyR VETERINARY THERAPEUTICS

SyRzh

BRÜSCH, Johannes. Über Homöopathie in der Veterinärmedizin. Ein Beitrag zu ihrer Geschichte und Versuch einer Nachprüfung. 87 p. Leipzig: Schwabe, 1934.

SyRF

SCHULZE, Walter. Therapeutische Tierquälerei in früherer Zeit. 14 p. (Diss. Leipzig) Bautzen: Gebr. Müller, 1923. Extract in *Mitt.Tierrätzl.Ges.Bekämpfung Kurpfuschertums*, 1930, 5: 4, 8.

SyRFzb

ENGERT, K. Geschichte des Aderlasses bei den Haustieren bis zur Gründung wissenschaftlicher Pflegstätten der Tierheilkunde. 43 p. (Diss. Leipzig) Dresden: 1912.

SA AGRICULTURE

SAc general history

ABEL, Wilhelm. Agrarpolitik. 419 p., diagr. (Grundriss der Sozialwissenschaft, 11) Göttingen: Vandenhoeck & Ruprecht, 1951.
Reviewed by P. Honigsheim, *Agr.Hist.*, 1952, 26: 156-60.

L'AGRICULTURE à travers les âges. Histoire des faits, des institutions, de la pensée et des doctrines économiques et sociales. 4 vol. 1. Quelques problèmes d'économie sociologique. Prolégomènes. Par E. Savoy. xvi, 667 p. 2. Première période: de Hammourabi à la fin de l'Empire romain. Par E. Savoy. xvi, 478 p. 3. L'agriculture au moyen âge, de la fin de l'empire romain au XVIe siècle. Par Roger Grand. 750 p. 4. L'agriculture du XVIIe siècle à la fin du XVIIIe. Par Edmond Soreau. 456 p. Paris: De Boccard, 1935. [CB 77/375]
Vol. 1-2 reviewed by Pierre Brunet, *Archeion*, 1936, 18: 291-2.

AUGÉ-LARIBÉ, Michel. La révolution agricole. xix, 435 p., 8 pl. (Bibliothèque historique: l'évolution de l'humanité, 83) Paris: Albin Michel, 1955.
Reviewed by Conway Zirkle, *Isis*, 1956, 47: 433.

CURWEN, E. Cecil; HATT, Gudmund. Plough and pasture: the early history of farming. xii, 329 p., 25 fig., 14 pl. New York: Schuman, 1953.
Reviewed by Conway Zirkle, *Isis*, 1954, 45: 301-2.

FOOD gathering to food production. Introduction, by Tom Jones; From cave to village in Iraq, by Robert J. Braidwood; Food sources in the New World, by Hugh C. Cutler. *Agr.Hist.*, 1954, 28: 39-49.

GRAS, Norman Scott Brien. A history of agriculture in Europe and America. 2nd ed. 496 p. New York: Crofts, 1940.
First published 1925.
Reviewed by Conway Zirkle, *Isis*, 1941, 33: 81.

HAHN, Eduard. Von der Hacke zum Pflug. 114 p. (Wissenschaft und Bildung, 127) Leipzig: Quelle und Meyer, 1914. [CB 10/194]

HONIGSHEIM, Paul. A new synopsis of agricultural history: a review of Abel's *Agrarpolitik*. *Agr.Hist.*, 1952, 26: 156-60.
For Abel's work *see* above.

LORD, Russell. The care of the earth. A history of husbandry. 384 p., ill. New York: New American Library, 1963.

MALIN, James C. Soil, animal and plant relations of the grass lands, historically considered. *Sci.Mon.*, 1953, 76: 207-20.

REVUE annuelle d'agronomie. *Rev.Gén.Sci.*, 1913, 24: 730-9; 1915, 26: 116-25; 1919, 30: 370-84, 411-18. [CB 4/781]

SLATER, William. The revolution in agriculture. *Advanc.Sci.*, 1961, 18: 249-56.

VAVILOV, Nikolai Ivanovich. The problem of the origin of the world's agriculture in the light of the latest investigations. 10 p., map. In: Science at the cross roads. Papers presented to the 2nd International Congress of the History of Science and Technology (London, 1931) by the delegates of the U.S.S.R. London: Kniga, 1931.

SAc-br

Agricultural History: quarterly journal of the Agricultural History Society of America. *Nature*, 1932, 129: 432.

The Annals of Applied Biology. The official organ of the Association of Economic (- of Applied) Biologists. 1- London: 1914- [CB 6/459]

Yearbook of Agriculture. United States Department of Agriculture. 1894- Washington, D.C.: Govt. Print. Off., 1895-
Volumes for 1936-42 reviewed by Conway Zirkle, *Isis*, 1938, 29: 182-3; 1943, 34: 525-6.

SAc-bv

THIRSK, J. List of books and articles on agrarian history issued September 1953-September 1963. *Agr.Hist.Rev.*, 1955, 3: 41-7; 1956, 4: 52-7; 1957, 5: 52-7; 1958, 6: 42-51; 1959, 7: 38-47; 1960, 8: 38-44; 1961, 9: 55-63; 1962, 10: 46-55; 1963, 11: 36-46; 1964, 12: 47-56; 1965, 13: 50-60.

SAc-bx

DIE ERSTE landwirtschaftlich-geschichtliche Ausstellung, Vippach-Edelhausen, 1-14 Februar 1917. [Catalogue of exhibition of objects, books and manuscripts] *Jahrb.Ges.Gesch. Lit.Landwirt.*, 1917, 16: 6-15. [CB 9/485]

SAcb

RASMUSSEN, Wayne D. The F. Hal Higgins Library of Agricultural Technology. *Technol.Cult.*, 1964, 5: 575-7.

SAce-bv

ASLIN, Mary S. Catalogue of the printed books on agriculture published between 1471 and 1840. With notes on the authors. 2nd ed. 293 p., ill. Harpenden: Rothamsted Experimental Station Library, 1940.
First published 1926 [CB 21/578]

ROYAL HORTICULTURAL SOCIETY. Lindley Library. Catalogue of books, pamphlets, manuscripts, and drawings. [By H.R. Hutchinson. Ed. by E.W. Hamilton] viii, 488 p. London: Royal Horticultural Society, 1927.

SAce-bx

BRITISH MUSEUM. Guide to an exhibition of manuscripts and printed books illustrating the history of agriculture. 30 p., 8 pl. London: British Museum, 1927.

SAda

DE KRUIF, Paul Henry. Hunger fighters. 377 p. New York: Harcourt, Brace, 1928.
German translation: Bezwinger des Hungers. Leipzig: Grethlein, 1930.

DIES, Edward Jerome. Titans of the soil: great builders of agriculture. ix, 213 p. Chapel Hill: University of North Carolina Press, 1949.

SAf

FUSSELL, G.E. Agricultural history in Holland. *Nature*, 1958, 182: 845.

KELSEY, R.W. Possibilities of intensive research in agricultural history. *Annu.Rep.Amer.Hist.Ass.1919*, (1), 377-83.

SAk/s special aspects

SAk

HILL, Johnson D.; STUERMANN, W.E. Roots in the soil. An introduction to the philosophy of agriculture. xi, 162 p., bibliogr. New York: Philosophical Library, 1964.

SAmzMY

BENNETT, M.K. Population and food supply: the current scare. *Sci.Mon.*, 1949, 68: 17-26.

CLARK, F. Le Gros; PIRIE, N.W.; ed. Four thousand million mouths. xii, 222 p. New York: Oxford University Press, 1952.

SAnh

BUTLIN, R.A. Some terms used in agrarian history. A glossary. (Glossaire de quelques termes utilisés en histoire agraire.) *Agr.Hist.Rev.*, 1961, 9: no. 2, 98-104.

SAqy

HOBSON, Asher. The International Institute of Agriculture (an historical and critical analysis of its organisation, activities and policies of administration.) vii, 356 p. Berkeley, Calif.: University of California Press, 1931.
Reviewed in *Nature*, 1931, 128: 737-8.

SAs

HALL, Daniel. Agricultural research in relation to the community. An address delivered before the Graduate School of the U.S. Department of Agriculture, January 26, 1925. *Science*, 1925, 61: 399-403.

SAsc

HONIGSHEIM, Paul. Max Weber as historian of agriculture and rural life. *Agr.Hist.*, 1949, 23: 179-213.

HYAMS, Edward. Soil and civilization. 312 p., 4 pl., 5 maps. London/New York: Thames and Hudson, 1952.
Reviewed by Jean-Paul Harroy, *Arch.Int.Hist.Sci.*, 1952, 5: 371-3.

SMITH, J. Russell. Grassland and farmland as factors in the cyclical development of Eurasian history. *Annu.Rep.Smithsonian Inst.for 1944*, p. 357-84, 1 pl., 18 fig. Washington, D.C.: 1945.

WHITNEY, Milton. Soil and civilisation: a modern concept of the soil and the historical development of agriculture. x, 278 p., 5 pl. (Library of Modern Sciences) London: Chapman and Hall, 1926.
Reviewed by W.E.B., *Nature*, 1927, 120: 436-7.

SAsy

DETURK, E.E., ed. Freedom from want: a survey of the possibilities of meeting the world's food needs. A symposium. *Chron.Bot.*, 1948, 11: 207-84.
Reviewed by Conway Zirkle, *Isis*, 1949, 40: 292.

PRENTICE, E. Parmalee. Food, war and the future. 164 p., 5 ill. New York: Harper, 1944.
Reviewed by Conway Zirkle, *Isis*, 1945, 36: 75-6.

SAw in different countries

CARTER, Jane. Man's place in the sun. *Agric.Hist.*, 1948, 22: 209-19.
Brief history of land tenure in England and the United States.

MASEFIELD, Geoffrey Bussell. A short history of agriculture in the British colonies. 186 p. Oxford: Clarendon Press, 1950.

SAwa

COOK, O.F. The debt of agriculture to tropical America. *Annu.Rep.Smithsonian Inst.for 1931*, p. 491-501, 7 pl. Washington, D.C.: 1932.

SAwb North America

BIDWELL, Percy Wells; FALCONER, John I. History of agriculture in the Northern United States, 1620-1860. xii, 512 p., 114 fig. Washington, D.C.: Carnegie Institution, 1925. [CB 18/621 and CB 23/249]
Reviewed by W.E.B., *Nature*, 1926, 117: 506-8.

BOGART, Ernest Ludlow. Economic history of American agriculture. x, 173 p. New York: Longmans, Green, 1923.

CARRIER, Lyman. Beginnings of agriculture in America. xvii, 323 p., 30 ill. New York: McGraw-Hill, 1923.

GRAY, Lewis Cecil. History of agriculture in the Southern United States to 1860. Assisted by Esther Katherine Thompson. With a foreword by H.C. Taylor. 2 vol. xxi, 7, 567 p., 1 map; x, p. 568-1086, 12 fig. Washington, D.C.: Carnegie Institution, 1933. [CB 39/459]
Reviewed by C.A. Kofoid, *Isis*, 1935, 23: 289.

HEDRICK, Ulysses Prentiss. A history of agriculture in the state of New York. xiv, 462 p., 82 pl., 41 fig., 2 maps. Geneva, N.Y.: New York State Agricultural Society, 1933.
Reviewed by C.A. Kofoid, *Isis*, 1935, 23: 287-8.

HIGGINBOTTOM, Sam. Sam Higginbottom: farmer, an autobiography. viii, 232 p., ill. New York: Scribners, 1949; London: Scribners, 1950.

HOWARD, Robert West. Two billion acre farm: an informal history of American agriculture. xi, 209 p. Garden City, N.Y.: Doubleday, Doran, 1945.
Reviewed by Conway Zirkle, *Isis*, 1947, 37: 111.

PFEIFER, Gottfried. Die räumliche Gliederung der Landwirtschaft im nördlichen Kalifornien. 309 p., ill. (*Wiss. Veröffentl.Ges.Erdk.Leipzig*, 10) Leipzig: F. Hirt, 1936. [CB 54/504]

SCHAFER, Joseph. The social history of American agriculture. x, 302 p., 2 pl., 6 fig. New York: Macmillan, 1936.
Reviewed by Charles A. Kofoid, *Isis*, 1938, 28: 149-50; by Harry J. Carman, *Amer.Hist.Rev.*, 1937, 42: 777-8.

TRUE, Alfred Charles. A history of agricultural experimentation and research in the United States, 1607-1925. Including a history of the United States Department of Agriculture. 321 p. (United States Department of Agriculture Miscellaneous Publications, 251) Washington: 1937.
Reviewed by C.Z., *Isis*, 1938, 29: 183.

SAwb-bv

EDWARDS, Everett Eugene. A bibliography of the history of agriculture in the U.S. iv, 307 p. (U.S. Dept. of Agriculture, Miscellaneous Publication, 84) Washington: Govt. Print. Off., 1930.

SAwb-cj

PINKETT, Harold T. *The American Farmer*, a pioneer agricultural journal. *Agr.Hist.*, 1950, 24: 146-50.

LANDON, Fred. The agricultural journals of upper Canada (Ontario). *Agr.Hist.*, 1935, 9: 167-75.

SAwb-da

IVINS, Lester Sylvan; WINSHIP, Albert Edward. Fifty famous farmers. xiv, 407 p. New York: Macmillan, 1924.

SAwb-daj

RASMUSSEN, Wayne D., ed. Readings in the history of American agriculture. ix, 304 p. Urbana: University of Illinois Press, 1960.
Reviewed by R.C. Loehr, *Agr.Hist.*, 1961, 35: 47-8.

SCHMIDT, Louis Bernard; ROSS, Earle Dudley. Readings in the economic history of American agriculture. xii, 591 p. New York: Macmillan, 1925.

SAwb-oq

MUMFORD, Frederick B. History of the Missouri College of Agriculture. 304 p. (Bulletin, 482) Columbia, Mo.: University of Missouri, College of Agriculture, 1946.
From its establishment in 1870 to the present.

STEVENS, Neil E. America's first agricultural school. *Sci. Mon.*, 1921, 13: 531-40. [CB 13/241]
The Gardiner Lyceum, Gardiner, Maine.

WILLARD, Julius Terrass. History of the Kansas State College of Agriculture and Applied Science. viii, 568 p., ill., portr. Manhattan, Kan.: Kansas State College Press, 1940. [CB 61/421]
This is a collection of data concerning the evolution of a state university in an agrarian society.

SAwb-or

GEISER, Samuel W. George Washington Curtis and Frank Arthur Gully: two early agricultural teachers in Texas. *Field Lab.*, 1946, 14: 1-12, portr.

SAwb-ph

FULLING, E.H. Plant life and the law of man. 2. Bounties. *J.N.Y.Bot.Gard.*, 1942, 43: 44-53.

SAwb-pw

BROWNE, Charles Albert. Some historical relations of agriculture in the West Indies to that of the United States. *Agr. Hist.*, 1927, 1: 23-33.

SAwb-qd

NEW JERSEY AGRICULTURAL SOCIETY. The history of the New Jersey Agricultural Society. Early attempts to form a society, proceedings, fairs, activities and accomplishments, 1781-1940. 70 p., ill. Trenton, N.J.: 1947.

MEMOIRS OF THE PHILADELPHIA SOCIETY FOR PROMOTING AGRICULTURE, vol. 6. Philadelphia, Pa.: 1939. [CB 59/476]
This volume contains a short history of the Society and reprints of some memorial addresses.

SAwb-qk

BAKER, Gladys L., et al. Century of service. The first 100 years of the United States Department of Agriculture. xv, 560 p. Washington, D.C.: Centennial Committee, U.S. Department of Agriculture, 1963.
Reviewed by Paul W. Gates, *Amer.Hist.Rev.*, 1963-64, 69: 793-4.

HARDING, T. Swann. Some landmarks in the history of the Department of Agriculture. 94 p. (Agricultural History Series, 2) Washington, D.C.: U.S. Department of Agriculture, 1942. [CB 64/452]
Material gleaned from the official annual reports relating to agriculture from 1837 to the present.

HARDING, T. Swann. Two blades of grass. A history of scientific developments in the U.S. Department of Agriculture. xi, 352 p. Norman: University of Oklahoma Press, 1947.
Reviewed by Mark Graubard, *Isis*, 1948, 38: 261-2; by G.H. Bailey, *Amer.Hist.Rev.*, 1947, 53: 186.

SAwc Latin America

SAwc-qg

COOK, Melville T. et al. History of the first quarter of a century of the Agricultural Experiment Station at Rio Piedras, Puerto Rico. 123 p., ill., bibliogr. (Bulletin, 44) San Juan, Puerto Rico: 1937. [CB 52/565]

SAwd Europe

CARRIER, Elsé Haydon. Water and grass. A study in the pastoral economy of Southern Europe. xi, 434 p. London: Christophers, 1932.

SLICHER VAN BATH, B.H. The agrarian history of Western Europe, A.D. 500-1850. ix, 364 p. London: Arnold, 1963; New York: St. Martin's Press, 1964.
English translation of: De agrarische geschiedenis van West-Europa, 500-1850. 416 p. Utrecht: Aula-Boeken, 1962. [CB 90/526]

SAwe

CHRISTIE, Mabel E. The evolution of the English farm. 376 p., ill. London: Allen & Unwin; Cambridge: Harvard University Press, 1927.
Reviewed by N. Neilson, *Amer.Hist.Rev.*, 1928, 33: 382-3.

ERNLE, Rowland Edmund Prothero, *baron*. English farming, past and present. 6th ed. Introd. by G.E. Fussell and O.R. McGregor. cxlv, 559 p. London: Heinemann, 1961.
First published 1912.
Reviewed by Douglas McKie, *Ann.Sci.*, 1961, 17: 123-4.

GAUT, R.C. A history of Worcestershire agriculture and rural evolution. xvi, 490 p. Worcester: Littlebury, 1939.
Reviewed by E.J. Russell, *Nature*, 1944, 154: 190-1.

HALL, Charles James. A short history of English agriculture and rural life. viii, 152 p., 8 pl. London: Black, 1924.

ORR, John. A short history of British agriculture. 96 p., ill. London: Oxford University Press, 1922.

ORWIN, C.S. A history of English farming. vii, 152 p., 24 pl. (Nelson's Agricultural Series) London: Nelson, 1949.

PORTEOUS, Crichton. Pioneers of fertility. 126 p., ill. London: Clareville Press, 1948.
Anecdotic history of agriculture in England from Fitzherbert (1523) to Robert Warington (1837-1907).

TROW-SMITH, Robert. English husbandry. From the earliest times to the present day. 240 p., ill. London: Faber & Faber, 1951.

SAwe-ce

FUSSELL, G.E. The old English farming books from Fitzherbert to Tull, 1523 to 1730. 141 p., 16 pl. London: Lockwood. 1947. [CB 72/273]

SAwe-qg

HOLMYARD, E.J. Priests of Pomoma. *Endeavour*, 1954, 13: 3-4.
An account of the Long Ashton Research Station, known informally as 'The Cider Institute.'

ROTHAMSTED centenary number. *MSN*, 1943, no. 24, 8 p., ill. [CB 66/266]
The hundredth anniversary of the foundation of the Rothamsted Experimental Station.

RUSSELL, E. John. British agricultural research: Rothamsted. 32 p., ill. London: British Council, 1942. [CB 69/56]

RUSSELL, E. John. Rothamsted and agricultural science. *Nature*, 1923, 111: 466-70. [CB 15/181]

TUBBS, F.R. The East Malling Research Station (1913-63). *Nature*, 1963, 198: 327-31.

SAwe-rx

GREEN, Frederick Ernest. A history of the English agricultural labourer, 1870-1920. x, 356 p. London: King, 1920.
Reprint. London: King, 1927.

SAwf

DEMOLON, Albert. L'évolution scientifique et l'agriculture française. 329 p. (Bibliothèque de Philosophie Scientifique) Paris: Flammarion, 1946.
Reviewed by Pierre Brunet, *Rev.Hist.Sci.*, 1948, 1: 374-5.

PARAIN, Charles. Les anciennes techniques agricoles. Aspects de la vie rurale en France. *Rev.Syn.*, 1957, 77: 317-46. [CB 84/327]
Part of a joint symposium sponsored by the Centre International de Synthèse and the Musée des Arts et Traditions Populaires.

SAwf-pq

CHOUARD, P. La recherche universitaire (période 1948-1961). *Compt.Rend.Séances Acad.Agr.Fr.*, 1961, no. 7, 368-72.

SAwg

ABEL, Wilhelm. Geschichte der deutschen Landwirtschaft vom frühen Mittelalter bis zum 19. Jahrhundert. 333 p., ill. Stuttgart: Eugen Ulmer, 1962.
Reviewed by Wolfgang Hartke, *Erde,* 1964, 95: 144-5.

SAwg-u

HALDY, Bruno. Die deutschen Bauernregeln, gesammelt und herausgegeben. Mit Monatsbildern von Josua Leander Gampp. 126 p., ill. Jena: Diederichs, 1923.

SAwh

INGLOT, Stefan. [Outline of the history of agricultural and forestry science in Poland. (In Polish with summary in French)] 53 p. (Polska Akademia Umiejetności, Historia, Nauki Polskiej w Monografiach, 11) Krakow: 1948.

SAwh-qg

STRZEMSKI, Michał. Instytut Gospodarstwa Wiejskiego i Leśnictwa w Puławach w latach 1869-1914. [The Institute of Rural Economy and Forestry in Puławy 1869-1914. (In Polish, with English and Russian summaries)] *Stud.Mater.Dziej. Nauk.Pol., ser. B,* 1961, 4: 3-57.

SAwi

PONI, Carlo. Gli aratri e l'economia agraria nel Bolognese, dal XVII al XIX secolo. viii, 274 p. Bologna: Zanichelli, 1963.
Reviewed by Douglas F. Dowd, *Technol.Cult.,* 1964, 5: 604-5.

SAwk

LINDEMANS, Paul. Geschiedenis van de landbouw in België. [History of agriculture in Belgium. (In Dutch)] 2 vol. 472 p.; 541 p., ill. Antwerpen: De Sikkel, 1952.

SAwn

FISH, Gennadi. A people's academy. 192 p. Moscow: Foreign Language Publishing House, 1949.
Reviewed by Conway Zirkle, *Isis,* 1951, 42: 85.
Agriculture in the Ukraine.

SAwp/wx Asia; Australia; Africa

SAwp

CALDER, Ritchie. Men against the desert. 186 p., 27 pl. London: Allen & Unwin, 1951.
Reviewed by G.V. Jacks, *Nature,* 1951, 167: 419.

SHORT, Albert K. Ancient and modern agriculture. Added scriptural references. xxii, 158 p. San Antonio, Tex.: Naylor, 1938. [CB 57/249]
Annotated compilation of Biblical references to agriculture and its techniques as related to social, industrial, and cultural factors in Palestine in ancient times and today.

UNITED STATES. AGRICULTURAL MISSION TO SAUDI ARABIA. Report. English text, 147 p.; Arabic, [192]p. [Cairo]: 1943.
K.S. Twichell, Chief of Mission.
Reviewed bv S.M. Zwemer, *Moslem World,* 1945, 35: 68.

SAwr

ANDERSON, George W. Agriculture in the undrained basin of Asia. *Agr.Hist.,* 1948, 22: 233-8.
Brief sketch of the development of modern agriculture in Turkestan and neighboring regions.

SAws

MUKHERJEE, J.N. Address of the General President to the Indian Science Congress, Calcutta, Jan. 1952. *Sci.Cult.,* 1952, 17: suppl. to no. 7, 17-32.
Review of science in India at present time, with particular reference to agriculture.

MUKERJEE, Radhakamal. The rural economy of India. xii, 262 p., plan. London: Longmans, Green, 1926.

SAwt

CHEN HAN-SENG. Frontier land systems in southernmost China. A comparative study of agrarian problems and social organization among the Pai Yi people of Yunnan and the Kamba people of Sikang. ix, 156 p. New York: International Secretariat, Institute of Pacific Relations, 1949. [CB 74/379]

FEI, Hsiao-Tung. Peasant life in China. A field study of country life in the Yangtze Valley. xxvi, 300 p. London: Routledge, 1939.
Reviewed in *Nature,* 1939, 144: 267; by Roger Pinto, *Bull. Ecole Franç.Extrême-Orient,* 1942, 41: 373-93.

FEI, Hsiao-Tung; CHANG, Chih-I. Earthbound China. A study of rural economy in Yunnan. Rev. English ed. prepared in collaboration with Paul Cooper and Margaret Park Redfield. xv, 319 p., ill. (International Library of Sociology and Social Reconstruction) London: Routledge, 1949. [CB 75/81]

WAGNER, Wilhelm. Die chinesische Landwirtschaft. xv, 668 p., ill, maps, plans, diagr. Berlin: Paul Parey, 1926.

SAww

MEINIG, Donald W. Goyder's line of rainfall. The role of a geographic concept in south Australian land policy and agricultural settlement. *Agr.Hist.,* 1961, 35: 207-14.

SAwx

GITHENS, Thomas S.; WOOD, Carroll E. The food resources of Africa. iv, 105 p., ill., bibliogr. (African Handbooks, 3) Philadelphia: University of Pennsylvania Press, University Museum, 1943.

SAx techniques and instruments; machinery

see also SCxb

KOHLMEYER, Fred W.; HERUM, Floyd L. Science and engineering in agriculture: a historical perspective. *Technol.Cult.,* 1961, 2: 368-80.

SAxb-pw

DALRYMPLE, Dana G. The American tractor comes to Soviet agriculture: the transfer of a technology. *Technol.Cult.,* 1964, 5: 191-214

SAxb-wb

HOLBROOK, Stewart H. Machines of plenty. Pioneering in American agriculture. 246 p., front. New York: Macmillan Company, 1955. [CB 81/339]
The presentation centers on the development of J.I. Case Company, manufacturers of agricultural machinery.

McMILLAN, Robert T. Effects of mechanization on American agriculture. *Sci.Mon.,* 1949, 69: 23-8.

SPENCE, Clark C. Early uses of electricity in American agriculture. *Technol.Cult.,* 1962, 3: 142-60.

SAxb-we

LONG, W. Harwood. The development of mechanization in English farming. *Agr.Hist.Rev.,* 1963, 11: 15-26.

SAxb-wn

ROKACH, J.A. [A contribution to the question of the origin of agricultural machine-building in Russia. (In Russian, with English summary)] *Arkh.Ist.Nauk.Tekh.,* 1934, 4: 323-35.

SAyBW AGRICULTURAL STATISTICS

SAyBWwe

FUSSELL, G.E. The collection of agricultural statistics in Great Britain: its origin and evolution. *Agr.Hist.,* 1944, 18: 161-86. [CB 68/55]

SB SOIL SCIENCE; AGRICULTURAL PHYSICS AND CHEMISTRY

for drainage and irrigation *see* TL

SBc general history

AMERICAN ASSOCIATION FOR THE ADVANCEMENT OF SCIENCE. Liebig and after Liebig. A century of progress in agricultural chemistry. Ed. by F.R. Moulton. iv, 111 p., portr., fig. (Publication, no. 16) Washington, D.C.: The Association, 1942. [CB 65/66]
Reviewed by Mark Graubard, *Isis*, 1943, 34: 369-70.

BROWNE, Charles A. The relation of chemistry to agriculture. *Science*, 1924, 60: 575-80.

FUSSELL, G.E. The early days of chemical fertilizers. *Nature*, 1962, 195: 750-4.

GARNER, H.V. The oldest experiment in the world. *Discovery*, 1959, 20: 296-301.
On agricultural chemistry and the first experimental farms in England.

HENRICK, James. Soil science in the twentieth century. *Advance.Sci.*, 1936, 233-48.

HONCAMP, Franz. Justus von Liebig und sein Einfluss auf die Entwicklung der Landwirtschaft. Rektoratsrede. 36 p. (Rostocker Universitäts-Reden, 6) Rostock: Verlag Hinstorff, 1928.

MAYER, Adolf. Zur Geschichte der Agrikulturchemie. *Naturwissenschaften*, 1924, 12: 885-7.

MEYER, L. 100 Jahre Agrikulturchemie; Justus v. Liebig und das Problem der Aufrechterhaltung der Bodenfruchtbarkeit. *Nova Acta Leopoldina*, 1941, 10: 1-28.

NEHRING, K. 100 Jahre landwirtschaftliche Chemie. 80 Jahre landwirtschaftliche Versuchsstation Rostock. *Beitr.Gesch. Landwirtschaftswiss.*, 1955, no. 2, 3-24.

POLYNOV, B.B. [Outline of the development of the study of the soil as a branch of natural sciences. (In Russian)] *Tr.Inst.Ist.Est.*, 1948, 2: 105-69.

RUFFIN, Edmund. An essay on calcareous manures. Ed. by J. Carlyle Sitterson. xxxv, 199 p., app., fig. Cambridge: Harvard University Press, 1961.

WILLIAMS, Robert R. Chemistry as a supplement to agriculture in meeting world food needs. *Amer.Scient.*, 1956, 44: 317-27. [CB 82/266]

SBce-bv

WULFF, Adolf. Bibliographia agrogeologica: essay of a systematic bibliography of agro-geology. iv, 286 p. (Mededeelingen van de Landbouwhoogeschool, 20) Wageningen: H. Veenman, 1921.

SBdaj

BROWNE, Charles A. A source book of agricultural chemistry. x, 290 p. (Chronica Botanica, 8) Waltham, Mass.: Chronica Botanica, 1944.
Reviewed by Conway Zirkle, *Isis*, 1946, 36: 149; by George Urdang, *J.Amer.Pharm.Ass.*, 1944, 33: 350-1.

SBwb

CRAVEN, Avery Odelle. Soil exhaustion as a factor in the agricultural history of Virginia and Maryland, 1606-1860. 179 p. (University of Illinois Studies in the Social Sciences, 13: no. 1) Urbana: University of Illinois, 1926.
Reviewed by Thomas J. Wertenbaker, *Amer.Hist.Rev.*, 1927, 32: 610-11.

JORDAN, Weymouth T. The Peruvian guano gospel in the old South. *Agr.Hist.*, 1950, 24: 211-21.
A study of the ante-bellum search for fertilizers.

SBwb-kq

SIMONSON, Roy W. Soil classification in the United States. *Science*, 1962, 137: 1027-34.

SBwg-qg

NEHRING, K. 100 Jahre landwirtschaftliche Chemie. 80 Jahre landwirtschaftliche Versuchsstation Rostock. *Beitr.Gesch. Landwirtschaftswiss.*, 1955, no. 2, 3-24.

SBwh

BALLENEGGER, Robert; FINÁLY, István. A magyar talajtani kutatás története 1944-ig. [The history of Hungarian soils research up to 1944. (In Hungarian)] 318 p., 30 ill. Budapest: Akademiai Kiado, 1963.

SBwn

VOL'FKOVICH, S.I. Osnovatel' otechestvennoi agrokhimii. D.N. Prianishnikov i khimizatsiia sel'skogo khoziaistva. [The founder of agricultural chemistry in Russia. D.I. Prianishnikov and the introduction of chemistry into agriculture. (In Russian)] *Priroda*, 1962, no. 10, 93-5.

SByJR

WAKSMAN, Selman A. Soil microbiology. vii, 356 p. New York: Wiley, 1952.
The first 28 pages are devoted to a history of the subject.

SC PLANT CULTIVATION AND HORTICULTURE

for plant genetics *see* KH

SCc general history

BROWNE, C.A. The spontaneous heating and ignition of hay and other agricultural products. *Science*, 1933, 77: 223-9. [CB 38/600]
Includes historical notes.

CARLES, Jules. Qu'est-ce qu'un cru? *Rev.Quest.Sci.*, 1949, 10: 239-54.

CHOUARD, Pierre. Cultures sans sol. 200 p. Paris: La Maison Rustique, 1952. [CB 79/179]
Historical development of techniques of crop production in water solutions on porous substances.

CHOUARD, Pierre. Dormances et inhibitions des graines et des bourgeons; préparation au forçage; thermopériodisme. 157 p., 22 fig. (Les Cours du Conservatoire National des Arts et Métiers) Paris: Centre de Documentation Universitaire, 1951. [CB 79/179]

JORGENSEN, Ingvar; STILES, Walter. The electroculture of crops. *Sci.Progr.*, 1918, 12: 609-21.

LEE, N.E. Harvests and harvesting through the ages. 208 p. London: Cambridge University Press, 1960.

LIPPMANN, Edmund O. von. Zur Geschichte der Samenbeizung. *Deut.Zuckerind.*, 1930, 55: 556.

SCHOPFER, W.H. La culture des plantes en milieu synthétique. Les précurseurs. *Act.VIe Congr.Int.Hist.Sci.* (Amsterdam, 1950), (1), p. 289-96; also in *Arch.Int.Hist.Sci.*, 1951, 4: 681-8.

WAHLEN, F.T. Plant sciences and world husbandry. *Proc.7th Int.Bot.Congr.* (Stockholm, 1950), p. 34-42. Stockholm: Almqvist & Wiksell; Waltham, Mass.: Chronica Botanica, 1953.

SCce-bv

Huntia: a yearbook of botanical and horticultural bibliography. 1- Pittsburgh: Hunt Botanical Library, Carnegie Institute of Technology, 1964-

SCw in different countries

SCwb

HEDRICK, Ulysses Prentiss. A history of horticulture in America to 1860. 551 p., 62 ill. London: Oxford University Press, 1950.

SCwb-oq

GAGER, C. Stuart. The school of horticulture in perspective. *Science,* 1936, 84: 357-65.
Address delivered at the 25th anniversary of the School of Horticulture for Women, Ambler, Pa.

SCwe

BUTTRESS, F.A.; DENNIS, R.W.G. The early history of seed treatment in England. *Agr.Hist.,* 1947, 21: 93-103. [CB 71/122]

SCwt

BUCK, John Lossing. Chinese farm economy: a study of 2866 farms in 17 localities and 7 provinces of China. xii, 476 p., 21 pl. Chicago: Chicago University Press, for the University of Nanking and the China Council of the Institute of Pacific Relations, 1931.
Reviewed by George B. Cressey, *Geogr.Rev.,* 1931, 21: 352.

SCxb plant and machinery

ANDERSON, Russell H. Grain drills through thirty-nine centuries. *Agr.Hist.,* 1936, 10: 157-205, 12 fig.

BISHOP, Carl Whiting. Origin and early diffusion of the traction plow. *Annu.Rep.Smithsonian Inst.for 1937,* p. 531-47, 4 pl., 7 fig. Washington, D.C.: 1938.

HOPKINS, L.C. The cas-chrom v. the lei-ssŭ. A study of th primitive forms of plough in Scotland and ancient China. *J. Roy.Asiatic Soc.,* 1935, 707-16; 1936, 45-54, ill.

LESER, Paul. Entstehung und Verbreitung des Pfluges. xv, 677 p., 351 fig., 22 pl. (Anthropos, vol. 3, pt. 3) Münster i. W.: Aschendorff, 1931.
Reviewed by Gustav Fischer, *Deut.Lit.Zeitung,* 1932, 3: 471-4.

LÖWE, Paul. Das Dreschen einst und jetzt. *Beitr.Gesch.Tech. Ind.,* 1928, 18: 139-42.

STEENSBERG, Axel. Ancient harvesting implements: a study in archeology and human geography. 275 p., 80 fig., 13 pl. Copenhagen: Nordisk Forlag, 1943.
Reviewed by E. Cecil Curwen, *Antiquity,* 1943, 17: 196-206, 11 fig.

SCxb-nh

PUHVEL, Jaan. The Indo-European and Indo-Aryan plough. A linguistic study of technological diffusion. *Technol.Cult.,* 1964, 5: 176-90.

SCxb-qx

CONGRÈS d'électroculture, (1er), Reims, octobre 1912. *Isis,* 1913, 1: 260-1.
Programme of the forthcoming conference.

SCxb-we

FUSSELL, G.E. The farmer's tools, 1500-1900. The history of British farm implements, tools and machinery before the tractor came. 246 p., 111 ill. London: A. Melrose, 1952.
Reviewed by R.J. Forbes, *Arch.Int.Hist.Sci.,* 1953, 6: 370.

PASSMORE, John B. The English plough. 84 p., 13 pl. (Reading University Studies) London: Oxford University Press, 1930.

SPENCE, Clark C. God speed the plow: the coming of steam cultivation to England. 183 p., ill. Urbana: University of Illinois Press, 1960.
Reviewed by Reynold M. Wik, *Technol.Cult.,* 1961, 2: 187-8; by F.H. Higgins, *Agr.Hist.,* 1961, 35: 104-5.

SD PLANT PATHOLOGY; PLANT PESTS

see also LUza APPLIED ENTOMOLOGY; INSECT CONTROL

SDc general history

BÖHNER, Konrad. Geschichte der Cecidologie. Ein Beitrag zur Entwicklungsgeschichte naturwissenschaftlicher Forschung und ein Führer durch die Cecidologie der Alten. Mit einer Vorgeschichte zur Cecidologie der klassischen Schriftsteller von Felix von Öfele. 2 vol. 1. Allgemeiner Teil. xxvii, 466 p., 27 fig.; 2. Besonderer Teil. 712 p., 138 fig. (Veröffentlichungen der Gesellschaft für Geschichte der Pharmazie) Mittenwald: Nemayer, 1933-35.
Reviewed by George Sarton, *Isis,* 1935, 24: 180-3, 2 fig.

FLINT, W.P.; METCALF, C.L. Insects, man's chief competitors. viii, 133 p., 12 fig. Baltimore: Williams & Wilkins, 1932. [CB 39/460]

HEUSINGER, Johann Christian Karl Friedrich von. Die Pflanzenwelt, ihr Wechsel und ihr Erkranken, in Beziehung auf die Geschichte und die Verbreitung der Krankheiten der Menschheit. *Henschel's Janus,* 1851, 1: 24-47; reprinted Leipzig: Alfred Lorentz, 1931.

KÜSTER, Ernst. Ueber die Gallen der Pflanzen. Neue Resultate und Streitfragen der allgemeinen Cecidologie. *Fortschr. Naturwiss.Forsch.,* 1913, 8: 115-60.

LARGE, E.C. The advance of the fungi. 488 p., ill. New York: Holt; London: Cape, 1940.
Reviewed by Morris C. Leikind, *Isis,* 1943, 34: 231-2.

LOFTIN, U.C. Living with the boll weevil for fifty years. *Annu.Rep.Smithsonian Inst.for 1945,* p. 273-91, 10 pl., 2 fig. Washington, D.C.: 1946.

MAGNUS, P. Zur Geschichte unserer Kenntnis der Kronenrostes der Gräser und einige sich daran knüpfende Bemerkungen. *Verhandl.Schweiz.Naturforsch.Ges.,* 1912, 95: 220-5.

MELHUS, Irving E.; KENT, George C. Elements of plant pathology. vii, 493 p., 254 fig. New York: Macmillan, 1939. [CB 58/574]
The first chapters contain historical data, and other data of that kind are scattered in the book.

MEYER, Erich. Beitrag zur Entwicklungsgeschichte der Phytopathologie und des Pflanzenschutzes. Unter besonderer Berücksichtigung folgender Krankheiten: Honigtaukrankheit, Mehltaukrankheit, Mutterkorn, Russtau, Rost des Getreides, Brand des Getreides. *Arch.Gesch.Math.Naturwiss.Tech.,* 1929, 12: 146-87; 1930, 12: 236-68.

ORLOB, Gert B. The concepts of etiology in the history of plant pathology. *Pflanzenschutz Nachr.Bayer,* 1964, 17: 186-268, bibliogr.

ROUSSY, Gust; WOLF, Maur. Le cancer des plantes. *Rev.Méd.,* 1922, 11: 75-86. [CB 13/284]

ROY, T.C. Origin and development of the views on virus diseases. *Sci.Cult.,* 1951, 17: 243-8.

SMITH, Erwin F. Les maladies bactériennes des plantes. *Rev. Gén.Sci.,* 1925, 36: 134-9. [CB 18/570]

SMITH, Kenneth M. Plant viruses. vii, 78 p. New York: Wiley, 1950.

SMITH, Kenneth M. Recent advances in the study of plant viruses. With a foreword by F.T. Brooks. xii, 423 p., 1 pl., 67 fig. Philadelphia: Blakiston, 1934. [CB 42/593]

VAYSSIÈRE, Paul. Le problème acridien et sa solution internationale. *Matér.Etud.Calamités,* 1924, no. 2, 122-58; no. 3, 274-82; 1925, no. 4, 361-72; no. 5, 67-74.
Reviewed by A.D. Imms, *Nature,* 1925, 115: 31.

WHETZEL, Herbert Hice. History of phytopathology. 250 p., ill. Philadelphia: Saunders, 1918.

WHETZEL, Herbert Hice. An outline of the history of phytopathology. 130 p., 22 portr. Philadelphia: Saunders, 1918.
Reviewed by George Sarton, *Isis,* 1923, 5: 461-4.

WILDEMAN, E. de. Allélopathie ou télétoxie, en particulier dans le règne végétal. *Bull.Acad.Roy.Belg.Cl.Sci.,* 1946, 32: 117-26.

SDp/u special aspects

SDpw

CUBONI, Giuseppe. Un accord international pour la lutte contre les maladies des plantes. *Rev.Hort.Belg.*, 1912, 38: 370-5.

NÉCESSITÉ d'un accord international pour la lutte contre les maladies des plantes. *Rev.Gén.Sci.*, 1913, 24: 173.

SDu

MARZELL, Heinrich. Pflanzengallen im Volksglauben. *Naturforscher*, 1930-31, 7: 430-6.

SDw in different countries

SDwb

RODGERS, Andrew Denny, III. Erwin Frink Smith. A story of North American plant pathology. x, 675 p., 4 pl. (*Mem. Amer.Phil.Soc.*, 31) Philadelphia, Pa.: American Philosophical Society, 1952. [CB 79/141]
Reviewed in *Nature*, 1953, 171: 764.

SWINGLE, Walter T.; *et al.* A Chinese insecticidal plant, *Tripterygium Wilfordii*, introduced into the United States. *Science*, 1941, 93: 60-1.

SDwb-ph

FULLING, E.H. Plant life and the law of man. 3. Barberry eradication. *J.N.Y.Bot.Gard.*, 1942, 43: 152-7.

FULLING, E.H. Plant life and the law of man. 4. Barberry, currant and gooseberry, and cedar control. *Bot.Rev.*, 1943, 9: 483-592.

SDwc

JENKINS, Anna E. On the history of phytopathology in Brazil. *Chron.Bot.*, 1941, 6: 224-6.

SDwf

VAYSSIÈRE, Paul. L'organisation de la lutte contre les ennemis des cultures et la protection de la séricículture en France. *Rev.Sci.*, 1924, 62: 238-43. [CB 16/351]

SDwn

DUNIN, M.S.; SEPESHSHI, Ishtvan. Ocherk razvitiya fitopatologii v Vengrii. [Outline of the development of phytopathology in Vengria. (In Russian)] *Vop.Ist.Est.Tekh.*, 1956, 2: 155-75.

SE CULTIVATED PLANTS IN GENERAL; ECONOMIC BOTANY

see also RQ NAMED MEDICINAL PLANTS

SEc general history

BOIS, Désiré G.J.M. Les plantes alimentaires chez tous les peuples et à travers les ages. Histoire, utilisation, culture. 3 vol. 1. Phanérogames légumières. 595 p., ill.; 2. Phanérogames fruitières. 636 p., 261 fig.; 3. Plantes à épices, à aromates, à condiments. iii, 289 p. Paris: Lechevalier, 1927-34.
Vol. 2 reviewed by G.D., *Rev.Gén.Sci.*, 1929, 40: 185-6; vol. 3 reviewed in *Nature*, 1935, 136: 663.

GUYOT, A.L. Histoire des plantes cultivées. 216 p. Paris: Armand Colin, 1963.
Reviewed by Albert Delorme, *Rev.Syn.*, 1963, 84: 623-4.

GUYOT, A.L. Origine des plantes cultivées. 126 p. (Que sais-je? 79) Paris: Presses Universitaires de France, 1942.

HAHN, Eduard. Die Pflanze als Begleiter der Menschheit. *Arch.Gesch.Math.Naturwiss.Tech.*, 1927, 10: 54-61.
General views on the dawn of agriculture.

HAYWARD, Herman E. The structure of economic plants. x, 674 p., 340 fig. New York: Macmillan, 1938. [CB 56/395]

HELBACK, Hans. Domestication of food plants in the old world: joint efforts by botanists and archeologists illuminate the obscure history of plant domestication. *Science*, 1959. 130: 365-72.

KAPLAN, Lawrence. Historical and ethnobotanical aspects of domestication in *Tagetes*. *Econ.Bot.*, 1960, 14: 200-2.

LEHNER, Ernst; LEHNER, Johanna. Folklore and odysseys of food and medicinal plants. 128 p. New York: Tudor Publishing Co., 1960.
Reviewed by Richard Evans Schultes, *Econ.Bot.*, 1963, 17: 154.

MERRILL, E.D. Some economic aspects of taxonomy. *Torreya*, 1943, 43: 50-64.

THELLUNG, Albert. Die Entstehung der Kulturpflanzen. Hrsg. v. J. Braun-Blanquet. 91 p. (Naturwissenschaft und Landwirtschaft, 16) Freising-München: Datterer, 1930.
Reviewed by Joh. Mattfeld, *Deut.Lit.Zeitung*, 1930, 1: 857-61.

VAVILOV, Nikolai Ivanovich. [The rôle of Central Asia in the origin of cultivated plants. (In Russian, with English summary)] *Tr.Prikl.Bot.Genet.Selek.*, 1931, 26: 1-44.

VERRILL, A. Hyatt; BARRETT, Otis W. Food America gave the world. xvi, 289 p., 10 pl. Boston: Page, 1937.
Reviewed by Conway Zirkle, *Isis*, 1938, 29: 153-5.

WALKER, Egbert H. The plants of China and their usefulness to man. *Annu.Rep.Smithsonian Inst.for 1943*, p. 325-61, 12 pl., map. Washington, D.C.: 1944.

WATKINS, A.E. The origin of cultivated plants. *Antiquity*, 1933, 7: 73-80, 1 pl., 1 map. [CB 38/601]

SEs relations with society

HAUDRICOURT, André G.; HEDIN, L. L'homme et les plantes cultivées. 233 p., ill. Paris: Galimard, 1943.

HUTCHINSON, G. Evelyn. Marginalia. *Amer.Scient.*, 1953, 41: 628-34.
The various historical and scientific problems to be found in the relationship of man to his domestic plants.

SEsk

HARLAN, Jack R. Crops, weeds and revolution. *Sci.Mon.*, 1955, 80: 299-303. [CB 81/274]

SEw in different countries

SEwb

KLOSE, Nelson. America's crop heritage: the history of foreign plant introduction by the federal government. x, 156 p., 6 ill. Ames: Iowa State College Press, 1950.
Reviewed by Conway Zirkle, *Isis*, 1951, 42: 86.

LAUFER, Berthold. The American plant migration. *Sci.Mon.*, 1929, 28: 239-51.

SEwd

HELBACK, Hans. Domestication of food plants in the old world. *Science*, 1959, 130: 365-72.

NETOLITZKY, Fritz. Unser Wissen von den alten Kulturpflanzen Mittel-Europas. *Ber.Röm.Ger.Komm.Deut.Arch.Inst.*, 1931, 20: 14-76.

SEwg

BERTSCH, Karl; BERTSCH, Franz. Geschichte unserer Kulturpflanzen. 268 p., 78 ill. Stuttgart: Wissenschaftliche Verlagsgesellschaft, 1947.
A history of the plants now cultivated in Germany.

GENTNER, Georg. Zur Geschichte unserer Kulturpflanzen. *Ber. Bayer.Bot.Ges.*, 1912, 13: 82-93.

SEwm

HOLMBOE, Jens. Gamle Norske Matplanter. [Old Norwegian food plants. (In Norwegian)] 36 p. (*Avhandl.Norske Vidensk.Akad. Oslo Math.Nat.Kl.*) Oslo: 1929.
Reviewed by H. Marzell, *Mitt.Gesch.Med.*, 1930, 29: 22.

SEwr

VAVILOV, Nikolai Ivanovich; BUKINICH, D.D. Agricultural Afghanistan. (In Russian and English) 610, xxxii p., ill. (*Tr.Prikl.Bot.Genet.Selek.*, Suppl. 33) Leningrad: 1929.
Reviewed by V. Minorsky, *J.Asiatique*, 1929, 215: 352-4.

SEwt

HO PING-TI. American food plants in China. *Plant Sci.Bull.*, 1956, 2: 1-3.
A description of the introduction of New World plants into Chinese agriculture.

SEyKH

DARLINGTON, C.D.; JANAKI-AMMAL, E.K. Chromosome atlas of cultivated plants. 397 p. London: Allen & Unwin, 1945. [CB 70/260]

SF GRAIN CROPS; CEREALS; GRASSES

for maize *see* SFzm
mills *see* UL

BULLER, A.-H. Reginald. Essays on wheat, including the discovery and introduction of marquis wheat, the early history of wheat-growing in western Canada, the origin of red bobs and kitchener and the wild wheat of Palestine. xv, 340 p., 50 ill. New York: Macmillan, 1919.

CHAMBLISS, Charles E. The botany and history of *Zizania aquatica* L. ("wild rice"). *Annu.Rep.Smithsonian Inst.for 1940*, p. 369-82, 9 pl. Washington, D.C.: 1941.

COPELAND, Edwin Bingham. Rice. xiv, 352 p., 18 pl. London: Macmillan, 1924.
Reviewed in *Nature*, 1924, 114: 455.

HUNTER, Herbert. The barley crop. A record of some recent investigations. viii, 166 p., diagr. London: Benn, 1926.
Reviewed by A.B.B., *Nature*, 1926, 118: 871.

KRAUSE, Ernst H.L. Die Gerste und die Indogermanen. *Naturwiss.Wochenschr.*, *new ser.*, 1913, 12: 199-202.

MESSEDAGLIA, Luigi. Per la storia delle nostre piante alimentari: il riso. *Riv.Stor.Sci.*, 1938, 29: 1-15, 49-64.

SAUER, Jonathan D. The grain amaranths: a survey of their history and classification. *Ann.Missouri Bot.Gard.*, 1950, 37: 561-632. [CB 77/374]

SCHULZ, August. Die Geschichte der kultivierten Getreide. Vol. 1. 134 p. Halle a. S.: Nebert, 1913.

SFnh

BLOCH, Jules. Le nom du riz. *Etudes asiatiques*, (1), p. 37-47. Paris: Van Ouest, 1925.

LIPPMANN, Edmund O. von. Ueber die Herkunft des Namen "Luzerne". *Chem.Zeitung*, 1925, 49: 517.

SFwb

WEAVER, John C. Barley in the United States: a historical sketch. *Geogr.Rev.*, 1943, 33: 56-73.

SFwe

PERCIVAL, John. Wheat in Great Britain. 125 p., 63 fig. Shinfield: The Author, 1934.
Reviewed by E. Cecil Curwen, *Antiquity*, 1934, 8: 240; by E.J. Russell, *Nature*, 1934, 134: 606.
2nd edition 132 p., pl. London: Duckworth, 1948.

WHITNEY, Milton. The yield of wheat in England during seven centuries. *Science*, 1923, 58: 320-4.

SFwt

LAUFER, Berthold. Rye in the Far East and the Asiatic origin of our word series "rye". *T'oung Pao*, 1935, 31: 237-73.

SFzm MAIZE

ANDERSON, Edgar. What is *Zea mays*? A report of progress. *Chron.Bot.*, 1945, 9: 88-92.

CLARK, J. Allen. Collection, preservation and utilization of indigenous strains of maize. *Econ.Bot.*, 1956, 10: 194-200. [CB 82/208]

COLLINS, G.N. Notes on the agricultural history of maize. *Annu.Rep.Amer.Hist.Ass.*, 1919, (1), 411-29.

CUTLER, H.C. The geographical origin of maize. *Chron.Bot.*, 1951, 12: 167-9.

FINAN, John J. Maize in the great herbals. *Ann.Missouri Bot.Gard.*, 1948, 35: 149-91, 25 fig. Reprinted in book form. Waltham: Chronica Botanica, 1950. [CB 73/174]
Reviewed by Agnes Arber, *Isis*, 1951, 42: 82.

KIESSELBACH, T.A. A half century of corn research. *Amer. Sci.*, 1951, 39: 629-55.

McNAIR, James Birtley. Indian corn. 33 p., fig. (Field Museum of Natural History, Dept. of Botany, leaflet 14) Chicago: Field Museum of Natural History, 1930.

MANGELSDORF, Paul C. Reconstructing the ancestor of corn. *Proc.Amer.Phil.Soc.*, 1958, 102: 454-63.

MANGELSDORF, Paul C.; REEVES, R.G. The origin of Indian corn and its relatives. 315 p., 95 fig. (Texas Agricultural Experiment Station, Bulletin 574) College Station, Tex.: Agricultural and Mechanical College of Texas, 1939. [CB 58/574]
Reviewed by Bruno Santini, *Archeion*, 1941, 23: 300-3.

MESSEDAGLIA, Luigi. Per la storia delle nostre piante alimentari: il mais o granoturco. *Riv.Stor.Sci.Med.*, 1935, 26: 59-84.

WEATHERWAX, Paul. The history of corn (*Zea mays*). *Sci.Mon.*, 1950, 71: 50-60.

WEATHERWAX, Paul. The story of the maize plant. xv, 247 p. Chicago: University of Chicago Press, 1923.

SFzm-wb

ANDERSON, Edgar; BROWN, William L. The history of the common maize varieties in the United States corn belt. *Agr.Hist.*, 1952, 26: 2-8. [CB 79/178]

CRABB, A. Richard. The hybrid-corn makers: prophets of plenty. xxv, 331 p. New Brunswick: Rutgers University Press, 1947. [CB 73/175]
Reviewed by Frederick D. Richey, *J.Hered.*, 1948, 39: 11-17; for comments on this review by Paul C. Mangelsdorf and Richey's reply, *see ibid.* 177-80, 185.

HAYES, Herbert K. A professor's story of hybrid corn. v, 237 p., ill. Minneapolis, Minn.: Burgess, 1963.
Reviewed by Conway Zirkle, *Isis*, 1964, 55: 399-400.

KEMPTON, J.H. Maize - our heritage from the Indian. *Annu.Rep. Smithsonian Inst.for 1937*, p. 385-408, 30 pl., 3 fig. Washington, D.C.: 1938.

MANGELSDORF, Paul C. The history of hybrid corn: critical comments on Richey's review of Crabb's book. *J.Hered.*, 1948, 39: 177-80. [CB 73/175]
For Crabb's book *see* above.

RICHEY, Frederick D. The lay of the corn-huckster. *J.Hered.*, 1948, 39: 11-17, 180, 185. [CB 73/175]

SHULL, George Harrison. Hybrid seed corn. *Science*, 1946, 103: 547-50. [CB 70/225]

SFzm-wc

MANGELSDORF, Paul C.; CAMERON, J.W. Western Guatemala: a secondary center of origin of cultivated maize varieties. *Bot.Mus.Leafl.Harvard Univ.*, 1942, 10: 217-52.
An application of cytology to the problem of the botanical and geographical origin of *Zea mays*.

SFzm-wh

SKRZEK, Miecyczyslaw. [Maize cultivation in the Wielkopolska Region between 1860 and 1912. (In Polish. Summary in Russian and English)] *Kwart.Hist.Kult.Mater.*, 1956, 4: 267-77, 3 fig.

SG FIBRE PLANTS

BROWN, H.B. Cotton: history, species, varieties, morphology, breeding, culture, diseases, marketing and uses. 2nd ed. xiv, 592 p. New York: McGraw-Hill, 1938.
First published 1927.
Reviewed by H.A. Hancock, *Sci.Progr.*, 1939, 34: 407-8.

EDWARDS, H.T. The introduction of abacá (Manila hemp) into the Western hemisphere. *Annu.Rep.Smithsonian Inst.for 1945*, p. 327-49, 10 pl. Washington, D.C.: 1946. [CB 70/260]

KUNDU, B.C. Jute - world's foremost bast fiber. 1. Botany, agronomy, diseases and pests. 2. Technology, marketing, production and utilization. *Econ.Bot.*, 1956, 10: 103-33, 203-40, ill., bibliogr.
Contains a short history of cultivated jute, *Corchorus capsularis* and *C. olitorius*.

SGxb

STREET, James H. Mechanizing the cotton harvest. *Agr.Hist.*, 1957, 31: 12-22, 4 fig.

SH ROOT CROPS

HODGE, W.H. The edible Arracacha - a little known root crop. *Econ.Bot.*, 1954, 8: 195-221. [CB 81/274]

HORNELL, James. How did the sweet potato reach Oceania? *J.Linnean Soc.Bot.*, 1946, 53: 41-62. [CB 70/260]

JACQUOT, Raymond; NATAF, Berthe. Le manioc et son utilisation alimentaire. Introduction de Emile F. Terroine. 56 p. (Actualités Scientifiques et Industrielles, 364, Nutrition, 1) Paris: Hermann, 1936.

SHzp POTATOES

LAUFER, Berthold. The American plant migration. 1. The potato. (Prepared for publication by C. Martin Wilbur.) 132 p., portr. (Field Museum of Natural History, Anthropological Series 28: no. 1, publication 418) Chicago: 1938.
Reviewed by Conway Zirkle, *Isis*, 1939, 30: 551; by L. Carrington Goodrich, *J.Amer.Orient.Soc.*, 1939, 59: 142.

LINNÉ, S. Potato problems. *Nature*, 1939, 143: 12-16, 3 fig. [CB 57/249]

SAFFORD, William E. The potato of romance and of reality. *Annu.Rep.Smithsonian Inst.for 1925*, p. 509-32, 12 pl. Washington, D.C.: 1926. [CB 22/276]
Reprinted slightly abridged, from *J.Hered.*, April 1925, 16: no. 4.

SALAMAN, Redcliffe N. The history and social influence of the potato. xxiv, 685 p., 32 pl. Cambridge University Press, 1949.
Reviewed by Conway Zirkle, *Isis*, 1951, 42: 85.

STEVENSON, F.J. The potato, its origin, cytogenetic relationships, production, uses and food value. *Econ.Bot.*, 1951, 5: 153-71.

TJOMSLAND, Anne. The white potato. *Ciba Symp.* (Summit, N.J.), 1950, 11: 1255-84, ill.

WISSLER, Clark. The saga of the "earth nut". *Natur.Hist.*, 1947, 56: 126-33, ill.
History of the potato.

SHzp-we-sc

SALAMAN, Redcliffe N. The influence of the potato on the course of Irish history. 32 p. (The tenth Finlay Memorial Lecture) Dublin: Browne and Nolan, 1944. [CB 68/56]

SHzp-wg

GUTTENBERG, Karl von. Die ersten Kartoffeln in Oberfranken. *Heimatbilder Oberfranken*, 1913, 1: 169-86.

SI SUGAR CANE AND BEET

COONS, George H. The sugar beet, product of science. *Sci.Mon.*, 1949, 68: 149-64.
A brief history of the creation of a crop plant and of the industry founded upon it.

LIPPMANN, Edmund O. von. Geschichte der Rübe (*Beta*) als Kulturpflanze von den ältesten Zeiten an bis zum Erscheinen von Achard's Hauptwerk (1809). Festschrift zum 75 jährigen Bestande des Vereins der deutschen Zuckerindustrie. viii, 184 p., pl. Berlin: J. Springer, 1925.
Reviewed by Julius Ruska, *Isis*, 1926, 8: 379-80.

LIPPMANN, Edmund O. von. Nachträge und Ergänzungen zu der Festschrift "Geschichte der Rübe (*Beta*) als Kulturpflanze". *Z.Ver.Deut.Zucker-Ind.Tech.Teil*, 1934, 84: 15-67.

LIPPMANN, Edmund O. von. Zur Geschichte der Rübe. *Leopoldina*, 1926, 1: 50-4.
Summary of the author's work *see* above.

SIwi-qg

ROUSSET, H. La station expérimentale de biéticulture de Rovigo. *Rev.Gén.Sci.*, 1913, 24: 872.

SJ PLANTS YIELDING STIMULANTS AND SPICES

for tobacco *see also* NP

CHATT, Eileen M. Cocoa. Cultivation, processing, analysis. 302 p., ill. New York: Interscience, 1953.
The first chapter is a history of the domestication and use of *Theobroma Cacao*.

CORRELL, Donovan S. Vanilla - its botany, history, cultivation and economic import. *Econ.Bot.*, 1953, 7: 291-358. [CB 80/134]

CORRELL, Donovan S. Vanilla: its history, cultivation and importance. *Lloydia*, 1944, 7: 236-64. [CB 68/55]

JOYCE, T.A. Use and origin of yerba maté. *Nature*, 1934, 134: 722-4, 760-2.

KLINKOWSKI, M. Die Wanderung des Kaffeebaumes. *Züchter*, 1947, 17: 247-55.

NETOLITZKY, Fritz. Zur Geschichte der ersten Auffindung der Heil- und Gewürzpflanzen. *Heil Gewürzpflanzen*, 1930, 12: 152-60.

SJce-bv

SPARN, Enrique. Bibliografía de la Yerba mate (*Ilex paraguayensis* St.-Hil.). 20 p. (Academia Nacional de Ciencias. Miscelánea, 22) Córdoba: 1937.

SJwb

KLOSE, Nelson. Experiments in tea production in the United States. *Agr.Hist.*, 1950, 24: 156-60.

SK PLANTS YIELDING OTHER USEFUL PRODUCTS

CHASE, Florence Meier. Useful algae. *Annu.Rep.Smithsonian Inst.for 1941*, p. 401-52, 9 pl. Washington, D.C.: 1942.

CLOW, Archibald; CLOW, Nan L. The natural and economic history of kelp. *Ann.Sci.*, 1947, 5: 297-316, 1 fig.

FULLING, Edmund H. American witch hazel - history, nomenclature and modern utilization. *Econ.Bot.*, 1953, 7: 359-81.

HOWES, F.N. Vegetable gums and resins. xxii, 188 p., 42 fig. Waltham, Mass.: Chronica Botanica, 1949. [CB 76/400]

HURRY, Jamieson B. The woad plant and its dye. xxviii, 328 p., 17 pl. London: Oxford University Press, 1930.
Reviewed by E.F. Armstrong, *Nature*, 1931, 127: 658-9.

SKce-bv

BOGUSCH, E.R. A bibliography on mesquite. *Tex.J.Sci.*, 1950, 2: 528-38. [CB 77/374]

SKwg

WILDE, Julius. Die Färberpflanzen der Bayerischen Rheinpfalz in der Zeit von 800-1800. *Mitt.Pfälz.Ver.Naturk.Pollichia*, 1930, 3: 147-200, 14 fig.
Reviewed by R. Zaunick, *Mitt.Gesch.Med.*, 1932, 31: 213.

SL GREEN VEGETABLES; FUNGI

ARNOULD, M.F. La vie et l'oeuvre du Dr. Berczeller, et le soja alimentaire. *Rev.Hist.Méd.Hébraique*, 1960, no. 50, 153-68.

PIPER, Charles Vancouver; MORSE, William Joseph. The soy bean. xv, 329 p., 84 ill. New York: McGraw-Hill, 1923.
Chapters 3 and 4 deal respectively with the botanical and the agricultural history of the soy bean.

SIGERIST, Henry E. American truffles. A Thanksgiving fantasia. *Bull.Hist.Med.*, 1944, 16: 402-9.

SLwf

LECLERC, Henri. Les légumes de France. Leur histoire, leurs usages alimentaires, leurs vertus thérapeutiques. 217 p. Paris: Masson, 1928.
Reviewed by M. Laignel-Lavastine, *Bull.Soc.Franç.Hist.Méd.*, 1928, 22: 221-2.

SLyRQ

KLEYN, H. Paddenstoelen en de geneeskunde. [Mushrooms in medicine. (In Dutch)] *Bijdr.Gesch.Geneesk.*, 1943, 23: 15-20.

SM FRUIT CULTIVATION

SMc general history

COLLINS, J.L. History, taxonomy and culture of the pineapple (*Ananas spp.*). *Econ.Bot.*, 1949, 3: 335-59.

CONDUIT, Ira J. The fig. xviii, 222 p., ill. Waltham: Chronica Botanica, 1947.
Reviewed by Conway Zirkle, *Isis*, 1949, 40: 290.

CORRELL, Donovan S. The African oil palm: its history, cultivation and importance. *Lloydia*, 1944, 7: 101-20. [CB 68/55]

DARROW, George M. Blackberry-raspberry hybrid. *J.Hered.*, 1955, 46: 67-71.
Includes a history of these hybrids from the creation of the loganberry in 1881 to the present.

GLIDDEN, Harold W. The lemon in Asia and Europe. *J.Amer. Orient.Soc.*, 1937, 57: 381-96.

HIGGINS, B.B. Origin and early history of the peanut. In: The peanut - the unpredictable legume, p. 18-27. Washington: National Fertilizer Association, 1951.

HILL, Arthur W. The original home and mode of dispersal of the coconut. *Nature*, 1929, 124: 133-4, 151-3.

JENKINS, J.A. The origin of the cultivated tomato. *Econ.Bot.*, 1948, 2: 379-92. [CB 74/389]

JOHNSON, Helen M. The lemon in India. *J.Amer.Orient.Soc.*, 1936, 56: 47-50. [CB 48/576]

LAUFER, Berthold. The lemon in China and elsewhere. *J.Amer. Orient.Soc.*, 1934, 54: 143-60. [CB 42/592]

MUKHERJEE, S.K. The mango - its botany, cultivation, uses and future improvement, especially in India. *Econ.Bot.*, 1953, 7: 130-62. [CB 80/134]

NEWBERRY, Percy Edward. On some African species of the genus Olea and the original home of the cultivated olive-tree. [With discussion] *Proc.Linnaean Soc.Lond.*, 1937-38, 150: 3-16, pl.
Reviewed by J. Capart, *Chron.Égypte*, 1940, 15: 237.

PEYRE, P. Sur l'olivier. L'histoire et la légende, les chantres sur l'olivier, l'arbre, ses fruits, son huile. Usages médicaux et pharmaceutiques. Ses parasites; la défense sanitaire des vergers. Intoxications professionnelles agricoles, soins d'urgence. 270 p. Paris: Le François, 1938.

REYNOLDS, Philip Keep. Earliest evidence of banana culture. v, 28 p., 8 pl. (Supplement *J.Amer.Orient.Soc.*, 12) Baltimore: American Oriental Society, 1951. [CB 79/179]

SCHNEIDER, Hildegard. On the pomegranate. *Bull.Metro.Mus. Art*, 1945, 4: 117-20, 2 ill.

TOLKOWSKY, S. Hesperides. A history of the culture and use of citrus fruits. xx, 371 p., 113 pl., 10 fig. London: Bale & Curnow, 1938. [CB 57/249 and CB 58/575]

VON LOESECKE, Harry W. Bananas; chemistry, physiology, technology. 189 p., 29 fig. New York: Interscience, 1949.

WEBBER, Herbert John; BATCHELOR, Leon Dexter; ed. The citrus industry. Vol. 1. History, botany and breeding. xx, 1028 p., 233 fig. Berkeley: University of California Press, 1943.
Reviewed by Conway Zirkle, *Isis*, 1945, 36: 76-7.

SMc-bv

McCUE, George Allen. The history of the use of the tomato: an annotated bibliography. *Ann.Missouri Bot.Gard.*, 1952, 39: 289-348.
Bibliographical entries are classified according to region.

SOULE, Mortimer J. A bibliography of the mango (*Mangifera indica* L.). vi, 89 p. Coral Gables, Flo.: Florida Mango Forum and University of Miami, 1950.

SMw in different countries

SMwb

KROCHMAL, Arnold; GRIERSON, W. Brief history of grape growing in the United States. *Econ.Bot.*, 1961, 15: 114-18.

MILLER, Erston V. The natural origins of some popular varieties of fruit. *Econ.Bot.*, 1954, 8: 337-8.

MILLER, Erston V. Our heritage of good fruits. *Sci.Mon.*, 1953, 77: 42-7.
An account of the origin and development of our present cultivated varieties.

TRUE, Rodney H. Notes on the early history of the pecan in America. *Annu.Rep.Smithsonian Inst.for 1917*, p. 435-48. Washington, D.C.: 1919.

SMwb-st

FULLING, E.H. Plant life and the law of man. 5. Right to fruit on overhanging branches. *J.N.Y.Bot.Gard.*, 1943, 44: 132-9.

SMwf

LECLERC, Henri. Les fruits de France, historique, diététique et thérapeutique. 274 p. Paris: Masson, 1925.

SMxd techniques

GODE, P.K. History of the art of grafting plants (between *c.* B.C. 500 and A.D. 1800). *Indian Cult.*, 1946, 13: no. 1, 25-34.

HAHN, Eduard. Das Pfropfen unserer Obstbäume. *Arch.Gesch. Math.Naturwiss.Tech.*, 1929, 11: 239-46.

LEICK, Erich. Die Kaprification und ihre Deutung im Wandel der Zeiten. *Mitt.Deut.Dendrolog.Ges.*, 1924, 263-83.

SMxd-ws

GODE, P.K. References to grafted mangoes in India between A.D. 1500 and 1800. *J.Amer.Orient.Soc.*, 1959, 79: 281-2.

SN GARDENING; FLOWERS

CLARKSON, Rosetta E. Magic gardens, a modern chronicle of herbs and savory seeds. 370 p., 60 ill. New York: Macmillan, 1939. [CB 59/475]

GOTHEIN, Marie Luise. Geschichte der Gartenkunst. 2 vol. viii, 446 p.; 506 p., 637 ill. Jena: Diederichs, 1914.

KRONFELD, E.M. Geschichte der Gartennelke. iv, 212 p., ill. Wien: Verlag der K.K. Gartenbau-Gesellschaft, 1913.

SHEPARD, Roy E. History of the rose. viii, 264 p., 26 pl. New York: Macmillan Co., 1954.
Reviewed by Conway Zirkle, *Isis*, 1954, 45: 302-3.

WRIGHT, Richardson. The story of gardening. From the Hanging Gardens of Babylon to the hanging gardens of New York. vi, 474 p., ill. New York: Dodd, Mead, 1934.
Reprinted 1964 (New York: Dover).

WYLIE, Ann. The history of garden roses. *Endeavour*, 1955, 14: 181-9. [CB 82/209]

ZANDER, Robert; TESCHNER, Clara. Der Rosengarten. Eine geschichtliche Studie durch zwei Jahrtausende. 78 p., 8 pl. Frankfurt/Oder: Trowitzsch, 1939.
Reviewed by H. Marzell, *Mitt.Gesch.Med.*, 1940, 39: 342.

SNce

LOWNES, Albert E. "Begynnynge of Marche". Old garden books have their place in collections. *Libr.J.*, 1947, 72: 430-2.

SNwe-ce

ROHDE, Eleanour Sinclair. The old English gardening books. xii, 144 p., 16 pl. (The New Aldine Library, 5) London: Martin Hopkinson, 1924.

SNwg

CHRIST, Hermann. Zur Geschichte des alten Bauerngartens der Schweiz und angrenzenden Gegenden. 2nd ed. 161 p., ill. Basel: Benno Schwabe, 1923.

SNxb-wb

MARX, Leo. The machine in the garden. Technology and the pastoral ideal in America. 392 p., 3 pl. New York: Oxford University Press, 1964.

SO FORESTRY

See also WB TIMBER
KX TREES AND SHRUBS

SOc

BELTRÁN, Enrique. Tom Gill y los bosques del mundo. *Rev.Soc. Mex.Hist.Natur.*, 1952, 13: 247-51.

BRUTTINI, Arturo. Dictionnaire de sylviculture. 384 p. Paris: Lechevalier, 1930.
Reviewed by G.D., *Rev.Gén.Sci.*, 1931, 42: 91.

CLEPPER, Henry. Forestry's first fifty years. *Sci.Mon.*, 1950, 71: 387-92.

COOK, O.F. Natural rubber. *Annu.Rep.Smithsonian Inst.for 1943*, p. 363-411, 20 pl. Washington, D.C.: 1944.

GREELEY, William B. Forests and men. 255 p., ill., bibliogr. Garden City, N.Y.: Doubleday, 1951. [CB 79/146]

HESKE, F. The history of forestry in the world: a short survey. *Cah.Hist.Mond.*, 1960, 5: 748-73.

SAGUI, C.-L. Forêts et déserts. *Bull.Soc.Etud.Sci.Natur.Vaucluse*, 1944, 15: 25 p.
Discussion of the need of afforestation, including abundant historical references.

STEBBING, E.P. A century of forestry. Forestry in the British Commonwealth in the last century. *Nature*, 1952, 169: 173-7.

SOwb

ROGERS, Andrew Denny, III. Bernard Eduard Fernow, a story of North American forestry. 621 p. Princeton: University Press, 1951.
Reviewed by Conway Zirkle, *Isis*, 1951, 42: 257.

SOwh-ce

ŻABKI-POTOPOWICZ, Antoni. Dzieje piśmiennictwa lésnego w Polsce do roku 1939. [History of the Polish forestry literature up to 1939. (In Polish with summaries in English and Russian)] *Stud.Mater.Dziej.Nauk.Pol.*, *ser. B.*, 1960, 3: 3-140.

SP ANIMAL HUSBANDRY

SPc

HILZHEIMER, Max. Ueberblick über die Geschichte der Haustierforschung, besonders der letzten 30 Jahren. *Zool.Ann.*, 1913, 5: 233-54.

KOPPERS, Wilhelm. Das Problem der Entstehung der Tierzucht. *Schr.Ver.Verbr.Naturwiss.Kennt.* (Wien), 1928-29, 69: 31-68.

ZEUNER, Frederick. The domestication of animals. *Scientia*, 1956, 91: 23-8.

ZEUNER, Frederick. A history of domesticated animals. 560 p., fig. New York: Harper and Row; London: Hutchinson, 1963.
Reviewed by Robert H. Dyson, *Science*, 1964, 144: 672-5; by E.S. Higgs, *Antiquity*, 1964, 38: 80-1; by Charles F. Bennett, *Geogr.Rev.*, 1964, 54: 142-4.

SPce-bv

ANGRESS, Shimon; REED, Charles A. An annotated bibliography on the origin and descent of domestic mammals, 1900-1955. 143 p. (*Fieldiana Anthropol.*, 54: no. 1) Chicago: Natural History Museum, 1962.

SPmzLG

KRAEMER, Hermann. Die Stellung der Tierzucht zur Abstammungslehre. *Arch.Gesch.Math.Naturwiss.Tech.*, 1930, 13: 113-32.

SPmzMF

LECLAINCHE, Emmanuel. Discours prononcé à l'Académie des Sciences, séance publique annuelle du lundi 20 décembre 1937. *Compt.Rend.Acad.Sci.*, 1937, 205: 1269-82.
Includes comparison of the concepts of human races and of domestic animal breeds.

SPs

EPSTEIN, H. Domestication in animals as functions of human society. *Agric.Hist.*, 1955, 29: 137-46.

SPvm-tc

SIMON, I. Les bases anatomiques, physiologiques et humanitaires de la Shehitah, ou méthode juive d'abbatage des animaux, avec une étude critique des autres methodes d'abbatage. *Rev.Hist.Méd.Hébraique*, 1954, 7: 37-46, 159-72, 217-18.

SPwb

THOMPSON, James Westfall. A history of livestock raising in the United States, 1607-1860. 182 p. (Agricultural History Series, 5) Washington: U.S. Dept. of Agriculture, 1942.
Reviewed by Conway Zirkle, *Isis*, 1944, 35: 195.

SPwe

MARSHALL, F.H.A.; HAMMOND, John. The science of animal breeding in Britain. A short history. vi, 24 p., ill. London/New York: Longmans, Green (for the British Council), 1946.

SPwj

DANTÍN CERECADA, J. La cañada ganadera de la Vizana. *Bol. Soc.Geogr.Madrid*, 1942, 78: 322-35, map. [CB 70/261]
Reviewed by Robert Aitken, *Geogr.J.*, 1945, 106: 59-69.

DANTÍN CERECADA, J. Las cañadas ganaderas del Reino de León. *Bol.Soc.Geogr.Madrid*, 1936, 76: 464-99, maps. [CB 70/261]
Reviewed by Robert Aitken, *Geogr.J.*, 1945, 106: 59-69.

DANTÍN CERECADA, J. Cañadas ganaderas españolas. *Mem.Com.I Congr.Pré e Proto-Hist.Portugal*, (18), p. 682-96, map, bibliogr. Lisboa: Comissão Executiva dos Centenários, Tip. Bertrand, 1940. [CB 70/261]
Reviewed by Robert Aitken, *Geogr.J.*, 1945, 106: 59-69.

SPyLS

KRAEMER, Hermann. Der Artbegriff in Anwendung auf die Haustiere. *Arch.Gesch.Math.Naturwiss.Tech.*, 1927, 10: 62-71.

SPC CATTLE

BÜHLER-OPPENHEIM, K. Verbreitung und Nutzung der Milchtiere. Milch und Milchtiere im Kult. Die Tiermilch in der Volksheilkunde und im Heilaberglauben. *Ciba Z.*, 1948, 10: 4244-64, ill.

HAMMOND, John. Polled cattle. *Endeavour*, 1950, 9: 85-90.
A brief history of hornless cattle.

SEMPLE, Arthur T. The origin of domestic cattle. The progenitors of one of the most important of our domestic animals - their wild forebears and the steps by which these wild creatures have been domesticated and the influences that have changed them. *Natur.Hist.*, 1931, 31: 287-99.

SPCnh

FORBES, Thomas R. The origin of *freemartin*. *Bull.Hist.Med.*, 1946, 20: 461-6.

SPCwb

LEMMER, George F. The spread of improved cattle through the eastern United States to 1850. *Agr.Hist.*, 1947, 21: 79-92.

PRENTICE, Ezra Parmalee. American dairy cattle. Their past and future. With chapters on dairy cattle in America, by Ernest L. Anthony, Lloyd Burlingham, Clifford L. Clevenger [and others]. xix, 453 p., 51 pl. New York: Harper, 1942.
Reviewed by G.E. Fussell, *Nature*, 1943, 152: 736-7.

SPCws

SCHNEIDER, B.H. *Ahimsa* and cattle breeding in India. *Sci.Mon.*, 1948, 67: 87-92. [CB 73/158]

SPH SHEEP AND GOATS

BELL, Alexander Graham. Saving the six-nippled breed. *J. Hered.*, 1923, 14: 98-111, ill. [CB 15/176]

BÜHLER-OPPENHEIM, K. *See* SPC

SPHwb

BONNER, James C. The Angora goat: a footnote in Southern agricultural history. *Agric.Hist.*, 1947, 21: 42-5.

SPHww

LUETKENS, Charlotte. Schafzucht und Wollerzeugung in Australien. *Ciba-Rundsch.*, 1948, 77: 2844-74, ill.

SPL DOGS AND CATS

ASH, Edward C. Dogs: their history and development. 2 vol. xviii, 384 p., 108 pl.; xvi, p. 385-778, pl. 109-60. London: Benn, 1927.

FEHRINGER, Otto. The oldest domestic animal [the dog]. *Res. Progr.*, 1942, 8: 225-9, 4 fig.

GUDGER, E.W. Dogs as fishermen. *Natur.Hist.*, 1923, 23: 559-68, 3 fig.

MONTAGU, M.F. Ashley. On the origin of the domestication of the dog. *Science*, 1942, 96: 111-12.

SCHWANGART, Friedrich. Stammesgeschichte, Rassenkunde und Zuchtsystem der Hauskatzen. 59 p., 10 fig. Leipzig: Heber, 1929.

SPLce-bv

BAEGE, Bruno. Kynologische Bibliographie. Zusammengestellt im Auftrage der Forschungsstelle des Reichsverbandes für das Deutsche Hundewesen (Gesellschaft für Hundeforschung). 126 p. Berlin: 1934.

SPLwg-u

KELLING, K. Der Hund im deutschen Volkstum. Seine Stellung und Bedeutung in Sage, Sitte, Brauch, Glaube und Sprache unseres Volkes. 83 p. Neudamm: J. Neumann, 1914.

SPLwt

COLLIER, V.W.F. Dogs of China and Japan in nature and art. xx, 208 p., ill. London: William Heinemann; New York: F.A. Stokes Co., 1921.
Reviewed by B. Laufer, *Isis*, 1923, 5: 444-6.

SPP HORSES AND OTHER EQUINES

DENHARDT, Robert M. The Chilean horse. *Agr.Hist.*, 1950, 24: 161-5.

GENELLIS, M.-F. de. Le cheval dans l'histoire. Préface du Général Donnio. 176 p. Paris: Peyronnet, 1956.
Reviewed by Y. Drieux, *Rev.Hist.Sci.*, 1957, 10: 285-6.

LEHMANN-NITSCHE, R. *See* SyPOwc

SCHILLER, Martin. Trense und Kandare. Ein Beitrag zur Heniastik des Pferdes unter besonderer Berücksichtigung der europäischen Formen. *Wiss.Z.Humboldt-Univ.Berlin Math.Naturwiss.Reihe*, 1957-58, 7: 465-94, 119 fig.

SIMPSON, George Gaylord. Horses: the story of the horse family in the modern world through sixty million years of history. xvi, 247 p., 32 pl., 34 fig. New York: Oxford University Press, 1951.
Reviewed by Conway Zirkle, *Isis*, 1952, 43: 80.

THOMAS, Fritz Carl. *See* SyOJ

TREW, Cecil G. From "Dawn" to the "Eclipse": the story of the horse. 142 p., 16 pl., 100 ill. London: Methuen, 1939.
Reviewed by M. Hilzheimer, *Antiquity*, 1940, 14: 322-3.

WENTWORTH, Judith Blunt-Lytton, *baroness*. The authentic Arabian horse and his descendants. Three voices concerning the horses of Arabia. Tradition (Nejd, Inner East), romantic fable (Islam), the outside world of the West. 395 p., 291 pl. London: Allen and Unwin, 1945.

WERTH, E. Zur Abstammung des Hausesels. (Zur Geographie und Geschichte der Kulturpflanzen und Haustiere, 2) *Sitzungsber.Ges.Naturforsch.Freunde*, 1929, 342-55.
Reviewed by R. Zaunick, *Mitt.Gesch.Med.*, 1932, 31: 35.

SPPce-bv

MENNESSIER DE LA LANCE, Gabriel René. Essai de bibliographie hippique. Donnant la description détaillée des ouvrages publiés ou traduits en latin et en français sur le cheval et la cavalerie avec de nombreuses biographies d'auteurs hippiques. 3 vol. 1. A à K. x, 760 p.; 2. L à Z. Supplément. 736 p.; [3]. Supplément. 64 p. Paris: Lucien Dorbon, 1915-21. [CB 18/623]

SPPtq

FLEITMANN, Lida L. The horse in art. From primitive times to the present. Foreword by A.J. Munnings. xxii, 372 p., ill. London: Medici Society; New York: W.F. Payson, 1931.

SPS REINDEER

LEHTISALO, T. Beiträge zur Kenntnis der Renntierzucht bei den Yuraksamojeden. 180 p., 32 ill., 2 maps, 16 pl. Oslo: 1932.
Reviewed by Kai Donner, *J.Roy.Asiatic Soc.*, 1933, 121-4.

SPT MONKEYS

GUDGER, E.W. Monkeys trained as harvesters. *Natur.Hist.*, 1923, 23: 272-9, 4 fig.

SPV POULTRY AND OTHER DOMESTIC BIRDS

ASMUNDSON, V.G.; LORENZ, F.W. Pheasant-turkey hybrids. *Science*, 1955, 121: 307-8.

COLE, Leon J. The origin of the domestic pigeon. *Proc.7th World Poultry Congr.* (Cleveland, 1939), p. 462-6. [Baltimore: Printed at the Waverly Press, 1939]

LANDAUER, Walter. The hatchability of chicken eggs as influenced by environment and heredity. 231 p., 46 fig. (A revision of Bulletins 216 and 236) Storrs, Conn.: Storrs Agricultural Experiment Station, College of Agriculture, University of Connecticut, 1948. [CB 75/93]
Includes history of artificial incubation in many parts of the world (p. 10-44, ill).

RIDDELL, W.H. The domestic goose. *Antiquity*, 1943, 17: 148-55, 2 pl.

SPVwt

LAUFER, Berthold. The domestication of the cormorant in China and Japan. *Field Mus.Natur.Hist.Publ.Anthropol.Ser.*, 1931, 18: 201-62, 4 pl.

SPVxd

ADJAN, A. [Contribution à l'histoire de l'incubateur. (In Russian with French summary)] *Arkh.Ist.Nauk.Tekh.*, 1935. 6: 287-98. [CB 45/243]

SQ BEES; APICULTURE

FRISCH, Karl v. Die "Sprache" der Bienen und ihre Nutzanwendung in der Landwirtschaft. *Experientia*, 1946, 2: 397-404, 8 fig.

HAMBLETON, James I. The indispensable honeybee. *Annu.Rep. Smithsonian Inst.for 1945*, p. 293-304, 4 pl. Washington, D.C.: 1946.

MÜLLER-GRAUPA, Edwin. Der Hochzeitsflug der Bienenkönigin. Die Geschichte eines biologischen Problems von Aristoteles bis Maeterlinck. *Arch.Gesch.Med.*, 1938, 31: 350-64.

RANSOME, Hilda M. The sacred bee in ancient times and folklore. 308 p., 12 pl., 35 fig. London: Allen & Unwin, 1937. [CB 51/271]

SHARP, Dallas Lore. The spirit of the hive. Contemplations of a beekeeper. 240 p. New York: Harpers, 1925.

TEALE, Edwin Way. The golden throng. A book about bees. 208 p., ill. New York: Dodd, Mead, 1940.

WILLEM, Victor. L'architecture des abeilles. *Bull.Acad.Roy. Belg.Cl.Sci.*, 1929, 14: 672-705, 5 pl., 9 fig. [CB 27/555]

SQsc

ARMBRUSTER, Ludwig. Der Bienenstand als völkerkundliches Denkmal. Zugleich Beiträge zu einer historischen Bienenzucht-Betriebslehre. 152 p., ill. (Bücherei für Bienenkunde, 8) Neumünster i. Holstein: K. Wachholtz, 1926.

SQwb

PELLETT, Frank Chapman. History of American beekeeping. ix, 213 p., fig. Ames, Iowa: Collegiate Press, 1938. [CB 57/252]

SQwd

BRINKMANN, Walter. Bienenstock und Bienenstand in den romanischen Ländern. xv, 200 p., 4 maps, 57 fig. (Hamburger Studien zu Volkstum und Kultur der Romanen, 30) Hamburg: Hansischer Gildenverlag, 1938.
Bee folklore and terminology in France, Spain, Portugal, Switzerland, Italy.

SQwg

SOODER, M. Bienen und Bienenhalten in der Schweiz. 341 p., ill. (Schriften der Schweizerischen Gesellschaft für Volkskunde, 34) Basel: Krebs, 1952.
Reviewed by F.S. Bodenheimer, *Arch.Int.Hist.Sci.*, 1953, 6: 336.

SQwg-da

KOCH, Karl. Die Grossmeister und Schöpfer unserer deutschen Bienenzucht von Nikol Jacob 1568 bis zur Gegenwart. Dargestellt in Bildern ihres Lebens, Schaffens und Forschens. iv, 198 p., fig. Berlin: Pfenningstorff, 1931.
Reviewed by R. Zaunick, *Mitt.Gesch.Med.*, 1934, 33: 336.

SQwn

SAMOJLOVIC, A. Beiträge zur Bienenzucht in der Krim im 14.-17. Jahrhundert. *Georg Jacob zum siebzigsten Geburtstag*, p. 270-5. Leipzig: Harrassowitz, 1932.

SR SILK WORM CULTURE

HANDSCHIN, E. The silkworm or *Bombyx mori* Linné. The breeding of silkworms and their diseases. Wild silk moths. Spiders and insects as producers of silk. *Ciba Rev.*, 1946, no. 53, 1902-30, ill.

ROLET, Antonin. Le crin de Florence. *Rev.Gén.Sci.*, 1930, 41: 81-7, 6 fig.

TOCCO, Roberto di. Saggio storico sull' origine, diffusione e caratteri delle varietà europee del *Bombyx mori*. *Annu.Sta. Bacol.Sperim.Padova*, 1925, 44: 387-447, ill.

SRwf

VAYSSIÈRE, Paul. L'organisation de la lutte contre les ennemis des cultures et la protection de la sériciculture en France. *Rev.Sci.*, 1924, 62: 238-43. [CB 16/351]

SS FISHERY; FISHING

SSc general history

BOLITHO, Hector. The glorious oyster: his history in Rome and in Britain, his anatomy and reproduction, how to cook him, and what various writers and poets have written in his praise; collected together as an acknowledgment of the supreme pleasure he has given to all persons of taste since Roman times. With certain chapters edited by Maurice Burton. x, 203 p. London: Knopf, 1929.
Reviewed by J.H.O., *Nature*, 1930, 125: 406.

COLLIER, H. Bruce. Fishing with otters. Answer to Query no. 108. [*See* Sarton, George, below] *Isis*, 1944, 35: 331.
Mentioned in the "Ko chih ching yüan" written in 1735 by Ch'ên Yüan-Lung.

CRONHEIM, Walther. Die wissenschaftliche und ökonomische Bedeutung der Teichwirtschaft. *Fortschr.Naturwiss.Forsch.*, 1913, 8: 94-114.

GREY, Zane. Tales of swordfish and tuna. 215 p. London: Hodder and Stoughton; New York: Harper, 1927.

GUDGER, E.W. Dogs as fishermen. *Natur.Hist.*, 1923, 23: 559-68, 3 fig.

GUDGER, E.W. Fishing with the otter. *Amer.Natur.*, 1927, 61: 193-225. [CB 25/425]

GUDGER, E.W. Fooling the fishes. Fishing with the bateau and the white varnished board in China and with similar devices in other parts of the world. *Sci.Mon.*, 1937, 44: 295-306.

GUDGER, E.W. On spider webs and spider web fish nets. *Zool. Soc.Bull.N.Y.*, 1918, 21: 1687-9.

SS

GUDGER, E.W. Wooden hooks used for catching sharks and *Ruvettus* in the south seas; a study of their variation and distribution. *Anthrop.Pap.N.Y.*, 1928, 28: 199-348, 92 fig. [CB 25/430]

HILLS, John Waller. A history of fly fishing for trout. 244 p., bibliogr. London: Allan, 1921.

HORNELL, James. Fishing in many waters. xv, 207 p. New York: Cambridge University Press, 1950. [CB 77/376]

INNIS, Harold A. The cod fisheries. The history of an international economy. xx, 520 p. (The Relations of Canada and the United States: a series of studies prepared under the direction of the Carnegie Endowment for International Peace, Division of Economics and History) New Haven: Yale University Press, 1940.
Reviewed by Michael Graham, *Nature*, 1941, 147: 208.

JENKINS, James Travis. The herring and the herring fisheries. xi, 175 p., ill., bibliogr. London: King, 1927.

RADCLIFFE, William. Fishing from the earliest times. xvii, 478 p., ill. New York: Dutton, 1921.
Reviewed by George Sarton, *Isis*, 1922, 4: 568-71.

ROULE, Louis. Les poissons migrateurs, leur vie et leur pêche. Un important problème d'histoire naturelle océanographique et économique. 175 p. (Bibliothèque de Culture Générale) Paris: Flammarion, 1922.

ROULE, Louis. Traité de la pisciculture et des pêches. 734 p., 301 fig. Paris: Baillière, 1914.

SARTON, George. Fishing with otters. (Query no. 108 and answer) *Isis*, 1944, 35: 178.
For another answer *see* Collier, H. Bruce, above.

SSc-br

Archiv für Fischereigeschichte. Vol. 1-9, 10-16. Berlin: Verlag des Deutschen Fischerei-Vereins, 1913-17, 1926-32.
Volume 10 reviewed by R. Zaunick, *Mitt.Gesch.Med.*, 1927, 26: 313.

SSce

ZAUNICK, Rudolph. Bitte um Mitteilungen über Fischereihandschriften. *Mitt.Gesch.Med.*, 1916, 15: 193-5.
Appeal for information on incunabula and Mss. dealing with fishing and fishery.

SSu

PLISCHKE, Hans. Der Fischdrachen. 46 p., 2 tables, map. (Veröffentlichungen des Städtischen Museums für Völkerkunde zu Leipzig, 6) Leipzig: Voigtländer, 1922.
Reviewed by F.M. Feldhaus, *Geschichtsbl.Tech.Ind.*, 1923, 10: 35.

SSw in different countries

SSwb

GUDGER, E.W. Swordfishing with the harpoon in New England waters. *Sci.Mon.*, 1942, 54: 418-30, 499-512, 20 fig.

HEDGPETH, Joel W. The United States Fish Commission steamer "Albatross". With an appendix by Waldo L. Schmitt. *Amer. Neptune*, 1945, 5: 5-26.

LOTURE, Robert de. Histoire de la grande pêche de Terre Neuve. 254 p., 2 maps, 1 fig. Paris: Gallimard, 1950.

SSwd

GUDGER, E.W. La pêche à la main en Europe. *La Nature*, 1951, 79: 43-4.

ZAUNICK, Rudolph. Die Fischerei-Tollköder in Europa vom Altertum bis zur Neuzeit. In: Geschichtliche Studien zur angewandten Naturwissenschaft, p. 527-736. (*Arch.Hydrobiol. Suppl.*, 4) Stuttgart: Schweizerbart, 1928.
Reviewed by H. Marzell, *Mitt.Gesch.Med.*, 1929, 28: 273.

SSwe

GUDGER, E.W. Fishing with the hand, "tickling trout" and other fishes in Great Britain, 1602-1943. *Australian Mus. Mag.*, 1950, 10: 61-4.

SSwf

VIVIER, P. Un important centenaire: Rémy, Géhin, Haxo, Coste, et l'établissement domanial de pisciculture d'Huningue, 1843, 1853, 1953. *Bull.Franç.Pisciculture*, 30 juin 1956, no. 181, 122-39.
Reviewed by P. Delaunay, *Arch.Int.Hist.Sci.*, 1956, 9: (35), 274-5.

SSwi

GUDGER, E.W. The perils and romance of swordfishing. The pursuit of *Xiphias gladius* with the trident in the Strait of Messina. *Sci.Mon.*, 1940, 51: 36-48.

SSwp

BOWEN, Richard LeBaron. Marine industries of Eastern Arabia. *Geogr.Rev.*, 1951, 41: 384-400.

SSwt

GUDGER, E.W. Fishing with the cormorant in Japan. *Sci.Mon.*, 1929, 29: 5-38, 31 fig.

LIGHT, S.F. Amphioxus fisheries near the University of Amoy, China. *Science*, 1923, 58: 57-60, 2 fig. [CB 15/193]

SSwx

GRUVEL, A. L'industrie des pêches sur la côte occidentale d'Afrique (du cap Blanc au cap de Bonne-Espérance). iii, 193 p., ill. Paris: E. Larose, 1913.

SSzp PEARL FISHING

BOUTAN, Louis Marie Auguste. La perle; étude générale de la perle, histoire de la méléagrine et des mollusques, producteurs de perles. 421 p., 167 fig. Paris: Doin, 1925.
Reviewed by L. Joubin, *Rev.Gén.Sci.*, 1925, 36: 248.

KORSCHELT, E. Perlen. Altes und neues über ihre Struktur, Herkunft und Verwertung. *Fortschr.Naturwiss.Forsch.*, 1913, 8: 110-90.

SSzp-s

KORNITZER, Louis. Pearls and men. 254 p. London: Bles, 1935.

SSzp-wp

BOWEN, Richard LeBaron. Pearl fisheries of the Persian Gulf. *Middle East J.*, 1951, 5: 161-80.

ST WHALING

AAGAARD, Bjarne. Den gamle hvalfangst. Kapitler av dens historie. [Whaling in olden days. Chapters from its history. (In Norwegian)] 166 p. Oslo: Gyldendal, 1933. [CB 43/278]
Reviewed by E. Lynam, *Geogr.J.*, 1934, 83: 439-40.

ANDREWS, Roy Chapman. Ends of the earth. x, 355 p., ill. New York: Putnam's 1929.
Covers whaling and hunting.
Reviewed in *Natur.Hist.*, 1930, 220.

DAKIN, William J. Whalemen adventurers. The story of whaling in Australian waters and other Southern Seas related thereto, from the days of sails to modern times. xx, 263 p., 42 pl., 2 maps. Sydney: Angus & Robertson, 1934. [CB 45/288]

GRANT, Gordon. Greasy luck. A whaling sketch book. With an introduction by William McFee. xiv, 126 p., ill. New York: W.F. Payson; London: Hopkinson, 1932.

HARMER, Sidney Frederic. The history of whaling. Presidential address delivered at the anniversary meeting of the Linnean Society of London on the 24th of May, 1928. *Proc.Linnean Soc.Lond.*, 1927-28, 140: 51-95.

JENKINS, James Travis. A history of the whale fisheries. From the Basque fisheries of the tenth century to the hunting of the finner whale at the present date. 336 p., 12 ill. London: Witherby, 1921. [CB 12/646]

JENKINS, James Travis. Whales and modern whaling. 239 p. London: Witherby, 1932.

LUBBOCK, Basil. The arctic whalers. xii, 484 p. Glasgow: Brown and Ferguson, 1937.
Reviewed by G.C.L. Bertram, *Geogr.J.*, 1938, 91: 188-9.

TOWNSEND, Charles Haskins. Where the nineteenth century whaler made his catch. The whaling season of 1929-30. *Bull.N.Y. Zool.Soc.*, 1931, 34: 173-9.
Reviewed in *Nature*, 1932, 129: 443-4.

VILLIERS, A.J. Whalers of the midnight sun. 285 p., ill. New York: Scribners; London: Bles, 1934.

STce-bv

JENKINS, James Travis. Bibliography of whaling. *J.Soc.Bibliogr.Natur.Hist.*, 1948, 2: 71-166. [CB 74/389]

STwb

DULLES, Foster Rhea. Lowered boats, a chronicle of American whaling. viii, 292 p., 9 pl. New York: Harcourt, Brace, 1934. [CB 42/594]
Reviewed by George Sarton, *Isis*, 1931, 16: 115-23.

STwg

BRINNER, Ludwig. Die deutsche Grönlandfahrt. xxiv, 540 p. (*Abhandl.Verkehrs- Seegesch.*, 7) Berlin: Carl Curtius, 1913.

STwm

AAGAARD, Bjarne. Fangst og forskning i Sydishavet. [Fishing and research in the Antarctic. (In Norwegian)] 3 vol. 1. Svunne dager. [Past days]; 2. Nye tider. [Recent times]; 3. Antarktikas historie. [The history of the Antarctic] (Kommandør Chr. Christensens Hvalfangstmuseum, Publikasjon 9-11) Oslo: Gyldendal, 1930-34.
The story of Norwegian endeavour in the Antarctic as far as it was connected with Norwegian whalers and whaling.
Reviewed by R.N.R. Brown, *Geogr.J.*, 1931, 77: 386-7; 1935, 86: 370-1.

STxx

SARTON, George. The Whaling Museums of New Bedford and Nantucket. *Isis*, 1931, 16: 115-23.

SU HUNTING; FALCONRY

ANDREWS, Roy Chapman. Ends of the earth. x, 355 p., ill. New York: Putnam's 1929.
Covers whaling and hunting.
Reviewed in *Natur.Hist.*, 1930, 220.

BOYER, Abel; PLANIOL, Maurice. Traité de fauconnerie et autourserie. 283 p., 25 ill. (Bibliothèque Scientifique) Paris: Payot, 1948. [CB 77/375]

FUERTES, Louis Agassiz. Falconry, the sport of kings. *Nat. Geogr.Mag.*, 1920, 38: 429-60, ill. [CB 11/453]

HODGKIN, Adrian Eliot. The archer's craft. A sheaf of notes on certain matters concerning archers and archery, the making of archer's tackle and the art of hunting with the bow. 222 p., ill. London: Faber, 1952.

RUSSELL, William F. Falconry, a handbook for hunters. x, 180 p., 12 fig., 7 ill. New York: Scribner's, 1940.

THOMAS, Joseph Brown. Hounds and hunting through the ages. xviii, 272 p., ill. New York: Derrydale Press, 1928.

VÖGELE, Hans-Heinrich. Die Falknerei. Eine ethnographische Darstellung. x, 106 p., 99 fig. (Veröffentlichungen des Geographischen Instituts der Albertus-Universität zu Königsberg Pr.) Königsberg: Neumann-Neudamm, 1931.
Reviewed by Joseph de Somogyi, *J.Roy.Asiatic Soc.*, 1933, 227.

SUsg

BRASS, Emil. Pelztierjagd und Pelzhandel. *Rohstoffe Tierreichs*, 1930, 1: 416-522, 70 fig.
Reviewed by R. Zaunick, *Mitt.Gesch.Med.*, 1932, 31: 35.

SUwb-sg

INNIS, Harold A. The fur trade in Canada: an introduction to Canadian economic history. 444 p., map, ill. New Haven: Yale University Press, 1930.
Reviewed by Charles C. Colby, *Geogr.Rev.*, 1931, 21: 336.

VANDIVEER, Clarence A. The fur trade and early western exploration. 316 p., front., pl., portr. Cleveland: Clark, 1929.
Reviewed by Wayne E. Stevens, *Amer.Hist.Rev.*, 1929, 35: 173.

SUwb-sk

SKINNER, Constance Lindsay. Beaver, kings and cabins. 273 p., 31 fig., maps. New York: Macmillan, 1933.
Reviewed by C.A. Kofoid, *Isis*, 1934, 22: 300.

SUxb

HORWITZ, Hugo Th. Ueber die Konstruktion von Fallen und Selbstschüssen. *Beitr.Gesch.Tech.Ind.*, 1924, 14: 85-100, 21 fig.

SUyS

KRAENNER, Paul. Falkenheilkunde. 76 p. (Diss.) Berlin: 1925.

SV FOOD TECHNOLOGY

see also NMzf FOODS: NUTRITIONAL VALUES

SVc

BITTING, A.W. Appertizing or the art of canning; its history and development. 852 p., ill. San Francisco: Trade Pressroom, 1937. [CB 51/265]

FILBY, Frederick A. A history of food adulteration and analysis. With a foreword by Bernard Dyer. 259 p., 3 facs., 8 fig. London: Allen & Unwin, 1934. [CB 44/273]

FORBES, R.J. The rise of food technology (1500-1900). *Janus*, 1958, 47: 101-27, 139-55.

FRANCIS, Clarence. A history of food and its preservation. A contribution to civilization. An address delivered before Princeton University on March 9, 1937, in the Cyrus Fogg Brackett lectureship in applied engineering and technology. 45 p. Princeton: Princeton University Press, 1937.

KALOYEREAS, Socrates A. On the history of food preservation. *Sci.Mon.*, 1950, 71: 422-4.

OSTERTAG, R. von. Beiträge zur Geschichte der Lebensmittelkonservierung. *Beitr.Gesch.Tech.Ind.*, 1933, 22: 87-92, 4 pl.

PLANK, Rudolf. Die Frischhaltung von Lebensmitteln durch Kälte. *Abhandl.Ber.Deut.Mus.*, 1940, 12: 139-72, ill.
Reviewed by R. Zaunick, *Mitt.Gesch.Med.*, 1941-42, 40: 180.

SCHUETTE, H.A.; ROBINSON, Francis J. Ice cream. *J.Chem.Educ.*, 1933, 10: 469-75.
Contains material on the history of artificially cooled beverages and foods.

ZBINDEN, Christian. Considérations sur l'origine, le développement et l'orientation de l'industrie alimentaire. *Act. Ve Congr.Int.Hist.Sci.* (Lausanne, 1947), p. 279-86. Paris: Hermann, 1948.

SVwb

MAYER, Oscar G. America's meat packing industry. A brief survey of its development and economics: a Newcomen address. 35 p. [Princeton, N.J.: Printed by Princeton University Press, 1939]

SW BEVERAGES

SCHELENZ, H. Zur Geschichte der Mineralwässer und ihrer Salze. *Z.Gesamte Kohlensäure-Ind.*, 1912, no. 28 and 29.

SWza ALCOHOLIC BEVERAGES

BETHGE, Karl. Aus der Zeit der alten Weinpressen. *Beitr. Gesch.Tech.Ind.*, 1924, 14: 210-16, 6 fig.

DAVIDSOHN, I.A. Die Erfindung der Distillation. Transl. from the Swedish by E. Hoffmann. *Int.Monatsschr.Erforsch. Alkoholismus*, 1912, no. 8.
Discussed by Edmund O. von Lippmann, *Chem.Zeitung*, 1913, 37: 1-2.

DIELS, H. Die Entdeckung des Alkohols. 35 p. (*Abhandl. Preuss.Akad.Wiss.Phil.Hist.Kl.*, 1913, no. 3) Berlin: 1913.
Discussed by L. Parmentier, *Rev.Instr.Publ.Belg.*, 1913, 56: 175-82.

GEISLER, Kurt W. Aus der Geschichte der Bierbrauerei. *Beitr. Gesch.Tech.Ind.*, 1930, 20: 130-6, 7 fig.

GEISLER, Kurt W. Zur Geschichte der Spirituserzeugung. Unter besonderer Berücksichtigung der landwirtschaftlichen Brennereien. *Beitr.Gesch.Tech.Ind.*, 1926, 16: 94-105, 7 fig.

HÄUSSER, Friedrich. Keltern einst und jetzt. Aus der Technik des Weines. *Beitr.Gesch.Tech.Ind.*, 1917, 7: 127-33, 6 fig.

JACQUET, L. L'alcool. Etude économique générale. 950 p., ill. Paris: Masson, 1913.

KING, F.A. Beer has a history. x, 180 p., 14 ill. London: Hutchinson, 1947.
Reviewed by R.J. Forbes, *Arch.Int.Hist.Sci.*, 1948, 2: 270-1.

LATRONICO, Nicola. I vini medicinali nella storia e nella scienza. Prefazione di Giovanni Dalmasso. 217 p. (Collana di Studi di Storia della Medicina, 4) Milano: Hoepli, 1947. [CB 71/132]

LIPPMANN, Edmund O. von. Beiträge zur Geschichte des Alkohols. *Chem.Zeitung*, 1913, 37: 1313-16, 1346-7, 1358-61, 1419-22, 1428-9; also in: Lippmann, Edmund O. von. Beiträge zur Geschichte der Naturwissenschaften und der Technik, (1), p. 60-107. Berlin: Springer, 1923. [CB 14/544]

LIPPMANN, Edmund O. von. Einige Bemerkungen zur Geschichte der Distillation und des Alkohols. *Z.Angew.Chem.*, 1912, 25: 1680-2.

LIPPMANN, Edmund O. von. Weitere Mitteilungen zur Geschichte des Alkohols. *Chem.Zeitung*, 1926, 50: 237-9.

LIPPMANN, Edmund O. von. Zur Geschichte der Destillation und des Alkohols. *Chem.Zeitung*, 1913, 37: 1-2; also in: Lippmann, Edmund O. von. Beiträge zur Geschichte der Naturwissenschaften und der Technik, (1), p. 56-9. Berlin: J. Springer, 1923.
Discussion of article by A. Davidsohn: Die Erfindung der Destillation. *See* above.

LIPPMANN, Edmund O. von. Zur Geschichte des Alkohols. Vortrag gehalten im Braunschweig-Hannoverschen Zweigverein des Vereins der Deutschen Zucker-Industrie am 24. März 1926 zu Hannover. *Deut.Zuckerind.*, 1926, 51: no. 17, 457-9.

LIPPMANN, Edmund O. von. Zur Geschichte des Alkohols und der Bezeichnung Gas. *Chem.Zeitung*, 1929, 53: 869-70.

LIPPMANN, Edmund O. von. Zur Geschichte des Alkohols und seines Namens. *Z.Angew.Chem.*, 1912, 25: 2061-5.

MAURIZIO, Adam. Geschichte der gegorenen Getränke. viii, 262 p. Berlin: Parey, 1933.
Reviewed in *Nature*, 1934, 133: 668.

PARMENTIER, L. La découverte de l'alcool. *Rev.Instr.Publique Belg.*, 1913, 56: 175-82.
Discussion of paper by H. Diels: Die Entdeckung des Alkohols, *see* above.

ROSE, Anthony H. Beer. *Sci.Amer.*, 1959, 200: no. 6, 90-100.

RUSKA, Julius. Alkohol und Al-kohl. Zur Geschichte der Entdeckung und des Namens. *Aus Natur*, 1913, 10: 97-111.

RUSKA, Julius. Ein neuer Beitrag zur Geschichte des Alkohols. *Islam*, 1913, 4: 320.

RUSKA, Julius. Wem verdankt man die erste Darstellung des Weingeistes? *Islam*, 1913, 4: 162.

SHAPIRO, N. [A history of opinions and theories of alcoholic fermentation. (In Hebrew, summary in English)] *Koroth*, 1957, 1: 400-8.

SHAPIRO, N. [History of the development of the concept of alcoholic fermentation. (In Hebrew)] *Koroth*, 1956, 1: 322-40.

SPETER, Max. Drei alkoholgeschichtliche Notizen. *Z.Spiritusind.*, 1938, 61: 71, 96.

STÜBE, R. Zur Ursprungsgeschichte der alkoholischen Getränke. *Beitr.Gesch.Tech.Ind.*, 1918, 8: 56-63.

SWza-ce-bv

SCHOELLHORN, Fritz. Bibliographie des Brauwesens. 436 p. Berlin: Gesellschaft für die Geschichte und Bibliographie des Brauwesens, 1928.

SWza-wb

WEISS, Harry B. The history of applejack or apple brandy in New Jersey from colonial times to the present. 265 p., ill. Trenton: New Jersey Agricultural Society, 1954. [CB 81/284]

WEISS, Harry B.; WEISS, Grace M. The early breweries of New Jersey. 98 p., 18 ill. Trenton, N.J.: New Jersey Agricultural Society, 1963.

SWza-we

HOLMYARD, E.J. Priests of Pomoma. *Endeavour*, 1954, 13: 3-4.
An account of the Long Ashton Research Station, known informally as 'The Cider Institute'.

SWza-wk

SLOOTMANS, C.J. De alcohol der nederlandsche suikerindustrie. [Alcohol from the Netherlands sugar industry. (In Dutch)] 149 p., 24 ill. Roosendaal: Van Poll Suykerbuyk, 1949.
Reviewed by R.J. Forbes, *Arch.Int.Hist.Sci.*, 1950, 3: 251.

SWzs STIMULANTS

for plants yielding stimulants *see* SJ

DUFRENOY, Marie-Louise; DUFRENOY, Jean. Coffee, the "exotick drug". *Sci.Mon.*, 1950, 70: 185-8.
Brief history of the introduction of coffee to Europeans.

FINCKE, Heinrich. Handbuch der Kakaoerzeugnisse. Ihre Geschichte, Rohstoffe, Herstellung, Beschaffenheit, Zusammensetzung, Anwendung, Wirkung, gesetzliche Regelung und Zahlberichte, dargestellt für Gewerbe, Handel und Wissenschaft. xvi, 568 p., 162 fig., 62 pl. Berlin: Springer, 1936.

HORWITZ, Hugo Th. Geschichte der Schokolade and Schokoladeindustrie. *Beitr.Gesch.Tech.Ind.*, 1923, 13: 125-45.

JACOB, Heinrich Eduard. The saga of coffee: the biography of an economic product. xiii, 296 p., ill. London: Allen & Unwin, 1935.
English translation of: Saga und Siegeszug des Kaffees (Berlin: Rowohlt, 1934). American edition entitled: The epic of a commodity. New York: Viking Press, 1935.

MENNELL, Robert O. Tea, an historical sketch. 63 p., portr., facs. London: Wilson, 1926.

RUSKA, Julius. Altes und Neues vom Kaffee. 1. Der Kaffee bei den Orientalen; 2. Kaffee und Kaffeehäuser in den europäischen Grosstädten; 3. Chemisches vom Kaffee; 4. Heilkräfte des Kaffees. *Med.Welt.*, 1929, 3: 473-4, 517-19.

SPRINGER, Walter, ed. Die blaue Blume. Von der Schwester des Kaffees, der Zichorie und ihrer Industrie. Mit einem Vorwort von Günther Schmid. 79 p., 25 fig. Berlin: Forschungen zur Geschichte der Industrie, 1940.
Reviewed by R. Zaunick, *Mitt.Gesch.Med.*, 1940, 39: 342.

STEINMANN, Alfred. Der Tee. Zur Geschichte des Teegenusses. Heimat, Verbreitung und Anbau der Teepflanze. Die Verarbeitung der Teeblätter. Teehandel und Teekonsum der Welt. Zur Pharmakologie des Tees. By Franz Gross. Zur Chemie des Tees. By Andreia Uffer. *Ciba Z.*, 1948, 10: no. 111, 4078-120, ill.

UKERS, William H. The romance of coffee: an outline history of coffee and coffee drinking through a thousand years. xvi, 280 p., 66 ill. New York: Tea and Coffee Trade Journal, 1948.
Reviewed by Conway Zirkle, *Isis*, 1949, 40: 291.

UKERS, William H. The romance of tea; an outline history of tea and tea-drinking through sixteen hundred years. 302 p., ill, map. New York: Knopf, 1936.
Reviewed by Clifford H. Pope, *Natur.Hist.*, 1937, 39: 74.

SWzs-wf

WICKERSHEIMER, Ernest. Les débuts en Alsace de l'industrie de la chicorée-café. *Rev.Hist.Pharm.*, 1951, 130: 193-201.

SX FOODS

SCHÄR, Eduard. Die kommerzielle und kulturgeschichtliche Bedeutung der Arznei- und Genussmittel. 28 p. (Rede.) Strassburg: 1913.

SXzb BREAD; CEREALS

ADRIAN, Walter. So wurde Brot aus Halm und Glut. 2nd ed. 120 p., ill., bibliogr. Bielefeld: Ceres Verlag, 1959. [CB 90/526]
First published 1951. Study of the technologies associated with bread-making, from sowing and harvesting to baking and serving.

ASHLEY, William. The bread of our forefathers. An enquiry in economic history. xii, 206 p., 4 pl. Oxford: Clarendon Press, 1928.

ERWIN, A.T. The origin and history of pop corn. *Econ.Bot.*, 1950, 4: 294-9.

JACOB, Heinrich Eduard. Bread in the ancient world. The rivalry of grains. Millers, bakers and the health of man. Bread in the twentieth century. *Ciba Symp.*, 1946, 8: 470-500, ill.

JACOB, Heinrich Eduard. Six thousand years of bread. Its holy and unholy history. xv, 399 p., 8 pl. Garden City, N.Y.: Doubleday, Doran, 1944.
Reviewed by Norah J. Watts, *Nature*, 1944, 154: 501-2.
Italian edition: I seimila anni del pane, storia sacra e storia profana. 470 p., ill. Milano: Garzanti, 1951, reviewed by Arturo Castiglioni, *Riv.Stor.Sci.*, 1952, 43: 136-7.

STORCK, John; TEAGUE, Walter Dorwin. Flour for man's bread. A history of milling. xiii, 382 p., 152 ill. Minneapolis: University of Minnesota Press, 1952.
Reviewed by Conway Zirkle, *Isis*, 1953, 44: 82-3.

SXzb-sc

McCANCE, R.A.; WIDDOWSON, E.M. Breads, white and brown: their place in thought and social history. xi, 174 p., 3 pl. London: Pitman Medical Publishing Co., 1956.
Reviewed by R.J. Forbes, *Arch.Int.Hist.Sci.*, 1957, 10: 83.

SXzc CONDIMENTS AND SPICES

for plants yielding spices *see* SJ

KOELNER, Paul. Die Safranzunft zu Basel und ihre Handwerke und Gewerbe, im Auftrage des Zunftvorstandes verfasst. xi, 684 p., 12 pl. Basel: Schwabe, 1935.
Reviewed by A. Bruckner, *Deut.Lit.Zeitung*, 1936, 57: 766-8.

McNAIR, James Birtley. Spices and condiments. 64 p., fig. (Botany, leaflet 15) Chicago: Field Museum of Natural History, 1930.

PARRY, J.W. The story of spices. viii, 208 p. New York: Chemical Publishing Co., 1953. [CB 81/275]
An epitome of this work published with same title in *Econ.Bot.*, 1955, 9: 190-207.

VERRILL, A. Hyatt. Perfumes and spices. Including an account of soaps and cosmetics. The story of the history, source, preparation, and use of the spices, perfumes, soaps, and cosmetics which are in everyday use. xvi, 304 p. Boston: Page, 1940.

SXzf FATS AND OILS

MENGHIN, Oswald. Geschichtliches zur Oelbereitung aus Traubenkernen. *Isis*, 1924, 6: 400-3.
Tracing back the extraction of oil from grapestones to the year 1569. The next records date from 1709, etc.

SXzs SALT

BLOCH, M.R. History of salt (NaCl) technology. *Act.VIIe Congr.Int.Hist.Sci.* (Jerusalem, 1953), p. 221-5. Paris: Hermann, [n.d.]

SCHOEN, Herbert M.; GROVE, C.S.; PALERMO, Joseph A. The early history of crystallization. *J.Chem.Educ.*, 1956, 33: 373-5, 4 fig.
Chiefly on the production of salt through the ages.

SXzs-sc

BLOCH, M.R. The social influence of salt. *Sci.Amer.*, 1963, 209: no. 1, 88-98.

HEHN, Victor. Das Salz. Eine kulturhistorische Studie. New ed. by Kurt Jagow. 71 p. Leipzig: Insel, 1919.
First published 1873.

SXzs-u

VORWAHL, Heinrich. Das Salz in der Volksmedizin. *Münch.Med. Wochenschr.*, 1931, 78: 595-6.

SXzs-wb

BATHE, Greville. The Onondaga Salt Works of New York State, 1646-1846. *Trans.Newcomen Soc.*, 1945-47, 25: 17-26, 4 fig.

TUNNELL, James M. Salt business in early Sussex County. *Delaware Hist.*, 1950, 4: 48-59.
History of the manufacture of salt from salt water, from colonial times to the middle of the 19th century.

SXzs-we

NEWBURY, N.F. The history of the common salt industry on Merseyside. *Ann.Sci.*, 1938, 3: 138-48, 2 fig.

SXzs-wg

LOCKEMANN, Georg. Die Gründung der Saline Sülbeck. *Arch.Gesch. Naturwiss.Tech.*, 1913, 6: 241-9.

SXzs-wh-ph

KECKOWA, Antonina, ed. Instrukcje górnicze dla żup krakowskich z XVI-XVIII wieku. [Mining instructions for the Cracow mines from the 16th to 18th century. (In Polish)] xv, 206 p. (Zakład Historii Nauki i Techniki Polskiej Akademii Nauk. Źródła do dziejów nauki i techniki, 4) Wroclaw: Zakład Narodowy im. Ossolińskich, 1963.

SXzs-wn

ROZEN, B.Ia. [Salt industry on the White Sea. (In Russian)] *Tr.Inst.Ist.Est.Tekh.*, 1955, 3: 53-67.

SXzs-wt

SPENCER, Joseph Earle. Salt in China. *Geogr.Rev.*, 1935, 25: 353-66, 5 fig. [CB 45/262]
Modern production and distribution.

SY SUGAR

BAXA, Jakob. Die Zuckererzeugung, 1600-1850. 231 p., 48 fig. Jena: Fischer, 1937.
Reviewed by Max Speter, *Isis*, 1938, 29: 184-5.

BIRCHER, E. Zur Geschichte der Milchzuckergewinnung, besonders in der Schweiz. *Gesnerus*, 1954, 11: 41-5.

COONS, George H. The sugar beet, product of science. *Sci. Mon.*, 1949, 68: 149-64.
A brief history of the creation of a crop plant and of the industry founded upon it.

DEERR, Noel; BROOKS, Alexander. Development of the practice of evaporation with special reference to the sugar industry. *Trans.Newcomen Soc.*, 1941-42, 22: 1-19, 16 fig.

DEERR, Noel. The history of sugar. 2 vol. xiv, 636 p., ill. London: Chapman and Hall, 1949-50.

LINDET, Léon. Histoire centennale de la fabrication du sucre de betteraves. *Rev.Sci.*, 1912, 50: 1er semestre, 481-91.

LIPPMANN, Edmund O. von. Aus den ersten Anfängen der Rübenzucker-Industrie. *Deut.Zuckerind.*, 1938, 63: 980.

LIPPMANN, Edmund O. von. Geschichte des Zuckers seit den ältesten Zeiten bis zum Beginn der Rübenzucker-Fabrikation. Ein Beitrag zur Kulturgeschichte. 2nd ed. ix, 824 p. Berlin: Springer, 1929.
First published 1890.
Reviewed by George Sarton, *Isis*, 1930, 13: 393-5.

LIPPMANN, Edmund O. von. Kleine Beiträge zur Geschichte des Zuckers. 1. Das erste Zuckerrohr in Amerika. 2. Arabische Zuckererzeugung in Spanien um 1400. 3. Ein "Zuckerbäcker" (Raffinerie-Arbeiter) von 1694. *Deut.Zuckerind.*, 1924, 49: 1015.

LIPPMANN, Edmund O. von. Kleine Beiträge zur Geschichte des Zuckers. 1. Zucker als Gift; 2. Karamel; 3. Die "Weihe" des Kalkofens; 4. Der erste deutsche Rübenzucker in England. *Deut.Zuckerind.*, 1926, 51: 532.

LIPPMANN, Edmund O. von. Das Leuchten des Zuckers. *Pharm. Ind.*, 1936, 3: 38-40.

LIPPMANN, Edmund O. von. Modifikationen des Rohrzuckers. *Chem.Zeitung*, 1927, 51: 873.

LIPPMANN, Edmund O. von. Nachträge und Ergänzungen zur "Geschichte des Zuckers". *Z.Ver.Deut.Zucker-Ind.*, 1934, 84: 806-936. [CB 43/274]

LIPPMANN, Edmund O. von. Nachträge zur "Geschichte des Zuckers". *Z.Wirtsch.Zuckerind.*, 1938, 88: 359-70, 639-81. [CB 56/395]

MUNDY, Norris Havemeyer, ed. A short history of sugar. Worthwhile facts about a valuable food. 85 p. Chicago: Havemeyer and Company, 1923. [CB 16/349]
Publication, serving as advertisement for the firm W.A. Havemeyer and Co., of Chicago. It was published to celebrate the golden jubilee of that firm (1873-1923).

PIQUE, René. Histoire du sucre. *Compt.Rend.VIe Congr.Chim. Ind.* (Paris, 1927), p. 625-36. (*Chim.Ind.*, 1927, special number) Paris: 1927. [CB 51/264]

SYvm

SHAPIRO, N. [The part played by Jews in the production of sugar. (In Hebrew)] *Koroth*, 1959, 2: 139-44.

SYwb

BROWNE, Charles Albert. The origins of sugar manufacture in America. 1. A sketch of the history of raw cane-sugar production in America. 2. A sketch of the history of sugar refining in America. *J.Chem.Educ.*, 1933, 10: 323-30, 421-7.

SYwg

LIPPMANN, Edmund O. von. Die Entwicklung der Zuckerindustrie 1888-1913. Kaisernummer der *Magdeburgischen Zeitung*, 15 Juni 1913. In: Lippmann, Edmund O. von. Beiträge zur Geschichte der Naturwissenschaften und der Technik, (1), p. 284-94. Berlin: J. Springer, 1923.
An account of the progress of the sugar industry in Germany during the reign of William II.

LIPPMANN, Edmund O. von. Fortschritte der Rübenzucker-Fabrikation (-Industrie).
This report on the beet sugar industry by E.O. von Lippmann appeared annually in *Chem.Zeitung* from 1892, vol. 16 until 1936, vol. 60, (no. [1]-44). From 1937 it was continued by W. Dörfeldt.

SYwk

HALLEMA, A. Van biet tot suiker. J.P. van Rossum als suikerindustrieel, koopman en organisator. [From beet to sugar. P.Van Rossum, sugar manufacturer, merchant and organizer. (In Dutch)] xv, 291 p., 27 ill., 4 maps. Baarn: Uitgeverij Schuyt, 1948.
Reviewed by R.J. Forbes, *Arch.Int.Hist.Sci.*, 1949, 28: 778.

SYwv

LIPPMANN, Edmund O. von. Die Zuckerindustrie Javas. (Vortrag, gehalten in der Generalversammlung des Sächsisch-Thüringischen Zweigvereins des Vereins der Deutschen Zucker-Industrie am 25. April 1929 in Halle a.S.) *Deut.Zuckerind.*, 1929, 54: 653-6, 677-8.

SYxb

DEERR, Noel; BROOKS, Alexander. The evolution of the sugar cane mill. *Trans.Newcomen Soc.*, 1940-41, 21: 1-9, 10 fig.

SYxk-wg

LIPPMANN, Edmund O. von. Zur Geschichte des Vakuum-Apparates. *Chem.Zeitung*, 1916, 40: 945. In: Lippmann, Edmund O. von. Beiträge zur Geschichte der Naturwissenschaften und der Technik, (1), p. 281-4. Berlin: J. Springer, 1923. [CB 14/521]

SYxp

LIPPMANN, Edmund O. von. Zur Geschichte des Saccharometers und der Senkspindel. *Chem.Zeitung*, 1912, 36: 385-6, 629-30, 1201.

SYySWxd

LIPPMANN, Edmund O. von. Ein Beitrag zur Geschichte der Saftreinigung. *Deut.Zuckerind.*, 1929, 54: 1143.

LIPPMANN, Edmund O. von. Verzeichnis von Mitteln zur Reinigung, Entfärbung und Klärung zuckerhaltiger Säfte und Erzeugnisse. *Deut.Zuckerind.*, 1937, 62: 67-9, 87-9, 105-6, 125-6, 151.

T TECHNOLOGY

Tc general history

for the history of science and technology *see* A

Tc-be *encyclopaedias*

DICTIONNAIRE archéologique des techniques. 2 vol. 1124 p., ill. Paris: Editions de l'Accueil, 1963-64.
Reviewed by R.J. Forbes, *Technol.Cult.*, 1964, 5: 69-74; for other reviews *see* CB 89/518 and CB 90/541.

EERSTE NEDERLANDSE SYSTEMATISCHE ENCYCLOPAEDIE. 9. Waterbouwkunde en wegenbouw, burgerlijke bouwkunde, verzorgende technieken en ambachten, levensvormen en vrije tijd, oorlog en oorlogvoering, uitvindingen en ontdekkingen, wetenschappelijk onderzoek. [Hydraulic engineering and road construction, civic architecture, techniques and crafts, ways of life in former days, war and military strategy, inventions and discoveries, scientific research. (In Dutch)] Edited by Jac. Bot and R.J. Forbes. x, 670 p. Amsterdam: E.N.S.I.E., 1950. [CB 78/185]

Tc-bm *large scale works*

ARMYTAGE, W.H.G. A social history of engineering. 378 p. London: Faber; New York: Pitman, 1961.
Reviewed by T.I. Williams, *J.Roy.Inst.Chem.*, 1961, 85: 275; by Sixten Rönnow, *Lychnos*, 1962, 525-7; by Melvin Kranzberg, *Victorian Stud.*, 1963, 6: 293-4.

BELLET, Daniel. L'évolution de l'industrie. 346 p. Paris: Flammarion, 1914.

BOWEN, Harold G.; KETTERING, Charles F. A short history of technology. 120 p. West Orange, N.J.: The Thomas Alva Edison Foundation, Inc., 1954.
Reviewed by Henry Noss, *Scr.Math.*, 1955, 21: 279-80.

BRAGG, William Henry. Old trades and new knowledge: six lectures delivered before a "Juvenile Auditory" at the Royal Institution, Christmas 1925. xii, 266 p., 42 pl. London: G. Bell, 1926.
Reviewed in *Nature*, 1927, 119: 272-3.

BRONOWSKI, J., *et al.*, ed. Technology: man remakes his world. 367 p., ill. New York: Doubleday, 1964.
Reviewed by Melvin Kranzberg, *Science*, 1964, 146: 237-8.

BUCCAR, M. de. Grandes inventions. 95 p., 95 ill. Paris: Larousse, 1953.
Reviewed by S. Colnort-Bodet, *Rev.Hist.Sci.*, 1954, 7: 196.

CALDER, Ritchie. L'homme et ses techniques de la préhistoire à nos jours. 376 p. Paris: Payot, 1963.
Reviewed by Pierre Huard, *Arch.Int.Hist.Sci.*, 1964, 17: 331-2.

CENTENNIAL OF ENGINEERING, 1952. Centennial of engineering, 1852-1952; history and proceedings of symposia; ed. by Lenox R. Lohr. 1079 p., ill. Chicago: Museum of Science and Industry, 1953. [CB 80/144]

CONTRIBUTIONS from the Museum of History and Technology, Papers 1-11. vi, 201 p., 128 ill. (United States National Museum Bulletin, 218) Washington, D.C.: Smithsonian Institution, 1959. [CB 85/403]
Reviewed by Robert S. Woodbury, *Technol.Cult.*, 1960, 1: 269-71.

CROWTHER, J.G. Discoveries and inventions of the twentieth century. 4th ed. 432 p. London: Routledge and Kegan Paul, 1955.
Previous editions by Edward Cressy; first published 1914.
Reviewed in *Sch.Sci.Rev.*, 1956, 37: 296.

DAUMAS, Maurice, ed. Histoire générale des techniques. Tome I. Les origines de la civilisation technique. xvi, 652 p., 113 ill., 48 pl. Paris: Presses Universitaires de France, 1962.
Reviewed by Lynn White, *Isis*, 1964, 55: 228-30; by R.J. Forbes, *Technol.Cult.*, 1963, 4: 336-7.

DERRY, T.K.; WILLIAMS, Trevor I. A short history of technology from the earliest times to A.D. 1900. xviii, 782 p., ill., bibliogr. New York/London: Oxford University Press, 1961.
Reviewed by Thomas P. Hughes, *Isis*, 1963, 54: 417-18; for other reviews *see* CB 87/576, CB 88/566 and CB 89/516.

DUCASSÉ, P. Histoire des techniques. 136 p. (Collection "Que sais-je?", 126) Paris: Presses Universitaires de France, 1945. [CB 69/228]
Reviewed by P. Sergescu, *Arch.Int.Hist.Sci.*, 1948, 2: 265-7.

DUNSHEATH, Percy, ed. A century of technology, 1851-1951. 346 p., 40 ill. London/New York: Hutchinson's Scientific and Technical Publications, 1951.
Reviewed by I. Bernard Cohen, *Isis*, 1952, 43: 377-8.

ECO, Umberto; ZORZOLI, G.B. The picture history of inventions. From plough to Polaris. Transl. from the Italian by Anthony Lawrence. 360 p., ill. London: Weidenfeld and Nicolson, 1962; New York: Macmillan, 1963.
Translation of: Storia figurata delle invenzioni dalla seice scheggiata al volo spaziale. (Milano: Bompiani, 1961)
Reviewed by Melvin Kranzberg, *Science*, 1963, 142: 657.

FELDHAUS, Franz M. Kulturgeschichte der Technik. 2 vol. 154 p., 60 fig.; 209 p., 47 fig. (Mathematisch-Naturwissenschaftlich-Technische Bücherei, 20-21) Berlin: Otto Salle, 1928. [CB 26/233]

FELDHAUS, Franz M. Ruhmesblätter der Technik. Von den Urerfindungen bis zur Gegenwart. 2nd ed. 2 vol. xi, 292 p.; 310 p., ill. Leipzig: Friedrich Brandstetter, 1924-26.
First published 1910.
Reviewed by Carl von Klinckowstroem, *Isis*, 1927, 9: 378-80.

FELDHAUS, Franz M. Die Technik der Vorzeit, der geschichtlichen Zeit und der Naturvölker. xv, 1400 p., 873 ill. Leipzig: W. Engelmann, 1914.

FINCH, James Kip. The story of engineering. xxvii, 528 p., 118 ill. Garden City, N.Y.: Anchor Books, Doubleday, 1960.
Reviewed by F. Klemm, *Isis*, 1962, 53: 401-2; by Eugene S. Ferguson, *Science*, 1960, 132: 464-5; by R.J. Forbes, *Technol.Cult.*, 1961, 2: 33-4.

FISKE, Bradley A. Invention: the master key to progress. ix, 356 p. New York: Dutton, 1921; London: Allen & Unwin, 1923.

FLAXMAN, Edward. Great feats of modern engineering. Rev. ed. 287 p., 32 pl., 47 fig., maps. London/Glasgow: Blackie; New York: Mill, 1938. [CB 57/245]
First published 1931.

FLEMING, A.P.M.; BROCKLEHURST, H.J. A history of engineering. vii, 312 p. (The Histories of English Industries Series) London: Black, 1925.

FORBES, R.J. Man the maker. A history of technology and engineering. Rev. ed. xv, 365 p., 41 pl., 27 fig. London/New York: Schuman, 1958. [CB 84/325]
First published 1950.
Reviewed by Cyril Stanley Smith, *Isis*, 1951, 42: 79; for other reviews *see* CB 85/403 and CB 88/567.

FORBES, R.J. De mens bouwt zich een wereld. Vijf duizend jaar techniek. 241 p. Amsterdam: N.V.Em. Querido's Uitgeversmij, 1952.
A Dutch translation of above.
Reviewed by E.J. Dijksterhuis, *Rev.Hist.Sci.*, 1953, 6: 287.

FORBES, R.J. Vom Steinbeil zum Ueberschall. Fünftausend Jahre Technik. 372 p., 44 ill., 36 fig., 16 pl. München: Paul List Verlag, 1954.
German translation of: Man the maker.
Reviewed by J.P., *Arch.Int.Hist.Sci.*, 1954, 7: 395; by Friedrich Klemm, *Sudhoffs Arch.*, 1954, 38: 287-8; by A.G. Drachmann, *Centaurus*, 1955, 4: 168.

GANZENMÜLLER, Wilhelm. Beiträge zur Geschichte der Technologie und der Alchimie. 389 p., 26 ill. Weinheim/Bergstr.: Verlag Chemie, GMBH., 1956.
Reviewed by W. Pagel, *Isis*, 1958, 49: 84-6; for other reviews *see* CB 82/205, CB 83/185 and CB 84/295.

GARTMANN, Heinz. Rings around the world: man's progress from steam engine to satellite. xv, 359 p., bibliogr., ill. New York: William Morrow, 1959.
American edition of "Science as history", *see* below.
Reviewed by Rudolf A. Clemen, *Technol.Cult.*, 1961, 2: 37-41.

GARTMANN, Heinz. Science as history. The story of man's technological progress from steam engine to satellite. Transl. from the German by Alan G. Readett. xii, 348 p., ill. London: Hodder and Stoughton, 1960.
German title: Sonst stünde die Welt still. (Düsseldorf: Econ-Verlag, 1957).
Reviewed by J.L. Stollery, *Nature*, 1960, 187: 8; by Ben Lockspeiser, *Advanc.Sci.*, 1960, 17: 185.

GEITEL, Max. Schöpfungen der Ingenieurtechnik der Neuzeit. 106 p., ill. (Aus Natur und Geisteswelt) Leipzig: Teubner, 1914.

HATFIELD, H. Stafford. The inventor and his world. 256 p. West Drayton: Penguin Books, 1948.
First published London: Kegan Paul, 1933.
Reviewed by H. Dopp, *Rev.Quest.Sci.*, 1948, 9: 619.

HENDRICHS, Franz. Der Weg aus der Tretmühle. Ein Abriss der Geschichte der Technik der Neueren Zeit. 236 p., 16 pl. Düsseldorf: VDI-Verlag, 1958.
Reviewed by Ladislao Reti, *Technol.Cult.*, 1961, 2: 41-2.

KIRBY, Richard Shelton, *et al.* Engineering in history. viii, 530 p., ill. London/Toronto/New York: McGraw-Hill, 1956.
Reviewed by Carl W. Condit, *Isis*, 1957, 48: 484-7; for other reviews *see* CB 82/216, CB 83/211, CB 84/326 and CB 89/517.

KLEMM, Friedrich. Technik. Eine Geschichte ihrer Probleme. xii, 454 p., 94 ill. (Orbis academicus. Problemgeschichten der Wissenschaft in Dokumenten und Darstellungen, 2: 5) Freiburg-München: K. Alber, 1954. [CB 80/143]
Reviewed by Otto Mahr, *Sudhoffs Arch.*, 1955, 39: 190-1; by Sixten Rönnow, *Lychnos*, 1956, 463-7.
For English translation *see* above.

KLEMM, Friedrich. Kurze Geschichte der Technik. 175 p., fig. Basel/Vienna: Herder, 1961.
Reviewed by M.-F. Hetier, *Doc.Hist.Tech.*, 1962, 2: 88-9; by J.B. Quintyn, *Tech.Wetensch.Tijdschr.*, 1962, 31: 57.

KLEMM, Friedrich. Technik. Eine Geschichte ihrer Problem. xii, 454 p., 94 ill. (Orbis academicus. Problemgeschichten der Wissenschaft in Dokumenten und Darstellungen, 2: 5) Freiburg-München: K. Alber, 1954. [CB 80/143]
Reviewed by Otto Mahr, *Sudhoffs Arch.*, 1955, 39: 190-1; by Sixten Rönnow, *Lychnos*, 1956, 463-7.
For English translation *see* above.

KLEMM, Friedrich, ed. Die Technik der Neuzeit. 3 vol. 1. Von der mittelalterlichen Technik zum Maschinenzeitalter. 48 p., ill.; 2. Rohstoffgewinnung und Verarbeitung. 240 p., ill.; 3. Verkehrs- und Bautechnik. 240 p., ill. Potsdam: Athenaion, 1941-42. [CB 73/172 and CB 77/372]
Incomplete; no more published.

LEITHÄUSER, Joachim G. Inventors' progress. Transl. from the German by Michael Bullock. 286 p., ill. Cleveland/New York: World Publishing Company, 1959.
Translation of: Die zweite Schöpfung der Welt. (Berlin: Safari Verlag, 1952). Title of London edition: Inventors of our world.
Reviewed by Abbott Payson Usher, *Isis*, 1960, 51: 103-4.

NEUDECK, Georg. Geschichte der Technik. 490 p., ill. Stuttgart: Walter Seifert, 1923.
Reviewed by Carl von Klinckowstroem, *Isis*, 1924, 6: 129-31.

OSGOOD, Ellen Louise. A history of industry. 2nd ed. 532 p. Boston: Ginn, 1935.
First published 1921.

POIRIER, René. The fifteen wonders of the world. Transl. by M. Crosland. 400 p., ill. London: Gollancz, 1960; New York: Random House, 1961.
Translation of: L'épopée des grands travaux de la Tour de Babel à la Cité de l'atome (Paris: Plon, 1957).
Reviewed by R.J. Forbes, *Technol.Cult.*, 1961, 2: 269-70.

QUINTYN, J.B. Historische opmars der techniek. [Historical advance of technology. (In Dutch)] 2nd rev. enl. ed. 270 p. Gent: De Vlam, 1963.
1960 edition reviewed by A. Van Winghem, *Technisch-Wetensch. Tijdschr.*, 1962, 31: 38.

RAPPORT, Samuel; WRIGHT, Helen; ed. Engineering. xiii, 378 p., fig. New York: New York University Press, 1963. [CB 89/518]

RICHARDSON, E.G. Physical science in art and industry. xi, 293 p., 73 fig. London: English Universities Press; New York: Macmillan, 1940. [CB 62/76]

ROUSSEAU, Pierre. Histoire des techniques. 528 p. (Les Grandes Études Historiques) Paris: Arthème-Fayard, 1956.
Reviewed by Maurice Daumas, *Rev.Hist.Sci.*, 1958, 11: 93-5.

SCHNITHALS, Hans; KLEMM, Friedrich. Handwerk und Technik vergangener Jahrhunderte. xv, 120 p., pl. Tübingen: Wasmuth, 1958.
Reviewed by M.D., *Doc.Hist.Tech.*, 1962, 2: 90.

SCHWARTE, M., ed. Die Technik im Weltkriege. Unter Mitwirkung von 45 technischen und militärischen sachwissenschaftlichen Mitarbeitern. x, 610 p., ill. Berlin: Mittler, 1920. [CB 11/422]

SINGER, Charles; HOLMYARD, E.J.; HALL, A.R.; WILLIAMS, Trevor I.; ed. A history of technology. 5 vol. London/New York: Oxford University Press, 1955-58.
Reviewed in *Isis*, 1955, 46: 294-6 (by George Sarton); 1958, 49: 89-90 (by C.S. Smith); 1959, 50: 163-5 (by Charles C. Gillispie); 1960, 51: 354-6 (by C.S. Smith); in *Technol.Cult.*, 1960, vol. 1 [CB 86/474]; for other reviews *see* CB 83/212, CB 84/327, CB 85/405 and 465 and CB 86/474.

UCCELLI, Arturo, ed. Storia della tecnica dal medio evo ai nostri giorni. Opera compilata con la collaborazione di eminenti specialisti. xii, 934 p., 2717 ill. Milan: Hoepli, 1944. Reprint 1945. [CB 75/91]

VIERENDEEL, Arthur. Esquisse d'une histoire de la technique. 2 vol. 348 p. Bruxelles: Vromant, 1921.
Reviewed by L. Guinet, *Isis*, 1923, 5: 486-7.

Tc-bn *essays; articles*

CUSHING, Harvey. One hundred and fifty years: from tallow-dip to television. *New Engl.J.Med.*, 1931, 204: 1234-55. [CB 33/391]

DYSKUSJA na temat historii kultury materialnej na plenarnym posiedzeniu Wydziału 1 PAN dn. 2II 1955r. [Discussion concerning the history of material culture. (In Polish, with summary in Russian and English)] *Kwart.Hist.Kult.Mater.*, 1955, 3: 586-621.

EWING, James Alfred. A century of inventions. *Nature*, 1928, 121: 947-55.
From the Thirty-fourth James Forrest Lecture, delivered before the Institution of Civil Engineers on June 4, 1928, on the occasion of the celebration of the centenary of its incorporation.

FORBES, R.J. La technique et l'énergie au cours des siècles. 47 p., 6 fig. (Les Conférences du Palais de la Découverte, D. 42) Paris: Université de Paris, 1956.

KILGOUR, Frederick G. How good are our science and engineering? *Yale Rev.*, Summer, 1955, 555-63.

MARSHALL, C.F. Dendy. The germs and development of some mechanical inventions. *Trans.Newcomen Soc.*, 1935-36, 16: 1-26, 12 fig.

MATSCHOSS, Conrad. Technische Kulturdenkmäler. *Beitr.Gesch. Tech.Ind.*, 1927, 17: 123-52, 92 fig.

ORROK, Geo. A. Engineering recollections: an informal address. *Trans.Newcomen Soc.*, 1934-35, 15: 153-67.

PARSONS, Charles A. Engineering science before, during and after the war. *Science*, 1920, 50: 333-8, 355-62, 383-6.
Address of the President of B.A.A.S., meeting of Bournemouth, 1919.

Quaderni di Merceologia (Pubblicati dall'Istituto di Merceologia dell'Università di Bari). Vol. 1, no. 1, 520 p. Bari: Editore Cressati, 1962. [CB 89/518]
25 papers on the theme of "technological progress and the improvement of quality" presented at a symposium of studies on the technology of commerce held at the University of Bari, 1962.
Reviewed by P.M.R., *Ambix*, 1963, 11: 159-60.

RUBIN, Z.A. Tekhnicheskii progress i inzhenernoe tvorchestvo. [Technical progress and engineering advances. (In Russian)] *Vop.Ist.Est.Tekh.*, 1958, 6: 12-23.

STRUMILIN, S.G. [Fortschritte der Technik in den letzten drei Jahrhunderten. (In Russian)] *Arkh.Ist.Nauk Tekh.*, 1934, 2: 81-104; 1935, 5: 435-72.

Tc-br *periodicals*

Beiträge zur Geschichte der Technik und Industrie see below *Technikgeschichte*

Cahiers de l'Institut de Science Économique Appliquée. Série AD, Evolution de Techniques et Progrès de l'Économie. 1- Paris: 1961-
No. 2 reviewed by M. Daumas, *Rev.Hist.Sci.*, 1963, 16: 405-6.

Documents pour l'Histoire des Techniques. Cahier no. 1-2. Paris: Centre de Documentation d'Histoire des Techniques, 1961-62.
Subsequent numbers appear as part of *Rev.Hist.Sci.*

Geschichtsblätter für Technik, Industrie und Gewerbe. Hrsg. von Carl v. Klinckowstroem und Franz M. Feldhaus. 11 vol. Berlin: Verlag der Quellenforschungen zur Geschichte der Technik und Industrie, 1914-27. [CB 6/459 and CB 8/370]
Suspended 1924-26.

S.É.T.: Structure et Évolution des Techniques. Bulletin mensuel de l'Association pour l'Etude des Techniques. Vol. 1- Paris: 1949- [CB 74/384]

Sbornik Narodniho Technickeho Musea. [Review of the National Technical Museum. (In Czech)] Vol. 1- Praha: Narodni Technické Muzeum, 1955-
For contents of volume 3, *see* CB 85/405.

Tage der Technik. Technisch-historischer Abreisskalender. Edited by F.M. Feldhaus (and Gilbert Feldhaus). 1, 1922 - 10, 1931. München: R. Oldenbourg; Hannover: Edler & Krische, 1921-30. [CB 18/617 and CB 22/271]

Technikgeschichte. Im Auftrage des Vereines Deutscher Ingenieure. Beiträge zur Geschichte der Technik und Industrie. Vol. 22-30. Berlin: 1933-41.
Vol. 1-21 (1909-32) entitled: *Beiträge zur Geschichte der Technik und Industrie.* Index to vol. 1-30 published as vol. 31 (1965); (Düsseldorf, 1965); vol. 32- Düsseldorf: 1965-

Technology and Culture. The international quarterly of the Society for the History of Technology. Vol. 1- Detroit: Wayne State University Press, 1959-

Transactions of the Newcomen Society for the study of the history of engineering and technology. Vol. 1 (1920-21)- London: Newcomen Society, 1922-
Volume 30 (1955-56 and 1956-57) reviewed by R.S. Woodbury, *Endeavour*, 1961, 20: 107.

Tc-bu/cv bibliography; literature; sources

Tc-bv

AKADEMIIA NAUK URSR. BIBLIOTEKA. Istoriia tekhniki: bibliografichnyi pokazhchik literatury, shcho vyishla na Ukraini v 1946-1955. rr. Pod. red. V.V. Danilevskogo. [History of technology. Bibliography of literature published in the Ukraine, 1946-1955. Edited by V.V. Danilevskii. (In Russian)] 98 p. Kiev: 1959.

ANALYTICAL bibliography of the history of engineering and applied science. *Trans.Newcomen Soc.*, 1921-22, 2: 141-55; 1922-23, 3: 122-7; 1923-24, 4: 135-40; 1924-25, 5: 100-24; 1925-26, 6: 203-21; 1926-27, 7: 132-45; 1927-28, 8: 161-83; 1928-29, 9: 113-33; 1929-30, 10: 121-34; 1930-31, 11: 171-87; 1931-32, 12: 112-18; 1932-33, 13: 187-95; 1933-34, 14: 213-25; 1934-35, 15: 233-48; 1935-36, 16: 161-78; 1936-37, 17: 221-31; 1937-38, 18: 281-94; 1938-39, 19: 269-79; 1939-40, 20: 161-73; 1940-41, 21: 158-73; 1941-42, 22: 188-203; 1945-47, 25: 211-21.

BRUNET, Lucien. Les techniques et leur histoire: essai de bibliographie pour 1936. *Thalès*, 1936, 3: 155-70. 11,522

COOPER UNION FOR THE ADVANCEMENT OF SCIENCE AND ART. LIBRARY. A guide to the literature on the history of engineering available in The Cooper Union Library: a classified bibliography. x, 46 p. (Cooper Union Bulletin, Engineering and Science Series, 28) New York: 1946. [CB 70/258]

FELDHAUS, Franz M.; KLINCKOWSTROEM, Carl von. Bibliographie der erfindungsgeschichtlichen Literatur. *Geschichtsbl.Tech. Ind.*, 1923, 10: 1-21. [CB 16/347]

FERGUSON, Eugene S. Contributions to bibliography in the history of technology. *Technol.Cult.*, 1962, 3: 73-84, 167-74, 298-306; 1963, 4: 318-30; 1964, 5: 416-34, 578-94; 1965, 6: 99-107. [CB 88/566 and 89/517]
Part 1 deals with sources in government records, Part 2 with encyclopedias, mechanical dictionaries and handbooks, Part 3 with biography, Part 4 with general works, bibliographies and directories, Part 5 with periodicals, Part 6 with early source books, travel and description, manuscripts and illustrations, Part 7 with technical museums and exhibitions.

HULME, E. Wyndham. Introductions to the literature of historical engineering to the year 1640. *Trans.Newcomen Soc.*, 1920-21, 1: 7-15.
Sketch of a bibliography with short introductions.

JOHN CRERAR LIBRARY, Chicago. A list of books on the history of industry and industrial arts. Prepared by A.G. Josephson. (9), 487 p. (Bibliographical Publications, 11) Chicago: 1915.

YAMAZAKI, Toshio. Japan's contributions to the modern history of technology. *Jap.Stud.Hist.Sci.*, 1962, 1: 45-7, bibliogr.
Review of the work of modern Japanese historians of technology.

Tc-bx

COLLINS, A. Frederick. The new world of science. 308 p., ill. Philadelphia: Lippincott, 1934. [CB 52/542]
An interpretative account of the Chicago Exposition of 1933 and 1934. For companion volume *see* Linn, James W., below.

LINN, James W. The official pictures of A century of progress exposition, Chicago, 1933. 10 p., 144 pl. Chicago: Donnelley, 1934. [CB 52/542]
For companion volume *see* Collins, A. Frederick, above.

Tcb

BIBLIOTHÈQUES techniques de Paris. *La Nature*, 1913, 41: 2e semestre, suppl., 189-90.

DEUTSCHES MUSEUM. Denkschrift über den Bibliothekbau des Deutschen Museums. 12 p., 10 ill., 3 pl. München: 1920. [CB 10/209]

Tcc

NICOL, Hugh. Agricultural sources of mechanical information. *Trans.Newcomen Soc.*, 1929-30, 10: 115-19, 1 fig.

Tcc-by

FELDHAUS, Franz M. Die Sammlungen Feldhaus und ihr neues Heim. *Geschichtsbl.Tech.Ind.*, 1927, 11: 6-10.

Tcd

ARCHIVE of science and technology [established by the Case Institute of Technology, Cleveland, Ohio]. *Isis*, 1961, 52: 417.

KLINCKOWSTROEM, Carl von. Technisches und Technologisches in den Akten der Bayerischen Akademie der Wissenschaften. *Geschichtsbl.Tech.Ind.*, 1921, 8: 11-16.

TREMAUD, Hélène. Documents pour l'histoire des techniques pré-industrielles au Musée des Arts et Traditions Populaires. *Doc.Hist.Tech.*, 1962, 2: 50-5.

Tce

COGS IN THE WHEEL: one hundred books from the Llewellyn Powell collection of early technology. 80 p., ill. (Library Handlist, 4) Durban: University of Natal Library, 1961.
Reviewed by Eugene S. Ferguson, *Technol.Cult.*, 1964, 5: 133-4.

Tce-bv

GERMANY. REICHSPATENTAMT. Katalog der Bibliothek des Reichspatentamts. Stand vom 1 Oktober 1922. 3 vol. Berlin: Reichsdruckerei, 1923.
Reviewed by Graf Carl von Klinckowstroem, *Isis*, 1924, 6: 131.

Technos: revue analytique des publications techniques françaises et étrangères. Année 1-4, no. 1-48. Paris: E. Chiron, 1920-24. [CB 12/645]

Tcj

LEAKE, C.D. Historical notes from commercial trade-journals. *Isis*, 1947, 32: 124.

Tcm

HORWITZ, Hugo Th. Technische Darstellungen in Bilderhandschriften des 13. bis 17. Jahrhunderts. *Beitr.Gesch.Tech.Ind.*, 1921, 11: 179-84, 7 fig.

Tcp

PAZDUR, Jan; WISLICKI, Alfred. Wokół sprawy ochrony zabytków przemysłu i techniki. [On the question of protection of monuments of industry and technology. (In Polish with summaries in Russian and English)] *Kwart.Hist.Kult.Mater.*, 1956, 4: 3-11.

Tcv

KHODORKOVSKII, V.R. [Summary of the history of technology collection kept in the Central State Archive of Cine-photo-phono-documents of the USSR (1884-1954). (In Russian)] *Vop.Ist.Est.Tekh.*, 1959, 7: 170-2.

Td biography

Td-bv

HIGGINS, Thomas James. Biographies of engineers and scientists. *Res.Publ.Ill.Inst.Tech.*, 1949, 7: 1-58.

HIGGINS, Thomas James. Book-length biographies of engineers, metallurgists and industrialists. *Bull.Bibliogr.*, 1946, 18: 207-10, 235-9; 19: 10-12.

Tda

FELDHAUS, Franz M. Ein Buch über die Leistungen der Techniker und Erfinder. *Geschichtsbl.Tech.Ind.*, 1927, 11: 13-22.

HENNIG, Richard. Buch berühmter Ingenieure. Grosse Männer der Technik, ihr Lebensgang und ihr Lebenswerk. 249 p., ill. Berlin: Verlag Neufeld & Henius, 1923. [CB 16/233]

LEPRINCE-RINGUET, Louis, ed. Les inventeurs célèbres. Sciences physiques et applications. 403 p. (La Galerie des Hommes Célèbres) Paris: Mazenod, 1950. [CB 77/370]
German translation (Cologne: 1963) reviewed by Heinz Degen, *Naturwiss.Rundsch.*, 1964, 17: 284.

MATSCHOSS, Conrad. Great engineers. Transl. by H. Stafford Hatfield. xi, 381 p. London: Bell, 1939.
Translation of: Grosse Ingenieure, *see* below.
Reviewed in *Nature*, 1939, 144: 690-1.

MATSCHOSS, Conrad. Grosse Ingenieure: Lebensbeschreibungen aus der Geschichte der Technik. 334 p., ill. München/Berlin: Lehmann, 1937.
4th edition by F. Hassler. 402 p. München: Lehmann, 1954.

MATSCHOSS, Conrad. Männer der Technik. Ein biographisches Handbuch. xi, 306 p., ill. Berlin: Verein Deutscher Ingenieure, 1925. [CB 19/804]
The work was criticized by Feldhaus, Franz M. Offener Brief an Herrn Dr. Ing. ehr. Conrad Matschoss. 24 p. Eberswalde: A. Arendt, 1925. A reply was published by the Verein deutscher Ingenieure on 22 February, 1926.

NEUBURGER, Albert. Erfinder und Erfindungen. 275 p. Berlin: Ullstein, 1913.

ROLT, L.T.C. Great engineers. xii, 244 p., 16 pl. London: Bell, 1962; New York: St. Martin's Press, 1963.

Tf history of technology as a study

BURSTALL, Aubrey F. A study of engineering history. *Trans.Newcomen Soc.*, 1953-55, 29: 247-54.
Concerning the study of the subject at King's College, Newcastle-on-Tyne.

FELDHAUS, Franz M. Die Geschichte der Technik, eine neue historische Hilfswissenschaft: Inhalt, gegenwärtiger Stand und Aufgaben. *Compt.Rend.1er Congr.Int.Hist.Sci.* (Paris, 1929) in *Archeion*, 1929, 11: x-xiii.

HAMILTON, S.B. Why engineers should study history. *Trans.Newcomen Soc.*, 1945-47, 25: 1-10.

HOLUBOWICZ, Wlodzimierz. [Remarks on the history of material culture as a science. (In Polish, with summary in English)] *Kwart.Hist.Kult.Mater.*, 1955, 3: 563-85.

MAHR, Otto. Zur Autonomie der Technikgeschichte. *Sudhoffs Arch.*, 1958, 42: 46-56.

MAJEWSKI, Kasimir. [The history of material culture. (In Polish, with English summary)] *Kwart.Hist.Kult.Mater.*, 1953, 1: 3-27.

MUMFORD, Lewis. History: neglected clue to technological change. *Technol.Cult.*, 1961, 2: 230-6.

OLSZEWSKI, E. [The scope of the history of technology and its place among other sciences. (In Polish)] *Kwart.Hist.Nauk.Tech.*, 1962, 6: (Special issue), 91-7.

PAZDUR, Jan. [The tasks of the history of material culture with reference to the present-day situation. (In Polish, with English summary)] *Kwart.Hist.Kult.Mater.*, 1954, 2: 331-45.

PENDRED, Loughnan St. L. The value of technological history. *Trans.Newcomen Soc.*, 1923-24, 4: 1-11.

SINGER, Charles. Technology and history. L.T. Hobhouse Memorial Trust Lecture No. 21 delivered on 23 October 1951 at the London School of Economics and Political Science. 19 p. London: Oxford University Press, 1952. [CB 79/177]

WEIHE, Carl. Geschichte und Kultur der Technik. *Proteus*, 1937, 2: 166-72.

WHITE, Lynn. The discipline of the history of technology. *J.Eng.Educ.*, 1964, 54: 349-51.

ZVORYKIN, A.A. The history of technology as a science and as a branch of learning: a Soviet view. *Technol.Cult.*, 1961, 2: 1-4.

Tfd

HASSLER, Friedrich. Conrad Matschoss' Weg zur Technikgeschichte. *Sudhoffs Arch.*, 1958, 42: 16-26.

SARTON, George. Charles Fremont, historien de la technologie (1855-1930). *Isis*, 1937, 27: 475-84.

SARTON, George. L'histoire de la technologie. *Rev.Gén.Sci.*, 1912, 23: 421.
The activities of F.M. Feldhaus and Carl von Klinckowstroem in the history of technology.

Tfp

SARTON, George. The organization of research in the history of technology on a commercial basis. *Isis*, 1921, 4: 44-5.
Apropos of the Quellenforschungen zur Geschichte der Technik und Industrie directed by F.M. Feldhaus and Carl von Klinckowstroem.

Tfqd

FELDHAUS, Franz M. "Geschichte der Technik". *Geschichtsbl. Tech.Ind.*, 1927, 11: 1-5. [CB 23/246]
Announcing the creation of a society bearing that name, in Berlin, February 18, 1927.

HASSLER, Friedrich. Die technisch-geschichtlichen Arbeiten des Vereines deutscher Ingenieure. *Arch.Gesch.Math.Naturwiss. Tech.*, 1929, 12: 188-94.

L'INSTITUT Autrichien de Recherches sur l'Histoire des Techniques. *Docum.Hist.Tech.*, 1962, 2: 70-2.
Account of the Forschungsinstitut für Technikgeschichte in Vienna.

NEWCOMEN SOCIETY FOR THE STUDY OF THE HISTORY OF ENGINEERING AND TECHNOLOGY. *Isis*, 1922, 4: 496-8.
Announcing the foundation of that society in London, 1920, and explaining its aim and plans.

UNION DES INGÉNIEURS ALLEMANDS. Section Histoire des Techniques. *Doc.Hist.Tech.*, 1962, 2: 69.

Tg teaching history of technology

COURTIN, M. Intérêt culturel de l'histoire de la technique dans l'enseignement des adolescents. *Act.VIIIe Congr.Int. Hist.Sci.* (Florence, 1956), p. 944-8. Paris: Hermann, 1958.

GILFILLAN, S. Colum. [Account of his course in the historical and social sides of technology, at Purdue University, entitled Social Aspects of Technology]. *Isis*, 1939, 30: 96-7.

Tgt

HOLLAND, Thomas Henry. Humanism in technical education. *Nature*, 1923, 111: 376-7.
From an address delivered at the Sir John Cass Technical Institute on January 31, 1923; London: M. Hopkinson, 1923.

Tgt-d

HIGGINS, Thomas J. The function of biography in engineering education. *J.Eng.Educ.*, 1941, 32: 82-92.

Th historiography and particular aspects of the history of technology

Thc

JEWSIEWICKI, Wladyslaw. Technika gromadzenia materiatéw naukowych do historii techniki droga wywiadów personalnych. [Technique of personal interviews for collecting scientific materials for the history of technology. (In Polish, with summary in Russian and English)] *Kwart.Hist.Nauk.Tech.*, 1963, 8: 393-408.

Thd

HORWITZ, Hugo Th. Systematik und Oekonomie bei technisch geschichtlicher Forschung. *Geschichtsbl.Tech.Ind.*, 1927, 11: 23-6.

NUNIS, Doyce B. Oral history and the history of technology. *Technol.Cult.*, 1963, 4: 149-53.

WAJDOWICZ, Roman. Z Dowwiadczen Badawczyca Historyka Techniki. [Some research experiences of a historian of technology. (In Polish, with summaries in Russian and English)] *Kwart.Hist. Nauk.Tech.*, 1961, 6: 93-109.

Thg

ERHARD, L. Der Weg des Geistes in der Technik. iv, 30 p., ill. (Deutsches Museum, Abhandlungen und Berichte, 1, no. 4) Berlin: VDI-Verlag, 1929. [CB 28/547]

FINCH, James Kip. The role of purely technical innovation in the history of engineering. *Technol.Cult.*, 1962, 3: 307-9.

GILFILLAN, S. Colum. The prediction of technical change. *Rev. Econ.Statist.*, 1952, 34: 368-85.

HARRISON, H.S. Evolution in material culture. *Nature*, 1930, 126: 726-9.
From the presidential address to Section H (Anthropology) of the British Association, Bristol, 1930.

HORWITZ, Hugo Th. Über das Gesetz vom Gebrauchswechsel und die Entwicklungsprinzipien bei einfachen technischen Gebilden. *Beitr.Gesch.Tech.Ind.*, 1932, 21: 123-30, 8 fig.

ISHIGAI, Seikan. Fundamental factors in the development of technics as manifested in the sequence of its historical stages. *Jap.Stud.Hist.Sci.*, 1962, 1: 125-32.
Abridged translation of paper published in *Kagakusi-Kenkyu*, 1955, no. 35, 28-38.

KULCZYCKI, Jerzy. [Theoretical foundations of the history of material culture. (In Polish, with summaries in Russian and Polish)] *Kwart.Hist.Kult.Mater.*, 1955, 3: 519-62.

SHUKHARDINE, S.V. On certain causes of the development of technology. *Kwart.Hist.Nauk.Tech.*, 1962, 6: (Special issue), 99-108.

Thg-mzWBwe

CLOW, Archibald; CLOW, Nan L. The timber famine and the development of technology. *Ann.Sci.*, 1956, 12: 85-102.

FLINN, Michael W. Timber and the advance of technology: a reconsideration. *Ann.Sci.*, 1959, 15: 109-20.

Thh

ATORS, Karlis I. Periodization of the history of technology. *Proc.10th Int.Congr.Hist.Sci.* (Ithaca, 1962), (1), p. 365-7. Paris: Hermann, 1964.

LORIA, Mario. Per una cronologia della tecnica. *Act.VIIIe Congr.Int.Hist.Sci.* (Florence, 1956), p. 962-5. Paris: Hermann, 1958.

Thj

LINDMARK, Gunnar. Teknikhistoriska notiser. [Condensed notes on origins and precursory concepts in technology. (In Swedish)] *Daedalus*, 1963, 151-64.

Thk

AIKAWA, Haruki. [Criticism of the "Second industrial revolution" theory. (In Japanese)] *J.Hist.Sci.Japan*, 1953, no. 25, 12-16.

DAUMAS, Maurice. Le mythe de la révolution technique. *Proc. 10th Int.Congr.Hist.Sci.* (Ithaca, 1962), (1), p. 415-18. Paris: Hermann, 1964. Also (in Polish, with French summary) *Kwart.Hist.Nauk.Tech.*, 1963, 8: 361-5.

DAUMAS, Maurice. Le mythe de la révolution technique. *Rev. Hist.Sci.*, 1963, 16: 291-302.

HORSKÁ-VRBOVÁ, Pavla. Problém tzv. druhé průmyslové revoluce v dějinách techniky. [The problem of the so-called second industrial revolution in the history of technology. (In Czech, with French summary)] *Sb.Dějiny Přírodn.Věd Tech.*, 1963, 8: 85-111. [CB 90/613]
Historico-materialistic interpretation.

KRANZBERG, Melvin. Criteria for an industrial revolution. *Arch.Int.Hist.Sci.*, 1960, 13: 256-62.

Thm

HUGHES, H. Stuart. Commentary: technology and the history of ideas. *Technol.Cult.*, 1961, 2: 237-9.

JONES, Howard Mumford. Ideas, history, technology. *Technol. Cult.*, 1959, 1: 20-7.

Tht

ROGERS, Everett M. Diffusion of innovations. xiii, 367 p., ill. New York: Free Press of Glencoe, 1962.

Tjg

JENNY, Jean. Brevets d'inventions, l'idée créatrice et le tour de main. 149 p., ill. Lausanne: Payot, 1946. [CB 73/172]

Tk/n philosophy and methodology; communication

Tk

ARMYTAGE, W.H.G. Origins and philosophy of technology. *Nature*, 1958, 182: 1349.

DUCASSÉ, Pierre. Les techniques et la philosophie contemporaine. *Proc.10th Int.Congr.Phil.* (Amsterdam, 1948), (1), p. 1048-50. Amsterdam: North Holland Publishing Co., 1949.

KIRCHVOGEL, P.A. Vom Wesen der Technik und ihrer Geschichte. *Abhandlungen zur Wissenschaftsgeschichte und Wissenschaftslehre*, p. 65-77. (Veröffentlichungen der Gesellschaft für internationale Wissenschaftsgeschichte, 1952, no. 1) Bremen: Carl Schünemann, [n.d.].

OBOUKHOFF, Nicholas M. Engineering as action and science. Abstract of the paper, "Empirico-logical and axio-teleological factors in engineering", presented before the Fifth International Congress for the Unity of Science, held at Harvard University, September 3-9, 1939. 9 p. (Oklahoma Agricultural and Mechanical College, Division of Engineering, publication, 41) Stillwater, Okla.: 1939.

SCHNEIDER, Gustav. Ueber Technik, technisches Denken und technische Wirkungen. vi, 88 p. (Diss.) Erlangen: 1912.

SCHUHL, Pierre Maxime. Machinisme et philosophie. 2nd ed. 131 p. (Nouvelle Encyclopédie Philosophique) Paris: Presses Universitaires de France, 1947. [CB 71/128]
First published 1938.

STERRETT, Frank W. Philosophical thoughts upon the life and work of the engineer in the advance of civilization. ... A Newcomen address, 1941. 24 p., ill. Princeton: Printed at the Princeton University Press, for the Newcomen Society, American Branch, 1941.

Tke-mzAke

HOSTELET, Georges. Confrontation entre la méthodologie scientifique des faits de nature et celle des faits d'activité humaine. *Compt.Rend.IIe Congr.Nat.Sci.* (Bruxelles, 1935), p. 60-7. Brussels: 1935.

HOSTELET, Georges. La méthodologie comparée des sciences et des techniques. [1]. 2. La méthodologie de l'investigation scientifique des faits d'activité humaine. *Rev.Syn.*, 1956, 77: 279-310; 1958, 79: 67-102.

HOSTELET, Georges. La méthodologie scientifique de l'investigation des faits de la nature et des faits de l'activité humaine. *Bull.Soc.Franç.Phil.*, 1935, 35: 1-3.

TmzA

CARUGO, Adriano. Sui rapporti tra progresso tecnico e pensiero scientifico. *Studi Storici*, 1959-60, 1: 835-47.

CASIMIR, H.B.G. Technological advance: a stimulus to basic research. In: Casimir, H.B.G.; Van Bleck, J.H. The Cherwell-Simon memorial lectures 1961 and 1962, p. 6-24. Edinburgh/London: Oliver and Boyd, 1962.
Reviewed by R. Bruce Lindsay, *Phys.Today*, 1964, 17: no. 4, 70.

DANNEMANN, Friedrich. Das Zusammenwachsen von Naturwissenschaft und Technik zur Einheit. *Tech.Kult.*, 1927, 18: 135-9.

DAUMAS, Maurice. Rapports entre sciences et techniques: étude générale du point de vue de l'histoire des sciences et des techniques. *Rev.Syn.*, 1962, 83: 15-37.

FINCH, James Kip. Engineering and science: a historical review and appraisal. *Technol.Cult.*, 1961, 2: 318-32.

HALL, A. Rupert. The historical relations of science and technology. In: Imperial College of Science and Technology. Inaugural Lectures, 1962-63 and 1963-64, p. 119-29. London: 1965. [CB 89/495]
See also Nature, 1963, 200: 1141-5.

HALL, A. Rupert. Technology and science. *Times Lit.Suppl.*, 6 January 1956, xxii-xxiii.

MULTHAUF, Robert P. The scientist and the "Improver" of technology. *Technol.Cult.*, 1959, 1: 38-47.

ODQVIST, Folke K.G. [The connections between science and engineering. (In Swedish with English summary)] *Lychnos*, 1937, 148-60. [CB 51/266]

SCHIMANK, Hans. Naturwissenschaften und Technik in ihrer Wechselwirkung. *Abhandlungen zur Wissenschaftsgeschichte und Wissenschaftslehre*, p. 1-20. (Veröffentlichungen der Gesellschaft für Internationale Wissenschaftsgeschichte, 1952, no. 2) Bremen: Carl Schünemann, [n.d.]

UBBELOHDE, A.R. Edwardian science and technology: their interactions. *Nature*, 1962, 194: 1110-14; also in *Brit. J.Hist.Sci.*, 1963, 1: 217-26.

WEYRAUCH, Robert. Die Technik, ihr Wesen und ihre Beziehungen zu anderen Lebensgebieten. x, 280 p. Stuttgart: Deutsche Verlags-Anstalt, 1922.
Reviewed by Carl v. Klinckowstroem, *Isis*, 1923, 5: 487-8.

TmzNA

ZEISS, H. Hygiene und Technik. *Technikgeschichte*, 1936, 25: 66-73.

Tnh

LIPPMANN, Edmund O. von. Zur Geschichte des Wortes "Technologie". *Chem.Zeitung*, 1927, 51: 189. [CB 22/272]

SHUKHARDIN, S.V. [Attempt to define the word "technology". (In Russian)] *Vop.Ist.Est.Tekh.*, 1959, 8: 144-7.

Tnq

HORWITZ, Hugo Theodor. Die Geschichte der Technik und die Sprachforschung. *Geschichtsbl.Tech.*, 1916, 3: 16-19.

To study and teaching

SKATKIN, M.N., ed. Rol'truda v politekhnicheskom obuchenii. [On technical education. (In Russian)] 237 p., ill. Moskva: Izd.-vo Akademii Pedagog. Nauk RSFSR, 1955.

WARREN, H.A. Technical education. 37 p. (Technics and Purpose, 3) London: Student Christian Movement Press, 1957.

To-bv

COOPER UNION FOR THE ADVANCEMENT OF SCIENCE AND ART. The non-technical aspects of engineering education. A bibliography compiled by the Cooper Union library. 10 p. (Cooper Union Bulletin, Engineering and Science Series, 18) New York: 1938.

Tog-B

OCAGNE, Maurice d'. Le rôle des mathématiques dans les sciences de l'ingénieur. *Rev.Gén.Sci.*, 1914, 25: 469-74.
Speech made at the opening session of the International Conference on Teaching Mathematics, 1914.

STAECKEL, Paul. La préparation mathématique des ingénieurs dans les différents pays. *Rev.Gén.Sci.*, 1914, 25: 474-8.
Summary of report presented to the International Conference on the Teaching of Mathematics, 1914.

Top

BRITISH COUNCIL OF CHURCHES. Technology and purpose in higher education. 25 p. London: 1959.

Toq

ASHBY, Eric. Technology and the academies; an essay on universities and the scientific revolution. vii, 118 p. London: Macmillan; New York: St. Martin's Press, 1958.
Reissued with alterations, 1963.
Reviewed in *Nature*, 1958, 182: 1256; by Asa Briggs, *Sci. Amer.*, 1959, 201: 201-6; by George A. Gullette, *Technol. Cult.*, 1964, 5: 600-1.

Tos

COTGROVE, Stephen F. Technical education and social change. 220 p. (Studies in Society) London: George Allen & Unwin; Fair Lawn, N.J.: Essential Books, 1958.

Tp/r organizational and professional aspects

Tp

GIBB, Alexander. Research in engineering. *Advance.Sci.*, 1937, 151-60.
Historical sketch as regards Britain and U.S.A.

KLINCKOWSTROEM, Carl von. Erfinderförderung gestern und heute. *Orion*, 1953, 8: 996-8.

Tpd

FELDHAUS, Franz M. Der Laie als Erfinder. Mit einem Vorwort von Hugo E. Bremer. *Geschichtsbl.Tech.Ind.*, 1918, 5: 1-53. [CB 8/370]

Tph

CLOW, Archibald. Fiscal policy and the development of technology. *Ann.Sci.*, 1954, 10: 342-58, 4 fig.

U.S. NATIONAL RESOURCES COMMITTEE. SCIENCE COMMITTEE. Technological trends and national policy. Including the social implications of new inventions. Report of the Subcommittee on Technology to the National Resources Committee. x, 388 p., ill. Washington: U.S. Govt. Print. Off., 1937. [CB 68/54]

Tps

KILLEFER, D.H. The genius of industrial research. ix, 263 p. New York: Reinhold, 1948. [CB 75/91]

MEES, C.E. Kenneth. The organisation of industrial scientific technical research. ix, 175 p. New York: McGraw-Hill, 1920.

Tpw

OGBURN, William Fielding, ed. Technology and international relations. 202 p. Chicago: Chicago University Press, 1949.

Tqx

INTERNATIONAL Engineering Congress. San Francisco, 1915. *Isis*, 1914, 1: 710-11.
Views of the executive committee on the choice of papers to be presented to the conference.

Tr

HATFIELD, Henry Stafford. The inventor and his world. v, 269 p. London: Kegan Paul, 1933.

KINGSFORD, P.W. Engineers, inventors, and workers. 272 p., ill. New York: St. Martin's, 1964.
Reviewed by Eugene S. Ferguson, *Science*, 1964, 146: 238.

STRUNZ, Franz. Der Erfinder, seine Idee und seine Geschichte. *Mitt.Gesch.Med.*, 1941-42, 40: 199-212.

Ts relations with society

ALLEN, Francis R. Technology and social change: current status and outlook. *Technol.Cult.*, 1959, 1: 48-59.

BOGGS, S.W. Mapping some effects of science on human relations. *Sci.Mon.*, 1945, 61: 45-50, 3 fig.
The effects of modern technology on man's affairs.

ENCYCLOPAEDIA BRITANNICA conference of the technological order. *Technol.Cult.*, 1962, 3: 381-658. [CB 88/535]

FORBES, R.J. Technology and society. *Impact*, 1951, 2: 7-9.

JACKSON, Dugald C. Man in an engineering world. *J.Franklin Inst.*, 1940, 230: 1-17.

JANNE, Henri. Notes critiques relatives à la sociologie de la technique. *Rev.Inst.Sociol.*, 1952, no. 4, 531-652.

WEYRAUCH, Robert. Die Technik, ihr Wesen und ihre Beziehungen zu anderen Lebensgebieten. x, 280 p. Stuttgart: Deutsche Verlags-Anstalt, 1922.
Reviewed by Carl v. Klinckowstroem, *Isis*, 1923, 5: 487-8.

ZVORYKIN, A.A. Technical progress and society. *Cah.Hist. Mond.*, 1960, 6: 183-98.

Tsb

GILFILLAN, S. Colum. The sociology of invention. xiii, 191 p. Chicago: Follett, 1935.
Reviewed by Robert K. Merton, *Isis*, 1936, 25: 166-7.

JEWKES, John; SAWERS, David; STILLERMAN, Richard. The sources of invention. 428 p. London: Macmillan; New York: St. Martin's Press. 1958.
Paperback reprint. 1963.

MAGET, Marcel. L'enquête ethnographique sur les techniques préindustrielles. *Tech.Civilisations*, 1951, 2: 21-7, 4 fig

MERTON, Robert K. Fluctuations in the rate of industrial invention. *Quart.J.Econ.*, 1935, 49: 454-74. [CB 44/533]

NEF, John U. Cultural foundations of industrial civilization. xv, 164 p. (The Wiles Lectures given at the Queen's University, Belfast, 1956) Cambridge University Press, 1958.
Reviewed in *Nature*, 1958, 181: 1427-8; by R.J. Forbes, *Arch.Int.Hist.Sci.*, 1958, 11: 180-1.

Tsc

ARMYTAGE, W.H.G. A social history of engineering. 378 p. London: Faber; New York: Pitman, 1961.
Reviewed by T.I. Williams, *J.Roy.Inst.Chem.*, 1961, 85: 275; by Sixten Rönnow, *Lychnos*, 1962, 525-7; by Melvin Kranzberg, *Victorian Stud.*, 1963, 6: 293-4.

BARNES, Harry Elmer. Living in the twentieth century. A consideration of how we got this way. 391 p. Indianapolis: Bobbs-Merrill, 1928. [CB 26/247]

BRIGGS, Asa. Technology and economic development. *Sci.Amer.*, 1963, 209: no. 3, 52-61.

BURLINGAME, Roger. The hardware of culture. *Technol.Cult.*, 1959, 1: 11-19.

BURLINGAME, Roger. Technology: neglected clue to historical change. *Technol.Cult.*, 1961, 2: 219-36.

CLOUGH, Shepard B. The rise and fall of civilization. An inquiry into the relationship between economic development and civilization. xiii, 291 p. New York: McGraw-Hill, 1951; London: Skeffington, 1953.
Reprinted New York: Columbia University Press, 1957.

CRAWFORD, O.G.S. Men, machines and history. *Antiquity*, 1949, 23: 100-6.
A discussion of Samuel Lilley's book, *see* below.

DELVILLE, Louis; GILLE, Bertrand. Techniques et civilisations. *Tech.Civilisations*, 1951, 2: 1-3.

DRUCKER, Peter F. The technological revolution: notes on the relationship of technology, science, and culture. *Technol. Cult.*, 1961, 2: 342-51.

FELDHAUS, Franz M. Kulturgeschichte der Technik. 2 vol. 154 p., 60 fig.; 209 p., 47 fig. (Mathematisch-Naturwissenschaftlich-Technische Bücherei, 20-21) Berlin: Otto Salle, 1928. [CB 26/233]

FINCH, James Kip. Engineering and western civilization. 407 p. New York: McGraw-Hill, 1951.
History of the ways in which advances in engineering have effected economic and social changes in western civilization.

FORBES, R.J. Science, technology and social evolution. *Congr. Int.Phil.Sci.* (Paris, 1949), (8), p. 51-8. (Actualités Scientifiques et Industrielles, 1166) Paris: Hermann, 1952.

GINSBERG, Eli, ed. Technology and social change. A seminar held at Columbia University. 168 p., ill. New York: Columbia University Press, 1964.

JACKSON, Dugald C. Engineering's part in the development of civilization. 114 p. New York: American Society of Mechanical Engineers, 1939. [CB 59/472]
Six lectures reprinted from *Mech.Eng.*, 1938, 60: 529-34. [CB 55/178]

LILLEY, Samuel. Men, machines and history; a short history of tools and machines in relation to social progress. 240 p. (Past and Present, Studies in the History of Civilization, 7) London: Cobbett Press, 1948.
Discussed by O.G.S. Crawford, *Antiquity*, 1949, 23: 100-6.

MUMFORD, Lewis. Art and technics. v, 162 p. (Bampton Lectures in America, 4) New York: Columbia University Press; London: Oxford University Press, 1952.
Reprinted 1960.
Reviewed in *Nature*, 1953, 171: 359-61.

MUMFORD, Lewis. An appraisal of Lewis Mumford's "Technics and civilization" (1934). *Daedalus Amer.Acad.Arts Sci.*, 1959, 88: 527-36.

MUMFORD, Lewis. Technics and civilization. xi, 495 p. New York: Harcourt Brace, 1934.
Reviewed by H.T. Davis, *Isis*, 1935, 22: 548-51.

NEF, John U. The conquest of the material world. xii, 408 p., bibliogr. Chicago/London: University of Chicago Press, 1964.
Collection of essays originally published in various places between 1934 and 1955, here revised ... to form an extended account of the coming of industrialism in Europe.

OAKESHOTT, Walter Fraser. Commerce and society. A short history of trade and its effects on civilization. xii, 418 p. Oxford: Clarendon Press, 1936.

STALEY, Eugene, *et al.*; ed. Creating an industrial civilization. A report on the Corning Conference. Held under the auspices of the American Council of Learned Societies and Corning Glass Works, 17-19 May 1951, Corning, New York. xvi, 368 p. New York: Harper, 1952.

WHITBECK, R.H. Our iron-clad civilization. *Sci.Mon.*, 1919, 9: 125-30.
Shows to what extent modern Western civilization is dominated and molded by iron and coal.

Tse

AYRES, Eugene. Social attitude toward invention. *Amer.Scient.*, 1955, 43: 521-40.

Tsg

SCHRIER, Elliot. Toward technology transfer. *Technol.Cult.*, 1964, 5: 344-58.
Summary of proceedings of Conference on "Technology and the civilian economy" sponsored by the Engineering Foundation.

SÉE, Henri. Remarques sur l'évolution du capitalisme et les origines de la grande industrie. *Rev.Syn.Hist.*, 1924, 37: 47-67.

STERN, Bernhard J. Frustration of technology. *Sci.Soc.*, 1937, 2: 1-28. [CB 54/567]

Tsp

NEF, John U. War and human progress. An essay on the rise of industrial civilization. ix, 464 p. Cambridge, Mass.: Harvard University Press, 1950. [CB 79/177]

WILLIAMS, Clement Clarence. Decisive inventions versus decisive battles. 36 p. Princeton: Printed at the Princeton University Press for the Newcomen Society, American Branch, 1940.

Tsy

THOMSON, George. The foreseeable future. 166 p. Cambridge University Press, 1955. [CB 82/263]

Tt relations with humanities

HUMANISM and technology and other essays. By Principal C. Grant Robertson, Sir Thomas H. Holland [*et al.*]. 91 p. London: Oxford University Press, 1924.

SPENGLER, Oswald. Der Mensch und die Technik. Beitrag zu einer Philosophie des Lebens. viii, 89 p. München: Beck, 1931.
Reviewed by Carl von Klinckowstroem, *Mitt.Gesch.Med.*, 1932, 31: 37-8.

TRACHTENBERG, Alan. Technology and human values. *Technol. Cult.*, 1964, 5: 359-76.
Summary of the December 1963 conference on "Technology and human values" at the Pennsylvania State University.

WEYRAUCH, Robert. Die Technik, ihr Wesen und ihre Beziehungen zu anderen Lebensgebieten. x, 280 p. Stuttgart: Deutsche Verlags-Anstalt, 1922.
Reviewed by Carl v. Klinckowstroem, *Isis*, 1923, 5: 487-8.

Tth

EBERMANN, Oskar. Sagen der Technik. Von Fliegern und Schiffern, Brücken und Bauten, Uhren, Glocken und Zauberspiegeln und wunderbarem Hausgerät. Nach alten Quellen berichtet. 140 p., 20 ill. Leipzig: Hegel u. Schade, 1930.

FELDHAUS, Franz M. Alte Technik auf der Bühne. *Geschichtsbl. Tech.Ind.*, 1914, 1: 8-10. [CB 24/458]

Ttp

DEONNA, Waldemar. L'influence de la technique sur l'oeuvre d'art. *Rev.Archéol.*, 1913, 2: 198-219. [CB 5/305]

EVANS, Joan. Pattern. A study of ornament in western Europe from 1180 to 1900. 2 vol. xxxvi, 179 p., pl.; xv, 249 p., pl. Oxford: Clarendon Press, 1931.

PANOFSKY, Erwin. The ideological antecedents of the Rolls-Royce radiator. *Proc.Amer.Phil.Soc.*, 1963, 107: 273-88.

SPELTZ, Alexander. The styles of ornament. From prehistoric times to the middle of the nineteenth century. A series of 3,500 examples arranged in historical order with descriptive text for the use of architects, designers, craftsmen, and amateurs. Transl. from the 2nd German ed., rev. and edited by R. Phene Spiers. 647 p. London: Batsford, 1910; reprinted 1924.
Translation of: Der Ornamentstil. 2nd ed. Berlin: 1907.

Tv ethnic groups

Tvn

BRUGSCH, Mohammed; KAMPFFMEYER, Georg. Arabische Technologie der Gegenwart. *Mitt.Seminar.Orient.Sprachen Friedrich-Wilhelms-Univ.Berlin*, 1926, 29: 1-98; 1927, 30: 58-139.

Tw in different countries

GILFILLAN, S. Colum. Inventiveness by nation. A note on statistical treatment. *Geogr.Rev.*, 1930, 20: 301-4.

JEFFERSON, Mark. The geographic distribution of inventiveness. *Geogr.Rev.*, 1929, 19: 649-61, 2 fig.

KAEMPFFERT, Waldemar. Bahnbrechende Erfindungen in Amerika und Europa. Geschichte ihrer Entstehung und ihrer Schöpfer. Transl. and enl. by Hans Klopstock. 430 p., 230 fig. Berlin: Rudolf Mosse, 1927.
Reviewed by R. Winderlich, *Mitt.Gesch.Med.*, 1928, 27: 18.

Twb North America

BEARD, Charles A., ed. A century of progress. viii, 452 p. New York: Harper, 1933. [CB 40/395]

BIRD, Viggo E. Early beginnings of Connecticut industry. 35 p., map. (The Newcomen Society, American Branch) Princeton: Princeton University Press, 1937.

CLARK, Victor Selden. History of manufactures in the United States. Rev. ed. 3 vol. 1. 1607-1860; 2. 1860-1893; 3. 1893-1928, ill. New York: McGraw-Hill (for the Carnegie Institution of Washington), 1929.
Reprinted New York: Peter Smith, 1949. First published 1916-28.

DE CAMP, L. Sprague. The heroic age of American invention. 290 p. Garden City, N.Y.: Doubleday, 1961.
Reviewed by Robert E. Carlson, *Isis*, 1963, 54: 168-9.

FERTIG, George J. The development of scientific research in the South. *Science,* 1932, 75: 595-9.

HALL, Courtney Robert. History of American industrial science. xix, 453 p. New York: Library Publishers, 1954. [CB 80/143]

KAEMPFFERT, Waldemar, ed. A popular history of American invention. 2 vol. New York: Scribner, 1924.

OLIVER, John W. History of American technology. viii, 676 p. New York: Ronald Press, 1956.
Reviewed by Carl W. Condit, *Isis,* 1957, 48: 484-7; for other reviews *see* CB 82/216, CB 83/211 and CB 84/327.

THOMPSON, Holland. The age of invention. A chronicle of mechanical conquest. xii, 267 p., 13 ill. (Chronicles of America Series, 37) New Haven: Yale University Press, 1921.
Reviewed by G. Sarton, *Isis,* 1922, 4: 517-19.

Twb-bv

LARSON, Henrietta M. Guide to business history. Materials for the study of American business history and suggestions for their use. Index by Elsie Hight Bishop. xxvi, 1181 p. (Harvard Studies in Business History, 12) Cambridge: Harvard University Press, 1948. [CB 75/91]

Twb-da

HYLANDER, C.J. American inventors. xvi, 216 p., 16 pl., 33 fig. New York: Macmillan, 1934. [CB 42/588]

SCHUYLER, Hamilton. The Roeblings. A century of engineers, bridge-builders, and industrialists. The story of three generations of an illustrious family, 1831-1931. xx, 425 p. Princeton, N.J.: University Press, 1931.

Twb-o

ANDERSON, Charnel. Technology in American education, 1650-1900. Principal investigator, James D. Finn; associate investigator, Lee E. Campion. vi, 53 p., ill. (New Media for Instruction, 1) Washington, D.C.: U.S. Department of Health, Education and Welfare, Office of Education, 1963.

Twb-oq

FINCH, James Kip. A history of the School of Engineering, Columbia University. vii, 138 p., front., 8 pl. New York: Columbia University Press, 1954. [CB 80/142]

KILLIAN, James R. Centenary of the Massachusetts Institute of Technology. *Nature,* 1961, 190: 948-53.

WOODBURY, Robert S. Courses at the Massachusetts Institute of Technology, Cambridge, Mass. *Isis,* 1936, 24: 432.

Twb-qk

BAXTER, James Phinney. Scientists against time. Foreword by Vannevar Bush. 473 p. Boston: Little, Brown, 1946.
Brief official history of the U.S. Office of Scientific Research and Development in World War II.

Twb-rw

BAKER, Elizabeth Faulkner. Technology and woman's work. xvi, 460 p., bibliogr. New York: Columbia University Press, 1964.

Twb-sc

MARX, Leo. The machine in the garden. Technology and the pastoral ideal in America. 392 p., 3 pl. New York: Oxford University Press, 1964.

RAE, John B. The "know-how" tradition: technology in American history. *Technol.Cult.,* 1960, 2: 139-50.

ROSEN, S. McKee; ROSEN, Laura. Technology and society. The influence of machines in the United States. xiv, 474 p. New York: Macmillan, 1941. [CB 61/401]
Reviewed by D. Caradog Jones, *Nature,* 1942, 149: 63-4.

Twc Latin America

WALLE, Paul. Bolivia. Its people and its resources, its railways, mines and rubber forests. Translated by B. Miall. 407 p. (The South American Series, 12) London: Fisher Unwin, 1914.
Translation of: La Bolivie et ses mines. (Paris: Librarie Orientale et Américaine, E. Guilmoto, 1913).

Twd Europe

DICKINSON, H.W.; GOMME, A.A. Some British contributors to continental technology (1600-1850). *Act.VI Congr.Int.Hist. Sci.* (Amsterdam, 1950), p. 307-23. Paris: Hermann, 1951-53. Also in *Arch.Int.Hist.Sci.,* 1951, 4: 706-22.

Twe British Isles

ARMYTAGE, W.H.G. Science and industry in Sheffield; some historical notes. *Proc.Chem.Soc.,* 1962, 51-5.
From about 1670 to 1900.

CHALONER, W.H.; MUSSON, A.E. Industry and technology. xiv, 202 p., 238 pl. (A Visual History of Modern Britain) London: Vista Books, 1963.

CLARK, H.O. Notes on local technology. *Trans.Newcomen Soc.,* 1925-26, 6: 184-7.
East Anglian technology: flint industry; monumental brasses; engineering; millwrighting.

COURT, W.H.B. The rise of the Midland industries, 1600-1838. viii, 272 p. London: Oxford University Press, 1938.
Reviewed by T.S.W., *Geogr.J.,* 1938, 92: 546-7.

FOX, Francis. Sixty-three years of engineering, scientific and social work. xii, 338 p. London: John Murray, 1924.

HAMILTON, S.B. Industries of West Hertfordshire, Watford and St. Albans. *Trans.Newcomen Soc.,* 1945-47, 25: 109-10.

HARRIS, T.R. Engineering in Cornwall before 1775. *Trans. Newcomen Soc.,* 1945-47, 25: 111-22.

HOFFMANN, Walther G. British industry, 1700-1950. Transl. by W.O. Henderson and W.H. Chaloner. xxiii, 338 p. Oxford: Blackwell, 1955.
Translation of: Wachstum und Wachstumsformen der englischen Industriewirtschaft von 1700 bis zur Gegenwart. (Jena: 1940) Reviewed by Judith Blow Williams, *Amer.Hist.Rev.,* 1956, 61: 631-2.

JENKINS, Rhys. Historical notes on some Derbyshire industries. *Trans.Newcomen Soc.,* 1933-34, 14: 163-77.

JENKINS, Rhys. Industries of Herefordshire in bygone times. *Trans.Newcomen Soc.,* 1936-37, 17: 175-89.

JENKINS, Rhys. Industries of Suffolk: a historical sketch. *Trans.Newcomen Soc.,* 1938-39. 19: 173-84.

JENKINS, Rhys. Links in the history of engineering and technology from Tudor times. Being the collected papers of Rhys Jenkins, M.I., Mech. E. Comprising articles published by him in the professional and technical press mainly prior to 1920 and a catalogue of his other published works. x, 248 p., 7 pl., 26 fig. Cambridge: Printed for the Newcomen Society by University Press, 1936.
Reviewed by E.A. Forward, *Antiquity,* 1937, 11: 244-5.

JENKINS, Rhys. Observations on the rise and progress of manufacturing industry in England. *Trans.Newcomen Soc.,* 1926-27, 7: 1-16.

JENKINS, Rhys. A sketch of the industrial history of the Coalbrookdale District. *Trans.Newcomen Soc.,* 1923-24, 4: 102-7, 7 pl.

McGOWAN, H. 1851-1951: a century of British industry. *J. Roy.Soc.Arts,* 1951, 99: 235-45.

O'DEA, W.T. 1851-1951: a century of British engineering. *J. Roy.Soc.Arts,* 1951, 99: 463-79, 6 fig.

PALFREY, H.E. Early Stourbridge industries. *Trans.Newcomen Soc.,* 1927-28, 8: 99-106.

TAYLOR, Frank Sherwood. British inventions. 44 p., 16 pl. (British Life and Thought Series) London: Longmans, Green, 1950.

USHER, Abbott Payson. The industrialization of modern Britain. *Technol.Cult.,* 1960, 2: 109-27.

THE WONDERFUL story of British industry, a record of the enterprise, skill and invention of the British people. 256 p., 155 ill. (Modern Knowledge Series, 1) London: Ward, Locke, 1951.
Reviewed by H.W. Dickinson, *Arch.Int.Hist.Sci.,* 1951, 4: 1090-1.

Twe-da

SCOTT, E. Kilburn. Memorials to pioneer Leeds engineers. *Trans.Newcomen Soc.*, 1930-31, 11: 164-7.

Twe-pw

DICKINSON, H.W.; GOMME, A.A. Netherlands contribution to Gt. Britain's engineering and technology to the year 1700. *Arch.Int.Hist.Sci.*, 1950, 3: 356-77.

DICKINSON, H.W.; GOMME, A.A. Some British contributors to continental technology (1600-1850). *Act.VI Congr.Int.Hist. Sci.* (Amsterdam, 1950), p. 307-23. Paris: Hermann, 1951-53. Also in *Arch.Int.Hist.Sci.*, 1951, 4: 706-22.

Twe-qd

LUCKHURST, Kenneth W. The Royal Society of Arts - bicentenary celebrations. *Nature*, 1954, 173: 656-7.

THE ROYAL SOCIETY OF ARTS. *Endeavour*, 1954, 13: 115-16.

Twe-sc

HODGEN, Margaret T. Change and history. A study of the dated distributions of technological innovations in England. 324 p., 5 tables, map series 1-10. (Viking Fund Publications in Anthropology, 18) New York: Wenner-Gren Foundation for Anthropological Research, 1952. [CB 80/143]

Twf France

BOUTARIC, Augustin. Les grandes inventions françaises. iii, 405 p., 27 fig. (La troisième république de 1870 à nos jours ...) Paris: Les Editions de France, 1932.
Reviewed by F.M., *Rev.Gén.Sci.*, 1933, 44: 348.

Twf-da

ALPHANDÉRY, Marie Fernande. Dictionnaire des inventeurs français. 408 p., pl. Paris: Seghers, 1963.
Reviewed by M. Daumas, *Rev.Hist.Sci.*, 1964, 17: 283.

Twf-oq

MONZIE, Anatole de. Le conservatoire du peuple. 154 p. Paris: Société d'Edition d'Enseignement Supérieur, 1948.
History of the Conservatoire National des Arts et Métiers in Paris.

MOUCHELET, E. Notice historique sur l'École Centrale des Arts et Manufactures. 56 p. Paris: Dunod & Pinat, 1913.

Twf-ps

U.S. ECONOMIC COOPERATION ADMINISTRATION. Report on the organization of industrial research in France. Findings and recommendations of Mission OEEC-84 to France, organized by the Economic Cooperation Administration in cooperation with the Organization for European Economic Cooperation, the Ministry of Industry and Energy, and the Ministry of Economic Affairs of the Fourth Republic. November-December 1951. 89 p. [Washington: U.S. Dept. of Commerce, Office of Technical Services, 195-].

Twf-qe

LEROY, Maxime. La coutume ouvrière; syndicats, bourses du travail, fédérations professionnelles, coopératives, doctrines et institutions. 2 vol., 934 p. (Bibliothèque Internationale d'Economie Politique) Paris: Giard et Brière, 1913.
Reviewed by G. Aillet, *Rev.Métaphys Morale*, 1914, 22: 517-47.

MARTIN SAINT-LÉON, Etienne. Histoire des corporations de métiers depuis leurs origines jusqu'à leur suppression en 1791. Suivie d'une étude sur l'évolution de l'idée corporative de 1791 à nos jours et sur le mouvement syndical contemporain. 3rd ed. xxviii, 876 p. Paris: Alcan, 1922.
First published 1897

Twf-se

BERNOT, L. Attitudes des français devant les techniques modernes. *Cah.Hist.Mond.*, 1960, 5: 975-96.

Twf-th

BRUYÈRE, Jean. Histoire littéraire des gens de métier en France. 264 p. Paris: Jouve, 1932.

Twg/wh Central Europe

Twg

DÄBRITZ, W. Entstehung und Aufbau des rheinisch-westfälischen Industriebezirks. *Beitr.Gesch.Tech.Ind.*, 1925, 15: 13-107, 31 fig.

FELDHAUS, Franz M.; KOLL, Karl. Die Technik, ihr Werden und Wirken. In: Die Hochschule des deutschen Volkes, vol. 3, p. 165-360, ill. Nordhausen: 1938.

HASSLER, Friedrich. Aus der Geschichte Augsburgs, seiner Gewerbe und seiner Industrie. *Beitr.Gesch.Tech.Ind.*, 1924, 14: 155-92, 10 fig., 3 portr.

MATSCHOSS, Conrad. Preussens Gewerbeförderung und ihre grossen Männer. Dargestellt im Rahmen der Geschichte des Vereins zur Beförderung des Gewerbfleisses, 1821-1921. 165 p., ill. Berlin: Verein Deutscher Ingenieure, 1921.
Reviewed by F.M. Feldhaus, *Geschichtsbl.Tech.Ind.*, 1920, 7: 82-3.

Twg-be

LÜDTKE, Gerhard; MACKENSEN, Lutz. Deutscher Kulturatlas. 6 vol. Berlin: de Gruyter, 1931-38. [CB 38/609]
The section on technology is by Franz M. Feldhaus. It includes 33 maps. [CB 48/572]

Twg-da

BERDROW, Wilhelm. Die Familie Krupp in Essen von 1587 bis 1887. Mit Anhang: 13 genealogische Tabellen, entworfen und zusammengest. von Fritz Gerhard Kraft. 2 vol. 400 p., 13 tables. Essen: Krupp, 1931.
Reviewed by Karl Lohmeyer, *Deut.Lit.Zeitung*, 1932, 3: 1286-8.

TANZER, Karl. Wegbereiter der oberschlesischen Industrie. *Beitr.Gesch.Tech.Ind.*, 1933, 22: 44-56, 2 pl.

Twg-oq

GOLLOB, Hedwig, ed. Geschichte der Technischen Hochschule in Wien. 104 p. Vienna: 1964.
The school was founded in 1805-1806.
Reviewed by M. Habacher, *Bl.Technikgesch.*, 1964, 26: 163-4.

100 Jahre Eidgenössische Technische Hochschule, 1855-1955. Le centenaire de l'École Polytechnique Fédérale. 256, 160 p. (*Schweiz.Hochschulzeitung*, 28, special number) Zurich: 1955.

NEUWIRTH, Joseph. Die K.K. Technische Hochschule in Wien 1815-1915. Gedenkschrift hrsg. vom Professorenkollegium. xi, 700 p. Wien: Gerold, 1915.

Twg-or

TROMMSDORFF, Paul. Der Lehrkörper der Technischen Hochschule Hannover 1831-1931. ix, 198 p., portr., 300 ill. Hannover: Osterwald, 1931.
Reviewed by Zaunick, *Mitt.Gesch.Med.*, 1932, 31: 188.

Twg-r

MATSCHOSS, Conrad. Vom Ingenieur, seinem Werden und seiner Arbeit in Deutschland. *Beitr.Gesch.Tech.Ind.*, 1930, 20: 1-20, 11 fig.

Twg-sy

KRETZMANN, Edwin M.J. German technological Utopias of the pre-war period. *Ann.Sci.*, 1938, 3: 417-30.

Twh

PURŠ, Jaroslav. [En marge des problèmes de la révolution industrielle dans la République Tchécoslovaque. (In Czech)] *Česk.Čas.Hist.*, 1956, 4: no. 1, 1-27.

Twi Italy

FERRARIO, Artemio. Invenzioni e inventori nel XX° secolo. 570 p., 33 pl. (Enciclopedia Scientifica Monografica Italiana del XX° Secolo, 1) Verona: Bompiani, 1938.
Restricted to Italian discoveries.

FORTI, Umberto. Storia della tecnica italiana. 336 p., 118 fig., 22 pl. Firenze: Sansoni, 1940.
Reviewed by Mario Gliozzi, *Arch.Int.Hist.Sci.*, 1948, 1: 541-3.

SAVORGNAN DE BRAZZÀ, Francesco. Da Leonardo a Marconi; invenzioni e scoperte italiane. vii, 368 p., 48 pl., ill. Milan: Hoepli, 1933.
Reviewed by Gino Testi, *Archeion*, 1933, 15: 268.

Twk/wm Low Countries; Scandinavia

Twk-da

MEYER, P. Grosse Leistungen holländischer Ingenieure. *Technikgeschichte*, 1937, 26: 84-92, 2 pl., 7 fig.

Twk-pw

DICKINSON, H.W.; GOMME, A.A. Netherlands contribution to Gt. Britain's engineering and technology to the year 1700. *Arch.Int.Hist.Sci.*, 1950, 3: 356-77.

Twm

LICHTENBERG, Niels. Dansk Teknik, dens Udvikling og Indsats. [Danish technology, its development and contribution. (In Danish)] 316 p. København: Hirschsprung, 1942.
Reviewed by Torsten Althin, *Lychnos*, 1943, 396.

Twm-tq

RÖNNOW, Sixten. Svensk teknik och industri i konsten. [Swedish technology and industry in art. (In Swedish)]. 334 p. Stockholm: Maskinaktibolaget Karlebo, 1943.
Chiefly illustrations.
Reviewed (in Swedish) by Efraim Lundmark, *Lychnos*, 1944-45, 471-3.

Twn Russia

GRAUBARD, Mark. Soviet technology, American education and our post-war hysteria. *Sci.Educ.*, 1960, 44: 331-45.

MALKIN, I. On the power of scientific tradition. *Scr.Math.*, 1961, 26: 339-46.
A review of the tradition of engineering science in Russia.

SAMSONOV, G.V. Osnovnye napravleniia razvitiia tekhnicheskikh nauk na Ukraine. [Fundamental trends in the development of technological sciences in the Ukraine. (In Russian)] *Vop. Ist.Est.Tekh.*, 1963, 14: 56-61.

Twn-hd

FELDHAUS, Franz M. Geschichte der Technik in Russland. *Isis*, 1934, 20: 445.

Twn-nh

KOSTROV, V.N. [From the history of Russian technical terminology. (In Russian)] *Tr.Inst.Ist.Est.Tekh.*, 1955, 3: 114-30.

Twn-o

MACHELSON, Sonya G. Technical education in the U.S.S.R. *J. Chem.Educ.*, 1955, 32: 481-3.

TRILLAT, Jean Jacques. Organisation et principes de l'enseignement en URSS. Les relations entre la science et l'industrie. 70 p., 3 pl. (Actualités Scientifiques et Industrielles, 67) Paris: Hermann, 1933.

Twn-sk

JORAVSKY, David. The history of technology in Soviet Russia and Marxist doctrine. *Technol.Cult.*, 1961, 2: 5-10.

Twp/wt Asia; Africa

Iz Istorii Nauki i Tekhniki v Stranakh Vostoka. [On the history of science and technology in the countries of the East. (In Russian)] Moskva: Izdatel'stvo Vostochnoi Literatury, 1960-
Volume 2, 1961, reviewed by M. Wong, *Arch.Int.Hist.Sci.*, 1962, 15: 419-20.

Twp

GRUNWALD, Kurt; RONALL, Joachim O. Industrialization in the Middle East. xx, 394 p. New York: Council for Middle Eastern Affairs Press, 1960.
Reviewed by S.K. Ghaswala, *Technol.Cult.*, 1961, 2: 79-82.

Twq

LE MAROC. *Rev.Gén.Sci.*, 1914, 25: 290-420. [CB 6/463]
Special number devoted to Morocco; contains 25 articles, many on economic and technical aspects.

Tws

RUTHERFORD, Ernest, *Lord Rutherford.* Science in industry in India. *Science*, 1938, 87: 75-9.

Twt

HUARD, Pierre. Sciences et techniques de l'Eurasie. *Bull. Soc.Étud.Indo-Chinoises Saïgon*, 1950, 25: 111-48.
Deals mostly with the Far East.

YOSIDA, Mitukuni. Studies on the history of the Japanese traditional arts and modern technology. 257 p., pl., fig. Kyoto: 1961. Abstract in *Jap.Stud.Hist.Sci.*, 1962, 1: 135-6.

Tx techniques and instruments

Txh

BOOKER, Peter Jeffrey. A history of engineering drawing. xvi, 239 p., ill., pl. London: Chatto and Windus, 1963; New York: Humanities Press, 1964.

FELDHAUS, Franz M. Geschichte des Technischen Zeichnens. 111 p., ill. Wilhelmshaven: Franz Kuhlmann K.G., 1953.
Reviewed by R.J. Forbes, *Arch.Int.Hist.Sci.*, 1955, 6: 205-6.
2nd edition, revised and enlarged with the assistance of Edmund Schruff. 121 p., ill. Wilhelmshaven: Franz Kuhlmann K.G., 1959.
Reviewed by R.S. Hartenberg, *Technol.Cult.*, 1961, 2: 45-9.

HEYMANN, Rudolf E. An approach to early art from technical drawing. *Proc.10th Int.Congr.Hist.Sci.* (Ithaca, 1962), (1), p. 373-5. Paris: Hermann, 1964.

Txw museology

DICKINSON, H.W. Presidential address: museums and their relation to the history of engineering and technology. *Trans. Newcomen Soc.*, 1933-34, 14: 1-12.

MILLER, O. von. Technische Museen als Stätten der Volksbelehrung. 27 p., 11 fig. (*Abhandl.Ber.Deut.Mus.*, 1: no. 5) Berlin: VDI-Verlag, 1929.

MULTHAUF, Robert P. The function of the technical museum in engineering education. *J.Eng.Educ.*, 1958, 49: 199-203

RICHARDS, Charles Russell. The industrial museum. x, 117 p. London: Macmillan, 1925.

Txx museums

BISHOP, P.W. Le Musée d'Histoire et de Technologie de la Smithsonian Institution. *Rev.Hist.Sci.*, 1963, 16: 380-6.

EDISON INSTITUTE. A guide book for the Edison Institute Museum. 72 p., ill. Dearborn, Mich.: 1941. [CB 62/77]
Illustrated description of the industrial museum established in Dearborn by Henry Ford.

FELDHAUS, Franz M. Technische Museen. *Archeion*, 1929, 11: 348-57. [CB 29/299]

GUIDE du Musée du Conservatoire National des Arts et Métiers. 16 p., ill. Paris: Ministère de l'Education National, 1954.

HANEKE, Hans. Die technischen Museen, 1927. *Beitr.Gesch.Tech. Ind.*, 1927, 17: 153-4.

HAMILTON, J.G. de Roulhac. The Ford Museum. *Amer.Hist.Rev.*, 1931, 36: 772-5.

HORWITZ, Hugo Th. Das technische Museum in Wien. 1. Die Sammlungen. *Geschichtsbl.Tech.Ind.*, 1921, 8: 1-10, 8 pl; 1922, 9: 1-12, 8 pl.

HOUGH, Walter. Synoptic series of objects in the United States National Museum illustrating the history of inventions. 47 p., 56 pl. (*Proc.U.S.Nat.Mus.*, 60) Washington, D.C.: 1922. [CB 13/311]

KAEMPFFERT, Waldemar. Revealing the technical ascent of man in the Rosenwald Industrial Museum. *Sci.Mon.*, 1929, 28: 481-98, 10 ill.

KLINCKOWSTROEM, Carl von. Schönfeld und sein technologisches Museum in Wien. *Geschichtsbl.Tech.Ind.*, 1927, 11: 96-101.

LEVEILLE, A. Dvorets Otkrytii. [Palais de la Découverte. (In Russian)] *Vop.Ist.Est.Tekh.*, 1961, 11: 130-6.

LEVEILLE, A. Le Palais de la Découverte. *Experientia*, 1945, 1: 345-6, ill.
Description of the technical museum created in Paris in 1937 and now a part of the University of Paris.

MATSCHOSS, Conrad. Die Heimatmuseen und die Technik. *Technikgeschichte*, 1933, 22: 1-6.

MITCHELL, Edwin Valentine. American village. Illustrated with material from the Henry Ford Collections in Greenfield Village, Michigan. 261 p., ill., pl. New York: Stackpole, 1938.

NATIONAL Museum of Engineering and Industry, Washington. To be under the direction of the Smithsonian Institution, Washington, D.C. 24 p. New York: 1924. [CB 17/605]

PALAIS DE LA DÉCOUVERTE. *Endeavour*, 1958, 17: 36.

SARTON, George. National Museum of Engineering, Washington, D.C. *Isis*, 1924, 6: 539-42.
A scheme to establish a museum under the direction of the Smithsonian Institution.

TAYLOR, Frank A. A national museum of science, engineering and industry. *Sci.Mon.*, 1946, 63: 359-65, ill.
An idea for a United States National Museum of Science, Engineering and Industry to be a part of the National Museum under the direction of the Smithsonian Institution.

Txx-br

Sbornik Narodniho Technickeho Musea. [Review of the National Technical Museum. (In Czech)] Vol. 1- Praha: Narodni Technické Museum, 1955-
For contents of volume 3, *see* CB 85/405.

TA INDUSTRIAL ORGANIZATION; PRODUCTION ENGINEERING

BARNARD, Chester I. The functions of the executive. xvi, 334 p. Cambridge: Harvard University Press, 1938. [CB 58/584]

GIEDION, Sigfried. Mechanization takes command. A contribution to anonymous history. xiv, 743 p., ill. New York: Oxford University Press, 1948.

LILLEY, Samuel. The scientific revolution and industrial processes. *Nature*, 1963, 198: 1132-7.
Automation in industry.

ROE, Joseph Wickham. Interchangeable manufacture. *Trans.Newcomen Soc.*, 1936-37, 17: 165-74.

STONE, Gilbert. A history of labour. 416 p. London: Harrap, 1921.
Reviewed by George Sarton, *Isis*, 1922, 4: 385-6.

TAYLOR, Frederick Winslow. La direction des ateliers. vi, 190 p. Paris: H. Dunod and E. Pinat, 1913.
Translation of: Shop management. 1911.
Reviewed by George Sarton, *Isis*, 1913, 1: 718.

TAYLOR, Frederick Winslow. Shop management. 207 p. New York/London: Harper, 1911.
Originally published in *Trans.Amer.Soc.Mech.Eng.*, 1903, vol. 24.

VAUCLAIN, Samuel M. Mass production within one lifetime. A Newcomen address ... 1937. 27 p. Princeton: Printed at the Princeton University Press for the Newcomen Society, American Branch, 1937.

TAce-bv

SELECT list of references on scientific management and efficiency. *Spec. Libr.*, May 1913, 72-109.

TAs

FRIEDMANN, Georges. Industrial society. The emergence of the human problems of automation. Edited and with an introduction by Harold L. Sheppard. 436 p. Glencoe, Ill.: Free Press, 1955.

TAwb

AITKEN, Hugh G.J. Taylorism at Watertown arsenal: scientific management in action 1908-1915. xiii, 269 p. Cambridge, Mass.: Harvard University Press, 1960.
Reviewed by R.H. Guest, *Technol.Cult.*, 1961, 2: 191-3.

ROE, Joseph Wickham. Interchangeable manufacture in American industry. 24 p. Birmingham, Ala.: Birmingham Publishing C Company (for the Newcomen Society, American Branch), 1939.

TAwb-s

WARNER, W. Lloyd; LOW, J.O. The social system of the modern factory. xvi, 245 p. (Yankee City Series, 4) New Haven: Yale University Press, 1947. [CB 71/127]

TAxu

CONWAY, H.G. Some notes on the origins of mechanical servomechanisms. *Trans.Newcomen Soc.*, 1953-55, 29: 55-75

KILGOUR, Frederick G. History and significance of automatic control. *Yale Sci.Mag.*, 1955, 29: 4 p., 3 fig.

RAMSEY, A.R.J. The thermostat or heat governor. An outline of its history. *Trans.Newcomen Soc.*, 1950, 25: 53-72, 19 fig.

SCIENTIFIC AMERICAN. Automatic control. 148 p. New York: Simon and Schuster, 1955.

TAyMG

MUENSTERBERG, H. Psychology and industrial efficiency. 321 p. Boston: Houghton Mifflin, 1913.

VERMILYE, William M. Human understanding in industry. 17 p. New York: National City Bank, 1939.

TB PATENTS AND INVENTIONS

for the psychology of invention *see* Tjg

FRUMKIN, Maximilian. Early history of patents for invention. *Trans.Newcomen Soc.*, 1947-48 and 1948-49, 26: 47-56.

NAUMBURG, Robert E. Patent engineering - a coming profession. *Tech*, 1924-25, 5: 211, 232.

POTTS, Harold Edwin. Patents, invention and method. A guide to the general lines of procedure in invention and discovery. vii, 160 p. London: Open Court, 1924.

SCHECHTER, Frank I. The historical foundations of the law relating to trade-marks. Table of cases, statutes, bibliography and index. 240 p., 4 pl. (Columbia Legal Studies, 1) New York: Columbia University Press, 1925.

TBkq

BALL, Norman T. The classification of patents. *Spec.Libr.*, 1947, 38: 11-16.

TBp

U.S. DEPARTMENT OF COMMERCE. ADVISTORY COMMITTEE ON APPLICATION OF MACHINES TO PATENT OFFICE OPERATIONS. Report. 76 p., bibliogr. Washington: Department of Commerce, 1954.
A report of a committee headed by Vannevar Bush.

TBwb-bv

DAVIS, Mrs. Watson. Classic inventions. [Listings of U.S. patents of basic inventions] *Sci.News Lett.*
Feature began August 1929.
Reviewed by G. Sarton, *Isis*, 1930, 13: 362.

TBwb-cd

REINGOLD, Nathan. U.S. Patent Office records as sources for the history of invention and technological property. *Technol.Cult.*, 1960, 2: 156-67.

TBwb-qk

FEDERICO, P.J., ed. Outline of the history of the United States Patent Office. *J.Pat.Office Soc.*, 1936, 18: no. 7, Centennial Number, 251 p.
Consists mainly of articles from *J.Pat.Office Soc.* during the previous 18 years.

TBwe

GOMME, Allan A. Patents of invention. Origin and growth of the patent system in Britain. v, 48 p., 8 ill. (Science in Britain) London: British Council, 1946. [CB 70/258]

TBwg

MELDAU, Robert. Hauptwurzeln des deutschen Patentrechts. *Technikgeschichte,* 1937, 26: 107-14.

TBwk

DOORMAN, G. Patents for inventions in the Netherlands during the 16th, 17th and 18th centuries. With notes on the historical development of technics. Abridged English version transl. by Joh. Meijer. 228 p. The Hague: Nijhoff, 1942. [CB 72/272]
Dutch original: Octrooien voor uitvindingen in de Nederlanden uit de 16e-18e eeuw. 1940.

TBwt

TOMITA, Tetsuo. The origin of patent system in Japan. *Jap. Stud.Hist.Sci.,* 1964, 3: 114-26.

TC CIVIL ENGINEERING

TCc

KIRBY, Richard Shelton; LAURSON, Philip Gustave. The early years of modern civil engineering. xvi, 325 p., 149 fig. New Haven: Yale University Press, 1932.

MERDINGER, Charles J. Civil engineering through the ages. 159 p., ill. Washington: Society of American Military Engineers, 1963.
Reviewed by James Kip Finch, *Technol.Cult.,* 1964, 5: 435-8.

PANNELL, J.P.M. An illustrated history of civil engineering. 376 p., ill. London: Thames & Hudson, 1964.
Reviewed in *Times Sci.Rev.,* 1964, no. 53, 17-18.

STRAUB, Hans. Die Geschichte der Bauingenieurkunst. Ein Überblick von der Antike bis in die Neuzeit. xii, 285 p., 79 pl., fig. (Wissenschaft und Kultur, 4) Basel: Verlag Birkhäuser, 1949. [CB 82/217]

TCwb-qt

BONNY, J.B. Morrison-Knudsen Company, Inc. Fifty years of construction progress. 24 p. Princeton, N.J.: Princeton University Press (for the Newcomen Society in North America), 1962.

TCwb-r

CALHOUN, Daniel Hovey. The American civil engineer. Origins and conflict. xiv, 295 p., map, bibliogr. Cambridge, Mass.: Technology Press, 1960.
Reviewed by Eugene S. Ferguson, *Isis,* 1962, 53: 269-70; for other reviews *see* CB 86/473 and CB 87/576.

TCwe-qd

SMITH, Edgar C. The centenary of the Institution of Civil Engineers. *Nature,* 1928, 121: 867-8.

TE STRUCTURES

FELDHAUS, Franz M. Geschichte der Träger. (Welt der Technik, Beilage zum "Deutschen Techniker", 9) Berlin: 1935. [CB 48/573]

HERTWIG, A. Aus der Geschichte der Gewölbe - Ein Beitrag zur Kulturgeschichte. *Technikgeschichte,* 1934, 23: 86-93, 4 pl., 8 fig.

TExd

BECKER, Fritz. Die Entwicklung der Eisenbetonbauweise. *Beitr. Gesch.Tech.Ind.,* 1932, 21: 43-58, 7 fig.

ROHLAND, Paul W. Aus der Geschichte des Eisenbetons. *Arch. Gesch.Naturwiss.Tech.,* 1912, 3: 423-9.

TF BRIDGES

BARMAN, Christian. The bridge: a chapter in the history of building. xvii, 249 p. London: John Lane; Bodley Head; New York: Dodd, Mead, 1926.

BLACK, Archibald. The story of bridges. xvi, 226 p. New York/London: McGraw-Hill, 1936.

FLETCHER, Robert; SNOW, J.P. A history of the development of wooden bridges. *Trans.Amer.Soc.Civil Eng.,* 1934, 99: 314-408, 47 fig.

HORWITZ, Hugo Th. Über urtümliche Seil-, Ketten- und Seilbahnbrücken. *Technikgeschichte,* 1934, 23: 94-8.

RATIGAN, William. Highways over broad waters: life and time of David B. Steinman, bridgebuilder. 360 p., ill. Grand Rapids, Mich.: William B. Eerdmans, 1959.
Reviewed by John A. Kouwenhoven, *Technol.Cult.,* 1961, 2: 204-5.

STEINMAN, D.B.; WATSON, S.R. Bridges and their builders. xvii, 401 p. London: Constable, 1958.
Reviewed in *Sch.Sci.Rev.,* 1958, 39: 545.

TFwb

EDWARDS, Llewellyn Nathaniel. The evolution of early American bridges. *Trans.Newcomen Soc.,* 1932-33, 13: 95-116, 2 fig.

EDWARDS, Llewellyn Nathaniel. A record of history and evolution of early American bridges. xii, 204 p., pl. Orono, Me.: Printed at the University Press, 1959.
Reviewed by Robert M. Vogel, *Science,* 1959, 130: 445-6.

TFwe

BECKER, M. Janet. Rochester Bridge, 1387-1856: a history of its early years compiled from the Wardens' Accounts. Foreword by S.C. Ratcliff. xvi, 123 p., 10 pl. London: Constable, 1930.
Reviewed in *Antiquity,* 1931, 5: 144.

TFwh

STERNER, Waclaw. Niezrealizowany project mostu lancuchowego przez Wisle pod Warszawa. [A scheme for a chain bridge across the Vistula at Warsaw that has never been realized. (In Polish)] *Kwart.Hist.Nauk.Tech.,* 1957, 2: 277-92.

TG TUNNELS

TGwb

GRAY, Carl C.; HAGEN, H.F. The eighth wonder: the Holland vehicular tunnel. *Annu.Rep.Smithsonian Inst.for 1930,* p. 577-607, 30 pl., 5 fig. Washington, D.C.: 1931.
Reprinted with a few omissions from the authors' pamphlet: The eighth wonder. 64 p., ill. Boston: B.F. Sturtevant Co., 1927.

TGwd

DULUC, Albert. Le Mont Cenis, sa route, son tunnel; contribution à l'histoire des grandes voies de communications. Préf. de Georges Friedmann. 151 p. (Actualités Scientifiques et Industrielles, 1177) Paris: Hermann, 1952.
Reviewed by Suzanne Delorme. *Rev.Hist.Sci.,* 1953, 6: 91-2.

TGxd

JANELID, Ingvar. The Swedish method. (In English) *Daedalus*, 1963, 113-43.
On the development of the so-called Swedish method of rock drilling for tunneling and mining.

TGxw

VOGEL, Robert M. Tunnel engineering, a museum treatment. (*Contrib.Mus.Hist.Technol.*, 41) *Bull.U.S.Nat.Mus.*, 1964, 240: 203-39.

TH HYDRAULIC ENGINEERING

CHOW, Ven-Te, ed. Handbook of applied hydrology. xiv, 1454 p., bibliogr. New York: McGraw-Hill, 1964. [CB 90/519]
Section 1 deals with the historical development of hydrology.

FRANK, Bernard; NETBOY, Anthony. Water, land and people. xviii, 329, xi p., 41 ill. New York: Knopf, 1950.
Reviewed by Conway Zirkle, *Isis*, 1951, 42: 273.

GARRISON, Fielding Hudson. The history of drainage, irrigation, sewage-disposal and water-supply. *Bull.N.Y.Acad.Med.*, 1929, 5: 887-938.

ROUSE, Hunter; INCE, Simon. History of hydraulics. xii, 269 p. Iowa City: State University of Iowa (for the Iowa Institute for Hydraulic Research), 1957.
Reprinted, with corrections, from separately paginated supplements to *La Houille Blanche*, 1954-56. Corrected reprint New York: Dover, 1963.
Reviewed by C. Truesdell, *Isis*, 1959, 50: 69-71.

THxm-wb

KOLUPAILA, S. Early history of hydrometry in the United States. *Proc.Amer.Soc.Civ.Eng.J.Hydraul.Div.*, 1960, 86: no. 1, 1-51; 1961, 87: no. 3, 175-81, ill.

TJ DAMS

TJwb

GABRIEL, Ralph Henry. The founding of Holyoke [Dam] A Newcomen Society (American Branch) address, 1936. 23 p. Princeton, N.J.: Princeton University Press, 1936.

LEGGET, Robert F. The Jones Falls Dam on the Rideau Canal, Ontario, Canada. *Trans.Newcomen Soc.*, 1957-58 and 1958-59, 31: 205-18.

TK WATER SUPPLY; SEWERAGE

BROMEHEAD, C.E.N. The early history of water-supply. *Geogr. J.*, 1942, 99: 142-51, 183-96.

BUFFET, Bernard; EVRARD, René. L'eau potable à travers les âges. 246 p., 195 fig. Liége: Solédi, 1950.
Reviewed in *Tech.Civilisations*, 1951, 2: 33.

ROBINS, F.W. The story of water supply. x, 207 p., 26 pl., 5 fig. London: Oxford University Press, 1946.
Reviewed by C.N.B., *Antiquity*, 1947, 21: 222.

SCHMASSMANN, H.; SCHMASSMANN, W. Water. (Waters of the earth. The nature of water. Water for trade and industrial uses. The purification of waste waters. Water supply past and present.) *Ciba Rev.*, 1950, no. 82, 2970-94, ill.

WAHL, Karl. Entwicklung der Wasserversorgung seit Einführung der Dampfmaschine. *Technikgeschichte*, 1936, 25: 26-42, 2 pl., 1 fig.

TKwb-bx

NEW YORK PUBLIC LIBRARY. An exhibition illustrating the history of the water supply of the city of New York from 1639 to 1917. *Bull.N.Y.Public Libr.*, 1917, 21: 407-12, pl.

TKwe-st

BROMEHEAD, C.E.N. Plato and the law of water supply. *Geogr. J.*, 1946, 108: 123-5.
Almost all the principles involved in the British Water Act of 1945 were laid down in Plato's "Laws", 844, a-d; 845, d-e.

TKwg

KLINCKOWSTROEM, Carl von. Beiträge zur Geschichte der Wassererschliessung. *Z.Ver.Gas- Wasserfachmänner*, 1913, 53: 321-4, 337-57, 370-6, ill., bibliogr.

SCHRÖDER, Albert. Die Wasserkunst und das Brunnennetz in Alt-Leipzig. *Beitr.Gesch.Tech.Ind.*, 1930, 20: 119-25, 17 fig.

TKwi

SALOMON, W. Die Brunnen von Venedig als Erzeuger von künstlichem Grundwasser. *Natur.Mus.*, 1930, 60: 227-31, 3 fig.

TL DRAINAGE AND IRRIGATION

TLwe

DARBY, Henry Clifford; RAMSDEN, P.M. The middle level of the Fens and its reclamation. With maps of the Fenland, by Edwart Lynam. In: Victoria history of the counties of England, Huntingdon (3), p. 249-90. London: Saint Catherine Press for the University of London, Institute of Historical Research, 1936.
Reviewed by E. Heawood, *Geogr.J.*, 1938, 91: 364-5.

TLwe-ph

OWEN, A.E.B. Land drainage authcrities and their records. *J. Soc.Arch.*, 1964, 2: 417-23.

TLwk

COOLS, R.H.A. De strijd om den grond in het lage Nederland. [The struggle for the land in the low-lying Netherlands. (In Dutch)] 300 p., 99 fig. The Hague: Van Ditmar, 1949.
History of the polders, dykes and land reclamation in Holland.
Reviewed by R.J. Forbes, *Arch.Int.Hist.Sci.*, 1950, 3: 246-8.

VEEN, Johan van. Dredge, drain, reclaim, the art of a nation. 3rd ed. 179 p., ill. The Hague: Nijhoff, 1950.
First published 1948.
A history of Dutch hydraulic engineering.

TLwp

EATON, Frank M. Irrigation along the Nile and Euphrates. *Sci. Mon.*, 1949, 69: 34-42.

TLws

WILLCOCKS, William. Lectures on the ancient system of irrigation in Bengal, and its application to modern problems. 128 p. Calcutta: University of Calcutta Press, 1930. [CB 33/387]
Reviewed by C.E.A.W. Odling, *Geogr.J.*, 1931, 77: 374-5.

TN TRANSPORT ENGINEERING

TNc

AVENEL, Georges d'. L'évolution des moyens de transport. Voyageurs, lettres, marchandises. 266 p. (Bibliothèque de Philosophie Scientifique) Paris: Flammarion, 1919.

BOULTON, W.H. The pageant of transport through the ages. Introduction by Sir Josiah Stamp. xviii, 238 p. London: Low, 1931.

FEUCHTINGER, Max-Erich. 100 Jahre Wettbewerb zwischen Eisenbahn und Landstrasse. *Technikgeschichte*, 1935, 24: 101-8, 5 fig.

MILLER, John Anderson. Fares please! From horse-cars to streamliners. xvii, 204 p., ill. New York: Appleton-Century, 1941.
History of urban transportation.

NANSOUTY, Max de. Chemins de fer. Automobiles. 396 p., 368 fig. (Les Merveilles de la Science, 5) Paris: Boivin, 1913.

SCHIELDROP, Edgar B. Conquest of space and time. 3 vol. 1. The railway. 256 p.; 2. The highway. 248 p.; 3. The high seas. 211 p. London: Hutchinson; Philadelphia: David McKay Co., 1939. [CB 61/401]

SHERRINGTON, Charles Ely Rose. A hundred years of inland transport. 376 p. (Hundred Years Series, 1830-1933) London: Duckworth, 1934. [CB 56/393]

SILLCOX, L.K. Speed! more speed! - in transport. 30 p. (Cyrus Fogg Brackett Lecture, Princeton University, 1939) Princeton: 1939.

TNwb

AMBLER, Charles Henry. A history of transportation in the Ohio Valley with special reference to its waterways, trade, and commerce from the earliest period to the present time. 465 p., maps, ill. Glendale, Calif.: Clark, 1932.
Reviewed by Guy-Harold Smith, *Geogr.Rev.*, 1933, 23: 520.

MacGILL, Caroline E., ed. History of transportation in the United States before 1860. Prepared under the direction of Balthasar Henry Meyer. xii, 678 p., 5 maps. Washington: Carnegie Institution, 1917.

TNwd

ENDERES, Bruno V. Die Geschichte der Alpenstrassen und Alpenbahnen. *Beitr.Gesch.Tech.Ind.*, 1933, 22: 7-17, 4 pl.

TNwe

JACKMAN, William T. The development of transportation in modern England. 2 vol. xv, vii, 820 p. Cambridge University, 1916.

TNxx

HORNIMAN MUSEUM AND LIBRARY. A handbook to the cases illustrating simple means of travel and transport by land and water. 71 p., 2 pl. (Publication, 11) London: London County Council, 1925.

TO MARINE ENGINEERING; CANALS; WATERWAYS

see also HC NAVIGATION
HO SEA TRAVEL
XX NAVAL FORCES

TOc

BRITTAIN, Robert. Gospodarka wodna a rozwöj historyczny. [River technology and historical development. (In Polish)] *Kwart.Hist.Nauk.Tech.*, 1963, 8: 355-9.

BRITTAIN, Robert. River technology and historical development. *Proc.10th Int.Congr.Hist.Sci.* (Ithaca, 1962), (1), p. 435-7. Paris: Hermann, 1964.
For a slightly longer version in Polish *see* above.

DENNY, Archibald. Fifty years' evolution in naval architecture and marine engineering. *Nature*, 1925, 116: 468-71.

SCHIELDROP, Edgar Bonsak. The high seas. With a foreword by Sir Archibald Hurd. 211 p. (Conquest of Space and Time, 3) London: Hutchinson; Philadelphia: McKay, 1939. [CB 61/401]

SMITH, Edgar C. A short history of naval and marine engineering. With a foreword by P.J. Cowan. xix, 376 p., ill., 16 pl. Cambridge University Press, 1938.

WREDEN, Richard. Vorläufer und Entstehen der Kammerschleuse, ihre Würdigung und weitere Entwicklung. *Beitr.Gesch.Tech. Ind.*, 1919, 9: 131-68, ill. [CB 10/218]

TOda

PAYNE, Pierre Stephen Robert. The canal builders. The story of canal engineers through the ages. 278 p., ill. New York: Macmillan, 1959.
Reviewed by Richard S. Kirby, *Isis*, 1960, 51: 580-2; by Eugene S. Ferguson, *Science*, 1959, 130: 383-4; by G.G. Meyerhof, *Technol.Cult.*, 1960, 2: 185-6.

TOwa

BENNETT, Ira E., ed. History of the Panama Canal. 543 p., ill. Washington, D.C.: Historical Publishing Company, 1915. [CB 16/248]

HENNIG, Rich. Die Geschichte der mittelamerikanischen Kanalunternehmungen. *Beitr.Gesch.Tech.Ind.*, 1912, 4: 113-46.

MACK, Gerstle. The land divided; a history of the Panama Canal and other Isthmian canal projects. xlix, 650 p., 45 ill., 17 maps. New York: Knopf, 1944.
Reviewed by Erwin H. Ackerknecht, *Bull.Hist.Med.*, 1944, 16: 93-4.

RECLUS, Armand. Le Canal de Panama; ses origines. *Géographie*, 1924, 41: 1-19, 3 maps. [CB 16/234]

TOwa-yQYwb

MEARS, J. Ewing. The triumphs of American medicine in the construction of the Panama canal. 25 p. Philadelphia: Wm. J. Dornan, 1912.

TOwb

STANFORD, Homer Reed. The historic Potomac - beginning with 1740. 47 p. Princeton: Princeton University Press (for Newcomen Society, American Branch), 1940.

VERMEULE, Cornelius C. The Morris Canal. *Trans.Newcomen Soc.*, 1934-35, 15: 195-202.

TOwc

JAGUARIBE DE MATTOS, Cel. F. Anteprojéto para o plano nacional de viação fluvial (linhas mestras). Acompanhado de 6 cartas parciais e de uma carta geral do Brasil reduzida, indicativas dos traçados dos canais. 1947. *Rev.Clube Eng.*, 1949, no. 151, 49-66. [CB 79/182]

TOwe

BROODBANK, Joseph-G. History of the Port of London. 2 vol., ill. London: Daniel O'Connor, 1921. [CB 11/441]

DE MARÉ, Eric Samuel. The canals of England. 124 p., ill. London: Architectural Press, 1950.

HADFIELD, Charles. British canals. An illustrated history. 259 p., 8 pl. London: Phoenix House, 1950.
Reviewed by K.G. Fenelon, *Nature*, 1951, 167: 417-19.

ROLT, L.T.C. The inland waterways of England. 221 p., front., 100 ill., map. London: Allen & Unwin, 1950.

TOwp

BARATTA, Mario. L'Italia e il canale di Suez. *Geografia*, 1929, 17: 85-124.

BIRK, Alfred. Die Geschichte des Suëzkanals. *Beitr.Gesch. Tech.Ind.*, 1923, 13: 17-29, 2 fig.

LE CANAL de Suez. *Vie Int.*, 1914, 5: 214-25. [CB 6/463]

TP SHIPS AND SHIPBUILDING

TPc general history

BATHE, Greville. The rise and decline of the paddle-wheel. x, 88 p., ill. Philadelphia: Allen, Lane & Scott, 1962.
Reviewed by Howard I. Chapelle, *Technol.Cult.*, 1964, 5: 611-12.

CHATTERTON, E. Keble. Sailing ships and their story. 2nd ed., with an additional chapter. xxii, 380 p. London: Sidgwick and Jackson, 1923.
First published in 1909. The new chapter is entitled "The sailing ship during the war, and after".

CLOWES, G.S. Laird. The story of sail. 148 p. London: Eyre and Spottiswoode, 1936.
Reviewed by F.G.G. Carr, *Geogr.J.*, 1937, 89: 483-4.

CRABBÉ, Raoul. De la pirogue aux navires atomiques. ii, 292 p., 48 ill. Bruxelles: A. Goemaere, 1951.
Reviewed by Wladyslaw Antoni Drapella, *Kwart.Hist.Nauk. Tech.*, 1956, 1: 391-405.

DANIEL, Hawthorne. Ships of the seven seas. With an introduction by Franklin D. Roosevelt. xvi, 321 p., ill. Garden City, N.Y.: Doubleday Page, 1925.

DAVIES, A.; ROBINSON, H. The evolution of the ship in relation to its geographical background. *Geography*, 1939, 24: 95-109.

FARIÑA, F. Historia de la navegación. Prólogo por Julio F. Guillén. 737 p., ill. Madrid: Departamento Editorial del Comisariado Español Maritimo, 1950.
A history of ships and shipping. Two appendices: 1. Algunos tipos de buques mercantes notables construidos de 1939 a 1950. 2. Los buques mercantes desde 1800.

GIBSON, Charles E. The story of the ship. 272 p., ill. (Life of Science Library) New York: Schuman, 1948.
Reviewed by Robert G. Albion, *Isis*, 1950, 41: 134.

GILFILLAN, S. Colum. Inventing the ship. A study of the inventions made in her history between floating log and rotor ship. 294 p., 80 fig. Chicago: Follett, 1935.
Reviewed by Abbott Payson Usher, *Isis*, 1936, 24: 450-3.

GILLE, Paul. La construction navale et les méthodes scientifiques. *Act.VIIe Congr.Int.Hist.Sci.* (Jerusalem, 1953), p. 313-15. Paris: Hermann, [n.d.].

HOBBS, Edward W. Sailing ships at a glance. A pictorial record of the evolution of the sailing ship from the earliest times until today. With an introduction by L.G. Carr Laughton. xviii, 114 p. London: Architectural Press, 1925.

HORNELL, James. Evolution of the clinker-built fishing lugger. *Antiquity*, 1936, 10: 341-5, 2 pl.

HORNELL, James. Origins of plank-built boats. *Antiquity*, 1939, 13: 35-44, 4 pl.
Deals with boats built in Greek and Roman times, with boats built by Vikings and with craft from Egypt and Sudan from ancient times until now; also with Indian and Chinese junks.

HORNELL, James. Water transport. Origins and early evolution. xv, 304 p., ill. Cambridge University Press, 1946. [CB 71/120]

JACKSON, George Gibbard. The ship under steam. 262 p., pl. London: Fisher Unwin. 1927: New York: Scribner's, 1928.

LANDSTRÖM, Björn. The ship. English transl. by Michael Phillips. 807 p., ill., bibliogr. London: Allen and Unwin, 1961.
A pictorial survey of the ship from the log of prehistoric man to the nuclear ship. Translation of: Skeppet (Stockholm: Bokförlaget Forum AB, 1961).
Reviewed by G.R.G. Worcester, *Mariner's Mirror*, 1962, 48: 150.

LA ROËRIE, Louis Guilleux; VIVIELLE, Jean. Navires et marins, de la rame à l'hélice. 2 vol. Paris: Duchartre & Van Buggenhoudt, 1930.

LETHBRIDGE, T.C. Boats and boatmen. viii, 199 p., 4 pl. (The Past in the Present Series) London: Thames and Hudson, 1952.
Reviewed by M.C. Burkitt, *Nature*, 1952, 169: 560.

MERRIEN, Jean. La grande histoire des bateaux. 254 p., 117 pl. Paris: Denoël, 1957.
Reviewed by Paul Gille, *Arch.Int.Hist.Sci.*, 1958, 11: 329-31.

REDMAYNE, P. Transport by sea. 48 p., ill., maps. London: Murray, 1950.
Reviewed by R.J. Forbes, *Arch.Int.Hist.Sci.*, 1951, 4: 558.

SAUSSURE, Hermine de. De la marine antique à la marine moderne. *Rev.Archéol.*, 1937, 10: 90-105.

SIVERZEV, I.N. Ein Abriss der Geschichte des Eisenbetonschiffbaues. [A sketch of the history of ship construction with reinforced concrete. (In Russian with German summary)] *Ark. Ist.Nauk.Tech.*, 1935, 6: 249-78, 21 fig.

SZYMANSKI, Hans. Zeittafel zur Geschichte des Handelsschiffes. *Technikgeschichte*, 1937, 26: 93-106.

TREBITSCH, R. Fellboote und Schwimmsäcke und ihre geographische Verbreitung in der Vergangenheit und Gegenwart. *Arch. Anthropol.*, 1912, 11: 161-84.

TPc-bv

LIBRARY OF CONGRESS. List of references on shipping and shipbuilding compiled under the direction of Hermann B. Meyer. 304 p. Washington: U.S. Govt. Print. Off., 1919. [CB 8/359]
2206 items, including history of shipping and history of shipbuilding, p. 189-97.

TPc-bx

LIÉGE. Exposition Internationale de la Technique de l'Eau. Historique de la construction navale et de la navigation. Catalogue. 72 p., ill. Liége: 1939.

TPcm

CHATTERTON, E. Keble. Chats on naval prints. 208 p., pl. (Books for Collectors) London: Fisher Unwin, 1926.

PARIS, François Edmond. Souvenirs de marine conservés, ou, Collections de plans de navires et de bateaux de tous les pays. 4 p., 57 pl. Paris: 1877.

POUJADE, Jean, ed. Collection de documents d'ethnographie navale, d'archéologie navale, d'ethnographie terrestre, d'archéologie terrestre. Fascicule introductif exposant les idées générales de cette collection et contenant la fiche signalétique et le questionnaire ethnographique du bateau, la réédition des planches no. 18, 19, 20, 22, et 23 et la table générale des "Souvenirs de marine conservés" par l'Amiral Paris. 67 p. (Publication du Centre de Recherche Culturelle de la Route des Indes) Paris: Gauthier-Villars, 1948.

ROUX, Antoine. Ships and shipping. A collection of pictures including many American vessels painted by Antoine Roux and his sons. With introductory text by Louis Bres and reminiscences by Edouard Gaubert. Translated and annotated by Alfred Johnson. ix, 270 p. Salem, Mass.: Marine Research Society, 1925.

TPs/t special aspects

TPsc

REEVE, Sidney A. Ship evolution and social evolution. *Geogr. Rev.*, 1933, 23: 61-76, 9 fig.

WESTINGHOUSE EDUCATIONAL FOUNDATION. Science and life in the world. The George Westinghouse centennial forum, May 16-18, 1946. 2. Transportation - a measure of civilization. Light, life and man. ix, 236 p., 12 pl. New York: McGraw Hill, 1946. [CB 40/166]

TPsg

COLLOQUE D'HISTOIRE MARITIME. Le navire et l'économie maritime du Moyen Age au XVIIIe siècle principalement en Méditerranée. Travaux du 2ième Colloque International d'Histoire Maritime, tenu ... mai 1957, à l'Académie de Marine. Ed. by Michel Mollat ... xii, 220 p., ill. (Bibliothèque Générale de l'Ecole Pratique des Hautes-Etudes) Paris: S.E.V.P.E.N., 1958.
Reviewed by Wladyslaw A. Drapella, *Arch.Int.Hist.Sci.*, 1959, 12: 404-5.

TPtq

LAUGHTON, L.G. Carr. Old ship figure-heads and sterns, with which are associated galleries, hancing-pieces, catheads, and divers other matters that concern the "grace and countenance" of old sailing ships. xv, 281 p., 55 pl. London: Halton and Truscott Smith, 1925.

TPw in different countries

CENTENARY of the Atlantic steam ferry. *Nature*, 1938, 141: 540-1.

MAYPER, Joseph. Atlantic transportation today! A centenary address. 28 p. (The Newcomen Society, American Branch ... address, 1938) [Princeton: Printed by the Princeton University Press, 1938]

PENROSE, Charles. 1838, April fourth, 1938. A century of Atlantic steam navigation. 31 p. Princeton, N.J.: Princeton University Press (for Newcomen Society, American Branch), 1938. Also in *Trans.Newcomen Soc.*, 1937-38, 18: 169-79.

SMITH, Edgar C. The centenary of transatlantic steam navigation. *Trans.Newcomen Soc.*, 1937-38, 18: 129-68, 4 fig.

TPwb

CHAPELLE, Howard Irving. The history of American sailing ships. xvii, 400 p., ill. London: Wales and Rusk, 1935.

CHAPELLE, Howard Irving. The migrations of an American boat type. (*Contrib.Mus.Hist.Technol.*, 25) *Bull.U.S.Nat.Mus.*, 1961, 228: 134-53.

FLEXNER, James Thomas. Steamboats come true: American inventors in action. x, 406 p. New York: Viking, 1944.
Reviewed by Carl W. Mitman, *Amer.Hist.Rev.*, 1945, 50: 351.

LASS, William E. A history of steamboating on the upper Missouri river. xiv, 215 p. Lincoln: University of Nebraska Press, 1962.
Reviewed by Carroll W. Pursell, *Technol.Cult.*, 1964, 5: 613-14.

LOREE, L.F. Steamboats of Lake Champlain. *Trans.Newcomen Soc.*, 1927-28, 8: 83-98.

NEWELL, William Stark. Shipbuilding in Maine. A brief history. 24 p., ill. Princeton, N.J.: Princeton University Press (for Newcomen Society, American Branch), 1938.

WALLACE, Frederick William. Wooden ships and iron men. The story of the square rigged merchant marine of British North America, the ships, their builders and owners and the men who sailed them. viii, 337 p. London: Hodder and Stoughton, 1924.

TPwb-cc

TAYLOR, Frank A. The Historic American Merchant Marine Survey. *Annu.Rep.Smithsonian Inst.for 1938*, p. 595-9, 11 pl. Washington, D.C.: 1939.
Records of old boats.

TPwb-qd

WHITEHILL, Walter Muir. The East India Marine Society and the Peabody Museum of Salem. A sesquicentennial history. xvi, 243 p., ill. Salem, Mass.: Peabody Museum, 1949. [CB 76/415]

TPwb-qt

ESKEW, Garnett Laidlaw. Cradle of ships. A history of the Bath Iron Works. 279 p., 34 ill., bibliogr. New York: G.P. Putnam's Sons, 1958.
Reviewed by Roger Burlingame, *Isis*, 1960, 51: 102.

TPwe

BACON, Frederic. Incidents in a century of ships, leading up to some remarks on the principles of engineering evolution. *Proc.S.Wales Inst.Eng.*, 1937, 53: 5-25. German transl. Aus der Geschichte des englischen Schiffbaues. *Technikgeschichte*, 1937, 26: 71-83.

HORNELL, James. British coracles and Irish curraghs, with a note on the quffah of Iraq. *Mariner's Mirror*, 1936, 22: 5-41, 261-304; 1937, 23: 74-83, 148-75; 1938, 24: 5-39, 153-9, 46 ill. Reprinted London: Quaritch (for the Society for Nautical Research), 1938 (with an introduction).

SCIENCE MUSEUM. British fishing boats and coastal craft. By E.W. White. 2 vol. London: H.M. Stationery Office, 1950-52. [CB 76/398]
Historical introduction to the catalogue of ship models exhibited in the Science Museum.

SMITH, Edgar C. The centenary of naval engineering. *Trans. Newcomen Soc.*, 1921-22, 2: 88-114.

TPwe-qd

BARNABY, K.C. The Institution of Naval Architects, 1860-1960. 645 p., ill. London: Royal Institution of Naval Architects, 1960.

TPwf

ANTHIAUME, A. Le navire. Sa construction en France et principalement chez les Normands. xvi, 482 p. Paris: Ernest Dumont, 1922. [CB 16/346]

LA RONCIERE, Charles B. de. Histoire de la marine française. 5 vol., ill. Paris: Plon, 1899-1920.

TPwj

ARTIÑANO Y DE GALDÁCANO, Gervasio de. La arquitectura naval española (en Madera). Bosquejo de sus condiciones y rasgos de su evolución. 428 p., 80 pl. (Conferencias organizados por el Instituto de ingenieros civiles de España en el Ateneo de Madrid, Mayo de 1914) Madrid: The author, 1920. [CB 10/216]

TPwn-nh

SMORGONSKII, I. [Foreign shipbuilding terms in the Russian language. (In Russian)] With a preface by A.N. Kriloff. xv, 180 p. (*Tr.Inst.Ist.Nauk.Tekh., ser. 2*, vol. 6) Moskva: Izdatel'stvo Akademii Nauk, SSSR, 1936.

TPwr

HORNELL, James. Primitive types of water transport in Asia: distribution and origins. *J.Roy.Asiatic Soc.*, 1946, 124-41, pl., 8 fig.

TPws

BERNSTEIN, Henry T. Steamboats on the Ganges. An exploration in the history of India's modernization through science and technology. xvi, 239 p., fig., bibliogr. Calcutta: Orient Longmans, 1960.

TPx techniques and instruments

TPxg

CHATTERTON, E. Keble. Ship-models. Edited by Geoffrey Holme. ix, 53 p., 142 pl. London: The Studio, 1923.

CHATTERTON, E. Keble. Steamship models. xii, 84 p., 128 pl. London: Laurie, 1924.

CLOWES, G.S. Laird. Sailing ships, their history and development as illustrated by the collection of ship models in the Science Museum. 2 vol. 1. Historical notes. 110 p.; 2. Catalogue of exhibits, with descriptive notes. 112 p. London: H.M. Stationery Office, 1930, 1932. [CB 35/300]
Reviewed by H.H. Bootes, *Geogr.J.*, 1931, 78: 85-7; 1932, 80: 355-6.
Part 1 reprinted 1947; Part 2 4th ed. 1952: reviewed by Eduard Fueter, *Centaurus*, 1955, 4: 83.

NANCE, R. Morton. Sailing ship models. A selection from European and American collections, with introductory text. 80 p. London: Halton and Truscott Smith, 1924.

TPxx museums

CHAPELLE, Howard Irving. The national watercraft collection. xi, 327 p., pl., fig., bibliogr. Washington, D.C.: Museum of History and Technology of the United States National Museum, 1960.

DODGE, Ernest S. The Peabody Museum of Salem, Massachusetts. *Mariner's Mirror*, 1961, 47: 90-100.

FERGUSON, Homer Lenoir. The Mariners' Museum (at Newport News, Va.). 9 p. New York: 1937.
Papers presented at the annual meeting of the Society of Naval Architects and Marine Engineers.

NATIONAL MARITIME MUSEUM. Guide. 230 p., pl. Greenwich: 1947.

ROBINSON, John. The Marine Room of the Peabody Museum of Salem. xiv, 188 p., ill. Salem, Mass.: Peabody Museum, 1921. [CB 16/349]
The Peabody Museum (founded in 1867 by George Peabody, 1795-1869) includes the Museum of the East India Marine Society (begun in 1799).

SCIENCE MUSEUM. Catalogue of the collections with descriptive and historical notes and illustrations. Water transport. 1. Sailing ships. Compiled by G.L. Overton. 71 p., 12 pl. London: H.M. Stationery Office, 1923.

WHITEHILL, Walter Muir. The East India Marine Society and the Peabody Museum of Salem. A sesquicentennial history. xvi, 243 p., ill. Salem, Mass.: Peabody Museum, 1949. [CB 76/415]

TPy related subjects

TPyB

GILLE, Paul. Les mathématiques et la construction navale. *Act.VIIIe Congr.Int.Hist.Sci.* (Florence, 1956), p. 57-63. Paris: Hermann, 1958.

NILSSON, Nils Gustaf. [The measurement of ships and mathematics. An historical survey. (In Swedish, with English summary)]. *Lychnos*, 1936, 1: 235-47, 248-50. [CB 48/567]

TPyHJ

CLOWES, G.S. Laird. Ships of early explorers. *Geogr.J.*, 1927, 69: 216-35, 10 fig. [CB 22/270]

TPyLPce-bv

CLAPP, W.F.; KENK, R. Marine borers. An annotated bibliography. xii, 1136 p. Washington, D.C.: Office of Naval Research, Department of the Navy, 1963.
Comprehensive bibliography covering the period from the earliest days of printing to 1954.

TPyTK

SCHADEWALDT, H. Die Wasserversorgung an Bord. *Gesnerus*, 1963, 20: 47-89.
A history of the technology of supplying ships with water.

TPyUK

GUTSCHE, Fritz. Die Entwicklung der Schiffsschraube. *Technikgeschichte*, 1937, 26: 37-50, 2 pl., 16 fig.

LEDERER, A. La propulsion des bateaux. *Rev.Quest.Sci.*, 1960, 21: 248-77.

SMITH, Edgar C. The progress of marine propulsion. *Nature*, 1929, 123: 352-4.

TQ LAND TRANSPORT

FORBES, R.J. Land transport and road-building (1000-1900). *Janus*, 1957, 46: 104-40, 201-23.

KORZENDORFER, Adolf. Post, Poststrassen, Postwagen. *Technikgeschichte*, 1934, 23: 79-85, 2 pl.

MITMAN, Carl W. An outline development of highway travel, especially in America. *Annu.Rep.Smithsonian Inst.for 1934*, p. 325-45, 12 pl. Washington, D.C.: 1935.

TQwb

HARLOW, Alvin Fay. Old waybills. The romance of the express companies. xii, 503 p., ill. New York/London: Appleton-Century, 1934.

TQwx

MAI, E. Strassen und Strassenfahrzeuge in Afrika. *Technikgeschichte*, 1934, 23: 118-23, 1 fig.

TR HORSE RIDING

LEFEBVRE DES NOËTTES, Richard. L'étrier à travers les âges. *Larousse Mens.*, 1926, 7: 11-14, 19 fig.

TS ROADS

FORBES, R.J. Roads of the past. *Chem.Ind.*, 1953, 70-4.

GREGORY, John Walter. The story of the road from the beginning to the present day. 2nd ed. rev. by C.J. Gregory. xii, 306 p., ill. London: Black, 1938.
First edition London: Maclehose, 1931.

HARTMANN, Cyril Hughes. The story of the roads. With an introduction by Alfred Hacking. xx, 194 p., 12 pl. London: Routledge, 1927.

HERTWIG, A. Aus der Geschichte der Strassenbautechnik. *Technikgeschichte*, 1934, 23: 1-5, 7 fig.

JENISON, Madge. Roads. 370 p. London: W.H. Allen, 1949.
Reviewed by R.J. Forbes, *Arch.Int.Hist.Sci.*, 1949, 2: 1241-2.

MACDONALD, John H.A. The road: past, present and future. *Proc. Roy.Inst.*, 1911-13, 20: 328-43. French transl. La route: passé, présent et futur. *Rev.Sci.*, 1913, 51: 1 semestre, 233-41.

SCHIELDROP, Edgar Bonsak. The highway. With a foreword by Sir Charles Bressey. 248 p. (Conquest of Space and Time, 2) London: Hutchinson; Philadelphia: McKay, 1939. [CB 61/401]

TSce-bv

FORBES, R.J. Bibliography of road building circa 300-1840. *Roads, Road Constr.*, 1938, 16: 189-96. [CB 55/177]

TSwe

DICKINSON, H.W. Alte Strassen und Pflasterungen in London. *Technikgeschichte*, 1934, 23: 45-50, 2 pl.

JEFFREYS, Rees. The King's Highway. xix, 292 p., 16 pl. London: Batchworth, 1949.

MALCOLM, L.W.G. Early history of the streets and paving of London. *Trans.Newcomen Soc.*, 1933-34, 14: 83-94.

WILKINSON, T.W. From track to by-pass: a history of the English road. xvi, 240 p., 39 pl. London: Methuen, 1934.
Reviewed in *Nature*, 1934, 134: 893.

TSwe-ce-bv

FORDHAM, Herbert George. The road-books and itineraries of Great Britain, 1570-1850: a catalogue with an introduction and a bibliography. xvi, 72 p. Cambridge University Press, 1924.

TSwf

ASSOCIATION POUR LA DIFFUSION DE LA PENSÉE FRANÇAISE. Les routes de France depuis les origines jusqu'à nos jours. 170 p., pl. (Colloques, Cahiers de Civilisation) Paris: 1959.
Reviewed by Jean-François Bergier, *Bibl.Hum.Renaiss.*, 1959, 21: 660-3; by J. Meuvret, *Rev.Belg.Philol.Hist.*, 1961, 39: 873-5.

TSwg

SCHULZE, Berthold. Geschichtliches über das Norddeutsche Strassenwesen. *Technikgeschichte*, 1934, 23: 30-5, 2 pl.

ZESCH, Erwin. Vom Jochweg zur Brenner-Autobahn. *Bl.Technikgesch.*, 1964, 26: 124-34.

TSwk

GENICOT, Léopold. Histoire des routes belges depuis 1704. 78 p. (Collection Nationale, 89) Bruxelles: Office de Publicité, 1948.

TT ROAD VEHICLES

BASCHMAKOFF, Alexandre. L'évolution de la charrue à travers les siècles au point de vue ethnographique. *Anthropologie* (Paris), 1932, 42: 82-90.

BOUMPHREY, Geoffrey Maxwell. The story of the wheel. 96 p., ill. (The How-and-Why Series, 7) London: Black, 1932.

FOX, Cyril. Sleds, carts, and waggons. *Antiquity*, 1931, 5: 185-99, 3 fig., 16 pl.

GROMODKA, Oskar; MÜLLER, Rudolf. Über Wagen und Wagenbau. *Technikgeschichte*, 1934, 23: 70-8, 2 pl., 14 fig.

KLEINSCHMIDT, H.E. Evolution of the wheel. *Sci.Mon.*, 1944, 59: 273-82, 10 ill.

MAHR, Otto. Zur Geschichte des Wagenrades. *Technikgeschichte*, 1934, 23: 51-61, 11 fig.

MÖTEFINDT, Hugo. Die Erfindung des Drehschemels am vierrädrigen Wagen. *Geschichtsbl.Tech.Ind.*, 1919, 6: 30-41, ill.

REID, James. The evolution of horse-drawn vehicles. With historical notes chronologically arranged and compiled. 109 p., pl. London: Institute of British Carriage and Automobile Manufacturers, 1933.

STURT, George. The wheelwright's shop. Passages selected and ed. by A.F. Collins. 2nd ed. 236 p., pl. Cambridge University Press, 1963.
First published 1923.
Reviewed by K.R. Gilbert, *Technol.Cult.*, 1964, 5: 610-11.

TU BICYCLES

CROON, Ludwig. Aus der Geschichte des Fahrrades. *Technikgeschichte*, 1934, 23: 62-9, 2 pl.

ROSTOVZOV, I.A. [Principal events in the evolution of the bicycle. (In Russian)] *Arkh.Ist.Nauk Tekh.*, 1934, 4: 411-26, 8 fig. [CB 43/233]

TV AUTOMOBILES

see also UP INTERNAL COMBUSTION ENGINES

ARNOLD, Gerhard. Zeittafel zur Geschichte des Kraftwagens. *Technikgeschichte*, 1934, 23: 113-17.

BARBER, Herbert Lee. Story of the automobile, its history and development from 1760 to 1917, with an analysis of the prospects of the automobile industry. 250 p., ill. Chicago: A. J. Murson, 1917.

CROSLEY, A.S. Early development of the railless electric trolleybus. In particular its application in Great Britain and elsewhere up to 1924. *Trans.Newcomen Soc.*, 1960-61, 33: 93-111.

DONGIER, R. Le propulseur à chenilles et la traversée du Sahara. *Rev.Sci.*, 1923, 61: 71-9. [CB 14/525]

ICKX, Jacques. Ainsi naquit l'automobile. 2 vol. 378 p., fig., pl.; 370 p., fig., pl. Lausanne: Edita, 1961.
Reviewed by M.D., *Doc.Hist.Tech.*, 1962, 2: 86-7.

TVdaj

NEUBURGER, Albert. Der Kraftwagen, sein Wesen und Werden. 82 p. (Voigtländers Quellenbücher, 41) Leipzig: R. Voigtländer, 1913.

TVwb

FIFTY years of progress. Some typical contributions of General Motors scientists and engineers, with foreword by Harlow H. Curtice. *Gen.Mot.Eng.J.*, 1958, 5: (3), 2-9, 11 fig.

GREENLEAF, William. Monopoly on wheels: Henry Ford and the Selden automobile patent. xii, 302 p. Detroit: Wayne State University Press, 1961.
Reviewed by John B. Rae, *Technol.Cult.*, 1961, 2: 289-90.

See also Ford, Henry 1: 426.

TVwe

CLARK, Ronald H. The development of the English traction engine. xxv, 390 p. Norwich: Goose, 1960.
Reviewed by Aubrey F. Burstall, *Technol.Cult.*, 1961, 2: 288-9; by J.J. Ermenc, *Ibid.*, 1964, 5: 258-9.

TVwe-qt

SMITH, G. Geoffrey. Frederick Henry Royce. An outline of his engineering achievement. iv, 31 p., 7 ill. (Science in Britain) London: Longmans Green, 1945.
Biography of the English creator of Royce cars and aircraft engines.

TVwg-da

DIESEL, Eugen; GOLDBECK, Gustav; SCHILDBERGER, Friedrich. From engines to autos: five pioneers in engine development and their contributions to the automotive industry. Translated by Peter White. vi, 302 p., ill. Chicago: Henry Regnery Co., 1960.
Translation of: Vom Motor zum Auto; fünf Männer und ihr Werk (Stuttgart: Deutsche Verlags-Anstalt, 1957).
The five pioneers were Benz, Bosch, Daimler, Diesel and Otto.
Reviewed by John B. Rae, *Technol.Cult.*, 1961, 2: 189-91; by Robert E. Carlson, *Isis*, 1962, 53: 272-3.

TVwg-qt

SEPER, Hans. 100 Jahre Steyr-Daimler Pusch AG. Der Werdegang eines österreichischen Industrie-Unternehmens. *Bl.Technikgesch.*, 1964, no. 26, 1-86.

TVwi

CONWAY, H.G. The automotive inventions of Ettore Bugatti. *Trans.Newcomen Soc.*, 1957-59, 31: 243-69.

TVxx

SCIENCE MUSEUM. Catalogue of the collections ... with descriptive and historical notes and illustrations. Land transport. 2. Mechanical road vehicles. Compiled by E.A. Forward. 87 p., 10 pl. London: H.M. Stationery Office, 1925.

TW RAILWAYS, INCLUDING TRACKS

TWc general history

BERGHAUS, Erwin. The history of railways. 215 p., ill., maps. London: Barrie & Rockcliff, 1964.

BOMBE, H. Die Entwicklung der Strassenbahnwagen. *Beitr.Gesch.Tech.Ind.*, 1913, 5: 214-29, 36 fig.

DICKERMAN, William Carter. Steam and the railroads. 22 p. Princeton: Princeton University Press, 1936. [CB 46/592]

DOLLFUS, Charles; GEOFFROY, Edgar de. Histoire de la locomotion terrestre. Les chemins de fer. xiv, 376 p., ill. Paris: L'Illustration, 1935.
Reviewed by Ph. T., *Rev.Gén.Sci.*, 1935, 46: 703.

FELDHAUS, Franz Maria. Vom Dampfross zum Schnellwagen. Eine kritische Studie. 32 p., 41 fig. Hannover: 1932. [CB 38/598]

GEISE, John. What is a railway? *Technol.Cult.*, 1959, 1: 68-77.

HERTWIG, A. Die Eisenbahn und das Bauwesen. *Technikgeschichte*, 1935, 24: 29-37, 6 pl.

LEE, Charles E. Some railway facts and fallacies. Presidential address. *Trans.Newcomen Soc.*, 1960-61, 33: 1-16.

LOREE, Leonor F. Locomotives! Past and present. An address delivered at the ninth annual American dinner of the Newcomen Society of England, held at New York, on April 24, 1933. 11 p., ill. New York: American Locomotive Co., 1933.

MAHR, Otto. Aus der Geschichte der Eisenbahnräder. *Technikgeschichte*, 1935, 24: 83-8.

MARTELL, Paul. Zur Geschichte des Eisenbahngleises. *Arch. Gesch.Naturwiss.Tech.*, 1917, 8: 41-8.

METZELTIN, E. Zur Geschichte der Druckluftlokomotive. *Technikgeschichte,* 1935, 24: 77-82, 2 pl.

RÖLL, Victor. Enzyklopädie des Eisenbahnwesens. 2nd ed. 10 vol. Berlin/Wien: 1912-23.

SCHIELDROP, Edgar Bonsak. The railway. With a foreword by Sir Ronald Matthews. 256 p. (Conquest of Space and Time, 1) London: Hutchinson; Philadelphia: McKay, 1939. [CB 61/401]

SMITH, Edgar C. The centenary of the railway. *Nature,* 1925, 116: 19-20.

UDE, Hans. Zur Geschichte der Eisenbahnwerkstoffe. *Technikgeschichte,* 1935, 24: 38-61, 2 pl., 13 fig.

TWce-bv

EWALD, Kurt. 20000 Schriftquellen zur Eisenbahnkunde. 928 p., 24 pl. Berlin: Springer, 1941.
Reviewed by R. Zaunick, *Mitt.Gesch.Med.*, 1941-42, 40: 354-5.

TWw in different countries

TWwb

BUDD, Ralph. Railway routes across the Rocky Mountains. *Trans.Newcomen Soc.*, 1937-38, 18: 205-23, 3 fig.

DICKERMAN, William Carter. 43 hours. My era in railway equipment life. A Newcomen address. 44 p., ill. Princeton, N.J.: Princeton University Press (for Newcomen Society, American Branch), 1943.

MINICK, Judd L. The Allegheny Portage Railroad. (Visit of the American Society of Mechanical Engineers to Altoona, Penna. October 5-7, 1925). 4 p., 1 ill. [n.p.]: Old Portage Railroad, 1925.

PASSER, Harold C. Frank Julian Sprague, father of electric traction, 1857-1934. In: Miller, William, ed. Men in business, p. 212-237, ill. Cambridge, Mass.: Harvard University Press, 1952.

RIEGEL, Robert E. The story of the western railroads. xv, 345 p. New York: Macmillan, 1926.

WHITE, John H. Introduction of the locomotive safety truck. (*Contrib.Mus.Hist.Technol.*, 24) *Bull.U.S.Nat.Mus.*, 1961, 228: 117-31.

TWwc

BRAZIL. CONSELHO NACIONAL DE GEOGRAFIA. I centenario das ferrovias brasileiras (diversos autores). 414 p., ill., portr., maps, tables, bibliogr. Rio de Janiero: Instituto Brasileiro de Geographia e Estatistica, 1954. [CB 83/211]

TWwe

FOWKES, E.H. Railway history and the local historian. 40 p. York, England: East Yorkshire Local History Society, 1963.
Reviewed by James L. Howgego, *J.Soc.Arch.*, 1964, 2: 488-9.

LEE, Charles E. The Haytor granite tramroad. *Trans.Newcomen Soc.*, 1962-63, 35: 237-41.

LEE, Charles E. Narrow-gauge railways in North Wales. 136 p. London: Railway Publishing Co., 1945. [CB 70/213]
Reviewed by S.H.R., *Geogr.J.*, 1945, 106: 227-8.

LEE, Charles E. The world's oldest railway. Three hundred years of coal conveyance to the Tyne Staiths. *Trans.Newcomen Soc.*, 1945-47, 25: 141-62.

MARSHALL, Chapman Frederick Dendy. Centenary history of the Liverpool and Manchester railway: to which is appended a transcript of the relevant portions of Rastrick's "Rainhill" notebook. ix, 192 p., 20 pl., ill. London: Locomotive Publishing Company, 1930.

ROLT, L.T.C. The Talyllyn Railway. *Trans.Newcomen Soc.*, 1960-61, 33: 17-29.

SKEAT, W.O. The Decapod locomotive of the Great Eastern Railway. *Trans.Newcomen Soc.*, 1951-52 and 1952-53, 28: 169-85; 1953-54 and 1954-55, 29: 263-4.

TWwf

ROBERT, Jean. De Nice à Chamonix. Les réseaux secondaires dans les Alpes françaises. 102 p., ill., maps. St. Germaine-en-Laye: Neuilly, 1961.
Reviewed by M. Daumas, *Rev.Hist.Sci.*, 1964, 17: 280.

TWwg

MAHR, Otto. Zeittafel zur Geschichte der Eisenbahnen, besonders in Deutschland. *Technikgeschichte,* 1935, 24: 109-15, 2 pl.

MATSCHOSS, Conrad. Hundert Jahre deutsche Eisenbahn. *Technikgeschichte,* 1935, 24: 1-22, 4 pl., 14 fig.

MOSER, Alfred. Der Dampfbetrieb der schweizerischen Eisenbahnen. Eine geschichtlich-technische Darstellung der im Bahnbetrieb der Schweiz gestandenen Dampflokomotiven, 1847-1936. Nachtrag umfassend die Jahre 1937-1946. 31 pl., ill. Basel: Verlag Birkhauser, 1947. [CB 82/216]

SCHWARZE, Bruno. Die theoretische Aus- und Fortbildung bei den deutschen Eisenbahnen. Ein geschichtlicher Abriss. *Technikgeschichte,* 1935, 24: 71-6.

VEREIN MITTELEUROPÄISCHER EISENBAHNVERWALTUNGEN. Die Entwicklung der Lokomotive im Gebiete des Vereins deutscher Eisenbahnverwaltungen. Vol. 1. 1835-1880. Von Richard von Helmholtz und W. Staby. Vol. 2. 1880-1920. 512 p. München: Oldenbourg, 1930, 1937.

TWwg-qt

KRAFT, Fritz Gerhard. "Hohenzollern, Aktiengesellschaft für Lokomotivbau" in Düsseldorf. Ein geschichtlicher Rückblick zu ihrer Stillegung im Jahre 1929. *Beitr.Gesch.Tech.Ind.*, 1932, 21: 79-84, 14 fig.

TWwh

KOZYREW, Aleksander. Udział Polaków w budowie kolei zelaznych południowego Uralu i kolei Zachodnio-syberysjskiej. [Participation of Poles in the construction of Russian railroads in the south of the Ural Mountains and the great Siberian Trail. (In Polish, with Russian and English summaries)] *Kwart.Hist. Nauk.Tech.*, 1961, 6: 288-301.

TWwk

LAMALLE, Ulysse. Histoire des chemins de fer belges. 158 p., 8 pl., 82 fig. (Collection Nationale, hors série) Bruxelles: Office de Publicité, 1943.

TWwn

KOZYREW, Aleksander. *See* TWwh

WESTWOOD, J.N. A history of Russian railways. 326 p., ill., maps. London: Allen and Unwin, 1964.

ZABARINSKII, P.P. [On the history of railway gauges in Russia. (In Russian)] *Arkh.Ist.Nauk Tekh.*, 1934, 4: 397-409, 4 fig.

TWx techniques and instruments

TWxb

ROWATT, Thomas. Railway brakes. *Trans.Newcomen Soc.*, 1927-28, 8: 19-32.

STABY, D. Die geschichtliche Entwicklung der Eisenbahnbremsen. *Beitr.Gesch.Tech.Ind.*, 1924, 14: 1-21, 26 fig.

TWxu

BORN, Erhard. Zur Entwicklungsgeschichte des Eisenbahnsignalwesens. *Technikgeschichte,* 1935, 24: 89-100, 2 fig.

DEAKIN, W.H. Development of railway signalling. *Trans.Newcomen Soc.*, 1929-30, 9: 1-11, 3 fig., 3 pl.

SPRAGUE, Frank J. The genesis of the multiple-unit system of electric train control. *Trans.Newcomen Soc.*, 1932-33, 13: 117-30.

TWxv

METZELTIN, E. Geschichte der Normung im Eisenbahnwesen. *Technikgeschichte,* 1935, 24: 62-70, 2 pl., 3 fig.

TX AERONAUTICS; AVIATION

see also XY AIR FORCES

TXc general history

ABBOT, C.G. The discovery of helium and what came of it. *Annu.Rep.Smithsonian Inst.for 1918*, p. 121-6. Washington, D.C.: 1920.
Popular account including the application to ballooning.

AMES, Joseph S. Aeronautic research. *J.Franklin Inst.*, 1922, 193: 15-28. Also in *Annu.Rep.Smithsonian Inst.for 1922*, p. 167-74, 7 fig., 5 pl. Washington, D.C.: 1924.

Astronautics and Aeronautics. Chronology on science, technology, and policy. 1963- Washington: National Aeronautics and Space Administration, 1964-

BRABAZON, John Theodore Cuthbert Moore-Brabazon, *baron.* The birth of flight. *Nature*, 1953, 171: 640-1.

BROWN, Cecil Leonard Morley. The conquest of the air: an historical survey. 126 p., 8 pl. (World's Manuals) London: Oxford University Press, 1927.

CROSS, Roy, ed. Early aeroplanes, 1907-18. Brattleboro, Vt.: Stephen Greene, 1962.
Twelve aircraft illustrate the early development of aviation.
Reviewed by Charles H. Hubbell, *Technol.Cult.*, 1964, 5: 98-9.

DAVY, M.J.B. Interpretative history of flight: a survey of the history and development of aeronautics, with particular reference to contemporary influences and conditions. 208 p., 31 pl. London: H.M. Stationery Off., 1937.
Reviewed in *Nature*, 1937, 140: 637.

DRYDEN, Hugh L. A half century of aeronautical research. *Proc.Amer.Phil.Soc.*, 1954, 98: 115-20.

DRYDEN, Hugh L. Supersonic travel within the last two hundred years. *Sci.Mon.*, 1954, 78: 289-95, 7 fig.

DUHEM, Jules. Histoire des idées aéronautiques avant Montgolfier. 458 p., ill. Paris: Sorlot, 1943.

DUHEM, Jules. Les origines de l'hélicoptère. *Thalès*, 1939, 4: 132-41.

DUKE, Neville; LANCHBERY, Edward. Sound barrier: the story of high-speed flight. 6th ed. 129 p., 27 pl. London: Cassell, 1954; New York: Philosophical Library, 1955.
First published 1953.

EMME, Eugene M.; DRYDEN, Hugh L. Aeronautics and astronautics: an American chronology of science and technology in the exploration of space, 1915-1960. xi, 240 p. Washington: National Aeronautics and Space Administration, 1961.
Reviewed by Melvin Kranzberg, *Amer.Hist.Rev.*, 1961-62, 67: 516.

FELDHAUS, Franz M. Luftfahrten einst und jetzt. 2nd rev. ed. 125 p., ill. Berlin: Hermann Paetel Verlag, 1923.
1st edition 1908.

FELDHAUS, Gilbert W. Die Entwicklung des Menschenfluges. *Weltall*, 1928, 28: 5-10, 2 fig.

GIBBS-SMITH, Charles H. The aeroplane: an historical survey of its origins and development. x, 375 p. London: H.M. Stationery Off., 1960.
Reviewed in *Sci.Amer.*, 1962, 207: no. 1, 175-6.

GIBBS-SMITH, Charles H. A history of flying. 304 p., ill., bibliogr. London: Batsford, 1953; New York: Praeger, 1954.

GOLDSTROM, John. A narrative history of aviation. xii, 319 p., 32 pl. New York: Macmillan, 1930.

HARPER, Harry. The evolution of the flying machine. Balloon, airship, aeroplane. 288 p. London: Hutchinson, 1930.

HENNIG, Richard. Beiträge zur Geschichte der Aeronautik. *Beitr.Gesch.Tech.Ind.*, 1918, 8: 100-16.
Down to the time of Leonardo da Vinci.

HENNIG, Richard. Zur Vorgeschichte der Luftfahrt. *Beitr. Gesch.Tech.Ind.*, 1928, 18: 87-94.

[HISTORY of aviation.] *Tech.Rundsch.*, 1953, 45: no. 51, 14 p.
The entire number is devoted to the history of aviation.

HOFF, N.J. A short history of the development of airplane structure. *Amer.Scient.*, 1946, 34: 212-24, 370-88.

HUNSAKER, Jerome C. A half century of aeronautical development. *Proc.Amer.Phil.Soc.*, 1954, 98: 121-30, 18 fig.

ICKX, Lucien. Il y a cinquante ans, l'avion. *Industrie*, 1961, 15: 555-64.

JAUNEAUD, Marcel. L'évolution de l'aéronautique. 284 p., 34 fig. Paris: Flammarion, 1923. [CB 15/249]

JOSEPHY, Alvin M., ed. The American Heritage history of flight. 416 p., ill. New York: American Heritage, 1962.
Also published with title: The adventure of man's flight. New York: Putnam, 1963.
Reviewed by Norwood Russell Hanson, *Isis*, 1964, 55: 230-3.

LARSEN, Egon. The day England ceased to be an island. *Discovery*, 1959, 20: 292-4.
On the airplane flight across the English Channel of 25 July 1909.

LAUFER, Berthold. The prehistory of aviation. 96 p., 12 pl. (Field Museum of Natural History, publication 253. Anthropological series, 18: no. 1) Chicago: 1928. [CB 26/234]

LOENING, Grover. Fifty years of flying progress. *Annu.Rep. Smithsonian Inst.for 1954*, p. 201-16, 26 pl. Washington, D.C.: 1955.

MAGOUN, Frederick Alexander; HODGINS, Eric. A history of aircraft. xx, 495 p. New York: McGraw-Hill, 1931.

MAURAIN, Charles. Les records de l'aviation. *Rev.Mois*, 1913, 16: 69-72.

MEANS, James Howard. James Means and the problem of man-flight during the period 1882-1920. xi, 143 p., ill. (Publication, 4526) Washington, D.C.: Smithsonian Institution, 1964.

PAINLEVÉ, Paul; BOREL, Émile; MAURAIN, Charles. L'aviation. [8th ed.] 308 p., 48 fig. (Nouvelle Collection Scientifique) Paris: Alcan, 1923.
First published 1910.

PITCAIRN, Harold F. The autogiro: its characteristics and accomplishments. *Annu.Rep.Smithsonian Inst.for 1930*, p. 265-71, 9 pl. Washington, D.C.: 1931.
Reprinted from *J.Franklin Inst.*, 1930, 209: 571-84.

RAE, John B. Science and engineering in the history of aviation. *Technol.Cult.*, 1961, 2: 391-9.

RUMPLER, Edmund. Technisches über das Trans-Ozeanflugzeug. *Arch.Gesch.Math.Naturwiss.Tech.*, 1927, 10: 185-206, ill.

SALATUN, R.J. Sedjarah penerbangan, melukiskan tjitatjita, perdjuangan, pengorbanan dan kemenangan manusia untuk menaklukkan angkasa-raya. (In Bahasa Indonesia) 84 p. Djakarta: Pustaka Rakjat, 1950.
Apropos of the history of aeronautics.

SCHIELDROP, Edgar Bonsak. The air. Foreword by J.T.C. Moore-Brabazon. vi, 327 p., ill. (Conquest of Space and Time, 4) London: Hutchinson; Philadelphia: McKay, 1940.

SCIENCE MUSEUM. Handbook of the collections illustrating aeronautics. 1. Heavier-than-air craft. Compiled by M.J.B. Davy. 3 vol. London: H.M. Stationery Office, 1929-34.
Revised edition 1949.

SCIENCE MUSEUM. Handbook of the collections illustrating aeronautics. 2. Lighter-than-air craft: a brief outline of the history and development of the balloon and the airship, with reference to the National Aeronautical Collection, and a catalogue of the exhibits. By M.J.B. Davy. 2nd ed. 112 p., 32 pl. London: H.M. Stationery Off., 1950.
First published 1934.

STEHLING, Kurt R.; BELLER, William. Skyhooks. 264 p., ill. Garden City, N.Y.: Doubleday, 1962.
History of ballooning from 1783 to the present.

STEWART, Oliver. First flights. 225 p. London: Routledge and Kegan Paul, 1957.
Reviewed in *Sch.Sci.Rev.*, 1957, 39: 178.

THURSTON, A.P. The evolution of rider planes for aircraft. *Trans.Newcomen Soc.*, 1941-42, 22: 107-15, 6 fig.

THURSTON, A.P. Reminiscences of early aviation. *Trans.Newcomen Soc.*, 1949-50 and 1950-51, 27: 1-6.

TURNER, Charles Cyril. The old flying days. x, 374 p., ill. London: Sampson Low, 1927.

TXc-bx

LIEBMANN, Louis; WAHL, Gustav. Katalog der historischen Abteilung der ersten internationalen Luftschiffahrt-Ausstellung (ILA) zu Frankfurt a. M. 1909. 536 p. Frankfurt a. M.: Wüsten, 1912.

TXcc

DUHEM, Jules. Musée aéronautique avant Montgolfier. Recueil de figures et de documents pour servir à l'histoire des idées aéronautiques avant l'invention des aérostats. 253 p., ill. Paris: Sorlot, 1944.

TXcm

MARSH, W. Lockwood. Aeronautical prints and drawings. xx, 36 p., 87 pl. London: Halton & Truscott Smith, 1924.
Reviewed by Hans W. Singer, *Deut.Lit.Zeitung,* 1927, 1116-17.

TXda

SCHAEFER, G.; NAUMANN, W. Physicians as pioneers of air travel. *Ciba Symp.* (Summit, N.J.), 1941, 3: 1026-32.

URDANG, George. Pharmacy and aviation. *Bull.Hist.Med.,* 1944, 15: 324-6.
Notes on pharmacists who were connected with balloon aviation.

TXdaj

DUKE, Neville; LANCHBERY, Edward; ed. The saga of flight: from Leonardo da Vinci to the guided missile. 406 p. New York: John Day Company, 1961. [CB 88/566]
An anthology of writings on flight.

THOMAS, Lowell. The first world flight: being the personal narratives of Lowell Smith, Erik Nelson, Leigh Wade, Leslie Arnold, Henry Ogden, John Harding, written by Lowell Thomas. xxii, 328 p., ill. Boston: Houghton Mifflin, 1925.

TXn/t special aspects

TXnh-be

IMPERIAL AERONAUTICAL SOCIETY OF JAPAN. Dictionary of aeronautical terms. English, Franch, Japanese, German. vii, 484 p. Washington: U.S. Govt. Print. Off., 1942.
Reproduced under the supervision of the Director of U.S. Intelligence Service from the 2nd edition, 1936.

TXth

BARRY, Mary Elizabeth; HANNA, Paul R.; ed. Wonder flights of long ago. Illustrated by Lynd Ward. x, 205 p. New York/London: Appleton, 1930.
A collection of flight legends, discovered by pupils of the intermediate grades of the Lincoln School of Teachers College, Columbia University.

TXw in different countries

TXwb

ABBOT, Charles G. The relations between the Smithsonian Institution and the Wright brothers. 27 p. (*Smithsonian Misc. Collect.,* 81: no. 5) Washington, D.C.: 1928.

BASSETT, Preston R. Aeronautics in New York State. *N.Y.Hist.,* 1962, 43: 115-48, portr., ill.

MILBANK, Jeremiah. The first century of flight in America. An introductory survey. x, 248 p., 24 pl. Princeton: Princeton University Press, 1943.
Reviewed by J.L. Pritchard, *Nature,* 1943, 152: 461-2.

PARKIN, J.H. Bell and Baldwin: their development of aerodromes and hydrodromes at Baddeck, Nova Scotia. xviii, 555 p., ill. Toronto: Univ. Toronto Press, 1964.

RAE, John B. Technology and entrepreneurship in the American aircraft industry. *Proc.10th Int.Congr.Hist.Sci.* (Ithaca, 1962), (1), p. 453-6. Paris: Hermann, 1964.

See also Langley, Samuel Pierpont 2: 45
Wright, Orville 2: 639

TXwb-bv

COHEN, I. Bernard. The development of aeronautics in America. A review of recent publications. *Isis,* 1947, 37: 58-64, 2 fig.

TXwb-qk

HISTORICAL origins of the National Aeronautics and Space Administration. 22 p., ill. Washington, D.C.: U.S. Government Printing Office, 1963.

TXwe

BOUGHTON, Terence. The story of the British light aeroplane. xiv, 321 p., ill., app., bibliogr. London: Murray, 1963.
Reviewed by Kenneth Razak, *Technol.Cult.,* 1964, 5: 457-9.

BRETT, R. Dallas. The history of British aviation, 1908-1914. xxiv, 388 p. London: Hamilton, 1934.

HODGSON, J.E. The history of aeronautics in Great Britain from the earliest times to the latter half of the nineteenth century. xxii, 436 p., 86 pl. London: Oxford University Press, 1924. [CB 17/605]
Reviewed by George Sarton, *Isis,* 1925, 7: 521-8.

TXwf-qd

FARIA, Antonio de Portugal de Faria, *Visconde de.* Académie aéronautique Bartholomeu de Gusmão, fondée en 1910 à Paris. Son rôle et son action dans les revendications émises en faveur de B. de Gusmão, inventeur des aérostats et précurseur des navigateurs aériens. 463 p., ill. Lausanne: Imprimeries Réunies, 1913. [CB 14/516]

TXwg

GEORGII, Walter. Ten years' gliding and soaring in Germany. *Annu.Rep.Smithsonian Inst.for 1930,* p. 273-83, 16 pl. Washington, D.C.: 1931.
Lecture delivered before the Royal Aeronautical Society, London, on Feb. 19, 1930.

SUPF, Peter. Das Buch der deutschen Fluggeschichte. Vorzeit. Wendezeit. Werdezeit. 518 p., 463 fig. Berlin: Klemm, 1935.

TXwi

BOFFITI, Giuseppe. Il volo in Italia. Storia documentata e aneddotica dell'aeronautica e dell'aviazione in Italia. xvii, 384 p. Firenze: Barbera, 1921. [CB 12/644]

TXwn

SOKOL'SKII, V.N. Iz istorii samoletstroeniia na Ukraine (Chervonskie aeroplannye masterskie). [From the history of aircraft construction in the Ukraine (the Chervonnom aeroplane workshops) (In Russian)] *Tr.Inst.Ist.Est.Tekh.,* 1962, 45: 222-35.
The eve of the First World War.

TXx techniques and instruments

TXxb

MURPHY, Charles J.V. Parachute. viii, 275 p. New York/London: Putnam, 1930.

TXxu

DOOLITTLE, James H. Early experiments in instrument flying. *Annu.Rep.Smithsonian Inst.for 1961,* p. 337-55. Washington, D.C.: 1962.

THURSTON, A.P. Automatic control of flying machines. *Trans. Newcomen Soc.,* 1939-40, 20: 151, 1 pl.
Apropos of Hiram S. Maxim.

TXxx museums

SCIENCE MUSEUM. Catalogue of the collections in the Museum with descriptive and historical notes and illustrations. Aeronautics. 71 p., 6 pl. London: H.M. Stationery Office, 1922.
Supplement compiled by B. Davy. 1924.

SCIENCE MUSEUM. Handbook. *See* TXc

UNITED STATES NATIONAL MUSEUM. National aircraft collection. 5th ed. [By Paul Edward Garber] 44 p. (Publication, 3635) Washington, D.C.: Smithsonian Institution, 1941.

TXy related subjects

TXyUK

SCIENCE MUSEUM. Handbook of the collections illustrating aeronautics. 3. The propulsion of aircraft. *See* UP

TAYLOR, C. Fayette. Aircraft propulsion: a review of the evolution of aircraft powerplants. *Annu.Rep.Smithsonian Inst.for 1962*, p.245-98, ill. Washington, D.C.: 1963.

TZ ASTRONAUTICS

Astronautics and Aeronautics. Chronology on science, technology, and policy. 1963- Washington: National Aeronautics and Space Administration, 1964-

EMME, Eugene M.; DRYDEN, Hugh L. *See* TXc

THE FIRST five years of the space age. *Sky Telesc.*, 1963, 25: 148-50.
A table of launchings and their experimental data, October 1957 to December 1962.

GATLAND, Kenneth W.; KUNESCH, Anthony M. Space travel. x, 11-205 p., ill., fig., tables. New York: Philosophical Library, 1953.
The first half of this book deals with the history of rockets; the second, with the possibilities of space travel.

MAXWELL, W.R. Some aspects of the origins and early development of astronautics. *J.Brit.Interplanet.Soc.*, 1961-62, 18: 415-25.

STUHLINGER, E., *et al.*; ed. Astronautical engineering and science from Peenemünde to planetary space. Honoring the fiftieth birthday of Wernher Von Braun. xviii, 394 p., ill. New York: McGraw-Hill, 1963.
Reviewed by Myron A. Hoffman, *Technol.Cult.*, 1964, 5: 264-5.

THOMAS, Shirley. Satellite tracking facilities; their history and operation. 159 p.. ill. New York: Holt. 1963.

TZda

THOMAS, Shirley. Men of space: profiles of the leaders in space research, development and exploration. Vol. 1-6. Philadelphia: Chilton, 1960-63.
Sub-title varies.

TZwb

EMME, Eugene M. Aeronautics as astronautics: an American chronology of science and technology in the exploration of space, 1915-1960. xi, 240 p. Washington, D.C.: National Aeronautics and Space Administration, 1961.

GRIMWOOD, James M. Project Mercury. A chronology. xiv, 238 p., ill. Washington: National Aeronautics and Space Administration, 1963.

HAYES, E. Nelson. The Smithsonian's satellite-tracking program. Its history and organization. *Annu.Rep.Smithsonian Inst. for 1961*, p. 275-322. Washington, D.C.: 1962.

HOLME, Molly. First five years of NASA. A concise chronology. 68 p. Washington, D.C.: National Aeronautics and Space Administration Historical Staff, 1963.

WATTS, Raymond N. Project Mercury concluded. *Sky Telesc.*, 1963, 26: 327-8.

TZwn

KRIEGER, F.J. Behind the sputniks. A survey of Soviet space science. vi, 380 p. Washington: Public Affairs Press, 1958.

TZyOF

HISTORY of research in space biology and biodynamics at the Air Force Missile Development Center, Holloman Air Force Base, New Mexico, 1946-1958. ix, 114 p., ill., portr. Holloman Air Force Base, N.M.: Historical Division, Office of Information Services, Air Force Missile Development Center, Air Research and Development Command, 1958.

HISTORY of research in subgravity and zero-g at the Air Force Missile Development Center, Holloman Air Force Base, New Mexico, 1948-1958. 46 p., bibliogr. Holloman Air Force Base, N.M.: Historical Branch, Office of Information Services, Air Force Missile Development Center, Air Research and Development Command, U.S. Air Force, 1958.

U MECHANICAL ENGINEERING

for special mechanical technologies *see* WQ

Uc

BURSTALL, Aubrey F. A history of mechanical engineering. 456 p., ill. London: Faber; New York: Pitman, 1963.
Reviewed by Eugene S. Ferguson, *Technol.Cult.*, 1964, 5: 438-40.

CRESSY, Edward. A hundred years of mechanical engineering. 340 p., 64 pl. London: Duckworth; New York: Macmillan, 1937.
Reviewed by Dugald C. Jackson, *Isis*, 1939, 31: 94-5.

ISTORIA mashinost-roenia. [The history of machinery construction. (In Russian)] *Tr.Inst.Ist.Est.Tekh.*, 1960, 29: 1-375, fig. [CB 86/473]
Whole volume on mechanical engineering.

USHER, Abbott Payson. A history of mechanical inventions. Rev. ed. x, 450 p., 159 fig. Cambridge: Harvard University Press, 1954.
Re-issued Boston: Beacon Press, 1959.
Reviewed by Lynn White, *Isis*, 1955, 46: 290-3; by I. Bernard Cohen, *J.Hist.Med.*, 1957, 12: 277; by Thomas M. Smith, *Technol.Cult.*, 1961, 2: 34-7.
First published New York: 1929 and reviewed by R.K. Merton, *Isis*, 1935, 24: 177-80.
Spanish translation (389 p., 148 fig. Mexico: Fondo de Cultura Económica, 1941) reviewed by Aldo Mieli, *Archeion*, 1942, 24: 112-17.

WESTCOTT, G.F. Mechanical and electrical engineering, including energy conversion, transmission and storage; atomic energy; pumping, blowing and compressing machinery; explosives and ordnance. 40 p. (Classified Lists of Historical Events) London: H.M. Stationery Off.(for the Science Museum), 1955.

Ucc

NICOL, Hugh. Agricultural sources of mechanical information. *Trans.Newcomen Soc.*, 1929-30, 10: 115-19, 1 fig.

Uwe-qt

HESKETH, Everard. J. and E. Hall Ltd., 1785 to 1935. viii, 58 p., pl. Glasgow University Press, 1935.
History of the engineering firm created by John Hall.

PETREE, J. Foster. Maudslay, Sons and Field as general engineers. *Trans.Newcomen Soc.*, 1934-35, 15: 39-61.

UB MACHINES AND MECHANISMS

for servomechanisms *see* TAxu

UBc

FERGUSON, Eugene S. Kinematics of mechanisms from the time of Watt. (*Contrib.Mus.Hist.Technol.*, 27) *Bull.U.S.Nat.Mus.*, 1962, 228: 186-230.

HORWITZ, Hugo Th. Über das Aufkommen des Zahnrades. *Beitr. Gesch.Tech.Ind.*, 1932, 21: 150-2, 6 fig.

ICHAK, Fr. Das perpetuum mobile. 98 p., 38 ill. (Aus Natur und Geisteswelt) Leipzig: Teubner, 1914.

KAMMERER, O. Die Entwicklung der Zahnräder. *Beitr.Gesch.Tech. Ind.*, 1912, 4: 242-73.

MICHEL, J. Mouvements perpétuels. Leur histoire et leurs particularités depuis les premières tentatives du XIIe s. jusqu'aux engins des inventeurs modernes. viii, 52 p., 82 fig. Paris: Desforges, Girardot, 1927. [CB 25/414]

O'BRIEN, Robert, *et al.* Machines. 200 p., ill. (Life Science Library) New York: Time, 1964.
Reviewed by Melvin Kranzberg, *Science*, 1964, 144: 666-7.

PUPIN, Michael I. Romance of the machine. vi, 111 p. New York: Scribner's, 1930.

REY, Jean. Auguste Rateau, turbomachines en général, ventilateurs, compresseurs, pompes rotatives. *Mém.Compt.Rend. Soc.Ing.Civils France*, 1930, 917-22.

SOULARD, Robert. A history of the machine. Adapted from the French by Peter Chaitin. 111 p., ill. (New Illustrated Library of Science and Invention, 11) New York: Hawthorn, 1963.
Translated and adapted from: Histoire de la machine (Lausanne: Editions Rencontre, 1962). There is also a German edition.

UBhh

KONFEDERATOV, I.Ia. Istoricheskaia klassifikatsiia tekhnologicheskikh mashin. [An historical classification of technological machines. (In Russian)] *Vop.Ist.Est.Tekh.*, 1962, 13: 26-36.

UBsc

LILLEY, S. Men, machines and history. A short history of tools and machines in relation to social progress. 240 p., 53 ill. (Past and Present Series, 7) London: Cobbett Press, 1948.
Reviewed by Sixten Rönnow, *Lychnos*, 1952, 454-5.

UBtq

WETTICH, Hans. Die Maschine in der Karikatur. Ein Buch zum Siege der Technik. 216 p., ill. Berlin: Eysler, 1920. [CB 10/218]

UBwb

BURLINGAME, Roger. Machines that built America. 214 p. New York: Harcourt Brace, 1953.
Reviewed by Clyde E. Dankert, *Sci.Mon.*, 1954, 78: 336.

UBwk

BOGAERT, Ed. W. Un peu d'histoire (les sciences mécaniques en Belgique pendant un siècle). *Bull.Tech.Ass.Ing.Bruxelles*, 1931, 27: 23-33.

UBwn-f

ANISIMOV, Iu. A.; DOBROV, G.M. Izucheniye istorii tekhniki v USSR. [The study of the history of machinery in the USSR. (In Russian)] *Vop.Ist.Est.Tekh.*, 1956, 1: 319-22.

UBwn-kq

ARTOBOLEVSKI, I.I. Evolution de la théorie de la structure et de la classification des mécanismes en Russie depuis le XIXe siècle à nous jours. *Act.VIIIe Congr.Int.Hist.Sci.* (Florence, 1956), p. 980-3. Paris: Hermann, 1958.

UBxh-wn

UVAROVA, L.I. O razvitii v Rossii nauchnykh osnov proektirovaniia mashin. [On the development in Russia of scientific bases for the projective representation of machines. (In Russian)] *Vop.Ist.Est.Tekh.*, 1961, 11: 116-19.

UBxx

UNITED STATES NATIONAL MUSEUM. Catalog of the mechanical collections of the Division of Engineering. By Frank A. Taylor. viii, 203 p., 37 pl. (*Bull.U.S.Nat.Mus.*, 173) Washington, D.C.: Smithsonian Institution, 1939.

UByTO

CONRADIS, Heinz. Alte Baggermaschinen. *Technikgeschichte*, 1937, 26: 51-61, 2 pl., 11 fig.

UC HAND AND MACHINE TOOLS; MACHINING

CLARK, E. Kitson. Humanity under the hammer. Presidential address to the Institution of Mechanical Engineers, 23rd October, 1931. *Proc.Inst.Mech.Eng.*, 1931, 121: 107-42.
Contains much information on the history of man's earliest tool: the hammer.

DICK, Otto. Die Feile und ihre Entwicklungsgeschichte. 251 p., 278 ill. Berlin: Springer, 1925.

DRUCKER, Peter F. Work and tools. *Technol.Cult.*, 1959, 1: 28-37.

FELDHAUS, Franz M. Die Geschichte der Schleifmittel. With appendix by H. Friederichs. 83 p., 49 ill. Hannover-Hainholz: Vereinigte Schmirgel- und Maschinenfabriken Aktien-Gesellschaft, 1919. [CB 10/217]
History of polishing from prehistoric times until the middle of last century.

FELDHAUS, Franz M. Die Säge. Ein Rückblick auf vier Jahrtausende. 72 p., ill. Berlin: J.D. Dominicus, 1921.

FISCHER, Hermann. Beiträge zur Geschichte der Werkzeugmaschinen. [1]. Bohrer und Bohrmaschinen für Holz und Metall. [2]. Spanabhebende Werkzeugmaschinen mit geradem Hauptweg (Metalhobelmaschinen). [3]. Schmiedemaschinen. *Beitr. Gesch.Tech.Ind.*, 1912, 4: 274-308: 1913, 5: 73-123; 1915, 6: 1-34, ill.

FORWARD, E.A. The early history of the cylinder boring machine. *Trans.Newcomen Soc.*, 1924-25, 5: 24-38, pl. v-viii. [CB 22/271]

GOODMAN, W.L. A history of woodworking tools. 208 p., pl., fig. London: Bell, 1964.

GRODZINSKI, P. Early history of diamond tool applications. *Act.VIIe Congr.Int.Hist.Sci.* (Jerusalem, 1953), p. 324-31. Paris: Hermann, [n.d.].

HÄNEKE, Hans. Aus der Geschichte der Zylinderbohrmaschine. *Beitr.Gesch.Tech.Ind.*, 1927, 17: 117-21, 12 fig.

HORWITZ, Hugo Th. Die Entwicklung der Drehbewegung. *Beitr. Gesch.Tech.Ind.*, 1920, 10: 179-95, 13 fig.

KURREIN, Max. The history of the machine-tool. *Act.VIIe Congr.Int.Hist.Sci.* (Jerusalem, 1953), p. 418-25. Paris: Hermann, [n.d.]

LISICHKIN, S.M. K istorii tekhniki turbinnogo bureniia. [On the history of the process of turbine drilling. (In Russian)] *Vop.Ist.Est.Tekh.*, 1962, 12: 195-7.

PETRIE, W.M. Flinders. History in tools. *Sci.Progr.*, 1917, 12: 71-82.

PRAUS, Alexis A. Mechanical principles involved in primitive tools and those of the machine age. *Isis*, 1948, 38: 157-60.

SCHROEDER, Alf. Entwicklung der Schleiftechnik bis zur Mitte des 19. Jahrhunderts. viii, 191 p., 153 fig. (Diss.) Braunschweig: 1930.

SPRINGER, Walter. Der Weg zur modernen Bohrmaschine. Eine technikgeschichtliche Skizze. 133 p., 94 fig. Berlin-Halensee: Forschungen zur Geschichte der Industrie, 1941.
Reviewed by R. Zaunick, *Mitt.Gesch.Med.*, 1941-42, 40; 178.

TÉTRY, Andrée. Les outils chez les êtres vivants. Préface de Lucien Cuénot. 337 p., 75 fig. (Avenir de la Science, 26) Paris: Gallimard, 1948.
Reviewed by P. Teilhard de Chardin, *Rev.Quest.Sci.*, 1949, 10: 298-9.

WITTMAN, Karl. Die Entwicklung der Drehbank bis zum Jahre 1939. 211 p., ill. Düsseldorf: VDI-Verlag, 1960.
Reviewed by Robert S. Woodbury, *Technol.Cult.*, 1961, 2: 176-8.

WOODBURY, Robert S. History of the gear-cutting machine. A historical study in geometry and machines. With a foreword by Abbott Payson Usher. iv, 135 p. (Technology Monographs, Historical Series, 1) Cambridge, Mass.: Technology Press of M.I.T., 1958.
Reviewed by Edwin A. Battison, *Isis*, 1960, 51: 582-3; for other reviews *see* CB 85/406 and CB 86/475.

WOODBURY, Robert S. History of the grinding machine. A historical study in tools and precision production. 191 p., ill., bibliogr. (Technology Monographs, Historical Series 2) Cambridge, Mass.: Technology Press of M.I.T., 1959.

WOODBURY, Robert S. History of the lathe to 1850. 124 p. Boston: Nimrod Press, 1961.

WOODBURY, Robert S. History of the milling machine: a study in technical development. 107 p., ill. (Technology Monographs, Historical Series, 3) Cambridge, Mass.: Technology Press of M.I.T., 1960.
Reviewed by Philip W. Bishop, *Isis*, 1961, 52: 610-11; for other reviews *see* CB 86/475 and CB 87/579.

WOODBURY, Robert S. The origins of the lathe. *Sci.Amer.*, 1963, 208: no. 4, 132-42.

UCda

ROE, Joseph Wickam. English and American tool builders. xv, 315 p. New Haven: Yale University Press, 1916. Reprinted 1926.

UCmzLO

HORWITZ, Hugo Th. Über den Gebrauch von Werkzeugen im Tierreich. *Geschichtsbl.Tech.Ind.*, 1927, 11: 26-9.

UCwb

ROE, Joseph Wickham. Aus der Geschichte der Amerikanischen Werkzeugmaschinen. *Beitr.Gesch.Tech.Ind.*, 1927, 17: 106-16, 4 fig.
Two chapters translated from the author's English and American tool-builders. New York: McGraw-Hill, 1916. Reprinted 1926. *See* UCda.

SLOANE, Eric. *See* UCxx

UCwb-qt

BROEHL, Wayne G., Jr. Precision Valley. The machine tool companies of Springfield, Vermont. Jones and Lamson Machine Company, Fellows Gear Shaper Company, Bryant Chucking Grinder Company. 274 p., 26 ill., 54 tables. Englewood Cliffs, N.J.: Prentice-Hall, 1959.
Reviewed by Robert S. Woodbury, *Technol.Cult.*, 1961, 2: 180-2.

TOURIN, R.H. Optical history of a machine tool builder. (Warner and Swasey). *Appl.Opt.*, 1964, 3: 1385-6.

UCwn

LISICHKIN, S.M. The history of turbine drilling technique in the USSR. *Act.VIIIe Congr.Int.Hist.Sci.* (Florence, 1956), p. 994-7. Paris: Hermann, 1958.

UCxx

MORGAN, F.C. Some old tools in Hereford Museum. *Trans.Newcomen Soc.*, 1942-43, 23: 55-65, fig.

SLOANE, Eric. A museum of early American tools. xii, 108 p., ill. New York: Funk, 1964.
Helpful in identifying tools.
Reviewed by Paul von Khrum, *Libr.J.*, 1964, 89: 2778.

UD MEANS OF JOINTING

BATTISON, Edwin A. Screw-thread cutting by the master-screw method since 1480. (*Contrib.Mus.Hist.Technol.*, 37) *Bull.U.S. Nat.Mus.*, 1964, 240: 106-19.

BELLUCCI, Giuseppe. I chiodi nell' etnografia antica e contemporanea. 266 p., 64 ill. Perugia: Unione Tipografica Cooperativa, 1919.

BERNDT, G. Die Entwicklung der Schraubengewinde. *Beitr.Gesch. Tech.Ind.*, 1924, 14: 101-20, 12 fig.

DICKINSON, H.W. Origin and manufacture of wood screws. *Trans. Newcomen Soc.*, 1941-42, 22: 79-89, 7 fig.

TREUE, Wilhelm. Kulturgeschichte der Schraube von der Antike bis zum achtzehnten Jahrhundert. Hrsg. im Auftrag der Kamax-Werke Rudolf Kellermann, Osterode am Harz. 170, 1 p., ill., bibliogr. München: F. Bruckman, 1955.

UE WELDING

FÜCHSEL, Max. Die Technik und der Schweisser. *Technikgeschichte*, 1933, 22: 103-8.

KHRENOV, Constantine C. History of electric arc welding in the USSR. *Proc.10th Int.Congr.Hist.Sci.* (Ithaca, 1962), (1), p. 463-6. Paris: Hermann, 1964.

UF HANDLING MACHINERY; VERTICAL TRANSPORT

BAUDET, Pierre. Histoire du transport verticale. *Bull.Soc. Ing.Civils France*, 1953, no. 1, 15-23.

GEYER, D.W. Beitrag zur Geschichte des elektrischen Hebezeuges. *Beitr.Gesch.Tech.Ind.*, 1926, 16: 261-79, 9 fig.

KAMMERER, O. Der Werkstoff im Kranbau. *Beitr.Gesch.Tech.Ind.*, 1924, 14: 130-54, 34 fig.

OSTOL'SKII, Vs. I. Pervye metallicheskie konstruktsii kranov v Rossii. [The first cranes of metal construction in Russia. (In Russian)] *Tr.Inst.Ist.Est.Tekh.*, 1962, 45: 204-13.

TAYLOR, F.R. Forbes. Heavy goods handling prior to the nineteenth century. *Trans.Newcomen Soc.*, 1962-63, 35: 179-91.

ZIMMER, G.F. The early history of mechanical handling devices. *Trans.Newcomen Soc.*, 1921-22, 2: 1-11, 8 pl.

UG MECHANICAL POWER TRANSMISSION; LUBRICATION

FELDHAUS, Franz M. Geschichte der Kugel-, Walzen- und Rollenlager. 56 p., 46 ill., bibliogr. Schweinfurt a. M.: Präcizions-Kugel-Lager-Werke Fichtel und Sachs, 1914. [CB 10/216]

HOPF, Ludwig, ed. Abhandlungen über die hydrodynamische Theorie der Schmiermittelreibung. vi, 227 p. (Ostwalds Klassiker, 218) Leipzig: Akademische Verlagsgesellschaft, 1927. [CB 22/265]
Collection of five works by N. Petrov, O. Reynolds, A. Sommerfeld and A.G. Michell.

HORWITZ, Hugo Th. Die Anfänge von Wellenkupplungen und Wellentransmissionen. *Beitr.Gesch.Tech.Ind.*, 1929, 19: 144-6, 10 fig.

HORWITZ, Hugo Th. Entwicklungsgeschichte der Traglager. *Geschichtsbl.Tech.Ind.*, 1914, 1: 45-59, 98-110, 165-203, 235-43; 1915, 2: 1-21, 59-92, 123-35.
Also revised edition. x, 137 p., 82 ill. Berlin: Fr. Zillessen, 1915.

HORWITZ, Hugo Th. Ueber eine Urform von Lager- und Scharnierkonstruktionen. *Beitr.Gesch.Tech.Ind.*, 1927, 17: 162-3, 3 fig.

HORWITZ, Hugo Th. Zur Geschichte der Kugel- und Walzenlager. *Geschichtsbl.Tech.Ind.*, 1921, 8: 32-5.

UVAROVA, L.I. Entwicklung der Mittel zur Fernübertragung mechanischer Energie. *NTM Z.Gesch.Naturwiss.Tech.Med.*, 1960, 1: no. 1, 94-118.

UVAROVA, L.I. On the history of the distant transmission of mechanical energy. *Act.VIIIe Congr.Int.Hist.Sci.* (Florence, 1956), p. 984-6. Paris: Hermann, 1958.

UH TRANSMISSION OF FLUIDS; PUMPING

BOOTSGEZEL, J.J. *See* UN

FELDHAUS, Franz M. Die Geschichte des Schlauches. In: Metallschlauchfabrik Pforzheim. 1885-1935. Fünfzig Jahre Metallschlauch, p. 12-27, ill. Pforzheim: 1935. [CB 48/572]

FREISE, Fer. W. Die brasilianische Schlauchpresse. *Geschichtsbl.Tech.Ind.*, 1922, 9: 41-4.

SHAPIRO, Sheldon. The origin of the suction pump. *Technol. Cult.*, 1964, 5: 566-74.

UHwb

MOORE, William Davis. Development of the cast iron pressure pipe industry in the Southern states, 1800-1938. 55 p., ill. Birmingham, Ala.: Birmingham Publishing Company (for the Newcomen Society, American Branch), 1939.

NOBLE, Henry Jeffers. History of the cast iron pressure pipe industry in the United States of America. 98 p., pl., fig. Princeton, N.J.: Princeton University Press (for the Newcomen Society, American Branch), 1940.

UHwg-qt

METALLSCHLAUCHFABRIK PFORZHEIM. 1885-1935. Fünfzig Jahre Metallschlauch. Zur 50 jährigen Wiederkehr des Jahres der Erfindung und ersten Herstellung des Metallschlauches. 68 p., ill. Pforzheim: 1935.

UHwi

BONI, Bruno. Sull'origine italiana delle trombe idroeoliche. *Fonderia Ital.*, 1958, 7: 161-8, ill.

UHxx

SCIENCE MUSEUM. Handbook of the collections illustrating pumping machinery. By G.F. Westcott. 2 vol. 1. Historical notes. 103 p., 30 pl.; 2. Descriptive catalogue. 195 p., 23 pl. London: H.M. Stationery Office, 1932, 1933.

UJ REFRIGERATION

LINDE, Carl von. Aus der Geschichte der Kältetechnik. *Beitr. Gesch.Tech.Ind.*, 1918, 8: 1-34, 17 ill.
Extracts from the great inventor's autobiography, published under the title: "Aus meinem Leben und von meiner Arbeit".

MARCHIS, L. Le froid industriel. 328 p. Paris: F. Alcan, 1913.

TURPAIN, Albert. L'air liquide, le froid industriel et son utilisation. x, 59 p. Paris: Gauthier-Villars, 1924.

WAGNER, J. Z dziejów chlodnictwa. [History of refrigeration. (In Polish)] *Kwart.Hist.Nauk.Tech.*, 1957, 2: 553-75.

UJc-bx

SCIENCE MUSEUM. Refrigeration exhibition, April-August 1934: a brief account of the historical development of mechanical refrigeration and a descriptive catalogue of the exhibits, with notes on the basic scientific principles. By T.C. Crawhall and B. Lentaigne. 28 p. London: H.M. Stationery Off., 1934.

UJda

SMITH, Edgar C. Some pioneers of refrigeration. *Trans.Newcomen Soc.*, 1942-43, 23: 99-107.
With chronological table, 1755 (William Cullen) to 1942.

UJqy

ASSOCIATION INTERNATIONALE DU FROID. [Report on the Association] *Isis*, 1913, 1: 500-1.

UJwb

ANDERSON, Oscar Edward. Refrigeration in America. A history of a new technology and its impact. ix, 344 p., 10 ill. Princeton, N.J.: Princeton University Press (for the University of Cincinnati), 1953. [CB 80/142]

UJwg-qt

LINDE, Carle Paul Gottfried. 50 Jahre Kältetechnik 1879-1929; Geschichte der Gesellschaft für Linde's Eismaschinen A.-G., Wiesbaden. iv, 192 p., 6 pl. Wiesbaden: Gesellschaft für Linde's Eismaschinen A.-G., 1929.

UK PRIME MOVERS; ENERGY CONVERSION

UKc

DECKER, Wilbur F. The story of the engine from lever to Liberty motor. xx, 277 p., ill. New York: Scribner's, 1920. [CB 9/496]

HOGBEN, Lancelot. Men, missiles and machines: the wonderful world of power. 70 p. London: Rathbone Books, 1957.
The American edition of the book is titled: The wonderful world of energy. (Garden City, N.Y.: Garden City Books, 1957).
Reviewed in *Sch.Sci.Rev.*, 1958, 39: 349.

MARCUS, Abraham; MARCUS, Rebecca B. Power unlimited! The story of power - from windmill to nuclear energy. viii, 152 p., ill. Englewood Cliffs, N.J.: Prentice-Hall, 1959.

RANSHAW, G.S. Great engines and their inventors: the story of machine power. 212 p., 39 fig., 20 pl. London: Burke, 1950.
Reviewed by R.J. Forbes, *Arch.Int.Hist.Sci.*, 1951, 4: 558.

SHUKHARDIN, Semen V. On the problem of motive forces in the development of technique. *Proc.10th Int.Congr.Hist.Sci.* (Ithaca, 1962), (1), p. 381-4. Paris: Hermann, 1964.

THIRRING, Hans. Energy for man. From windmills to nuclear power. 409 p., ill., bibliogr. Bloomington: Indiana University Press, 1958. [CB 88/569]
Reprinted New York: Harper Torchbook, 1962. 2nd edition of Power production (London: Harrap, 1956).

UBBELOHDE, A.R. Man and energy. 247 p., 13 pl. London: Hutchinson's Scientific and Technical Publications, 1954.
Reviewed by F. Sherwood Taylor, *Nature*, 1955, 175: 1055.

VOWLES, Hugh P. Early evolution of power engineering. *Isis*, 1932, 17: 412-20, 4 pl.

VOWLES, Hugh P.; VOWLES, Margaret W. The quest for power: from prehistoric times to the present day. xv, 354 p., 88 pl. London: Chapman and Hall, 1931.
Reviewed in *Nature*, 1932, 129: 380-1.

UKs

UNESCO. DEPARTMENT OF THE NATURAL SCIENCES. Energy in the service of man. 7 vol. (Unesco discussion theme 1951, papers) Paris: 1951-52. [CB 79/168]
Mimeographed.

UKwb

MARTIN, Thomas W. Economics of power in Alabama. 44 p. Birmingham, Ala.: Birmingham Publishing Company (for Newcomen Society, American Branch), 1939.

UL ANIMAL POWER; WIND AND WATER MILLS

ATKINSON, Frank. The horse as a source of rotary power. *Trans. Newcomen Soc.*, 1960-61, 33: 31-55.

BURNE, E. Lancaster; RUSSELL, John; WAILES, Rex. Windmill sails. *Trans.Newcomen Soc.*, 1943-45, 24: 147-61, 13 fig.

CLARK, H.O. Notes on horse-mills. *Trans.Newcomen Soc.*, 1927-28, 8: 33-9.

DEERR, Noel; BROOKS, Alexander. The evolution of the sugar cane mill. *Trans.Newcomen Soc.*, 1940-41, 21: 1-9, 10 fig.

HOPKINS, Robert Thurston. Old watermills and windmills. Introduction by Arthur Beckett. viii, 245 p. London: Allan, 1930.

HORWITZ, Hugo Th. Über das Aufkommen, die erste Entwicklung und die Verbreitung von Windrädern. *Technikgeschichte*, 1933, 22: 93-102.

MELLER, Emil. Aus der Geschichte des Getreidemühlenbaus. *Beitr.Gesch.Tech.Ind.*, 1930, 20: 111-18, 9 fig.

RUSSELL, John. Millstones in wind and water mills. *Trans.Newcomen Soc.*, 1943-45, 24: 55-64, 5 fig.

TITLEY, Arthur. Notes on old windmills. *Trans.Newcomen Soc.*, 1922-23, 3: 41-51.

TURRIÈRE, Emile. Histoire des moulins à vent. *Compt.Rend. Trav.Congr.Eau* (Montpellier, 1923), p. 119-32. Montpellier: Rouméqous et Déhan, 1923. [CB 16/349]

VOWLES, Hugh P. An inquiry into origins of the windmill. *Trans.Newcomen Soc.*, 1930-31, 11: 1-14, 5 fig.
Contents: 1. Introductory; 2. Héron's "windmill"; 3. Early Persian windmills; 4. Transition from Persia to Western Europe.

WAILES, Rex. The drive to the stones in windmills. *Trans.Newcomen Soc.*, 1957-58 and 1958-59, 31: 289-99.

WAILES, Rex. Windmill winding gear. *Trans.Newcomen Soc.*, 1945-46 and 1946-47, 25: 27-35, 15 fig.

ULsc

BLOCH, Marc. Technique et évolution sociale. A propos de l'histoire de l'attelage et de celle de l'esclavage. *Rev. Syn.Hist.*, 1926, 41: 91-9. [CB 21/575]
A propos of Lefebvre des Noëttes, Richard, *see* below.

LEFEBVRE DES NOËTTES, Richard. L'attelage, le cheval de selle à travers les âges. Contribution à l'histoire de l'esclavage. Préface de Jérome Carcopino. 2 vol. Paris: A. Picard, 1931. [CB 35/300]
2nd edition of: La force motrice animale à travers les âges (132 p. Paris: Berger-Levrault, 1924) reviewed by Paul Pelliot, *T'oung Pao*, 1926, 24: 256-68; *see also J. Savants, 4th ser.*, 1924, 22: 229-32.

LEFEBVRE DES NOËTTES, Richard. La force motrice animale à travers les âges et la question de l'esclavage. *Anthropologie*, 1926, 36: 297-308. [CB 10/278]

LEFEBVRE DES NOËTTES, Richard; BLOCH, Marc. La force motrice animale et le rôle des inventions techniques. *Rev.Syn.Hist.*, 1927, 43: 83-91.

ULst

KOEHNE, Carl. Die Mühle im Rechte der Völker. *Beitr.Gesch. Tech.Ind.*, 1913, 5: 27-53.

ULwb

HAMILTON, Edward Pierce. Some windmills of Cape Cod. *Trans. Newcomen Soc.*, 1924-25, 5: 39-44, pl.

WAILES, Rex. Windmills of eastern Long Island. *Trans.Newcomen Soc.*, 1934-35, 15: 117-51, 10 fig.

WEISS, Harry B.; SIM, Robert J. The early grist and flouring mills of New Jersey. 135 p., ill. Trenton: New Jersey Agricultural Society, 1956. [CB 82/217]

WEISS, Harry B.; WEISS, Grace M. The early snuff mills of New Jersey. 117 p., ill. Trenton: New Jersey Agricultural Society, 1962.

WEISS, Harry B.; WEISS, Grace M. Forgotten mills of early New Jersey. 94 p., 27 ill. Trenton: New Jersey Agricultural Society, 1960.

ULwe

ADAMS, James W.R. Windmills in Kent. 32 p., 12 pl. Maidstone, Eng.: Kent County Council, 1955. [CB 82/215]

ADDISON, Joseph; WAILES, Rex. Dorset watermills. *Trans.Newcomen Soc.*, 1962-63, 35: 193-216.

BAKER, P.H.J.; WAILES, Rex. The windmills of Derbyshire, Leicestershire and Nottinghamshire. 1. Post mills; 2. Tower mills. *Trans.Newcomen Soc.*, 1960-61, 33: 113-28; 34: 89-104.

BATTEN, M.I. English windmills. 1. Containing a history of their origin and development, with records of mills in Kent, Surrey and Sussex. xviii, 128 p. London: Architectural Press, 1930.
For Part 2 *see* under Smith, Donald, below.

DICKINSON, H.W.; STRAKER, E. The Shetland watermill. *Trans. Newcomen Soc.*, 1932-33, 13: 89-94.

FINCH, William Coles. Watermills and windmills. A historical survey of their rise, decline and fall as portrayed by those of Kent. 336 p., ill. London: Daniel, 1933.

PELHAM, R.A. Old mills of Southampton. 39 p. (Southampton Papers, 3) Southampton, Eng.: Southampton Corporation, 1963.

SMITH, Donald. English windmills. 2. Containing a record of the mills in Buckinghamshire, Essex, Hertfordshire, Middlesex and London. 152 p. London: Architectural Press, 1932.
For Part 1 *see* under Batten, M.I., above.

WAILES, Rex. Essex windmills. *Trans.Newcomen Soc.*, 1957-58 and 1958-59, 31: 153-80.

WAILES, Rex. Lincolnshire windmills. 1. Post mills; 2. Tower mills. *Trans.Newcomen Soc.*, 1951-52 and 1952-53, 28: 245-53; 1953-54 and 1954-55, 29: 103-22.

WAILES, Rex. Suffolk windmills. 1. Post mills; 2. Tower mills. *Trans.Newcomen Soc.*, 1941-42, 22: 41-63, 13 fig; 1942-43, 23: 37-54, fig.

WAILES, Rex. Tide mills in England and Wales. *Trans.Newcomen Soc.*, 1938-39, 19: 1-33, 12 fig.

WAILES, Rex. Windmills in England, a study of their origin, development and future. viii, 47 p., 109 ill. London: Architectural Press, 1948.

WAILES, Rex. The windmills of Cambridgeshire. *Trans.Newcomen Soc.*, 1950-51, 27: 97-119, 5 fig.

WAILES, Rex; RUSSELL, John. Windmills in Kent. *Trans.Newcomen Soc.*, 1953-54 and 1954-55, 29: 221-39.

WILSON, Paul N. Watermills: an introduction. 16 p., pl. (Society for the Protection of Ancient Buildings, Wind and Watermills Section, Booklet no. 1) London: 1956. Reprinted in *Edgar Allen News*, 1956, 35: 247-9, ill.

ULwf

CLARK, H.O. Notes on French windmills. *Trans.Newcomen Soc.*, 1928-29, 9: 52-9, 4 pl.

HUARD, M.G.; WAILES, Rex; WEBSTER, H.A. Three types of windmills in Southern Brittany. *Trans.Newcomen Soc.*, 1949-50 and 1950-51, 27: 203-10, 5 fig.

ULwg

CLAAS, Wilhelm. Die Wassermühlen der ehemaligen Grafschaft Mark. Ihr Werden, Sein und Vergehen. *Beitr.Gesch.Tech.Ind.*, 1932, 21: 165-9, 8 fig.

MUGGERIDGE, D.W. The windmills of Hanover. *Trans.Newcomen Soc.*, 1945-46 and 1946-47, 25: 199-205.

PESCHKE, Werner. Das Mühlenwesen der Mark Brandenburg. Von den Anfängen der Mark bis um 1600. viii, 110 p. (Schriftenreihe der Arbeitsgemeinschaft für Technikgeschichte des Vereins Deutscher Ingenieure) Berlin: VDI-Verlag, 1937.
Reviewed by R. Zaunick, *Mitt.Gesch.Med.*, 1940, 39: 249.

ULwk

BOORSMA, P. Duizend Zaansche Molens. [A thousand Zaan mills. (In Dutch)] xii, 291 p., 16 pl. Wormerveer: Drukkerij Meijer, 1950.
Reviewed by R.J. Forbes, *Arch.Int.Hist.Sci.*, 1951, 4: 557.

GARDNER, E.M. Some notes on Dutch watermills. *Trans.Newcomen Soc.*, 1949-50 and 1950-51, 27: 199-202.

ULwm

JESPERSEN, Anders. Danish windmills. The outlines of a pattern of millwright tradition. *Trans.Newcomen Soc.*, 1957-58 and 1958-59, 31: 301-10.

UM WATER TURBINES AND TIDAL POWER

BIED-CHARRETON, René. L'utilisation de l'énergie hydraulique. Ses origines, ses grandes étapes. *Rev.Hist.Sci.*, 1955, 8: 53-72.

CROZET-FOURNEYRON, Marcel. Invention de la turbine: historique suivi d'une note sur un régulateur à mouvement louvoyant applicable aux turbines hydrauliques. Ouvrage couronné par l'Académie des Sciences. 55 p. Paris: Ch. Béranger, 1927.

DAVEY, Norman. Studies in tidal power. xiii, 255 p. London: Constable, 1923.

DURAND, W.F. The Pelton water wheel. 1. Developments by Pelton and others prior to 1880; 2. Developments by Doble and others, 1880 to date. *Mech.Eng.*, 1939, 61: 447-54, 511-18.

REICHEL, Ernst. Aus der Geschichte der Wasserkraftmaschinen. *Beitr.Gesch.Tech.Ind.*, 1928, 18: 57-68, 30 fig.

UMwe

WAILES, Rex. Tide mills in England and Wales. *Trans.Newcomen Soc.*, 1938-39, 19: 1-33, 12 fig.

WILSON, Paul N. Early water turbines in the United Kingdom. *Trans.Newcomen Soc.*, 1957-58 and 1958-59, 31: 219-41.

UN STEAM ENGINES AND STEAM TURBINES

BOOTSGEZEL, J.J. The Cruquius engine and its history. *Trans. Newcomen Soc.*, 1934-35, 15: 1-16, 3 fig.

DICKINSON, H.W. A short history of the steam engine. xvi, 255 p. Cambridge University Press, 1939. [CB 57/245]

GLIOZZI, Mario. Breve historia de machinas thermico. [Short history of heat engines. (In Interlingua)] *Schola Vita*, 1931, 6: 169-72.

KERKER, Milton. Science and the steam engine. *Technol.Cult.*, 1961, 2: 381-90.

MONTEIL, C. Auguste Rateau, la thermodynamique et les machines motrices. *Mém.Compt.Rend.Soc.Ing.Civils France*, 1930, 912-16.

MORGAN, David P., ed. Steam's finest hour. 128 p., ill. Milwaukee: Kalmbach Publishing Company, 1959.
Reviewed by Paul E. Guenther, *Technol.Cult.*, 1960, 1: 273-6.

NEEDHAM, Joseph. The pre-natal history of the steam-engine. *Trans.Newcomen Soc.*, 1962-63, 35: 3-58.

OTANI, Ryoichi. [Relation between science and technique in the development of the steam engine. (In Japanese)] *J.Hist. Sci.Japan*, 1953, no. 25, 23-8.

THURSTON, Robert H. A history of the growth of the steam-engine. Centennial edition. With a supplementary chapter by William N. Barnard. xii, 555 p., 181 fig., portr. Ithaca: Cornell University Press, 1939. [CB 59/473]
First published 1878; 2nd edition 1907.

VAUCLAIN, Samuel M. What steam has meant to us. 19 p. Princeton, N.J.: Princeton University Press (for Newcomen Society, American Branch), 1936.

UNda

SCHAEFER, G.; NAUMANN, W. Physicians as inventors of steam engines. *Ciba Symp.* (Summit, N.J.), 1941, 3: 1033-6.

UNwg

JOCHMANN, Ernst-Otto. Die Entwicklung des Hochdruckdampfes in Deutschland. 164 p., ill., bibliogr. Düsseldorf: VDI-Verlag, 1958.
Reviewed by Glenn R. Frying, *Technol.Cult.*, 1961, 2: 178-80.

UP INTERNAL COMBUSTION ENGINES

EVANS, Arthur F. The history of the oil engine. A review in detail of the development of the oil engine from the year 1680 to the beginning of the year 1930. With illustrations and name index and an index of important patents. Foreword by Sir Dugald Clerk. xviii. 318 p. London: Sampson Low, 1932.

GAGARIN, E.I. [From the history of the development of the construction of automobile motors. (In Russian)] *Vop.Ist. Est.Tekh.*, 1959, 7: 86-94.

LE GALLEC, Yves. Les origines du moteur à combustion interne. *Tech.Civilisations*, 1951, 2: 28-33, 1 fig.

MEYER, Robert B. Three famous early aero engines. *Annu.Rep. Smithsonian Inst.for 1961*, p. 357-71, ill. Washington, D.C.: 1962.

PAL'NIKOV, M.P. O razvitii porshnevykh aviatsionnykh dvigatelei. [On the development of piston-driven aviation engines. (In Russian)] *Vop.Ist.Est.Tekh.*, 1963, 14: 117-26.

SCIENCE MUSEUM. Handbook of the collections illustrating aeronautics. 3. The propulsion of aircraft. A brief outline of the history and development of the aero-engine and the airscrew with reference to the National Aeronautical Collection, and a catalogue of the exhibits. By M.J.B. Davy and G.T. Richards. 2nd rev. and enl. ed. 104 p., 18 pl. London: H.M. Stationery Off., 1936. [CB 51/178]
First published 1930.

TIULINA, I.A. Iz istorii vodometnogo dvizhitelia. [On the history of hydro-jet propulsion. (In Russian)] *Vop.Ist.Est. Tekh.*, 1961, 11: 107-16.

WHITTLE, Frank. Jet: the story of a pioneer. [Reminiscences.] 320 p., portr., pl. London: Muller, 1953; New York: Philosophical Library, 1954.

WITZ, Aimé. Traité théorique et pratique des moteurs à gaz, à essence et à pétrole. 5th ed. 2 vol., ill. Paris: Albin Michel, 1923.
First published 1886; 4th edition 1903.
Reviewed by George Sarton, *Isis*, 1924, 6: 454-6.

YOUNG, J.W. Notes on the practical development of the oil engine. *Trans.Newcomen Soc.*, 1936-37, 17: 109-29, 1 fig.

UPwg

DIESEL, Eugen; GOLDBECK, Gustav; SCHILDBERGER, Friedrich. From engines to autos: five pioneers in engine development and their contributions to the automotive industry. Translated by Peter White. vi, 302 p., ill. Chicago: Henry Regnery Co., 1960.
Translation of: Vom Motor zum Auto; fünf Männer und ihr Werk (Stuttgart: Deutsche Verlags-Anstalt, 1957).
The five pioneers were Benz, Bosch, Daimler, Diesel and Otto.
Reviewed by John B. Rae, *Technol.Cult.*, 1961, 2: 189-91; by Robert E. Carlson, *Isis*, 1962, 53: 272-3.

SASS, Friedrich. Geschichte des deutschen Verbrennungsmotorenbaues von 1860 bis 1918. xii, 667 p., fig., portr., chart. Berlin: Springer-Verlag, 1962.
Reviewed by Lynwood Bryant, *Technol.Cult.*, 1964, 5: 82-6.

UQ ROCKET TECHNOLOGY

EMME, Eugene M., ed. The history of rocket technology. Essays on research, development, and utility. 320 p., ill. Detroit: Wayne State University Press, 1964.

GATLAND, Kenneth W.; KUNESCH, Anthony M. Space travel. x, 11-205 p., ill., fig., tables. New York: Philosophical Library, 1953.
The first half of this book deals with the history of rockets.

THE HISTORY of rocket technology. *Technol.Cult.*, 1963, 4: 377-528. [CB 89/587]

SIRY, Joseph W. The early history of rocket research. *Sci. Mon.*, 1950, 71: 326-31.

SIRY, Joseph W. Rocket research in the twentieth century. *Mon.*, 1950, 71: 408-21.

SOKOL'SKII, V.N. Iz istorii porokhovykh raket (XVII-XIX vv.). [From the history of powder rockets (17th-19th centuries). (In Russian)] *Tr.Inst.Ist.Est.Tekh.*, 1962, 45: 48-106.

UQwm

STRANDH, Sigvard. Wilhelm Teodor Unge - a Swedish pioneer in rocketry. *Daedalus*, 1964, 87-108, bibliogr.

UQwn

KAPLUN, A.B. Pioneer Sovetskogo raketostroeniia. 75 let so dnia rozhdeniia F.A. Tsandera. [On the 75th anniversary of the birth of F.A. Tsander, pioneer of Soviet rocket construction. (In Russian)] *Priroda*, 1962, no. 12, 82-4.

UR ATOMIC ENERGY

URc general history

ALLIBONE, T.E. The industrial development of nuclear power. (Rutherford Memorial Lecture, 1963) *Proc.Roy.Soc., Ser. A.*, 1964, 282: 447-63.

BALKE, Siegfried. Verwertung der Kernenergie in geschichtlicher Sicht. 17 p. (Beiträge zur Geschichte der Wissenschaft und der Technik, 1) Wiesbaden: Franz Steiner Verlag, 1961.

DARROW, Karl K. Atomic energy. 80 p. (The Norman Wait Harris Lectures delivered at Northwestern University) New York: Wiley, 1948. [CB 73/169]

FEARNSIDE, K.; JONES, E.W.; SHAW, E.N. Applied atomic energy. viii, 156 p., front., 14 pl. New York: Philosophical Library, 1954. [CB 80/204]

FEINBERG, J.G. The story of atomic theory and atomic energy. (Formerly titled: The atom story) 2nd ed. viii, 264 p., ill. New York: Dover Publications, 1960.
Reviewed by M. Courtin, *Arch.Int.Hist.Sci.*, 1962, 15: 434-5
First published 1953.

GAMOW, George. Atomic energy in cosmic and human life. x, 161 p. Cambridge University Press; New York: Macmillan Co., 1946.

GLASSTONE, Samuel. Sourcebook on atomic energy. With an introduction by Gordon Dean. 546 p., ill. New York: Van Nostrand, 1950.
Reviewed by I. Bernard Cohen, *Isis*, 1951, 42: 272-3.

GOLDSCHMIDT, Bertrand. The atomic adventure, its political and technical aspects. Transl. from the French by Peter Beer. (2nd ed.) xii, 259 p., ill., bibliogr. Oxford: Pergamon; New York: Macmillan, 1964.
Translation of L'aventure atomique.
First published Paris: Fayard, 1962.

GREEN, T.S. Thermonuclear power. 168 p., fig. New York: Philosophical Library, 1964.

HEWLETT, Richard G. Pioneering on nuclear frontiers: two early landmarks in reactor technology. *Technol.Cult.*, 1964, 5: 512-22.
The first self-sustained nuclear chain reaction, 2 Dec. 1942, directed by Enrico Fermi; and the first generation of electricity from atomic energy 21 Dec. 1951, under the responsibility of Walter Zinn.

KEYS, David A. Rutherford and nuclear power. *Nature*, 1963, 197: 842-3.

LANSDELL, Norman. The atom and energy revolution. 200 p. New York: Philosophical Library, 1958.

MASSEY, H.S.W. Atoms and energy. 174 p., 37 fig. London: Elek Books; New York: Philosophical Library, 1956.

ROTHMANN, S.C., ed. Constructive uses of atomic energy. ix, 257 p., 52 fig. New York: Harper, 1949.
Parts of this book are concerned with the evolution of nuclear science.
Reviewed by I. Perlman, *J.Chem.Educ.*, 1950, 27: 49-50.

SACKS, Jacob. The atom at work. Illustrations by George R. Cox. xii, 327 p., 54 fig. New York: Ronald Press, 1951.
Reviewed by I. Bernard Cohen, *Isis*, 1951, 42: 272-3.

SCIENTIFIC AMERICAN. Atomic power. 180 p. New York: Simon & Schuster, 1955.

SODDY, Frederick. The story of atomic energy. viii, 136 p. London: Nova Atlantis, 1949.

TELLER, E. The work of many people. *Science*, 1955, 121: 267-74.
A history of the discovery of atomic power by the man who found out how to make the hydrogen bomb feasible.

U.S. SENATE. SPECIAL COMMITTEE ON ATOMIC ENERGY. Essential information on atomic energy (including a glossary and bibliography). 94 p., diagr., bibliogr. Washington, D.C.: U.S. Govt. Print. Off., 1946.

URc-be

GAYNOR, Frank. Pocket encyclopedia of atomic energy. 204 p. New York: Philosophical Library, 1950. [CB 76/366]

URce-bv

UNITED NATIONS. SECRETARIAT. ATOMIC ENERGY COMMISSION GROUP. An international bibliography on atomic energy. 2 vol. 1. Political, economic and social aspects; 2. Scientific aspects. Lake Success, N.Y.: 1949-51. [CB 76/391 and CB 78/156]

URp/s organizational and social aspects

URph

BOHR, Niels. Open letter to the United Nations. *Science*, 1950, 112: 1-6.
Apropos of the use and misuse of atomic energy.

THE CONTROL of atomic energy. Proposals before the United Nations Atomic Energy Commission and unofficial plans. *Int. Conciliation*, 1946, no. 423, 307-438.

UNITED NATIONS. ATOMIC ENERGY COMMISSION. Scientific and technical aspects of the control of atomic energy. The full text of the first report of the Scientific and Technical Committee of the Atomic Energy Commission, the background of the report, a glossary of scientific terms and biographical notes. v, 42 p. Lake Success, N.Y.: United Nations, Department of Public Information, 1946.

UNITED NATIONS. ATOMIC ENERGY COMMISSION. Recommendations of the Atomic Energy Commission for the international control of atomic energy and the prohibition of atomic weapons ... iv, 75 p. (Official records: Fourth Year, Special Supplement, 1) Lake Success, N.Y.: Columbia University Press, 1949.

UNITED NATIONS. GENERAL ASSEMBLY. International control of atomic energy. iii, 37 p. (Official Records: Fourth Session, Supplement, 15) Lake Success, N.Y.: 1950.

URqy

THE UNITED NATIONS ATOMIC ENERGY COMMISSION. An historical survey of the period June 1946 to March 1947. *Int.Conciliation*, 1947, no. 430, 166-292.

UNITED NATIONS. ATOMIC ENERGY COMMISSION. Report to the Security Council. iv, 141 p. (Official Records: Special Supplement) Lake Success, N.Y.: 1946. [CB 71/115]
Collection of all the documents printed in parallel columns in English and French.

URs

GRAUBARD, Mark. Science, humanity and politics face the atom. 32 p. Orono: Extension Service College of Agriculture, University of Maine, 1947.

HIEBERT, Erwin N. The impact of atomic energy; a history of responses by governments, scientists, and religious groups. 312 p. Newton, Kans.: Faith and Life Press, 1961.
Reviewed by Everett Mendelsohn, *Isis*, 1964, 55: 470-2; by Arthur H. Compton, *Science*, 1961, 134: 1232-3; by Klaus Fuchs, *NTM Z.Gesch.Naturwiss.Tech.Med.*, 1963, 1: no. 4, 138-43.

MUMFORD, Lewis. Anticipations and social consequences of atomic energy. *Proc.Amer.Phil.Soc.*, 1954, 98: 149-52.

NEWMAN, James R.; MILLER, Byron S. The control of atomic energy. A study of its social, economic, and political implications. xiii, 434 p. New York: McGraw-Hill, 1948.
Reviewed by Louis N. Ridenour, *Isis*, 1949, 40: 75-6.

UREY, Harold C. The atom and humanity. *Science*, 1945, 102: 435-9.

URs-bv

LIBRARY OF CONGRESS. GENERAL REFERENCE AND BIBLIOGRAPHY DIVISION. The social impact of science: a select bibliography with a section on atomic power. vii, 51 p. (Sub-committee on War Mobilization of the Committee on Military Affairs, United States Senate) Washington: U.S. Gov. Print. Off., 1945.
This includes 505 items divided as follows: 1. Government publications, 50 items; 2. Books and pamphlets, 172; 3. Periodical articles, 260; 4. Atomic power, 23.

URsc

WESTINGHOUSE EDUCATIONAL FOUNDATION. Science and life in the world. The George Westinghouse centennial forum, May 16-18, 1946. 1. Science and civilization. The future of atomic energy. ix, 125 p., 11 pl. New York: McGraw Hill, 1946. [CB 40/166]

URw in different countries

URwb

BISHOP, Amasa S. Project Sherwood - The U.S. program in controlled fusion. vii, 227 p., fig. Garden City: Doubleday, 1960.

FERMI, Laura. Atoms for the world. United States participation in the Conference on the Peaceful Uses of Atomic Energy. (Geneva, August 1955) xii, 227 p., 34 ill. Chicago: University of Chicago Press, 1957. [CB 83/278]

SNELL, Arthur H.; WEINBERG, Alvin M. History and accomplishments of the Oak Ridge graphite reactor, [1943-63]. *Phys. Today*, 1964, 17: no. 8, 32-8.

URwb-hd

HEWLETT, R.G. A pilot study in contemporary scientific history. *Isis*, 1962, 53: 31-8.
Regarding the feasibility of a general history of the Atomic Energy Commission and raising some general points on methods of historical research

URwb-ph

STRAUSS, Lewis L. Men and decisions. viii, 468 p. Garden City, N.Y.: Doubleday, 1962. [CB 88/535]
Personal recollections of events involving atomic energy and public policy.

U.S. SENATE. SPECIAL COMMITTEE ON ATOMIC ENERGY. Atomic energy act of 1946. Hearings ... on S. 1717, a bill for the development and control of atomic energy. 5 pt., 539 p. Washington: U.S. Govt. Print. Off., 1946.

U.S. SENATE. SPECIAL COMMITTEE ON ATOMIC ENERGY. Hearings ... pursuant to S. Res. 179. A resolution creating a special committee to investigate problems relating to the development, use, and control of atomic energy. 5 pt., iii, 573 p. Washington: U.S. Govt. Print. Off., 1945-46.

URwb-qk

HEWLETT, Richard G.; ANDERSON, Oscar E. Jr. A history of the United States Atomic Energy Commission. Vol. 1. xvi, 766 p., ill. (New World, 1939-46, 1) University Park, Pa.: Pennsylvania State University Press, 1962.
Reviewed by Morgan Thomas, *Miss.Val.Hist.Rev.*, 1962, 49: 537-9; by Stanley Klein, *Technol.Cult.*, 1963, 4: 227-31.

KOMONS, Nick A.; BUSHNELL, David. The Air Force and nuclear physics. A history of the Air Force Office of Scientific Research Nuclear Physics Program. v, 142 p. Washington, D.C.: Office of Aerospace Research, 1963.

URwb-sk

NIEBURG, Harold L. Nuclear secrecy and foreign policy. Intro. by Hans J. Morgenthau. 236 p. Washington: Public Affairs Press, 1964.

URwd

MODELSKI, G.A. Atomic energy in the communist bloc. 226 p., tables. New York: Cambridge University Press; Calton: Melbourne University Press on behalf of the Australian National University; London: Macmillan, 1959.

URwe

GOWING, Margaret M. Britain and atomic energy, 1939-1945. Introd. by Kenneth Jay. xvi, 464 p., ill., portr. New York: St Martin's; London: Macmillan, 1964.
First instalment of an official history of the United Kingdom atomic energy project.

URwe-qk

THE BRITISH Atomic Energy Research Establishment, 1946-1951. 128 p., 32 pl., 9 diagr. London: Ministry of Supply; Central Office of Information, 1952. [CB 79/144]
Explaining the atomic research done at Harwell from 1946 to 1951.

URwn

KRAMISH, Arnold. Atomic energy in the Soviet Union. x, 232 p., bibliogr. (Rand Series) Stanford: Stanford University Press, 1959; London: Oxford University Press, 1960.
Reviewed by Thomas P. Hughes, *Technol.Cult.*, 1961, 2: 85-6.

US SOLAR AND GEOTHERMAL POWER

ACKERMANN, A.S.E. The utilization of solar energy. *J.Roy.Soc. Arts*, 1914-15, 63: 538-65; also *Annu.Rep.Smithsonian Inst. for 1915*, p. 141-66. Washington: 1916.

ROBINSON, N. A brief history of utilisation of the sun radiation. *Act.VIIe Congr.Int.Hist.Sci.* (Jerusalem, 1953), p. 510-15. Paris: Hermann, [n.d.].

UT ELECTRICAL ENGINEERING; POWER PRODUCTION

UTc general history

DUNSHEATH, Percy. A history of electrical engineering. 368 p., ill. New York: Pitman Publishing Corp.; London: Faber, 1962.
Reviewed by Douglas McKie, *Ann.Sci.*, 1961, 17: 122-3; for other reviews *see* CB 88/566 and CB 89/516.

FLEMING, John Ambrose. Fifty years of electricity. The memories of an electrical engineer. xii, 371 p., ill. London: Wireless Press, [1921].
Reviewed by George Sarton, *Isis*, 1924, 6: 71-3.

FLEMING, John Ambrose. A hundred years of electrical engineering: an address delivered at University College on Tuesday, June 14, 1927. 31 p. London: University of London Press, 1927.

FUCHS, Franz. Die Entwicklung der Hochfrequenztechnik. *Beitr. Gesch.Tech.Ind.*, 1927, 17: 55-9, 6 fig.

GROSS, Arnold Th. Zeittafel zur Entwicklung der Elektrizitätsversorgung. *Technikgeschichte*, 1936, 25: 126-38, 2 pl.

HOWE, G.W.O. A hundred years of electrical engineering. *Nature*, 1924, 114: 277-80.

MITKEWICH, W.Th. The work of Faraday and modern developments in the application of electrical energy. 4 p. In: Science at the cross roads. Papers presented to the International Congress of the History of Science and Technology (London, 1931) by the delegates of the U.S.S.R. London: Kniga, 1931.

NATIONAL ELECTRICAL MANUFACTURERS ASSOCIATION. Chronological history of electrical development from 600 B.C. 106, 37 p. New York: The Association, 1946.
Reviewed by Mario Gliozzi, *Arch.Int.Hist.Sci.*, 1949, 2: 761-3.

O'DEA, W.T. Electrical invention and re-invention. *Trans. Newcomen Soc.*, 1939-40, 20: 75-91, 4 pl.

POSCHENRIEDER, P. Errinnerungen aus der Elektrotechnik. *Gesch.Einzeldarstell.Elektrotech.*, 1931, 3: 89-125.

SCIENCE MUSEUM. Handbook of the collections illustrating electrical engineering. I. Electric power. By W.T. O'Dea. Part 1. History and development. 78 p., 19 pl. Part 2. Descriptive catalogue. 96 p., 19 pl. London: H.M. Stationery Office, 1933.

SHARLIN, Harold Isadore. The making of the electrical age; from the telegraph to automation. 248 p., ill. New York: Abelard-Schuman, 1963.
Reviewed by Bern Dibner, *Isis*, 1964, 55: 382-3; and *Technol.Cult.*, 1964, 5: 441-3.

SWEZEY, Kenneth M. Nikola Tesla. Electricity today is generated, transmitted, and converted to mechanical power by means of his inventions. *Science*, 1958, 128: 1147-59, 12 fig.

UTce-bv

AMERICAN INSTITUTE OF ELECTRICAL ENGINEERS. Catalogue of the Wheeler gift of books, pamphlets and periodicals in the Library. Ed. by William D. Weaver. With introd., descriptive and critical notes by Brother Potamian. 2 vol. 504; 475 p., ill. New York: The Institute, 1909.
Reviewed by George Sarton, *Isis*, 1924, 6: 104-7.

UTda

ETTLINGER, H.J. Four sparkling personalities. *Scr.Math.*, 1941, 8: 237-50, 4 pl.
Heaviside, Pupin, Steinmetz, Karapetoff stand out as luminaries amongst those who have contributed to electrical engineering and electrical science.

HIGGINS, Thomas James. A biographical bibliography of electrical engineers and electrophysicists. *Technol.Cult.*, 1961, 2: 28-32, 146-65.

UTqy

THOMPSON, Silvanus P. The aims and work of the International Electrotechnical Commission. [With discussion.] *J.Inst. Elec.Eng.*, 1913, 50: 306-26; French version: Le but et l'oeuvre de la Commission Électrotechnique Internationale. *Vie Int.*, 1914, 5: 5-26, 163-5.

UTw in different countries

UTwb-qg

BIRR, Kendall. Pioneering in industrial research. The story of the General Electric Research Laboratory. vii, 204 p. Washington, D.C.: Public Affairs Press, 1957. [CB 83/280]

COMPTON, Karl T. Edison's laboratory in war time. *Science*, 1932, 75: 70-1.

JEHL, Francis. Menlo Park reminiscences. Written in Edison's restored Menlo Park laboratory. 430 p., fig. Dearborn, Mich.: Edison Institute, 1936.

WILSON, Chas.E. The General Electric Research Laboratory, 1900-1950. *Amer.Scient.*, 1951, 39: 262-7.

UTwb-qt

ADAMS, Edward Dean. Niagara power. History of the Niagara Falls Power Company, 1886-1918. Evolution of its central power station and alternating current system. (The fiftieth anniversary of [the Company's] foundation, 1927.) 2 vol. 1. History and power projects. xxii, 455 p.; 2. Construction and operation. xv, 504 p. Niagara Falls, N.Y.: The Company, 1927.
Reviewed by A.R., *Nature*, 1928, 122: 916-17.

FISHER, W.B. Twenty-five years of TVA. *Advance Sci.*, 1960, 17: 162-70.

KYLE, John H. The building of TVA. An illustrated history. xiii, 162 p., ill. Baton Rouge, La.: Louisiana State University Press, 1958.
Reviewed by Carl W. Condit, *Technol.Cult.*, 1960, 2: 189-91.

UTwe-qd

APPLEYARD, Rollo. The history of the Institution of Electrical Engineers (1871-1931). 342 p., 38 pl. London: The Institution, 1939.
Reviewed by A.P.M. Fleming, *Nature*, 1940, 145: 914-15.

UTwg

FISCHINGER, G. Die Entstehungsgeschichte der ersten 100 kV-Anlage in Europa, in Lauchhammer. *Gesch.Einzeldarstell. Elektrotech.*, 1931, 3: 67-88.

MILLER, Rudolf v. Ein Halbjahrhundert deutsche Stromversorgung aus öffentlichen Elektrizitätswerken. *Technikgeschichte*, 1936, 25: 111-25, 2 pl., 14 fig.

UTwg-qt

VOIGT, H. Die Firma Voigt und Haeffner. Das Werden eines Ingenieurs und eines Unternehmens zur Frühzeit der Elektrotechnik. *Beitr.Gesch.Tech.Ind.*, 1923, 13: 30-60.

UTwh

TSVERAVA, G.K. [The history of electroenergetics in Czechoslovakia in the first half of the 20th century. (In Russian)] *Vop.Ist.Est.Tekh.*, 1960, 9: 62-70.

UTwn

ALEKSEEV, V.V. Pervye gidroelektrostantsii v Sibiri. [The first hydroelectric stations in Siberia. (In Russian)] *Vop. Ist.Est.Tekh.*, 1963, no. 14, 109-11.

DAVYDOVA, L.G. Iz istorii elektrifikatsii silovykh protseesov v promyshlennosti SSSR. [From the history of the electrification of power operations in the industry of the USSR. (In Russian)] *Tr.Inst.Ist.Est.Tekh.*, 1962, 44: 116-60.

MATVEEV, G.A. Puti razvitiia teplovykh elektrostantsii SSSR. [Paths of development of thermal electric stations in the USSR. (In Russian)] *Vop.Ist.Est.Tekh.*, 1962, 13: 7-18.

NESTERUK, F. Ia. Krengol'mskaia (Narvskaia) gidrosilovaia ustanovska. [Krengolm [Narva] hydroelectric power station. (In Russian)] *Tr.Inst.Ist.Est.Tekh.*, 1962,

VINTER, A.V. Twenty five years of power development in the U.S.S.R. With: Ioffe, A.F. Development of the exact sciences in the U.S.S.R., p. 27-47. New York: American-Russian Institute, 1943.

ZOLOTAREY, T.L. Razvitie gidroenergetiki v SSSR. [Development of hydroelectricity in the USSR. (In Russian)] *Vop. Ist.Est.Tekh.*, 1961, 11: 40-50.

UTxp measuring instruments

see also CMxm electrical measurement

JABŁONSKI, Bolesław. De quelques régularités du développement des mécanismes sur l'exemple des appareils électriques de mesure. *Kwart.Hist.Nauk.Tech.*, 1957-58, special issue, 35-53.

SUKHOV, B.P. Razvitie logometrov magnitoelektricheskoi sistemy. [The development of logometers of an electromagnetic system. (In Russian)] *Tr.Inst.Ist.Est.Tekh.*, 1962, 44: 161-70.

UTxx museums

SCIENCE MUSEUM. Catalogue of the collections with descriptive and historical notes and illustrations. Electrical engineering. By F.St. A. Hartley. 116 p., 14 pl. London: H.M. Stationery Off., 1927.

SCIENCE MUSEUM. Handbook ... *See* UTc

UV ELECTRIC MACHINES; MOTORS AND GENERATORS

BECKMANN, H. Zur Geschichte des Akkumulators und der Akkumulatoren-Fabrik Aktiengesellschaft. *Beitr.Gesch.Tech.Ind.*, 1924, 14: 242-61, 28 fig.

BODY, J.H.R. A note on electro-magnetic engines. *Trans.Newcomen Soc.*, 1933-34, 14: 103-7.

EFREMOV, D.V.; RADOVSKII, M.I.; comp. Dinamomashina v ee istoricheskom razvitii. Documenty i materialy. [Dynamo-electric machine in its historical development. Documents and materials. (In Russian)] xviii, 560 p., ill. (*Tr.Inst. Ist.Nauk.Tekh.*, *ser. 3*, no. 1) Moskva: Izdatelstvo Akademii Nauk SSSR, 1934. [CB 43/233 and CB 44/518]

EFREMOV, D.V.; RADOVSKII, M.I.; comp. Elektrodvighatel' v egho istoricheskom razvitii. Dokumenty i materialy. [The electromotor in its historical development. (In Russian)] xiv, 660 p., ill. (*Tr.Inst.Ist.Nauk.Tekh.*, *ser. 3*, no. 2) Moskva: Izdatelstvo Akademii Nauk SSSR, 1934. [CB 46/590]
Continuation of: Dinamomashina v ee istoricheskom razvitii, *see* above.

HEINTZENBERG, Fr. Vom Werden der Starkstromtechnik. Ein Rückblick aus Anlass des 75. Geburtstages der Dynamomaschine. *Naturwissenschaften*, 1942, 30: 175-8.

MAHR, Otto. Die Entstehung der Dynamomaschine. v, 159 p., 103 fig. (*Gesch.Einzeldarstell.Elektrotech.*, 5) Berlin: Springer, 1941.

SCHOOF, Fr. Entwicklung von einigen wichtigen elektrischen Installations-Apparaten. *Beitr.Gesch.Tech.Ind.*, 1929, 19: 99-112, 62 fig.

TSCHANTER, Ernst. Das Erwärmungsproblem in der Geschichte des Elektromaschinenbaues. *Technikgeschichte*, 1933, 22: 63-9, 2 pl.

UW POWER TRANSMISSION; INSULATION

CERNYŠEV, A.A. [Geschichte der Übertragung der elektrischen Energie. (In Russian)] *Arkh.Ist.Nauk Tekh.*, 1934, 4: 269-98, 10 fig.

FORETAY, E. Les câbles électriques, leur développement et leurs perspectives d'avenir. *Act.Ve Congr.Int.Hist.Sci.* (Lausanne, 1947), p. 266-78. Paris: Hermann, 1948.

HIGGINS, Thomas James. Evolution of the three-phase 60-cycle alternating-current system. *Amer.J.Phys.*, 1945, 13: 32-6. Also in *Ill.Tech.Eng.Alumnus*, 1944, 9: 10-15, 42 fig.

HORWITZ, Hugo Th. Ueber die Anfänge von Relais-Schaltungen. *Geschichtsbl.Tech.Ind.*, 1921, 8: 27-31.

MELLANBY, John. The history of electric wiring. 224 p. London: MacDonald, 1957.
Reviewed in *Sch.Sci.Rev.*, 1957, 39: 175-6.

PIONEER of electric power transmission. An account of some of the early work of Sebastian Ziani de Ferranti, D.Sc., F.R.S. (1864-1930). *Notes Roy.Soc.Lond.*, 1964, 19: 33-41.

ROBERTSON, A.W. About George Westinghouse and the polyphase electric current. 44 p., portr., ill. Princeton, N.J.: Princeton University Press (for the Newcomen Society, American Branch), 1943.

WEICKER, W. Die Entwicklung des Freileitungs-Stützen-Isolators. *Beitr.Gesch.Tech.Ind.*, 1927, 17: 60-71, 76 fig.

WEICKER, W. Zur Geschichte des Freileitungs-Isolators. *Gesch. Einzeldarstell.Elektrotech.*, 1931, 3: 1-66.

UWxf-WA

GOLUBTSOVA, V.A. From the history of the application of high-molecular polymers to electrical insulation. *Act.VIIIe Congr.Int.Hist.Sci.* (Florence, 1956), p. 1083-6. Paris: Hermann, 1958.

UX ELECTRONICS TECHNOLOGY

for electrical communications *see* XJ

BERKNER, L.V. Electronics comes of age. *Elec.Eng.*, 1948, 67: 32-7, ill.

BOTTOM, Virgil E. Invention of the solid-state amplifier. *Phys.Today*, 1964, 17: no. 2, 24-6.

BOUTHILLON, Léon. L'invention de la diode. *Rev.Hist.Sci.*, 1956, 9: 354-6.

BOWEN, Harold G. The Edison effect. 72 p., fig., ill. West Orange, N.J.: Thomas Alva Edison Foundation, 1951. [CB 79/173]

BOWN, Ralph. The transistor as an industrial research episode. *Sci.Mon.*, 1955, 80: 40-6, 8 fig.

INSTITUTE OF PHYSICS. The electron jubilee exhibition, held at the Science Museum, London, Sept. 1947-Jan.1948, to illustrate the discovery of the electron in 1897, phenomena in which the electron plays a major part, and the scientific and industrial developments and applications arising from those phenomena. By D.H. Follett. 48 p., front., 7 fig. London: The Institute, 1947.

IVANOV, A.B. Predistoriia i pervye etapy razvitiia priemno-usilitel'nykh lamp. [The prehistory and first stages of the development of receiving-amplifying tubes. (In Russian)] *Tr. Inst.Ist.Est.Tekh.*, 1962, 44: 213-32.

JOHNSON, J.B. More on the solid-state amplifier and Dr. Lilienfeld. *Phys.Today*, 1964, 17: no. 5, 60-1.

KOMPFNER, Rudolf. The invention of the traveling-wave tube. iii, 30 p., 18 fig., facs. (History of Technology Monographs) San Francisco, Calif.: San Francisco Press, 1964.
Reviewed by Robert Chipman, *Isis*, 1964, 55: 458-9.

KOMPFNER, Rudolf. Some recollections of the early history of the travelling wave tube. *Yearbook Phys.Soc.*, 1956, 30-3.
Address delivered at the award of the Duddell Medal on 18 October 1955.

RENARD, G. La découverte et le perfectionnement des transistors. *Rev.Hist.Sci.*, 1963, 16: 323-58.

SKOWRONNEK, Karl. Zur Entwicklung der Elektronenverstärker-Röhre (Lieben-Röhre). *Arch.Gesch.Math.Naturwiss.Tech.*, 1931, 13: 225-76, 36 fig.

V MATERIALS AND PROCESSES

Vc

BEERY, Pauline Gracia. Stuff: the story of materials in the service of man. xiii, 504 p., ill. New York: Appleton, 1930.

FORBES, R.J. Materialen voor 1850. [Materials before 1850. (In Dutch)] Causerie, gehouden ter gelegenheid van het 25-jarig bestaan van de Bond voor Materialenkennis, 21.11. '51. *Metalen*, 1951, 12 p.

FURNAS, Clifford Cook. The storehouse of civilization. xx, 562 p. New York: Teachers College, Columbia University, 1939.
Reviewed by M.F. Ashley Montagu, *Isis*, 1949, 32: 405-6.
The raw materials with which man has to work and their use in technology.

HAYNES, Williams. Chemistry's contribution. The economics of new materials. An address delivered before Princeton University on December 10, 1935, in the Cyrus Fogg Brackett lectureship in applied engineering and technology. 31 p. Princeton, N.J.: The Guild of Brackett Lecturers, 1936.

Vws

THE WEALTH of India. A dictionary of Indian raw materials and industrial products. Delhi: Council of Scientific and Industrial Research, 1948-
Issued in 2 sections. Raw materials. Vol. 1-6, A-M. 1948-62. Industrial products. Vol. 1-4, A-L. 1948-60.
Reviewed by J.L. Simonsen, *Nature*, 1949, 163: 743; 1951, 168: 618.

Vwt-bx

NEEDHAM, Joseph. Chungking industrial and mining exhibition. *Nature*, 1944, 153: 672-5, ill.

Vxj testing materials

BAUMANN, R. Das Materialprüfungswesen und die Erweiterung der Erkenntnisse auf dem Gebiet der Elastizität und Festigkeit in Deutschland während der letzten vier Jahrzehnte. *Beitr. Gesch.Tech.Ind.*, 1912, 4: 147-95.

GIBBONS, Chester H. History of testing machines for materials. *Trans.Newcomen Soc.*, 1934-35, 15: 169-84.

GIBBONS, Chester H. Materials testing machines. An account of their development, with special reference to the tension - compression - transverse group. 89 p., fig. Pittsburgh: Instruments Publishing Co., 1935. [CB 59/472]

TIMOSHENKO, Stephen P. History of strength of materials. 452 p., 245 fig. New York/London: McGraw-Hill, 1953.
Reviewed by R.J. Forbes, *Arch.Int.Hist.Sci.*, 1953, 6: 533-4.

VA CHEMICAL ENGINEERING; PROCESS ENGINEERING

see also VP CHEMICAL INDUSTRY

VAwh-o-ce

SARNECKI, Kazimierz. Dawne podreczniki technologii chemicznej w Polsce. [Old-time textbooks of chemical technology in Poland. (In Polish, with English summary)] *Stud.Mater.Dziej. Nauk.Pol., Ser. C*, 1964, 9: 3-28.

VAwn-qg

BOL'SHAKOV, K.A.; PLOTKIN, S. Ia. Moskovskii institut tonkoi khimicheskoi tekhnologii im. M.V. Lomonosova. [The Moscow institute of chemical engineering named in honor of M.V. Lomonosov. (In Russian)] *Vop.Ist.Est.Tekh.*, 1962, no. 12, 160-1.

VAxd

FARRAR, W.V. The strange history of intensive drying. *Proc. Chem.Soc.*, 1963, 125-8.
A critical account of the work of H.B. Baker on the physical properties of anhydrous liquids.

MIKHAILOV, Iu.A. [From the history of desiccation by means of superheated steam. (In Russian)] *Vop.Ist.Est.Tekh.*, 1959, 7: 166-70.

VAze INDUSTRIAL EFFLUENTS

BOYNE, Rolf. Vom Entwicklungsgang der Abwasserbeseitigung in den letzten hundert Jahren. *Technikgeschichte*, 1936, 25: 57-65, 3 pl., 5 fig.

ROHLAND, Paul W. Zur Geschichte der Abwässeranlagen. *Arch. Gesch.Naturwiss.Tech.*, 1912, 4: 215-17.

VB MINING TECHNOLOGY (also MINING AND METALLURGY combined)

VBc general history

AMERICAN INSTITUTE OF MINING AND METALLURGICAL ENGINEERS. Seventy-five years of progress in the mineral industry, 1871-1946, including Proceedings of the 75th anniversary of the ... Institute ... and World Conference on Mineral Resources, March 1947, ed. by A.B. Parsons. xii, 817 p., 111 portr., 58 fig. New York: The Institute, 1947.
Reviewed by L. Don Leet, *Isis*, 1949, 40: 82-3.

BERGBAU und Bergleute. Neue Beiträge zur Geschichte des Bergbaus und der Geologie. 294 p., ill. (Freiberger Forschungshefte. Kultur und Technik, D 11) Berlin: Akademie-Verlag, 1955. [CB 84/312]
Reviewed by Felix F. Strauss, *Isis*, 1962, 53: 521-3.

ISTORIA gornoi tekhniki i metallurgii. [History of mining technology and metallurgy. (In Russian)] *Tr.Inst.Ist.Est. Tekh.*, 1960, 33: 1-309, ill.
For contents of this volume *see* CB 86/473.

PARMA, Jan Boris. Rozvoj dobývacích metod rudného hornictví v první třetině 20. století. [The development of ore mining methods in the first third of the twentieth century. (In Czech, with Russian summary)] *Sb.Dějiny Přírodn.Věd Tech.*, 1963, 8: 113-37.

PARMA, Jan Boris. Vznik dobývacích metod v rudném hornictví a jejich vyvoj do konce 19. století. [The origin and development of working methods in ore mining up to the end of the 19th century. (In Czech, with German summary)] *Sb.Dějiny Přírodn.Věd Tech.*, 1962, 7: 137-58.

SCHREIBER, Georg. Der Bergbau in Geschichte, Ethos und Sakralkultur. 757 p., ill. (Wissenschaftliche Abhandlungen der Arbeitsgemeinschaft für Forschung des Landes Nordrhein-Westfalen, 21) Köln und Opladen: Westdeutscher Verlag, 1962.
Reviewed by M. Habacher, *Bl.Technikgesch.*, 1964, 26: 157-8.

TREPTOW, E. Bergmännische Kunst. *Beitr.Gesch.Tech.Ind.*, 1922, 12: 173-212, 41 fig.

VBc-br

Studia z Dziejow Gornictwa i Hutnictwa. [Studies on the history of mining and metallurgy. (In Polish)] Vol. 1 - (Polska Akademia Nauk Instytut Historii Kultury Materialnej. Studia i materialy z historii kultury materialne) Warszawa: Geologiczne, 1957 -

VBc-bv

[DISSERTATIONS on the history of geology, geography, mining, and metallurgy published 1944-1954. (In Russian)] *Tr.Inst. Ist.Est.Tekh.*, 1955, 3: 232-7.

VBce

KOCH, Manfred. Geschichte und Entwicklung des bergmännischen Schrifttums. 176 p., ill. (Schriftenreihe Bergbau-Aufbereitung, 1) Goslar: Hermann Hübener Verlag K.G., 1963.

VBce-bx

HAWKES, Arthur J. Jubilee exhibition of early mining literature, Wigan public libraries. May 1 to September 29, 1928. Annotated catalogue compiled and arranged, with an introduction. Foreword by the Earl of Crawford and Balcarres. xiv, 38 p. Wigan: Public Library, 1928.

VBn/t special aspects

VBnh

TAUBE, Edward. Mining terms of obscure origins. *Sci.Mon.*, 1944, 58: 454-6.
The origin and history of matte, mispickel, quartz, shaft, and shode.

VBnh-be

KRYGIER, Eugenius. [The need for a dictionary of mining and smelting terms. (In Polish with summaries in Russian and English)] *Kwart.Hist.Kult.Mater.*, 1955, 3: 119-23.

VBsc

RICKARD, T.A. Man and metals. A history of mining in relation to the development of civilization. 2 vol. xiii, 1068 p., 108 fig. New York: McGraw-Hill, 1932.
Reviewed by George Sarton, *Isis*, 1934, 21: 334-6.

VBt

HADDOCK, M.H. Cultural contacts of mining. 144 p. London: Routledge and Kegan Paul, 1949.

VBw in different countries

VBwa-o

MORRAL, F.R. The beginning of mining and metallurgical education in the New World. *Mining Eng.*, 1963, 15: 40.
References to early mineral industry education in the United States from 1864 and from 1777 in Mexico.

VBwb

PAIN, S.A. The way north: men, mines and minerals. vi, 249 p., ill. Toronto: Ryerson, 1964.

RAYMOND, Rossiter W. Old mines of California and Nevada. 133 p. Toyahville, Texas: Frontier Book Co., 1964.

VBwc

BARGALLO, Modesto. La minería y la metalurgía en la America española durante la época colonial. 442 p., ill., bibliogr. Mexico City/Buenos Aires: Fondo de Cultura Económica, 1955.
Reviewed by Bailey W. Diffie, *Hispanic-Amer.Hist.Rev.*, 1957, 37: 96-7.

VBwe

BARTON, Denys B. A historical survey of the mines and mineral railways of East Cornwall and West Devon. 102 p., ill., maps. Truro, Eng.: Truro Bookshop, 1964.

GOUGH, J.W. The mines of Mendip. x, 269 p. Oxford: Clarendon Press; New York: Oxford University Press, 1930.
Reviewed by E.F. Armstrong, *Nature*, 1930, 126: 345-6; by Abbott Payson Usher, *Amer.Hist.Rev.*, 1931, 36: 422-3.

JENKIN, A.K. Hamilton. Mines and miners of Cornwall. Pt. 1-9. Truro, Eng.: Truro Bookshop, 1961-64.
In progress.
Reviewed by Douglas McKie, *Ann.Sci.*, 1963, 19: 150-1.

LONES, T.E. The South Staffordshire and North Worcestershire mining district and its relics of mining appliances. *Trans. Newcomen Soc.*, 1930-31, 11: 42-54.

PAULL, Clarence V. South Crofty: past and present. *Trans. Newcomen Soc.*, 1932-33, 13: 147-50.
Cornish mines.

VBwe-r

JENKIN, A.K. Hamilton. The Cornish miner, an account of his life above and underground from early times. 3rd ed. 351 p. London: Allen and Unwin, 1962.
First published 1927.

VBwg

BERGBAU und Bergleute. *See* VBc

TREPTOW, Emil. Der Bergbau des Oberharzes, seine Ausbeutemünzen und Ausbeutefahnen. *Beitr.Gesch.Tech.Ind.*, 1928, 18: 1-14, 22 fig.

VBwg-or

SCHIFFNER, Carl. Aus dem Leben alter Freiberger Bergstudenten. xv, 375 p., fig., pl. Freiberg i. Sa.: Mauckisch, 1935.
Reviewed by R. Zaunick, *Mitt.Gesch.Med.Naturwiss.Tech.*, 1937, 36: 286.

VBwg-r

KLINCKOWSTROEM, Carl von. Die Weltgeltung des deutschen Bergmannes. *Deut.Erde* (Munich), 1933, 4: 380-6, 3 fig.

VBwg-st

HUFFMANN, Fritz Robert. Über die sächsische Berggerichtsbarkeit vom 15. Jahrhundert bis zu ihrem Ende. Ein Beitrag zur Geschichte der Sondergerichte. viii, 149 p. Weimar: Böhlaus, 1935.
Reviewed by Paul Rehme, *Deut.Lit.Zeitung*, 1937, 58: 1861-4.

VBwg-tk

HEILFURTH, Gerhard. Das erzgebirgische Bergmannslied. Ein Aufriss seiner literarischen Geschichte. 142 p. Schwarzenberg/Erzgebirge: Glückauf-Verlag, 1936.
Reviewed by Wilhelm Heiske, *Deut.Lit.Zeitung*, 1937, 58: 148-9.

WOLF, Herbert. Studien zur deutschen Bergmannssprache in den Bergmannsliedern des 16.-20. Jahrhunderts, vorwiegend nach Mitteldeutschen Quellen. 238 p., bibliogr. (Mitteldeutsche Forschungen, 11) Tübingen: Max Niemeyer, 1958.
Reviewed by Gerhard Eis, *Centaurus*, 1963, 8: 298-300.

VBwg-tq

TREPTOW, Emil. Deutsche Meisterwerke bergmännischer Kunst. iv, 46 p., 42 fig. (*Abhandl.Ber.Deut.Mus.*, 1: no. 1) Berlin: VDI Verlag, 1929.

VBwh

KORAN, Jan. Mining technology on the territory of Czechoslovakia in the old days. *Act.VIIIe Congr.Int.Hist.Sci.* (Florence, 1956), p. 1040-5. Paris: Hermann, 1958.

PAZDUR, Jan. [A study of the history of mining and foundry technology in Poland (a scheme for future research). (In Polish, with English summary)] *Kwart.Hist.Kult.Mater.*, 1953, 1: 44-77.

VBwh-st

KORAN, Jan; VANECEK, Vaclav. Czech mining and mining laws. *Cah.Hist.Mond.*, 1962, 7: 27-45.

VBwi-p

ALBERTI, Annibale; CESSI, Roberto. La politica mineraria della repubblica Veneta. Con lettera del ministro Belluzzo al capo del governo. viii, 455 p. Roma: Libreria dello Stato, 1927.

VBwn

ISTORIA gornoi tekhniki i metallurgi. *See* VBc

OSTROMETSKII, A.A. Ocherki po istorii russkoi gornoi mekhaniki. [Sketch of the history of Russian mining engineering. (In Russian)] 155 p., ill., portr. Moskva: Ugletekhizdat, 1953.

TIGRANIAN, S.T. [New information on mining business in the Armenian SSR. (In Russian)] *Tr.Inst.Ist.Est.Tekh.*, 1955, 3: 170-5.

VBwq

GSELL, Stéphane. Vieilles exploitations minières dans l' Afrique du Nord. *Hespéris*, 1928, 8: 1-21.

VBws

WADIA, D.N. Mineral industries in India. *Sci.Cult.*, 1962, 28: 49-52.

VBwx

BANCROFT, J. Austen. Mining in Northern Rhodesia - A chronology of mineral exploration and mining development. Arranged and prepared by T.D. Gurney. 174 p., front., pl. London: British South Africa Company, 1961. [CB 88/548]
History from early times to the present of prospecting, geological exploration, engineering and business development of the Northern Rhodesian copper deposits.

VBx techniques and instruments

VBxb-wh

ZWOLINSKI, Stefan. Urzadzenia kopalni na Kunsztach w Dolinie Koscieliskiej w Tatrach. [The equipment of a mine called "Na Kunsztach" in the Koscieliska valley in the Tatra mountains. (In Polish with summaries in Russian and English)] *Kwart.Hist.Nauk.Tech.*, 1961, 6: 457-67.

VBxb-wn

DOBROV, G.M. [On the first projects of the multi-purpose mining machinery in Russia. (In Russian)] *Tr.Inst.Ist.Est.Tekh.*, 1955, 3: 36-44.

VBxd

JANELID, Ingvar. The Swedish method. (In English) *Daedalus*, 1963, 113-43.
On the development of the so-called Swedish method of rock drilling for tunneling and mining.

VBxd-wn

SHEVYAKOV, L.D. The development of the analytic method in mining. *Act.VIIIe Congr.Int.Hist.Sci.* (Florence, 1956), p. 990-3. Paris: Hermann, 1958.

VBxm-wg

KIRNBAUER, Franz. Die Entwicklung des Markscheidewesens im Lande Österreich. vii, 154 p., 102 fig., 2 pl. (Blätter für Technikgeschichte, Forschungsinstitut für Technikgeschichte in Wien, 7) Wien: Springer, 1940.
Reviewed by R. Zaunick, *Mitt.Gesch.Med.*, 1940, 39: 189-90.

VBxx museums

FALUN. BERGSLAGETS MUSEUM. Plan av Byggnaden och Samlingarna. [The mining museum of Falun, Sweden. A plan of the building and its collection. (In Swedish)] 27 p. Falun: 1947. [CB 71/124]

VBy SPECIAL PROCESSES

VByUH

MULTHAUF, Robert P. Mine pumping in Agricola's time and later. (*Contrib.Mus.Hist.Technol.*, 7) *Bull.U.S.Nat.Mus.*, 1959, 218: 113-20.

VByUV

PHILIPPI, Wilhelm. Die Entwicklung der Elektrizitätsverwendung im Bergbau. *Beitr.Gesch.Tech.Ind.*, 1928, 18: 19-36, 27 fig.

VC METALLURGY

VCc general history

AITCHISON, Leslie. A history of metals. 2 vol. xxi, 304 p.; xvii, 305-647 p., front., pl., fig., tables, bibliogr. New York: Interscience; London: Macdonald and Evans, 1960.
Reviewed by Robert F. Mehl, *Isis*, 1962, 53: 242-4; for other reviews *see* CB 86/473, CB 87/576 and CB 88/565.

DENNIS, W.H. A hundred years of metallurgy. x, 342 p., ill. London: Duckworth, 1963; Chicago: Aldine, 1964.
Reviewed by Cyril Stanley Smith, *Arch.Int.Hist.Sci.*, 1964, 17: 334-5; by B.R. Queneau, *Science*, 1964, 144: 727-8.

DESCH, Cecil H. The services of Henry Clifton Sorby to metallurgy. Being the second Sorby lecture, delivered on October 31, 1921. 20 p., 7 fig. [Sheffield: Sheffield Society of Engineers and Metallurgists, 1921.] [CB 17/557]

FORBES, R.J. Metallurgy. *Metalen*, 1958, 13: 6-8, 26-9, 46-8, 71-4, 90-1, 111-14, 129-33, ill., bibliogr.

GUERTLER, W. Der gegenwärtige Stand der Forschungen auf dem Gebiete der Metallographie. *Fortschr.Naturwiss.Forsch.*, 1913, 8: 1-50.

GUILLET, Léon. L'évolution de la métallurgie. ii, 196 p., 37 fig. (Nouvelle Collection Scientifique) Paris: Alcan, 1928. [CB 29/299]

SMITH, Cyril Stanley. A history of metallography. The development of ideas on the structure of metals before 1890. xxi, 291 p., front., fig., pl., bibliogr. Chicago: University of Chicago Press, 1960.
Reviewed by Herbert Maryon, *Isis*, 1962, 53: 244-6; for other reviews *see* CB 86/475 and CB 87/578.

SMITH, Cyril Stanley. The interaction of science and practice in the history of metallurgy. *Technol.Cult.*, 1961, 2: 357-67.

THOMAS, Pierre-Julien le. La métallurgie. 192 p., ill. (Le Rayon de la Science, 19) Paris: Éditions du Seuil, 1963.
Reviewed by Jacques Payen, *Rev.Hist.Sci.*, 1964, 17: 281-2.

VCc-bx

NIMAL, H. de. La métallurgie à l'Exposition de Charleroi en 1911, avec des notes historiques sur la Forgerie. In: Drèze, Gustave, ed. Livre d'or de l'Exposition de Charleroi, vol. 1, 150 p. Liége: Imprimerie Bénard, 1913.

VCcp

WEILL, Adrienne R. De l'analyse des objets à l'histoire des techniques de métallurgie. *Act.VIIIe Congr.Int.Hist.Sci.* (Florence, 1956), p. 949-61. Paris: Hermann, 1958.

VCj/t special aspects

VCjg

LODGE, Oliver. States of mind which make and miss discoveries: with some ideas about metals. Nineteenth May lecture to the Institute of Metals, delivered May 7, 1929. *J.Inst.Metals*, 1929, 41: 345-76.

VCmzD

DESCH, C.H. A chemist's view of metallurgy. Presidential address. *J.Inst.Metals*, 1938, 62: 41-61.

VCmzDY

ELIADE, Mircea. Metallurgy, magic and alchemy. *Zalmoxis*, 1938, 1: 85-129.

MAHDIHASSAN, S. Alchemy and its connection with astrology, pharmacy, magic and metallurgy. *Janus*, 1957, 46: 81-103.

VCmzYC

FORBES, R.J. Archaeology and metallurgy. *Edgar Allen News*, 1953, 32: 89-92.

READ, Thomas T. Metallurgical fallacies in archaeological literature. *Amer.J.Archaeol.*, 1934, 38: 382-9.

for the application of metallurgy to archaeological technique *see* YCxf-VC

VCnh

CRIVELLI, Epaminonda. Le vicende dei nomi dei metalli. *Arch. Stor.Sci.*, 1921, 2: 1-45. [CB 10/195]

VCtq

SMITH, Cyril Stanley. Decorative etching and the science of metals. *Endeavour*, 1957, 16: 199-208, 22 fig.

VCw in different countries

VCwf

GILLE, Bertrand. Les origines de la grande industrie métallurgique en France. Introduction d'Edouard Dolléans. xxxii, 212 p. Paris: Domat-Montchrestien, 1947.

VCwg

SIEBER, Siegfried. Aus der Geschichte der Industrie des Erzgebirges. *Beitr.Gesch.Tech.Ind.*, 1928, 18: 129-34, 1 map.

VCwg-oq

BIALETSKIN, K.A. [The metallurgical laboratory of the Berg Collegium. (In Russian)] *Tr.Inst.Ist.Est.Tekh.*, 1955, 3: 176-83.

VCwh

ZIENTARA, Benedykt. [A note concerning the history of metallurgy in Malopolska. (In Polish, with summary in Russian and English)] *Kwart.Hist.Kult.Mater.*, 1955, 3: 809-11.

VCwn

STRUMILIN, S.G. [Technical progress during three centuries. (In Russian)] *Arkh.Ist.Nauk.Tekh.*, 1934, 3: 51-76, 1 fig; 4: 149-90.
A sketch of Russian metallurgy since the XVIIth century.

VCxd METAL PROCESSING

CHEREPNEV, A.I. K voprosu razvitiia mekhanizatsii i avtomatizatsii obrabotki metallov rezaniem. [On the question of the development of mechanization and automation in metal cutting processes. (In Russian)] *Tr.Inst.Ist.Est.Tekh.*, 1962, 45: 28-47.

CLAAS, Wilhelm. Vom Draht und den Altenaer Drahtrollen. *Beitr. Gesch.Tech.Ind.*, 1932, 21: 133-42, 8 fig.

DICKINSON, H.W. A study of galvanised and corrugated sheet metal. *Trans.Newcomen Soc.*, 1943-44 and 1944-45, 24: 27-36.

DICKMANN, H. Die Erfindung des Stacheldrahtes. *Beitr.Gesch. Tech.Ind.*, 1927, 17: 161, 5 fig.

LAMAN, N.K. Iz istorii tekhniki volocheniia metallov. [From the history of the technology of the wire-drawing of metals. (In Russian)] *Vop.Ist.Est.Tekh.*, 1963, no. 14, 111-16.

PEARSON, C.E. The history of the hydraulic extrusion process. *Trans.Newcomen Soc.*, 1940-41, 21: 109-21, 13 fig.

PLOTKIN, S.Ia. Iz istorii poroshkovoi metallurgii. [On the history of powder metallurgy. (In Russian)] *Vop.Ist.Est. Tekh.*, 1961, 11: 119-24.

READ, Thomas T. The earliest industrial use of coal. *Trans. Newcomen Soc.*, 1939-40, 20: 119-33.
For smelting.

WEDEL, Ernst von. Geschichtliche Entwicklung des Umformens in Gesenken. (Bericht Nr. 36 des Geschichtsausschusses des Vereins Deutscher Eisenhüttenleute) *Stahl Eisen*, 1959, 79: 1419-27.

VCxd-we

GALE, W.K.V. Soho Foundry. Some facts and fallacies. *Trans. Newcomen Soc.*, 1961-62, 34: 73-87.

VCxd-wn

ROUBTSOV, N.N. Les fondeurs moscovites du XIVe au XVIIe siècles. *Act.VIIIe Congr.Int.Hist.Sci.* (Florence, 1956), p. 1065-8. Paris: Hermann, 1958.

VD IRON AND STEEL

VDc general history

AUGER, Paul E. Iron, its history and its economic fluctuations through the ages. *Proc.Geol.Ass.Can.*, 1963, 15: 21-32.

BENT, Quincy. 75 years of steel. 24 p. Princeton, N.J.: Princeton University Press (for Newcomen Society, American Branch), 1939.

HATFIELD, W.H. Economy in the use of ferro-alloys. *Nature*, 1942, 150: 509-12.
Including historical table of ferro-alloys.

JOHANNSEN, Otto. Geschichte des Eisens. 3rd ed. viii, 622 p., ill. Düsseldorf: Verlag Stahleisen, 1953.
Reviewed by R.J. Forbes, *Arch.Int.Hist.Sci.*, 1955, 8: 206-7. First published 1924. 2nd edition (1925) reviewed by H. Th. Horwitz, *Geschichtsbl.Tech.Ind.*, 1927, 11: 199-201.

JÜPTNER VON JONSTORFF, H. Das Eisenhüttenwesen. Eine Uebersicht seiner Entwicklung sowie seiner kulturellen und volkswirtschaftlichen Bedeutung. xii, 212 p., ill. Leipzig: Akademische Verlagsgesellschaft, 1912.

KLINCKOWSTROEM, Karl von. Die Herkunft des Eisens. *Stahl Eisen*, 1951, 71: 362-73.

LARKE, William J. Iron and steel. *Nature*, 1935, 136: 19-26.
Friday evening discourse delivered at the Royal Institution on March 22, 1935. Includes historical summary.

LEROI-GOURHAN, A. Notes pour une histoire des aciers. *Tech. Civilisations*, 1951, 2: 4-10, 14 fig.

LOUIS, Henry. Iron manufacture and heat generation. *Nature*, 1929, 123: 762-5, 3 fig.

MARS, G. Die Spezialstähle: ihre Geschichte, Eigenschaften, Behandlung und Herstellung. 2nd ed. viii, 675 p. Stuttgart: F. Enke, 1923.
First published 1912.

PARKER, Charles M. Steel in action. viii, 221 p., 16 fig. (Science for War and Peace Series) Lancaster, Pa.: Jaques Cattell Press, 1943. [CB 66/264]
Contains a chapter on the history of the manufacture of iron and steel.

PEAKE, Harold. The origin and early spread of ironworking. *Geogr.Rev.*, 1933, 23: 639-52, 1 fig. [CB 40/407]

PECKITT, Leonard. Iron in industry - progress of 100 years, with a tribute to David Thomas. 31 p., ill. Princeton, N.J.: Princeton University Press (for Newcomen Society, American Branch), 1940.

PRŮMYSLOVA revoluce v železářství. [Industrial revolution in iron industry. (In Czech)] 93 p. (Rozpravy Narodnihe Technického Muzea v Praze. Rada Populárně Vědecká, 10) Prague: Národní Technické Muzeum, 1964.

TYRKIEL, Eugeniusz. Wykres żelazo-węgiel w rozwoju historycznym. [History of the iron-carbon diagram. (In Polish)] 308 p., ill. (Monografie z dziejów nauki i techniki, 21) Wroclaw: Zaklad Narodowy im. Ossolińskich, 1963.

WERTIME, Theodore A. The coming of the age of steel. xvi, 330 p., 10 ill., bibliogr. Leiden: Brill, 1961; Chicago: University of Chicago Press, 1962.
Reviewed by Leslie Aitchison, *Isis*, 1964, 55: 234-5; by James B. Austin, *Technol.Cult.*, 1963, 4: 71-2; by Cyril Stanley Smith, *Ibid.*, 1964, 5: 87-8.

WILLIAMS, E. Two metallurgical discoveries. *Ann.Sci.*, 1955, 11: 93-8.
The discovery of manganese steel by Robert A. Hadfield and of high-speed tool steel by Frederick W. Taylor.

VDc-br

Revue d'Histoire de la Sidérurgie. Vol. 1- Nancy: Centre de Recherches de l'Histoire de la Sidérurgie, 1960-.
Reviewed by M. Daumas, *Rev.Hist.Sci.*, 1963, 16: 404-5.

VDc-bu

GILLE, Bertrand. Programmes et méthodes de documentation du Centre de Recherches de l'Histoire de la Sidérurgie de Nancy. *Doc.Hist.Tech.*, 1962, 2: 62-7.

VDc-bv

DICKMANN, H. Zur Geschichte des Eisens. *Beitr.Gesch.Tech.Ind.*, 1933, 22: 120-2.
A review of some literature on the subject.

VDcb

McHUGH, Jeanne. The Iron Library of the George Fischer Company [Schaffhausen, Switzerland.] *Technol.Cult.*, 1963, 4: 331-5.
A collection of over 20,000 books and manuscripts related to iron. Established in 1948.

SCHIB, K. Die "Eisenbibliothek" im ehemaligen Kloster "Paradies", Zentrum industriegeschichtlicher Forschung. *Schweiz. Arch.Angew.Wiss.Tech.*, 1960, 26: no. 6, 217-20.

VDce

HATFIELD, W.H. The association of the Royal Society with the iron and steel industry. *Notes Roy.Soc.Lond.*, 1940, 3: 64-79.
Apropos of the work on iron and steel found in the *Philosophical Transactions* and *Proceedings*.

VDfd

SHEEP, James T. James M. Swank, pioneer historian of the iron and steel industry. *West.Penn.Hist.Mag.*, 1951, 34: 260-9.

VDw in different countries

VDwb

BOYER, Charles Shimer. Early forges and furnaces in New Jersey. xv, 287 p. Philadelphia: University of Pennsylvania Press; London: Oxford University Press, 1931.

JOURNAL OF METALS. History of iron and steelmaking in the United States. x, 101 p., ill. New York: Metallurgical Society, American Institute of Mining, Metallurgical, and Petroleum Engineers, 1961. [CB 88/567]
This book consists of seventeen articles that appeared in the *Journal of Metals* on various phases of the iron and steel industry.

STARKEY, J. Albert. The bog ore and bog iron industry of South Jersey. *Bull.N.J.Acad.Sci.*, 1962, 7: 5-8.

VDwe

BREARLEY, Harry. Knotted string: autobiography of a steelmaker. ix, 198 p. London: Longmans, Green, 1941.
Reviewed by C.H. Desch, *Nature*, 1942, 149: 397.

DAVIES, A. Stanley. The early iron industry in North Wales. *Trans.Newcomen Soc.*, 1945-46 and 1946-47, 25: 83-90.

DELANY, Mary Cecilia. The historical geography of the Wealden iron industry. 62 p., 3 maps. (Historico-Geographical Monographs) London: Benn, 1921.

DESCH, Cecil H. The steel industry of South Yorkshire: a regional study. Being a paper read to the Sociological Society on 24th January, 1922. *Sociol.Rev.*, 1922, 14: 131-7. [CB 17/583]

GALE, W.K.V. Notes on the Black country iron trade. *Trans. Newcomen Soc.*, 1943-44 and 1944-45, 24: 13-26.

HALL, J.W. Notes on Coalbrookdale, and the Darbys. *Trans. Newcomen Soc.*, 1924-25, 5: 1-8, 1 pl.

JENKINS, Rhys. Early engineering and ironfounding in Cornwall. *Trans.Newcomen Soc.*, 1942-43, 23: 23-35.

JENKINS, Rhys. Iron-making in the Forest of Dean. *Trans.Newcomen Soc.*, 1925-26, 6: 42-65.

JENKINS, Rhys. Notes on the early history of steel making in England. *Trans.Newcomen Soc.*, 1922-23, 3: 16-40.

JENKINS, Rhys. The rise and fall of the Sussex iron industry. *Trans.Newcomen Soc.*, 1921-22, 1: 16-33, 10 pl. [CB 13/311]

SCHUBERT, H.R. History of the British iron and steel industry from c. 450 B.C. to A.D. 1775. xxi, 445 p., ill. London: Routledge & Kegan Paul, 1957.
Reviewed by F.W. Gibbs, *Ambix*, 1958, 6: 162-3; by F.C. Thompson, *Nature*, 1958, 182: 349; by H.W.M. Hodges, *Proc. Prehist.Soc.*, 1959, 25: 287.

STRAKER, Ernest. Wealden iron. xiv, 488 p., ill. London: Bell, 1931. [CB 32/583]
Reviewed by S.E. Winbolt, *Geogr.J.*, 1931, 78: 365.

VDwg

ANSELM, H. Die Stubaier Kleineisenindustrie. *Abhandl.Ber. Deut.Mus.*, 1930, 2: no. 3, 65-84, 10 fig. [CB 30/470]

BREMECKER, Ernst. Aus der Entwicklungsgeschichte der Kleineisenindustrie in der ehemaligen Grafschaft Mark und dem Herzogtum Berg. *Beitr.Gesch.Tech.Ind.*, 1928, 18: 135-8.

ILLIES, -. Aus der geschichtlichen Entwicklung des Eisenhüttenwesens Oberschlesiens an Hand der Geschichte der Königshütte. *Beitr.Gesch.Tech.Ind.*, 1922, 12: 1-39, 27 fig.

KRÄMER, Wolfgang. Geschichte des Eisenwerkes zu St. Ingbert mit besonderer Berücksichtigung der Frühzeit. Ein Beitrag zur Geschichte der pfälzisch-saarländischen Eisenverhüttung nach archivalischen Quellen. 188 p., 44 fig. (Veröffentlichungen der Pfälzischen Gesellschaft zur Förderung der Wissenschaften, 22) Speyer: Pfälzische Gesellschaft, 1933.

SIEBER, Siegfried. Vom eisernen Erzgebirge. *Forsch.Fortschr.*, 1964, 38: 265-70.
On the history of iron production in the Erzgebirge.

TANZER, K. Vom norischen Eisen zum steirischen Stahl. ii, 32 p., 11 fig. (*Abhandl.Ber.Deut.Mus.*, 2: no. 4) Berlin: VDI Verlag, 1930. [CB 30/471]

WEVER, Franz. Henry Clifton Sorby und die deutsche Metallographie. *Z.Metallk.*, 1964, 55: 1-4.

VDwg-qt

FISCHER, Georg. Hundertfünfzig Jahre Georg Fischer Werke 1802-1952. 192 p., 20 pl. Schaffhausen: Georg Fischer, 1952. [CB 79/176]

VDwh

PIASKOWSKI, Jerzy. Le développement de la technologie d'acier et du fer en Pologne d'après les examinations métallographiques des produits anciens. *Kwart.Hist.Nauk.Tech.*, 1957-58, special issue, 55-76.

PIASKOWSKI, Jerzy. Preliminary report on early iron technology in Poland. *Technol.Cult.*, 1961, 2: 245-8.

VDwi

BONI, Bruno. Vecchia metallurgia toscana: la ferriera di Follonica e i Medici; la fonderia di Follonica e i Lorena. *Fonderia Ital.*, 1957, 6: 3-21, 9 fig.

VDwk

BOURGUIGNON, Marcel. Les anciennes forges de Pierrard et de Rabais. *Pays Gaumais*, 1961, 22: 129-50.

EVRARD, René; DESCY, Armand. Histoire de l'usine des Vennes, suivie de considérations sur les fontes anciennes, 1548-1948. 381 p. Liége: Soledi, 1948.

WESTERMANN, J.C. Geschiedenis van de ijzer en staalgieterij in Nederland. [History of iron and steel foundries in Holland. (In Dutch)] 392 p., 45 ill. Utrecht: 1948.
Reviewed by R.J. Forbes, *Arch.Int.Hist.Sci.*, 1950, 3: 250-1.

VDwm

JOHANNSEN, Otto. Die Geschichte des schwedischen Stahls. *Technikgeschichte*, 1933, 22: 122-6.
A review of Carl Sahlin's book, *see* below.

SAHLIN, Carl. Svenskt stål före de stora götstålprocessernas inforande; historiska anteckningar. [Swedish steel before the introduction of the great steel casting process: historical notes. (In Swedish)] 242 p., ill. Stockholm: I. Haeggström, 1931.
Reviewed by O. Johannsen, *Beitr.Gesch.Tech.Ind.*, 1933, 22: 122-6.

VDwn

ROMANCHENKO, G.N. [On the history of Krivoi Rog basin. (In Russian)] *Tr.Inst.Ist.Est.Tekh.*, 1955, 3: 19-35.

STRUMILIN, S.G. [Iron metallurgy in Russia and in the USSR. Technological progress during three centuries. (In Russian)] 324 p., ill. (*Tr.Inst.Ist.Nauk.Tekh.*, *ser. 2*, no. 4) Moskva: Izdatelstvo Akademii Nauk SSSR, 1935. [CB 45/285]

VDx techniques and instruments

VDxd

DARMSTAEDTER, Ernst. Eisenhärtung mit Pflanzen. *Geschichtsbl. Tech.Ind.*, 1927, 11: 163-9.

DÖHNER, O.H. Die Entwicklung der Mechanisierung bei der Herstellung von Eisen- und Stahldrähten. *Beitr.Gesch.Tech.Ind.*, 1924, 14: 193-204, 10 fig.

GILLE, Bertrand. Notes d'histoire de la technique métallurgique. 2. L'utilisation de la houille en sidérurgie. *Métaux Civilisations*, 1946, 1: 99-104.

HALL, John W. The making and rolling of iron. *Trans.Newcomen Soc.*, 1927-28, 8: 40-55.

HULME, E. Wyndham; BONE, William A. The invention of the hot blast in iron-smelting. *Nature*, 1928, 122: 728.

JOHANNSEN, Otto. Der Ursprung des Hochofens und der Eisengiesserei. Zwei schwierige Fragen aus der Geschichte des Eisens. *Korrespondenzbl.Gesamtver.Deut.Geschichts-Altertumsver.*, 1912, 60: 126-9.

MURAMATSU, Teijiro. [Recent state of the "Tatara" method of iron smelting. (In Japanese)] *J.Hist.Sci.Japan*, 1953, no. 26, 30-6.

SCHULTZ, Ernst-Hermann. Die Möglichkeit eines Zusammenhanges zwischen Dreckapotheke und Stahlhärtungsmitteln. *Sudhoffs Arch.*, 1958, 42: 62-4.

VDxd-wn

SAMARIN, A.M. Early stage of development of the converter method of steel production in Russia. *Act.VIIIe Congr.Int.Hist. Sci.* (Florence, 1956), p. 998-1000. Paris: Hermann, 1958.

VDxf-DH

MATHEWS, John A. Comments on the electric steel industry. [With discussion.] *Trans.Amer.Electrochem.Soc.*, 1917, 31: 43-52.

VE NON-FERROUS METALS

VEc

DAWKINS, J.M. Zinc and spelter. Notes on the early history of zinc from Babylon to the 18th century, compiled for the curious. 35 p. Oxford: Zinc Development Association, 1950. [CB 79/175]
Development of a text first published in *Chem.Ind.*, 1949, 515-20.

GADEAU, R. Historique de la fabrication de l'aluminium. *Chim. Ind.*, 1964, 92: 180-7.

GÁLVEZ-CAÑERO, A. de. La metalurgia de la plata y del mercurio (bosquejo histórico). *IX Congr.Int.Quím.Pura Apl.* (Madrid, 1934), Conferencias generales, p. 133-67. Madrid: Imprenta C. Bermejo, 1934.

GHASWALA, S.K. Development in aluminium and its alloys. *Act. VIe Congr.Int.Hist.Sci.* (Amsterdam, 1950), p. 609-17. Paris: Hermann, 1953. Also in *Arch.Int.Hist.Sci.*, 1953, 6: 444-52.

HOMMEL, W. Zur Geschichte des Zinks. Ursprung des Namens Zink. Erkennung des Zinks als Metall. *Chem.Zeitung*, 1912, 36: 905-6, 918-20.

HOWARD-WHITE, F.B. Nickel. An historical review. xiv, 350 p., ill. New York: Van Nostrand, 1963.
Reviewed by Earl R. Parker, *Science*, 1963, 142: 218; by H.J.S., *Ambix*, 1963, 11: 99-100.

KIRCHHEIMER, Franz. Das Uran und seine Geschichte. 372 p., ill., pl. Stuttgart: E. Schweizerbart'sche, 1963.
The early history of uranium up to the discovery of radium in 1898.
Reviewed by H. Seper, *Bl.Technikgesch.*, 1964, 26: 147.

MARÉCHAL, Jean R. Petite histoire du laiton et du zinc. *Tech. Civilisations*, 1954, 3: 109-28, 10 fig.

ROLANDI, Giovanni. Lo Zinco; notizie storiche. *Ind.Mineraria, 2nd ser.*, 1959, 10: 191-207, 327-41, 479-98, 641-65, 787-800; 1960, 11: 255-83, bibliogr., ill.

SAINTE-CLAIRE DEVILLE, H. Aluminium (its manufacture, properties, and uses). Transl. from the French by Robert J. Anderson. 204 p., 13 ill. Cleveland, Ohio: Sherwood Press, 1933.
Translation of: De l'aluminium, ses propriétés, sa fabrication et ses applications. Paris: 1859.

STERNER-RAINER, Roland. Zur Geschichte des Aluminiums und seiner leichten Legierungen. *Beitr.Gesch.Tech.Ind.*, 1924, 14: 121-9.

VEc-bx

NATIONAL MUSEUM OF WALES. Tin through the ages in arts, crafts and industry: handbook to a temporary exhibition, July-December 1941, by F.J. North. 38 p. Cardiff: 1941.

NORTH, F.J. Tin through the ages. An experiment in museum synthesis. *Nature*, 1941, 148: 413-14. [CB 62/80]
An account of the exhibition, Tin through the ages in arts, crafts and industry, at the National Museum of Wales, Cardiff, 1941.

VEsc

HEDGES, Ernest S. Tin in social and economic history. vii, 194 p., 32 pl. London: Arnold; New York: St. Martin's, 1964.

VEwb-qt

CARR, Charles C. Alcoa, an American enterprise. ix, 292 p., 9 ill., 2 maps. New York: Rinehart, 1952. [CB 79/175]
The Aluminium Company of America, founded in 1886.

VEwc

WHITAKER, Arthur Preston. The Huancavelica mercury mine. A contribution to the history of the Bourbon renaissance in the Spanish Empire. xvi, 150 p. (Harvard Historical Monographs, 16) Cambridge: Harvard University Press, 1941. [CB 66/267]
Reviewed by J. Fred Rippy, *Amer.Hist.Rev.*, 1941, 46: 1000.

VEwe

GIBBS, F.W. The rise of the tinplate industry. 1. The tinplate workers; 2. Early tinplate manufacture to 1700; 3. John Hanbury, 1664-1734; 4. An eighteenth century tinplate mill; 5. Cockshutt on tinplate manufacture. *Ann.Sci.*, 1950, 6: 390-403; 1951, 7: 25-42, 43-61, 113-27; 1955, 11: 145-53.

JENKINS, Rhys. The zinc industry in England. The early years up to about 1850. *Trans.Newcomen Soc.*, 1945-46 and 1946-47, 25: 41-52.

KIRKHAM, Nellie. Derbyshire lead mining glossary. 34 p., 1 fig. (Cave Research Group Publication, 2) Leamington Spa, Eng.: Binns, 1949.

MINCHINTON, W.E. The British tinplate industry. xvi, 286 p., ill. Oxford: Clarendon Press, 1957.
Reviewed by R.J. Forbes, *Arch.Int.Hist.Sci.*, 1957, 10: 286-7.

RAISTRICK, A. Notes on lead mining and smelting in West Yorkshire. *Trans.Newcomen Soc.*, 1926-27, 7: 81-96.

VEwe-qt

RAISTRICK, A. The London Lead Company, 1692-1905. *Trans. Newcomen Soc.*, 1933-34, 14: 119-48.

VEwg

PELTZER, R.A. Geschichte der Aachen-Stolberger Messingindustrie. *Beitr.Gesch.Tech.Ind.*, 1925, 15: 196-209, 9 fig.

SIEBER, Siegfried. Erzbergischer Zinnbergbau. *Forsch.Fortschr.*, 1962, 36: 369-72.

VEwk-qt

BOURGUIGNON, Marcel. Histoire de la platinerie de Bonnert. *Ann.Inst.Archéol.Luxemb.*, 1961, 92: 81-115.

VIEILLE MONTAGNE: a hundred years of zinc melting. *Trans.Newcomen Soc.*, 1937-38, 18: 266-7. [CB 59/436]
Apropos of La Société des Mines et Fonderies de Zinc de la Vieille Montagne.

VEwm-qt

LINDROTH, Sten. Gryvbrytning och kopparhantering vid Stora Kopparberg intill 1800-talets börrjan. [Mining and copper metallurgy in Stora Kopparberg until the beginning of the nineteenth century. (In Swedish, with German summary)] 2 vol. 700 p.; 454 p., 461 ill. Uppsala: Almqvist & Wiksell, 1955.
Reviewed by George Sarton, *Isis*, 1956, 47: 441-3; by Arthur Birembaut, *Rev.Hist.Sci.*, 1958, 11: 187-8.

STORA KOPPARBERGS BERGSLAGS AKTIEBOLAG. Stora Kopparberg. Six hundred years of industrial enterprise. [Written and ed. by G. Olsson and B. Anderson.] 82 p., ill., portr. Falun: 1951.

TUNBERG, Sven. Stora Kopparbergets historia. Förberedande undersökningar. [History of the coppermine Stora Kopparbergs Bergslag. (In Swedish)] 197 p., 39 ill. Uppsala: Almqvist & Wiksell, 1922. [CB 71/124]

VEwn

ROZENBAUM, S.A. [The development of the mercury industry in Russia. (In Russian)] *Tr.Inst.Ist.Est.Tekh.*, 1955, 3: 45-52.

VF PRECIOUS METALS

FLECK, Alexander Fleck, *baron*. Industrial chemistry surrounding gold. *Nature*, 1962, 195: 222-5.

McDONALD, Donald. A history of platinum: from the earliest times to the eighteen-eighties. x, 254 p., pl. London: Johnson Matthey, 1960.
Reviewed by W.A.S., *Ambix*, 1963, 11: 98-9; for other reviews *see* CB 87/565 and CB 88/545.

MÜNZER, Gustav. Das Platin. Gewinnung. Handel, Verwendung. 136 p. Leipzig: Diebener, 1929.

QUIRING, Heinrich. Geschichte des Goldes; die Goldenen Zeitalter in ihrer kulturellen und wirtschaftlichen Bedeutung. 318 p., 102 fig., map. Stuttgart: Enke, 1948.
Reviewed by R. Hooykaas, *Arch.Int.Hist.Sci.*, 1951, 4: 833.

SCHOFIELD, M. The story of malleable platinum. *Endeavour*, 1947, 6: 125-8, portr.

VFsg

KEMP, William. Precious metals as money: a study of the prehistoric origin and historic development of this use. 336 p. Paisley: A. Gardner, 1923.

VFwc

FREISE, F. Skizzen der Entwicklung der Goldgewinnungstechnik in Brasilien mit besonderer Berücksichtigung der älteren kolonialen Zeit. *Arch.Gesch.Naturwiss.Tech.*, 1912, 3: 429-51.

MÁRQUEZ MIRANDA, Fernando. Ensayo sobre los artífices de la platería en el Buenos Aires colonial. 235, lxxvii p., 10 pl. (Publicaciones del Instituto de Investigaciones Históricas de la Facultad de Filosofía y Letras de Buenos Aires, 62) Buenos Aires: Imprenta de la Universidad, 1933.
Reviewed by A. Quintana y Marí, *Archeion*, 1934, 16: 433.

VFwf

SAGUI, Cornelio L. Les gîtes aurifères du Limousin. *VII Congr. Int.Mines Mét.Géol.Appl.* (Paris, 1935), Section de géologie appliquée, p. 15-19. Paris: 1936.

VFwg

KLEIN, Walter. Geschichte der Gmünder Edelmetallindustrie. *Beitr.Gesch.Tech.Ind.*, 1927, 17: 72-9, 14 fig.

REINDL, Jos. Goldwäschereien und Goldbergbau in Bayern. *Naturwiss.Wochenschr.*, 1913, 12: 694-7.

VFwn

PLAKSINE, I. L'extraction et la métallurgie des métaux précieux en Russie et en URSS. *Act.VIIIe Congr.Int.Hist.Sci.* (Florence, 1956), p. 1057-60. Paris: Hermann, 1958.

VFxd-wb

SAWIN, Herbert A. One hundred years of California placer mining. *Sci.Mon.*, 1949, 69: 56-62.

VFxj

HRADECKY, Karl. Geschichte und Schrifttum der Edelmetallstrichprobe. Ein Beitrag zur Geschichte der Probierkunde. ii, 46 p., 4 fig. (Schriftenreihe der Arbeitsgemeinschaft f. Technikgeschichte des Vereins Deutscher Ingenieure im NSBDT, 18) Berlin: VDI-Verlag, 1942.
Reviewed by R. Zaunick, *Mitt.Gesch.Med.*, 1941-42, 40: 352.

VG MINERALS

for mineral deposits *see* GS
for technology of salt *see* SXzs

VGc

AMERICAN INSTITUTE OF MINING AND METALLURGICAL ENGINEERS. Seventy-five years of progress in the mineral industry, 1871-1946, including Proceedings of the 75th anniversary of the ... Institute ... and World Conference on Mineral Resources, March 1947, ed. by A.B. Parsons. xii, 817 p., 111 portr., 58 fig. New York: The Institute, 1947.
Reviewed by L. Don Leet, *Isis*, 1949, 40: 82-3.

JACOBY, Adolf. Aus der Geschichte des Asbestes. *Bull.Mens. Soc.Natur.Luxembourgeois*, 1924, 18: 132-53.

VGwb

BOYD, M.L.; MONTGOMERY, D.S. A study of the Athabasca bitumen from the Abasand Quarry, Alberta, Canada. 1. Early history, analysis of the bituminous sand, and isolation and structural analysis of the asphaltene fraction. 67 p. (Mines Branch Research Report, R 78) Ottawa: Department of Mines and Technical Surveys, 1961.
A summary of the observations and investigations from 1778 to the present.

GWYNNE, Charles S. Quarrying in Iowa. *Palimpsest*, 1957, 38: 177-208, ill. [CB 83/200]

VGwh-ph

KECKOWA, Antonina, ed. Instrukcje górnicze dla żup krakowskich z XVI-XVIII wieku. [Mining instructions for the Cracow mines from the 16th to 18th century. (In Polish)] xv, 206 p. (Zakład Historii Nauki i Techniki Polskiej Akademii Nauk. Źródia do dziejów nauki i techniki, 4) Wroclaw: Zakład Narodowy im. Ossolińskich, 1963.

VGws

VISWANATHAN, P. The beach sands industry in South India: a fifty year review. *Sci.Cult.*, 1961, 27: 16-22.

VH PRECIOUS AND SEMI-PRECIOUS MINERALS

See also GU GEM STONES

DOERMER, L. Künstliche (synthetische) Edelsteine. *Chem. Zeitung*, 1912, 36: 200.

GRODZINSKI, P. *See* UC

LONSDALE, Kathleen. Further comments on attempts by H. Moissan, J.B. Hannay and Sir Charles Parsons to make diamonds in the laboratory. *Nature*, 1962, 196: 104-6.

RAYLEIGH, 4th Baron. J.B. Hannay and the artificial production of diamonds. *Nature*, 1943, 152: 597.

RUSKA, Julius. Über Nachahmung von Edelsteinen. *Quellen Stud. Gesch.Naturwiss.Med.*, 1933, 3: no. 4, 108-19.
1. Die Rezepte des Papyrus Holmiensis; 2. Spätgriechische Rezepte; 3. Syroarabische Rezepte; 4. Rezepte für farbige Gläser.

TRAVERS, M.W. J.B. Hannay and the artificial production of diamonds. *Nature*, 1943, 152: 726.

VHu

LIPPMANN, Edmund O. von. Diamant und Bocksblut; ein Beitrag zur Volkskunde. *Chem.Zeitung*, 1921, 45: 42-3, 62-4. [CB 10/216]

VHwg

REICHELT, Hans. Geschichte der Idar-Obersteiner Edelsteinindustrie. *Beitr.Gesch.Tech.Ind.*, 1932, 21: 74-8, 5 fig.

VI FUEL TECHNOLOGY

ELLIS, Oliver Coligny de Champleur. A history of fire and flame. xxiv, 436 p., 22 pl. London: Simpkin, Marshall, 1932.

GOLDSMITH, J.N.; HULME, E. Wyndham. History of the grated hearth, the chimney, and the air-furnace. *Trans.Newcomen Soc.*, 1942-43, 23: 1-12.

NIEMANN, W. Ueber die älteste Art der Feuererzeugung. *Geschichtsbl.Tech.Ind.*, 1915, 2: 216-24.

SCHULZ, Bruno. Die technische Entwicklung der Ölfeuerung. *Beitr.Gesch.Tech.Ind.*, 1926, 16: 106-20, 13 fig.

WATSON, Warren N. Early fire-making methods and devices. 75 p. Washington, D.C.: Priv. print., 1939. [CB 58/572]

VIsc

HOUGH, Walter. Fire as an agent in human culture. xiv, 270 p. (*Bull.U.S.Nat.Mus.*, 139) Washington, D.C.: Smithsonian Institution, 1926.

VIwb

PHILLIPS, George Lewis. American chimney sweeps. An historical account of a once important item. With an introduction by John Hurd and drawings by Everett Gee Jackson. x, 88 p., front., ill. Trenton, N.J.: Past Times Press, 1957. [CB 84/327]

VIxx

BRYANT AND MAY MUSEUM OF FIRE MAKING APPLIANCES. Catalogue of the exhibits. Compiled, with an introduction and notes, by Robert Miller Christy. viii, 255 p. London: Simpkin Marshall, 1926.

HOUGH, Walter. Fire-making apparatus in the United States National Museum. 72 p., pl. (*Proc.U.S.Nat.Mus.*, 73) Washington, D.C.: 1929.

VJ FIREWORKS; EXPLOSIVES; MATCHES

BROCK, Alan St. H. A history of fireworks. 280 p., ill. London: Harrap, 1949.

BROCK, Alan St. H. Pyrotechnics. The history and art of firework making. xv, 197 p., ill. London: O'Connor, 1922.

DAVIS, Tenney L. The chemistry of powder and explosives. vol. New York: Wiley; London: Chapman & Hall, 1941-43.
Vol. 1 reviewed by Eduard Färber, *Isis*, 1942, 34: 35-6.

DAVIS, Tenney L. Pulvis Fulminans. *Chymia*, 1949, 2: 99-110, 1 ill.

DESMARETS, M. Un siecle d'industrie des allumettes. *Rev.Gen. Sci.*, 1913, 24: 291.
Apropos of article by P. Fischer, *J.Gasbeleucht.*, 1913, *see* below.

DIXON, William Hepworth. The match industry, its origin and development. x, 150 p. (Pitman's Common Commodities and Industries) London: Pitman, 1925.

FISCHER, P. 100 Jahre Zündholzindustrie. *J.Gasbeleucht.*, 1913, 56: 115-16, 239.
Reviewed by M. Desmarets, *Rev.Gen.Sci.*, 1913, 24: 291.

GODE, P.K. The history of fireworks in India between A.D. 1400 and 1900. 26 p. (Transaction 17) Basavangudi, Bangalore: Indian Institute of Culture, May 1953.
Includes brief general history of fireworks.

KLINCKOWSTROEM, Carl von. Ein Beitrag zur Geschichte der chemischen Feuerzeuge. *Geschichtsbl.Tech.Ind.*, 1915, 2: 226-33.

MARSHALL, Arthur. Explosives. Their manufacture, properties, tests and history. xvi, 624 p. London: Churchill, 1915.
Part 1. Historical. p. 1-43: summary based on the works of H.W.L. Hime and Oscar Guttmann.

NIEMANN, W. Die ersten chemischen Feuerzeuge. *Arch.Gesch. Naturwiss.Tech.*, 1916, 7: 299-309, 390-403, ill.

OBERHUMMER, Wilfrid. Zur Geschichte des Reibzündholzes. *Forsch.Fortschr.*, 1963, 37: 14-16.

READ, John. Explosives. 160 p., ill. (Pelican Book) Harmondsworth/New York: Penguin Books, 1942. [CB 63/271]

THIEME, -. Die Entwicklung und wirtschaftliche Bedeutung der Zündholzindustrie. Vortrag. *Chem.Zeitung*, 1912, 36: 915.
Brief note on lecture delivered at the Handels-Hochschule, Berlin, 22 May 1912.

VJwb

VAN GELDER, Arthur Pine; SCHLATTER, Hugo. History of the explosives industry in America. (Prepared from data collected by and published under the direction of the Institute of Makers of Explosives) With an introduction by Charles E. Munroe. xxxviii, 1132 p. New York: Columbia University Press, 1927.

VJwg-qt

DYNAMIT Actien-Gesellschaft, vormals Alfred Nobel & Co. Festschrift, 1865-1925. 72 p. Hamburg: 1925.

VJwm-qt

WETTERHOLM, Allan. Nitroglycerin Aktiebolaget 1864-1964. [Nitroglycerin Ltd. (In Swedish)] *Svensk Kem.Tidskr.*, 1964, 76: 609-16.
On the 100th anniversary of nitroglycerin.

VK WOOD; CHARCOAL BURNING

VKwb

SIM, Robert J.; WEISS, Harry B. Charcoal-burning in New Jersey from early times to the present. 62 p., 25 fig. Trenton: New Jersey Agricultural Society, 1955.

VL COAL AND COAL MINING

BARROIS, Charles. Discours prononcé à la Séance publique annuelle du lundi 12 décembre 1927 par le Président de l'Académie des sciences. *Compt.Rend.Acad.Sci.*, 1927, 185: 1331-46.
Apropos of the history of coal.

GILLE, Bertrand. *See* VDxd

MINING ASSOCIATION OF GREAT BRITAIN. Historical review of coal mining. xv, 377, 86 p., ill. London: Fleetway Press, [1924]. [CB 16/348]
Compiled primarily with the object of supplementing and elucidating the historical exhibit of models in the Exhibition Hall at the Wembley Coal Mine.

READ, Thomas T. *See* VCxd

SUTHERLAND, D. The story of coal. 96 p., 54 ill. London: Burke, 1949.

VLwb

McAULIFFE, Eugene. Early coal mining in the West, beginning with 1868. 32 p., ill. New York: Newcomen Society of England, American Branch, 1948.
Address delivered during the 1948 Nebraska dinner of the Newcomen Society of England, held at Omaha, 8 October 1948.

VLwe

JENKINS, W.J. The early history of coal-mining in the Black Country and especially around Dudley. *Trans.Newcomen Soc.*, 1927-28, 8: 107-12.

VLwg

PIEPER, Wilhelm. Die Entwicklung des Kohlenbergbaus im Gebiet um Halle bis zum Bau der Eisenbahnen. *Beitr.Gesch.Tech.Ind.*, 1926, 16: 133-52.

VLwg-cd

GRUNEWALD, -; EICHENBERG, -. Urkundliche Beiträge zur Geschichte des rheinischen Braunkohlenbergbaues. *Beitr.Gesch. Tech.Ind.*, 1925, 15: 126-47, 16 fig.

VLwk

BERCK, Fr. Histoire de nos charbonnages. Les anciennes houillères de La Haye, Pévy et Champay à Saint-Nicolas. *Chron. Archéol.Pays Liége*, 1949, 40: 37-72.

VLwk-cd

HANSOTTE, Georges. Inventaire des archives du Charbonnage des Six-Bonniers à Seraing. 19 p. Brussels: 1959.
Reviewed by H. Watelet, *Revue Belg.Philol.Hist.*, 1961, 39: 658.

VLwn-qt

DOBROV, G.M. K istorii razvitia Sovetskikh ugledobyvayushchikh kombainov. [On the history of the development of Soviet coalmining combines. (In Russian)] *Tr.Inst.Ist.Est.Tekh.*, 1959, 25: 161-76.

VLxb

NEMCHINOV, V.P. [Early period of development of coal-cutting machinery. (In Russian)] *Vop.Ist.Est.Tekh.*, 1960, 9: 143-9.

VLxd-bv

RUDOMETOV, I.I. [Bibliography; on the history of techniques of mining peat. (In Russian)] *Tr.Inst.Ist.Est.Tekh.*, 1955, 3: 216-32.

VLyWM

MORGAN, J.R. The search for a safety-lamp in mines. *Ann.Sci.*, 1936, 1: 302-29, 7 fig.

VM COAL GAS; COKE

HAFFNER, A.E. A century of gas engineering. *Nature*, 1963, 198: 1137-40.

KÖRTING, A. Geschichte der Gastechnik. *Technikgeschichte*, 1936, 25: 84-110, 2 pl., 10 fig.

OECHELHAEUSER, Wilhelm von. Ein Beitrag zur Geschichte der Grossgasmaschine. *Beitr.Gesch.Tech.Ind.*, 1915, 6: 109-51, 21 fig.

VMwd

ELTON, Arthur. The rise of the gas industry in England and France. *Arch.Int.Hist.Sci.*, 1952, 5: 320-32. Also in *Act. VIe Congr.Int.Hist.Sci.* (Amsterdam, 1950), p. 492-504. Paris: Hermann, 1953.

VMwe

CHANDLER, Dean; LACEY, A. Douglas. The rise of the gas industry in Britain. 156 p., 51 fig., map. London: British Gas Council, 1949.
Reviewed by R.J. Forbes, *Arch.Int.Hist.Sci.*, 1951, 4: 560.

VN OIL; NATURAL GAS

BEEBY-THOMPSON, A. Oil pioneer; selected experiences and incidents associated with sixty years of world-wide petroleum exploration and oil field development. 544 p., pl. London: Sidgwick and Jackson, 1961. [CB 88/625]

FORBES, R.J. History of petroleum. *Isis*, 1938, 28: 465.
Short account of the session of the 2nd World Petroleum Congress (Paris, 1937) devoted to "The archaeology and history of petroleum".

FORBES, R.J. Sketch of the history of the petroleum industry. *Act.IIe Congr.Mond.Pétrol.* (Paris, 1937), (4), p. 15-20. Paris: Omnes et Cie, [?1938]

FORBES, R.J. Studies in early petroleum history. x, 202 p., 16 pl., 32 fig. Leiden: E.J. Brill, 1958.
Reviewed by A.G. Drachmann, *Isis*, 1959, 50: 498-9.

FORBES, R.J. Techniek. Zestig jaar ontwikkeling der aardolieindustrie. [Sixty years of development in the petroleum industry. (In Dutch)] *Olie*, 1950, 3: no. 10, 1-8, ill.

GIDDENS, Paul H. Early days of oil. viii, 150 p., 365 ill. Princeton: Princeton University Press, 1948.

HUNTER, Leslie. Oil. 96 p. (Science in Industry, 2) London: Burke, 1961.
Reviewed by B.K.M., *Sci.Cult.*, 1962, 28: 71.

LEES, G.M. The search for oil. *Annu.Rep.Smithsonian Inst.for 1940*, p. 231-48, 4 pl. Washington, D.C.: 1941.

MERCIER, Maurice. Quelques points de l'histoire du pétrole. Vérifications par le laboratoire. *Bull.Ass.Franç.Tech. Pétrol.*, 1937, no. 39, 121-42.

PEABODY, Ernest H. Oil fuel, a world-wide adventure. 96 p. Princeton: Princeton University Press for the Newcomen Society, American Branch, 1942.

ROY, H.L. Centenary of petroleum industry. *Sci.Cult.*, 1959, 25: 51-7.

TESTI, Gino. Appunti storici sui gas naturali spontaneamente infiammabili all'aria. *Riv.Stor.Sci.*, 1934, 25: 144-8.

VNqt

FORBES, R.J.; O'BEIRNE, D.R. The technical development of the Royal Dutch Shell Group, 1890-1940. ix, 670 p., ill., maps. Leiden: E.J. Brill, 1957.
Reviewed by John W. Oliver, *Isis*, 1959, 50: 500-1.

VNqx

BIREMBAUT, A. Les premiers congrès internationaux du pétrole. *Act. 3e Congr.Mond.Pétrol.* (The Hague, 1951), p. 203-4. Leiden: E.J. Brill, 1951.

VNwb

BYLES, Axtell J. America's petroleum industry. A review and a commentary. An address delivered before Princeton University on December 14, 1937, in the Cyrus Fogg Brackett lectureship in applied engineering and technology. 28 p. Princeton: Guild of Brackett Lecturers, 1938.

CROSS, Roy. From a chemist's diary. iv, 315 p., ill. (Kansas City Testing Laboratory Bulletin, 29) Kansas City, Mo.: 1943. [CB 69/194]
Throws light on the history of petroleum and petroleum technology in the United States.

RISTER, Carl Coke. Oil! Titan of the Southwest. xxiii, 467 p., ill. Norman: University of Oklahoma Press, 1949. [CB 76/398]

VNwb-qt

LOOS, John L. Oil on stream! A history of Interstate Oil Pipe Line Company, 1909-1959. xii, 411 p., ill., maps., bibliogr. Baton Rouge: Louisiana State University Press, 1959.
Reviewed by Arnold R. Daum, *Technol.Cult.*, 1960, 1: 276-8.

NICHOLS, Stuart H. The natural gas story from the ground down. The history of National Fuel Gas Company. 24 p. Princeton, N.J.: Princeton University Press (for the Newcomen Society in North America), 1963.

TAYLOR, Frank J.; WELTY, Earl M. Black bonanza. 280 p., 180 ill. New York: McGraw-Hill, 1950.
A history of the Union Oil Company of California.
Reviewed by R.J. Forbes, *Arch.Int.Hist.Sci.*, 1951, 4: 1091.

VNwh

MIKUCKI, Tadeusz. L'histoire de l'industrie polonaise du pétrole. *Act.IIe Congr.Mond.Pétrol.* (Paris, 1937), (4), p. 81-5. Paris: Omnes et Cie, [?1938]

VNwp

KALUGAI, I. Moshe Wilbushewitz, a pioneer of the new oil-industry in Israel. *Act.VIIe Congr.Int.Hist.Sci.* (Jérusalem, 1953), p. 391-4. Paris: Hermann, [n.d.]

VO OTHER COAL AND PETROLEUM BY-PRODUCTS

BEER, John J. *See* VYc

BOJUNGA, R.G.; FELDHAUS, Franz M. Bereitung und Verwendung des Russes im Wandel der Zeiten. *Festschrift zum 75 jährigen Bestehen der Russbetriebe der August Wegelin Aktiengesellschaft*, p. 7-18, ill. Kalscheuren bei Köln a. Rh.: 1937.

FORBES, R.J. Het Bitumen in de Verfindustrie. [Bitumen in the paint industry. (In Dutch)] *Verfkroniek*, 1936, 9: 263-71.

FORBES, R.J. Das Bitumen in den fünfzehn Jahrhunderten vor Drake (300-1860). *Bitumen*, 1937, 7: 11 (28 pages up to 134).

FORBES, R.J. 5000 Jaar Asphalt. *Chem.Weekbl.*, 1936, 33: 264-6.

FORBES, R.J. The story of bitumen. From the earliest times up to the nineteenth century. 63 p., 37 fig. [The Hague: Royal Dutch Shell, 1934]

WALDEN, Paul. "100 Jahre Benzol". Das Benzol als wissenschaftliches Problem und weltwirtschaftlicher Faktor, Betrachtungen zur Jahrhundertfeier seiner Entdeckung. *Z.Angew. Chem.*, 1926, 39: 125-32.
Reviewed by G. Lockemann, *Mitt.Gesch.Med.*, 1926, 25: 231.

VOwe

CROOKS, James. The history of the refining of paraffin wax in Scotland. *Chem.Ind.*, 1925, 44: 599-602.

GARDNER, Walter Myers. The British coaltar industry. Its origin, development and decline. ix, 437 p. London: Williams and Norgate, 1915.

VOwg-qt

AUGUST WEGELIN AKTIENGESELLSCHAFT. Festschrift zum 75 jährigen Bestehen der Russbetriebe der August Wegelin Aktiengesellschaft. 55 p., ill. Kalscheuren bei Köln a. Rh.: 1937.

VOxb

FELDHAUS, Franz M. Zur Geschichte der Brikett-Pressen. *Deut. Bergwerkszeitung Tech.Bl.*, 1936, no. 17, 3 fig. [CB 48/572]

VP CHEMICAL INDUSTRY

see also VA CHEMICAL ENGINEERING
RT CHEMICAL DRUGS
SV FOOD TECHNOLOGY

VPc

FESTER, Gustav. Die Entwicklung der chemischen Technik bis zu den Anfängen der Grossindustrie. Ein technologisch-historischer Versuch. viii, 225 p. Berlin: Julius Springer, 1923.
Reviewed by Julius Ruska, *Isis*, 1924, 6: 89-90.

LEICESTER, Henry M. Chemistry, chemical technology, and scientific progress. *Technol.Cult.*, 1961, 2: 352-6.

SCHMIDT, Albrecht. Die industrielle Chemie in ihrer Bedeutung im Weltbild und Erinnerungen an ihren Aufbau, nach 25 Vorlesungen an der Johann Wolfgang Goethe-Universität. xxix, 829 p. Berlin: De Gruyter, 1934.

TAYLOR, E. Sherwood. A history of industrial chemistry. xvi, 467 p., front., 22 pl., 62 fig. Melbourne/London/Toronto: William Heinemann, Ltd.; New York: Abelard-Schumann, 1957.
Reviewed by Aaron Ihde, *Isis*, 1958, 49: 352; for other reviews *see* CB 83/200 and CB 84/312.

ZART, A. Die Entwicklung der chemischen Grossindustrie. 48 p., 10 fig. (Der Werdegang der Entdeckungen, 5) München: Oldenbourg, 1922. [CB 14/545]

VPce-bv

SCIENCE MUSEUM, London. Books on the chemical and allied industries. A subject catalogue of books in the Science Library. Compiled by L.R. Day. ix, 118 p. London: H.M. Stat. Off., 1961.

VPqx

CONGRÈS de Chimie Appliquée, (VIIIe), Washington et New York, septembre 1912. *Isis*, 1913, 1: 258-9.
Short account of conference.

VPwb

BROWNE, Charles Albert. Chronological table of some leading events in the history of industrial chemistry in America from earliest colonial settlements until the outbreak of the World War. *Ind.Eng.Chem.*, 1926, 18: 884-92.

BROWNE, Charles Albert. Early chemical industry in America - a few comparisons of past and present conditions. *Ind.Eng. Chem.*, 1922, 14: 1066-71.

HAYNES, Williams. American chemical industry. 6 vol. 1. Background and beginning, 1608-1910. lxxvii, 512 p., ill.; 2,3. The World War I period, 1912-1922. xliii, 440 p.; xv, 606 p.; 4. The merger era, 1923-1929. xli, 638 p., ill.; 5. The decade of new products, 1930-1939. li, 622 p., ill.; 6. The chemical companies. viii, 559 p. New York: Van Nostrand, 1945-54.
Vol. 1 and 5 reviewed by Aaron J. Ihde, *Isis*, 1956, 47: 430-1; vol. 2 and 3 reviewed by Morris C. Leikind, *Amer. Hist.Rev.*, 1947, 52: 349-50; vol. 6 reviewed in *Nature*, 1950, 166: 413.

VPwb-da

HAYNES, Williams. Chemical pioneers; the founders of the American chemical industry. The story of fifteen pioneers, from J. Winthrop, Jr. to H.H. Dow. 288 p. New York: Van Nostrand, 1939.

VPwe

HARDIE, D.W.F. The chemical industry of Merseyside. *Proc. Chem.Soc.*, 1961, 52-7. [CB 87/628]
The development of heavy chemical manufacturing since 1800.

HARDIE, D.W.F. A history of the chemical industry in Widnes. xii, 250 p., 38 pl. Liverpool: Imperial Chemical Industries, 1950.
Reviewed by T.P. Hilditch, *Nature*, 1951, 167: 581-2.

MIALL, Stephen. A history of the British chemical industry. Written for the Society of Chemical Industry on the occasion of the fiftieth anniversary of its foundation. xvi, 273 p. London: Benn, 1931.

MORGAN, Gilbert T.; PRATT, David Doig. British chemical industry: its rise and development. xii, 387 p., 32 pl. London: Arnold; New York: Longmans, Green, 1938. [CB 56/390]
Reviewed in *Nature*, 1939, 143: 6-7.

VPwe-da

ARMSTRONG, Henry E. The Monds and chemical industry: a study in heredity. *Nature* 1931, 127: 238-40.

VPwe-qd

SOCIETY OF CHEMICAL INDUSTRY. Special jubilee number, July 1931. 272 p., fig. London: Society of Chemical Industry, 1931.
Founded in 1881.

VPwf-oq

CINQUANTENAIRE de l'Ecole de Chimie Industrielle de Lyon. 12 mai 1934. 6 p., ill. Lyon: Ecole de Chimie Industrielle de Lyon, 1934.

VPwg

BASLE and the chemical industry. *Ciba Rev.*, 1959, 11: 33-40.

CHRISTIANSEN, C.C. Chemische und Farben-Industrie. iv, 99 p. Tübingen: Mohr, 1914.

LEPSIUS, B. Deutschlands Chemische Industrie 1888-1913. 108 p. Berlin: Georg Stilke, 1914.
Reviewed by Ernst Bloch, *Isis*, 1922, 4: 335.

THE STORY of chemical industry in Basle. (Published by CIBA Limited on the occasion of its 75th Anniversary.) 234 p. Basle: CIBA Limited, 1959.
Reviewed by L.K. Sharp, *Nature*, 1960, 187: 540-1; by Paul Meier, *Isis*, 1960, 57: 579-80.

VPwg-qt

MERCK, E. E. Merck Chemische Fabrik Darmstadt. 127 p., ill. Darmstadt: 1928. [CB 25/439]

VPwh-ce

SARNECKI, Kazimierz. Dawne podreczniki technologii chemicznej w Polsce. [Old-time textbooks of chemical technology in Poland. (In Polish, with English summary)] *Stud.Mater.Dziej. Nauk.Pol., Ser. C*, 1964, 9: 3-28.

VPwi-ph

SPADA, Nicolo. Leggi veneziane sulle industrie chimiche a tutela della salute pubblica del secolo XIII al XVIII. 33 p. Venezia: R. Deputazione di Storia Patria, 1930.
Reviewed by C.R. de Gino Testi, *Archeion*, 1931, 13: 278-9.

VPyDCzc

WEIL, Herbert. Chromatographische Fabrikation. *Chem.Zeitung*, 1955, 79: 206-8, 5 fig. [CB 81/270]

VPyDK

WALDEN, Paul. Stereochemie und Technik. *Z.Angew.Chem.*, 1925, 38: 429-39.

VQ INORGANIC CHEMICALS

BALDWIN, Robert T. History of the chlorine industry. *J.Chem. Educ.*, 1927, 4: 313-19.

THE BEGINNINGS of phosphorus manufacture. *Endeavour*, 1961, 20: 40-1.
Account of Arthur Albright's work.

CLAUDE, Georges. La recherche scientifique, ses applications à l'industrie et à la synthèse industrielle de l'ammoniaque. *Rev.Gén.Sci.*, 1921, 32: 534-43, 570-81.

MITTASCH, Alwin. Salpetersäure aus Ammoniak. Geschichtliche Entwicklung der Ammoniakoxydation bis 1920. 136 p., ill. Weinheim/Bergstr.: Verlag Chemie, 1953.
Reviewed by Eduard Farber, *Isis*, 1954, 45: 224.

SCHROETER, J. Discovery of chlorine and the beginnings of the chlorine industry. The story of chlorine down to the present. *Ciba Rev.*, 1960, 12: no. 139, 5-23.

SINGER, Charles. The earliest chemical industry. An essay in the historical relations of economics and technology illustrated from the alum trade. With a preface by Derek Spence. 352 p., ill. London: Folio Society, 1948.
Reviewed by George Sarton and comments by Charles Singer, *Isis*, 1950, 41: 128-31.

THRELFALL, Richard E. The story of 100 years of phosphorus making, 1851-1951. 400 p., 72 ill. Oldbury: Albright and Wilson, 1951.
Reviewed by R.J. Forbes, *Arch.Int.Hist.Sci.*, 1953, 6: 372.

VQwb

BROWNE, Charles Albert. Historical notes upon the domestic potash industry in early colonial and later times. *J.Chem. Educ.*, 1926, 3: 749-56.

TAFT, Robert. The beginning of liquid ammonia research in the United States. *J.Chem.Educ.*, 1933, 10: 34-9.

VQwc

DONALD, M.B. History of the Chile nitrate industry. *Ann.Sci.*, 1936, 1: 29-47, 193-216, ill.

VQwe

DICKINSON, H.W. The history of vitriol making in England. *Trans.Newcomen Soc.*, 1937-38, 18: 43-60, 2 fig.

VQwf

RANC, Albert. La question des nitrates sous la Restauration. *Rev.Sci.*, 1923, 61: 615-18. [CB 15/216]
French legislation concerning saltpetre from the 14th century until 1819.

VQwg

SCHÖNEMANN, Josef. Die deutsche Kali-industrie und das Kaligesetz. Eine volkswirtschaftliche Studie. viii, 152 p., ill. Hannover: Hahn, 1912.

VQwn

SEGAL, V.A. K istorii organizatsii proizvodstva glinozema iz zaglikskikh alunitov Azerbaidzhanskoi SSR. [On the history of the organization of the production of alumina from alunites of the Azerbaijan SSR. (In Russian)] *Tr.Inst.Ist.Est. Tekh.*, 1962, 39: 248-57.

SEGAL, V.A.; ZVIAGINTSEV, O.E. Raboty sovetskikh uchenykh po polucheniiu glinozema. [Works of Soviet scientists on obtaining alumina. (In Russian)] *Tr.Inst.Ist.Est.Tekh.*, 1961, 35: 351-75.

VOL'FKOVICH, S.I. Razvitiia proizvodstv neorganicheskoi khimii v SSSR. [Development of manufacture of inorganic chemicals in the U.S.S.R. (In Russian)] *Tr.Inst.Ist.Est.Tekh.*, 1961, 35: 330-50.

VR ORGANIC CHEMICALS

HALE, William J. A decade of advance in organic chemical manufacture. *J.Chem.Educ.*, 1933, 10: 464-8.

VRwb

STINE, C.M.A. The rise of the organic chemical industry in the United States. *Ind.Eng.Chem.*, 1940, 32: 137-44. Reprinted in *Annu.Rep.Smithsonian Inst.for 1940*, p. 177-92, 4 pl. Washington, D.C.: 1941.

VS CEMENT; LIME; MORTAR; CONCRETE

DAVIS, Arthur Charles. A hundred years of Portland cement, 1824-1924. xxi, 282 p. London: Concrete Publications, 1924.

GRÜN, Richard. Der Zement. Herstellung, Eigenschaften und Verwendung. ix, 173 p., 90 fig., 35 tables. Berlin: Springer, 1927.

NICHOLS, Henry Windsor. Cement. 15 p., 4 pl. (Field Museum of Natural History. Geology, 12) Chicago: 1929.

SCHARROO, P.W. Beton, oud en nieuw. [Concrete, old and new. (In Dutch)] *Ingenieur*, 1946, 58: no. 26, 4 p.

SCHARROO, P.W. Cement en Beton, oud en nieuw. [Cement and concrete, old and new. (In Dutch)] 306 p., 164 ill. Amsterdam: Veen, 1948.
Reviewed by R.J. Forbes, *Arch.Int.Hist.Sci.*, 1948, 2: 268-70.

YOUNG, Joseph Samuel. A brief outline of the history of cement. 27 p., ill. Allentown, Pa.: Lehigh Portland Cement Co., 1955.

VSce-bv

SPACKMAN, Charles. Some writers on lime and cement from Cato to present time. xvii, 287 p. Cambridge: Heffer, 1929.
Reviewed by S.R. Hind, *Nature*, 1931, 127: 156-8.

VT CERAMICS; POTTERY

BURTON, William. A general history of porcelain. 2 vol. London: Cassell, 1921.

EVANS, Maria Millington, *Lady*. Lustre pottery. xx, 148 p., 24 pl. London: Methuen, 1920. [CB 10/183]

HANNOVER, Emil. Pottery and porcelain: a handbook for collectors. Transl. from the Danish. Edited with notes and appendices by Bernard Rackham. 3 vol. 1. Europe and the Near East: earthenware and stoneware. 589 p., 7 pl.; 2. The Far East. 287 p., 2 pl.; 3. European porcelain. 571 p., 2 pl. London: Benn, 1925.
Translation of: Keramisk Haandbog. 3 vol. København: H. Koppel, 1919-24.

VTwf

DESVERGNES, Louis. Analyse de poteries ligures provenant de l'ancien oppidum gaulois de "Vindalium" (Vaucluse). *Ann. Chim.Anal.*, 1926, 8: 40-1.
The composition of this pottery is very similar to that of modern ware.

VTwg

ANTZ, E.L. Aus der Geschichte der Keramik in Deutschland. *Beitr.Gesch.Tech.Ind.*, 1922, 12: 136-58, 45 fig.

VTwk

NEURDENBURG, Elisabeth. Old Dutch pottery and tiles. Transl. with annotations by Bernard Rackham. xv, 155 p., 69 pl. New York: Himebaugh and Browne, 1923.

VTwn

BEZBORODOV, M.A. [History of the origin of the first Russian porcelain. (In Russian)] *Tr.Inst.Ist.Est.*, 1948, 2: 269-87.

VTxb

RIETH, Adolf. The development of the potter's wheel during five thousand years. *Res.Progr.*, 1942, 8: 193-8, 2 fig.

VU GLASS

HODGEN, Margaret T. Glass and paper; an historical study of acculturation. *Southwest.J.Anthropol.*, 1945, 1: 466-97.

KNOWLES, John A. The history of copper ruby glass. *Trans.Newcomen Soc.*, 1925-26, 6: 66-74.

PELLIOT, Marianne. Verres anciens. viii, 153 p., 48 pl. Paris: Van Oest, 1929.
Reviewed by Gustav E. Pazaurek, *Deut.Lit.Zeitung*, 1930, 51: 699-702.

PHILLIPS, C.J. Glass: the miracle maker. Its history, technology and applications. xii, 424 p. New York: Pitman, 1941. [CB 62/77]

SCHLOSSER, Ignaz. Le verre ancien. Traduit de l'allemand par Madeleine Maas-Auclert. 46 p., 22 ill. (Mémentos Illustrés) Paris: Presses Universitaires de France, 1957.
Translation of: Altes Glas: ein Brevier (Braunschweig: Klinkhardt & Biermann, 1957).
Reviewed by Yolande Amic, *Arch.Int.Hist.Sci.*, 1958, 11: 327-8.

SCOVILLE, V. Candler. Revolution in glassmaking. 398 p., 11 ill. Cambridge, Mass.: Harvard University Press, 1948.

VUce-bv

DUNCAN, George Sang. Bibliography of glass (from the earliest records to 1940). 544 p. London: Dawson, 1960.
A definitive bibliography of all aspects of the production and use of glass.

VUda

DRAKE, Wilfred James. A dictionary of glasspainters and "glasyers" of the tenth to eighteenth centuries. 224 p., ill., bibliogr. New York: Metropolitan Museum of Art, 1955.

VUhc

BRILL, Robert H.; HOOD, Harrison P. A new method for dating ancient glass. *Nature*, 1961, 189: 12-14.

VUwb

REVI, Albert Christian. American pressed glass and figure bottles. xi, 446 p., ill. New York: Nelson, 1964.
Reviewed by H.J. Haden, *Technol.Cult.*, 1964, 5: 605-8.

VUwd

BUCKLEY, Wilfred. European glass; a brief outline of the history of glass making, with notes on various methods of glass decoration, illustrated by examples in the collection of the author. With a foreword by Bernard Rackham, and with an essay on Dutch glass engravers by Ferrand Hudig. xxiv, 96 p., 104 pl. London: Benn; Boston: Houghton Mifflin, 1926.

VUwe

BUCKLEY, Francis. A history of old English glass. xxvii, 154 p., 60 pl. London: Benn, 1925.

HULME, E. Wyndham. On the invention of English flint glass. *Trans.Newcomen Soc.*, 1925-26, 6: 75-85.

POWELL, Harry J. Glass-making in England. x, 183 p. Cambridge University Press, 1923.
Reviewed by W.E.S. Turner, *Nature*, 1923, 112: 612-14.

THORPE, William Arnold. A history of English and Irish glass. 2 vol. xv, 372 p.; xii, 168 p., pl. London: Medici Society, 1929.

VUwe-qt

BARKER, T.C. Pilkington brothers and the glass industry. 296 p., 20 pl. London: George Allen and Unwin, Ltd., 1960.
Reviewed by R.W. Douglas, *Nature*, 1961, 189: 342-3; by T.K. Derry, *Endeavour*, 1961, 20: 170.

VUwg

GRUNDMANN, Günther. Die Geschichte der Glasmacherkunst im Hirschberger Tale. *Z.Tech.Phys.*, 1927, 8: 329-37.

PETERSEN, Kurt. Die geschichtliche Entwicklung der Glasindustrie im Rheinland. 104 p. Mülheim-Ruhr: Rühl, 1930.

VUwg-mzJN

GROSSMANN, H. Der Einfluss der alten Glashütten auf den schweizerischen Wald. *Ber.Geobot.Forschungsinst.Rübel Zürich*, 1933, 15-32. [CB 42/588]

VUwg-qt

KÜHNERT, Herbert. Otto Schott. Eine Studie über seine Wittener Zeit bis zur Gründung des Jenaer Glaswerkes. xiii, 281 p., 41 fig. (Jahrbuch des Vereins für Orts- und Heimatkunde in der Grafschaft Mark, 54) Witten-Ruhr: Märkische Druckerei Aug. Pott, 1940.
Reviewed by R. Zaunick, *Mitt.Gesch.Med.*, 1941-42, 40: 130.

VUwh

ZUMAN, Franz. Die böhmischen Glashütten und Industrie der Glaskompositionssteine. *Beitr.Gesch.Tech.Ind.*, 1929, 19: 54-60, 7 fig.

VUwn

BEZBORODOV, M.A. Steklodelie v drevnei Rusi. [Glassmaking in ancient Russia. (In Russian)] 306 p., 37 fig., 38, 40 tables. Minsk: Izdatelstvo Akademii Nauk BSSR, 1956. [CB 83/210]

VUxf-DC

CALEY, Earle R. Analysis of ancient glasses 1790-1957: a comprehensive and critical survey. 118 p. New York: Corning Museum of Glass, 1962.
Reviewed by H.J. Haden, *Technol.Cult.*, 1963, 4: 58-61.

VUxx

VICTORIA AND ALBERT MUSEUM. Glass. A handbook for the study of glass vessels of all periods and countries and a guide to the Museum collection. By W.B. Honey. xii, 169 p., 72 pl. (Handbook, 1) London: Victoria and Albert Museum, 1946.

VW SOAPS; DETERGENTS

EVIEUX, Ernest. Contribution à l'étude des détersifs et du savon. *Parfum.Mod.*, 1925, 18: 255-60.
Résumé de l'histoire du savon.

GIBBS, F.W. The history of the manufacture of soap. *Ann.Sci.*, 1939, 4: 169-90, 50 fig.

SCHAEFER, G. Historical facts concerning the production and use of soap. Development of soap boiling. Some old-fashioned ways of cleaning textiles. *Ciba Rev.*, 1947, 56: 2014-37, ill.

VY DYES AND PAINTS

VYc general history

BEER, John J. Coal tar dye manufacture and the origins of the modern industrial research laboratory. *Isis*, 1958, 49: 123-31.

BÜHLER, A. Plangi - tie and dye work. *Ciba Rev.*, 1954, no. 104, 3726-48.

COLEBY, L.J.M. A history of Prussian blue. *Ann.Sci.*, 1939, 4: 206-11.

EDELSTEIN, Sidney M. Historical notes on the wet-processing industry. Published in commemoration of the Perkin Centennial. 54 p., ill. New York: American Dyestuff Reporter, 1956.
A collection of articles on various aspects of the history of dyeing that appeared in the *American Dyestuff Reporter* between 1954 and 1956.

EDELSTEIN, Sidney M. Lo Kao - the story of Chinese green. *Amer.Dyestuff Reporter*, 1957, 46: 433-6, bibliogr.

EDELSTEIN Sydney M. Old dyers, old books and old methods. Remarks on the history of dyeing and finishing. *Amer.Dyestuff Reporter*, 1947, 36: 523-32.

FORBES, R.J. Het Bitumen in de Verfindustrie. [Bitumen in the paint industry. (In Dutch)] *Verfkroniek*, 1936, 9: 263-71.

FRITZ, Felix. Leuchtfarben. Geschichte, Herstellung, Eigenschaften und Anwendung. 228 p. Berlin: Chemisch-technischer Verlag Bodenbender, 1940.
Reviewed by R. Zaunick, *Mitt.Gesch.Med.*, 1940, 39: 330.

GETTENS, Rutherford J.; STOUT, George L. Painting materials: a short encyclopedia. vii, 333 p. New York: Van Nostrand, 1942.
Reviewed by F. Ian G. Rawlins, *Nature*, 1943, 151: 262-3.

GIBBS, F.W. Historical survey of the japanning trade. 1. Eastern and western lacquer. 2. Early British japanning. 3. Pontypool and Usk. 4. The Midlands. *Ann.Sci.*, 1951, 7: 401-16; 1953, 9: 88-95, 197-213, 214-32, ill.

GINZBURG, O.F. Razvitie predstavlenii o stroenii trifenilmetanovykh krasitelei. [The development of conceptions about the structure of triphenylmethyl pigments. (In Russian)] *Tr.Inst.Ist.Est.Tekh.*, 1962, 39: 176-94.

HIGGINS, Sydney Herbert. A history of bleaching. viii, 176 p., 9 pl. London: Longmans, 1924.

HURRY, Jamieson B. The woad plant and its dye. xxviii, 328 p., 17 pl. London: Oxford University Press, 1930.
Reviewed by E.F. Armstrong, *Nature*, 1931, 127: 658-9.

INDIGO. The history of indigo, by W.A. Vetterli. The production of indigo. The history of indigo dyeing. The application of indigo in textile printing, by R. Haller. Indigo dyeing among primitive races, by A. Bühler. Modern trends in printing, dyeing and finishing. *Ciba Rev.*, 1951, no. 85, 3066-96, ill.

KALUGAY, J. [Centenary of the discovery of the synthesis of organic dyes and its influence on the chemical industry. (In Hebrew)] *Koroth*, 1956, 1: 341.

KURDIAN, H. Kirmiz. *J.Amer.Orient.Soc.*, 1941, 61: 105-7. [CB 62/79]
Dried insect used for dyeing.

MELLOR, C.M.; CARDWELL, D.S.L. Dyes and dyeing. *Brit.J.Hist. Sci.*, 1963, 1: 265-79.

VYc-bx

LERNER, F. Textiles and dyestuffs at the Frankfort fairs. *Ciba Rev.*, 1954, no. 103, 3690-712, ill.

VYce-bv

LIBRARY OF CONGRESS. List of references on dyestuffs. Chemistry, manufacture, trade. Compiled under the direction of Herman H.B. Meyer. 186 p. Washington: U.S. Govt. Print. Off., 1919. [CB 9/485]

VYmzDY

FORBES, R.J. Alchemy and colour. (Modern chemistry and alchemy. Alchemy, dye and colour. The pots of Gerber's cooks.) *Ciba Rev.*, 1961, no. 5, 2-32.

VYn/t special aspects

VYnh

OBERMILLER, Julius. Die Purpurfarbe im Sprachgebrauch. *Arch. Gesch.Math.Naturwiss.Tech.*, 1931, 13: 416-34. [CB 48/571]

VYtq

EIBNER, Alexander. Entwicklung und Werkstoffe der Wandmalerei vom Altertum bis zur Neuzeit. xvi, 618 p., pl. Supplement. vii, 195 p., pl. München: Heller, 1926-28.

LAURIE, A.P. The pigments and mediums of the old masters, with a special chapter on the microphotographic study of brushwork. xiv, 192 p., 34 pl. London: Macmillan, 1914.

LIPPMANN, Edmund O. von. Name und Geschichte des "Galizensteins". *Chem.Zeitung*, 1923, 47: 2-3, 41-2.
History of the sulphate of zinc (white vitriol, couperose blanche, etc.) which was used by painters already before 1400 as a siccative substance.

PARTINGTON, J.R. The discovery of mosaic gold. *Isis*, 1934, 21: 203-6.
History of *aurum musivum* (mosaic gold; crystalline stannic sulphide, SnS^2). The earliest recipe is the *De arte illuminandi* (a XIV Ms. of Italian origin).

WARD, James. History and methods of ancient and modern painting. 4 vol., ill. London: Chapman and Hall, 1913-21.

VYw in different countries

VYwe

BRITISH Dyestuffs Corporation. The British dyestuffs industry, 1856-1924. A booklet issued on the occasion of the British Empire Exhibition, 1924. 28 p., ill. Manchester: 1924. [CB 17/557]

CLARK, H.O.; WAILES, Rex. The preparation of woad in England. *Trans.Newcomen Soc.*, 1935-36, 16: 69-95, ill.

PERKIN Centenary, London. 100 years of synthetic dyestuffs. xii, 136 p., 8 pl. (*Tetrahedron Suppl.*, 1) London/New York: Pergamon Press, 1958.
Reviewed by R. Brightman, *Nature*, 1959, 183: 709; by O.T. Benfey, *J.Chem.Educ.*, 1959, 36: A638.

SIR WILLIAM HENRY PERKIN. The age; Perkin, the man; chemistry and chemical education in Perkin's student days; Perkin as a scientist; Perkin the manufacturer; the legacy of Perkin; dyestuffs research and application. *Ciba Rev.*, June 1956, no. 115, 2-49, ill., bibliogr.

VYwe-da

ROBINSON, Robert. The Perkin family of organic chemists. *Endeavour*, 1956, 15: 92-102, 4 pl., 2 fig., 1 chart. [CB 82/257]

VYwg

BEER, John J. The emergence of the German dye industry. 168 p. (Illinois Studies in the Social Sciences, 44) Urbana: University of Illinois Press, 1959.
Reviewed by Henry M. Leicester, *Isis*, 1960, 51: 366-7; for further reviews *see* CB 85/403, CB 86/511, CB 89/574.

WALTER, Gustav Adolf. Die geschichtliche Entwicklung der rheinischen Mineralfarben-Industrie vom Beginn des 19. Jahrhunderts bis zum Ausbruch des Weltkrieges. Ein Beitrag zur rheinischen Industriegeschichte. xx, 204 p. (Veröffentlichungen des Archivs für Rheinisch-Westfälische Wirtschaftsgeschichte, 6) Essen: Baedeker, 1922.

WILDE, Julius. Die Färberpflanzen der Bayerischen Rheinpfalz in der Zeit von 800-1800. *Mitt.Pfälz.Ver.Naturk.Pollichia*, 1930, 3: 147-200, 14 fig.
Reviewed by R. Zaunick, *Mitt.Gesch.Med.*, 1932, 31: 213.

VYwi

TESTI, Gino. Le antiche miniere di allume e l'arte tintoria in Italia. *Archeion*, 1931, 13: 440-8.

VYwn-tq

LOUKIANOV, P.M. Les couleurs dans la Russie ancienne. *Act. VIIIe Congr.Int.Hist.Sci.* (Florence, 1956), (2), p. 581-3. Paris: Hermann, 1958.
History of colours used in painting.

VYws

PHADKE, B.N. The history of dyes and dyeing in the Bombay Presidency. xx, 152 p. Poona City: Dastane, 1947.
Reviewed by Mata Prasad, *Arch.Int.Hist.Sci.*, 1950, 3: 239.

VZ COSMETICS; PERFUMES

COLA, Félix. Le parfum à travers les âges. 780 p., ill. Paris: Casterman, 1931.
Reviewed by Jean Hesse, *Larousse Mens.*, 1931, 8: 873-5.

HELMAN, M.D. [Perfume and smoking incense. (In Hebrew)] *Koroth*, 1962, 3: 73-5.

WALKER, N.W. Gregory. The mystery of ambergris. *Discovery*, 1937, 18: 52-3.

VZwd

PRINS, Isaac. Aperçu sur l'histoire de l'industrie européenne de la civette. *Act.VIIe Congr.Int.Hist.Sci.* (Jerusalem, 1953), p. 493-7. Paris: Hermann, [n.d.].

VZws

GODE, P.K. History of ambergris in India between about A.D. 700 and 1900. *Chymia*, 1949, 2: 51-6.

WA PLASTICS; RUBBER, NATURAL AND SYNTHETIC

BAEKELAND, Leo Hendrik. Impress of chemistry upon industry. Bakelite an example. *Ind.Eng.Chem.*, 1935, 27: 538-43.

BALLY, W. Rubber. *Ciba Rev.*, 1951, no. 87, 3130-56, ill.

BLAKEY, W. The history of aminoplastics. Sixth Chance Memorial Lecture of the Society of Chemical Industry. *Chem.Ind.*, 1964, 1349-57.

CALDER, Ritchie. Speculative research. *Discovery*, 1960, 21: 420-5.
Speculative research is defined and examined in the light of the history of the development of polythene.

COOK, O.F. Natural rubber. *Annu.Rep.Smithsonian Inst. for 1943*, p. 363-41, 20 pl. Washington, D.C.: 1944.

DIJKMAN, M.J. Hevea. Thirty years of research in the Far East. With a foreword by R.D. Rands. xxii, 327 p., 116 fig. Coral Gables, Fla.: University of Miami Press, 1951.
This includes a historical account of natural rubber.

GERČIKOV, M.G. [On the history of plastic materials. (In Russian with English summary)] *Arkh.Ist.Nauk Tekh.*, 1936, 9: 259-88.
Includes chronological table, 1832 to 1932.

GIBBONS, W.A. The rubber industry, 1839-1939. *Annu.Rep.Smithsonian Inst.for 1940*, p. 193-214, 4 pl. Washington, D.C.: 1941.

KLINE, Gordon M. Plastics. *Annu.Rep.Smithsonian Inst.for 1941*, p. 225-38, 5 pl. Washington, D.C.: 1942.

PIETSOVSKI, C. Sulla storia della sintesi industriale del caucciù col metodo di Sergio Lebedev. *Act.VIIIe Congr.Int. Hist.Sci.* (Florence, 1956), (2), p. 584-6. Paris: Hermann, 1958.

WILSON, Charles Morrow. Trees and test tubes: the story of rubber. xii, 352 p., 27 fig. New York: Holt, 1943.
Reviewed by Conway Zirkle, *Isis*, 1944, 35: 45-6.

WOLF, Ralph F. Eighty-eight years of synthetic rubber. *Sci. Mon.*, 1948, 66: 221-30.

WOLF, Ralph F. Richman, poorman. *Sci.Mon.*, 1952, 74: 69-75. [CB 79/146]
Julius Arthur Nieuwland and Wallace Carothers and the development of synthetic rubber.

WAnh

SCHURER, Heinz. The origin of the word "caoutchouc". *J.Rubber Res.*, 1949, 18: 45-9.
Caoutchouc is derived from "cauchuc", a word of the Kechua language spoken by the Incas.

WAwb

CHALMERS, Douglas. Breakthroughs in American rubber technology 1940-1950. *Proc.10th Int.Congr.Hist.Sci.* (Ithaca, 1962), (1), p. 443-52. Paris: Hermann, 1964.

WAwf

LE THANH KHOI. La propogation de l'innovation dans le domaine du caoutchouc en France. *Cah.Inst.Sci.Écon.Appl.Sér.AD*, 1963, 2: 2-208.
Reviewed by M. Daumas, *Rev.Hist.Sci.*, 1963, 16: 405-6.

WB TIMBER

BOERHAAVE-BEEKMAN, W. Hout in alle tijden. [Wood in all periods. (In Dutch)] 6 vol. ill., bibliogr. Deventer: Kluwer, 1949-55.
Vol. 1 reviewed by R.J. Forbes, *Arch.Int.Hist.Sci.*, 1950, 3: 490-3.

BOULTON, Harold Edwin. A century of wood preserving. Ed. by Sir Harold Boulton. x, 150 p., 3 pl. London: Allan, 1930.
Reviewed in *Nature*, 1931, 127: 195-6.

FÄRBER, Eduard. Aus der Geschichte der chemischen Holzverwertung mit besonderer Berücksichtigung der Zellstoffgewinnung. *Beitr.Gesch.Tech.Ind.*, 1926, 16: 121-32.

GLESINGER, Egon. Le bois en Europe: origines et étude de la crise actuelle. Préface par Jacob Viner. xxxix, 742 p., ill., bibliogr. Paris: Librairie du Receuil Sirey, 1932.

GLESINGER, Egon. The coming age of wood. xv, 279 p. New York: Simon and Schuster, 1949; London: Secker and Warburg, 1950.

LATHAM, Bryan. Timber, its development and distribution, a historical survey. 303 p., 70 ill. London: Harrap, 1957.
Reviewed by R.J. Forbes, *Arch.Int.Hist.Sci.*, 1958, 11: 97-8.

MOLL, Friedrich. Holzschutz. Seine Entwicklung von der Urzeit bis zur Umwandlung des Handwerkes in Fabrikbetrieb. *Beitr. Gesch.Tech.Ind.*, 1920, 10: 66-92.

WBwe-mzThg

CLOW, Archibald; CLOW, Nan L. The timber famine and the development of technology. *Ann.Sci.*, 1956, 12: 85-102.

FLINN, Michael W. Timber and the advance of technology: a reconsideration. *Ann.Sci.*, 1959, 15: 109-20.

WBwe-mzXX

ALBION, Robert Greenhalgh. Forests and sea power; the timber problem of the Royal Navy 1652-1862. xv, 485 p., ill., bibliogr. (Harvard Economic Studies, 29) Cambridge: Harvard University Press, 1926.
Reviewed by Eleanor Louisa Lord, *Amer.Hist.Rev.*, 1927, 32: 590-1; by Lawrence S. Mayo, *Geogr.Rev.*, 1928, 341-2.

WBwg

MOLL, Friedrich. Geschichte der Holzschutzindustrie in Deutschland. *Beitr.Gesch.Tech.Ind.*, 1930, 20: 26-30, 7 fig.

WC PAPER

LES ARTS de reproduction graphique. L'histoire de la gravure. Le papier à travers les âges. 104 p. (*Bull.Synd.Maîtres Imprimeurs France,* special number) Paris: 1925. [CB 18/644]

BLUM, André. Les origines du papier, de l'imprimerie et de la gravure. 252 p., ill. Paris: Editions de la Tournelle, 1935.
Reviewed by Axel Nelson, *Lychnos*, 1937, 2: 430.

BLUM, André. On the origin of paper. Transl. from the French by Harry Miller Lydenberg. 79 p. New York: Booker, 1934. [CB 43/274]
Translation of: Les origines du papier (Paris: 1932).

CLAPPERTON, Robert Henderson. Paper. An historical account of its making by hand from the earliest times down to the present day. xvi, 158 p., ill. Oxford: Shakespeare Head Press, 1934.

HODGEN, Margaret T. Glass and paper; an historical study of acculturation. *Southwest.J.Anthropol.*, 1945, 1: 466-97.

HÖSSLE, Friedrich von. Die Geschichte des Papiers, die Roh- und Halbstoffe der Papierfabrikation mit Ausnahme des Holzzellstoffes. New ed. viii, 278 p. (Technik und Praxis der Papierfabrikation, 1: pt. 1) Berlin: Elsner, 1929.

HUNTER, Dard. Laid and wove. *Printing Art*, 1921, 38: 33-40. Reprinted in *Annu.Rep.Smithsonian Inst.for 1921*, p. 587-93, 6 pl. Washington, D.C.: 1922.
Brief history of hand-made paper.

HUNTER, Dard. Papermaking: the history and technique of an ancient craft. 2nd ed. rev. and enl. xxiv, 611, xxvii p., ill. New York: Knopf, 1957.
First published 1943.
Reviewed by Douglas C. McMurtrie, *Amer.Hist.Rev.*, 1943, 49: 82-3.

ISENBERG, Irving H. Papermaking fibers. *Econ.Bot.*, 1956, 10: 176-93.
A brief history of papermaking together with a list and description of plants used.

LATOUR, A. Paper, a historical outline. *Ciba Rev.*, 1949, 72: 2630-9, ill.

LECLERC, Emile; *et al.* Les transformations du papier et du carton. 160 p., ill. Paris: Les Publications Papyrus, 1926. [CB 23/247]

SCHAEFER, G. The development of papermaking. *Ciba Rev.*, 1949, 72: 1641-8, ill.

STEVENSON, Allan. Paper as bibliographical evidence. *Library, 5th ser.*, 1962, 17: 197-212.
Discussion of watermarks, paper moulds, etc.

WCc-br

Papier Geschichte. Zeitschrift der Forschungsstelle Papiergeschichte in Mainz. Vol. 1- Darmstadt: 1951-

WCsc

VON HAGEN, Victor W. Paper and civilization. *Sci.Mon.*, 1943, 62: 301-14.
An account of the origin of true paper and paperlike substances in China, Egypt, and Yucatan.

WCwb-qt

SCHMON, Arthur A. Papermakers and pioneers. The Ontario Paper Company Limited and Quebec North Shore Paper Company. 24 p. Princeton, N.J.: Princeton University Press (for the Newcomen Society in North America), 1963.

WCwe

JERVIS, W.W.; JONES, S.J. The paper-making industry in Somerset. *Geography*, 1930, 15: 625-9.
Historical notes covering the last two hundred years.

SHORTER, Alfred H. Paper-making in Devon and Cornwall. *Geography*, 1938, 23: 164-76.
From 1684 to present.

WCwf-qt

ALIBAUX, Henri. Les premières papeteries françaises. 215 p. Paris: Les Arts et le Livre, 1926.

AUDIN, Marius. La Papeterie du Suchet aux Ardillats. *Pap. Gesch.*, 1960, 10: 22-8.

HÖSSLE, Friedrich von. Histoire de quelques anciennes papeteries françaises. *Papyrus*, 1926, 7: 337-40, 412-13, 485-7. [CB 22/271]

WCwg

JAFFÉ, Albert. Zur Geschichte des Papieres und seiner Wasserzeichen. Eine kulturhistorische Skizze unter besonderer Berücksichtigung des Gebietes der Rheinpfalz. 29 p., 10 pl., 73 fig. Kaiserlautern: Pirmasens, Lützel, 1930.
Extract from *Pfalzisches Museum*, 1930, vol. 47.

THIEL, Viktor. Die geschichtliche Entwicklung der Papiererzeugung in Österreich. *Beitr.Gesch.Tech.Ind.*, 1932, 21: 103-10, 11 fig.

WCwg-bx

HAUSEN, J. Die Geschichte der Papierindustrie auf der Jahresschau Deutscher Arbeit, Dresden, 1927. *Beitr.Gesch.Tech.Ind.*, 1927, 17: 154-5, 2 fig.

WCwh

ZUMAN, Franz. Die Papiermachéindustrie in Böhmen. *Beitr. Gesch.Tech.Ind.*, 1932, 21: 111-14.

ZUMAN, Franz. Die Prager Altstädter Papiermühlen. *Beitr. Gesch.Tech.Ind.*, 1929, 18: 168-9.

WCws

DUTT, Asoka K. Papermaking in India. A resumé of the industry from the earliest period until the year 1949. *Pap.Maker* (Wilmington), 1955, 24: no. 2, 11-19, ill.

WCxb

RASKIN, N. [Sur l'histoire du cylindre (hollander). (In Russian, with French summary)] *Ark.Ist.Nauk.Tekh.*, 1935, 6: 117-37.

WCxx

DARD HUNTER Paper Museum of the Institute of Paper Chemistry. *Pap.Maker* (Wilmington), 1955, 24: 43-8, 9 fig.

WCyKU effect of fungi

SÉE, Pierre. Champignons chromogènes causes de l'altération des papiers. *Ann.Chim.Anal., 2nd ser.*, 1920, 2: 94. [CB 18/622]

SÉE, Pierre. Les moisissures des livres et des estampes. *Compt.Rend.Acad.Sci.*, 1917, 164: 230. [CB 51/299]

WD TEXTILES

WDc

BRATKOWSKI, Wladyslaw. Z historii technologii włókienniczej. [Some glimpses of the history of textile technology. (In Polish, summaries in Russian and English)] *Stud.Mater.Dziej. Nauk.Pol.*, 1956, no. 4, 63-78, map.

BRAUN-RONSDORF, M. Mixture fabrics of later times. *Ciba Rev.*, 1960, 12: no. 141, 16-28.

CHERBLANC, Emile. L'archéologie textile et l'histoire générale du tissu. *Thalès*, 1937-39, 4: 142-7.

CHERBLANC, Emile. Mémoire sur l'invention du tissu. 75 p., 6 pl. (Histoire Générale du Tissu. Document, 1) Paris: Éditions d'Art et d'Histoire, 1935.
Reviewed in *Ethnographie*, 1935, no. 31, 164-6.

JOHANNSEN, Otto. Die Geschichte der Textil-Industrie. 543 p., 514 fig., 1 pl. Zürich: Füssli, 1932.

LATOUR, A. The stocking: modern stocking manufacture; the knitted stocking; the stocking frame; the growth of the hose knitting industry; fashions in stockings. *Ciba Rev.*, 1954, no. 106, 3794-825.

SAGHER, Henri de. Essai d'une historiographie de l'industrie drapière avant la période du mécanisme. *Ann.XXIIIe Congr. Fédération Archéol.Hist.Belg.* (Gand, 1913), (2), p. 307-47. Gand: W. Siffer, 1914.

WDc-bx

LERNER, F. Textiles and dyestuffs at the Frankfort fairs. *Ciba Rev.*, 1954, no. 103, 3690-712, ill.

WDfqy

MICHEAUX, R. de. Le Centre International d'Étude des Textiles Anciens. *Rev.Hist.Sci.*, 1964, 17: 243-9.

WDwe

FRAZER, Grace Lovat. Textiles by Britain. x, 181 p., 52 pl. London: Allen and Unwin, 1948.
Reviewed by R.J. Forbes, *Arch.Int.Hist.Sci.*, 1949, 2: 801.

RUDD, W.R. The strangers in Norwich, a page in the history of our ancient textile industry. *Trans.Newcomen Soc.*, 1925-26, 6: 188-95.

WDwe-qe

JOHNSON, Arthur Henry. The history of the Worshipful Company of the Drapers of London preceded by an introduction on London and her gilds up to the close of the XVth century. 5 vol. Oxford: Clarendon Press, 1914-22.

WDwf

WESCHER, H. Rouen - French textile centre. *Ciba Rev.*, 1959, 12: no. 135, 2-33, ill. [CB 85/406]

WDxb

LEWTON, Frederick L. The servant in the house: a brief history of the sewing machine. *Annu.Rep.Smithsonian Inst.for 1929*, p. 559-83, 8 pl. Washington, D.C.: 1930.

NAHLIK, Adam. W sprawie rozwoju krosna tkackiego. [On the development of the weaving loom. (In Polish, summaries in Russian and English)] *Kwart.Hist.Kult.Mater.*, 1956, 4: 519-40, 26 pl.

NAUMBURG, Robert E. The development of the spinning frame; its history, present status, and future possibilities. *Mech.Eng.*, 1924, 46: 825-40, 51 fig. [CB 17/605]

ORTH, Friedrich. Der Werdegang wichtiger Erfindungen auf dem Gebiete der Spinnerei und Weberei. *Beitr.Gesch.Tech.Ind.*, 1922, 12: 61-108, 34 fig.; 1927, 17: 89-105, 39 fig.

ROTH, H. Ling. Studies in primitive looms. 151 p., ill. Halifax: King, 1918. Reprinted from *J.Roy.Anthropol.Soc.*, vol. 48.

VERMILYE, William Moorhead. Power in the textile industry. A brief historical review. 34 p., fig. Princeton: Princeton University Press (for the Newcomen Society, American Branch), 1938.

WDxb-wb

DANILOFF, Serge. Some unusual American spinning wheels. *Trans. Newcomen Soc.*, 1925-26, 6: 144-8.

WDxj

WAGNER, E. History of textile testing. *Ciba Rev.*, 1959, 12: no. 134, 6-14.

WDxx

BUEHLER-OPPENHEIM, Kristin; BUEHLER-OPPENHEIM, Alfred. Die Textiliensammlung Fritz Iklé-Huber im Museum für Völkerkunde und Schweizerischen Museum für Volkskunde, Basel. vi, 184 p., 159 ill., 3 pl. (Mémoires de la Société Helvetique des Sciences Naturelles, 78: no. 2) Zurich: Fretz, 1948.

DUBUISSON, Marguerite. Le Musée de la Bonneterie à Troyes et ses ressources documentaires. *Doc.Hist.Tech.*, 1962, 2: 56-61.

WDyVY textile dyeing and printing

see also VY DYES; PAINTS
for cotton printing *see* WEyVY

INDIGO. The history of indigo, by W.A. Vetterli. The production of indigo. The history of indigo dyeing. The application of indigo in textile printing, by R. Haller. Indigo dyeing among primitive races, by A. Bühler. Modern trends in printing, dyeing and finishing. *Ciba Rev.*, 1951, no. 85, 3066-96, ill.

SCIENCE and technology - pacemakers in textile processing. *Ciba Rev.*, 1959, 11: no. 131, 4-11.

WDyVYce-bv

LAWRIE, L.G. A bibliography of dyeing and textile printing. 143 p. London: Chapman and Hall, 1949.

WDyVYwe

FLOUD, Peter. The development of design in English printed textiles. *Ciba Rev.*, 1961, no. 1, 15-20.

WE COTTON, FLAX AND OTHER PLANT FIBRES

CRAWFORD, Morris De Camp. The heritage of cotton, the fibre of two worlds and many ages. 224 p., pl. New York: Putnam, 1924.

HUTCHINSON, Joseph. The history and relationships of the world's cottons. *Endeavour*, 1962, 21: 5-15.

LEGGETT, William F. The story of linen. xi, 103 p. Brooklyn, N.Y.: Chemical Publishing Co., 1945. [CB 69/230]

LUETKENS, Charlotte. Early origins of the textile industry. Cotton's rise. *Ciba Rev.*, 1962, no. 2, 18-33.

MOORE, Alfred S. Linen. viii, 204 p. (Staple Trades and Industries, 3) London: Constable, 1922.

WEwb

PALMER, Arthur W. The growth of cotton fiber science in the United States. *Annu.Rep.Smithsonian Inst.for 1960*, p. 473-508. Washington, D.C.: 1961.

WEwd

HORNER, John. The linen trade of Europe during the spinning wheel period. xiv, 591 p. Belfast: McCaw, Stevenson and Orr, 1920. [CB 12/629]

WEwe

GILL, Conrad. The rise of the Irish linen industry. vii, 539 p., 2 maps. Oxford: Clarendon Press, 1925.

STREAT, E. Raymond. Manchester and cotton - today. *Ciba Rev.*, 1962, no. 2, 2-9.

WEwg

LÜTHY, H. The linen industry of St. Gall. *Ciba Rev.*, 1952, no. 91, 3262-86, ill.

WEwn

ZEITLIN, E.A. [The technical revolution in flax-spinning and the beginning of the machine manufacture of flax yarn in Russia. (In Russian)] 223 p., 46 fig. (*Tr.Inst.Ist.Nauk Tekh.*, *Ser. 2*, no. 9) Moskva: Izdatelstvo Akademii Nauk SSSR, 1936.

WEyVYwe

FLOUD, Peter. The British calico-printing industry, 1676-1840. *Ciba Rev.*, 1961, no. 1, 2-7.

WEyVYwh

KOMASZYNSKI, Michal. [The building of the old cotton printing works at Wroclaw. (In Polish, with English summary)] *Kwart. Hist.Kult.Mater.*, 1954, 2: 140-66, 20 fig.

WF WOOL

LEGGETT, William F. The story of wool. 304 p. New York: Chemical Publishing Co., 1947. [CB 71/122]

LIPSON, E. A short history of wool and its manufacture (mainly in England). 205 p. Melbourne: Heinemann, 1953.
Reviewed by G. de Poerck, *Arch.Int.Hist.Sci.*, 1954, 7: 397.

WFwe

JUMP, Percy. The Cotswold countryside: an engineer's thoughts on the past and present. *Trans.Newcomen Soc.*, 1962-63, 35: 225-36.
Evidence in the Cotswolds of the woollen industry - inns, mills, engines, fulling.

WFww

LUETKENS, Charlotte. Schafzucht und Wollerzeugung in Australien. *Ciba-Rundsch.*, 1948, 77: 2844-74, ill.

WFxd

SCOTT, E. Kilburn. Early cloth fulling and its machinery. *Trans.Newcomen Soc.*, 1931-32, 12: 31-52, 6 fig.

WFxd-wb

WEISS, Harry B.; ZIEGLER, Grace M. The early fulling mills of New Jersey. 79 p., ill. Trenton, N.J.: New Jersey Agricultural Society, 1957.

WG SILK

ALGOUD, Henri. La soie, art et histoire. 256 p., 24 fig., 16 pl. Paris: Payot, 1928. [CB 28/562]

CHERBLANC, Emile. Soie et soie artificielle. *Thalès*, 1948, 5: 85-99.

WGc-bx

LOS ANGELES COUNTY MUSEUM. Two thousand years of silk weaving. An exhibition sponsored by the Los Angeles County Museum in collaboration with the Cleveland Museum of Art and the Detroit Institute of Arts. xi, 63 p., 88 pl. New York: Weyhe, 1944.
Exhibition of 484 specimens of silk fabrics dating from the Han dynasty to 1850.

WGwe

WARNER, Frank. The silk industry of the United Kingdom. Its origin and development. 664 p., 54 pl. London: Drane, 1921.

WGwf

CLOUZOT, Henri. Le métier de la soie en France 1466-1815, suivi d'un historique de la toile imprimée 1759-1815. 178 p., pl. Paris: Devambez, [1914].

WGwi

BRENNI, Luigi. La tessitura serica attraverso i secoli. Cenni sulle sue origini e il sio sviluppo in Como, nelle altre città italiane ed in alcuni stati europei. 136 p. Como: Cesarie Nanie, 1925. [CB 21/576]

WGwt

KATŌ, Sōichi. [Short history of silk manufacture in Japan. (In Japanese)] *J.Hist.Sci.Japan*, 1951, 20: 16-20.

SIAO TSEN-TSAN. Die chinesische Seidenindustrie. 92 p. (Klepzigs Textilbücherei, 6-7) Leipzig: Klepzig Verlag, 1929.

TSING TUNG-CHUN. De la production et du commerce de la soie en Chine. 228 p. (*Etudes et documents publiés par l'Institut Franco-Chinois de Lyon*, 4) Paris: Geuthner, 1928.
Reviewed by Walther Trittel, *Deut.Lit.Zeitung*, 1930, 1: 1145-7.

WH MINERAL FIBRES; MIXED AND SYNTHETIC FABRICS

BEER, Edwin J. The birth of viscose rayon. *Trans.Newcomen Soc.*, 1962-63, 35: 109-16.

BRAUN-RONSDORF, M. Gold and silver fabrics from medieval to modern times. *Ciba Rev.*, 1961, no. 3, 2-16.

WI LEATHER

GANSSER, A. The early history of tanning. *Ciba Rev.*, 1950, no. 81, 2938-68, ill.

KOBERT, R. Beiträge zur Geschichte des Gerbens und der Adstringentien. *Arch.Gesch.Naturwiss.Tech.*, 1916, 7: 185-206. [CB 8/370]

POSTL, H. Le parchemin et ses imitations. *Chim.Ind.*, 1924, 11: 959. [CB 56/403]

RYDER, Michael L. Parchment - its history, manufacture and composition. *J.Soc.Arch.*, 1964, 2: 391-9.

STICKELBERGER, Emanuel. Versuch einer Geschichte der Gerberei. 95 p., 36 ill. Berlin: Springer, 1915.

WIyLW

GUDGER, E.W. Helmets from skins of the porcupine-fish. *Sci.Mon.*, 1930, 30: 432-42.

GUDGER, E.W. The Puffer fishes and some interesting uses of their skins. *Zool.Soc.Bull.*, 1919, 22: 126-31, 10 fig.

WIyPJ

THOMPSON, Lawrence S. Tanned human skin. *Bull.Med.Libr.Ass.*, 1946, 34: 93-102.

WJ TOWN AND COUNTRY PLANNING

WJc

ADAMS, Charles C. The relation of natural resources to regional and county planning. *Bull.N.Y.State Mus.*, 1937, 310: 121-41.

BELLET, Daniel; DARVILLÉ, Will. Ce que doit être la cité moderne. Plan, aménagements, organes, hygiène, monuments et vie. 328 p., 81 fig. Paris: H. Nolo, 1914.

HUGHES, Thomas Harold; LAMBORN, E.A.G. Towns and town-planning: ancient and modern. xii, 156 p., ill. Oxford: Clarendon Press, 1923.

LE CORBUSIER, *pseud.* The city of to-morrow, and its planning. Transl. from the eighth French edition with an introduction by Frederick Etchells. xxvii, 302 p. London: Rodker, 1929.
Translation of: Urbanisme (Paris: G. Crès, 1925).

POËTE, Marcel. Introduction à l'urbanisme. L'évolution des villes. La leçon de l'antiquité. 364 p., 32 pl. Paris: Boivin, 1929. [CB 28/561]

POLLOCK, H.M.; MORGAN, W.S. Modern cities. Progress of the awakening for their betterment here and in Europe. 418 p. New York: Funk and Wagnall, 1914. [CB 6/471]

PURDOM, Charles Benjamin. The building of satellite towns, a contribution to the study of town development and regional planning. xv, 368 p. London: Dent, 1925.

SERT, José Luis. Can our cities survive? An A B C of urban problems, their analysis, their solutions. Based on the proposals formulated by the C.I.A.M. xii, 259 p., fig., maps. Cambridge: Harvard University Press, 1942. [CB 63/277]

WJwa

LEIPZIGER, Hugo. The architectonic city in the Americas. Significant forms, origins, and prospects. 68 p., 40 pl. (University of Texas Publication, 4407. Bureau of Municipal Research, Municipal studies, 21) Austin: University of Texas, 1944. [CB 66/269]

WK MUNICIPAL ENGINEERING

for water supply and sewerage *see* TK

WKzf FIRE FIGHTING AND FIRE PROTECTION

HEINRICHS, Wilhelm. Der Werdegang der Feuerwehrleiter. *Beitr. Gesch.Tech.Ind.*, 1928, 18: 118-28, 24 fig.

MERZ, Leopold. Die Geschichte des Feuerlöschwesens. *Beitr. Gesch.Tech.Ind.*, 1926, 16: 162-82, 13 fig.

RETI, Ladislao. Historia del atanor desde Leonardo da Vinci hasta l'"Encyclopédie" de Diderot. *Ind.Quím.*, 1952, 14: 11 p., 18 fig.

RUPPEL, S. Gebäudeblitzschutz. *Elektrotech.Z.*, 1913, 34: 643-7.

WL BUILDING AND ARCHITECTURE; BUILDING CRAFTS

WLc general history

BECKER, Fritz. Die betriebswirtschaftliche Entwicklung im Baugewerbe. *Beitr.Gesch.Tech.Ind.*, 1930, 20: 137-46, 8 fig.

BOUMPHREY, Geoffrey. Your house and mine. xvi, 253 p. New York: Norton, 1938. [CB 62/77]

BRIGGS, Martin Shaw. A short history of the building crafts. 312 p. Oxford: Clarendon Press, 1925.

CHARLTON, T.M. Development of architectural science. *Nature*, 1958, 181: 1315-16.

JOPE, E.M., ed. Studies in building history. Essays in recognition of the work of B.H. St. J. O'Neil. xxxii, 287 p., ill. London: Odhams Press, 1961.
Reviewed by Peter Eden, *Antiquity*, 1962, 36: 307-8.

MICHAELS, Leonard. Contemporary structure in architecture. xix, 229 p., ill. New York: Reinhold, 1950.
Reviewed by Carl W. Condit, *Isis*, 1952, 43: 382-3.

POSTGATE, Raymond William. The builders' history. xxx, 487 p., ill., bibliogr. London: Labour Publishing Company for the National Federation of Building Trade Operatives, 1923.

RABUT, Charles. L'évolution scientifique de l'art de bâtir. *Rev.Gén.Sci.*, 1918, 29: 229-45, ill.

STURGIS, Russell; FROTHINGHAM, A.L. A history of architecture. 4 vol. New York: Doubleday, 1906-15.
The first volume alone is by Sturgis. After his death, Frothingham undertook the completion of his work.

WLda

ARCHITECTS and craftsmen in history. Festschrift für Abbott Payson Usher. xiii, 172 p. (Veröffentlichungen der List Gesellschaft E.V., 2) Tübingen: J.C.B. Mohr (Paul Siebeck), 1956.
Reviewed by F.L. Nussbaum, *Amer.Hist.Rev.*, 1958, 63: 638-9.

LUKOMSKII, Georgii Kreskent'evich. I maestri della architettura classica da Vitruvio allo Scamozzi: con 350 illustrazioni. Transl. by Lino Cappuccio. xiii, 455 p. Milan: Hoepli, 1933.

WLm/t special aspects

WLmc

GIEDION, Sigfried. Space, time and architecture. xvi, 601 p. Cambridge: Harvard University Press, 1941.
Reviewed by M.F. Ashley Montagu, *Isis*, 1942, 33: 640-1.

WLmzGP

FRECH, F. Baukunst und Erdbeben. *Fortschr.Naturwiss.Forsch.*, 1913, 8: 287-308.

WLr

BRIGGS, Martin Shaw. The architect in history. xii, 400 p., ill., bibliogr. Oxford: Clarendon Press, 1927.

WLtd

WHITE, James F. Protestant worship and church architecture. Theological and historical considerations. xi, 224 p., 60 fig., bibliogr. New York: Oxford University Press, 1964.

WLtp

LUND, Fredrik Macody. Ad quadratum. A study of the geometrical bases of classic and medieval religious architecture with special reference to their application in the restoration of the cathedral of Nidaros (Trondjem), Norway, profusely illustrated by plans, sections, views, and details of notable temples, churches, cathedrals, and other buildings in Greece, Italy, Germany, Denmark, France, England, and Norway. Printed by order of the Norwegian Parliament. xxiv, 385 p., ill., with portfolio of 32 pl. London: Batsford, 1921.

NEWCOMB, Rexford. The volute in architecture and architectural decoration. 85 p., 55 fig., bibliogr. (University of Illinois. Engineering Experiment Station Bulletin, 121) Urbana: University of Illinois, 1921. [CB 14/539]

WLw in different countries

WLwb

CONDIT, Carl W. The Chicago school of architecture. A history of commercial and public building in the Chicago area, 1875-1925. xviii, 238 p., 196 ill. Chicago/London: University of Chicago Press, 1964.

CONDIT, Carl W. The rise of the skyscraper. xi, 255 p., 108 ill. Chicago: University of Chicago Press, 1952. [CB 80/201]

CONNELY, Willard. Louis Sullivan as he lived. The shaping of American architecture. 322 p., pl., front., bibliogr. New York: Horizon Press, 1960.
Reviewed by Carl W. Condit, *Isis*, 1962, 53: 270-2.

FITCH, James Marston. American building. The forces that shape it. xvi, 382 p., ill. Boston: Houghton-Mifflin, 1948.
Reviewed by Carl W. Condit, *Isis*, 1952, 43: 382-3.

RANDALL, Frank A. History of the development of building construction in Chicago. xvi, 388 p., ill. Urbana: University of Illinois Press, 1949.
Reviewed by Carl W. Condit, *Isis*, 1952, 43: 382-3.

WLwb-sc

MUMFORD, Lewis. Sticks and stones. A study of American architecture and civilization. 2nd rev. ed. 237 p., 21 pl. New York: Dover Publications, 1955.
A reprint of a work first published in 1924, with a new preface dated 1954 by the author.

WLwe-rf

JENKINS, Frank. Architect and patron: a survey of professional relations and practice in England from the sixteenth century to the present day. xvi, 254 p., front., pl., index. London: Oxford University Press, 1961.

WLwf

MONITEUR DES TRAVAUX PUBLICS ET DU BÂTIMENT. Un demi-siècle de progrès dans les travaux publics et le bâtiment (1903-1953). Numéro spécial. cxxvii, 211, cxxix-cxci p., ill. Paris: 1953.
Reviewed by S. Colnort, *Rev.Hist.Sci.*, 1954, 7: 294.

WLws

HAVELL, E.B. Indian architecture. Its psychology, structure and history from the first Muhammadan invasion to the present day. 2nd ed. xxii, 282 p., pl. London: Murray, 1927.

WLx techniques and instruments

WLxf-D

HEDVALL, J. Arvid. Chemie im Dienst der Archäologie, Bautechnik, Denkmalpflege. x, 236 p., pl. Göteborg: Gumperts, 1962.
Reviewed by L. Biek, *Antiquity*, 1964, 38: 240-1.

WLxf-VD

GLOAG, John; BRIDGWATER, Derek. A history of cast iron in architecture. xx, 395 p., 507 ill. London: Allen and Unwin, 1948.
Reviewed by R.J. Forbes, *Arch.Int.Hist.Sci.*, 1949, 2: 802.

HAMILTON, S.B. The use of cast iron in building. *Trans.Newcomen Soc.*, 1940-41, 21: 139-55, 8 fig.

WLxf-VT

NEWCOMB, Rexford. Ceramics in architecture. 28 p., 24 fig. (Architectural Monographs on Tiles and Tilework, 1) Beaver Falls, Mass.: Associated Tile Manufacturers, 1924. [CB 16/283]

WLxh-wn

KUZIN, A.A. [The development of draughtsmanship in Russia (up to the 18th century). (In Russian)] *Tr.Inst.Ist.Est.Tekh.*, 1955, 3: 131-69, 22 ill.
Architectural drawings.

WM LIGHTING

ALDINGTON, J.N. The evolution of the electric lamp. *Endeavour*, 1943, 2: 62-8, 9 fig.

ARTAMONOV, I.D. Dal'nee osveshchenie. [Long-range illumination. (In Russian)] *Tr.Inst.Ist.Est.Tekh.*, 1962, 44: 43-115.

BRIGHT, Arthur A. The electric lamp industry: technological change and economic development from 1800 to 1947. xxviii, 526 p., 43 fig. (Massachusetts Institute of Technology Studies of Innovation) New York: Macmillan, 1949. [CB 75/90]

BURGER, D. De electrische gloeilamp 75 jaar geleden uitgevonden. [The electric bulb invented 75 years ago. (In Dutch)] *Faraday*, 1953-54, 23: 131-2.

CHATELAIN, M. A. [Sur l'histoire de l'invention des lampes à incandescence. (In Russian with French summary)] *Arkh.Ist.Nauk.Tekh.*, 1934, no. 4, 299-312. [CB 43/232]

COUSTET, Ernest. Les progrès de la lampe électrique à incandescence. *Rev.Gén.Sci.*, 1916, 27: 88-93.

DERIBERE, M. Évolution dans les sources de lumière. *Scientia*, 1964, 99: 69-74.

FÜRST, Artur. Das elektrische Licht, von den Anfängen bis zur Gegenwart, nebst einer Geschichte der Beleuchtung. 222 p., 136 fig. München: Albert Langen, 1926.

GROSS, Arnold Th. Die Glühlampe als Wegbereiterin der Elektrizitätswirtschaft. *Technikgeschichte*, 1933, 22: 70-6, 2 fig.

JOSEPHSON, Matthew. The invention of the electric light. *Sci. Amer.*, 1959, 201: no. 5, 98-114.
A discussion of Edison's incandescent lamp as part of a larger invention, that of a complete electrical lighting system.

LEWIS, Floyd A. The incandescent light. A review of its invention and application. With a foreword by Charles F. Kettering. v, 79 p., ill. West Orange, N.J.: Thomas Alva Edison Foundation, 1949.
Describing the history and development of incandescent electric light with abundant illustrations.

LOKKER, J.C. Fifty years of the gas-filled lamp. *Philips Tech.Rev.*, 1963-64, 25: no. 1, 2-15.

LUCKIESH, Matthew. Contributions of science to the lighting art. *Science*, 1927, 65: 531-5.

MORGAN, J.R. The search for a safety-lamp in mines. *Ann.Sci.*, 1936, 1: 302-29, 7 fig.

NIEMANN, W. Weitere Beitraege zur Geschichte des Beleuchtungswesens. *Geschichtsbl.Tech.Ind.*, 1918, 5: 137-41.
The original article (*ibid.* 1916, 3: 281-303, ill.) deals with the lamp in the 19th century only, whereas the above article is more general.

NIEMANN, W. Wer hat die Sicherheitslampe erfunden? *Über Land Meer*, 1912, 107: 575, 5 fig.

RISLER, Jacques. Historique de l'éclairage par fluorescence. *Bull.Soc.Franç.Elec.*, *7e sér.*, 1956, 6: 752-66, 2 fig.
Reviewed by J.P., *Arch.Int.Hist.Sci.*, 1957, 10: 283.

ROBINS, F.W. The story of the lamp (and the candle). xiv, 155 p., ill. London/New York: Oxford University Press, 1939.

SCHROEDER, Henry. History of electric light. xiii, 95 p., ill. (*Smithsonian Misc.Collect.*, 76: no. 2) Washington, D.C.: Smithsonian Institution, 1923. [CB 16/235]

TURPAIN, Albert. L'éclairage et le chauffage électrique, la naissance d'une lampe à incandescence. x, 64 p. Paris: Gauthier-Villars, 1924.

WATSON, H.E. The development of the neon glow lamp (1911-61). *Nature*, 1961, 191: 1040-1.

WMsc

LUCKIESH, Matthew. Artificial light. Its influence upon civilization. xiv, 366 p., ill. New York: Century, 1920.

O'DEA, William T. The social history of lighting. xiii, 254 p., ill. London: Routledge and Kegan Paul; New York: Macmillan, 1958.
Reviewed by C. Malcom Watkins, *Science*, 1959, 130: 1468.

WMxx

UNITED STATES NATIONAL MUSEUM. Collection of heating and lighting utensils in the United States National Museum. By Walter Hough. viii, 113 p., 99 pl. (*Bull.U.S.Nat.Mus.*, 141) Washington, D.C.: Government Printing Office, 1928. [CB 25/419]

WMy0Qzv

FERREE, C.E. The problem of lighting in its relation to the efficiency of the eye. *Science*, 1914, 40: 84-91. [CB 6/458]

WN HEATING; VENTILATION

DICKINSON, H.W. Utilization of waste heat from industrial operations. *Trans.Newcomen Soc.*, 1943-45, 24: 1-11.

KÖRTING, Johannes. Aus der Geschichte der Zentralheizung bis zur Gegenwart. *Technikgeschichte*, 1937, 26: 115-29, 2 pl., 27 fig.

SCHULZ, E. Geschichte der Städteheizung. *Technikgeschichte*, 1936, 25: 74-83, 3 fig.

TURPAIN, Albert. *See* WM

WNwg-qs

VEREIN Schweizerischer Centralheizungsindustrieller. Zum 25 jährigen Bestehen. Publication à l'occasion du 25e anniversaire, 1906-1931. 195 p. [Zurich: 1932]. [CB 38/599]

WNwn

RADZIG, A.A. [Die Entwicklung der Wärmetechnik in der USSR. (In Russian, with German summary)] *Arkh.Ist.Nauk Tekh.*, 1934, 4: 1-19, 7 fig.
Comparison of the achievements of the old regime with those of the new.

WNxx

UNITED STATES NATIONAL MUSEUM. *See* WMxx

WP DOMESTIC APPLIANCES AND FURNISHINGS

BOOTH, H. Cecil. The origin of the vacuum cleaner. *Trans. Newcomen Soc.*, 1934-35, 15: 85-98, 3 fig.

FELDHAUS, Franz M. Die Wandlung des Teppichs von der Wand-Bekleidung zum Boden-Belag. *Halbmond-Teppich-Zeitung*, 1936, no. 30, fig. [CB 48/572]

LEWTON, Frederick L. The servant in the house: a brief history of the sewing machine. *Annu.Rep.Smithsonian Inst.for 1929*, p. 559-83, 8 pl. Washington, D.C.: 1930.

WALTON, Frederick. The infancy and development of linoleum floorcloth. 56 p. London: Simpkin Marshall, 1925.

WHITING, Gertrude. Tools and toys of stitchery. xiii, 357 p. New York: Columbia University Press, 1928.

WQ SPECIAL MECHANICAL TECHNOLOGIES; INSTRUMENT TECHNOLOGY

for theoretical aspects and applications of scientific instruments *see* INDEX

WQc

WHIPPLE, Robert S. Instruments in science and industry. *Advance.Sci.*, 1940, 1: 175-90; *Nature*, 1939, 144: 461-5.
General historical outline of progress in instrument making.

WQda

DAUMAS, Maurice. Quelques fabricants d'instruments scientifiques anciens. *Rev.Hist.Sci.*, 1950, 3: 364-70.

WQwg-qt

BISCHOFF, Ig. Hundert Jahre deutscher Präzisionsmechanik 1812-1912. T. Ertel u. Sohn, G.m.b.H. Reichenbachsches Mathematisch-Mechanisches Institut München. *Z.Vermessungswesen* 1913, 42: 309-19, 400.

WQwk

ROOSEBOOM, Maria. Bijdrage tot de geschiedenis der instrumentmakerskunst in de noordelijke Nederlanden tot omstreeks 1840. [A contribution to the history of the art of instrument making in the Northern Netherlands to about 1840. (In Dutch)]. 156 p. (Mededeling uit het Rijkmuseum voor de Geschiedenis der Natuurwetenschappen, 74) Leiden: 1950.
Reviewed by P.H. van Cittert, *Arch.Int.Hist.Sci.*, 1951, 4: 560-3.

WR CLOCKS

see also Axr TIME MEASUREMENT (in general; for specific applications *see* INDEX)
FV ASTRONOMICAL CHRONOLOGY
for marine chronometers *see* HCxs

WRc general history

ANDRADE, Jules. Les organes réglants des chronomètres. 146 p., ill. (Bibliothèque Horlogère) Besançon: E. Magron, 1922.
The first two chapters are historical.
Reviewed by Léopold Reverchon, *Rev.Gén.Sci.*, 1922, 33: 525.

ANDRADE, Jules. Problemes mécaniques et chronométriques actuels. *Rev.Gén.Sci.*, 1922, 33: 463-71. [CB 13/311]

BAILLIE, G.H. Watches, their history, decoration, and mechanism. xxiv, 384 p. London: Methuen, 1929.

BASSERMANN-JORDAN, Ernst von. Alte Uhren und ihre Meister. viii, 179 p., ill. Leipzig: Diebener, 1926.

BASSERMAN-JORDAN, Ernst von. The book of old clocks and watches. 4th ed., rev. by Hans von Bertele. 522 p., 700 ill., 20 col. pl. London: Allen & Unwin; New York: Crown, 1964. [CB 90/538]
Translation of "Uhren", *see* below.

BASSERMANN-JORDAN, Ernst von. Uhren: ein Handbuch für Sammler und Liebhaber. 4th ed. rev. by Hans von Bertele. 518 p., ill. (Bibliothek für Kunst- und Antiquitätenfreunde, 7) Braunschweig: Klinkhardt und Biermann, 1961.
Reviewed by Emmanuel Poulle, *Rev.Hist.Sci.*, 1963, 16: 399-400.

BEDINI, Silvio A. The compartmented cylindrical clepsydra. *Technol.Cult.*, 1962, 3: 115-41.

BERTELE, Hans von. Zur Geschichte der Äquationsuhren-Entwicklung. *Bl.Technikgesch.*, 1956, no. 16, 78-121, 26 fig.

BLOCK, W. Die Entwicklung der neueren Uhrentechnik. *Technikgeschichte*, 1933, 22: 77-82, 5 fig.

BREARLEY, Harry Chase. Time telling through the ages. 294 p., ill. New York: Doubleday, Page (for Robert H. Ingersoll and Company), 1919. [CB 16/346]
Publication prepared to celebrate the twenty-fifth anniversary of the entrance of Robt. H. Ingersoll and Co. into the watch industry.

BRITTEN, Frederick James. Old clocks and watches and their makers. Being a historical and descriptive account of the different styles of clocks and watches of the past in England and abroad, to which is added a list of nearly 12,000 makers. 5th ed. xii, 822 p. London: Spon, 1922. [CB 16/346]
6th edition 1933; 7th edition 1956.

CHAMBERLAIN, Paul M. It's about time. 490 p., ill. New York: Richard R. Smith, 1940.
Studies on watches and watchmaking. 1. Escapements; 2. Experiments and unusual timepieces; 3. Famous watchmakers (17th to 19th centuries).

CONSERVATOIRE DES ARTS ET MÉTIERS. Conférences prononcées au Musée du Conservatoire à l'Exposition: Les chefs-d'oeuvre de l'horlogerie (mars, avril et mai 1949). 375 p., ill. Paris: Revue Française des Bijoutiers-horlogers, 1949.
Reviewed by C.A. Crommelin, *Arch.Int.Hist.Sci.*, 1951, 4: 1088-90.

CROMMELIN, C.A. Les horloges publiques ou de clocher et l'application du pendule à ces horloges. (Communications du Musée National de l'Histoire des Sciences exactes et naturelles à Leiden, 84) *J.Suisse Horlogerie*, édition suisse, 1952, 77: no. 5-6, 1-6, 4 fig.

DITISHEIM, Paul. Pendules à une seule roue. *Astronomie*, 1913, 27: 33-5.

DITISHEIM, Paul. Le spiral réglant et le balancier depuis Huygens jusqu'à nos jours. 117 p., 117 ill. Lausanne: Editions du Journal suisse d'Horlogerie, 1945. [CB 71/120]

GORDON, G.F.C. Clockmaking, past and present. 2nd ed., enlarged by Arthur V. May. xvii, 232 p. London: Technical Press, 1949.
Reviewed by C.A. Crommelin, *Arch.Int.Hist.Sci.*, 1951, 4: 269.
First published London: Crosby Lockwood and Son, 1925.

GROS, Charles. Echappements d'horloges et de montres. Exposé technique, descriptif et historique des échappements d'horlogerie. 2nd ed. 263 p., 277 fig. Paris: Bureau de l'Almanach de l'Horlogerie-Bijouterie, 1913. [CB 5/291]

HOPE-JONES, F. Clocks showing mean and sidereal time simultaneously. *Nature*, 1936, 138: 931.

HOWGRAVE-GRAHAM, R.P. New light on ancient turret clocks. *Trans.Newcomen Soc.*, 1953-55, 29: 137-49.

HOWGRAVE-GRAHAM, R.P. Some clocks and jacks, with notes on the history of horology. *Archaeologia*, 1928, 77: 257-312, 10 pl., 4 fig. [CB 28/548]

KRASSOIEVITCH, André G. Horology: past, transitional and future. *Discovery*, 1959, 20: 238-43.

LEGRAND, Charles. Les horloges à eau. *Larousse Mens.*, March 1929, 8: 60-2, 6 fig.

LLOYD, H. Alan. Some outstanding clocks over seven hundred years, 1250-1950. xx, 160 p., ill. London: Leonard Hill, 1958.
Reviewed by Derek J. de Solla Price, *Arch.Int.Hist.Sci.*, 1962, 15: 436-7.

LÜBKE, Anton. Die Uhr, von der Sonnenuhr zur Atomuhr. 441 p., 476 pl. Düsseldorf: VDI-Verlag, 1958.
Reviewed by Torsten Althin, *Lychnos*, 1960-61, 419-21; by Derek J. de Solla Price, *Technol.Cult.*, 1961, 2: 49-50.

MESNAGE, P. Esquisse d'une histoire de la montre. *Ann.Litt. Franche-Comté*, 1947, 2: 3-32, ill.
Reviewed by P. Ducassé, *Thalès*, 1948, 5: 113-27.

MICHEL, Henri. Les instruments primitifs de mesure du temps. (Conference prononcée au Musée du Conservatoire des Arts et Métiers à l'exposition: Les chefs d'oeuvre de l'horlogerie) *Rev.Franc.Bijout.Horlogers*, 1949, no. 106, 61-71.

MILHAM, Willis Isbister. Time and timekeepers. Including the history, construction, care and accuracy of clocks and watches. xx, 609 p., 339 fig. New York: Macmillan, 1923. [CB 16/347]

PIPUNYROV, V.N. Razvitie teorii chasov. [The development of the theory of clocks. (In Russian)] *Tr.Inst.Ist.Est.Tekh.*, 1962, 45: 174-203.

PRICE, Derek J. de Solla. Clockwork before the clock. Lecture given to a joint meeting of the British Horological Institute and the Antiquarian Horological Society, 5 October 1955. *Horological J.*, 1955, 97: 810-14; 1956, 98: 31-4. [CB 83/211]

PRICE, Derek J. de Solla. On the origin of clockwork, perpetual motion devices and the compass. (*Contrib.Mus.Hist. Technol.*, Paper 6) *Bull.U.S.Nat.Mus.*, 1959, 218: 82-112.
Reviewed by Henri Michel, *Ciel Terre*, 1960, 76: 64.

ROBERTSON, J. Drummond. The evolution of clockwork, with a special section on the clocks of Japan, fully illustrated from the author's collection. Together with a comprehensive bibliography of horology covering over six hundred authors. xvi, 358 p., ill. London: Cassell, 1931. [CB 51/179]

SENAC, E.J. La pendule astronomique. 16 p., 8 fig. (Les Conférences du Palais de la Découverte) Paris: Université de Paris, 1948. [CB 84/310]

UNGERER, Alfred. Les horloges astronomiques et monumentales les plus remarquables de l'antiquité jusqu'à nos jours. Préface de E. Esclangon. 514 p., 458 ill. Strasbourg: The author; Paris: Berger-Levrault, 1931.

UNGERER, Alfred. Les horloges d'édifice: leur construction, leur montage, leur entretien, guide pratique à l'usage des personnes qui s'interessent aux horloges monumentales, suivi d'une nomenclature des horloges monumentales et astronomiques les plus remarquables. vi, 334 p. Paris: Gauthier-Villars, 1926.

WIEDEMANN, Eilhard. Gefäss zum Regeln des Wasserausflusses bei Wasseruhren. (Beiträge zur Geschichte der Naturwissenschaften, 59) *Sitzungsber.Phys.Med.Soz.Erlangen*, 1918-19, 50-1: 272-4. [CB 11/432]

WINS, Alphonse. L'horloge à travers les âges. Préface de Jean Chalon. xxx, 343 p., 163 gravures. Mons: Léon Duquesne, 1924.

WOODBURY, Robert S. Une invention importante de la mécanique de précision. L'origine des calibres d'épaisseur. *Rev.Hist. Sci.*, 1963, 16: 303-16.

ZINNER, Ernst. Die ältesten Räderuhren und moderne Sonnenuhren. Forschungen über den Ursprung der modernen Wissenschaft. 148 p., 96 fig. on 50 pl. (*Ber.Naturforsch.Ges. Bamberg*, 28) Bamberg: 1939. [CB 60/148]

ZINNER, Ernst. Die Sanduhr. *Uhr*, 1955, 9: 37-40, 4 fig.

WRc-be

BRITTEN, Frederick James. The watch and clockmaker's handbook, dictionary and guide. 15th ed. rev. by J.W. Player. vii, 598 p., ill. London: Spon, 1955.

LLOYD, H. Alan. The collector's dictionary of clocks. 214 p., over 500 ill. London: Country Life, 1964.
A collection of horological material, including numerous significant items illustrated here for the first time.

WRda

BAILLIE, G.H. Watchmakers and clockmakers of the world. xiv, 416 p. (The Connoisseur's Library) London: Methuen, 1929. [CB 49/178]

BRITTEN, Frederick James. *See* WRc

HILL, R. Noel. Huguenot clock and watch makers. [Additions and amendments to Britten, Frederick James, *see* WRc] *Connoisseur*, March 1948, 26-30, 12 ill.

WRtq

ZINNER, Ernst. Uhren auf Bildnissen. *Neue Uhrmacher-Zeitung*, 1957, no. 20, 21-4, 5 fig.

WRw in different countries

WRwb-qt

BATTISON, Edwin A. The Auburndale Watch Company: First American attempt toward the dollar watch. (*Contrib.Mus.Hist.Technol.*) *Bull.U.S.Nat.Mus.*, 1959, 218: 50-68.

WRwe

SYMONDS, R.W. A history of English clocks. 79 p., 72 pl. (King Penguin Book, K 28) London/New York: Penguin Books, 1947.
Reviewed by A. Thompson-Allen, *Antiquity*, 1948, 22: 163.

WRwe-da

CESCINSKY, Herbert. The old English master clockmakers and their clocks, 1670-1820. xii, 182 p., 277 ill. London: Routledge, 1938.

SMITH, John. Old Scottish clockmakers. From 1453 to 1850. Compiled from original sources with notes. 2nd rev. ed. 452 p., 25 ill. Edinburgh: Oliver and Boyd, 1930.

WRwf

POULLE, Emmanuel. L'horloge astronomique de la cathédrale de Bourges. *Bull.Soc.Nat.Antiquair.Fr.*, 1961, 168-75.

UNGERER, Alfred. L'horloge astronomique de la cathédrale de Strasbourg. *Compt.Rend.Ie Congr.Int.Math.* (Strasbourg, 1920), p. 656-63. Toulouse: E. Privat, 1921. [CB 14/567]

UNGERER, Alfred. L'horloge astronomique de la cathédrale de Strasbourg. Avec la collaboration de A. Danjon et G. Rougier. 60 p. Paris: Société astronomique de France, 1922.

WRwg

CHAPUIS, Alfred. Relations de l'horlogerie suisse avec la Chine: la montre "chinoise". Avec la collaboration de Gustave Loup. Introduction sur l'horométrie et le système cosmologique des Chinois, par Léopold de Saussure. xiii, 272 p., 33 pl., 245 fig. Neuchâtel: Attinger, [1919]. [CB 12/644]

KISTNER, Adolf. Die Geschichte der Schwarzwalduhr und das Badische Landesmuseum. *Geschichtsbl.Tech.Ind.*, 1920, 7: 30-42.

KISTNER, Adolf. Die Schwarzwälder Uhr. 164 p. (Heimatblätter "Vom Bodensee zum Main", 31) Karlsruhe: C.F. Müller, 1927.
Reviewed by J. Ruska, *Mitt.Gesch.Med.*, 1927, 26: 121.

SCHWENNINGER, Oskar. Die Entwicklung der Schwarzwälder Uhrenindustrie. *Beitr.Gesch.Tech.Ind.*, 1930, 20: 91-8, 11 fig.

ZINNER, Ernst. Von alter süddeutscher Uhrmacherei. *Neue Uhrmacher-Zeitung*, 1955, no. 9, 17-20, 3 fig.

WRwk

CROMMELIN, C.A. La contribution de la Hollande à l'horlogerie. *Bull.Annu.Soc.Suisse Chronom.*, 1949, 2: 653-63, 20 fig.

PHOLIEN, Florent. L'horlogerie et ses artistes au pays de Liége. Etude rétrospective. 131 p., 65 ill. Liége: Imprimeries Nationales des Militaires Mutilés et Invalides de la Guerre, 1934.

WRxx museums

ARTHUR, James. Timepieces of the James Arthur Collection at New York University. *Science*, 1940, 91: 284.

CONSERVATOIRE NATIONAL DES ARTS ET MÉTIERS. MUSÉE. Catalogue, section JB: Horlogerie. 330 p., ill. Paris: 1949.
Reviewed by P. Ducassé, *Thalès*, 1948, 5: 113-27.

HERING, Daniel Webster. The lure of the clock. An account of the James Arthur Collection of clocks and watches at New York University. xiv, 121 p., 12 pl. New York: New York University Press, 1932.

KISTNER, Adolf, ed. Die Historische Uhrensammlung Furtwangen. [Catalogue] iv, 173 p., ill. Furtwangen: Uttenweiler, 1925.

LOISEAU, J. L'exposition des chefs-d'oeuvre de l'horlogerie au Musée du Conservatoire National des Arts et Métiers. *Rev. Hist.Sci.*, 1950, 3: 88-9.

ZINNER, Ernst. Alte Uhren in Russland. *Uhr*, 1959, 13: no. 2, 26-7.

ZINNER, Ernst. Clocks in Russian Museums. *Antiq.Horology*, 1959, 2: 206-9.

WS AUTOMATA

BEDINI, Silvio A. The role of automata in the history of technology. *Technol.Cult.*, 1964, 5: 24-42.

BERNARD-MAITRE, Henri. Le problème du robot scientifique. *Rev.Hist.Sci.*, 1950, 3: 370-5.

BLIND, Adolphe. Les automates truqués. 82 p. Genève: Eggimann, 1927.
Reviewed by F.M. Feldhaus, *Geschichtsbl.Tech.Ind.*, 1927, 11: 202.

CHAPUIS, Alfred; DROZ, Edmond. Les automates. Figures artificielles d'hommes et d'animaux; histoire et technique. 425 p. Neuchâtel: Éditions du Griffon, 1949.

CHAPUIS, Alfred; GÉLIS, Edouard. Le monde des automates. Etude historique et technique. 2 vol. 348 p.; 352 p. Neuchâtel: Chapuis, 1928.
Reviewed by Giulio Panconcelli-Calzia, *Deut.Lit.Zeitung*, 1930, 1: 1628-9.

PRICE, Derek J. de Solla. Automata in history. Automata and the origins of mechanism and mechanistic philosophy. *Technol.Cult.*, 1964, 5: 9-23.

RUNGE, Wilhelm T. Automates anciens et nouveaux. *Industrie*, 1961, 15: 519-23.

WT CALCULATING MACHINES

see also XP COMPUTERS
for other aids to numerical calculation *see* BCxk and BFza-xk

WTc

BRAUNER, Ludwig. Wichtige Abschnitte in der Rechenmaschinen-Entwicklung. *Beitr.Gesch.Tech.Ind.*, 1926, 16: 248-60, 9 fig.

CALCULATEURS automatiques depuis Pascal jusqu'à Hollerith. *Larousse Mens.*, 1931, 8: 715-17, 8 fig.

COUFFIGNAL, Louis. Les machines à calculer, leurs principes, leur évolution. 88 p., ill. Paris: Gauthier-Villars, 1933.

DAVIS, Harry M. Mathematical machines. Some measure, others count. The latter, with which this article is principally concerned, are the focus of much feverish activity not all of it purely scientific. *Sci.Amer.*, 1949, 180: no. 4, 29-31, ill.

FELDHAUS, F.M. Rechenapparate mit Kugeln oder Knöpfen. *Masch.Buchhaltung Euklid-Feldhaus-Beil.*, June 1928, no. 3, 9-12.

FELDHAUS, F.M. Rechenbehelfe des 17.-19. Jahrhunderts. *Masch. Buchhaltung Euklid-Feldhaus-Beil.*, Feb. 1929, no. 11, 45-8, 3 fig.

FELDHAUS, F.M. Rechenkästen. *Masch.Buchhaltung Euklid-Feldhaus-Beil.*, Dec. 1928, no. 9, 33-6, 1 fig.

HARVARD UNIVERSITY. COMPUTATION LABORATORY. Proceedings of a symposium on large-scale digital calculating machinery. Jointly sponsored by the Navy Department Bureau of Ordnance and Harvard University. 334 p. (Annals of the Computation Laboratory, 16) Cambridge, Mass.: 1948.
Some historical material.

IZ ISTORII Vychislitel'nykh Ustroĭstv publikatsiia no materialam arkhiva AN SSSR i primechaniia M.I. Radovskogo; predislovie E. Kol'mana. [Documents on the history of calculating apparatus published from materials in the USSR Academy of Science with notes by M.I. Radovsky and preface by E. Kolman. (In Russian)]. *Ist.Mat.Issled.*, 1961, 14: 551-86.

KIRCHVOGEL, Paul Adolf. Zahlen und Räder aus der Geschichte der Rechenmaschinen. *B.A.S.F.*, 1964, 14: no. 3, 136-44. [CB 90/510]

KOBORI, Akira. [History of computing machines. (In Japanese)]. *J.Hist.Sci.Japan*, May 1952, no. 22, 3-6.

LEHMER, D.H. A photo-electric number sieve. *Amer.Math.Mon.*, 1933, 40: 401-6.

LILLEY, S. Mathematical machines. *Nature*, 1942, 149: 462-5.

LOCKE, L. Leland. Synchronism and anachronism. *Scr.Math.*, 1932, 1: 147-52.
Apropos of synchronic and anachronic inventions. Illustrated by the history of calculating machines from Pascal and Leibnitz to modern times.

LORIA, Gino. Veicoli al servizio dei calcolatori. *Scientia*, 1920, 28: 77-93.
History of appliances used for computing.

McCORMICK, E.M. Digital computers. Their history, operation, and use. *Annu.Rep.Smithsonian Inst.for 1960*, p. 281-99. Washington, D.C.: 1961.

MURRAY, Francis J. The theory of mathematical machines. Rev. ed. vii, 139 p., fig. New York: King's Crown Press, 1948. [CB 75/58]
Some attention is paid to the older instruments, planimeters, integrometers, integraph, and harmonic analyzers.

TAKEDA, Kusuo. [Development of the electronic calculating machine. (In Japanese)] *J.Hist.Sci.Japan*, 1952, no. 22, 6-11; no. 23, 6-11.

TATON, René. Le calcul mécanique. 126 p. (Que Sais-Je?) Paris: Presses Universitaires de France, 1949. [CB 76/395]
Brief history of mathematical machines.

TATON, René; FLAD, Jean Paul. Le calcul mécanique. 2nd rev. ed. 128 p., fig. Paris: Presses Universitaires de France, 1963.
Reviewed by Jean Itard, *Rev.Hist.Sci.*, 1964, 17: 169.

TRINKS, F. Geschichtliche Daten aus der Entwicklung der Rechenmaschine von Pascal bis zur Nova-Brunswiga. *Braunschweiger G-N-C-Monatsschr.*, 1927, 14: 249-75.

WTc-bx

MICHEL, Henri. Le calcul mécanique. A propos d'une exposition récente. *J.Suisse Horlogeri*, July-August 1947, 72: 307-16.

WTmzBkk

BERKELEY, Edmund C. The relations between symbolic logic and large-scale calculating machines. *Science*, 1950, 112: 395-9.

WTwb

LOCKE, L. Leland. The history of modern calculating machines, an American contribution. *Amer.Math.Mon.*, 1924, 31: 422-9. [CB 17/590]

LOCKE, L. Leland. Early calculating machines of American invention. *Typewriter Top.*, June 1922; March 1925.

WTxx

SCIENCE MUSEUM. Catalogue of the collections with descriptive and historical notes and illustrations. Mathematics. I. Calculating machines and instruments. Compiled by D. Baxandall. 85 p., 13 pl. London: H.M. Stationery Office, 1926.

WU OPTICAL INSTRUMENTS: TECHNOLOGY

see also FAxk TELESCOPES
ORzs SPECTACLES
CJxk OPTICAL INSTRUMENTS (theoretical aspects)
for photographic equipment *see* XFxb

WUc

GLAZE, Francis W. The optical glass industry, past and present. *Sky Telesc.*, 1947, 6: no. 3, 3-5; no. 4, 9-11. Reprinted in *Annu.Rep.Smithsonian Inst.for 1948.* p. 217-25, 4 pl., 2 fig. Washington, D.C.: 1949.

ROHR, Moritz von. Ein Beitrag zur Geschichte des optischen Glases. (Bis zur Eröffnung des Jenaer Glaswerks) *Nova Acta Leopoldina*, 1934, 2: 147-202.

ROHR, Moritz von. Die Erkenntnis von dem wahren Wesen des Lichtbildes und ihr Einfluss auf das Verständnis für die optischen Geräte im allgemeinen. *Naturwissenschaften*, 1932, 20: 496-501, 514-20.

ROHR, Moritz von. Die optischen Instrumente. Brille, Lupe, Mikroskop, Fernrohr, Aufnahmelinse und ihnen verwandte Vorkehrungen. 4th ed. vi, 130 p., 91 fig. Berlin: Springer, 1930.

TURRIÈRE, Emile. Introduction à l'histoire de l'optique. Le développement de l'industrie verrière d'art depuis l'époque vénitienne jusqu'à la fondation des verreries d'optique. *Isis*, 1925, 7: 77-104. [CB 19/802]
This article forms the introduction to the author's works on optical instruments.

TURRIÈRE, Emile. Optique industrielle. 2 vol. in 1. 1. Verres et verreries d'optique. Objectifs photographiques. (Petzval, Steinheil, Goerz, Taylor, Zeiss) Téléobjectifs. 264 p. [2]. Appendice. Calcul des objectifs astronomiques de Fraunhofer. 2e éd. 112 p. (Travaux du Bureau d'Etudes d'optique du Service géographique de l'Armée, fasc. 1) Paris: Delagrave, 1920.

TURRIÈRE, Emile. Pour l'histoire de l'optique: le développement de l'industrie verrière d'art, des origines jusqu'à la fondation des verres d'optique. *Bull.Union Mat.Assoc.Etudiants France*, 1923, no. 6, 1-6; no. 7, 1-11. [CB 16/350]

TURRIÈRE, Émile. Le problème des objectifs de longues-vues dans la dioptrique contemporaine. Exposition des recherches de M.H. Harting. iv, 150 p., 2 pl. (Travaux du Bureau d'Études d'Optique du Service Géographique de l'Armée) Paris: 1918. [CB 8/344]

WUda

SCHAEFER, G.; NAUMANN, W. Physicians as builders of optical instruments. *Ciba Symp.* (Summit, N.J.), 1941, 3: 1042-6.

WUwb-qt

TOURIN, R.H. Optical history of a machine tool builder. (Warner and Swasey.) *Appl.Optics*, 1964, 3: 1385-6.

WUwe-qt

NEGRETTI AND ZAMBRA. Centenary. 1850-1950. 24 p., ill. London: 1950. [CB 79/140]
The history of a famous firm.

WUwg-qt

AUERBACH, Felix. The Zeiss works and the Carl Zeiss foundation in Jena. Their scientific, technical and sociological development and importance popularly described. Transl. from the 5th German ed. by R. Kanthack. iv, 273 p. London: W. and G. Foyle, 1927.

AUERBACH, Felix. Das Zeisswerk und die Carl-Zeiss Stiftung in Jena. Ihre wissenschaftliche, technische und soziale Entwicklung und Bedeutung. 5 umgearb. Aufl. vi, 258 p., 252 fig., portr. Jena: G. Fischer, 1925.

ROHR, Moritz V. Zur Geschichte der Zeissischen Werkstätte bis zum Tode Ernst Abbes. Mit Beiträgen von Max Fischer und August Köhler. *Forsch.Gesch.Opt.*, 1930, 1: 91-202, 10 p., 49 fig.

WV MUSICAL INSTRUMENTS; BELLS

ANDERSON, E.W. Development of the organ. *Trans.Newcomen Soc.*, 1927-28, 8: 1-18, 11 fig.

ANDERSSON, Otto. The bowed-harp. A study in the history of early musical instruments. From the original Swedish edition revised by the author. The translation edited with additional footnotes by Kathleen Schlesinger. xviii, 319 p., 116 fig. London: Reeves, 1930.
Reviewed by Curt Sachs, *Deut.Lit.Zeitung*, 1931, 2: 2188-9.

CELLIER, Alexandre; BACHELIN, Henri. L'orgue. Ses éléments, son histoire, son esthétique. Préface de C.M. Widor. 255 p., ill. Paris: Delagrave, 1933.

HUGHES, A.A. Bell founding. *Trans.Newcomen Soc.*, 1929-30, 10: 36-45.

MOSORIAK, Roy. The curious history of music boxes. 242 p., 40 pl., fig. Chicago: Lightner, 1943. [CB 66/270]

NICHOLS, John Robert. Bells thro' the ages: the founders' craft and ringers' art. xi, 320 p. London: Chapman and Hall, 1928.

PRICE, Frank Percival. The carillon. Preface by Herbert Austin Fricker. Drawings by Leonard Eldon Shore. xi, 288 p., 38 pl. London: Oxford University Press, 1933.

REBER, B. Ein Beitrag zur Geschichte der Glocken. 25 p. Baden: Heller, 1912.

RUPP, Emile. Die Entwicklungsgeschichte der Orgelbaukunst. xvi, 480 p., 97 fig. Einsiedeln: Benziger, 1929.

SACHS, Curt. Geist und Werden der Musikinstrumente. xii, 284 p., 48 pl. Berlin: Reimer, 1929.
Reviewed by J. Nippgen, *Ethnographie*, 1930, 23: 128-9.

SUMNER, William Leslie. The organ, its evolution, principles of construction and use. xiv, 429 p., 19 pl. New York: Philosophical Library, 1952. [CB 79/189]

WVwd

GALPIN, Francis W. A textbook of European musical instruments. Their origin, history and character. 256 p., ill. London: Williams and Norgate; New York: Dutton, 1937.

WW SPECIAL CRAFTS

WWc

DICKINSON, H.W. Besoms, brooms, brushes and pencils: the handicraft period. *Trans.Newcomen Soc.*, 1943-44 and 1944-45, 24: 99-108.

GRAESSE, J.G.Th. Kunstgewerbliche Altertümer und Kuriositäten. Führer für Sammler und Liebhaber von Gegenständen der Kleinkunst, von Antiquitäten sowie von Kuriositäten. Begründet von J.G.Th. Graesse, fortgeführt von F. Jennicke. 6th ed. 262 p. Berlin: R.C. Schmidt, 1920.
First published 1871: Guide de l'amateur d'objets d'art et de curiosité.
Reviewed by George Sarton, *Isis*, 1921, 4: 82.

HUGHES, C. Bernard. Living crafts. 192 p., ill. New York: Philosophical Library, 1954. [CB 80/143]
Study of the older handcrafts which have survived to the present, including metal-working, paper-making, soap-making, various textile crafts, etc.

WWwb

ANDREWS, Edward D. The New York Shakers and their industries. 8 p., 8 fig. (*Circ.N.Y.State Mus.*, 2) Albany, N.Y.: 1930. [CB 32/518]

WWwe

WYMER, Norman. English town crafts, a survey of their developments from early times to the present day. viii, 128 p., 131 ill. London: Batsford, 1949.

WWxx-wb

ADAMS, Charles C. The New York State Museum's historical survey and collection of the New York Shakers. *Bull.N.Y. State Mus.*, 1941, no. 323, 77-111, ill.

WWxx-we

PEATE, Iorwerth Cyfeiliog. Guide to the collection of Welsh bygones. A descriptive account of old-fashioned life in Wales. Together with a catalogue of the objects exhibited. svi, 148 p., lii pl. Cardiff: National Museum of Wales, 1929.

WX METALWORK; JEWELLERY

DARMSTAEDTER, Ernst. Subaerate Münzen und ihre Herstellung. *Mitt.Bayer.Numismat.Ges.*, 1929, 47: 27-38.

HÖVER, Otto. A handbook of wrought iron from the Middle Ages to the end of the eighteenth century. Transl. by Ann C. Weaver. xxxiii p., 320 pl. London: Thames and Hudson, 1962.
Translation of: Das Eisenwerk. Translation of 1st edition entitled: An encyclopedia of ironwork. New York: Weyhe, 1927.

HÖVER, Otto. Das Eisenwerk: die Kunstformen des Schmiedeeisens vom Mittelalter bis zum Ausgang des 18. Jahrhunderts. 4th ed. xxxiv p., 320 pl. Tübingen: Wasmuth, 1961.
First published 1927.

HOPKINS, Albert A. The lure of the lock. A short treatise on locks to elucidate the John M. Mossman Collection of locks in the Museum of the General Society of Mechanics and Tradesmen in the City of New York, including some of the Mossman Papers. ix, 246 p., 500 ill. New York: General Society of Mechanics and Tradesmen, 1928.

LLOYD, Godfrey Isaac Howard. The cutlery trades; an historical study in the economics of small-scale production. xvi, 493 p., 16 ill., 3 maps. London: Longmans, 1913.

SMITH, Cyril Stanley. Methods of making chain mail (14th to 18th centuries): a metallographic note. *Technol.Cult.*, 1959, 1: 60-7.

WHITE, George. A history of early needle-making. *Trans.Newcomen Soc.*, 1940-41, 21: 81-7, 4 fig.

WXtq

SUTHERLAND, C.H.V. Art in coinage. 223 p., 147 fig. New York: Philosophical Library, 1956. [CB 82/217]

WXwe

CRAIG, John. A history of the London Mint from A.D. 287 to 1948. xviii, 450 p., 16 pl. Cambridge University Press, 1953. [CB 80/142]
Reviewed by F.C. Thompson, *Nature*, 1953, 172: 221.

WXwe-qe

WELCH, Charles. History of the Cutlers' Company of London. 2 vol. London: The Company, 1916-23.

WXwg

HENDRICHS, Franz. Carl Friedrich Ern (1850-1924), der Bahnbrecher für die Solinger Rasiermesserindustrie. *Beitr.Gesch. Tech.Ind.*, 1930, 20: 47-62, 22 fig.

HENDRICHS, Franz. Von der Handschmiede zur Schlägerei: der Tischmesserschmied. 72 p., ill. (Aus der Geschichte der Solinger Industrie, 2) Köln: Verein für Technik und Industrie, Solingen, 1922. [CB 26/234]

HENDRICHS, Franz. Die Schleifkotten an der Wupper. 96 p., ill. (Aus der Geschichte der Solinger Industrie, 1) Köln: Verein für Technik und Industrie, Solingen, 1922.

WXwg-qe

HENDRICHS, Franz. Die Entwicklung der Solinger Schwert- und Messerzünfte bis zum Dreissigjährigen Krieg. *Beitr.Gesch. Tech.Ind.*, 1929, 19: 113-20, 8 fig.

WY WOODWORK; LEATHER AND BASKETWORK

BAKER, Oliver. Black Jacks and leather bottells. Being some account of leather drinking vessels in England and incidentally of other ancient vessels. 190 p. Stratford-on-Avon: Priv. print., 1921.

BOBART, Henry Hodgkinson. Basketwork through the ages. xv, 174 p., ill. London: Oxford University Press, 1936.

DICKINSON, H.W. A condensed history of rope-making. *Trans. Newcomen Soc.*, 1942-43, 23: 71-91.

HENNELL, Thomas B. Men of straw: an account of surviving straw handicraft. *Trans.Newcomen Soc.*, 1931-32, 12: 15-29, 5 fig.

STENGER, Erich. Phelloplastik, die Kleinkunst der Korkbildnerei. *Arch.Gesch.Math.Naturwiss.Tech.*, 1929, 12: 194-209, 1 fig.

WYxb

GOODMAN, W.L. A history of woodworking tools. 208 p., pl., fig. London: Bell, 1964.

WZ CLOTHING; COSTUME

LATOUR, A. The stocking: modern stocking manufacture; the knitted stocking; the stocking frame; the growth of the hos knitting industry; fashions in stockings. *Ciba Rev.*, 1954, no. 106, 3794-825.

SCHRAMM, Hans. Journeymen's dress. *Ciba Rev.*, 1960, 12: no. 138, 14-17.

SCHRAMM, Hans. Occupational and festive costumes in pre-industrial times. *Ciba Rev.*, 1960, 12: no. 138, 2-13.

TILKE, Max. Oriental costumes: their designs and colours. Transl. by L. Hamilton. 32 p., 128 pl. London: Kegan Paul, 1923.
Translation of: Orientalische Kostüme in Schnitt und Farbe (Berlin: Wasmuth, 1923).

WZwb

DAVIDSON, Daniel Sutherland. Snowshoes. 207 p. (*Mem.Amer. Phil.Soc.*, 6) Philadelphia: 1937.
A study of the distribution of the various kinds of snowshoes in North America.

WZwe

KELLY, Francis Michael; SCHWABE, Randolph. A short history of costume and armour chiefly in England (1066-1800). 2 vol. London: Batsford, 1931.
Reviewed by M. Calberg, *Bull.Mus.Roy.Art Hist.*, 1932, 4: 79-80.

WRIGHT, Thomas. The romance of the shoe. Being the history of shoe-making in all ages and especially in England and Scotland. xvi, 317 p. London: Farncombe, 1922.

WZwg

SCHRAMM, Hans. Die deutsche Knopfindustrie, ihre Geschichte, Volkswirtschaft und Weltwirtschaft. vii, 113 p. Leipzig: Gunz und Eule, 1921.
Reviewed by F.M. Feldhaus, *Geschichtsbl.Tech.Ind.*, 1922, 9: 75.

X COMMUNICATIONS

Xc

ALBION, Robert G. The communication revolution, 1760-1933. *Trans.Newcomen Soc.*, 1933-34, 14: 13-25.

CHERRY, Colin. On human communication. A review, a survey, and a criticism. xiv, 333 p., ill. (Studies in Communication) New York/London: Technology Press of Massachusetts Institute of Technology; Wiley; Chapman & Hall, 1957. [CB 82/210]

FABRE, Maurice. A history of communications. vii, 105 p., ill. New York: Hawthorn, 1964.
Reviewed by Melvin Kranzberg, *Science*, 1964, 144: 531.

XyFE

MORRISON, Philip. Interstellar communication. *Bull.Phil.Soc. Wash.*, 1962, 16: 59-81.

XyFF

VOROB'EV, B.N. Nachalo rabot K.E. Tsiolkovskogo po mezhplanetnym soobshcheniiam. [Early work of K.E. Tsiolkovskii on interplanetary communications. (In Russian)] *Vop.Ist. Est. Tekh.*, 1958, no. 6, 30-8.

XyFFwn-qd

KRAMAROV, G.M. Obshchestvo izucheniia meshplanetnykh soobshchenii. [The Society for the Study of Interplanetary Communication. (In Russian)] *Tr.Inst.Ist.Est.Tekh.*, 1962, 45: 107-14.

XA INFORMATION THEORY; CYBERNETICS

GEORGE, F.H. Automation, cybernetics and society. 283 p., fig. New York: Philosophical Library, 1959.

GOLDSTINE, H.H. Information theory. *Science*, 1961, 133: 1395-9.

McCULLOCH, W.S. Mysterium iniquitatis of sinful man aspiring into the place of God. *Sci.Mon.*, 1955, 80: 35-9.

MACKAY, D.M. The use of behavioural language to refer to mechanical processes. *Brit.J.Phil.Sci.*, 1962, 13: 89-103.

REISER, Oliver L. Unified symbolism for world understanding in science, including Bliss symbols (semantography) and logic, cybernetics and semantics. 52 p. Sydney, Australia: Semantography Publishing Company, 1953.

SAYRE, Kenneth M.; CROSSON, Frederick J.; ed. The modeling of mind. Computers and intelligence. xi, 275 p. Notre Dame, Ind.: University of Notre Dame Press, 1963. [CB 89/490]

XAmzJ

DAVID, Aurel. Morale, cybernétique et biologie. *Act.VIIIe Congr.Int.Hist.Sci.* (Florence, 1956), p. 668-72. Paris: Hermann, 1958.
The author claims that the distinction between physical and biological sciences is disappearing.

XB WRITING MATERIALS; TYPEWRITERS

FELDHAUS, F.M. Bleistifte schreiben Weltgeschichte. Privatdruck zum 275 jährigen Jubiläum der Bleistiftfabrik Staedtler. 54 p., 39 fig. Nürnberg: 1937. [CB 46/585]

KRCAL, Richard. 100 Jahre Schreibmaschine 1864-1964. Die Schreibmaschine Peter Mitterhofers. Tatsachen und Irrtüme über seine Modelle. *Bl.Technikgesch.*, 1964, no. 26, 87-111.

MAGINNIS, James P. Histoire du porte-plume réservoir et du stylographe. *Papyrus*, 1923, 4: 142, 177, 252, 573, 651, 717, 778. [CB 18/618]

PFEIFFER, Otto. Die Schreibmaschine bis 1900. *Beitr.Gesch. Tech.Ind.*, 1923, 14: 89-124, 30 fig.

PFEIFFER, Otto. Zur Vorgeschichte der Schreibmaschine. Die Modelle des Technischen Museums in Wien. *Beitr.Gesch.Tech. Ind.*, 1930, 20: 149-68, 5 fig.

SCIENCE MUSEUM. The history and development of typewriters. by G. Tilghman Richards. Rev. ed. by W.E. Church. 49 p., ill. London: H.M. Stationery Off., 1964.
First published 1938 with title: Handbook of the collection illustrating typewriters. [CB 54/531]; revised and amended reprint published 1948.

TESTI, Gino. Nel centenario della macchina da scrivere. *Archeion*, 1934, 16: 98-9.

VOICE, Eric H. The history of the manufacture of pencils. *Trans.Newcomen Soc.*, 1949-50 and 1950-51, 27: 131-41, 4 fig.

XBwg-qt

STAEDTLER, J.S., Firm. 275 Jahre Staedtlerstifte, 1662-1937. 80 p., 49 fig. Nürnberg: 1937. [CB 52/587]
Festschrift celebrating the history of the Nuremberg concern devoted to the making of pencils.

XC BOOKMAKING AND PRINTING

XCc general history

ALDIS, Harry G. The printed book. 2nd ed. by John Carter and E.A. Crutchley. x, 142 p. Cambridge University Press, 1941. [CB 61/421]
First published 1916.

BLUM, André. Les origines du papier, de l'imprimerie et de la gravure. 252 p., ill. Paris: Editions de la Tournelle, 1935.
Reviewed by Axel Nelson, *Lychnos*, 1937, 2: 430.

DIEHL, Edith. Bookbinding, its background and technique. 2 vol. xxi, 251 p., 91 pl.; vi, 406 p. New York/Toronto: Rinehart, 1946. [CB 72/277]

DIRINGER, David. The hand-produced book. A companion volume to The alphabet, a key to the history of mankind. xii, 603 p., ill. New York: Philosophical Library, 1953. [CB 80/145]

DOWDING, Geoffrey. An introduction to the history of printing types; an illustrated summary of the main stages in the development of type design from 1440 up to the present day; an aid to typeface identification. 277 p. London: Wace, 1962.

JACKSON, Hartley E. 26 lead soldiers: a textbook of printing types, methods and processes for journalism students. xiv, 214 p. Stanford: Stanford University Press, 1937. [CB 51/290]
The methods and processes of printing.

MORISON, Stanley. Four centuries of fine printing. One hundred and ninety two facsimiles of pages of books printed at presses established between 1465 and 1924. With an introductory text and indexes. 4th rev. ed. 254 p. London: Benn; New York: Barnes and Noble, 1960.
First edition 1924.

MORISON, Stanley. The typographic book, 1450-1935; a study of fine typography through five centuries. With an introductory essay by S. Morison and supplementary material by Kenneth Day. xiii, 98 p., 377 facs. London: Benn; Chicago: University of Chicago Press, 1963.
Designed to supersede the author's Four centuries of fine printing.

MORTET, Charles. Le format des livres. Notions pratiques suivies de recherches historiques. 50 p., ill. Paris: Ed. Champion, 1925. [CB 20/213]

PEDDIE, Robert Alexander. Printing: a short history of the art. x, 390 p. London: Grafton, 1927.

POTTINGER, David. Printers and printing. xi, 143 p. Cambridge: Harvard University Press, 1941. [CB 62/89]

SCHOTTENLOHER, Karl. Das alte Buch. 3rd ed. 467 p., 132 fig. Braunschweig: Klinkhardt und Biermann, 1956.
First published 1919.
Reviewed by Marc Klein, *Arch.Int.Hist.Sci.*, 1957, 10: 115-16.

TURPAIN, Albert. De la presse à bras à la linotype et à l'électrotypographe. x, 97 p. Paris: Gauthier-Villars, 1924.

UPDIKE, Daniel Berkeley. Printing types, their history, forms, and uses; a study in survivals. 2nd ed. 2 vol. xl, 292 p.; xix, 326 p., 367 ill. Cambridge: Harvard University Press, 1951.
First edition 1922. [CB 13/313]
Reviewed by Sonia S. Wohl, *Isis*, 1952, 43: 303-4.

WIBORG, Frank Bestow, ed. Printing ink. A history. With a treatise on modern methods of manufacture and use. xx, 299 p., 10 ill. New York: Harpers, 1926.
Reviewed by George Sarton, *Isis*, 1927, 9: 134-8.

XCce-bv

LEHMANN-HAUPT, Hellmut. Seventy books about bookmaking: a guide to the study and appreciation of printing. v, 60 p. New York: Columbia University Press, 1941.

XCda

JENNETT, Sean. Pioneers in printing. Johann Gutenberg, William Caxton, William Caslon, John Baskerville, Alois Senefelder, Frederick Koenig, Ottmar Mergenthaler, Tolbert Lanston. xi, 196 p., ill. London: Routledge & Kegan Paul; Fair Lawn, N.J.: Essential Books, 1959.
Reviewed by Lubomyr Wynar, *Technol.Cult.*, 1960, 1: 264-6.

XCn/t special aspects

XCnb

GERMANY. REICHSDRUCKEREI. Alphabete und Schriftzeichen des Morgen- und Abendlandes zum allgemeinen Gebrauch, mit besonderer Berücksichtigung des Buchgewerbes, unter Mitwirkung von Fachgelehrten zusammengestellt in der Reichsdruckerei. 86 p. Berlin: 1924.
Reviewed by Ernst Lewy, *Deut.Lit.Zeitung*, 1926, 1681-3.

XCqt

RANSOM, Will. Private presses and their books. 493 p. New York: Bowker, 1929.

XCth

LEENER, G. de. Effets juridiques et économiques de l'invention de l'imprimerie sur les activités littéraires. *Bull.Inst. Sociol.Solvay*, 1913, no. 26, 648-51. [CB 2/315]

XCw in different countries

XCwb

LEHMANN-HAUPT, Hellmut; *et al.* The book in America; a history of the making and selling of books in the United States. 2nd American ed. xiv, 493 p. New York: Bowker, 1951. [CB 78/197 and CB 79/196]
Revised and enlarged English text from 1937 German edition of: Das amerikanische Buchwesen (Leipzig: Hiersemann, 1937).

XCwb-qt

WILEY AND SONS, INC. The first one hundred and fifty years. A history of John Wiley and Sons, Incorporated, 1807-1957. xxv, 242 p., front., 31 ill. New York: John Wiley & Sons, Inc., 1957. [CB 83/212]

XCwc

MEDINA, José Toribio. Historia de la imprenta en los antiguos dominios españoles de América y Oceanía. Prologo de Guillermo Feliu Cruz. Complemento bibliográfico by José Zamudio Z. 2 vol. cxli, 542 p.; xv, 540 p., ill. Santiago: Fondo Histórico y Bibliográfico José Toribio Medina, 1958.
Reviewed by Lota M. Spell, *Hispanic-Amer.Hist.Rev.*, 1960, 40: 139.

XCwc-bx

LIBRARY OF CONGRESS. Colonial printing in Mexico. Catalog of an exhibition held at the Library of Congress in 1939 commemorating the four hundredth anniversary of printing in the New World. 60 p. Washington: U.S. Govt. Print. Off., 1939. [CB 61/422]

XCwe

HANDOVER, Phyllis Margaret. Printing in London from 1476 to modern times. Competitive practice and technical invention in the trade of book and bible printing, periodical production, jobbing, etc. 224 p., 77 ill. Cambridge, Mass.: Harvard University Press, 1960.
Reviewed by Frederic J. Mosher, *Renaiss.News*, 1961, 14: 125-6.

JONES, Ifano. A history of printing and printers in Wales to 1810; and of successive and related printers to 1923. Also a history of printing and printers in Monmouthshire to 1923. x, 367 p. Cardiff: William Lewis, 1925.

XCwf

PASQUIER, Émile. Imprimeurs et libraires de l'Anjou. 403 p. Angers: Société anonyme des éditions de l'Ouest, 1932.
Reviewed by A.H. Shearer, *Amer.Hist.Rev.*, 1933, 39: 166.

XCwf-bx

LE LIVRE français, des origines à la fin du Second Empire, par Henry Martin, André Blum, Ch. Mortet [*et al.*]. Exposition du pavillon de Marsan, avril 1923. ix, 184 p., ill. Paris: van Oest, 1924.
Reviewed by Gustave Hirschfeld, *Larousse Mens.*, 1925, 6: 679-82.

XCwf-r

RENARD, Georges. Les travailleurs du livre et du journal. 3 vol. 278 p.; 352 p.; 304 p. (Bibliothèque Sociale des Métiers) Paris: G. Doin, 1925-26.
Reviewed by L. Guinet, *Isis*, 1927, 9: 143-4.

XCwg

MORI, Gustav. Das Schriftgiessergewerbe in Süddeutschland und den angrenzenden Ländern. Ein Abschnitt aus der Geschichte des deutschen Schriftgiessergewerbes. xx, 76 p., pl., portr. Stuttgart: Schriftgiesserei Bauer & Co., 1924.

XCwg-qt

LEEMANN-VAN ELCK, Paul. Die Offizin Froschauer, Zürichs berühmte Druckerei im 16. Jahrhundert. Ein Beitrag zur Geschichte der Buchdruckerkunst anlässlich der Halbjahrtausendfeier ihrer Erfindung. 215 p., ill., 3 pl. Zürich: Füssli, 1940.
Reviewed by Hans Sallander, *Lychnos*, 1941, 310.

XCwk

BOCK, Eugeen de. Beknopte geschiedenis van de boekhandel in de Nederlanden. [Short history of book production in the Netherlands. (In Dutch)] 2nd ed. 144 p., ill. (De Seizoenen, 43) Antwerp: Nederlandsche Boekhandel, 1943. [CB 71/127]
First published Brussels: 1939.

XCwk-bv

BIBLIOGRAPHIE de l'histoire du livre en Belgique, 1959. (Bibliografie van de geschiedenis van het boek in België) *Gulden Passer*, 1960, 38: 211-32.
This bibliography continued annually for 10 years.

XCwn

AKADEMIIA NAUK SSSR. OTDELENIE ISTORICHESKIKH NAUK. U istokov russkogo knigopechataniia. [Sources of Russian printing. (In Russian)] 268 p., ill. Moskva: Akademiia Nauk SSSR, 1959.
Reviewed by Lubomyr Wynar, *Technol.Cult.*, 1960, 1: 264-6.

XCwt

CARTER, Thomas Francis. The invention of printing in China and its spread westward. Rev. by L.C. Goodrich. 2nd ed. xxiv, 293 p., ill. New York: Ronald Press, 1955.
First published 1925 (New York: Columbia University Press); corrected reprint with additions 1931. [CB 36/426]
Reviewed by G. Sarton, *Isis*, 1926, 361-73.
Chinese translation: Chung-kuo yinshua-shu ti fa-ming ho t'a-ti hsi ch'uan. Shanghai: Commercial Press, 1957. [CB 85/419]

XCxx museums

RUPPEL, Aloys, ed. Gutenberg-Festschrift zur Feier des 25. jährigen Bestehens des Gutenberg-Museums in Mainz. xvi, 448 p., 50 pl., fig. Mainz: Gutenberg-Gesellschaft, 1925.

SARTON, George. Gutenberg Museum und Gesellschaft (Mainz). *Isis*, 1919, 2: 399-400.
Short note to explain the aims of this society with list of its most important publications.

XCzp PROOF-READING

SIMPSON, Percy. Proof-reading in the sixteenth, seventeenth and eighteenth centuries. vii, 251 p. London: Oxford University Press, 1935.

XD GRAPHIC PROCESSES

LES ARTS de reproduction graphique. L'histoire de la gravure. Le papier à travers les âges. 104 p. (*Bull.Synd.Maîtres Imprimeurs France*, special number) Paris: 1925. [CB 18/644]

BLAND, David. A history of book illustration; the illuminated manuscript and the printed book. 448 p., ill. Cleveland/New York: World Publishing Company, 1958. [CB 84/329]

BLISS, Douglas Piercy. A history of wood engraving. xvi, 263 p., 120 ill. London: Dent, 1928.

BLUM, André. *See* WC

BRITTON, Roswell S. A horn printing block. *Harvard J.Asiatic Stud.*, 1938, 3: 99-103, 3 fig. [CB 55/166]

DURRIEU, Paul. Les origines de la gravure. *J.Savants*, 1917, 15: 205-12, 251-64.
Review of Gusman, Pierre, below.

GUSMAN, Pierre. La gravure sur bois et d'épargne sur métal du XIVe au XXe siècle. 299 p., ill. Paris: R. Roger et F. Chernoviz, 1916.

HIND, Arthur M. A history of engraving and etching from the fifteenth century to the year 1914, being the third and fully revised edition of "A short history of engraving and etching". xx, 487 p. London: Constable, 1923.
First published 1908.

KÖDITZ, Emil. Ein halbes Jahrhundert Autotypie. *Arch.Buchgewerbe*, 1931, 68: 147-8, 2 fig.

LILIEN, Otto M. Early history of industrial gravure printing to 1900. *Act.VIIIe Congr.Int.Hist Sci.* (Florence, 1956), p. 970-9. Paris: Hermann, 1958.

SUDHOFF, Karl. Drei Jahrtausende Graphik im Dienste der Wissenschaft (1914). *Sudhoffs Arch.*, 1929, 21: 283-95.
Originally published in Internationale Ausstellung für Buchgewerbe und Graphik, Leipzig, 1914. Amtlicher Führer, p. 251-62. Leipzig: R. Schick, 1914.

VILLERS, R. La simili-gravure et son histoire. *La Nature*, 1913-14, 1: 227-30, 7 fig.

WEBER, Wilhelm. Saxa loquuntur (Steine reden). Geschichte der Lithographie. 156 p., ill. Heidelberg/Berlin: Impuls Verlag Heinz Moos, 1961.
Reviewed by F. Stegmüller, *Bl.Technikgesch.*, 1964, 26: 161.

XF PHOTOGRAPHY

for applications of photography *see* INDEX

XFc general history

BAIER, Wolfgang. Quellendarstellung zur Geschichte der Fotografie. 703 p., ill. Halle: VEB Fotokinoverlag Halle, 1964.
Reviewed by R. Niederhuemer, *Bl.Technikgesch.*, 1964, 26: 153-4.

BURGER, D. De uitvinding der photografie. [The invention of photography. (In Dutch)] *Faraday*, 1939, 10: 52-9.

CROMER, G. Quelques épreuves et documents relatifs à l'histoire de la photographie panoramique. *Bull.Soc.Franç.Photogr.*, 1931, 17: 170-82.

EDER, Josef Maria. History of photography. Transl. by Edward Epstean. xx, 860 p. New York: Columbia University Press, 1945.
Translated from the 4th edition of: Geschichte der Photographie (Halle a.S.: Knapp, 1932).
Reviewed by I. Bernard Cohen, *Isis*, 1947, 37: 103-4.
German edition reviewed by Aldo Mieli, *Archeion*, 1933, 15: 117-18.

FRIEDMAN, Joseph S. History of color photography. x, 514 p. Boston: American Photographic Publishing Co., 1944.
Reviewed by I. Bernard Cohen, *Isis*, 1947, 37: 103-4.

GERNSHEIM, Helmut; GERNSHEIM, Alison. The history of photography from the earliest use of the camera obscura in the eleventh century up to 1914. xxviii, 395 p., 359 ill., bibliogr. London/New York/Toronto: Oxford University Press, 1955.
Reviewed by I. Bernard Cohen, *Isis*, 1958, 49: 449-51; by D. Burger, *Arch.Int.Hist.Sci.*, 1956, 9: 83-4.

GIBSON, Charles R. The history of photography. 34 p. In: Photography as a scientific implement; a collective work by A.E. Conrady [*et al.*]. London: Blackie, 1923.

JACOB, G. Die Erwähnungen der Schattenstheater und der Zauberlaternen bis zum Jahre 1700. 18 p., bibliogr. Berlin: Mayer & Müller, 1912.

MEES, C.E. Kenneth. Photography. xvi, 227 p. London: Bell, 1936; New York: Macmillan, 1937. [CB 51/261]

MEES, C.E. Kenneth. The theory of the photographic process. x, 1124 p., 406 fig. New York: Macmillan, 1942. [CB 63/271]

MOHOLY, Lucia. A hundred years of photography, 1839-1939. 182 p., 40 ill. (A Pelican Special) Harmondsworth: Penguin Books, 1939. [CB 59/471]

NEWHALL, Beaumont. A brief history of photographic techniques. *Ciba Symp.* (Summit, N.J.), 1942, 4: 1330-43, fig.

NEWHALL, Beaumont. Photography, a short critical history. 220 p., 95 pl. New York: Museum of Modern Art, 1938. [CB 56/389]
First edition Photography, 1839-1937. 130 p., 95 pl. New York: Museum of Modern Art, 1937.
Reviewed by Daniel Norman, *Isis*, 1939, 30: 127-8.

PAUSCHMANN, G. Zur Geschichte der linsenlosen Abbildung. *Arch.Gesch.Naturwiss.Tech.*, 1922, 9: 86-103.

POTONNIÉE, Georges. The history of the discovery of photography. Transl. by Edward Epstean. x, 272 p. New York: Tennant and Ward, 1936.
French edition (Paris: Paul Montel, 1925) reviewed by L. Guinet, *Isis*, 1926, 8: 511-13.

SHEPPARD, S.E. The chemistry of photography. 1. Historical considerations; 2. The latent image; 3. Development of negative and positive images. *J.Chem.Educ.*, 1927, 4: 298-312, 465-73, 749-57.
Some historical notes in the technical articles.

SPETER, Max. Photohistorica antiqua-nova varia. *Photogr.Korresp.*, 1937, 73: 33-7. [CB 51/205]

STENGER, Erich. Geschichte der Photographie. vi, 44 p., ill. (*Abhandl.Ber.Deut.Mus.*, 6) Berlin: VDI-Verlag, 1929. [CB 28/498]

STENGER, Erich. The history of photography, its relation to civilization and practice. Transl. and footnotes by Edward Epstean. xiv, 204 p., ill. Easton, Pa.: Mack Printing Company, 1939.
Translation of: Die Photographie in Kultur und Technik. Ihre Geschichte während hundert Jahren (Leipzig: Seemann, 1938) reviewed by R. Zaunick, *Mitt.Gesch.Med.*, 1941-42, 40: 143.

STEVENS, G.W.W. Microphotography since 1839. *Photogr.J.*, 1950, 90B: 150-6, 9 fig. [CB 78/152]

WALL, Edward John. The history of three-color photography. x, 747 p., ill. Boston, Mass.: American Photographic Publishing Co., 1925.

XFc-bv

BONI, Albert, ed. Photographic literature. 333 p. New York: Morgan and Morgan, 1962.
A comprehensive, international guide to general and specialized literature on photography; with a section on the history of photography.

COLUMBIA UNIVERSITY. LIBRARY. A catalogue of the Epstean Collection on the history and science of photography and its applications especially to the graphic arts. 109 p., ill. New York: Columbia University Press, 1937.

NEUERES Schriftum zur Geschichte der Photographie. *Mitt.Gesch. Med.*, 1941, 40: 137-50.
Brief comments (mainly by R. Zaunick) on recent books and articles by Erich Stenger and others.

XFw in different countries

XFwb-qg

ABETTI, Giorgio. C.E. Kenneth Mees e i laboratori di ricerca della compagnia Kodak. *Atti Fond.Ronchi*, 1957, 12: 7-9.

XFwk

COREMANS, P. Le rôle de la Belgique dans l'histoire de la photographie. *Bull.Mus.Roy.Art Hist.*, 1939, 11: 2-8, 5 fig.

XFx techniques and instruments

XFxb

CLAY, Reginald S. The photographic lens from the historical point of view. (25th annual Traill-Taylor Memorial Lecture) *Photogr.J.*, 1922, 46: 459-76. Summary in *Nature*, 1922, 110: 739-40.

WUERSCHMIDT, J. Zur Geschichte, Theorie und Praxis der Camera Obscura. *Z.Math.Naturwiss.Unterricht*, 1915, 46: 466-76.

XFxx museums

GEORGE EASTMAN HOUSE OF PHOTOGRAPHY. Illustrated guide to the George Eastman house of photography. 31 p. Rochester: George Eastman House, 1952.

PELSENEER, Jean. Musée de la photographie à Bruxelles. *Isis*, 1947, 32: 130.
To contain a reconstruction of the laboratory of D. van Monckhoven as well as his library and instruments.

XG CINEMA

BARDÈCHE, Maurice; BRASILLACH, Robert. The history of motion pictures. Transl. and ed. by Iris Barry. xii, 412 p., ill. New York: Norton, 1938. [CB 56/391]
Translation of: Histoire du cinéma (Paris: Denoël et Steele, 1935).

BENOIT-LÉVY, Jean. Les grandes missions du cinéma. 349 p., ill. Montréal: Parizeau, 1945. [CB 69/228]
Includes a brief history of the basic inventions.

BUHOT, René. Un prochain cinquantenaire. Comment le cinématographe est né de la physiologie. *Rev.Gén.Sci.*, 1937, 48: 365-8.

COISSAC, G. Michel. Histoire du cinématographe. Préface de J.-L. Breton. xvi, 604 p., 136 fig. Paris: Gauthier-Villars, 1925.
Reviewed by L. Guinet, *Isis*, 1927, 9: 125-7.

HENDRICKS, Gorden. The Edison motion picture myth. 216 p., fig. Berkeley/Los Angeles: University of California Press, 1961.
Reviewed by R.S., *Doc.Hist.Tech.*, 1962, 2: 86.

LIESEGANG, F. Paul. Aus der Entwicklungsgeschichte der Kinematographie. *Mitt.Gesch.Med.*, 1912, 11: 543.

LIESEGANG, F. Paul. Zahlen und Quellen zur Geschichte der Projektionskunst und Kinematographie. 125 p. Berlin: Deutsches Druck- und Verlagshaus, 1926.

LO DUCA, Giuseppe. Histoire du cinéma. 136 p., 85 ill. (Que Sais-Je? Le Point des Connaissances Actuelles, 81) Paris: Presses Universitaires de France, 1942.

LUMIÈRE, Auguste Marie Louis Nicolas; LUMIÈRE, Louis Jean. Résumé des travaux scientifiques, 1887-1914. 308 p. Lyon: Union Photographique Industrielle, 1914.

QUIGLEY, Martin. Magic shadows (the story of the origin of motion pictures). 191 p., 27 ill. Washington, D.C.: Georgetown University Press, 1948.
Reviewed by R.J. Forbes, *Arch.Int.Hist.Sci.*, 1948, 2: 228-30.

REGNAULT, Félix. L'évolution du cinéma. *Rev.Sci.*, 1922, 60: 79-86.
The author considers Marey the father of the cinema and not Démeny.

RICHTER, Wilhelm. Ueber einige neuere Probleme der wissenschaftlichen Kinematographie. *Akad.Rundsch.*, 1914, 2: 466-71.

SADOUL, Georges. L'invention du cinéma. 364 p., 143 ill. (Histoire Générale du Cinéma, 1) Paris: Édition Denoël, 1946.

THUN, Rudolph. Entwicklung der Kinotechnik. iv, 28 p., ill. (*Abhandl.Ber.Deut.Mus.*, 8: no. 5) Berlin: VDI-Verlag, 1936.
Reviewed by R. Zaunick, *Mitt.Gesch.Med.*, 1941-42, 40: 353.

TURPAIN, Albert. Le cinématographe, histoire de son invention, son développement, son avenir. xii, 83 p. Paris: Gauthier-Villars, 1924.

see also LUMIÈRE, Louis Jean, 2: 119

XGwg

LIESEGANG, F. Paul. Die Stellung Deutschlands in der Entwicklungsgeschichte der Kinematographie. *Proteus*, 1937, 2: 31-41.

XGyL

MAGNAN, A. Cinématographie jusqu'à 12.000 vues par seconde (avec application à l'étude du vol des insectes). 20 p., ill. (Actualités Scientifiques et Industrielles, 46. Exposés de Morphologie Dynamique et de Mécanique du Mouvement, 3) Paris: Hermann, 1932.

MAGNAN, A. Premiers essais de cinématographie ultra-rapide. 26 p., ill. (Actualités Scientifiques et Industrielles, 35. Exposés de Morphologie Dynamique et de Mécanique du Mouvement, 1) Paris: Hermann, 1932.
Study of the wingbeats of birds and insects made with the Huguenard and Magnan apparatus (1931) which allows 3000 exposures per second.

XH POSTAL SERVICES

BATTEUX, L.A. La poste. Organe de distribution des imprimés et correspondances. *Mus.Livre Publ.Fasc.*, 1912, 23-24: 351-66.

HARLOW, Alvin Fay. Old post bags: the story of the sending of a letter in ancient and modern times. Introduction by Joseph Stewart. xviii, 500 p. New York: Appleton, 1928.

XHwb

RICH, Wesley Everett. The history of the United States Post Office to the year 1829. vii, 190 p. Cambridge, Mass.: Harvard University Press, 1924.

XHwe

JACKSON, George Gibbard. From post boy to air mail. The story of the British post office. xii, 244 p. London: Sampson, 1930.

MARSHALL, Chapman Frederick Dendy. The British post office, from its beginnings to the end of 1925. vi, 354 p., ill., bibliogr. London: Oxford University Press, 1926.

WATSON, Edward. The Royal Mail to Ireland, or an account of the origin and development of the Post between London and Ireland through Holyhead and the use of the line of communication by travellers. vi, 244 p. London: Arnold, 1917.

XHwf

VAILLÉ, Eugène. Histoire des postes jusqu'à la Révolution. 128 p. (Collection "Que sais-je?") Paris: Presses Universitaires de France, 1946.

XJ ELECTRICAL COMMUNICATIONS

for electronics technology *see* UX

A CHRONOLOGICAL history of electrical communication, telegraph, telephone, and radio. *Radio Eng.*, 1932, 12: 6.

CRAWLEY, Chetwode. From telegraphy to television: the story of electrical communications. xii, 212 p., 24 pl. London: Warne, 1931.
Reviewed in *Nature*, 1932, 130: 418.

HARLOW, Alvin Fay. Old wires and new waves: the history of the telegraph, telephone, and wireless. xiv, 548 p. New York: Appleton-Century, 1936.
Reviewed by Harry J. Carman, *Amer.Hist.Rev.*, 1937, 43: 93-4.

LEE, George. Oliver Heaviside and the mathematical theory of electrical communications. vii, 32 p., front., 5 fig. (Science in Britain) London: Longmans, Green, 1947. [CB 71/97]

McADIE, Alexander. The Kennelly-Heaviside layer. *Science*, 1925, 61: 540. [CB 18/565]

PUPIN, Michael Idvorsky. Fifty years' progress in electrical communications. Address of the retiring president of the American Association for the Advancement of Science, Philadelphia, December 27, 1926. *Science*, 1926, 64: 631-8.

SHARLIN, Harold Isadore. The making of the electrical age; from the telegraph to automation. 248 p., ill. New York: Abelard-Schuman, 1963.
Includes some fresh insights into the story of electric power at Niagara.
Reviewed by Bern Dibner, *Isis*, 1964, 55: 382-3; and *Technol.Cult.*, 1964, 5: 441-3.

STOKLEY, James. Electrons in action. x, 320 p., ill. New York: McGraw Hill, 1946. [CB 70/256]
An account of the applications of electronics.

XJda

APPLEYARD, Rollo. Pioneers of electrical communication. ix, 347 p. London: Macmillan, 1930.
Reviewed by A.R., *Nature*, 1930, 125: 300.

DUNLAP, Orrin E. Radio's 100 men of science: biographical narratives of pathfinders in electronics and television. xx, 294 p. New York: Harper, 1944.
Reviewed by W.F.G. Swann, *Science*, 1945, 101: 224.

PERUCCA, Eligio; GORI, Vittorio. Pioneers in electrical communications. *J.Franklin Inst.*, 1956, 261: 61-79.

XJwn

TITOVA, V.M. Razvitie rannikh tekhnicheskikh sredstv sviazi v Rossii. [The development of early technical means of communication in Russia. (In Russian)] *Tr.Inst.Ist.Est.Tekh.*, 1962, 44: 179-212.

XK TELEGRAPH AND TELEPHONE

for radiotelegraphy *see* XM

AITKEN, William. Who invented the telephone? x, 196 p., ill. London: Blackie, 1939.

BLAKE, G.G. History of radio telegraphy and telephony. xix, 425 p., ill. London: Chapman and Hall, 1926.
Reviewed by E.E.F. d'Albe, *Nature*, 1927, 120: 868.

CARTY, John J. Ideals of the telephone service. A tribute to the memory of Alexander Graham Bell. Presidential address delivered at the ninth annual meeting of the Telephone Pioneers of America at Cleveland, Ohio, Sept. 29, 1922. *Annu. Rep.Smithsonian Inst.for 1922*, p. 533-40. Washington, D.C.: 1924.

COSTAIN, Thomas B. The chord of steel. The story of the invention of the telephone. 238 p., plates. New York: Doubleday and Co., 1960.

DIBNER, Bern. The Atlantic cable. 2nd ed. 190 p., ill. New York: Blaisdell, 1964.
First published Norwalk, Conn.: 1959 and reviewed by John W. Oliver, *Isis*, 1960, 51: 367-9; by L.R. Hickernell, *Technol.Cult.*, 1959, 1: 102-4; by S.B. Hamilton, *Arch. Int.Hist.Sci.*, 1960, 13: 133-5.

FEYERABEND, Ernst. Der Telegraph von Gauss und Weber im Werden der elektrischen Telegraphie. viii, 221 p., 72 fig., 13 pl. Berlin: Reichspostministerium (VDI-Verlag), 1933.

GLIOZZI, Mario. Una rivendicazione italiana: il telefono automatico. *Archeion*, 1934, 16: 205-8, 2 facs. [CB 46/552]
The author claims that it was invented by Ranieri Antoni and Giuseppe Pacini.
Reviewed by R. Zaunick, *Mitt.Gesch.Med.*, 1936, 35: 131-2.

KINGSBURY, John E. The telephone and telephone exchanges. Their invention and development. x, 588 p., ill. London: Longmans Green, 1915.

LANGDON, W.C. Myths of telephone history. *Bell Telephone Quart.*, 1933, 12: 123-40.
Apropos of the claims of Antonio Meucci and of Elisha Gray.

LODGE, Oliver. The history and development of the telephone. *J.Inst.Elec.Eng.*, 1926, 64: 1098-114.
Reviewed in *Nature*, 1927, 119: 244-5.

MARTIN, William Hennick. Seventy-five years of the telephone; an evolution in technology. *Bell Syst.Tech.J.*, 1951, 30: 214-38. [CB 79/177]

ROTTH, August. Das Telephon und das Werden. Mit einem Geleitwort des Staatssekretärs Dr. Feyerabend. v, 148 p., ill. Berlin: Springer, 1927.
Reviewed by F.M. Feldhaus, *Mitt.Gesch.Med.*, 1927, 26: 280.

see also BELL, Alexander Graham, 1: 126

XKsc

[EFFECT of transoceanic cables on naval history.] *Proc.U.N. Nav.Inst.*, 1956, 82: 797-911, ill.

XKsg

LEE, John. The economics of telegraphs and telephones. vii, 86 p. London: Pitman, 1913.

XKwb

CAMPBELL, George Ashley. The collected papers of George Ashley Campbell, research engineer of the American Telephone and Telegraph Company. xii, 581 p., 1 pl. New York: American Telephone and Telegraph Co., 1937.
Reviewed by A.R., *Nature*, 1938, 142: 591.

XKwe

BALDWIN, F.G.C. The history of the telephone in the United Kingdom. With a foreword by Frank Gill. xxvi, 788 p., 75 pl. London: Chapman and Hall, 1925; cheaper ed. 1938.
Reviewed by L.E.C.H., *Nature*, 1939, 143: 185.

XKwg

FEYERABEND, Ernst. 50 Jahre Fernsprecher in Deutschland 1877-1927. Herausgegeben vom Reichspostministerium, Berlin. 231 p., ill. Berlin: Reichsdruckerei, 1927.

XKwk-bx

NETHERLANDS, STAATSBEDRIJF DER POSTERIJEN, TELEGRAFIE EN TELEFONIE. Centenary of the Netherlands Telegraph Service. Exhibition at the Hague, July 19th through September 28th 1952. Bulletin of the Organizing Committee. 20 p., 22 ill. The Hague: 1952.

XKxw

SCHELL, C.W.L. The problems involved in exhibiting the development of telegraphs and telephones. *Act.VIe Congr.Int.Hist. Sci.* (Amsterdam, 1950), p. 618-23. Paris: Hermann, 1953.
Also in *Arch.Int.Hist.Sci.*, 1954, 7: 324-9.

XKxx

HENRIQUEZ-PHILIPPE. Un musée de la télégraphie. *La Nature*, 26 juillet 1913, 146-9, 3 fig. [CB 3/565]
A propos du Musée des Postes et Télégraphes, Paris.

SCIENCE MUSEUM. Catalogue of the collections with descriptive and historical notes and illustrations. Electrical communication. Compiled by R.P.G. Denman. 1. Line telegraphy and telephony. 2. Wireless telegraphy and telephony. 2 vol. London: H.M. Stationery Office, 1926, 1925.

XKyB

KORN, Arthur. Some mathematical problems in early telegraphic transmission of pictures. *Scr.Math.*, 1941, 8: 93-7.

XL SOUND REPRODUCTION; TAPE RECORDERS

GELATT, Roland. The fabulous phonograph, from tinfoil to high fidelity. xiii, 250 p., 40 ill. London: Cassell, 1956.
Reviewed by R. Forbes, *Arch.Int.Hist.Sci.*, 1956, 9: 362.

HUNT, Frederick V. Electroacoustics: the analysis of transduction, and its historical background. x, 260 p., fig. (Harvard Monographs in Applied Science, 5) Cambridge, Mass.: Harvard University Press, 1954.

NIEMANN, W. Sprechende Figuren. Ein Beitrag zur Vorgeschichte des Phonographen. *Geschichtsbl.Tech.Ind.*, 1920, 7: 2-30.

VOSKUIL, J. The speaking machine through the ages. *Trans.Newcomen Soc.*, 1947-48 and 1948-49, 26: 259-67, 4 fig.

WAJDOWICZ, Roman. Zarys rozwoju techniki dzwiekowej do Poczatkow Powstania kinematografii. [An outline of sound technique development from the first attempts at recording sounds to the beginning of motion pictures. (In Polish, summaries in English and Russian)] *Kwart.Hist.Nauk.Tech.*, 1959, 4: 495-520.

XLwh

WAJDOWICZ, Roman. Polskie osiagnięcia techniczne z dziedziny utrwalania i odtwarzania dźwięku do roku 1939. [Polish technological achievements in the recording and reproduction of sound until 1939. (In Polish)] 268 p., ill. (Zakład Historii Nauki i Techniki Polskiej Akademii Nauk. Monografie z dziejów nauki i techniki, 19) Wroclaw: Zaktad Narodowy im. Ossolińskich, 1962.

XM RADIO

AKADEMIIA NAUK SSSR. INSTITUT ISTORII ESTESTVOZNANIIA I TEKHNIKI. Ocherki istorii radiotekhniki. [Essays on the history of radio technology. (In Russian)] Edited by B.S. Sotin. 448 p., ill., bibliogr. Moskva: Izdatel'stvo Akademii Nauk SSSR, 1960. [CB 86/512]
Reviewed by Stanislaw Furman, *Kwart.Hist.Nauk.Tech.*, 1961, 6: 325-6.

ARCHER, Gleason L. History of radio to 1926. vi, 421 p. New York: American Historical Society, 1938.
Reviewed by I. Bernard Cohen, *Isis*, 1947, 32: 210-11.

CAHEN, Louis. Retour aux origines dans les radio-communications. *Rev.Hist.Sci.*, 1958, 11: 274-6.

EICHHORN, Gustave. Neuere Fortschritte in der Radiotelegraphie. *Fortschr.Naturwiss.Forsch.*, 1913, 7: 191-209.

GUINCHANT, Joseph. Les grandes étapes de la radio. Fasc. 1. Les premières découvertes. 90 p. Paris: Dunod, 1925. [CB 20/170]

HALSTEAD, Philip E. Oliver Heaviside and his influence on modern radio research. *Amer.Scient.*, 1950, 78: 610-11.

HAMMOND, J.H.; PURRINGTON, E.S. A history of some foundations of modern radio-electronic technology. *Proc.Inst.Radio.Eng.*, 1957, 45: 1191-208. [CB 85/469]
For discussion of this article, by Lloyd Espenscheid, with rebuttals by Hammond and Purrington, *see ibid.*, 1958, 47: 1253-68.

HARBORD, James G. The 40 year march of radio. 24 p., ill. Princeton, N.J.: Princeton University Press (for the Newcomen Society, American Branch), 1943.

LODGE, Oliver. Talks about wireless: with some pioneering history and some hints and calculations for wireless amateurs. xiii, 251 p. London: Cassell, 1925.

MACLAURIN, W. Rupert. Invention and innovation in the radio industry. With the technical assistance of R. Joyce Harman. Foreword by Karl T. Compton. xxi, 304 p. (Massachusetts Institute of Technology Studies of Innovation) New York: Macmillan, 1949. [CB 75/91]

MIESSNER, Benjamin Franklin. On the early history of radio guidance. vi, 86 p., 12 fig., app. San Francisco: San Francisco Press, 1964.
Setting the record straight on work with Hammond.
Reviewed by Robert Chipman, *Isis*, 1964, 55: 458-9.

RODIONOV, V.M. Osnovnye napravleniia razvitiia tekhniki generirovaniia radiovoln. [Basic trends in the development of the technology of generating radio waves. (In Russian)] *Tr.Inst.Ist.Est.Tekh.*, 1962, 44: 257-74.

SCIENTIFIC discovery and the wireless telephone. 28 p. [n.p.: 1920]. [CB 9/494]
Issued on the occasion of an exhibition of apparatus in 1920, sponsored by the National Research Council, prepared by the American Telephone and Telegraph Company and the Western Electric Company.
Reviewed by G. Sarton, *Isis*, 1920-21, 3: 274-6.

SOVIET UNION celebrates the fiftieth anniversary of radio. *Isis*, 1947, 38: 101.
Apropos of Popov's inventions of 1895 and following years.

SUSSKIND, Charles. Popov and the beginnings of radiotelegraphy. 30 p., 3 fig. (History of Technology Monographs) San Francisco, Calif.: San Francisco Press; Cambridge: Heffer, 1964.
Reviewed by Robert Chipman, *Isis*, 1964, 55: 458-9.

TAYLOR, J.E. Notes on wireless history. *Post Office Elec.Eng. J.*, 1933, 25: 295-9.

WENSTROM, W.H. Historical review of the ultra-short-wave progress. *Proc.Inst.Radio Eng.*, 1932, 20: 95-112.

see also MARCONI, Guglielmo, 2: 145-6

XMr

HARBORD, James G. World wireless. The engineer's place in radio communication. An address delivered before Princeton University on November 12, 1935, in the Cyrus Fogg Brackett lectureship in applied engineering and technology. 37 p. Princeton: Guild of Brackett Lecturers, 1936.

XMwg

BREUNIG, Erwin. Deutschlands Anteil an der Entwicklung des Rundfunks. *Proteus*, 1937, 2: 41-7.

XMwn

OSTROUMOV, B.A. Radiotekhnika v Rossii posle A.S. Popova (1906-1912). [Radio engineering in Russia after A.S. Popov. (In Russian)] *Tr.Inst.Ist.Est.Tekh.*, 1962, 44: 233-56.

XMwn-qg

OSTROUMOV, B.A. Nezhegorodskaia Radiolaboratoriia im. V.I. Lenina. [Nizhegorod Lenin Radiolaboratory. (In Russian)] *Vop.Ist.Est.Tekh.*, 1961, 11: 105-7.

XMxb

BEDEAU, François. Le quartz piézo-électrique: ses applications à la T.S.F. 32 p. Paris: Hermann, 1931.
Conférence faite au Conservatoire des arts et métiers le 8 mai 1931.

XN TELEVISION

LAUFER, Berthold. The prehistory of television. *Sci.Mon.*, 1928, 27: 455-9.

McGEE, J.D. Campbell Swinton and television. *Nature*, 1936, 138: 674-6.

XO RADAR

GUERLAC, Henry. The radio background of radar. *J.Franklin Inst.*, 1950, 250: 284-308. [CB 77/341]

PAGE, Robert Morris. The early history of radar. *Proc.Inst. Radio Eng.*, 1962, 50: 1232-6; reprinted in *Annu.Rep.Smithsonian Inst.for 1962*, p. 315-21. Washington, D.C.: 1963.

PAGE, Robert Morris. The origin of radar. 196 p., ill. (Anchor Books Science Study Series) Garden City, N.Y.: Doubleday & Company, 1962.

ROWE, Albert Percival. One story of radar. xi, 207 p., 7 ill. Cambridge University Press, 1948.
Reviewed by A. Proca, *Arch.Int.Hist.Sci.*, 1949, 2: 765-9.

XO

U.S. JOINT BOARD ON SCIENTIFIC INFORMATION POLICY. Radar: a report on science at war. Released by the Joint Board on Scientific Information Policy for: Office of Scientific Research and Development, War Department, Navy Department. iii, 53 p. Washington: Office of War Information, 1945.

U.S. OFFICE OF SCIENTIFIC RESEARCH AND DEVELOPMENT. [History of the development of radar, ed. by Henry L. Guerlac.] 4 pt. 1300 p. (PB 93618-93621) Washington, D.C.: [1949?]
Note on availability *Isis*, 1949, 40: 121.

WATSON-WATT, Robert Alexander. The pulse of radar: the autobiography of Sir Robert Watson-Watt. x, 438 p. New York: Dial Press, 1959. [CB 85/467-8]
Published in Britain with the title "Three steps to victory" (Odhams Press: 1957).
Reviewed by W.A. Higinbotham, *Science*, 1959, 129: 1135-6; by Jean Pelseneer, *Rev.Univ.Bruxelles*, 1959, 328-9; by George Raynor Thompson, *Technol.Cult.*, 1960, 2: 193-4.

WATSON-WATT, Robert Alexander. Le radar. 19 p. (Conférences du Palais de la Découverte, 18 déc. 1946) Paris: Université de Paris, 1948.

WATSON-WATT, Robert. Three steps to victory. 480 p., 25 pl. London: Odhams Press, 1957.
This book has appeared in the United States under the title The pulse of radar, New York: The Dial Press, 1959.
Reviewed by R.L. Smith-Rose, *Nature*, 1958, 182: 415-16.

XP COMPUTERS

see also WT CALCULATING MACHINES

BERKELEY, Edmund C. Giant brains or machines that think. 270, xvi p. New York: Wiley; London: Chapman & Hall, 1949.

FREUDENTHAL, H. Machines pensantes. 16 p. (Conférences du Palais de la Découverte, D, 24) Paris: Université de Paris, 1953.

HILTON, Alice Mary. Logic, computing machines, and automation. 427 p., ill. Washington, D.C.: Spartan Books, 1963.

LATIL, Pierre de. La pensée artificielle. 332 p., ill. Paris: Gallimard, 1953.
Reviewed by Suzanne Colnort-Bodet, *Rev.Hist.Sci.*, 1954, 7: 196.

SAYRE, Kenneth M.; CROSSON, Frederick J. *See* XA

XPk

HAMMING, R.W. Intellectual implications of the computer revolution. *Amer.Math.Mon.*, 1963, 70: 4-12. [CB 89/576]

VON NEUMANN, John. The computer and the brain. xiv, 82 p. New Haven: Yale University Press, 1958.
Paperback reprint. 1963.

XR MILITARY TECHNOLOGY

for ballistics *see* CDzb

XRc

FALLS, Cyril. The art of war from the age of Napoleon to the present day. viii, 240 p. New York: Oxford University Press, 1961.

GENEZ, A. Historique de la guerre souterraine. 297 p., 37 fig., 13 pl. Paris: Berger-Levrault, 1914.

MONTROSS, Lynn. War through the ages. Rev. ed. xiv, 1007 p., 114 plans, ill. New York: Harper, 1946.
First published 1944.
Reviewed by R.J. Forbes, *Arch.Int.Hist.Sci.*, 1949, 2: 538-40.

POKROVSKII, G.I. Science and technology in contemporary war. Transl. by Raymond L. Garthoff. ix, 180 p., ill. (Praeger Publications in Russian History and World Communism, 74) New York: Frederick A. Praeger, 1959.
An unabridged translation of his key writings on the subject.

SCHMITTHENNER, Paul. Krieg und Kriegführung im Wandel der Weltgeschichte. 452 p. (Museum der Weltgeschichte) Wildpark-Potsdam: Athenaion, 1930.
Reviewed by Robert G. Albion, *Amer.Hist.Rev.*, 1931, 36: 787-8.

SPAULDING, Oliver Lyman; NICKERSON, Hoffman; WRIGHT, John Womack. Warfare: a study of military methods from the earliest times. xiii, 601 p. New York: Harcourt, Brace, 1925.
Reviewed by A.E.R. Boak, *Amer.Hist.Rev.*, 1925, 31: 102-4.

TOUT, Thomas Frederick. Medieval and modern warfare. Lecture. 30 p. Manchester: University Press; London: Longmans, 1919.
Reprinted from *Bull.John Rylands Libr.*, 1919, vol. 5.

XRce-by

SPAULDING, Thomas M.; KARPINSKI, Louis C. Early military books in the University of Michigan libraries. xvi, 45 p., 35 pl. (University of Michigan General Library Publications) Ann Arbor, Mich.: University of Michigan Press, 1941. [CB 62/77]

XRda

EARLE, Edward Mead, ed. Makers of modern strategy. Military thought from Machiavelli to Hitler. With the collaboration of Gordon A. Craig and Felix Gilbert. xi, 553 p. Princeton: Princeton University Press, 1943. [CB 65/86]

XRwe

FORBES, Arthur. A history of the army ordnance services. 3 vol. London: Medici Society, 1929.

FORTESCUE, John William. The Royal Army Service Corps: a history of transport and supply in the British Army. 2 vol., pl., maps. Cambridge University Press (for the R.A.S.C. Record Office), 1930.

INSTITUTION OF ROYAL ENGINEERS. The work of the Royal Engineers in the European War, 1914-1918. Miscellaneous; the organization and expansion of the Corps, 1914-18; organization of engineer intelligence and information; camouflage service; concrete defence works and factories; forward communications; machinery, workshops and electricity; anti-aircraft searchlights; inundations; schools. (Ed. by G.H. Addison) iii, 372 p., 100 pl. Chatham: W. and J. Mackay, 1927.

SANDES, E.W.C. The Royal Engineers in Egypt and the Sudan. xxvii, 571 p., ill., maps. Chatham: Institution of Royal Engineers, 1937.
Reviewed by Henri Dehérain, *J.Savants*, 1938, 81-4.

XRwe-o

ARMSTRONG, Anthony, pseud. Science in the army. A brief account of the scientific training and technical work of the soldier to-day, as illustrated by a special War Office exhibition held at the Science Museum - November 1938-February 1939. 20 p., front. London: H.M.S.O., 1938.

XRxx

GENERAAL C.J. SNIJDERS en het Nederlandsch Legermuseum [General C.J. Snijders and the Nederlandsch Legermuseum. (In Dutch)] *Ingenieur*, 1946, 58: A.255-8, 3 fig.

XRyB

SCHAAF, William L. A survey of the recent literature of military mathematics. *Scr.Math.*, 1945, 11: 57-74.

XRyTE

TOY, Sidney. Castles. A short history of fortifications from 1600 B.C. to A.D. 1600. xiv, 241 p., pl. London: Heinemann, 1939.

TOY, Sidney.. A history of fortification from 3000 B.C. to A.D. 1700. xxiv, 262 p. London: Heinemann; New York: Macmillan, 1955.
Reviewed by John Beeler, *Amer.Hist.Rev.*, 1956, 61: 602-3.

XRyTEwe

BELL, Walter G.; COTTRILL, F.; SPON, Charles. London wall through eighteen centuries. A history of the ancient town wall of the City of London, with a survey of the existing remains. 8 original drawings by A.A. Moore. x, 124 p. London: Council for Tower Hill Improvement, 1937.

XRyUXwb

APPLIED physics. Electronics, a history of Divisions 13 and 15 and the Committee on Propogation, NDRC, ed. by C.G. Suits. Optics, a history of Divisions 16 and 17, NDRC, by H.K. Stephenson and E.L. Jones, ed. by G.R. Harrison. Metallurgy, a history of Division 18, NDRC, by Louis Jordan. xiii, 456 p. (Science in World War II; Office of Scientific Research and Development) Boston: Little, Brown, 1948.
Prepared under the direction of the respective administrative units of the National Defense Research Committee.

XS ARMS AND ARMOUR

CARMAN, W. A history of firearms, from earliest times to 1914. 207 p., ill. London: Routledge & Paul, 1955.

DEAN, Bashford. Helmets and body armour in modern warfare. 325 p. New Haven: Yale University Press, 1920.

FELDHAUS, Franz M. Modernste Kriegswaffen, alte Erfindungen. 240 p., ill. Leipzig: Abel und Mueller, 1915. [CB 10/216]

GORDON, D.H. Fire and sword: the technique of destruction. *Antiquity*, 1953, 27: 149-52, ill.

GREENER, C.E. Gun-making handicrafts. *Trans.Newcomen Soc.*, 1924-25, 5: 57-71, pl.

HAYWARD, J.F. The art of the gunmaker. 2 vol. 1. 1500-1660. 303 p., ill.; 2. Europe and America, 1660-1830. 379 p., ill. London: Barrie and Rockcliff; New York: St. Martin's Press, 1962-64.

JENKINS, Rhys. "Shrinking-on". *Trans.Newcomen Soc.*, 1934-35, 15: 73-5. [CB 49/179]

OAKESHOTT, R. Ewart. The archaeology of weapons: arms and armour from prehistory to the age of chivalry. 359 p., ill. London: Lutterworth Press; New York: Praeger, 1960.
Reviewed by Stephen V. Grancsay, *Technol.Cult.*, 1961, 2: 171-4.

PÖHLMANN, Martin. Untersuchungen der älteren Geschichte des antiken Belagerungsgeschützes. 47 p. (Diss.) Erlangen: Druck von Junge und Sohn, 1912.

POPE, Saxton Temple. A study of bows and arrows. iv, 102 p., 20 pl. Berkeley: University of California Press, 1930.

SMITH, Cyril Stanley. Methods of making chain mail (14th to 18th centuries): a metallographic note. *Technol.Cult.*, 1959, 1: 60-7.

STEIN, Henri. Archers d'autrefois; archers d'aujourd'hui. 305 p., 20 pl., ill. Paris: Longuet, 1925.
Reviewed in *Amer.Hist.Rev.*, 1926, 31: 753.

STONE, George Cameron. A glossary of the construction, decoration and use of arms and armor in all countries and in all times. Together with some closely related subjects. x, 694 p., 875 ill., bibliogr. Portland, Me.: Southworth Press, 1934.

WILBUR, C. Martin. The history of the crossbow, illustrated from specimens in the United States National Museum. *Annu. Rep.Smithsonian Inst.for 1936*, p. 427-38, 6 pl. Washington, D.C.: 1937.

XSsg

PECK, Merton J.; SCHERER, Frederic M. The weapons acquisition process: an economic analysis. xxx, 736 p. Boston: Division of Research, Graduate School of Business Administration, Harvard University, 1962. [CB 88/649]

XSwb

BROWNING, John; GENTRY, Curt. John M. Browning, American gunmaker: an illustrated biography of the man and his guns. lx, 323 p., ill., notes, bibliogr. Garden City, N.Y.: Doubleday, 1964.

SHIELDS, Joseph W. From flintlock to M 1. 220 p., ill. New York: Coward-McCann, 1954. [CB 80/144]
A history of shoulder-arms in the United States from the American Revolution to World War II.

XSwd

JACKSON, Herbert J. European hand firearms of the sixteenth, seventeenth and eighteenth centuries. With a treatise on Scottish hand firearms by Charles E. Whitelaw. xvi, 108 p., 72 pl. Chicago: Quadrangle Books; Toronto: Burns & MacEachern, 1960.
First edition London: Chiswick Press, 1923.

LAKING, Guy Francis. A record of European armour and arms through seven centuries. With an introduction by the Baron de Cosson. 5 vol. London: Bell, 1920-22.

XSwd-da

FFOULKES, Charles. *See* XSwe-da

XSwe

GLENDENNING, Ian. British pistols and guns, 1640-1840. viii, 195 p. London: Cassell; New York: British Book Centre, 1951. [CB 79/177]

KELLY, Francis Michael; SCHWABE, Randolph. *See* WZwe

XSwe-da

FFOULKES, Charles. The gun-founders of England. With a list of English and continental gun-founders from the XIV to the XIX centuries. Preface by Lord Cottesloe. xvi, 134 p., 15 pl., 38 ill. Cambridge University Press, 1937.

XSwe-qt

JENKINS, Rhys. The Hollow Sword Blade Company and sword making at Shotley Bridge. *Trans.Newcomen Soc.*, 1934-35, 15: 185-94.

XSwj

LARCHER, Jorge. Armaria portuguesa. 1. Breves notas acêrca da sua história e terminologia. 2. Descrição de algunas armas e engenhos. *Petrus Nonius*, 1939, 2: 117-20; 1940, 3: 52-8.

XSxx

HORNIMAN MUSEUM. War and the chase: handbook to the collection of weapons of savage, barbaric and civilised people. 2nd ed. by H.S. Harrison. 85 p., 2 pl. (Horniman Museum and Library Publications, 8) London: King, 1929.
First edition, 1908.

METROPOLITAN MUSEUM OF ART. Handbook of arms and armor, European and oriental. By Bashford Dean. 4th ed. With additions, corrections, and a chapter on the Bashford Dean Memorial Gallery by Stephen V. Grancsay. xviii, 331 p. New York: 1930.
First edition 1915.

VICTORIA AND ALBERT MUSEUM. European firearms, by J.F. Hayward. 53 p., 34 pl. London: H.M. Stationery Off.; New York: Philosophical Library, 1955. [CB 81/284]
A guide to the collection of firearms in the Victoria and Albert Museum.

XSyTV ARMOURED VEHICLES

FULLER, John Frederick Charles. Tanks in the Great War, 1914-1918. xxiv, 331 p., 7 pl. London: Murray, 1920.

HASSLER, Fr. Aus der Geschichte der Kampfwagen. *Technikgeschichte*, 1934, 23: 99-112, 2 pl., 3 fig.

XSyVJ GUNPOWDER

FENG CHIA-SHENG. Huo-yao ti fa-ming ho hsi ch'uan. [The invention and westward transmission of gunpowder. (In Chinese)] iv, 86 p. Shanghai: Shanghai People's Press, 1962.

MERCIER, Maurice. Le feu grégeois: les feux de guerre depuis l'antiquité; la poudre à canon. vi, 164 p., ill. Paris: Geuthner, 1952.
Reviewed by R.J. Forbes, *Arch.Int.Hist.Sci.*, 1953, 6: 369-70.

PARTINGTON, J.R. A history of Greek fire and gunpowder. xvi, 381 p., front., fig. Cambridge: W. Heffer, 1960.
Reviewed by Eduard Farber, *Science*, 1960, 121: 1726-7; by R.J. Forbes, *Nature*, 1960, 187: 272; by D. Geoghegan, *Ambix*, 1960, 8: 120-1.

PIQUE, René. Histoire de la pyrotechnie de guerre. *Compt.Rend. IXe Congr.Chim.Ind.* (Barcelona, 1929), p. 347-58. (*Chim.Ind.*, 1930, special number) Paris: 1930. [CB 51/264]

XT NUCLEAR WEAPONS

see also UR ATOMIC ENERGY

AMRINE, Michael. The great decision. The secret history of the atomic bomb. 251 p. New York: Putnam, 1959.
Reviewed by E.U. Condon, *Science*, 1959, 130: 32-3.

BLACKETT, P.M.S. Military and political consequences of atomic energy. (3rd impression, revised) viii, 222 p. London: Turnstile Press, 1949.
First published 1948. American edition: Fear, war, and the bomb; military and political consequences of atomic energy. ix, 244 p. New York: Whitlesey House, 1949. [CB 75/86]
Reviewed by J.R. Newman, *New Repub.*, 29th November 1948; by I.I. Rabi, *Atlantic Mon.*, April 1949.

CLARK, Ronald W. The birth of the bomb. The untold story of Britain's part in the weapon that changed the world. Preface by Sir George Thomson. 209 p. New York: Horizon Press; London: Phoenix House, 1961.
Reviewed by Malcolm C. Henderson, *Science*, 1961, 134: 661-2; in *Times Lit.Suppl.*, 1961, 211.

HERSEY, John. Hiroshima. *New Yorker*, August 31st 1946, 15-60. [CB 70/250]

JUNGK, Robert. Brighter than a thousand suns. A personal history of the atomic scientists. xiv, 369 p. Transl. from the German by James Cleugh. New York: Harcourt, Brace, 1958.
Reviewed by Oscar E. Anderson, *Isis*, 1960, 51: 117-19. For further reviews *see* CB 84/387.

MASTERS, Dexter; WAY, Katharine; ed. One world or none. Foreword by Niels Bohr. Introduction by Arthur H. Compton. x, 79 p., fig. New York: Whittlesey House, 1946. [CB 70/224]

OPPENHEIMER, Robert. Niels Bohr and atomic weapons. *N.Y.Rev. Books*, 1964, 3: (9), 6-8.

PURCELL, John Francis. The best-kept secret; the story of the atomic bomb. 188 p., pl. New York: Vanguard Press, 1963.

ROSECRANCE, R.N., ed. The dispersion of nuclear weapons. Strategy and politics. xii, 343 p., bibliogr. New York/London: Columbia University Press, 1964.

SAHA, M.N.; CHAUDHURI, B.D. Nag. The story of the 'atomic bomb'. *Sci.Cult.*, 1945, 11: 111-18, fig.

SEN, Samarendra Nath. Ānabik bomā. [Atomic bomb. (In Bengali)] xiii, 175 p., ill. Calcutta: 1946.
Bengali account of atomic energy and the atomic bomb, with many illustrations. Preface by M.N. Saha.

SMYTH, Henry DeWolf. Atomic energy for military purposes. The official report on the development of the atomic bomb under the auspices of the United States Government, 1940-1945. ix, 264 p., pl. Princeton: Princeton University Press, 1945. [CB 69/204]

TELLER, Edward; BROWN, Allen. The legacy of Hiroshima. 325 p. New York: Doubleday, 1962.
Reviewed in *Sci.Amer.*, 1962, 206: no. 5, 185-9.

THIRRING, Hans. Die Geschichte der Atombombe. Mit einer elementaren Einführung in die Atomphysik auf Grund der Originalliteratur gemeinverständlich dargestellt. 150 p. (Wissenschaft für Jedermann) Wien: "Neues Österreich" Zeitungs- und Verlagsgesellschaft, 1946.
Reviewed by E. Broda, *Nature*, 1947, 159: 792.

XTqy

SALTER, Arthur. The United Nations and the atomic bomb. *Int. Conciliation*, 1946, no. 417, 40-8.

XTs

EINSTEIN, Albert. Only then shall we find courage. *Sci.Cult.*, 1947, 13: 46-8.
First published in *N.Y.Times Mag.*
Effect of atom bomb on society.

XTsk

BLACKETT, P.M.S. Military and political consequences of atomic energy. (3rd impression, revised) viii, 222 p. London: Turnstile Press, 1949.
First published 1948. American edition: Fear, war, and the bomb; military and political consequences of atomic energy. ix, 244 p. New York: Whittlesey House, 1949. [CB 75/86]
Reviewed by J.R. Newman, *New Repub.*, 29th November 1948; by I.I. Rabi, *Atlantic Mon.*, April 1949.

XU GUIDED MISSILES

GATLAND, Kenneth W. Development of the guided missile. 2nd ed. 292 p., ill. London: Iliffe; New York: Philosophical Library, 1954. [CB 79/144]
First published 1952.
Reviewed by Howard S. Seifert, *Sci.Mon.*, 1955, 81: 153-4.

KELLER, Charles L. The first guided missile program: the aerial torpedo. *Sperry Eng.Rev.*, 1961, 14: 11-18.

XUhc

MILES, Wyndham D. Usefulness of oral history in writing the story of a large scientific project. *Proc.10th Int.Congr. Hist.Sci.* (Ithaca, 1962), (1), p. 351-3. Paris: Hermann, 1964.
On the development of the Polaris missile.

XUnh-be

U.S. RESEARCH AND DEVELOPMENT BOARD. Dictionary of guided missile terms. By the Committee on Guided Missiles. Issued in cooperation with the Antiaircraft Journal. 57 p. Washington: Public Affairs Press, 1949. [CB 74/388]

XV CHEMICAL WARFARE

BROWNE, Charles Albert. Early references pertaining to chemical warfare. *J.Ind.Eng.Chem.*, 1922, 14: 646.

CATTELAIN, Eugène. L'ypérite ou gaz moutarde. Son histoire, le secret de sa puissance, son avenir. *Rev.Gén.Sci.*, 1938, 49: 205-11, 322-7.

HALDANE, J.B.S. Callinicus. A defence of chemical warfare. viii, 84 p. (Today and Tomorrow Series) London: Kegan Paul, 1925.

LEROUX, Lucien. La guerre chimique. 2nd enl. ed. 163 p. Paris: Spes, 1933. [CB 46/591]
First edition 1932.

MILES, Wyndham D. Fritz Haber, father of chemical warfare. *Armed Forces Chem.J.*, 1960, 14: 28-30.

XVwb

BROPHY, Leo P. The Chemical Warfare Service: from laboratory to field. xviii, 498 p. (U.S. Army in World War II: The Technical Services) Washington: Office of the Chief of Military History, Department of the Army, 1959.
Reviewed by H. Fabian Underhill, *Amer.Hist.Rev.*, 1961-62, 67: 236-7.

NOYES, W.A., ed. Chemistry. A history of the chemistry components of the National Defense Research Committee, 1940-1946. With a foreword by James Bryant Conant and Roger Adams. xviii, 524 p. Boston: Little, Brown, 1948. [CB 73/170]

XVwg

WACHTEL, Curt. Chemical warfare. ix, 312 p. Brooklyn: Chemical Publishing Co., 1941. [CB 61/400]
Includes a discussion of the influence of Fritz Haber in coordinating research and industry in Germany for the effective use of war gas.

XW BIOLOGICAL WARFARE

ROSEBURY, Theodor. Peace or pestilence. 218 p., ill. New York: Whittlesey House, 1949.
On biological warfare.
Reviewed by James R. Newman, *Sci.Amer.*, 1949, 180: no. 6, 56-8.

XX NAVAL FORCES

ANDERSON, R.C. Oared fighting ships. xiii, 99 p., ill. London: Percival Marshall, 1962.
Reviewed by J.S. Morrison, *Mariner's Mirror*, 1963, 49: 79-80.

BRODIE, Bernard. Sea power in the machine age. viii, 466 p. Princeton: Princeton University Press, 1941.
Reviewed by Alfred Romer, *Isis*, 1943, 34: 230-1.

ERBACH, R. Die geschichtliche Entwicklung der Kampfmittel zur See. *Technikgeschichte*, 1937, 26: 15-36, 8 pl., 17 fig.

HEYMAN, R. The development of the armoured battleship. *Act. VIIe Congr.Int.Hist.Sci.* (Jerusalem, 1953), p. 372-6. Paris: Hermann, 1954.

REHLER, J.E.; BOTTGER, G.C. Submarines through twenty centuries. *Mil.Engineer*, 1963, 55: 327-31.

SHERR, S.A. [On the history of the construction of submarines. (In Russian)] *Vop.Ist.Est.Tekh.*, 1959, 7: 95-106.

VAGTS, Alfred. Landing operations from antiquity to 1945. 831 p., 16 ill., 18 maps. Harrisburg, Pa.: Military Service Publishing Co., 1946.
Reviewed by R.J. Forbes, *Arch.Int.Hist.Sci.*, 1949, 2: 538-40.

XXwb

ROSENBERG, Herbert H.; BAIN, Henry M. Program planning for research and development in the Navy. 1 vol. (various paging). [Washington]: Syracuse University, The Maxwell Graduate School of Citizenship and Public Affairs, Washington Research Office, 1954.

XXwe

ALBION, Robert Greenhalgh. Forests and sea power; the timber problem of the Royal Navy 1652-1862. xv, 485 p., ill., bibliogr. (Harvard Economic Studies, 29) Cambridge: Harvard University Press, 1926.
Reviewed by Eleanor Louisa Lord, *Amer.Hist.Rev.*, 1927, 32: 590-1; by Lawrence S. Mayo, *Geogr.Rev.*, 1928, 18: 341-2.

MARCUS, G.J. The formative centuries. 494 p. (A Naval History of England, 1) London: Longmans, 1961; Boston: Little, Brown, 1962.
Covers 1407-1783.
Reviewed by Christopher Lloyd, *Mariner's Mirror*, 1963, 48: 152-3.

SMITH, Edgar C. The centenary of naval engineering. *Trans. Newcomen Soc.*, 1921-22, 2: 88-114.

XXwe-o

SMITH, Edgar C. Sir Alfred Ewing and naval education. *Nature*, 1935, 135: 140.

XXwf

LA RONCIÈRE, Charles B. de. Histoire de la marine française. 5 vol., ill. Paris: Plon, 1899-1920.

XXxx

SCIENCE MUSEUM. Catalogue of the collections ... with descriptive and historical notes and illustrations. Water transport. 3. Steam ships of war. Compiled by G.L. Overton. 102 p., 8 pl. London: H.M. Stationery Office, 1925.

SCIENCE MUSEUM. Naval mining and degaussing. An exhibition of representative British and German naval mining and degaussing material used during the war, 1939-1945. viii, 27 p. London: H.M. Stationery Off., 1946.

XXyUNwb

BOWEN, H.G. 100 years of steam in the United States navy. 32 p. (Newcomen Society, American Branch, ... address, 1937) [Princeton: 1937]

XXyXJwb

HOWETH, L.S. History of communications: electronics in the United States navy. Introd. by Chester W. Nimitz. 656 p., ill. Washington: U.S. Govt. Print. Off., 1963.

XXyXS

ROBERTSON, Frederick Leslie. The evolution of naval armament. vi, 307 p., ill. London: Constable, 1921.

XY AIR FORCES

XYwb

BUSHNELL, David; KOMONS, Nick A. History of the Office of the Research Analyses. vii, 120 p. Washington, D.C.: Office of Aerospace Research, 1963.

XYwe

SPAIGHT, James Molony. The beginnings of organised air power; a historical study. London: Longmans, 1927.
Describes "the events connected with the creation of the British Air Ministry and Air Force in 1918".

XYwf

MARIE, Félix. Les origines de l'aéronautique militaire, (novembre 1909-novembre 1910). 124 p., ill. Paris: Lavauzelle, 1924.
Reviewed by J. Voyer, *Rev.Gén.Sci.*, 1925, 36: 277.

XYyXXwb

FULTON, Garland. The general climate for technological developments in naval aeronautics on the eve of World War I. *Technol.Cult.*, 1963, 4: 154-65.
Personal recollections.

McCARTHY, Charles J. Naval aircraft design in the mid-1930s. *Technol.Cult.*, 1963, 4: 165-74.
From personal experience.

Y ANCILLARY DISCIPLINES

YA HISTORICAL SCIENCES

YAc general history

BRANDI, Karl. Geschichte der Geschichtswissenschaft. 2nd ed. rev. and enl. by W. Graf. 147 p. (Geschichte der Wissenschaften, 1. Geisteswissenschaften) Bonn: Athenäum Verlag, 1952.
First published 1948. [CB 78/196]
Reviewed by J. Stengers, *Arch.Int.Hist.Sci.*, 1953, 6: 90-1, by E.J. Dijksterhuis, *Rev.Hist.Sci.*, 1953, 6: 279-80.

BUTTERFIELD, Herbert. Man on his past. The study of the history of historical scholarship. xvii, 238 p. Cambridge/New York: Cambridge University Press, 1955. [CB 83/188]
The inaugural series of lectures given at the Queen's University of Belfast under the Wiles Trust.
Reviewed by Boyd C. Shafer, *Amer.Hist.Rev.*, 1956, 61: 930-1.

CROCE, Benedetto. Theory .. *See* YAhd

FITZSIMONS, Matthew A.; PUNDT, Alfred G.; NOWELL, Charles E.; ed. The development of historiography. xxxii, 471 p. Harrisburg, Pa.: Stackpole Company, 1955.
Reviewed by B.C.S., *Amer.Hist.Rev.*, 1958, 63: 453.

FUETER, Eduard. Geschichte der neueren Historiographie. 3rd ed. by Dietrich Gerhard und Paul Sattler. xxii, 670 p. (Handbuch der mittelalterlichen und neueren Geschichte) München: Oldenburg, 1936.
First published 1911.
Reviewed by Frank J. Manheim, *Amer.Hist.Rev.*, 1936, 42: 86.
French translation of first edition Paris: Alcan, 1914.

HISTOIRE et historiens depuis cinquante ans: méthodes, organisation et résultats du travail historique de 1876 à 1926. 2 vol. xii, 758 p. Paris: Alcan, 1927.
Collection of essays to celebrate the golden jubilee of the *Revue Historique*.
Reviewed by J.F. Jameson, *Amer.Hist.Rev.*, 1928, 34: 92-3.

LELAND, Waldo G. Recent trends in the humanities. *Science*, 1934, 79: 281-5.
Address of the retiring vice-president and chairman of Section L - Historical and philological sciences, American Association for the Advancement of Science, Boston, December 1933.

SHOTWELL, James T. The history of history. Vol. 1. Rev. ed. of "An introduction to the history of history". xii, 407 p. New York: Columbia University Press, 1939.
Reviewed by W.S. Ferguson, *Amer.Hist.Rev.*, 1940, 45: 849-51.

SHOTWELL, James T. An introduction to the history of history. xii, 339 p., 1 pl. (Records of Civilization) New York: Columbia University Press, 1922.
Reviewed by George Sarton, *Isis*, 1923, 5: 174-6.

THOMPSON, James Westfall; HOLM, Bernard J. A history of historical writing. 2 vol. 1. From the earliest times to the end of the seventeenth century. xvi, 676 p.; 2. The eighteenth and nineteenth centuries. ix, 674 p. New York: Macmillan, 1942.
Reviewed by J.W. Swain, *Amer.Hist.Rev.*, 1943, 48: 291-3.

YAc-br-bd

CARON, P.; JARYC, M.; ed. World list of historical periodicals and bibliographies. xvi, 391 p. Oxford: International Committee of Historical Sciences, 1939.

YAc-bv

AMERICAN HISTORICAL ASSOCIATION. Guide to historical literature. Board of editors: George Frederick Howe, chairman, [*et al.*]. xxxv, 962 p. New York: Macmillan, 1961.
Successor to the Association's A guide to historical literature published in 1931.
Reviewed by Joseph Mayer, *Isis*, 1932, 17: 453-64; by Godfrey Davies, *Amer.Hist.Rev.*, 1932, 37: 290-6.

International Bibliography of Historical Sciences. Edited for the International Committee of Historical Sciences. 1st year, 1926- Paris, etc.: 1930-
Volume for 1928 (3rd year) and for 1930 (7th year) reviewed by Heinrich Sproemberg, *Deut.Lit.Zeitung*, 1934, 5: 126-31; 1935, 6: 1878-80.

JARYC, Marc. La "Bibliographie internationale des sciences historiques." *Rev.Livre*, 1936, 4: 9.

List of doctoral dissertations in history now in progress at Universities in the United States. Washington: 1909-
Published annually and now issued by the American Historical Association approximately every 3 years.

LIST of research projects in history, exclusive of doctoral dissertations, now in progress in the United States and the Dominion of Canada. *Amer.Hist.Rev.*, 1934, 39: no. 3, suppl. 54 p.
Results of questionnaire sent to universities; additions to the list. *Amer.Hist.Rev.*, 1934, 39: 800-2; 1935, 40: 182-3, 389-91, 585-6, 800-1; 1937, 42: 194, 408, 624, 849.

YAcd

BUCHNER, Eberhard. Das Neueste von gestern. Kulturgeschichtlich interessante Dokumente aus alten deutschen Zeitungen. 5 vol. 1. Das 16. und 17. Jahrhundert. xv, 330 p.; 2. 1700-1750. vii, 491 p.; 3. 1750-1787. v, 437 p.; 4. Die Zeit der französischen Revolution. Pt. 1. Bis zur Hinrichtung Ludwigs XVI, 1788-1793. vi, 390 p. 1913; 5. — Pt. 2. Bis zur Errichtung des Konsulats, 1793-1799. vi, 444 p. München: Albert Langen, 1911-13. [CB 4/767]

HAMER, Philip M., comp. A guide to archives and manuscripts in the United States, compiled for the National Historical Publications Committee. 775 p. New Haven: Yale University Press, 1961.
Reviewed in *Pharm.Hist.*, 1962, 7: 53.

INTERNATIONAL COMMITTEE OF HISTORICAL SCIENCES. Enquête de la Commission des Archives sur les fonds étrangers. *Bull. Int.Comm.Hist.Sci.*, 1932, 4: 206-77.
Reports from various countries on archives concerning their own histories found in foreign collections.

YAcn-bv

TREHARNE, R.F. Bibliography of historical atlases and handmaps for use in schools. 24 p. (Historical Association Pamphlet, 114) London: 1939.

TREHARNE, R.F. Handlist of historical wall-maps. 72 p. (Historical Association, special series: S 1) London: 1945.

YAda

HALPERIN, S. William, ed. Some 20th century historians. xxiv, 298 p. Chicago: University of Chicago Press, 1961.
Reviewed by Sven Ulric Palme, *Lychnos*, 1962, 370-3.

YAdaj

STEINBERG, Sigfrid, ed. Die Geschichtswissenschaft der Gegenwart in Selbstdarstellungen. 2 vol. viii, 274 p.; iv, 222 p. Leipzig: Felix Meiner, 1925-26.
Reviewed by Walter L. Dorn, *Amer.Hist.Rev.*, 1925, 30: 860-1; 1927, 32: 606-7.

STERN, Fritz, ed. The varieties of history, from Voltaire to the present. 427 p. New York: Meridian Books, 1956.
Selections illustrating historical writing, and points of view from Voltaire's time to the present, including Russian selections.

YAf

AUSUBEL, Herman. Historians and their craft: a study of the presidential addresses of the American Historical Association, 1884-1945. 373 p. (Studies in History, Economics, and Public Law, 567) New York: Columbia University Press, 1950.
Reviewed by Waldo Gifford Leland, *Amer.Hist.Rev.*, 1951, 56: 528-9.

HALPHEN, Louis. Introduction à l'histoire. 100 p. Paris: Presses Universitaires de France, 1946. [CB 71/127]

LHÉRITIER, Michel. L'histoire du point de vue international. *Livre*, 1931, 5: no. 8, 1-5.

MORISON, Samuel Eliot. Faith of a historian. *Amer.Hist.Rev.*, 1951, 56: 261-75.
Presidential address read at the annual dinner of the American Historical Association in Chicago on December 29, 1950.

POWICKE, F.M. Modern historians and the study of history. Essays and papers. 256 p. London: Odhams Press; New York: Oxford University Press, 1955.
Reviewed by Charles F. Mullett, *Amer.Hist.Rev.*, 1956, 61: 675.

Revue de Synthèse Historique, vol. 26. 240 p. Paris: Michel, 1950. [CB 77/381]
This volume celebrates three anniversaries. The fiftieth of the RSH, the twenty-fifth of the Centre International de Synthèse, and the fifteenth Semaine de Synthèse.

ROSENSTOCK-HÜSSY, Eugen. The predicament of history. *J. Phil.*, 1935, 32: 93-100. [CB 43/287]

SIGERIST, Henry E. The significance of history in a period of emergency. *Virginia Med.Mon.*, 1942, 69: 409-11.

THOMSON, S. Harrison. The historian and crisis. *Prairie Schooner*, 1951, 25: no. 2, 166-78.

YAh historiography and particular aspects of history

for the historiography of science *see* Ah
the historiography of the separate sciences *see* INDEX
the history of historiography *see* YAc

YAhc historical techniques

BROWNE, Charles Albert. The comparative value of methods for estimating fame. *Science*, 1911, 33: 770-3.
Reply to F.A. Woods' article, *see* below.

BUTTERFIELD, Lyman H. Archival and editorial enterprise in 1850 and in 1950: some comparisons and contrasts. *Proc. Amer.Phil.Soc.*, 1954, 98: 159-70.

CAPPON, Lester J. The historian as editor. *In support of Clio: essays in memory of Herbert A. Kellar*, p. 173-93. Madison: State Historical Society of Wisconsin, 1958.

CLARK, Albert Curtis. The descent of manuscripts. xv, 464 p. Oxford University Press, 1918.

ERSLEV, Kr. Historische Technik. Die historische Untersuchung in ihren Grundzügen dargestellt. Transl. from the Danish by Ebba Brandt. 100 p. München: Oldenbourg, 1928.
Translation of: Historisk teknik: den historiske undersøgelse fremstillet i sine grundlinier. 2nd ed. 100 p. København: Gyldendal, 1926. First published 1911.
Reviewed by Percy Ernst Schramm, *Deut.Lit.Zeitung*, 1929, 6: 479-83.

GRANT, Julius. Analytical methods in the dating of books and documents. *Nature*, 1938, 142: 239-41.

HASELDEN, R.B. Scientific aids for the study of manuscripts. x, 108 p., fig. Oxford University Press, 1935. [CB 47/288]

MACDONALD, Arthur. History as a science. *Calcutta Rev.*, 1926, *3rd ser.*, 18: 277-302.
An attempt to introduce quantitative method in historical research.

PASQUALI, Giorgio. Storia della tradizione e critica del testo. xx, 485 p. Florence: Le Monnier, 1934.
Reviewed by Félix Peeters, *Chron.Égypte*, 1935, 10: 139-46.

SANDOZ, Edouard. Suggestions for dating and identification by heraldry and armor. *Colophon*, 1937, 2: 323-37.
An introduction to the methods to be followed in dating MSS and other works by heraldry and armor.

STEVENSON, Allan. Paper as bibliographical evidence. *Library, 5th ser.*, 1962, 17: 197-212.
Reviewed in *Times Lit.Suppl.*, 14 June 1963: 451.

TATE, Vernon D. Photographic and other scientific aids to the editor and curator. *Proc.Amer.Phil.Soc.*, 1954, 98: 179-84.

WOODS, Frederick Adams. Historiometry as an exact science. *Science*, 1911, 33: 568-74.

YAhc-cv

GOWER, H.D.; JAST, L. Stanley; TOPLEY, W.W. The camera as historian. A handbook to photographic record work for those who use a camera and for survey or record societies. xv, 259 p., ill. London: Sampson Low, Marston; New York: Stokes, 1916.

TATE, Vernon D. *See* YAhc

YAhd historical method

ALTAMIRA Y CREVEA, Rafael. Proceso histórico de la historiografia humana. 257 p. México: El Colegio de México, 1948.

BARNES, Sherman B. Historiography under the impact of rationalism and revolution. (Historians in the Age of Enlightenment. By S.B. Barnes. Modern Russian historiography. By Alfred A. Skerpan.) p. 60. (Kent State University Research Series, 1) Kent, Ohio: 1952.

CROCE, Benedetto. History as the story of liberty. Transl. from the Italian by Sylvia Sprigge. 324 p. New York: Norton, 1941.
Reviewed by J. Salwyn Schapiro, *J.Hist.Ideas*, 1941, 2: 505-8.
Italian original: La storia come pensiero e come azione. Bari: 1938.

CROCE, Benedetto. Theory and history of historiography. Transl. from the Italian by Douglas Ainslie. 317 p. London: Harrap, 1921. [CB 11/444]
Title of American edition: History: its theory and practice.
Translation of: Teoria e storia della storiografia. 2nd edition 1919; 8th Italian edition Bari: 1963.

CRUMP, Charles George. History and historical research. x, 178 p. London: Routledge, 1928.

DOMANOVSZKY, Sándor. La méthode historique de M. Nicolas Iorga (à propos d'un compte rendu), par Alexandre Domanovszky. 323 p. [Budapest]: Imprimerie de l'Université royale hongroise, [1938?].

FUETER, Eduard. Wichtige Beiträge zur modernen Historiographie. *Schweiz.Z.Gesch.*, 1955, 5: 376-82.

GARRAGHAN, Gilbert J. A guide to historical method. Edited by Jean Delanglez. xv, 482 p. New York: Fordham University Press, 1946.
Reviewed by Joseph T. Clark, *Isis*, 1950, 41: 139-43; by Homer G. Hockett, *Amer.Hist.Rev.*, 1947, 52: 764.

HEARNSHAW, F.J.C. History as a science. *Scientia*, 1932, 51: 228-36.

JOHNSON, Allen. The historian and historical evidence. 179 p. New York: Scribner, 1926.

JUSSERAND, Jean Jules; *et al.* The writing of history. xii, 143 p. New York: Scribner, 1926.
Reviewed by Allen Johnson, *Amer.Hist.Rev.*, 1927, 32: 293-5.

KAHLER, Erich. Man the measure. A new approach to history. x, 700 p. New York: Pantheon Books, 1943.
Reviewed by M.F. Ashley Montagu, *Isis*, 1946, 36: 147.

KEYSER, Erich. Die Geschichtswissenschaft. Aufbau und Aufgaben. v, 243 p. München: Oldenbourg, 1931.
Reviewed by Rudolf Stadelmann, *Deut.Lit.Zeitung*, 1932, 3: 464-8.

KNOWLES, David. The historian and character. Inaugural lecture delivered at Cambridge 17 November 1954. 22 p. Cambridge University Press, 1955.

MASSON-OURSEL, Paul. Les objections des Orientaux contre notre critique historique. *Rev.Hist.Phil.*, 1927, 1: 261-8.

MILLÁS-VALLICROSA, J.M. En torno al método histórico de Toynbee. *Arch.Int.Hist.Sci.*, 1958, 11: 153-9.

PARKER, Donald Dean. Local history. How to gather it, write it, and publish it. Revised and edited by Bertha E. Josephson. xiv, 186 p. New York: Social Science Research Council, 1944. [CB 68/59]

PIRENNE, Henri. De la méthode comparative en histoire. Discours prononcé à la séance d'ouverture. *Compt.Rend.Ve Congr.Int.Sci.Hist.* (Brussels, 1923), p. 19-32. Bruxelles: Weissenbruch, 1923. [CB 15/224]

REIS, Lincoln; KRISTELLER, Paul Oskar. Some remarks on the method of history. *J.Phil.*, 1943, 40: 225-45.

ROBINSON, James Harvey. The newer ways of historians. *Amer. Hist.Rev.*, 1930, 35: 245-55.
Presidential address delivered before the American Historical Association at Durham, December 30, 1929.

SOCIAL SCIENCE RESEARCH COUNCIL. COMMITTEE ON HISTORIOGRAPHY. Theory and practice in historical study: a report of the Committee. xi, 177 p. (*Bull.Soc.Sci.Res.Counc.*, 54) New York: Social Science Research Council, [1946].
Includes selective reading list on historiography and the philosophy of history by Ronald Thompson.

SPRANGER, E. Allgemeine Kulturgeschichte und Methodenlehre. *Arch.Kulturgesch.*, 1912, 9: 363-81.

WILLIAMS, Charles Harold. The modern historian. 309 p. London: Nelson, 1938.
Extracts on historical method from the works of representative historians of the early twentieth century.

YAhd-da

CHRISTERN, Hermann. Entwicklung und Aufgaben biographischer Sammelwerke. Ein Beitrag zur Geschichte der Historiographie. *Abhandl.Preuss.Akad.Wiss.Phil.Hist.Kl.*, 1933, 1069-148, 1 pl.

YAhf philosophical aspects of history

BERLIN, Isaiah. Historical inevitability. Delivered on 12 May 1953 at the London School of Economics and Political Science. 79 p. (Auguste Comte Memorial Trust Lecture, 1) London/New York: Oxford University Press, 1955.
Reviewed by Maurice Mandelbaum, *Amer.Hist.Rev.*, 1956, 61: 675-6.

BERR, Henri. En marge de l'histoire universelle. xii, 303 p. Paris: La Renaissance du Livre, 1934.
Reviewed by Hélène Metzger, *Archeion*, 1934, 16: 463-4.

BURKE, Marjorie L. Origin of history as metaphysic. 61 p. New York: Philosophical Library, 1950. [CB 78/196]

COHEN, Morris R. The meaning of human history. ix, 304 p. (The Paul Carus Lectures, Sixth Series, 1944) La Salle, Ill.: Open Court Publishing Co., 1947.
Reviewed by Sidney Ratner, *Amer.Hist.Rev.*, 1949, 54: 97-8.

COLLINGWOOD, Robin George. The idea of history. xxvi, 339 p. Oxford: Clarendon Press; New York: Oxford University Press, 1946. Reprinted 1956.
Reviewed by Charles A. Beard, *Amer.Hist.Rev.*, 1947, 52: 704-8.

CROCE, Benedetto. Il concetto della storia. Antologia a cura di A. Parente. 256 p. Bari: G. Laterza, 1954.

DELEVSKY, J. La prévision dans l'histoire humaine. *Rev. Phil.*, 1936, 61: 145-78.

FARRINGTON, Benjamin. Has history a meaning? x, 40 p. (Conway Memorial Lecture, 1950) London: South Place Ethical Society, 1950.

GARDINER, Patrick, ed. Theories of history. ix, 549 p., bibliogr. Glencoe, Ill.: Free Press; London: Allen & Unwin, 1959.

GOETZ, Walter. Kultur- und Universalgeschichte. Walter Goetz zu seinem 60. Geburtstage dargebracht von Fachgenossen, Freunden und Schülern. iv, 567 p. Leipzig: Teubner, 1927.
Reviewed by Percy Ernst Schramm, *Deut.Lit.Zeitung*, 1929, 6: 373-9.

GOHEEN, John D. Philosophy and history. *Pakistan Phil.J.*, July 1957, 1: 1-9.

GRANT, C.K. Collingwood's theory of historical knowledge. *Renaiss.Mod.Stud.*, 1957, 1: 65-90.

HALDANE, Richard Burdon Haldane, *1st Viscount*. The meaning of truth in history. 35 p. (Creighton Lecture, 1913-14) London: University of London Press, 1914.

HARNACK, Adolf von. Ueber die Sicherheit und die Grenzen geschichtlicher Erkenntnis. Vortrag. 23 p. München: Oldenburg, 1917.

HOLBORN, Hajo. Wilhelm Dilthey and the critique of historical reason. *J.Hist.Ideas*, 1950, 11: 93-118.

JASPERS, Karl. The origin and goal of history. xvi, 294 p. New Haven: Yale University Press, 1953. [CB 80/116]

KLIBANSKY, Raymond; PATSON, H.J. Philosophy and history. Essays presented to Ernst Cassirer. xii, 360 p. New York: Oxford University Press, 1936.
Reviewed by M.F. Ashley-Montagu, *Isis*, 1937, 27: 358-60.

LE BON, Gustave. Bases scientifiques d'une philosophie de l'histoire. 325 p. Paris: Flammarion, 1931.
Reviewed by Philippe Tongas, *Rev.Gén.Sci.*, 1931, 42: 483; by M.M. Knight, *Amer.Hist.Rev.*, 1932, 37: 361-2.

MARROU, Henri-Irenée. De la connaissance historique. 299 p. (Collection "Esprit") Paris: Editions du Seuil, 1954.

MEHLIS, Georg. Geschichtsphilosophie. *Jahrb.Phil.*, 1913, 1: 270-300, 377-8.

MULLER, Herbert J. The uses of the past. 394 p. New York: Oxford University Press, 1952.
Reviewed by Mark Graubard, *Isis*, 1953, 44: 84-6.

RÁDL, Emanuel. Natur und Geschichte. *Festschrift Th.G. Masaryk zum 80. Geburtstage 7. März 1930*, Pt. 1, p. 241-64. (Ergänzungsband zur Zeitschrift *Der russische Gedanke*) Bonn: F. Cohen, 1930. [CB 29/311]

ROSENTHAL, Jerome. Attitudes of some modern rationalists to history. *J.Hist.Ideas*, 1943, 4: 429-56.

ROTENSTREICH, Nathan. Between past and present. An essay on history. With a foreword by Martin Buber. xxix, 329 p. New Haven: Yale University Press, 1958. [CB 84/299]

SAXL, Fritz. Veritas filia temporis. *Philosophy & history, essays presented to Ernst Cassirer*, p. 197-222, 13 fig. Oxford: Clarendon Press; New York: Oxford University Press, 1936.

SCHRECKER, Paul. Work and history: an essay on the structure of civilization. xviii, 322 p. Princeton: Princeton University Press, 1948.
Reviewed by Ernest Nagel, *Isis*, 1949, 40: 83-5; by Henry David, *Amer.Hist.Rev.*, 1949, 54: 94-6.

SÉE, Henri. Science et philosophie de l'histoire. 513 p. Paris: Alcan, 1928.
Reviewed by Abbott Payson Usher, *Amer.Hist.Rev.*, 1929, 34: 787-8.

SLOTKIN, J.S. Reflections on Collingwood's "Idea of History". *Antiquity*, 1948, 22: 98-102.

SPENGLER, Oswald. Der Untergang des Abendlandes. Umrisse einer Morphologie der Weltgeschichte. 2 vol. 1. Gestalt und Wirklichkeit. 2. Welthistorische Perspektiven. 635 p. München: Oskar Beck, 1922.
Reviewed by J. Ruska, *Isis*, 1923, 5: 176-81.

STRAYER, Joseph Reese, ed. The interpretation of history, by Jacques Barzun, Hajo Holborn, Herbert Heaton [*et al.*]. 186 p. Princeton: Princeton University Press, 1943.
Reviewed by Wallace K. Ferguson, *Amer.Hist.Rev.*, 1944, 49: 262-3.

SUTER, Jean François. Philosophie et histoire chez Wilhelm Dilthey. xi, 204 p. (Studia Philosophica, suppl. 8) Basel: Verlag für Recht und Gesellschaft, 1960.
Reviewed by Rolf Torstendahl, *Lychnos*, 1962, 369-70.

TEGGART, Frederick John. Theory of history. xix, 231 p. New Haven: Yale University Press, 1925.

TOYNBEE, Arnold Joseph. A study of history. 12 vol. (Issued under the auspices of the Royal Institute of International Affairs) London: Oxford University Press, 1934-61.
The study of civilizations.
Volumes 1-3 reviewed by Jules Menken, *Nature*, 1935, 135: 636-8.

TROELTSCH, Ernst. Der Historismus und seine Probleme. Book 1. Das logische Problem der Geschichtsphilosophie. 2 pts. xi, 777 p. Tübingen: J.C. Mohr, 1923.
2nd book not published.

WIENER, Philip P. On methodology in the philosophy of history. *J.Phil.*, 1941, 38: 309-24.

YAhg evolutionary aspects of history

BURY, John Bagnell. The idea of progress. An inquiry into its origin and growth. xv, 377 p. London: Macmillan, 1920.
Reviewed by G. Sarton, *Isis*, 1921-23, 4: 373-5.
American edition. Introduction by Charles A. Beard. xl, 357 p. New York: Macmillan, 1932. Reprinted 1955 (New York: Dover Publications). Reviewed by Carl Becker, *Amer. Hist.Rev.*, 1933, 38: 404-6.

YAhh

BELOW, Georg von. Ueber historische Periodisierungen, mit einer Beigabe: Wesen und Ausbreitung der Romantik. 108 p. (Einzelschriften zur Politik und Geschichte, 11) Berlin: Deutsche Verlagsgesellschaft für Politik und Geschichte, 1925.
Reviewed by H.P. Gallinger, *Amer.Hist.Rev.*, 1926, 31: 559.

CAVAIGNAC, Eugène. Chronologie. 214 p. Paris: Payot, 1925. [CB 18/643]

INTERNATIONAL COMMITTEE OF HISTORICAL SCIENCES. Enquête de la Commission de Chronologie pour la révision des listes chronologiques. *Bull.Int.Comm.Hist.Sci.*, 1932, 4: 278-337.
Reports from countries on chronological lists in existence for their histories.

YAj psychological aspects

ARENS, Franz. La psychologie en histoire et la "métaethnique". *Rev.Synthèse*, 1937, 13: 7-15.
Apropos of a world "Geistesgeschichte" developed from the teaching of Karl Lamprecht (1856-1915).

NÄCKE, P. Die Psychiatrie als Hilfswissenschaft, auch in der Historik. Die Pathographien, insbesondere die von Jesus-Christus. *Neurol.Zentralbl.*, 1913, 32: 1074-80.

YAm/u other special aspects of historical studies

YAmzMP

BARNES, Harry Elmer. The new history and the social studies. xvii, 605 p. New York: Century, 1925.
Reviewed by Gaston G. Dept, *Isis*, 1926, 8: 380-2.

SALVEMINI, Gaetano. Historian and scientist. An essay on the nature of history and the social sciences. ix, 203 p. Cambridge Mass.: Harvard University Press, 1940.
Reviewed by M.F. Ashley Montagu, *Isis*, 1941, 33: 82-3.

YAnh

BERR, Henri. Le vocabulaire historique du Centre International de Synthèse. 4 p. In: Deuxième Congrès National des Sciences Historiques (14-16 avril 1930). Alger: 1932.

YAnp

CLARK, George Norman. Historical reviewing. *Essays in history presented to Reginald Lane Poole*, p. 115-26. Oxford: Clarendon Press, 1927.

YAns

KERR, Chester. Publishing historical sources. A prejudiced view of the problem of finance. *Proc.Amer.Phil.Soc.*, 1954, 98: 273-8.

UNITED STATES NATIONAL HISTORICAL PUBLICATIONS COMMISSION. A national program for the publication of historical documents. viii, 106 p. Washington: U.S. Govt. Print. Off., 1954.
Reviewed by John B. Blake, *J.Hist.Med.*, 1955, 10: 451.

WHITEHILL, Walter Muir, *et al.* Publishing the papers of great men. *Daedalus Amer.Acad.Arts Sci.*, 1955-57, 86: 47-79.
A session at the 69th Annual Meeting of the American Historical Association.

YAom

INTERNATIONAL COMMITTEE OF HISTORICAL SCIENCES. L'enseignement de l'histoire dans les écoles primaires. Rapports nationaux précédés d'un rapport général. Enquête de la Commission pour l'enseignement de l'histoire. *Bull.Int. Comm.Hist.Sci.*, 1931, 3: 319-480; 1932, 4: 554-757.

YAqv

THE UNITY History Schools, (1st-15th). *Isis*, 1938, 28: 96-8; 1939, 30: 97-9. [CB 21/590]
Seminars in historical studies on the lines of unity and progress, initiated and led by Francis Sydney Marvin.

YAqx

INTERNATIONAL CONGRESS OF HISTORICAL SCIENCES. [Publication dates of Proceedings and accounts of Congresses.]
4th (London, 1913) London: 1913.
5th (Brussels, 1923) Bruxelles: 1923.
Isis, 1923, 5: 142.
6th (Oslo, 1928) Oslo: 1928.
7th (Warsaw, 1933) Warsaw: 1933.
8th (Zurich, 1938) Paris: 1938-39.
9th (Paris, 1950) Paris: 1950-51.
10th (Rome, 1955) Firenze: 1955.
11th (Stockholm, 1960) Göteborg: 1960.
Bibl.Hum.Renaiss., 1961, 23: 157-66.

YAqy

LELAND, Waldo G. L'organisation internationale des études historiques. In: Histoire et historiens depuis cinquante ans, methodes, organisation et résultats du travail historique de 1876 à 1926, (2), p. 741-56. Paris: Alcan, 1928.

YAs

WARE, Caroline F., ed. The cultural approach to history, edited for the American Historical Association. ix, 357 p. New York: Columbia University Press, 1940. [CB 61/414]

YAtd

BUTTERFIELD, Herbert. Christianity and history. vii, 146 p. London: Bell, 1949.
Reviewed by Sydney W. Jackman, *Isis*, 1950, 41: 326.

YAth

MORISON, Samuel Eliot. History as a literary art: an appeal to young historians. 13 p. (Old South Leaflets, series 2, no. 1) Boston: Old South Association, 1947.
Reviewed by I. Bernard Cohen, *Isis*, 1948, 39: 197-8.

YAtp

NEFF, Emery. The poetry of history. viii, 258 p. New York: Columbia University Press, 1947.
Reviewed by Solomon Gandz, *Isis*, 1948, 39: 198-9.

YAtt

LÁNG, Paul Henry. Music in Western civilization. xvi, 1107 p., ill., maps. New York: Norton, 1941.
Reviewed by George Sarton, *Isis*, 1942, 34: 182-6, map.

YAw in different countries

YAwb

HASKINS, Charles H. European history and American scholarship. *Amer.Hist.Rev.*, 1923, 28: 215-27.
Review of American work in the field of European history.

SHRYOCK, Richard H. American historiography: a critical analysis and a program. *Proc.Amer.Phil.Soc.*, 1943, 87: 35-46.

YAwb-o

PIERCE, Bessie Louise. Public opinion and the teaching of history in the United States. xi, 380 p. New York: Knopf, 1926.
Reviewed by Carlton J.H. Hayes, *Amer.Hist.Rev.*, 1928. 33: 360-1.

YAwb-qd

LITERARY AND HISTORICAL SOCIETY OF QUEBEC. The centenary volume of the Society, 1824-1924. 2 pt. 196, 109 p. Quebec: The Society, 1924.

YAwb-qk

DREWRY, Elizabeth B. Historical units of agencies of the first World War. *Bull.Nat.Arch.*, 1942, no. 4, 61-91.

YAwf

HALPHEN, L. Les historiens français et la science historique allemande. *Scientia*, 1923, 33: 333-41. [CB 15/224]

YAwg

HALPHEN, L. Les historiens français et la science historique allemande. *Scientia*, 1923, 33: 333-41. [CB 15/224]

PIRENNE, Henri. De l'influence allemande sur le mouvement historique contemporain. *Scientia*, 1923, 34: 173-8.

SRBIK, Heinrich von. Geist und Geschichte vom deutschen Humanismus bis zur Gegenwart. 2 vol. München: Bruckmann, 1950-51.
Reviewed by E. Fueter, *Schweiz.Z.Gesch.*, 1955, 5: 376-82.

YAwg-oq

SCHERER, Emil Clemens. Geschichte und Kirchengeschichte an den deutschen Universitäten. xxx, 522 p. Freiburg i. Br.: Herder, 1927.
Reviewed by Francis A. Christie, *Amer.Hist.Rev.*, 1928, 33: 390-2.

YAwh

PLASCHKA, Richard Georg. Von Palacký bis Pekař. Geschichtswissenschaft und Nationalbewusstsein bei den Tschechen. Mit einem Nachwort von H.F. Schmid. xi, 119 p. (Wiener Archiv für Geschichte des Slawentums und Osteuropas, 1) Graz: Böhlaus, 1955.
Reviewed by František Graus, *Česk.Čas.Hist.*, 1956, 4: 672-5.

SEMKOWICZ, Wladyslaw. Rozwój nauk pomocniczych historii w Polsce. [The development of the sciences auxiliary to history in Poland. (In Polish, with French summary)] 49 p. (Polska Akademia Umiejetności, Historia Nauki Polskiej w Monografiach, 20) Krakow: 1948.

TYMIENIECKI, Kazimierz. [Esquisse de l'historiographie polonaise. (In Polish with French summary)] 143 p. (Polska Akademia Umiejetności, Historia Nauki Polskiej w Monografiach 19a) Krakow: 1948.

YAwm-qd

UPPSALA. UNIVERSITET. HISTORISKA FÖRENINGEN. Hundra års historisk diskussion: Historiska Föreningen i Uppsala 1862-1962. [A hundred years of historical debate: The Historical Society of Upsala, 1862-1962. (In Swedish)] 124 p. (Studia Historica Uppsaliensia, 8) Stockholm: Svenska Bokförlaget, 1962.
Reviewed by Nils Runeby, *Lychnos*, 1962, 388-90.

YAwn

AKADEMIIA NAUK SSSR. INSTITUT ISTORII. Ocherki istorii istoricheskoi nauki v SSSR. Ed. by M.N. Tikhomirov. [Outlines of the history of the historical sciences in the U.S.S.R. (In Russian)] Vol. 1. Moskva: Akademia Nauk SSSR, 1955.
Volume 1 covers up to the mid 19th century.

BUZESKUL, V.P. Vseobshchaia istoriia i ee predstaviteli v Rossii v XIX i nachale XX veka. [General history and its exponents in Russia, in the XIXth and in the beginning of the XXth century. (In Russian)] 2 vol. (Komissiia po Istorii Znanii, Trudy, 7) Leningrad: Akademiia Nauk SSSR, 1929-31. [CB 29/311]

YAwn-hf

MASARYK, Th.G. Zur russischen Geschichts- und Religionsphilosophie. Soziologische Skizzen. 2 vol. Jena: Diederichs, 1913.
Reviewed by G. Sarton, *Isis*, 1919, 2: 238-9.

YB GENEALOGY

DIMPFEL, Rudolf. Biographische Nachschlagewerke, Adelslexica, Wappenbücher. Systematische Zusammenstellung für Historiker und Genealogen. 128 p. Leipzig: Heims, 1922.

HILDEBRAND, Bengt. Handbok i släkt- och personforskning. Pt. 1. Metodlära, medeltidsförhållanden, historiografi och bibliografi. [Handbook for genealogical and biographical research. Pt. 1. Methodology, mediaeval periods, historiography and bibliography. (In Swedish)] 400 p. Stockholm: Wahlström & Widstrand, 1961.
Reviewed by Bror Olsson, *Lychnos*, 1962, 373-5.

YBmzMD

LEMARCHAL, Robert. Hérédité et généalogie. *Act.IIIe Congr. Bénélux Hist.Sci.* (Luxembourg, 1960). *Janus*, 1960, 49: 175-81.

YC ARCHAEOLOGY

for dating with the aid of tree rings *see* KXyJ0

YCc general history

BIBBY, Geoffrey. The testimony of the spade. xviii, 414, x p., ill. New York: Knopf, 1956. [CB 83/213]

BREASTED, James H. The place of archaeology in the modern world. *Southwest.Lore*, 1939, 43-8.

CERAM, C.W., *pseud.* of Kurt W. Marek. Gods, graves, and scholars. The story of archaeology. Transl from the German by E.B. Garside. xii, 426, xvi p., ill., bibliogr. New York: Knopf, 1951. [CB 79/185]
Translation of: Götter, Gräber und Gelehrte: Roman der Archäologie (Hamburg: Rowohlt, 1949).

CORNWALL, I.W. Bones for the archaeologist. 255 p., ill. London: Phoenix House, 1956; New York: Macmillan, 1957.
Reviewed by Lucille E. Hoyme, *Antiquity*, 1958, 32: 49-50.

DANIEL, Glyn E. A hundred years of archaeology. 344 p. (The Hundred Years Series) London: Duckworth; New York: Macmillan, 1950. [CB 76/405]

DE CAMP, L. Sprague; DE CAMP, Catherine C. Ancient ruins and archaeology. 294 p., ill., bibliogr. Garden City, N.Y.: Doubleday, 1964.

HAWKES, Jacquetta, ed. The world of the past. 2 vol. New York: Knopf; London: Thames & Hudson, 1963.
An anthology of archaeological history.

MAGOFFIN, Ralph van Deman. The lure and lore of archaeology. x, 107 p. Baltimore: Williams & Wilkins, 1930; London: Baillière, Tindall and Cox, 1931.

MAGOFFIN, Ralph van Deman; DAVIS, Emily C. The romance of archaeology. xv, 348 p. London: Bell, 1930.

OPPELN-BRONIKOWSKI, Friedrich von. Archäologische Entdeckungen im 20. Jahrhundert. 165 p., ill. Berlin: Keller, 1931.
Reviewed by R.A.S. Macalister, *Antiquity*, 1932, 6: 114.

RAPPORT, Samuel; WRIGHT, Helen; ed. Archaeology. xiii, 367 p., ill. New York: New York University Press, 1963. [CB 89/520]

WHEELER, Mortimer. Archaeology from the earth. xi, 221 p., ill. Oxford: Clarendon Press, 1954. [CB 80/146]

WOOLLEY, C. Leonard. Dead towns and living men: being pages from an antiquary's notebook. Rev. enl. ed. 220 p., ill. London: Lutterworth Press, 1954; New York: Philosophical Library, 1956.
First edition. vii, 259 p. London: Oxford University Press, 1920.

WOOLLEY, C. Leonard. Digging up the past. 2nd ed. xiii, 125 p., 32 pl. London: Benn; New York: Crowell, 1954.
Also (Pelican Books, A.4) Harmondsworth: Penguin Books, 1960. First published 1930.

WOOLLEY, C. Leonard. Spadework: adventures in archaeology. 124 p., ill. London: Lutterworth Press; New York: Philosophical Library, 1953. [CB 80/146]
American edition has title: Spadework in archaeology.

YCc-be

RÉAU, Louis. Dictionnaire d'art et d'archéologie. viii, 487 p., ill. Paris: Larousse, 1930.
Reviewed by H. Lemonnier, *J.Savants*, 1931, 136.

YCcb

BIBLIOTHÈQUE D'ART ET D'ARCHÉOLOGIE. Note signée R.J. *Rev. Syn.Hist.*, 1914, 28: 168-9. [CB 5/476]

YCcc

BURKITT, M.C. Correlation of the archaeological and geological records. *Nature*, 1930, 126: 509-10.
Including a table of correlation.

YCce-bv

DOW, Sterling. Archaeological indexes. *Amer.J.Archaeol.*, 1950, 54: 41-57.

YChh

FRANCHET, L. Les éléments chronologiques en archéologie. *Rev. Sci.*, 1919, 57: 331-4.

YCht

WHEELER, Mortimer. Archaeology and the transmission of ideas. *Antiquity*, 1952, 26: 180-92.

YCke methodology

CHAPOT, Victor. Les méthodes archéologiques. *Rev.Syn.Hist.*, 1914, 28: 1-18. [CB 6/475]
Most of article is review of: Deonna, W. L'archéologie, *see* below.

CHILDE, V. Gordon. The constitution of archeology as a science. *Science, Medicine and History. Essays in honour of Charles Singer*, 1: 1-15, 2 pl. London: Oxford University Press. 1953. [CB 80/145]

DANIEL, Glyn E. The three ages. An essay on archaeological method. 60 p. Cambridge University Press, 1943. [CB 65/85; CB 66/268]

DEONNA, Waldemar. L'archéologie, sa valeur, ses méthodes. 3 vol. Paris: Laurens, 1912.
Reviewed by George Sarton, *Isis*, 1913, 1: 745-54; by Victor Chapot, *Rev.Syn.Hist.*, 1914, 28: 1-18.

DEONNA, Waldemar. L'archéologie. Ses principes, son utilité. Leçon d'ouverture du cours d'archéologie classique et orientale à l'Université de Genève, 17 janvier 1921. 16 p. Genève: Sonor, 1921.

DEONNA, Waldemar. Etudes d'archéologie et d'art. 66 p., ill. Genève: Albert Kündig, 1914. [CB 6/475]

DEONNA, Waldemar. Les lois et les rythmes dans l'art. 188 p. (Bibliothèque de Culture Générale) Paris: Flammarion, 1914. [CB 9/481]
A summary of the author's L'archéologie, sa valeur, ses méthodes (*see* above).

DEONNA, Waldemar. Qu'est-ce que l'archéologie? *Scientia*, 1914, 16: 3-20.

MAGOFFIN, Ralph van Deman. Archaeology as a science. *J.Urusvati*, 1931, 1: 7-11.

RANDALL-MacIVER, David. Archaeology as a science. *Antiquity*, 1933, 7: 5-20.

RICHMOND, Ian A. The nature and scope of archaeology. *Advance. Sci.*, 1959, 15: 95-101.

YCm/t other special aspects

YCmzFD

DINSMOOR, William Bell. Archaeology and astronomy. *Proc. Amer.Phil.Soc.*, 1939, 80: 95-173, 10 fig.

YCnb

ALLCROFT, Arthur Hadrian. The circle and the cross: a study in continuity. 2 vol. 1. The circle. x, 370 p., 4 pl.; 2. The cross. vii, 454 p., 4 pl. London: Macmillan, 1927-30.

YCtp

DEONNA, Waldemar. Unité et diversité. *Rev.Archeol.*, 1914, *4th ser.*, 23: 39-58. [CB 6/475]

YCw in different countries

YCwb-ke

WILLEY, Gordon R.; PHILLIPS, Philip. Method and theory in American archaeology. 270 p. Chicago: University of Chicago Press, 1958. [CB 84/330]

YCwb-qh

STRONG, William Duncan; KIDDER, Alfred, II; PAUL, A.J. Drexel, Jr. Preliminary report on the Smithsonian Institution - Harvard University Archeological Expedition to Northwestern Honduras, 1936. 129 p., 16 pl. (*Smithsonian Misc.Collect.*, 97: no. 1) Washington, D.C.: 1938.

YCwe

KENDRICK, Thomas Downing; HAWKES, C.F.C. Archaeology in England and Wales, 1914-1931. xix, 379 p. London: Methuen, 1932. [CB 51/280]

YCwe-da

WALTERS, Henry Beauchamp. The English antiquaries of the sixteenth, seventeenth, and eighteenth centuries. viii, 80 p., 6 portr. London: Walters, 1934.
Reviewed by Roland Austin, *Antiquity*, 1934, 8: 494.

YCwm

SHETELIG, Haakon; FALK, Hjalmar. Scandinavian archaeology. Transl. by E.V. Gordon. viii, 435 p. Oxford: Clarendon Press; New York: Oxford University Press, 1937.

YCwn

MARINUS, Albert. Ethnographie, folklore et archéologie en Russie soviétique. *Bull.Soc.Belge Anthrop.Préhist.*, 1934, 49: 173-86.

MILLER, Mykhaĭlo. Archaeology in the U.S.S.R. 232 p. (Research Monographs of the Research Program on the U.S.S.R., 3) New York: Praeger, 1956.
Reviewed by Alexander Vucinich, *Isis*, 1959, 50: 517-18; by Marija Gimbutas, *Sci.Mon.*, 1957, 85: 207-8.

MONGAIT, A.L. Archaeology in the U.S.S.R. Transl. and adapted by M.W. Thompson. 320 p., ill. (Pelican Books, A.495) Harmondsworth/Baltimore: Penguin Books, 1961.
Translation of: Arkheologia v SSSR. Moskva: 1955.

YCx techniques and instruments

YCxd

BOAS, George F. The promise of underwater archaeology. *Amer. Sch.*, 1963, 32: 241-54.

DU MESNIL DU BUISSON, Robert, *Comte*. The art of excavation. *Urusvati*, 1931, 1: 13-26, ill.

DU MESNIL DU BUISSON, Robert, *Comte*. La technique des fouilles archéologiques. Les principes généraux. 256 p., 8 pl. Paris: Geuthner, 1934. [CB 42/598]

DU MESNIL DU BUISSON, Robert, *Comte*. La technique des fouilles archéologiques. Les principes généraux. Conférences de première année faites à l'Ecole du Louvre, dans les années scolaires 1928-1929 et 1931-1932. 224 p., 3 pl., 11 fig. Paris: Geuthner, 1932.

KENYON, Kathleen M. Beginning in archaeology. 203 p., 11 pl. London: Phoenix House; New York: Praeger, 1952. [CB 79/185]
Introduction to practical archaeology.

PLACE, Robin. Down to earth. A practical guide to archaeology. xvi, 173 p., ill. New York: Philosophical Library, 1955.

YCxf

BROTHWELL, Don; HIGGS, Eric; ed. Science in archaeology. With a foreword by Grahame Clark. 595 p., ill. New York: Basic Books, 1963. [CB 89/520]

FORBES, R.J. Archaeologie en exacte wetenschappen. [Archaeology and the exact sciences. (In Dutch)] *Chem.Weekbl.*, 1939, 36: 356-62.

HOLMYARD, E.J. Archaeology and other sciences. *Endeavour*, 1953, 12: 59-60.

JUDSON, Sheldon. Archaeology and the natural sciences. *Amer. Scient.*, 1961, 49: 410-14.
On various scientific techniques used in archaeology.

YCxf-CJxkm

BIEK, Leo. Archaeology and the microscope. 287 p., ill. New York/London: Praeger, 1963.

YCxf-D

CALEY, Earle R. On the application of chemistry to archaeology. *Ohio J.Sci.*, 1948, 48: 1-14, bibliogr.

HEDVALL, J. Arvid. Chemie im Dienst der Archäologie, Bautechnik, Denkmalpflege. x, 236 p., pl. Göteborg: Gumperts, 1962.
Reviewed by L. Biek, *Antiquity*, 1964, 38: 240-1.

KAPUSTINSKAIA, K.A. K istorii vozniknoveniia arkheologicheskoi khimii. [On the history of the emergence of archeological chemistry. (In Russian)] *Tr.Inst.Ist.Est.Tekh.*, 1962, 39: 258-65.

MATIGNON, Camille. La chimie et l'archéologie. *Chim.Ind.*, 1930, 24: 124-9. [CB 51/299]

YCxf-RE

HUMPHREYS, Humphrey. Dental evidence in archaeology. *Antiquity*, 1951, 25: 16-18.

YCxf-VC

DESCH, C.H. Metallurgical aids to archaeology. Presidential address. *Trans.Newcomen Soc.*, 1949-50 and 1950-51, 27: 121-9.

FORBES, R.J. Archaeology and metallurgy. *Edgar Allen News*, 1953, 32: 89-92.

READ, Thomas T. Metallurgical fallacies in archaeological literature. *Amer.J.Archaeol.*, 1934, 38: 382-9.

TYLECOTE, R.F. Metallurgy in archaeology. xvi, 368 p., pl. London: Arnold, 1962.

YCxf-XF

CRAWFORD, O.G.S. A century of airphotography. *Antiquity*, 1954, 28: 206-10.

RICKERTSON, Oliver; KIDDER, A.V. An archeological reconnaissance by air in central America. With photographs by Mrs. Lindbergh and Oliver Ricketson. *Geogr.Rev.*, 1930, 20: 177-206, ill.

YCxw

PLENDERLEITH, Harold James. The preservation of antiquities. viii, 71 p., 2 pl. London: The Museums Association, 1934.
Reviewed by P.D.R., *Nature*, 1934, 134: 516.

YG WRITING; PALAEOGRAPHY

YGc general history

BALOGH, Josef. Voces paginarum: Beiträge zur Geschichte des lauten Lesens und Schreibens. 66 p. (*Philologus*, 82: 1 and 2) Leipzig: Dieterich, 1927.
Reviewed by W.B. Sedgwick, *Speculum*, 1928, 3: 116-17.

BATTELLI, Giulio. Lezioni di palaeografia. 2nd ed. x, 241 p. (Pont. Scuola Vaticana di Paleografia e Diplomatica) Città del Vaticano: Arti Grafiche e Fotomeccaniche Sansaini, 1936.
1st edition reviewed by Charles H. Beeson, *Amer.Hist.Rev.*, 1938, 43: 574-5.

CALLEWAERT, H. Physiologie de l'écriture cursive, avec 56 figures groupant des croquis de U. Wernaers, des photogravures extraites de films, des reproductions d'écritures, etc. 122 p., ill. Paris: De Brouwer, 1937.

COHEN, Marcel. La grande invention de l'écriture et son évolution. 2 vol. 1. Texte. xii, 471 p.; 2. Documentation et index. 228 p.; portfolio of 95 pl. Paris: Imprimerie Nationale, 1958.
Reviewed by J.G. Février, *J.Asiatique*, 1958, 246: 469-71.

DANZELL, T.W. Die Anfänge der Schrift. 219 p. Leipzig: Voigtländer, 1912.

DEGERING, Hermann. Lettering: a series of 240 plates illustrating modes of writing in Western Europe from antiquity to the end of the 18th century. xxxvii p., 240 pl. London: Benn, 1929.
English edition of: Die Schrift, *see* below.

DEGERING, Hermann. Die Schrift. Atlas der Schriftformen des Abendlandes vom Altertum bis zum Ausgang des 18. Jahrhunderts. xxxvii p., 240 p. (Wasmuths Werkkunst-Bücherei, 6) Berlin: Wasmuth, 1929.
French edition Paris: Calavas, 1929. English edition London: Benn, 1929 (*see* above).
Reviewed by Ernst Crous, *Deut.Lit.Zeitung*, 1930, 1: 1633-5; by H. Jensen, *Orient.Lit.Zeitung*, 1930, 33: 863-5.

DELITSCH, Hermann. Geschichte der abendländischen Schreibschriftformen. xliii, 290 p., 16 pl. Leipzig: Hiersemann, 1928.
Reviewed by Anton Chroust, *Deut.Lit.Zeitung*, 1930, 1: 193-5.

FÉVRIER, James G. Histoire de l'écriture. 608 p., 135 fig., 16 pl. Paris: Payot, 1948.
Reviewed by J. Filliozat, *J.Asiatique*, 1949, 237: 363.

GELB, Ignace J. A study of writing. xv, 295 p. Chicago: University of Chicago Press, 1952. [CB 79/190]

HERTZ, Amelia. Les débuts de l'écriture. *Rev.Archéol.*, 1934, 4: 109-34, 8 fig.

JENSEN, Hans. Geschichte der Schrift. viii, 231 p., ill. Hannover: Heinz Lafaire, 1925. [CB 19/814]
Reviewed by Julius Ruska, *Isis*, 1926, 8: 382-5, 814.

JENSEN, Hans. Die Schrift in Vergangenheit und Gegenwart. viii, 418 p., 445 ill. Glückstadt: Augustin, 1935.
Reviewed by Willy Hartner, *Isis*, 1939, 30: 132-7; by G. v. Selle, *Orient.Lit.Zeitung*, 1936, 39: 489-91.

MASON, William A. A history of the art of writing. 502 p. New York: Macmillan, 1920.
Reviewed by Walter Libby, *Isis*, 1922, 4: 367-8.

MEILLET, Antoine. La langue et l'écriture. *Scientia*, 1919, 26: 290-3. [CB 9/488]

MOORHOUSE, A.C. The triumph of the alphabet: a history of writing. xiv, 223 p., ill. (The Life of Science Library, 28) New York: Henry Schuman, 1953.
Reviewed by Robert H. Pfeiffer, *Isis*, 1953, 44: 397-8.

ULLMAN, B.L. The origin and development of humanistic script. 146 p., ill. Rome: Edizioni di Storia e Letteratura, 1960.
Reviewed by Bror Olsson, *Lychnos*, 1962, 235-6.

YGc-bv

SATTLER, Paul; SELLE, Götz von. Bibliographie zur Geschichte der Schrift bis in das Jahr 1930. xx, 234 p. (Archiv für Bibliographie, Beiheft 17) Linz a.d.: Winkler, 1935.
Reviewed by H. Jensen, *Orient.Lit.Zeitung*, 1936, 39: 674-6.

YGce-bv

IVINS, William M. List of lettering and writing books in the print room of the Metropolitan Museum of Art. *Bull.Metrop. Mus.Art*, 1929, 23: 297-9, ill.

YGhc

AINSWORTH, Michell. Evaluation de l'âge d'une écriture. *Ann. Chim.Anal.*, *2e ser.*, 1921, 3: 126-9.

YGj psychological aspects; graphology

GROSSMANN, Karl Josef. Aus der Geschichte der Graphologie. *Ciba Z.*, 1960, 9: 3246-58.

MENARD, Pierre. L'écriture et le subconscient. Psychanalyse et graphologie. 172 p., 62 autographes et fig. Paris: Alcan, 1931. [CB 33/405]

PREYER, William. Zur Psychologie des Schreibens mit besonderer Rücksicht auf individuelle Verschiedenheiten der Handschriften. 2nd ed. with supplement by Th. Preyer. vi, 256 p. Leipzig: Voss, 1919.
First published 1895.

ROUGEMONT, E. de. La graphologie, science d'observation. *Rev. Idées*, 1913, 10: 179-216, bibliogr.

SAUDEK, Robert. Experimentelle Graphologie. xii, 347 p. Berlin: Metzner, 1929.
Reviewed by Karl Birnbaum, *Deut.Lit.Zeitung*, 1929, 6: 2080-2.

SAUDEK, Robert. Experiments with handwriting. 395 p. London: Allen and Unwin, 1928.

SAUDEK, Robert. The handwriting of identical twins. *Ciba Symp.* (Summit, N.J.), 1941, 2: 717-20, fig.

YGv/x other special aspects

YGvd

WIRTH, Herman. Der Aufgang der Menschheit. Untersuchungen zur Geschichte der Religion, Symbolik und Schrift der atlantisch-nordischen Rasse. Vol. 1. Die Grundzüge. 632 p., 68 fig., 11 pl., 28 ill. Jena: Diederichs, 1928.
No more published.
Reviewed by Adolf Meyer, *Arch.Gesch.Math.Naturwiss.Tech.*, 1930, 12: 433-41.

YGvf

PROU, Maurice. Manuel de paléographie latine et française. 4th ed. reset with the collaboration of Alain de Bouärd. xii, 511 p., with album of 24 pl. Paris: Picard, 1924.
First published 1890.

YGwe-da

HEAL, Ambrose. The English writing-masters and their copybooks, 1570-1800. A biographical dictionary and a bibliography. With an introduction on the development of handwriting by Stanley Morison. Illustrated with portraits of the masters and specimens of their hands. xl, 225 p., 81 pl. Cambridge University Press, 1931.

YGwj

MARTINS, João. De l'histoire de la paléographie en Portugal. *Act.IIIe Congr.Int.Hist.Sci.* (Portugal, 1934), p. 127-36. Lisbon: 1936.

MILLARES CARLO, Augustin. Paleografía española: ensayo de una historia de la escritura en España desde el siglo VIII al XVII. 2 vol. 359 p., ill.; 131 p., ill. (Colección Labor, 192-4) Barcelona: Editorial Labor, 1929.
Reviewed by Charles Upson Clark, *Speculum*, 1930, 5: 454.

YGwo

BIANU, Ioan; CARTOGAN, N. Album de paleografie romaneasca (Scrierea Chirlica). 35 pl. Bucharest: Socec, 1929.
Reviewed by Samuel H. Cross, *Speculum*, 1930, 5: 326-7.

YH ALPHABET

CLODD, Edward. The story of the alphabet. ix, 209 p. New York: Appleton-Century, 1938. [CB 54/574]
First published 1900; re-issued with a foreword by George H. McKnight.

DIRINGER, David. The alphabet: a key to the history of mankind. Foreword by Sir Ellis Minns. 607 p. New York: Philosophical Library, 1948.
Reviewed by Robert H. Pfeiffer, *Isis*, 1949, 40: 87-8.

DORNSEIFF, Franz. Das Alphabet in Mystik und Magie. 2nd ed. vi, 195 p. (Stoicheia: Studien zur Geschichte des antiken Weltbildes und der griechischen Wissenschaft, 7) Leipzig: Teubner, 1925.
First edition 1922.

FÉVRIER, J.G. La genèse de l'alphabet d'après les découvertes récentes. *Rev.Hist.Phil.*, 1933, 1: 100-20.

GANDZ, Solomon. The dawn of literature. Prolegomena to a history of unwritten literature. *Osiris*, 1939, 7: 261-522. [CB 58/585]
Extension of the author's article, *see* below.

GANDZ, Solomon. The knot in Hebrew literature, or from the knot to the alphabet. *Isis*, 1930, 14: 189-214.

PETRIE, W.M. Flinders. The formation of the alphabet. iv, 20 p. (British School of Archeology in Egypt. Studies Series, 3) London: Macmillan, 1912.

SPRENGLING, Martin. The alphabet: its rise and development from the Sinai inscriptions. 71 p., 4 pl. Chicago: University of Chicago Press, 1931.
Reviewed by Flinders Petrie, *Antiquity*, 1932, 6: 375.

STÜBE, Rudolf. Der Ursprung des Alphabetes und seine Entwicklung. viii, 36 p. Berlin: Heintze & Blanckertz, 1921. [CB 18/646]

YHnb

GERMANY. REICHSDRUCKEREI. Alphabete und Schriftzeichen des Morgen- und Abendlandes zum allgemeinen Gebrauch, mit besonderer Berücksichtigung des Buchgewerbes, unter Mitwirkung von Fachgelehrten zusammengestellt in der Reichsdruckerei. 86 p. Berlin: 1924.
Reviewed by Ernst Lewy, *Deut.Lit.Zeitung*, 1926, 1681-3.

YJ LINGUISTICS

for linguistic and semantic aspects in the philosophy of science *see* Akn
for linguistic problems of communication in science *see* Anq
for terminology in science *see* Anh
for these aspects in the separate sciences *see* INDEX

YJc

GRAFF, Willem Laurens. Language and languages. An introduction to linguistics. xlvi, 487 p. London: Appleton, 1932.

GRAY, Louis H. Foundation of language. xv, 530 p. New York: Macmillan, 1939. [CB 58/585]
The last chapter is devoted to "The history of the study of language".

JESPERSEN, Otto. The classification of languages. A contribution to the history of linguistic science. *Scientia*, 1920, 28: 109-20. [CB 10/197]

MAROUZEAU, J. La linguistique ou science du langage. 190 p. Paris: Geuthner, 1921. [CB 10/197]
Concludes with a history of linguistics.

YJc-be

PEI, Mario A.; GAYNOR, Frank. A dictionary of linguistics. 238 p. New York: Philosophical Library, 1954.

YJcn

DAUZAT, Albert. Les atlas linguistiques et leurs progrès récents. *La Nature*, 1929, 57: 2e semestre, 4-7, 1 map.

JABERG, Karl; JUD, J. Der Sprachatlas als Forschungsinstrument, kritische Grundlegung und Einführung in den Sprach-und Sachatlas Italiens und der Südschweiz. iii, 243 p. Halle: Niemeyer, 1928.
Reviewed by A. Meillet, *J.Asiatique*, 1929, 215: 343.

YJhc

MEILLET, Antoine. Ce que les linguistes peuvent souhaiter d'une édition. *Bull.Ass.Guillaume Budé*, 1923, 1: 33-7.

YJj

LAFFAL, J. Freud's theory of language. *Psychoanal.Quart.*, 1964, 33: 157-75.

OGDEN, C.K.; RICHARDS, I.A. The meaning of meaning: a study of the influence of language upon thought and of the science of symbolism. With supplementary essays by B. Malinowski and F.G. Crookshank. 6th ed. London: Kegan Paul; New York: Harcourt Brace, 1944.
Third edition reviewed by A.K. Coomaraswamy, *J.Amer. Orient.Soc.*, 1933, 53: 298-303.

PAGET, Richard A.S. Sign language as a form of speech. *Nature*, 1936, 137: 384-8, 3 fig.

PILLSBURY, Walter Bowers; MEADER, Clarence L. The psychology of language. vii, 306 p. London: Appleton, 1928.

PSYCHOLOGIE du langage. [Articles by various authors.] *J. Psychol.Norm.Pathol.*, 1933, 30: 1-496.

RICHTER, Friedrich. Die Entwicklung der psychologischen Kindersprachforschung bis zum Beginn des 20. Jahrhunderts. Ein Beitrag zur Geschichte der Kinderseelenkunde. v, 116 p. Münster i. w.: Münsterverlag, 1927.

SCHILLER, F.C.S. The meaning of 'Meaning': a symposium by F.C.S. Schiller, B. Russell and H.H. Joachim. *Mind*, 1920, 29: 385-414.

YJk

BRUNOT, Ferdinand. La pensée et la langue. Méthode, principes et plan d'une théorie nouvelle du langage appliquée au français. xxxvi, 955 p. Paris: Masson, 1922. [CB 14/549]

CARNOY, Albert Joseph. La science du mot. Traité de sémantique. vii, 426 p. Louvain: Editions Universitas, 1927.
Reviewed in *Mélanges Univ.Saint-Joseph*, 1929, 14: 207-8.

DELACROIX, Henri. Le langage et la pensée. 602 p. Paris: F. Alcan, 1924.
Essay review by L. Weber, *Rev.Métaphys.Morale*, 1926, 33: 93-125.

GARDINER, Alan Henderson. Linguistic theory. *Eng.Stud.*, 1937, 19: 58-65.

GARDINER, Alan Henderson. The theory of speech and language. 2nd ed. xii, 348 p. Oxford: Clarendon Press, 1951.
1st published 1932.
Reviewed by N.B. Hunter, *Antiquity*, 1933, 7: 120-2.

HAYAKAWA, S.I. Language in action. ix, 245 p. New York: Harcourt Brace, 1941. [CB 62/84]
Reviewed by Eliseo Vivas, *Amer.Sociol.Rev.*, 1942, 7: 256-60.

JESPERSEN, Otto. The philosophy of grammar. 359 p. London: Allen and Unwin, 1924.

JOHNSON, Alexander Bryan. A treatise on language. Edited with a critical essay on his philosophy of language, by David Rynin. ix, 443 p. Berkeley: University of California Press, 1947.
Reviewed by I.A. Richards, *Isis*, 1948, 38: 251-2.

MacKAYE, James. The logic of language. 303 p. Hanover: Dartmouth College Publications, 1939. [CB 59/485]

SPITZER, Leo. Milieu and ambiance: an essay in historical semantics. *Phil.Phenomenol.Res.*, 1942, 3: 1-42, 169-218.

YJnb

BAYLEY, Harold. The lost language of symbolism; an inquiry into the origin of certain letters, words, names, fairy-tales, folklore, and mythologies. 2 vol. ix, 375 p.; viii, 388 p. New York: Barnes and Noble, 1912; reprinted 1951, 1952.
Reviewed by Sonia S. Wohl, *Isis*, 1952, 43: 301-2.

MEYER, Heinrich. Symbolgebilde der Sprache. *Stud.Gen.*, 1953, 6: 197-206.

URBAN, Wilbur Marshall. Language and reality. The philosophy of language and the principles of symbolism. 755 p. (Library of Philosophy). London: Allen & Unwin, 1939. [CB 79/190]
Reprinted 1951 (London: Allen & Unwin; New York: Macmillan Company).

YJnh-be

MAROUZEAU, J. Lexique de la terminologie grammaticale et linguistique. iv, 182 p. Paris: Geuthner, 1932.

MAROUZEAU, J. Lexique de la terminologie linguistique. 205 p. Paris: Geuthner, 1933. [CB 40/412]

YJs

DOROSZEWSKI, W. Quelques remarques sur les rapports de la sociologie et de la linguistique: Durkheim et F. de Saussure. *J.Psychol.Norm.Pathol.*, 1933, 30: 82-91.

SAPIR, Edward. Selected writings in language, culture and personality. Ed. by David G. Mandelbaum. xv, 617 p., bibliogr. Berkeley, Calif.: University of California Press, 1949. [CB 77/342]

YJsc

SCHMIDT-ROHR, Georg. Die Sprache als Bildnerin der Völker. Eine Wesens- und Lebenskunde der Volkstümer. 418 p. (Schriften der Deutschen Akademie, 12) Jena: Diederichs, 1932.
Reviewed by Friedrich Panzer, *Deut.Lit.Zeitung*, 1932, 3: 2262-9.

VOSSLER, Karl. The spirit of language in civilization. Transl. by Oscar Oeser. vii, 247 p. (International Library of Psychology, Philosophy and Scientific Method) London: Kegan Paul, 1932.
Reviewed in *Nature*, 1933, 131: 152.

YJv

SCHEFTELOWITZ, J. Gleichklangzauber in Indien und im jüdischen Volksglauben. *Z.Deut.Morgenländ.Ges.*, *new ser.*, 1924, 3: no. 2, 106-10. [CB 18/645]

YJwg

MEILLET, Antoine. Ce que la linguistique doit aux savants allemands. *Scientia*, 1923, 33: 263-71. [CB 14/550]

YJxd

BOOTH, Andrew D.; BRANDWOOD, L.; CLEAVE, J.P. Mechanical resolution of linguistic problems. vii, 306 p. London: Butterworths Scientific Publication; New York: Academic Press, 1958. [CB 84/329]

YJyBW

DUFRENOY, M.L. Analyse statistique du langage. *J.Soc. Statist.Paris*, 1946, 87: 208-19.

YULE, G. Udny. The statistical study of literary vocabulary. ix, 306 p. Cambridge University Press; New York: The Macmillan Co., 1944. [CB 68/59]
Reviewed by M.G. Kendall, *Nature*, 1944, 153: 570-1.

YJzp PHONETICS

PANCONCELLI-CALZIA, Giulio. Quellenatlas zur Geschichte der Phonetik. 86 p., ill. Hamburg: Hansischer Gildenverlag, 1940.
Reviewed by J.A.V., *Janus*, 1940, 44: 316-17.

YJzp-s

PANCONCELLI-CALZIA, Giulio. Phonetik und Kultur. 78 p., 12 pl. Hamburg: Hansischer Gildenverlag, 1938. [CB 56/402]
Reviewed by J.A.V., *Janus*, 1940, 44: 316-17.

YL HISTORY OF LANGUAGE

BEKHTEREV, Vladimir M. Ueber die biologische Entwicklung der menschlichen Sprache. *Folia Neuro-Biol.*, Sept. 1913, 7: 595-610.

BLOOMFIELD, Leonard. Language. ix, 564 p. New York: Holt, 1933.
Reviewed by Franklin Edgerton, *J.Amer.Orient.Soc.*, 1933, 53: 295-7.

DAUZAT, Albert. La géographie linguistique. *Rev.Mois*, 1913, 16: 279-95.

FEBVRE, Lucien. Le développement des langues et l'histoire. *Rev.Syn.Hist.*, 1913, 27: 52-65.

FRIEDRICH, Johannes. Extinct languages. (Transl. by Frank Gaynor from the original German) x, 182 p., front., 73 fig. New York: Philosophical Library, 1957.
Translation of: Entzifferung verschollener Schriften und Sprachen (Berlin: Springer, 1954).

HOVELACQUE, Abel. La linguistique. Histoire naturelle du langage. 5th ed. xv, 448 p. (Bibliothèque des Sciences Contemporaines) Paris: Costes, 1922.
1st edition 1876.

JESPERSEN, Otto. Language. Its nature, development and origin. 448 p. London: Allen & Unwin; New York: Holt, 1922.
Reprinted New York: Macmillan, 1947.

KIECKERS, Ernst. Die Sprachstämme der Erde. Mit einer Anzahl grammatischer Skizzen. xii, 257 p. (Kultur und Sprache, 7) Heidelberg: Winter, 1931.
Reviewed by Ernst Lewy, *Deut.Lit.Zeitung*, 1932, 3: 534-7.

LAGUNA, Grace (Mead) Andrus de. Speech; its function and development. xii, 363 p. New Haven: Yale University Press, 1927.

LIDDELL, Mark H. New light on the physical data of language. *Sci.Mon.*, 1925, 21: 487-502.

LITTMANN, Enno. Deutschland und Morgenland im Lichte der Lehnwörter. *Z.Deut.Morgenländ.Ges.*, 1924, *new ser.* 3: no. 2, 73-87. [CB 18/588]

MEILLET, Antoine. Les langues dans l'Europe nouvelle. Un appendice de L. Tesnière sur la statistique des langues de l'Europe. xii, 495 p. Paris: Payot, 1928.

MEILLET, Antoine. Linguistique historique et linguistique générale. viii, 334 p. (Collection linguistique publiée par la Société de Linguistique de Paris, 8) Paris: Champion, 1921.
Reviewed by A. Ernout, *J.Savants*, 1921, 205-14, 258-64; by Ed. Hermann, *Deut.Lit.Zeitung*, 1921, 349.

MEILLET, Antoine. La méthode comparative en linguistique historique. viii, 117 p. (Instituttet for Sammenlignende Kulturforskning, ser. A, 2) Oslo: Aschehovg; Cambridge: Harvard University Press, 1925.

MEILLET, Antoine. Le problème de la parenté des langues. *Scientia*, 1914, 15: 403-25. [CB 6/477]

MEILLET, Antoine; COHEN, Marcel; ed. Les langues du monde, par un groupe de linguistes. xvi, 812 p., maps. (Collection Linguistique publiée par la Société de Linguistique de Paris, 16) Paris: Champion, 1924. [CB 22/298]

PAGET, Richard A.S. Babel: or the past, present and future of human speech. 93 p. (To-day and To-morrow Series) London: Kegan Paul, 1930.

REISS, Samuel. The rise of words and their meanings. 301 p. New York: Philosophical Library, 1950. [CB 77/382]

SARTON, George. The tower of Babel. (Preface to volume 39) *Isis*, 1948, 39: 3-15, 2 facs.

SCHLAUCH, Margaret. The gift of tongues. ix, 348 p. New York: Modern Age Books, 1942.
An introduction to the science of language.

SCHMIDT, Wilhelm. Die Sprachfamilien und Sprachenkreise der Erde. xvi, 596 p., with atlas of 14 maps. (Kulturgeschichtliche Bibliothek, ser. 1: Ethnologische Bibliothek, 5) Heidelberg: C. Winter, 1926. [CB 28/563]
Reviewed in *Nature*, 1927, 120: 288-90.

TERRACHER, Louis Adolphe. L'histoire des langues et la géographie linguistique. 31 p. (The Zaharoff Lecture. 1929) Oxford: Clarendon Press, 1929.

VENDRYES, Joseph. Le langage. Introduction linguistique à l'histoire. xxxii, 440 p. (Évolution de l'humanité, 3) Paris: Renaissance du livre, 1921.
[With a new bibliographical appendix] xxxii, 456 p. Paris: Michel, 1939. Reprinted 1950.

VENDRYES, Joseph. Language: a linguistic introduction to history. Transl. by Paul Radin. xxviii, 378 p. (The History of Civilization) London: Kegan Paul, 1925.
Translation of: Le langage, *see* above.

YLnh-be

HALLIWELL PHILLIPPS, James Orchard. A dictionary of archaic and provincial words, obsolete phrases, proverbs and ancient customs from the XIV century. 7th ed. xxxvi, 960 p. London: Routledge; New York: Dutton, 1924.
First edition, 2 volumes, 1846 (1847); 2nd edition, 1850; 6th edition, 2 volumes, London: Routledge, 1904.

YLvp-j

JÓHANNESSON, Alexander. Gesture origin of Indo-European languages. *Nature*, 1944, 153: 171-2.

YLsc

WOOLNER, A.C. Languages in history and politics. xii, 167 p. London: Oxford University Press, 1939.

YLza ARTIFICIAL LANGUAGES

EATON, Helen S. The educational value of an artificial language. *Mod.Lang.J.*, 1927, 12: 8 p.

FOSTER, Edward Powell. Alphabet of ideas or dictionary of Ro. The world language. 159 p. Waverly, W.Va.: Roia, 1928.

GODE, Alexander. The case for Interlingua. *Sci.Mon.*, 1953, 77: 88-90. [CB 80/120]

GUÉRARD, Albert Léon. A short history of the international language movement. 268 p. London: Fisher Unwin, 1922.

GUIGNON, J. L'état actuel du problème d'une langue auxiliaire internationale. [With comments by Charles Lyon-Caen and André Lalande] *Compt.Rend.Acad.Sci.Morales Polit.*, oct-déc. 1926, 381-404. [CB 23/263]

MACAULAY, T.C.; SMITH, J.A. Interlanguage. By T.C. Macaulay. Artificial languages. By J.A. Smith. With an introd. by Elizabeth Daryush. p. 451-77. (Society for Pure English. Tract no. 34) Oxford: Clarendon Press, 1930.

PANKHURST, Estelle Sylvia. Delphos: the future of international language. 95 p. (To-day and To-morrow Series) London:

YR EDUCATION

for education in science *see* Ao
education in the separate sciences *see* INDEX

YRc general history

COMPAYRÉ, Gabriel. Histoire de la pédagogie. 29th ed. 512 p. Paris: Delaplane, 1922. [CB 14/546]
First published 1884.

CUBBERLEY, Ellwood Patterson. The history of education. Educational practice and progress considered as a phase of the development and spread of Western civilization. xxiv, 849 p. Boston: Houghton Mifflin, 1920.

GARCIA Y BARBARIN, Eugenio. Historia de la pedagogia. 5th ed. by Gerardo Rodriguez Garcia. 399 p. Madrid: Hernando, 1932.
First published 1903.

GOLLANCZ, Hermann. Pedagogics of the Talmud and that of modern times. A comparative study. viii, 120 p. London: Oxford University Press, 1924. [CB 18/595]

HÉGER, Paul. Les bases de la pédagogie moderne, à propos de l'inauguration de l'Institut Buls-Tempels. *Rev.Univ. Bruxelles*, 1914, 9 p. [CB 5/299]

MARCHESINI, Giovanni. Disegno storico delle dottrine pedagogiche. 4th ed. 294 p. Roma: Athenaeum, 1918.

MULHERN, James. A history of education. 2nd ed. 754 p. New York: Ronald Press, 1959.
First edition 1946.
Reviewed by Robert Ulich, *Amer.Hist.Rev.*, 1947, 52: 708-9.

OSBORN, Henry Fairfield. Creative education in school, college, university and museum: personal observation and experience of the half-century 1877-1927. xiv, 360 p. New York: Scribner, 1927.

ULICH, Robert. History of educational thought. xii, 412 p., bibliogr. New York: American Book Company, 1945.
Reviewed by Theodore Brameld, *Amer.Hist.Rev.*, 1946, 51: 352.

WIFSTRAND, Albert. Bildning. Ett begrepps historia. [Bildung. Die Geschichte eines Begriffs. (In Swedish, with German summary)] *Lychnos*, 1946-47, 1-10.

WOLFENDEN, John. The educated man today and tomorrow. 26 p. (Technics & Purpose, 6) London: Student Christian Movement Press, 1959.

YRc-be

SCHWARTZ, Hermann, ed. Pädagogisches Lexikon. In Verbindung mit der Gesellschaft für evangelische Pädagogik und unter Mitwirkung zahlreicher Fachmänner. 4 vol. Bielefeld: Velhagen, 1928-31.
Volume 1 reviewed by Fr. Delakat, *Deut.Lit.Zeitung*, 1929, 6: 511-14.

WATSON, Foster, ed. The encyclopaedia and dictionary of education. 4 vol., ill. London/New York: Pitman, 1921-22.

YRdaj

HADLICH, Hermann. Quellenhefte zur Geschichte der Pädagogik. 4 vol. 1. Aus dem Altertum, dem Mittelalter, der Humanisten- und Reformationszeit. iv, 58 p.; 2. Aus der Zeit der Aufklärung und des Pietismus. iv, 52 p.; 3. Aus der Zeit vor hundert Jahren. iv, 52 p.; 4. Aus der Gegenwart. iv, 58 p. Leipzig: Teubner, 1913. [CB 5/306]

MIELI, Aldo. Pedagogisti ed educatori antichi e moderni. *Isis*, 1919, 2: 399.
Short note to announce the publication of a new collection edited by Giuseppe Lombardo-Radice and published by Sandron, Palermo.

ULICH, Robert, ed. Three thousand years of educational wisdom: selections from great documents. x, 614 p. Cambridge: Harvard University Press, 1947.
Reviewed by Richard Boyd Ballou, *Isis*, 1948, 38: 272.

YRhd

TITS, Désiré. Projet d'une histoire universelle de l'éducation. *Act.VIIIe Congr.Int.Hist.Sci.* (Florence, 1956), (3), p. 1165-70. Paris: Hermann, 1958.

YRj psychological aspects

BERTRAND, François Louis. L'analyse psycno-sensorielle et ses applications à l'éducation intégrale. 302 p., 4 pl. Paris: Alcan, 1930. [CB 33/419]

CLAPARÈDE, Edouard. Comment diagnostiquer les aptitudes chez les écoliers. 300 p. (Bibliothèque de Philosophie Scientifique) Paris: Flammarion, 1924.
Reviewed by L. Guinet, *Isis*, 1924, 6: 571-2.

LASCARIS, P.A. L'éducation esthétique de l'enfant. 508 p. (Thèse) Paris: Alcan, 1928. [CB 27/584]
The first sixty pages of this thesis give the history of aesthetic education.

PFISTER, O. Psychoanalysis in the service of education, being an introduction to psychoanalysis. Authorized translation. xii, 176 p. London: H. Kimpton, 1922.
Translation of: Was bietet die Psychoanalyse dem Erzieher (Leipzig: Klinkhardt, 1917; 2nd ed. 1923). For French translation (Berne: 1921) *see* CB 13/303.

SARTON, George. Ugly ducklings. (Preface to vol. XXX) *Isis*, 1939, 30: 6-16.
Apropos of the education of gifted children.

WATSON, Robert I. A brief history of educational psychology. *Psychol.Rec.*, 1961, 11: 209-42.

YRk philosophy of education

BERKSON, L.B. Preface to an educational philosophy. xvi, 250 p. New York: Columbia University Press, 1940. [CB 60/171]

FISCHER, Aloys. Der Einheitsgedanke in der Schulorganisation. 38 p. Jena: Diederichs, 1914. [CB 6/477]

HILDEBRAND, Joel H. A philosophy of teaching. *J.Chem.Educ.*, 1949, 26: 450-5.

KANDEL, I.L. Conflicting theories of education. xiii, 177 p. New York: Macmillan, 1938.

KILPATRICK, William Heard. Source book in the philosophy of education. Rev. ed. xviii, 535 p. New York: Macmillan, 1934.
First published 1923.

LILGE, Fritz. Revitalizing learning. *Educ.Forum*, 1940, 389-99.

LIVINGSTONE, Richard. Education and the spirit of the age. 114 p. Oxford: Clarendon Press, 1952. [CB 79/196]

YRo method of teaching; primary, secondary and higher education

YRod

ADAMS, Charles Christopher. School museums, field trips and travel as phases of objective education. *Bull.N.Y. State Mus.*, 1942, no. 330, 75-118, 27 fig.

GRAVES, Frank Pierrepont. Is the Montessori method a fad? *Pop.Sci.Mon.*, June 1914, 84: 609-14.

SUCHODOLSKI, Bogdan. Investigation and teaching. *Organon*, 1938, 2: 43-78.

YRom

DESFORGE, J.; ILIOVICI, G.; ROBERT, P. L'oeuvre de M. Jacques Hadamard et l'enseignement secondaire. *Enseign.Sci.*, 1936, 9: 97-117.

YRop

CORRIGAN, Joseph Moran. University and universality. Rectorial oration, November 13, 1939. 33 p. Washington, D.C.: Catholic University of America Press, 1940.

KENYON, Frederic George. Education, secondary and university. A report of conferences between the Council for Humanistic Studies and the Conjoint Board of Scientific Societies. 47 p. London: Murray, 1919.

LINDBERG, Sten G. Tredje opponenten, terrae filius och quodlibetarius. Till det akademiska disputationsväsendets historia. [The "third opponent", the "ivy orator", the "praevaricator", the "terrae filius" and the "quodlibetarius". A contribution to the history of academical disputations. (In Swedish, with English summary)] *Lychnos*, 1950-51, 59-103.

PAYNE, Fernandus; SPIETH, Evelyn Wilkinson. An open letter to college teachers. xi, 380 p. Bloomington, Ind.: Principia Press, 1935. [CB 46/603]

YRoq

AIGRAN, René. Les universités catholiques. 81 p. Paris: Picard, 1935.
Reviewed by Pierre Brunet, *Archeion*, 1936, 18: 292-4.

CATTELL, J. MacKeen. University control. viii, 484 p. New York: Science Press, 1913.

IRSAY, Stephen d'. Histoire des universités françaises et étrangères des origines à nos jours. 1. Moyen âge et renaissance. xii, 372 p., ill. 2. Du XVIe siècle à 1860. 451 p. Paris: Picard, 1933-35.
No more published.
Volume 1 reviewed by G.C. Sellery, *Amer.Hist.Rev.*, 1933, 39: 301-3; by Hélène Metzger, *Archeion*, 1933, 15: 298-300; by Gaines Post, *Speculum*, 1934, 9: 102-5; volume 2 by Pierre Brunet, *Archeion*, 1936, 18: 292-4.

ORTEGA Y GASSET, José. Mission of the university. Transl., with an introduction, by Howard Lee Nostrand. 103 p. Princeton: Princeton University Press, 1944. [CB 68/63]
Translation of the Spanish work first published Madrid: 1936.

SIGERIST, Henry E. The university at the crossroads. Addresses and essays. ix, 162 p. New York: Schuman, 1946. [CB 70/275]

SIGERIST, Henry E. The university's dilemma. *Bull.Hist.Med.*, 1943, 14: 1-13.

SPRANGER, Eduard. Wandlungen im Wesen der Universität seit 100 Jahren. 39 p. Leipzig: E. Wiegandt, 1913.

YRorw

WHITE, Lynn. Educating our daughters: a challenge to the colleges. x, 166 p. New York: Harper, 1950. [CB 77/388]

YRov

GRUENBERG, Benjamin C. The diffusion and dissipation of learning. *J.Adult Educ.* (New York), April 1934, 3-18.

YRp/t other special aspects

YRpw

COMMISSION FOR RELIEF IN BELGIUM EDUCATIONAL FOUNDATION. C.R.B. exchanges. Biographical records, Belgium and the United States, 1920-1936. 131 p. New York: C.R.B. Educational Foundation, 1937. [CB 55/163]

YRr

WILSON, Logan. The academic man. viii, 248 p. New York: Oxford University Press, 1942.
Reviewed by M.F. Ashley Montagu, *Isis*, 1943, 34: 528-9.

YRs

GREENE, Theodore M.; *et al.* Liberal education re-examined. xiv, 134 p. New York: Harper, 1943. [CB 65/89]
This is the report of a committee appointed by the American Council of Learned Societies on the role of education in a democracy.

MONTAGU, M.F. Ashley. The improvement of human relations through education. *Sch.Soc.*, 1947, 65: 465-9.

RUSSELL, Bertrand. Education and the social order. 254 p. London: Allen and Unwin, 1932.
Reviewed by R. Brightman, *Nature*, 1932, 130: 863-5.

YRsc

CHEVALIER, Jacques. En quoi consiste le progrès de l'humanité. Habitudes transmises ou éducation reçue? *Compt.Rend.Acad. Sci.Morales Polit.*, 1930, 293-310.

YRsr

TAYLOR, Henry Osborn. Freedom of the mind in history. xii, 297 p. London: Macmillan, 1923.

YRt

MILNER, Alfred Milner, *Viscount*. On classical education and humanism. *Isis*, 1923, 5: 137-40.
Reprinted from the presidential address to the Classical Association, January 1922.

YRv/w ethnic groups; different countries

YRvm-qg

WEINREICH, M. Ein jiddisches wissenschaftliches Institut. Z. *Deut.Morgenländ.Ges.*, 1926, 5: 68-70. [CB 21/558]

YRvm-r

GINZBERG, Louis. Students, scholars and saints. xi, 291 p. Philadelphia: Jewish Publication Society of America, 1928.
Reviewed by Julius H. Greenstone, *Jew.Quart.Rev.*, 1931, 22: 69-71.

YRw-oq

FLEXNER, Abraham. Universities: American, English, German. x, 381 p. New York: Oxford University Press, 1930.
German translation Berlin: Springer, 1932.

THWING, Charles Franklin. The American and the German university. One hundred years of history. 238 p. London: Macmillan, 1928.

YRwb North America

BROWN, Rollo Walter. The creative spirit. An inquiry into American life. 233 p. New York: Harper, 1925. [CB 18/641]

COHN, Alfred E. Minerva's progress. Tradition and dissent in American culture. 101 p. New York: Harcourt, Brace, 1946. [CB 70/274]

CONANT, James Bryant. The citadel of learning. vii, 79 p. New Haven: Yale University Press; London: Oxford University Press, 1956.
The three chapters discuss: The citadel of learning; An old tradition in a new world; Some basic problems of American education.

KALLEN, Horace M. The education of free men. An essay toward a philosophy of education for Americans. xx, 332 p. New York: Farrar, Straus, 1949. [CB 76/415]

ULICH, Robert. Crisis and hope in American education. xiv, 235 p. Boston: Beacon Press, 1951.
Reviewed by Aaron J. Ihde, *Isis*, 1952, 43: 301.

YRwb-ce

MORISON, Samuel Eliot. Old school and college books in the Prince library. *Bull.Boston Publ.Libr.*, 1936, 11: 77-93, 3 facs. [CB 47/258]

YRwb-da

CATTELL, J. McKeen, ed. Leaders in education. A biographical directory. 2nd ed. vi, 1134 p. New York: Science Press, 1941. [CB 35/314]
First published 1932.

YRwb-om

HOLMES, Pauline. A tercentenary history of the Boston Public Latin School. xxiv, 541 p. (Harvard Studies in Education, 25) Cambridge, Mass.: Harvard University Press, 1935.

YRwb-op

SCHMIDT, George P. Intellectual crosscurrents in American colleges, 1825-1955. *Amer.Hist.Rev.*, 1936, 42: 46-67.

STORR, Richard J. The beginnings of graduate education in America. ix, 195 p. Chicago, Ill.: University of Chicago Press; London: Cambridge University Press, 1953. [CB 80/119]
An account of graduate education chiefly in reference to Columbia University.

YRwb-oq

BEACH, Arthur Granville. A pioneer college. The story of Marietta. xiv, 325 p. Chicago: Cuneo Press, 1935.
Reviewed by Homer C. Hockett, *Amer.Hist.Rev.*, 1936, 41: 392.

BRONSON, Walter Cochrane. The History of Brown University, 1764-1914. ix, 547 p., ill. Providence, R.I.: Brown University, 1916.

CHEYNEY, Edward Potts. History of the University of Pennsylvania. 1740-1940. x, 461 p. Philadelphia, Pa.: University of Pennsylvania Press, 1940.
Reviewed by Donald G. Tewksbury, *Amer.Hist.Rev.*, 1942, 47: 616-17.

COLUMBIA UNIVERSITY. The rise of a university. 2 vol. New York: Columbia University Press, 1937.

CROSBIE, Laurence M. The Phillips Exeter Academy. A history. xii, 347 p. Norwood, Mass.: Plimpton Press, 1923.

DEMAREST, William H.S. A history of Rutgers College, 1766-1924. x, 570 p. New Brunswick, N.J.: The College, 1924.
Reviewed by J.W.T., *Amer.Hist.Rev.*, 1924, 30: 164-6.

ELLIOTT, Orrin Leslie. Stanford University. The first twenty-five years. xiii, 624 p. Stanford, Calif.: University Press, 1937.

FUESS, Claude Moore. Amherst: the story of a New England college. xiii, 372 p. Boston: Little, Brown, 1935.
Reviewed by J.F. Jameson, *Amer.Hist.Rev.*, 1935, 41: 197.

GOODSPEED, Thomas Wakefield. The story of the University of Chicago, 1890-1925. xv, 244 p., 16 pl. Chicago, Ill.: University of Chicago Press, 1925.

HATCH, Louis C. The history of Bowdoin College. xii, 500 p. Portland, Me.: Loring, Short and Harmon, 1927.
Reviewed by W.E. Lunt, *Amer.Hist.Rev.*, 1928, 33: 705.

HEPBURN, William Murray; SEARS, Louis Martin. Purdue University. Fifty years of progress. vi, 203 p. Indianapolis, Ind.: Hollenbeck Press, 1925.

JONES, Rufus Matthew. Haverford College. A history and an interpretation. xi, 244 p. London: MacMillan, 1933.

MORISON, Samuel Eliot. The tercentennial history of Harvard College and University, 1636-1936. 4 vol. 1. The development of Harvard University since the inauguration of President Eliot, 1869-1929. xc, 660.p.; 2. The founding of Harvard College. xxvi, 472 p.; 3. Harvard College in the seventeenth century. 2 vol. Cambridge, Mass.: Harvard University Press, 1930-36.
Reviewed by George Sarton, *Isis*, 1936, 25: 513-20, fig. [CB 44/485]

PIRENNE, Henri. Les universités américaines. New ed. 31 p. New York: Belgian American Educational Foundation, 1939.

SEELYE, Laurenus Clark. The early history of Smith College, 1871-1910. xi, 242 p. Boston, Mass.: Houghton Mifflin, 1923.

SMYTHE, George Franklin. Kenyon College: its first century. x, 349 p. New Haven, Conn.: Yale University Press, 1924.

STEWART, Wallace William. A history of the University of Toronto, 1827-1927. 308 p. Toronto: University Press, 1927.

WALTON, Clarence Eldon. An historical prospect of Harvard College, 1636-1936. 48 p., 8 pl. Boston, Mass.: Society for the Preservation of New England Antiquities, 1936.

YRwb-orw

WOODY, Thomas. A history of women's education in the United States. 2 vol. xvi, 608 p., 70 fig.; xii, 646 p., 54 fig. New York: Science Press, 1929. [CB 42/612]

YRwb-ov

PARK, Charles F. A history of the Lowell Institute School (1903-1928). 192 p. Cambridge, Mass.: Harvard University Press, 1931.
An account of an educational experiment begun in 1903 and continued for more than twenty-five years.

YRwb-r

BARZUN, Jacques. Teacher in America. vi, 321 p. Boston: Little, Brown, 1945.
Reviewed by M.F. Ashley Montagu, *Isis*, 1947, 37: 125.

YRwb-sc

BUCK, Paul H.; *et al.* The role of education in American history. 16 p. New York: Fund for the Advancement of Education, 1957

YRwc Latin America

YRwc-oq

BONAVIT, Julian. Fragmentos de la historia de Colegio Primitivo y Nacional de San Nicolás de Hidalgo. 344 p., ill. Morelia, Mexico: Departamento de Extensión Universitaria, 1940.
Reviewed by José Babini, *Archeion*, 1940, 22: 358-9.

ENGERRAND, Jorge. L'école nationale des hautes études de Mexico. *Isis*, 1914, 2: 170-1. [CB 7/152]
Created by Ezequiel Chavez.

YRwd Europe

ULICH, Robert. The dilemma of European education. *Harvard Educ.Rev.*, 1947, 17: 85-90.

YRwd-rg

HARGREAVES-MAWDSLEY, W. A history of academical dress in Europe. xiii, 235 p. Oxford: Clarendon Press, 1963.

YRwe British Isles

ARMYTAGE, W.H.G. Four hundred years of English education. viii, 353 p., index. Cambridge University Press, 1964.

CLARKE, M.L. Classical education in Britain 1500-1900. viii, 234 p., bibliogr. Cambridge/New York: Cambridge University Press, 1959.
Reviewed by E.V.C. Plumptre, *Gnomon*, 1959, 31: 465-9; by Donald Lemen Clark, *Renaiss.News*, 1959, 12: 277-8.

DRESSLER, Bruno. Geschichte der englischen Erziehung. Versuch einer ersten kritischen Gesamtdarstellung der Entwicklung der englischen Erziehung. xii, 340 p. Leipzig: Teubner, 1928.
Reviewed by Paul Meissner, *Deut.Lit.Zeitung*, 1928, 5: 2398.

JARMAN, T.L. Landmarks in the history of education. English education as part of the European tradition. viii, 323 p. London: Cresset Press, 1951; New York: Philosophical Library, 1952. [CB 79/195]

JESSOP, J.C. Education in Angus. An historical survey of education up to the Act of 1872 from original and contemporary sources. viii, 328 p. London: University of London Press, 1931.

JONES, Evan J. History of education in Wales. Vol. 1. x, 300 p. Wrexham: Hughes, 1931.
No more published.

YRwe-of-bv

CHAMPNEYS, M.C. An English bibliography of examinations, 1900-1932. xxiv, 141 p. London: Macmillan, 1934.
Bibliography of books and articles published in Great Britain, 1900-1932 (and a short list from 1700 onwards), which have influenced the examination question.
Reviewed by T.A.A. Broadbent, *Math.Gaz.*, 1935, 19: 64.

YRwe-om

BIRCHENOUGH, Charles. History of elementary education in England and Wales: from 1800 to the present day. 2nd edition. viii, 514 p. London: University Tutorial Press, 1925.
First edition London: W.B. Clive, 1914.

GREAT BRITAIN. BOARD OF EDUCATION. Report of the consultative committee on secondary education with special reference to grammar schools and technical high schools. [Chairman: Will Spens]. xxxviii, 477 p. London: H.M. Stationery Off., 1938.
Reviewed by George Sarton, *Isis*, 1940, 31: 488-90.

MACK, Edward C. Public schools and British opinion since 1860. xii, 511 p. New York: Columbia University Press, 1941. [CB 64/457]

YRwe-on

BARNES, Arthur Stapylton. The Catholic schools of England. xi, 255 p. London: Williams and Norgate, 1926.

BRADLEY A.G.; CHAMPNEYS, A.C.; BAINES, J.W. A history of Marlborough College. Now rev. and continued by J.R. Taylor, H.C. Brentnall, and G.C. Turner. xii, 332 p., 16 pl. London: Murray, 1923.

DRUETT, Walter W. Harrow through the ages. xvi, 239 p. Uxbridge: King and Hutchings, 1935.

GRAY, John Milner. A history of the Perse School. 162 p., 7 ill. Cambridge: Bowes and Bowes, 1921.

LEMPRIERE, William. A history of the girls' school of Christ's Hospital, London, Hoddesdon, and Hertford. xiv, 98 p. Cambridge University Press, 1924.

MERCHANT TAYLORS' SCHOOL. Its origin, history and present surroundings. [Ed. by W.C. Farr.] 170 p., pl. Oxford: Blackwell, 1929.

RAINE, Angelo. History of St. Peter's School, York, A.D. 627 to the present day. xii, 212 p., pl. London: Bell, 1926.

RIVINGTON, Septimus. The history of Tonbridge School: from its foundation in 1553 to the present date. 4th ed., rev. xi, 372 p., 44 pl. London: Rivingtons, 1925.
First edition 1869, third 1910.

SARGANT, Walter Lee, ed. The book of Oakham School. 79 p., pl. Cambridge: University Bookshop, 1928.

SARGEAUNT, John. A history of Bedford School. Ed. and completed by Ernest Hockliffe. xii, 260 p. London: Fisher Unwin, 1925.

SYMONS, Katherine Elizabeth. The grammar school of King Edward VI, Bath, and its ancient foundation. x, 372 p. Bath: Wood, 1934.

TANNER, Lawrence Edward. Westminster School. A history. 132 p. London: Westminster Abbey, 1934.

WILKINS, Harold Tom. Great English schools. Wood engravings by H. George Webb. xv, 320 p. London: Noel Douglas, 1926.

YRwe-oq

ATTWATER, Aubrey. Pembroke College, Cambridge. A short history. Ed., with an introduction and a postscript, by S.C. Roberts. viii, 129 p. Cambridge University Press, 1936.

BARKER, Ernest. Universities in Great Britain, their position and their problems. 98 p. London: Student Christian Movement, 1931.

BELLOT, Hugh Hale Leigh. University College, London, 1826-1926. xvi, 464 p., front., pl., map. London: University of London Press, 1929.

BURNS, Cecil Delisle. A short history of Birkbeck College (University of London). 170 p. London: University of London Press, 1924.

CHARLTON, H.B. Portrait of a university, 1851-1951. To commemorate the centenary of Manchester University. x, 185 p., 23 pl. Manchester: Manchester University Press, 1951.
Reviewed by A.D. Ritchie, *Nature*, 1951, 168: 846.

DAVIS, Valentine David. A history of Manchester College, from its foundation in Manchester to its establishment in Oxford. 216 p. London: Allen and Unwin, 1932.

FORBES, Mansfield D., ed. Clare College, 1326-1926. University Hall, 1326-1346. Clare Hall, 1346-1856. 2 vol. xxxvi 270 p.; xl, 389 p., pl. Cambridge: Clare College, 1928.

HAMILTON, Mary Agnes. Newnham. An informal biography. 199 p., pl. London: Faber and Faber, 1936.

HEARNSHAW, Fossey John Cobb. The centenary history of King's College, London, 1828-1928. 543 p. London: Harrap, 1929.

JONES, William Henry Samuel. A history of St. Catharine's College, once Catharine Hall, Cambridge. xiv, 413 p. Cambridge University Press, 1936.

MAGRATH, John Richard. The Queen's College. 2 vol., 46 pl. Oxford: Clarendon Press, 1921.

MALLET, Charles Edward. A history of the University of Oxford. 3 vol. London: Methuen, 1924-27.

MANSBRIDGE, Albert. The older universities of England: Oxford and Cambridge. xxiv, 296 p., 8 pl. London: Longmans, Green, 1923; Boston: Houghton Mifflin, 1924. [CB 16/296]
Reviewed by S.E. Morison, *New Republic*, April 16, 1924.

MORGAN, Alexander. Scottish university studies. viii, 216 p. London: Oxford University Press, 1933.

MORGAN, Alexander. University of Edinburgh: charters, statutes, and acts of the town council and the senatus, 1583-1858. Historical introductions by Robert Kerr Hannay. xi, 294 p. London: Oliver and Boyd, 1937.

MURRAY, David. Memories of the old College of Glasgow. Some chapters in the history of the University. xv, 631 p. Glasgow: Jackson, Wylie, 1927.

UNIVERSITY COLLEGE, UNIVERSITY OF LONDON. Centenary addresses. Preface by R.W. Chambers. 12 pt. in 1 vol. London: University of London Press, 1927.
Reviewed in *Nature*, 1928, 121: 271-4.

WALKER, Thomas Alfred. Peterhouse. xvii, 157 p. Cambridge: Heffer, 1935.

WHITING, Charles Edwin. The University of Durham, 1832-1932. xiii, 345 p. London: Sheldon Press, 1932.

WIGHTMAN, William P.D. The founding of Edinburgh University. *Isis*, 1955, 46: 367.

YRwe-orw

GARDINER, Dorothy. English girlhood at school. A study of women's education through twelve centuries. xiii, 501 p., pl. London: Oxford University Press, 1929.
Reviewed by Paul Meissner, *Deut.Lit.Zeitung*, 1929, 6: 1758-63.

YRwe-qb

MORRAH, Herbert Arthur. The Oxford Union, 1823-1923. x, 326 p. London: Cassell, 1923.

YRwe-r

WELLS, Herbert George. The story of a great schoolmaster: being a plain account of the life and ideas of Sanderson of Oundle. vi, 151 p., 3 pl., portr. London: Chatto and Windus; New York: Macmillan, 1924.

YRwf France

BARNARD, Howard Clive. The French tradition in education. Ramus to Mme Necker de Saussure. vii, 319 p., ill. Cambridge University Press, 1922.

DURKHEIM, Emile. L'évolution pédagogique en France. 2 vol. 1. Des origines à la renaissance. 2. De la renaissance à nos jours. (Bibliothèque de Philosophie Contemporaine) Paris: Alcan, 1938.

YRwf-aq

GAUDEFROY-DEMOMBYNES, Roger. L'oeuvre française en matière d'enseignement au Maroc. 247 p. Paris: Geuthner, 1928.
Reviewed by Gabriel Ferrand, *J.Asiatique*, 1929, 214: 181-4.

YRwf-oq

BOISSONNADE, et al. Histoire de l'Université de Poitiers, passé et présent (1432-1932). 573 p. Poitiers: Renault, 1932.
Reviewed by Laignel-Lavastine, *Bull.Soc.Franç.Hist.Méd.*, 1935, 24: 60-2.

BONNEROT, Jean. La Sorbonne, sa vie, son rôle, son oeuvre à travers les siècles. viii, 328 p., 28 pl. Paris: Presses Universitaires de France, 1927. [CB 26/259]

CHARLÉTY, Sébastien. Les universités de France. *Organon*, 1938, 2: 79-85.

PFISTER, Christian. L'Université de Strasbourg. *Rev.Bleue*, Déc. 1921, 721-8. [CB 12/629]
History of the University, written for its 300th Anniversary.

PRENTOUT, Henri. Esquisse d'une histoire de l'Université de Caen. 193 p. Caen: Malherbe, 1932.

YRwf-tf

DAINVILLE, François de. La naissance de l'humanisme moderne. Vol. 1. Les jésuites et l'humanisme. xx, 391 p. (Les Jésuites et l'Education de la Société Française) Paris: Beauchesne, 1940. [CB 76/415]

YRwg/wh Central Europe

YRwg-on

GESCHICHTE der Annenschule in Dresden. Festschrift zur 350-Jahrfeier (1579-1929). 191 p. Dresden: 1929.
Reviewed by R. Zaunick, *Mitt.Gesch.Med.*, 1932, 31: 12.

YRwg-op

STRICH, Fritz, ed. Schweizerische Akademiereden. xvii, 501 p. Bern: Haupt, 1945.
Reviewed bv Bror Olsson, *Lychnos*, 1946-47, 297-8.

YRwg-oq

BEZOLD, Friedrich von. Geschichte der Rheinischen Friedrich Wihelms-Universität von der Gründung bis zum Jahr 1870. x, 535 p. Bonn: Marcus und Weber, 1920. [CB 12/603]

BONJOUR, Edgar. The history of Basle University. *Ciba Symp.*, 1959, 6: 227-41.

BUCHHOLZ, Erich; HEINIG, Karl, ed. Forschen und Wirken. Festschrift zur 150-Jahr-Feier der Humboldt-Universität zu Berlin. Bd. 1: Beiträge zur wissenschaftlichen und politischen Entwicklung der Universität. 754 p., pl. Berlin: VEB Deutscher Verlag der Wissenschaften, 1960.
Reviewed by Alexander Mette, *N.T.M. Z.Gesch.Naturwiss. Tech.Med.*, [1962], 1: (3), 144-5.

CRUCHET, René. Les universités allemandes au XXe siècle. Préface de C. Julian. 450 p. Paris: A. Colin, 1914.

ENGELHARDT, Roderich von. Die Deutsche Universität Dorpat in ihrer geistesgeschichtlichen Bedeutung. x, 570 p., 25 pl. München, Reinhardt, 1933.

HINZ, Gerhard, ed. Aus der Geschichte der Universität Heidelberg und ihrer Fakultäten. Aus Anlass des 575 jährigen Bestehens der Ruprecht-Karl-Universität Heidelberg. Hrsg. im Auftrag der Vereinigung der Freunde der Studentenschaft der Universität Heidelberg e.V. 455 p. (Ruperto-Carola. Sonderband.) Heidelberg: Brausdruck, 1961.
Reviewed by H. Degen, *Naturwiss.Rundsch.*, 1962, 15: 333.

HUMBOLDT UNIVERSITÄT ZU BERLIN. Die Humboldt-Universität gestern, heute, morgen. Zum einhundertfünfzigjährigen Bestehen der Humboldt-Universität zu Berlin und zum zweihundertfünfzigjährigen Bestehen der Charité, Berlin ... 250 p., ill. Berlin: Deutscher Verlag der Wissenschaften, 1960.
Reviewed by Alexander Mette, *NTM Z.Gesch.Naturiwss.Tech. Med.*, [1962], 1: (3), 145-6.

KAUFMANN, Georg. Die Geschichte der deutschen Universitäten. 2 vol. in 1. Stuttgart: I.G. Cotta, 1888-96; reprinted 2 vol. Graz: Akademische Bruck- und Verlagsanstalt, 1958.

KREMERS, Edward. Alma mater Dorpatensis 1632-1932. *Isis*, 1934, 20: 448.

LANG, Max. Die Universität Berlin. 84 p., 79 fig. Wien: Lindner, 1931.

RITTER, Gerhard. Die Heidelberger Universität. Ein Stück deutscher Geschichte. Vol. 1. Das Mittelalter (1386-1508). xiii, 533 p., 7 pl. Heidelberg: Winter, 1936.

STAEHELIN, Andreas. Geschichte der Universität Basel. 2 vol. 1. 1632-1818. xix, 643 p. 2. 1818-1835. 203 p. (Studien zur Geschichte der Wissenschaften in Basel, 4/5, 7) Basel: Helbing & Lichtenhahn, 1957-59. [CB 85/447 and CB 88/192]
Reviewed by W.H. Schopfer, *Arch.Int.Hist.Sci.*, 1958, 11: 48-9; by Bror Olsson, *Lychnos*, 1959, 241.

UNIVERSITÉ DE BÂLE, 1460-1960. 232 p. (*Schweiz.Hochschulzeitung*, 33) Zürich: 1960.
A special issue devoted to the 500th anniversary of the founding of the University of Basle.

WALTHER, Johannes. Aus der Geschichte der Universität Wittenberg. Vortrag, gehalten am 18. Juli 1929 im Schloss zu Wittenberg. *Leopoldina, new ser.*, 1929, 5: 1-8.

YRwg-or

HEER, Georg. Marburger Studentenleben, 1527-1927. 222 p., tables. Marburg: N.G. Elwertsche Verlag, 1927.
Reviewed by Ernst Heymann, *Deut.Lit.Zeitung*, 1927, 449-52.

PECHNER, G. Russkie studenty vo Freiberge. [Russian students at Freiberg. (In Russian)] *Vop.Ist.Est.Tekh.*, 1962, 12: 163-4.
18th century to the present.

YRwg-r

GUNDLACH, Franz, ed. Catalogus professorum Academiae Marburgensis. Die akademischen Lehrer der Philipps-Universität in Marburg von 1527-1910. xxvii, 607 p. (Veröffentlichungen der Historischen Kommission für Hessen und Waldeck, 15) Marburg: Elwert, 1927.

VOLBEHR, Friedrich. Professoren und Dozenten der Christian-Albrechts-Universität zu Kiel 1665-1954. Mit Angaben über die sonstigen Lehrkräfte und die Universitäts-Bibliothekare und einem Verzeichnis der Rektoren. 4th ed. [rev. by C.F. W.R. Weyl.] Bearb. von Rudolf Bülck. 293 p. Kiel: Ferdinand Hirt, 1956.
3rd ed., 1665-1933 (Kiel, 1934).
Reviewed by Herbert Böttger, *Sudhoffs Arch.*, 1957, 41: 91; 3rd ed. by R. Bülck, *Deut.Lit.Zeitung*, 1934, 5: 2017-19.

YRwg-sk-oq

HARTSHORNE, Edward Y. German universities and National Socialism. 179 p. Cambridge: Harvard University Press, 1937.
Well documented and well balanced account.

WEINREICH, Max. Hitler's professors. The part of scholarship in Germany's crimes against the Jewish people. 291 p. New York: Yiddish Scientific Institute, 1946. [CB 70/240]

YRwg-sr

LUTHER, Wilhelm. Vom Wesen menschlicher Freiheit. Erziehung zu Freiheit und Mitverantwortung an den deutschen Höheren Schulen, insbesondere am Humanistischen Gymnasium. 2nd ed. 106 p. (Schriftenreihe der Bundeszentrale für Heimatdienst, 29) Bonn: 1959.

YRwh-oq

BARYCZ, Henryk. [Jagellonian University. Six hundred years of activity. (1364-1964). (In Polish)] *Kwart.Hist.Nauk. Tech.*, 1964, 9: 173-97.

BOYCE, Gray C.; DAWSON, W.H. The University of Prague. Modern problems of the German University in Czechoslovakia. ix, 117 p. London: Hale, 1937.
Story of the university founded by Pope Clement VI in 1347 and by Charles IV of Bohemia in 1348.

SKUBALA, Zofia; TOKARSKI, Zbigniew. Polish universities. 175 p., ill. Warsaw: Polonia Publishing House, 1959.

YRwh-vm-oq

KISCH, Guido. Die Prager Universität und die Juden, 1348-1848. Mit Beiträgen zur Geschichte des Medizinstudiums. x, 239 p. Mährisch-Ostrau: 1935. [CB 56/374]

YRwi/wj Southern Europe

YRwi-oq

BOLOGNA. UNIVERSITÀ. L'Università di Bologna nel passato e nel presente. A cura di un comitato di professori della stessa università. xvi, 198 p., ill. Bologna: Zanichelli, 1919.

CONTRIBUTI alla storia dell' Università di Pavia. Pubblicati nell' XI centenario dell' ateneo. 529 p., ill. Pavia: Tip. Cooperativa, 1925.

FAVARO, Antonio. Per la storia dello studio di Padova. Autobibliografia. *Atti Ist.Veneto Sci.*, 1922, 81: (2), 211-32.
List of Favaro's papers devoted to the history of his Alma Mater. 105 titles dating from 1875 to 1922.

FAVARO, Antonio. L'Università di Padova. Notizie raccolte. 222 p., ill. Venezia: Ferrari, 1922. [CB 13/286]
The university of Padova originated in 1222 as a *studium generale*, with a migration of students from Bologna. It celebrated in 1922 the seventh centenary of its birth.

FAVARO, Antonio. La Università di Padova ed il suo settimo centenario (1222-1922). *Arch.Stor.Sci.*, 1920, 1: 151-2.
Program of work it is proposed to undertake to commemorate this 7th centenary.

FEDELI, Carlo. Documenti e pagine di storia universitaria, 1427-1800. 140 p. (*Ann.Univ.Toscane*, 32) Pisa: 1913.

POLSKA AKADEMIJA UMIEJETNOŚCI. Omaggio dell'Accademia Polacca di Scienze e Lettere all'Università di Padova nel settimo centenario della sua fondazione. 364 p. Cracovia: 1922.

SPANO, Nicola. L'Università di Roma. xxix, 336 p. Rome: Casa Editrice Mediterranea, 1935.

TANFANI, Gustavo. Gli antichi collegi degli scolari dello studio di Padova. *Atti.Soc.Ital.Stor.Sci.Med.Natur.IV.Congr. Naz.*(Roma, 1933), p. 200-10, 5 fig. In: *Riv.Stor.Sci.*, 1934, vol. 15.

YRwj-oq-nb

ALCALDE, Alfonso Fernandez de. Brèves considérations sur une collection d'anciens sceaux académiques espagnols. *Compt. Rend.IIe Congr.Int.Hist.Méd.* (Paris, 1921), p. 314-20, 1 pl. Évreux: Imprimerie Ch. Hérissey, 1922.

YRwj-sc

CASTILLEJO, José. Wars of ideas in Spain, philosophy, politics and education. With an introduction by Sir Michael Sadler. x, 168 p. London: Murray, 1937. [CB 53/282]

YRwk/wm Low Countries; Scandinavia

YRwk-oq

ESSEN, Léon van der. L'Université de Louvain (1425-1940). 293 p. (Collection Leo Belgicus) Bruxelles: Editions Universitaires, Les Presses de Belgique, 1945.

FLORKIN, Marcel. Les origines françaises de la Faculté des Sciences de Liége. *Vieux-Liége*, 1954, no. 104-105, 302-6.

LADEUZE, P. L'Université de Louvain, 1426-1927. *Rev.Quest. Sci.*, 1927, 12: 5-16. [CB 24/566]

L'UNIVERSITÉ DE LOUVAIN à travers cinq siècles: études historiques. Publiées avec une introduction par Léon van der Essen, avec le concours de E. van Cauwenbergh [and others]. 308 p., ill. Brussels: A. Lesigne, 1927.
Reviewed in *Amer.Hist.Rev.*, 1928, 33: 685-6.

UTRECHT. UNIVERSITEIT. Album Promotorum der Rijksuniversiteit Utrecht, 1815-1936. [Album promotorum of the State University at Utrecht. (In Dutch)] 350 p. Leiden: Brill, 1963.

VAUTHIER, Marcel. 1940-1944. L'Université de Bruxelles sous l'occupation allemande. Préface de Charles Frerichs. iv, 158 p. Bruxelles: Cock, 1944.

YRwm-oq

UNIVERSITETET I OSLO, 1911-1961. [In Norwegian] 2 vol. 709 p.; 385 p. Oslo: Universitetsforlaget, 1961.
Reviewed by Chr. Callmer, *Lychnos*, 1962, 243-4.

VÄRMLANDS Nation i Uppsala från år 1595. [The Värmlands Society at Upsala from the year 1595. (In Swedish)] Ed. by Erik Gren. 211 p., ill. (Nationen och hembygden, Bilaga, 8) Uppsala: Värmlands Nation, 1960.
Reviewed by Gösta Elvin, *Lychnos*, 1962, 246.

WILSTADIUS, Paul. Smålands nation i Uppsala. Biografiska och genealogiska anteckningar. 2: 1845-1950. [The Småland society at Uppsala. Biographical and genealogical notes. 2. 1845-1950. (In Swedish)] xvi, 380 p. Uppsala: Smålands Nations Förlag, 1961.
Reviewed by Bror Olsson, *Lychnos*, 1962, 245-6.

YRwm-oq-ch

SMITH, Fritze. Bidrag til doktordisputatsens historie ved Københavns universitet. [Contributions to the history of doctoral theses in the University of Copenhagen. (In Danish)] x, 134 p. København: Ejnar Munksgaard, 1950.
Reviewed by E. Louis Backman, *Lychnos*, 1952, 288-91.

YRwn/wo Russia; South Eastern Europe

YRwn

PECHNER, G. *See* YRwg-or

SARAFIAN, Kevork Avedis. History of education in Armenia. With introductions by Lester B. Rogers and Bishop Karekin. xi, 320 p. La Verne, Calif.: Leader Press, 1930.

TRILLAT, Jean Jacques. Organisation et principes de l'enseignement en URSS. Les relations entre la science et l'industrie. 70 p., 3 pl. (Actualités Scientifiques et Industrielles, 67) Paris: Hermann, 1933.

YOUNG, R. Fitzgibbon. Practical trends in Russian education. *Contemp.Rev.*, 1946, 169: 348-53. [CB 70/275]

YRwn-oq

KORBUT, Mikhail Ksaverevich. [The state university of Kazan known as V.I. Ulanov-Lenin during 125 years (1804/05-1929/30). (In Russian)] 2 vol. Kazan: Izdanie Kazanskogo Universiteta, 1930.

VOVCHENKO, G.D.; SALTANOV, Iu. A. Moskovskii gosudarstvennyi universitet im. M.V. Lomonosova. [The Moscow State University named in honor of M.V. Lomonosov. (In Russian)] *Vop.Ist.Est. Tekh.*, 1962, no. 12, 157-60.

YRwo-oq

SERGESCU, Petre. L'Université de Cluj et ses relations avec l'étranger. *Rev.Transylvanie*, 1945, 10: 33-51.

SERGESCU, Petre. L'Université Roumaine de Cluj en exil. *Archeion*, 1942, 24: 284-8.

YRwp/wq Middle East

YRwp-oq

HEBREW UNIVERSITY Issue. *New Palestine*, 1925, 8: no. 13, 281-456, ill. [CB 18/596]
Special number to celebrate the formal inauguration of the Hebrew University, on Mount Scopus, just outside of Jerusalem, on April 1, 1925.

THE HEBREW UNIVERSITY OF JERUSALEM, 1925-1950. Jubilee volume. Ed. by Manka Spiegel. xvi, 207 p., pl. Jerusalem: 1950. [CB 77/356]

PENROSE, Stephen B.L., Jr. That they may have life. The story of the American University of Beirut, 1866-1941. xviii, 347 p., ill. New York: American University of Beirut, 1941.
Reviewed by George Sarton, *Isis*, 1942, 34: 40-1.

YRwq

HEYWORTH-DUNNE, J. An introduction to the history of education in modern Egypt. xiv, 503 p. London: Luzac, 1939.
Reviewed by I.L. Kandel, *Amer.Hist.Rev.*, 1940, 45: 683; by Victor Watson, *J.Roy.Asiatic Soc.*, 1940, 364-5.

YRwq-oq

BERCHER, L. Nouvelle charte de l'Université d'al-Azhar au Caire. Loi n° 49 de 1930. *Rev.Étud.Islamiques*, 1931, 241-75.

BRUNET, Emmanuel. Rapport sur l'organisation de l'université musulmane el-Azhar. 28 p. (*Nouv.Arch.Missions Sci.Lit.*, 18 no. 1) Paris: 1909.

PAUTY, Edmond. Le plan de l'Université Qarawiyin à Fès. *Hespéris*, 1930, 3: 515-23, 3 pl.

SÉKALY, Achille. L'Université d'el-Azhar et ses transformations. *Rev.Étud.Islamiques*, 1927, 1: 95-116, 465-529; 1928, 2: 47-165, 255-337, 401-73. [CB 23/230]

YRws/wx Asia; Africa

YRws-oq

SANKALIA, Hasmukh D. The university of Nālandā. With a preface by H. Heras. 400 p., ill. Madras: Paul, 1934.

YRwt-sk

PEAKE, Cyrus Henderson. Nationalism and education in modern China. xiv, 240 p. New York: Columbia University Press, 1932.
Reviewed by K.S. Latourette, *Amer.Hist.Rev.*, 1933, 38: 598.

YRwv

DJAJADINIGRAT, Loekman. From illiteracy to university. Educational development in the Netherlands Indies. 68 p., ill. (*Bull.Neth.Neth.Indies Counc.Inst.Pacific Relat.*, 3) New York: 1944.

YRwx

HUXLEY, Julian. Africa view. viii, 455 p., pl., map. London: Chatto & Windus, 1936.
Reviewed by George Sarton, *Isis*, 1938, 28: 150-1.
A report on the progress of native education.

YRyBW STATISTICS IN EDUCATION

WALKER, Helen M. Studies in the history of statistical method. With special reference to certain educational problems. viii, 229 p., 12 ill. Baltimore: Williams and Wilkins, 1929.
Reviewed by George Sarton, *Isis*, 1930, 13: 382-3.

YT LIBRARIES

for libraries in special subject fields *see* INDEX

YTc

CHANGING patterns of scholarship and the future of research libraries. A symposium in celebration of the establishment of the University of Pennsylvania Library. x, 133 p. Philadelphia: University of Pennsylvania Press, 1951. [CB 79/196]
Reviewed by Henry R. Viets, *J.Hist.Med.*, 1953, 8: 95-6.

ESDAILE, Arundell. National libraries of the world. Their history, administration and public services. Second ed. completely revised by F.J. Hill. xv, 413 p., 12 pl. London: Library Association, 1957.
First published 1934 (London: Grafton).
Reviewed by R. Brightman, *Nature*, 1958, 182: 758.

KOCH, Theodore Wesley. On university libraries. 2nd ed. 55 p. Paris: E. Champion, 1924.

SPARN, Enrique. El crecimiento de las grandes bibliotecas de la tierra durante el primer cuarto del siglo XX. 4 pt. 1. Las bibliotecas universitarias y afines con más de 100,000 volúmenes. 46 p. 2. Las bibliotecas nacionales, provinciales municipales y populares con más de 100,000 volúmenes. 62 p. 3, 4. Las bibliotecas especiales con 100,000 y más volúmenes. Resumen tabulario de las partes 1-3. 87 p. Cordoba (Argentina): Academia Nacional de Ciencias, 1926.
Pt. 1 reviewed by W. Giese, *Deut.Lit.Zeitung*, 1926, 1585-6.

UHLENDAHL, Heinrich. Bibliotheken gestern und heute. Vortrag zur Einweihung der Bibliothek des Deutschen Museums in München am 7. Mai 1932. *Abhandl.Ber.Deut.Mus.*, 1932, 4: 131-51. [CB 38/616]

YTwb

JOHN CRERAR LIBRARY. Handbook. 16 p. Chicago, Ill.: 1913. [CB 5/305]

LINDA HALL LIBRARY, Kansas City, Missouri. [Notice of its holdings.] *Isis*, 1956, 47: 420-1.

LYDENBERG, Harry Miller. History of the New York Public Library, Astor, Lenox and Tilden Foundations. xii, 643 p., pl. New York: The Library, 1923.
Reprinted from papers published in *Bull.N.Y.Public Libr.* from 1916 to 1921.

PIERPONT MORGAN LIBRARY. A review of the growth, development and activities of the Library during the period between its establishment as an educational institution in February 1924 and the close of the year 1929. (- from 1936 through 1940; - 1941/1948). 3 vol. 148 p., ill; xiii, 127 p., ill.; 108 p. New York: 1930, 1941, 1949. [CB 31/574 and CB 63/280]

RANEY, M. Llewellyn. The university libraries. xv, 250 p. (University of Chicago Survey, 7) Chicago: University Press, 1933. [CB 38/615]

STILLWELL, Margaret Bingham. The Annmary Brown memorial. A descriptive essay. 24 p. Providence, R.I.: Trustees of the Annmary Brown Memorial, 1925.

WALTON, Clarence Eldon. The three-hundredth anniversary of the Harvard College Library. iv, 46 p. Cambridge, Mass.: Harvard College Library, 1939.

YTwe

BARWICK, George Frederick. The Reading Room of the British Museum. 175 p. London: Benn, 1929.

CRASTER, Edmund. History of the Bodleian Library, 1845-1945. xii, 372 p. Oxford: Clarendon Press, 1952.
Reviewed by Donald G. Wing, *J.Hist.Med.*, 1953, 8: 234-5.

GUPPY, Henry. The John Rylands Library, Manchester. (1899-1924). A record of its history, with brief descriptions of the building and its contents. In commemoration of the twenty-fifth anniversary of its inauguration. xviii, 144 p., ill., facs. Manchester: University Press, 1924.

YTwe-bd

RYE, Reginald Arthur. The student's guide to the libraries of London. With an account of the most important archives and other aids to study. 3rd ed. rev. and enl. xxv, 580 p. London: University of London Press, 1927.

YTwf-bd

LEROY, Émile. Le guide pratique des bibliothèques de Paris. 283 p. Paris: Editions des Bibliothèques Nationales, 1937.

YTwg

GÖBER, Willi. Die Universitätsbibliothek. Grundzüge ihrer Entwicklung. *Wiss.Z.Humboldt Univ.Berlin*, Beiheft zum Jubiläumsjahrgang, 1959-60, 9: 1-14.

KUHNERT, Ernst. Geschichte der Staats- und Universitätsbibliothek zu Königsberg. Von ihrer Begründung bis zum Jahre 1810. 317 p. Leipzig: O.W. Hiersemann, 1926.
Reviewed by Alfred Schulze, *Deut.Lit.Zeitung*, 1927, 1993-6.

LEYH, Georg. Die deutschen wissenschaftlichen Bibliotheken nach dem Krieg. 222 p. Tübingen: Mohr, 1947. [CB 71/133]

OESER, Max. Kurzer Führer durch die Bibliothek Desbillons und die ihr angeschlossenen Büchersammlungen. Städt.Schlossbücherei Mannheim. Einleitung zum Katalog. 34 p., 11 pl., 5 tables. Mannheim: Städt.Schlossbücherei, 1926. [CB 21/530]
Library of F.J.T. Desbillons.

SENSBURG, Waldemar. Die bayerischen Bibliotheken. Ein geschichtlicher Überblick mit besonderer Berücksichtigung der öffentlichen wissenschaftlichen Bibliotheken. viii, 172 p., ill. München: Bayerland-Verlag, 1926.

YTwg-bv

BALCKE, Curt. Bibliographie zur Geschichte der Preussischen Staatsbibliothek. x, 102 p. (Mitteilungen aus der Preussischen Staatsbibliothek, 6) Leipzig: K.W. Hiersemann, 1925.
Reviewed by Otto Pniower, *Deut.Lit.Zeitung*, 1927, 593-5.

YTwh

BIRKENMAJER, Aleksander. L'état actuel des bibliothèques en Pologne. *Procès-verbaux Mém.Congr.Int.Bibl.Bibliophiles* (Paris, 1923), 10 p. Paris: Jouve, 1925.

YTwm

BRING, Samuel E. C.G. Warmholtz och Louis de Geers bibliotek på Christineholm. [The libraries of C.G. Warmholtz and Louis de Geer in Christineholm. (In Swedish, with French summary)] 249 p., fig. Uppsala: Almqvist & Wiksell, 1941. [CB 62/55]

YTwp-bv

HOWARD, Harry N. Preliminary materials for a survey of the libraries and archives of Istanbul. *J.Amer.Orient.Soc.*, 1939, 59: 227-46.

YTwt

BRANDT, Fre. J. van den. La Bibliothèque du Pé-t'ang. Notes historiques. *Monumenta Serica*, 1939-40, 4: 616-21.

GOODRICH, L. Carrington. Note on the Pei-t'ang Library in Peking apropos of the article by Boleslaw Szczesniak. *Isis*, 1950, 41: 195.

SZCZESNIAK, Boleslaw. Note on Kepler's "Tabulae Rudolphinae" in the Library of Pei-t'ang in Pekin. *Isis*, 1949, 40: 344-7.
Includes account of Library.

VERHAEREN, H. La Bibliothèque Chinoise du Pet'ang. *Monumenta Serica*, 1939-40, 4: 622-6.

A Classification Scheme for the History of Science, Medicine and Technology

It is not surprising that during the whole time that George Sarton edited the *Isis* Critical Bibliographies he was preoccupied with the problems of organizing the entries. As late as December 1950 he wrote, 'It is certain that I am almost always thinking of the Critical Bibliography'.[1] The difficulties are indeed formidable. The subject of the history of science is a hybrid one. It is one aspect of science. It has special relations with social conditions, with the history of civilization, and with cultural activities. It has philosophical aspects, and as such presents one facet of the philosophy of history. It is also closely related to the philosophy of science, and psychological factors shed light on the way discoveries are made.

To these difficulties are added the confusions arising from the different meanings of the word 'history'. 'It may mean either the records of events or events themselves ... It is unfortunate that such a double meaning of the word should have grown up for it is productive of not a little confusion of thought.'[2] In a bibliography of the history of science a third meaning must be considered, namely 'history as a subject of study'. For example, in the history of seismology we may have to consider the history of seismological studies, the history of earthquakes which form the basis of these studies, and the 'history of seismology' as a subject for study. In many cases, a separation of the history of the study and the phenomena studied is not helpful and often not even possible, but it is always necessary to distinguish between the history of science and the 'history of science' as a discipline.

Before I began work on this project I made a comparative study of classification schemes for the history of science,[3] with special emphasis on the different schemes Sarton evolved during the time he edited the *Isis* Critical Bibliographies. I had been struck by the fact that Sarton had developed a scheme with a 'faceted' structure long before the technique of facet analysis became generally known. Facet analysis is, in essence, somewhat similar to systematic classification carried out on the usual logical principles. The subject field is analysed into mutually exclusive facets, or categories, derived by using a single characteristic of division. However, unlike the traditional systems of classification in which every term is enumerated, in a faceted scheme the terms in each category are listed and then when it is necessary to represent a multi-faceted subject the terms can be combined in a predetermined order to form the appropriate code or classmark. The fact that the order is predetermined helps to solve the classifier's difficulty in deciding where to class a composite subject that might well fit into more than one category. For example, the history of botanical societies in the eighteenth century has three 'facets': (a) eighteenth century history, (b) botany, and (c) societies. We therefore have to decide whether to enter this title in the order (a) (b) (c), (a) (c) (b), (b) (c) (a), (b) (a) (c), (c) (a) (b) or (c) (b) (a). The arrangement (a) (b) (c), or (a) (c) (b), may be preferred by the historian specializing in the eighteenth century, (b) (a) (c) (botany, eighteenth century history, societies), or (b) (c) (a), by the historian of botany, and (c) (b) (a) (societies, botany, eighteenth century), or (c) (a) (b), by the sociologist. If we decide not to repeat the entry under all these permutations, which would tend to make a bibliography bulky and difficult to produce and use, then we must adopt a preferred order, that is the entries must be collected under one heading with index entries made for those aspects that are distributed. However, even the index cannot contain all permutations and a selection must be made of those most likely to be sought.

Both Sarton and the committee that considered the *Isis* classification scheme when Sarton retired as Editor of *Isis*, were most concerned with the problem of whether period (and civilization) or subject should be the preferred facet. The committee decided, as Sarton had done, that the chronological and civilization aspects is the more important. In the scheme that I have developed and used this rule has been retained. All those entries that relate to the history of science or the sciences in one particular civilization or period and to not more than two centuries during the modern period (from 1500) will appear in Volume 4. Entries of a more general nature are included in this Volume. The rule that I have adopted is as follows: all material that brings the subject into the modern period is cumulated in the present volume. Moreover, as I have mentioned in the Introduction, I have also included in this volume titles that deal with the twentieth century or with the nineteenth and twentieth centuries combined.* This is a departure from the arrangement in the *Isis* Critical Bibliographies. My reasons for making this change were as follows: (1) when all the material for the present volume (subjects) had been cumulated, all those sections covering subjects that originated in the nineteenth or twentieth centuries contained no entries because so much of modern science is of comparatively recent origin; and (2) it was impossible to decide whether entries relating to philosophical, educational and sociological aspects considered from a contemporary point of view should be classed in the twentieth century section of the periods volume or in the general subject volume (it was clear from a study of the annual bibliographies that the editors had difficulties in deciding how to classify such entries).

Although in the scheme currently used in the annual *Isis* Critical Bibliographies there is a strict rule that all material that fits into the chronological sections is classed there (a rule which, as I have explained, I have retained), nc consistent citation order is adhered to regarding aspect or point of view on the one hand and subject field on the other. For example, some titles dealing with the philosophy of biology have been classed under philosophy of science, others under biology; similarly, the section on Institutions has sometimes contained references to botanical gardens, at other times these have been classed under botany. In the *Cumulative Bibliography* I have consistently adopted the following rule: first classify by period, then by subject, and finally by aspect (or point of view) and bibliographical form. This means that all aspects of a subject, however narrow, are classed under that subject, so that, for example, entries on the philosophy of science and the sciences or on the social relations of science and the sciences are distributed among the subject fields. Of course, a philosopher of science might prefer to have all references to philosophical aspects collected under that heading, subdivided by subject, and similarly the sociologist might like to find all material on the social relations of all the subject fields brought together. However, since the *Cumulative Bibliography* is a bibliography of the history of science, the emphasis is on the *history* of each subject and consequently, however narrow the subject, all aspects of it are gathered together.

To recapitulate: in the present scheme there are three main facets, namely (1) civilization and periods, (2) subjects, (3) aspects and forms. The notation has been chosen to emphasize these: numerals denote civilizations and periods, capital letters subject fields, and lower case letters aspects and forms. Lower case letters are also used to form compound subjects and to extend subjects in a non-systematic order.

Notation and code-building

It must be emphasized that the notation does *not* set out to reflect the hierarchy of the classification; it is *ordinal*. Although frequently one letter represents a main subject, this is not always so. Thus, FZ, indicating earth sciences has a two letter code, but meteorology, which is one of the earth sciences, is represented by one letter, G. Similarly, RB, standing for surgery, contains as many letters as RC, meaning regional surgery, although the latter is a subdivision of the former. The codes are arranged in alphabetical order. It is essential to remember that in the filing sequence a stop must be imagined between the capital letters and the lower case letters, with the result that Bce (B.ce) files before BAce (BA.ce). Apart from capital and lower case letters, the only other symbols used are the hyphen and the oblique stroke, both with their conventional filing values. The hyphen separates two sets of codes and in filing is considered like a stop; for example, Lc-be (L.c.be) files before Lcb (L.cb). The oblique stroke is an inclusion sign meaning that p/s includes sections p, q, r, s, and consequently precedes them, e.g. LUp/s comes before LUp, LUq, LUr, LUs. It is mainly used to indicate the range of sections in the body of the Bibliography.

The code is made up of figures, capitals and lower case letters. No figures are used in this volume since the subjects are treated generally without reference to a special period or civilization. The capital letters (usually one or two) are followed by lower case letters (also generally one or two) without an intervening punctuation sign. If the subject is considered from more than one aspect, these are combined by a hyphen and are alphabetized in the way described. Thus, SAwb-qd signifies North American agricultural learned societies (SA = agriculture; wb = North America; qd = learned societies). A compound subject is represented by two subjects being joined together by the letter y. For example, LUyLO stands for insect behaviour (LU = animal behaviour; LO = insects). Two subjects may also be joined together by mz if a conceptual or comparative relationship is involved, for example TmzA, relation of technology and science.

---

* I was gratified to find that in the classification scheme used by *Technology and Culture*[4] a similar rule is adopted.

Aspects and forms

Since all those entries for which the primary facet is civilizations and periods will be cumulated in Volume 4, I shall discuss that facet in detail in that volume. Here I shall deal only with the other two main facets, subjects, and aspects and forms, beginning with the latter.

In the scheme used in this volume* each subject, however narrow, is subdivided in the same way into what may broadly be described as: its general history, including bibliographical, biographical and historiographical aspects; its psychology and philosophy; communication in, and teaching of, the subject; its sociology, including organization, institutions, the profession and its relation with society as a whole; its relations with the humanities; its popular aspects; and finally its history in different linguistic and ethnic groups and in different countries. The order of the aspect subdivisions was not an easy problem to solve. They are a mixture of subfacets and what are termed common subdivisions; that is, they concern the external (bibliographical form) and internal form (aspect) in which the subject is presented and the relations with other subjects. I was anxious to choose an arrangement that would satisfy the historian. At the same time I had to fix the order in which these subdivisions were to be cited when combined. I shall revert to this problem when I have discussed the aspect and form divisions in more detail.

Each subject begins with the general history of the subject (section c)**. This is followed by libraries (cb), historical sources in general (cc), the different kinds of primary literature (cd through cm) and non-bibliographical sources (cn through cv). Since the general history, c, is subdivided by the terms listed in section b (bibliographical forms divisions and terms relating to documentation), the bibliographical aspects of history and the bibliography of historical literature follow one another closely. The bibliographical terms in c are similar to those in b, the difference being that in b they designate form, whereas in cc through cm they denote subjects. For example, encyclopaedias of science (usually of a historical nature) are Ac-be, but the history of scientific encyclopaedias is Acf; periodicals on the history of medicine are Nc-br, whereas the history of medical periodicals is Ncj.

Section d, biography, contains mainly collective material: collective biography, references to collections of portraits, and collections of texts. Individual biographies and references to individual men of science are, of course, contained in Volumes 1 and 2 of the *Cumulative Bibliography*.

As I have already emphasized, it is necessary to distinguish between the subject in its various aspects, including its history, and the 'history of the subject' as an academic discipline. Sections f and g contain references to the study and teaching of the history of the subject. The study of history in f is organized in a similar way to the arrangement of the subject as a whole. For example, research institutes in mathematics are found under Bqg; research institutes in the history of mathematics, under Bfqg. The construction of section g (teaching the history of the subject) mirrors that of the teaching of the subject in o. For example, methods of teaching physics (physics: teaching: method), are under Cod: methods of teaching the history of physics (history of physics: teaching: method), under Cgd.

In section h are references to historiography and particular aspects of the history of the subject. This section begins with historical techniques, historiography and historical method, followed by divisions on philosophical and evolutionary aspects of the history of the subject and the history of ideas of the subject and their transmission.

Section j covers psychological aspects of the subject, including the psychology of men of science, particularly the psychology of discovery. This aspect is, of course, of interest to both the historian and philosopher of science. Section k contains a fairly detailed schedule of the philosophy and methodology of the subject. The divisions on 'philosophical aspects of the history of the subject' (hf) and the 'philosophy of the subject' (k) are very closely allied; nevertheless, I think that there is a clear distinction. In the former division the philosophical point of view is used to illustrate the history, whereas in the latter historical examples serve to elucidate

---

* In the faceted scheme that I first proposed,[3] I introduced in the civilization and period facet a category 'all periods' (including general history and national histories), with the result that different aspects of the subject such as philosophy, education and sociology were completely separated from its history, unless they were entirely historical in character. In practice I found that, for the material in the *Isis* Critical Bibliographies, it was difficult and not helpful to the user to make such a distinction because whatever book or article was included had some relevance to the history of the subject.

**As section c is always the first section, the letter c is sometimes omitted in the narrower subjects. The reason for beginning with c is explained later.

the philosophy. The last subdivision, kz, in the philosophy section is concerned with speculations on the future of the subject. The following two entries illustrate very well the difference between this subdivision and the subdivision, sy, under the sociology section which includes entries on the subject in future society: Bertrand Russell's *Icarus; or the future of science* (classed in kz), and J.B.S. Haldane's *Daedalus; or science and the future* (classed in sy). Material on fundamental concepts, even when not strictly philosophical, is usually of a methodological nature and therefore fits in well after section k. Subdivision mz indicates a conceptual relationship between two subject fields.

The next two sections concern problems of communication and teaching. Section n deals with both the means of communication and the communication of knowledge. It leads naturally into section o, the study and teaching of the subject. Although most other institutions are classed in q, schools, colleges and universities are included in o. It was found that references to university departments were so closely connected with the teaching in those departments that they are better classed with university teaching (oq) than with institutions (q); and similarly, that schools should be associated with school-teaching.

Sections p, q, r and s are devoted to social relations of the subject. Section p deals with the organization of, and research in, the subject. Section q concerns institutions involved in the organization of the subject, unlike the three types of institutions classed elsewhere (libraries cb, educational institutions on and oq and museums xx and xy). Section r deals with the profession as a whole and its role in the organization of the subject, not with individual members of the profession as section d. Section s contains entries on the relation of the subject with society: the relation of the subject with society in general, s, is followed by the impact of society on the subject, sb; sc represents the relation of science with the history of civilization; sd references to important personages; later sections concern more specific social relations, e.g. with economics (sg), with politics (sk), and with the law (st).

Section t contains entries on cultural and humanistic relations of the subject and its history, including ethics, religion, literature, art and music. As regards ethics, only references to ethical aspects of the subject as a whole are classed here. Professional ethics are in rj, and ethics as a subject for historical study is included in the philosophy of values (classmark AJ). Similarly, the relation of the subject with organized religion is classed here (in general under td, and in its historical context under tf); but religious beliefs of the professions are classed in rd and religious folklore in ud. The relation of the subject with philosophy, with the exception of ethics and aesthetics, is *not* included in this section; philosophy of science or the sciences is classed in k; philosophy as a subject for historical study is one of the main subject sections (classmark AF).

In section u are classed popular and folkloric aspects of the subject. The history of superstitions in general is a division of social and cultural anthropology (classmark MR).

Section v contains the histories of ethnic and linguistic groups. This section is used only where section w (national histories) is too restrictive. For example, a history of Slav science is classed in Avh, but Czech science is Awh.

The national histories are in section w. The order of countries is based on the contemporary situation. In particular, it must be emphasized that in the present volume entries under Asian countries refer to Western science, medicine, etc. as practised there and not to science, medicine, etc. of indigenous cultures which will appear in Volume 4. The reasons which have led me to place the national histories in section w and not to include them with the general history, as in the present practice in the *Isis* Critical Bibliographies, will be discussed later.

Section x differs somewhat from the preceding sections. It contains entries on equipment used (xb), on methods of experimentation (xe), on techniques (xd), and on instruments (xk). Instrument technology, however, is a subdivision of technology. The history of instruments and their use is classed with the subject. For example, surgical instruments are in RBxk, but instruments used in gynaecological surgery are in RCTxk. Section x also includes the topic of measurement which is, therefore, distributed among all the subjects to which it is applied. Measurement in general (metrology) is under science: measurement (Axm). Similarly, although there is a subdivision under astronomy for astronomical chronology, time measurement in general goes under Axr since the subject is no longer confined to measurement based on astronomy. Section x ends with subsections on museology (xw) and museums (xx). This may seem a strange location, but in practice it works out well because much of museology is closely related to equipment, techniques and instruments.

I have not yet mentioned section a, and I have referred to section b only incidentally. They are never used on their own, but only in conjunction with one of the other subdivisions (this is the reason for c being the first section in the arrangement of aspects and forms under each subject). Section a represents geographical subdivisions, which must be distinguished from the national subdivisions in w although they follow exactly the same pattern. They are rarely used (mostly in connection with the 'history of the subject') and only to indicate location, for example, history of science teaching at university level in the British Isles, Agp-ae. Section b contains bibliographical form divisions, many of them being used only when the amount of material warrants subdivision.

The letters y and z do not, strictly speaking, represent sections. They are symbols to facilitate the ordering of subject extensions. As already explained, the symbol y is used to form compound subjects and certain relations between subjects. The symbol z serves to form non-systematic alphabetical extensions of the subject. I had originally planned verbal extensions, but instead decided on the letter z followed by the first letter, or if necessary by the first two or three letters, of the subject to shorten the heading and to facilitate the addition of aspect or form codes.

Order and combination of aspects and forms

As I have already mentioned, the order of the aspect and form divisions and the way in which they are combined to form a classmark presented the most difficult problems in constructing these classification schedules. It was essential for the order to be helpful to the user of the bibliography and for the code to be representative of the semantic analysis of the subject. At the same time, rules had to be made for the combination of the different aspects and forms. The citation order chosen, that is the order in which the facets are joined up to form the classmark, is in reverse of schedule order, following many makers of faceted classification schemes: that is later terms in the schedules are quoted before the earlier ones. One of the most tricky problems that had to be solved concerned the position of the national histories. In my previous studies on the classification scheme[3] the national histories were placed immediately after general history and all succeeding aspects were divided by the different countries. In the current *Isis* Critical Bibliographies they are classed with the general history, and the Editor, Mr. John Neu, was at first somewhat sceptical regarding the advisability of putting them in section w. However, it was finally agreed that this was the best position, since much of the material on organizational, professional and general social aspects is most relevant to the history of the subject in that country and is therefore better classed with the latter. Even the teaching of the subject in a country is part of the history of the subject there. Consequently, the national histories listed in w are subdivided by the preceding aspects. For example: the study of the history of science is under Af; the study of the history of American science is under Awb-f; exhibitions on the history of medicine are under Nc-bx; exhibitions on the history of Italian medicine are under Nwi-bx; scientific learned societies are under Aqd; British scientific learned societies are under Awe-qd; Jews in medicine under Nvm; Jews in American medicine under Nwb-vm.

The other problems that caused considerable difficulty were the need to distinguish between the history of the subject and the study of its history, and between the subject and its teaching. To achieve this and at the same time retain the rule regarding the order of citation, part of section f (fd through fs) mirrors the construction of the subject as a whole and section g is built up in the same way as section o. I have already quoted examples (*see* page 624) which illustrate the way I have solved the problem. For the same reason section o includes a division on social aspects of the teaching of special subjects, to avoid making provision for changing the combination order. Sociological aspects of science teaching is Aov to avoid confusion with Asb-o which represents teaching the sociology of science.

The only instances where the code for aspects and forms is built in a forward direction is 'philosophy of science: teaching', Ak-o, collective biography of Nobel prize winners, da-py, and of women scientists, da-rw. It was felt that the biography of these scientists is better classed with biography in general than with these specific categories.

Subject fields

A classification scheme for the history of science, medicine and technology does not fall within the category of a general scheme for the classification of knowledge (it clearly does not cover the whole of knowledge), but neither can it be properly described as a special scheme which organizes a limited field of knowledge. It deals with some aspects of the whole field of scientific, medical and technological knowledge. Consequently, the subject facet covers the whole of science, medicine and technology. Even if a satisfactory faceted general scheme were in existence, it is doubtful whether it would be suitable for classifying historical material. Most modern schemes aim at providing a framework for the classification of contemporary literature. Moreover, historical writings seem to cover the scientific subject fields unevenly. Although there are fashions in science and there will always be some fields that are more written about than others, in our field spotlights are turned on here and there in a manner that is probably accounted for by historical rather than scientific reasons. For example, a scheme for organizing writings on 'Medical bacteriology' would provide for the systematic arrangement of all the causal agents; historical writings, on the other hand, spotlight certain diseases, very often just because they were historically far more important and had more serious social consequences.

In the *Isis* Critical Bibliographies somewhat different subject schemes are used for ancient and modern periods. Lund and Taube some time ago[5] proposed that literature should first be divided by the period in which it was written and that a different scheme of classification should be used for each of these periods. Of course, they must have had mainly primary literature in mind. For a number of reasons I plan to apply the same overall scheme to all periods. First, the task of making a comprehensive index for different schemes would be very difficult. Secondly, using the same subject scheme would make it possible to change the citation order as between subjects and periods, if desired. However, the way the scheme is constructed allows considerable latitude both for subject extensions, if necessary by using the non-systematic extension device z, and by choosing the more general subject headings where the borderlines between subjects are vaguer. Clearly, some of the divisions which now contain references to modern developments will remain empty, but I do not think that there will be any difficulty in applying the scheme to special periods and civilizations.

I have already drawn attention to the difference between the history of the subject and the history of the phenomena which form the basis of these studies. In my paper on 'Classification schemes for the history of science'[3] I discussed some recent attempts to discard the traditional subject classes for purposes of classification and to order the phenomena without reference to these classes, which present a somewhat similar problem. Indeed, the aim to make classification schemes discipline-independent continues. In the history of science and the sciences, this would not only be very difficult, but quite useless. Even a cursory glance at the literature makes it evident that historical writings, particularly large-scale works, deal with the history of the traditional disciplines and it would hardly be convenient for the user to find these widely separated from the histories of specific topics.

I have, therefore, not generally made this distinction nor have I introduced any substantial changes to the order of subjects now used in the arrangement of the Critical Bibliographies for the modern periods, based on Sarton's original scheme, which in turn leans heavily on the traditional Comtian classification of knowledge. I have retained the division between science and technology, although this causes some difficulties. I have changed in some respects the order of subjects within the main subject fields, particularly in the earth sciences and biology, and I have moved the sections on general anatomy and physiology into the medical sciences.

In the *Isis* Critical Bibliographies there are no subdivisions in the main subjects, but in the *Cumulative Bibliography* I have had to draw up schemes for classifying entries not only to make consultation of the greater number of entries easier, but also to allow for more specific entries in the index to subject divisions and thus to achieve more efficient information retrieval. (An alphabetical subject index to individual entries would not have been practicable.) For the schemes that I have devised I have leant heavily on schedules prepared by others, particularly the draft revisions of the Bliss classification,[6] the draft of the scheme for classifying medical literature prepared by Miss Ruth Daniel for the Wessex Regional Hospital Board[7] and Barnard's *Classification for Medical and Veterinary Libraries*.[8] Although no detailed classifications of subjects were required, I was anxious to introduce a faceted structure in all the schemes used and to allow for expansion if needed at a later date. For simple subjects I have devised a one to two letter notation (capitals), a third letter being used only in very few instances and always where the further breakdown is of a systematic nature. This occurs mostly in subjects of a geographical character where the third letter stands for the country, in regional surgery where the third letter is used in an enumerative manner to indicate the system of the body concerned and in animal husbandry. Consequently, although I have used a faceted structure, I have in some cases had recourse to an enumerative notation rather than a faceted one to simplify the codes. For example, instead of using RCyOZ for gastrointestinal surgery, this is notated as RCK.

I have emphasized the way in which quite specific topics tend to be spotlighted in historical writings. To avoid complicated systematic schedules to accommodate these topics I have used the device of non-systematic extensions, introduced by the letter z. For example, again in the field of 'medical bacteriology', it would require a complicated scheme to order all the diseases caused by viruses, bacilli and bacteria systematically; instead these diseases are ordered alphabetically.

Before I comment briefly on the schemes adopted for the individual sciences, medicine and technology, I must draw attention to some of the difficulties that have arisen which affect the structure of the scheme as a whole. These concern the subjects that figure both as subject fields and in the aspect subdivisions. They are: magic and superstitions; history of ideas; philosophy, including ethics and aesthetics, and logic; sociology; and the ancillary disciplines which form the last section in the subject fields, including historical sciences, linguistics and education. I will deal with these separately when discussing the organization of each subject field, but here I would like to mention the criterion that has been adopted for deciding how to classify entries that fall within them. When the subject is treated generally, without reference to science, medicine or technology, it is classed with the appropriate subject field, particularly if it is concerned with the history of that field. If, however, it is treated as an aspect of science, medicine or technology, it goes with whatever subject is involved.

A Science

The section on science includes not only entries dealing with science, but also those dealing with science, medicine and technology combined. It is subdivided, as is every other subject field, according to the aspect and form divisions described above.

AC/AK Natural magic, mythology and pseudo-sciences; History of ideas; Philosophy; Logic

All these subjects figure also in the aspect subdivisions and I have already discussed the criterion that governs the classification of entries referring to these topics. The subjects are placed here because in their historical context they are related to the origin of science, particularly natural magic and philosophy. History of ideas (AD) precedes philosophy (AF) as it is the more general subject. It must be emphasized that the ideas treated here are of a general nature; the history of comprehensive *scientific* ideas goes under Ahm and of particular scientific ideas under the relevant subject followed by hm. Similarly, the philosophy and logic of science and of the sciences are aspect subdivisions. Only general references to the history of philosophy and logic are classified in AF and AK respectively.

B Mathematics

The section on mathematics contains entries on pure mathematics only, mathematical physics and applied mathematics being classified under the appropriate sections in physics. No attempt at rigorous faceting has been made. I have kept to a rather traditional, largely nineteenth century, arrangement of topics, which seems to suit the material in this volume best. At the same time I have had to bear in mind modern developments and accommodate them in the scheme. A modern scheme, like that used in *Mathematical Reviews*, was found unsuitable. So was the new Dewey scheme[9] where algebra now precedes arithmetic, number theory, including analytic aspects, is classed under algebra, and topology comes between arithmetic and analysis. In the revised Bliss scheme[6] there is no special section on arithmetic, and set theory and number theory are under algebra. In the scheme devised for the present Bibliography, mathematics is divided into arithmetic (BA), algebra (BF), set theory (BG), number theory (BH), concept of number (BI), analysis (BJ), vectors and tensors (BN), geometry (BO), topology (BU), and probability and statistics (BV). Thus, elementary arithmetic comes first, followed by numerical mathematics; higher arithmetic (number theory) is placed between set theory and the concept of number which precedes analysis.

BZ Physical sciences

In this volume of the Bibliography this title is only used as a section heading. There are so few entries that deal with more than one of the physical sciences that, rather than introduce more subsections, I have repeated these entries under the relevant subjects. The code (BZ) was used in the first two volumes for the purpose of arranging entries and will probably be used again in Volume 4 where the distinction between the individual physical sciences becomes vaguer.

C Physics

In physics, as in mathematics, the arrangement is a traditional one, although account has, of course, been taken of modern developments. Modern physical theory, relativity and quantum theory are placed in fundamental physics, as they are in most current schemes. They are followed by the classical subdivisions: mechanics, heat, optics (classical), magnetism and electricity. The latter part of the physics schedule includes all modern atomic physics. The schedule has a faceted structure, beginning with phenomena and properties, followed by the structural components of matter and ending with the states of matter. Compound subjects are formed by joining the codes in reverse schedule order. For example, the spectroscopy of X-rays is CPyCOzx (spectroscopy = CP; X-rays = COzx).

D Chemistry

Although the traditional subdivisions of chemistry (analytical, physical, inorganic and organic) have been retained, the schedule has a faceted structure: operations; processes and properties; chemical substances. The citation order is the reverse of schedule order. Consequently, physical inorganic chemistry is classed at DRyDD (inorganic chemistry = DR; physical chemistry = DD); physical organic chemistry at DUyDD (organic chemistry = DU; physical chemistry = DD). Most of the entries on the structure of matter are in CQ although they are of as much interest to the chemist as to the physicist. Crystallography is a section in physics (CW), but if the entry deals with the structure of a particular compound it is classed with the compound; for example, the crystallography of organic compounds is DVyCW (organic compounds = DV; crystallography = CW).

F Astronomy

The order of facets in this field is similar to that in chemistry: operations; phenomena and properties; heavenly bodies, and again they are cited in reverse of schedule order. The celestial body or system of bodies concerned is cited first, with the result that references to the origin of the solar system are classed with the latter under FG, but cosmogony in general may be found in the section on the universe (FU). This schedule differs from some of the standard classification systems, where cosmology is classed with general astronomy. I found that the material fitted better into my scheme, which begins with the history of astronomy in general and ends with the galaxies, systems of galaxies, and the universe. Astronomical instruments are not classed in one single division: telescopes are filed under observational astronomy (FAxk), astrolabes under spherical astronomy (FDxk) and sundials under astronomical chronology (FVks). This separation is inevitable because the subject is the primary facet.

FZ Earth sciences

Unlike the present *Isis* arrangement and most current classification schemes, meteorology (G) has been put first. It seemed better here than placed between geology (GG) and physical geography (GV) or between the latter and geography (H). The arrangement under geology begins with the study of the earth as a whole, its physics (GI), chemistry (GM) and chronology (GN). It is followed by subjects related to the interior of the earth: seismology and tectonics (GP/GQ); the science of the rocks (GR/GU); and finally by physical geography and geomorphology (GV/GY). Geography (H) is divided into geodesy and surveying (HB); navigation (HC); charting (HF/HI); and travel and exploration (HJ/HQ). The earth sciences, as well as natural history, botany and zoology, have a regional aspect, and to differentiate between the region which forms the subject of the study and the country responsible for the study I have used different notations. For example, the history of American geology is GGwb; the history of the geology of America GHB (I have used the same letters to represent any particular country throughout the classification schedules: a capital letter when the country is the subject of the study and a lower case letter following w when the country is responsible for the study); French studies of American geology GGBwf; American studies of French geology GGFwb. Similarly, the history of the study of French geology of Europe is GFD; European studies of the climate of America GFBwd. Palaeontology (HU/HW) is the last division of the earth sciences. This position may be debatable since palaeontology is related to petrology and stratigraphy. However, it is no less closely related to the biological sciences and so I have placed it here.

HY Natural history

Natural history is often defined in two ways: (1) the study of flora and fauna; and (2) the study of rocks, fossils, flora and fauna. I have interpreted it in the second sense and have placed it between the earth sciences and biology. It also has a regional aspect and this is treated in the same way as explained under the earth sciences.

J Biology; K Botany; L Zoology

All biological sciences easily lend themselves to a faceted arrangement since they are generally viewed from two main aspects: the process, structure or function on the one hand and the organism on the other. When the subject is treated without special reference to an organism, it is classed in biology, for example, evolution (JG), genetics (JH). If it deals with a microorganism it is in microbiology (JR), with a plant in botany (K), with an animal in zoology (L). For example, plant evolution is KG, animal evolution LG and human evolution MC. Both botany and zoology are divided in the same way as biology J. Although the notation is not completely faceted, the structure of facets is the same. The code is again made up in reverse of schedule order. For example, animal physiology is LK; bird physiology LYyLK (ornithology = LY; animal physiology = LK).

M Sciences of man

A difficulty encountered in constructing this section was the position of anthropology, which includes both physical, and social and cultural anthropology. Many entries deal with the history of both and it was, therefore, necessary to make three sections which, because of their nature, are separated in the schedule. The sciences of man fall into three parts: human biology, psychology and the social sciences. I have put anthropology in general at the head of the whole section at MA, but physical anthropology (ME) is one of the sections concerning physical aspects of the sciences of man, whereas social and cultural anthropology are treated as one of the social sciences. I have already mentioned that anatomy and physiology are classed in the medical sciences.

The position of psychology at MG/MO needs some explanation. It is closely related to neurology, since it is concerned with the function of the brain. In the older schemes it used to be classed with philosophy, with which it has close affinities, particularly in its historical context. However, its primary significance for our field, at any rate, is as one of the sciences of man. Clinical psychology and psychoanalysis are among the medical specialties, OM and OMP respectively.

As far as the social sciences are concerned, there are two points that need stressing. General entries on folklore and superstitions are classed in social and cultural anthropology (MR), but the folkloric aspects of special subjects are under the subject followed by the small letter u. Similarly, the sociology section MU contains entries on the history of sociology, social relations, social psychology, but sociological aspects of the different sciences are classed with aspect divisions p/s of the subjects.

N Medicine

The classification scheme for the medical sciences (N/R) was comparatively straightforward and easy to deal with, partly because there was a faceted scheme (the Wessex scheme[7]) that I was able to draw upon and partly because the subject lends itself easily to a faceted structure. The Wessex scheme is, of course, much more detailed. Moreover, to simplify the scheme and the notation I have omitted the organ and part of the body facet which is subsumed in the system of the body concerned, for example, heart under cardiology and the liver under gastroenterology. The main facets that I have taken into account are: systems of the body; structure (anatomy), function (physiology) and malfunction (pathology); causal agents of disease; specific therapeutic methods, including surgery, drugs and medicaments; environmental factors; public health and safety. The order of the schedule is: medicine, general (N), public health and social medicine, including hospitals and nursing (NA/NZ), anatomy and physiology, general (O/OG), special systems of the body (the medical specialties) (OH/PZ), pathology and clinical medicine (Q), environmental medicine (QU/QX), therapeutics (R), including surgery (RB) and dental surgery (RE) and pharmacy and materia medica (RM/RZ). Unlike the rules governing most other subject fields, the citation order, that is the order in which the facets are joined up to form the classmark, which is generally in reverse of schedule order, is sometimes in a forward direction.

The central part of the medical schedules is PH/PZ which covers the anatomy, physiology and pathology of the systems of the body. Disorders and diseases, their diagnosis and treatment are classed under the part of the body affected unless the disease is caused by a live organism (in which case it goes under medical bacteriology, entomology or mycology) or if the treatment is specified. For example, cancer of the liver goes in OZyQF (gastrointestinal diseases = OZ; cancer QF), but the surgery of this condition is RCKyQF (gastrointestinal surgery = RCK; cancer = QF). Similarly, the treatment of locomotor diseases is OJ, but the hydrotherapy of such disorders is RGyOJ (hydrotherapy = RG; locomotor diseases = OJ). As will be clear from these examples, the code is made up in reverse of schedule order except where the nature of the disease (unless caused by a live orgamism) is stated. This has the effect that, unlike the usual practice, general entries on pathology follow specific cases. For example, a reference to cancer in general at QF comes after a particular case of the disease, for example cancer of the liver, OZyQF.

The notation in the medical section is not fully faceted. To avoid the repetition of pathology. a subsection dealing with disorders and diseases is added to each of the sections on the systems of the body. Moreover, under regional surgery, instead of repeating the code for the system concerned, I have introduced a third letter, but the subject is divided like OH/PZ.

S Veterinary medicine

Veterinary medicine is arranged in exactly the same way as human medicine. The code is made up by joining the appropriate medical code to S by means of y. For example, veterinary bacteriology is SyQN.

SA Agriculture

Since the history of agriculture is usually studied in all its aspects, that is biological as well as technological, I have placed it here rather than splitting it into agricultural botany, agricultural zoology, and agricultural technology, as is still being done in the *Isis* Critical Bibliographies. The product is the primary facet, and agricultural technology is distributed among the different agricultural activities to which it is applied.

T Technology

The classification scheme for the technology section has been largely based on that used in the bibliographical section of *Technology and Culture*,[4] which lists references to the history of technology and its cultural relations, but the scheme used here is far more detailed. The main divisions are: Technology, general (T); Civil engineering (TC); Transport engineering (TN); Mechanical engineering (U); Prime movers and energy conversion (UK); Electrical engineering and power production (UT); Materials and processes (V) (including chemical engineering, mining and metallurgy and the chemical technologies); Town and country planning (WJ) (including building and building crafts); Special mechanical technologies (WQ); Special crafts (WW); Communications (X) (including electrical electrical communications); Military technology (XR). Although the traditional disciplines have been retained (mainly because literature is still being written on the history of civil engineering, mechanical engineering, electrical engineering, and so forth), some of the subdivisions that might have been expected either under civil engineering or mechanical engineering will be found under transport engineering. For example, roads and road vehicles are classed under land transport, internal combustion engines are classed under prime movers. Another unusual feature is that, although electronics technology comes under electrical engineering, electrical communications is a subdivision of communications. With a few exceptions, code building is once again in reverse of schedule order.

Y Ancillary disciplines

As I have already mentioned, all the fields classed under this section are those which, when applied to any particular subject field, appear in the aspect subdivisions. Under the historical sciences (YA) are listed all entries relating to the history of 'history' and to historiography in general. This is followed by the auxiliary historical sciences, genealogy (YB), archaeology (YC), writing and palaeography (YG). Linguistics (YJ) includes entries on the history of the subject. the history of language being in YL. I must emphasize that there are several aspect subdivisions that relate to linguistic problems: linguistic problems of communication concerning special subject fields are in nq; terminology in nh; and linguistic problems in the philosophy of particular subjects in kn.

The history of education in general is in YR, but educational problems related to science and the special sciences are symbolized by o following the subject, and those related to the teaching of history of science and the special sciences in g following the subject. Similarly, the history of universities is classed under YRoq, if treated in general, or under the country (for example, German universities = YRwg-oq); but the history of a university department and the teaching therein is classed with the subject of the department, for example, the medical department of a Polish university is Nwh-oq.

The section on Bibliography (YS) has no entries in this volume, as there were hardly any references to bibliography that did not concern a special subject. However, there are quite a number of references to general libraries which are in YT.

Relations between subject disciplines

The subtitle of *Isis* is 'An international review devoted to the history of sciences and its cultural influences'. In my discussion of the aspect subdivisions I have already covered the philosophical, psychological, social and humanistic aspects of our subject field. However, these do not cover relations between the subject disciplines. With these I have dealt in three different ways. They do not exhaust the possible relationships that may exist, but the instances in which these relations occur are comparatively few and it would have been uneconomic to devise codes to express a great variety of relationships.

I have already given many examples of how compound subjects are formed and of how the letter y is used to join two facets of a subject. It also serves to indicate the application of one subject to another, for example, statistics applied to population studies, MYyBW.

I have also mentioned that mz is used to indicate a conceptual relationship or a comparison between two subjects (mz may be used at any point in making up the code), for example, relation of chemistry with alchemy, DYmzD).

The third way in which relations between two subject disciplines are indicated is illustrated by the following examples: (1) the use of a method or material developed in one field in another (for example, electrochemistry in metallurgical technique, VDxf-DH); (2) a subject used in the teaching of another (for example, mathematics in the technology curriculum, Tog-B); and (3) activities of men in one profession in another subject field (for example, medical men as geologists, Nrk-GG).

Alphabetical index

The alphabetical index is an index to subject headings represented by classmarks (irrespective of whether these are followed by the description of the subject treated), not an index to individual entries. Since the entries in the Bibliography are arranged in a classified order, the index has a twofold purpose: first, it must lead the user to the page on which he will find the entries relating to the subject on which he seeks information; and secondly, it must collect all those aspects of a subject that are distributed, or scattered, in the systematic arrangement. As far as the subject fields are concerned, I have adhered to the rules of chain indexing. This is a semi-mechanical method of producing the necessary subject index entries that avoids unnecessary inversion of terms. For example, since all of medicine is in one classified sequence which can be consulted in full in the subject schedules or in summarized form in the Contents, reference is made to the main code N only. There are no inverted terms, such as medicine, tropical, or medicine, social, but, of course, there are index entries under tropical medicine, social medicine, etc. Similarly, since each subject is subdivided in exactly the same way into its different aspects, the index only gives the main code; no index entries are made under, for example, medicine: history, or medicine: philosophy. A brief summary of the aspects is set out on page 2 of Guide to Users. On the other hand, the same aspects of different subjects, such as philosophy, sociology, etc. are brought together in the index, so that anyone, such as the philosopher of science or the sociologist of science, interested in one particular aspect of several subjects may find all the references that he requires.

As far as the aspect subdivisions are concerned, I have found that the usual rules regarding chain indexing are not entirely satisfactory. For example, a reference to British ornithological societies (code LYwe-qd) would require entries under ornithology LY (without qualification for the reason explained above), under British Isles: ornithology (LYwe) and under learned societies: British Isles: ornithology (LYwe-qd). However, I decided that the last order was not helpful and should instead be: learned societies: ornithology: British Isles. It seemed to me that learned societies should first be subdivided by the subject and then by the country concerned.

The other entry, British Isles: ornithology, seemed to be insufficient, and I decided that a reference was needed under British Isles: zoology, so that anyone requiring information on the history of British zoology would not have to scan the whole of the section on the history of the British Isles. This situation applies to all countries and also to some other frequently occurring aspects, literature, etc. To distinguish between references to entries in the body of the index and to references to headings within these large sections, I have used capitals as initial letters for the former and lower case letters for references to headings for the latter.

REFERENCES

1. George Sarton. The Critical Bibliographies of Isis. *Isis*, 1950, 41: p.292.
2. *Encyclopaedia Britannica*. 13th ed. London: 1926. Volume 13, p.527 ('History')
3. Magda Whitrow. Classification schemes for the history of science. *Journal of Documentation*, 1964, 20: pp.120-36.
4. *Technology and Culture*. The international quarterly of the Society for the History of Technology. Vol. 1- . Detroit: Wayne State University Press, 1959- . The first of the annual bibliographies was published in 1964, 5: pp.138-48, an outline of the classification scheme used being on page 139.
5. John J. Lund and Mortimer Taube. A nonexpansive classification system: an introduction to period classification. *Library Quarterly*, 1937, 7: pp.373-94.
6. *Bliss Bibliographic Classification*. 2nd greatly enlarged and completely revised edition. In the press, due to be published by Butterworth in the autumn of 1976.
7. Classification of the health sciences by Ruth Daniel (for the Wessex Regional Hospital Board) to be incorporated in the revised Bliss Classification (*see* 6. above).
8. Cyril C. Barnard. *A classification for medical and veterinary libraries*. London: H.K. Lewis, 1955.
9. *Dewey Decimal Classification*. 18th edition.

Form and Aspect Subdivisions

a geographical subdivisions (divided like w) use for location only; for national sciences use w

b common form subdivisions (form of presentation) to be used always in conjunction with c-w
bb reference works in general
bc study guides; handbooks
bd directories
be encyclopaedias; dictionaries; systematic compendia
bg formularies; specifications; tables
bk theses
bm monographs; textbooks
bn essays; articles
bp collections; anthologies
bq conference proceedings
br periodicals; serials; yearbooks
bs broadsheets; advertisements
bt charts; diagrams
bu sources of information; documentation
bv bibliographies; indexes; book catalogues; literature surveys
bw catalogues of non-book material
bx special exhibitions; catalogues and guides
by collections; collecting

c general history
cb libraries and archives
cc historical sources (the primary material)
cd archives and manuscripts
ce literature
cf encyclopaedic literature
cg formularies; specifications; tables
ch thesis literature
ci Festschriften; anthologies
cj periodical literature
ck occasional publications; broadsheets
cm pictorial records; illustrations; illustrated books; bookplates
cn maps
co 3-dimensional representations
cp other non-bibliographical sources; objects of historical interest
cq monuments; inscriptions; epigraphs
cr tables; papyri
cs coins, medals and seals
ct postage stamps
cv photographs; slides and films
cw aural records

d biography
da collective biography
dae portraits; iconography
daj collections of texts
db-ds biographies of individual personalities (*see* volumes 1 and 2; for detailed schedule *see* Volume 1, p.xv)

f the history of the subject as a study
fb history and philosophy of the subject as a study
fd biographical studies of historians of science
fn problems of communication in history (divide like n)
fp historical studies: organization (divide like p)
fq historical studies: institutions (divide like q)
fr historians of the subject (divide like r)

g teaching the history of the subject (divided like o, except for the omission of gb and the addition of gt)
gd methods of teaching history
gf examinations
gg curriculum
gm primary and secondary level
gp university level
gr teachers and students of the history of the subject
gt teaching history of the subject as a means of teaching the subject
gv popularizing the history of the subject

h history of the subject: historiography; philosophical and evolutionary aspects
hc historical techniques; textual criticism; editing
hd historiography; historical method
hf philosophical aspects
hg evolutionary aspects and progress
hh historical chronology; periodization
hj precursors and influences; priority in discovery
hk revolutions in the subject
hm ideas in the subject
ht transmission of ideas

j psychological aspects
jd personality of the person in the subject; temperament
jg psychology of discovery; creativity
jj age and creativity; the nature of genius

k philosophy and methodology
kb the nature of the subject
kd explanation; hypotheses and theories
ke method
kg inference; induction and deduction; probability
kh quantification and statistical aspects
kk logic and foundations of the subject
km verification and falsification
kn linguistics and semantics of the subject (but *see* nh for terminology and nq for linguistic problems of communication)
kq classification of knowledge
ks epistemology; theory of knowledge
kt philosophical systems
kv causality; determinism and indeterminism
kw positivism
kx mechanism and vitalism
ky transformism
kz speculations on the future of the subject (but *see* sy for science in a future society; utopias)

m fundamental concepts
mc time and space, combined
md time
me space
mf symmetry
mh infinity
mj forces and fields
mk energy; mass; momentum
mz relation with other scientific subject fields

n communication
nb symbolism; type of symbol
nc figures; ideographs
nd scripts; transcription; transliteration

nf shorthand notations
ng anagrams; codes; cryptographs
nh terminology; nomenclature
nj eponyms
nk methods of communication
nm speaking; lecturing
nn broadcasting
np writing; reporting; reviewing
nq translating; linguistic problems of communication
ns publishing

o the study and teaching of the subject
ob study of the subject
oc theoretical aspects of teaching the subject
od methods of teaching
of examinations
og curriculum
om primary and secondary education
on schools
op university and higher education in general
oq universities
or teachers and students
os social relations of education
ov adult education; popularization

p organization of the subject
pd professional or amateur
pe specialization
pf team or single work
pg crown sponsored
ph government sponsored, including administrative measures for control
pq academically sponsored
pr privately sponsored
ps sponsored by industry
pv relations within one country
pw international relations
px prizes and awards
py Nobel prize

q societies and institutions
(for libraries *see* cb
for museums xx
for universities oq)
qb invisible colleges; clubs
qc national academies
qd learned and professional societies
qe guilds; trade unions
qg research institutes; research and observational stations
qh expeditions and field work
qk Government departments; Government sponsored surveys
qm welfare institutions
qp religious institutions
qq missions
qr trusts and foundations
qs trade associations
qt companies; shops
qu congresses in general
qv national congresses
qw relations between institutions
qx international congresses
qy international institutions

r the profession: the person in the subject
rc social background
rd his social responsibility and attitude to society; religious beliefs
rf professional qualifications; status; remuneration
rg costumes
rh his place of work; transport
rj professional ethics; conduct; discipline
rk activities outside his or her field
rn leisure activities; travel
rw women in the subject
rx auxiliary personnel

s the subject in relation with society as a whole
sb impact of society on the subject; sociology of knowledge
sc the subject in relation with the history of civilization
sd important figures in history
se the subject and public opinion
sf the subject and social welfare
sg the subject in its relation to economic factors; to industry
sh the subject in its relation to transport
sk the subject in its relation to politics
sm manpower and emigration
sp peace and war
sq refugees
sr freedom and secrecy
st the subject in its relation to the law
sy the future of the subject; utopias

t the subject in relation to culture and the humanities in general
tc the subject in relation to ethics
td the subject in relation to religion
tf religion in history
th the subject in relation to literature in general
tk to poetry
tn to fiction
tp aesthetic aspect of the subject
tq the subject in relation to art
tt the subject in relation to music

u popular aspects of the subject
ud religious folklore

v ethnic and linguistic subdivisions
vb white races
vc Anglo-Saxons
vd Germanic races (Germanic languages)
vf Latin races (Romance or neo-Latin languages)
vg Latin and Greek languages
vh Slavs (Slavonic languages)
vj Semites (Semitic languages)
vk Aramaic
vm Jews (Hebrew)
vn Arabs (Arabic)
vo Hamitic races and languages
vp Indo-European races and languages
vq Celts
vr Gipsies
vs Turkish and Finno-Ugrian group of languages
vt Mongolian and other Asiatic languages
vu Chinese and Japanese
vv Amerindians
vw Australasian races and languages
vx African races and languages

w national subdivisions (these subdivisions are only used for Western science, as practised in the different countries; for indigenous science, *see* Civilizations and periods)
wa America (North and South combined)
wb North America (not including Mexico)
wc Latin America
wd Europe
we British Isles
wf France
wg Central Europe: Germany, Austria, Switzerland Czechoslovakia, Poland, Hungary
wh
wi Italy
wj Spain and Portugal
wk Low Countries: Belgium, Holland, Luxembourg
wm Scandinavia: Denmark, Sweden, Norway
wn Russia, Baltic States, Finland
wo South Eastern Europe: the Balkans; Yugoslavia, Greece, Bulgaria, Rumania
wp Near or Middle East; including Turkey
wq Egypt and North Africa
wr Asia in general; Central and Northern Asia
ws Indian subcontinent: India, Pakistan
wt Far East: China, Japan
wv South Eastern Asia: Malaya, Indo-China, East Indies and the Oceanic Islands
ww Australia and New Zealand
wx Africa (for Egypt and North Africa *see* wq)
wy South Africa
wz Polar regions

x techniques and instruments
xb laboratories and instrumentation in general; equipment and machinery
xc practical aspects of research (for organization of research *see* p)
xd techniques and processes
xe experiments on self; experiments endangering experimenter
xf methods using techniques from other subjects
xg models and their use (distinguish from co 3-dimensional representations)
xh drawing and designing
xj testing
xk instruments in general
xm measurement; metrology
xn systems of measurement; metric system
xp measuring instruments
xq measuring volume, density, pressure, temperature
xr time measurement
xs time measuring instruments
xt recording and recording instruments; graphical methods
xu control instruments
xv standardization
xw museology
xx museums
xy exhibitions of live specimens

y facet indicator: used for compound subjects or application of one subject to another

z subject extension: used for alphabetical, non-systematic breakdown of subject

Scientific Subject Fields

A S C I E N C E
AC NATURAL MAGIC; MYTHOLOGY; PSEUDO-SCIENCES
AD HISTORY OF IDEAS
AF PHILOSOPHY
AG PHILOSOPHICAL SYSTEMS
AH METAPHYSICS
AJ PHILOSOPHY OF VALUES
AK LOGIC

B M A T H E M A T I C S
BA ARITHMETIC
BB NUMERALS; NUMERICAL SYSTEMS
BBzn NUMEROLOGY
BC ARITHMETICAL OPERATIONS; NUMERICAL MATHEMATICS
BD LOGARITHMS
BE TABLES
BF ALGEBRA
BFza ALGEBRAIC EQUATIONS
BFzd DETERMINANTS; MATRICES
BFzg GROUPS
BG SET THEORY
BH NUMBER THEORY (HIGHER ARITHMETIC)
BHzf FERMAT'S PROBLEM
BHzm MAGIC SQUARES
BI CONCEPT OF NUMBER
BIzc COMPLEX NUMBERS
BIzi IRRATIONAL NUMBERS
BJ ANALYSIS
BK SERIES AND FUNCTIONS
BL CALCULUS
BM DIFFERENTIAL AND INTEGRAL EQUATIONS
BN VECTORS AND TENSORS
BO GEOMETRY
BP EUCLIDEAN GEOMETRY (plane and solid)
BPzc SQUARING THE CIRCLE
BQ ANALYTICAL AND DIFFERENTIAL GEOMETRY
BR PROJECTIVE AND DESCRIPTIVE GEOMETRY
BRzp PERSPECTIVE
BS TRIGONOMETRY
BT NON-EUCLIDEAN GEOMETRY
BU TOPOLOGY
BV PROBABILITY AND STATISTICS
BW APPLIED STATISTICS
BX MERCANTILE AND INDUSTRIAL MATHEMATICS
BY RECREATIONAL MATHEMATICS

BZ P H Y S I C A L S C I E N C E S

C P H Y S I C S
CA FUNDAMENTAL PHYSICS
CB RELATIVITY
CBze EINSTEIN'S SPECIAL THEORY
CBzg GENERAL THEORY
CBzt TESTS OF RELATIVITY
CC QUANTUM THEORY
CD MECHANICS IN GENERAL; SOLID MECHANICS
CDzb BALLISTICS
CDzg GRAVITATION
CDzi INERTIA
CDzv VARIATIONAL PRINCIPLES
CE FLUID MECHANICS
CF ELASTICITY AND PLASTICITY
CG ACOUSTICS; VIBRATIONS
CH HEAT; THERMODYNAMICS
CHzl LOW TEMPERATURES
CI KINETIC THEORY; STATISTICAL MECHANICS
CJ OPTICS (classical)
CJzv VELOCITY OF LIGHT
CK COLOUR SCIENCE
CL MAGNETISM
CM ELECTRICITY; ELECTRICITY AND MAGNETISM (combined)
CMzs SUPERCONDUCTIVITY
CN ELECTROMAGNETISM; ELECTRODYNAMICS
CNze ELECTRON PHYSICS; IONIZATION
CO ELECTROMAGNETIC WAVES; RADIATION
COze ETHER
COzx X-RAYS
CP SPECTROSCOPY
CQ STRUCTURE OF MATTER
CR SUBATOMIC PARTICLES
CRzc COSMIC RAYS
CS NUCLEAR AND ATOMIC PHYSICS
CT NUCLEUS
CU NUCLEAR PROCESSES; RADIOACTIVITY
CV MOLECULES
CW CRYSTALLOGRAPHY
CX X-RAY CRYSTALLOGRAPHY
CY SOLID STATE
CZ LIQUID AND GASEOUS STATES; PLASMA

D C H E M I S T R Y
DA THEORY OF THE ELEMENTS AND CONSTITUTION
DAzi ISOTOPES
DAzp PERIODIC SYSTEM
DC ANALYTICAL CHEMISTRY
DCzc CHROMATOGRAPHY
DCzm MASS SPECTROSCOPY
DCzs SPECTROCHEMISTRY
DD PHYSICAL CHEMISTRY
DE CHEMICAL STATICS AND DYNAMICS
DEzc CATALYSIS
DEzd DISTILLATION
DF TYPES OF REACTIONS
DFzc COMBUSTION
DG THERMOCHEMISTRY
DH ELECTRO- AND MAGNETOCHEMISTRY
DI RADIO-, RADIATION AND PHOTOCHEMISTRY
DJ STRUCTURAL CHEMISTRY
DJza AFFINITY
DJzb VALENCY; BONDS
DK STEREOCHEMISTRY
DL STATES OF MATTER
DM SURFACE CHEMISTRY
DN SOLUTIONS
DO COLLOID CHEMISTRY
DP TYPES OF SUBSTANCES; COMPLEX CHEMISTRY
DQ ELEMENTS AND COMPOUNDS IN GENERAL
DR INORGANIC CHEMISTRY
DS NON-METALS AND NON-METALLIC COMPOUNDS
DT METALS AND METALLIC COMPOUNDS
DU ORGANIC CHEMISTRY
DV ORGANIC COMPOUNDS
DW NATURAL PRODUCTS AND BIOCHEMICAL SUBSTANCES
DY ALCHEMY

F A S T R O N O M Y
FA OPTICAL ASTRONOMY
FB RADIO ASTRONOMY; INFRA-RED AND RADAR ASTRONOMY
FC SPACE RESEARCH AND EXPLORATION
FD SPHERICAL ASTRONOMY AND ASTROMETRY

F A S T R O N O M Y (Cont.)
FE HEAVENLY BODIES
FF SOLAR SYSTEM (including the planets in general)
FG ORIGIN OF THE SOLAR SYSTEM
FH MOTIONS; CELESTIAL MECHANICS
FJ ECLIPSES, TRANSITS AND OCCULTATIONS
FK SUN
FL EARTH AS A PLANET
FM MOON
FN OTHER PLANETS AND SATELLITES
FO COMETS AND METEORS
FOzm METEORITES
FP STARS AND STAR CLUSTERS
FQ CONSTELLATIONS
FR INTERSTELLAR MATTER
FS THE GALAXY (MILKY WAY)
FT GALAXIES AND GALACTIC CLUSTERS
FU THE UNIVERSE; COSMOLOGY AND COSMOGONY
FV ASTRONOMICAL CHRONOLOGY
FW CALENDAR
FY ASTROLOGY

FZ E A R T H S C I E N C E S
FZzc NATURAL CALAMITIES

G M E T E O R O L O G Y
Gzm WEATHER MODIFICATION
GA THE ATMOSPHERE IN GENERAL
GB WINDS
GC PRECIPITATIONS; FLOODS
GD ELECTRICAL AND OPTICAL PHENOMENA
GE WEATHER FORECASTING
GF CLIMATOLOGY
GFA* REGIONAL CLIMATOLOGY

GG G E O L O G Y
GH* REGIONAL GEOLOGY
GI GEOPHYSICS
GJ GRAVITATIONAL FIELD; ISOSTASY
GK TERRESTRIAL HEAT
GL GEOMAGNETISM; ELECTRICAL AND RADIATION PHENOMENA
GM GEOCHEMISTRY
GN GEOCHRONOLOGY; AGE AND HISTORY OF THE EARTH; HISTORICAL GEOLOGY
GO SEISMOLOGY AND VULCANOLOGY
GP VOLCANIC ERUPTIONS; EARTHQUAKES
GPA* REGIONAL SEISMOLOGY AND VULCANOLOGY
GQ TECTONICS; STRUCTURAL GEOLOGY
GR STRATIGRAPHY; PETROLOGY AND PETROGRAPHY
GS MINERAL DEPOSITS
GT MINERALOGY
GU GEM STONES

GV G E O M O R P H O L O G Y; P H Y S I O G R A P H Y
GW GLACIOLOGY
GWA* REGIONAL GLACIOLOGY
GX HYDROLOGY AND HYDROGRAPHY
GXA* REGIONAL HYDROLOGY
GY OCEANOGRAPHY
GYzc CURRENTS
GYzt TIDES
GYA* REGIONAL OCEANOGRAPHY
GZ WATER DIVINING

H G E O G R A P H Y
HB GEODESY; SURVEYING
HC NAVIGATION
HD AIR NAVIGATION
HF CARTOGRAPHY
HG* REGIONAL CARTOGRAPHY
HH CHARTING THE SEAS
HI AIR CHARTING
HJ TRAVEL AND EXPLORATION
HK* BY REGION
HL POLAR EXPLORATION
HLN NORTH POLE; the ARCTIC
HLP GREENLAND
HLS ANTARCTIC
HM MOUNTAIN EXPLORATION; MOUNTAINEERING
HN MOUNT EVEREST
HO SEA TRAVEL
HP IMAGINARY LANDS
HQ ATLANTIS

HU P A L A E O N T O L O G Y
HV PALAEOBOTANY
HW PALAEOZOOLOGY

HY N A T U R A L H I S T O R Y
HYA* BY REGION

J B I O L O G Y
JA EXPERIMENTAL BIOLOGY; MICROSCOPY
JB THEORETICAL BIOLOGY
JC BIOPHYSICS
JD BIOCHEMISTRY
JE VITAMINS; HORMONES; ENZYMES
JF ORIGIN OF LIFE; SPONTANEOUS GENERATION
JG EVOLUTION
JH GENETICS
JI MORPHOLOGY
JJ COMPARATIVE ANATOMY
JK COMPARATIVE PHYSIOLOGY
JKzf FERTILIZATION; SEX
JL EMBRYOLOGY
JM CYTOLOGY
JN ECOLOGY
JNzm MARINE AND CAVE BIOLOGY
JO EFFECT OF RADIATIONS, CLIMATE AND EXTRA-TERRESTRIAL PHENOMENA
JP PARASITISM, in general
JQ COMPARATIVE PATHOLOGY

JR M I C R O B I O L O G Y
JRzf FERMENTATION

K B O T A N Y
KC/KN PLANT BIOLOGY
KC PLANT PHYSICS
KD PLANT CHEMISTRY AND BIOCHEMISTRY
KE PLANT VITAMINS AND HORMONES
KG PLANT EVOLUTION
KH PLANT GENETICS; HYBRIDIZATION
KI PLANT MORPHOLOGY
KK PLANT PHYSIOLOGY
KL PLANT EMBRYOLOGY
KM PLANT CYTOLOGY
KN PLANT ECOLOGY
KR* PLANT GEOGRAPHY; FLORA
KS SYSTEMATIC BOTANY
KT FLOWERLESS PLANTS
KU MYCOLOGY
KV SEED AND FLOWERING PLANTS
KX TREES AND SHRUBS
KY SPECIFIC TREES AND SHRUBS

L Z O O L O G Y
LG/LQ ANIMAL BIOLOGY
LG ANIMAL EVOLUTION
LH ANIMAL GENETICS
LI ANIMAL MORPHOLOGY
LJ ANIMAL ANATOMY
LK ANIMAL PHYSIOLOGY
LL ANIMAL EMBRYOLOGY
LM ANIMAL CYTOLOGY
LN ANIMAL ECOLOGY
LO ANIMAL PSYCHOLOGY AND BEHAVIOUR
LP ANIMAL PARASITOLOGY
LQ ANIMAL PATHOLOGY
LR* ZOOGEOGRAPHY; FAUNA
LS SYSTEMATIC ZOOLOGY
LT INVERTEBRATE ZOOLOGY
LU ENTOMOLOGY
LUza APPLIED ENTOMOLOGY; INSECT CONTROL
LV VERTEBRATE ZOOLOGY
LW ICHTHYOLOGY
LX HERPETOLOGY
LY ORNITHOLOGY
LZ MAMMALOGY

*** Subdivided by A-Z, representing the different countries, as second letter in section w (Form and aspect subdivisions).**

M SCIENCES OF MAN

MA ANTHROPOLOGY in general
MB HUMAN PALAEONTOLOGY
MBzp PILTDOWN MAN
MC HUMAN EVOLUTION
MD HUMAN GENETICS
ME PHYSICAL ANTHROPOLOGY
MF ETHNOLOGY; ETHNOGRAPHY
MFA RACES

MG PSYCHOLOGY
MH PERSONALITY; TEMPERAMENT
MHzp PHRENOLOGY; PHYSIOGNOMY
MI ABILITY; INTELLIGENCE
MJ PHYSIOLOGICAL PSYCHOLOGY; PERCEPTION
MK MIND AND BODY
MKzf FIREWALKING
ML FEELING AND EMOTION; MOTIVES
MM HIGHER MENTAL PROCESSES: LEARNING; MEMORY
MMzc CREATIVITY; GENIUS
MN DEPTH PSYCHOLOGY
MNzd DREAMS; SOMNAMBULISM
MO SPECIAL PSYCHIC PHENOMENA; ESP

MP SOCIAL SCIENCES
MQ SOCIAL AND CULTURAL ANTHROPOLOGY
MQzs SEXUAL BEHAVIOUR; MARRIAGE
MQzt TOTEMS AND TABOOS
MR FOLKLORE; SUPERSTITIONS
MS WITCHCRAFT
MU SOCIOLOGY
MV SOCIAL RELATIONS; SOCIAL GROUPS
MW SOCIAL PSYCHOLOGY
MX CRIMINOLOGY
MY POPULATION; DEMOGRAPHY

N MEDICINE

NA PUBLIC HEALTH AND SOCIAL MEDICINE
NB MEDICAL STATISTICS
NC ENVIRONMENTAL HYGIENE; HUMAN ECOLOGY
ND SANITATION; REFUSE HANDLING; WATER SUPPLY
NE AIR POLLUTION
NF DISPOSAL OF THE DEAD; EMBALMING
NG PREVENTIVE MEASURES
NH PHYSICAL AND CHEMICAL HAZARDS
NJ QUARANTINE
NK PERSONAL HYGIENE AND HEALTH
NL PHYSICAL TRAINING
NM NUTRITION; DIETETICS
NMzf FOODS; NUTRITIONAL VALUES
NO NARCOTICS; ALCOHOL
NP TOBACCO
NQ SEXUAL HYGIENE
NR PROSTITUTION
NS EUGENICS; APPLIED GENETICS
NT HEALTH SERVICES; SOCIAL WELFARE
NU MOTHERS AND CHILDREN
NV PRISONERS
NW HOSPITALS
NX AUXILIARY SERVICES
NY DOCTORS AND PATIENTS
NZ NURSING

O ANATOMY AND PHYSIOLOGY (including human biology and constitution)

OB ANATOMY
OC DISSECTION
OD REGIONAL ANATOMY
OE HISTOLOGY

OF PHYSIOLOGY
OFzd DEVELOPMENT AND GROWTH; LIFE AND DEATH
OFze ELECTROPHYSIOLOGY
OFzh HEAT AND COLD
OFzr REST AND SLEEP
OG METABOLISM; PHYSIOLOGICAL CHEMISTRY

OH SYSTEMS OF THE BODY; SPECIALTIES OF MEDICINE
OI LOCOMOTOR SYSTEM
OJ LOCOMOTOR SYSTEM: DISORDERS AND DISEASES
OK NEUROLOGY
OL NERVOUS DISEASES AND DISORDERS
OLza APHASIA
OLze EPILEPSY
OM MEDICAL PSYCHOLOGY AND PSYCHIATRY
OMP PSYCHOANALYSIS
ON SPECIFIC MENTAL DISEASES
OO MENTAL DEFICIENCY
OP** SPECIAL SENSE ORGANS
OQ OPHTHALMOLOGY
OQzv VISION
OR EYE DISORDERS AND DISEASES
ORzs SPECTACLES
OS OTOLOGY
OT EAR DISORDERS AND DISEASES
OU OTO-RHINO-LARYNGOLOGY
OV NOSE AND THROAT: DISORDERS AND DISEASES
OW RESPIRATORY SYSTEM
OX RESPIRATORY DISORDERS AND DISEASES
OY GASTROENTEROLOGY
OZ DIGESTIVE DISORDERS AND DISEASES

PA CARDIOVASCULAR SYSTEM; CARDIOLOGY
PB CIRCULATION OF THE BLOOD
PC CARDIAC AND CIRCULATORY DISORDERS AND DISEASES
PD HAEMOPOIETIC SYSTEM; HAEMATOLOGY
PE BLOOD DISORDERS AND DISEASES
PF LYMPHATIC AND RETICULOENDOTHELIAL SYSTEM
PG LYMPHATIC DISORDERS AND DISEASES
PH ENDOCRINOLOGY
PI ENDOCRINE DISORDERS AND DISEASES
PIzd DIABETES
PIzg GOITER
PJ DERMATOLOGY
PK SKIN DISEASES
PKzs SAINT ANTHONY'S FIRE
PL UROLOGY
PM URINARY DISORDERS AND DISEASES
PN SEXOLOGY
PO FAMILY PLANNING; CONTRACEPTION; ARTIFICIAL INSEMINATION
PP DISEASES AFFECTING THE GENITAL SYSTEM; VENEREAL DISEASES
PQ GYNAECOLOGY AND OBSTETRICS
PR WOMEN: ANATOMY AND PHYSIOLOGY
PS OBSTETRICS
PSza ABORTION
PT WOMEN'S DISORDERS AND DISEASES
PU HUMAN EMBRYOLOGY
PUzm MULTIPLE BIRTHS
PV TERATOLOGY
PW PAEDIATRICS
PX CHILDREN'S DISORDERS AND DISEASES
PY GERONTOLOGY
PZ GERIATRICS; DISEASES OF OLD AGE

Q PATHOLOGY AND CLINICAL MEDICINE
QA* MEDICAL GEOGRAPHY; AETIOLOGY
QB DISEASES: THEORETICAL ASPECTS
QC MORBID ANATOMY; EXPERIMENTAL PATHOLOGY
QD DIAGNOSIS; SYMPTOMS
QDze ELECTRODIAGNOSIS
QDzu URINE ANALYSIS
QE RADIOLOGY; RADIOGRAPHY
QF TUMOURS; CANCER
QG DISEASES OF UNKNOWN CAUSATION
QH PSYCHOSOMATIC MEDICINE
QI CONGENITAL DISEASES
QJ DISEASES DUE TO PHYSICAL FACTORS
QK TOXICOLOGY
QL METABOLIC AND DEFICIENCY DISEASES
QM ALLERGIC DISEASES
QN MEDICAL BACTERIOLOGY; INFECTIOUS AND COMMUNICABLE DISEASES
QO IMMUNOLOGY
QP SPECIFIC DISEASES CAUSED BY MICROORGANISMS

* Subdivided by A-Z, representing the different countries, as second letter in section w (Form and aspect subdivisions).

** Heading not used in this volume.

Q P A T H O L O G Y A N D C L I N I C A L M E D I C I N E (Cont.)
QPza ANTHRAX
QPZC CHOLERA
QPzdi DIPHTHERIA
QPzdy DYSENTERY
QPze ENCEPHALITIS LETHARGICA
QPzga GAS GANGRENE
QPzgo GONORRHEA
QPzi INFLUENZA
QPzl LEPROSY
QPzm MEASLES
QPzpl PLAGUE
QPzpo POLIOMYELITIS
QPzpu PUERPURAL FEVER
QPzra RABIES
QPzrat RAT-BITE FEVER
QPzrh RHEUMATIC FEVER
QPzsm SMALLPOX
QPzsw SWEATING SICKNESS
QPzsy SYPHILIS
QPzte TETANUS
QPztu TUBERCULOSIS
QPzty TYPHUS
QPzw WHOOPING COUGH
QPzya YAWS
QPzye YELLOW FEVER
QR MEDICAL MYCOLOGY
QS MEDICAL ENTOMOLOGY AND PARASITOLOGY
QT SPECIFIC DISEASES CAUSED BY PARASITES AND INSECTS
QTzm MALARIA
QTzsc SCABIES
QTzsl SLEEPING SICKNESS
QU/QY ENVIRONMENTAL MEDICINE
QU INDUSTRIAL MEDICINE
QV ARMY MEDICINE
QW NAVAL AND MARITIME MEDICINE
QX AVIATION MEDICINE
QY TROPICAL MEDICINE
QZ FORENSIC MEDICINE
QZzs SUICIDE

R T H E R A P E U T I C S
Rzh HOMOEOPATHY
Rzm MESMERISM
Rzn NATURE CURES
Rzy QUACKERY
RA FIRST AID; ACCIDENTS
RB S U R G E R Y
RBzh HAEMOSTASIS; WOUND HEALING
RBzp PLASTIC SURGERY
RC REGIONAL SURGERY
RCC SURGERY OF THE LOCOMOTOR SYSTEM; ORTHOPAEDIC SURGERY
RCD NEUROSURGERY
RCF EYE SURGERY
RCG LUNG SURGERY; CHEST SURGERY IN GENERAL
RCJ SURGERY IN OTO-RHINO-LARYNGOLOGY
RCK GASTRO-INTESTINAL SURGERY
RCL HEART AND CARDIOVASCULAR SURGERY
RCN SURGERY OF ENDOCRINE GLANDS
RCQ UROLOGICAL SURGERY
RCR SURGERY OF MALE SEX ORGANS
RCS CIRCUMCISION
RCT SURGERY IN GYNAECOLOGY AND OBSTETRICS
RCU CAESAREAN SECTION
RD ANAESTHESIA
RE DENTAL SURGERY
RF THERAPEUTIC ARTS AND PRACTICE
RFzb BLOODLETTING
RG AERO- AND HYDROTHERAPY
RH LIGHT AND HEAT THERAPY
RI ELECTRO- AND RADIOTHERAPY
RJ PHYSIOTHERAPY; MECHANOTHERAPY; PROSTHETICS
RJzo OSTEOPATHY
RK OCCUPATIONAL AND PSYCHOTHERAPIES
RL DIET THERAPY

RM P H A R M A C Y; M A T E R I A M E D I C A; P H A R M A C O T H E R A P Y
RN PRACTICAL PHARMACY
RO MODE OF ADMINISTRATION OF DRUGS
RP PHARMACO-BOTANY; PHARMACOGNOSY
RQ NAMED MEDICINAL PLANTS
RQzci CINCHONA
RQzcu CURARE
RQzd DIGITALIS
RQzm MANDRAGORA
RR PHARMACO-ZOOLOGY (including materia medica of human origin)
RS PHARMACO-MINERALOGY
RT CHEMICAL DRUGS
RU NAMED CHEMICAL DRUGS
RV BIO- AND ORGANOTHERAPY
RVzb BLOOD TRANSFUSION
RW CHEMOTHERAPY
RX ANTIBIOTICS
RY ANTISEPSIS
RZ PHARMACOLOGY

S* V E T E R I N A R Y M E D I C I N E

SA A G R I C U L T U R E
SB SOIL SCIENCE; AGRICULTURAL PHYSICS AND CHEMISTRY
SC PLANT CULTIVATION AND HORTICULTURE
SD PLANT PATHOLOGY; PLANT PESTS
SE CULTIVATED PLANTS IN GENERAL; ECONOMIC BOTANY
SF GRAIN CROPS; CEREALS; GRASSES
SFzm MAIZE
SG FIBRE PLANTS
SH ROOT CROPS
SHzp POTATOES
SI SUGAR CANE AND BEET
SJ PLANTS YIELDING STIMULANTS AND SPICES
SK PLANTS YIELDING OTHER USEFUL PRODUCTS
SL GREEN VEGETABLES; FUNGI
SM FRUIT CULTIVATION
SN GARDENING; FLOWERS

SO F O R E S T R Y

SP A N I M A L H U S B A N D R Y
SPC CATTLE
SPH SHEEP AND GOATS
SPL DOGS AND CATS
SPP HORSES AND OTHER EQUINES
SPS REINDEER
SPT MONKEYS
SPV POULTRY AND OTHER DOMESTIC BIRDS
SQ BEES; APICULTURE
SR SILK WORM CULTURE
SS FISHERY; FISHING
SSzp PEARL FISHING
ST WHALING
SU HUNTING; FALCONRY

SV F O O D T E C H N O L O G Y
SW BEVERAGES
SWza ALCOHOLIC BEVERAGES
SWzs STIMULANTS
SX FOODS
SXzb BREAD; CEREALS
SXzc CONDIMENTS AND SPICES
SXzf FATS AND OILS
SXzs SALT
SY SUGAR

T T E C H N O L O G Y
TA INDUSTRIAL ORGANIZATION; PRODUCTION ENGINEERING
TB PATENTS AND INVENTIONS

TC C I V I L E N G I N E E R I N G
TD FOUNDATIONS; SOIL MECHANICS; ROCK MECHANICS
TE STRUCTURES
TF BRIDGES
TG TUNNELS
TH HYDRAULIC ENGINEERING
TJ DAMS
TK WATER SUPPLY; SEWERAGE
TL DRAINAGE AND IRRIGATION

* Subdivided as medicine N/R.

TN T R A N S P O R T   E N G I N E E R I N G
TO MARINE ENGINEERING; CANALS; WATERWAYS
TP SHIPS AND SHIPBUILDING
TQ LAND TRANSPORT
TR HORSE RIDING
TS ROADS
TT ROAD VEHICLES
TU BICYCLES
TV AUTOMOBILES
TW RAILWAYS, INCLUDING TRACKS
TX AERONAUTICS; AVIATION
TZ ASTRONAUTICS

U M E C H A N I C A L   E N G I N E E R I N G
UB MACHINES AND MECHANISMS
UC HAND AND MACHINE TOOLS; MACHINING
UD MEANS OF JOINTING
UE WELDING
UF HANDLING MACHINERY; VERTICAL TRANSPORT
UG MECHANICAL POWER TRANSMISSION; LUBRICATION
UH TRANSMISSION OF FLUIDS; PUMPING
UJ REFRIGERATION

UK P R I M E   M O V E R S;   E N E R G Y   C O N - V E R S I O N
UL ANIMAL POWER; WIND AND WATER MILLS
UM WATER TURBINES AND TIDAL POWER
UN STEAM ENGINES AND STEAM TURBINES
UP INTERNAL COMBUSTION ENGINES
UQ ROCKET TECHNOLOGY
UR ATOMIC ENERGY
US SOLAR AND GEOTHERMAL POWER

UT E L E C T R I C A L   E N G I N E E R I N G;   P O W E R   P R O D U C T I O N
UV ELECTRICAL MACHINES; MOTORS AND GENERATORS
UW POWER TRANSMISSION; INSULATION
UX ELECTRONICS TECHNOLOGY

V M A T E R I A L S   A N D   P R O C E S S E S
VA CHEMICAL ENGINEERING; PROCESS ENGINEERING
VAze INDUSTRIAL EFFLUENTS
VB MINING TECHNOLOGY (also MINING AND METALLURGY combined)
VC METALLURGY
VD IRON AND STEEL
VE NON-FERROUS METALS
VF PRECIOUS METALS
VG MINERALS
VH PRECIOUS AND SEMI-PRECIOUS MINERALS
VI FUEL TECHNOLOGY
VJ FIREWORKS; EXPLOSIVES; MATCHES
VK WOOD; CHARCOAL BURNING
VL COAL AND COAL MINING
VM COAL GAS; COKE
VN OIL; NATURAL GAS
VO OTHER COAL AND PETROLEUM BY-PRODUCTS
VP CHEMICAL INDUSTRY
VQ INORGANIC CHEMICALS
VR ORGANIC CHEMICALS
VS CEMENT; LIME; MORTAR; CONCRETE
VT CERAMICS; POTTERY
VU GLASS
VV OILS; FATS; WAXES
VW SOAPS; DETERGENTS
VX** GUMS; RESINS
VY DYES; PAINTS
VZ COSMETICS; PERFUMES

WA PLASTICS; RUBBER, NATURAL AND SYNTHETIC
WB TIMBER
WC PAPER
WD TEXTILES
WE COTTON, FLAX AND OTHER PLANT FIBRES
WF WOOL
WG SILK
WH MINERAL FIBRES; MIXED AND SYNTHETIC FABRICS
WI LEATHER

WJ T O W N   A N D   C O U N T R Y   P L A N N I N G
WK MUNICIPAL ENGINEERING
WKzf FIRE FIGHTING AND PROTECTION
WL BUILDING AND ARCHITECTURE; BUILDING CRAFTS
WM LIGHTING
WN HEATING; VENTILATION
WP DOMESTIC APPLIANCES AND FURNISHINGS

WQ S P E C I A L   M E C H A N I C A L   T E C H N O L - O G I E S;   I N S T R U M E N T   T E C H N O L O G Y
WR CLOCKS
WS AUTOMATA
WT CALCULATING MACHINES
WU OPTICAL INSTRUMENTS
WV MUSICAL INSTRUMENTS; BELLS

WW S P E C I A L   C R A F T S
WX METALWORK; JEWELLERY
WY WOODWORK; LEATHER AND BASKETWORK
WZ CLOTHING; COSTUME

X C O M M U N I C A T I O N S
XA INFORMATION THEORY; CYBERNETICS
XB WRITING MATERIALS; TYPEWRITERS
XC BOOKMAKING AND PRINTING
XCzp PROOF-READING
XD GRAPHIC PROCESSES
XF PHOTOGRAPHY
XG CINEMA
XH POSTAL SERVICES

XJ E L E C T R I C A L   C O M M U N I C A T I O N S
XK TELEGRAPH AND TELEPHONE
XL SOUND REPRODUCTION; TAPE RECORDERS
XM RADIO
XN TELEVISION
XO RADAR
XP COMPUTERS

XR M I L I T A R Y   T E C H N O L O G Y
XS ARMS AND ARMOUR
XT NUCLEAR WEAPONS
XU GUIDED MISSILES
XV CHEMICAL WARFARE
XW BIOLOGICAL WARFARE
XX NAVAL FORCES
XY AIR FORCES

Y* A N C I L L A R Y   D I S C I P L I N E S

YA H I S T O R I C A L   S C I E N C E S
YB GENEALOGY
YC ARCHAEOLOGY
YG WRITING; PALAEOGRAPHY
YH ALPHABET

YJ L I N G U I S T I C S
YJzp PHONETICS
YL HISTORY OF LANGUAGE
YLza ARTIFICIAL LANGUAGES

YR E D U C A T I O N

YS** B I B L I O G R A P H Y
YT LIBRARIES

* Only references of a general nature are classed here; historiographical, linguistic and educational aspects of the preceding subject fields are classed there, as are special libraries.
** Heading not used in this volume.

Index to Subject Classmarks

N.B. *See* and *see also* references with a lower case initial letter are to headings within the same section; references with an upper case initial letter are to other main headings in the index.